Seeley's

ANATOMY & PHYSIOLOGY

Thirteenth Edition

Cinnamon VanPutte
Southern Illinois University School of Dental Medicine

Jennifer Regan
The University of Southern Mississippi

Andrew Russo
University of Iowa

Mc Graw Hill

SEELEY'S ANATOMY & PHYSIOLOGY

Published by McGraw Hill LLC, 1325 Avenue of the Americas, New York, NY 10019.

Some ancillaries, including electronic and print components, may not be available to customers outside the United States.

This book is printed on acid-free paper.

1 2 3 4 5 6 7 8 9 LWI 27 26 25 24 23 22

ISBN 978-1-265-12958-3
MHID 1-265-12958-4

Cover Image: *Rattanasak Khuentana/Shutterstock*

mheducation.com/highered

ABOUT THE Authors

Howard Ash

Cinnamon L. VanPutte

Associate Professor
Growth, Development and Structure
Southern Illinois University School of Dental Medicine

Cinnamon has been teaching biology and human anatomy and physiology for over two decades. At SIU School of Dental Medicine she is the course director for the Integrated Biomedical Science courses and teaches physiology to first-year dental students and participates in dental-based physiology research. Cinnamon is an active member of several professional societies, including the Human Anatomy and Physiology Society (HAPS) and American Dental Education Association (ADEA). Her Ph.D. in zoology, with an emphasis in endocrinology, is from Texas A&M University. She worked in Dr. Duncan MacKenzie's lab, where she was indoctrinated in the major principles of physiology and the importance of critical thinking. The critical thinking component of *Seeley's Human Anatomy & Physiology* epitomizes Cinnamon's passion for the field of human anatomy and physiology; she is committed to maintaining this tradition of excellence. Cinnamon and her husband, Robb (also a biology professor), have two children: a daughter, Savannah, and a son, Ethan. Savannah is studying to become an elementary school teacher. Ethan is involved in 4-H and shows steers and lambs. He is working on his future endeavors. Cinnamon and her family live on a farm with her parents, Tom and Bobbie, where they raise sheep and cattle.

Bridget Reeves

Jennifer L. Regan

Teaching Professor
The University of Southern Mississippi

For over 20 years, Jennifer has taught introductory biology, human anatomy and physiology, and genetics at the university and community college level. She has received the Instructor of the Year Award at both the departmental and college level while teaching at USM. In addition, she has been recognized for her dedication to teaching by student organizations such as the Alliance for Graduate Education in Mississippi and Increasing Minority Access to Graduate Education. Jennifer has dedicated much of her career to improving lecture and laboratory instruction at her institutions. Critical thinking and lifelong learning are two characteristics Jennifer hopes to instill in her students. She appreciates the Seeley approach to learning and is excited about contributing to further development of the textbook. She received her Ph.D. in biology at the University of Houston, under the direction of Edwin H. Bryant and Lisa M. Meffert. She is an active member of several professional organizations, including the Human Anatomy and Physiology Society. During her free time, Jennifer enjoys spending time with her husband, Hobbie, a GIS analyst supervisor. They have two sons, Patrick and Nicholas.

Andrew F. Russo

Andrew F. Russo

Professor of Molecular Physiology and Biophysics
University of Iowa

Andrew has over 30 years of classroom experience with human physiology, neurobiology, molecular biology, and cell biology courses at the University of Iowa. He is a recipient of the Collegiate Teaching Award and the J.P. Long Teaching Award in Basic Sciences. He is currently the course director for a new medical school course called Mechanisms of Health and Disease that integrates physiology, histology, and genetics. He is a member of several professional societies, including the Society for Neuroscience. Andrew received his Ph.D. in biochemistry from the University of California at Berkeley. His research interests are focused on the molecular basis of migraine. His decision to join the author team for *Seeley's Human Anatomy & Physiology* is the culmination of a passion for teaching that began in graduate school. He is excited about the opportunity to hook students' interest in learning by presenting cutting-edge clinical and scientific advances. Andrew is married to Maureen, a physical therapist, and has three daughters, Erilynn, Becky, and Colleen, and six grandchildren. He enjoys all types of outdoor sports, especially bicycling, skiing, running, and open water swimming.

Dedication

This text is dedicated to the students of human anatomy and physiology. Helping students develop a working knowledge of anatomy and physiology is a satisfying challenge, and we have a great appreciation for the effort and enthusiasm of so many who want to know more. It is difficult to imagine anything more exciting, or more important, than being involved in the process of helping people learn about the subject we love so much.

Acknowledgments

A great deal of effort is required to produce a heavily illustrated textbook like *Seeley's Anatomy & Physiology*. Many hours of work are required to organize and develop the components of the textbook while also creating and designing illustrations, but no text is solely the work of the authors. It is not possible to adequately acknowledge the support and encouragement provided by our loved ones. They have had the patience and understanding to tolerate our absences and our frustrations. They have also been willing to provide assistance and unwavering support.

Many hands besides our own have touched this text, guiding it through various stages of development and production. We wish to express our gratitude to the staff of McGraw Hill for their help and encouragement. We appreciate the guidance and tutelage of portfolio manager Matthew Garcia. We are sincerely grateful to product developer Melisa Seegmiller for her careful scrutiny of the manuscript, her creative ideas and suggestions, and her tremendous patience and encouragement. Special thanks are also offered to copyeditor Sharon O'Donnell for her attention to detail and for carefully polishing our words. A special acknowledgment of gratitude is owed to content project manager Ann Courtney for her patience and detail-tracking abilities. Content licensing specialist Lori Hancock, designer David Hash, and assessment project manager Brent Dela Cruz, we thank you for your time spent turning our manuscript into a book and its accompanying digital program. The McGraw Hill employees with whom we have worked are excellent professionals. They have been consistently helpful and their efforts are truly appreciated. Their commitment to this project has clearly been more than a job to them.

Finally, we sincerely thank the past reviewers and instructors who have provided us time and time again with remarkable feedback. We have continued their recommendations in this edition, while remaining true to our overriding goal of writing a text that is comprehensive enough to provide the depth necessary for a two-semester course, yet ensuring it is presented with such clarity that it nicely balances the thorough coverage to be more student centered. Each feature incorporated into this edition has been carefully considered in how it may be used to support student learning and understanding.

It takes teamwork to ensure the highest accuracy and greatest clarity within a textbook of this magnitude. We would like to extend a very heartfelt thank you to our Board of Advisors for their feedback on our new art program. With their keen eyes and innovative ideas, we are very excited to present this edition of the text. However, without a strong foundation provided by the previous authors of this text, the changes we've made simply wouldn't be possible and so our gratitude to the founders of this text is ever-present.

Also, in this edition, we are very pleased to have been able to incorporate real student data points and input, derived from thousands of our LearnSmart users, to help guide our revision. LearnSmart Heat Maps provided a quick visual snapshot of usage of portions of the text and the relative difficulty students experienced in mastering the content. With these data, we were able to hone not only our text content but also the LearnSmart probes.

Cinnamon VanPutte
Jennifer Regan
Andy Russo

Reviewers

Nahel Awadallah, *Nash Community College*

Jessica K. Baack, *Southwestern Illinois College*

Corinne Carey, *Southwestern Illinois College*

Maria Figueiredo-Pereira, *Hunter College, CUNY*

Sharada Gollapudi, *San Jacinto College South*

Clare Hays, *Metropolitan State University of Denver*

Shannon Larson, *College of Southern Nevada*

Cynthia Littlejohn, *The University of Southern Mississippi*

Lauren E. McDaniel, *Kansas State University*

Judy Metcalf, *Texas A&M University–Corpus Christi*

Jean Mitchell, *University of Florida College of Medicine and Northwest Florida State College*

Justicia Opoku, *University of Maryland, College Park*

Nicole Pinaire, *St. Charles Community College*

Ann Raddant, *University of Wisconsin–Milwaukee*

Achint Utreja, *Southern Illinois University School of Dental Medicine*

Nichole Watkins, *The University of Southern Mississippi*

Ronika Williams, *Coastal Bend College*

Brief Contents

Contents

DYNAMIC NEW **Art** PROGRAM

Our new art program has created more vibrancy and more three-dimensionality to our art, making it look more realistic.

12th Edition

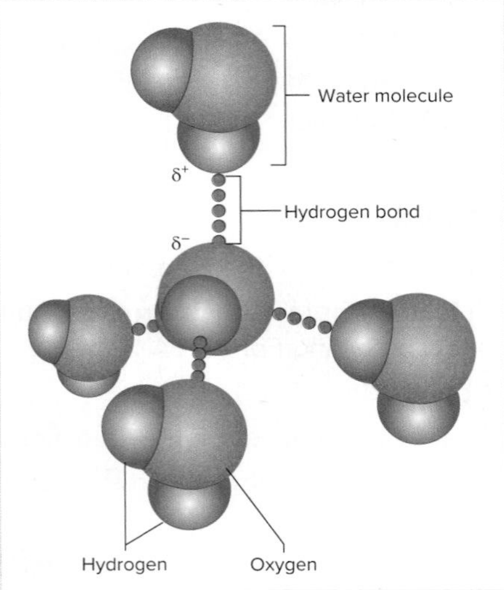

The previous version of this figure did not illustrate the connection between formation of polar covalent bonds and the potential for hydrogen bonds to occur. The new art builds from previous art illustrating polar covalent bond formation.

13th Edition

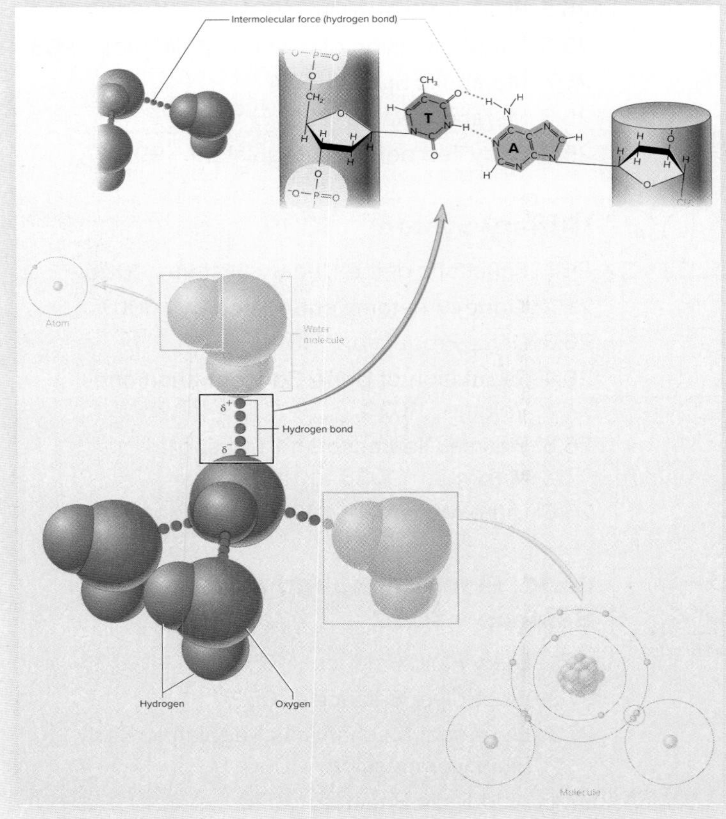

12th Edition

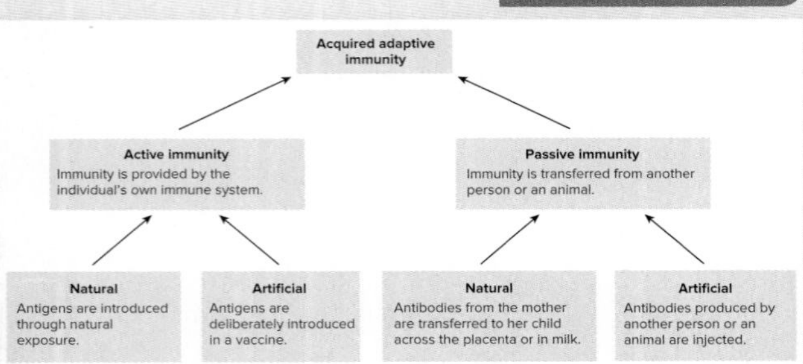

The 12/e version of this figure is a flat, two-dimensional, simplistic flow-chart. The 13/e version is colorful and engaging, as well as relatable. Having images that illustrate each component provides realistic context for students.

(Young woman feeling) Brothers91/Getty Images; (Doctor vaccinating girl) valentinrussanov/Getty Images; (Breastfeeding Mother) FatCamera/Getty Images; (Doctor holds a vial of monoclonal antibodies) Cristian Storto/Alamy Stock Photo

13th Edition

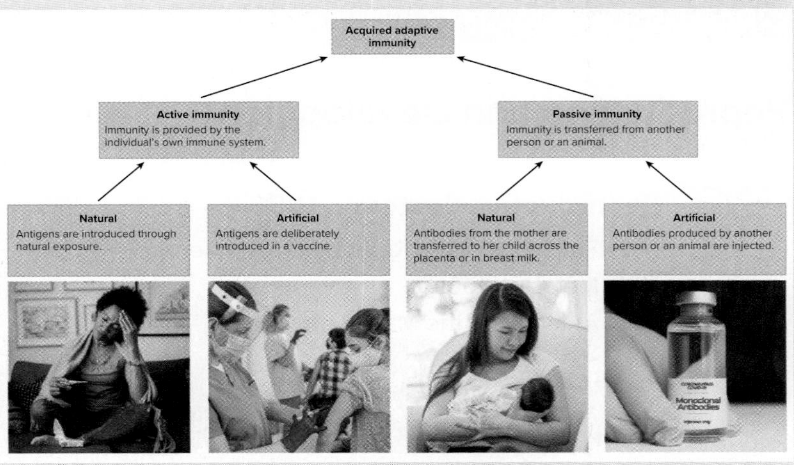

12th Edition

The 12/e version of this figure was two-dimensional, muted in color, and small, while the 13/e version of this figure is three-dimensional, vibrant in color, and a two-page spread to help students tie all the concepts together from beginning to end.

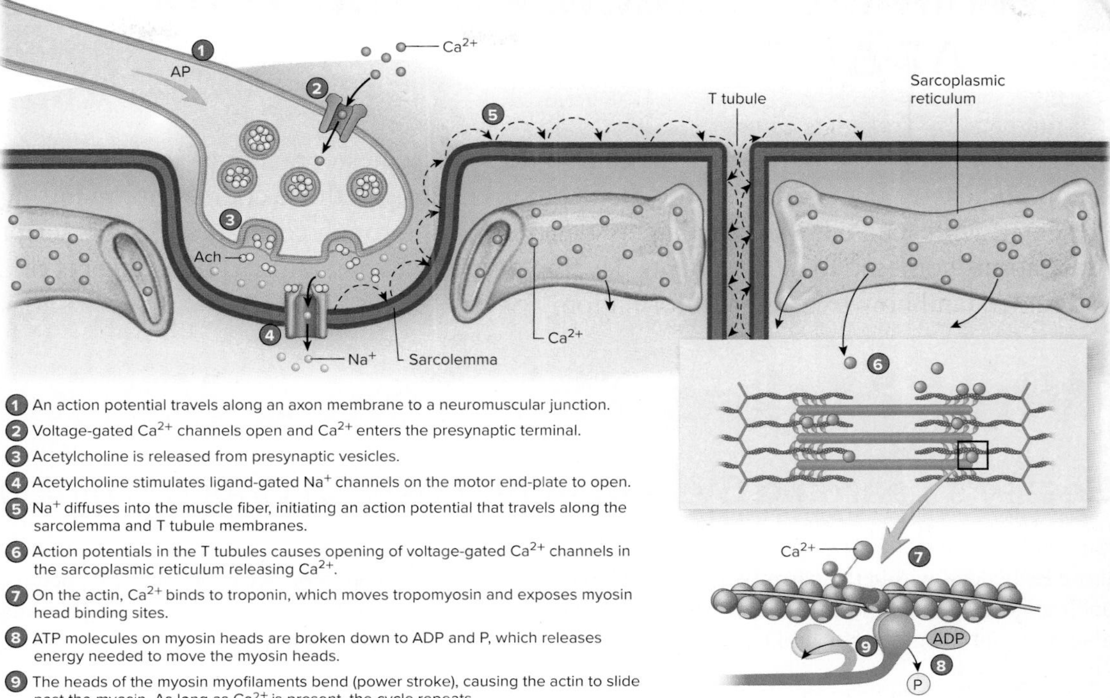

1. An action potential travels along an axon membrane to a neuromuscular junction.
2. Voltage-gated Ca^{2+} channels open and Ca^{2+} enters the presynaptic terminal.
3. Acetylcholine is released from presynaptic vesicles.
4. Acetylcholine stimulates ligand-gated Na^+ channels on the motor end-plate to open.
5. Na^+ diffuses into the muscle fiber, initiating an action potential that travels along the sarcolemma and T tubule membranes.
6. Action potentials in the T tubules causes opening of voltage-gated Ca^{2+} channels in the sarcoplasmic reticulum releasing Ca^{2+}.
7. On the actin, Ca^{2+} binds to troponin, which moves tropomyosin and exposes myosin head binding sites.
8. ATP molecules on myosin heads are broken down to ADP and P, which releases energy needed to move the myosin heads.
9. The heads of the myosin myofilaments bend (power stroke), causing the actin to slide past the myosin. As long as Ca^{2+} is present, the cycle repeats.

13th Edition

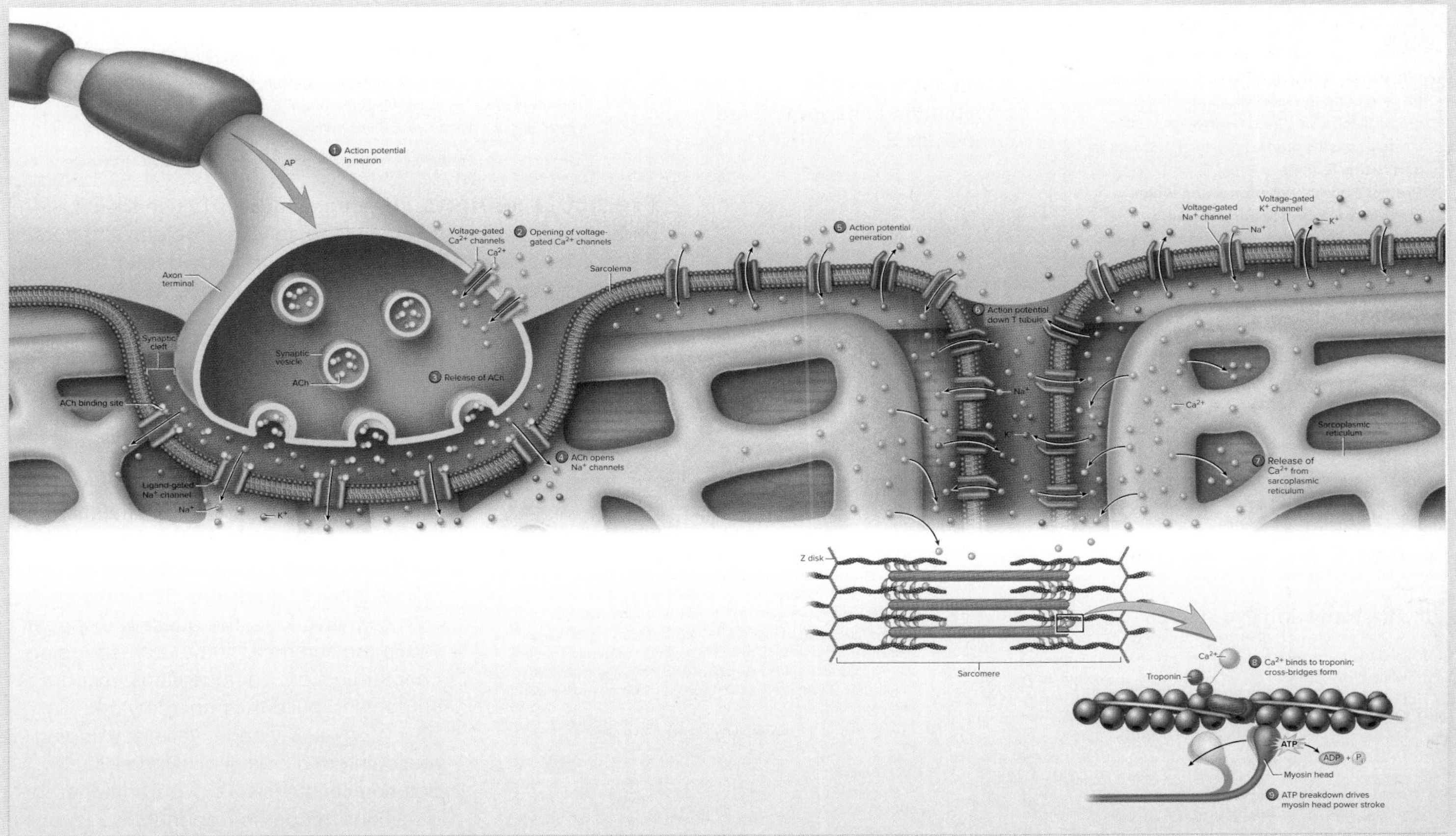

AP
1 Action potential in neuron
Axon terminal
Voltage-gated Ca^{2+} channels
Ca^{2+}
2 Opening of voltage-gated Ca^{2+} channels
Sarcolema
Synaptic cleft
Synaptic vesicle
ACh
3 Release of ACh
ACh binding site
Ligand-gated Na^+ channel
Na^+
K^+
4 ACh opens Na^+ channels
5 Action potential generation
Voltage-gated Na^+ channel
Na^+
Voltage-gated K^+ channel
K^+
6 Action potential down T tubule
Na^+
K^+
Ca^{2+}
Sarcoplasmic reticulum
7 Release of Ca^{2+} from sarcoplasmic reticulum
Z disk
Sarcomere
Ca^{2+}
Troponin
8 Ca^{2+} binds to troponin; cross-bridges form
ATP
ADP + P_i
Myosin head
9 ATP breakdown drives myosin head power stroke

WHAT SETS Seeley's Anatomy & Physiology APART?

Seeley's Anatomy & Physiology is written for the two-semester anatomy and physiology course. The writing is comprehensive enough to provide the depth necessary for those courses not requiring prerequisites, and is presented with such clarity that it nicely balances the thorough coverage. Clear descriptions and exceptional illustrations combine to help students develop a firm understanding of the concepts of anatomy and physiology and understand how to use that information.

What Makes This Text a Market Leader?

Seeley's Learning System—*Emphasis on Critical Thinking*

An emphasis on critical thinking is integrated throughout this textbook. This approach is found in questions that begin each chapter and those embedded within the narrative; in clinical material that is designed to bridge concepts explained in the text with real-life applications and scenarios; in end-of-chapter questions that go beyond rote memorization; and in a visual program that presents material in understandable, relevant images, with application questions that follow each Process Figure.

- Problem-solving perspective from the book's inception
- Pedagogy that builds student comprehension from knowledge to application (**Learn to Predict** questions, **Predict** questions, **Concept Check** questions)

Understand **Learn to Predict**

While weight training, Pedro strained his back injuring the following muscles: psoas major, iliacus, pectineus, sartorius, vastus lateralis, vastus medius, vastus intermedius, and rectus femoris.

Predict Pedro's symptoms and which movements of his lower limb were affected, other than walking on a flat surface. What types of daily tasks would be difficult for Pedro to perform?

Answers to this question and the chapter's odd-numbered Predict questions can be found in Appendix E.

Learn to Predict questions are found at the beginning of each chapter, with the corresponding answer located in Appendix E.

Explain the difference between doing chin-ups with the forearm supinated and doing them with it pronated. The action of which muscle predominates in each type of chin-up? Which type is easier? Why?

Predict Questions challenge students to use their understanding of new concepts to solve a problem. Answers to the odd-numbered Predict questions are provided in Appendix E, allowing students to evaluate their responses and to understand the logic used to arrive at the correct answer. All Predict question answers have been written in teaching style format to model the answer for students, to help them learn how to think critically.

Concept Check

Knowledge of anatomy and physiology can be used to solve problems concerning the body when healthy or diseased.

1.1 Anatomy and Physiology

A. Anatomy is the study of the body's structures.
B. Developmental anatomy considers anatomical changes over time, while gross anatomy studies organs from a systemic or regional perspective; surface anatomy uses superficial structures to locate internal structures.
C. Physiology is the study of the body's functions.
D. Cellular physiology studies functions of a cell; systems-level physiology considers functions of a system; exercise physiology examines changes caused by exercise.
E. Pathology is concerned with all aspects of disease.

B. Basic chemical characteristics are responsible for the body's structures with cells being the simplest unit of an organism. Cells contain specialized structures called organelles that perform specific functions. Groups of cells form tissues and two or more tissues form organs.
C. Organs are arranged into the 11 organ systems of the human body (integumentary, skeletal, muscular, nervous, endocrine, cardiovascular, lymphatic, respiratory, digestive, urinary, and reproductive; see figure 1.3). These organ systems interact to form a whole, functioning organism.

2. *The following are organizational levels for considering the body.*

(1) cell
(2) chemical
(3) organ
(4) organ system
(5) organism

Concept Check is a place to review and practice critical thinking. The chapter summary is interwoven with review and comprehension questions as well as critical thinking questions. To help students with cognitive load, the questions appear within the summary of the corresponding chapter section. The questions encourage students to build their anatomy and physiology knowledge while developing reasoning and critical thinking skills. Solution-style answers to odd-numbered questions appear in Appendix F.

Clinical Emphasis—*Case Studies Bring Relevance to the Reader*

- Chapter opening photos and scenarios have been correlated to provide a more complete story and begin critical thinking from the start of the chapter
- Learn to Predict and chapter Predict questions, with unique Learn to Predict answers
- Clinical Impact boxes (placed at key points in the text)
- Case Studies
- Clinical Genetics essays have been updated and streamlined for accuracy and impact
- Diseases and Disorders tables
- Systems Pathology boxes with System Interactions illustration

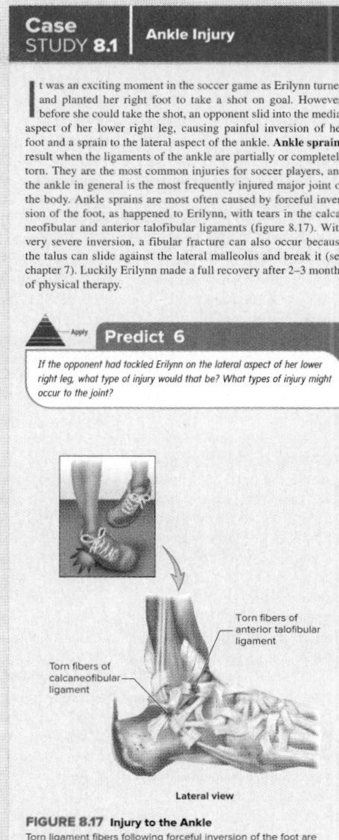

Case STUDY 8.1 | **Ankle Injury**

It was an exciting moment in the soccer game as Erilynn turned and planted her right foot to take a shot on goal. However, before she could take the shot, an opponent slid into the medial aspect of her lower right leg, causing painful inversion of her foot and a sprain to the lateral aspect of the ankle. **Ankle sprains** result when the ligaments of the ankle are partially or completely torn. They are the most common injuries for soccer players, and the ankle in general is the most frequently injured major joint of the body. Ankle sprains are most often caused by forceful inversion of the foot, as happened to Erilynn, with tears in the calcaneofibular and anterior talofibular ligaments (figure 8.17). With very severe inversion, a fibular fracture can also occur because the talus can slide against the lateral malleolus and break it (see chapter 7). Luckily Erilynn made a full recovery after 2–3 months of physical therapy.

Apply **Predict 6**

If the opponent had tackled Erilynn on the lateral aspect of her lower right leg, what type of injury would that be? What types of injury might occur to the joint?

FIGURE 8.17 Injury to the Ankle
Torn ligament fibers following forceful inversion of the foot are shown in a lateral view of the right ankle.

Clinical IMPACT 8.2 | **Arthritis**

Osteoarthritis is the most common type of arthritis; over 85% of Americans age 70 and older are affected by osteoarthritis. This type of arthritis is a noninflammatory condition and is characterized by the gradual degeneration of the articular cartilage due to overuse or advancing age. Referring to osteoarthritis as "noninflammatory" can be confusing, especially when considering it is often treated with anti-inflammatory medications. As a practical rule of thumb, joints with osteoarthritis do not typically swell and feel warm to the touch. The pain and swelling associated with osteoarthritis is often isolated to the soft tissues around the joint. In addition, with osteoarthritis other tissues of the body are not generally affected as is the case with rheumatoid arthritis. Heredity or obesity can be contributing factors to development of osteoarthritis. Individuals with osteoarthritis experience symptoms such as pain within the affected joint or swelling of the soft tissues around the joint, which can cause the joint to be misshapen or reduce the range of motion. To diagnose osteoarthritis, a physician may perform any one of several procedures with the common theme of taking a sample of the tissue or fluid that makes up the joint to look for signs of damage. Treatment of osteoarthritis includes certain medications to reduce swelling and pain, physical therapy to strengthen the muscles around the affected joint, or surgery to fuse the existing bones of the joint, or to replace the damaged bone with a prosthetic joint. **Rheumatoid arthritis (RA)** is the second most common type of arthritis. It affects about 3% of all females and about 1% of all males in the United States. RA is a general, inflammatory connective tissue disorder that affects the skin, vessels, lungs, and other organs, but it is most pronounced in the joints. RA is severely disabling and most commonly destroys small joints, such as those in the hands and feet (figure 8.8*b,c*).

The initial cause of RA is unknown but may involve a transient infection or an autoimmune disease (an immune reaction to one's own tissues; see chapter 22) that develops against collagen. A genetic predisposition may also exist. Whatever the cause, the ultimate course appears to be immunological. In RA, the synovial fluid and associated connective tissue cells proliferate, forming a *pannus* (clothlike layer), which causes the joint capsule to become thickened and destroys the articular cartilage. In advanced stages, opposing joint surfaces can become fused. Table 8.3 contrasts osteoarthritis with rheumatoid arthritis.

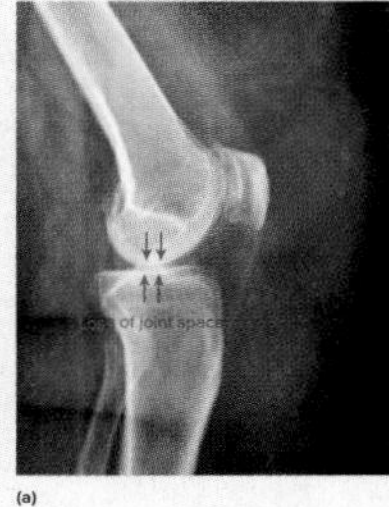

(a)

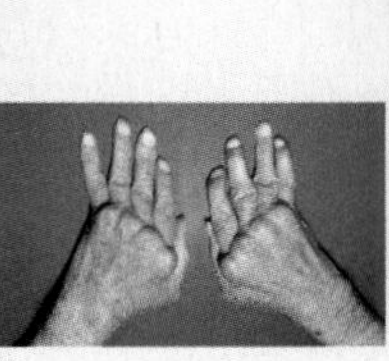

(b)

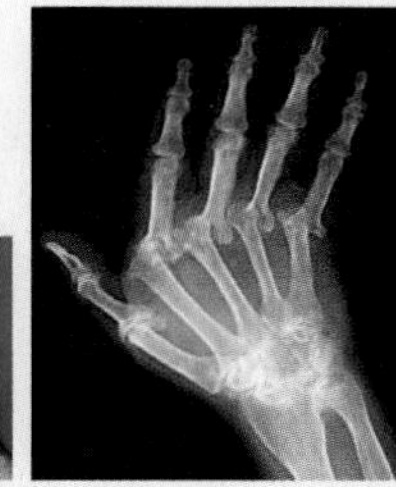

(c)

FIGURE 8.8 Rheumatoid Arthritis
(*a*) X-ray of a knee with osteoarthritis. Note the loss of space within the synovial cavity with osteoarthritis. (*b*) Photograph of hands with rheumatoid arthritis. (*c*) Radiographs of the same hands shown in (*b*). (a) ZEPHYR/SCIENCE PHOTO LIBRARY/Alamy Stock Photo; (b) ©James Stevenson/Science Photo Library/Science Source; (c) ZEPHYR/SPL/Alamy Stock Photo

Clinical Impact boxes These in-depth boxed essays explore relevant topics of clinical interest. Subjects covered include pathologies, current research, sports medicine, exercise physiology, and pharmacology.

Systems PATHOLOGY | Duchenne Muscular Dystrophy

Background Information

A couple became concerned about their 3-year-old son, Greger, when they noticed that he was much weaker than other boys his age and his muscles appeared poorly developed. Eventually, it was readily apparent that Greger had difficulty sitting, standing, climbing stairs, and even walking. When Greger tried to stand, he would use his hands and arms to climb up his legs. Finally, the couple took Greger to his pediatrician, who, after several tests, informed them that Greger had Duchenne muscular dystrophy. **Duchenne muscular dystrophy (DMD)** is usually identified in children around 3 years of age, when their parents notice slow motor development with progressive weakness and muscle wasting (atrophy). Typically, muscular weakness begins in the hip muscles, which causes a waddling gait. Temporary enlargement of the calf muscles is apparent in 80% of cases. The enlargement is paradoxical because the muscle fibers are actually getting smaller, but the amount of fibrous connective tissue and fat between the muscle fibers is increasing (figure 9.29*a,b*). The protein that normally protects muscle against mechanical stress is not functional in patients with DMD. This is thought to be the primary cause of the muscle weakness and other symptoms. Rising from the floor by using the hands and arms is characteristic and is caused by weakness of the lumbar and hip muscles (figure 9.29*c*). Within 3 to 5 years, the muscles of the shoulder girdle become involved. The replacement of muscle with connective tissue contributes to muscular atrophy and shortened, inflexible muscles called contractures. The contractures limit movements and can cause severe deformities of the skeleton. By 10 to 12 years of age, people with DMD are usually unable to walk, and few live beyond age 20. DMD is genetic, but because of its inheritance pattern, mostly males are affected. There is no effective treatment to prevent the progressive deterioration of muscles in DMD. Therapy primarily involves exercises to help strengthen muscles and prevent contractures. Figure 9.30 demonstrates the impact DMD has on other organ systems. Table 9.6 lists other diseases and disorders of the muscular system.

Predict 10

A boy with advanced Duchenne muscular dystrophy developed pulmonary edema (accumulation of fluid in the lungs) and pneumonia caused by a bacterial infection. His physician diagnosed the condition in the following way: The pulmonary edema was the result of heart failure, and the increased fluid in the lungs provided a site where bacteria could invade and grow. The fact that the boy could not breathe deeply or cough effectively made the condition worse. How would the muscle tissues in a boy with advanced DMD differ from the muscle tissues in a boy with less-advanced DMD?

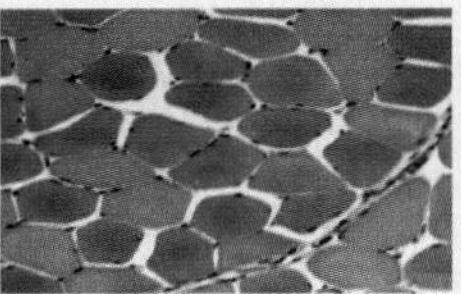

(a) Normal muscle tissue

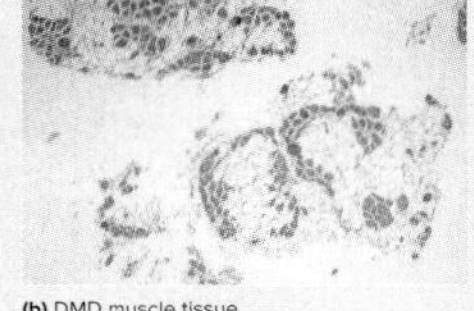

(b) DMD muscle tissue

(c) A DMD patient

FIGURE 9.29 Effects of DMD on Skeletal Muscle Tissue
(*a*) Cross section of normal skeletal muscle tissue. Note the lesser amount of adipose and connective tissue between muscle fibers than seen in (*b*). (*b*) Cross section of DMD skeletal muscle tissue. Skeletal muscle fibers decrease in size and have increased amount of adipose and connective tissue distributed among the muscle fibers. (*c*) Patients with DMD must support themselves whether sitting or standing on the ground. (a) Biophoto Associates/Science Source; (b) Dr. Edwin P. Ewing, Jr./Centers for Disease Control and Prevention; (c) Jaren Jai Wicklund/Shutterstock

SKELETAL
Shortened, inflexible muscles (contractures) cause severe skeletal deformities. Curvature of the spinal column laterally and anteriorly (kyphoscoliosis) can be so severe that normal respiratory movements are impaired. Surgery is sometimes required to prevent contractures from making it impossible for the individual to sit in a wheelchair.

DIGESTIVE
Smooth muscle tissue is affected by DMD, and the reduced ability of smooth muscle to contract can result in disorders of the digestive system, including enlarged colon diameter and twisting of the small intestine that leads to intestinal obstruction, cramping, and reduced absorption of nutrients.

Duchenne Muscular Dystrophy

Symptoms
- Muscle weakness
- Muscle atrophy
- Contractures

Treatment
- Physical therapy to prevent contractures
- No effective treatment to prevent atrophy

NERVOUS
Some degree of intellectual disability occurs in a large percentage of people with DMD, although the specific cause is unknown.

LYMPHATIC AND IMMUNE
Although the lymphatic system is not directly affected, damaged muscle fibers are phagocytized by macrophages.

URINARY
Reduced smooth muscle function and wheelchair dependency increase the frequency of urinary tract infections.

CARDIOVASCULAR
Cardiac muscle is affected by DMD; consequently, heart failure occurs in many patients with advanced DMD. Cardiac involvement becomes serious in as many as 95% of cases and is one of the leading causes of death for DMD patients.

RESPIRATORY
Deformity of the thorax and increasing weakness of the respiratory muscles result in inadequate respiratory movements, which cause an increase in respiratory infections, such as pneumonia. Insufficient movement of air into and out of the lungs due to weak respiratory muscles is a major contributing factor in many deaths.

FIGURE 9.30 Interactions Between DMD and Other Organ Systems
DMD affects most systems of the body because muscle tissue is used for many body functions.

Systems Pathology boxes These two-page spreads explore a specific condition or disorder related to a particular body system. Presented in a simplified case study format, each Systems Pathology vignette begins with a patient history, followed by background information about the featured topic.

- **Microbes In Your Body** features discuss the many important and sometimes little-known roles of microbes and the physiology of homeostasis.

MICROBES In Your Body 22.1 | **Do Our Gut Bacteria Drive Immune Development and Function?**

"All disease begins in the gut." This quote from Hippocrates (460–377 B.C.), the father of Western medicine, is still relevant today. Over the last four decades, increasing numbers of people have suffered from allergies and autoimmune disorders. Researchers hypothesize that the increase in these conditions stems from inadequate development of immune function. In turn, they hypothesize that underdeveloped immune function is due to deficiencies in our gut microbiota. This has led to the Hygiene Hypothesis, which states that the increased use of antibiotics and antimicrobial chemicals damages the normal gut microbiota and other microbiota that are critical for immune system development and function.

Could the Hygiene Hypothesis explain the observed increases in allergies and autoimmune disorders? Much of the evidence for the importance of gut microbiota for immune function is derived from studies with germ-free mice. These lab-raised mice lack the natural microorganisms in their gut and in their body. As a result, the mice have multiple defects with their lymphatic tissues, such as fewer and smaller Peyer patches in the gut and fewer B and T lymphocytes. However, if scientists place intestinal or fecal microbiota from normal mice into the gut of germ-free mice, the immune tissues of the germ-free mice begin developing and functioning normally.

The importance of the gut in immune development is further supported by the fact that it contains the largest concentration of lymphatic tissue and microbiota in the human body. In the gut there are between 500 and 1000 species of bacteria, compared with a few hundred associated with the skin or fewer than 10 species associated with the conjunctiva of the eye. In humans, the gut microbiota begin to appear just before birth. As the baby passes through the birth canal, more microorganisms are transferred from the mother to the baby. The makeup of a baby's microbiota is influenced by many factors, including genetics, the mode of delivery (vaginal or C-section), antibiotic use, stress, and the mother's diet during late pregnancy. The first year of life is the most critical for the accumulation of gut bacteria, but this process continues through childhood. At about 10 years of age, a person's gut microbiota are established and remain similar in composition throughout life. Humans and their gut microbiota have a symbiotic relationship, in that the gut provides space and nutrients for the microbiota, which in turn provide their host with specialized nutrition, physiological regulators, and protection against pathogens. Because of these ever-present microbiota ("good" bacteria), human gut epithelial and immune cells must maintain tolerance to them yet still protect against invading gut pathogens ("bad" bacteria).

How do our cells distinguish between "good" and "bad" bacteria? As it turns out, gut microbiota help stimulate the development of immune cells by triggering the production of different receptors. These receptors are found in the plasma membranes of white blood cells, such as macrophages and neutrophils, as well as in the plasma membranes of intestinal epithelial cells. The surface of all bacterial cells has bacteria-specific molecules that can be recognized by the receptors of defense cells, which is what allows for distinction between "good" and "bad" microorganisms. Activation of the receptors triggers a cascade of events, which result in immune responses such as T-lymphocyte activation and the production of immunity chemicals. In addition, the "good" bacteria attack invading "bad" bacteria by secreting antimicrobial substances against them and competing with them for nutrients and space. Thus, without appropriate amounts and/or types of gut microbiota, the body's immune system may not have all of the messages that are essential for producing specific immune cells and chemicals that kill pathogenic intestinal microorganisms.

Medical professionals are interested in manipulating gut microbiota to reduce allergies and other diseases and to promote healing. First, and perhaps most importantly, is to get the desired population of gut microbiota started immediately in infancy through breastfeeding. Human breast milk contains carbohydrates that stimulate the growth of specific intestinal microbiota while preventing infection by some pathogens. And the use of prebiotics (nondigestible carbohydrates that promote the growth of healthy microbiota) and probiotics (live normal gut microbiota) is being actively explored for the treatment of problems that arise later in life. However, there is still much work to be done before we fully understand the extent to which gut microbiota are involved in human immune function.

Predict 2

In some underdeveloped countries, children are nutritionally deprived. Studies of twins in these countries have demonstrated that sometimes one of the twins thrives, whereas the other twin is malnourished. In the malnourished twin, the gut microbiota population is far less diverse and much smaller than that of the thriving twin. Using what you have learned about the role of gut microbiota in immune function, predict a possible developmental repercussion in the malnourished twin. Propose some possible solutions that might result in both twins having a normal gut microbe population.

- **Clinical Genetics** features have been updated and streamlined to provide the newest and most accurate information available.
- Online clinical study questions are based on clinical features within the text, including Microbes In Your Body and Systems Pathology vignettes, and are correlated with Learning Outcomes and HAPS Learning Objectives to further develop and measure higher-level thinking and application of learned content.

Clinical GENETICS 25.1 | **Newborn Screening of Metabolic Disorders**

Metabolic disorders, sometimes called inborn errors of metabolism, are a large class of genetic disorders that result in biochemical defects. Metabolic disorders affect the body's ability to break down or use nutrients needed for energy, growth, and repair. Too little synthesis of certain substances or a buildup of toxic compounds can cause significant health problems. Although the frequency of any given individual disorder is rare, the overall incidence of metabolic disorders is estimated to be up to 1 in 1000 births.

Early detection through newborn screening is vital. Metabolic disorders can hinder early mental and physical development. Depending on the disorder, specific treatment can prevent or limit harm if it is started early. In the United States, most states require the screening of newborns. However, there is no national standard for newborn screening, so the specific disorders for which tests are performed vary from state to state. Although over several hundred genetic disorders are known, most are so rare that it is not cost-effective to test for them.

Table 25.5 lists the most common blood tests performed for metabolic disorders. All of the disorders listed are autosomal recessive.

TABLE 25.5 Metabolic Disorders

Disorder	Description	Effect	Treatment
Phenylketonuria (PKU)	Inability to metabolize the amino acid phenylalanine (see chapter 29)	Intellectual disability	Restrict dietary phenylalanine.
Galactosemia	Inability to convert the sugar galactose to glucose, resulting in a buildup of galactose	Intellectual disability, growth deficiency, cataracts, severe infections, death	Eliminate milk and other dairy products from the diet. Galactose is one of two sugars in lactose (milk sugar).
Biotinidase deficiency	Inability to separate the vitamin biotin from other chemicals, resulting in a biotin deficiency	Seizures, hearing loss, optic atrophy, intellectual disability, poor muscle control	Take oral biotin supplements.
Maple syrup urine disease	Deficiency in an enzyme complex, resulting in an inability to metabolize the amino acids leucine, isoleucine, and valine	Intellectual disability in those surviving past 3 months of age	Restrict dietary intake of the affected amino acids.
Homocystinuria	Defect in methionine metabolism, leading to an accumulation of homocysteine	Dislocated lenses of the eyes, intellectual disability, skeletal abnormalities, abnormal blood clotting	Take high doses of vitamin B_6; eat methionine-restricted diet supplemented with cysteine.
Tyrosinemia	Deficiency in a series of enzymes that break down the amino acid tyrosine	Mild intellectual disability, language skill difficulties, liver and kidney failure	Restrict dietary tyrosine and phenylalanine.

Chapter-by-Chapter Changes

Global Changes

- Added Chapter 0 to assist students with studying techniques and provide an understanding of the language and conceptual framework of anatomy and physiology.
- Added Vision and Change information to relevant locations within the text. For example, when discussing membrane potentials, we point out that ion gradients follow the key concept of concentration gradients found within many systems.
- Added tips for students to aid them in answering the Learn to Predict questions at the beginning of the chapter by adding the statement, This information may help you in answering this chapter's Learn to Predict.
- Added some active learning activities. For example, in chapter 6, the students are prompted to soak a chicken bone in vinegar for some time and evaluate the change in texture. In chapter 3, the students are encouraged to sketch, using "dots," a representation of two solutions, each with a different pH, and then evaluate whether the more acidic solution had more "dots" (H^+).
- Replaced chapter opener photos with summary figures that provide an overview of the concepts presented in that chapter.
- Added roadmap figures (often a two-page spread) to help students see an entire concept from beginning to end. These roadmap figures then reappear throughout the chapter, with a particular portion of the figure (the one being discussed) highlighted.
- Changed pronunciations to phonetic (e.g., isometric [eye-soh-MET-rik]).
- Updated art throughout using more vibrant colors, modernized the images, created a more 3D image that doesn't look cartoony, and improved connections between separate ideas.
- Added Bloom's icons next to in-chapter questions.
- Moved "Effects of Aging" section to a boxed reading.
- Changed the "Summary" section to the "Concept Check" section with the review and comprehension questions and the critical thinking questions integrated into the corresponding section.
- Removed the purple circle text lists from process figures and integrated them into the narrative text. The purple circles remain in the figure art and have statement-style descriptors for the student to follow the process. The lengthy descriptions of the process are integrated into the narrative with corresponding purple circles to provide a complete explanation. This will help with projection of the figures in a lecture hall as well as cognitive load for the students.
- For accessibility, discontinued referring to objects within the line art by color only to help students with visual impairments, including students who are color blind.
- Used gender-neutral terms throughout (*male* and *female* rather than *man, boy, woman, girl*).

Chapter 1

- Added new chapter opener with an overview of the major body systems.
- Introduced four key concepts consistent with Vision and Change to be carried throughout the text.
- Modified table 1.1 to be one column and reduced the amount of text to reduce cognitive load.
- Modified figure 1.1 to correlate each level more clearly with the next.
- Moved section 1.4 "Biomedical Research" earlier in chapter to avoid interrupting the flow of the remaining chapter material.
- Revised section on homeostasis for clarity and accuracy based on reviewer feedback.
- Added a new figure to introduce feedback loops.
- Added art to figure 1.6 to explain positive-feedback mechanisms.
- Deleted former figure 1.7 based on reviewer feedback.
- Added some active learning activities to section on directional terms.

Chapter 2

- Added new chapter opener with an overview of interconnections between major concepts.
- Converted figure 2.7 to a process figure and added an image highlighting the electron density.
- Revised figure 2.9 to show connections between different bond types.

Chapter 3

- Added new chapter opener with an overview of major components of a cell.
- Revised table 3.1 to designate "cytoplasmic extensions."
- Added description of transcytosis.
- Added description of the polarity of the Golgi apparatus (*cis* v. *trans*).

- Added information about spliceosome in discussion of gene expression.
- Added prometaphase in discussion of mitosis.

Chapter 4

- Added new chapter opener summarizing tissue types throughout the body.
- Reorganized the introduction to section 4.1 for clarity.
- Added a new figure 4.1 to introduce the basic epithelial tissue types first.
- Revised descriptions of epithelial tissues for clarity.
- Revised tables 4.2, 4.3, and 4.4 to illustrate tissue types more clearly.
- Revised section on cell layers and cell shapes for clarity.
- Split former table 4.5 into two tables to separate simple and stratified.
- Revised section on cell connections for clarity.
- Rewrote section on glands to organize material to compare structure vs. mode of secretion.
- Added new table 4.5 to organize glands by structure and secretion mode.
- Combined old figures 4.3 and 4.4 into one figure for closer comparison.
- Revised tables 4.7–4.14 to illustrate tissue types more clearly.

Chapter 5

- Added new chapter opener with an overview of components of the integumentary system.
- Added some receptors to skin figure.
- Added new dermis figure identifying papillary and reticular layers and sensory receptors.
- Added new figure of types of injections.
- Added vitamin D production figure.

Chapter 6

- Added new chapter opener with an overview of bone anatomy.
- Added more micrographs of hyaline cartilage to figure 6.1.
- Added photomicrograph of osteoclast to figure 6.3.
- Added image of infant's legs to osteogenesis Clinical Genetics box.
- Replaced figure 6.16 with a more accurate depiction of this process.
- Added a photograph of a sectioned long bone to figure 6.8.
- Added photographs of different bone shapes to figure 6.9.
- Revised the introduction under calcium homeostasis for clarity.
- Added information about toll-like receptors to discussion of osteoclasts and osteoblast regulation of bone deposition and reabsorption.

Chapter 7

- Added new chapter opener with an overview of skeletal system functions.
- Added photographs to skull figures as well as some analogy images as learning devices (e.g., an image of crown placement to draw link for coronal suture).
- Replaced x-ray with MRI images in figure 7.13 for paranasal sinuses.
- Reorganized art of cervical vertebrae to compare atlas and axis directly as well to compare lateral and superior views of cervical vertebrae to each other.
- Added color coding to table 7.7 to better correlate each bone to overall location within skull and to all other colored skull images throughout chapter.
- Revised figure in table 7.9 to add a color gradient to spine to more readily differentiate between different regions of spinal column.
- Added x-rays of the other spinal deformations to Clinical Impact 7.1.
- Added color coding to figures 7.25–7.37 for better orientation of bone within overall skeleton.
- Added images of separated radius and ulna, and tibia and fibula.

Chapter 8

- Added new chapter opener with an overview of joint types.
- Added x-ray image of osteoarthritic knee to Clinical Impact 8.2.
- Added table 8.3 highlighting differences between osteoarthritis and rheumatoid arthritis.
- Combined figures 8.9–8.19 into one figure, separating them into angular movements, circular movements, and special movements.
- Added an x-ray to each joint image.

Chapter 9

- Added new chapter opener that provides organizational understanding of skeletal muscle structure.
- Added photomicrographs to table 9.1 for each muscle tissue type.
- Added photomicrograph of skeletal muscle cross section to figure 9.1.
- Revised figure 9.3 to clarify relationship between T tubules and terminal cisternae.

- Revised figure 9.5 into two-page spread to help students make connections between sarcomere structure, NMJ, and myofilament structure.
- Changed myosin head orientation in figure 9.6 to show contracted state.
- Added two-page spread on action potential generation, correlation with ion channels, and electrical output.
- Added Ca^{2+} channels to figure highlighting muscle relaxation.
- Updated figure 9.26 on mechanism of smooth muscle contraction.

Chapter 10

- Added new chapter opener with an overview of the muscles of the body.
- Added organizing bracket for muscle groups to figure 10.3*a,b*.
- Placed tables highlighting muscle functions on facing pages with the art of each group of muscles.
- Reorganized table 10.3 by body region (mouth, eye, neck, etc.).
- Reorganized table 10.19 by muscle group rather than directionally (e.g., gluteal group, adductor group, etc.).
- Replaced figures showing leg muscles with a figure organized by group as they are in table 10.19.

Chapter 11

- Added new chapter opener with an overview of the nervous system.
- Revised figure 11.2 to include visual references for sensory and motor divisions of the PNS.
- Added photomicrograph of neuromuscular junction to figure 11.3 neuron.
- Created new glial cell figures to summarize structure and function.
- Added two new summary figures of neuron communication highlighting action potential generation, action propagation, and synaptic communication.
- Revised figure 11.12 graded potential to include image of neuron for clarity.
- Updated figures 11.16 and 11.17 illustrating action propagation to include shaded areas indicating state of membrane potential changes.

Chapter 12

- Added new figure and text describing methods of classifying reflexes.
- Revised images of withdrawal reflex to be a more accurate representation.

Chapter 13

- Added new chapter opener that highlights the regions of the brain.
- Added labels to cranial nerves in table 13.5 for better reference.

Chapter 14

- Added new chapter opener with an overview of the integration of nervous system functions.
- Revised table 14.1 to provide specific examples of special senses receptors.
- Added new figure 14.5 illustrating the three major sensory pathways for better comparison.
- Added posterior view to figure 14.6 illustrating areas of referred pain on the body surface.
- Added new figure 14.10 illustrating the somatic motor pathways for better comparison.

Chapter 15

- Added new chapter opener with an overview of the special senses.
- Added new figure 15.13, which provides a summary of the physiology of vision.
- Revised figure 15.15 to match terminology of text and better represent tension levels in suspensory ligaments.
- Revised figure 15.20 to reinforce light conditions for each scenario.
- Used *external acoustic meatus* throughout description of the ear.

Chapter 16

- Added new chapter opener with an overview of the two divisions of the autonomic nervous system.
- Revised figure 16.1 to include all categories of tissues innervated by the ANS.
- Revised figures 16.2 and 16.4 to depict the CNS more accurately.
- Added new figure 16.5 to illustrate the sympathetic pathways.
- Added new figure 16.6 to illustrate the parasympathetic pathways.

Chapter 17

- Completely reorganized this chapter.
- Added new chapter opener with an overview of the major mechanisms of action in hormones.
- Revised figure 17.4 to show a side-by-side comparison of types of hormonal secretion controls.

- Redrew all the hormonal feedback figures in a more streamlined fashion as a flow chart, rather than being as loosely constructed.
- Revised figure 17.10 to demonstrate cytoplasmic receptors and thyroid hormone transporters.
- Revised figure 17.11 to include the three different types of alpha subunits.
- Revised figure 17.12 to include the phosphodiesterase icon.
- Redrew figure 17.13 to more accurately represent the tyrosine kinase receptor mechanism and structure.
- Redrew figure 17.15 (originally 17.11) to more clearly illustrate up- and down-regulation.
- Added information about hormone interactions as well as an illustration to the chapter.

Chapter 18

- Added new chapter opener with an overview of the interactions among all the components of a particular hormone system (thyroid hormones).
- Redrew figure 18.1 to more accurately reflect the correct vascular anatomy of the anterior pituitary.
- Revised figure 18.3 to more clearly show the release of neurohormones into the circulation.
- Redrew figure 18.4 to correlate ADH delivery to kidney more closely.
- Revised figure 18.7 to more visually represent muscle, bone, adipose, etc.
- Redrew figure 18.10 to be more clear.
- Added line art for regions of the adrenal cortex to figure 18.14.
- Revised figure 18.15 to show the breakdown of adrenal medulla actions on various tissues more clearly.
- Redrew figure 18.20 for clarity.
- Redrew figure 18.21 for clarity.

Chapter 19

- Added new chapter opener with an overview of blood composition.
- Added new process figure 19.6 to illustrate the role of EPO in red blood cell production.
- Revised process figure 19.7 to illustrate the breakdown of hemoglobin clearly.
- Revised process figure 19.15 to illustrate the sequence of events that often result in sensitization of an Rh-negative female.

Chapter 20

- Added new chapter opener with an overview of the heart anatomy.
- Added new figure 20.11, which provides a clearer representation of cardiac muscle.
- Revised process figure 20.12 with an overview of the conducting system of the heart as well as the electrical and mechanical events of contraction of the heart.
- Revised figure 20.15 to clearly illustrate refractory period and timing of maximum tension.
- Revised figure 20.18 to include images to better correlate events of the cardiac cycle.
- Revised table 20.1 to include ECG tracings of specific cardiac arrythmias.
- Revised discussion of ECG for clarity.
- Revised figure 20.20 to better illustrate the relationships among cardiac output, peripheral resistance, and mean arterial pressure.

Chapter 21

- Added new figure 21.2, which represents all major categories of blood vessels.
- Updated figures 21.14 and 21.15.
- Revised figure 21.25 to include additional information about blood pressure differences in various blood vessels.
- Updated figure 21.28 for clarity.
- Revised Clinical Impact on circulatory shock.

Chapter 22

- Revised “Lymphatic Tissue and Organs” section to include description of primary lymphatic organs and secondary lymphatic organs and tissues.
- Added new figure 22.10 with an overview of the components of immunity.
- Added images of cells to table 22.2.
- Added illustration of tissue damage to figure 22.12 for clarity.
- Added new figures representing MHC classes separately to better align with placement in text.
- Updated figure 22.20 to better illustrate the increase in immunity cells.
- Revised figure 22.23 to distinguish between primary and secondary immune response.
- Reorganized Section 22.5 “Adaptive Immunity” for clarity.
- Updated figure 22.6 to include images representing ways to acquire adaptive immunity.

Chapter 23

- Added new chapter opener with an overview of the functions of the respiratory system.
- Revised figure 23.1 to include alveoli and zones of the respiratory system.
- Changed the term *ventilation* to *pulmonary ventilation*.
- Changed the term *respiration* to *pulmonary gas exchange* or *tissue gas exchange*.

- Added color coding to the regions of the pharynx in figure 23.2 for clarity.
- Added line art to figure 23.4 showing vocal cord structure in high- vs. low-pitch sound production.
- Added a cross-sectional photomicrograph of the trachea to figure 23.5.
- Added an image of a cast of the tracheobronchial tree to figure 23.6.
- Added labels for the fissures as well as names of lung lobes to figure 23.8.
- Deleted table 23.1 and replaced with new figure demonstrating gas laws.
- Revised figure 23.11 to show changes in lung volume in a side-by-side manner with inspiration vs. expiration.
- Removed numbers from figure 23.13 and added them to a table to accompany the graph of lung volumes and lung capacities.
- Added labels to figure 23.15 for clarity.
- Created a two-page spread for figure 23.16 to help make connections between gas exchange at the tissues vs. the lungs.
- Deleted figure 23.17 because it was too simplistic.
- Added hemoglobin line art to cytoplasm of red blood cell to help students make the connection that O_2 binds to Hb within the red blood cell.
- Added values to figure 23.18 for Hb saturation at various P_{O_2}.
- Combined parts *a* and *b* for figure 23.19 to more clearly compare the curve shift to the right vs. a shift to the left.
- Updated the text in the "Generation of Rhythmic Pulmonary Ventilation" section to more accurately reflect the current understanding of the regulation of respiration.
- Redrew figure 23.20 to be more realistic and to more accurately reflect the effectors of the efferent nerves.
- Added a new figure for the chemoreceptor reflex to integrate the regulation of the respiratory rate.

Chapter 24

- Added new chapter opener with an overview of the functions of the digestive system.
- Deleted table 24.1 and replaced with the new figure 24.2 that is less visually intimidating to students.
- Updated the information on the mesentery to reflect its status as a continuous organ subdivided into six regions. This leads to the separation of the abdomen into two domains: the mesenteric domain and the nonmesenteric domain.
- Revised figure 24.5 to show the newly elucidated anatomy of the mesentery.
- Added a surface view of the tongue and its papillae to figure 24.6.
- Added tables to figure 24.6 with tooth numbers and names of the teeth to clean up the art.
- Deleted table 24.2 and replaced with new figure 24.9, which decreases the cognitive load.
- Placed figure 24.10 into a vertical format with brackets and labels to help discern the different stages of deglutition.
- Updated figure 24.11 to differentiate the various cell types in the gastric glands.
- Revised figure 24.12 to reflect the appropriate structure of a parietal cell.
- Throughout the chapter, made the arrow color for the vagus nerve one consistent color.
- Added color coding to figure 24.15 for the different regions of the small intestine.
- Revised the colon in figure 24.25 to show more detail and to include the vasculature.
- Combined section 24.10 to include the liver, pancreas, and gallbladder.
- Simplified figure 24.27 for clarity.
- Added a two-page spread linking region of the digestive system with specific nutrients digested within the portion.
- Redrew figure 24.35 to correlate source of fluid with reabsorbed fluid.

Chapter 25

- Added new chapter opener highlighting the concept of macronutrients.
- Updated discussion of *Dietary Guidelines for Americans*.
- Included terms *dispensable* and *indispensable* in discussion of essential nutrients.
- Revised description of amino acids to include description of conditionally essential amino acids.
- Added new Process figure 25.4 with an overview of the use of the three major nutrients (carbohydrates, lipids, and proteins) for ATP production.
- Revised figure 25.14 to better represent text, including description of lipogenesis.

Chapter 26

- Added new chapter opener summarizing the functions of the urinary system.
- Updated figure 26.1 to include more detail internally for kidney anatomy.
- Changed terminology to include *glomerular capsule, nephron loop, cortical radiate artery* or *vein, renal threshold,* and *transport maximum.*
- Added figure summarizing urine flow from kidneys to urinary bladder.
- Added electron micrographs to figure 26.5.
- Added photomicrographs to figure 26.6.
- Added a flow chart for blood flow through kidney to figure 26.7.

- Revised figure 26.8 to be more realistic to summarize the three steps in urine production.
- Revised figure 26.9 to look more realistic for calculation of filtration pressures.
- Added an orientation inset to figures 26.10–26.13 that correlates with a two-page spread summarizing events in urine production.
- Added interstitial fluid gradient background to figure 26.14.
- Revised figure 26.17 RAAS art to include organ icons to help students make those connections.
- Added an image of an aquaporin to figure 26.19.
- Added comparison of male vs. female urethra to figure 26.22.

Chapter 27

- Added new chapter opener summarizing the movements of ions and fluid into and out of the cell.
- Added new figure 27.1 to visually represent the distribution of water throughout the body.
- Added new figure 27.2 to visually represent the distribution of ions between the intracellular and extracellular fluid.
- Added line art to figure 27.3 to illustrate the different forces within the capillary.
- Reorganized section 27.1 and deleted section 27.2.
- Added headings "Fluid Input" and "Fluid Output."
- Added a figure on the baroreceptor reflex to integrate with fluid input.
- Reorganized section on thirst to regulation of intake vs. regulation of output.
- Added a summary figure on changes in blood osmolality to replace deleted table 27.5.
- Rearranged tables containing information about abnormal ion levels so that there can be a side-by-side comparison of *hypo-* vs. *hyper-*.
- Reorganized each section on a particular ion to discuss the material in the same order: Function, Regulation, Imbalances.
- Deleted figures 27.9 and 27.10.
- Created new section "Hormonal Mechanisms Regulating Body Fluid Composition."
- Deleted table 27.11.
- Rearranged the "Acid-Base Imbalances" section so all "acidosis" information is together and under the "Acidosis" head and all "alkalosis" information is together and under the "Alkalosis" head.

Chapter 28

- Added new figure 28.1 as an overview of the organs of the male and female reproductive systems.
- Added new chapter opener comparing spermatogenesis and oogenesis.
- Removed information about reproductive hormones and effects in females from table 28.1 and used it to create new table 28.2 so that the information is located in the proper area of the chapter.
- Added new figure and description of oogenesis, with a separate panel for ovarian follicle development.
- Revised description of ovarian cycle for clarity.
- Revised figure 28.19 to include panel labels for easier referencing in text.
- Revised figure 28.20 for clarity and to better correlate with description in text.
- Converted table 28.4 to new figure.

Chapter 29

- Added new chapter opener and figure 29.1 illustrating the life stages.
- Added description of *SRY* gene in discussion of development of male reproductive system.

Remote Proctoring & Browser-Locking Capabilities

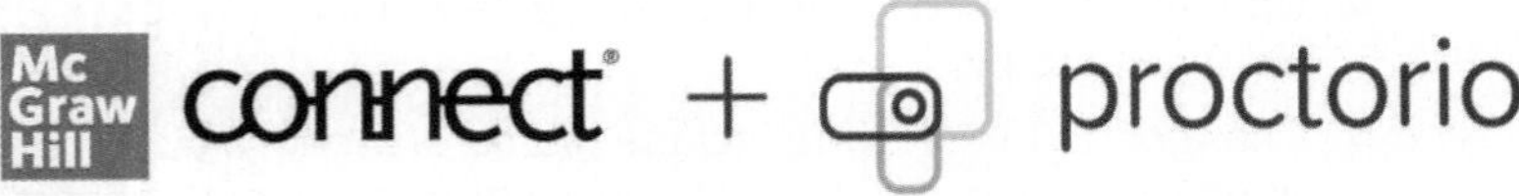

New remote proctoring and browser-locking capabilities, hosted by Proctorio within Connect, provide control of the assessment environment by enabling security options and verifying the identity of the student.

Seamlessly integrated within Connect, these services allow instructors to control students' assessment experience by restricting browser activity, recording students' activity, and verifying students are doing their own work.

Instant and detailed reporting gives instructors an at-a-glance view of potential academic integrity concerns, thereby avoiding personal bias and supporting evidence-based claims.

50% of the country's students are unable to pass the A&P course*

McGraw Hill empowers students to learn and succeed in the Anatomy and Physiology course.

SMARTBOOK®

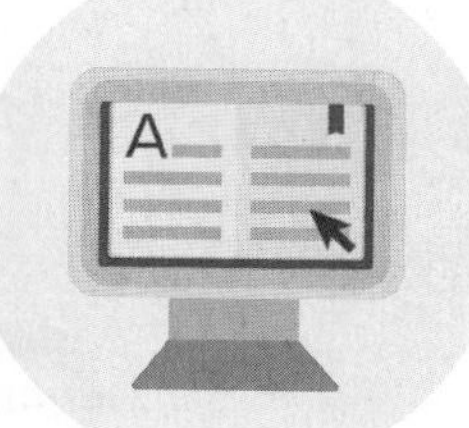

SmartBook provides personalized learning to individual student needs, continually adapting to pinpoint knowledge gaps and focus learning on concepts requiring additional study. The result? Students are highly engaged in the content and better prepared for lecture.

PREP

A&P Prep helps students thrive in college-level A&P by helping solidify knowledge in the key areas of cell biology, chemistry, study skills, and math. The result? Students are better prepared for the A&P course.

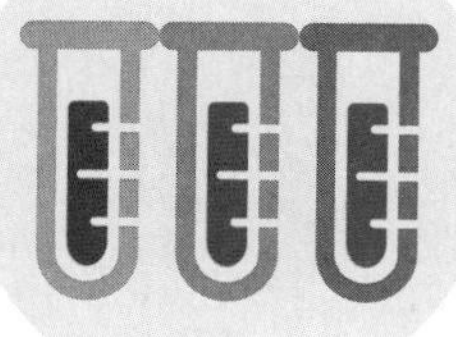

PhILS

Ph.I.L.S. 4.0 (Physiology Interactive Lab Simulations) software is the perfect way to reinforce key physiology concepts with powerful lab experiments. The result? Students gain critical thinking skills and are better prepared for lab.

Concept Overview Interactives are groundbreaking interactive animations that encourage students to explore key physiological processes and difficult concepts. The result? Students are engaged and able to apply what they've learned while tackling difficult A&P concepts.

Practice ATLAS

Practice Atlas for A&P is an interactive tool that pairs images of common anatomical models with stunning cadaver photography, allowing students to practice naming structures on both models and human bodies, anytime, anywhere. The result? Students are better prepared, engaged, and move beyond basic memorization.

Virtual Labs

Connect Virtual Labs helps connect the dots between lab and lecture, boosts student confidence and knowledge, and improves student success rates. The result? Students are engaged, prepared, and utilize critical thinking skills.

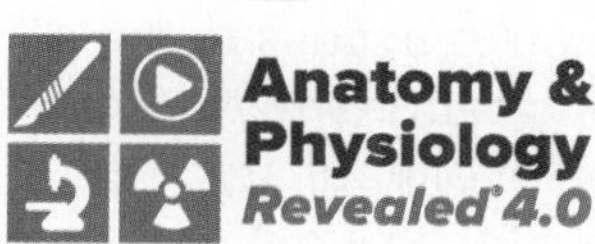

Anatomy & Physiology Revealed® (APR) 4.0 is an interactive cadaver dissection tool to enhance lecture and lab that students can use anytime, anywhere. The result? Students are prepared for lab, engaged in the material, and utilize critical thinking.

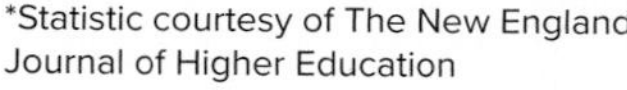

*Statistic courtesy of The New England Journal of Higher Education

Instructors: Student Success Starts with You

Tools to enhance your unique voice

Want to build your own course? No problem. Prefer to use an OLC-aligned, prebuilt course? Easy. Want to make changes throughout the semester? Sure. And you'll save time with Connect's auto-grading too.

65%
Less Time Grading

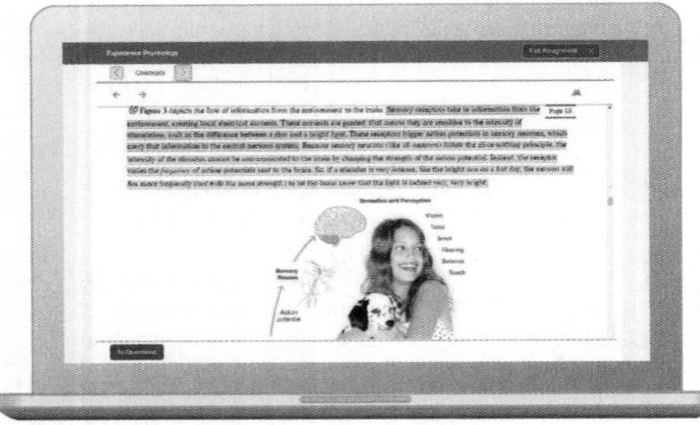

Laptop: McGraw Hill; Woman/dog: George Doyle/Getty Images

Study made personal

Incorporate adaptive study resources like SmartBook® 2.0 into your course and help your students be better prepared in less time. Learn more about the powerful personalized learning experience available in SmartBook 2.0 at **www.mheducation.com/highered/connect/smartbook**

Affordable solutions, added value

Make technology work for you with LMS integration for single sign-on access, mobile access to the digital textbook, and reports to quickly show you how each of your students is doing. And with our Inclusive Access program you can provide all these tools at a discount to your students. Ask your McGraw Hill representative for more information.

Padlock: Jobalou/Getty Images

Solutions for your challenges

A product isn't a solution. Real solutions are affordable, reliable, and come with training and ongoing support when you need it and how you want it. Visit **www.supportateverystep.com** for videos and resources both you and your students can use throughout the semester.

Checkmark: Jobalou/Getty Images

Students: Get Learning that Fits You

Effective tools for efficient studying

Connect is designed to help you be more productive with simple, flexible, intuitive tools that maximize your study time and meet your individual learning needs. Get learning that works for you with Connect.

Study anytime, anywhere

Download the free ReadAnywhere app and access your online eBook, SmartBook 2.0, or Adaptive Learning Assignments when it's convenient, even if you're offline. And since the app automatically syncs with your Connect account, all of your work is available every time you open it. Find out more at **www.mheducation.com/readanywhere**

"I really liked this app—it made it easy to study when you don't have your text-book in front of you."

- Jordan Cunningham, Eastern Washington University

Calendar: owattaphotos/Getty Images

Everything you need in one place

Your Connect course has everything you need—whether reading on your digital eBook or completing assignments for class, Connect makes it easy to get your work done.

Learning for everyone

McGraw Hill works directly with Accessibility Services Departments and faculty to meet the learning needs of all students. Please contact your Accessibility Services Office and ask them to email accessibility@mheducation.com, or visit **www.mheducation.com/about/accessibility** for more information.

Top: Jenner Images/Getty Images, Left: Hero Images/Getty Images, Right: Hero Images/Getty Images

CHAPTER

How to Be Successful in A&P

dotshock/Shutterstock

Hello, Students! Author Cinnamon VanPutte would like to share something with you: She failed her college organic chemistry course. Later, she retook it and earned an "A." Why does this matter to you? We hope this helps you understand that your authors have been there. Yes, we've earned an "A" in hard classes—but we also know what it is to struggle in a class. We've had to retool our study habits; we've had to learn how to effectively use a textbook. These experiences have helped inform our approach to this textbook, and we hope this helps you. We know that many of you will sail right through A&P and would have done so even without reading this success guide, while others may be retaking A&P for the second or third time. By taking the time to read this guide, you have already taken a positive first step toward succeeding in A&P. You have entered a partnership with your instructor and us, the authors. If you utilize the tips, techniques, and information that we, as well as your instructors, are providing to you, we know you will learn a lot of information and you will be positioned to succeed in this course.

0.1 The World of A&P

If you search online for "hardest classes in college," A&P will show up on many lists. But don't worry! We are here to help! We have each taught A&P for more than 20 years and have seen countless students, who were very nervous on the first day, successfully move through the course—all the while gaining self-assurance, confidence, and a deep understanding of the fundamental concepts needed to perform well in the course.

The study of A&P entails a lot of information. Depending on the particular course, the first semester of A&P may start with a discussion of matter and chemical bonds, and end with the complexities of the nervous system (such as action potentials). Truthfully, this means progressing from introductory material to more advanced material within a single semester.

In addition, you will be learning the vocabulary of A&P, which means you are essentially learning a foreign language—you might even feel like you're learning more new vocabulary than if you were actually learning a foreign language! In an effort to make this task easier, our textbook provides phonetic pronunciations of these vocabulary terms, similar to those found on Facebook for people's names. For example, the gluteus maximus pronunciation would be: GLOO-tee-us MAX-ih-mus. We think this type of guide will help you learn the terminology very readily and be more confident speaking the language—if you can say it out loud, then you can probably spell it and are better poised to remember it.

It's also important to realize that the information in A&P cannot be effectively understood through memorization alone. Several of the physiology concepts require that you use critical thinking skills. Many of you may be planning careers in science or health professions, such as nursing or pharmacy—professions in which the ability to problem solve is essential. In this book we will help you develop critical thinking skills and thus a deeper understanding of complex concepts.

0.2 Developing Critical Thinking Skills

So, what is required to develop critical thinking skills? What are critical thinking skills? To understand these questions, we need to explore the difference between simple memorization—what you may have always called "studying"—and **conceptual learning.** Many of you have enjoyed much success in high school and in some of your early introductory-level college classes through "studying." However, to be successful in most A&P classes, you will also need to develop skills for conceptual learning. The basis for this difference is best described using Bloom's taxonomy, originally published by B. Bloom and colleagues in 1956. Over time, Bloom's taxonomy has been modified and can be best thought of as a model for the gradual increase in the amount of abstract thought required to achieve a particular level of learning. The simplest, most concrete level of learning is *remembering*, or simply memorizing. As you climb the levels of Bloom's, your ability to put ideas into your own words (*understanding*) and then to solve problems you've never seen before (*applying*) increases. Thus, as you gain these skills, you are now *learning* the material and can answer **how** and **why** a particular process happens, and you can predict outcomes to unfamiliar scenarios. This textbook will guide you in developing those skills.

To do this, you will begin to use **metacognition** in your learning. *Metacognition* was first defined by Flavell in 1976 as "thinking about your own thinking"—in other words, deciding whether you truly understand and can apply fundamental physiological and anatomical principles. We are going to provide you with five metacognitive learning strategies to ensure your success in A&P.

0.3 Five Metacognitive Learning Strategies

What will you need to do to achieve the goal of being successful in A&P? There are five specific tasks you can employ to be successful in A&P. These tasks are adapted from the book *Teach Students How to Learn* by S. Y. McGuire. They are the following:

1. Attend every class session and take notes with a pen and paper.
2. Read, read, read!
3. Work with other students.
4. Do homework as if it were the test.
5. Engage in concentrated study sessions.

We will address each of these tasks in the remainder of this success guide with specific information on how to use this textbook.

0.4 Using the Five Metacognitive Learning Strategies with This Textbook

1. *Attendance and Note-Taking.* It is essential that you attend each class session. As you can see, this book has 29 chapters, each of which covers a topic for which you could take an entire semester class, or more! Your instructor will decide what material you will cover. Some instructors may expect you to glean specific information directly from the book. Therefore, to make sure you hear, firsthand, all the information and messages your instructor presents in class, it is critical you be in class. Then, while in class, take notes by hand! Students who handwrite their notes outperform students who take notes with their laptops. The difference is that taking notes by hand requires you to use your own words, which helps you remember the information better. After the class session, it is also helpful to take notes by hand directly from the assigned chapters.
2. *Read, Read, Read!* Possibly one of the biggest misconceptions regarding reading a textbook is that it is no different from reading a novel—which couldn't be farther from the truth. Reading a science textbook involves a slow and systematic process. There are three types of reading strategies you'll need to employ to get the most information from each chapter: (a) preview, (b) prepare for active reading, (c) actively read.
   a. Preview
      Previewing a chapter is like watching a movie trailer or reading the description of a book to see what it's about and whether it interests you. Skim the section headings. Each system chapter of this textbook is laid out in the following way:
      - Anatomy of the System
        - Organs
        - Histology
      - Functions of the System
        - Major Functions
        - Integration of Functions for Homeostasis

      Some sections are further subdivided into specialized topics to walk you through a process step-by-step.
      While you're previewing the chapter, pay attention to bolded terms, phonetic pronunciations, and word origins. Root words tell a lot of information about a process or structure; for example, *hyper-* indicates higher or above, and *hypo-* indicates lower or below, and they are used both anatomically and physiologically.
   b. Prepare for Active Reading
      As you're previewing, or as a next step, write out questions you'd like answered as you read. The bold terms can be used as a guide to the questions.
   c. Actively Read
      After you've previewed the chapter and have done the preparations for active reading, the next step is to actively read. This can be done one paragraph, or one concept in SmartBook 2.0, at a time. Write notes in your own words as you read. Add a paragraph, or concept, at a time, all the while adding ideas from the previous paragraph. In this way, you're "taking one bite at a time" of the chapter's information. This helps your brain integrate information and keeps it from suffering information overload. As you actively read, there are several features that are consistent throughout this text that can serve as guideposts for you. We present these features in the section "Textbook Features and Figure Colors and Symbols."
3. *Work with Other Students Enrolled in the Same Class.* Author C. VanPutte would like to share something else with you: She did not fully comprehend the concept of osmosis until she taught her first college-level class. Once she had to explain the concept out loud and in her own words, a light

clicked on! So, form study groups! Assign each other topics on which to lecture to the group. Write practice exams for each other. Sometimes your peers can help you as much as, or perhaps more than, the instructor.

4. *Do Homework as If It Were the Test.* For most lecture exams you will not be allowed to use your notes, the textbook, or the Internet. So you need to practice for that situation. Don't simply copy answers onto your homework assignments. Instead, study first, then do the homework without assistance. If you get stuck, use your resources. For example, you could do a "recharge" in SmartBook 2.0, or visit your instructor during their office hours.
5. *Utilize Multiple, Intense, Short Study Sessions.* Our brains work more efficiently when we stay focused for a relatively brief period of time: approximately 30–50 minutes. Staring blankly at your notes for 3 hours is not helpful. Therefore, decide what you're going to focus on, then study with intent for 30–50 minutes. Studying with intent involves actively engaging with the material. This can include making a concept map, expanding on your notes and rephrasing them, writing out a summary, and simply thinking about the material. Take a short 10- to 15-minute break, then briefly review what you just studied. Do this 3–5 times a day for each class in which you're enrolled.

0.5 Textbook Features and Figure Colors and Symbols

Throughout this textbook you will see certain repeating features and symbols. These symbols are always a particular color; however, for our students with vision disabilities, these colored symbols are also uniquely labeled.

1. In-Text Numbering
   As you're reading, look for areas where we've tried to make complex topics clearer by numbering steps or components. This ensures that you don't miss a step or a part.

> In an unstimulated cell, this charge difference is called the **resting membrane potential.** Although we call it the resting membrane potential, the cell is more like a sprinter in starting blocks; it is ready to respond at a moment's notice. The resting membrane potential is the result of three factors: (1) The concentration of K^+ inside the cell membrane is higher than that outside the cell membrane, (2) the concentration of Na^+ outside the cell membrane is higher than that inside the cell membrane, and (3) the cell membrane is more permeable to K^+ than to Na^+.

2. Process Figures
   For complex processes, we have process figures that break down the step-by-step sequence of events. The in-text explanations directly correlate to portions of the figure by the use of purple-circled numbers.

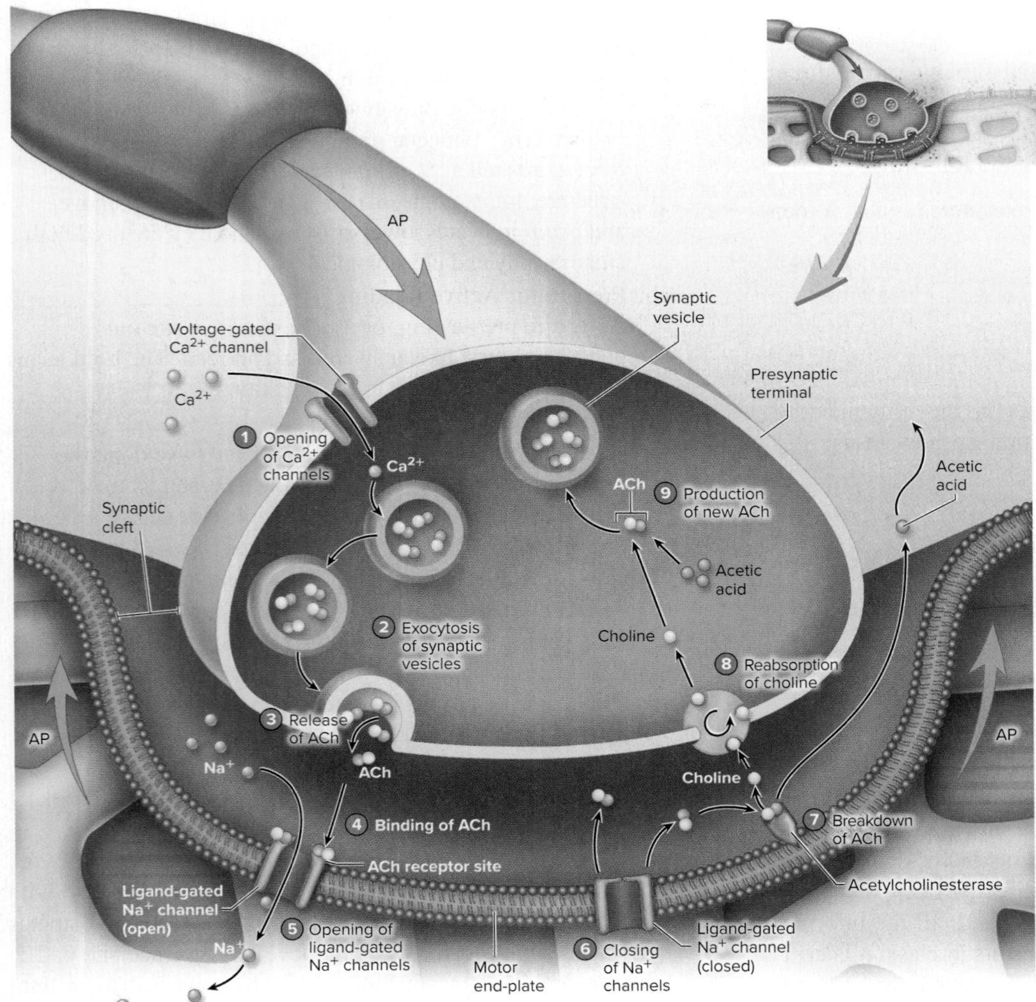

3. Side-by-Side Anatomy Figures
   In certain anatomy figures, we have placed a photograph next to an artistic rendering. This allows for accurate interpretation of artist-generated figures.

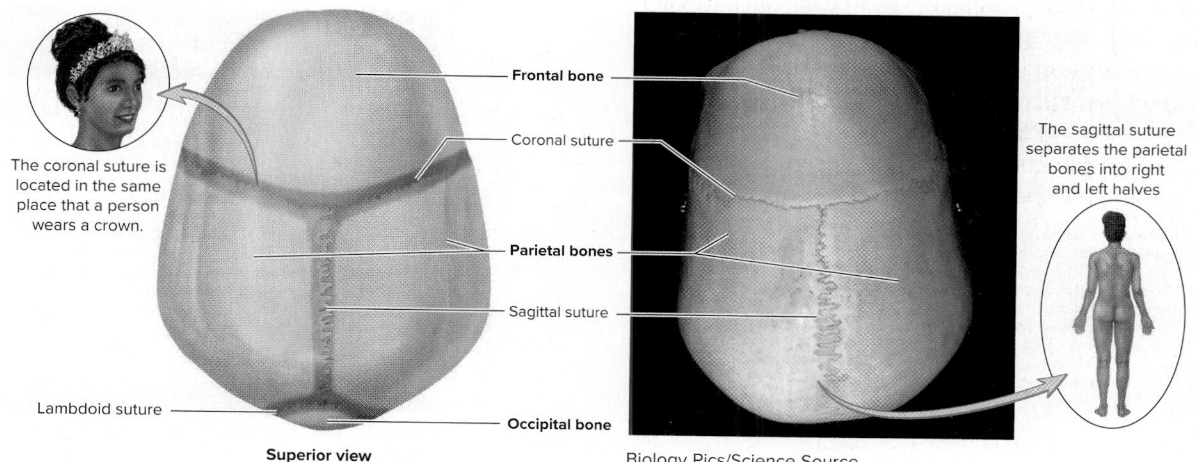

4. Homeostasis Figures
   These figures walk you through certain critical physiological mechanisms involved in the maintenance of homeostasis. Icons depict the particular organs discussed, in order to help strengthen associations between anatomy and physiology.

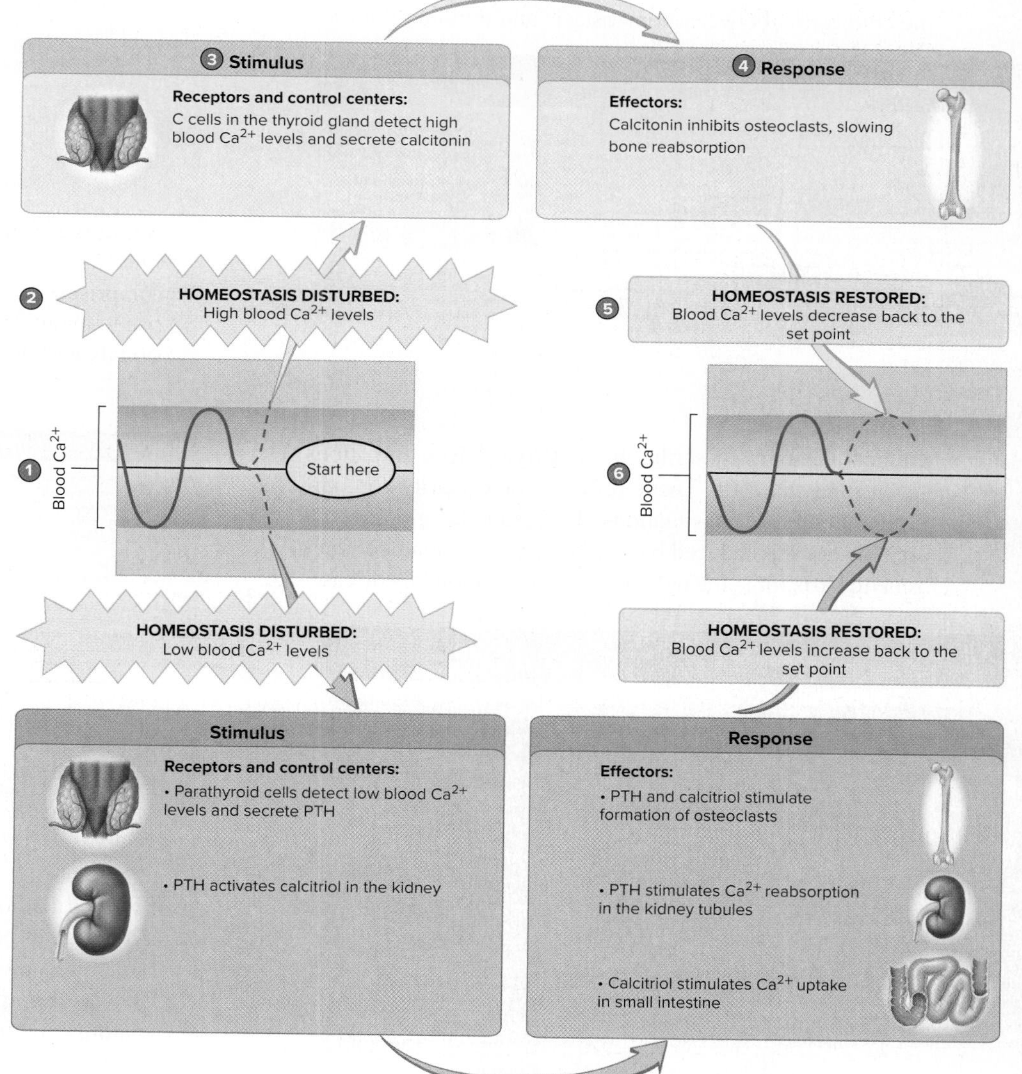

5. Clinical Content
   a. Clinical Impact: explore interesting clinical aspects of the body system being discussed. These are like commercial breaks in the reading, allowing you to relate the content to a "real-world" example.

Clinical IMPACT 12.3

Sciatic Nerve Damage

If a person sits on a hard surface for a considerable time, the sciatic nerve may be compressed against the ischial portion of the hip bone. When the person stands up, he or she feels a tingling sensation, described as "pins and needles," throughout the lower limb and often remarks that the limb has "gone to sleep." This condition is temporary, but the sciatic nerve can be seriously injured in a number of ways. A ruptured intervertebral disk or pressure from the uterus during pregnancy may compress the roots of the sciatic nerve. Other causes of sciatic nerve damage include hip injury, compression of the nerve by the piriformis muscle (piriformis syndrome), and an improperly administered injection in the hip region (see Clinical Impact 7.3).

   b. Microbes in Your Body: highlight the role of microbes in maintaining homeostasis. With the ever-expanding understanding of the microbiome, these provide some context of the connection between homeostasis and the microbiome.

MICROBES In Your Body 20.1 | **How Bacteria Affect Cardiac Muscle**

You've learned that the majority of bacteria are either harmless or an integral part of our well-being. Unfortunately, there are a handful of pathogenic bacteria that can interfere with the body's homeostasis.

Most people associate bacterial pneumonia with the lungs only. However, in the medical community, it is well known that pneumonia can cause serious heart problems. In fact, cardiac problems cause 70% of the deaths in individuals with other types of severe bacterial infections. Most bacterial pneumonia is caused by the bacterium *Streptococcus pneumoniae*, but until recently the mechanism by which this pathogen damages the heart had not been well understood. It seems that these bacteria induce the cells lining blood vessels to endocytose them and deposit them in cardiac muscle tissue. There, the bacteria release a toxin, called pneumolysin, that kills the cardiac muscle cells. These areas of dead cardiac muscle are called microlesions. In addition, during recovery from the infection, scars may form within the myocardium. Thus, the bacteria physically damage the heart, which interrupts the electrical signal necessary for cardiac muscle contraction. In addition, simply treating pneumonia with the traditional antibiotic ampicillin may actually worsen damage to the heart. Ampicillin causes the bacterial cell walls to burst, which releases a surge of pneumolysin, creating even more microlesions. Use of an antibiotic that does not destroy the bacterial cell walls will help reduce cardiac muscle death. Further, a vaccine against the bacterial molecule that induces the bacterial transport and against pneumolysin has shown great promise in minimizing the tissue damage caused by these bacteria.

Although pathogenic bacteria exist, modern medicine continues to make great strides to reduce their damaging effects on our bodies. In addition, the more we learn about our microbiome, the more effectively we may be able to prevent bacterial infections from occurring in the first place.

Apply **Predict 4**

Given that S. pneumoniae *microlesions interrupt the electrical activity that flows between cardiac muscle cells, the heart can experience severe stress and may malfunction or stop contracting altogether. Using what you learned about skeletal muscle contraction, would microlesions in skeletal muscle cause the same type of reaction as in cardiac muscle?*

   c. Clinical Genetics: describe the underlying gene alterations for certain diseases. These provide some clarity for otherwise confounding situations. For example, emphysema isn't always self-induced by smoking; there is an underlying genetic basis for some individuals who develop this disease.

Clinical GENETICS 15.1 | **Color Blindness**

Color blindness results from the dysfunction of one or more of the three photopigments (red, green, blue) involved in color vision. If one pigment is dysfunctional and the other two are functional, the condition is called **dichromatism.** An example of dichromatism is red-green color blindness (figure 15.22).

Red-green color blindness is common in males, but not females. About 7% of males have some degree of color blindness, which is over eight times more common than in females. The basis for this male prevalence is that the genes for the red and green photopigments are arranged in tandem on the X chromosome (see chapter 29). Because males have only one X chromosome, they are more likely to be affected by an X-linked mutation than females, who have a higher probability of having a good gene on one of their two X chromosomes.

The vast majority, over 95%, of color blindness involves red-green color vision, not blue vision. The reason can be traced to the tandem arrangement of the red and green photopigment genes. Not only are the two genes next to each other, but they are also nearly identical; differences in only 3 of the 360 amino acids determine the red versus green wavelength absorption characteristics. Because the red and green genes are so similar and adjacent to each other, it is relatively easy for mistakes to occur during development as DNA is replicated and exchanged between chromosomes (see chapter 29). Hence, an X chromosome may lack one or both genes, or it may have a hybrid gene containing exons from both red and green genes, which may or may not alter their degree of functionality. The blue photopigment gene is rarely associated with color blidness because it is not adjacent to another photopigment gene. It is also not X-linked, so it is equally rare in males and females.

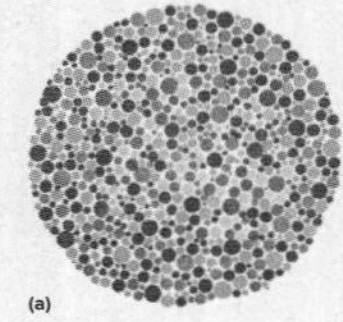

(a)

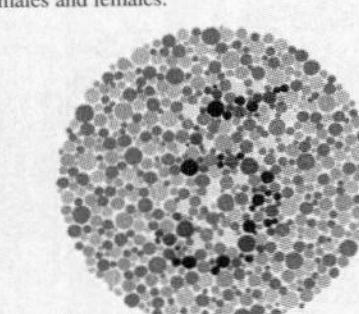

(b)

FIGURE 15.22 Color Blindness Charts
(*a*) A person with normal color vision can see the number 74, whereas a person with red-green color blindness sees the number 21. (*b*) A person with normal color vision can see the number 5, whereas a person with red-green color blindness sees the number 2. (a) Steve Allen/Brand X Pictures/Getty Images; (b) Prisma Bildagentur AG/Alamy Stock Photo

Reproduced from Ishihara's Tests for Colour Blindness published by Kanehara & Co., Ltd., Tokyo, Japan, but tests for color blindness cannot be conducted with this material. For accurate testing, the original plates should be used.

   d. Case studies: these allow you to be the expert! The case studies present a clinical situation and then ask you to problem solve to predict the connections.

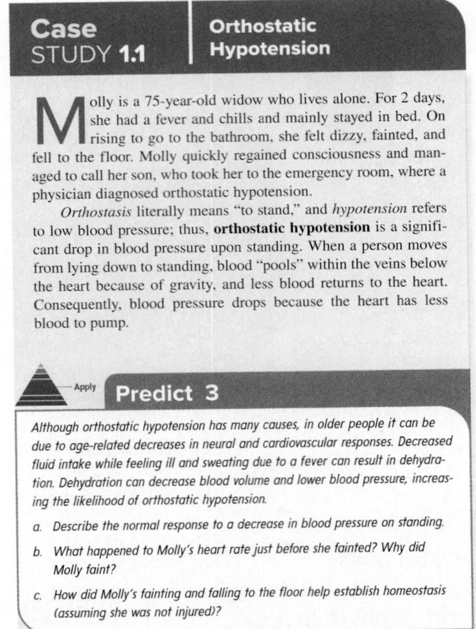

Case STUDY 1.1 | **Orthostatic Hypotension**

Molly is a 75-year-old widow who lives alone. For 2 days, she had a fever and chills and mainly stayed in bed. On rising to go to the bathroom, she felt dizzy, fainted, and fell to the floor. Molly quickly regained consciousness and managed to call her son, who took her to the emergency room, where a physician diagnosed orthostatic hypotension.

Orthostasis literally means "to stand," and *hypotension* refers to low blood pressure; thus, **orthostatic hypotension** is a significant drop in blood pressure upon standing. When a person moves from lying down to standing, blood "pools" within the veins below the heart because of gravity, and less blood returns to the heart. Consequently, blood pressure drops because the heart has less blood to pump.

Apply **Predict 3**

Although orthostatic hypotension has many causes, in older people it can be due to age-related decreases in neural and cardiovascular responses. Decreased fluid intake while feeling ill and sweating due to a fever can result in dehydration. Dehydration can decrease blood volume and lower blood pressure, increasing the likelihood of orthostatic hypotension.

a. Describe the normal response to a decrease in blood pressure on standing.
b. What happened to Molly's heart rate just before she fainted? Why did Molly faint?
c. How did Molly's fainting and falling to the floor help establish homeostasis (assuming she was not injured)?

   e. Aging: describe changes to the body systems as we age. Currently, approximately 15% of the U.S. population is comprised of adults older than 65. This percentage will rise to about 21% by the year 2030, and health-care professionals will need an understanding of the aging process.

EFFECTS OF AGING ON THE RESPIRATORY SYSTEM

Most aspects of the respiratory system are affected by aging. However, even though vital capacity, maximum pulmonary ventilation rates, and gas exchange decrease with age, older people can engage in light to moderate exercise because the respiratory system has a large reserve capacity.

Vital capacity declines with age because of a decreased ability to fill the lungs (inspiratory reserve volume) and a decreased ability to empty the lungs (expiratory reserve volume). As a result, maximum minute volume rates are reduced, which in turn limits the ability to perform intense exercise. These changes are related to weakening of respiratory muscles and to reduced compliance of the thoracic cage caused by the stiffening of cartilage and ribs. Lung compliance increases with age because parts of the alveolar walls are lost, which reduces lung recoil. No significant age-related changes take place in lung elastic fibers or surfactant.

Alveolar ducts and many of the larger bronchioles expand in diameter with age, which increases residual volume. Larger bronchioles and alveolar ducts create more dead space, lowering the amount of air available for gas exchange (alveolar ventilation). In addition, gas exchange across the respiratory membrane is reduced because parts of the alveolar walls are lost, creating less surface area available for gas exchange. A gradual rise in resting tidal volume with age compensates for these changes.

With age, mucus accumulates within the respiratory passageways because it becomes more viscous and because there are fewer cilia. As a consequence, older people are more susceptible to respiratory infections and bronchitis. Table 23.2 describes several other diseases and disorders of the respiratory system that can occur during any stage of life.

   f. Systems Pathologies: discuss a disorder or disruption in a particular body system. These readings are a deeper look into clinical correlations than the clinical impacts. They will help you make a connection between studying anatomy and physiology and situations you may encounter in a health-care setting.

Systems PATHOLOGY | Burns

A **burn** is injury to a tissue caused by heat, cold, friction, chemicals, electricity, or radiation. Burns are classified according to the extent of surface area involved and the depth of the burn.

On the basis of depth, burns are classified as either partial-thickness or full-thickness burns (figure 5.14). **Partial-thickness burns** are subdivided into first- and second-degree burns. **First-degree burns** involve only the epidermis and may result in redness, pain, and slight edema (swelling). **Second-degree burns** damage the epidermis and dermis. Minimal dermal damage causes redness, pain, edema, and blisters.

Full-thickness burns are also called **third-degree burns.** The epidermis and dermis are completely destroyed, and tissue just below the skin may be involved. Third-degree burns are often surrounded by first- and second-degree burns. Although the areas that have first- and second-degree burns are painful, the region of third-degree burn is usually painless because the sensory receptors have been destroyed.

Fourth-degree burns are extremely severe burns that affect tissues deeper than the subcutaneous tissue, often damaging tendons, fascia, muscle, and bone. Because of the severity of tissue damage, fourth-degree burns often require amputation or removal of damaged tissue.

Sam received severe burns across his body after he fell asleep while smoking. He was admitted to the emergency room and later transferred to the burn unit in critical condition, suffering from shock (figure 5.15). Large volumes of intravenous fluids were administered and Sam's condition improved. He was given a high-protein, high-caloric diet, as well as topical antimicrobial drugs to treat infection of his wounds the first few weeks of treatment. Sam developed venous thrombosis in his left leg, which required additional treatment. Later, his physician recommended debridement of his wounds.

When large areas of skin are severely burned, there are systemic effects that can be life-threatening (figure 5.16). Within minutes of a major burn injury, there is increased permeability of the capillaries. This increased permeability occurs at the burn site and throughout the body, resulting in loss of fluid and electrolytes (see chapter 2) at the burn wound and into tissue spaces. The loss of fluid decreases blood volume, which decreases the heart's ability to pump blood. The resulting decrease in blood delivery to tissues can cause tissue damage, shock, and even death. Treatment consists of administering intravenous fluid at a faster rate than it leaks out of the capillaries, though fluid continues to leak into tissue spaces, causing pronounced **edema** (swelling). Capillary permeability returns to normal typically within 24 hours, reducing the need for intravenous fluids.

Substances released from the burn may alter capillary permeability as well as cause cells to function abnormally. Burn injuries result in an almost immediate hypermetabolic state, which persists until wound closure. Two other factors contributing to the increased metabolism are (1) a resetting of the temperature control center in the brain to a higher temperature and (2) hormones released by the endocrine system (e.g., epinephrine and norepinephrine from the adrenal glands), which can increase cell metabolism. The increased metabolism can result in a loss of 30–40% of the patient's preburn weight, requiring a specialized diet to compensate. Compared with a normal body temperature of approximately 37°C (98.6°F), a typical burn patient may have a body temperature of 38.5°C (101.3°F) despite the higher loss of water by evaporation from the burn.

Because burns damage and sometimes completely destroy the skin, microorganisms can cause infections. Burn patients are maintained in an aseptic (sterile) environment in an attempt to prevent the entry of microorganisms into the wound. They are also given antimicrobial drugs, which kill microorganisms or suppress their growth.

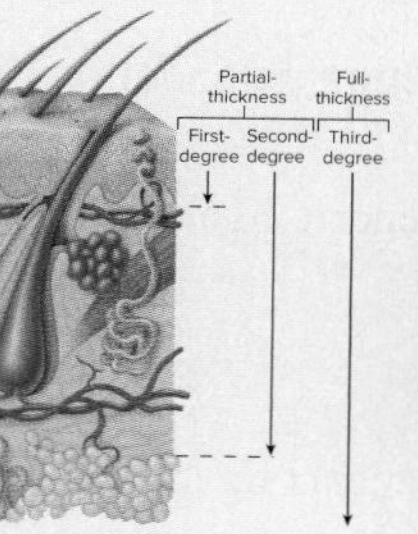

FIGURE 5.14 Partial- and Full-Thickness Burns

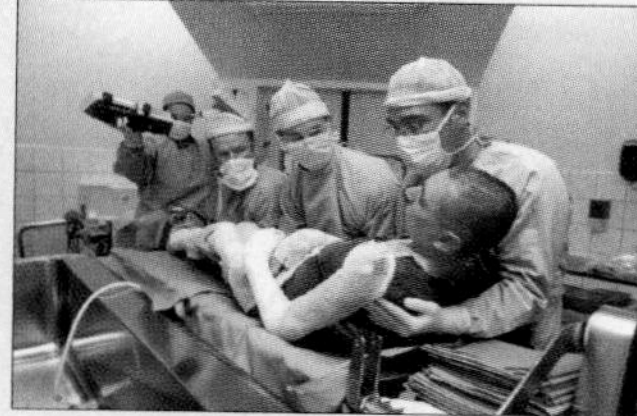

FIGURE 5.15 Patient in a Burn Unit
Phanie/Science Source

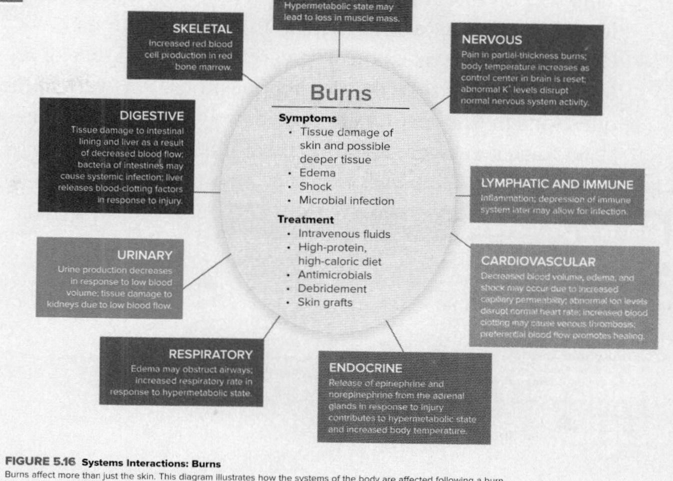

FIGURE 5.16 Systems Interactions: Burns
Burns affect more than just the skin. This diagram illustrates how the systems of the body are affected following a burn.

Debridement (dah-BREED-ment, day-breed-MON), the removal of dead tissue from the burn, helps prevent infections by cleaning the wound and removing tissue in which infections could develop. Skin grafts, performed within a week of the injury, also help close the wound and prevent the entry of microorganisms.

Despite these efforts, infections are still the major cause of death for burn victims. Depression of the immune system during the first or second week after the injury contributes to the high infection rate. The greater the magnitude of the burn, the greater the depression of the immune system and the greater the risk for infection.

Venous thrombosis, the development of a clot in a vein, is another complication of burns. Blood normally forms a clot when exposed to damaged tissue, such as at a burn site, but clotting can also occur elsewhere, such as in veins, where clots can block blood flow, resulting in tissue destruction. The concentration of chemicals that cause clotting (called clotting factors) increases for two reasons: (1) Loss of fluid from the burn patient concentrates the chemical and (2) the liver releases an increased amount of clotting factors.

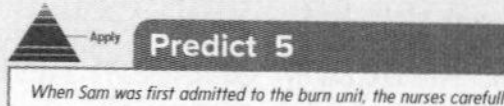

When Sam was first admitted to the burn unit, the nurses carefully monitored his urine output. Why does that make sense in light of his injuries?

6. Critical Thinking Practice
   The textbook presents you with multiple opportunities to practice applying the information you've learned to particular situations. Critical thinking questions require a higher-order level of thinking than simple fact-based questions. The Bloom's taxonomy icon indicates the level at which a given question is ranked.

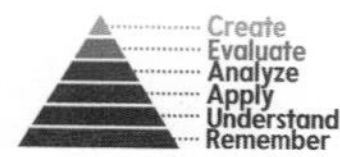

   a. Learn to Predict
      This feature appears at the beginning of each chapter and integrates information from earlier chapters or asks you to think about a scenario as you read the chapter. Answers to odd-numbered questions are provided in appendix E. Answers to even-numbered questions are provided online. The answers are written in a solution-style format. We walk you through the logic of each answer.

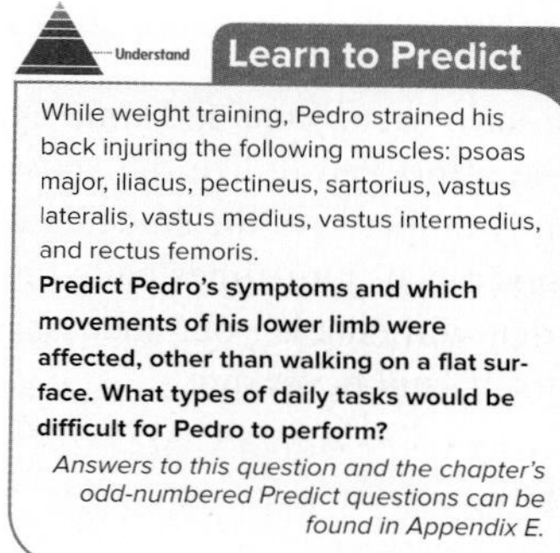

Chapter 10
Learn to Predict

The description of Pedro's injury provided specific information about the regions of the body affected: the left hip and thigh. These facts will help us determine Pedro's symptoms and predict the movements that may be affected by his injury.

We read in this chapter that the muscles affected by Pedro's injury (psoas major, iliacus, pectineus, sartorius, vastus lateralis, vastus medius, vastus intermedius, and rectus femoris) are involved in flexing the hip, the knee, or both. Therefore, we can conclude that movements involving hip and knee flexion, such as walking

   b. Predict
      Predict questions are distributed throughout each chapter and pertain to information presented prior to each question. The same solution-style format answers to the odd-numbered questions are provided.

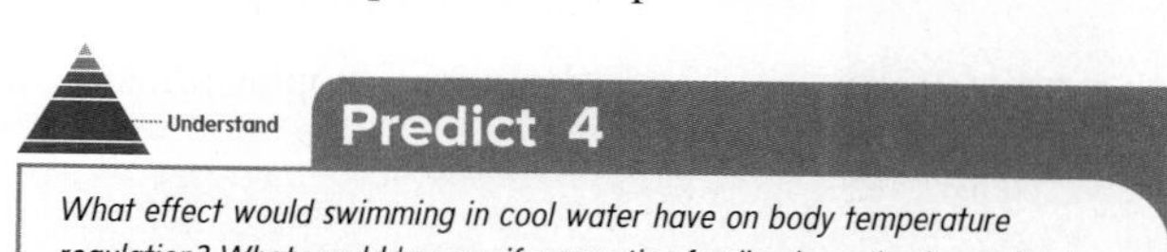

c. Concept Check
This section integrates a chapter review with remember-level questions as well as critical thinking questions. Critical thinking questions typically require a higher-order level of thinking than the Predict questions. Answers to the questions in this section are provided, including solution-style-format answers for the critical thinking questions.

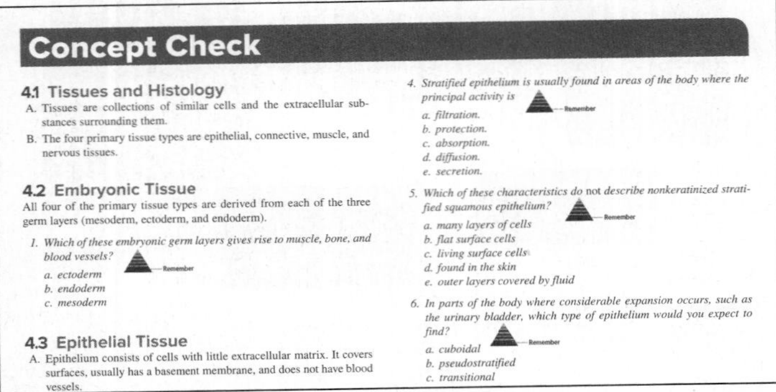
Concept Check

4.1 Tissues and Histology

A. Tissues are collections of similar cells and the extracellular substances surrounding them.

B. The four primary tissue types are epithelial, connective, muscle, and nervous tissues.

4.2 Embryonic Tissue

All four of the primary tissue types are derived from each of the three germ layers (mesoderm, ectoderm, and endoderm).

1. Which of these embryonic germ layers gives rise to muscle, bone, and blood vessels? Remember

a. ectoderm
b. endoderm
c. mesoderm

4.3 Epithelial Tissue

A. Epithelium consists of cells with little extracellular matrix. It covers surfaces, usually has a basement membrane, and does not have blood vessels.

4. Stratified epithelium is usually found in areas of the body where the principal activity is Remember

a. filtration.
b. protection.
c. absorption.
d. diffusion.
e. secretion.

5. Which of these characteristics do not *describe nonkeratinized stratified squamous epithelium?* Remember

a. many layers of cells
b. flat surface cells
c. living surface cells
d. found in the skin
e. outer layers covered by fluid

6. In parts of the body where considerable expansion occurs, such as the urinary bladder, which type of epithelium would you expect to find? Remember

a. cuboidal
b. pseudostratified
c. transitional

7. Figure Colors and Symbols
Following are symbols used consistently to indicate the same structure or event in all chapters. If in some chapters a symbol is given a different usage, that usage for the symbol is always labeled or defined.

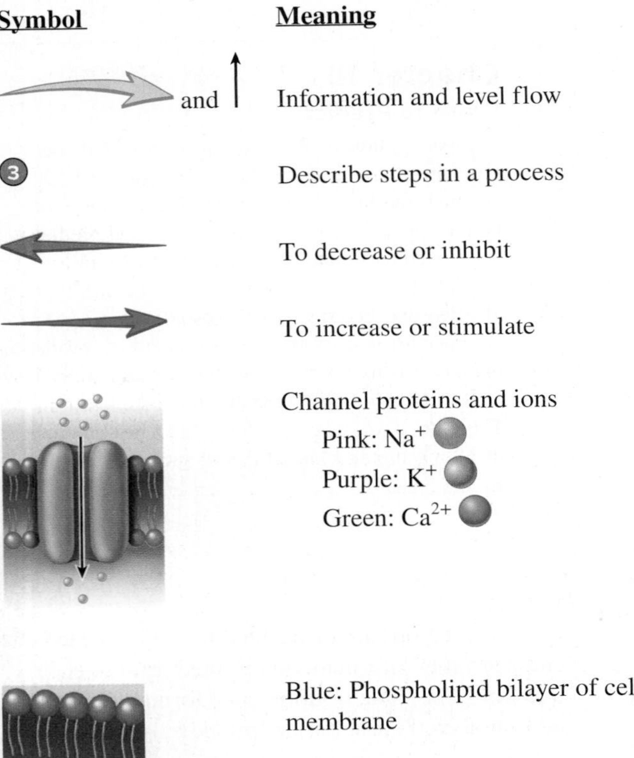

Symbol	Meaning
and	Information and level flow
	Describe steps in a process
	To decrease or inhibit
	To increase or stimulate
	Channel proteins and ions Pink: Na^+ Purple: K^+ Green: Ca^{2+}
	Blue: Phospholipid bilayer of cell membrane Yellow: Cytoplasm/inside of cell

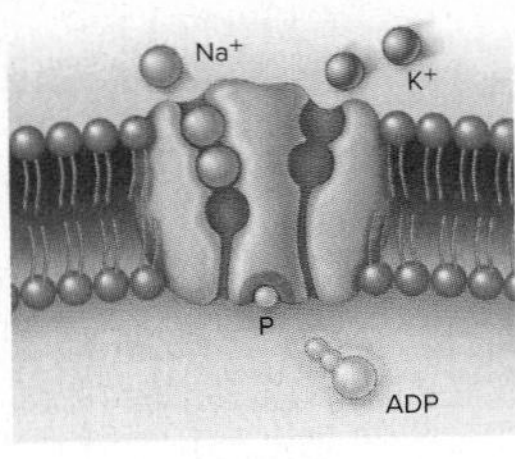

Sodium-potassium (Na^+–K^+) pump

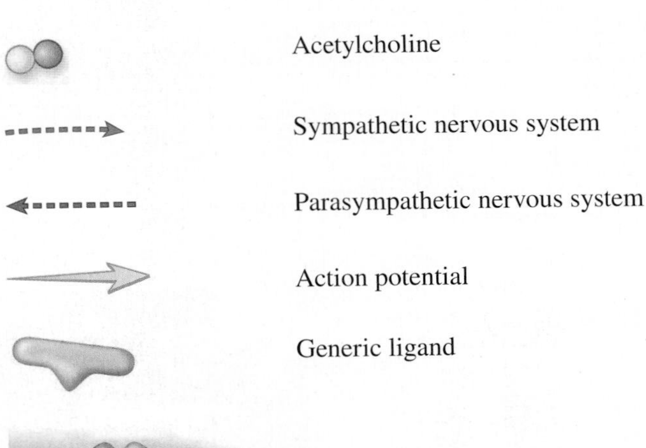

Acetylcholine

Sympathetic nervous system

Parasympathetic nervous system

Action potential

Generic ligand

Generic ligand receptor

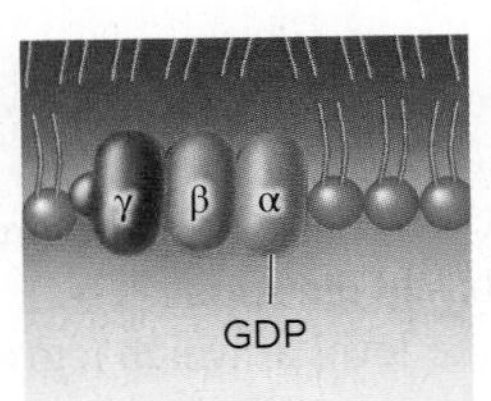

G protein

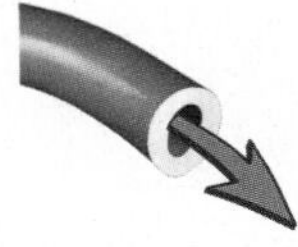

Veins with deoxygenated blood

Arteries with oxygenated blood

Conclusions

In our teaching we have seen, time and time again, that the students who put in the effort and utilize the activities described in this guide consistently outperform the students who do not. Thus, it will be your perseverance, sometimes called *grit*—and not how "smart" you are—that will enable your success. Encourage yourself, believe in yourself, and never quit.

1

CHAPTER

The Human Organism

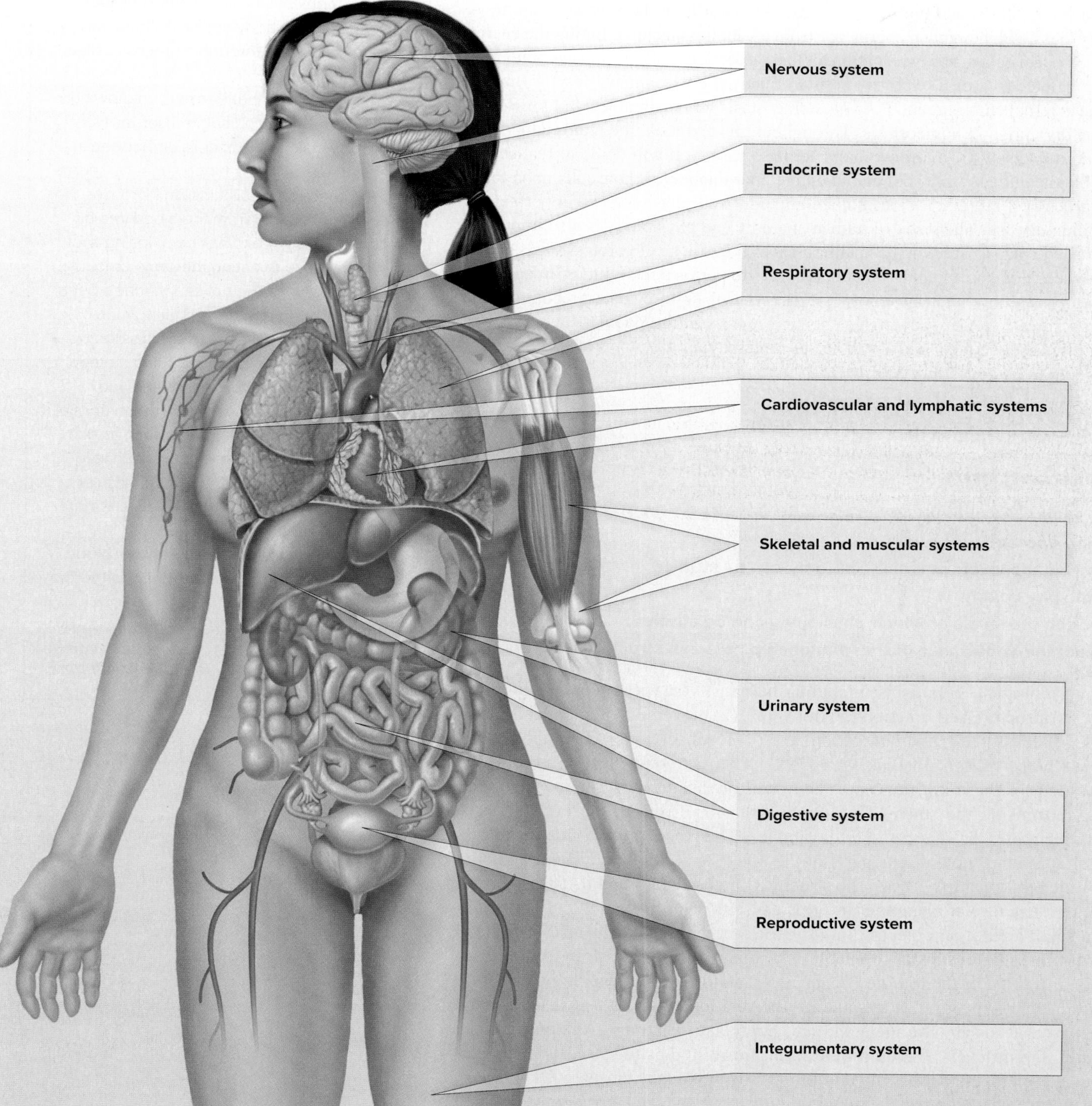

The human body is a complex system. The structures in the body work in concert to maintain homeostasis, a balance in the body's internal environment.

What lies ahead is an astounding adventure—learning about the structure and function of the human body and the intricate checks and balances that regulate it. Renzo's (the dancer featured in this chapter's Learn to Predict) blood sugar disorder is a good example of how important this system of checks and balances is in the body. Perhaps you have had the experience of oversleeping, rushing to your 8 a.m. class, and missing breakfast. Afterward, on the way to Anatomy & Physiology class, you bought an energy bar from a vending machine. Eating the energy bar helped you feel better. The explanation for these experiences is the process of homeostasis, the maintenance of a relatively constant internal environment, despite fluctuations in the external environment. For you, homeostasis was maintained, but for Renzo, there was a disruption in homeostasis. Throughout this textbook, the major underlying theme is homeostasis. As you think about Renzo's case, you will come to realize just how capable the human body is of an incredible coordination of thousands upon thousands of processes. Learning about human anatomy and physiology is important for understanding disease. The study of human anatomy and physiology is also important for students who plan a career in the health sciences because health professionals need a sound knowledge of structure and function in order to perform their duties. In addition, understanding anatomy and physiology prepares all of us to evaluate recommended treatments, critically review advertisements and reports in the popular literature, and rationally discuss the human body with health professionals and nonprofessionals.

Learn to Predict

Renzo, a dancer, can perfectly balance on the ball of one foot, yet a slight movement in any direction causes him to adjust his position. The human body adjusts its balance among all its parts through a process called homeostasis.

Let's imagine that Renzo is unknowingly suffering from a blood sugar disorder. Normally, tiny collections of cells embedded in the pancreas regulate blood sugar by secreting the chemical insulin. Insulin increases the movement of sugar from the blood into his cells. However, Renzo has been losing a lot of weight, despite eating the same amount of food as always. He noticed that he's been fatigued, very thirsty, and urinating more than normal. Renzo went to see his doctor, who ordered some tests, including a blood glucose challenge. The results showed Renzo's blood sugar was higher than normal. After trying several treatments such as diet and prescription oral medication with little effect, Renzo was outfitted with an insulin pump. Now, his blood sugar levels are more consistent.

Develop an explanation for Renzo's blood sugar levels before and after his visit to the doctor.

Answers to this question and the chapter's odd-numbered Predict questions can be found in Appendix E.

1.1 Anatomy and Physiology

LEARNING OUTCOMES

After reading this section, you should be able to

A. **Define *anatomy*.**
B. **Describe the levels at which anatomy can be studied.**
C. **Define *physiology*.**
D. **Describe the levels at which physiology can be studied.**
E. **Explain the importance of the relationship between structure and function.**

In studying biological organisms, including humans, you will encounter four key concepts: (1) structure and function relationships, (2) movement of chemicals along gradients, (3) cell-to-cell communication, and (4) feedback loops. Throughout this chapter, we will highlight these key concepts. Then as you progress through the textbook, look for these key concepts. They will be discussed within every organ. system. **Anatomy** is the scientific discipline that investigates the body's structures—for example, the shape and size of bones. The word *anatomy* means to dissect or cut apart and separate the parts of the body for study. In addition, anatomy examines the relationship between the structure of a body part and its function. For example, the structure of a hammer informs us of its primary use: to deliver a hard blow to a small area of an object. Similarly, the fact that bone cells are surrounded by a hard, mineralized substance enables the bones to provide strength and support. This is the first of the four key concepts of anatomy and physiology: structure and function relationships. Understanding the relationship between structure and function makes it easier to understand and appreciate anatomy. Anatomy can be studied at different levels. **Developmental anatomy** studies the structural changes that occur between conception and adulthood. **Embryology** (em-bree-OL-oh-jee), a subspecialty of developmental anatomy, considers changes from conception to the end of the eighth week of development.

Module 1
Body Orientation

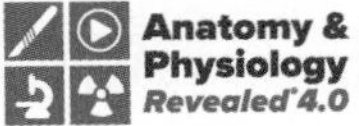

Some structures, such as cells, are so small that they must be studied using a microscope. **Cytology** (sigh-TOL-oh-jee; *cyto,* cell) examines the structural features of cells, and **histology** (his-TOL-oh-jee; *hist,* tissue) examines tissues, which are composed of cells and the materials surrounding them.

Gross anatomy, the study of structures that can be examined without the aid of a microscope, can be approached either systemically or regionally. A **system** is a group of structures that have one or more common functions, such as the cardiovascular, nervous, respiratory, skeletal, or muscular systems. In systemic anatomy, the body is studied system by system. In regional anatomy, the body is studied area by area. Within each region, such as the head, abdomen, or arm, all systems are studied simultaneously. The regional approach is taken in many graduate programs at medical and dental schools. The systemic approach is used in this and most other introductory textbooks.

Surface anatomy involves looking at the exterior of the body to visualize structures deeper inside the body. For example, the sternum (breastbone) and bulges from the ribs can be seen and palpated (felt) on the front of the chest. Health professionals use these structures as anatomical landmarks to identify regions of the heart and points on the chest where certain heart sounds can best be heard. **Anatomical imaging** uses radiographs (x-rays), ultrasound, magnetic resonance imaging (MRI), and other technologies to create pictures of internal structures (table 1.1). Anatomical imaging has revolutionized medical science. Anatomical imaging allows medical personnel to look inside the body with amazing accuracy and without the trauma and risk of exploratory surgery. The risk of anatomical imaging is minimized by using the lowest possible number of doses providing the necessary information. No known risks exist from ultrasound or electromagnetic fields at the levels used for diagnosis. Both surface anatomy and anatomical imaging provide important information for diagnosing disease.

However, no two humans are structurally identical. **Anatomical anomalies** are physical characteristics that differ from the normal pattern. Anatomical anomalies can vary in severity from relatively harmless to life-threatening. For example, each kidney is normally supplied by one blood vessel, but in some individuals a kidney is supplied by two blood vessels. Either way, the kidney receives adequate blood. On the other hand, in the condition called "blue baby" syndrome, certain blood vessels arising from an infant's heart are not attached in their correct locations; blood is not effectively pumped to the lungs, and so the tissues do not receive adequate oxygen.

Physiology is the scientific investigation of the processes or functions of living things. There are two major goals when studying human physiology: (1) examining the body's responses to stimuli and (2) examining the body's maintenance of stable internal conditions within a narrow range of values in a constantly changing environment.

Like anatomy, physiology can be considered at many levels. **Cell physiology** examines the processes occurring in cells such as energy production from food, and **systemic physiology** considers the functions of organ systems. Types of systemic physiology are

TABLE 1.1 Anatomical Imaging

Imaging Technique	Clinical Examples
X-ray 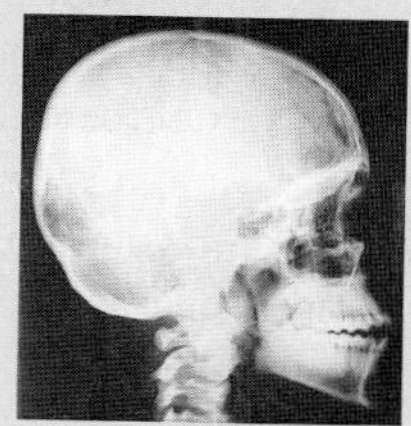 Omikron/Science Source	This extremely short-wave electromagnetic radiation moves through the body, exposing a photographic plate to form a **radiograph** (RAY-dee-oh-graf). Radiographs create flat, two-dimensional (2D) image.
Ultrasound 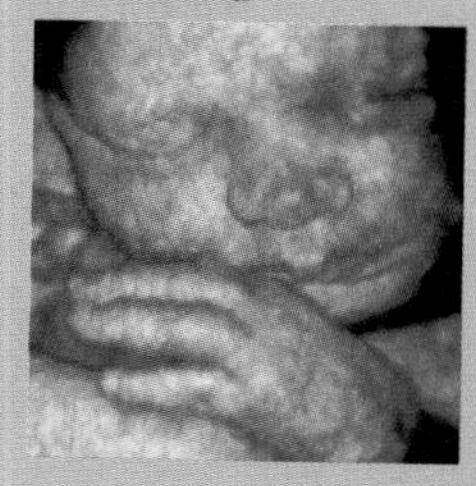 Bernard Benoit/Science Photo Library/Science Source	**Ultrasound** uses high-frequency sound waves, which strike internal organs and bounce back to the receiver on the skin. Among other medical applications, ultrasound is commonly used to evaluate the condition of the fetus during pregnancy.
Computed Tomography (CT) RGB Ventures/SuperStock/Alamy Stock Photo 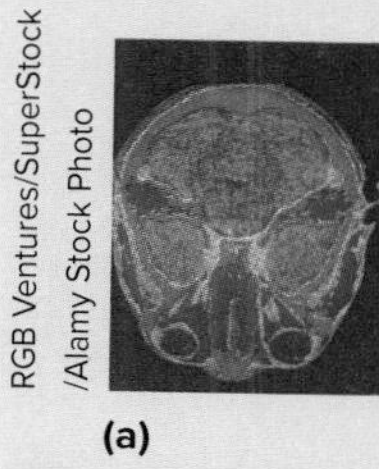 (a) (b) Ribotsky D.P.M./Custom Medical Stock Photo	**Computed tomographic** (TOH-moh-GRAF-ik) **(CT) scans** are computer-analyzed x-ray images (*a*). Some computers are able to take several scans short distances apart and stack the slices to produce a 3D image of a body part (*b*).
Digital Subtraction Angiography (DSA) 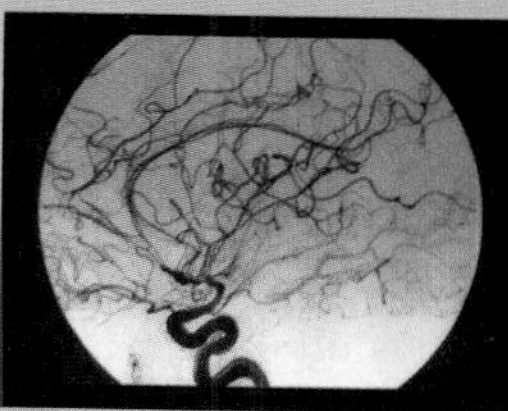 Living Art Enterprises, LLC/Science Source	**Digital subtraction angiography** (an-jee-OG-rah-fee) **(DSA)** is one step beyond CT scanning. A radiopaque dye is injected into the blood, which allows for enhanced differences when compared to a noninjected scan.
Magnetic Resonance Imaging (MRI) 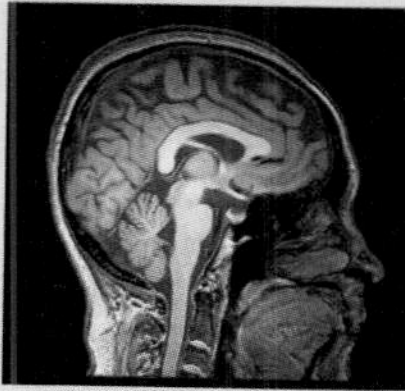 MriMan/Shutterstock	**Magnetic resonance imaging (MRI)** directs radio waves at a person lying inside a large electromagnetic field. An MRI is more effective at detecting some forms of cancer than a CT scan.
Positron Emission Tomography (PET) 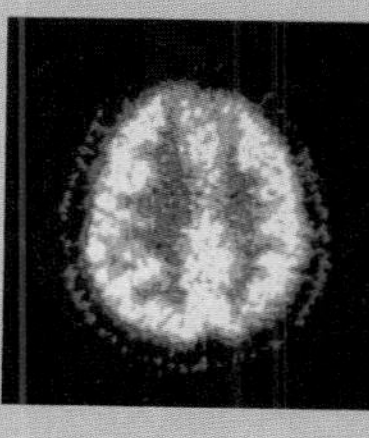 Science Source	**Positron emission tomographic (PET) scans** can identify the metabolic states of various tissues. This technique is particularly useful in analyzing the brain. Radiation pinpoints cells that are metabolically active.

cardiovascular physiology, which focuses on the heart and blood vessels, and **neurophysiology,** which focuses on the function of the nervous system. Physiology often examines systems rather than regions because a particular function can involve portions of a system in more than one region. The second key concept of anatomy and physiology is integral to studying physiology as you will learn: Chemicals move along gradients. We will examine that more in chapter 3.

Studies of the human body must encompass both anatomy and physiology because structures, functions, and processes are interwoven. **Pathology** (pa-THOL-oh-jee) is the medical science dealing with all aspects of disease, with an emphasis on the cause and development of abnormal conditions, as well as the structural and functional changes resulting from disease. **Exercise physiology** focuses on the changes in function and structure caused by exercise.

ASSESS YOUR PROGRESS

Answers to these questions are found in the section you have just completed. Re-read the section if you need help in answering these questions.

1. *How does the study of anatomy differ from the study of physiology?*
2. *What is studied in gross anatomy? In surface anatomy?*
3. *What type of physiology is employed when studying the endocrine system?*
4. *Why are anatomy and physiology normally studied together?*

1.2 Biomedical Research

LEARNING OUTCOME

After reading this section, you should be able to

A. **Explain why it is important to study other organisms along with humans.**

Much of what we know about our own physiology is based on physiological studies of other organisms. Humans share many characteristics with other organisms. For example, studying single-celled bacteria has allowed scientists to utilize bacteria to synthesize certain human medicines such as insulin. However, some biomedical research cannot be accomplished using single-celled organisms or isolated cells. Sometimes other mammals must be studied, as evidenced by the great progress in open-heart surgery and kidney transplantation made possible by perfecting surgical techniques on other mammals before attempting them on humans. Strict laws govern the use of animals in biomedical research; these laws are designed to ensure minimal suffering on the part of the animal and to discourage unnecessary experimentation.

Although much can be learned from studying other organisms, the ultimate answers to questions about humans can be obtained only from humans because other organisms differ from humans in significant ways. A failure to appreciate the differences between humans and other animals led to many misconceptions by early scientists. One of the first great anatomists was a Greek physician, Claudius Galen (ca. 130–201). Galen described a large number of anatomical structures supposedly present in humans but observed only in other animals. For example, he described the liver as having five lobes. This is true for rats, but not for humans, who have four-lobed livers. The errors introduced by Galen persisted for more than 1300 years until a Flemish anatomist, Andreas Vesalius (1514–1564), who is considered the first modern anatomist, carefully examined human cadavers and began to correct the textbooks. This example should serve as a word of caution: Some current knowledge in molecular biology and physiology has not been confirmed in humans.

ASSESS YOUR PROGRESS

5. *Why is it important to recognize that humans share many, but not all, characteristics with other animals?*

1.3 Structural and Functional Organization of the Human Body

LEARNING OUTCOMES

After reading this section, you should be able to

A. **Name the six levels of organization of the body.**
B. **Describe the major characteristics of the six levels of organization.**
C. **List the 11 organ systems and identify their components.**
D. **Describe the major functions of each system.**

The body can be studied at six levels of organization: chemical, cell, tissue, organ, organ system, and whole organism (figure 1.1). As you move through levels, you will notice that each builds on the previous level. Disruption of this organized state can result in loss of functions or even death.

1. *Chemical level.* The structural and functional characteristics of all organisms are determined by their chemical makeup. The chemical level of organization involves how atoms, such as hydrogen and carbon, interact and combine to form molecules. This is important because a molecule's structure determines its function. For example, collagen molecules are strong ropelike protein fibers that give skin structural strength and flexibility. With aging, the structure of collagen changes, and the skin becomes fragile and more easily torn during everyday activities. We present a brief overview of chemistry in chapter 2.
2. *Cell level.* **Cells** are the basic structural and functional units of all living organisms. Combinations of molecules form cells. Structures inside cells called **organelles** (OR-gah-nellz; little organs) carry out particular functions, such as digestion and movement, for the cell. For example, the nucleus is an organelle that contains the cell's hereditary information, and mitochondria are organelles that manufacture

FUNDAMENTAL Figure

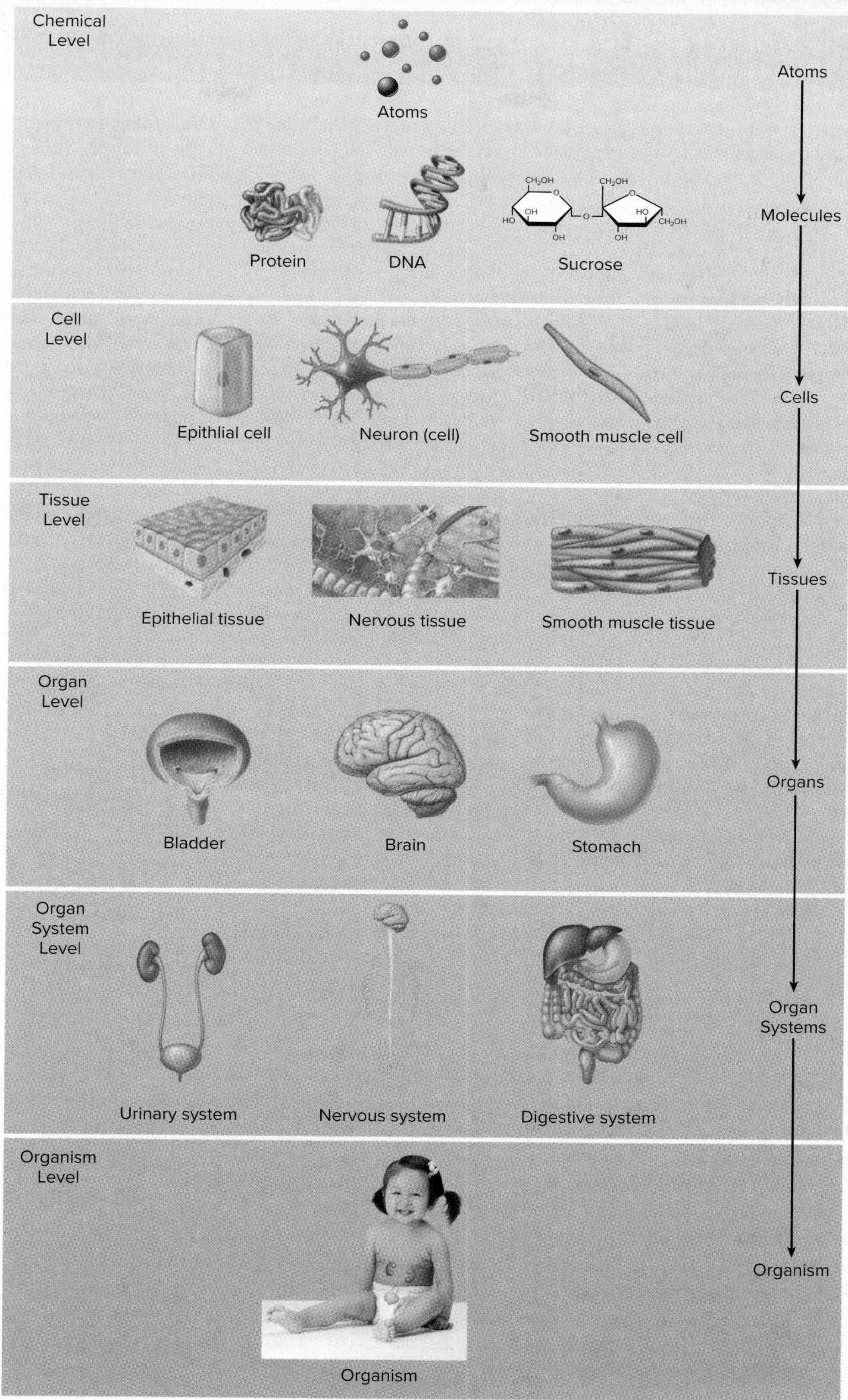

FIGURE 1.1 Levels of Organization for the Human Body

The simplest level of organization in the human body is the atom. Atoms combine to form molecules. Molecules aggregate into cells. Cells form tissues, which combine with other tissues to form organs. Organs work in groups called organ systems. All organ systems work together to form an organism.

(baby girl) BJI/Blue Jean Images/Getty Images

MICROBES In Your Body 1.1 Getting to Know Your Bacteria

Did you know that you have as many microbial cells as human cells in your body? Astoundingly, for every cell in your body, there is at least one microbial cell. That's as many as 40 trillion microbial cells, which can collectively account for between 2 and 6 pounds of your body weight! A microbe is any life form that can only be seen with a microscope (for example, bacteria, fungi, and protozoa). All living organisms fit into one of three domains of living organisms: (1) Bacteria, (2) Archaea, and (3) Eukarya. The cells of organisms in each domain are unique. Bacterial cells' genetic material is not separated from the rest of the cell by a barrier. In addition, bacterial cells have far fewer separate structures made of membrane for carrying out the cell's metabolic processes than eukaryotic cells. Archaea cells are constructed similarly to bacteria; however, they share certain structures, called ribosomes, with eukaryotic cells. We discuss cell structure in detail in chapter 3. Commonly, the term *prokaryotic* is used to describe bacterial and archaea cells. Eukaryotic cells, which include human cells, have the most structural complexity with many smaller structures, called organelles, made with membrane. These smaller structures conduct the metabolic processes of the cell.

In addition to structural differences, there are many other differences far too numerous to adequately describe here. However, size differences between bacteria and archaea and cells of eukaryotes are quite evident with most eukaryotic cells being significantly larger than most prokaryotic cells. The total population of microbial cells on the human body is referred to as the microbiota, while the collection of all the microbial cell genes is known as the microbiome. The microbiota includes so-called good bacteria, which do not cause disease and may even help us. It also includes pathogenic, or "bad," bacteria.

With that many microbes in and on our bodies, you might wonder how they affect our health. To answer that question, the National Institutes of Health (NIH) initiated the Human Microbiome Project. Five significant regions of the human body were examined: the airway, skin, mouth, gastrointestinal tract, and vagina. This project identified over 5000 species and sequenced over 20 million unique microbial genes.

What did scientists learn from the Human Microbiome Project? Human health is dependent upon the health of our microbiota, especially the "good" bacteria. More specifically, the human microbiome is intimately involved in the development and maintenance of the immune system. And more evidence is mounting for a correlation between a host's microbiota, digestion, and metabolism. Researchers have suggested that microbial genes are more responsible for our survival than human genes. There are even a few consistent pathogens that are present without causing disease, suggesting that their presence may be good for us. However, there does not seem to be a universal healthy human microbiome. Rather, the human microbiome varies across life span, ethnicity, nationality, culture, and geographic location. Instead of being a detriment, this variation may actually be very useful for predicting disease. There seems to be a correlation between autoimmune and inflammatory diseases (Crohn disease, asthma, multiple sclerosis), which have become more prevalent, and a "characteristic microbiome community." Early research seems to indicate that any significant change in the profile of the microbiome of the human gut may increase a person's susceptibility to autoimmune diseases. It has been proposed that these changes may be associated with exposure to antibiotics, particularly in infancy. Fortunately, newer studies of microbial transplantations have shown that the protective and other functions of bacteria can be transferred from one person to the next. However, this work is all very new, and much research remains to be done.

Throughout this text, we will highlight specific instances in which our microbes influence our body systems. In light of the importance of our bodies' bacteria and other microbes, the prevalence of antibacterial soap and hand gel usage in everyday life may be something to think about.

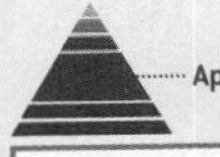

Predict 1

Predict some possible consequences of high-dose, intravenous (IV) antibiotic administration on the homeostasis of a person's digestive function.

adenosine triphosphate (ATP), a molecule cells use for energy. Although cell types differ in their structure and function, they have many characteristics in common. Knowledge of these characteristics, as well as their variations, is essential to understanding anatomy and physiology. We discuss the cell in chapter 3.

3. *Tissue level.* Groups of cells combine to forms **tissues.** A tissue is composed of a group of similar cells and the materials surrounding them. The characteristics of the cells and surrounding materials determine the functions of the tissue. The body is made up of four basic tissue types: (1) epithelial, (2) connective, (3) muscle, and (4) nervous. We discuss tissues in chapter 4.
4. *Organ level.* Different tissues combine to form **organs.** An organ is composed of two or more tissue types that perform one or more common functions. Examples of organs include the urinary bladder, heart, stomach, and lung (figure 1.2).
5. *Organ system level.* Multiple organs combine to form an **organ system** (figure 1.3). An organ system is a group of organs that together perform a common function or set of functions and are therefore viewed as a unit. For example, the urinary system consists of the kidneys, ureters, urinary bladder, and urethra. The kidneys produce urine, which the ureters transport to the urinary bladder, where it is stored until being eliminated from the body through the urethra. In this text, we consider 11 major organ systems: (1) integumentary, (2) skeletal, (3) muscular, (4) nervous, (5) endocrine, (6) cardiovascular, (7) lymphatic, (8) respiratory, (9) digestive, (10) urinary, and (11) reproductive. Figure 1.3 presents a brief summary of these organ systems and their functions. Throughout this textbook, Systems Pathology essays present a specific disease state and consider how this affects the interactions of the organ systems.

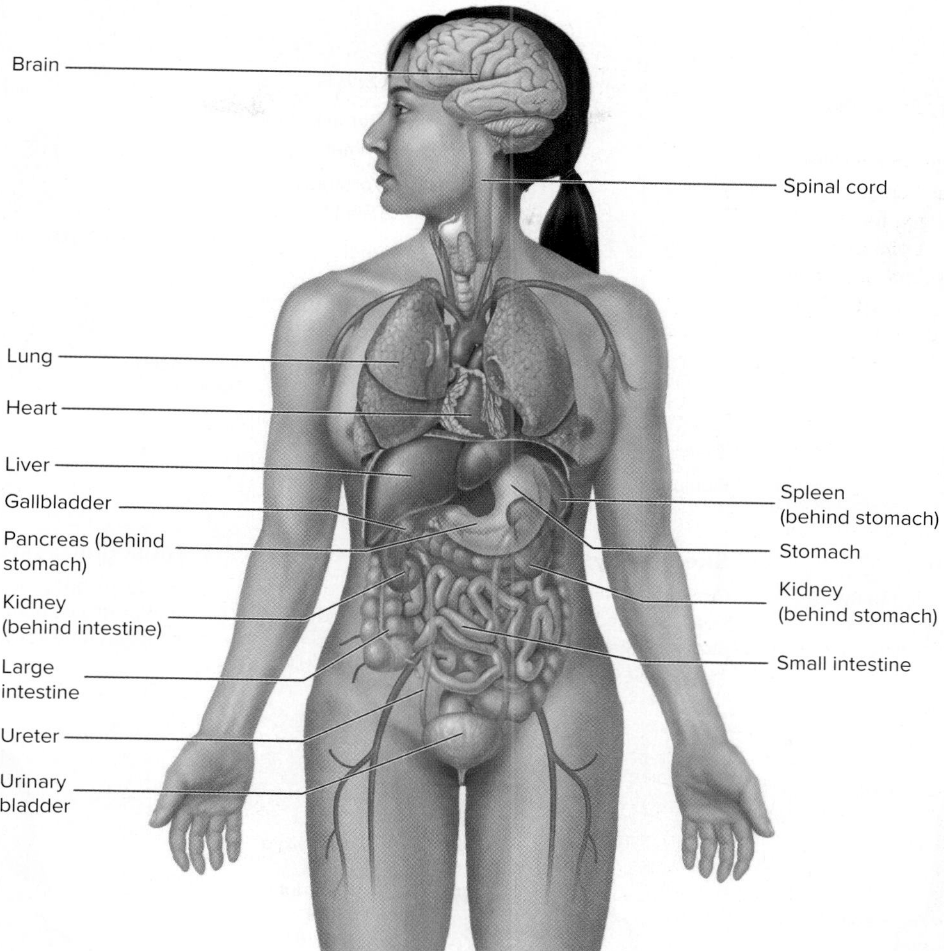

FIGURE 1.2 Major Organs of the Body
The body's major organs include the brain, lungs, heart, liver, pancreas, spleen, stomach, gallbladder, kidneys, large intestine, small intestine, urinary bladder, ureters, and urethra. APR

6. *Organism level.* An **organism** is any living thing considered as a whole—whether composed of one cell, such as a bacterium, or of trillions of cells, such as a human. The human organism is the combination of all the organ systems. These form a network of systems that are all mutually dependent on one another.

Understand **Predict 2**

In one type of diabetes, the pancreas fails to produce insulin, a chemical normally made by pancreatic cells and released into the blood. List as many levels of organization as you can at which this disorder could be corrected.

ASSESS YOUR PROGRESS

6. *From simplest to complex, list and define the body's six levels of organization.*
7. *What are the four basic types of tissues?*
8. *Referring to figure 1.3, which two organ systems are responsible for regulating the other organ systems? Which two are responsible for support and movement?*

1.4 Characteristics of Life

LEARNING OUTCOME

After reading this section, you should be able to

A. **List and define the six characteristics of life.**

Humans are organisms, sharing characteristics with other organisms. The most important common feature of all organisms is life. This textbook recognizes six essential characteristics of life:

1. **Organization** refers to the specific interrelationships among the parts of an organism and how those parts interact to perform specific functions. As we discussed in section 1.3, there are six levels of organization in the body (see figure 1.1).

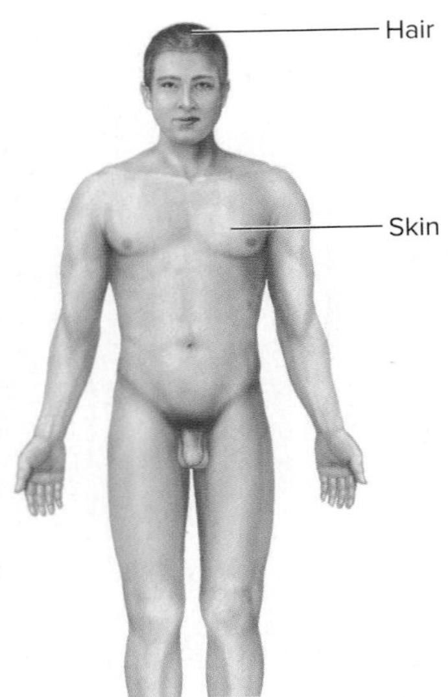

Integumentary System

Provides protection, regulates temperature, prevents water loss, and helps produce vitamin D. Consists of skin, hair, nails, and sweat glands.

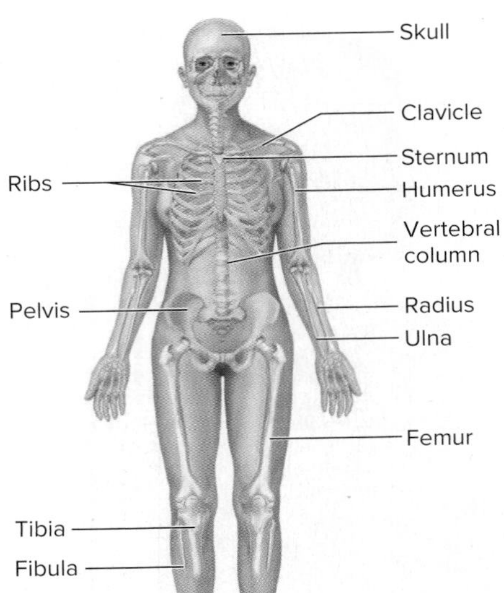

Skeletal System

Provides protection and support, allows body movements, produces blood cells, and stores minerals and adipose. Consists of bones, associated cartilages, ligaments, and joints.

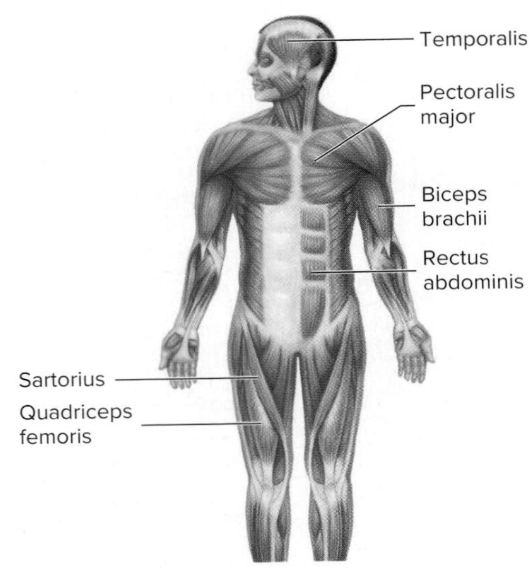

Muscular System

Produces body movements, maintains posture, and produces body heat. Consists of muscles attached to the skeleton by tendons.

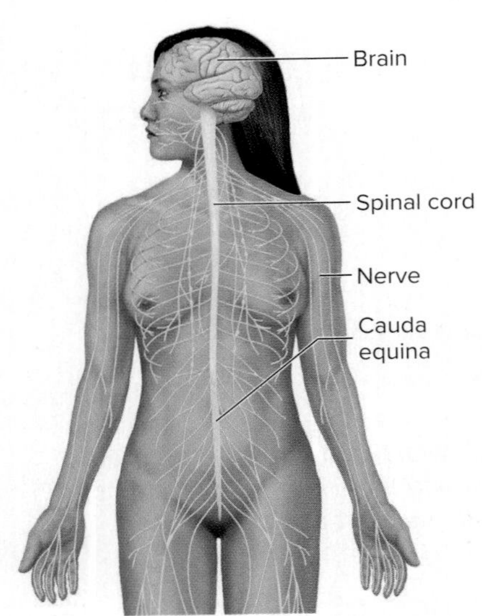

Nervous System

A major regulatory system that detects sensations and controls movements, physiological processes, and intellectual functions. Consists of the brain, spinal cord, nerves, and sensory receptors.

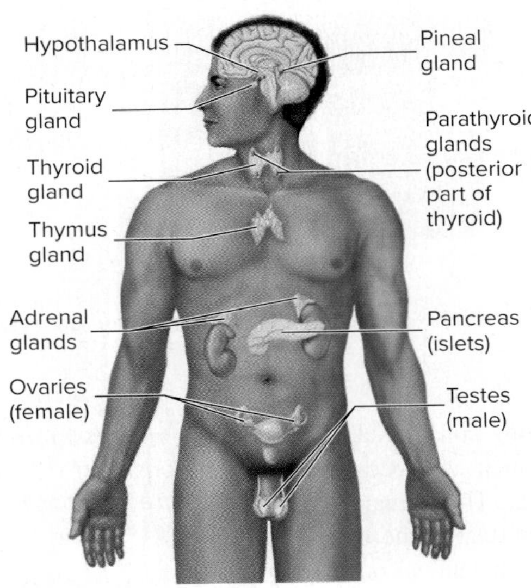

Endocrine System

A major regulatory system that influences metabolism, growth, reproduction, and many other functions. Consists of glands, such as the pituitary, that secrete hormones.

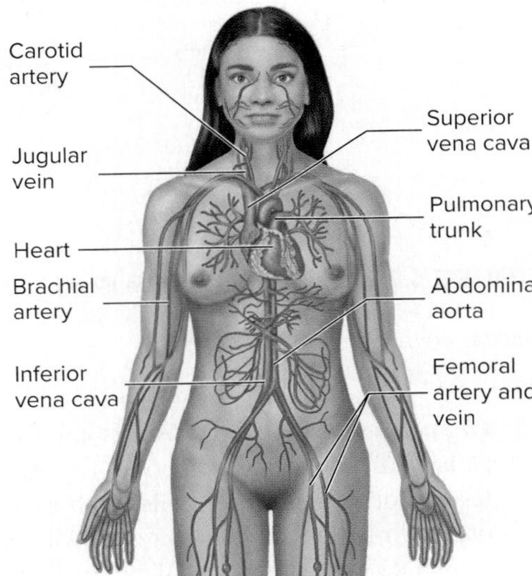

Cardiovascular System

Transports nutrients, waste products, gases, and hormones throughout the body; plays a role in the immune response and the regulation of body temperature. Consists of the heart, blood vessels, and blood.

FIGURE 1.3 Organ Systems of the Body
There are 11 body systems: integumentary, skeletal, muscular, lymphatic, respiratory, digestive, nervous, endocrine, cardiovascular, urinary, and reproductive.

2. **Metabolism** (meh-TAB-oh-lizm) is the ability to use energy and to perform other vital functions. Metabolism refers to all of the chemical reactions taking place in the cells and internal environment of an organism. For example, within our digestive system, we possess specialized proteins that break down food molecules (see figure 1.3). The organism then uses the nutrients from the food as a source of energy and raw materials to synthesize new molecules. Energy is also used to rearrange the shape of molecules. The shape of a molecule determines its function (recall the first key

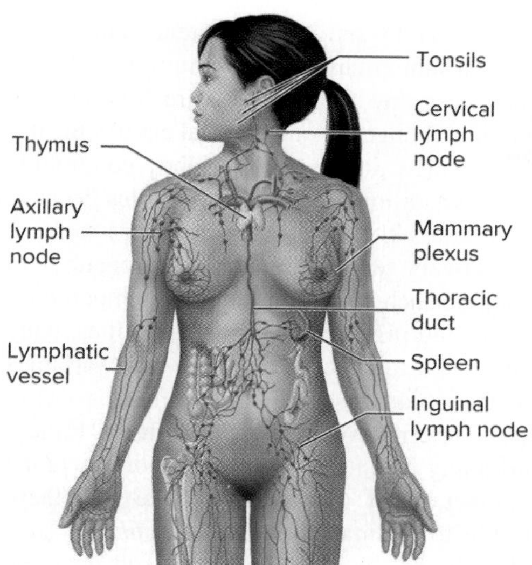

Lymphatic System

Removes foreign substances from the blood and lymph, combats disease, maintains tissue fluid balance, and absorbs dietary fats from the digestive tract. Consists of the lymphatic vessels, lymph nodes, and other lymphatic organs.

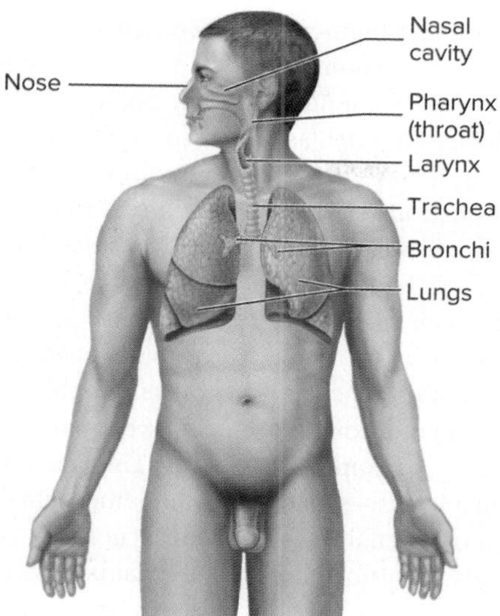

Respiratory System

Exchanges oxygen and carbon dioxide between the blood and air and regulates blood pH. Consists of the lungs and respiratory passages.

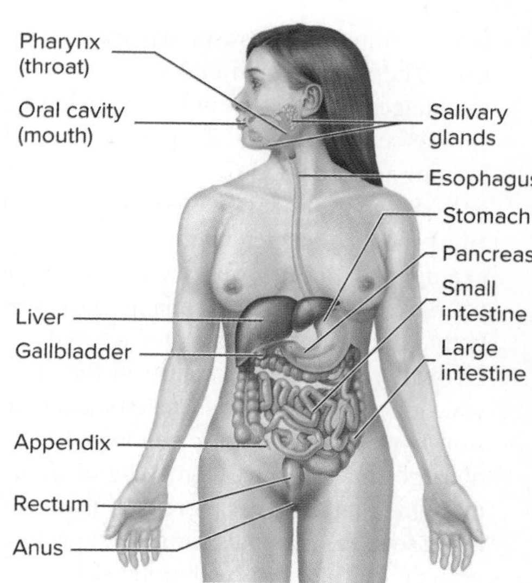

Digestive System

Performs the mechanical and chemical processes of digestion, absorption of nutrients, and elimination of wastes. Consists of the mouth, esophagus, stomach, intestines, and accessory organs.

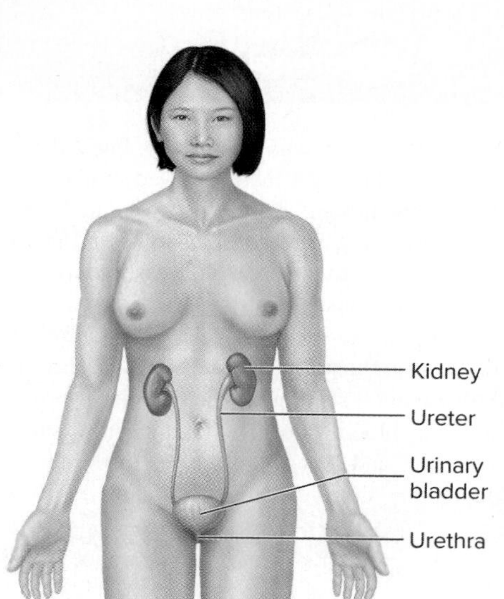

Urinary System

Removes waste products from the blood and regulates blood pH, ion balance, and water balance. Consists of the kidneys, urinary bladder, and ducts that carry urine.

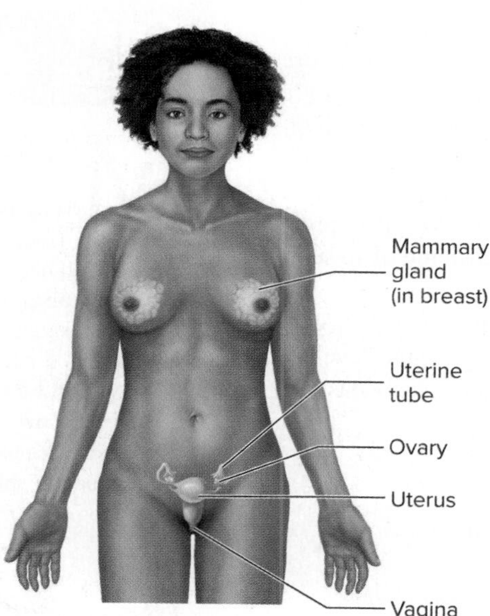

Female Reproductive System

Produces oocytes and is the site of fertilization and fetal development; produces milk for the newborn; produces hormones that influence sexual function and behaviors. Consists of the ovaries, uterine tubes, uterus, vagina, mammary glands, and associated structures.

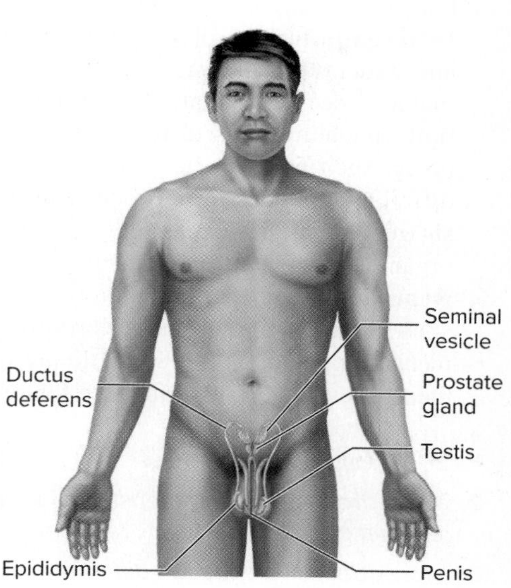

Male Reproductive System

Produces and transfers sperm cells to the female and produces hormones that influence sexual functions and behaviors. Consists of the testes, accessory structures, ducts, and penis.

FIGURE 1.3 **(continued)**

concept of anatomy and physiology). Some changes in molecular shape can allow certain cells to change shape. For example, specialized white blood cells can surround and engulf potentially dangerous foreign invaders, such as certain bacteria. Metabolism is necessary for other vital functions, such as responsiveness, growth, development, and reproduction.

3. **Responsiveness** is an organism's ability to sense changes in its external or internal environment and adjust to those changes. The third key concept of anatomy and physiology

is very important for responsiveness: cell-to-cell communication. The nervous and endocrine systems regulate responses to changes in the environment through cell-to-cell communication (see figure 1.3). Responses can include actions such as moving toward food or water and moving away from danger or poor environmental conditions. Organisms can also make adjustments that maintain their internal environment. For example, if the external environment causes the body temperature to rise, sweat glands produce sweat, which can lower body temperature down to the normal range.

4. **Growth** refers to an increase in the size or number of cells, which produces an overall enlargement of all or part of an organism. For example, a muscle enlarged by exercise is composed of larger muscle cells than those of an untrained muscle, and the skin of an adult has more cells than the skin of an infant. An increase in the materials surrounding cells can also contribute to growth. For instance, within the skeletal system, we see bones grow because of an increase in cell number and the deposition of mineralized materials around the cells (see figure 1.3).
5. **Development** includes the changes an organism undergoes through time, beginning with fertilization and ending at death. The greatest developmental changes occur before birth, but many changes continue after birth, and some go on throughout life. Development usually involves growth, but it also involves differentiation and morphogenesis. **Differentiation** involves changes in a cell's structure and function from an immature, generalized state to a mature, specialized state. For example, following fertilization, immature cells differentiate to become specific cell types, such as skin, bone, muscle, or nerve cells. These differentiated cells form tissues and organs. **Morphogenesis** (mohr-foh-JEN-eh-sis) is the change in shape of tissues, organs, and the entire organism.
6. **Reproduction** is the formation of new cells or new organisms. Reproduction of cells allows for growth and development. Reproduction allows all living organisms to pass on their genes to their offspring (see figure 1.3).

ASSESS YOUR PROGRESS

9. *What are the six characteristics of living things? Briefly explain each.*
10. *How does differentiation differ from morphogenesis?*

1.5 Homeostasis

LEARNING OUTCOMES

After reading this section, you should be able to

A. **Define *homeostasis.***
B. **Explain why homeostasis is important for proper body function.**
C. **Describe a negative-feedback mechanism and give an example.**
D. **Describe a positive-feedback mechanism and give an example.**

Homeostasis (hoh-mee-oh-STAY-sis) is the existence and maintenance of a relatively constant environment within the body. As our bodies undergo their everyday processes, we are continuously exposed to new conditions. Changes in our external environmental conditions can result in changes in our internal body conditions. Changes in internal body conditions are called **variables** because their values are not constant. To achieve and maintain homeostasis, the body must actively regulate responses to changes in variables. Variables include such conditions as body temperature, volume, chemical content and pH of body fluids, as well as many other variables. For our cells to function normally, all variables must be maintained within a narrow range.

This narrow range is referred to as a **normal range.** Homeostatic mechanisms normally maintain body conditions near an ideal normal value or **set point** (figure 1.4). Note that these mechanisms are not able to maintain body conditions *precisely* at the set point. Rather, body conditions increase and decrease slightly around the set point. Keep in mind that these fluctuations are minimal. For example, normal body temperature does not typically vary more than 1°F above or below normal. Our *average* body temperature is 98.6°F. Just as your home's thermostat does not keep the air temperature exactly at 75°F at all times, your body

Case STUDY 1.1 Orthostatic Hypotension

Molly is a 75-year-old widow who lives alone. For 2 days, she had a fever and chills and mainly stayed in bed. On rising to go to the bathroom, she felt dizzy, fainted, and fell to the floor. Molly quickly regained consciousness and managed to call her son, who took her to the emergency room, where a physician diagnosed orthostatic hypotension.

Orthostasis literally means "to stand," and *hypotension* refers to low blood pressure; thus, **orthostatic hypotension** is a significant drop in blood pressure upon standing. When a person moves from lying down to standing, blood "pools" within the veins below the heart because of gravity, and less blood returns to the heart. Consequently, blood pressure drops because the heart has less blood to pump.

Apply

Predict 3

Although orthostatic hypotension has many causes, in older people it can be due to age-related decreases in neural and cardiovascular responses. Decreased fluid intake while feeling ill and sweating due to a fever can result in dehydration. Dehydration can decrease blood volume and lower blood pressure, increasing the likelihood of orthostatic hypotension.

a. *Describe the normal response to a decrease in blood pressure on standing.*
b. *What happened to Molly's heart rate just before she fainted? Why did Molly faint?*
c. *How did Molly's fainting and falling to the floor help establish homeostasis (assuming she was not injured)?*

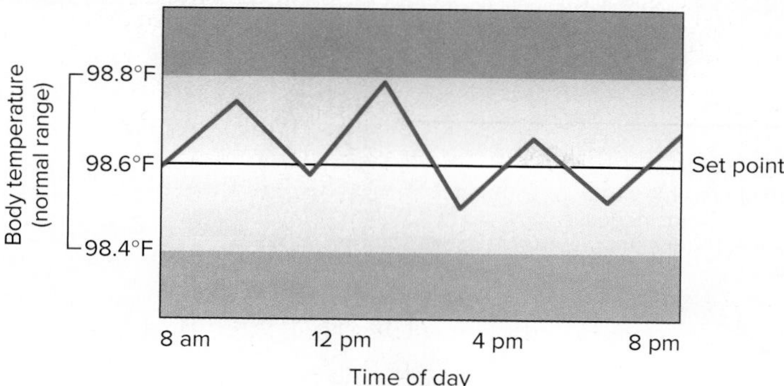

FIGURE 1.4 Fluctuation Around a Set Point
Body temperature is an example of a variable maintained near an ideal value, or set point.

conditions do not stay perfectly stable. As long as body conditions remain within the normal range, homeostasis is maintained.

It is the body's network of organ systems that helps keep the body's internal environment relatively constant. For example, the digestive, respiratory, cardiovascular, and urinary systems work together to ensure that each cell in the body receives adequate oxygen and nutrients, while also ensuring that waste products do not accumulate to toxic levels. Disease states can disrupt these processes and disturb homeostasis in such a way that death could result. Modern medicine attempts to understand disturbances in homeostasis and works to reestablish a normal range of values.

Feedback Loops

Homeostasis is regulated by **feedback loops.** Here we will examine our fourth key concept of anatomy and physiology: feedback loops. A feedback loop allows for a process to be regulated by the outcome. In biological systems, there are two types of feedback loops: (1) negative feedback and (2) positive feedback. Note that a common misconception is that negative feedback is the decrease of a body parameter, while positive feedback is the increase of a body parameter. For example, students sometimes think a drop in blood glucose levels is negative feedback and an increase in blood glucose is positive feedback. Rather, blood glucose increases and decreases are both controlled by negative feedback. As you read about each type of feedback loop, keep in mind that both types of feedback loops regulate the body's *responses* to either increased or decreased parameters.

Feedback loops have three components: (1) a **receptor,** which monitors the value of a variable by detecting stimuli; (2) a **control center,** such as a part of the brain, which determines the set point for the variable and receives input from the receptor about the variable; and (3) an **effector,** which generates the **response** that adjusts the value of a changed variable. A changed variable is a **stimulus** because it initiates a homeostatic mechanism.

Negative Feedback

Negative-feedback mechanisms are more commonly involved in maintenance of homeostasis than are positive-feedback mechanisms. In everyday terms, the word *negative* is used to mean "bad" or "undesirable." In the context of homeostasis mechanisms, negative means "to decrease." *Negative feedback* is when any deviation from the set point is made smaller or is resisted. In other words, the response by the effector is stopped once the variable returns to its set point (figure 1.5).

One of the most familiar examples of a negative-feedback mechanism is maintenance of body temperature. Normal body temperature is critical to our health because it allows molecules and enzymes to keep their normal shape so they can function optimally. An optimal body temperature prevents molecules from being destroyed. For example, picture the change in appearance of egg whites as they are cooked; the egg whites change from a transparent fluid to a white solid because heat changes the shape of the egg white molecules. Similarly, if the body were to be exposed to extreme heat, the shape of the molecules in the body could change, thus preventing them from functioning normally. Figure 1.6*a* demonstrates the steps in the negative-feedback mechanism regulating body temperature if it becomes too high. Normal body temperature depends on the

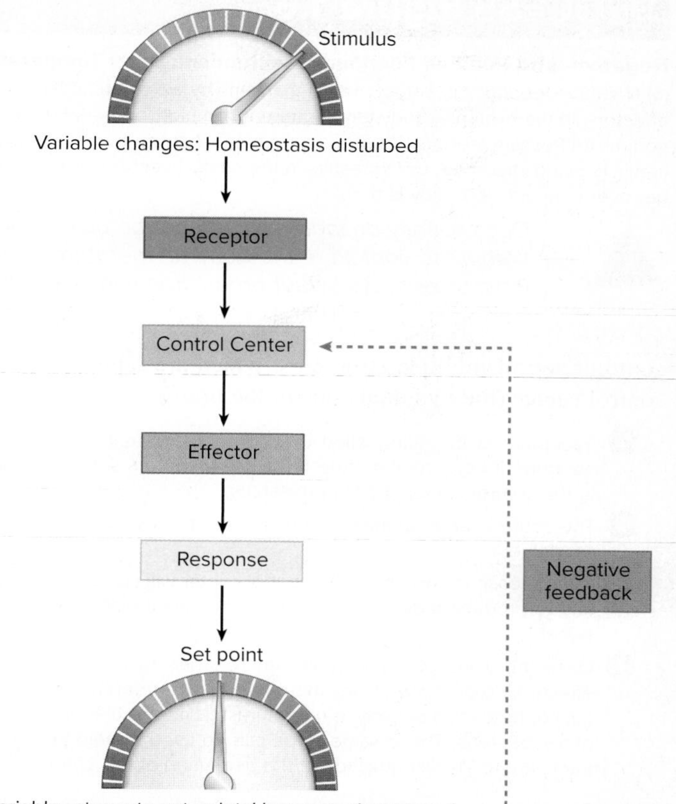

FIGURE 1.5 Feedback Loop
Feedback loops maintain homeostasis. Receptors signal the control center that a variable has deviated outside its normal range. The control center regulates the action of the effectors, which produce a response that returns the variable to the set point. In negative feedback, the return to set point stops the response.

FUNDAMENTAL **Figure**

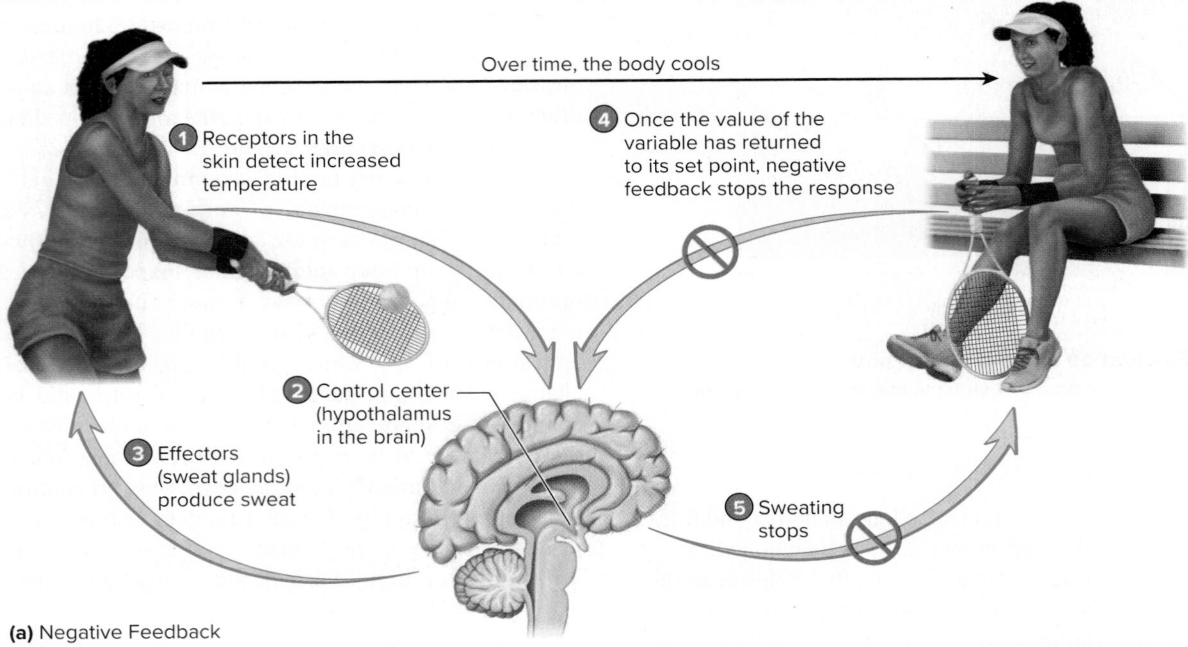

(a) Negative Feedback

PROCESS **Figure 1.6**

Negative- and Positive Feedback Mechanism: Body Temperature

(*a*) Negative feedback is one of the mechanisms by which homeostasis is maintained. Receptors signal the control center, which regulates the action of the effectors. In the example, body temperature is too high, so sweating occurs. Negative feedback stops the sweating when the body temperature returns to normal. (*b*) Positive feedback is also a type of mechanism that works to maintain homeostasis. In this example, receptors signal the control center that the cervix is being stretched, which results in the control center sending signals to increase the contractions of the uterus. This cycle continues, becoming stronger over time until the baby is born.

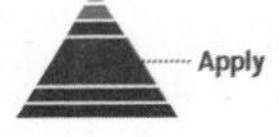

Occasionally an individual will not be able to produce sweat and can overheat, potentially suffering a heat stroke. Within the context of the body temperature homeostatic mechanism, where might the disruption occur? Propose at least three ways sweat production might be inhibited when the body temperature rises above the set point.

coordination of multiple structures, which are regulated by the control center (the hypothalamus in the brain).

1. Receptors in the skin (called thermoreceptors) monitor body temperature. If body temperature rises, the receptors send a message to the control center, the hypothalamus.
2. The control center compares the value of the variables against the set point.
3. If a response is necessary, the control center will stimulate the effectors to produce their response. Here, the sweat glands will secrete sweat.
4. Once the value of the variable has returned to the set point, the effectors do not receive any more information from the control center. For regulation of body temperature, this means that the secretion of sweat stops. These same steps can be used to help you answer the Learn to Predict question at the beginning of this chapter.

Often there is more than one effector for a particular homeostatic mechanism. In these cases, the control center must coordinate the effectors' responses. For example, cooling the body involves not only the production of sweat by the sweat glands, but also the action of the blood vessels to alter blood flow to the skin (see chapter 5). Once body temperature has returned to normal, the effectors stop. This is the hallmark of negative feedback—effectors stop their response once the variable has returned to it set point. They do not produce an infinite response (figure 1.7).

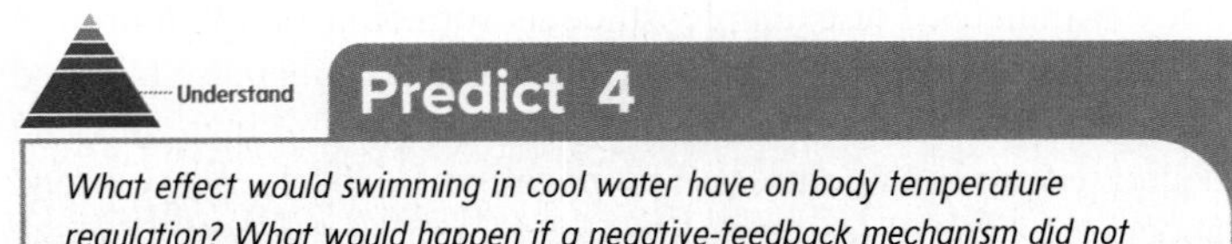

Predict 4

What effect would swimming in cool water have on body temperature regulation? What would happen if a negative-feedback mechanism did not return the value of a variable, such as body temperature, to its normal range?

Positive Feedback

Positive-feedback mechanisms occur when a response to the original stimulus results in the deviation from the set point becoming even greater. In other words, *positive* means "to increase." You may have experienced this: Perhaps you became embarrassed and realized your face was turning red, which caused you to become more embarrassed and your face turned even more red. Though not the typical physiological type of positive feedback, this example may help you understand the concept of positive feedback.

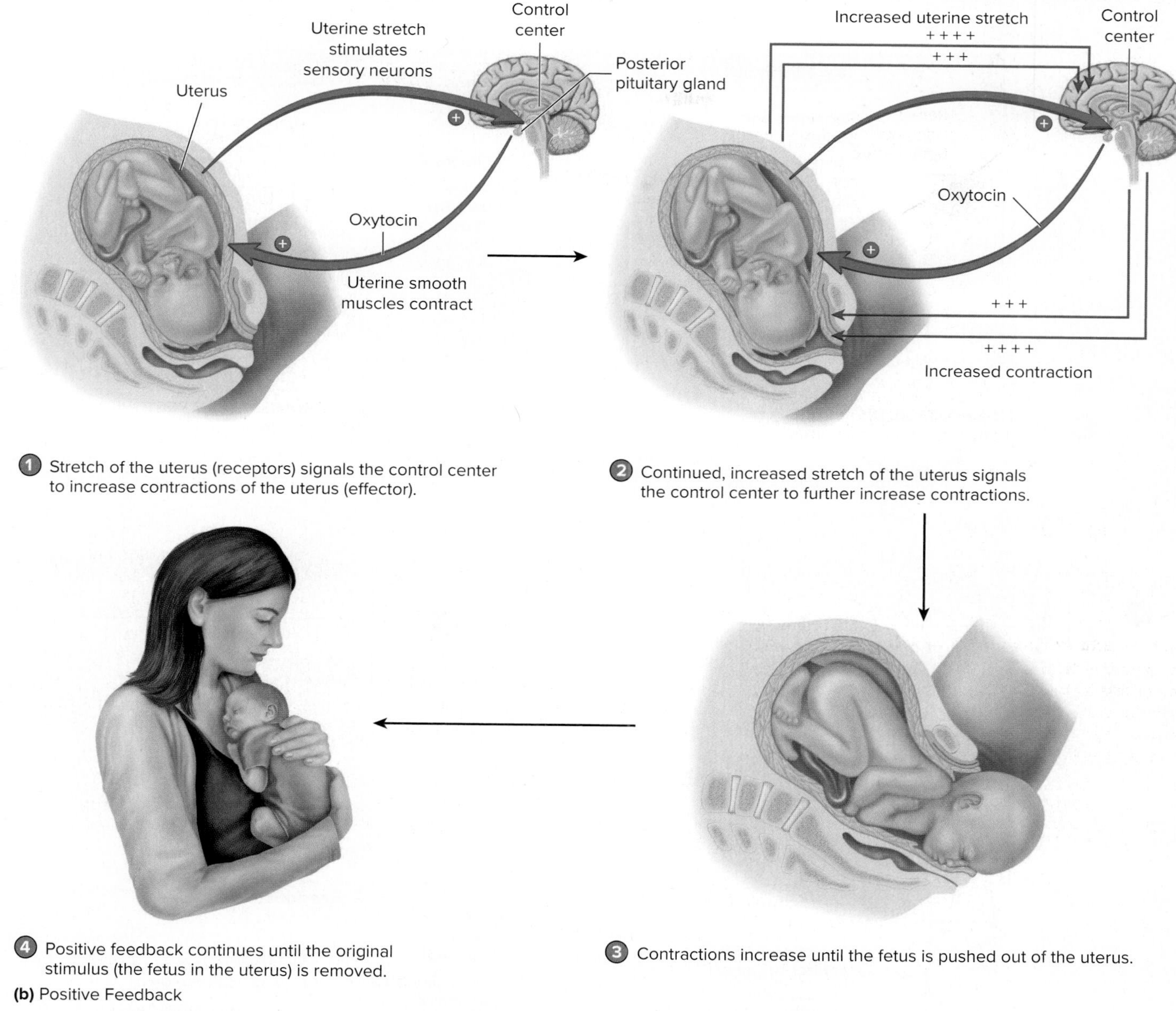

1 Stretch of the uterus (receptors) signals the control center to increase contractions of the uterus (effector).

2 Continued, increased stretch of the uterus signals the control center to further increase contractions.

3 Contractions increase until the fetus is pushed out of the uterus.

4 Positive feedback continues until the original stimulus (the fetus in the uterus) is removed.

(b) Positive Feedback

PROCESS **Figure 1.6 (Continued)**

1 Near the end of pregnancy, the baby's larger size stretches the uterus, especially near its opening.
2 This stretching stimulates contractions of the uterine muscles.
3 The contractions push the baby against the opening and stretch it further. This stimulates additional contractions, which result in additional stretching.
4 This positive-feedback sequence ends only when the baby is delivered from the uterus and the stretching stimulus is eliminated.

A physiological example of positive feedback occurs during blood loss. A chemical responsible for blood clot formation, called thrombin, stimulates production of even more thrombin. By continuing to produce thrombin, a disruption in homeostasis (blood loss) is resolved through a positive-feedback mechanism (blood clotting). But why doesn't this continued production of thrombin lead to the entire vascular system forming a clot? Because the clot formation process is self-limiting. Eventually, the chemicals needed for clot formation will be depleted in the area of blood loss and no further clotting can occur.

As shown in figure 1.6*b*, birth is another example of a normally occurring positive-feedback mechanism.

This continued response is the hallmark of positive feedback—the effectors continue the response beyond the set point until the original stimulus is removed.

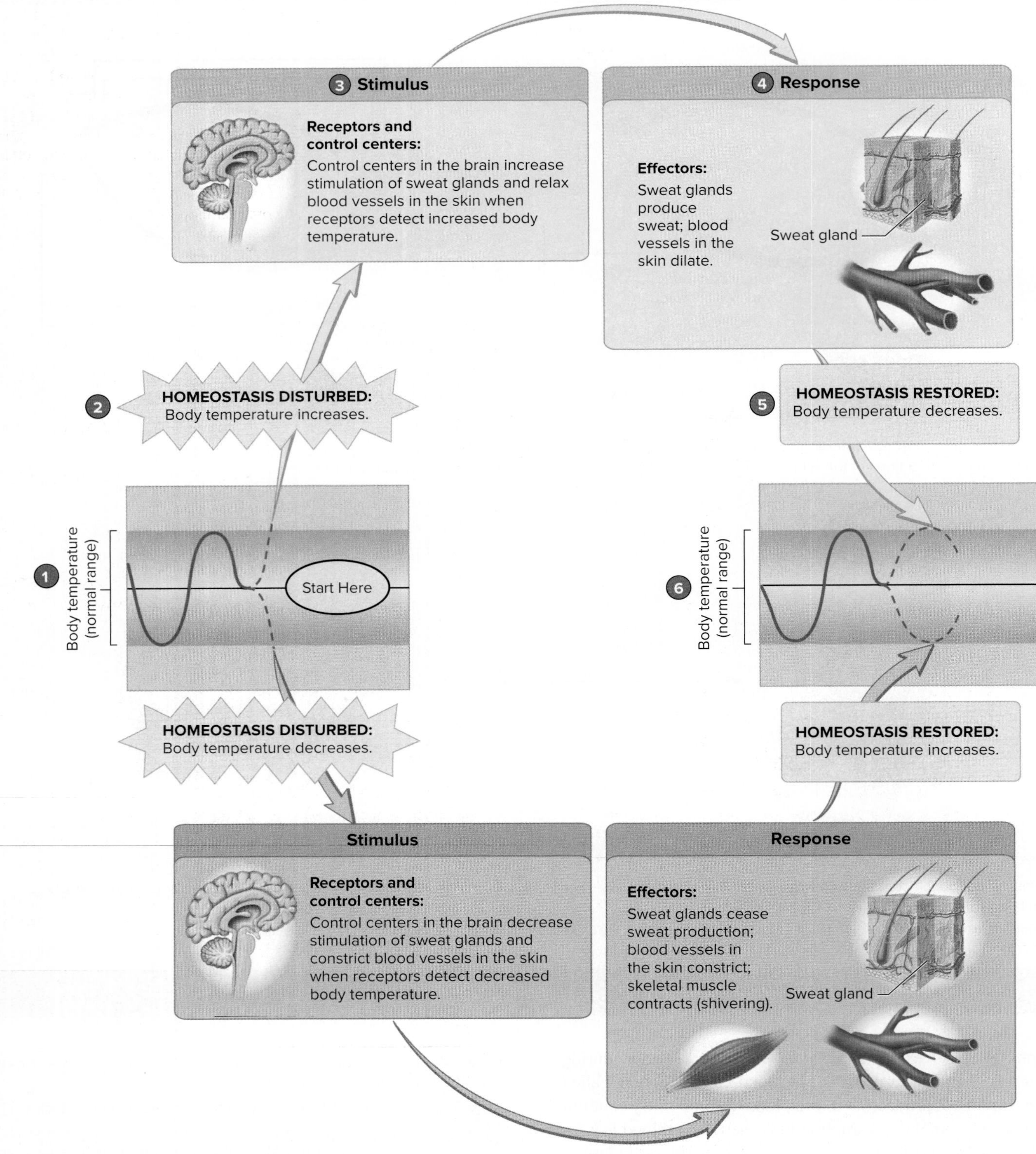

HOMEOSTASIS FIGURE 1.7 Negative-Feedback Control of Body Temperature

Throughout this book, all homeostasis figures have the same format as shown here. The changes caused by the increase of a variable outside the normal range are shown in the *top blue boxes,* and the changes caused by a decrease are shown in the *bottom pink boxes*. To help you learn how to interpret homeostasis figures, some of the steps in this figure are numbered. (1) Body temperature is within its normal range. (2) Body temperature increases outside the normal range, which causes homeostasis to be disturbed. (3) The body temperature control center in the brain responds to the change in body temperature. (4) The control center causes sweat glands to produce sweat and blood vessels in the skin to dilate. (5) These changes cause body temperature to decrease. (6) Body temperature returns to its normal range, and homeostasis is restored. Observe the responses to a decrease in body temperature outside its normal range by following the *bottom pink arrows*.

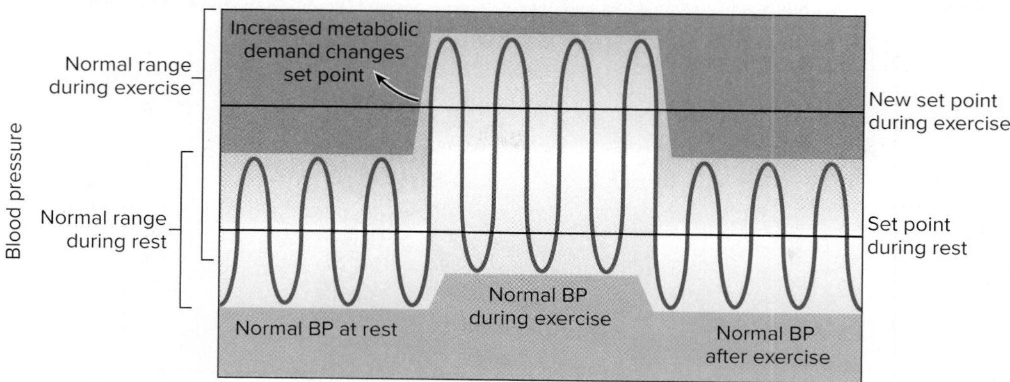

FIGURE 1.8 Changes in Blood Pressure During Exercise
During exercise, muscle tissue demands more oxygen. To meet this demand, blood pressure (BP) increases, resulting in an increase in blood flow to the tissues. The increased blood pressure is not an abnormal or nonhomeostatic condition but a resetting of the normal homeostatic range to meet the increased demand. The reset range is higher and broader than the resting range. After exercise ceases, the range returns to that of the resting condition.

There are two basic principles about homeostatic mechanisms to remember: (1) many disease states result from the failure of negative-feedback mechanisms to maintain homeostasis and (2) some positive-feedback mechanisms can be detrimental instead of helpful. One example of a detrimental positive-feedback mechanism is inadequate delivery of blood to cardiac (heart) muscle. Contraction of cardiac muscle generates blood pressure and the heart pumps blood to itself through a system of blood vessels on the outside of the heart. Just as with other tissues, blood pressure must be maintained to ensure adequate delivery of blood to the cardiac muscle. Following extreme blood loss, blood pressure decreases to the point that the delivery of blood to cardiac muscle is inadequate. As a result, cardiac muscle does not function normally. The heart pumps less blood, which causes the blood pressure to drop even further—a deviation further from the set point. The additional decrease in blood pressure further reduces blood delivery to cardiac muscle, and the heart pumps even less blood, which again decreases the blood pressure. The process self-propagates until the blood pressure is too low to sustain the cardiac muscle, the heart stops beating, and death results. In this example, we see the deviation from the heart rate set point becoming larger and larger—this is a positive-feedback mechanism. Thus, if blood loss is severe, negative-feedback mechanisms may not be able to maintain homeostasis, and the postive feedback of ever-decreasing blood pressure can develop. On the other hand, following a moderate amount of blood loss (e.g., after donating a pint of blood), *negative-feedback mechanisms* result in an *increase* in heart rate, which restores blood pressure.

Although homeostasis is the maintenance of a normal range of values, this does not mean that all variables remain within the same narrow range of values at all times. Sometimes a deviation from the usual range of values can be beneficial. For example, during exercise the normal range for blood pressure increases above the resting range (figure 1.8). The increase in blood pressure helps supply muscle cells with the greater amount of oxygen and nutrients needed to support increased activity during exercise.

Predict 5

Ashley is on the track team and is running an 800-meter race. Throughout the race, her respiratory rate increases rapidly. Does this represent negative or positive feedback? Explain.

ASSESS YOUR PROGRESS

11. *How do variables, set points, and normal ranges relate to homeostasis?*
12. *Distinguish between negative feedback and positive feedback.*
13. *What are the three components of a negative-feedback mechanism?*
14. *Give an example of how a negative-feedback mechanism maintains homeostasis.*
15. *Give an example of a positive-feedback mechanism that may be harmful to the body and an example of one that is not harmful.*

1.6 Terminology and the Body Plan

LEARNING OUTCOMES

After reading this section, you should be able to

A. **Describe a person in the anatomical position.**
B. **Define the directional terms for the human body and use them to locate specific body structures.**
C. **Know the terms for the parts and regions of the body.**
D. **Name and describe the three major planes of the body.**
E. **Name and describe the three major ways to cut an organ.**
F. **Describe the major trunk cavities and their divisions.**
G. **Locate organs in their specific cavity, abdominal quadrant, or region.**
H. **Describe the serous membranes, their locations, and their functions.**

As you study anatomy and physiology, you will be learning many new words. Knowing the derivation, or **etymology** (ET-ee-MOL-oh-jee), of these words can make learning them easy and fun. Most anatomical terms are derived from Latin or Greek. For example, *foramen* is a Latin word for "hole," and *magnum* means "large." The foramen magnum is therefore a large hole in the skull through which the spinal cord attaches to the brain.

Prefixes and suffixes can be added to words to expand their meaning. For example, the suffix *-itis* means an inflammation, so

FUNDAMENTAL **Figure**

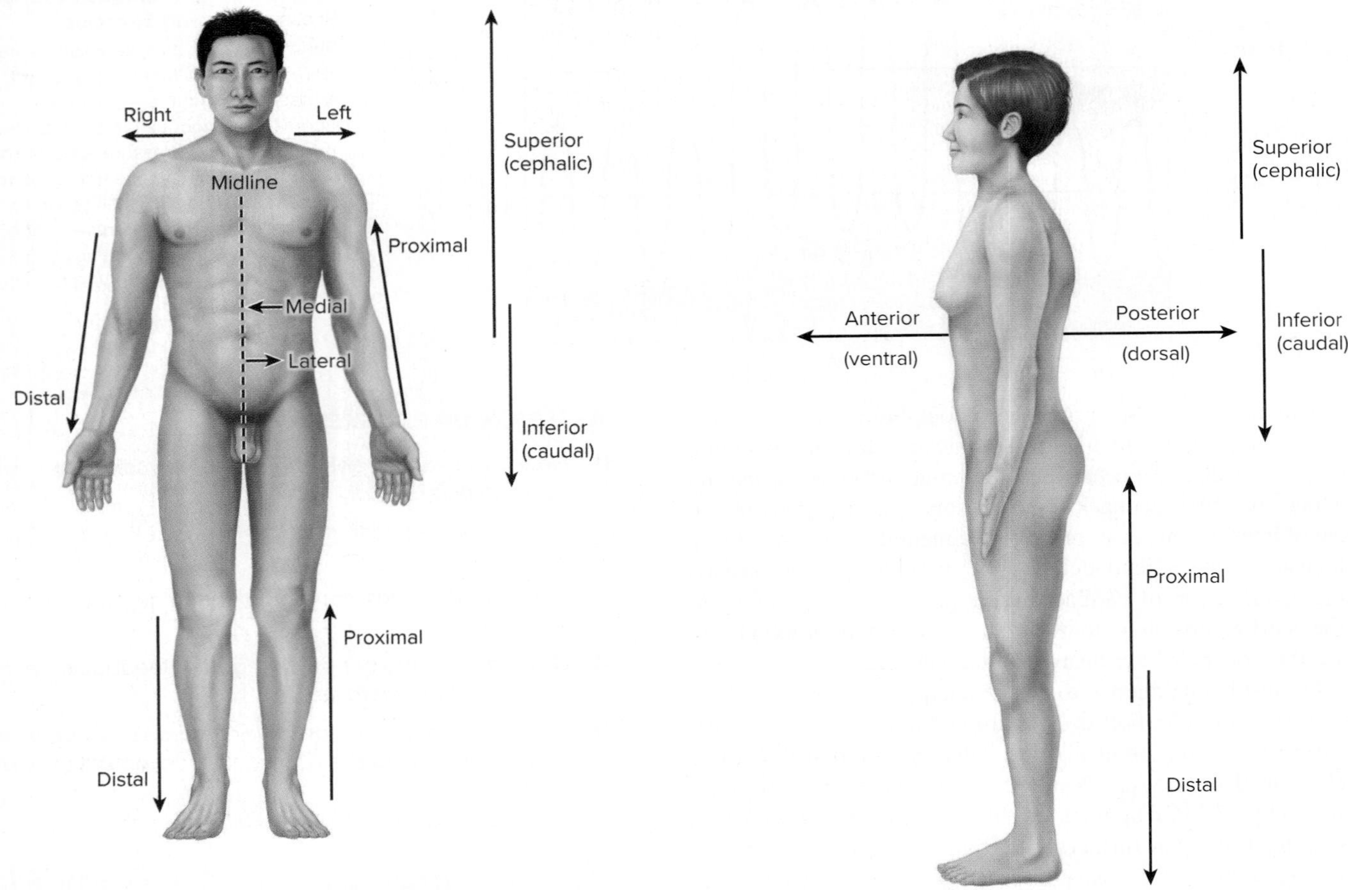

FIGURE 1.9 Directional Terms
All directional terms are in relation to the body in the anatomical position: a person standing erect with the face directed forward, the arms hanging to the sides, and the palms of the hands facing forward. APR

appendicitis is an inflammation of the appendix. As new terms are introduced in this text, their meanings are often explained. The glossary and the list of word roots, prefixes, and suffixes in appendix B of this textbook provide additional information about the new terms.

It is very helpful to learn these new words, so that your message is clear and correct when you speak to colleagues or write reports. Additionally, you will find many of the roots of words appearing over and over again. For example, in chapter 7, you will learn a specific region of the scapula called the *infraspinous fossa.* Later, in chapter 10, you learn that the muscle in that region is named the *infraspinatus.*

Body Positions

Anatomical position refers to a person standing erect with the face directed forward, the upper limbs hanging to the sides, and the palms of the hands facing forward (figure 1.9). A person is **supine** when lying face upward and **prone** when lying face downward.

In anatomical position, the head is above the feet, but if a person were to do a handstand, the head would be closer to the ground than the feet. However, we would still refer to the position of the head as being above the feet because the point of reference for anatomical structures is the body, not the position of the body structure compared to the earth.

Directional Terms

Directional terms describe parts of the body relative to each other. Important directional terms are illustrated in figure 1.9 and summarized in table 1.2. It is important to become familiar with these directional terms as soon as possible because you will see them repeatedly throughout this textbook. **Right** and **left** are used as directional terms in anatomical terminology. **Superior** means above, and **inferior** means below; **anterior** is used for "in front of," and **posterior** is used for "behind."

For human anatomy, the term *superior* is used interchangeably with the term *cephalic* (SE-FAL-ik; head), and the term *inferior* is used interchangeably with *caudal* (KAW-dal; tail). In

TABLE 1.2 Directional Terms for Humans

Term	Etymology*	Definition	Example
Right		Toward the right side of the body	Right ear
Left		Toward the left side of the body	Left eye
Superior	L. higher	A structure above another	The chin is superior to the navel.
Inferior	L. lower	A structure below another	The navel is inferior to the chin.
Cephalic	G. *kephale*, head	Closer to the head than another structure (usually synonymous with *superior*)	The chin is cephalic to the navel.
Caudal	L. *cauda*, a tail	Closer to the tail than another structure (usually synonymous with *inferior*)	The navel is caudal to the chin.
Anterior	L. before	The front of the body	The navel is anterior to the spine.
Posterior	L. *posterus*, following	The back of the body	The spine is posterior to the breastbone.
Ventral	L. *ventr-*, belly	Toward the belly (synonymous with *anterior*)	The navel is ventral to the spine.
Dorsal	L. *dorsum*, back	Toward the back (synonymous with *posterior*)	The spine is dorsal to the breastbone.
Proximal	L. *proximus*, nearest	Closer to the point of attachment to the body than another structure	The elbow is proximal to the wrist.
Distal	L. *di-* plus *sto*, to stand apart or be distant	Farther from the point of attachment to the body than another structure	The wrist is distal to the elbow.
Lateral	L. *latus*, side	Away from the midline of the body	The nipple is lateral to the breastbone.
Medial	L. *medialis*, middle	Toward the midline of the body	The nose is medial to the eye.
Superficial	L. *superficialis*, toward the surface	Toward or on the surface (not shown in figure 1.10)	The skin is superficial to muscle.
Deep	O.E. *deop*, deep	Away from the surface, internal (not shown in figure 1.10)	The lungs are deep to the ribs.

*Origin and meaning of the word: L., Latin; G., Greek; O.E., Old English.

animals that do not walk upright, such as a cat, the terms *cephalic* and *caudal* can be used to describe the relative position of anatomical structures on the trunk, but not on the limbs. In addition, *anterior* is synonymous with *ventral* (belly) and *posterior* is synonymous with *dorsal* (back).

Predict 6

The anatomical position of a cat refers to the animal standing erect on all four limbs and facing forward. On the basis of the etymology of the directional terms, which two terms indicate movement toward the cat's head? What two terms mean movement toward the cat's back? Compare these terms with those referring to a human in the anatomical position.

Proximal means "close to," whereas **distal** means "far from." These terms are used to refer to relative positions of structures, such as on the limbs. Each limb is attached at its proximal end to the body, and the distal end, such as the hand, is farther away. Proximal and distal can also describe a structure's position relative to another, such as the kidney structures the proximal and distal convoluted tubules. Their position is described relative to another kidney structure used for filtration.

Medial means "toward the midline," and **lateral** means "away from the midline." The nose is in a medial position in the face, and the eyes are lateral to the nose. **Superficial** describes a structure close to the surface of the body, and **deep** is toward the interior of the body. The skin is superficial to muscle and bone.

Predict 7

Use as many directional terms as you can to describe the relationship between your kneecap and your heel.

ASSESS YOUR PROGRESS

16. *What is anatomical position in humans? Why is it important?*

17. *What two directional terms indicate "toward the head" in humans? What are the opposite terms?*

18. *What two directional terms indicate "the back" in humans? What are the opposite terms?*

19. *Define the following directional terms and give the term that means the opposite:* proximal, lateral, *and* superficial.

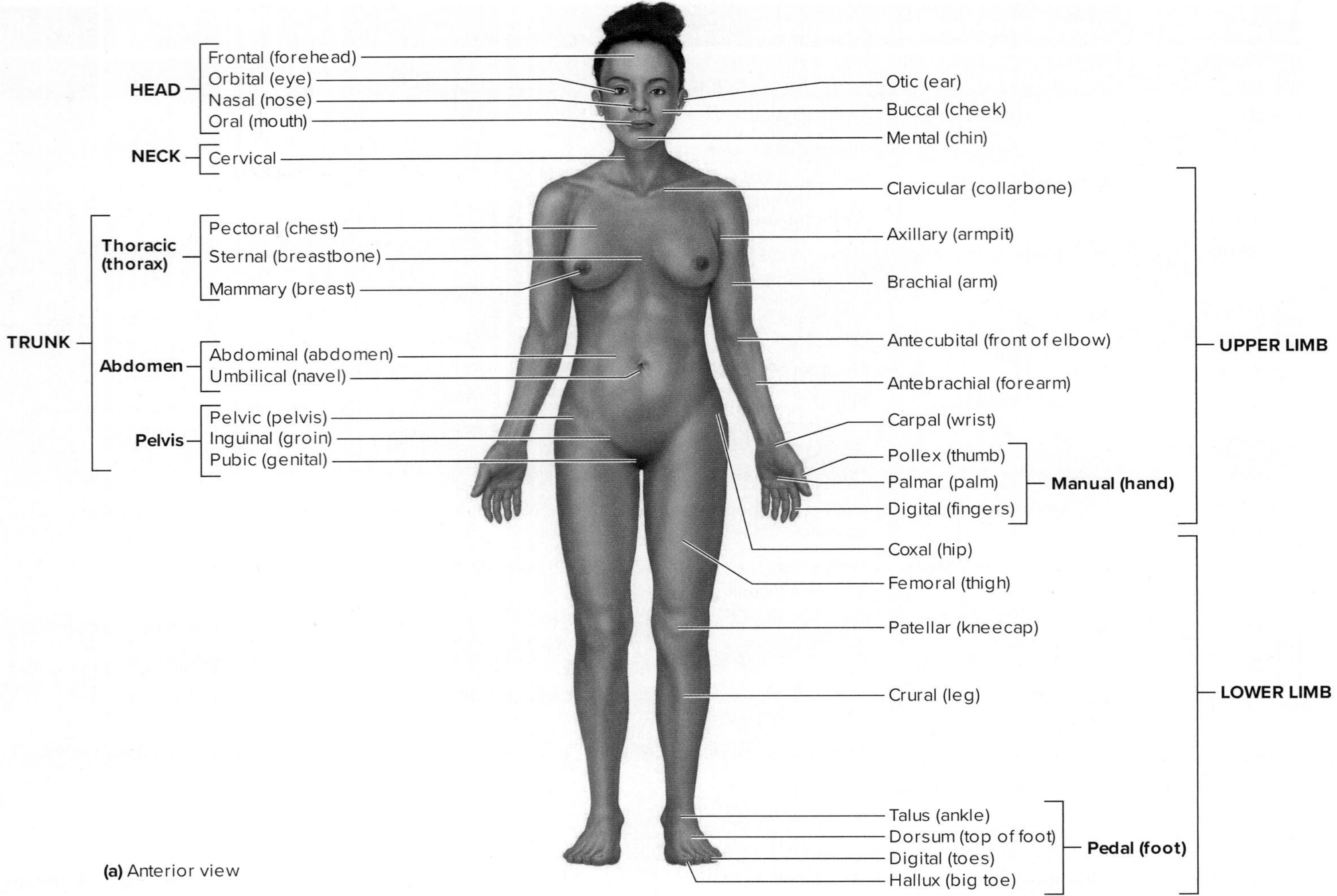

FIGURE 1.10 Body Parts and Regions
The anatomical and common (*in parentheses*) names are indicated for the major parts and regions of the body. (*a*) Anterior and (*b*) posterior views. APR

Body Parts and Regions

Health professionals use a number of terms when referring to different parts or regions of the body. Figure 1.10 (*a*, anterior; *b*, posterior) shows the anatomical terms, with the common terms in parentheses.

The central region of the body consists of the **head, neck,** and **trunk.** The trunk can be further divided into three regions: (1) the **thorax,** (2) the **abdomen,** and (3) the **pelvis.** The thorax is the chest cavity where the heart and lungs are located. The abdomen contains organs such as (1) the liver, (2) the stomach, and (3) the intestines. The pelvis contains the bladder and reproductive organs. The upper limb is divided into (1) the arm, (2) the forearm, (3) the wrist, and (4) the hand. The **arm** extends from the shoulder to the elbow, and the **forearm** extends from the elbow to the wrist. The lower limb is divided into (1) the thigh, (2) the leg, (3) the ankle, and (4) the foot. The **thigh** extends from the hip to the knee, and the **leg** extends from the knee to the ankle. Note that, contrary to popular usage, the terms *arm* and *leg* refer to only a part of the limb.

The abdomen is often subdivided superficially into **quadrants** by two imaginary lines—one horizontal and one vertical—that intersect at the navel (figure 1.11*a*). The quadrants formed are (1) the right-upper, (2) the left-upper, (3) the right-lower, and (4) the left-lower quadrants. In addition to these quadrants, the abdomen is sometimes subdivided into **regions** by four imaginary lines: two horizontal and two vertical. These four lines create a "virtual" tic-tac-toe grid on the abdomen, resulting in nine regions: (1) epigastric, (2) right and left hypochondriac, (3) umbilical, (4) right and left lumbar, (5) hypogastric, and (6) right and left iliac (figure 1.11*b*). Health professionals use the quadrants and regions as reference points for locating underlying organs. For example, the appendix is in the right-lower quadrant, and the pain of an acute appendicitis is usually felt there. Practice using these body part and region terms with the directional terms in figure 1.9. For example, "Your lungs (in the thorax) are ______ compared to your stomach (in the abdomen). The calcaneal region of the lower limb is ______ to the popliteal region of the lower limb.

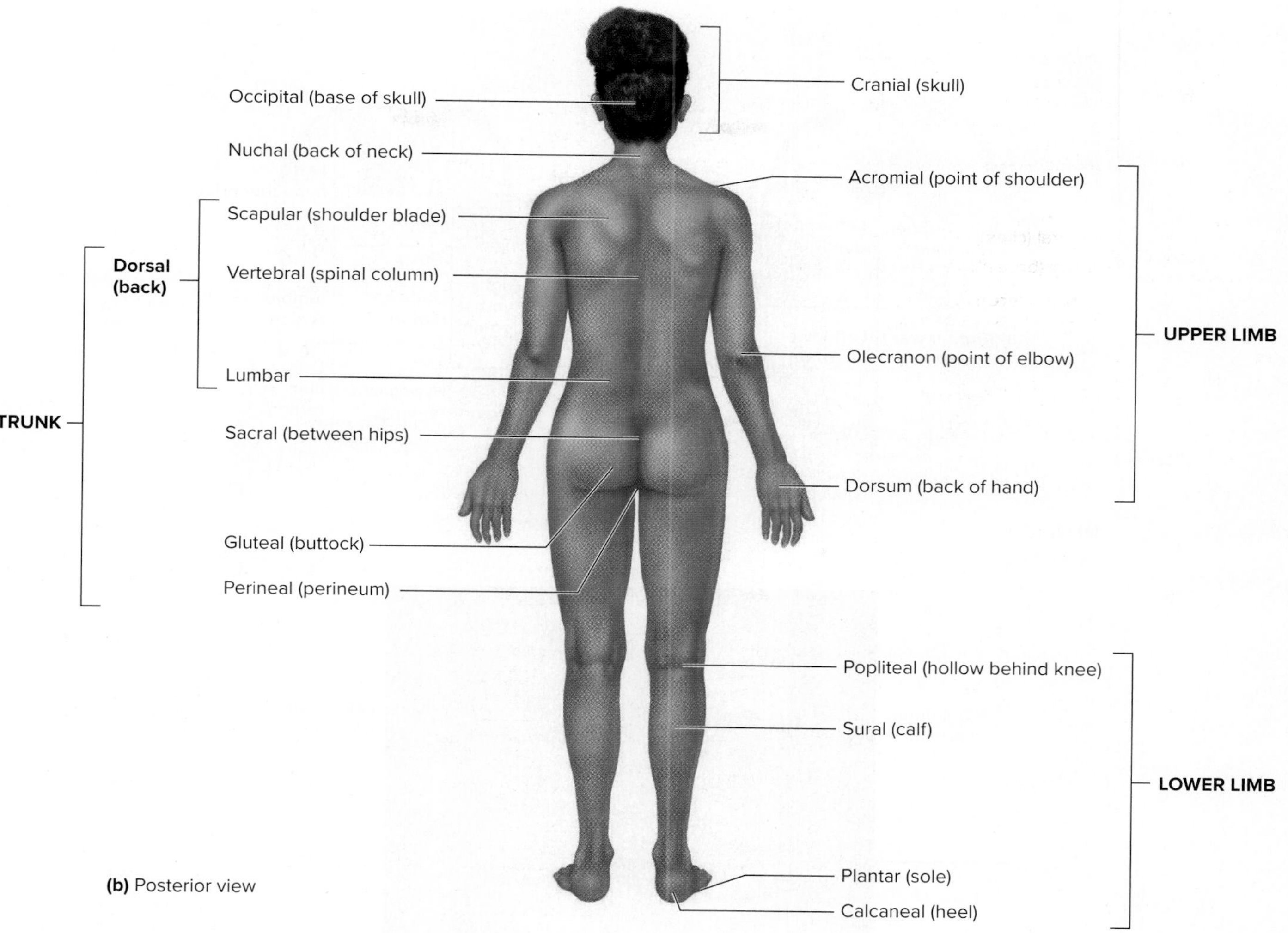

(b) Posterior view

FIGURE 1.10 (continued)

Planes

At times, it is useful to describe the body as having imaginary flat surfaces, called **planes,** passing through it (figure 1.12). A plane divides, or sections, the body, making it possible to "look inside" and observe the body's structures.

1. A **sagittal** (SAJ-ih-tal) **plane** separates the body or a structure into right and left halves. The word *sagittal* means "the flight of an arrow" and refers to the way the body would be split by an arrow passing anteriorly to posteriorly.
2. A **median plane** is a sagittal plane that passes through the midline of the body, dividing it into equal right and left halves.
3. A **transverse** (**horizontal**) **plane** runs parallel to the ground, dividing the body into superior and inferior portions.
4. A **frontal** (**coronal**) (KOHR-oh-nal, koh-ROH-nal; crown) **plane** divides the body into front (anterior) and back (posterior) halves. For example, the coronal suture on the skull is located across the top, where a person might wear a crown.

Organs are often sectioned to reveal their internal structure (figure 1.13). A cut through the length of the organ is a **longitudinal section,** and a cut at a right angle to the length of an organ is a **transverse** (**cross**) **section.** If a cut is made across the the length of an organ at other than a right angle, it is called an **oblique section.**

ASSESS YOUR PROGRESS

20. *What makes up the central region of the body?*
21. *What is the difference between the arm and the upper limb? Between the leg and the lower limb?*
22. *What are the anatomical terms for the following common body terms—neck, mouth, hand, front of elbow, calf, sole?*
23. *In what quadrant would the majority of the stomach be located? In which region(s)?*
24. *List and describe the three planes of the body.*
25. *In what three ways can you cut an organ?*

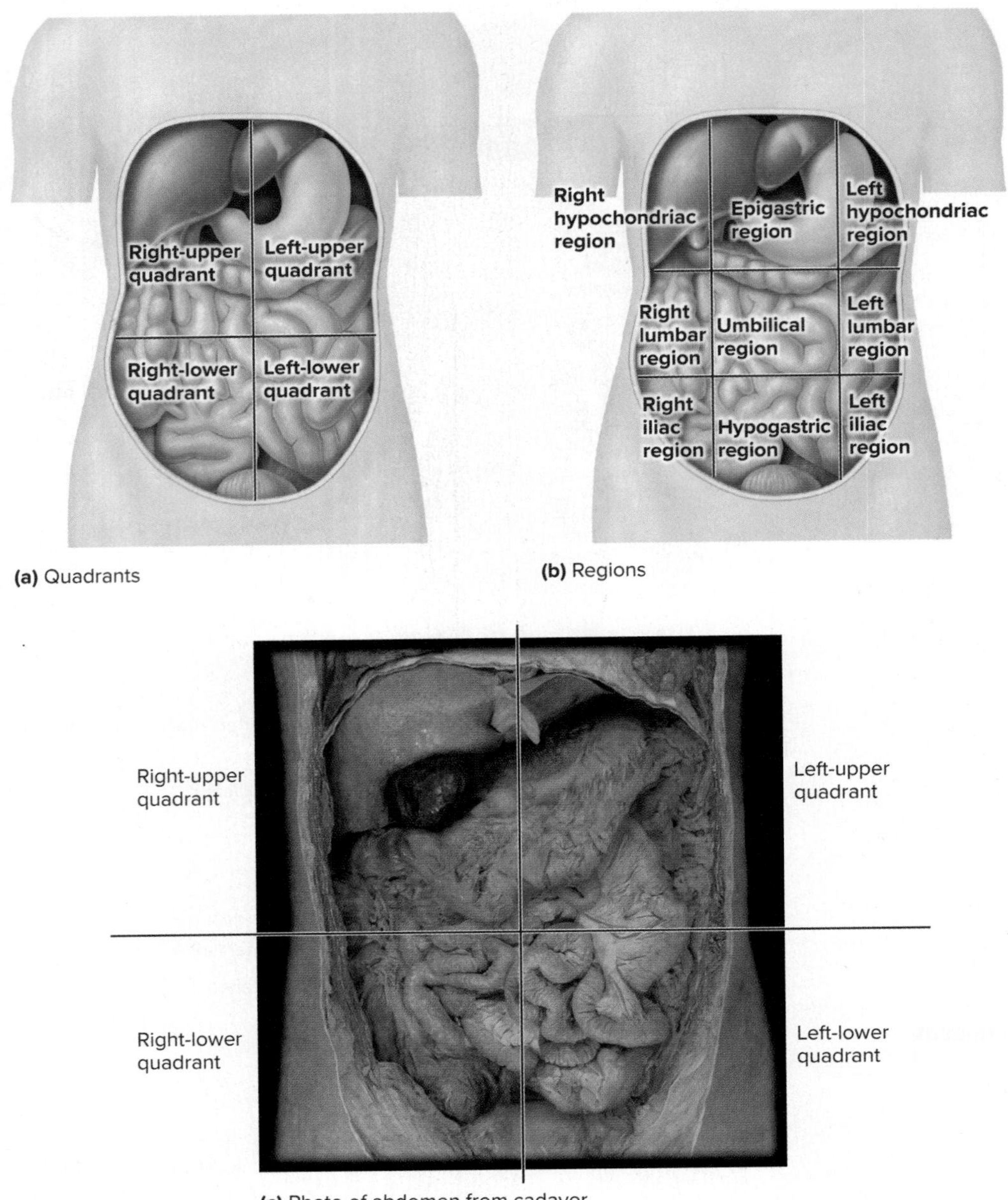

FIGURE 1.11 Subdivisions of the Abdomen
Lines are superimposed over internal organs to demonstrate the subdivisions they lie in. (*a*) Abdominal quadrants. (*b*) There are nine abdominal regions. (c) Cadaver photo of abdominal cavity. (c) McGraw Hill APR

Body Cavities

The body contains two types of internal cavities: (1) the dorsal body cavity and (2) the ventral body cavity (figure 1.14). These cavities, which are closed to the outside, contain our internal organs, providing protection for them. Some anatomy textbooks do not use the dorsal body cavity designation; however, in this textbook we have chosen to use the two internal body cavities model.

Dorsal Body Cavity

The dorsal body encloses the organs of the nervous system, the brain and spinal cord. The two subdivisions of the dorsal body cavity are (1) the cranial cavity, which houses the brain, and (2) the vertebral canal, which houses the spinal cord. Both the brain and spinal cord are covered by membranes called meninges (figure 1.14*a*). We discuss the anatomy of the nervous system further in chapters 12 and 13.

Ventral Body Cavity

The ventral body cavity houses the vast majority of our internal organs, collectively referred to as the **viscera** (VIS-er-ah; internal organs) (figure 1.14*b*). The ventral body cavity also has two major subdivisions, which are (1) the thoracic cavity and (2) the abdominopelvic cavity.

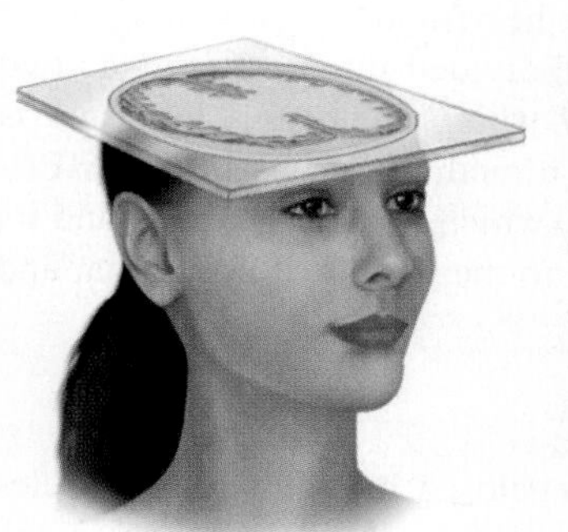

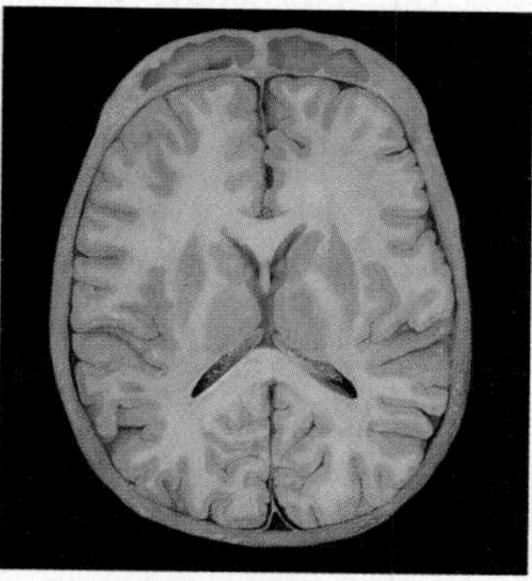

Transverse Section (from the top)

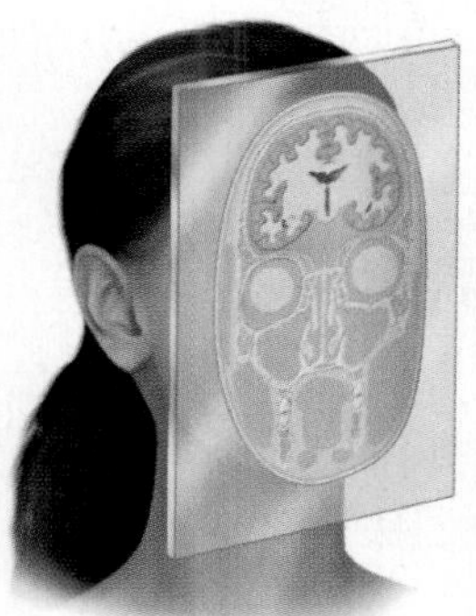

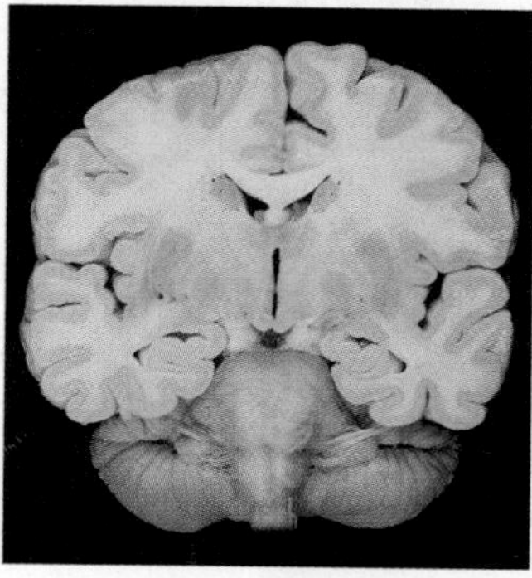

Coronal Section (from the front)

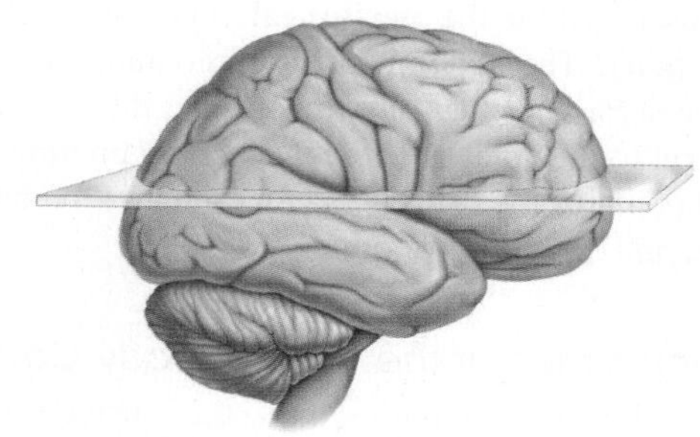

(a) Transverse Section

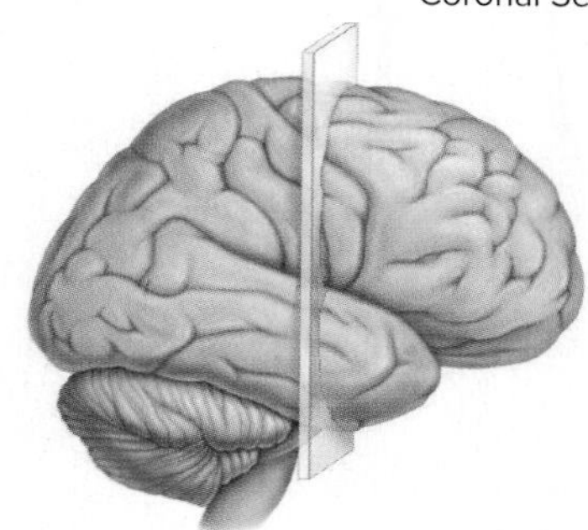

(b) Coronal Section

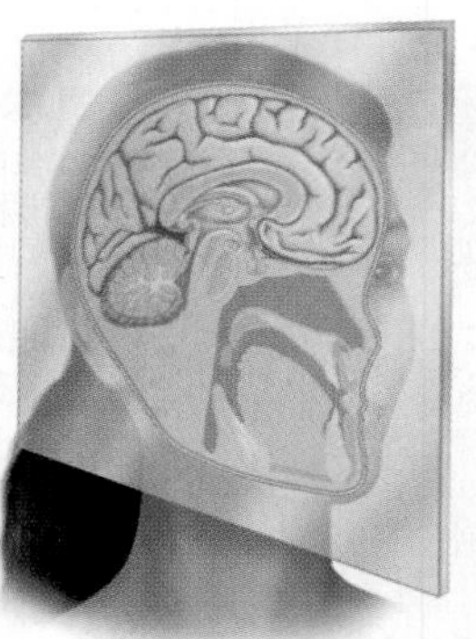

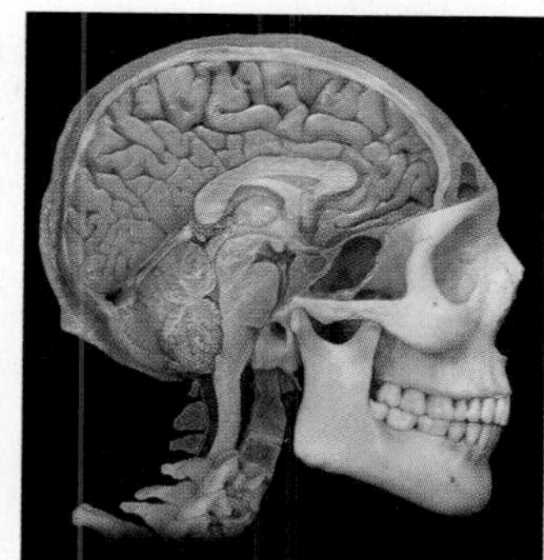

Sagittal Section (right and left halves)

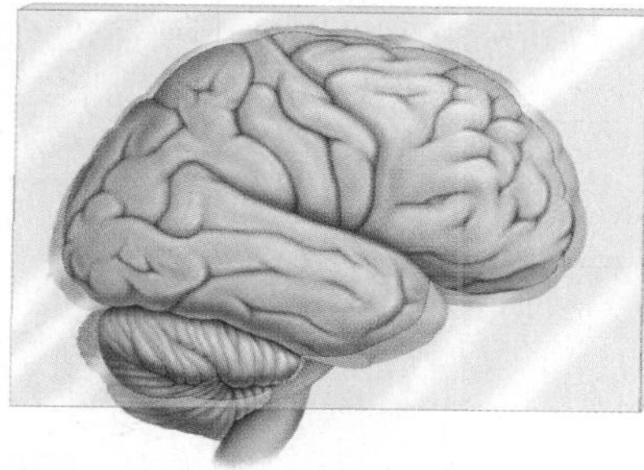

(c) Sagittal Section

FIGURE 1.12 Planes Through the Body

Planes through the head are indicated by "glass" sheets. (*a*) Transverse sections are made to separate a structure into superior and inferior portions. (*b*) Coronal sections are made to separate a structure into anterior and posterior portions. (*c*) Sagittal sections are made to separate a structure into right and left halves. (a, b, c) McGraw Hill APR

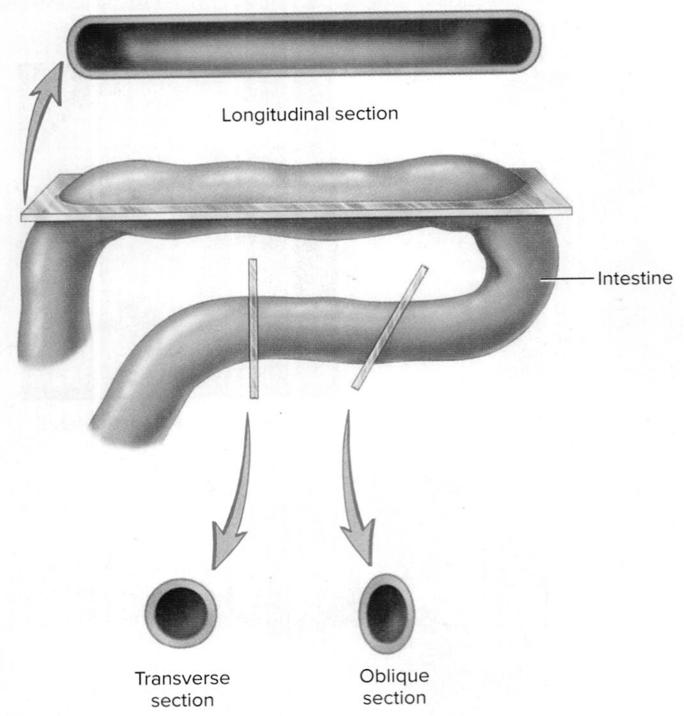

FIGURE 1.13 Planes Through an Organ
Planes through the small intestine are indicated by "glass" sheets. The views of the small intestine after sectioning are also shown. Although the small intestine is basically a tube, the sections appear quite different in shape.

The Thoracic Cavity

The **thoracic cavity** is more superior to the abdominopelvic cavity and houses primarily the heart and lungs, among other organs. This cavity is further subdivided into sections: (1) two lateral **pleural cavities,** each of which encloses a lung and is surrounded by the ribs, and (2) a medial **mediastinum** (MEE-dee-ah-STIE-num; middle wall), which houses the heart and its major blood vessels, in addition to the thymus, the trachea, and the esophagus.

The Abdominopelvic Cavity

The **abdominopelvic cavity** is enclosed by abdominal muscles and consists of (1) the more superior **abdominal cavity** and (2) the more inferior **pelvic cavity.** The organs of the abdominopelvic cavity are housed within the **peritoneal** (per-ih-toh-NEE-al; to stretch over) **cavity.** The abdominal cavity contains the majority of the digestive organs, such as the stomach, the intestines, and the liver, in addition to the spleen. The pelvic cavity continues below the pelvis and contains the urinary bladder, urethra, rectum of the large intestine, and reproductive organs.

Serous Membranes of the Ventral Body Cavity

The walls of the body cavities and the surface of internal organs are in contact with membranes called **serous** (SEER-us) **membranes.** These membranes are double layered. The layer that lines the walls of the cavities is called the

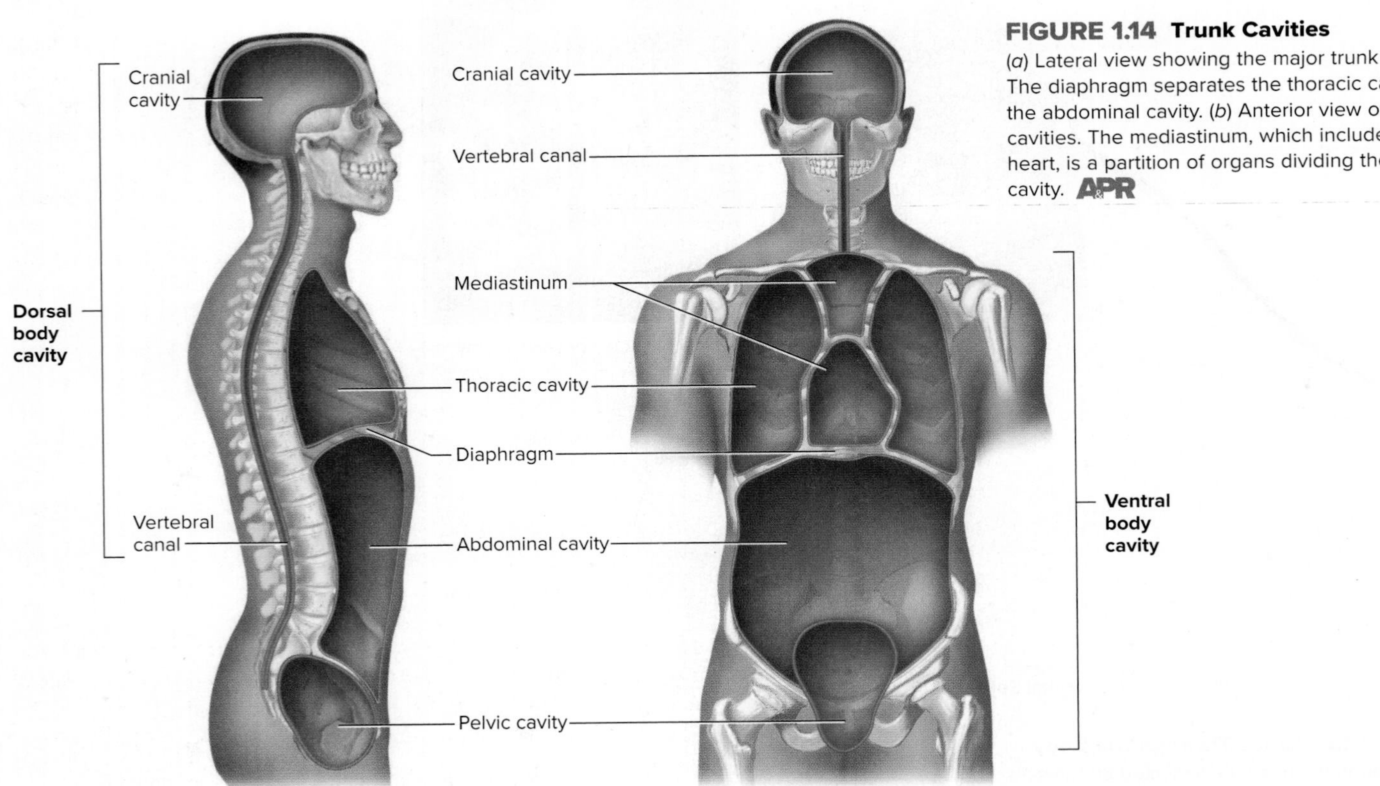

FIGURE 1.14 Trunk Cavities
(*a*) Lateral view showing the major trunk cavities. The diaphragm separates the thoracic cavity from the abdominal cavity. (*b*) Anterior view of the trunk cavities. The mediastinum, which includes the heart, is a partition of organs dividing the thoracic cavity. APR

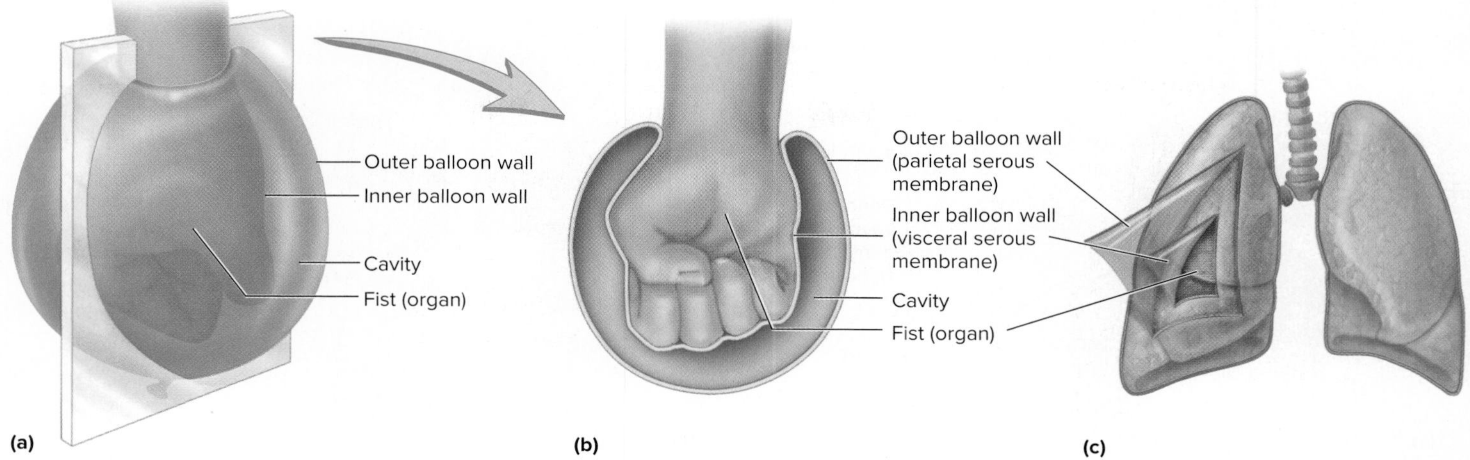

FIGURE 1.15 Serous Membranes

(*a*) A fist pushing into a balloon. A "glass" sheet indicates the location of a section through the balloon. (*b*) Interior view produced by the section in (*a*). The fist represents an organ, and the walls of the balloon represent the serous membranes. The inner wall of the balloon represents a visceral serous membrane in contact with the fist (organ). The outer wall of the balloon represents a parietal serous membrane. (*c*) The relationship of the parietal and serous membranes to the lungs. Figure 1.16 shows the relationship of the parietal and visceral membranes to the heart.

parietal (pa-RYE-ee-tal; wall) **serous membrane.** The layer covering the internal organs (the viscera) is the **visceral serous membrane.** To understand the relationship between the parietal and the visceral serous membranes, imagine pushing your fist (representing an organ) into a slightly deflated balloon (representing the membranes and the cavity) (figure 1.15). Because your fist represents the internal organs, the portion of the balloon in contact with your fist represents the visceral serous membrane, and the outer part of the balloon wall represents the parietal serous membrane. However, in the body, the parietal serous membrane is in close contact with the body cavity wall. Furthermore, in the body, there is no air between the visceral and parietal serous membranes as there is in the balloon; rather, the two membranes are separated by a thin film of serous fluid produced by the membranes. As organs move around in the cavities, the combination of serous fluid and smooth serous membranes reduces friction.

Thoracic Cavity Membranes

The serous membranes are named for the specific cavity and organs they are in contact with. They include:

1. Pericardial Cavity
   The pericardial cavity (peri = around; cardi = heart), containing the heart, is housed in the mediastinum. The parietal serous membrane is called the **parietal pericardium** and the visceral serous membrane is called the **visceral pericardium.** The space between the two pericardial membranes is called the **pericardial cavity** and is filled with **pericardial fluid** (figure 1.16*a*).
2. Pleural Cavities
   Each of the two pleural cavities (pleuron = side of body, rib) houses a lung. The parietal serous membrane lining the pleural cavities is called the **parietal pleura,** while the visceral serous membrane covering the lungs is called the **visceral pleura** (figure 1.16*b*). The space between the two pleural membranes is called the **pleural cavity** and is filled with **pleural fluid.**
3. Peritoneal Cavity
   The peritoneal cavity (peri = around; -tonos = stretched; stretched around) houses many internal organs, such as the liver, the digestive organs, and the reproductive organs. The parietal serous membrane in the peritoneal cavity is called the **parietal peritoneum.** The visceral serous membrane is called the **visceral peritoneum.** The space between the two serous membranes is the specific location of the **peritoneal cavity** and is filled with **peritoneal fluid** (figure 1.16*c*). In addition to covering organs, a double-folded sheet of visceral peritoneum attaches the digestive organs at certain points to the posterior abdominopelvic cavity wall. These regions of double-folded visceral peritoneum form the mesentery. The mesentery also provides a pathway for nerves and blood vessels to reach the digestive organs (figure 1.16*d*). The most notable mesenteric structure is an enormous pouch containing adipose tissue that is suspended from the inferior border of the stomach. In some people, this pouch contributes to their "big belly" (see chapter 24).

Some abdominal organs are tightly adhered to the posterior body wall and are covered by peritoneum only on their peritoneal cavity side. These organs have a **retroperitoneal** (RE-troh-PER-i-toh-NEE-uhl; behind the peritoneum) location and include the kidneys, ureters, adrenal glands, a large portion of the pancreas, parts of the large intestine, and the urinary bladder (see figure 1.16*c*). This will be further discussed in chapter 24.

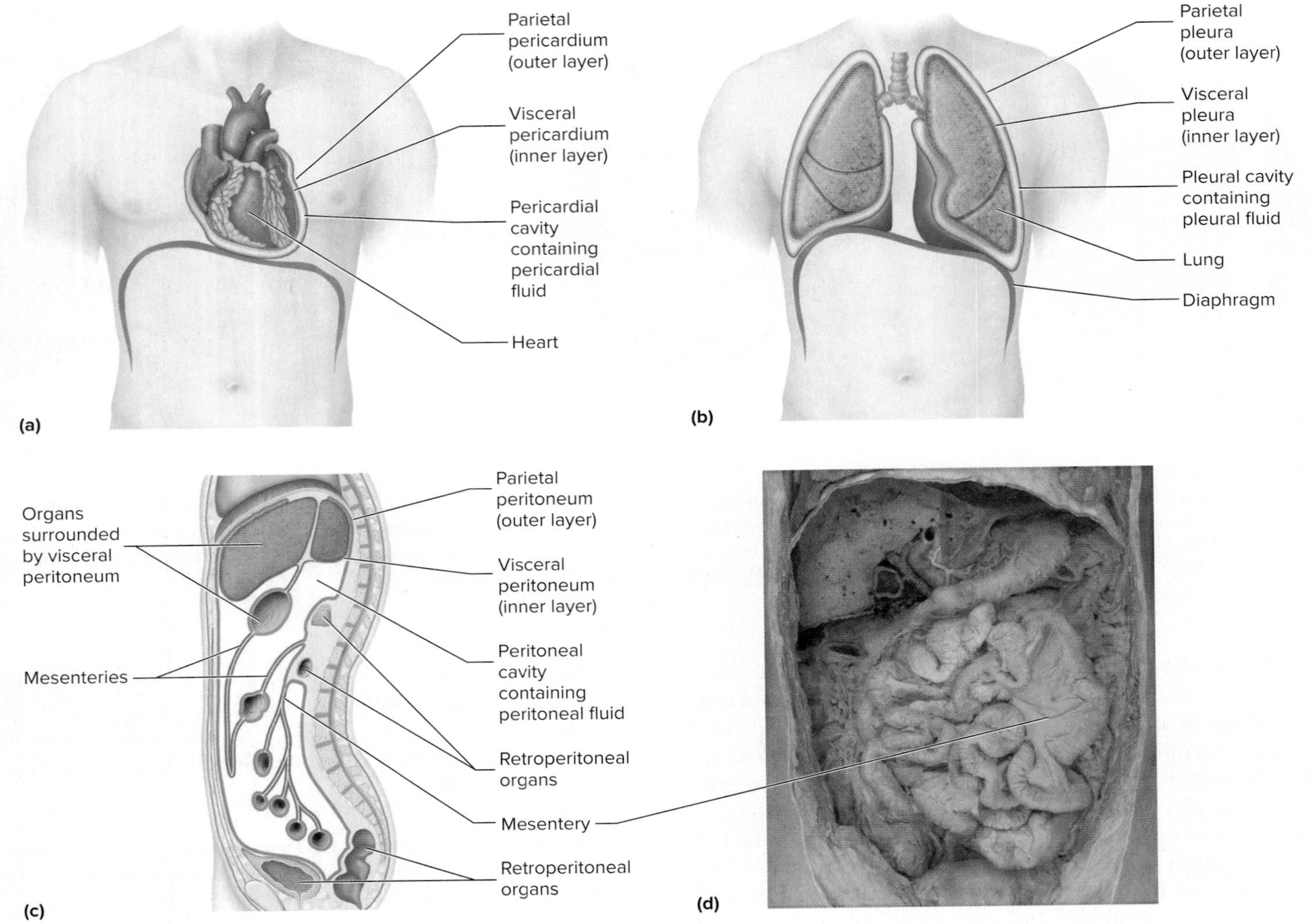

FIGURE 1.16 Location of Serous Membranes
(*a*) Frontal section showing the parietal pericardium (*outer, blue*), the visceral pericardium (*inner, red*), and the pericardial cavity. (*b*) Frontal section showing the parietal pleura (*outer, blue*), the visceral pleura (*inner, red*), and the pleural cavities. (*c*) Sagittal section through the abdominopelvic cavity showing the parietal peritoneum (*outer, blue*), the visceral peritoneum (*inner, red*), the peritoneal cavity, mesenteries (*central, purple*), and parts of the retroperitoneal organs. (*d*) Photo of mesentery (*highlighted*) in a cadaver. (d) MCOF Enterprises, Ltd./McGraw Hill Education

Inflammation, often due to an infection, of the serous membranes in the ventral body cavities sometimes occurs. Serious consequences can arise if the inherent infection or problem cannot be resolved (see Clinical Impact 1.1). The following is a list of the conditions caused by inflammation of the serous membranes:

1. **Pericarditis** (PER-i-kar-DIE-tis; *-itis,* inflammation) is inflammation of the pericardium.
2. **Pleurisy** (PLOOR-ih-see) is inflammation of the pleura.
3. **Peritonitis** (PER-i-toh-NIGH-tis) is inflammation of the peritoneum.

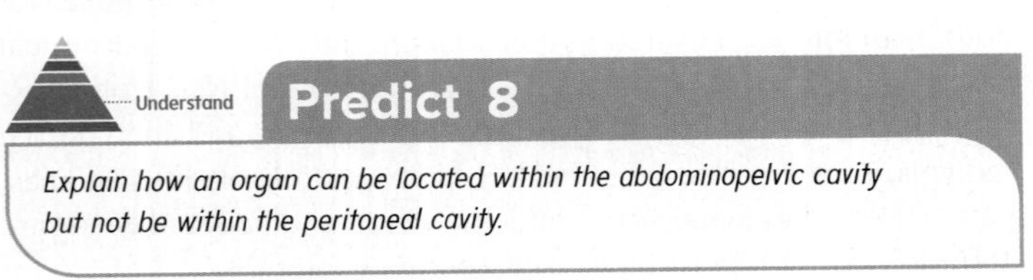

Explain how an organ can be located within the abdominopelvic cavity but not be within the peritoneal cavity.

ASSESS YOUR PROGRESS

26. *What structure separates the thoracic cavity from the abdominal cavity? The abdominal cavity from the pelvic cavity?*
27. *What structure divides the thoracic cavity into right and left parts?*
28. *What is a serous membrane and its function? Differentiate between the parietal and visceral portions of a serous membrane.*
29. *Name the serous membrane–lined cavities of the trunk.*
30. *What are mesenteries? Explain their function.*
31. *What are retroperitoneal organs? List five examples.*

Clinical IMPACT 1.1 — Pericarditis and Cardiac Tamponade

Pericarditis is an inflammation of the serous pericardium. The cause is frequently unknown, but it can result from infection, diseases of connective tissue, or damage due to radiation treatment for cancer. The condition can cause extremely painful sensations that are referred to the back and chest and can be confused with a myocardial infarction (heart attack). Pericarditis can lead to fluid accumulation within the pericardial sac.

Cardiac tamponade (tam-puh-naad) is a potentially fatal condition in which a large volume of fluid or blood accumulates in the pericardial cavity and compresses the heart from the outside. Although the heart is a powerful muscle, it relaxes passively. When it is compressed by fluid within the pericardial cavity, it cannot expand when the cardiac muscle relaxes. Consequently, it cannot fill with blood during relaxation; therefore, it cannot pump blood. Cardiac tamponade can cause a person to die quickly unless the fluid is removed. Causes of cardiac tamponade include rupture of the heart wall following a myocardial infarction, rupture of blood vessels in the pericardium after a malignant tumor has invaded the area, damage to the pericardium due to radiation therapy, and trauma, such as that resulting from a traffic accident.

Concept Check

Knowledge of anatomy and physiology can be used to solve problems concerning the body when healthy or diseased.

1.1 Anatomy and Physiology

A. Anatomy is the study of the body's structures.

B. Developmental anatomy considers anatomical changes over time, while gross anatomy studies organs from a systemic or regional perspective; surface anatomy uses superficial structures to locate internal structures.

C. Physiology is the study of the body's functions.

D. Cellular physiology studies functions of a cell; systems-level physiology considers functions of a system; exercise physiology examines changes caused by exercise.

E. Pathology is concerned with all aspects of disease.

1. Physiology

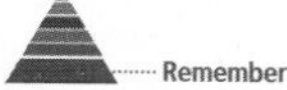

a. deals with the processes of functions of living things.
b. is the scientific discipline that investigates the body's structures.
c. is concerned with organisms and does not deal with levels of organization, such as cells and systems.
d. recognizes the static (as opposed to the dynamic) nature of living things.
e. can be used to study the human body without considering anatomy.

1.2 Biomedical Research

Much of our knowledge about humans is derived from research on other organisms.

1.3 Structural and Functional Organization of the Human Body

A. There are six organizational levels within the body. From simple to complex they are chemical, cell, tissue, organ, organ system, and organism.

B. Basic chemical characteristics are responsible for the body's structures with cells being the simplest unit of an organism. Cells contain specialized structures called organelles that perform specific functions. Groups of cells form tissues and two or more tissues form organs.

C. Organs are arranged into the 11 organ systems of the human body (integumentary, skeletal, muscular, nervous, endocrine, cardiovascular, lymphatic, respiratory, digestive, urinary, and reproductive; see figure 1.3). These organ systems interact to form a whole, functioning organism.

2. The following are organizational levels for considering the body.

Remember

(1) cell
(2) chemical
(3) organ
(4) organ system
(5) organism
(6) tissue

Choose the correct order for these organizational levels, from simplest to most complex.

a. 1,2,3,6,4,5
b. 2,1,6,3,4,5
c. 3,1,6,4,5,2
d. 4,6,1,3,5,2
e. 1,6,5,3,4,2

For questions 3–7, match each organ system with one of the following functions.

Remember

a. regulates other organ systems
b. removes waste products from the blood; maintains water balance
c. regulates temperature; reduces water loss; provides protection
d. removes foreign substances from the blood; combats disease; maintains tissue fluid balance
e. produces movement; maintains posture; produces body heat

3. *Endocrine system*

4. *Integumentary system*

5. *Muscular system*

6. *Nervous system*

7. *Urinary system*

1.4 Characteristics of Life

Humans share many characteristics with other organisms, such as organization, metabolism, responsiveness, growth, development, and reproduction.

8. *The characteristic of life that is defined as "all the chemical reactions taking place in an organism" is* Remember
   - *a. development*
   - *b. growth.*
   - *c. metabolism.*
   - *d. organization.*
   - *e. responsiveness.*

1.5 Homeostasis

Homeostasis is the condition in which body functions, body fluids, and other factors of the internal environment are maintained at levels suitable to support life.

Feedback Loops

A. There are two types of feedback loops: negative feedback and positive feedback.

B. There are three components in a feedback loop: (1) receptor, (2) control center, and (3) effector.

Negative Feedback

Negative-feedback mechanisms maintain homeostasis by stopping a response once a variable has returned to its set point.

9. *The following events are part of a negative-feedback mechanism.*

   (1) Blood pressure increases.
   (2) The control center compares actual blood pressure to the blood pressure set point.
   (3) The heart beats faster.
   (4) Receptors detect a decrease in blood pressure.

   Choose the arrangement that lists the events in the order they occur.
   - *a. 1,2,3,4*
   - *b. 1,3,2,4*
   - *c. 3,1,4,2*
   - *d. 4,2,3,1*
   - *e. 4,3,2,1*

Positive Feedback

A. Positive-feedback mechanisms usually result in deviations farther from the set point. A few of these mechanisms are normal for homeostasis; some can be harmful.

B. Normal instances include blood clotting and childbirth labor. Harmful instances include decreased blood flow to the heart.

10. *Which of these statements concerning positive feedback is correct?*

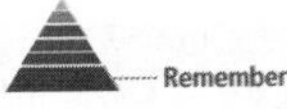

   - *a. Positive-feedback responses maintain homeostasis.*
   - *b. Positive-feedback responses occur continuously in healthy individuals.*
   - *c. Birth is an example of a normally occurring positive-feedback mechanism.*
   - *d. When cardiac muscle receives an inadequate supply of blood, positive-feedback mechanisms increase blood flow to the heart.*
   - *e. Medical therapy seeks to overcome illness by aiding positive-feedback mechanisms.*

11. *Exposure to a hot environment causes the body to sweat. The hotter the environment, the greater the sweating. Two anatomy and physiology students are arguing about the mechanisms involved. Student A claims they are positive feedback, and student B claims they are negative feedback. Do you agree with student A or student B, and why?* Understand

12. *A male has lost blood as a result of a gunshot wound. Even though the bleeding has been stopped, his blood pressure is low and dropping and his heart rate is elevated. Following a blood transfusion, his blood pressure increases and his heart rate decreases. Which of the following statement(s) is (are) consistent with these observations?* Understand
   - *a. Negative-feedback mechanisms can be inadequate without medical intervention.*
   - *b. The transfusion interrupted a positive-feedback mechanism.*
   - *c. The increased heart rate after the gunshot wound and before the transfusion is a result of a positive-feedback mechanism.*
   - *d. a and b*
   - *e. a, b, and c*

1.6 Terminology and the Body Plan

A. A human standing erect with the face directed forward, the arms hanging to the sides, and the palms facing forward is in the anatomical position.

B. A person lying face upward is supine; a person lying face downward is prone.

Directional Terms

Directional terms always refer to the anatomical position, no matter what the actual position of the body (see table 1.2).

13. *A term that means nearer the attached end of a limb is*

   - *a. distal.*
   - *b. lateral.*
   - *c. medial.*
   - *d. proximal.*
   - *e. superficial.*

14. *Which of these directional terms are paired most appropriately as opposites?* Remember
   - *a. superficial and deep*
   - *b. medial and proximal*
   - *c. distal and lateral*
   - *d. superior and posterior*
   - *e. anterior and inferior*

15. *Provide the correct directional term for the following statement: When a boy is standing on his head, his nose is ___________ to his mouth.* Understand

Body Parts and Regions

A. The body can be divided into a central region and the appendages. The central region consists of the head, neck, and trunk. The appendages consist of the upper and lower limbs.

B. Superficially, the abdomen is divided into quadrants, or into nine regions.

16. *The part of the upper limb between the elbow and the wrist is called the* Remember
    a. *arm.*
    b. *forearm.*
    c. *hand.*
    d. *inferior arm.*
    e. *lower arm.*

17. *A patient with appendicitis usually has pain in the ___________ quadrant of the abdomen.* Remember
    a. *left-lower*
    b. *right-lower*
    c. *left-upper*
    d. *right-upper*

Planes

A. The three main planes of the body are sagittal (right and left), transverse (superior and inferior), and frontal (anterior and posterior).

B. Organs can be sectioned longitudinally (lengthwise), transversely (at a right angle), or obliquely (across the length at more than a right angle).

18. *A plane that divides the body into anterior and posterior parts is a* Remember
    a. *frontal (coronal) plane.*
    b. *sagittal plane.*
    c. *transverse plane.*

Body Cavities

A. There are two internal body cavities: the dorsal (houses the brain and spinal cord) and the ventral (subdivided into thoracic, abdominal, and pelvic) cavities.

B. The thoracic cavity, with a center mediastinum for the heart, houses the lungs and is separated from the abdominal cavity by the diaphragm. The pelvic cavity is bordered by pelvic bones.

C. Serous membranes line the trunk cavities. The parietal portion of a serous membrane lines the wall of the cavity, and the visceral portion is in contact with the internal organs. Retroperitoneal organs are not in the abdominal or pelvic cavity; they are "behind" the peritoneum. The peritoneum forms mesenteries that hold the abdominal organs in place and provide a passageway for blood vessels and nerves to the organs.

19. *The lungs are*

    a. *part of the mediastinum.*
    b. *surrounded by the pericardial cavity.*
    c. *found within the thoracic cavity.*
    d. *separated from each other by the diaphragm.*
    e. *surrounded by mucous membranes.*

20. *Given the following organ and cavity combinations:* Remember
    (1) heart and pericardial cavity
    (2) lungs and pleural cavity
    (3) stomach and peritoneal cavity
    (4) kidney and peritoneal cavity

    Which of the organs is correctly paired with a space that surrounds that organ?
    a. *1,2*
    b. *1,2,3*
    c. *1,2,4*
    d. *2,3,4*
    e. *1,2,3,4*

21. *Which of the following membrane combinations are found on the superior and inferior surface of the diaphragm?* Remember
    a. *parietal pleura—parietal peritoneum*
    b. *parietal pleura—visceral peritoneum*
    c. *visceral pleura—parietal peritoneum*
    d. *visceral pleura—visceral peritoneum*

22. *Which of the following organs are* not *retroperitoneal?*

    a. *adrenal glands*
    b. *urinary bladder*
    c. *kidneys*
    d. *pancreas*
    e. *stomach*

23. *During pregnancy, which of the mother's body cavities increases most in size?* Understand

24. *A woman falls while skiing and is accidentally impaled by her ski pole. The pole passes through the abdominal body wall and into and through the stomach, pierces the diaphragm, and finally stops in the left lung. List, in order, the serous membranes the pole pierces.* Understand

Answers to this chapter's odd-numbered Concept Check questions appear in Appendix F.

2
CHAPTER

The Chemical Basis of Life

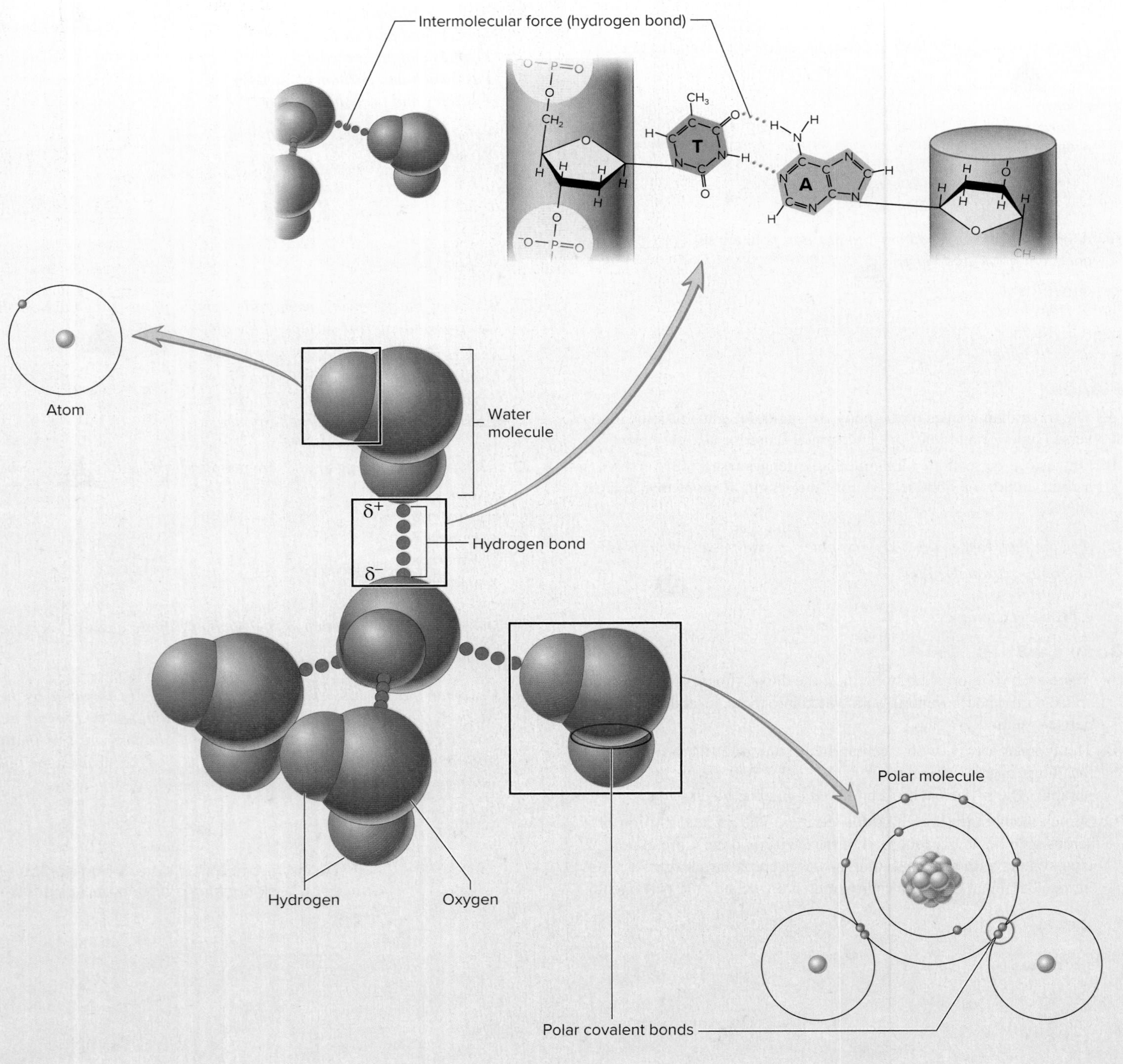

To thoroughly understand the structure and function of the human body, it helps to begin with the materials that compose our bodies and how those materials interact.

Life is chemistry. Chemicals compose the structures of the body, and the interactions of chemicals with one another are responsible for the body's functions. Nerve impulse generation, digestion, muscle contraction, and metabolism can be described in chemical terms, and so can many abnormal conditions and illnesses, as well as their treatments. These diverse functions all involve intricate interactions between molecules. For example, chemicals in saliva interact with food to aid in digestion, and membrane proteins assemble to form a pore for ions to pass into and out of our cells to aid in nerve impulse generation and muscle contraction. To understand anatomy and physiology, it is essential to have a basic knowledge of chemistry—the scientific discipline concerned with the atomic composition of substances and the reactions they undergo. This chapter is not a comprehensive treatment of chemistry, but it does review some of the basic chemical concepts related to living systems. When necessary, refer back to this chapter when chemical processes are discussed later in the textbook.

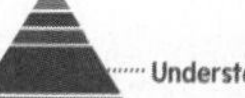

Learn to Predict

Brad and his lab partner, Angie, mixed a small amount of starch into a test tube of water. Then they added iodine, which stained the starch molecules blue. Next they added saliva to the test tube. After 30 minutes, the blue color disappeared. This exercise demonstrates the consequences of metabolism in the absence of homeostasis (described in chapter 1). Homeostasis often involves a balance of chemical reactions that will make and break apart molecules, such as starch. In the test tube, only one reaction occurred. After reading the chapter, you will have learned that the rate of a chemical reaction can be greatly increased by enzymes in cells and body fluids, and you will understand the roles of two chemical phenomena—activation energy and decomposition reactions. **Considering the properties of enzymes and chemical reactions, can you explain why the blue color in the test tube disappeared?**

Answers to this question and the chapter's odd-numbered Predict questions can be found in Appendix E.

2.1 Basic Chemistry

LEARNING OUTCOMES

After reading this section, you should be able to

A. **Define *matter, mass,* and *weight*.**
B. **Distinguish between elements and atoms.**
C. **State the four most abundant elements in the body.**
D. **Name the subatomic particles of an atom, and indicate their mass, charge, and location in an atom.**
E. **Define *atomic number, mass number, isotope, atomic mass,* and *mole*.**
F. **Compare and contrast ionic and covalent bonds.**
G. **Differentiate between a molecule and a compound.**
H. **Explain what creates a hydrogen bond, and relate its importance.**
I. **Describe solubility and the process of dissociation.**
J. **Predict if a compound or molecule is an electrolyte or a nonelectrolyte.**

Matter, Mass, and Weight

All living and nonliving things are composed of **matter,** which is anything that occupies space and has mass. **Mass** is the amount of matter in an object, and **weight** is the gravitational force acting on an object of a given mass. For example, the weight of an apple results from the force of gravity "pulling" on the apple's mass.

Predict 1

The difference between mass and weight can be illustrated by considering an astronaut. How do an astronaut's mass and weight in outer space compare with the astronaut's mass and weight on the earth's surface?

The international unit for mass is the **kilogram (kg),** which is the mass of a platinum-iridium cylinder kept at the International Bureau of Weights and Measurements in France. The mass of all other objects is compared with this cylinder. For

example, a 2.2-pound lead weight and 1 liter (L) (1.06 qt) of water each has a mass of approximately 1 kg. An object with 1/1000 the mass of a kilogram has a mass of 1 **gram (g).**

Elements and Atoms

An **element** is the simplest type of matter, having unique chemical properties. A list of the elements commonly found in the human body appears in table 2.1. About 96% of the body's weight results from the elements oxygen, carbon, hydrogen, and nitrogen. The majority of the body's weight is from oxygen. Oxygen is also the most abundant element in the earth's crust. Carbon plays an especially important role in the chemistry of the body, due in part to its propensity to form covalent bonds with itself and other molecules. Many elements are present in only trace amounts but still play essential roles in the body. Elements can have multiple roles and exist in different states in the body. For example, mineralized calcium contributes to the solid matrix of bones, while dissolved calcium helps regulate enzyme activities and nervous system signaling.

An **atom** (*atomos,* indivisible) is the smallest particle of an element that has the chemical characteristics of that element. An element is composed of atoms of only one kind. For example, the element carbon is composed of only carbon atoms, and the element oxygen is composed of only oxygen atoms.

An element, or an atom of that element, is often represented by a symbol. Usually, the symbol is the first letter or letters of the element's name—for example, C for carbon, H for hydrogen, and Ca for calcium. Occasionally, the symbol is taken from the Latin, Greek, or Arabic name for the element—for example, the symbol for sodium is Na, from the Latin word *natrium.* The symbols for common elements will be used throughout the textbook and the reader should refer to table 2.1 for any needed clarification.

Atomic Structure

The characteristics of matter result from the structure, organization, and behavior of atoms. Atoms are composed of subatomic particles, some of which have an electrical charge. The three major types of subatomic particles are (1) neutrons, (2) protons, and (3) electrons (figure 2.1). A **neutron** has no electrical charge, a **proton** has one positive charge, and an **electron** has one negative charge. Because each atom has an equal number of protons and electrons, the positive and negative charges cancel each other. Therefore, each atom is electrically neutral.

Protons and neutrons are found in the center of an atom, which is called the **nucleus** (NOO-klee-us; kernel, inner part). The electrons are found in an **electron cloud** and are constantly orbiting the nucleus (figure 2.1). The nucleus accounts for 99.97% of an atom's mass but only 1 ten-trillionth of its volume. Most of the volume of an atom is occupied by the electrons.

Atomic Number and Mass Number

Each element is uniquely defined by the number of protons in the atoms of that element. For example, only hydrogen atoms have 1 proton, only carbon atoms have 6 protons, and only oxygen atoms have 8 protons (figure 2.2; table 2.1). The **atomic number** of an element is equal to the number of protons in each atom and, because the number of electrons is equal to the number of protons, the atomic number is also the number of electrons. There are 90 naturally occurring elements, but additional elements have been synthesized by altering atomic nuclei. See the periodic table in appendix A for additional information about the elements.

TABLE 2.1 Common Elements in the Human Body

Element	Symbol	Atomic Number	Mass Number	Atomic Mass	Percent by Weight	Percent by Number of Atoms
Hydrogen	H	1	1	1.008	9.5	63.0
Carbon	C	6	12	12.01	18.5	9.5
Nitrogen	N	7	14	14.01	3.3	1.4
Oxygen	O	8	16	16.00	65.0	25.5
Fluorine	F	9	19	19.00	Trace	Trace
Sodium	Na	11	23	22.99	0.2	0.3
Magnesium	Mg	12	24	24.31	0.1	0.1
Phosphorus	P	15	31	30.97	1.0	0.22
Sulfur	S	16	32	32.07	0.3	0.05
Chlorine	Cl	17	35	35.45	0.2	0.03
Potassium	K	19	39	39.10	0.4	0.06
Calcium	Ca	20	40	40.08	1.5	0.31
Iron	Fe	26	56	55.85	Trace	Trace
Iodine	I	53	127	126.9	Trace	Trace

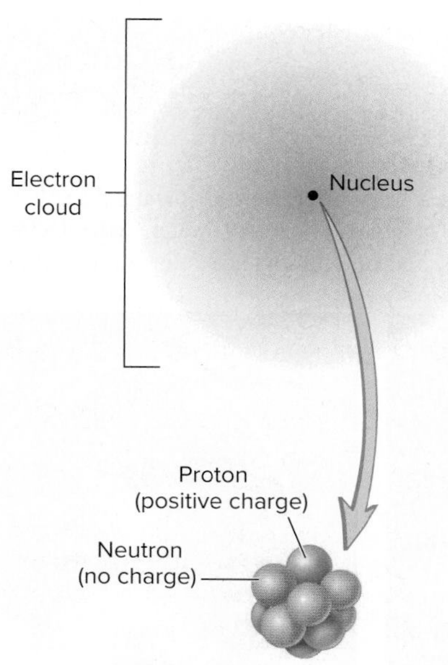

FIGURE 2.1 Model of an Atom
The tiny, dense nucleus consists of positively charged protons and uncharged neutrons. Most of the volume of an atom is occupied by rapidly moving, negatively charged electrons, which can be represented as an electron cloud. The probable location of an electron is indicated by the color of the electron cloud. The darker the color in each small part of the electron cloud, the more likely the electron is located there. APR

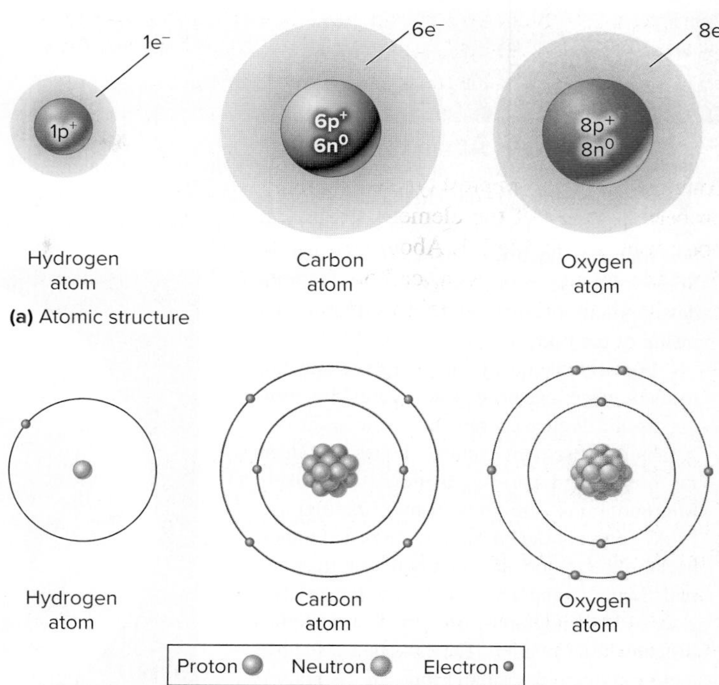

FIGURE 2.2 Hydrogen, Carbon, and Oxygen Atoms
(*a*) Within the nucleus, the number of positively charged protons (p^+) and uncharged neutrons (n^0) is indicated. The negatively charged electrons (e^-) are around the nucleus. Atoms are electrically neutral because the number of protons and the number of electrons within an atom are equal.
(*b*) Electrons occupy separate electron shells. A maximum of 2 electrons can occupy the innermost shell closest to the nucleus. All other shells contain a maximum of 8 electrons.

Protons and neutrons have about the same mass, and they are responsible for most of the mass of atoms. Electrons, on the other hand, have very little mass. The **mass number** of an element is the number of protons plus the number of neutrons in each atom. For example, the mass number for carbon is 12 because it has 6 protons and 6 neutrons.

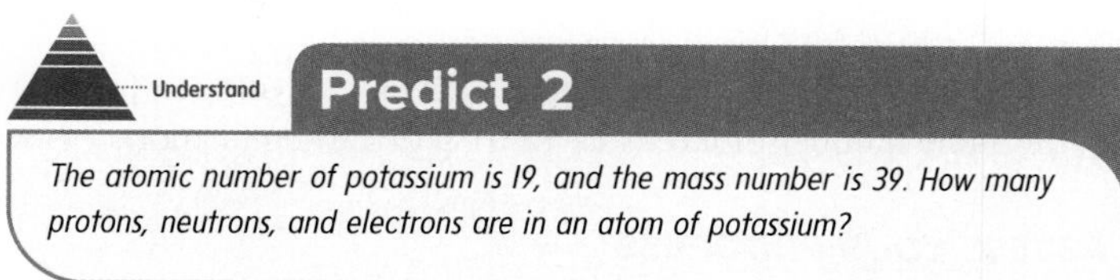

The atomic number of potassium is 19, and the mass number is 39. How many protons, neutrons, and electrons are in an atom of potassium?

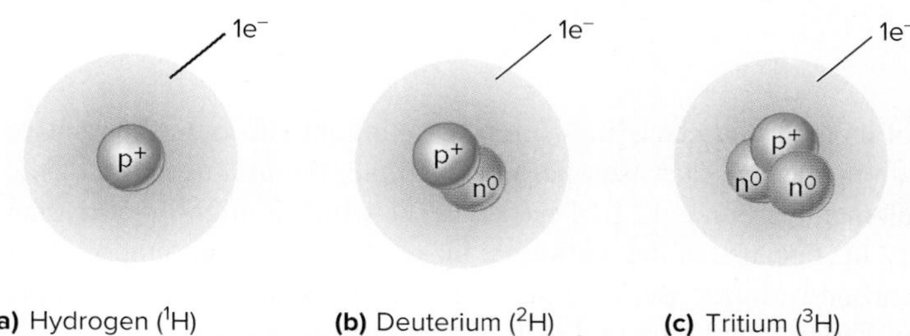

FIGURE 2.3 Isotopes of Hydrogen
(*a*) Hydrogen has 1 proton and no neutrons in its nucleus. (*b*) Deuterium has 1 proton and 1 neutron in its nucleus. (*c*) Tritium has 1 proton and 2 neutrons in its nucleus.

Isotopes and Atomic Mass

Isotopes (EYE-soh-topes) are two or more forms of the same element that have the same number of protons and electrons but a different number of neutrons. Thus, isotopes have the *same* atomic number but *different* mass numbers. There are three isotopes of hydrogen: hydrogen, deuterium, and tritium. All three isotopes have 1 proton and 1 electron, but hydrogen has no neutrons in its nucleus, deuterium has 1 neutron, and tritium has 2 neutrons (figure 2.3). Isotopes can be denoted using the symbol of the element preceded by the mass number (number of protons and neutrons) of the isotope. Thus, hydrogen is ^{1}H, deuterium is ^{2}H, and tritium is ^{3}H.

Individual atoms have very little mass. A hydrogen atom has a mass of 1.67×10^{-24} g (see appendix B for an explanation of the scientific notation of numbers). To avoid working with such small numbers, scientists use a system of relative atomic mass. In this system, a **dalton (Da),** or *unified atomic mass unit* (*u*), is 1/12 the mass of ^{12}C, a carbon atom with 6 protons and 6 neutrons. Thus, ^{12}C has an atomic mass of exactly 12 Da. However, a naturally occurring sample of carbon contains mostly ^{12}C and a small quantity of other carbon isotopes, such as ^{13}C, which has 6 protons and 7 neutrons. The **atomic mass** of an element is the *average* mass

Clinical IMPACT 2.1

Clinical Uses of Atomic Particles

Protons, neutrons, and electrons are responsible for the chemical properties of atoms. They also have other properties that can be useful in a clinical setting. Some of these properties have enabled the development of methods for examining the inside of the body.

For example, x-rays are a type of radiation formed when electrons lose energy by moving from a higher energy state to a lower one. X-rays are used to examine bones and teeth for breaks and caries (cavities), respectively. Mammograms are low-energy radiographs (x-ray films) of the breast that can reveal tumors because the tumors are slightly denser than normal tissue. Computers can be used to analyze a series of radiographs, each made at a slightly different body location. The computer assembles these radiographic "slices" through the body to form a three-dimensional image. A **computed tomography** (toh-MOG-rah-fee) **(CT) scan** is an example of this technique (figure 2.4*a*). CT scans are used to detect tumors and other abnormalities in the body.

Magnetic resonance imaging (MRI) is another method for looking into the body (figure 2.4*b*). The patient is placed into a very powerful magnetic field, which aligns the hydrogen nuclei. Radio waves given off by the hydrogen nuclei are monitored, and a computer uses these data to make an image of the body. Because MRI detects hydrogen, it is very effective for visualizing soft tissues that contain a lot of water. MRI technology can reveal tumors and other abnormalities.

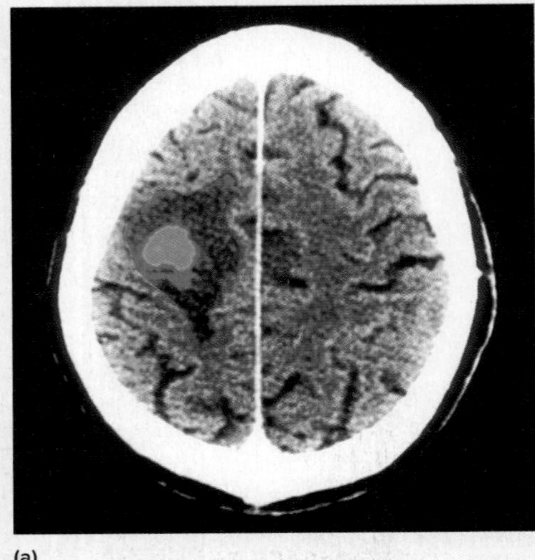

(a)

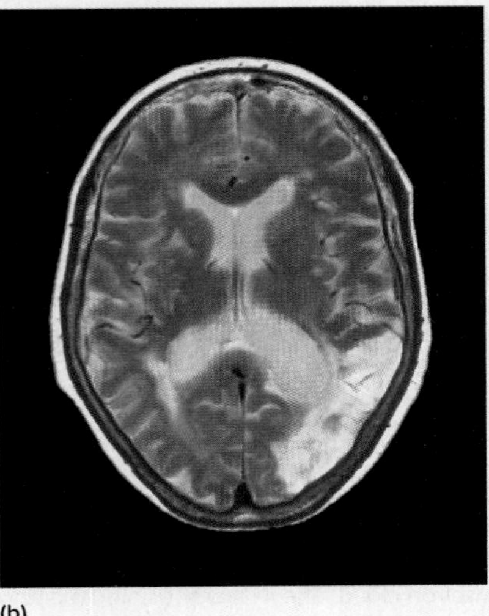

(b)

FIGURE 2.4 Use of atomic particles to view inside the body
(*a*) CT scan of the brain with iodine injection, showing one large brain tumor (*green area*) that has metastasized (spread) to the brain from cancer in the large intestine. (*b*) Colorized MRI brain scan showing a stroke. The whitish area in the lower right part of the MRI is blood that has leaked into the surrounding tissue. (a) Scott Camazine/Alamy Stock Photo; (b) Simon Fraser/Royal Victoria Infirmary, Newcastle upon Tyne/Science Source

of its naturally occurring isotopes, taking into account the relative abundance of each isotope. For example, the atomic mass of the element carbon is 12.01 Da (table 2.1), which is slightly more than 12 Da because of the additional mass of the small amount of other carbon isotopes. Because the atomic mass is an average, a sample of carbon can be treated as if all the carbon atoms had an atomic mass of 12.01 Da.

The Mole and Molar Mass

Just as a grocer sells eggs in lots of a dozen, a chemist groups atoms in lots of 6.022×10^{23}, which is called **Avogadro's number,** or 1 **mole** (abbreviated **mol**). Stated another way, a mole of a substance contains Avogadro's number of entities, such as atoms, ions, or molecules. The mass of 1 mole of a substance expressed in grams is called the **molar mass.** Molar mass is a convenient way to determine the number of atoms in a sample of an element. Because 12 g of ^{12}C is used as the standard, the atomic mass of an entity expressed in unified atomic mass units is the same as the molar mass expressed in grams. Thus, carbon atoms have an atomic mass of 12.01 Da, and 12.01 g of carbon has Avogadro's number (1 mol) of carbon atoms. By the same token, 1.008 g of hydrogen (1 mol) has the same number of atoms as 12.01 g of carbon (1 mol).

ASSESS YOUR PROGRESS

Answers to these questions are found in the section you have just completed. Re-read the section if you need help in answering these questions.

1. *Define matter. How are the mass and the weight of an object different?*
2. *Differentiate between element and atom. What four elements are found in the greatest abundance in the human body?*
3. *For each subatomic particle of an atom, state its charge and location. Which region of an atom is most responsible for the mass of the atom? Its volume?*
4. *Which subatomic particle determines the atomic number? What determines the mass number?*
5. *What is an isotope? How are isotopes denoted?*
6. *What is Avogadro's number? How is it related to a mole and molar mass?*

Electrons and Chemical Bonding

Recall from chapter 1 that the human body has six levels of organization. The key to the first level, the chemical level, is the concept of how atoms interact to form molecules by sharing and transferring their outermost electrons to form **chemical bonds.**

The *chemical behavior* of an atom is dependent on its electrons. The electron cloud around an atom's nucleus is organized into different energy levels, depending on the distance from the nucleus. For simplicity, the energy levels are often depicted as concentric rings, called **electron shells,** around the nucleus (see figure 2.2*b*). Each shell can hold a maximum number of electrons. Outer shells do not contain electrons until the inner shells have reached their maximum. The innermost shell (the shell closest to the nucleus) holds a maximum of 2 electrons, and the remaining shells hold a maximum of 8 electrons. The outermost shell is called the **valence shell.** The number of electrons in the valence shell determines an atom's chemical nature. If the valence shell is full (contains 8 electrons), the atom is *inert,* that is, it does not form chemical bonds with other atoms. For example, helium has 2 electrons in its valence shell and does not naturally form chemical bonds with other atoms. However, if an atom's valence shell is not full, the atom is *chemically reactive* and forms chemical bonds with other atoms to achieve a full valence shell, called an octet. Thus, most atoms follow the **octet rule,** the tendency of atoms to combine with other atoms until each has 8 electrons (2 electrons for hydrogen) in its valence shell.

Atoms achieve an octet in two major ways: (1) the transfer of electrons between atoms and (2) the sharing of electrons between atoms. The fate of electrons as being either transferred or shared determines the type of chemical bond: ionic or covalent, as discussed in the following paragraphs.

The outcome as to whether an electron is transferred or shared between two atoms is determined by the relative electronegativity of the two atoms. **Electronegativity** is the ability of an atom's nucleus to attract electrons. In general, atoms that lack only 1 or 2 electrons from having an octet in their valence shell have a strong electronegativity. In contrast, atoms that lack 6 or 7 electrons from having an octet in their valence shell have a weak electronegativity. The major exception to this generalization is hydrogen. Hydrogen lacks only 1 electron from its valence shell to be full. Based on the definition, it might seem that hydrogen should be strongly electronegative; however, hydrogen's pull on electrons is less than that of other atoms with more protons, which means hydrogen's electronegativity is lower than that of other atoms.

Thus, the relative electronegativity of two atoms dictates the degree of sharing of electrons between those atoms (see figure 2.5). Atoms that have the same electronegativities, such as two carbon atoms, will equally share electrons. When atoms have some differences in electronegativities, then there will be unequal sharing of electrons. For example, oxygen has a relatively strong electronegativity, so it will complete its valence shell octet by pulling electrons unequally from other atoms that have a weaker electronegativity. When there are very different electronegativities between two atoms, such as Na and Cl, then there is a transfer, not sharing, of electrons between the atoms.

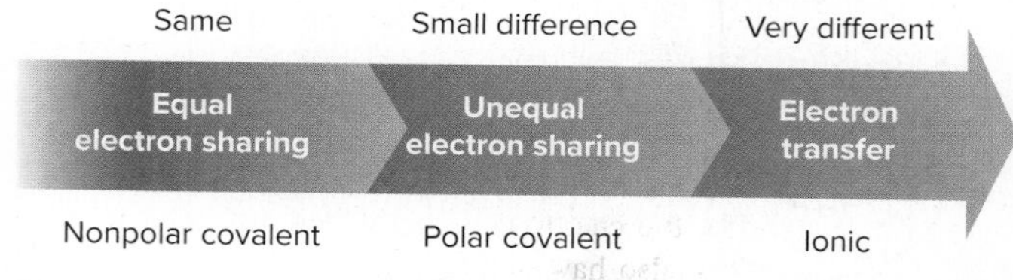

FIGURE 2.5 Relationship Between Electronegativity and Chemical Bonding

Electronegativity is a measure of how much an atom attracts electrons from another atom to form a chemical bond. Covalent bonds are formed by the sharing of electrons between atoms that have the same electronegativity (nonpolar covalent bond, e.g., H_2) or a relatively small difference in electronegativities (polar covalent bond, e.g., H_2O). Ionic bonds are formed by the transfer of electrons between two atoms that have very different electronegativities (e.g., NaCl). APR

In a chemical bond, the fate of the electrons between two atoms depends on the relative difference in electronegativity between the atoms. When the electronegativities of two atoms forming a chemical bond are similar, the atoms tend to share, rather than transfer, the electrons. Under these conditions, covalent bonds are formed. In contrast, when electronegativities are very different, the atoms tend to transfer electrons. For example, an atom with 7 electrons in its valence shell has a strong pull on electrons, while an atom with 1 electron in its valence shell has a weak pull on electrons. Thus, the "strong" atom can "steal" the valence electron from the "weak" atom, resulting in a transfer of electrons. The relationship between electronegativity and the resultant chemical bond types is illustrated in figure 2.5. The two major types of chemical bonds are ionic and covalent bonds.

Ionic Bonds

Recall that an atom is electrically neutral because it has equal numbers of protons and electrons. However, an atom can donate or lose electrons to other atoms depending on its electronegativity. When this occurs, the numbers of protons and electrons are no longer equal, and a charged particle, called an **ion** (EYE-on), is formed. After a weakly electronegative atom loses an electron, it has 1 more proton than it has electrons and is positively charged. A sodium atom (Na) can lose an electron to become a positively charged sodium ion (Na^+) (figure 2.6*a*). After an atom gains an electron, it has 1 more electron than it has protons and is negatively charged. A chlorine atom (Cl) can accept an electron to become a negatively charged chloride ion (Cl^-). After this transfer of electrons, both chlorine and sodium have full valence shells.

Positively charged ions are called **cations** (KAT-eye-onz), and negatively charged ions are called **anions** (AN-eye-onz). Because oppositely charged ions are attracted to each other, cations and anions tend to remain close together. Thus, an **ionic** (eye-ON-ik) **bond** forms when electrons are transferred between atoms, creating oppositely charged ions. For example, Na^+ and Cl^- are held

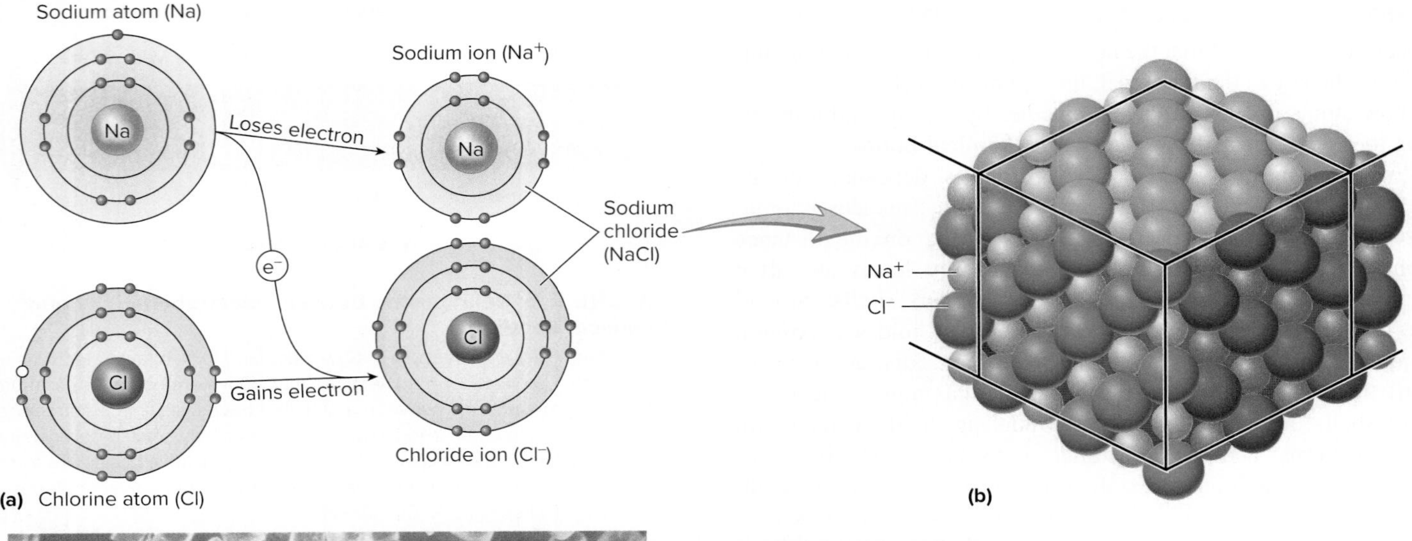

FIGURE 2.6 Ionic Bonds
(*a*) A sodium atom (Na) loses an electron to become a smaller, positively charged ion, and a chlorine atom (Cl) gains an electron to become a larger, negatively charged ion. The attraction between the oppositely charged ions results in ionic bonding and the formation of sodium chloride. (*b*) The sodium ions (Na^+) and the chlorine ions (Cl^-) are organized to form a cube-shaped array. (*c*) A photomicrograph of salt crystals reflects the cubic arrangement of the ions. (c) ©Trent Stevens APR

together by ionic bonding to form an array of ions called sodium chloride (NaCl), or table salt (figure 2.6*b,c*). Some ions commonly found in the body are listed in table 2.2.

Covalent Bonds

A **covalent bond** forms when atoms share one or more pairs of electrons. The sharing of electrons, rather than transfer of electrons, occurs because the atoms have similar electronegativities. The resulting combination of atoms is called a molecule. Figure 2.7 illustrates the formation of a covalent bond between two hydrogen atoms to form a hydrogen molecule.

1. Initially, the two atoms do not interact because they are too far apart. Each hydrogen atom has 1 electron.
2. As the two hydrogen atoms get closer together, the positively charged nucleus of each atom begins to attract the electron of the other hydrogen atom.
3. A **nonpolar covalent bond** forms when the electrons are shared equally between the nuclei because the electrons have the same attraction to each nucleus. The two hydrogen atoms are held together by a nonpolar covalent bond and now form a **nonpolar molecule.**

The sharing of one pair of electrons by two atoms results in a **single covalent bond.** A single line between the symbols of the atoms involved (e.g., H—H) represents a single covalent bond. A **double covalent bond** results when two atoms share 4 electrons, 2 from each atom. When a carbon atom combines with two oxygen atoms to form carbon dioxide (CO_2), two double covalent bonds form. Double covalent bonds are indicated by a double line between the atoms (O═C═O).

However, covalent bonds are not always the result of equal sharing of electrons between atoms. In cases where the two atoms involved in a covalent bond have different electronegativities, **polar covalent bonds** will form (see figure 2.5). Polar covalent bonds can result in polar molecules, which are electrically asymmetric. For example, oxygen atoms have a higher electronegativity than do hydrogen atoms. When covalent bonding between an oxygen atom

TABLE 2.2 Important Ions in the Human Body

Ion	Symbol	Significance*
Calcium	Ca^{2+}	Part of bones and teeth; functions in blood clotting, muscle contraction, release of neurotransmitters
Sodium	Na^+	Membrane potentials, water balance
Potassium	K^+	Membrane potentials
Hydrogen	H^+	Acid-base balance
Hydroxide	OH^-	Acid-base balance
Chloride	Cl^-	Water balance
Bicarbonate	HCO_3^-	Acid-base balance
Ammonium	NH_4^+	Acid-base balance
Phosphate	PO_4^{3-}	Part of bones and teeth; functions in energy exchange, acid-base balance
Iron	Fe^{2+}	Red blood cell formation
Magnesium	Mg^{2+}	Necessary for enzymes
Iodide	I^-	Present in thyroid hormones

*The ions are part of the structures or play important roles in the processes listed.

PROCESS Figure

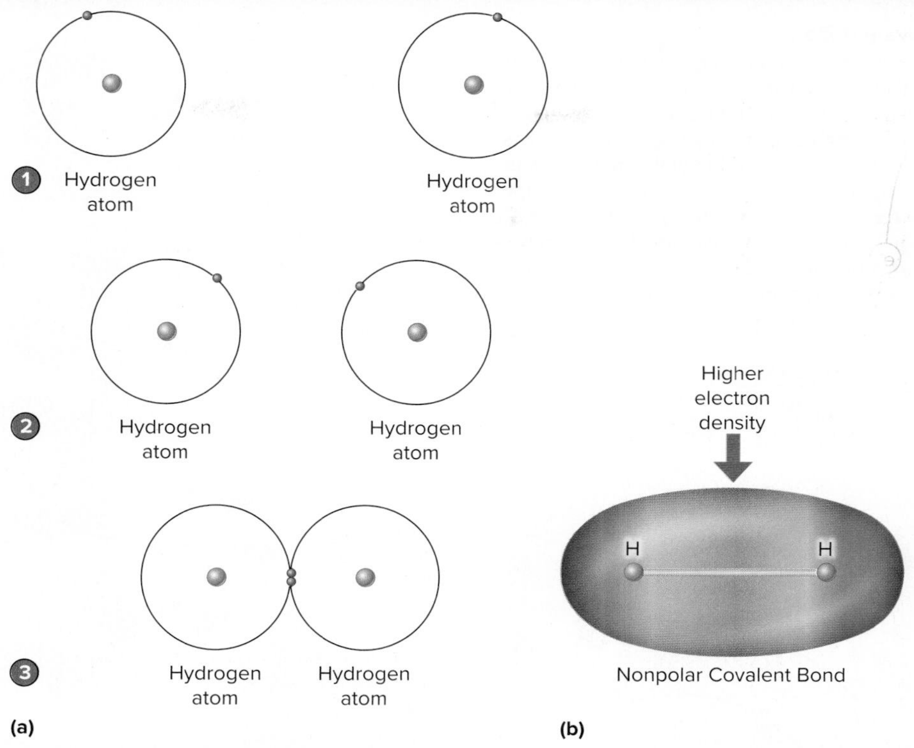

PROCESS **Figure 2.7**

Nonpolar Covalent Bonds

(*a*) In a nonpolar bond, there is an even distribution of electrons due to the equal electronegativities of the two atoms. (*b*) Molecules formed by nonpolar covalent bonds are neutral. The electron distribution (*arrow*) is equal between the two nuclei.

What type of bond would form when electrons are shared between an atom with stronger electronegativity and an atom with weaker electronegativity?

and two hydrogen atoms forms a water molecule, the electron cloud is closer to the oxygen nucleus than to the hydrogen nuclei. Because electrons have a negative charge, the oxygen side of the molecule is slightly more negative than the hydrogen side (figure 2.8).

Molecules and Compounds

A **molecule** is composed of two or more atoms chemically combined to form a structure that behaves as an independent unit. Sometimes the atoms that combine are of the same type, such as two hydrogen atoms combining to form a hydrogen molecule. However, more typically, a molecule consists of two or more different types of atoms, such as two hydrogen atoms and an oxygen atom combining to form water. Thus, a glass of water consists of a collection of individual water molecules positioned next to one another.

A **compound** is a substance resulting from the chemical combination of two or more *different types* of atoms. Water is a molecule that is also a compound because it is a combination of two different atoms, hydrogen and oxygen. But not all molecules are compounds. For example, a hydrogen molecule is not a compound because it does not consist of different types of atoms.

Some compounds are molecules and some are not. (Remember that to be a molecule, a structure must be an independent unit.) Covalent compounds, in which different types of atoms are held together by covalent bonds, are molecules because the sharing of electrons results in distinct units. On the other hand, ionic compounds, in which ions are held together by the force of attraction between opposite charges, are not molecules because they do not consist of distinct units. Table salt (NaCl) is an example of a substance that is a compound but not a molecule. A piece of NaCl does not consist of individual sodium chloride molecules positioned next to one another. Instead, NaCl is an organized array of individual Na^+ and individual Cl^- in which each charged ion is surrounded by several ions of the opposite charge (see figure 2.6*b*).

The properties of elements can change when they are combined to form compounds. For example, the element hydrogen is extremely flammable, and oxygen, although not flammable on its own, promotes fire. However, when combined, hydrogen and oxygen form the very nonflammable compound water. Likewise, elements that are dangerous or toxic to humans can become useful as compounds. For example, sodium is very explosive when

FIGURE 2.8 Polar Covalent Bonds

(*a*) A water molecule forms when one oxygen atom forms polar covalent bonds with two hydrogen atoms. In a polar covalent bond, such as with water, there is an uneven distribution of electrons due to the stronger electronegativity of oxygen compared to that of hydrogen. This creates charged regions of the molecule. The oxygen side of the molecule has a slight negative charge (*indicated by* δ^-), and the hydrogen side of the molecule has a slight positive charge (*indicated by* δ^+). (*b*) Molecules formed by polar covalent bonds have charged portions. The electron distribution is unequal between two nuclei and the electron density is greater around the nucleus with the stronger electronegativity.

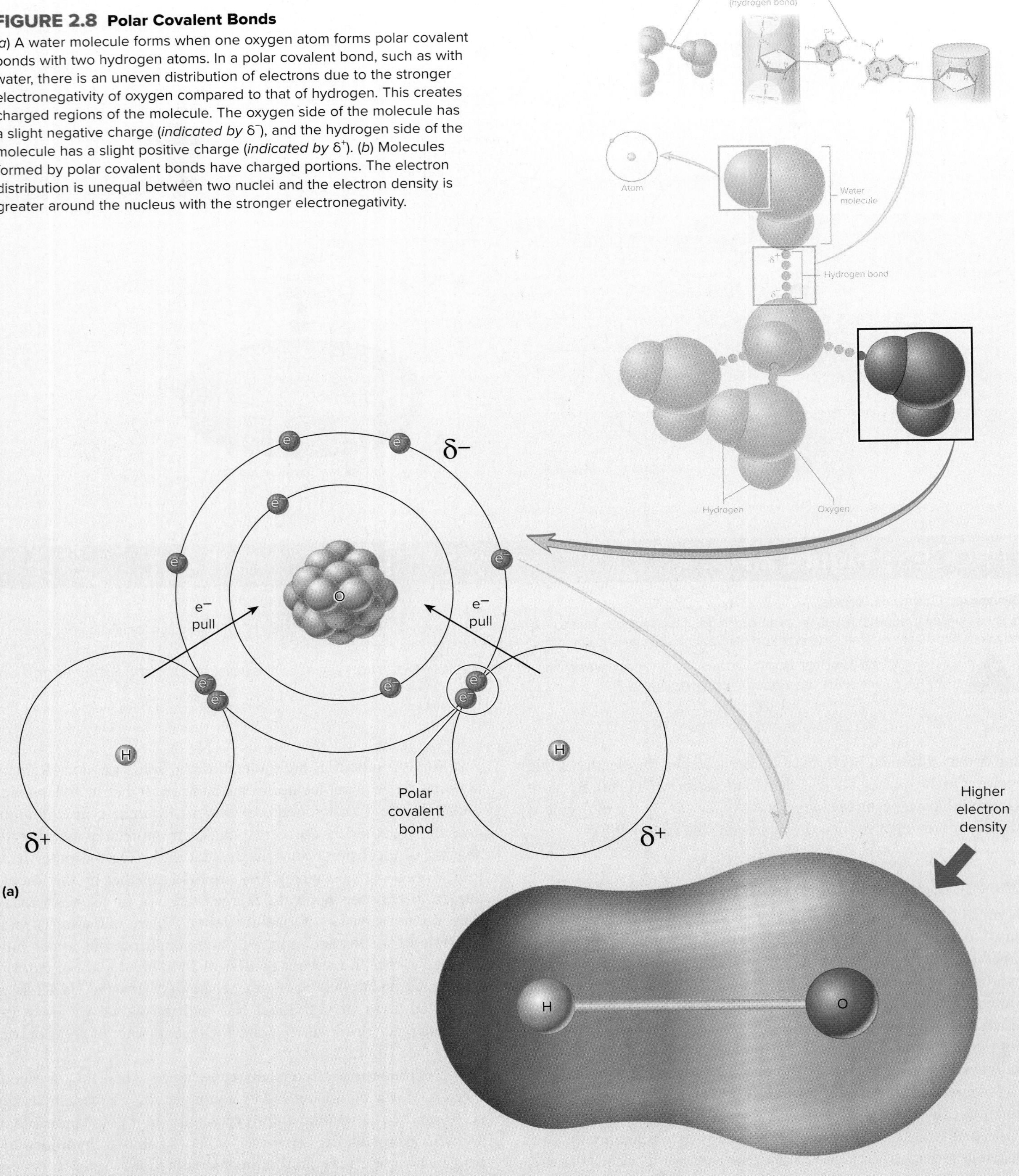

TABLE 2.3 Picturing Molecules

Representation	Hydrogen	Carbon Dioxide	Glucose
Chemical Formula The formula shows the kind and number of atoms present.	H_2	CO_2	$C_6H_{12}O_6$
Electron-Dot Formula The bonding electrons are shown as dots between the symbols of the atoms.	H:H Single covalent bond	O::C::O Double covalent bond	Not used for complex molecules
Bond-Line Formula The bonding electrons are shown as lines between the symbols of the atoms.	H—H Single covalent bond	O=C=O Double covalent bond	CH_2OH, O, HO, OH, OH, OH
Models Atoms are shown as different-sized and different-colored spheres.	Hydrogen atom	Oxygen atom, Carbon atom	

placed in water, and chlorine is a strong disinfectant in solutions, such as bleach and swimming pool water. Chlorine is so toxic that it was used as a poison gas in World War I, yet, when combined, sodium and chloride form the relatively safe and nonexplosive compound table salt.

The kinds and numbers of atoms (or ions) in a molecule or compound are typically represented by a formula consisting of the symbols of the atoms (or ions) plus subscripts denoting the quantity of each type of atom (or ion). The formula for glucose (a sugar) is $C_6H_{12}O_6$, indicating that a molecule of glucose consists of 6 carbon, 12 hydrogen, and 6 oxygen atoms (table 2.3). The formulas for some common substances, such as O_2 for oxygen and CO_2 for carbon dioxide, will be used throughout the textbook.

The **molecular mass** of a molecule or compound can be determined by adding up the atomic masses of its atoms (or ions). The term *molecular mass* is used for convenience for ionic compounds, even though they are not molecules. For example, the atomic mass of sodium is 22.99 and that of chloride is 35.45. The molecular mass of NaCl is therefore 58.44 (22.99 + 35.45).

Intermolecular Forces

Intermolecular forces are the weak electrostatic attractions that exist between oppositely charged parts of molecules, or between ions and molecules. There is no exchange of electrons in intermolecular forces. This differs from other chemical bonds. Intermolecular forces are much weaker than the forces producing chemical bonding. Intermolecular forces include hydrogen bonds and the properties of solubility and dissociation.

Hydrogen Bonds

Molecules with polar covalent bonds have positive and negative "ends." Intermolecular force results from the attraction of the positive end of one polar molecule to the negative end of another polar molecule. For example, when hydrogen forms a covalent bond with oxygen, nitrogen, or fluorine, the resulting molecule becomes very polarized. If the positively charged hydrogen of one molecule is attracted to the negatively charged oxygen, nitrogen, or fluorine of another molecule, a **hydrogen bond** forms. A common example of hydrogen bonding occurs between water molecules and other polar molecules (figure 2.9). These hydrogen bonds are essential for the unique properties of water (see section 2.3).

In addition to intermolecular bonds between molecules, hydrogen bonds form intramolecular bonds within the same molecule. Intramolecular hydrogen bonds form the more complex structure of proteins and nucleic acids and help stabilize their final three-dimensional shape (see section 2.4).

Table 2.4 summarizes the important characteristics of chemical bonds (ionic and covalent) and intermolecular forces (hydrogen bonds).

Solubility and Dissociation

Solubility is the ability of one substance to dissolve in another—for example, sugar dissolving in water. Charged substances, such as sodium chloride, and polar substances, such as glucose, readily dissolve in water, whereas nonpolar substances, such as oils, do not. We all have seen how oil floats on water. Substances dissolve in water when they become surrounded by water molecules. If the positive

FUNDAMENTAL **Figure**

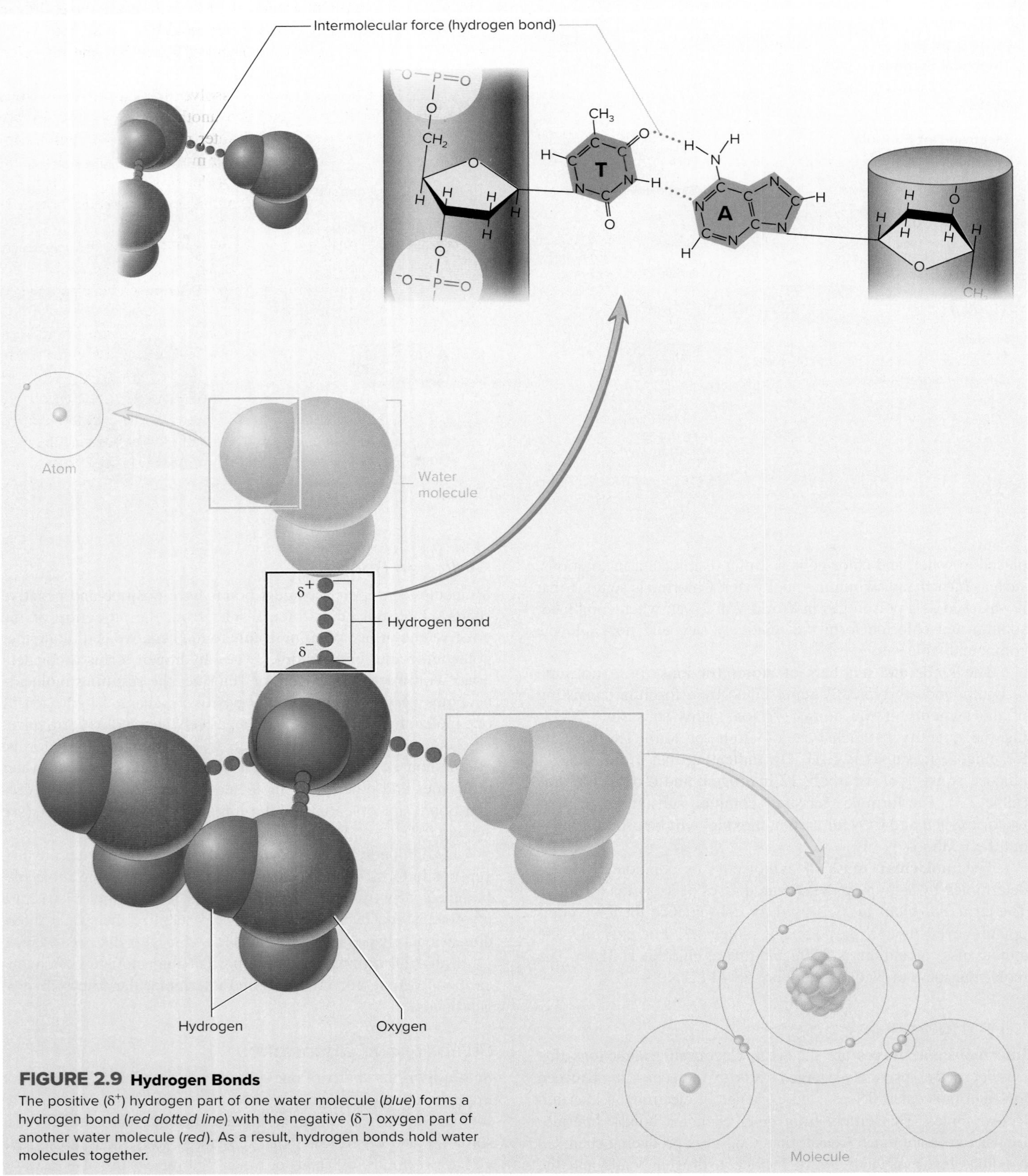

FIGURE 2.9 Hydrogen Bonds
The positive (δ^+) hydrogen part of one water molecule (*blue*) forms a hydrogen bond (*red dotted line*) with the negative (δ^-) oxygen part of another water molecule (*red*). As a result, hydrogen bonds hold water molecules together.

TABLE 2.4 Comparison of Bonds

Chemical Bond	Example
Ionic Bond A complete transfer of electrons between two atoms results in separate positively charged and negatively charged ions.	Na^+Cl^- Sodium chloride
Polar Covalent Bond An unequal sharing of electrons between two atoms results in a slightly positive charge (δ^+) on one side of the molecule and a slightly negative charge (δ^-) on the other side of the molecule.	H δ^+ \ O δ^- / H δ^+ Water
Nonpolar Covalent Bond An equal sharing of electrons between two atoms results in an even charge distribution among the atoms of the molecule.	H—H Hydrogen
Intermolecular Bond	
Hydrogen Bond The attraction of oppositely charged ends of one polar molecule to another polar molecule holds molecules or parts of molecules together.	H, O•••H—O, H, H Water molecules

and negative ends of the water molecules are more attracted to the charged ends of other molecules than to each other, the hydrogen bonds between the ends of the water molecules break, and water molecules surround the other molecules, which become dissolved in water.

When ionic compounds dissolve in water, their ions **dissociate,** or separate, from one another because cations are attracted to the negative ends of water molecules and anions are attracted to the positive ends of water molecules. When NaCl dissociates in water, sodium and chloride ions separate, and water molecules surround and isolate the ions, thereby keeping them in solution (figure 2.10).

When molecules (covalent compounds) dissolve in water, they usually remain intact, even though they are surrounded by water molecules. Thus, in a glucose solution, glucose molecules are surrounded by water molecules.

Cations and anions that dissociate in water are sometimes called **electrolytes** (ee-LEK-troh-lytes) because they have the capacity to conduct an electric current, which is the flow of charged particles. An electrocardiogram (ECG) is a recording of electric currents produced by the heart. These currents can be detected by electrodes on the surface of the body because the ions in the body fluids conduct electric currents. Molecules that do not dissociate form solutions that do not conduct electricity and are called **nonelectrolytes.** Pure water is a nonelectrolyte.

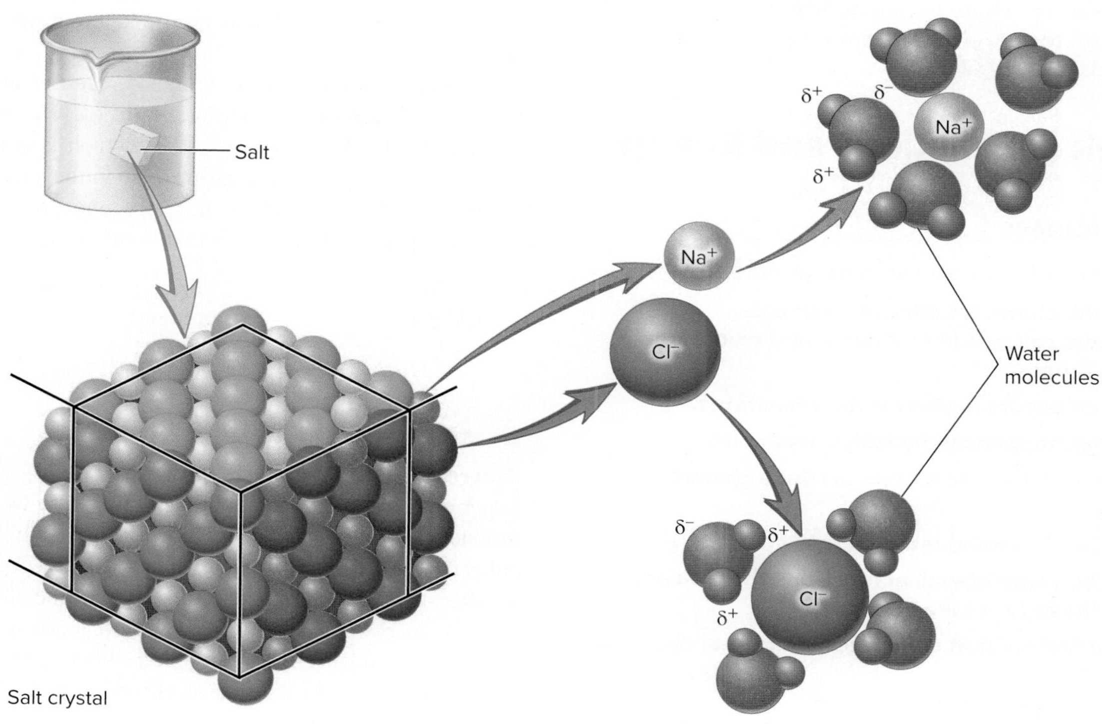

FIGURE 2.10 Dissociation

Sodium chloride (table salt) dissociates in water. The positively charged Na^+ are attracted to the negatively charged (δ^-) oxygen (*red*) end of the water molecule, and the negatively charged Cl^- are attracted to the positively charged (δ^+) hydrogen (*blue*) end of the water molecule. APR

Maintaining the proper balance of electrolytes is important for keeping the body hydrated, controlling blood pH, and ensuring the proper function of muscles and nerves. Under most conditions, including moderate exercise, the body's usual regulatory mechanisms are sufficient to maintain electrolyte homeostasis. However, people engaging in prolonged exercise, such as competing in a triathlon, are advised to consume sports drinks containing electrolytes. In an emergency, administering intravenous solutions can restore electrolyte and fluid balance.

ASSESS YOUR PROGRESS

7. *Describe how an ionic bond is formed. What are cations and anions?*
8. *What occurs in the formation of a covalent bond? What is the difference between polar and nonpolar covalent bonds?*
9. *Distinguish between a molecule and a compound. Give an example of each. Are all molecules compounds? Are all compounds molecules?*
10. *What are intermolecular forces, and how do they create a hydrogen bond?*
11. *What is meant by the statement "table sugar is soluble in water"?*
12. *Describe what occurs during the dissociation of NaCl in water. What occurs when glucose ($C_6H_{12}O_6$) dissolves in water?*
13. *Explain the difference between electrolytes and nonelectrolytes. Classify each of the following water solutions as an electrolyte or a nonelectrolyte: potassium iodide (KCl), sucrose ($C_{12}H_{22}O_{11}$), magnesium bromide ($MgBr_2$), lactose ($C_{12}H_{22}O_{11}$).*

2.2 Chemical Reactions and Energy

LEARNING OUTCOMES

After reading this section, you should be able to

A. **Summarize the characteristics of synthesis, decomposition, reversible reactions, and oxidation-reduction reactions.**
B. **Illustrate what occurs in dehydration reactions.**
C. **Illustrate what happens in hydrolysis reactions.**
D. **Explain how reversible reactions produce chemical equilibrium.**
E. **Contrast potential and kinetic energy.**
F. **Distinguish between chemical reactions that release energy and those that take in energy.**
G. **Describe the factors that can affect the rate of chemical reactions.**

A **chemical reaction** occurs when atoms, ions, molecules, or compounds interact either to form or to break chemical bonds. The substances that enter into a chemical reaction are called **reactants,** and the substances that result from the chemical reaction are called **products.**

For our purposes, three important points can be made about chemical reactions. (1) In some reactions, less complex reactants are combined to form a larger, more complex product. An example is the synthesis of the complex proteins of the human body from amino acid "building blocks" obtained from food (figure 2.11*a*). (2) In other reactions, a reactant can be broken down, or decomposed, into simpler, less complex products. An example is the breakdown of carbohydrate molecules into glucose molecules (figure 2.11*b*). (3) Atoms are generally associated with other atoms through chemical bonding or intermolecular forces; therefore, to synthesize new products or break down reactants, it is necessary to change the relationship between atoms. You may find the information that follows helpful to answer the Learn to Predict question at the beginning of this chapter.

Synthesis Reactions

A **synthesis reaction** is when two or more reactants chemically combine to form a new and larger product. The collective term for synthesis reactions in the body is **anabolism** (an-AB-oh-lizm). These reactions produce the molecules characteristic of life, such as ATP, proteins, carbohydrates, lipids, and nucleic acids. The growth, maintenance, and repair of the body could not take place without anabolic reactions.

Another example of a synthesis reaction is the combination of two amino acids to form a dipeptide (figure 2.11*a*). As the amino acids are bound together, water is also produced. Synthesis reactions in which water is a product are called **dehydration** (water out) **reactions.** As the atoms rearrange as a result of a synthesis reaction, old chemical bonds are broken and new chemical bonds are formed.

Another example of a synthesis reaction in the body is the formation of **adenosine triphosphate (ATP;** see section 2.4 for the details of ATP structure). ATP, which is composed of adenosine and three phosphate groups, is synthesized from adenosine diphosphate (ADP), which has two phosphate groups, and an inorganic phosphate (H_2PO^4) that is often symbolized as P_i:

A-P-P	+	P_i	→	A-P-P-P
(ADP)		(Inorganic phosphate)		(ATP)

Decomposition Reactions

A **decomposition reaction** is the reverse of a synthesis reaction—a larger reactant is chemically broken down into two or more smaller products. The decomposition reactions occurring in the body are collectively called **catabolism** (kah-TAB-oh-lizm). They include the digestion of food molecules in the intestine and within cells, the breakdown of stored lipids, and the breakdown of foreign matter and microorganisms in certain blood cells that protect the body. All of the anabolic and catabolic reactions in the body are collectively defined as **metabolism.**

Another example of a decomposition reaction is the breakdown of a disaccharide (a type of carbohydrate) into glucose molecules (figure 2.11*b*). Note that this reaction requires that water be split into two parts and that each part be contributed to one of the new

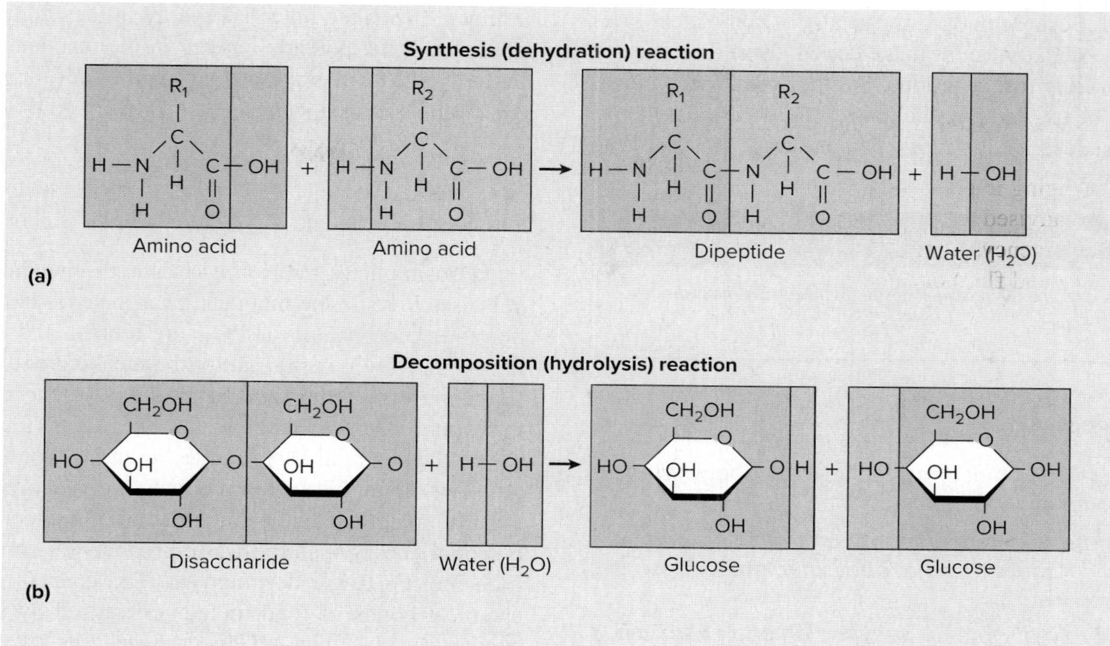

FIGURE 2.11 Synthesis and Decomposition Reactions
(*a*) A synthesis reaction in which two amino acids combine to form a dipeptide. This reaction is also a dehydration reaction because it results in the removal of a water molecule from the amino acids. (*b*) A decomposition reaction in which a disaccharide breaks apart into individual glucose molecules. This reaction is also a hydrolysis reaction because it involves the splitting of a water molecule.

glucose molecules. Reactions that use water in this manner are called **hydrolysis** (high-DROL-ih-sis; water dissolution) **reactions.**

The breakdown of ATP to ADP and an inorganic phosphate is another example of a decomposition reaction:

A-P-P-P	$\rightarrow$	A-P-P	+	P_i
(ATP)		(ADP)		(Inorganic phosphate)

Reversible Reactions

Some chemical reactions are reversible. A **reversible reaction** is when the reaction can run in the opposite direction, so that the products are converted back to the original reactants. When the rate of product formation is equal to the rate of the reverse reaction, the reaction system is said to be at **equilibrium.** At equilibrium, the amount of reactants relative to the amount of products remains constant.

The following analogy may help clarify the concept of reversible reactions and equilibrium. Imagine a football team. The team is divided into two groups: players on the field and those on the bench. Because the players can move in either direction (on or off the field), this is like a reversible reaction. Imagine that the players on the bench are the reactant and the players on the field (lined up in formation) are the product. At equilibrium, the amount of reactant relative to the amount of product is always the same. When some players on the bench run onto the field, an equal number of players run off the field, so equilibrium is maintained.

A reversible reaction that is very important in the human body involves carbon dioxide and hydrogen ions. Carbon dioxide (CO_2) and water (H_2O) combine to form carbonic acid (H_2CO_3). Carbonic acid then separates by a reversible reaction to form hydrogen ions (H^+) and bicarbonate ions (HCO_3^-):

$$CO_2 + H_2O \rightleftarrows H_2CO_3 \rightleftarrows H^+ + HCO_3^-$$

If more CO_2 is added to the reaction, then additional H_2CO_3 forms, which causes more H^+ and HCO_3^- to form. The amount of H^+ and HCO_3^- relative to CO_2 therefore remains constant. Maintaining a constant level of H^+ in the body can be achieved, in part, by regulating blood CO_2 levels. For example, slowing down the respiration rate causes blood CO_2 levels to increase and thus increase H^+ levels.

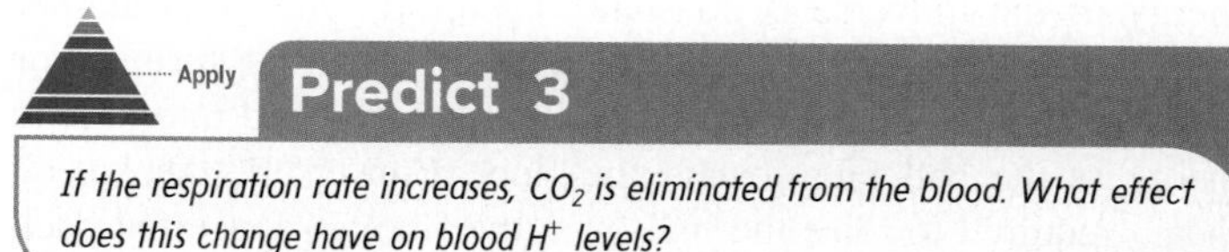

If the respiration rate increases, CO_2 is eliminated from the blood. What effect does this change have on blood H^+ levels?

Oxidation-Reduction Reactions

Chemical reactions that result from the exchange of electrons between the reactants are called oxidation-reduction reactions. When Na^+ and Cl^- react to form NaCl, the sodium atom loses an electron and the chlorine atom gains an electron. The loss of an electron by an atom is called **oxidation,** and the gain of an electron is called **reduction.** The transfer of the electron can be complete, resulting in an ionic bond, or it can be partial, resulting in a covalent bond. Because one atom partially or completely loses an electron and another atom gains that electron, these reactions are called **oxidation-reduction reactions.** Synthesis and decomposition reactions can be oxidation-reduction reactions. Thus, a chemical reaction can be described in more than one way.

Predict 4

When hydrogen gas combines with oxygen gas to form water, is the hydrogen reduced or oxidized? Explain.

ASSESS YOUR PROGRESS

14. *Using the terms* reactant *and* product, *describe what occurs in a chemical reaction.*

15. *Contrast synthesis and decomposition reactions, and explain how catabolism and anabolism relate to these two types of reactions.*

16. *Describe the role of water in dehydration and hydrolysis reactions.*

17. *What is a reversible reaction? How does this type of reaction lead to chemical equilibrium?*

18. *What are oxidation-reduction reactions?*

Energy

Energy is the capacity to do **work.** So, what is the definition of *work?* Work is the movement of matter. That means that *energy is the ability to put matter into motion.* In this straightforward definition of energy, you can clearly see the importance of *understanding* a definition, rather than simply *memorizing* it. Energy can be subdivided into potential energy and kinetic energy. **Potential energy** is stored energy that could do work but is not doing so. **Kinetic** (ki-NET-ik) **energy** is the form of energy that is actually doing work and moving matter. A ball held at arm's length above the floor has potential energy. No energy is expended as long as the ball does not move. However, if the ball is released and falls toward the floor, it has kinetic energy.

According to the conservation of energy principle, the total energy of the universe is constant. Therefore, energy is neither created nor destroyed, but it can take on different forms. For example, the potential energy in the ball is converted into kinetic energy as the ball falls toward the floor. Conversely, the kinetic energy required to raise the ball from the floor is converted back into potential energy.

Potential and kinetic energy exist in many different forms. Here we consider mechanical, chemical, and heat energy. **Mechanical energy** results from the position or movement of objects. Many of the activities of the human body, such as moving a limb, breathing, and circulating blood, involve mechanical energy.

Chemical Energy

Chemical energy is a form of potential energy stored within the chemical bonds of a substance. In any chemical reaction, the potential energy in the chemical bonds of the reactants can be compared with the potential energy in the chemical bonds of the products. If the potential energy in the reactants is *less* than that in the products, energy must be supplied for the reaction to occur. An example is the synthesis of ATP from ADP:

$$\underset{\text{(Less potential energy in reactants)}}{ADP + H_2PO_4^-} \quad + \quad \text{Energy} \quad \rightarrow \quad \underset{\text{(More potential energy in products)}}{ATP + H_2O}$$

For simplicity, the H_2O is often not shown in this reaction, and P_i is used to represent inorganic phosphate ($H_2PO_4^-$). For this reaction to occur, bonds in $H_2PO_4^-$ are broken, and bonds are formed in ATP and H_2O. As a result of the breaking of existing bonds, the formation of new bonds, and the input of energy, these products have more potential energy than the reactants (figure 2.12*a*).

If the potential energy in the chemical bonds of the reactants is *greater* than that of the products, the reaction releases energy. For example, the chemical bonds of food molecules contain more potential energy than the waste products that are produced when food molecules are decomposed. The energy released from the chemical bonds of food molecules is used by living systems to synthesize ATP. Once ATP is produced, the breakdown of ATP to ADP results in the release of energy:

$$\underset{\text{(More potential energy in reactants)}}{ATP + H_2O} \quad \rightarrow \quad \underset{\text{(Less potential energy in products)}}{ADP + H_2PO_4^-} \quad + \quad \text{Energy}$$

For this reaction to occur, the bonds in ATP and H_2O are broken and bonds in $H_2PO_4^-$ are formed. As a result of breaking the existing bonds and forming new bonds, these products have less potential energy than the reactants, and energy is released (figure 2.12*b*). Note that there are two quantities of energy in this

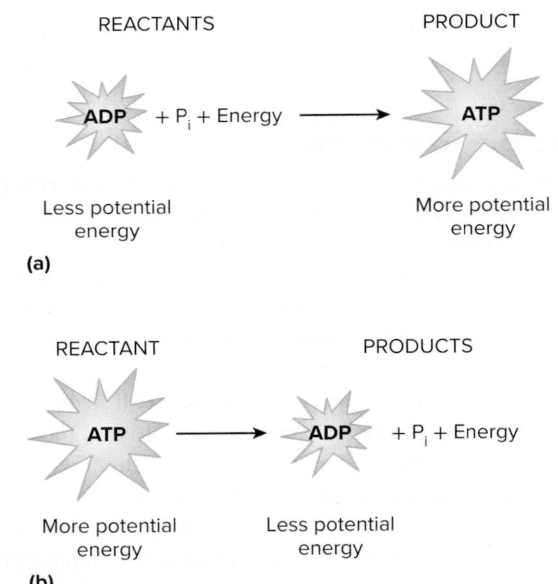

FIGURE 2.12 Energy and Chemical Reactions
In the two reactions shown here, the larger "sunburst" represents greater potential energy and the smaller "sunburst" represents less potential energy. (*a*) The input of energy is required for the synthesis of ATP. (*b*) Energy is released as a result of the breakdown of ATP. APR

The normal pH range for human blood is 7.35 to 7.45. **Acidosis** results if blood pH drops below 7.35. In this case, the nervous system becomes depressed and the individual may become disoriented and possibly comatose. **Alkalosis** results if blood pH rises above 7.45. In this case, the nervous system becomes overexcitable, and the individual may become extremely nervous or have convulsions. Both acidosis and alkalosis can be fatal.

Salts

A **salt** is a compound consisting of a cation other than H^+ and an anion other than OH^-. Salts are formed by the interaction of an acid and a base in which the H^+ of the acid are replaced by the positive ions of the base. For example, in a solution in which hydrochloric acid (HCl) reacts with the base sodium hydroxide (NaOH), the salt sodium chloride (NaCl) is formed:

$$\underset{\text{(Acid)}}{HCl} + \underset{\text{(Base)}}{NaOH} \rightarrow \underset{\text{(Salt)}}{NaCl} + \underset{\text{(Water)}}{H_2O}$$

Typically, when salts such as sodium chloride dissociate in water, they form positively and negatively charged ions (see figure 2.10).

Buffers

The chemical behavior of many molecules changes as the pH of the solution in which they are dissolved changes. For example, many enzymes work best within narrow ranges of pH. The survival of an organism depends on its ability to maintain homeostasis by keeping body fluid pH within a narrow range. Deviations from the normal pH range for human blood are life-threatening.

One way body fluid pH is regulated involves the use of buffers. **Buffers** are chemicals that resist changes in pH when either acids or bases are added to a solution. For example,

1. when an acid is added to a buffered solution,
2. the buffer binds to the H^+,
3. preventing these ions from causing a decrease in the pH of the solution (figure 2.15).

Important buffers in living systems are composed of bicarbonate, phosphates, amino acids, and proteins. Buffers prevent large changes in pH values by acting as **conjugate acid-base pairs.** A conjugate base is what remains of an acid after the H^+ (proton) is lost. A conjugate acid is formed when a H^+ is transferred to the conjugate base. Two substances related in this way are a conjugate acid-base pair.

A major buffer in our body fluids is the bicarbonate system. A bicarbonate ion (HCO_3^-) is formed by the ionization of carbonic acid (H_2CO_3):

$$H_2CO_3 \rightleftarrows H^+ + HCO_3^-$$

Carbonic acid and bicarbonate are a conjugate acid-base pair. The sodium salt of bicarbonate ($NaHCO_3$), also known as baking soda, is an active ingredient in some antacids taken to reduce stomach acidity. In the forward reaction, H_2CO_3 loses a H^+ to produce HCO_3^-, which is a conjugate base. In the reverse reaction, a H^+ is transferred to the HCO_3^- (conjugate base) to produce H_2CO_3, which is a conjugate acid.

PROCESS **Figure**

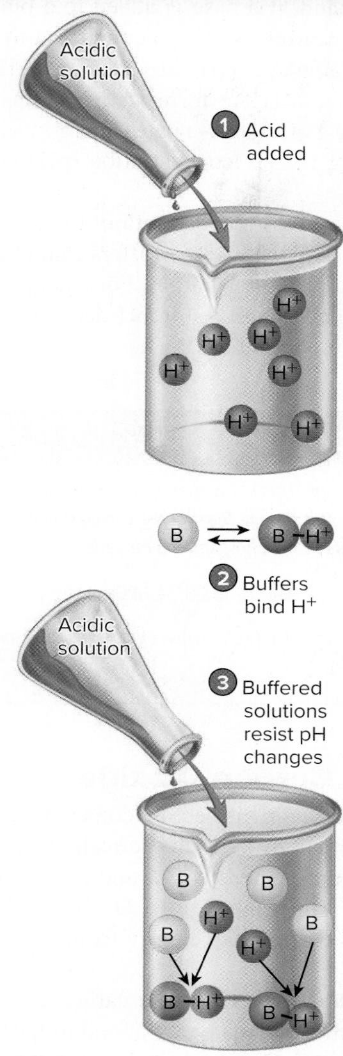

PROCESS **Figure 2.15**

Buffers

The addition of an acid to a nonbuffered solution of water results in an increase of H^+ that causes a large decrease in pH. The addition of an acid to a buffered solution results in a much smaller change in pH. The added H^+ bind to the buffer (symbolized by the letter *B*). The buffer acts as a conjugate acid-base pair, in which buffer molecules not bound with H^+ are the conjugate base and buffer molecules bound with H^+ are the conjugate acid.

What would happen if a basic solution instead of an acidic solution is added to the beakers?

For a given condition, this reversible reaction results in an equilibrium, in which the amounts of H_2CO_3 relative to the amounts of H^+ and HCO_3^- remain constant. The conjugate acid-base pair can resist changes in pH because of this equilibrium. If an acid is added to a buffer, the H^+ from the added acid can combine with the base component of the conjugate acid-base pair. As a result, the concentration of H^+ does not increase as much as it would without this reaction. If H^+ is added to a H_2CO_3 solution, many of the H^+ combine with HCO_3^- to form H_2CO_3.

On the other hand, if a base is added to a buffered solution, the conjugate acid can release H^+ to counteract the effects of the added base. For example, if OH^- are added to a H_2CO_3 solution, the OH^- combine with H^+ to form water. As the H^+ are incorporated into water, H_2CO_3 dissociates to form H^+ and HCO_3^-, thereby maintaining the H^+ concentration (pH) within a normal range.

The greater the buffer concentration, the more effectively it can resist a change in pH; however, buffers cannot entirely prevent some change in the pH of a solution. For example, when an acid is added to a buffered solution, the pH decreases, but not to the extent it would have without the buffer.

Predict 6

Dihydrogen phosphate ion ($H_2PO_4^-$) and monohydrogen phosphate ion (HPO_4^{2-}) form the phosphate buffer system. Identify the conjugate acid and the conjugate base in the phosphate buffer system:

$$H_2PO_4^- \rightleftarrows H^+ + HPO_4^{2-}$$

Explain how they function as a buffer when either H^+ or OH^- are added to the solution.

Oxygen and Carbon Dioxide

Oxygen is an inorganic molecule consisting of two oxygen atoms bound together by a double covalent bond. About 21% of the gas in the atmosphere is O_2, and it is essential for most living organisms. Humans require O_2 in the final step of a series of reactions that extract energy from food molecules (see chapter 25).

Carbon dioxide consists of one carbon atom bound to two oxygen atoms. Each oxygen atom is bound to the carbon atom by a double covalent bond. Carbon dioxide is produced when organic molecules, such as glucose, are metabolized within the cells of the body (see chapter 25). Much of the energy stored in the covalent bonds of glucose is transferred to other organic molecules when glucose is broken down and CO_2 is released. Once carbon dioxide is produced, it is eliminated from the cell as a metabolic by-product, transferred to the lungs by the blood, and exhaled during respiration. If CO_2 is allowed to accumulate within cells, it becomes toxic.

ASSESS YOUR PROGRESS

29. *Define* acid *and* base, *and describe the pH scale.*
30. *What is the difference between a strong acid or base and a weak acid or base?*
31. *The blood pH of a patient is 7.30. What condition does this patient have, and what are the symptoms?*
32. *How are salts related to acids and bases?*
33. *What is a buffer, and why are buffers important in the body?*
34. *What is a conjugate acid-base pair?*
35. *What are the functions of O_2 and CO_2 in living systems?*

2.4 Organic Chemistry

LEARNING OUTCOMES

After reading this section, you should be able to

A. **Describe the structural organization and major functions of carbohydrates, lipids, proteins, and nucleic acids.**
B. **Explain how enzymes work.**
C. **Describe the roles of nucleotides in the structures and functions of DNA, RNA, and ATP.**

Carbon's ability to form covalent bonds with other atoms makes possible the formation of the large, diverse, complicated molecules necessary for life. These are called organic molecules, or sometimes biomolecules. Our cells utilize some of these molecules to synthesize ATP, while others are used as structural components and regulatory molecules, among many other functions. Carbon atoms bound together by covalent bonds constitute the "backbone" of many large molecules. Two mechanisms that allow the formation of a wide variety of molecules are (1) variation in the length of the carbon chains and (2) the combination of the atoms involved. For example, some protein molecules have thousands of carbon atoms bound by covalent bonds to one another or to other atoms, such as nitrogen, sulfur, hydrogen, and oxygen. A functional group gives distinctive properties, such as polarity, to organic molecules. Selected major functional groups of organic compounds are listed in table 2.5.

The four major groups of organic molecules essential to living organisms are (1) carbohydrates, (2) lipids, (3) proteins, and (4) nucleic acids. In addition, a high-energy form of a nucleic acid building block, called ATP, is an important organic molecule in cellular processes. Each of these groups and ATP have specific structural and functional characteristics.

Carbohydrates

Carbohydrates are organic molecules composed primarily of carbon, hydrogen, and oxygen atoms and range in size from small to very large. Carbohydrates have three major roles in the body (table 2.6): (1) They are parts of other organic molecules, (2) they are broken down to provide energy, and (3) when undigested they provide bulk in feces. In most carbohydrates, there are approximately two hydrogen atoms and one oxygen atom for each carbon atom. Note that this two-to-one ratio is the same as in water (H_2O). The molecules are called carbohydrates because carbon (*carbo*) atoms are combined with the same atoms that form water (*hydrated*). The large number of oxygen atoms in carbohydrates makes them relatively polar molecules. Consequently, they are soluble in polar solvents, such as water.

Monosaccharides

Large carbohydrates are composed of numerous, relatively simple building blocks called **monosaccharides** (MON-oh-SACK-ah-rides; *mono-*, one + *saccharide,* sugar), or simple sugars. Monosaccharides commonly contain 3 carbons (trioses), 4 carbons (tetroses), 5 carbons (pentoses), or 6 carbons (hexoses).

TABLE 2.5 Major Functional Groups of Organic Compounds

Name and Structural Formula*	Functional Significance
Hydroxyl R — O — H	*Alcohols* contain a hydroxyl group, which is polar and hydrophilic. Hydroxyl groups greatly increase the solubility of molecules in water.
Sulfhydryl R — S — H	*Thiols* have a sulfhydryl group, which is polar and hydrophilic. The amino acid cysteine contains a sulfhydryl group that can form a disulfide bond with another cysteine to help stabilize protein structure.
Carbonyl $R-\overset{\overset{\displaystyle O}{\|}}{C}-R$	*Ketones* and *aldehydes* have a carbonyl group, which is polar and hydrophilic. Ketones contain a carbonyl group within the carbon chain. Ketones are formed during normal metabolism, but they can be elevated in the blood during starvation or certain diabetic states. Aldehydes are similar to ketones, but they have the carbonyl group at the end of the carbon chain.
Carboxyl $R-\overset{\overset{\displaystyle O}{\|}}{C}-OH$	*Carboxylic acids* have a carboxyl group, which is hydrophilic and can act as an acid by donating a hydrogen ion. All amino acids have a carboxyl group at one end. At physiological pH, the amino acid carboxyl group is predominantly negatively charged.
Ester $R-\overset{\overset{\displaystyle O}{\|}}{C}-O-R$	*Esters* are structures with an ester group, which is less hydrophilic than hydroxyl or carboxyl groups. Triglycerides and dietary fats are esters. Other types of esters include the volatile compounds in perfumes.
Amino $R-N\begin{smallmatrix}\diagup H\\ \diagdown H\end{smallmatrix}$	*Amines* have an amino group, which is less hydrophilic than carboxyl groups. Amines can act as a base by accepting a hydrogen ion. All amino acids have an amine group at one end. At physiological pH, the amino acid amine group is predominantly positively charged.
Phosphate $R-O-\overset{\overset{\displaystyle O}{\|}}{\underset{\underset{\displaystyle O^-}{\vert}}{P}}-O^-$	*Phosphates* have a phosphate group, which is very hydrophilic due to the double negative charge. Phosphates are used as an energy source (adenosine triphosphate) in biological membranes (phospholipids) and as intracellular signaling molecules (protein phosphorylation).

*R = variable group.

TABLE 2.6 Roles of Carbohydrates in the Body

Role	Example
Structure	Ribose forms part of RNA and ATP molecules. Deoxyribose forms part of DNA.
Energy	Monosaccharides (glucose, fructose, galactose) can be used as energy sources. Disaccharides (sucrose, lactose, maltose) and polysaccharides (starch, glycogen) must be broken down to monosaccharides before they can be used for energy. Glycogen is an important energy-storage molecule in muscles and in the liver.
Bulk	Cellulose forms bulk in the feces.

The monosaccharides most important to humans include both 5- and 6-carbon sugars. Common 6-carbon sugars, such as glucose, fructose, and galactose, are **isomers** (EYE-soh-merz). Isomers are molecules that have the same number and types of atoms but differ in their three-dimensional arrangement (figure 2.16). Glucose, or blood sugar, is the major carbohydrate in the blood and a major nutrient for most cells of the body. In fact, cells preferentially use glucose to synthesize ATP. Blood glucose levels are tightly regulated by insulin and other hormones. In people with diabetes, the body is unable to regulate glucose levels properly. Diabetics need to monitor their blood glucose carefully to minimize the deleterious effects of this disease. Fructose and galactose are also important dietary nutrients. Important 5-carbon sugars include ribose and deoxyribose (see figure 2.26), which are components of ribonucleic acid (RNA) and deoxyribonucleic acid (DNA), respectively.

Disaccharides

Disaccharides (die-SACK-ah-rides; *di-*, two) are composed of two monosaccharides bound together through a dehydration reaction. For example, glucose and fructose combine to form a disaccharide called **sucrose** (table sugar) plus a molecule of water (figure 2.17*a*). In addition to sucrose, two other disaccharides important to humans are lactose and maltose. Lactose, or milk sugar, is glucose combined with galactose. Lack of the enzyme required to break down lactose leads to lactose intolerance (see chapter 24). Maltose, or malt sugar, is two glucose molecules joined together.

Structural isomer

Stereoisomer

Fructose ($C_6H_{12}O_6$)

Glucose ($C_6H_{12}O_6$)

Galactose ($C_6H_{12}O_6$)

FIGURE 2.16 Monosaccharides

These monosaccharides almost always form a ring-shaped molecule. Although not labeled with a C, carbon atoms are located at the corners of the ring-shaped molecules. Fructose is a structural isomer of glucose because it has identical chemical groups bonded in a different arrangement in the molecule (*red shading*). Galactose is a stereoisomer of glucose because it has exactly the same groups bonded to each carbon atom but located in a different three-dimensional orientation (*yellow shading*).

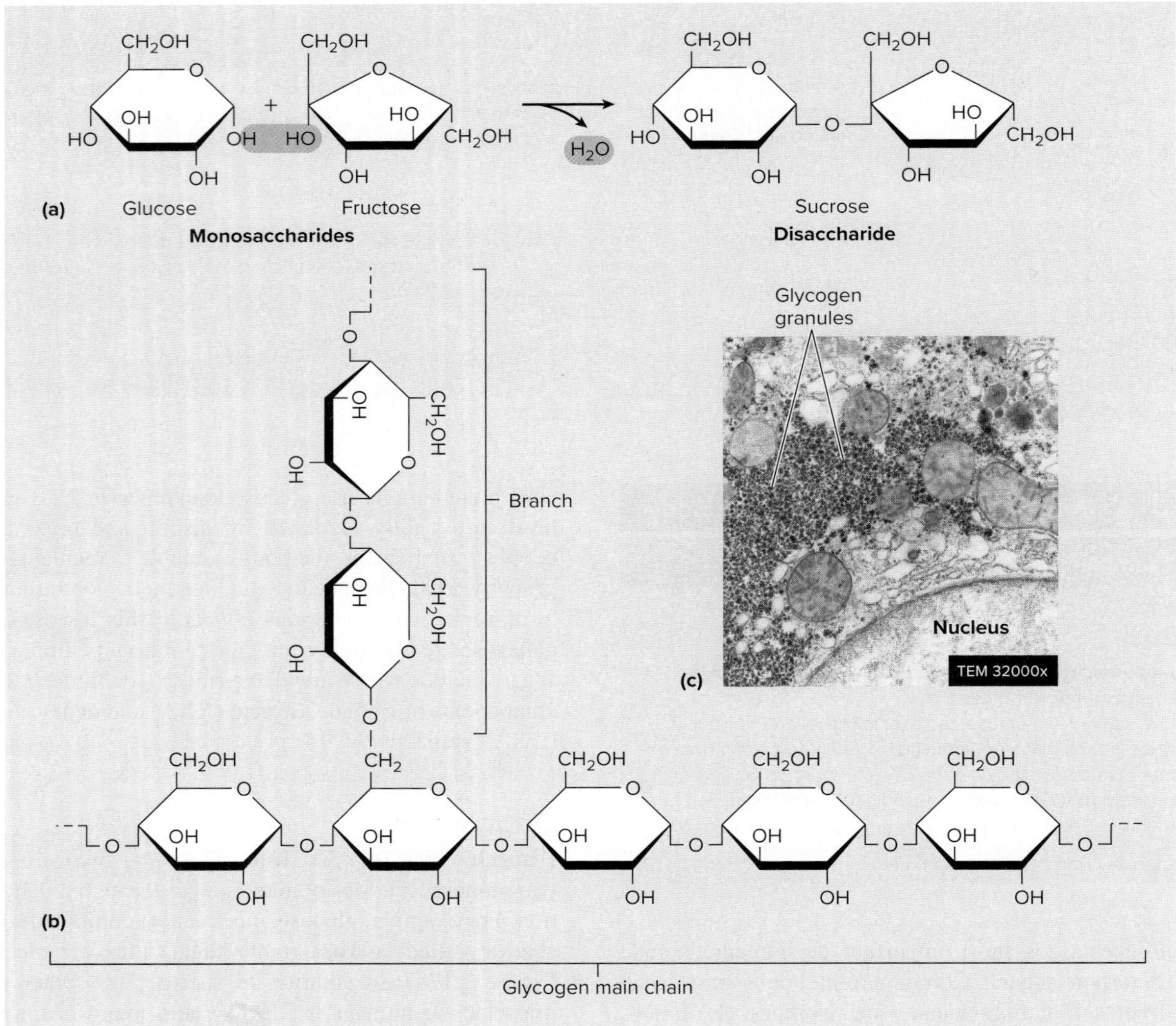

FIGURE 2.17 Carbohydrates

(*a*) Sucrose, a disaccharide, forms by a dehydration reaction involving glucose and fructose (monosaccharides). (*b*) Glycogen is a polysaccharide formed by combining many glucose molecules. (*c*) The transmission electron micrograph shows glycogen granules in a liver cell. (c) Biophoto Associates/Science source

Polysaccharides

Polysaccharides (pol-ee-SACK-ah-rides; *poly-*, many) are long chains of monosaccharides covalently linked together (figure 2.16*b*). These chains can be either straight or branched. Three important polysaccharides are glycogen, starch, and cellulose. **Glycogen,** or animal starch, is a multibranched polysaccharide composed of many glucose molecules (figure 2.17*b*). Glycogen is the main storage form of glucose in humans. Because glucose can be metabolized rapidly and the resulting energy can be used by cells, glycogen is an important energy-storage molecule. A substantial amount of the glucose that is metabolized to produce energy for muscle contraction during exercise is stored in the form of glycogen in the cells of the liver and skeletal muscles.

Starch and **cellulose** are two important polysaccharides found in plants. Like glycogen, both are composed of long chains of glucose. Starch is an energy-storage molecule in plants, similar to the role of glycogen in animals. Cellulose is an important structural component of plant cell walls. When humans ingest plants, the starch can be broken down and used as an energy source. Humans, however, do not have the digestive enzymes necessary to break down cellulose. Cellulose is eliminated in the feces, where it provides bulk. Clinically, the presence of cellulose (fiber) in our diet is important for regularity of bowel movements and has been reported to help reduce cholesterol and control blood sugar levels.

ASSESS YOUR PROGRESS

36. *Why is carbon such a versatile element?*

37. *What is the building block of carbohydrates? What are isomers?*

38. *List the 5- and 6-carbon sugars that are important to humans.*

39. *What are disaccharides and polysaccharides, and what type of reaction is used to make them?*

40. *Which carbohydrates are used for energy? What is the function of starch and cellulose in plants? What is the function of glycogen and cellulose in animals?*

Lipids

Lipids are a major group of organic molecules that are defined as being relatively insoluble in water. Lipids have many important functions in the body (table 2.7). They (1) provide protection and insulation, (2) help regulate many physiological processes, (3) form plasma membranes, and (4) act as major energy-storage molecules. Like carbohydrates, lipids are composed principally of carbon, hydrogen, and oxygen, but lipids have a lower ratio of oxygen to carbon than do carbohydrates. This makes them less polar. Consequently, lipids can be readily dissolved in nonpolar organic solvents, such as alcohol or acetone, but they are relatively insoluble in water. Some lipids also contain small amounts of other elements, such as phosphorus and nitrogen, which can aid solubility in water. The major classes of lipids are (1) fats, which are mostly triglycerides; (2) phospholipids; (3) eicosanoids; (4) steroids; and (5) fat-soluble vitamins.

TABLE 2.7 Roles of Lipids in the Body

Role	Example
Protection	Adipose tissue surrounds and pads organs.
Insulation	Adipose tissue under the skin prevents heat loss. Myelin surrounds nerve cells and electrically insulates the cells from one another.
Regulation	Steroid hormones regulate many physiological processes. For example, estrogen and testosterone are the reproductive hormones responsible for many of the differences between males and females. Prostaglandins help regulate tissue inflammation and repair.
Vitamins	Fat-soluble vitamins perform a variety of functions. Vitamin A forms retinol, which is necessary for seeing in the dark; active vitamin D promotes calcium uptake by the small intestine; vitamin E promotes wound healing; and vitamin K is necessary for the synthesis of proteins responsible for blood clotting.
Structure	Phospholipids and cholesterol are important components of the membranes of cells.
Energy	Lipids can be stored and broken down later for energy; per unit of weight, they yield more energy than carbohydrates or proteins.

Fats are a major type of lipid. Like carbohydrates, the fats humans ingest are broken down by hydrolysis reactions in cells to release energy for use by those cells. Conversely, if fat intake exceeds need, excess chemical energy from any source can be stored in the body as adipose tissue for later use. Adipose tissues also provide protection by surrounding and padding organs, and under-the-skin adipose acts as an insulator to prevent heat loss.

Triglycerides (trie-GLISS-eh-ridez) constitute 95% of the fats in the human body. Triglycerides consist of two different types of building blocks: (1) one glycerol and (2) three fatty acids. **Glycerol** is a 3-carbon molecule with a hydroxyl group attached to each carbon atom. A **fatty acid** is a straight chain of carbon atoms with a carboxyl group attached at one end (figure 2.18). A **carboxyl** (kar-BOK-sil) **group** (—COOH) consists of both an oxygen atom and a hydroxyl group attached to a carbon atom:

$$-\overset{\overset{\displaystyle O}{\|}}{C}-OH \quad \text{or} \quad HO-\overset{\overset{\displaystyle O}{\|}}{C}-$$

The carboxyl group is responsible for the acidic nature of the molecule because it releases hydrogen ions into solution. Glycerides can be described according to the number and kinds of fatty acids that combine with glycerol through dehydration reactions. Monoglycerides have one fatty acid, diglycerides have two fatty acids, and triglycerides have three fatty acids bound to glycerol.

Fatty acids differ from one another according to the length and the degree of saturation of their carbon chains. Most naturally occurring fatty acids contain an even number of carbon atoms, with 14- to 18-carbon chains the most common. *Saturation* refers to the number of hydrogen atoms in the carbon chain. A fatty acid is **saturated** if it contains only single covalent bonds

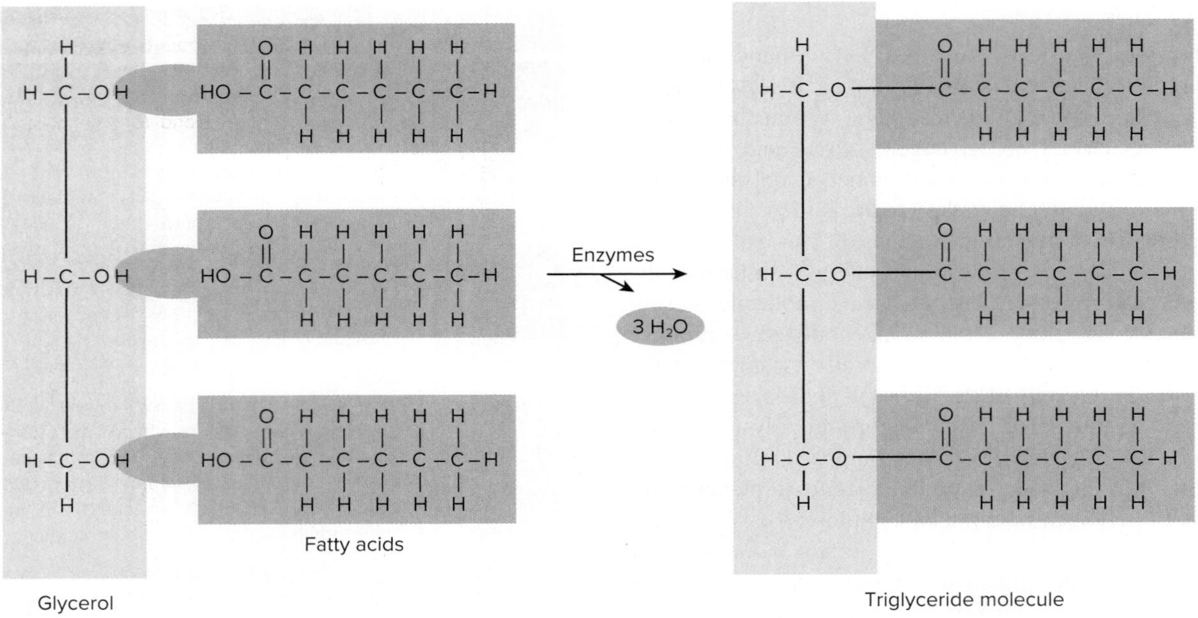

FIGURE 2.18 Triglyceride
A triglyceride is produced from a backbone of one glycerol molecule and three fatty acid molecules. One water molecule (H_2O) is given off for each covalent bond formed between a fatty acid and glycerol.

between the carbon atoms and consequently it is saturated with the maximum number of H atoms (figure 2.19*a*). Sources of saturated fats include beef, pork, whole milk, cheese, butter, eggs, coconut oil, and palm oil. The carbon chain is **unsaturated** if it has one or more double covalent bonds between carbon atoms (figure 2.19*b*). The double covalent bond introduces a kink into the carbon chain, which tends to keep them liquid at room temperature. **Monounsaturated fats,** such as olive and peanut oils, have one double covalent bond between carbon atoms. **Polyunsaturated fats,** such as safflower, sunflower, corn, and fish oils, have two or more double covalent bonds between carbon atoms. Unsaturated fats are the best type of fats in the diet because, unlike saturated fats, they do not contribute to the development of cardiovascular disease.

***Trans* fats** are unsaturated fats that have been chemically altered by the addition of hydrogen. The process makes the fats more saturated and hence more solid and stable (longer shelf life). However, the double covalent bonds that do not become saturated are changed from the usual *cis* configuration (H on the same side of the double bond) to a *trans* configuration (H on different sides). This change in structure makes the consumption of *trans* fats an even greater factor than saturated fats in the risk for cardiovascular disease.

Phospholipids are similar to triglycerides, except that one of the fatty acids bound to the glycerol is replaced by a phosphate-containing region (figure 2.20). A phospholipid is polar at the end of the molecule to which the phosphate is bound and nonpolar at the other end. The polar end of the molecule is attracted to water and is said to be hydrophilic (water-loving). The nonpolar end is repelled by water and is said to be hydrophobic (water-fearing). Phospholipids are important structural components of the membranes of cells (see figure 3.2). The presence of phospholipids with unsaturated fatty acids contributes to the fluidity of the plasma membrane (see chapter 3).

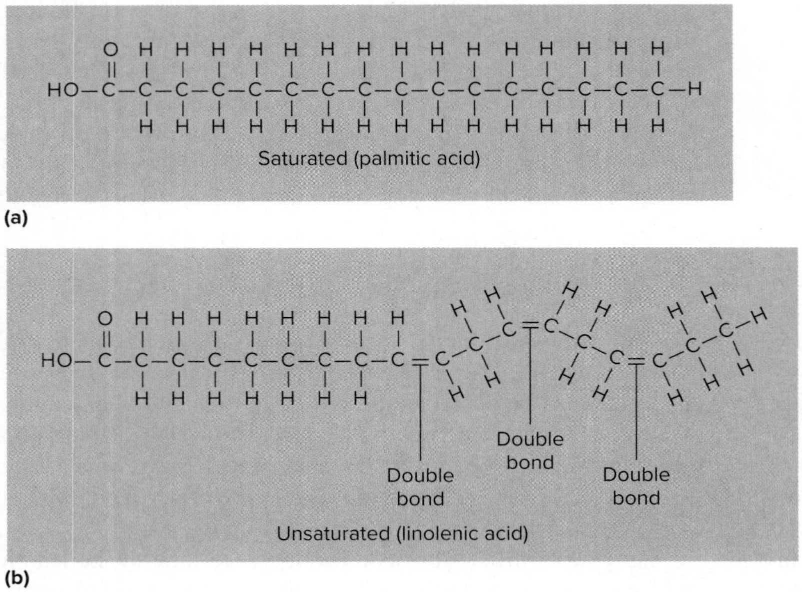

FIGURE 2.19 Saturated and Unsaturated Fatty Acids
(*a*) A saturated fatty acid contains no double bonds between the carbons. An example is palmitic acid. (*b*) An unsaturated fatty acid has double bonds between the carbons. An example is linolenic acid, which has three double bonds.

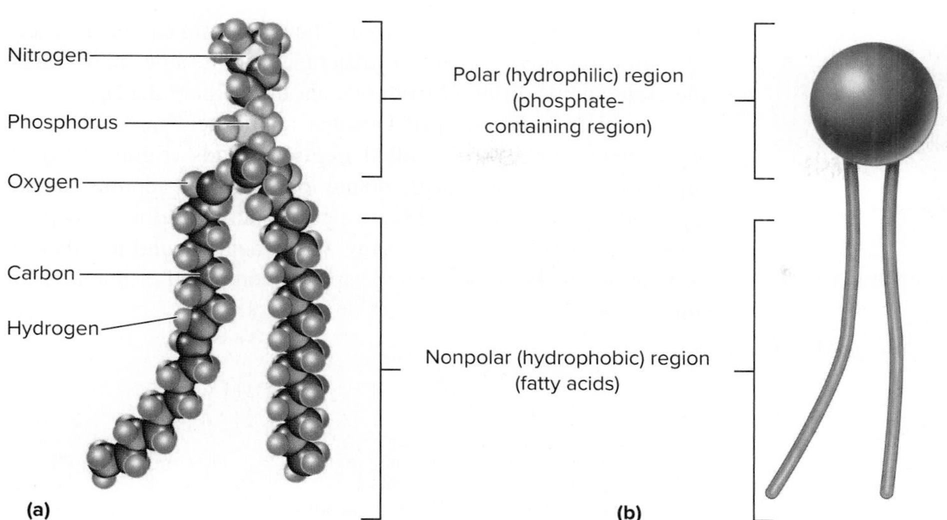

FIGURE 2.20 Phospholipids

(*a*) A molecular model of a phospholipid. The phosphate-containing region usually includes a nitrogen. The bent carbon chain indicates a kink from a double covalent bond. (*b*) A simplified depiction of a phospholipid.

The **eicosanoids** (EYE-koh-sah-noyds) are a group of important chemicals derived from fatty acids. They include **prostaglandins** (PROS-tah-GLAN-dins), **thromboxanes** (THROM-bok-zanes), and **leukotrienes** (loo-koh-TRY-eens). Eicosanoids are made in most cells and are important regulatory molecules. Among their numerous effects is their role in the response of tissues to injuries. Prostaglandins have been implicated in regulating the secretion of certain hormones, blood clotting, some reproductive functions, and many other processes. Many of the therapeutic effects of aspirin and other anti-inflammatory drugs result from their ability to inhibit prostaglandin synthesis.

Steroids are lipids that have four ringlike structures (figure 2.21). Steroids differ in chemical structure from other lipid molecules, but their solubility characteristics are similar. **Cholesterol** is a particularly important steroid because it serves as the starting point for the synthesis of many other steroid molecules.

Steroids derived from cholesterol include (1) bile salts (aid in lipid digestion and absorption) and (2) the reproductive steroid hormones estrogen, progesterone, and testosterone. In addition, cholesterol is an important component of the plasma membrane of all cells in the body. Although high levels of cholesterol in the blood increase the risk for cardiovascular disease, a certain amount of cholesterol is vital for normal function.

Another class of lipids is the **fat-soluble vitamins.** Their structures are not closely related to one another, but they are nonpolar molecules essential for many normal body functions.

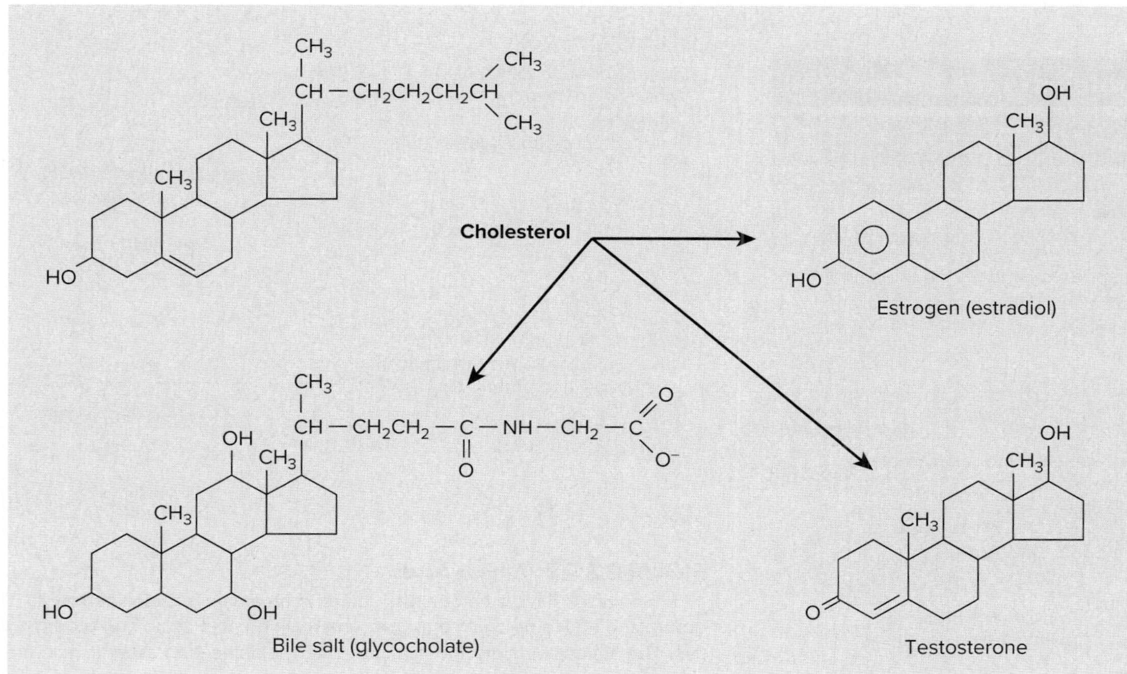

FIGURE 2.21 Steroids

Steroids are four-ringed molecules that differ from one another according to the groups attached to the rings. Cholesterol, the most common steroid, can be modified to produce other steroids.

ASSESS YOUR PROGRESS

41. *State six roles of lipids in the body, and give an example of each.*
42. *What is the most common fat in the body, and what are its basic building blocks?*
43. *What is the difference between a saturated fat and an unsaturated fat? What is a trans fat?*
44. *Describe the structure of a phospholipid. Which end of the molecule is hydrophilic? Explain why.*
45. *What are three examples of eicosanoids and their general functions?*
46. *Why is cholesterol an important steroid?*

Proteins

All **proteins** are organic macromolecules that contain carbon, hydrogen, oxygen, and nitrogen bound together by covalent bonds. Most proteins also contain some sulfur. In addition, some proteins contain small amounts of phosphorus, iron, and iodine. Proteins have many important functions in the body (table 2.8): (1) regulate body processes, (2) act as transportation molecules, (3) provide protection, (4) help muscles contract, and (5) provide structure and energy. The molecular mass of proteins can be very large. For the purpose of comparison, the molecular mass of water is approximately 18, sodium chloride 58, and glucose 180, but the molecular mass of proteins ranges from approximately 1000 to several million.

Protein Structure

The basic building blocks for proteins are the 20 **amino acid** (ah-MEE-noh ASS-id) molecules. Each amino acid has an amine (ah-MEEN) group ($—NH_2$), a carboxyl group ($—COOH$), a hydrogen atom, and a side chain designated by the symbol **R** attached to the same carbon atom. The side chain can be a variety of chemical structures, and the differences in the side chains make the amino acids different from one another (figure 2.22).

Covalent bonds formed between amino acid molecules during protein synthesis are called **peptide bonds** (figure 2.23). A dipeptide is two amino acids bound together by a peptide bond, a tripeptide is three amino acids covalently bound together by peptide bonds, and a polypeptide is many amino acids bound together by peptide bonds. Proteins are polypeptides composed of hundreds of amino acids.

TABLE 2.8 Roles of Proteins in the Body

Role	Example
Regulation	Enzymes control chemical reactions. Hormones regulate many physiological processes; for example, insulin affects glucose transport into cells.
Transport	Hemoglobin transports O_2 and CO_2 in the blood. Plasma proteins transport many substances in the blood. Proteins in plasma membranes control the movement of materials into and out of the cell.
Protection	Antibodies protect against microorganisms and other foreign substances.
Contraction	Actin and myosin in muscle are responsible for muscle contraction.
Structure	Collagen fibers form a structural framework in many parts of the body. Keratin adds strength to skin, hair, and nails.
Energy	Proteins can be broken down for energy; per unit of weight, they yield as much energy as carbohydrates do.

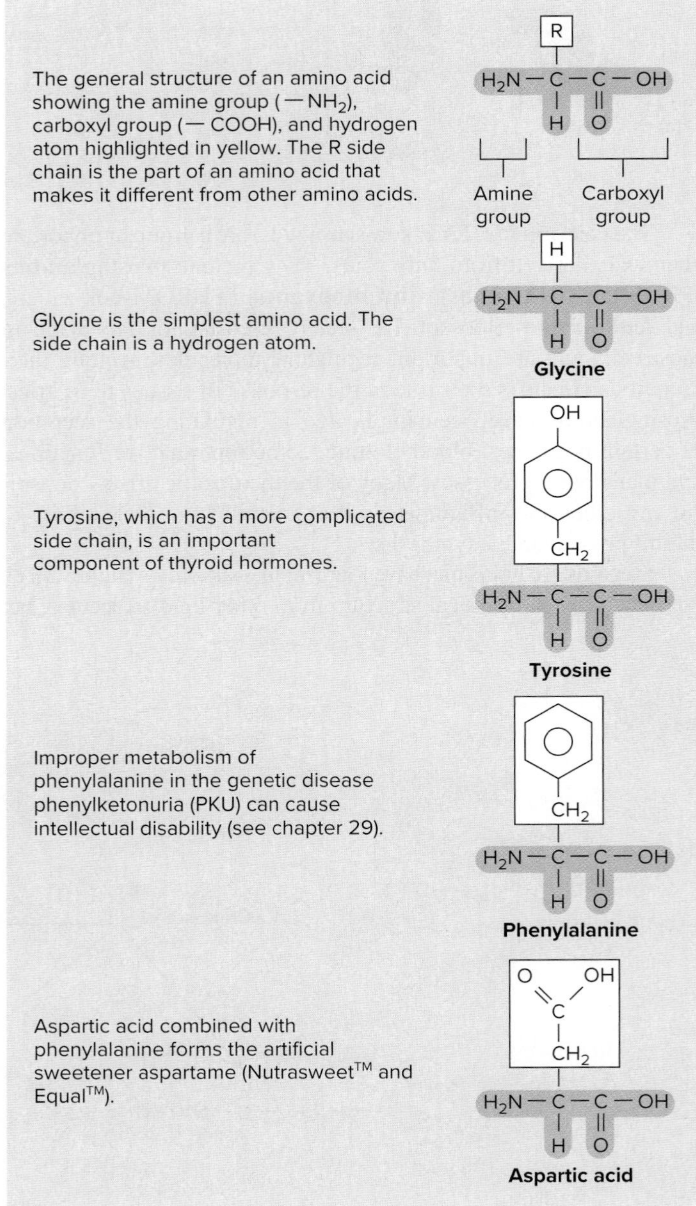

FIGURE 2.22 Amino Acids
All amino acids have a common structure of an amine group, a carboxyl group, and an R side chain that gives each amino acid its unique properties. The amino acids glycine, tyrosine, phenylalanine, and aspartic acid are shown as representative examples.

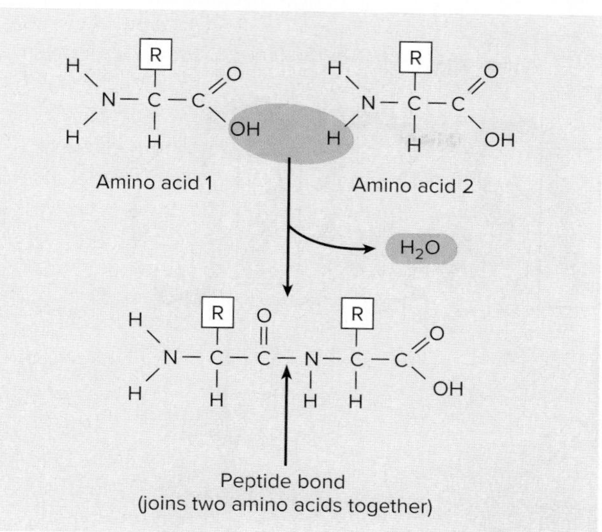

FIGURE 2.23 Peptide Bond

A dehydration reaction between two amino acids forms a dipeptide and a water molecule. The covalent bond between the amino acids is called a peptide bond.

The **primary structure** of a protein is determined by the sequence of the amino acids bound by peptide bonds (figure 2.24*a*). The potential number of different protein molecules is enormous because 20 different amino acids exist, and each amino acid can be located at any position along a polypeptide chain. The characteristics of the amino acids in a protein ultimately determine the three-dimensional shape of the protein, and the shape of the protein determines its function. A change in one or a few amino acids in the primary structure can alter protein function, usually making the protein less functional or even nonfunctional.

The **secondary structure** results from the folding or bending of the polypeptide chain caused by the hydrogen bonds between amino acids (figure 2.24*b*). Two common shapes that result are pleated (folded) sheets and helices (sing. helix, coil). If the hydrogen bonds that maintain the shape of the protein are broken, the protein becomes denatured and nonfunctional. **Denaturation** is the change in shape caused by the breaking of hydrogen bonds. It can be caused by abnormally high temperatures or changes in the pH of body fluids. An everyday example of denaturation is the change in the proteins of egg whites when they are cooked.

The **tertiary structure** results from large-scale folding of the protein driven by interactions within the protein and with the immediate environment (figure 2.24*c*). These interactions allow the pleated sheets and helices of the secondary structure to be arranged and organized relative to each other. Some amino acids are quite polar (hydrophilic) and therefore form hydrogen bonds with water. The polar portions of proteins tend to remain unfolded, maximizing their contact with water, whereas the less polar (hydrophobic) regions tend to fold into a globular shape, minimizing their contact with water. The formation of covalent bonds between sulfur atoms located at different locations along the polypeptide chain produces disulfide bridges that hold different regions of the protein together in the tertiary structure. The tertiary structure determines the shape of a **domain,** which is a folded sequence of 100–200 amino acids within a protein. The domain structure dictates protein functions. For example, fibrous proteins are relatively rigid and hence often play structural roles, while globular proteins tend to be more flexible and play regulatory roles as enzymes. Changes in the primary or secondary structure that affect the shape of the domain can change protein function.

The **quaternary structure** results from the association of two or more proteins to form a functional unit (figure 2.24*d*). The individual proteins are called subunits. Interactions between subunits result in the quaternary structure.

In summary, protein structure is determined by the following sequence of events.

1. Primary structure: bonding together of a specific sequence of amino acids.
2. Secondary structure: hydrogen bonding between neighboring amino acids within the primary structure polypeptide causes it to fold and bend into helices and sheets.
3. Tertiary structure: hydrophilic and hydrophobic interactions drives large-scale folding of the secondary structure polypeptide. The tertiary structure is stabilized by disulfide bridges.
4. Quaternary structure: chemical interactions between separate tertiary structure polypeptides form multisubunit complexes. Not all proteins have a quaternary structure.

Enzymes

Proteins perform many roles in the body, including acting as enzymes. An **enzyme** is a protein catalyst that increases the rate at which a chemical reaction proceeds without the enzyme being permanently changed. Synthesis and decomposition reactions in the body require enzymes to proceed at a rate that supports life. The **active site** is the region of the enzyme that binds reactants and catalyzes their conversion to products. According to the **lock-and-key model** of enzyme action, a reaction occurs when the reactants (key) bind to the active site (lock) on the enzyme. This view of enzymes and reactants as rigid structures fitting together has been modified by the **induced fit model,** in which the enzyme is able to change shape slightly and better fit the reactants. The enzyme is like a glove that does not achieve its functional shape until the hand (reactants) moves into place.

At the active site, reactants are brought into close proximity and the reaction occurs (figure 2.25). After the reactants combine, they are released from the active site, and the enzyme is unchanged and capable of catalyzing additional reactions. The activation energy required for a chemical reaction to occur is lowered by enzymes (see figure 2.13) because they orient the reactants toward each other in such a way that a chemical reaction is more likely to occur.

Slight changes in the structure of an enzyme can destroy the active site's ability to function. Enzymes are very sensitive to changes in temperature or pH, which can break the hydrogen bonds within them. As a result, the relationship between amino acids changes, thereby producing a change in shape that prevents the enzyme from functioning normally.

FUNDAMENTAL **Figure**

(a) Primary structure—the amino acid sequence. A protein consists of a chain of different amino acids (represented by different-colored spheres).

(b) Secondary structure results from hydrogen bonding (*dotted red lines*). The hydrogen bonds cause the amino acid chain to form pleated (folded) sheets or helices (coils).

(c) Tertiary structure with secondary folding caused by interactions within the polypeptide and its immediate environment

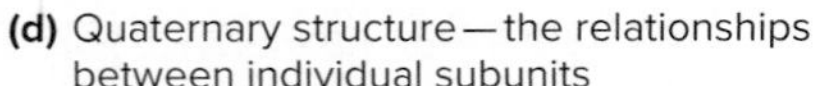

(d) Quaternary structure—the relationships between individual subunits

FIGURE 2.24 Protein Structure

When a chain of amino acids is formed, chemical interactions between amino acids cause the entire chain to fold upon itself in predictable patterns. (*a*) Primary structure results from the amino acid sequence. (*b*) Secondary structure results from hydrogen bonds. (*c*) Tertiary structure results from folding of the protein. (*d*) Quaternary structure results from association of subunits.

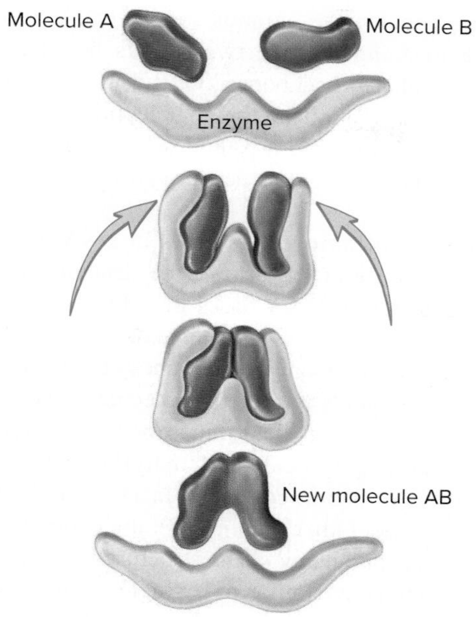

FIGURE 2.25 Enzyme Action

The enzyme brings the two reacting molecules together. After the reaction, the unaltered enzyme can be used again.

To be functional, some enzymes require additional, nonprotein substances called **cofactors.** A cofactor can be an ion, such as magnesium or zinc, or an organic molecule. Cofactors that are organic molecules, such as certain vitamins, may be referred to as **coenzymes.** Cofactors normally form part of the enzyme's active site and are required to make the enzyme functional.

The remarkable specificity of enzymes for only certain reactants is due to the unique three-dimensional structure of each active site. Therefore, each enzyme catalyzes a specific chemical reaction and no others. This specificity has also allowed scientists to design drugs that block specific active sites to treat diseases, such as Gleevec® for treating certain cancers. An important consequence of the specificity of active sites is that many different enzymes are needed to catalyze the many chemical reactions of the body. Enzymes are often named by adding the suffix *-ase* to the name of the molecules on which they act. For example, an enzyme that catalyzes the breakdown of lipids is a **lipase** (LIE-pase), and an enzyme that breaks down proteins is a **protease** (PROH-tee-ayse).

Enzymes control the rate at which most chemical reactions proceed in living systems. Consequently, they control essentially all cellular activities. At the same time, the activity of enzymes themselves is regulated by several mechanisms within the cells. Some mechanisms control the enzyme concentration by influencing the rate at which the enzymes are synthesized; others alter the activity of existing enzymes. Much of our knowledge about the regulation of cellular activity involves understanding how enzyme activity is controlled.

ASSESS YOUR PROGRESS

47. *What are the building blocks of proteins? What type of bond chemically connects these building blocks? What is the importance of the R group?*
48. *What determines the primary, secondary, tertiary, and quaternary structures of a protein?*
49. *What is denaturation? Name two factors that can cause it.*
50. *Compare the lock-and-key and the induced fit models of enzyme activity. What determines the active site of an enzyme? State the difference between a cofactor and a coenzyme.*

Nucleic Acids: DNA and RNA

The **nucleic** (noo-KLEE-ik, KLAY-ik) **acids** are large molecules composed of carbon, hydrogen, oxygen, nitrogen, and phosphorus. There are two types of nucleic acids: (1) **Deoxyribonucleic** (dee-OCK-see-RYE-boh-noo-KLEE-ik) **acid (DNA)**, which is the genetic material of cells. Copies of DNA are transferred from one generation of cells to the next generation. DNA contains the information that determines the structure of proteins. (2) **Ribonucleic** (RYE-boh-noo-KLEE-ik) **acid (RNA)**, which is structurally related to DNA, and important in protein synthesis. In chapter 3, we describe the means by which DNA and RNA direct the functions of the cell.

The basic building blocks of DNA and RNA are called **nucleotides** (NOO-klee-oh-tides). Nucleotides are composed of (1) a monosaccharide, (2) a nitrogenous base, and (3) a phosphate group (figure 2.26). The monosaccharides are **deoxyribose** for DNA and **ribose** for RNA. The **nitrogenous bases** consist of carbon and nitrogen atoms organized into rings. They are bases because the nitrogen atoms tend to take up H^+ from solution. The nitrogenous bases are (1) cytosine (SIGH-toh-seen; C), (2) thymine (THIGH-meen, THIGH-min; T),

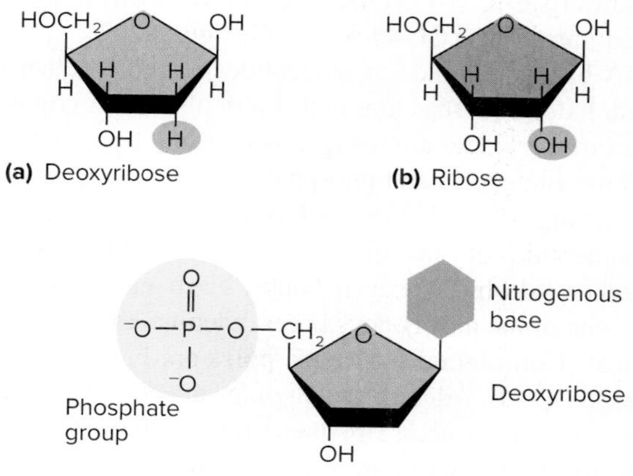

FIGURE 2.26 Components of Nucleotides

(*a*) Deoxyribose sugar, which forms nucleotides used in DNA production. (*b*) Ribose sugar, which forms nucleotides used in RNA production. Note that deoxyribose is ribose minus an oxygen atom. (*c*) A deoxyribonucleotide consists of deoxyribose, a nitrogenous base, and a phosphate group.

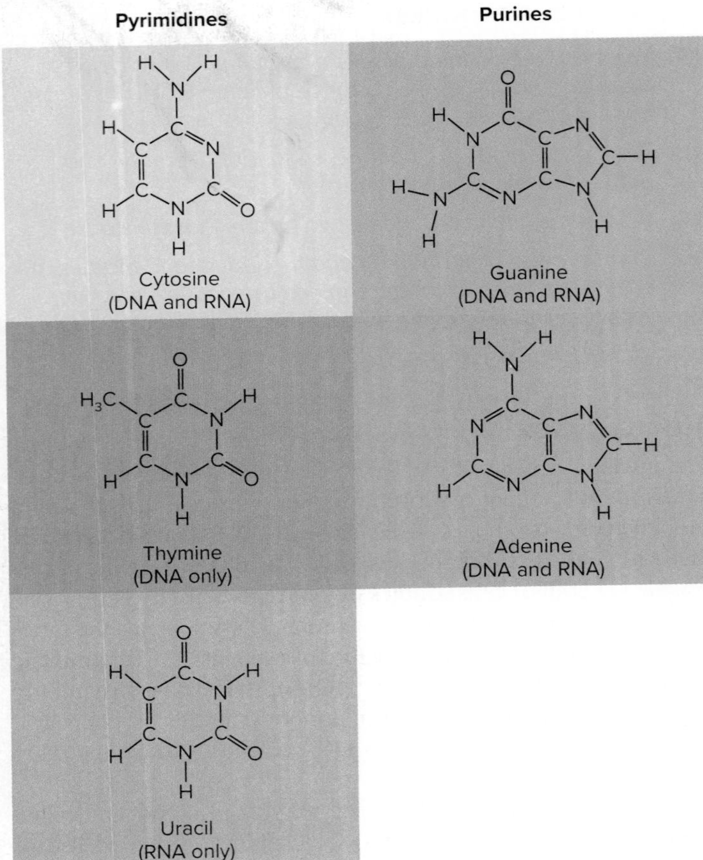

FIGURE 2.27 Nitrogenous Bases
The organic bases found in nucleic acids are separated into two groups. Pyrimidines are single-ringed molecules, and purines are double-ringed molecules.

(3) uracil (YOOR-ah-sil; U), (4) guanine (GWAHN-een; G), and (5) adenine (AD-eh-neen; A). Bases with a single ring are called pyrimidines (pye-RIM-i-deenz; C, U, T). Bases with double rings are called purines (PYOO-reenz; A, G; figure 2.27).

DNA has two strands of nucleotides joined together to form a twisted, ladderlike structure called a double helix (figure 2.28). The sides of the ladder are formed by covalent bonds between the deoxyribose molecules and phosphate groups of adjacent nucleotides. The rungs of the ladder are formed by the nitrogenous bases of the nucleotides of one side connected to the nitrogenous bases of the other side by hydrogen bonds. Each nucleotide of DNA contains one of the nitrogenous bases: adenine, thymine, cytosine, or guanine. **Complementary base pairs** are bases held together by hydrogen bonds. Adenine and thymine are complementary base pairs because the structure of these bases allows two hydrogen bonds to form between them. Cytosine and guanine are complementary base pairs because the structure of these bases allows three hydrogen bonds to form between them. The two strands of a DNA molecule are said to be complementary. If the sequence of bases in one DNA strand is known, the sequence of bases in the other strand can be predicted because of complementary base pairing.

The two nucleotide strands of a DNA molecule are **antiparallel,** meaning that the two strands lie side by side but their sugar-phosphate "backbones" extend in opposite directions because of the orientation of their nucleotides (figure 2.28). A nucleotide has a 5′ end and a 3′ end. The prime sign is used to indicate the carbon atoms of the deoxyribose sugar, which are numbered 1′ to 5′.

The sequence of nitrogenous bases in DNA is a "code" that stores information used to determine the structures and functions of cells. A sequence of DNA bases that directs the synthesis of proteins or RNA molecules is called a **gene** (see chapter 3, section 3.9, for more information on genes). Genes determine the type and sequence of amino acids in protein molecules. Because enzymes are proteins, DNA structure determines the rate and type of chemical reactions that occur in cells by controlling enzyme structure. Therefore, the information contained in DNA ultimately defines all cellular activities. Other proteins that are coded by DNA, such as collagen, determine many of the structural features of humans.

RNA's structure is similar to a single strand of DNA. Like DNA, four different nucleotides make up the RNA molecule, and the nitrogenous bases are the same, except that thymine is replaced with uracil (see figure 2.27). Uracil can bind only to adenine.

Adenosine Triphosphate

Adenosine triphosphate (ah-DEN-o-seen try-FOS-fate; **ATP**) is the most important molecule for storing and providing energy in all living organisms. ATP consists of (1) adenosine (ribose with adenine) and (2) three phosphate groups (figure 2.29). The close proximity of the three negatively charged phosphate groups makes ATP a very unstable molecule. As a result, cleavage of the phosphate bonds releases a large amount of energy; hence, the second and third phosphate bonds are referred to as "high-energy" bonds. In particular, the potential energy stored in the covalent bond between the second and third phosphate groups of ATP is important to living organisms because it provides the energy used in nearly all of the chemical reactions within cells. Removal of the third phosphate generates **adenosine diphosphate (ADP),** which has only two phosphate groups and much less potential energy than ATP.

The catabolism of glucose and other nutrient molecules results in chemical reactions that release energy. Some of that energy is used to synthesize ATP from ADP and an inorganic phosphate group (P_i):

$$\text{ADP} + P_i + \text{Energy (from catabolism)} \rightarrow \text{ATP}$$

The transfer of energy from nutrient molecules to ATP involves a series of oxidation-reduction reactions in which a high-energy electron is transferred from one molecule to the next molecule in the series. In chapter 25, the oxidation-reduction reactions of metabolism are considered in greater detail.

Once produced, ATP is used to provide energy for other chemical reactions (anabolism) or to drive cell processes, such as muscle contraction. In the process, ATP is converted back to ADP and an inorganic phosphate group:

$$\text{ATP} \rightarrow \text{ADP} + P_i + \text{Energy (for anabolism and other cell processes)}$$

Solution Concentrations

A. One measurement of solution concentration is the osmole, which contains Avogadro's number (6.022 × 1023) of particles (i.e., atoms, ions, or molecules) in 1 kilogram of water.

B. A milliosmole is 1/1000 of an osmole.

Acids and Bases

A. Acids are proton (H^+) donors, and bases (e.g., OH^-) are proton acceptors.

B. A strong acid or base almost completely dissociates in water. A weak acid or base partially dissociates.

C. A neutral solution has an equal number of H^+ and OH^- and is assigned a pH of 7.

D. Acidic solutions, in which the number of H^+ is greater than the number of OH^-, have pH values less than 7.

E. Basic, or alkaline, solutions have more OH^- than H^+ and a pH greater than 7.

F. A salt is a molecule consisting of a cation other than H^+ and an anion other than OH^-. Salts form when acids react with bases.

G. A buffer is a solution of a conjugate acid-base pair that resists changes in pH when acids or bases are added to the solution.

22. *A solution with a pH of 5 is ________ and contains ________ H^+ than (as) a neutral solution.*
    - *a. a base, more*
    - *b. a base, fewer*
    - *c. an acid, more*
    - *d. an acid, fewer*
    - *e. neutral, the same number of*

23. *A buffer*
    - *a. slows down chemical reactions.*
    - *b. speeds up chemical reactions.*
    - *c. increases the pH of a solution.*
    - *d. maintains a relatively constant pH.*
    - *e. works by forming salts.*

24. *A conjugate acid-base pair* 

    - *a. acts as a buffer.*
    - *b. can combine with H^+ in a solution.*
    - *c. can release H^+ to combine with OH^-.*
    - *d. describes carbonic acid (H_2CO_3) and bicarbonate ions (HCO_3^-).*
    - *e. All of these are correct.*

25. *Solution A is a strong acid of pH 2, and solution B is an equally strong base of pH 8. Each chemical can donate or receive a single proton. If equal amounts of solutions A and B are mixed, is the resulting solution acidic or basic?*

26. *Carbon dioxide that accumulates in the blood can become toxic, in part because it alters the blood pH. Some of the carbon dioxide molecules react with water to form carbonic acid ($CO_2 + H_2O \rightarrow H_2CO_3$). Ned can swim across the swimming pool under water. Before diving into the water, he breathes rapidly for a few seconds, and while he is under the water, he does not breathe at all. Explain how the pH of his blood changes while breathing rapidly and while swimming under water. Also explain why the pH of his blood does not change dramatically.*

Oxygen and Carbon Dioxide

Oxygen is necessary for the reactions th om food molecules in living organisms. When the org e broken down during metabolism, carbon dioxide and en eased.

2.4 Organic Chemistry

Organic molecules contain carbon and h gen atoms bound together by covalent bonds.

Carbohydrates

A. Monosaccharides are the basic building blocks of other carbohydrates. Examples are ribose, deoxyribose, glucose, fructose, and galactose. Glucose is an especially important source of energy.

B. Disaccharide molecules are formed by dehydration reactions between two monosaccharides. Examples of disaccharides are sucrose, lactose, and maltose.

C. A polysaccharide is composed of many monosaccharides bound together to form a long chain. Examples include cellulose, starch, and glycogen.

27. *The polysaccharide used for energy storage in the human body is*
    - *a. cellulose.*
    - *b. glycogen.*
    - *c. lactose.*
    - *d. sucrose.*
    - *e. starch.*

Lipids

A. Triglycerides (fats) are composed of glycerol and fatty acids and store energy. Fatty acids are straight chains of carbon molecules with a carboxyl group. Fatty acids can be saturated (single covalent bonds) or unsaturated (double covalent bonds).

B. Phospholipids are lipids in which a fatty acid is replaced by a phosphate-containing molecule. Phospholipids are a major structural component of plasma membranes.

C. Steroids are lipids composed of four interconnected ring molecules. Examples are cholesterol, bile salts, and sex hormones.

D. Other lipids include fat-soluble vitamins, prostaglandins, thromboxanes, and leukotrienes.

28. *The basic units or building blocks of triglycerides are* 

    - *a. simple sugars (monosaccharides).*
    - *b. double sugars (disaccharides).*
    - *c. amino acids.*
    - *d. glycerol and fatty acids.*
    - *e. nucleotides.*

29. *A ________ fatty acid has one double covalent bond between carbon atoms.*
    - *a. cholesterol*
    - *b. monounsaturated*
    - *c. phospholipid*
    - *d. polyunsaturated*
    - *e. saturated*

Prot[illegible]

A. The build[illegible]otein are amino acids, which are joined by peptide[illegible]

B. The number, ki[illegible]rangement of amino acids determine the primary structure [illegible]ein. Hydrogen bonds between amino acids determine secondary[illegible]ure, and hydrogen bonds between amino acids and water deter[illegible] tertiary structure. Interactions between different protein subunits determine quaternary structure.

C. Enzymes are protein catalysts that speed up chemical reactions by lowering their activation energy. The active sites of enzymes bind only to specific reactants.

30. *The ________ structure of a protein results from the folding of the pleated sheets or helices.*

a. primary
b. secondary
c. tertiary
d. quaternary

31. *According to the lock-and-key model of enzyme action,* Remember

a. reactants must first be heated.
b. enzyme shape is not important.
c. each enzyme can catalyze many types of reactions.
d. reactants must bind to an active site on the enzyme.
e. enzymes control only a small number of reactions in the cell.

32. *Using the materials commonly found in a kitchen, explain how to distinguish between a protein and a lipid.* Apply

Nucleic Acids: DNA and RNA

A. The basic unit of nucleic acids is the nucleotide, which is a monosaccharide with an attached phosphate and a nitrogenous base.

B. DNA nucleotides contain the monosaccharide deoxyribose and the nitrogenous base adenine, thymine, guanine, or cytosine. DNA occurs as a double strand of joined nucleotides. Each strand is complementary and antiparallel to the other strand.

C. A gene is a sequence of DNA nucleotides that determines the structure of a protein or RNA.

D. RNA nucleotides are composed of the monosaccharide ribose. The nitrogenous bases are the same as for DNA except that thymine is replaced with uracil.

33. *DNA molecules*

a. contain genes.
b. contain a single strand of nucleotides.
c. contain the nucleotide uracil.
d. are of three different types that have roles in protein synthesis.
e. contain up to 100 nitrogenous bases.

Adenosine Triphosphate

Adenosine triphosphate (ATP) stores energy derived from catabolism. The energy released from ATP is used in anabolism and other cell processes.

34. *ATP* Remember

a. is formed by the addition of a phosphate group to ADP.
b. is formed with energy released during catabolic reactions.
c. provides the energy for anabolic reactions.
d. contains three phosphate groups.
e. All of these are correct.

Answers to this chapter's odd-numbered Concept Check questions appear in Appendix F.

CHAPTER 3

Cell Biology

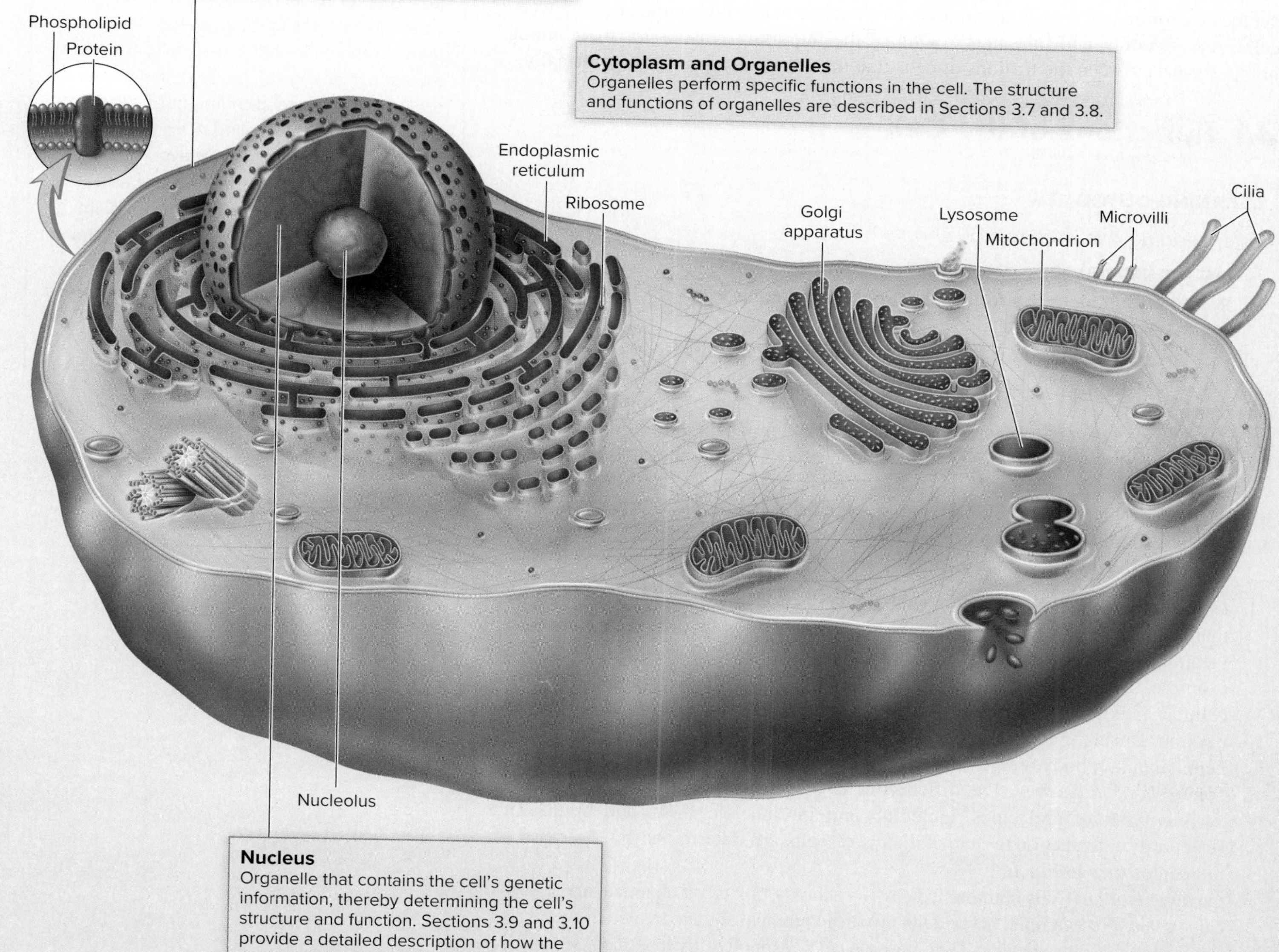

The cell is the basic unit of life and is composed of a plasma membrane and the cytoplasm, which includes a nucleus and cytoplasmic organelles.

The human [illegible]posed of trillions of cells. If each of these cells were the size of a sta[illegible]ck, the colossal human statue erected from those bricks would be 6 mi[illegible]! In reality, an average-sized cell is only one-fifth the size of the smallest dot you c[illegible] make on a sheet of paper with a sharp pencil. Although they are minute, cells act as complex factories to carry out the functions of life.

All of the cells of an individual originate from a single fertilized cell. During development, cell division and specialization give rise to a wide variety of cell types, such as nerve, muscle, bone, and blood cells. Each cell type has important characteristics that are critical to normal body function, including cell metabolism and energy use; synthesis of molecules, such as proteins and nucleic acids; communication between cells; reproduction; and inheritance. One of the important reasons for maintaining homeostasis is to keep the trillions of cells that form the body functioning normally.

Learn to Predict

Carlos always carries a water bottle, and he never likes to be too far from a restroom. Carlos has diabetes insipidus, an incurable disease that causes his kidneys to produce an unusually large volume of dilute urine. To keep his body fluids in a state of homeostasis (see chapter 1), Carlos has to drink enough water and solutes to replace what he loses as urine. Diabetes insipidus results from a gene mutation, a change in the DNA, that prevents the kidneys from responding normally to an important hormone, called ADH, that regulates water loss from the kidneys.

After reading about cell structure and gene expression in this chapter, explain how Carlos's condition developed at the cellular level.

Answers to this question and the chapter's odd-numbered Predict questions can be found in Appendix E.

3.1 Functions of the Cell

LEARNING OUTCOMES

After reading this section, you should be able to

A. **List the general parts of a cell.**

B. **Relate and explain the four main functions of cells.**

Cells are the basic units of all living things, including humans. Cells of the human body are diverse in size, structure, and function, yet they share several common characteristics (figure 3.1; table 3.1). The **plasma** (PLAZ-mah) **membrane,** or *cell membrane,* forms the outer boundary of the cell, through which the cell interacts with its external environment. The **nucleus** (NYU-klee-us / NOO-klee-us) is usually located centrally; it directs cell activities, most of which take place in the **cytoplasm** (SIGH-toh-plazm), located between the plasma membrane and the nucleus. Within cells, specialized structures called **organelles** (OR-gah-nellz) perform specific functions.

The characteristic functions of the cell include the following:

1. *Cell metabolism and energy use.* Cell metabolism involves all chemical reactions that occur within a cell. These metabolic reactions often involve energy transfers, meaning the energy released by one reaction is then used in another reaction. For example, the energy released from the digestion of large nutrient molecules fuels cellular activities, such as the synthesis of other molecules and muscle cell contraction. During many metabolic reactions, energy is also released as heat, which helps maintain body temperature.
2. *Synthesis of molecules.* The different cells of the body synthesize, or produce, various types of molecules, including proteins, nucleic acids, and lipids. The structural and functional characteristics of cells are determined by the types of molecules they produce.
3. *Communication.* Cells communicate with each other by using chemical and electrical signals. For example, nerve cells produce chemical signals by which they communicate with muscle cells. Then, muscle cells respond to the chemical signals by contracting or relaxing.
4. *Reproduction and inheritance.* Most cells contain a complete copy of all the genetic information (DNA molecules) of the individual. This genetic information ultimately determines the structural and functional characteristics of the cell. As a person grows, cells divide to produce new cells, each containing the same genetic information. Inheritance refers to the transmission of traits from one generation to the next. Specialized cells called gametes are responsible for the transmission of genetic information to the next generation.

Module 2
Cells & Chemistry

TABLE 3.1 Summary of Cell Parts and Functions

Cell Parts	Structure	Function
Plasma Membrane	Lipid bilayer composed of phospholipids and cholesterol; proteins are incorporated or attached to the lipid bilayer	Functions as the outer boundary of the cell; controls the entry and exit of substances; receptor proteins function in intercellular communication; marker molecules enable cells to recognize one another
Nucleus	Enclosed by nuclear envelope, a double membrane with nuclear pores; contains chromatin (dispersed, thin strands of DNA and associated proteins), which condenses to become visible mitotic chromosomes during cell division; also contains one or more nucleoli, dense bodies consisting of ribosomal RNA and proteins	Acts as the control center of the cell; DNA within the nucleus regulates protein synthesis and therefore the chemical reactions of the cell
Cytoplasmic Organelles		
Ribosome	Ribosomal RNA and proteins form large and small subunits; some are attached to endoplasmic reticulum, whereas others (free ribosomes) are distributed throughout the cytoplasm	Serves as site of protein synthesis
Rough endoplasmic reticulum	Membranous tubules and flattened sacs with attached ribosomes	Synthesizes proteins, which are usually transported to Golgi apparatus
Smooth endoplasmic reticulum	Membranous tubules and flattened sacs with no attached ribosomes	Manufactures lipids and carbohydrates; detoxifies harmful chemicals; stores calcium
Golgi apparatus	Flattened membrane sacs stacked on each other	Modifies, packages, and distributes proteins and lipids for secretion or internal use
Lysosome	Membrane-bound vesicle pinched off Golgi apparatus	Contains digestive enzymes
Peroxisome	Membrane-bound vesicle	Serves as one site of lipid and amino acid degradation; breaks down hydrogen peroxide
Proteasomes	Tubelike protein complexes in the cytoplasm	Break down proteins in the cytoplasm
Mitochondria	Spherical, rod-shaped, or threadlike structures; enclosed by double membrane; inner membrane forms projections called cristae	Are major sites of ATP synthesis when O_2 is available
Centrioles	Pair of cylindrical organelles consisting of triplets of parallel microtubules; located in the centrosome, a specialized area of the cytoplasm where microtubule formation occurs	Serve as centers for microtubule formation; determine cell polarity during cell division; form the basal bodies of cilia and flagella
Extensions of plasma membrane		
Cilia	Extensions of the plasma membrane containing doublets of parallel microtubules; 10 μm in length	Move materials over the surface of cells
Flagellum	Extension of the plasma membrane containing doublets of parallel microtubules; 55 μm in length	In humans, propels spermatozoa
Microvilli	Extensions of the plasma membrane containing microfilaments	Increase surface area of the plasma membrane for absorption and secretion; modified to form sensory receptors

FUNDAMENTAL Figure

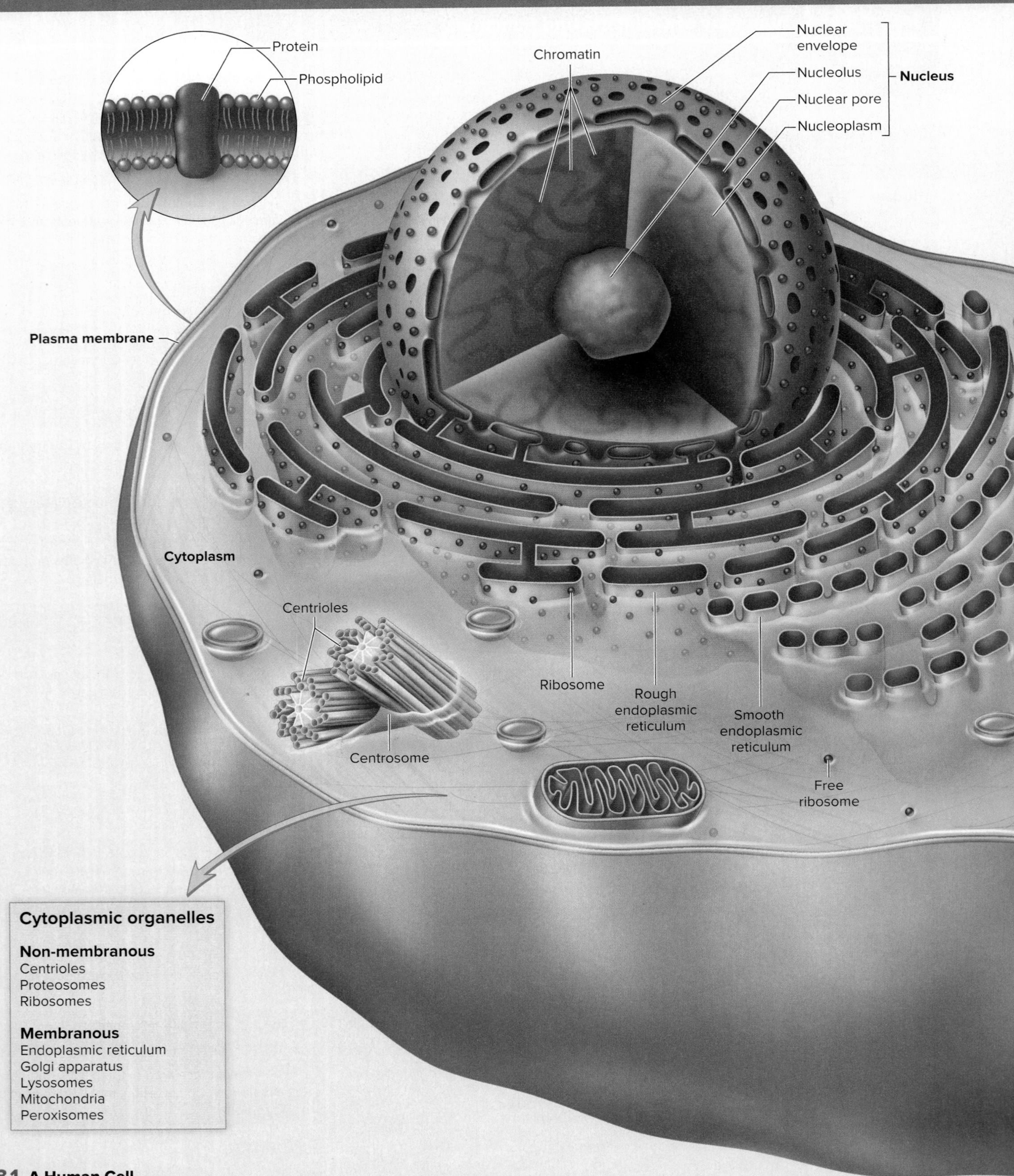

FIGURE 3.1 A Human Cell
A generalized human cell showing the plasma membrane, nucleus, and cytoplasm with its organelles. Although no single cell contains all these organelles, many cells contain a large number of them. APR

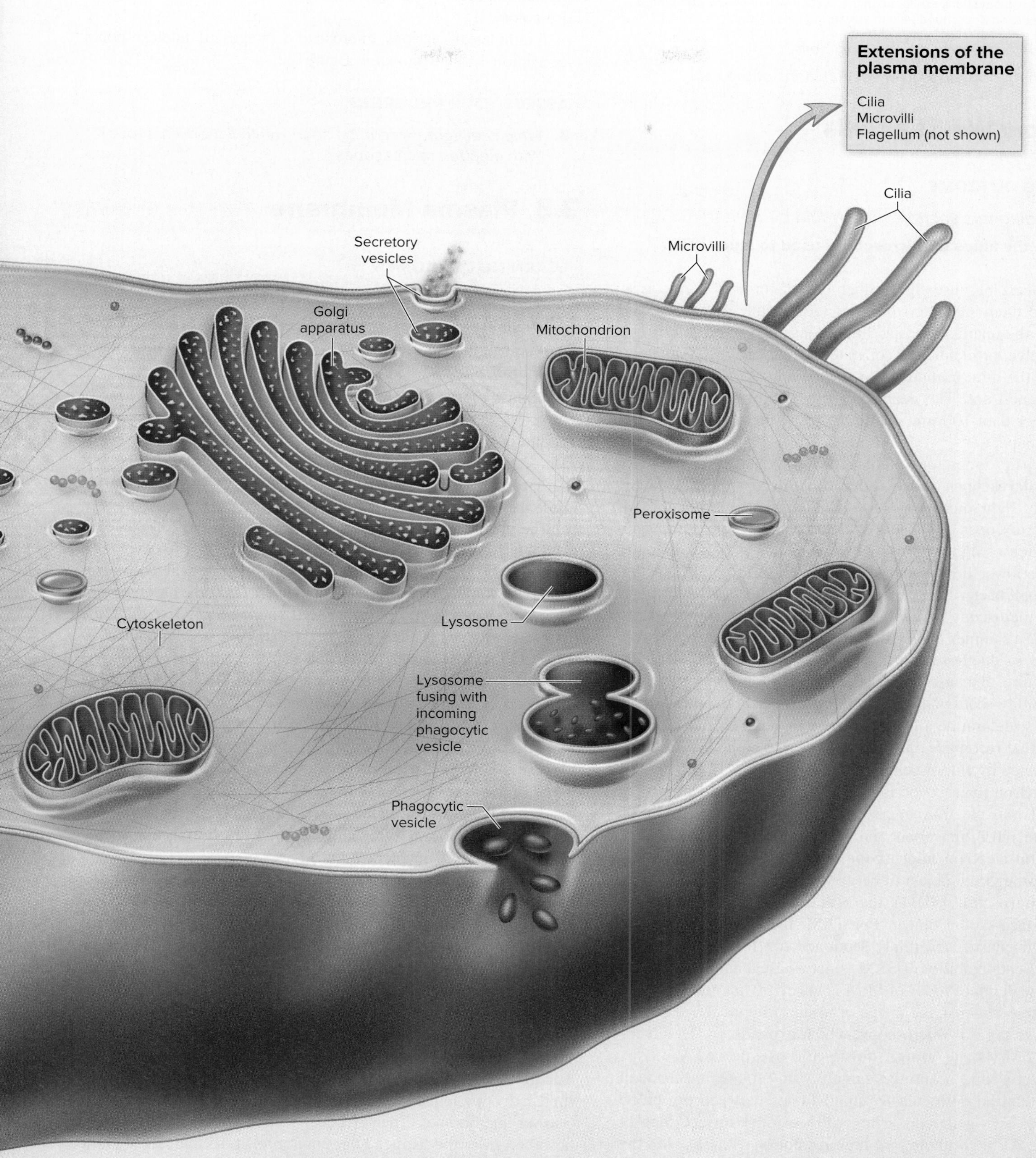

FIGURE 3.1 (continued)

ASSESS YOUR PROGRESS

Answers to these questions are found in the section you have just completed. Re-read the section if you need help in answering these questions.

1. *What parts are common to most cells?*
2. *Explain the four characteristic functions of the cell.*

3.2 How We See Cells

LEARNING OUTCOME

After reading this section, you should be able to

A. **Relate the kinds of microscopes used to study cells.**

We see objects because light either passes through them or is reflected off them and enters our eyes (see chapter 15). However, vision with the unaided eye has limitations. The smallest objects we can resolve, or identify as separate objects, are approximately 100 μm, or 0.1 mm, in diameter, which is approximately the size of a fine pencil dot. The details of cells and tissues, which are much smaller than 100 μm, cannot be examined without the aid of a microscope.

Two basic types of microscopes have been developed: (1) **light microscopes** and (2) **electron microscopes.** As their names imply, light microscopes use light to produce an image, and electron microscopes use beams of electrons to produce an image. The resolution of light microscopes is limited by the wavelength of light, the lower limit being approximately 0.1 μm—about the size of a small bacterium.

Light microscopy is regularly used to examine biopsy specimens because samples can be quickly prepared and the resolution is adequate to diagnose most conditions that cause changes in tissue structure. Because most tissues are colorless and transparent when thinly sectioned, the tissue must be stained with a dye, so that the structural details can be seen, or must be stained with antibodies that recognize specific molecules. The bound antibodies are detected by fluorescent tags.

An electron microscope is used to see objects much smaller than a cell. An electron microscope has a resolution limit of approximately 0.1 nm, about the size of some molecules. In a **transmission electron microscope (TEM),** a beam of electrons is passed through the object to be viewed, whereas in a **scanning electron microscope (SEM),** the beam of electrons is reflected off the surface of the object. For TEM, the specimen must be embedded in plastic and thinly sectioned (0.01–0.15 μm thick). The magnification ability of SEM is not as great as that of TEM; however, the depth of focus of SEM is much greater and produces a clearer three-dimensional image of tissue structure.

A newer type of microscopy, which expands on the advantages of SEM, is the **atomic force microscope (AFM).** This type of microscope scans the sample using a tiny mechanical probe that can be deflected by small forces between the probe and sample. This generates a three-dimensional surface map of the sample. AFM combines the high resolution of TEM with the topographical visualization of SEM. AFM also has the benefit that samples can generally be viewed under more physiological conditions. Because TEM, SEM, and AFM do not transmit color information, the micrographs are black and white unless assigned false colors.

Examples of various microscopic images of nuclear pores (see section 3.8) are shown in figure 3.2.

ASSESS YOUR PROGRESS

3. *Which cell features can be seen with a light microscope? With electron microscopes?*

3.3 Plasma Membrane

LEARNING OUTCOMES

After reading this section, you should be able to

A. **Describe the functions of the plasma membrane.**
B. **List the main chemical components of the plasma membrane.**
C. **Relate why a membrane potential is formed.**

The plasma membrane is the outermost component of a cell, and as such, serves several important functions. (1) It functions as a boundary separating the **cytoplasmic,** *intracellular,* substances, those inside the cell, from **extracellular** substances, those outside the cell. (2) The plasma membrane encloses and supports the cell contents. (3) It attaches cells to the extracellular environment or to other cells. (4) The cells' ability to recognize and communicate with each other takes place through the plasma membrane. (5) Also, the plasma membrane determines what moves into and out of cells. As a result, the cytoplasm of a cell is different from the extracellular environment.

An electrical charge difference across the plasma membrane called the **membrane potential** is a result of the cell's regulation of ion movement into and out of the cell. There are more positively charged ions along the outside of the plasma membrane and more negatively charged ions and proteins along the inside of the plasma membrane. As a result, the outside of the plasma membrane is positively charged, compared with the negatively charged inside of the plasma membrane. The membrane potential, an important feature of a living cell's normal function, is considered in greater detail in chapters 9 and 11.

The plasma membrane consists primarily of lipids and proteins, with a very small amount of carbohydrates. Most of the weight of the plasma membrane is determined by the lipids and proteins, each making up about 45–50% of the total. However, these values can vary depending on the specific type of cell analyzed. Carbohydrates make up a small percentage of the plasma membrane (4–8%) and are found only on the outer surface of the plasma membrane (figure 3.3). The carbohydrates combine with lipids to form glycolipids and with proteins to form glycoproteins. The **glycocalyx** (GLYE-koh-KAY-liks) is the collection of glycolipids, glycoproteins, and carbohydrates on the outer surface of the plasma membrane. The glycocalyx also contains molecules absorbed from the extracellular environment, so there is often no precise boundary between the plasma membrane and the extracellular environment.

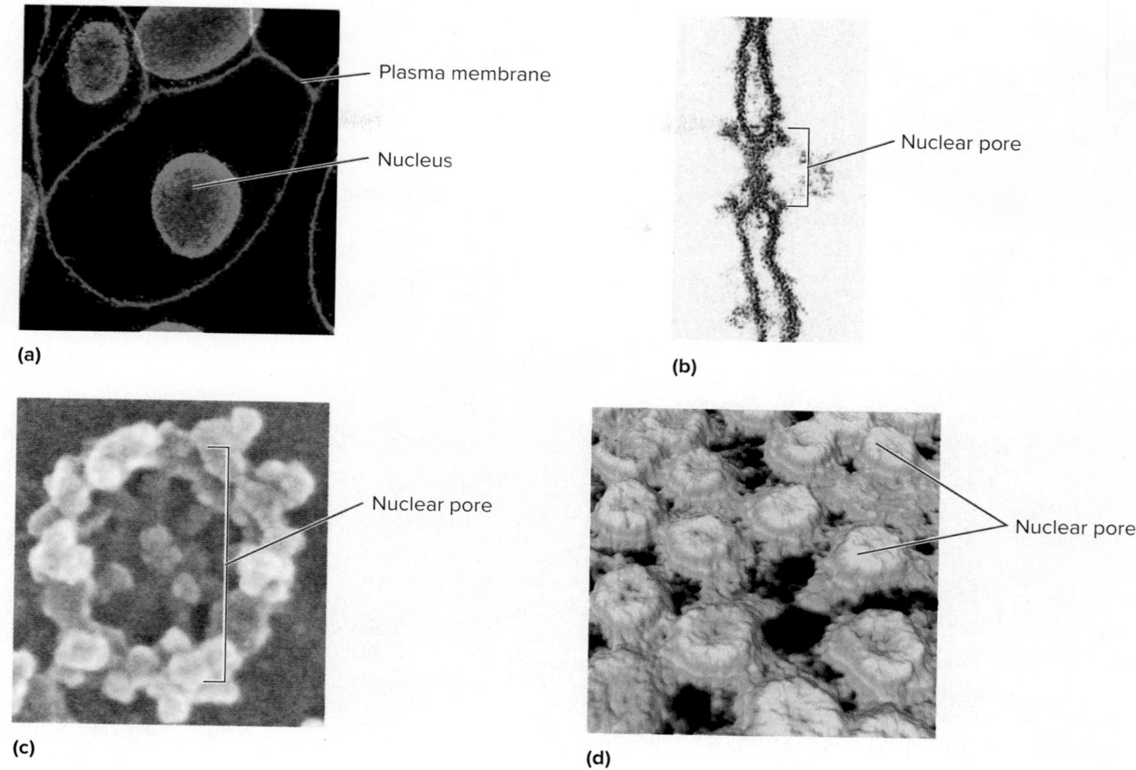

FIGURE 3.2 Microscopic Images of Nuclear Pores
(*a*) Light microscopy image of a cell. The nucleus is labeled with antibodies that bind nuclear pores and proteins on the plasma membrane. (*b*) Transmission electron micrograph of a single nuclear pore. (*c*) Scanning electron micrograph of a single nuclear pore. View is from the cytoplasm of the cell into the pore. (*d*) Color-enhanced atomic force microscopy image of nuclear pores. (a) National High Magnetic Field Laboratory, The Florida State University; (b) Courtesy of Werner Franke and Ulrich Scheer; (c) Courtesy of Dr. Martin W. Goldberg; (d) Shahin, Schillers & Oberleithner, Institute of Physiology II, Medical Faculty, University of Muenster, Germany

ASSESS YOUR PROGRESS

4. *Explain five functions of the plasma membrane.*
5. *Differentiate between cytoplasmic and extracellular.*
6. *What is the membrane potential? Is the outside of the plasma membrane positively or negatively charged compared with the inside?*
7. *What are the main chemical components of the plasma membrane?*

3.4 Membrane Lipids

LEARNING OUTCOMES

After reading this section, you should be able to

A. **List and describe the functions of membrane lipids.**
B. **Explain the nature of the fluid-mosaic model of membrane structure.**

The two predominant lipids of the plasma membrane are phospholipids and cholesterol. **Phospholipids** readily assemble to form a **lipid bilayer,** a double layer of phospholipid molecules, because they have a polar (charged) head and a nonpolar (uncharged) tail (see chapter 2). The polar heads are attracted to water molecules, so they are also called **hydrophilic** (water-loving) heads. The polar, hydrophilic heads are exposed to the extracellular fluid and cytoplasm of the cell, both of which are aqueous solutions. The tails of the phospholipids are nonpolar and are not attracted to water molecules, so the tails are also called **hydrophobic** (water-fearing). The nonpolar, hydrophobic tails face one another in the interior of the plasma membrane (figure 3.3). The **fluid-mosaic model** of the plasma membrane describes the plasma membrane as being neither rigid nor static in structure. Instead, the plasma membrane is highly flexible and can change its shape and composition through time. The lipid bilayer functions as a dense liquid in which other molecules, such as proteins, are suspended. The fluid nature of the lipid bilayer has several important consequences: (1) It provides an important means of distributing molecules within the plasma membrane. (2) Slight damage to the membrane can be repaired because the phospholipids tend to reassemble around damaged sites and close them. (3) The fluid nature of the lipid bilayer also enables membranes to fuse with one another.

Phospholipids are not the only lipid of the plasma membrane. **Cholesterol** is the other major lipid, though it is present in much

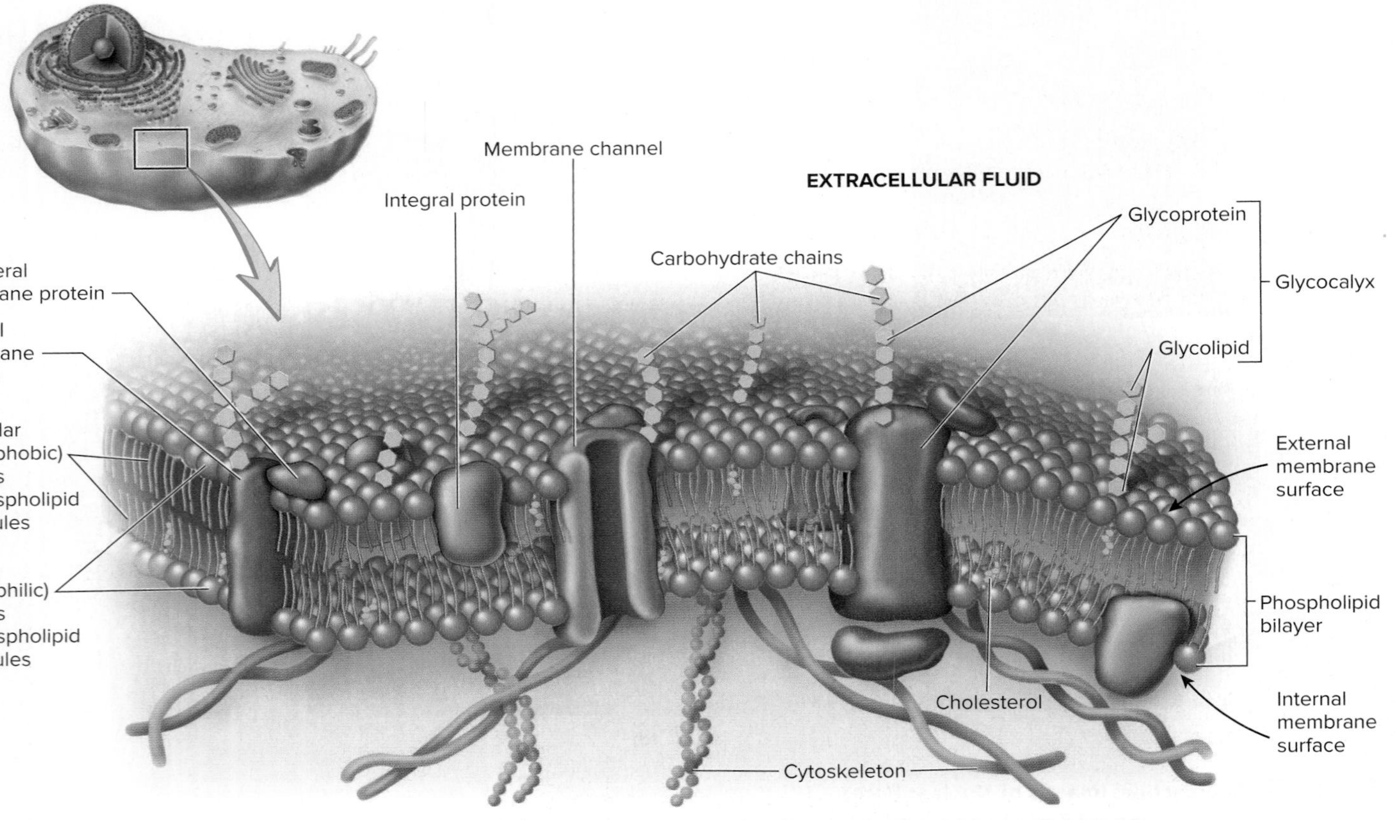

Membrane channel
Integral protein
EXTRACELLULAR FLUID
Glycoprotein
Carbohydrate chains
Glycocalyx
Peripheral membrane protein
Integral membrane protein
Glycolipid
Nonpolar (hydrophobic) regions of phospholipid molecules
External membrane surface
Polar (hydrophilic) regions of phospholipid molecules
Phospholipid bilayer
Cholesterol
Internal membrane surface
Cytoskeleton
(a)
CYTOPLASM (intracellular fluid)

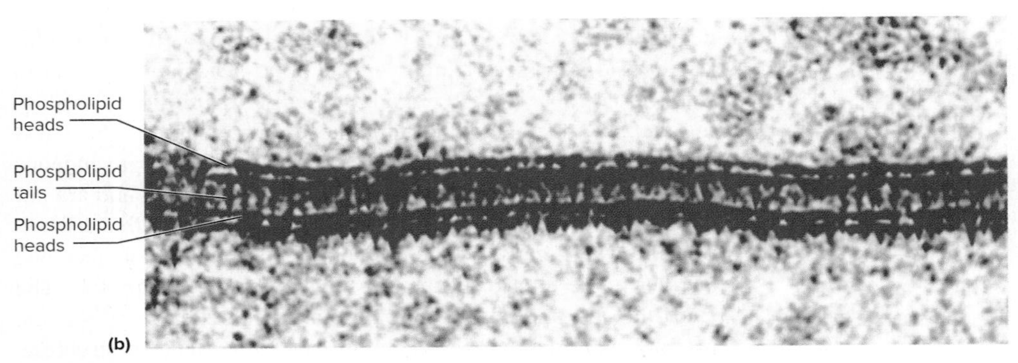

FIGURE 3.3 Plasma Membrane
(*a*) Fluid-mosaic model of the plasma membrane. The membrane is composed of a bilayer of phospholipids and cholesterol with proteins "floating" in the membrane. The nonpolar, hydrophobic region of each phospholipid molecule is directed toward the center of the membrane, and the polar, hydrophilic region is directed toward either the extracellular fluid or the cytoplasm. (*b*) Transmission electron micrograph showing the plasma membrane of a single cell. Proteins at either surface of the lipid bilayer stain more readily than the lipid bilayer does and give the membrane the appearance of having three parts: The two outer parts consist of proteins and the phospholipid heads, and the central part is composed of the phospholipid tails and cholesterol. (b) Don Fawcett/Science Source APR

smaller amounts compared to phospholipids. It is interspersed among the phospholipids and accounts for about one-third of the total lipids in the plasma membrane. The hydrophilic hydroxyl (–OH) group of cholesterol extends between the phospholipid heads to the hydrophilic surface of the membrane, whereas the hydrophobic part of the cholesterol molecule lies within the hydrophobic region of the phospholipids. The amount of cholesterol in a particular plasma membrane is a major factor in determining the fluid nature of the membrane. An important function of cholesterol as part of the plasma membrane is that it limits the movement of phospholipids, providing stability to the plasma membrane.

ASSESS YOUR PROGRESS

8. *Describe the arrangement of the hydrophilic heads and hydrophobic tails of phospholipid molecules in a plasma membrane.*
9. *Summarize the characteristics of the fluid-mosaic model of membrane structure.*
10. *What is the function of cholesterol in plasma membranes?*

3.5 Membrane Proteins

LEARNING OUTCOMES

After reading this section, you should be able to

A. **Describe the difference between integral and peripheral membrane proteins.**
B. **List and explain the functions of membrane proteins.**
C. **Describe the characteristics of specificity, competition, and saturation of transport proteins.**

Although the basic structure of the plasma membrane and some of its functions are determined by its lipids, many of its other functions are determined by its proteins. Based on their location among or attached to the phospholipid molecules, membrane proteins can be classified as integral or peripheral. **Integral membrane proteins** penetrate deeply into the lipid bilayer, in many cases extending from one surface to the other (figure 3.3). **Peripheral membrane proteins** are attached to either the inner or the outer surfaces of the lipid bilayer. Integral membrane proteins consist of regions made up of amino acids with hydrophobic R groups and other regions of amino acids with hydrophilic R groups (see chapter 2). The hydrophobic regions are located within the hydrophobic part of the membrane, and the hydrophilic regions lie at the inner or outer surface of the membrane or line channels through the membrane. Some peripheral proteins may be bound to integral membrane proteins, whereas others are bound to the polar heads of the phospholipid molecules. Membrane proteins have many functions. Protein function is determined by (1) the protein's chemical characteristics and (2) the three-dimensional shape of the protein. In addition, whether a protein is integral or peripheral is important as to how it carries out its functions. Membrane proteins can function as marker molecules, attachment proteins, transport proteins, receptor proteins, or enzymes (table 3.2).

ASSESS YOUR PROGRESS

11. *Describe the difference between integral and peripheral proteins in the plasma membrane.*
12. *What are the five roles that proteins can play as part of the plasma membrane?*

Marker Molecules

Marker molecules are cell surface molecules that allow cells to identify other cells or other molecules. They are mostly **glycoproteins** (proteins with attached carbohydrates; table 3.2) or **glycolipids** (lipids with attached carbohydrates). The protein portions of glycoproteins may be either integral or peripheral membrane proteins. Examples of marker molecule function include a sperm cell's recognition of an oocyte and the immune system's ability to distinguish between self-cells and foreign cells, such as bacteria or donor cells in an organ transplant. Intercellular communication and recognition are important because cells are not isolated entities; they must work together to ensure normal body function.

TABLE 3.2 Functions of Membrane Proteins

Membrane Protein	Protein Function
Marker molecules 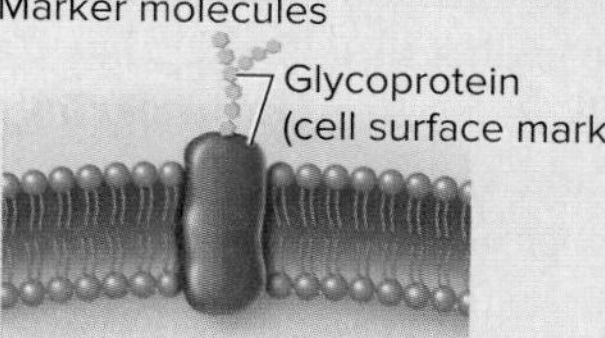	Allow cells to identify other cells or other molecules
Attachment proteins 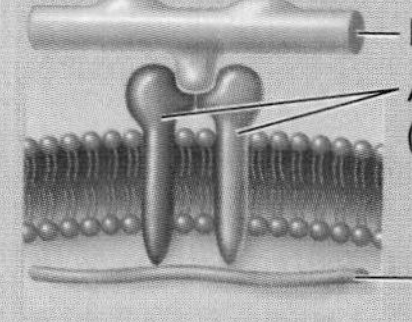	Anchor cells to other cells (cadherins) or to extracellular molecules (integrins)
Transport Proteins	
Channel proteins 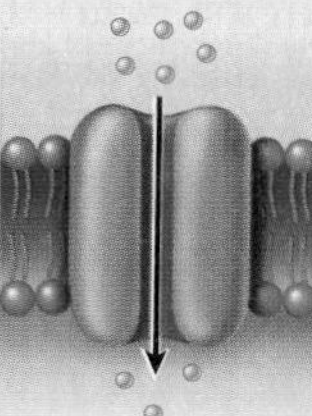	Form passageways through the plasma membrane, allowing specific ions or molecules to enter or exit the cell; may be leak or gated
Carrier proteins (transporters) 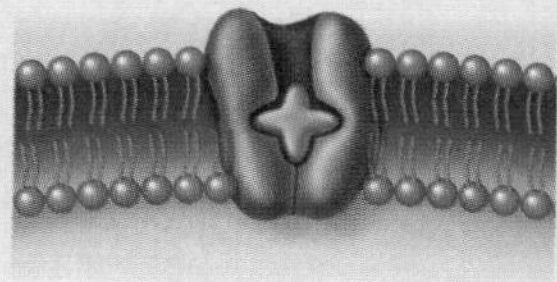	Move ions or molecules across the plasma membrane; binding of specific chemical to carrier proteins causes changes in the shape of the carrier proteins; the carrier proteins then move the specific chemical across the plasma membrane
ATP-powered pumps 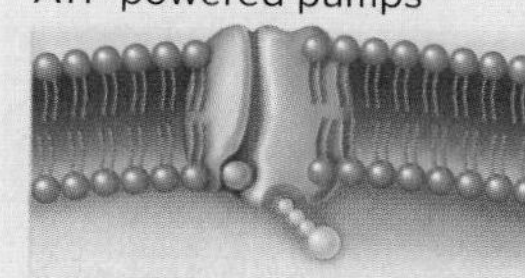	Move specific ions or molecules across the plasma membrane; require ATP molecules to function
Receptor proteins 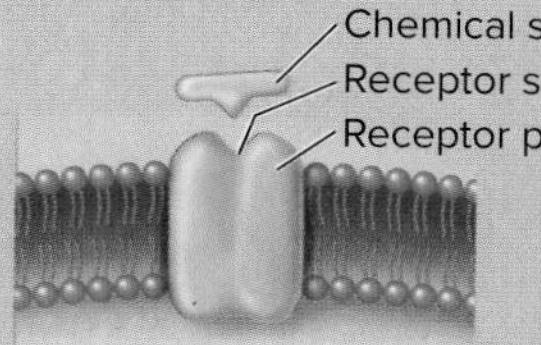	Function as binding sites for chemical signals in the extracellular fluid; binding of chemical signals to receptors triggers cellular responses
Enzymes 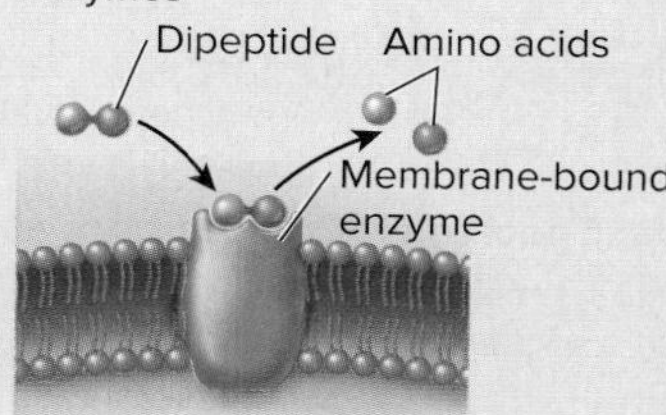	Catalyze chemical reactions either inside or outside cells

Attachment Proteins

Attachment proteins are integral proteins that allow cells to attach to other cells or to extracellular molecules (table 3.2). Many attachment proteins also attach to cytoplasmic molecules. Two examples of attachment proteins are cadherins and integrins. **Cadherins** are proteins that attach cells to other cells; **integrins** are proteins that attach cells to extracellular molecules. Integrins function in pairs of integral membrane proteins, which interact with both cytoplasmic and extracellular molecules. Because of the interaction with cytoplasmic molecules, integrins also function in cellular communication.

Transport Proteins

Transport proteins are integral proteins that allow ions or molecules to move from one side of the plasma membrane to the other. Transport proteins have three characteristics that are important to their function: (1) specificity, (2) competition, and (3) saturation. **Specificity** means that each transport protein binds to and transports only a certain type of molecule or ion (figure 3.4*a*). For example, the transport protein that moves glucose does not move amino acids. The chemical structure of the binding site determines the specificity of the transport protein because only substances that are the right shape can bind to the protein. **Competition** is the result of molecules with simlilar shape binding to the transport protein (figure 3.4*b*). Although the binding sites of transport proteins exhibit specificity, closely related substances that have the same shape may bind to the same binding site. The substance in the greater concentration or the substance that binds to the binding site more readily is moved across the plasma membrane at the greater rate. **Saturation** means that the rate of movement of molecules across the membrane is limited by the number of available transport proteins (figure 3.4*c*). As the concentration of a transported substance increases, more transport proteins have their binding sites occupied, so the rate at which the substance is moved across the plasma membrane increases. However, once the concentration of the substance is increased so that all the binding sites are occupied, the rate of movement remains constant, even though the concentration of the substance increases further. There are three major classes of transport proteins: (1) channel proteins, (2) carrier proteins, and (3) ATP-powered pumps.

Channel Proteins

Channel proteins are one or more integral membrane proteins arranged so that they form a tiny channel through the plasma membrane (figure 3.5; table 3.2). The hydrophobic regions of the proteins face outward toward the hydrophobic part of the plasma membrane, and the hydrophilic regions of the protein face inward and line the channel. Ions or small molecules of the right size, charge, and shape can pass through the channel. The charges in the hydrophilic part of the channel proteins determine which types of ions can pass through the channel.

Channel proteins include leak ion channels and gated ion channels. **Leak ion channels,** or *nongated ion channels,* are

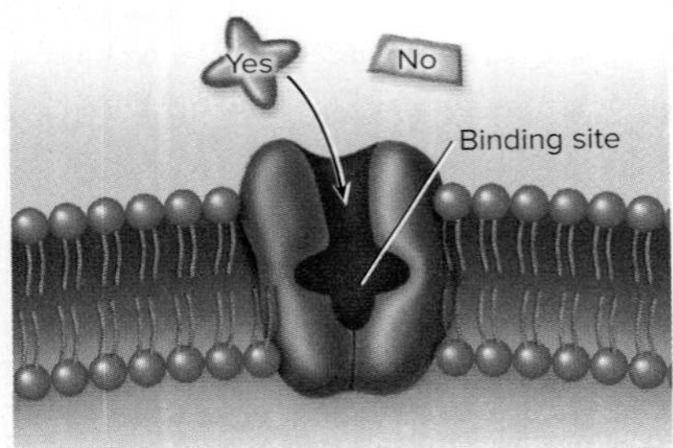

(a) Specificity: Only molecules that are the right shape to bind to the binding site are transported.

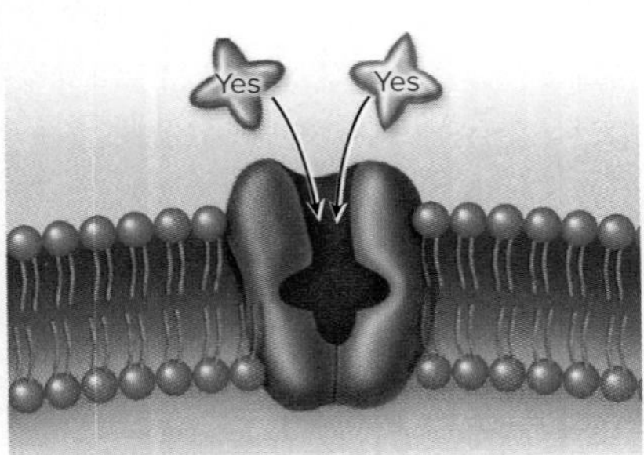

(b) Competition: Similarly shaped molecules can compete for the same binding site.

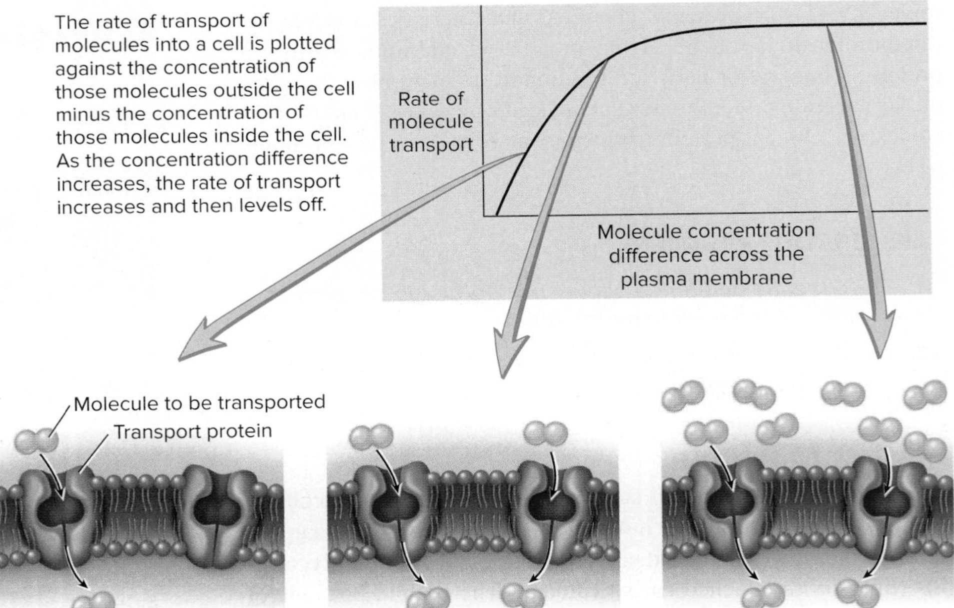

(c) Saturation: The rate of movement of a substance across the membrane is limited by the number of available transport proteins.

FIGURE 3.4 Transport Proteins: Specificity, Competition, and Saturation
(*a*) Transport proteins are specific to the type of substance they transport. (*b*) Competition at transport proteins may occur between substances that have similar shapes. (*c*) Transport of a specific substance across the membrane is limited by the number of available transport proteins.

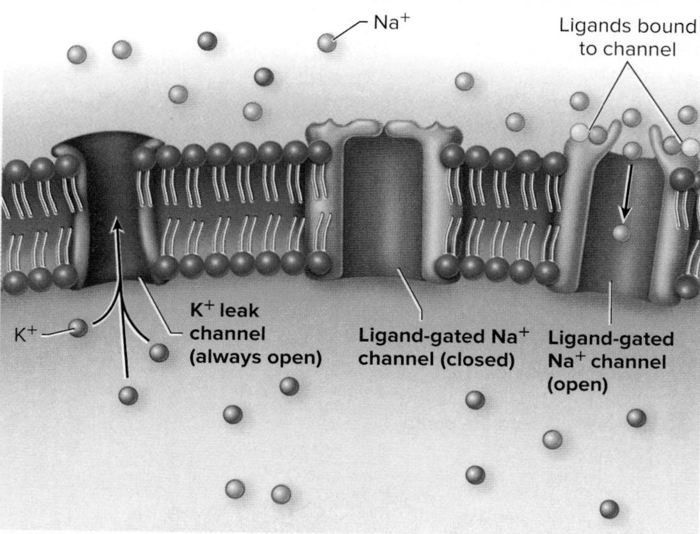

FIGURE 3.5 Leak and Gated Membrane Channels
Leak channels are always open. Gated channels open and close depending on certain cell conditions.

always open and are responsible for the plasma membrane's permeability to ions when the plasma membrane is at rest. **Gated ion channels** open and close depending on certain conditions of the cell. Some gated ion channels open or close in response to chemical signals binding to the ion channel. **Ligand** (LIG-and, LYE-gand) is a generic term for any chemical signal molecule that binds an area of a cell to change the activity of that cell. Ion channels that respond to these signals are called **ligand-gated ion channels.** Other gated ion channels open or close when there is a change in the membrane potential. These are called **voltage-gated ion channels.**

The functioning of membrane ion channels is so vital to homeostasis that serious disease can occur if a type of channel does not function properly. **Cystic fibrosis** is a genetic disorder that affects chloride ion channels. The failure of these ion channels to function causes the affected cells to produce thick, viscous secretions. Although cystic fibrosis affects many cell types, its most profound effects are in the pancreas and the lungs. In the pancreas, the thick secretions block the release of digestive enzymes, resulting in an inability to digest certain types of food and sometimes leading to serious cases of pancreatitis (inflammation of the pancreas). In the lungs, the thick secretions block airways and make breathing difficult.

Channel proteins were once thought of as simple tubes, with or without gates, through which ions pass. Many channel proteins, however, are more complex than that. It now appears that ions briefly bind to specific sites inside channels and that the shapes of those channels change as ions are transported through them. The size and charge within a channel determine the channel's specificity. For example, Na^+ channels do not transport K^+, and vice versa. In addition, similar ions moving into and binding within a channel protein are in competition with each other. Furthermore, the number of ions moving into a channel protein can exceed the capacity of the channel, thus saturating the channel. Therefore, channel proteins exhibit specificity, competition, and saturation.

Carrier Proteins

Carrier proteins, or *transporters,* are integral membrane proteins that move ions or molecules from one side of the plasma membrane to the other. Figure 3.6 illustrates how a carrier protein transports a molecule into the cell.

1. A specific molecule enters the carrier protein from the extracellular fluid.
2. The molecule attaches to a binding site within the carrier protein.
3. The binding of the molecule causes the carrier proteins to change shape and release the bound molecule to the other side of the plasma membrane. The carrier protein then resumes its original shape and is available to transport more molecules (as shown in *step 1*).

Some carrier proteins transport one ion or molecule at a time, but other carrier proteins can transport more than one type of substance at a time. Because of this difference, the movement of ions or molecules by carrier proteins can be classified in three ways.

1. **Uniport** is the movement of one specific ion or molecule across the membrane, as illustrated in figure 3.6.
2. **Symport** (*cotransport*) is the movement of two different ions or molecules in the same direction across the plasma membrane (see figure 3.16 later in the chapter for an example).
3. **Antiport** (*countertransport*) is the movement of two different ions or molecules in opposite directions across the plasma membrane (see figure 3.15 later in the chapter for an example).

Carrier proteins involved in these types of movement are called **uniporters, symporters,** and **antiporters,** respectively.

ATP-Powered Pumps

ATP-powered pumps are transport proteins that require cellular energy to move specific ions or molecules from one side of the plasma membrane to the other. The activity of ATP-powered pumps is fueled by the breakdown of adenosine triphosphate (ATP). Recall from chapter 2 that energy stored in ATP molecules is used to power many cellular activities. Figure 3.7 illustrates an ATP-powered pump transporting an ion into the cell.

1. ATP-powered pumps have binding sites, to which specific ions or molecules can bind, as well as a binding site for ATP.
2. The breakdown of ATP to adenosine diphosphate (ADP) releases energy, changing the shape of the protein, which moves the ion or molecule across the membrane.
3. The ion and phosphate are released from the ATP-powered pump. The pump resumes its original shape (as shown in *step 1*).

Receptor Proteins

Receptor proteins are membrane proteins or glycoproteins that have an exposed **receptor site** on the outer cell surface. Specific substances, such as chemical signals, can attach to the receptor site. Cells commonly use receptors and the chemical signals

PROCESS **Figure**

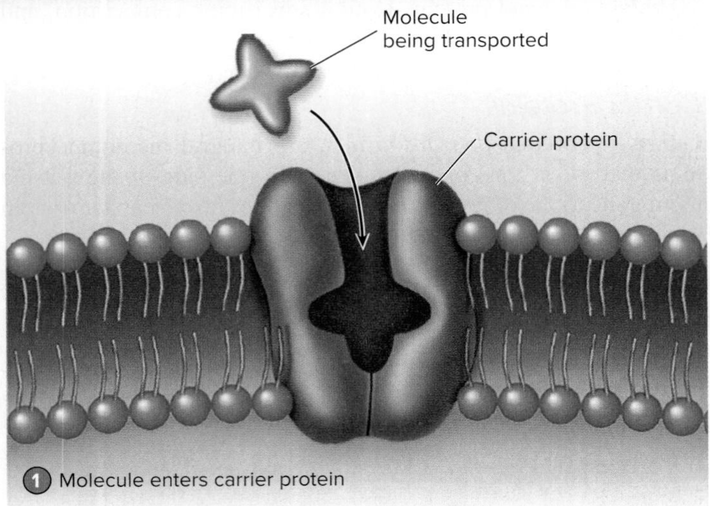

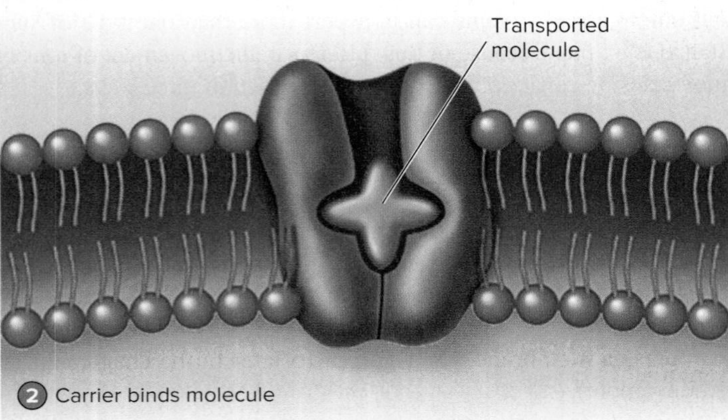

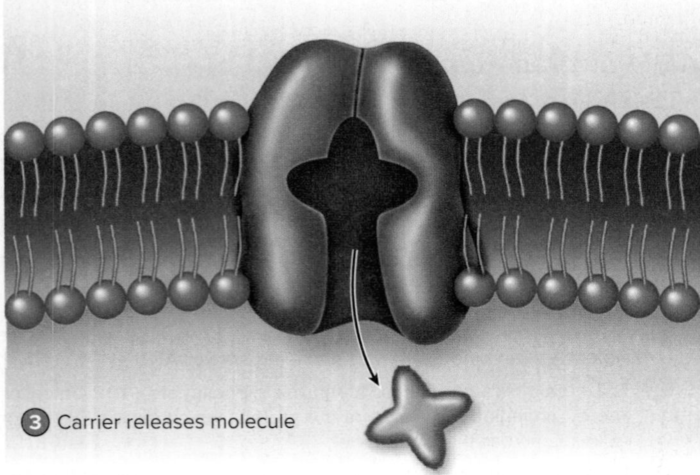

PROCESS **Figure 3.6**

Transport by a Carrier Protein

Some substance must bind to specific sites on carrier proteins for transport across the membrane.

Gene mutations ultimately alter protein structure. In which region of a carrier protein would a change in structure be most critical?

PROCESS **Figure**

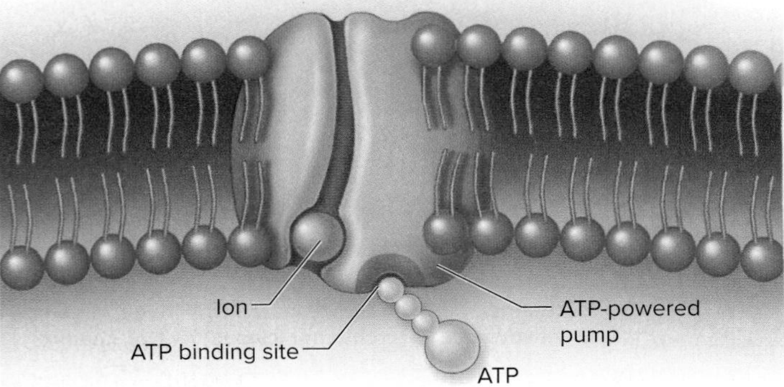

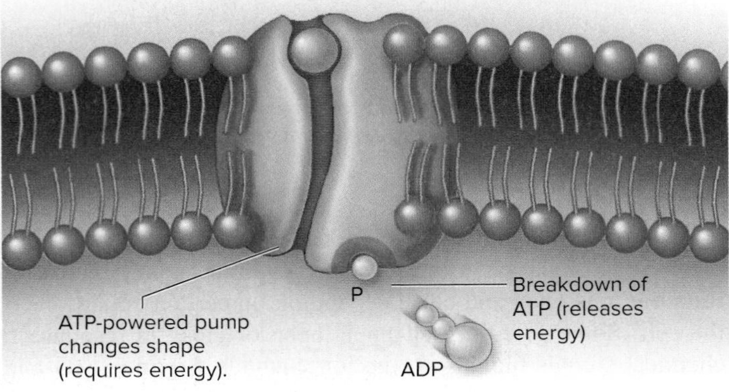

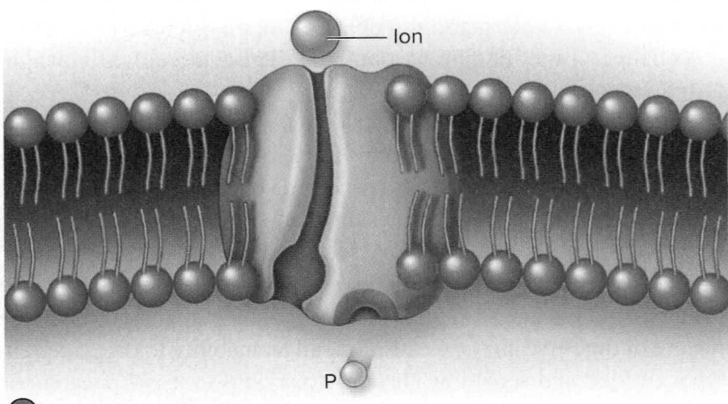

PROCESS **Figure 3.7**

Transport by an ATP-Powered Pump

ATP-powered pumps require cellular energy (ATP) to move a specific substance across the membrane.

Is the protein shown in this figure an integral membrane protein or a peripheral membrane protein? Explain your answer.

they bind as part of an intercellular communication system that coordinates activities among the various parts of the body. One cell can release a chemical signal that diffuses to another cell and binds to its receptor. The binding acts as a signal that triggers a response. An important part of this intercellular communication system depends on the characteristic of specificity. The same chemical signal would have no effect on other cells that lacked the specific receptor molecule. This ensures that only the appropriate cells receive a given signal. Cell communication is discussed more thoroughly in chapters 11 and 17.

Receptors Linked to Channel Proteins

Some membrane-bound receptors also help form ligand-gated ion channels. The ion channels are composed of proteins that span the plasma membrane. Parts of one or more of the channel proteins form receptors on the cell surface. When chemical signals, or ligands, bind to these receptors, the combination alters the three-dimensional structure of the proteins of the ion channels, causing the channels either to open or to close. The result is a change in the permeability of the plasma membrane to the specific ions passing through the ion channels. Figure 3.8 illustrates the effect of the ligand acetylcholine as it binds to a receptor linked to a Na^+ channel.

1. Acetylcholine binds to the receptor sites linked to a Na^+ channel. When the receptor sites are not occupied by acetylcholine, the Na^+ channel remains closed.
2. The binding of acetylcholine molecules to the receptor sites opens Na^+ channels in the plasma membrane, allowing Na^+ to move into the cell.

Receptors Coupled to G Protein Complexes

Some membrane-bound receptor proteins function by altering the activity of a **G protein complex** located on the inner surface of the plasma membrane. The G protein complex acts as an intermediary between a receptor and other cellular proteins. The G protein complex consists of three proteins: alpha (α), beta (β), and gamma (γ) proteins. Figure 3.9 illustrates how a G protein complex interacts with a receptor protein when a ligand is bound to the receptor protein.

1. When the G protein complex is not interacting with a receptor protein, the α subunit of the G protein complex has guanosine diphosphate (GDP) attached to it.
2. When a chemical signal binds to the receptor, the receptor becomes associated with the G protein complex. The α subunit releases the GDP and attaches to guanosine triphosphate (GTP). At this point the α subunit is considered activated.
3. The G protein complex separates from the receptor, and the activated α subunit separates from the β and γ subunits.
4. The activated α subunit can stimulate a cell response in at least three ways: (a) by means of intracellular chemical signals, (b) by the opening of ion channels in the plasma membrane, and (c) by the activation of enzymes associated with the plasma membrane.

Drugs with structures similar to those of specific chemical signals may compete with those chemical signals for their receptor sites. Depending on the exact characteristics of a drug, it binds to a receptor site and either activates or inhibits the action of the receptor. For example, some drugs compete with the chemical signal epinephrine for its receptor sites. Some of these drugs activate epinephrine receptors; others inhibit them.

PROCESS **Figure**

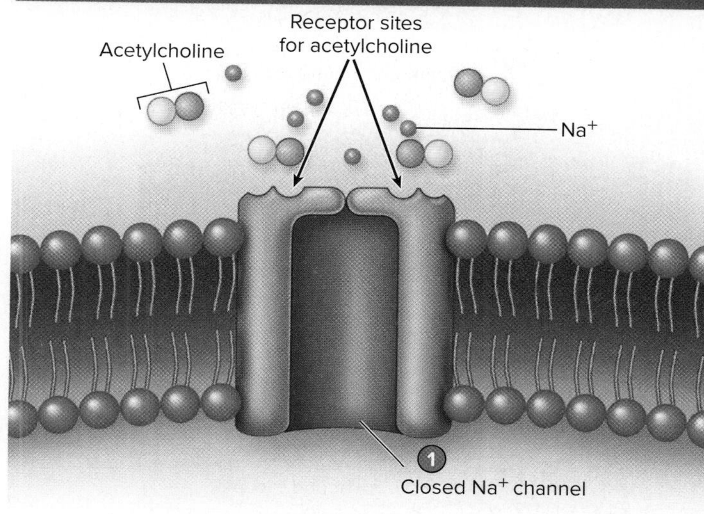

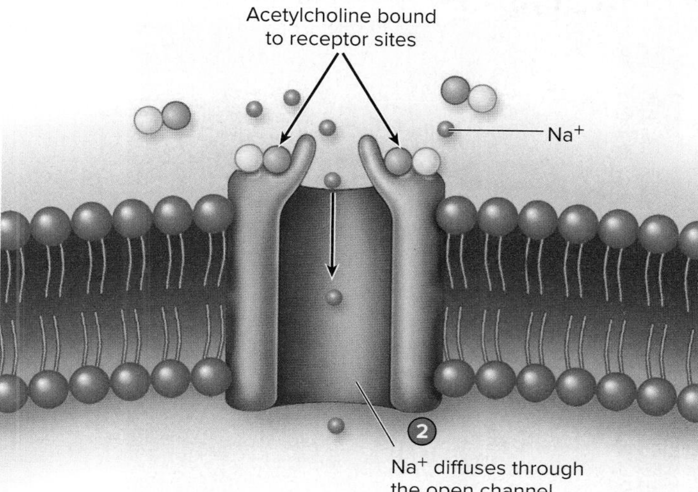

PROCESS **Figure 3.8**

Opening and Closing of a Ligand-Channel Protein

Ligand-gated ion channels open or close in response to a specific ligand binding to the appropriate receptor site.

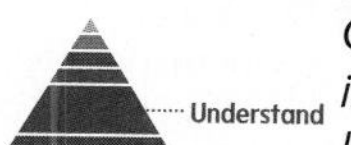

Certain toxins disrupt normal cell activity by blocking acetylcholine binding sites. Which of the following explains this type of interaction: specificity, competition, or saturation? Explain your answer.

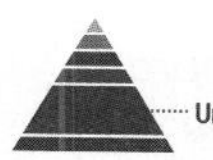

Predict 1

A research scientist is developing a new drug that blocks muscle cell receptors that, when activated, stimulate a muscle contraction. In her first experiment, she used 250 mg of the new drug but saw no effect. In her second experiment, she increased the dosage to 750 mg. This dosage was successful in blocking the muscle stimulation. Explain why increasing the dosage would affect the outcome of the experiment.

PROCESS **Figure**

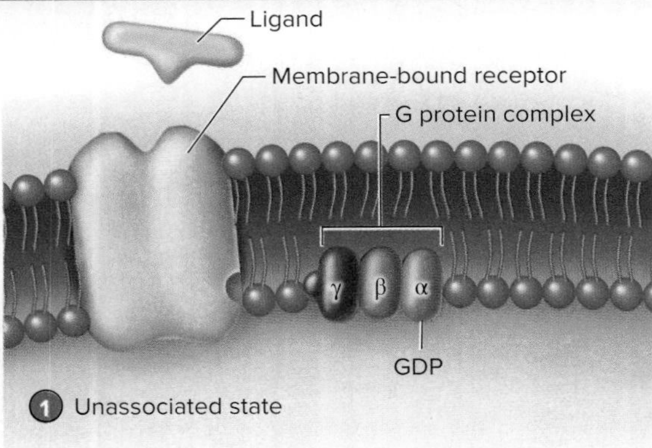

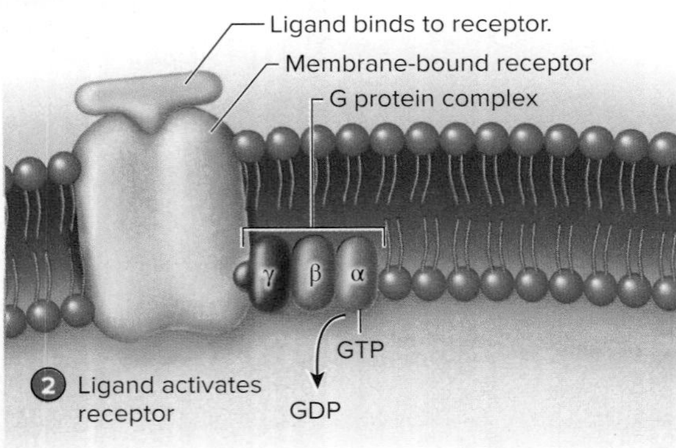

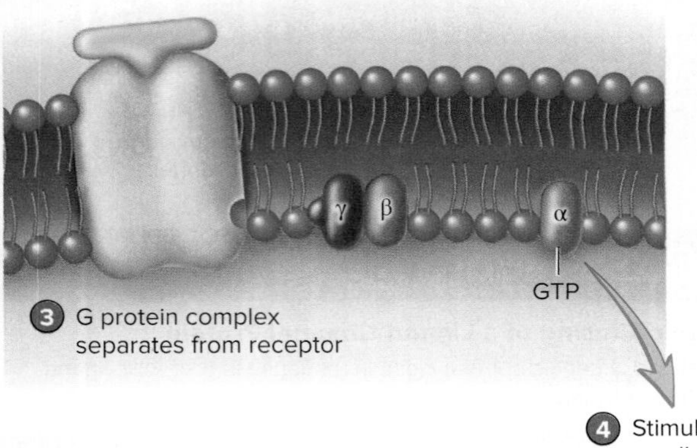

4 Stimulates a cell response

PROCESS **Figure 3.9**

Receptor Coupled to a G Protein Complex

Binding of a ligand to a receptor coupled to a G protein complex can alter cell activity in multiple ways.

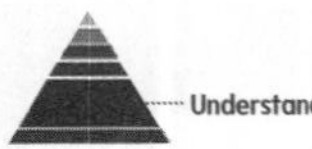

What characteristic of the plasma membrane allows for the movement of the G protein complex toward and away from the receptor protein?

Enzymes

Some membrane proteins function as **enzymes,** which can catalyze chemical reactions on either the inner or the outer surface of the plasma membrane. For example, some enzymes on the surface of cells in the small intestine break the peptide bonds of dipeptides to form two single amino acids (table 3.2). Some membrane-associated enzymes are always active; others are activated by membrane-bound receptors or G protein complexes.

ASSESS YOUR PROGRESS

13. *What are the three classes of transport proteins?*
14. *Describe specificity, competition, and saturation as characteristics of transport proteins.*
15. *What are the three types of channel proteins, and what signal causes each to open or close?*
16. *Define* uniport, symport, *and* antiport.
17. *Compare and contrast how carrier proteins and ATP-powered pumps move ions or molecules across the plasma membrane.*
18. *To what part of a receptor molecule does a chemical signal attach? Explain how a chemical signal can bind to a receptor on a channel protein and cause a change in membrane permeability.*
19. *Describe how receptors alter the activity of G protein complexes. List three ways in which activated α subunits can stimulate a cell response.*
20. *Give an example of the action of a plasma membrane enzyme.*

3.6 Movement Through the Plasma Membrane

LEARNING OUTCOMES

After reading this section, you should be able to

A. **Describe the nature of the plasma membrane in reference to the passage of materials through it.**
B. **List and explain the three ways that molecules and ions can pass through the plasma membrane.**
C. **Discuss the process of diffusion and relate it to a concentration gradient.**
D. **Explain the role of osmosis and osmotic pressure in controlling the movement of water across the plasma membrane.**
E. **Illustrate the differences among hypotonic, isotonic, and hypertonic solutions in terms of water movement.**
F. **Describe mediated transport.**
G. **Compare and contrast facilitated diffusion, active transport, and secondary active transport.**
H. **Describe the processes of endocytosis and exocytosis.**

The plasma membrane separates extracellular material from the cytoplasm and is **selectively permeable**—that is, it allows only certain substances to pass through it. The cytoplasm has a different composition than the extracellular material, and the cell's survival depends on the maintenance of these differences. Enzymes, other proteins, glycogen, and K^+ are present in higher concentrations in the cytoplasm; Na^+, Ca^{2+}, and Cl^- exist in higher concentrations extracellularly. In addition, even though nutrients must continually enter the cell and waste products must exit, the cell's volume remains unchanged. Because of the plasma membrane's permeability and its ability to transport molecules selectively, the cell is able to maintain homeostasis. Rupture of the membrane, alteration of its permeability characteristics, or inhibition of transport processes can disrupt the normal concentration differences across the plasma membrane and lead to cell death.

Molecules and ions can move across the plasma membrane in different ways, depending on the chemical characteristics of the molecules and ions and the structure and function of the cell (figure 3.10). Molecules that are soluble in lipids, such as O_2, CO_2, and steroids, pass through the plasma membrane readily by dissolving in the lipid bilayer. Some small, non-lipid-soluble molecules, such as urea, can diffuse between the phospholipid molecules of the plasma membrane. Large, non-lipid-soluble molecules and ions cannot move across the phospholipid bilayer independently. Transport proteins provide a means for specific non-lipid-soluble molecules or ions to move across the plasma membrane. Large, non-lipid-soluble molecules, as well as small pieces of matter and even whole cells, can be transported across the plasma membrane in a **vesicle,** a small, membrane-bound sac. Table 3.3 lists the specific

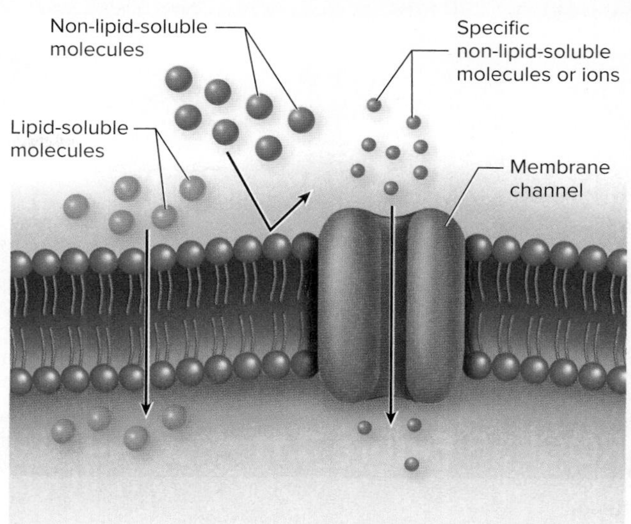

FIGURE 3.10 Diffusion Through the Plasma Membrane
Movement of substances across the plasma membrane depends on their chemical characteristics. Substances that are non-lipid-soluble are less likely to diffuse through the plasma membrane so they must move through transport proteins. Lipid-soluble substances diffuse directly through the membrane.

TABLE 3.3 Comparison of Membrane Transport Mechanisms

Transport Mechanism	Description	Substances Transported	Example
Passive Transport Mechanisms			
Diffusion	Net movement from areas of higher to lower concentration	Lipid-soluble molecules	Oxygen, CO_2, and lipids
Osmosis	Water diffuses across a selectively permeable membrane.	Water	Water movement from the intestines into blood
Facilitated diffusion	Carrier proteins move substances across the plasma membrane without ATP. Facilitated diffusion exhibits the characteristics of specificity, saturation, and competition.	Some substances too large to pass through membrane channels; ions and small molecules diffuse through membrane channels.	Glucose movement into muscle cells and adipocytes
Active Transport Mechanisms			
Active transport	ATP-powered pumps bind to substances and move them across the plasma membrane; ATP is used.	Substances accumulated in concentrations higher on one side of the membrane than on the other are transported.	Ions, such as Na^+, K^+, and Ca^{2+}, are actively transported.
Secondary active transport	Ions are moved across the plasma membrane by active transport, which establishes an ion concentration gradient; ATP is required; ions then move back down their concentration gradient by facilitated diffusion, and another ion or molecule moves with the diffusion ion (symport) or in the opposite direction (antiport).	Some sugars, amino acids, and ions are transported.	Glucose transport into intestinal epithelial cell using Na^+ concentration gradient
Vesicular Transport			
Endocytosis	Vesicle is taken into the cell; requires ATP; in receptor-mediated endocytosis, specific substances are ingested.	Phagocytosis takes in cells and solid particles; pinocytosis takes in molecules dissolved in liquid.	Immune system cells ingest bacteria and cellular debris; most cells take in substances through pinocytosis.
Exocytosis	Secretory vesicles that fuse with the plasma membrane and release contents to the outside of the cell; requires ATP.	Proteins and other water-soluble molecules are transported out of cells.	Digestive enzymes, hormones, neurotransmitters

PROCESS **Figure**

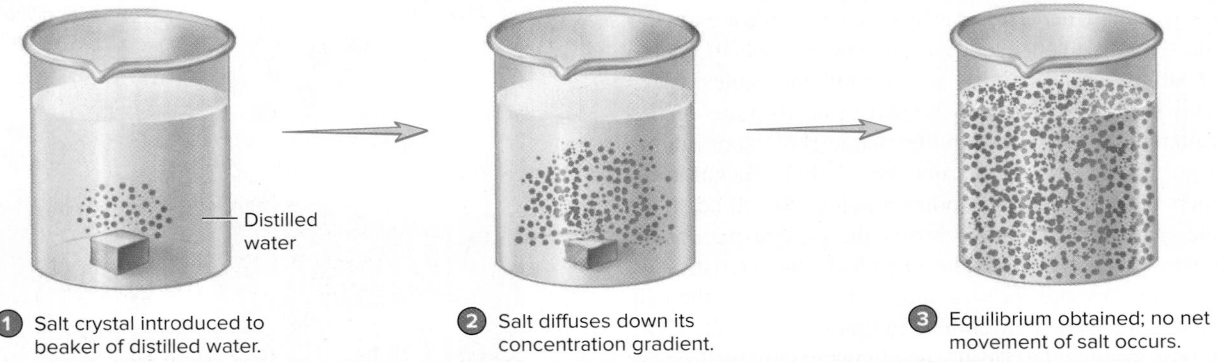

PROCESS **Figure 3.11**

Diffusion

Salt ions (*green dots*) diffuse from areas of higher concentration to areas of lower concentration until the salt ions are evenly distributed throughout the beaker of water. APR

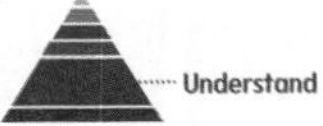

How would the rate of diffusion change if the temperature of the water were decreased?

types of movement across plasma membranes, and each of these methods is described in detail in the following sections.

Passive Membrane Transport

Membrane transport mechanisms are classified as either passive or active based on whether or not the cell expends metabolic energy, in the form of ATP, during the transport process. During passive membrane transport, the cell does not expend metabolic energy. Active membrane transport requires the cell to expend metabolic energy. Passive membrane transport includes diffusion, osmosis, and facilitated diffusion. Active membrane transport will be discussed later in the chapter.

Diffusion

The environment within and around cells is an aqueous, or water, solution. A **solution** consists of one or more substances dissolved in the predominant liquid or gas. The liquid or gas is called the **solvent** and the substances dissolved in it are called **solutes.** When describing the solutions associated with cells, the solvent is water and the solutes vary.

When solutes are first added to a solvent, the molecules of the solute are concentrated in one area, but eventually they will spread out through the solvent in a process called diffusion. **Diffusion** is the movement of solutes from an area of higher solute concentration to an area of lower solute concentration. Diffusion results from the constant random motion of all atoms, molecules, or ions in a solution. Because there are more solute particles in an area of higher concentration than in an area of lower concentration and because the particles move randomly, the chances are greater that solute particles will move from the higher to the lower concentration than in the opposite direction. Thus, the overall, or net, movement is from the area of higher solute concentration to that of lower solute concentration. Figure 3.11 illustrates the diffusion of salt in a beaker of water.

1. A salt crystal is placed in a beaker of water. A concentration difference exists between the salt crystal and the water surrounding it.
2. Salt ions, moving randomly, spread through the column of water.
3. Eventually, the salt ions will become evenly distributed throughout the water.

The solutes and solvent molecules will continue to move randomly, but an equilibrium will exist because no net movement of solutes will occur. Additional examples of diffusion include the movement and distribution of smoke or perfume throughout a room without air currents and the dispersion of a dye throughout a beaker of still water.

A concentration difference occurs when the solutes are not evenly distributed in a solvent. The concentration difference between two points, divided by the distance between the two points, is called the **concentration gradient.** Solutes diffuse *down* their concentration gradients (from a higher to a lower solute concentration) until an equilibrium is achieved. The greater the concentration gradient, the greater the rate of diffusion of a solute down that gradient. Adjusting the concentration difference or distance between the two points changes the concentration gradient. Increasing the concentration difference between the two points or reducing the distance between the two points results in a greater concentration gradient. Conversely, decreasing the concentration difference between the two points or increasing the distance between the two points causes the concentration gradient to decrease.

The rate of diffusion is influenced by several factors, including (1) the magnitude of the concentration gradient, (2) the temperature of the solution, (3) the size of the diffusing molecules, and (4) the viscosity of the solvent. The rate of diffusion increases as the concentration gradient increases. The greater the concentration gradient, the greater the number of solute particles moving from a higher to a lower solute concentration. As the temperature of a solution increases, the speed at which all molecules move increases, resulting in a greater diffusion rate. Small molecules diffuse through a solution more readily than do large ones, so smaller molecules diffuse faster than larger molecules. **Viscosity** is a measure of a fluid's resistance to flow. A fluid with a low viscosity flows more easily, and a fluid with a high viscosity flows less easily. Thick solutions, such as syrup, are more viscous than water. Diffusion occurs more slowly in viscous solvents than in thin, less viscous solvents.

Diffusion of molecules is an important means by which substances move between the extracellular fluid and cytoplasm of the body's cells. Substances that can diffuse through either the lipid bilayer or the membrane channels can pass through the plasma membrane (see figure 3.10). Some nutrients enter and some waste products leave the cell by diffusion, and maintenance of the appropriate cytoplasmic concentration of these substances depends to a large degree on diffusion. For example, if the extracellular concentration of O_2 is reduced, the concentration gradient decreases, inadequate O_2 diffuses into the cell, and the cell cannot function normally.

ASSESS YOUR PROGRESS

21. *Explain why the plasma membrane is selectively permeable.*
22. *List three ways that substances can move across the plasma membrane.*
23. *Describe how the amount of solute in a solvent creates a concentration gradient. Do solutes diffuse with (down) or against their concentration gradient?*
24. *How is the rate of diffusion affected by an increased concentration gradient? By increased temperature of a solution? By increased viscosity of the solvent?*

Predict 2

Samuel is suffering from chronic renal failure, characterized by a gradual decrease in his kidneys' ability to perform their normal functions. Over the past few months, blood tests have indicated an increasing concentration of urea in his blood, which is a sign that the concentration of urea in the extracellular fluid is also increasing. Urea, a toxic waste produced inside cells, diffuses across the plasma membrane into the extracellular fluid. The kidneys eliminate excess urea in the urine. Explain why the extracellular concentration of urea is increasing, and predict how the intracellular concentration of urea is changing.

Osmosis

Osmosis (oz-MOH-sis) is the diffusion of water (solvent) across a selectively permeable membrane, such as a plasma membrane (figure 3.12). *Selectively permeable* means that the membrane allows water but not all the solutes dissolved in the water to diffuse through it. Interestingly, the permeability of some kidney cells to water can be regulated. Researchers found that the cells of kidneys have **aquaporins,** or water channel proteins, that open and close to adjust membrane permeability to water. (*Note:* This will be helpful in answering the Learn to Predict question at the beginning of the chapter.)

Water diffuses from a solution with proportionately more water, across a selectively permeable membrane, and into a solution with proportionately less water. Because solution concentrations are defined in terms of solute concentrations, not in terms of solvent content (see chapter 2), water diffuses from the less concentrated solution (fewer solutes, more water) into the more concentrated solution (more solutes, less water). Osmosis is important to cells because large volume changes caused by water movement disrupt normal cell function.

Osmotic pressure is the force required to prevent water from moving by osmosis across a selectively permeable membrane. Figure 3.12 illustrates osmosis across a selectively permeable membrane.

1. The osmotic pressure of a solution can be determined by placing the solution into a tube that is closed at one end by a selectively permeable membrane. The tube is then immersed in distilled water.
2. Water molecules move by osmosis through the membrane into the tube, forcing the solution to move up the tube. As the solution rises into the tube, its weight produces hydrostatic pressure, which opposes osmosis and forces water out of the tube back into the distilled water surrounding the tube.
3. At equilibrium, net movement of water stops, which means that the movement of water into the tube by osmosis is equal to the movement of water out of the tube caused by hydrostatic pressure. The osmotic pressure of the solution in the tube is equal to the hydrostatic pressure that prevents net movement of water into the tube.

The osmotic pressure of a solution provides information about the tendency for water to move by osmosis across a selectively permeable membrane. Because water moves from less concentrated solutions (fewer solutes, more water) into more concentrated solutions (more solutes, less water), the greater the solute concentration of a solution, the greater the tendency for water to move into the solution, and the greater the osmotic pressure to prevent that movement.

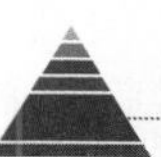

Predict 3

Given the demonstration in figure 3.12, what happens to osmotic pressure if the membrane is not selectively permeable but instead allows all solutes and water to pass through it?

Three terms describe the osmotic pressure of solutions: (1) isosmotic, (2) hyperosmotic, and (3) hyposmotic. Solutions with the same concentration of solute particles (see chapter 2) have the same osmotic pressure and are referred to as **isosmotic** (EYE-sos-MOT-ik). The solutions are isosmotic even if the types of solute particles in the two solutions differ from each other. If one solution has a greater concentration of solute particles, and therefore a greater osmotic pressure than another solution, the first solution is said to be **hyperosmotic** (HIGH-per-oz-MOT-ik) compared with the more dilute solution. The more dilute solution, with the lower osmotic pressure, is **hyposmotic** (HIGH-pos-MOT-ik) compared with the more concentrated solution.

Three additional terms describe the tendency of cells to shrink or swell when placed into a solution: (1) isotonic, (2) hypertonic, and (3) hypotonic (figure 3.13). If a cell placed into a solution neither shrinks nor swells, the solution is said to be **isotonic** (EYE-soh-TON-ik). In an isotonic solution, the shape of the cell remains constant, maintaining its internal tension or tone, a condition called

PROCESS Figure

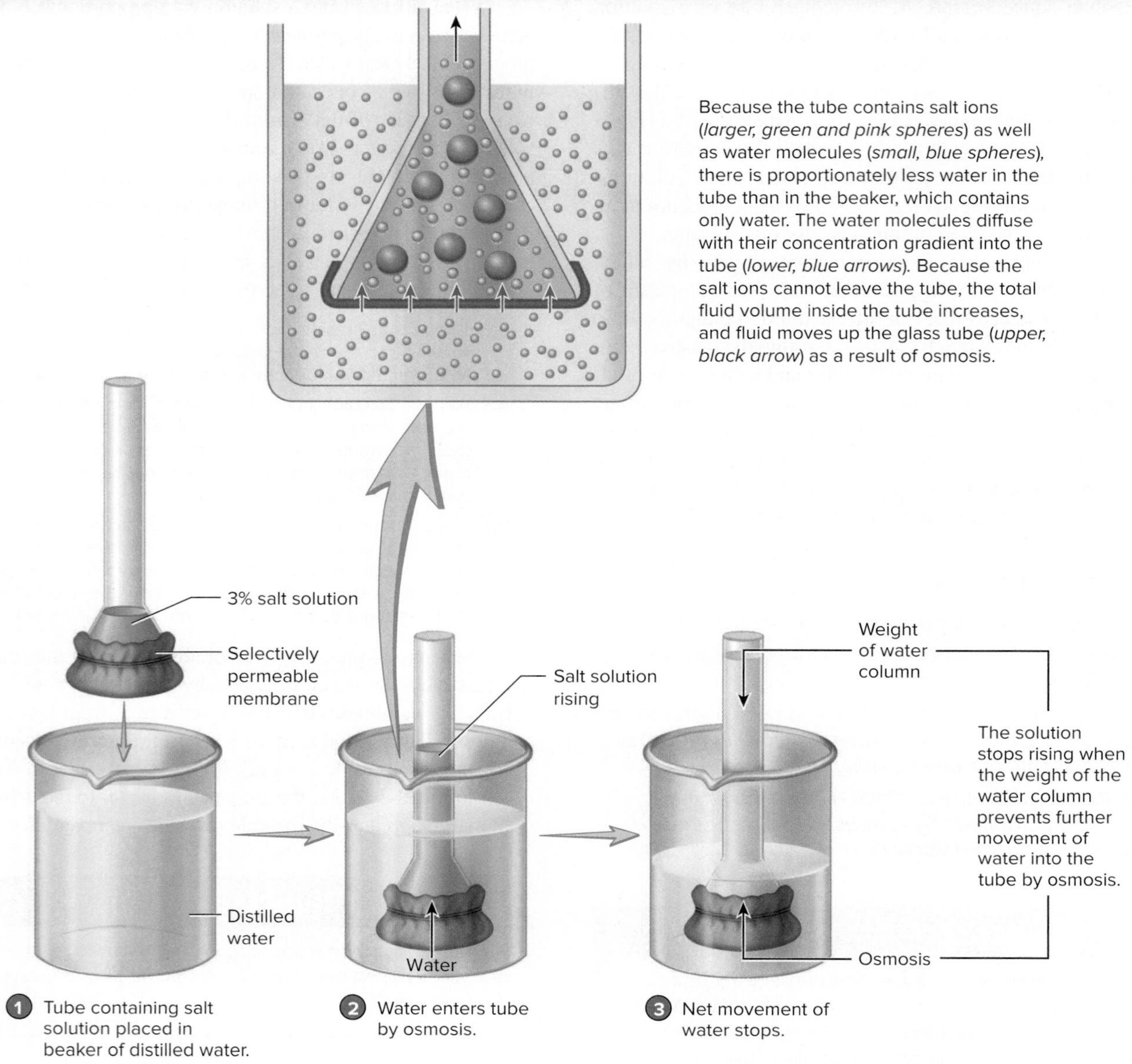

Because the tube contains salt ions (*larger, green and pink spheres*) as well as water molecules (*small, blue spheres*), there is proportionately less water in the tube than in the beaker, which contains only water. The water molecules diffuse with their concentration gradient into the tube (*lower, blue arrows*). Because the salt ions cannot leave the tube, the total fluid volume inside the tube increases, and fluid moves up the glass tube (*upper, black arrow*) as a result of osmosis.

3% salt solution

Selectively permeable membrane

Distilled water

Salt solution rising

Water

Weight of water column

The solution stops rising when the weight of the water column prevents further movement of water into the tube by osmosis.

Osmosis

1. Tube containing salt solution placed in beaker of distilled water.
2. Water enters tube by osmosis.
3. Net movement of water stops.

PROCESS Figure 3.12

Osmosis

In osmosis, water diffuses across a selectively permeable membrane from an area of lower solute concentration to an area of higher solute concentration. 

 Understand *What would happen if the tube shown in the above diagram were shorter by half?*

tonicity (toh-NIS-i-tee). If a cell is placed into a solution and water moves out of the cell by osmosis, causing the cell to shrink, the solution is called **hypertonic** (high-per-TON-ik). If a cell is placed into a solution and water moves into the cell by osmosis, causing the cell to swell, the solution is called **hypotonic** (high-poh-TON-ik).

An isotonic solution may be isosmotic to the cytoplasm. Because isosmotic solutions have the same concentration of solutes and water as the cytoplasm of the cell, no net movement of water occurs, and the cell neither swells nor shrinks (figure 3.13*b*). Hypertonic solutions can be hyperosmotic and have a greater concentration of solute molecules and a lower concentration of water than the cytoplasm of the cell. Therefore, water moves by osmosis from the cell into the hypertonic solution, causing the cell to shrink, a process called **crenation** (kreh-NAY-shun) in red blood cells (figure 3.13*c*). Hypotonic solutions can be hyposmotic and have a smaller concentration of solute molecules and a greater concentration of water than the cytoplasm of the cell. Therefore, water moves by osmosis into the cell, causing it to swell. If the cell swells enough, it can rupture, a process called **lysis** (LYE-sis; figure 3.13*a*). Solutions injected into the bloodstream or the tissues must be isotonic because shrinkage or swelling of cells disrupts their normal function and can lead to cell death.

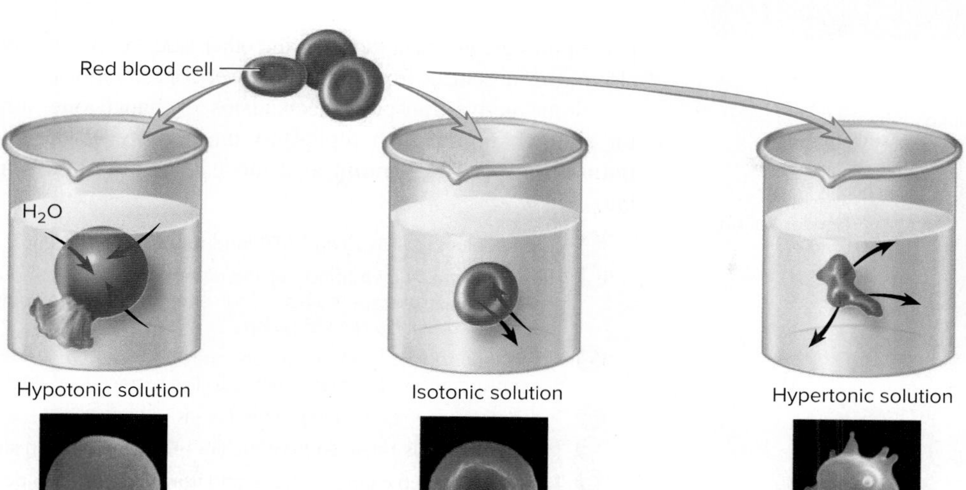

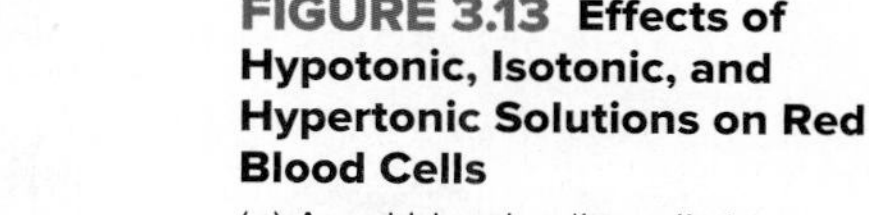

(a) When a red blood cell is placed in a hypotonic solution (one having a low solute concentration), water enters the cell by osmosis (*arrows*), causing the cell to swell or even burst (lyse; *puff of cytoplasm in lower part of cell*).

(b) When a red blood cell is placed in an isotonic solution (one having a concentration of solutes equal to that inside the cell), water moves into and out of the cell at the same rate (*arrows*). No net water movement occurs, and the cell shape remains normal.

(c) When a red blood cell is placed in a hypertonic solution (one having a high solute concentration), water moves by osmosis out of the cell and into the solution (*arrows*), resulting in shrinkage (crenation).

FIGURE 3.13 Effects of Hypotonic, Isotonic, and Hypertonic Solutions on Red Blood Cells

(*a*) A red blood cell swells in a hypotonic solution. This could cause the cell to lyse, or burst, if the difference is great enough. (*b*) A red blood cell submerged in an isotonic solution does not change shape. (*c*) A red blood cell submerged in a hypertonic solution loses water and shrinks, a condition called crenation.
David M. Phillips/Science Source

The *-osmotic* terms refer to the concentration of the solutions, and the *-tonic* terms refer to the tendency of cells to swell or shrink. These terms should not be used interchangeably. Not all isosmotic solutions are isotonic. For example, it is possible to prepare a solution of glycerol and a solution of mannitol that are isosmotic to the cytoplasm of the cell. Because the solutions are isosmotic, they have the same concentration of solutes and water as the cytoplasm. However, glycerol can diffuse across the plasma membrane, whereas mannitol cannot. When glycerol diffuses into the cell, the solute concentration of the cytoplasm increases, and its water concentration decreases. Therefore, water moves by osmosis into the cell, causing it to swell, and the glycerol solution is both isosmotic and hypotonic. In contrast, mannitol cannot enter the cell, and the isosmotic mannitol solution is also isotonic.

Facilitated Diffusion

Because of their chemical structure or size, many essential molecules, such as amino acids and glucose, cannot enter or exit the cell by diffusing directly through the plasma membrane. Instead, these molecules and ions cross the membrane by **mediated transport,** a membrane transport process by which membrane transport proteins mediate, or assist, the movement of large, water-soluble molecules or electrically charged molecules or ions across the plasma membrane.

Facilitated diffusion is a mediated transport process that moves substances into or out of cells from a higher to a lower concentration. Carrier proteins and channel proteins carry out facilitated diffusion. Facilitated diffusion does not require metabolic energy to transport substances across the plasma membrane. Figure 3.14 illustrates the facilitated diffusion of glucose into a cell.

1. A glucose molecule enters a carrier protein from the extracellular fluid. The glucose binds to the carrier protein.
2. The carrier protein changes shape and releases the glucose molecule into the cell. The carrier protein then resumes its original shape to transport additional glucose molecules.

The rate at which molecules or ions are transported is directly proportional to their concentration gradient up to the point of saturation, when all the carrier proteins or channels are occupied. Then the rate of transport remains constant at its maximum rate (see figure 3.4*c*).

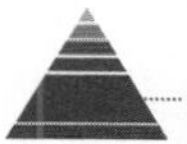

Predict 4

The transport of glucose into and out of most cells, such as muscle cells and adipocytes, occurs by facilitated diffusion. Once glucose enters a cell, it is rapidly converted to another molecule, such as glucose-6-phosphate or glycogen. What effect does this conversion have on the cell's ability to acquire glucose? Explain.

Active Membrane Transport

Active Transport

Active transport is a mediated transport process that requires energy provided by ATP. Movement of the transported substance to the opposite side of the membrane and its subsequent release from the ATP-powered pump are fueled by the breakdown of ATP. The maximum rate at which active transport proceeds depends on the number of ATP-powered pumps in the plasma membrane and the availability of adequate ATP. Active transport is important because it can move substances against their concentration gradients—that is, from lower concentrations to higher concentrations. Consequently, it can accumulate substances on one side of the plasma membrane at concentrations

PROCESS **Figure**

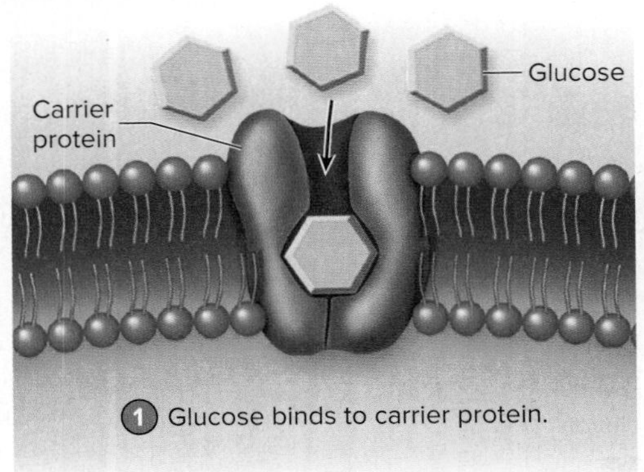

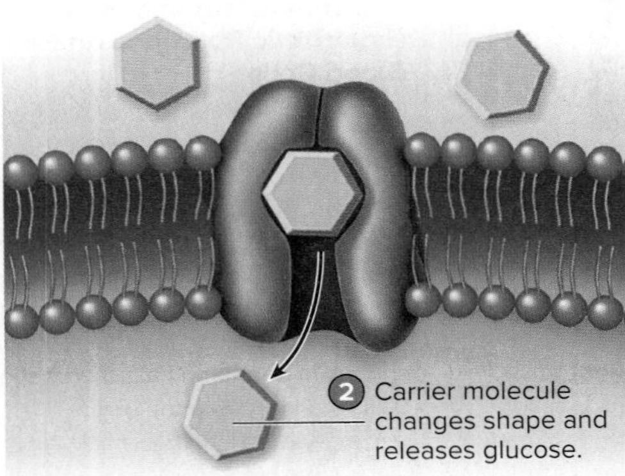

PROCESS **Figure 3.14**

Facilitated Diffusion

During facilitated diffusion, a carrier protein binds with a specific molecule, changes shape, and moves the molecule across the membrane.

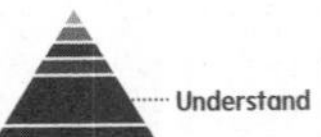

Is the carrier protein in the above figure moving the substance with or against the substance's concentration gradient? How do you know?

Case STUDY 3.1 | **Addison Disease**

James experienced unexplained weight loss, fatigue, and low blood pressure. After running several tests, his physician concluded that James had Addison disease, which involves decreased aldosterone production by the adrenal gland. When aldosterone production falls too low, certain kidney cells are unable to transport Na^+ back into the blood.

Predict 5

1) *How does Addison disease affect Na^+ levels in the urine?*
2) *Would you expect James's urine volume to be higher or lower than normal? Explain your answer.*

many times greater than those on the other side. Active transport can also move substances from higher to lower concentrations.

Some active-transport mechanisms exchange one substance for another. Figure 3.15 represents the activity of the **sodium-potassium (Na^+–K^+) pump** as it moves Na^+ out of cells and K^+ into cells.

1. Three sodium ions (Na^+) and ATP bind to the Na^+–K^+ pump.
2. The ATP breaks down to adenosine diphosphate (ADP) and a phosphate (P) and releases energy. That energy is used to power the shape change in the Na^+–K^+ pump.
3. The Na^+–K^+ pump changes shape, and the three sodium ions are transported across the membrane into the extracellular fluid.
4. Two potassium ions (K^+) bind to the Na^+–K^+ pump.
5. The phosphate is released from the Na^+–K^+ pump binding site.
6. The Na^+–K^+ pump changes shape and transports the two potassium ions across the membrane and into the cytoplasm. The Na^+–K^+ pump can again bind to Na^+ and ATP.

The result of the Na^+–K^+ pump activity is a higher concentration of Na^+ outside the cell and a higher concentration of K^+ inside the cell. Because ATP is broken down during the transport of Na^+ and K^+, the pump is also called **sodium-potassium ATP-ase.** The Na^+–K^+ pump is very important to a number of cell functions, as discussed in chapters 9 and 11.

Secondary Active Transport

Secondary active transport involves the active transport of an ion, such as Na^+, out of a cell, establishing a concentration gradient, with a higher concentration of the ions outside the cell. The tendency for the ions to move back into the cell (down their concentration gradient) provides the energy necessary to move a different ion or some other molecule into the cell. For example, glucose moves from the lumen of the intestine into epithelial cells by secondary active transport. This process requires two transport proteins: (1) A Na^+–K^+ pump actively moves Na^+ out of the cell, and (2) a carrier protein facilitates the movement of Na^+ and glucose into the cell. Both Na^+ and glucose are necessary for the carrier protein to function. The process of transporting glucose into a cell by secondary active transport is shown in figure 3.16.

1. A Na^+–K^+ pump maintains a concentration gradient of Na^+ that is higher outside the cell than inside the cell.
2. Sodium ions move back into the cell through a transport protein that also moves glucose. The concentration gradient for Na^+ provides energy required to move glucose against its concentration gradient.

The movement of Na^+ down its concentration gradient provides the energy to move glucose molecules into the cell against their concentration gradient. Thus, glucose can accumulate at concentrations higher inside the cell than outside. Because the movement of glucose molecules against their concentration gradient results from the formation of a concentration gradient of Na^+ by an active-transport mechanism, the process is called secondary active transport.

Vesicular Transport

Vesicular transport is the movement of larger volumes of substances across the plasma membrane through the formation or release of vesicles, membrane-bound sacs. Vesicular transport includes endocytosis and exocytosis.

PROCESS **Figure**

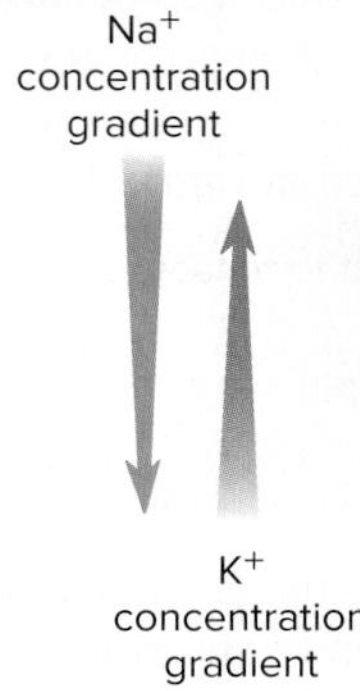

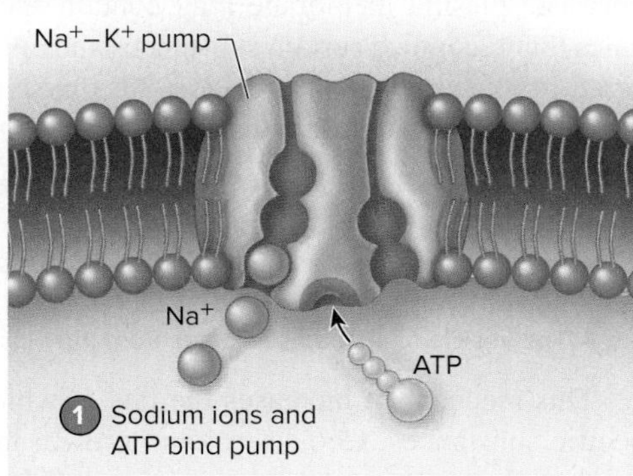

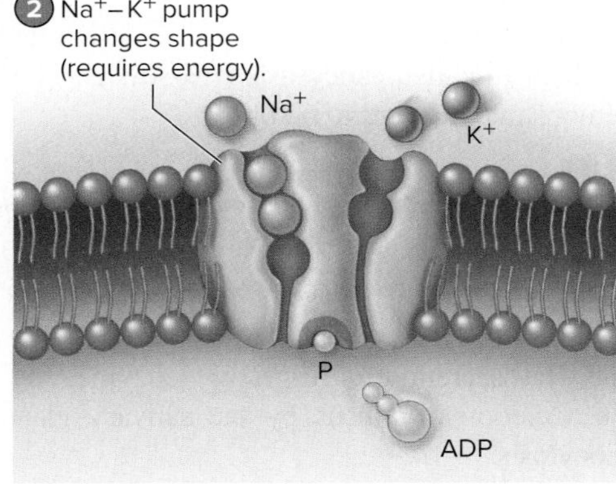

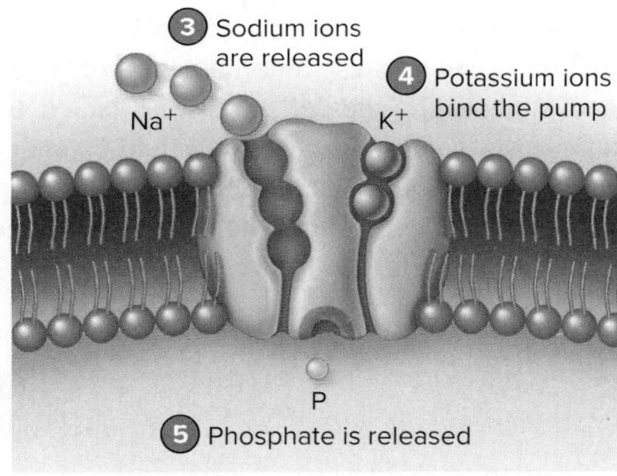

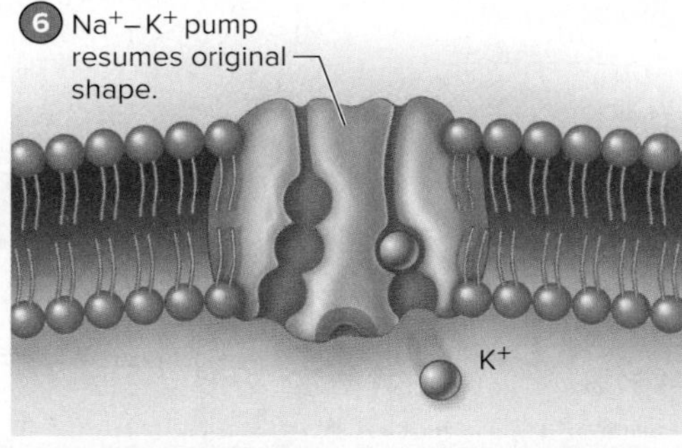

PROCESS **Figure 3.15**

Active Transport: Sodium-Potassium Pump

During a single cycle of the Na^+–K^+ pump, one ATP molecule is used to transport 3 Na^+ out of the cell and 2 K^+ into the cell. APR

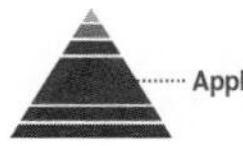

How many ATP molecules would be spent to transport 12 Na^+ out of the cell? How many K^+ would be transported into the cell during the same cycles?

PROCESS **Figure**

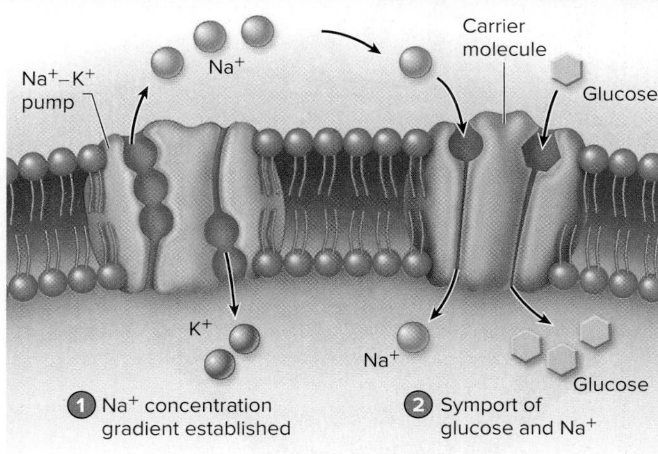

PROCESS **Figure 3.16**

Secondary Active Transport (Symport) of Na^+ and Glucose

The active transport of Na^+ (step 1) maintains a Na^+ concentration gradient, which provides the energy to transport glucose against its concentration gradient (step 2).

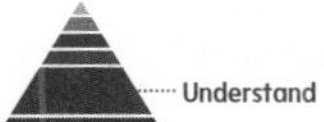

In which step is the cell "paying" the energy cost to transport glucose against its concentration gradient? Explain your answer.

Vesicular transport requires energy in the form of ATP and therefore is an active membrane transport process. However, because it involves the bulk movement of material into the cell, vesicular transport does not demonstrate the degree of specificity or saturation that other forms of active membrane transport exhibit.

Endocytosis (EN-doh-sigh-TOH-sis) occurs when material moves through the plasma membrane and into the cytoplasm by the formation of a vesicle. A portion of the plasma membrane wraps around a particle or droplet in the extracellular fluid. The portion of the plasma membrane then fuses, so that the particle or droplet is surrounded by a membrane. That portion of the membrane then "pinches off," so that the enclosed particle or droplet is within the cytoplasm of the cell, and the plasma membrane is left intact.

There are two types of endocytosis: (1) phagocytosis and (2) pinocytosis. In **phagocytosis** (FAG-oh-sigh-TOH-sis), which means "cell-eating," solid particles are ingested and phagocytic vesicles are formed (figure 3.17). White blood cells and some other cell types phagocytize bacteria, cell debris, and foreign particles. Phagocytosis is therefore important in eliminating harmful substances from the body.

Pinocytosis (PIN-oh-sigh-TOH-sis), which means "cell-drinking," is distinguished from phagocytosis in that smaller vesicles form, and they contain molecules dissolved in liquid rather than particles (figure 3.18). Pinocytosis often forms vesicles near the tips of deep invaginations of the plasma membrane. It is a common transport phenomenon in a variety of cell types, occurring in certain cells of the kidneys, epithelial cells of the intestines, cells of the liver, and cells that line capillaries.

Endocytosis can exhibit specificity. For example, cells that phagocytize bacteria and necrotic tissue do not phagocytize healthy

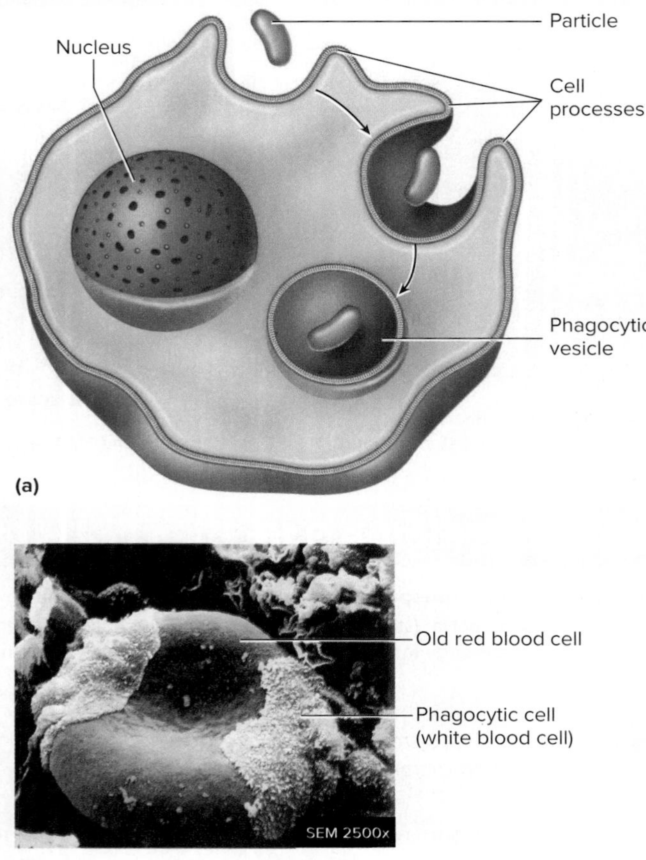

FIGURE 3.17 Phagocytosis
(*a*) In this type of endocytosis, a solid particle is ingested, and a phagocytic vesicle forms around it. (*b*) Colorized scanning electron micrograph of phagocytosis of a red blood cell. (b) Profs. P.M. Motta, T. Fujita & M. Muto/ Science Source

cells. The plasma membrane may contain specific receptor molecules that recognize certain substances and allow them to be transported into the cell by phagocytosis or pinocytosis. This is called **receptor-mediated endocytosis,** and is illustrated in figure 3.19.

1. Specific molecules in the extracellular fluid bind to receptors in the plasma membrane.
2. The receptors and the bound molecules are taken into the cell as a vesicle begins to form.
3. The vesicle fuses and separates from the plasma membrane.

This mechanism increases the rate at which the cells take up specific substances. Cholesterol and growth factors are examples of molecules that can be taken into a cell by receptor-mediated endocytosis.

Some cells release material through a vesicular transport mechanism called **exocytosis** (EK-so-sigh-TOH-sis). Exocytosis is demonstrated in figure 3.20.

1. Within the cell, secretions accumulate within vesicles. These secretory vesicles then move to the plasma membrane.
2. The vesicle membrane fuses with the plasma membrane.
3. The vesicle contents are expelled from the cell into the extracellular fluid.

The secretion of digestive enzymes by the pancreas and the secretion of mucus by the salivary glands are examples of exocytosis.

Vesicular transport is important for moving substances into or out of cells. However, cells, such as the endothelial cells of blood capillaires, can also use a combination of both types to move substances "through" the cell, a process called **transcytosis.** During transcytosis, a substance enters the cell by endocytosis. The vesicle containing the substance moves through the cytoplasm to the opposite side of the cell. There the substance is released from the cell through exocytosis (see figure 3.18).

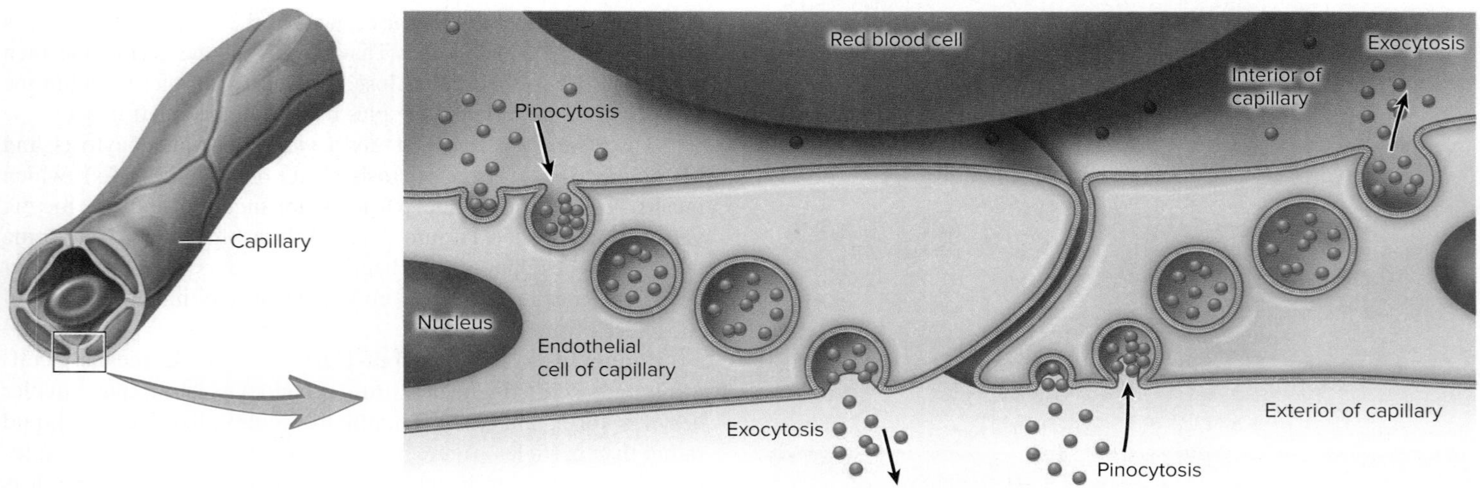

FIGURE 3.18 Pinocytosis and Transcytosis
Pinocytosis is much like phagocytosis, except that the cell processes—and therefore the vesicles formed—are much smaller and the material inside the vesicle is liquid rather than particulate. Pinocytotic vesicles form on the internal side of a capillary, are transported across the cell, and open by exocytosis outside the capillary. Transcytosis is the movement of a substance through a cell by a combination of endocytosis on one cell surface and exocytosis on the opposite cell surface.

PROCESS **Figure**

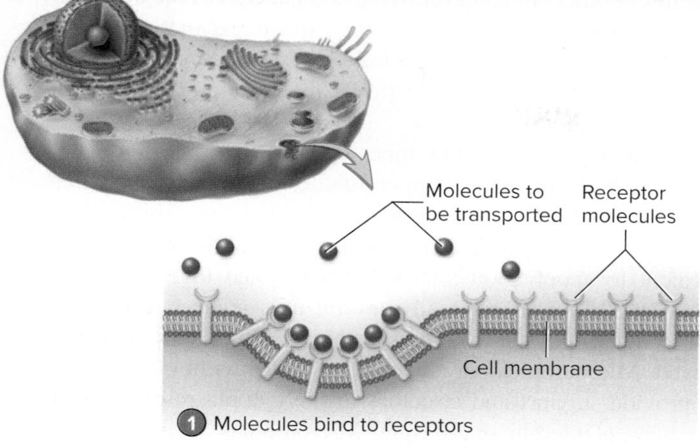

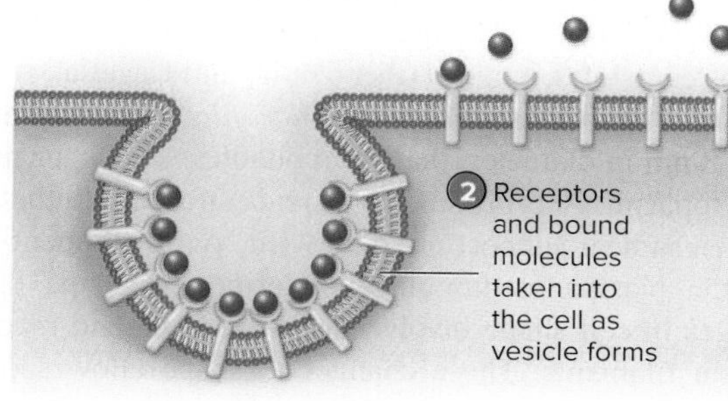

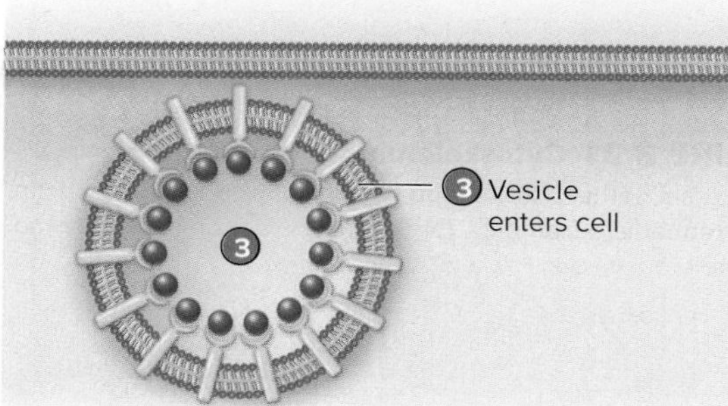

PROCESS **Figure 3.19**

Receptor-Mediated Endocytosis

Molecules bind to receptors on the plasma membrane and a vesicle forms to transport the molecules into the cell.

How is receptor-mediated endocytosis similar to facilitated diffusion? How is it different?

PROCESS **Figure**

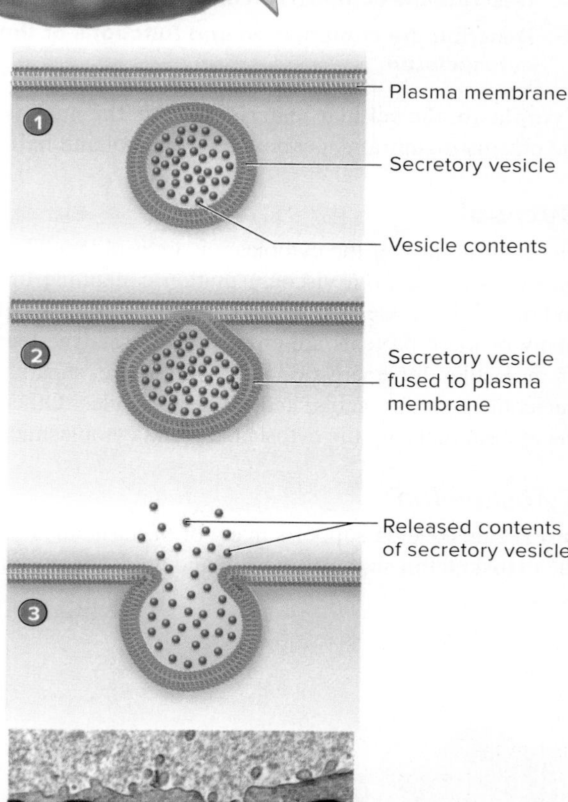

PROCESS **Figure 3.20**

Exocytosis

(*a*) Diagram of exocytosis. (*b*) Transmission electron micrograph of exocytosis.
(b) JOSE CALVO/Science Source

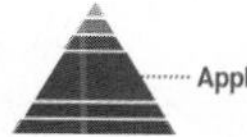

Exocytosis often involves the release of proteins manufactured in the cell. Why do you suppose these proteins are not transported across the membrane by transport proteins?

ASSESS YOUR PROGRESS

25. *Define osmosis, and describe how osmotic pressure is created. As the concentration of a solution increases, what happens to its osmotic pressure and to the tendency for water to move into the solution?*

26. *Compare isosmotic, hyperosmotic, and hyposmotic solutions with isotonic, hypertonic, and hypotonic solutions.*

27. *What is mediated transport? What types of particles move through the plasma membrane by mediated transport?*

28. *Contrast facilitated diffusion and active transport in relation to energy expenditure and direction of movement with respect to the concentration gradient.*

29. *What is secondary active transport? Describe how it functions.*

30. *What occurs during endocytosis? What role do vesicles play?*

31. *How do phagocytosis and pinocytosis differ from each other?*

32. *What is receptor-mediated endocytosis?*

33. *Describe and give examples of exocytosis.*

3.7 Cytoplasm

LEARNING OUTCOMES

After reading this section, you should be able to

A. **Describe the composition and functions of the cytoplasm.**
B. **Describe the composition and functions of the cytoskeleton.**

Cytoplasm, the cellular material outside the nucleus but inside the plasma membrane, is about half cytosol and half organelles.

Cytosol

The fluid portion of the cytoplasm is **cytosol** (SIGH-toh-sol). The cytosol is a colloid, a viscous solution containing dissolved ions and molecules as well as suspended molecules, especially proteins. Many of these proteins are enzymes that catalyze the breakdown of molecules for energy or the synthesis of sugars, fatty acids, nucleotides, amino acids, and other molecules. Other proteins in the cytosol make up the cytoskeleton and cytoplasmic inclusions.

Cytoskeleton

Just as our skeleton supports many of the structures of our bodies, the **cytoskeleton** supports the cell and holds the nucleus and other organelles in place. In addition, some components of the cytoskeleton are responsible for changes in cell shape and the movement of cell organelles. The cytoskeleton consists of three groups of proteins: (1) microtubules, (2) actin filaments, and (3) intermediate filaments (figure 3.21).

Microtubules are hollow tubes composed primarily of protein units called **tubulin.** The microtubules are about 25 nanometers (nm) in diameter, with walls about 5 nm thick. (For comparison, the width of a human hair is 60,000 nm, which is equivalent to about 2000 microtubules bundled together.) They vary in length but are normally several micrometers (μm) long. Microtubule length can change as tubulin subunits are added or removed. Microtubules play a variety of roles within cells. They help provide support and structure to the cytoplasm of the cell, much like an internal scaffolding. Microtubules are involved in cell division and in the transport of intracellular materials. Microtubules also form essential components of certain cell organelles, such as centrioles, spindle fibers, cilia, and flagella.

Actin filaments, also called *microfilaments,* are small fibrils, about 8 nm in diameter, that form bundles, sheets, or networks in the cytoplasm. Actin filaments provide structure to the cytoplasm and mechanical support for microvilli. Actin filaments also support the plasma membrane and define the shape of the cell. Changes in cell shape involve the breakdown and reconstruction of actin filaments. These changes in shape allow some cells to

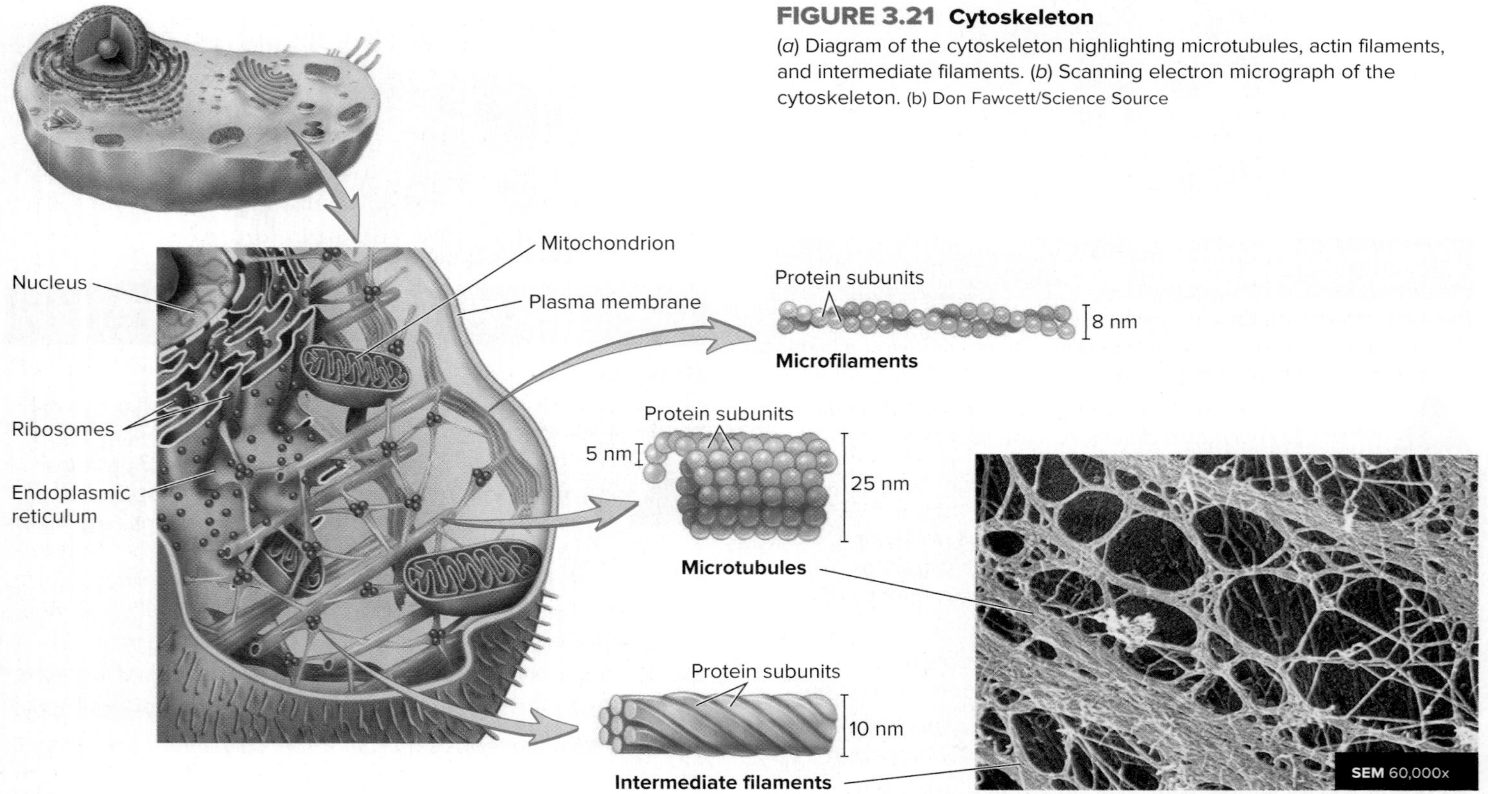

FIGURE 3.21 Cytoskeleton
(*a*) Diagram of the cytoskeleton highlighting microtubules, actin filaments, and intermediate filaments. (*b*) Scanning electron micrograph of the cytoskeleton. (b) Don Fawcett/Science Source

move about. Muscle cells contain a large number of highly organized actin filaments, which are responsible for the muscle's ability to contract (see chapter 9).

Intermediate filaments are protein fibers about 10 nm in diameter that provide mechanical strength to cells. For example, intermediate filaments support the extensions of nerve cells. These nerve cell extensions have a very small diameter but can be up to a meter in length.

Cytoplasmic Inclusions

The cytosol also contains **cytoplasmic inclusions,** which are aggregates of chemicals either produced or taken in by the cell. For example, lipid droplets or glycogen granules store energy-rich molecules; hemoglobin in red blood cells transports O_2; the pigment melanin colors the skin, hair, and eyes; and **lipochromes** (LIP-oh-krohmz) are pigments that increase in amount with age. Dust, minerals, and dyes can also accumulate in the cytoplasm.

ASSESS YOUR PROGRESS

34. *Differentiate between the cytoplasm and the cytosol.*
35. *What are the general functions of the cytoskeleton?*
36. *List and describe the functions of microtubules, actin filaments, and intermediate filaments.*
37. *What are cytoplasmic inclusions? Give several examples.*

3.8 The Nucleus and Cytoplasmic Organelles

LEARNING OUTCOMES

After reading this section, you should be able to

A. **Define *organelle*.**
B. **Describe the structure and function of the nucleus.**
C. **Describe the structure and function of the nucleoli.**
D. **Explain the structure and function of ribosomes.**
E. **Compare the structures and functions of rough and smooth endoplasmic reticula.**
F. **Discuss the structure and function of the Golgi apparatus.**
G. **Describe the role of secretory vesicles in the cell.**
H. **Compare the structures and roles of lysosomes and peroxisomes in digesting material within the cell.**
I. **Relate the structure and function of proteasomes.**
J. **Describe the structure and function of mitochondria.**
K. **Explain the structure and function of the centrosome.**
L. **Compare the structures and functions of cilia, flagella, and microvill.**

Organelles are structures within cells that are specialized for particular functions, such as manufacturing proteins or producing ATP. Organelles can be thought of as individual workstations within the cell, each responsible for performing specific tasks. One class of organelles has membranes that are similar to the plasma membrane, whereas other organelles are clusters of proteins and other molecules not surrounded by a membrane. The interior of the membrane-bound organelles is separated from the cytoplasm, creating subcellular compartments having their own enzymes capable of carrying out unique chemical reactions. The nucleus is the largest organelle of the cell. The remaining organelles are considered cytoplasmic organelles (see table 3.1).

Recall that the first key concept of anatomy and physiology is structure and function relationships. Thus, the number and type of cytoplasmic organelles within each cell are related to the specific structure and function of the cell. Cells secreting large amounts of protein contain well-developed organelles that synthesize and secrete protein, whereas cells actively transporting substances, such as Na^+ across their plasma membrane, contain highly developed organelles that produce ATP. The following sections describe the structures and main functions of the nucleus and major cytoplasmic organelles in cells.

The Nucleus

The **nucleus** is a large, membrane-bound structure usually located near the center of the cell. It may be spherical, elongated, or lobed, depending on the cell type. All body cells have a nucleus at some point in their life cycle (see section 3.10), although some cells, such as red blood cells, lose their nuclei as they develop. Other cells, such as skeletal muscle cells contain more than one nucleus.

The nucleus consists of **nucleoplasm** surrounded by a **nuclear envelope** (figure 3.22). The nuclear envelope is composed of two membranes separated by a space. At many points on the surface of the nuclear envelope, the inner and outer membranes fuse to form porelike structures called **nuclear pores.** Molecules move between the nucleus and the cytoplasm through these openings.

Deoxyribonucleic acid (DNA) is mostly found within the nucleus, although small amounts of DNA are also found within mitochondria (described later in this section). The DNA and associated proteins are organized into discrete structures called **chromosomes** (KROH-moh-sohmz; figure 3.23). **Nucleosomes** are structural units of chromosomes, consisting of DNA wrapped around proteins called **histones** (HIS-tohnz) Other proteins associated with chromosomes regulate DNA function. During most of the cell's life cycle, the chromosomes are dispersed throughout the nucleus as delicate filaments collectively referred to as **chromatin** (KROH-ma-tin; figures 3.22 and 3.23). During cell division (see section 3.10), the chromatin filaments become densely coiled, forming compact chromosomes.

DNA determines the structural and functional characteristics of the cell by specifying the structure of proteins. Proteins form many of a cell's structural components, as well as all the enzymes that regulate most of the chemical reactions in the cell. DNA establishes the structure of proteins by specifying the sequence of their amino acids (see figure 2.24*a*). DNA is a large molecule, however, and cannot leave the nucleus. Instead DNA directs protein synthesis by means of an intermediate, **ribonucleic acid (RNA)**, which can leave the nucleus through nuclear pores. Three types of RNA molecules are important to protein synthesis: (1) messenger

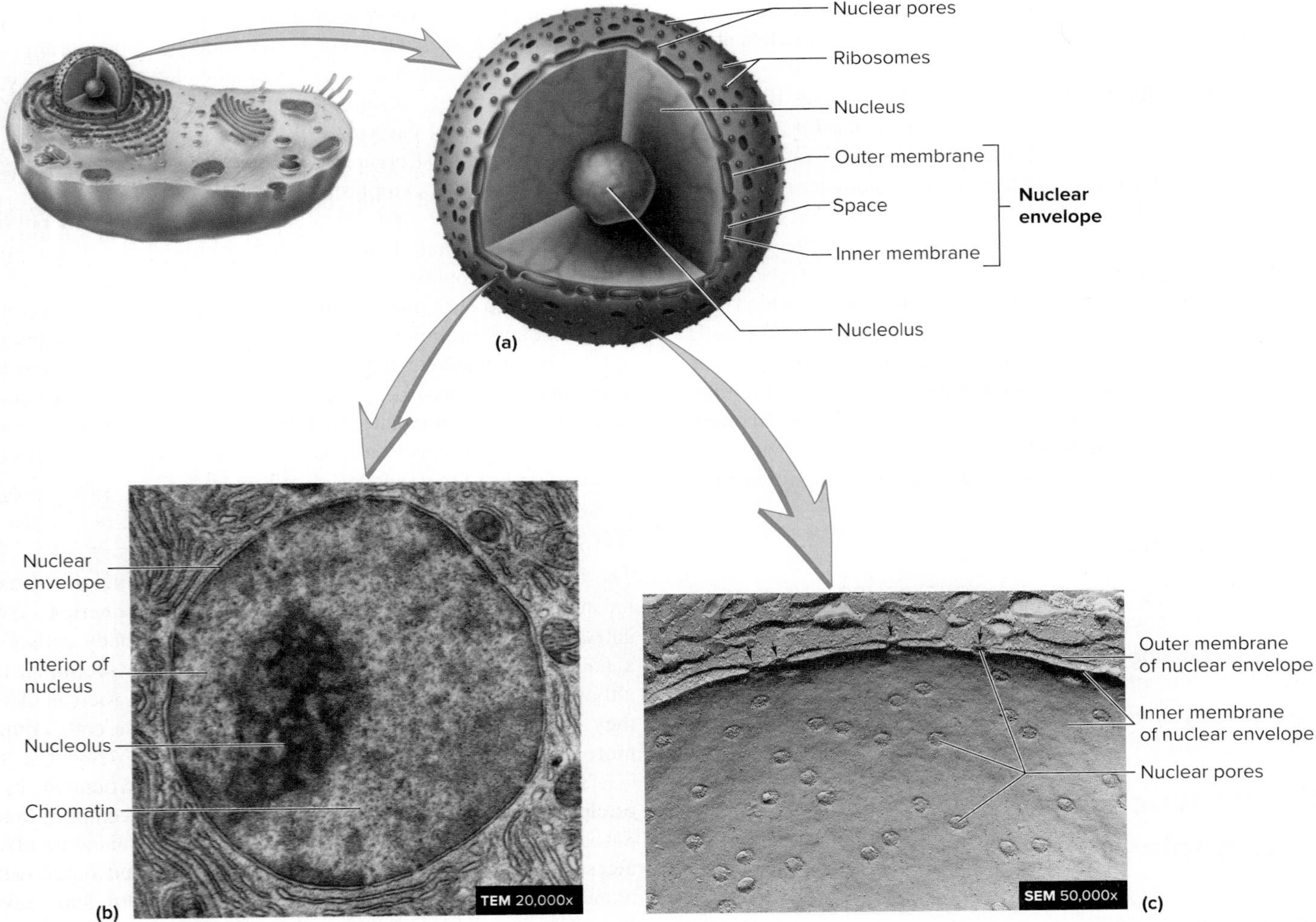

FIGURE 3.22 Nucleus
(*a*) The nuclear envelope consists of inner and outer membranes that become fused at the nuclear pores. The nucleolus is a condensed region of the nucleus not bound by a membrane and consisting mostly of RNA and protein. (*b*) Transmission electron micrograph of the nucleus. (*c*) Scanning electron micrograph showing the inner surface of the nuclear envelope and the nuclear pores. (b) Don W. Fawcett/Science Source; (c) Bernard Gilula/Science Source APR

RNA (mRNA), (2) ribosomal RNA (rRNA), and (3) transfer RNA (tRNA). The exact roles of these molecules are described in more detail in section 3.9.

Because RNA synthesis occurs within the nucleus, cells without nuclei accomplish protein synthesis only as long as the RNA produced before the nucleus degenerates remains functional. For example, red blood cells lack nuclei—the nuclei of developing red blood cells are expelled from the cells before the red blood cells enter the blood. Red blood cells survive without a nucleus for about 120 days and must be continually replaced. In comparison, many cells with nuclei, such as nerve and skeletal muscle cells, potentially survive as long as the person is alive.

A **nucleolus** (noo-KLEE-oh-lus) is a dense region within the nucleus and lacks a surrounding membrane (see figure 3.1). Usually, one nucleolus exists per nucleus, but several nucleoli may be seen in the nuclei of rapidly dividing cells. The subunits for ribosomes are manufactured in the nucleolus, so the portions of chromosomes that contain DNA from which rRNA is produced are located in the nucleolus.

Ribosomes

Ribosomes (RYE-boh-sohmz) are the sites of protein synthesis. Each ribosome is composed of a large subunit and a small subunit. The ribosomal subunits consist of **ribosomal RNA (rRNA)** produced in the nucleolus of the nucleus and proteins produced in the cytoplasm. Figure 3.24 illustrates the production of ribosomes.

1. Ribosomal proteins, produced in the cytoplasm, are transported through nuclear pores into the nucleolus.
2. Ribosomal proteins combine with rRNA, most of which is produced in the nucleolus, to form small and large subunits.
3. The small and large ribosomal subunits leave the nucleolus and the nucleus through nuclear pores.
4. The small and large subunits, now in the cytoplasm, combine with each other and with mRNA during protein synthesis.

Ribosomes can be found free in the cytoplasm or attached to an intracellular membrane complex called the endoplasmic reticulum. **Free ribosomes** primarily synthesize proteins used inside the cell, whereas ribosomes attached to the endoplasmic

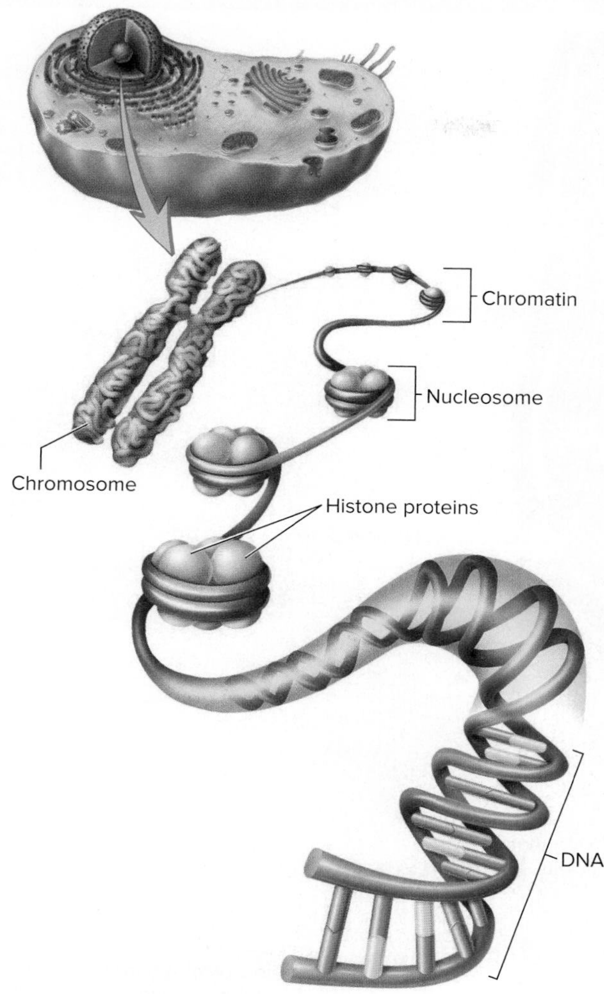

FIGURE 3.23 Chromosome Structure

DNA associated with globular histone proteins form units called nucleosomes. DNA molecules and bound proteins are called chromatin. During cell division, the chromatin condenses, so that individual structures, called chromosomes, become visible.

reticulum produce integral membrane proteins and proteins that are secreted from the cell.

ASSESS YOUR PROGRESS

38. *Define* organelles. *Are all organelles found in all cells?*
39. *Describe the structure of the nucleus and the nuclear envelope. What is the function of the nuclear pores?*
40. *Distinguish between chromatin and a chromosome. What molecule is found in chromatin? What are histones?*
41. *How can DNA control the structural and functional characteristics of the cell without leaving the nucleus? List the types of RNA.*
42. *What is the function of the nucleolus?*
43. *What molecules combine to form ribosomes? Where are ribosomal subunits formed?*
44. *Compare the functions of free ribosomes and ribosomes attached to the endoplasmic reticulum.*

Endoplasmic Reticulum

The outer membrane of the nuclear envelope is continuous with a series of membranes distributed throughout the cytoplasm of the cell (see figure 3.1), collectively referred to as the **endoplasmic reticulum** (EN-doh-PLAZ-mik reh-TIC-you-lum; network inside the cytoplasm). The endoplasmic reticulum consists of broad, flattened, interconnecting sacs and tubules (figure 3.25). The interior spaces of those sacs and tubules are called **cisternae** (sis-TER-nee) and are isolated from the rest of the cytoplasm.

The **rough endoplasmic reticulum** is called "rough" because ribosomes are attached to it. The ribosomes of the rough endoplasmic reticulum are sites where proteins are produced and modified for use as integral membrane proteins and for secretion into the extracellular space. The amount and configuration of the endoplasmic reticulum within the cytoplasm depend on the type and function of the particular cell. Cells with abundant rough endoplasmic reticulum synthesize large amounts of protein, which are secreted for use outside the cell.

Smooth endoplasmic reticulum, which is endoplasmic reticulum without attached ribosomes, manufactures lipids, such as phospholipids, cholesterol, and steroid hormones, as well as carbohydrates. Enzymes required for lipid synthesis are associated with the membranes of the smooth endoplasmic reticulum, and cells that synthesize large amounts of lipids contain dense accumulations of smooth endoplasmic reticulum. Many phospholipids produced in the smooth endoplasmic reticulum help form vesicles within the cell and contribute to the plasma membrane. Smooth endoplasmic reticulum also participates in **detoxification,** the processes by which enzymes act on chemicals and drugs to change their structure and reduce their toxicity. The smooth endoplasmic reticulum of skeletal muscle stores Ca^{2+} that function in muscle contraction.

Golgi Apparatus

The **Golgi** (GOL-jee) **apparatus** is composed of flattened, membranous sacs, containing cisternae, stacked on each other like dinner plates (figure 3.26). The Golgi apparatus can be thought of as a packaging and distribution center because it modifies, packages, and distributes proteins and lipids manufactured by the rough and smooth endoplasmic reticula. Material from the endoplasmic reticulum enters the Golgi apparatus on the *cis* face. After modification in the Golgi, the material is released from the *trans* face (see figure 3.26).

Figure 3.27 summarizes the movement of substances to and from the Golgi apparatus.

1. Proteins produced at the ribosomes attached to the rough endoplasmic reticulum move into the endoplasmic reticulum.
2. These proteins are later packaged into **transport vesicles** that then move to the *cis* face of the Golgi apparatus. These transport vesicles fuse with the Golgi apparatus membrane and release the proteins into the Golgi apparatus cisterna.
3. The Golgi apparatus concentrates and, in some cases, chemically modifies the proteins by synthesizing and attaching carbohydrate molecules to the proteins to form glycoproteins or by attaching lipids to the proteins to form lipoproteins.

PROCESS Figure

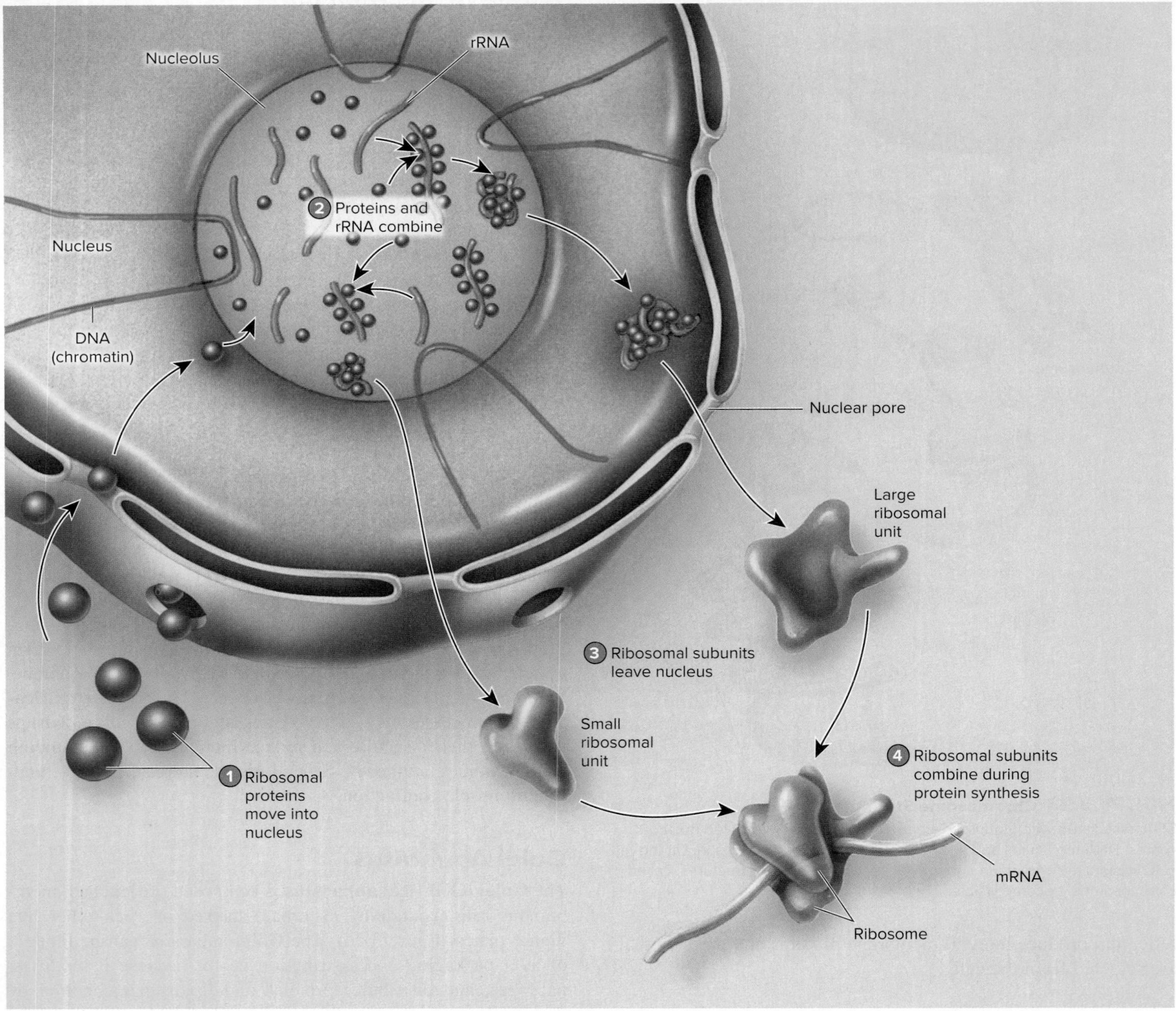

Nucleolus

rRNA

2 Proteins and rRNA combine

Nucleus

DNA (chromatin)

Nuclear pore

Large ribosomal unit

3 Ribosomal subunits leave nucleus

Small ribosomal unit

4 Ribosomal subunits combine during protein synthesis

mRNA

Ribosome

1 Ribosomal proteins move into nucleus

PROCESS Figure 3.24

Production of Ribosomes

Ribosomal subunits are produced in the nucleus and then move into the cytoplasm, where they form ribosomes during protein synthesis.

What are the two major molecules that make up ribosomal subunits? Recalling information from chapter 2, identify the building blocks for each of these molecule types.

4 The proteins are then packaged into vesicles that pinch off from the margins of the *trans* face of the Golgi apparatus and are distributed to various locations.

5 Some vesicles contain enzymes that are used by the cell.

6 Some vesicles carry proteins to the plasma membrane, where the proteins are secreted from the cell by exocytosis.

7 Other vesicles contain proteins that become part of the plasma membrane.

The Golgi apparatus is most highly developed in cells that secrete large amounts of protein or glycoproteins, such as cells in the salivary glands and the pancreas.

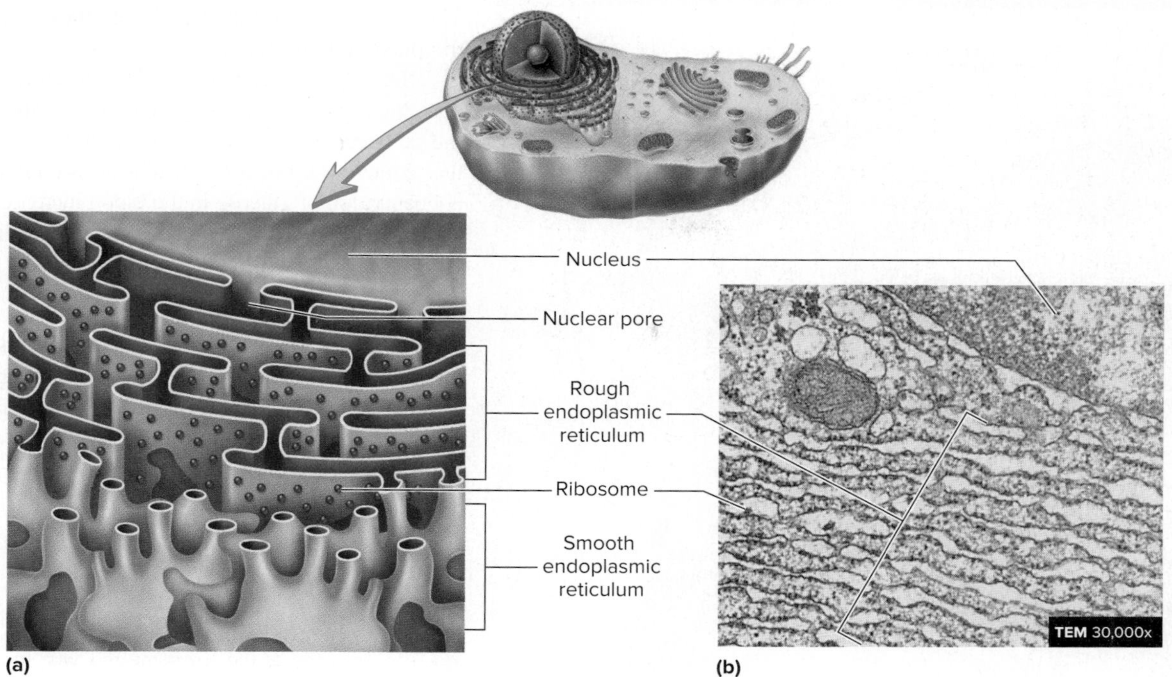

FIGURE 3.25 Endoplasmic Reticulum

(*a*) The endoplasmic reticulum is continuous with the nuclear envelope and occurs either as rough endoplasmic reticulum (with ribosomes) or as smooth endoplasmic reticulum (without ribosomes). (*b*) Transmission electron micrograph of the rough endoplasmic reticulum. (b) J. David Robertson, from Charles Flickinger, Medical Cell Biology, Philadelphia APR

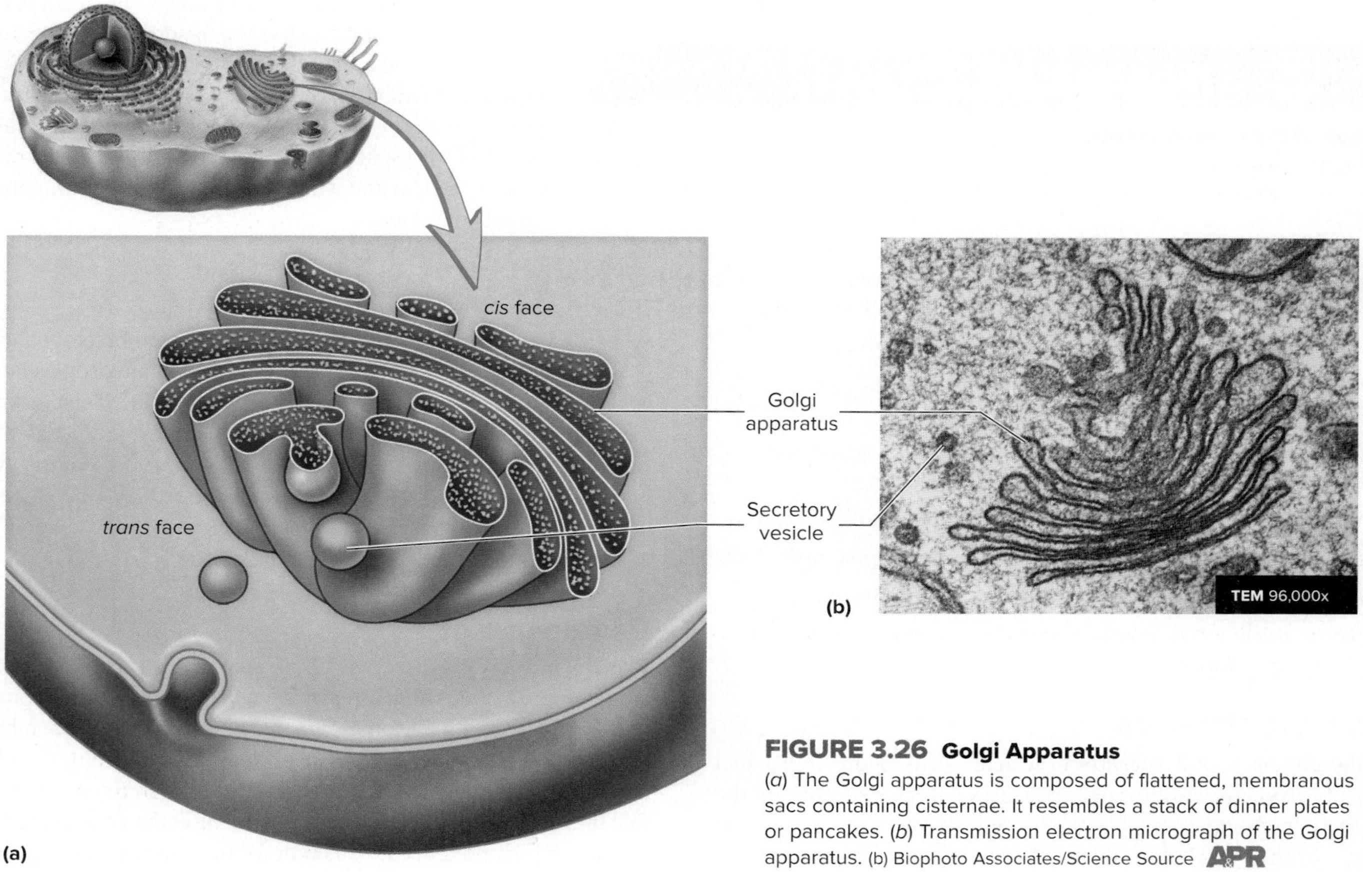

cis face
Golgi apparatus
Secretory vesicle
trans face
TEM 96,000x
(a)
(b)

FIGURE 3.26 Golgi Apparatus

(*a*) The Golgi apparatus is composed of flattened, membranous sacs containing cisternae. It resembles a stack of dinner plates or pancakes. (*b*) Transmission electron micrograph of the Golgi apparatus. (b) Biophoto Associates/Science Source APR

PROCESS **Figure**

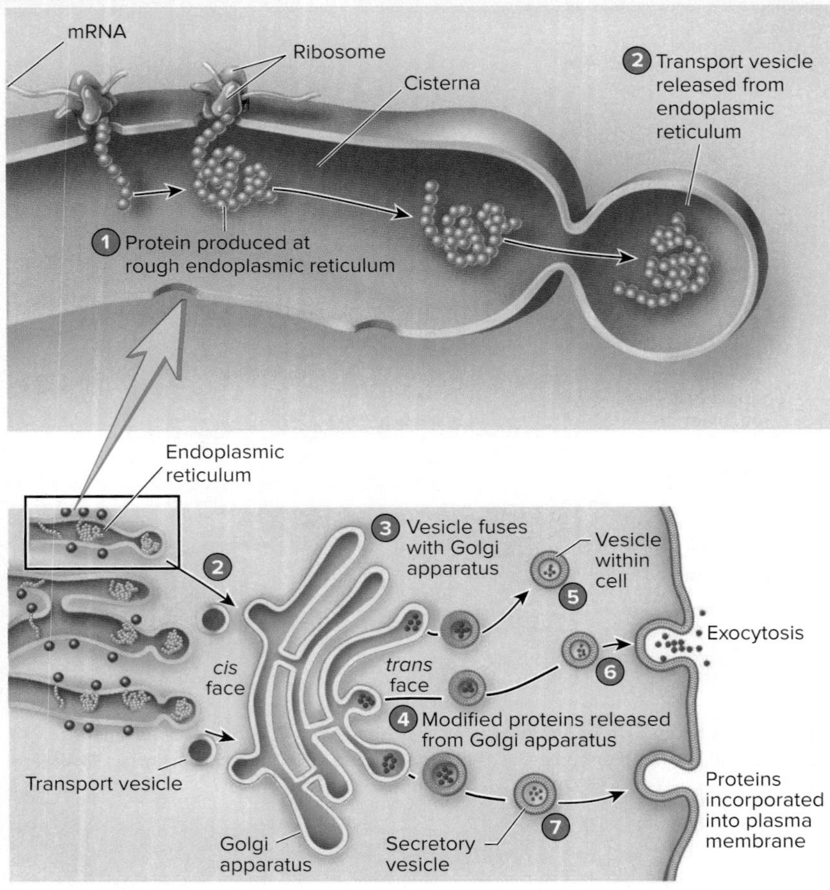

PROCESS **Figure 3.27**

Function of the Golgi Apparatus

The Golgi apparatus receives transport vesicles from the endoplasmic reticulum. The contents of these vesicles are concentrated and packaged for distribution within or outside of the cell.

Contents of transport vesicles can originate at the rough ER or smooth ER. What types of molecules are expected to be transported from the rough ER? From the smooth ER?

ASSESS YOUR PROGRESS

45. *Describe the structure and location of the endoplasmic reticula.*

46. *What are the functions of the rough endoplasmic reticulum?*

47. *Explain the functions of the smooth endoplasmic reticulum.*

48. *Relate the structure and function of the Golgi apparatus.*

49. *Name three ways in which proteins are distributed from the Golgi apparatus.*

Secretory Vesicles

The membrane-bound **secretory vesicles** (see figure 3.26) that pinch off from the Golgi apparatus move to the surface of the cell, their membranes fuse with the plasma membrane, and the contents of the vesicles are released to the exterior by exocytosis. The membranes of the vesicles are then incorporated into the plasma membrane.

Secretory vesicles accumulate in some cells, but their contents frequently are not released to the exterior until the cell receives a signal. For example, secretory vesicles that contain the hormone insulin do not release it until the concentration of glucose in the blood increases and acts as a signal for the secretion of insulin from the cells.

Lysosomes

Lysosomes (LIE-soh-sohmz) are membrane-bound vesicles that form at the Golgi apparatus (figure 3.27). They contain a variety of hydrolytic enzymes that function as intracellular digestive systems. Figure 3.28 illustrates the action of a lysosome in the digestion of phagocytized material.

1. A vesicle forms and enters the cytoplasm as the cell phagocytizes extracellular material.
2. A lysosome, formed at the Golgi apparatus, migrates to and fuses with the vesicle.
3. The enzymes of the lysosome mix with the material in the vesicle and digest the material.

Various enzymes within lysosomes digest nucleic acids, proteins, polysaccharides, and lipids. Certain white blood cells have large numbers of lysosomes that contain enzymes to digest phagocytized bacteria. Lysosomes also digest the organelles of the cell that are no longer functional, a process called **autophagy** (aw-toh-FAY-jee; self-eating). In other cells, the lysosomes move to the plasma membrane, and the enzymes are secreted by exocytosis. For example, the normal process of bone remodeling involves the breakdown of bone tissue by specialized bone cells. Lysosomes produced by those cells release the enzymes responsible for that degradation into the extracellular fluid.

Peroxisomes

Peroxisomes (per-OK-si-sohmz) are membrane-bound vesicles that are smaller than lysosomes. Peroxisomes contain enzymes that break down fatty acids and amino acids. The breakdown of these molecules can produce hydrogen peroxide (H_2O_2) as a toxic by-product. Peroxisomes also contain the enzyme **catalase,** which breaks down hydrogen peroxide to water and oxygen, thereby eliminating the toxic substance. Cells that are active in detoxification, such as liver and kidney cells, have many peroxisomes.

Proteasomes

Proteasomes (PROH-tee-ah-sohmz) are large protein complexes containing enzymes that break down and recycle other proteins within the cell. Proteasomes are not surrounded by membranes but instead are a collection of specific proteins forming barrel-like structures. The inner surfaces of the barrel have enzymatic regions that break down the proteins. Other proteins at the ends of the barrel regulate which proteins are taken in for breakdown and recycling.

PROCESS Figure

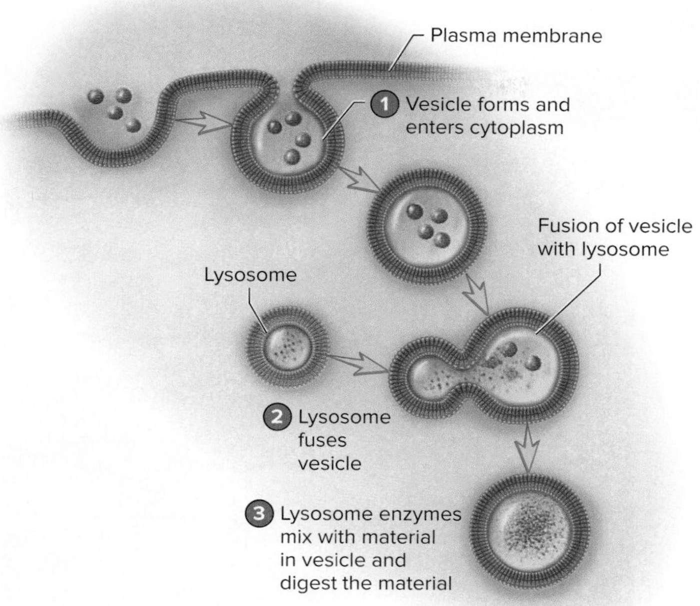

PROCESS Figure 3.28

Action of Lysosomes

Digestive enzymes in lysosomes are used to break down substances in the cytoplasm.

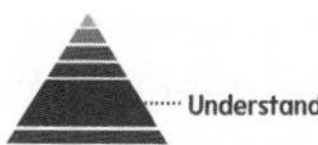

What is the benefit of having digestive enzymes isolated to lysosomes as opposed to free in the cytoplasm?

Clinical IMPACT 3.1

Tay-Sachs Disease

Some diseases result from nonfunctional lysosomal enzymes. For example, **Tay-Sachs disease** is a rare genetic disorder caused by the inability of lysosomal enzymes to break down **gangliosides,** specialized membrane lipids of neurons. These lipids accumulate in the cells and damage them. The common symptoms of Tay-Sachs disease include paralysis, blindness, and death, usually before age 5. Damage to the central nervous system begins in the fetus, but other symptoms do not become apparent until several months after birth. The infant appears to develop normally but then begins to regress, losing motor function and vision, experiencing seizures, and exhibiting delayed mental development. As a result of the destruction of cells of the nervous system, the individual usually dies by the age of 4 or 5.

Unfortunately, there is no known cure or treatment for Tay-Sachs disease. However, genetic counseling of high-risk couples accompanied by prenatal screening has greatly reduced the incidence of the disease.

Mitochondria

Mitochondria (mye-toh-KON-dree-ah) are the organelles that provide the majority of the energy for the cell. Consequently, they are often called the cell's power plants. Mitochondria are usually depicted as small, rod-shaped structures (figure 3.29). However, in living cells, mitochondria are very dynamic and constantly change shape and number as they split and fuse with each other. Mitochondria are the major sites for the production of ATP, which is the primary energy source for most energy-requiring chemical reactions within the cell. Each mitochondrion has an inner and an outer membrane, separated by an intermembrane space. The outer membrane has a smooth contour, but the inner membrane has numerous infoldings called **cristae** (KRIS-tee; sing. *crista*) that project into the interior of the mitochondrion. The material located inside the inner membrane is called the **matrix.**

Complex series of mitochondrial enzymes form the two major enzyme systems responsible for most ATP synthesis (see chapter 25). The enzymes of the citric acid (Krebs) cycle are in the matrix. The enzymes of the electron-transport chain are embedded within the inner membrane. Cells with a greater energy requirement have more mitochondria with more cristae than do cells with lower energy requirements. Within the cytoplasm of a cell, the mitochondria are more numerous in areas where ATP is used. For example, mitochondria are numerous in cells that perform active transport and are packed near the membrane where active transport occurs.

Increases in the number of mitochondria result from the division of preexisting mitochondria. When muscles enlarge as a result of exercise, the number of mitochondria within the muscle cells increases to provide the additional ATP required for muscle contraction.

Predict 6

Describe the structural characteristics of cells that are highly specialized to do the following: (a) synthesize and secrete proteins, (b) actively transport substances into the cell, (c) synthesize lipids, and (d) phagocytize foreign substances.

ASSESS YOUR PROGRESS

50. *How are secretory vesicles formed?*
51. *Describe the process by which lysosomal enzymes digest phagocytized materials. What is autophagy?*
52. *What is the function of peroxisomes? How does catalase protect cells?*
53. *What are the structure and function of proteosomes?*
54. *Describe the structure of a mitochondrion. How does its nickname, the cell's power plant, relate to its function?*
55. *What enzymes are found on the cristae? In the matrix? How can the number of mitochondria in a cell increase?*

Centrioles and Spindle Fibers

The **centrosome** (SEN-troh-sohm), a specialized zone of cytoplasm close to the nucleus, is the center of microtubule formation

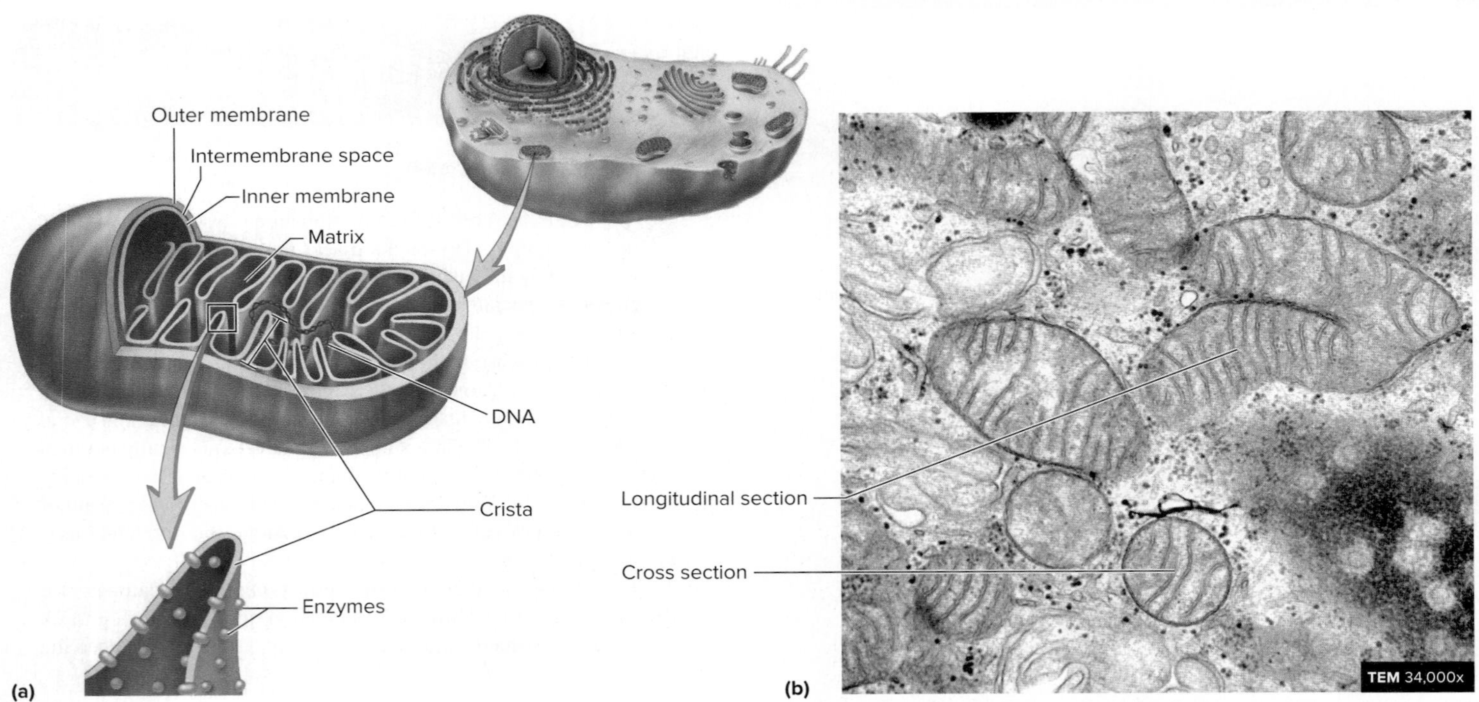

FIGURE 3.29 Mitochondrion
(*a*) Typical mitochondrion structure. (*b*) Transmission electron micrograph showing mitochondria in longitudinal and cross section. (b) EM Research Services/Newcastle University APR

in the cell. Within the centrosome are two **centrioles** (SEN-tree-ohlz). Each centriole is a small, cylindrical organelle about 0.3–0.5 μm in length and 0.15 μm in diameter, and the two centrioles are normally oriented perpendicular to each other within the centrosome (see figure 3.1). The wall of the centriole is composed of nine evenly spaced, longitudinally oriented, parallel units, or triplets. Each unit consists of three parallel microtubules joined together (figure 3.30).

Microtubules appear to influence the distribution of actin and intermediate filaments. Through its control of microtubule formation, the centrosome is closely involved in determining cell shape and movement. The microtubules extending from the centrosomes are very dynamic—constantly growing and shrinking.

Before cell division, the two centrioles double in number; the centrosome divides into two; and one centrosome, containing two centrioles, moves to each end of the cell. Microtubules

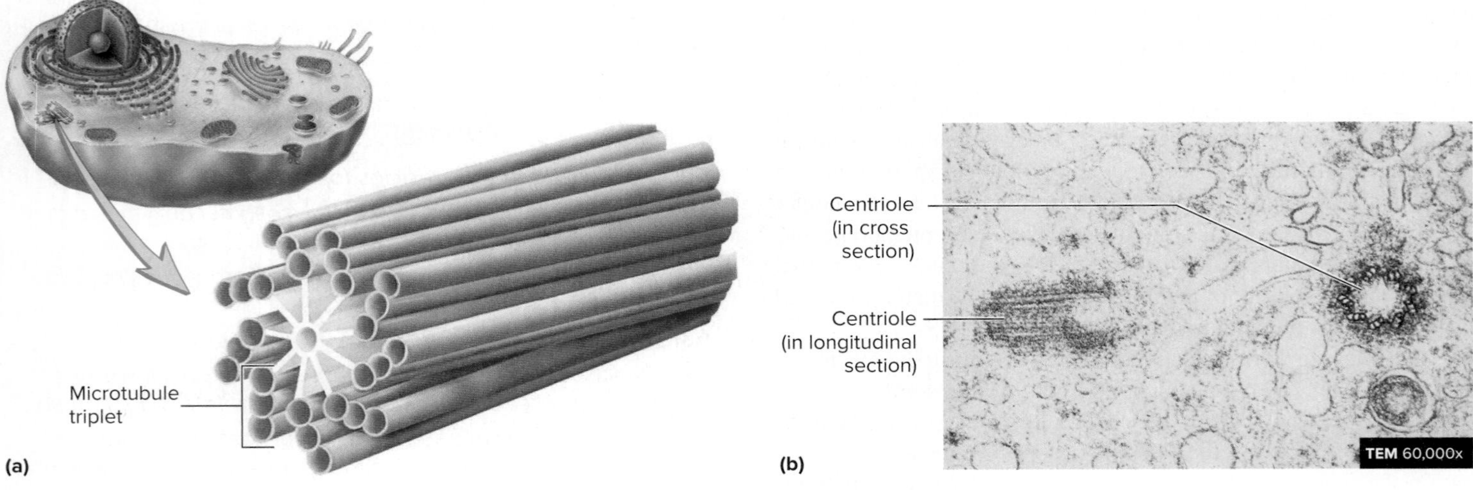

FIGURE 3.30 Centriole
(*a*) Structure of a centriole, which is composed of nine triplets of microtubules. Each triplet contains one complete microtubule fused to two incomplete microtubules. (*b*) Transmission electron micrograph of a pair of centrioles, which are normally located together near the nucleus. One is shown in cross section and one in longitudinal section. (b) Biology Media/Science Source APR

called **spindle fibers** extend out in all directions from the centrosome. These microtubules grow and shrink even more rapidly than those of nondividing cells. If the extended end of a spindle fiber comes in contact with a chromosome, the spindle fiber attaches to the chromosome and stops growing or shrinking. Eventually, spindle fibers from each centrosome bind to all the chromosomes. During cell division, the spindle microtubules facilitate the movement of chromosomes toward the two centrosomes (see section 3.10).

Cilia and Flagella

Cilia (SIL-ee-ah) are structures that project from the surface of cells and are capable of movement. They vary in number from one to thousands per cell. Cilia are cylindrical in shape, measuring about 10 μm in length and 0.2 μm in diameter. The shaft of each cilium is enclosed by the plasma membrane. Each cilium contains two centrally located microtubules and nine peripheral pairs of fused microtubules (the so-called 9 + 2 arrangement) that extend from the base to the tip of the cilium (figure 3.31). Movement of the cilium results when the microtubules move past each other, a process that requires energy from ATP. **Dynein arms,** proteins connecting adjacent pairs of microtubules, push the microtubules past each other. A **basal body** (a modified centriole) is located in the cytoplasm at the base of the cilium.

Cilia are numerous on surface cells that line the respiratory tract and the female reproductive tract. In these regions, cilia move in a coordinated fashion. Their motion moves materials over the surface of the cells. For example, cilia in the trachea move mucus containing trapped dust particles upward and away from the lungs, thus helping keep the lungs clear of debris.

Flagella (fla-JELL-ah) have a structure similar to that of cilia, but they are longer (45 μm). Sperm cells are the only human cells that possess flagella, and usually only one flagellum exists per cell. Furthermore, whereas cilia move small particles across the cell surface, flagella move the entire cell. For example, each sperm cell is propelled by a single flagellum. In contrast to cilia, which have a power stroke and a recovery stroke, flagella move in a wavelike fashion.

Microvilli

Microvilli (mye-kroh-VIL-eye; figure 3.32) are cylindrically shaped extensions of the plasma membrane about 0.5–1.0 μm in length and 90 nm in diameter. Normally, each cell has many microvilli. The presence of microvilli increases the cell surface area. A student looking at photographs may confuse microvilli with cilia, but microvilli are only one-tenth to one-twentieth the size of cilia. Individual microvilli can usually be seen only with an electron microscope, whereas cilia can be seen with a light microscope. Microvilli do not move, and they are supported with actin filaments, not microtubules. Microvilli are found on the cells of the intestine, kidney, and other areas where absorption is an important function. In certain locations of the body, microvilli are highly modified to function as sensory receptors. For example, elongated microvilli in hair cells of the inner ear respond to sound.

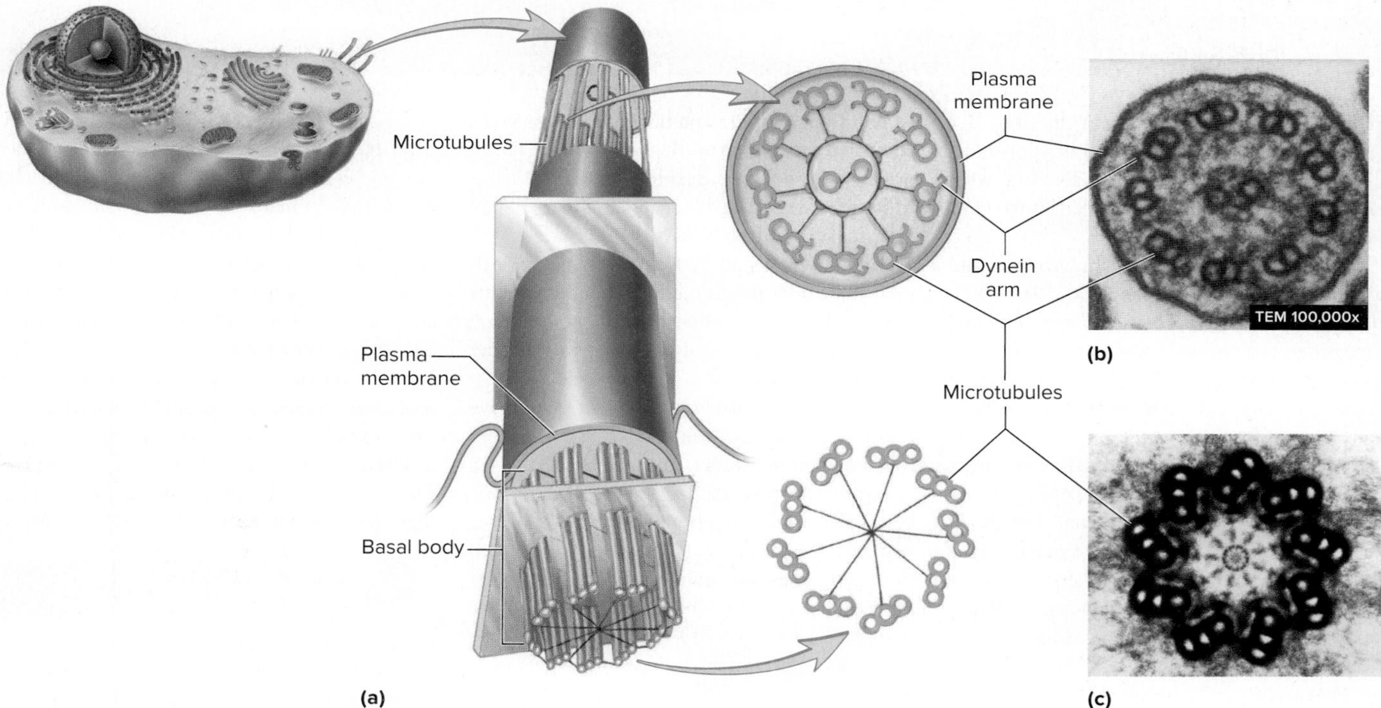

FIGURE 3.31 Structure of Cilia and Flagella

(*a*) The shaft of a cilium or flagellum has nine microtubule doublets around its periphery and two in the center. Dynein arms are proteins that connect one pair of microtubules to another pair. Dynein arm movement, which requires ATP, causes the microtubules to slide past each other, resulting in bending or movement of the cilium or flagellum. A basal body attaches the cilium or flagellum to the plasma membrane. (*b*) Transmission electron micrograph through a cilium. (*c*) Transmission electron micrograph through the basal body of a cilium. (b) Biophoto Associates/Science Source; (c) Don W. Fawcett/Science Source

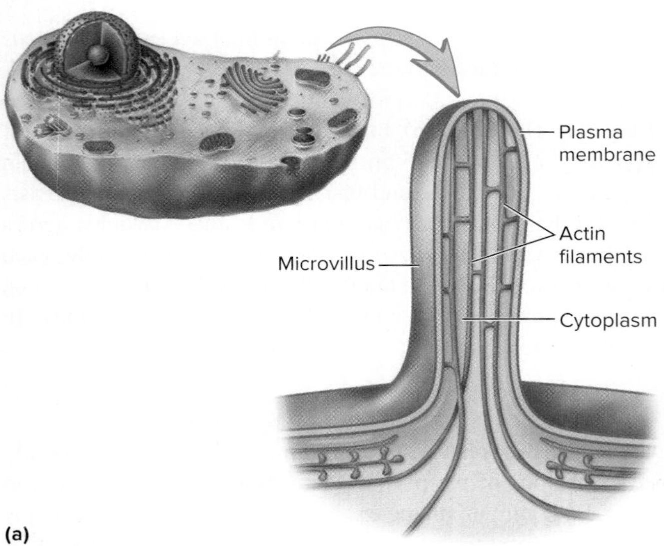

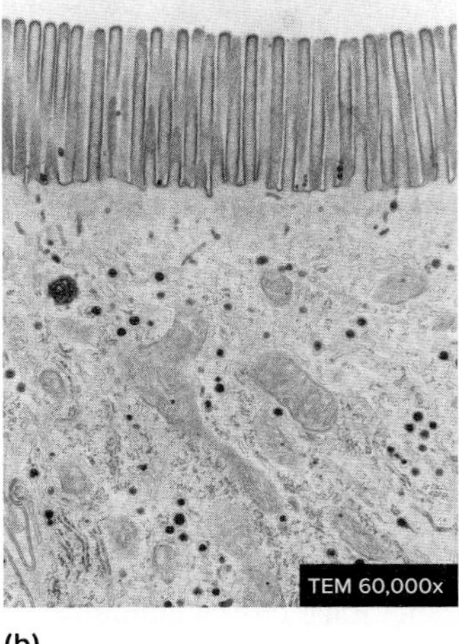

FIGURE 3.32 Microvillus
(*a*) A microvillus is a tiny, tubular extension of the cell; it contains cytoplasm and some actin filaments (microfilaments). (*b*) Transmission electron micrograph of microvilli. (b) Don W. Fawcett/Science Source

ASSESS YOUR PROGRESS

56. *What is the centrosome? Relate the structure of centrioles.*
57. *What are spindle fibers? Explain the relationship among centrosomes, spindle fibers, and chromosomes during cell division.*
58. *Contrast the structure and function of cilia with those of flagella.*
59. *Describe the structure and function of microvilli. How are microvilli different from cilia?*

MICROBES In Your Body 3.1 — Differences Between Prokaryotic and Eukaryotic Cells

Recall from Microbes In Your Body 1.1 that for every human cell in your body, there are 10 bacterial cells. But what are the major differences between those cells and human cells?

All living organisms can be grouped into two classes based on their cell structure: eukaryotes and prokaryotes. Human cells and some microbes in our bodies are eukaryotes. However, all bacteria cells are prokaryotes. It is this fundamental distinction that explains many facets of our biology.

Breaking down the term *prokaryotic* sheds light on the nature of this cell type: *pro* means pre, or before, and *karyon* means kernel, or nucleus—in other words, *before nuclei*. True to their name, prokaryotic cells do not have a formed, membrane-bound nucleus. Prokaryotes are also very ancient, appearing on earth at least 3 billion years ago.

Prokaryotic cells are ubiquitous—they are found in almost every location on earth and live many places other organisms cannot. Though we often associate bacteria with diseases, most prokaryotes are harmless; it is a small minority that is pathogenic. Prokaryotes comprise a majority of the total mass of living organisms on earth, despite their small size. Most prokaryotic cells are much smaller than most eukaryotic cells, which are, in general, 10 times longer and 1000 times larger in volume than prokaryotic cells. Prokaryotic cells are usually single-celled organisms, although some can be found living in groups with other prokaryotic cells.

Although prokaryotic cells do not have a formed nucleus, their DNA is clustered together among other cellular materials in a region termed the *nucleoid*. Prokaryotic cells also lack membrane-bound organelles or internal membranes. Their DNA is located in a single chromosome, which is circular in shape. Generally, most prokaryotes have between 1000 and 4000 genes, compared with eukaryotes, which have more genes—approximately 20,000 in humans. However, despite what some humans might view as limitations (small cell size, fewer genes), prokaryotes are impressively varied in their biochemical capabilities.

Bacterial cells are fundamentally different from human cells in their structure and their biology. Bacteria have molecules and mechanisms that humans do not, which allow for pathogenic bacteria to be targeted by antibiotics without harm to human cells. On the other hand, the immense population of bacteria in and on our bodies, referred to as commensal bacteria, are critical to our health. Commensal bacteria provide humans with materials and processes our cells are incapable of performing. For example, *E. coli* in our intestine produce a significant amount of required vitamin K. Throughout the rest of this book, we will highlight the importance of bacteria to homeostasis.

Apply

Predict 7

Viruses are also a type of microbe, yet they are not cells. Viruses consist of a molecule of nucleic acid (RNA or DNA) surrounded by protein. They must enter other organisms' cells and use their molecules and machinery to replicate themselves. Why aren't antibiotics prescribed for viral infections?

3.9 Genes and Gene Expression

LEARNING OUTCOMES

After reading this section, you should be able to

A. **Describe the two-step process that results in gene expression.**

B. **Explain the roles of DNA, mRNA, tRNA, and rRNA in the production of a protein.**

C. **Explain what the genetic code is and what it is coding for.**

D. **Describe what occurs during posttranscriptional processing.**

E. **Describe what occurs during posttranslational processing.**

F. **Describe the regulation of gene expression.**

Genes are the functional units of **heredity.** Heredity is the transmission of genetic traits from parent to offspring. Each gene is a segment of a DNA molecule that specifies the structure of an RNA molecule. This RNA can be functional on its own, or it can produce a protein. The production of RNA and/or proteins from the information stored in DNA is called **gene expression.** Gene expression that produces proteins involves two steps: (1) transcription and (2) translation, which are illustrated in figure 3.33.

1. Transcription occurs in the nucleus. During this process, information stored in a segment of DNA is used to produce a complementary RNA molecule, called **messenger RNA (mRNA)**.
2. The mRNA molecule moves to the ribosomes in the cytoplasm, where **translation** occurs. During this process, the nucleotide sequence of the mRNA is used to determine the composition of a polypeptide chain, a precursor to a protein.

This process can be illustrated with an analogy. Suppose a cook wants a cake recipe that is found only in a reference book in the library. Because the book cannot be checked out, the cook makes a copy, or **transcription,** of the recipe. Later, in the kitchen, the information contained in the copied recipe is used to make the cake. The changing of something from one form to another (from recipe to cake) is called **translation.** In this analogy, DNA is the reference book that contains many recipes (genes) for making different proteins. DNA, however, is too large a molecule to pass through the nuclear envelope to go to the cytoplasm (the kitchen), where the proteins are synthesized. Just as the reference book stays in the library, DNA remains in the nucleus. Therefore, through transcription, the cell makes a copy of the gene (the recipe) necessary to make a particular protein (the cake). The copy, which is called mRNA, travels from the nucleus to ribosomes (the kitchen) in the cytoplasm, where the information in the copy is used to construct a protein (i.e., translation). Of course, to turn a recipe into a cake, ingredients are needed. The ingredients necessary to synthesize a protein are amino acids. Specialized transport molecules, called **transfer RNA (tRNA)**, carry the amino acids to the ribosomes (see figure 3.33).

In summary, gene expression involves transcription (making a copy of a small part of the stored information in DNA) and translation (converting that copied information into a protein). The details of transcription and translation are considered next.

FUNDAMENTAL **Figure**

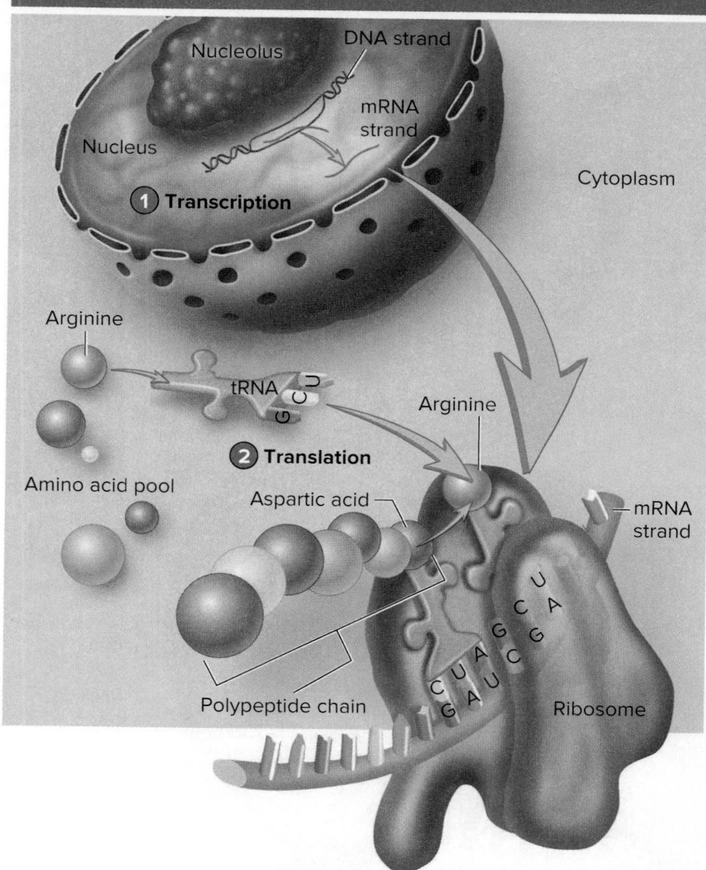

PROCESS **Figure 3.33**

Overview of Gene Expression

Gene expression occurs in two steps: transcription, which occurs in the nucleus, and translation, which occurs in the cytoplasm at ribosomes.

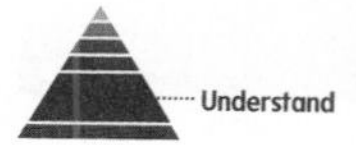

In bacterial cells, translation can begin before transcription of a gene is complete. Can this happen in our cells? Why or why not?

Transcription

Transcription is the synthesis of mRNA, tRNA, and rRNA molecules based on the nucleotide sequence of a gene in a DNA molecule (figure 3.34). Transcription occurs when a section of a DNA molecule unwinds and its complementary strands separate. One of the DNA strands serves as the template strand for the process of transcription. Nucleotides that form RNA align with the DNA nucleotides in the template strand by complementary base pairing. For example, suppose the DNA base sequence TGCA is to be transcribed. An adenine aligns with the thymine of DNA, cytosine aligns with guanine, and guanine aligns with cytosine. Instead of thymine, uracil of RNA (see figure 2.27) aligns with adenine of DNA. Thus, the sequence of bases that aligns with the TGCA sequence of DNA is ACGU. This pairing relationship between

PROCESS Figure

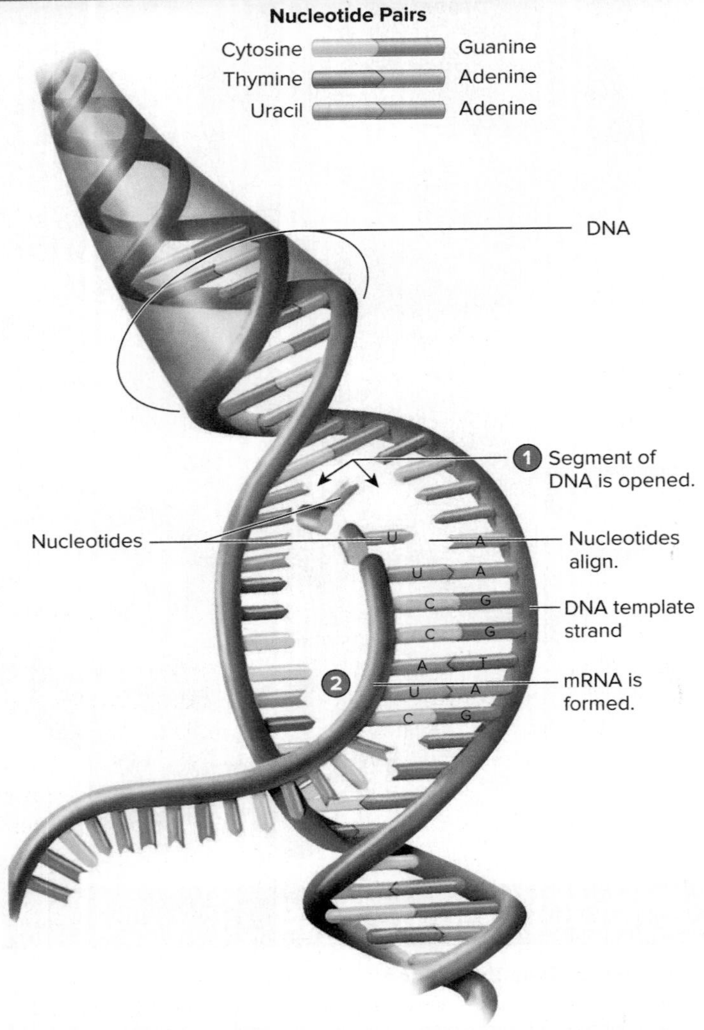

PROCESS Figure 3.34

Formation of mRNA by Transcription of DNA

RNA nucleotides pair with specific DNA nucleotides of a gene during transcription. APR

Other than the substitution of uracil for thymine, how do RNA nucleotides differ from DNA nucleotides? (*Hint:* Review section 2.4.)

nucleotides ensures that the information in DNA is transcribed correctly into RNA.

Predict 8

Given the following sequence of nucleotides of a template DNA strand, predict the sequence of mRNA that is transcribed from it. What is the nucleotide sequence of the complementary strand of the DNA molecule? How does it differ from the nucleotide sequence of RNA?

DNA nucleotide sequence: CGTACGCCGAGACGTCAAC

RNA polymerase is an enzyme that synthesizes the complementary RNA molecule from DNA. RNA polymerase must attach to the DNA molecule near the beginning of the gene. A DNA nucleotide sequence called a **promoter** signals the beginning of the gene and is the site for initial RNA polymerase binding; however, RNA polymerase does not attach to the promoter by itself. It must first associate with other proteins called **transcription factors** in order to interact with the DNA. Figure 3.34 illustrates the process of transcription.

1. The strands of the DNA molecule separate from each other as a result of the binding of RNA polymerase to the promoter (not shown in figure). One DNA strand serves as a template for mRNA synthesis.
2. Nucleotides that will form mRNA pair with DNA nucleotides according to the base-pair combinations shown in the key at the top of the figure. Thus, the sequence of nucleotides in the template DNA strand determines the sequence of nucleotides in the mRNA. Nucleotides are joined through the action of the RNA polymerase.

The termination of transcription in eukaryotic cells is not completely understood. When the RNA polymerase encounters the end of the gene sequence, interactions with other proteins cause the release of the newly formed RNA. The type of RNA that will make proteins is called messenger RNA (mRNA).

The region of a DNA molecule between the promoter and termination of transcription is a gene. The structure of a gene is more complex than just the nucleotides that code for a protein; some regions that are transcribed as part of the mRNA do not code for parts of a protein. Regions of the mRNA that do code for proteins are called **exons,** whereas the regions that do not code for a protein are called **introns.** An mRNA that contains introns is called a **pre-mRNA.** The introns are removed from the pre-mRNA and the remaining exons are spliced together through the activity of a **splicesome,** a complex structure composed of RNA and proteins. After intron removal and splicing, the functional mRNA will then consist only of exons.

Before a pre-mRNA leaves the nucleus, it undergoes several modifications called **posttranscriptional processing,** which produces the functional mRNA that is used in translation to produce a protein. Figure 3.35 illustrates these modifications.

1. Introns within a pre-mRNA are removed through the activity of splicesomes (not shown in figure).
2. A **7-methylguanosine cap** is added to one end of mRNA.
3. A series of adenine nucleotides, called a **poly-A tail,** is added to the other end. These modifications to the ends of the mRNA ensure that mRNA travels from the nucleus to the cytoplasm and interacts with ribosomes during translation.

In a process called **alternative splicing,** various combinations of exons are incorporated into mRNA. Which exons—and how many—are used to make mRNA can vary between cells of different tissues, resulting in different mRNAs transcribed from the same gene. Alternative splicing allows a single gene to produce more than one specific protein; however, the various proteins usually have similar functions in different tissues. In humans, nearly all mRNAs undergo alternative RNA splicing.

PROCESS Figure

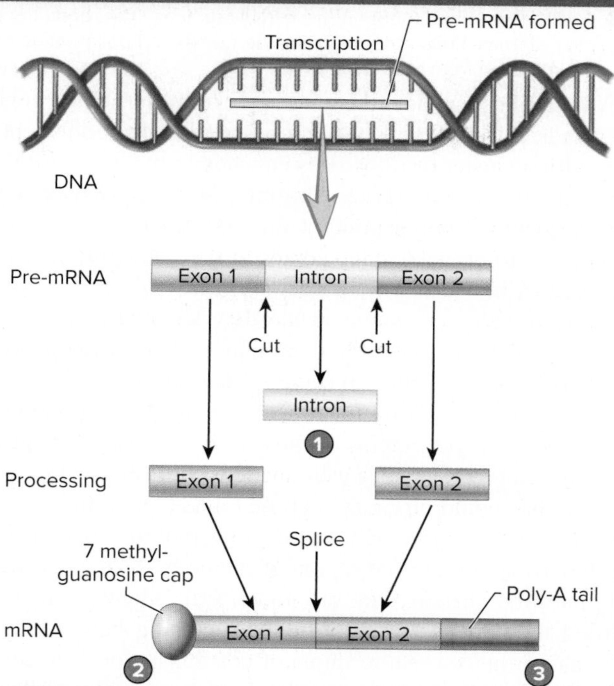

PROCESS **Figure 3.35**

Posttranscriptional Change in mRNA

The original RNA molecule that is produced during transcription is modified. Introns are removed and exons are spliced to form the functional mRNA. Modifications also are made to both ends of the molecule.

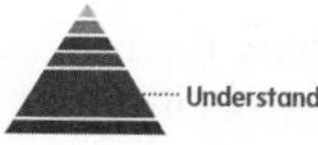

How would the length of the gene sequence in the DNA molecule differ from the length of the mRNA molecule?

Genetic Code

The **genetic code** is the information contained in mRNA and it relates the nucleotide sequence of mRNA to the amino acid sequence of a protein. The mRNA is organized into three nucleotide sequences called **codons,** each of which specifies an amino acid during translation. For example, the codon GAU specifies the amino acid aspartic acid, and the codon CGA specifies arginine. Although there are only 20 different amino acids commonly found in proteins, 64 possible codons exist. Therefore, an amino acid can have more than one codon. The codons for arginine include CGA, CGG, CGU, and CGC. Furthermore, some codons act as signals during translation. AUG, which specifies methionine, also acts as a **start codon,** which signals the beginning of translation. UAA, UGA, and UAG act as **stop codons,** which signal the end of translation. Unlike the start codon, stop codons do not specify amino acids. If you think of the mRNA as a sentence describing the structure of a protein, the start codon is the capital letter at the beginning of the sentence and the stop codon is the period at the end. Therefore, the protein-coding region of an mRNA begins at the start codon and ends at a stop codon.

Translation

Translation is the synthesis of a protein at the ribosome based on the sequence of the codons of mRNA. In addition to mRNA, translation requires ribosomes and tRNA. Ribosomes consist of

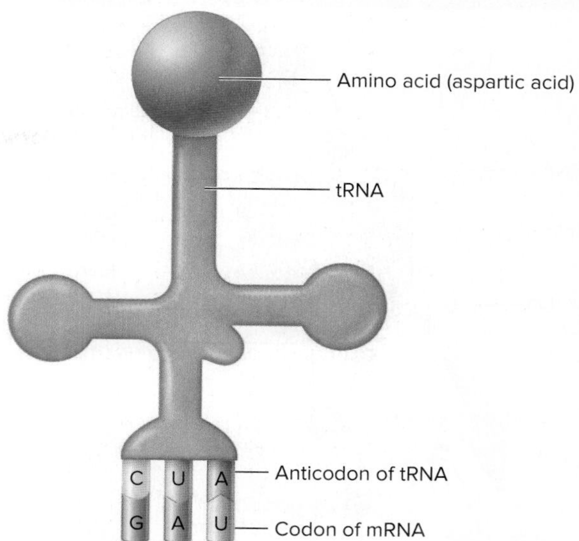

FIGURE 3.36 Transfer RNA (tRNA)

An amino acid binds to one end of a tRNA. The anticodon on the tRNA is complementary to the codon on an mRNA.

ribosomal RNA (rRNA) and proteins. Like mRNA, tRNA and rRNA are produced in the nucleus by transcription.

The function of tRNA is to match a specific amino acid to a specific codon of mRNA (figure 3.36). There are multiple types of tRNA, each specific to one amino acid. The amino acid binds to one end of its specific tRNA molecule. Another part of the tRNA, called the **anticodon,** consists of three nucleotides and is complementary to a particular codon of mRNA. On the basis of the pairing relationships between nucleotides, the anticodon can combine only with its matched codon. For example, the tRNA that has the anticodon CUA combines with the codon GAU of mRNA. The codon GAU of mRNA codes for aspartic acid, so the matching tRNA will have aspartic acid attached to it.

Ribosomes align the codons of the mRNA with the anticodons of tRNA and then enzymatically join the amino acids of adjacent tRNA molecules. The mRNA moves through the ribosome one codon at a time. With each move, a new tRNA enters the ribosome and the amino acid is linked to the growing chain, forming a polypeptide. The step-by-step process of translation at the ribosome is described in detail in figure 3.37.

1. To start protein synthesis, a ribosome binds to mRNA. The ribosome has two binding sites for tRNA, one of which is occupied by a tRNA with its amino acid. Note that the first codon of mRNA to associate with a tRNA is AUG, the start codon, which codes for methionine. The codon of mRNA and the anticodon of tRNA are aligned and joined. The other tRNA binding site is open.
2. By occupying the open tRNA binding site, the next tRNA is properly aligned with mRNA and the other tRNA.
3. An enzyme catalyzes a synthesis reaction to form a peptide bond between the amino acids. Note that the amino acids are now associated with only one of the tRNAs.
4. The ribosome shifts position by three nucleotides along the mRNA. The tRNA without the amino acid is released from the ribosome, and the tRNA with the amino acids takes its position. A tRNA binding site is left open by this shift. Additional amino acids can be added by repeating *steps 2* through *4*.

PROCESS **Figure**

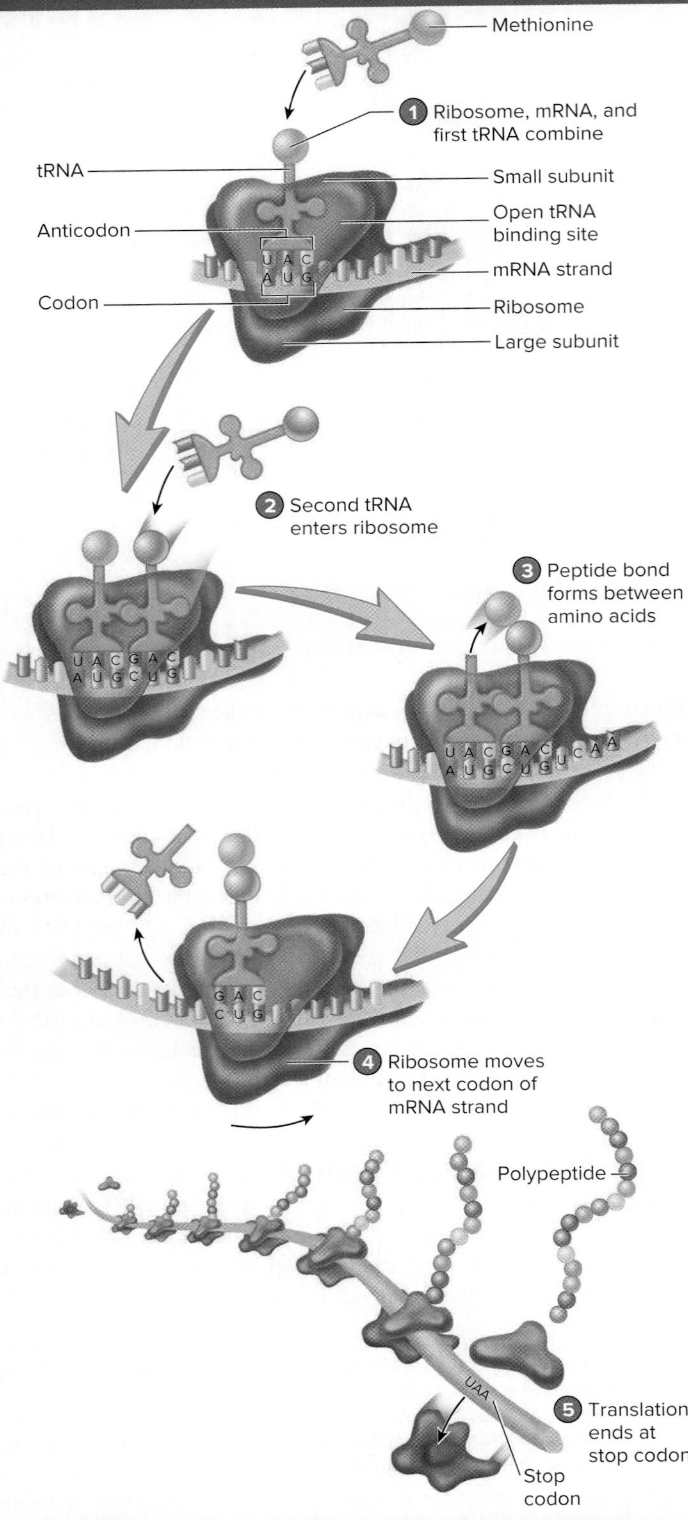

PROCESS **Figure 3.37**

Translation of mRNA to Produce a Polypeptide

Amino acids are linked together based on the codon sequence on the mRNA. APR

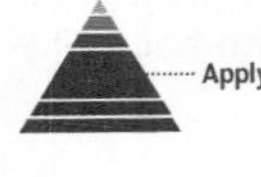

If a polypeptide chain consisted of 50 amino acids, how many codons, not counting the stop codon, are specified by the mRNA? How many nucleotides would that be?

5 Eventually, a stop codon in the mRNA, such as UAA, ends the process of transcription. At this point, the mRNA and polypeptide chain are released from the ribosome.

After a ribosome uses the initial part of mRNA, another ribosome can attach to the mRNA and begin to make a polypeptide. The resulting cluster of ribosomes attached to the same mRNA is called a **polyribosome.** Each ribosome in a polyribosome produces an identical polypeptide chain, and polyribosomes are an efficient way to produce many copies of the same protein using a single mRNA molecule.

Many proteins are longer when they are first made than in their final, functional state. These proteins are called **proproteins,** and the extra piece of the molecule is cleaved off by enzymes to make the proprotein into a functional protein. Many proteins are enzymes, and the proproteins of those enzymes are called **proenzymes.** If many proenzymes were made within cells as functional enzymes, they could digest the cell that made them. Instead, they are made as proenzymes and are not converted to active enzymes until they reach a protected region of the body, such as inside the small intestine, where they are functional. Many proteins are modified through **posttranslational processing** before they are functional in the cell. An example of posttranslational processing is the addition of side chains, such as polysaccharides, following translation. Another example is the assembly of complex proteins, where two or more polypeptide chains are joined after each chain is produced on separate ribosomes.

Regulation of Gene Expression

Most of the cells in the body have the same DNA. However, the transcription of mRNA in cells is regulated so that only the necessary genes are transcribed in each cell. The proteins associated with DNA in the nucleus play a role in regulating transcription. As cells differentiate and acquire specialized functions during development, part of the DNA is no longer transcribed, whereas other segments of DNA become more active. For example, the DNA coding for hemoglobin is not expressed in most cells, and little, if any, hemoglobin is synthesized. But in developing red blood cells, the DNA coding for hemoglobin is transcribed, and hemoglobin synthesis occurs rapidly.

Gene expression in a single cell is not normally constant but fluctuates in response to changes in signals from within and outside the cell. Regulatory molecules that interact with nuclear proteins can either increase or decrease the transcription rate of specific DNA segments. For example, triiodothyronine (T_3), a hormone released by cells of the thyroid gland, enters cells, such as skeletal muscle cells; interacts with specific nuclear proteins; and increases transcription of mRNAs from specific genes. Consequently, the production of certain proteins increases. As a further result, an increase in the number of mitochondria and an increase in metabolism occur in these cells.

ASSESS YOUR PROGRESS

60. *What is gene expression, and what two processes result in gene expression?*

61. *What type of molecule results from transcription? Where do the events of transcription occur?*

62. *Describe the events of transcription.*
63. *What are exons and introns? How do they relate to pre-mRNA and posttranscriptional processing?*
64. *What is the role of alternative splicing in variation?*
65. *What is the genetic code?*
66. *What are start and stop codons? How is a start codon different from a promoter?*
67. *Describe the steps of translation. In what molecules are codons and anticodons found? What is a polyribosome?*
68. *What occurs in posttranslational processing? How does it relate to proproteins and proenzymes?*
69. *State two ways the cell controls what part of DNA is transcribed.*

3.10 Cell Cycle

LEARNING OUTCOMES

After reading this section, you should be able to

A. **Describe the stages of the cell cycle.**
B. **Give the details of DNA replication.**
C. **Explain what occurs during mitosis.**
D. **Explain the process of cytokinesis.**
E. **Define *apoptosis*.**

The **cell cycle** includes the changes a cell undergoes from the time it is formed until it divides to produce two new cells. The cell cycle has two stages: (1) interphase and (2) cell division (figure 3.38). Cell division includes mitosis, the division of the nucleus, and cytokinesis, the division of the cytoplasm.

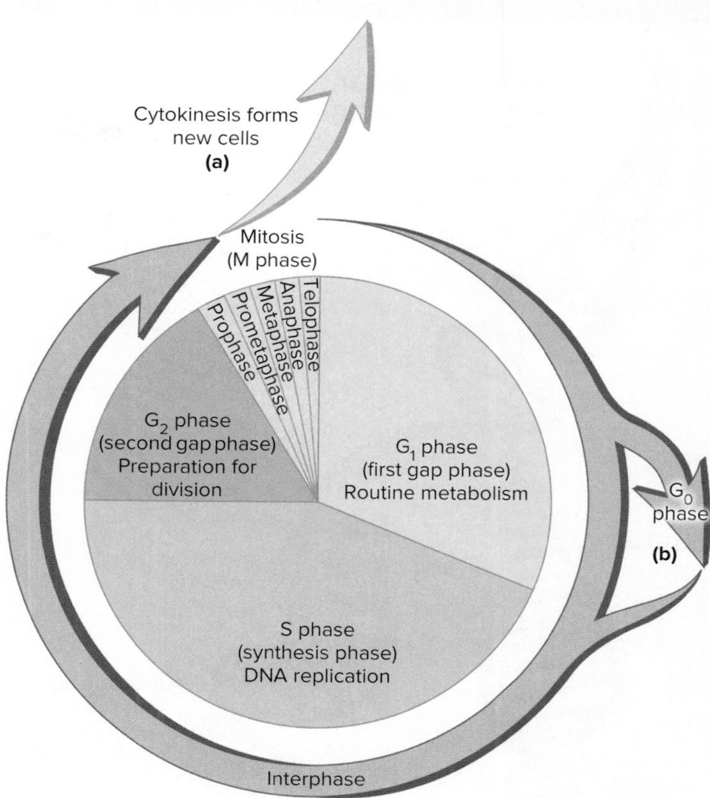

FIGURE 3.38 Cell Cycle

The cell cycle is divided into interphase (*blue*) and cell division (mitosis and cytokinesis). Interphase is divided into G_1, S, and G_2 subphases. During G_1, the cell carries out routine metabolic activities. During the S phase, DNA is replicated. During the G_2 phase, the cell prepares for division. (*a*) Following mitosis, two cells are formed by the process of cytokinesis. Each new cell begins a new cell cycle. (*b*) Many cells exit the cell cycle and enter the G_0 phase, where they remain until stimulated to divide, at which point they reenter the cell cycle.

Interphase

Interphase is the phase between cell divisions; nearly all of the life cycle of a typical cell is spent in interphase. During this time, the cell carries out the metabolic activities necessary for life and performs its specialized functions—for example, secreting digestive enzymes. In addition, the cell prepares to divide. This preparation includes both an increase in cell size as many cell components double in quantity and a doubling of the DNA content during DNA replication. The centrioles within the centrosome are also duplicated. Consequently, when the cell divides, each new cell receives the organelles and DNA necessary for continued functioning.

Interphase can be divided into three subphases: (1) G_1, (2) S, and (3) G_2. During G_1 (the first *gap* phase), the cell carries out routine metabolic activities. During the S phase (the *synthesis* phase), the DNA is replicated (new DNA is synthesized). During the G_2 phase (the second *gap* phase), the cell prepares for cell division. Many cells of the body do not divide for days, months, or even years. These "resting" cells do not follow the normal pattern of the cell cycle but instead enter what is called the G_0 phase, in which they remain unless stimulated to divide.

DNA Replication

Recall from chapter 2 that each DNA molecule is composed of two strands of DNA nucleotides. **DNA replication** is the process in which the two strands of a DNA molecule separate and each serves as the template for making complementary new strands of nucleotides. The two old strands combine with their respective complementary new strand, thereby producing two molecules of DNA. Figure 3.39 illustrates the process of DNA replication.

1. During interphase, DNA and its associated proteins appear as dispersed chromatin threads within the nucleus. When DNA replication begins, the two strands of each DNA molecule separate from each other for some distance.
2. Each strand then functions as a template, or pattern, for the production of a new, complementary strand of DNA. Each new strand forms as complementary nucleotides pair with the nucleotides of each template strand of the original DNA molecule.
3. DNA replication results in two identical DNA molecules. Each of the two new DNA molecules has one strand of nucleotides derived from the original DNA molecule and one newly synthesized strand.

PROCESS **Figure**

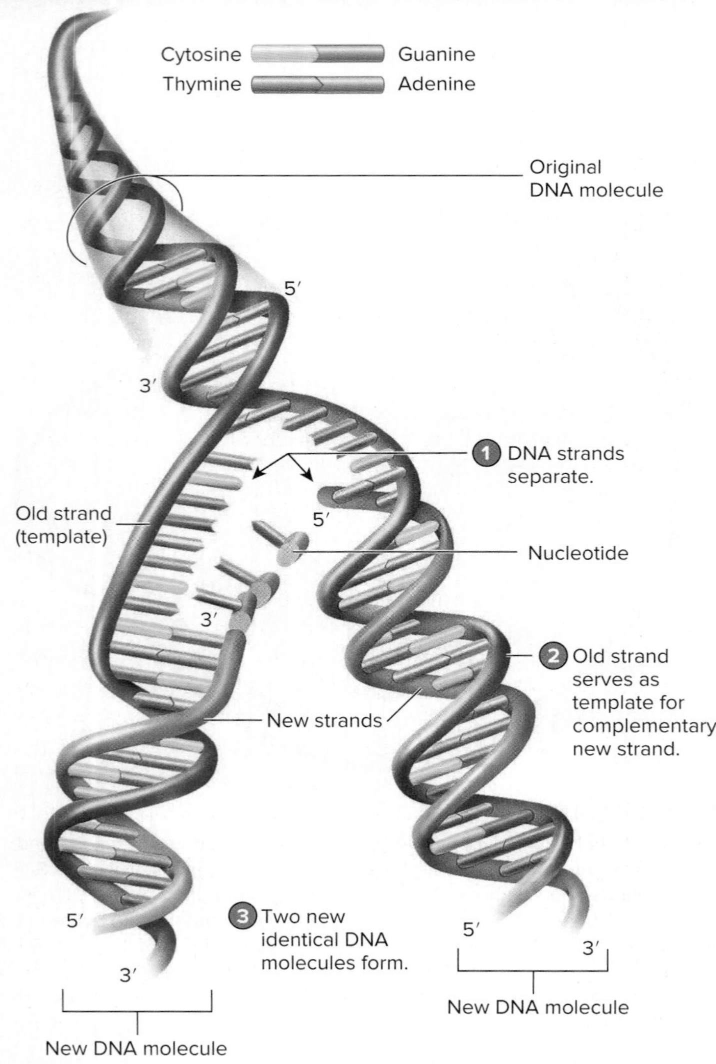

PROCESS **Figure 3.39**

Replication of DNA

Replication during the S phase of interphase produces two identical molecules of DNA. APR

How are the processes of DNA replication and transcription similar? How are they different?

The production of the new nucleotide strands is catalyzed by **DNA polymerase,** an enzyme that adds new nucleotides to the 3′ end of the growing strands. Because of the antiparallel orientation of the two DNA strands, the strands form differently. One strand, called the **leading strand,** forms as a continuous strand, whereas the other strand, called the **lagging strand,** forms in short segments called *Okazaki fragments*. The Okazaki fragments are then spliced by **DNA ligase.**

Each cell of the human body, except for sex cells, contains a specific number of chromosomes, known as the **diploid number.** The diploid number in humans is 46 chromosomes. Sex cells have the **haploid number** of chromosomes, which is half the diploid number, or 23 (see chapter 28, section 28.2).

Cell Division

Cell division produces the new cells necessary for growth and tissue repair. A parent cell divides to form two daughter cells, each having the same amount and type of DNA as the parent cell. The daughter cells also tend to have the same structure and perform the same functions as the parent cell. However, during development and cell differentiation, the functions of daughter cells may differ from each other and from that of the parent cell.

Cell division involves two major events: (1) division of the chromosomes into two new nuclei and (2) division of the cytoplasm to form two new cells, each of which contains one of the newly formed nuclei. The nuclear events are called mitosis, and the cytoplasmic division is called cytokinesis.

Mitosis

Mitosis (my-TOH-sis) is the division of a cell's nucleus into two new nuclei, each containing the same amount and type of DNA as the original nucleus. During mitosis, the chromatin becomes very densely coiled to form compact chromosomes called **mitotic chromosomes.** Mitotic chromosomes are discrete bodies that can be stained and easily seen with a light microscope. Recall that the DNA has been replicated during interphase of the cell cycle. As a result, each mitotic chromosome consists of two copies of the original chromosome. Each copy is called a **chromatid** (KROH-mah-tid). The chromatids are attached at the **centromere** (SEN-tro-meer) (figure 3.40; see figure 3.23). The **kinetochore** (ki-NET-oh-kohr, ki-NEE-toh-kohr) is a protein structure that binds the centromere and provides a point of attachment for microtubules that will separate and move the chromatids during mitosis. As two daughter cells form, a nucleus is re-formed around the chromatids. After the chromatids have separated, each is considered a chromosome. Each daughter cell receives a copy of the chromosomes. Thus, the daughter cells receive the same complement of chromosomes and are genetically identical.

Mitosis is divided into five phases: (1) prophase, (2) prometaphase, (3) metaphase, (4) anaphase, and (5) telophase. The process of mitosis is illustrated in figure 3.41.

1. Interphase is the time between cell divisions. DNA is present as thin threads of chromatin in the nucleus. DNA replication occurs during the S phase of interphase. Organelles, other than the nucleus, and centrioles duplicate during interphase.
2. In **prophase** the chromatin condenses to form mitotic chromosomes. The chromosomes are visible with a light microscope, and it is evident that each has replicated. Also, the centrioles in the cytoplasm divide and migrate to each pole of the cell.
3. During prometaphase, microtubules called spindle fibers extend from the centrioles to the centromeres of the chromosomes. Also, the nucleolus and nuclear envelope disappear.
4. In **metaphase** the chromosomes align near the center of the cell.

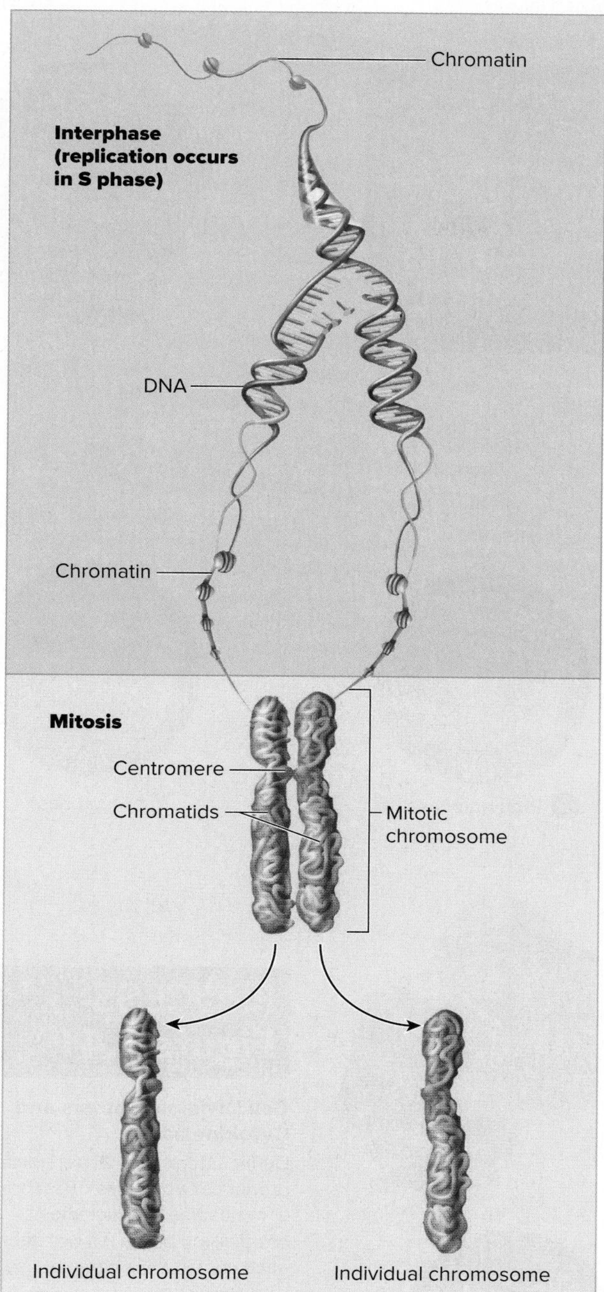

FIGURE 3.40 Structure of a Mitotic Chromosome
During mitosis, chromatin condenses to form visible mitotic chromosomes. Each mitotic chromosome consists of two chromatids.

5. At the beginning of **anaphase** the chromatids separate. At this point, one of the two identical sets of chromosomes is moved by the spindle fibers toward the centrioles at each of the poles of the cell. At the end of anaphase, each set of chromosomes has reached an opposite pole of the cell, and the cytoplasm begins to divide.

6. During **telophase** nuclear envelopes form around each set of chromosomes to form two separate nuclei. The chromosomes begin to uncoil and resemble the genetic material characteristic of interphase.

7. Following cytokinesis (described below), two new cells are formed. The chromosomes have unraveled to become chromatin. Cell division has produced two daughter cells, each with DNA that is identical to the DNA of the parent cell.

Cytokinesis

Cytokinesis (SIGH-toh-ki-NEE-sis) is the division of the cell's cytoplasm to produce two new cells. Cytokinesis begins in anaphase and continues through telophase (figure 3.41; *steps 5 through 7*). The first sign of cytokinesis is the formation of a **cleavage furrow,** an indentation of the plasma membrane that forms midway between the centrioles. A contractile ring composed primarily of actin filaments pulls the plasma membrane inward, dividing the cell into halves. Cytokinesis is complete when the membranes of the halves separate at the cleavage furrow to form two separate cells.

Apoptosis

Apoptosis (AP-op-TOH-sis), or programmed cell death, is a normal process by which cell number within various tissues is adjusted and controlled. In the developing fetus, apoptosis removes extra tissue, such as cells between the developing fingers and toes. In some adult tissues, apoptosis eliminates excess cells to maintain a constant number of cells within the tissue. Damaged or potentially dangerous cells, virus-infected cells, and potential cancer cells are also eliminated by apoptosis induced by immune cells.

Apoptosis is regulated by specific genes. The proteins coded for by those genes initiate events within the cell that ultimately lead to the cell's death. These proteins include some that are released from mitochondria. Once these proteins enter the cytosol, they activate other proteins that carry out many of the events of apoptosis. As apoptosis begins, the chromatin within the nucleus condenses and fragments. This is followed by fragmentation of the nucleus and finally by death and fragmentation of the cell. Specialized cells called macrophages phagocytize the cell fragments.

ASSESS YOUR PROGRESS

70. *What are the two stages of the cell cycle? Which stage is the longest?*
71. *Describe the cell's activities during the G_1, S, and G_2 phases of interphase.*
72. *Describe the process of DNA replication. What are the functions of DNA polymerase and DNA ligase?*
73. *What are the two major events of cell division? What happens in each?*
74. *Differentiate among chromatin, chromatids, and chromosomes.*
75. *List the events that occur during prophase, prometaphase, metaphase, anaphase, and telophase of mitosis.*
76. *What is the end result of mitosis and cytokinesis?*
77. *What is apoptosis? How is it beneficial to the body?*

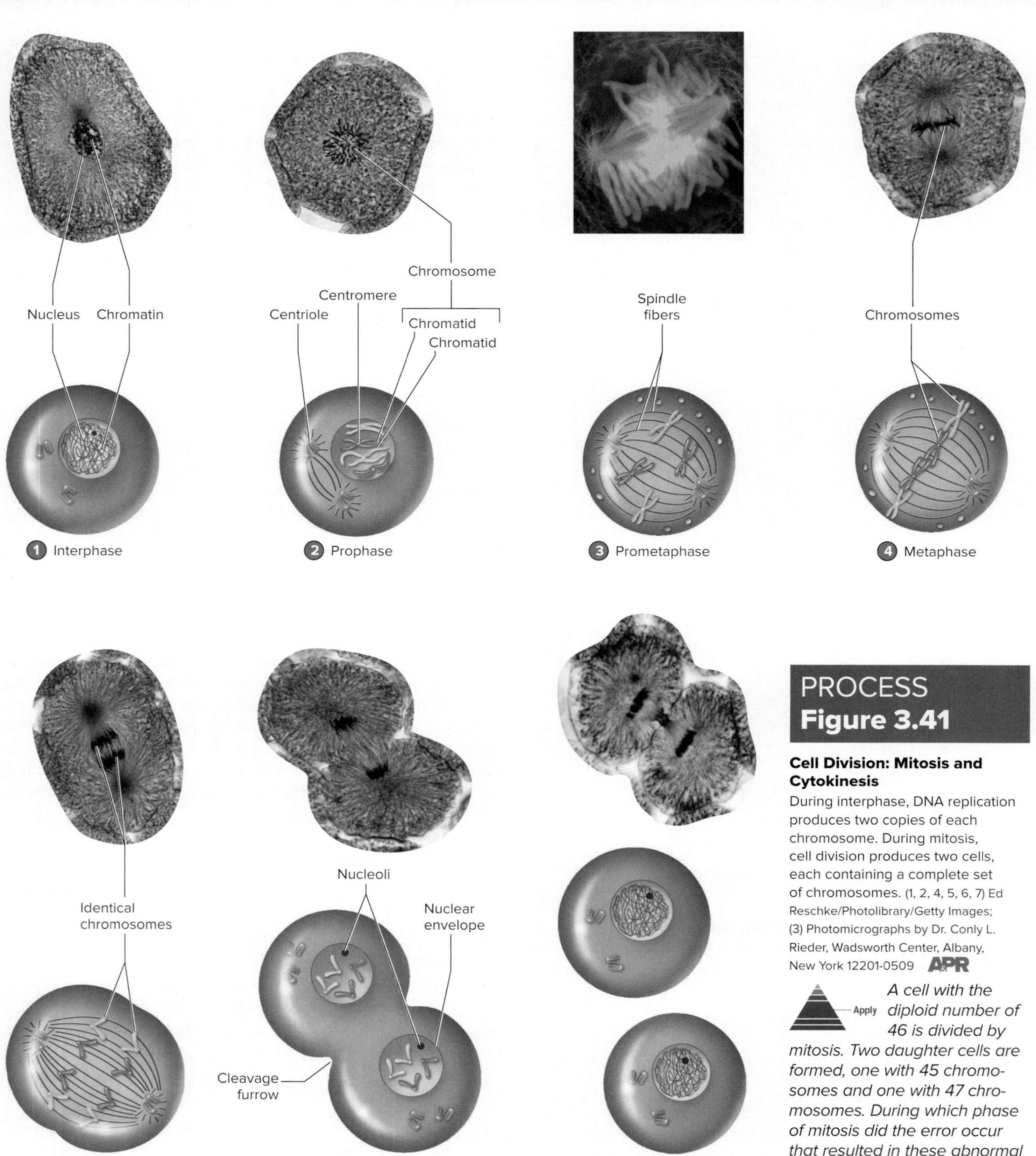

PROCESS Figure 3.41

Cell Division: Mitosis and Cytokinesis

During interphase, DNA replication produces two copies of each chromosome. During mitosis, cell division produces two cells, each containing a complete set of chromosomes. (1, 2, 4, 5, 6, 7) Ed Reschke/Photolibrary/Getty Images; (3) Photomicrographs by Dr. Conly L. Rieder, Wadsworth Center, Albany, New York 12201-0509 APR

Apply *A cell with the diploid number of 46 is divided by mitosis. Two daughter cells are formed, one with 45 chromosomes and one with 47 chromosomes. During which phase of mitosis did the error occur that resulted in these abnormal chromosome numbers?*

EFFECTS OF AGING ON **CELLS**

We are all familiar with the outward signs of aging, such as wrinkled skin, gray hair, and reduced vision. A number of cellular structures or events appear to be involved in causing these effects. The major hypotheses that attempt to explain how aging occurs concentrate on molecules within the cell, such as lipids, proteins, and nucleic acids. It is estimated that at least 35% of the factors affecting aging are genetic.

1. *Cellular clock.* One hypothesis of aging suggests the existence of a cellular clock that, after a certain passage of time or a certain number of cell divisions, results in the death of a given cell line.
2. *Death genes.* Another hypothesis suggests that there are "death genes," which turn on late in life, or sometimes prematurely, causing cells to deteriorate and die.
3. *DNA damage.* Other hypotheses suggest that, through time, DNA is damaged, resulting in cell degeneration and death.
4. *Free radicals.* DNA is also susceptible to direct damage, resulting in mutations that may result in cellular dysfunction and, ultimately, cell death. One of the major sources of DNA damage is apparently **free radicals,** which are atoms or molecules with an unpaired electron.
5. *Mitochondrial damage.* Mitochondrial DNA may be more sensitive to free-radical damage than is nuclear DNA. Mitochondrial DNA damage may result in loss of proteins critical to mitochondrial function. Because the mitochondria are the primary source of ATP, loss of mitochondrial function could lead to the loss of energy critical to cell function and, ultimately, to cell death. One proposal suggests that reduced caloric intake may reduce free-radical damage to mitochondria.

Concept Check

3.1 Functions of the Cell

A. The plasma membrane forms the outer boundary of the cell.

B. The nucleus directs the cell's activities.

C. The cytoplasm, between the nucleus and the plasma membrane, is where most cell activities take place.

D. Cells perform the following functions:

- Cells metabolize and release energy.
- Cells synthesize molecules.
- Cells provide a means of communication.
- Cells reproduce and provide for inheritance.

3.2 How We See Cells

A. Light microscopes allow us to visualize the general features of cells.

B. Electron microscopes allow us to visualize the fine structure of cells.

3.3 Plasma Membrane

A. The plasma membrane passively or actively regulates what enters or leaves the cell.

B. The plasma membrane is composed of a phospholipid bilayer, in which proteins are suspended (commonly depicted by the fluid-mosaic model).

3.4 Membrane Lipids

Lipids give the plasma membrane most of its structure and some of its function.

3.5 Membrane Proteins

A. Membrane proteins function as marker molecules, attachment proteins, transport proteins, receptor proteins, and enzymes.

B. Transport proteins include channel proteins, carrier proteins, and ATP-powered pumps.

C. Some receptor proteins are linked to and control channel proteins.

D. Some receptor molecules are coupled to G protein complexes, which control numerous cellular activities.

1. *In the plasma membrane, __________ form(s) the lipid bilayer, __________ determine(s) the fluid nature of the membrane, and __________ mainly determine(s) the function of the membrane.* Understand

   a. phospholipids, cholesterol, proteins
   b. phospholipids, proteins, cholesterol
   c. proteins, cholesterol, phospholipids
   d. cholesterol, phospholipids, proteins
   e. cholesterol, proteins, phospholipids

2. *Which of the following functioning proteins are found in the plasma membrane?* Remember

   a. channel proteins
   b. marker molecules
   c. receptor molecules
   d. enzymes
   e. All of these are correct.

3.6 Movement Through the Plasma Membrane

A. Lipid-soluble molecules pass through the plasma membrane readily by dissolving in the lipid bilayer. Small molecules diffuse between the phospholipid molecules of the plasma membrane.

B. Large, non-lipid-soluble molecules and ions (e.g., glucose and amino acids) are transported through the membrane by transport proteins.

C. Large, non-lipid-soluble molecules, as well as very large molecules and even whole cells, can be transported across the membrane in vesicles.

3. *In general, lipid-soluble molecules diffuse through the ________; small, water-soluble molecules diffuse through the ________.*

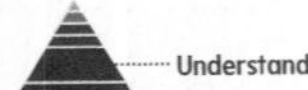
Understand

   a. membrane channels, membrane channels
   b. membrane channels, lipid bilayer
   c. lipid bilayer, carrier proteins
   d. membrane channels, carrier proteins
   e. carrier proteins, membrane channels

Passive Membrane Transport

A. Diffusion is the movement of a substance from an area of higher solute concentration to one of lower solute concentration (down a concentration gradient).

B. The concentration gradient is the difference in solute concentration between two points divided by the distance separating the points.

C. The rate of diffusion increases with an increase in the concentration gradient, an increase in temperature, a decrease in molecular size, and a decrease in viscosity.

D. The end result of diffusion is uniform distribution of molecules.

E. Diffusion requires no expenditure of energy.

F. Osmosis is the diffusion of water (solvent) across a selectively permeable membrane.

G. Osmotic pressure is the force required to prevent the movement of water across a selectively permeable membrane.

H. Isosmotic solutions have the same concentration of solute particles, hyperosmotic solutions have a greater concentration of solute particles, and hyposmotic solutions have a lower concentration of solute particles.

I. Cells placed in an isotonic solution neither swell nor shrink. In a hypertonic solution, they shrink (crenate); in a hypotonic solution, they swell and may burst (lyse).

J. Mediated transport is the movement of a substance across a membrane by means of a transport protein. The substances transported tend to be large, water-soluble molecules.

K. Facilitated diffusion moves substances down their concentration gradient and does not require energy (ATP).

4. *The rate of diffusion increases if the*

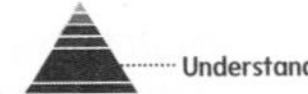
Understand

   a. concentration gradient decreases.
   b. temperature of a solution decreases.
   c. viscosity of a solution decreases.
   d. All of these are correct.

5. *Concerning the process of diffusion, at equilibrium*

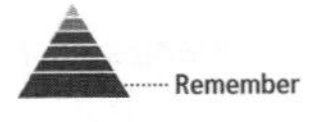
Remember

   a. the net movement of solutes stops.
   b. random molecular motion continues.
   c. there is an equal movement of solute in opposite directions.
   d. the concentration of solute is equal throughout the solution.
   e. All of these are correct.

6. *If a cell is placed in a(n) ________ solution, lysis of the cell may occur.* Remember

   a. hypertonic *b. isotonic* *c. hypotonic* *d. isosmotic*

7. *Suppose that a woman runs a long-distance race in the summer. During the race, she loses a large amount of hyposmotic sweat. You would expect her cells to* Understand

   a. shrink. *b. swell.* *c. stay the same.*

8. *Which of these statements about facilitated diffusion is true?*

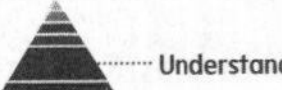
Understand

   a. In facilitated diffusion, net movement is down the concentration gradient.
   b. Facilitated diffusion requires the expenditure of energy.
   c. Facilitated diffusion does not require a carrier protein.
   d. Facilitated diffusion moves materials through ion pumps.
   e. Facilitated diffusion moves materials in vesicles.

9. *Why does a surgeon use sterile distilled water rather than sterile isotonic saline to irrigate a surgical wound from which a tumor has been removed?* Apply

10. *Solution A is hyperosmotic to solution B. If solution A is separated from solution B by a selectively permeable membrane, does water move from solution A into solution B, or vice versa? Explain.* Apply

11. *A dialysis membrane is selectively permeable, and substances smaller than proteins are able to pass through it. If you wanted to use a dialysis machine to remove only urea (a small molecule) from blood, what could you use for the dialysis fluid?* Apply

   a. a solution that is isotonic and contains only large molecules, such as protein
   b. a solution that is isotonic and contains the same concentration of all substances except that it has no urea
   c. distilled water, which contains no ions or dissolved molecules
   d. blood, which is isotonic and contains the same concentration of all substances, including urea

Active Membrane Transport

A. Active transport can move substances against their concentration gradient and requires ATP. An exchange pump is an active-transport mechanism that simultaneously moves two substances in opposite directions across the plasma membrane.

B. In secondary active transport, an ion is moved across the plasma membrane by active transport, and the energy produced by the ion diffusing back down its concentration gradient can transport another molecule, such as glucose, against its concentration gradient.

C. Vesicular transport is the movement of large volumes of substances across the plasma membrane through the formation or release of vesicles.

D. Endocytosis is the bulk movement of materials into cells.
   - Phagocytosis is the bulk movement of solid material into cells by the formation of a vesicle.
   - Pinocytosis is similar to phagocytosis, except that the ingested material is much smaller and is in solution.

E. Receptor-mediated endocytosis allows for endocytosis of specific molecules.

F. Exocytosis is the secretion of materials from cells by vesicle formation.

G. Both endocytosis and exocytosis require energy.

12. *Small pieces of matter, and even whole cells, can be transported across the plasma membrane in* Remember

   a. membrane channels. *c. receptor molecules.* *e. vesicles.*
   b. carrier molecules. *d. marker molecules.*

13. *Which of these statements concerning the symport of glucose into cells is true?* Understand
    a. *The sodium-potassium exchange pump moves Na^+ into cells.*
    b. *The concentration of Na^+ outside cells is less than inside cells.*
    c. *A carrier protein moves Na^+ into cells and glucose out of cells.*
    d. *The concentration of glucose can be greater inside cells than outside cells.*
    e. *As Na^+ are actively transported into the cell, glucose is carried along.*

14. *A white blood cell ingests solid particles by forming vesicles. This describes the process of* Remember
    a. *exocytosis.*
    b. *facilitated diffusion.*
    c. *secondary active transport.*
    d. *phagocytosis.*
    e. *pinocytosis.*

15. *Given these characteristics:* Remember
    (1) requires energy
    (2) requires carrier proteins
    (3) requires membrane channels
    (4) requires vesicles

    Choose the characteristics that apply to exocytosis.
    a. *1,2* b. *1,4* c. *1,3,4* d. *1,2,3* e. *1,2,3,4*

16. *A researcher wants to determine the nature of the transport mechanism that moved substance X into a cell. She could measure the concentration of substance X in the extracellular fluid and within the cell, as well as the rate of movement of substance X into the cell. She does a series of experiments and gathers the data shown in the accompanying graph. Choose the transport process that is consistent with the data.* Apply
    a. *diffusion*
    b. *active transport*
    c. *facilitated diffusion*
    d. *There is not enough information to make a judgment.*

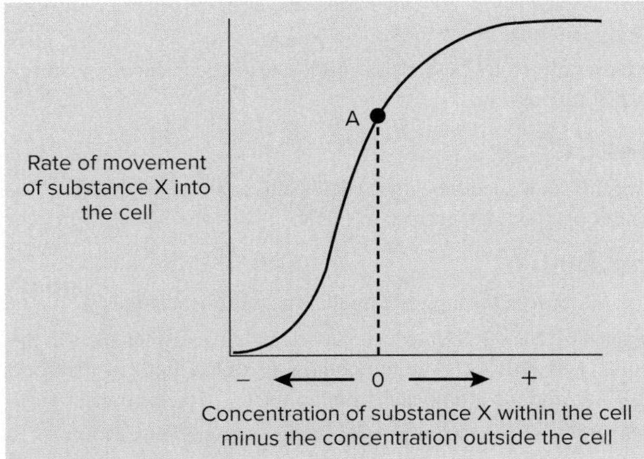

Graph depicting the rate of movement of substance X from a fluid into a cell (*y* axis) versus the concentration of substance X within the cell minus the concentration outside the cell (*x* axis). At point *A*, the extracellular concentration of substance X is equal to the intracellular concentration of substance X (designated 0 on the *x* axis).

3.7 Cytoplasm

The cytoplasm is the material outside the nucleus and inside the plasma membrane.

Cytosol

A. Cytosol consists of a fluid part (the site of chemical reactions), the cytoskeleton, and cytoplasmic inclusions.

B. The cytoskeleton supports the cell and is responsible for cell movements. It consists of protein fibers.
- Microtubules are hollow tubes composed of the protein tubulin. They form spindle fibers and are components of centrioles, cilia, and flagella.
- Actin filaments are small protein fibrils that provide structure to the cytoplasm or cause cell movements.
- Intermediate filaments are protein fibers that provide structural strength to cells.

C. Cytoplasmic inclusions, such as lipochromes, are not surrounded by membranes.

17. *Cytoplasm is found* 

    a. *in the nucleus.*
    b. *outside the nucleus and inside the plasma membrane.*
    c. *outside the plasma membrane.*
    d. *inside mitochondria.*
    e. *everywhere in the cell.*

18. *Which of these elements of the cytoskeleton is composed of tubulin and forms essential components of centrioles, spindle fibers, cilia, and flagella?* Remember
    a. *actin filaments* b. *intermediate filaments* c. *microtubules*

3.8 The Nucleus and Cytoplasmic Organelles

Organelles are subcellular structures specialized for specific functions.

The Nucleus

A. The nuclear envelope consists of a double membrane with nuclear pores.

B. DNA and associated proteins are found inside the nucleus as chromatin.

C. DNA is the hereditary material of the cell. It controls cell activities by producing proteins through RNA.

D. A gene is a portion of a DNA molecule. Genes determine the proteins in a cell.

E. Nucleoli consist of RNA and proteins and are the sites of ribosomal subunit assembly.

Ribosomes

A. Ribosomes consist of small and large subunits manufactured in the nucleolus and assembled in the cytoplasm.

B. Ribosomes are the sites of protein synthesis.

C. Ribosomes can be free or associated with the endoplasmic reticulum.

Endoplasmic Reticulum

A. The endoplasmic reticulum is an extension of the outer membrane of the nuclear envelope; it forms tubules or sacs (cisternae) throughout the cell.

B. The rough endoplasmic reticulum has ribosomes and is a site of protein synthesis and modification.

C. The smooth endoplasmic reticulum lacks ribosomes and is involved in lipid production, detoxification, and calcium storage.

Golgi Apparatus

The Golgi apparatus is a series of closely packed, modified cisternae that modify, package, and distribute lipids and proteins produced by the endoplasmic reticulum.

Secretory Vesicles

Secretory vesicles are membrane-bound sacs that carry substances from the Golgi apparatus to the plasma membrane, where the contents of the vesicles are released by exocytosis.

Lysosomes

A. Lysosomes are membrane-bound sacs containing hydrolytic enzymes. Within the cell, the enzymes break down phagocytized material and nonfunctional organelles (autophagy).
B. Enzymes released from the cell by lysis or enzymes secreted from the cell can digest extracellular material.

Peroxisomes

Peroxisomes are membrane-bound sacs containing enzymes that digest fatty acids and amino acids, as well as enzymes that catalyze the breakdown of hydrogen peroxide.

Proteasomes

Proteasomes are large, multienzyme complexes, not bound by membranes, that digest selected proteins within the cell.

Mitochondria

A. Mitochondria are the major sites for the production of ATP, which cells use as an energy source.
B. The mitochondria have a smooth outer membrane and an inner membrane that is infolded to form cristae.
C. Mitochondria contain their own DNA, can produce some of their own proteins, and can replicate independently of the cell.

Centrioles and Spindle Fibers

A. Centrioles are cylindrical organelles located in the centrosome, a specialized zone of the cytoplasm that serves as the site of microtubule formation.
B. Spindle fibers are involved in the separation of chromosomes during cell division.

Cilia and Flagella

A. Cilia facilitate the movement of materials over the surface of the cell.
B. Flagella, which are much longer than cilia, propel sperm cells.

Microvilli

Microvilli increase the surface area of the plasma membrane for absorption or secretion.

19. *A large structure, normally visible in the nucleus of a cell, where ribosomal subunits are produced is called a(n)* Remember

    a. endoplasmic reticulum. *c. nucleolus.*
    b. mitochondrion. *d. lysosome.*

20. *A cell that synthesizes large amounts of protein for use outside the cell has a large* Understand

    a. number of cytoplasmic inclusions.
    b. number of mitochondria.
    c. amount of rough endoplasmic reticulum.
    d. amount of smooth endoplasmic reticulum.
    e. number of lysosomes.

21. *Which of these organelles produces large amounts of ATP?* Understand

    a. nucleus *c. ribosomes* *e. lysosomes*
    b. mitochondria *d. endoplasmic reticulum*

22. *Cylindrically shaped extensions of the plasma membrane that do not move, are supported by actin filaments, and may function in absorption or as sensory receptors are* Remember

    a. centrioles. *c. cilia.* *e. microvilli.*
    b. spindle fibers. *d. flagella.*

23. *Luke started a training program at the beginning of the summer. For the first week, he jogged 1 mile. Each week after that, he increased the distance he jogged by about 0.5 mile and increased his speed. At the end of 2 months, he was able to jog 4.5 miles each day at a faster pace than he had been able to jog at the beginning of the summer. During the 2-month period, the muscle cells in his heart and his legs increased in size. Identify a critical membrane-bound organelle that increased in number and made it possible for Luke to run the longer distance. Also, explain how these organelles increased in number, and describe the location of the genetic code for the proteins in the organelles.* Apply

3.9 Genes and Gene Expression

A. During transcription, information stored in DNA is copied to form mRNA.
B. During translation, the mRNA goes to ribosomes, where it directs the synthesis of proteins.

Transcription

A. DNA unwinds and, through nucleotide pairing, produces pre-mRNA (transcription).
B. Introns are removed and exons are spliced together during posttranscriptional processing.
C. Modifications to the ends of mRNA also occur during posttranscriptional processing.

Genetic Code

The genetic code specifies amino acids and consists of codons, which are sequences of three nucleotides in mRNA.

Translation

A. mRNA moves through the nuclear pores to ribosomes.
B. Transfer RNA (tRNA), which carries amino acids, interacts at the ribosome with mRNA. The anticodons of tRNA bind to the codons of mRNA, and the amino acids join to form a protein (translation).
C. During posttranslational processing, proproteins, some of which are proenzymes, are modified into proteins, some of which are enzymes.

Regulation of Gene Expression

A. Cells become specialized because certain parts of the DNA molecule are activated but other parts are not.
B. The level of DNA activity and thus protein production can be controlled internally or can be affected by regulatory substances secreted by other cells.

24. *A portion of an mRNA molecule that determines one amino acid in a polypeptide chain is called a(n)*

Remember

a. nucleotide. *b. gene.* *c. codon.* *d. exon.* *e. intron.*

25. *In which of these organelles is mRNA synthesized?*

a. nucleus
b. ribosome
c. endoplasmic reticulum
d. nuclear envelope
e. peroxisome

26. *If you had the ability to inhibit mRNA synthesis with a drug, explain how you could distinguish between proteins released from secretory vesicles in which they had been stored and proteins released from cells in which they had been newly synthesized.*

Apply

3.10 Cell Cycle

The cell cycle has two stages: interphase and cell division.

Interphase

A. Interphase, the period between cell divisions, is the time of DNA replication.

B. During replication, DNA unwinds, and each strand produces a new DNA molecule.

Cell Division

A. Cell division includes nuclear division and cytoplasmic division.

B. Mitosis is the replication of the cell's nucleus, and cytokinesis is division of the cell's cytoplasm.

C. Most of the cells of the body contain the diploid number of chromosomes, which is 46. Sex cells contain the haploid number of chromosomes, which is 23.

D. Mitosis is a continuous process divided into five phases.

- *Prophase*. Chromatin condenses to become visible as chromosomes. Each chromosome consists of two chromatids joined at the centromere. Centrioles move to opposite poles of the cell.
- *Prometaphase*. Spindle fibers attach to centromeres. Nucleoli disappear, and the nuclear envelope degenerates.
- *Metaphase*. Chromosomes align at the center of the cell.
- *Anaphase*. The chromatids of each chromosome separate at the centromere. Each chromatid is then called a chromosome. The chromosomes migrate to opposite poles.
- *Telophase*. Chromosomes unravel to become chromatin. The nuclear envelope and nucleoli reappear.

E. Cytokinesis begins with the formation of the cleavage furrow during anaphase. It is complete when the plasma membrane comes together at the equator, producing two new daughter cells.

Apoptosis

Apoptosis, or programmed cell death, is a normal process by which cell number within various tissues is adjusted and controlled.

27. *During the cell cycle, DNA replication occurs during the*

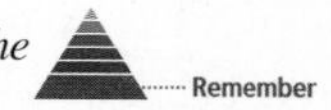

a. G_1 *phase.* *b.* G_2 *phase.* *c. M phase.* *d. S phase.*

28. *Given the following activities:*

Remember

(1) repair
(2) growth
(3) gamete production
(4) differentiation

Which of the activities is (are) the result of mitosis?

a. 2 *b. 3* *c. 1,2* *d. 3,4* *e. 1,2,4*

29. *Apoptosis*

a. is a programmed cell death.
b. removes excess cells between the developing fingers and toes of a fetus.
c. eliminates virally infected cells and cancer cells from the body.
d. All of these are correct.

Answers to this chapter's odd-numbered Concept Check questions appear in Appendix F.

4

CHAPTER

Tissues

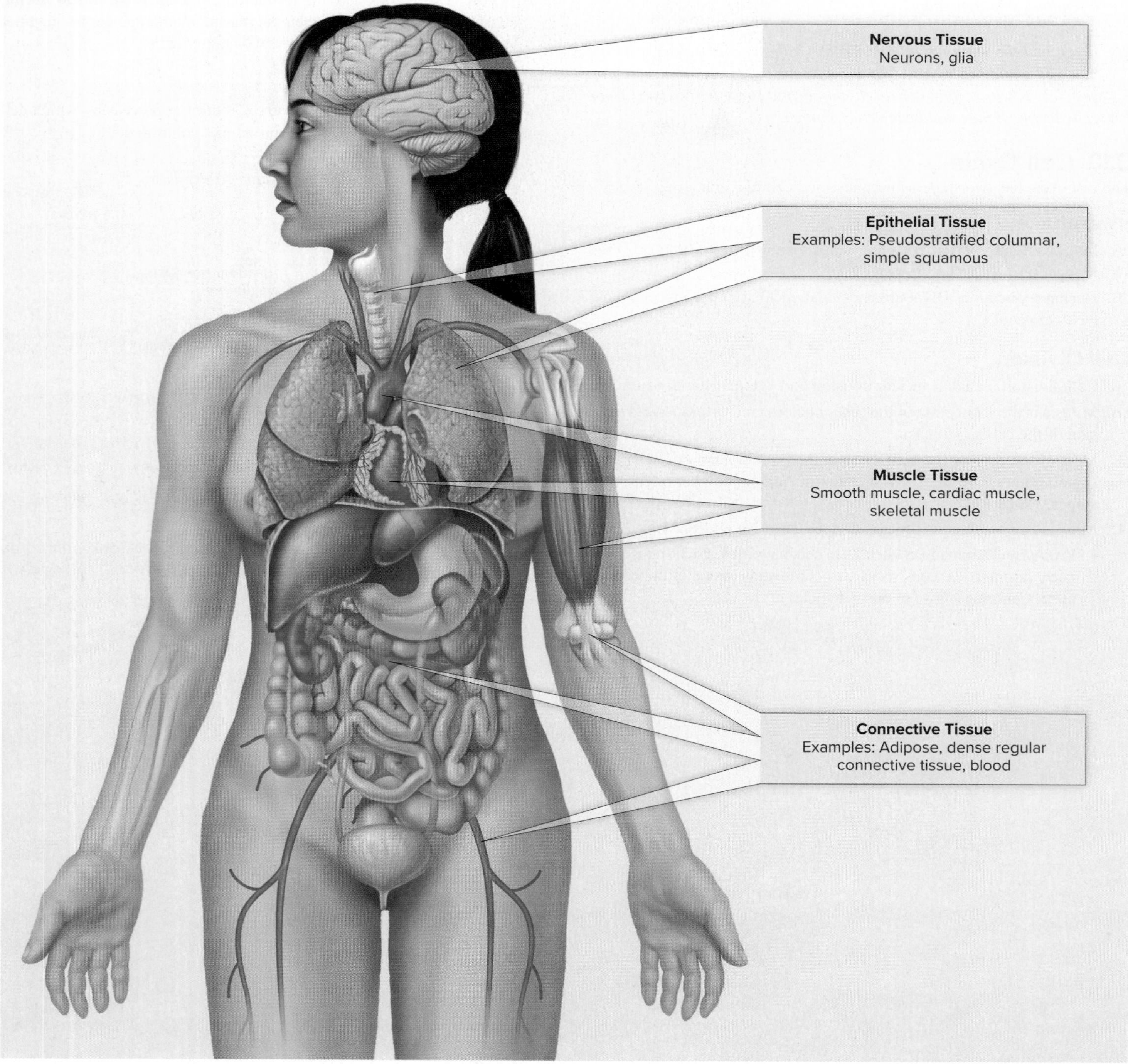

Nervous Tissue
Neurons, glia

Epithelial Tissue
Examples: Pseudostratified columnar, simple squamous

Muscle Tissue
Smooth muscle, cardiac muscle, skeletal muscle

Connective Tissue
Examples: Adipose, dense regular connective tissue, blood

As we learn more about the structure of the human body, it is evident that the complexity of the body increases as we consider more structures. In this chapter we will learn how groups of cells interact to form tissues. Additionally, as illustrated in this figure, there are many subtypes of each tissue. You will also notice a pattern: form follows function. For example, in areas of the body where protection is the primary function, the tissues are dense or consist of many cell layers. On the other hand, in areas of the body where materials move across a barrier, the tissues are very thin and composed of only one cell layer.

In some ways, the human body is like a car. Both consist of many parts that are made of materials consistent with their specialized functions. For example, car tires are made of synthetic rubber reinforced with a variety of fibers, the engine is composed of various metal parts, and the windows are transparent glass. Similarly, the many parts of the human body are made of groups of specialized cells and the materials surrounding them. Muscle cells, which contract to produce body movements, differ both structurally and functionally from epithelial cells, which protect, secrete, or absorb. Conversely, cells in the retina of the eye, which are specialized to detect light and enable us to see, do not contract as muscle cells do—nor do they exhibit the functions of epithelial cells.

The structure and the function of tissues are so closely related that we can often predict the function of a tissue when given its structure, and vice versa. Knowledge of tissue structure and function is critical in understanding organs, organ systems, and the complete organism.

Learn to Predict

It is Matt's birthday, but he will not be eating any cake. Matt has gluten enteropathy, also called celiac disease, which results from an inappropriate immune response to gluten, a group of proteins found in wheat and various other grains. After eating food containing gluten, such as most breads and cereals, Matt has bouts of diarrhea because his intestinal lining is unable to properly absorb water and nutrients. The poor absorption is due to a reduced number of villi, or fingerlike protrusions of the intestinal lining, and reduced transport capacity of the remaining cells within the villi. In chapter 3 we learned that water and nutrients enter and exit the body's cells by osmosis and other transport processes. Chapter 4 describes how tissues are specialized to allow this flow of water and nutrients.

After reading this chapter, identify the type of tissue affected by Matt's disease and which parts of the cells in this tissue are damaged, thus reducing their ability to absorb water and nutrients. Then explain why Matt has diarrhea after eating food containing gluten.

Answers to this question and the chapter's odd-numbered Predict questions can be found in Appendix E.

4.1 Tissues and Histology

LEARNING OUTCOMES

After reading this section, you should be able to

A. **Describe the general makeup of a tissue.**
B. **List the four primary tissue types.**
C. **Explain how histology relates to biopsies and autopsies.**

Tissues (TISH-yous) are groups of specialized cells and the extracellular substances surrounding them. **Histology** (his-TOL-oh-jee; *histo*, tissue + *ology*, study) is the microscopic study of tissue structure. Microscopic examination of tissues can identify abnormalities, including cancer, resulting from changes in a tissue. The structure and function of a tissue are so closely related that we can often predict the function of a tissue when given its structure, and vice versa. Knowledge of tissue structure and function is important in understanding organs, organ systems, and the complete organism. With each major tissue type, it is evident that the structure of each tissue informs you of the function of the organ, or portion of the organ, where the tissue is found. For example, bone is our densest tissue and provides significant protection for our body. As we discuss each tissue, we will include information examining the relationship between the structure and function of the tissue. Body tissues are classified into four types, based on the structure of the cells; the composition of the noncellular substances surrounding the cells, called the **extracellular matrix;** and the functions of the cells.

The four primary tissue types, from which all organs of the body are formed, are (1) epithelial tissue, (2) connective tissue, (3) muscle tissue, and (4) nervous tissue. Muscle and nervous tissues are more fully examined in later chapters.

Remember, the relationship between the function and structure of body parts is one of four key concepts in anatomy and physiology. For example, the lungs have a thin layer of specialized epithelial tissue that enhances the exchange of gases between air and blood. In contrast, the outer layer of the skin is composed of a different type of epithelial tissue, which provides protection to underlying tissues.

The tissues of the body are interdependent. For example, muscle tissue cannot produce movement unless it receives O_2 carried by red blood cells, and new bone tissue cannot form unless epithelial tissue absorbs Ca^{2+} and other nutrients from the

Module 3 Tissues

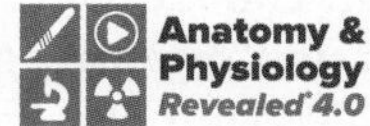

digestive tract. Also, the loss of one vital tissue through disease or injury can lead to organ failure and death.

Much information about a person's health can be gained by examining tissues. A **biopsy** (BIE-op-see) is the process of removing tissue samples from patients surgically or with a needle for diagnostic purposes. Examining tissue samples can distinguish various disorders. For example, some red blood cells have an abnormal shape in people suffering from sickle-cell disease, and red blood cells are smaller than normal in people with iron-deficiency anemia. Cancer is identified and classified based on characteristic changes in tissues. For example, changes in the structure of epithelial cells can indicate cancer of the uterine cervix, and changes in white blood cells identify people who have leukemia. Also, a greatly increased number of white blood cells can be a sign of infection. Epithelial cells from respiratory airways have an abnormal structure in people with chronic bronchitis, as well as in people with lung cancer.

Tissue samples can be sent to a laboratory for examination. In some cases, tissues are removed surgically and examined quickly, so that the results can be reported and decisions about the action to be taken can be made while the patient is still anesthetized.

An **autopsy** (AW-top-see) is a postmortem examination of the organs to determine the cause of death or to study the changes caused by a disease including microscopic examination of tissues.

ASSESS YOUR PROGRESS

Answers to these questions are found in the section you have just completed. Re-read the section if you need help in answering these questions.

1. *What components make up a tissue?*
2. *Name the four primary tissue types and the characteristics that are used to classify them.*
3. *Define* histology. *Explain how the histology of tissues taken by biopsy or autopsy is used to diagnose some diseases.*

4.2 Embryonic Tissue

LEARNING OUTCOMES

After reading this section, you should be able to

A. **Identify the three embryonic germ layers.**
B. **Name the adult structures that are derived from each of the three germ layers.**

Approximately 13 or 14 days after fertilization, the embryonic stem cells that give rise to a new individual form a slightly elongated disk consisting of two layers, the epiblast and the hypoblast (the suffix *-blast* means bud or germ). Cells of the epiblast then migrate between the two layers to form the three embryonic germ layers: (1) the endoderm, (2) the mesoderm, and (3) the ectoderm. They are called germ layers because they give rise to all the tissues of the body (see chapter 29).

The **endoderm** (EN-doh-derm), the inner layer, forms the lining of the digestive tract and its derivatives. The **mesoderm** (MEZ-oh-derm), the middle layer, forms tissues such as muscle, bone, and blood vessels. The **ectoderm** (EK-toh-derm), the outer layer, forms the skin; a portion of the ectoderm called **neuroectoderm** (noor-oh-EK-toh-derm) becomes the nervous system. Groups of cells that break away from the neuroectoderm during development, called **neural crest cells,** give rise to parts of the peripheral nerves, skin pigment cells (see chapter 5), the medulla of the adrenal gland (see chapter 18), and many tissues of the face.

ASSESS YOUR PROGRESS

4. *Name the three embryonic germ layers.*
5. *What adult structures are derived from each layer?*
6. *What is formed from neural crest cells?*

4.3 Epithelial Tissue

LEARNING OUTCOMES

After reading this section, you should be able to

A. **List and explain the general characteristics of epithelial tissue.**
B. **Describe the major functions of epithelial tissue.**
C. **Classify epithelial tissues based on the number of cell layers and the shape of the cells.**
D. **Name and describe the various types of epithelial tissue, including their chief functions and locations.**
E. **Relate the structural specializations of epithelial tissue with the functions they perform.**
F. **Differentiate between exocrine and endocrine glands, and unicellular and multicellular glands.**
G. **Categorize glands based on their structure and function.**

Epithelial (ep-ih-THEE-lee-al) **tissue,** or *epithelium* (ep-ih-THEE-lee-um), covers and protects surfaces, both outside and inside the body. The characteristics common to most types of epithelial tissue are shown in figure 4.1 and listed here:

1. *Mostly composed of cells.* Epithelial tissue consists almost entirely of cells, with very little extracellular matrix between them.
2. *Covers body surfaces.* Epithelial tissue covers body surfaces and forms glands that are derived developmentally from body surfaces. The body surfaces include the exterior surface, the lining of the digestive and respiratory tracts, the heart and blood vessels, and the linings of many body cavities.
3. *Has an exposed surface.* Because epithelial tissues form coverings and linings, one surface of their cells is in direct contact with either the outside environment or the contents of our hollow organs. For example, our skin is in contact with air in the atmosphere, and the lining of the stomach is in contact with food we eat. The surface that is exposed is called the **free surface,** or *apical* (AY-pi-kal) *surface*. Epithelial cells are always oriented such that the free surface points toward the space inside a hollow organ or the

FUNDAMENTAL **Figure**

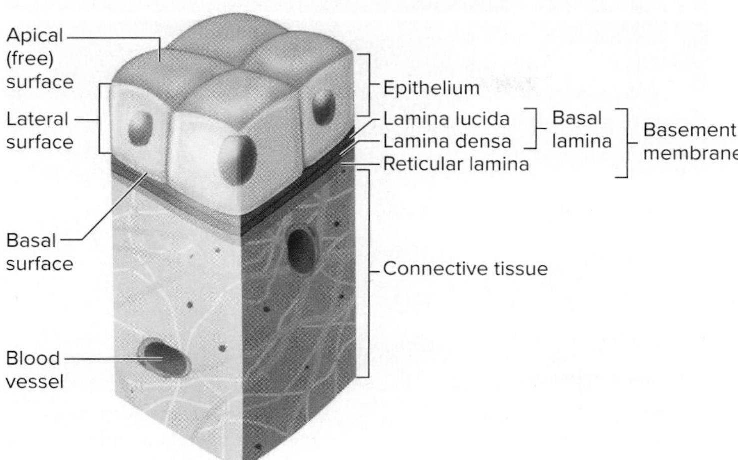

(a) Structure of Epithelial Tissue

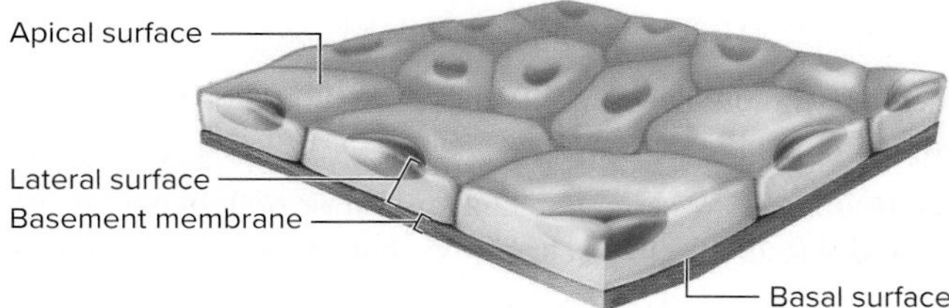

Simple epithelium

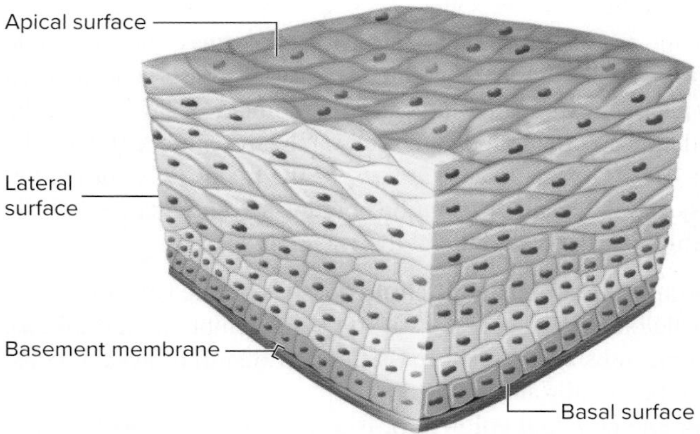

Stratified epithelium

(b) Epithelium classified by number of cell layers

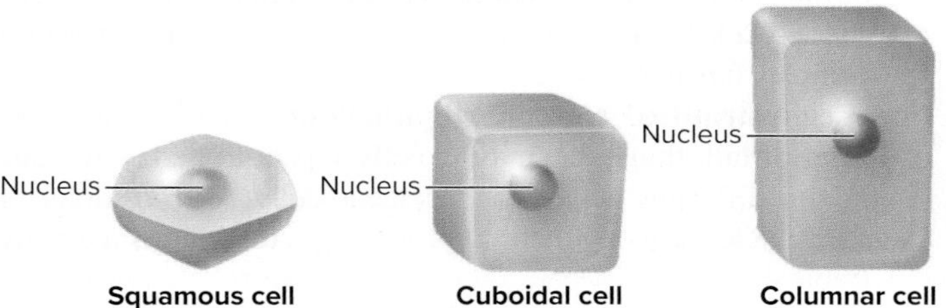

(c) Epithelium classified by cell shape

external environment, even when part of a multilayered epithelial tissue. However, only the most superficial layer of cells is in contact with the environment.

4. *Attaches at the basal surface*. The surface of the cells that is anchored in place is called the **basal surface.** The basal surface is held in place through attachment to a noncellular material that is somewhat like mortar for brick. This material is called the **basement membrane.** The basement membrane consists of two layers visible only with a light microscope. These two layers are the: (a) basal lamina and (b) reticular lamina. The basal lamina can be further subdivided into two layers, which are the (a) lamina lucida and (b) lamina densa. The basement membrane is composed of specialized extracellular material secreted by the epithelial cells, which includes collagen, glycoproteins (laminin, fibronectin), and proteoglycans. The basement membrane plays an important role in supporting and guiding cell migration during tissue repair. It is typically porous and regulates the movement of substances to and from the epithelial tissue above it. Epithelial cells are always oriented such that their basal surface contacts the basement membrane, even as part of a multilayered epithelial tissue. However, only the deepest layer of cells is in contact with the basement membrane. Between the epithelial cells is the **lateral surface,** where the epithelial cells are attached to each other. We will consider specialized attachments at the lateral surface later in this chapter.
5. *Has specialized cell connections and matrix attachments.* Specialized cell contacts bind adjacent epithelial cells together and to the extracellular matrix of the basement membrane.
6. *Is avascular.* Blood vessels in the underlying connective tissue do not penetrate the basement membrane to reach the epithelium; thus, all gases and nutrients carried in the blood must reach the epithelium by diffusing from blood vessels across the basement membrane. In epithelial tissues with many layers of cells, diffusion must also occur across cells, and the most metabolically active cells are close to the basement membrane.
7. *Is capable of regeneration.* Epithelial tissue has the ability to regenerate and replace damaged cells with new epithelial cells. Undifferentiated cells (stem cells) continuously divide and produce new cells. In some types of epithelial tissues, such as those in the skin and the digestive tract, new cells continuously replace cells that die.

FIGURE 4.1 Characteristics of Epithelial Tissue

(a) Epithelial tissue has the following characteristics: little extracellular material between cells, an apical surface, and a basement membrane attaching the basal surface of epithelial cells to underlying tissues. Nutrients, oxygen, and waste products diffuse across the basement membrane. *(b)* Epithelial tissues can be classified based on the number of cell layers in the tissue (simple or stratified). *(c)* Epithelial tissues can also be classified based on the shape of the cells at the superficial layer (squamous, cuboidal, or columnar).

Functions of Epithelial Tissues

The major functions of epithelial tissue are

1. *Protecting underlying structures.* Examples include the outer layer of the skin and the epithelium of the oral cavity, which protect the underlying structures from abrasion.
2. *Acting as a barrier.* Epithelium prevents many substances from moving through it. For example, the skin acts as a barrier to water and reduces water loss from the body. The epithelium of the skin also prevents many toxic molecules and microorganisms from entering the body.
3. *Permitting the passage of substances.* Though epithelium acts as a barrier for some substances, it also permits many other substances to move through it. For example, O_2 and CO_2 are exchanged between the air and blood by diffusion through the epithelium in the lungs. Epithelium acts as a filter in the kidney, allowing many substances to pass from the blood into the urine but retaining other substances, such as blood cells and proteins, in the blood.
4. *Secreting substances.* Mucous glands, sweat glands, and the enzyme-secreting portions of the pancreas are all composed of epithelial cells that secrete their products onto surfaces or into ducts that carry them to other areas of the body.
5. *Absorbing substances.* The plasma membranes of certain epithelial cells contain carrier proteins (see chapter 3), which regulate the absorption of materials.

ASSESS YOUR PROGRESS

7. *List seven characteristics common to most types of epithelial tissue.*
8. *What are the distinct cell surfaces found in epithelial tissue? Describe them.*
9. *List and describe the major functions of epithelial tissue.*

Classification of Epithelial Tissues

Epithelial tissues are classified primarily according to the number of cell layers and the shape of the superficial cells. There are four major types of epithelium based on the number of cell layers in each:

1. **Simple epithelium** consists of a single layer of cells, with each cell extending from the basement membrane to the free surface.
2. **Stratified epithelium** consists of more than one layer of cells, but only the basal layer attaches the deepest layer to the basement membrane.
3. **Pseudostratified columnar epithelium** is a special type of simple epithelium. The prefix *pseudo-* means false, so this type of epithelium appears to be stratified but is not. It consists of one layer of cells, with all the cells attached to the basement membrane. There appear to be two or more layers of cells because some of the cells are tall and extend to the free surface, whereas others are shorter and do not extend to the free surface.
4. **Transitional epithelium** is a special type of stratified epithelium. The shape of its cells changes from cuboidal and columnar to squamouslike when stretched.

TABLE 4.1 Classification of Epithelium

Number of Layers or Category	Shape of Cells
Simple (single layer of cells)	Squamous Cuboidal Columnar
Stratified (more than one layer of cells)	Squamous Nonkeratinized (moist) Keratinized Cuboidal (very rare) Columnar (very rare)
Pseudostratified (modification of simple epithelium)	Columnar
Transitional (modification of stratified epithelium)	Roughly cuboidal to columnar when not stretched and squamouslike when stretched

There are three types of epithelium based on idealized shapes of the epithelial cells:

1. **Squamous** (SKWAY-mus) cells are flat or scalelike.
2. **Cuboidal** (cubelike) cells are cube-shaped—about as wide as they are tall.
3. **Columnar** (tall and thin, similar to a column) cells tend to be taller than they are wide.

In most cases, an epithelium is given two names, such as simple squamous, stratified squamous, simple columnar, or pseudostratified columnar. The first name indicates the number of layers, and the second indicates the shape of the cells at the free surface (table 4.1). Tables 4.2–4.3 provide an overview of the major types of epithelial tissues and their distribution. Figure 4.2 summarizes all the epithelial tissue types in the body.

1. **Simple squamous epithelium** consists of one layer of flat, or scalelike, cells that rest on a basement membrane (table 4.2*a*). Some substances easily pass through this thin layer of cells, but other substances do not.
2. **Simple cuboidal epithelium** is a single layer of cubelike cells (table 4.2*b*) that carry out active transport, facilitated diffusion, or secretion.
3. **Simple columnar epithelium** is a single layer of tall, thin cells (table 4.2*c*). The large size of these cells enables them to perform complex functions.
4. **Pseudostratified columnar epithelium** is actually a single layer of tall, thin cells, but the cells appear to be layered due to the differing heights of adjacent cells and positions of their nuclei. This epithelium provides protection for the body (table 4.2*d*).
5. **Stratified squamous epithelium** forms a thick epithelium because it consists of several layers of flat cells (table 4.3*a*). The deepest cells are cuboidal or columnar and are capable of dividing and producing new cells. As these newly formed cells are pushed to the surface, they become flat and thin.

TABLE 4.2 Simple Epithelium

(a) Simple Squamous Epithelium APR

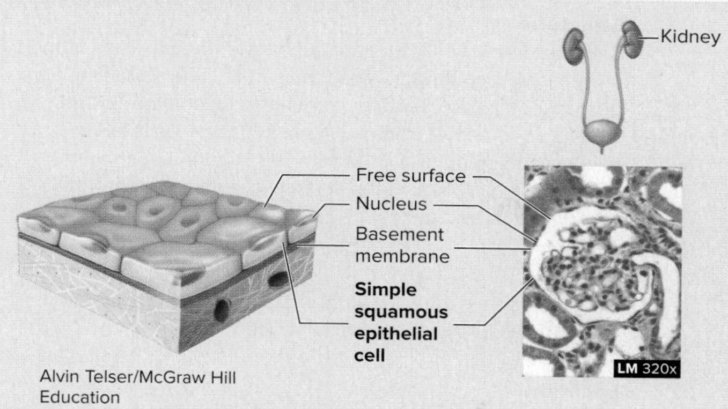

Structure:
Single layer of flat, often hexagonal cells; the nuclei appear as bumps when viewed in cross section because the cells are so flat

Function:
Diffusion, filtration, some secretion, and some protection against friction

Location:
Lining of blood vessels and the heart, lymphatic vessels, alveoli of the lungs, portions of the kidney tubules, lining of serous membranes of body cavities (pleural, pericardial, peritoneal)

(b) Simple Cuboidal Epithelium APR

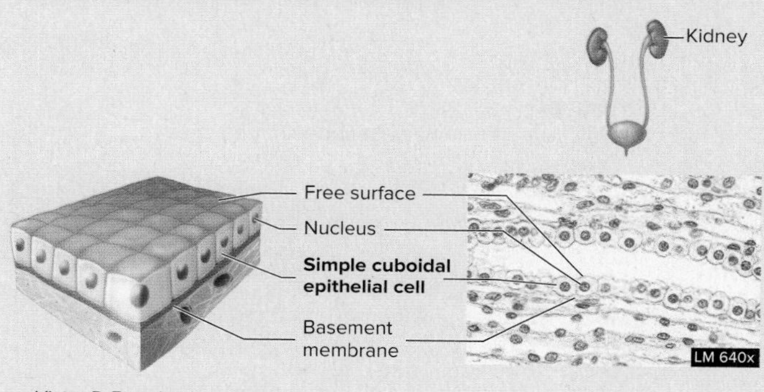

Structure:
Single layer of cube-shaped cells; some cells have microvilli (kidney tubules) or cilia (terminal bronchioles of the lungs)

Function:
Secretion and absorption by cells of the kidney tubules; secretion by cells of glands and choroid plexuses; movement of particles embedded in mucus out of the terminal bronchioles by ciliated cells

Location:
Kidney tubules, glands and their ducts, choroid plexuses of the brain, lining of terminal bronchioles of the lungs, and surfaces of the ovaries

(c) Simple Columnar Epithelium APR

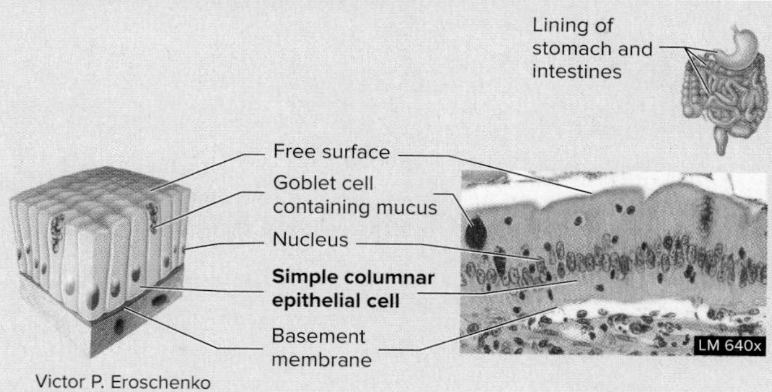

Structure:
Single layer of tall, narrow cells; some cells have cilia (bronchioles of lungs, auditory tubes, uterine tubes, and uterus) or microvilli (intestines)

Function:
Movement of particles out of the bronchioles of the lungs by ciliated cells; partially responsible for the movement of oocytes through the uterine tubes by ciliated cells; secretion by cells of the glands, the stomach, and the intestines; absorption by cells of the intestines

Location:
Glands and some ducts, bronchioles of lungs, auditory tubes, uterus, uterine tubes, stomach, intestines, gallbladder, bile ducts, and ventricles of the brain

(d) Pseudostratified Columnar Epithelium APR

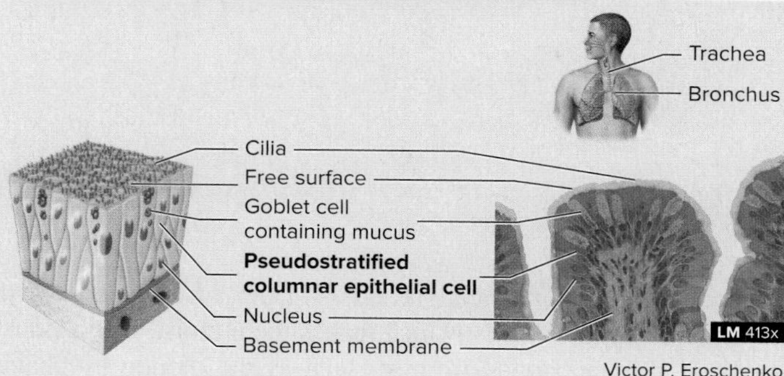

Structure:
Single layer of cells; some cells are tall and thin and reach the free surface, and others do not; the nuclei of these cells are at different levels and appear stratified; the cells are almost always ciliated and are associated with goblet cells that secrete mucus onto the free surface

Function:
Synthesize and secrete mucus onto the free surface and move mucus (or fluid) that contains foreign particles over the surface of the free surface and from passages

Location:
Lining of nasal cavity, nasal sinuses, auditory tubes, pharynx, trachea, and bronchi of lungs

TABLE 4.3 Stratified Epithelium

(a) Stratified Squamous Epithelium APR

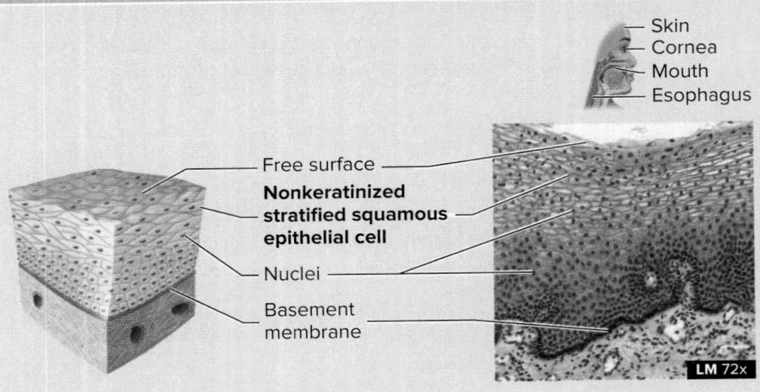

Al Telser/McGraw Hill

Structure:
Several layers of cells that are cuboidal in the basal layer and progressively flattened toward the surface; the epithelium can be nonkeratinized (moist) or keratinized; in nonkeratinized stratified squamous epithelium, the surface cells retain a nucleus and cytoplasm; in keratinized stratified epithelium, the cytoplasm of cells at the surface is replaced by a protein called keratin, and the cells are dead

Function:
Protects against abrasion, forms a barrier against infection, and reduces loss of water from the body

Location:
Keratinized—outer layer of the skin; nonkeratinized—mouth, throat, larynx, esophagus, anus, vagina, inferior urethra, and corneas

(b) Stratified Cuboidal Epithelium

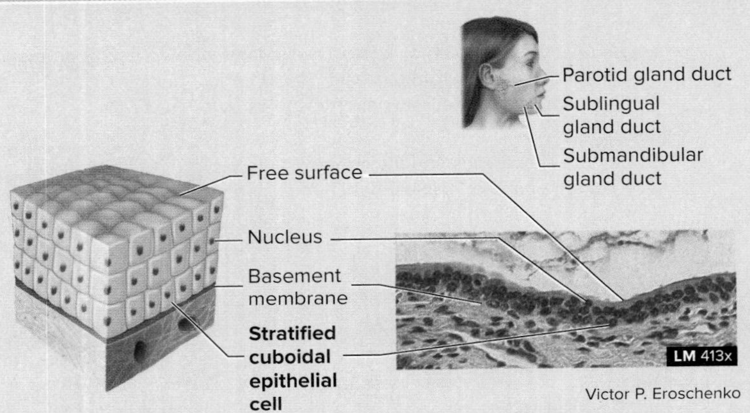

Victor P. Eroschenko

Structure:
Multiple layers of somewhat cube-shaped cells

Function:
Secretion, absorption, protection against infection

Location:
Sweat gland ducts, ovarian follicular cells, salivary gland ducts

(c) Stratified Columnar Epithelium

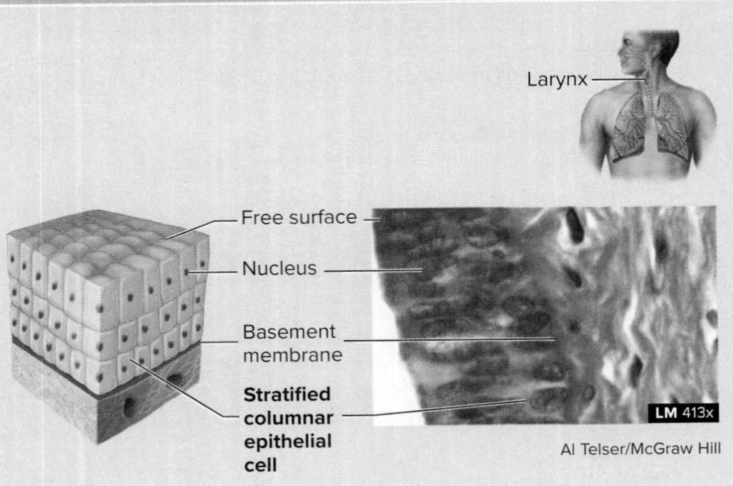

Al Telser/McGraw Hill

Structure:
Multiple layers of cells with tall, thin cells resting on layers of more cube-shaped cells; the cells are ciliated in the larynx

Function:
Protection, secretion

Location:
Mammary gland ducts, larynx, a portion of the male urethra

Stratified squamous epithelium can be classified further as either nonkeratinized or keratinized, according to the condition of the outermost layer of cells. **Nonkeratinized (moist) stratified squamous epithelium** (table 4.3*a*) consists of living cells in both the deepest and superficial layers. A layer of fluid covers the superficial layers of cells, which makes them moist. These nonkeratinized cells are found in areas such as the mouth, esophagus, rectum, and vagina. In contrast, **keratinized** (KER-ah-ti-nyezd)

TABLE 4.3 **Stratified Epithelium—Continued**

(d) Transitional Epithelium APR

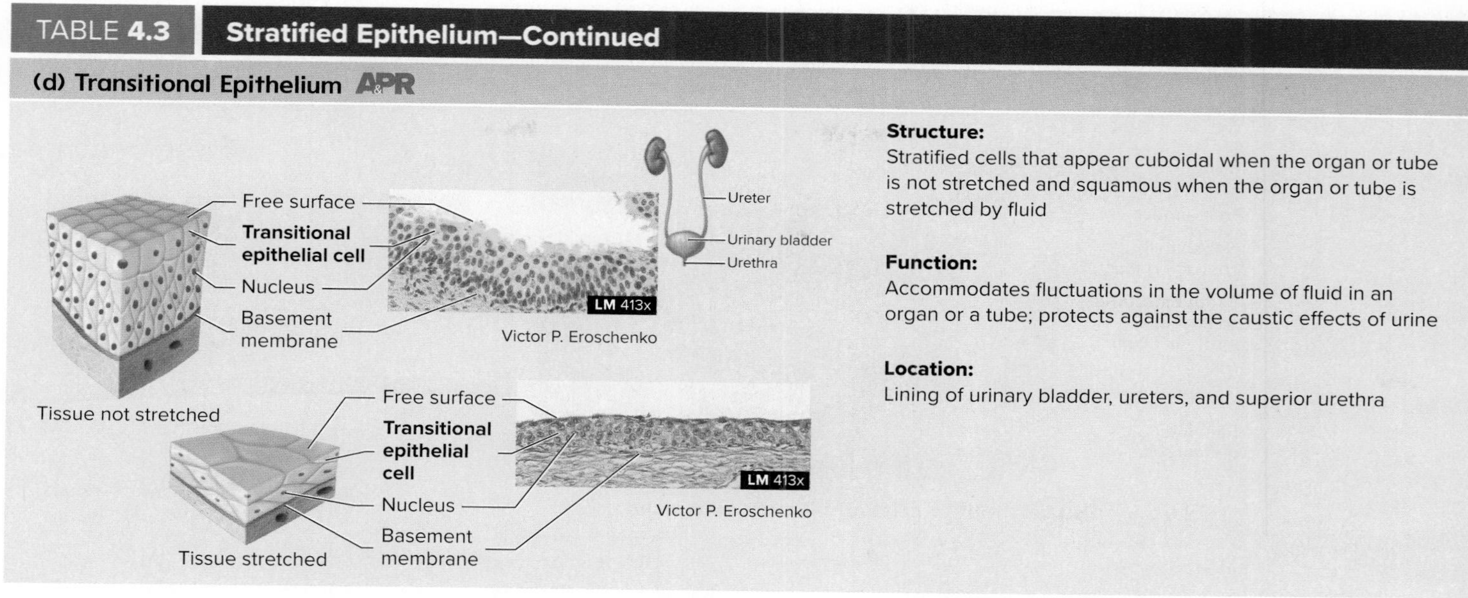

Structure:
Stratified cells that appear cuboidal when the organ or tube is not stretched and squamous when the organ or tube is stretched by fluid

Function:
Accommodates fluctuations in the volume of fluid in an organ or a tube; protects against the caustic effects of urine

Location:
Lining of urinary bladder, ureters, and superior urethra

stratified squamous epithelium consists of living cells only in the deepest layers, while the superficial layers are composed of dead cells containing the protein keratin. The dead, keratinized cells give the tissue a dry, durable, moisture-resistant character. These keratinized cells are found in the skin (see chapter 5). In addition to the skin, keratinized stratified squamous epithelium is also found in the gums and hard palate of the mouth.

A unique type of stratified epithelium called **transitional epithelium** (table 4.3*d*) lines the urinary bladder, ureters, pelvis of the kidney (including the major and minor calyces; KAL-i-seez), and superior part of the urethra (see chapter 26). These are structures where considerable expansion can occur. The shape of the cells and the number of cell layers vary, depending on the degree to which transitional epithelium is stretched. The surface cells and the underlying cells are roughly cuboidal or columnar when the epithelium is not stretched, and they become more flattened or squamouslike as the epithelium is stretched. Also, as the epithelium is stretched, the epithelial cells can shift on one another, so that the number of layers decreases from five or six to two or three.

Relationship Between Structure and Function of Epithelial Tissues

As the number of cell layers increases and the shape of the cells becomes more robust, we see a proportional increase in the degree of protection an epithelial tissue provides and increased complexity of the function it performs (table 4.4).

Number of Cell Layers and Cell Shapes

1. *One layer of flat cells.* Simple squamous epithelium is best adapted for areas of the body where filtration and diffusion are common. For example, simple squamous epithelium of the alveoli (air sacs) in the lungs allows diffusion of gases between the air and blood. In the kidneys, simple squamous epithelium in special structures allows wastes, but not blood cells, to be filtered from the blood. In addition, simple squamous epithelium protects organs in the pericardial, pleural, and peritoneal cavities (see chapter 1) by covering them with a thin, lubricated layer of tissue to allow the organs to easily slide past each other without friction-induced damage occurring.
2. *One layer of cubelike cells.* Simple cuboidal epithelium, due to the larger volume of these cells, has a greater secretory capacity than simple squamous epithelium. In fact, most glands in the body and other secretory structures are frequently composed of simple cuboidal epithelium. Additionally, the larger size of cuboidal cells can create tubes that are sturdy and provide more protection than tubes composed of simple squamous epithelium.
3. *One layer of tall, rectangular cells.* Simple columnar epithelial cells are much taller than those of cuboidal epithelium. Draw a sketch of squamous, cuboidal, and columnar epithelial cells side-by-side. Which cell type provides the thickest barrier? Simple columnar epithelium of the small intestine produces digestive enzymes, absorbs nutrients, and secretes mucus, which protects the lining of the intestine. Also, because these cells are tall, bacteria cannot easily penetrate the lining of the intestine (see chapter 24). Pseudostratified columnar epithelium, like simple columnar epithelium, is composed of tall cells and secretes mucus, which provides protection such as trapping inhaled debris in the trachea (see chapter 23). Both simple and pseudostratified columnar epithelia contain large goblet cells. It is the **goblet cells** that are responsible for synthesizing and secreting the large amounts of mucus common to these two tissues.
4. *Multiple layers of flat cells.* Stratified squamous epithelium forms a thick barrier, which can be as many as 30–40 cells thick. One type of stratified squamous epithelium forms the

Simple Epithelial Tissues

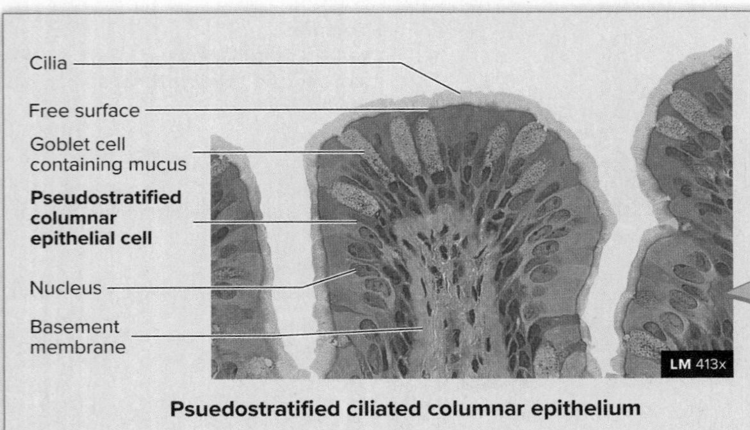

Psuedostratified ciliated columnar epithelium

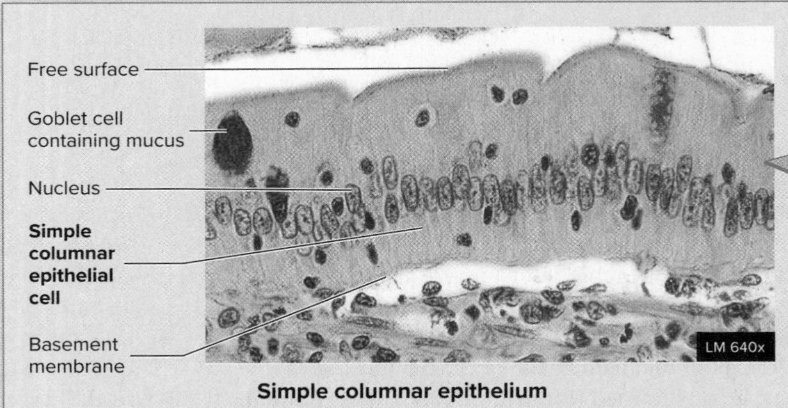

Simple columnar epithelium

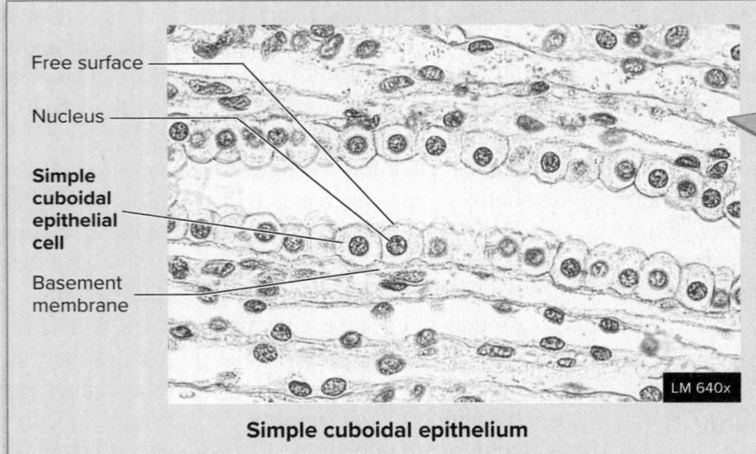

Simple cuboidal epithelium

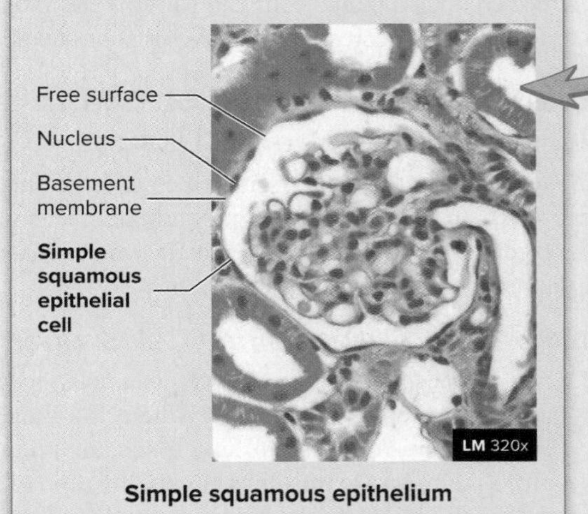

Simple squamous epithelium

FIGURE 4.2 Epithelial Tissue

The two main types of epithelial tissues are simple and stratified. Within these two categories, cell shape determines the specific epithelial tissue and influences the function. (Pseudostratified, simple columnar, simple cuboidal, transitional epithelium) Victor P. Eroschenko; (Renal corpuscle, esophagus, mediium power) Alvin Telser/McGraw Hill Education

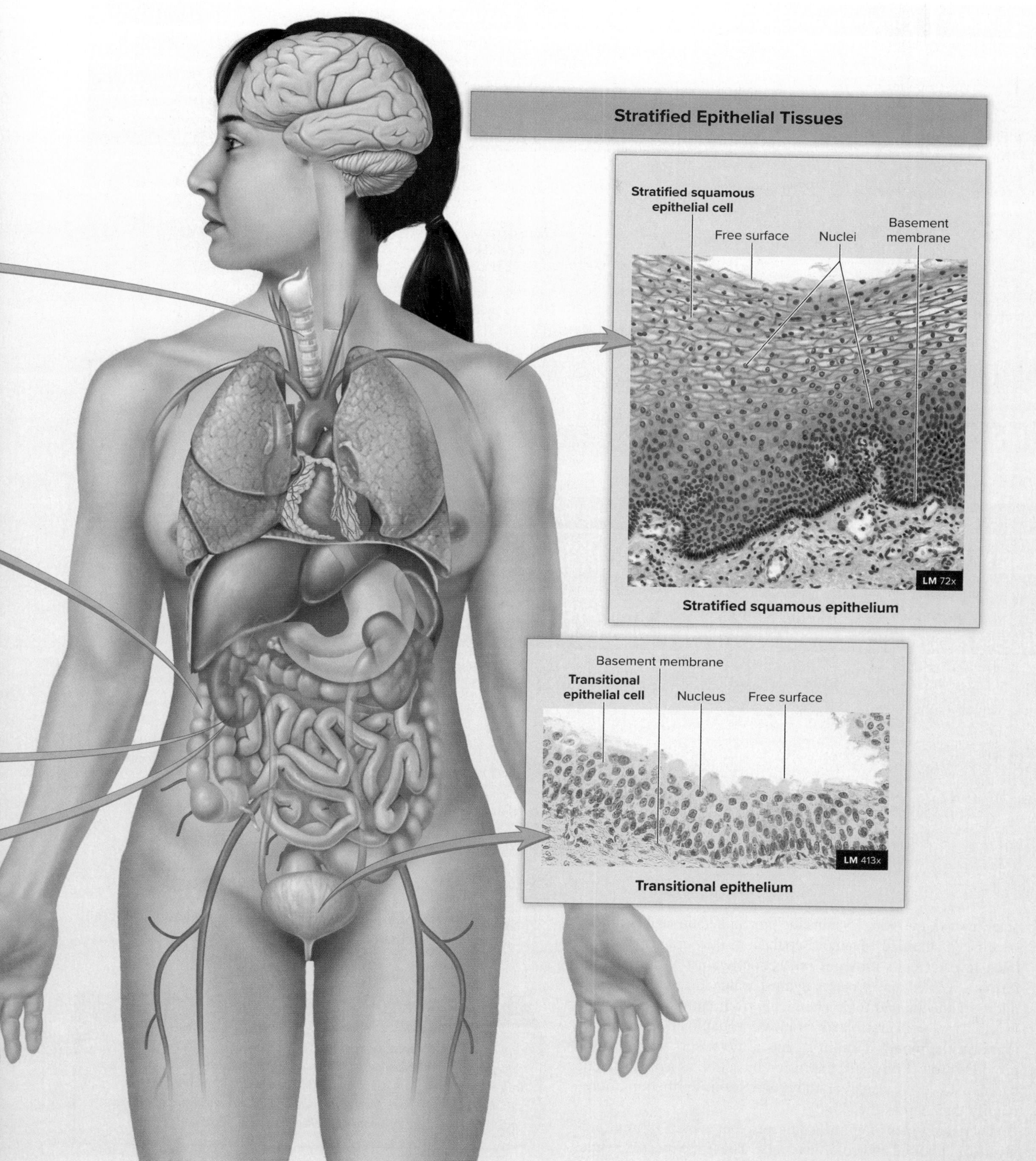
Stratified Epithelial Tissues
Stratified squamous epithelial cell
Free surface
Nuclei
Basement membrane
LM 72x
Stratified squamous epithelium
Basement membrane
Transitional epithelial cell
Nucleus
Free surface
LM 413x
Transitional epithelium

TABLE 4.4A Functions and Locations of Simple Epithelial Tissues

Simple Epithelia			
	LOCATION		
Function	**Simple Squamous Epithelium**	**Simple Cuboidal Epithelium**	**Pseudostratified Columnar Epithelium**
Diffusion	Blood and lymphatic capillaries, alveoli of lungs	—	—
Filtration	Bowman capsules of kidneys	—	—
Secretion or absorption	Mesothelium (serous fluid)	Choroid plexus (cerebrospinal fluid), part of kidney tubules, many glands and their ducts	—
Protection (against abrasion and friction)	Endothelium (e.g., blood vessels) Mesothelium (e.g., body cavities)	Terminal bronchioles of lungs	—
Movement of mucus (ciliated)	—	—	Trachea, bronchi of lungs, larynx, nasal cavity, auditory tubes
Miscellaneous	Inner part of tympanic membrane; smallest ducts of glands	Surface of ovaries	

TABLE 4.4B Functions and Locations of Stratified Epithelial Tissues

Stratified Epithelia				
	LOCATION			
Function	**Stratified Squamous Epithelium**	**Stratified Cuboidal Epithelium**	**Stratified Columnar Epithelium**	**Transitional Epithelium**
Protection (against abrasion and friction)	Skin (epidermis), corneas, mouth, esophagus	—	—	—
Movement of mucus (ciliated)	—	—	Larynx	—
Capable of stretch	—	—	—	Urinary bladder, ureters, superior part of urethra
Miscellaneous	Lower part of urethra, sebaceous gland ducts	Sweat gland ducts, salivary gland ducts, ovarian follicular cells	Part of male urethra, epididymides, ductus deferens, mammary gland ducts	—

outer layer of the skin, contains the protein keratin, and is called keratinized stratified squamous epithelium (see chapter 5). The thick layer of cells provides protection against abrasion, and forms a barrier that protects against water loss and prevents microorganisms and toxic chemicals from entering the body. In contrast, nonkeratinized stratified squamous epithelium, found in the mouth and throat, has a moist surface, but also provides protection against abrasion by acting as a mechanical barrier. However, water can move across this epithelium more readily than across the skin.

There are types of epithelial tissues that consist of multiple layers of cuboidal and columnar cells. These are more rare but generally provide a greater level of protection and strength to structures in which they are found.

Predict 1

Explain the consequences of having (a) nonkeratinized stratified epithelium rather than simple columnar epithelium lining the digestive tract, (b) nonkeratinized stratified squamous epithelium rather than keratinized stratified squamous epithelium in the skin, and (c) simple columnar epithelium rather than stratified squamous epithelium lining the mouth.

ASSESS YOUR PROGRESS

10. *Describe simple, stratified, and pseudostratified epithelial tissues. Distinguish among squamous, cuboidal, and columnar epithelial cells.*
11. *How do nonkeratinized stratified squamous epithelium and keratinized stratified squamous epithelium differ? Where is each type found?*
12. *Describe the changes in cell shape and number of cell layers in transitional epithelium as it is stretched. Where is transitional epithelium found?*
13. *List the types of epithelial tissue, giving the structure, functions, and major locations of each.*
14. *What functions would a single layer of epithelial cells be expected to perform? A stratified layer?*
15. *Why are cuboidal or columnar cells found where secretion or absorption is occurring?*

Free Surface Modifications

The free surfaces of epithelial tissues are not in contact with other cells. The free surfaces can be smooth or folded; they may also have microvilli or cilia. Smooth surfaces reduce friction. For example, the lining of blood vessels is a specialized simple squamous epithelium with a smooth surface called **endothelium** (en-doh-THEE-lee-um). The smooth surface reduces friction as blood flows through the vessels (see chapter 21).

Microvilli and cilia were described in chapter 3. Microvilli are nonmotile and contain microfilaments. They are extensions of the cell that greatly increase free surface area. They occur in cells that absorb or secrete, such as serous membranes and the lining of the small intestine (see chapter 24). Specialized microvilli found primarily in sensory structures, such as the inner ear (see chapter 15), are called stereocilia, but are microvilli and should not be confused with cilia. In contrast, cilia are motile and contain microtubules, which allow them to move materials across the free surface of the cell (see chapter 3). For example, cilia move mucus containing foreign particles out of the respiratory airways (see chapter 23). Cilia are also found on the apical surface of the simple columnar epithelial cells of the uterus and uterine tubes, where the cilia help move mucus and oocytes.

Transitional epithelium has cells with a rather unusual plasma membrane specialization: rigid sections of membrane separated by very flexible regions in which the plasma membrane is folded. When transitional epithelium is stretched, the folded regions of the plasma membrane can unfold. Transitional epithelium is specialized to expand in tissues such as the urinary bladder.

Cell Connections

Cells have structures that hold them to one another or to the basement membrane (figure 4.3). These structures do three things: (1) mechanically bind the cells together, (2) help form a permeability barrier, and (3) provide a mechanism for intercellular communication.

FUNDAMENTAL **Figure**

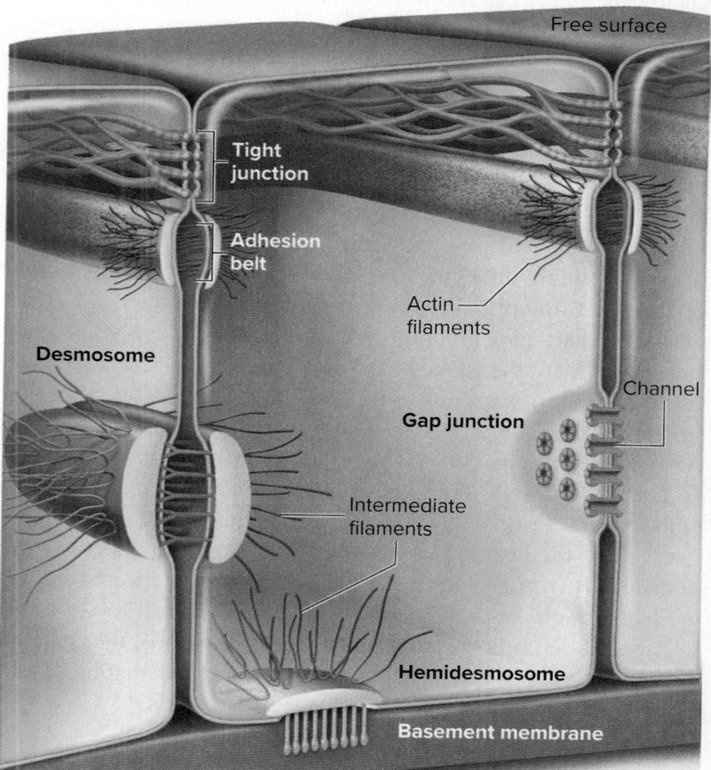

FIGURE 4.3 Cell Connections
Desmosomes, adhesion belts, and tight junctions anchor cells to one another, and hemidesmosomes anchor cells to the basement membrane. Gap junctions allow adjacent cells to communicate with each other. Few cells have all of these different connections.

Cell connection structures that mechanically bind epithelial cells together are called **desmosomes** (DEZ-moh-somes; *desmos*, a band + *soma*, body), while those that bind cells to the basement membrane are called **hemidesmosomes** (HEM-ee-dez-moh-sohms; *hemi*, half; see figure 4.3). Both types of mechanical linkages consist of adhesive material between the cells and intermediate filaments that extend into the cytoplasm of adjacent cells. Many desmosomes are found in epithelial tissues subjected to mechanical stress, such as the stratified squamous epithelium of the skin. Hemidesmosomes are the anchors of epithelial tissues to the underlying basement membrane, preventing the movement of the tissue.

Tight junctions are cell connection structures that (1) form barriers and (2) anchor cells to each other (see figure 4.3). Tight junctions form a barrier to movement of molecules or ions between epithelial cells. In addition, tight junctions anchor cells together. Structures called **adhesion belts** are found just below the tight junctions, and help the tight junctions anchor the epithelial cells to each other. Tight junctions are located near the free surface of the epithelial cells and form rings that completely surround each cell. These arrangements bind adjacent cells together to prevent passage of materials between cells, thus the name *tight* junctions. For example, in the stomach and urinary bladder, chemicals cannot pass between cells—water and other substances must pass through the epithelial cell membranes. This allows tight regulation of what is absorbed or secreted. The adhesion belt provides additional strength for the binding together of cells at at locations of tight junctions.

Cell connection structures that allow for intercellular communication include **gap junctions.** A gap junction is a small, specialized contact region between cells containing protein channels that aid intercellular communication by allowing ions and small molecules to pass from one cell to another (figure 4.3). In epithelium, the function of gap junctions is not entirely clear; gap junctions between ciliated epithelial cells may coordinate the movements of cilia. In cardiac and smooth muscle tissues, gap junctions are important in coordinating important functions. Because ions can pass through the gap junctions from one cell to the next, electrical signals can pass from cell to cell to coordinate the contraction of cardiac and smooth muscle cells. Thus, electrical signals that originate in one cell of the heart can spread from cell to cell and cause the entire heart to contract. In the heart, the gap junctions between cardiac muscle cells are found in specialized cell-to-cell connections called **intercalated disks** (see chapter 20). Intercalated disks contain both gap junctions and desmosomes that help hold adjacent cells in close contact.

Predict 2

If a simple epithelium has well-developed tight junctions, explain how NaCl can move from one side of the epithelial layer to the other, what type of epithelium it is likely to be, and how the movement of NaCl causes water to move in the same direction.

ASSESS YOUR PROGRESS

16. *What is the function of each of the following characteristics of an epithelial free surface: is smooth, has cilia, has microvilli, is folded? Give an example of where each surface type is found in the body.*
17. *Name the possible ways by which epithelial cells are bound to one another and to the basement membrane.*
18. *What role do desmosomes play in the skin?*
19. *What is the general function of gap junctions?*

Glands

Now that you've learned that many epithelial tissues are capable of secretion, let's examine specialized secretory organs, called glands. **Glands** are composed of epithelium supported by a network of connective tissue. These glands develop from an infolding or an outfolding of epithelium in the embryo. There are two major types of glands in the body: (1) endocrine glands and (2) exocrine glands.

Endocrine (EN-doh-krin) **glands** produce chemicals called **hormones** and are often termed ductless glands based on their structure and mode of secretion. Endocrine glands become separated from the epithelium of their origin and thus do not have ducts into which their secretions empty. These glands are associated with an extensive network of blood vessels, and their hormones are transported throughout the body by way of the blood. Hormones are discussed in more detail in chapters 17 and 18.

Exocrine (EK-soh-krin) **glands** produce a wide variety of products, such as saliva, sweat, and digestive tract secretions. These secretions enter ducts, which are continuous with the epithelial tissue surface from which the gland developed. At the appropriate location, the secretions exit onto the free surface of the target organ's tissue. Exocrine glands are primarily categorized on the basis of their structure, but they are also separated on the basis of their mode of secretion. For example, there are exocrine glands that have the same structure but utilize different modes of secretion. By the same token, there are glands that utilize the same mode of secretion but have very different structures.

The three specific distinctions we use in this textbook are (1) structure of the duct, (2) structure of the secretory portion of the gland, and (3) mode of secretion within the secretory portion (figure 4.4).

Structure of Exocrine Glands

First, it's important to distinguish between the duct and the secretory portion of the gland. The duct refers to the tube in contact with the epithelial tissue free surface, which transports the secreted material. Second, the secretory portion of the gland is found deeper in the epithelium and is composed of the cells responsible for producing the secreted material. The three major categories of exocrine glands are (1) unicellular, (2) simple, and (3) compound.

Unicellular

Some exocrine glands are composed of only a single cell, such as **goblet cells** that secrete mucus (figure 4.4*a*, table 4.5).

Simple

Simple glands are multicellular glands that have a single, nonbranched duct (figure 4.4*b*; see table 4.5). The secretory portions

TABLE 4.5 Representative Exocrine Glands

Structure	Structural Subtype	Example	Mode of Secretion
Unicellular	—	Goblet cell	Merocrine
Multicellular Simple	Simple tubular	Glands in stomach	Merocrine
	Simple branched tubular	Gastric glands in stomach	Merocrine
	Simple acinar	Sebaceous glands	Holocrine
	Simple branched acinar	Thyroid gland	Merocrine
Compound	Compound tubular	Mucous glands of duodenum	Merocrine
	Compound acinar	Mammary glands	Apocrine for fatty portion Merocrine for protein-rich portion
	Compound tubuloacinar	Pancreas	Merocrine

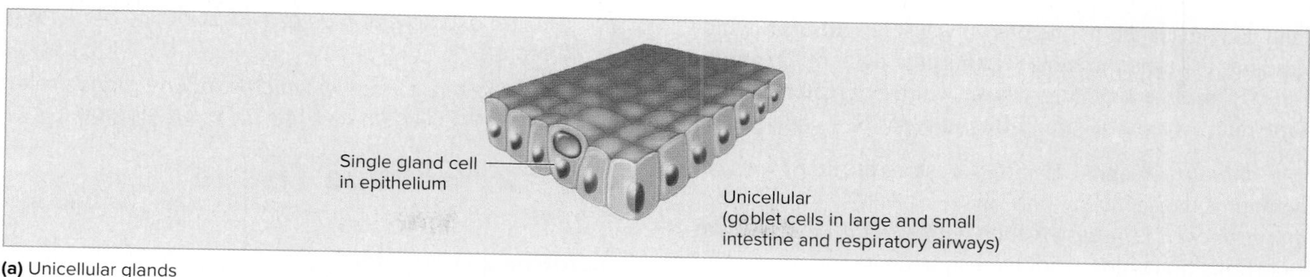

(a) Unicellular glands

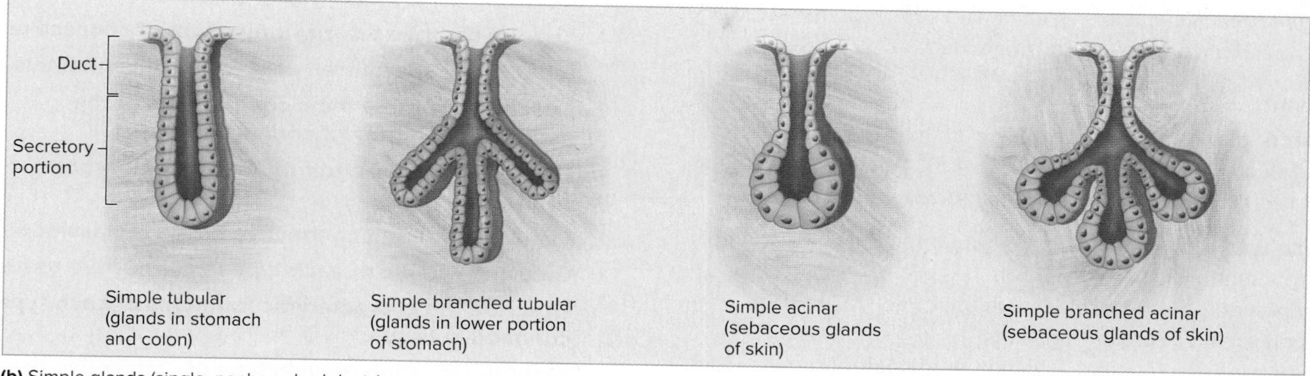

(b) Simple glands (single, nonbranched ducts)

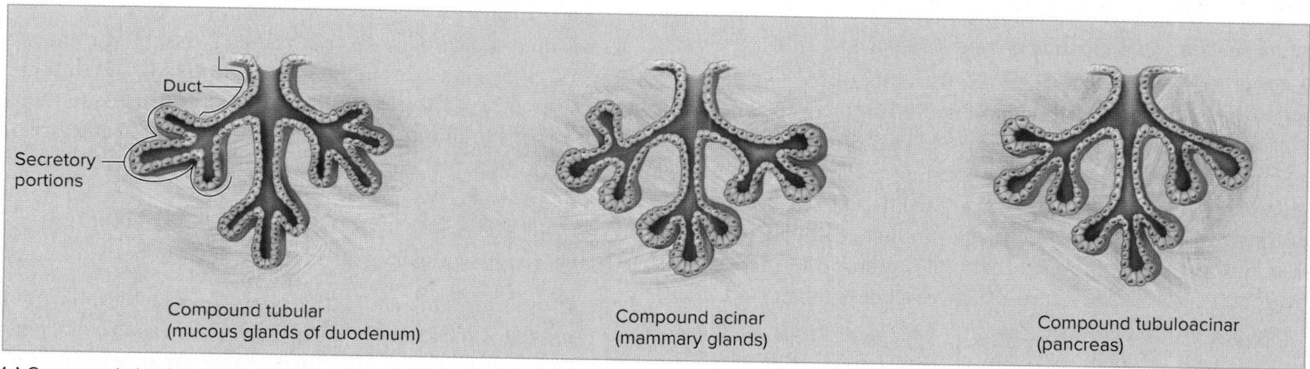

(c) Compound glands (multiple, branched ducts)

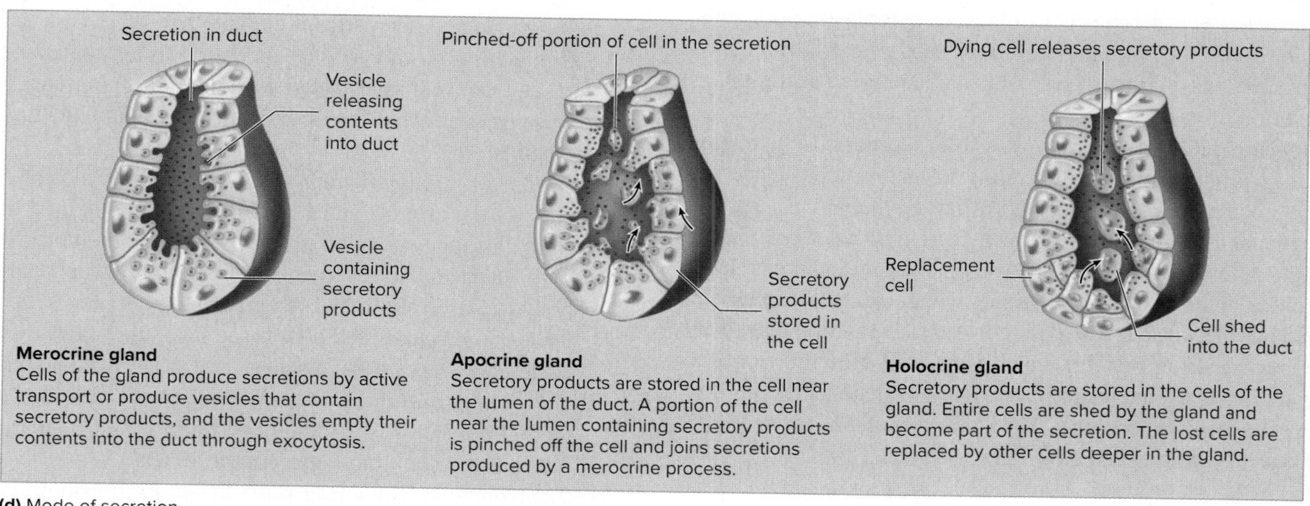

(d) Mode of secretion

FIGURE 4.4 Structure of Exocrine Glands

(*a*) Unicellular glands. Exocrine glands can be unicellular, but are most often multicellular. (*b*) Simple glands. These have single, nonbranched ducts. (*c*) Compound glands. These have multiple, branched ducts. (*d*) Modes of secretion: merocrine glands, apocrine glands, and holocrine glands.

of the gland can be shaped in one of two ways: (1) **tubular,** which is a straight, narrow tube the same width as the duct, or (2) **acinar** (ASS-ih-nar), a saclike structure whose width is greater than the width of the duct. We see several different types of simple glands.

- *Simple tubular*—glands forming a straight tube with no branching of the secretory portion
- *Simple branched tubular*—glands with several tubular secretory portions branching from the single duct
- *Simple acinar*—glands with a single saclike secretory portion
- *Simple branched acinar*—glands with several acinar secretory portions branching from the single duct

Compound

Compound glands are multicellular glands that have several branched ducts (figure 4.4*c*; see table 4.5). Again, the secretory portions can be either tubular or acinar, or a mixture of both.

- *Compound tubular*—glands with multiple ducts, each with a narrow tubular secretory portion
- *Compound acinar*—glands with multiple ducts, each with several saclike secretory portions
- *Compound tubuloacinar*—glands with multiple ducts, each with several tubular and acinar secretory portions

Modes of Secretion by Exocrine Glands

Within each of the structural categories, the cells of the secretory portion may use one of three modes of secretion or even a combination of secretion modes (figure 4.4*d*). The three modes are (1) merocrine, (2) apocrine, and (3) holocrine.

Merocrine (MARE-oh-krin; *mero*, partial + *crine*, to separate) **secretion** is the release of secretory products through exocytosis and is the most common. For example, merocrine secretion is used by goblet cells, temperature-sensitive sweat glands, and the exocrine portion of the pancreas.

Apocrine (AP-oh-krin; *apo*, away from) **secretion** is the release of secretory products when a portion of the free surface of the epithelial cell pinches off, releasing cytoplasmic contents. The remainder of the cell is repaired. Release of the fatty portion of milk by mammary glands occurs through apocrine secretion, as does secretion of earwax.

Holocrine (HOL-oh-krin; *holos,* whole) **secretion** is the release of secretory products through shedding of entire cells. Once the secretory products have accumulated in the epithelial cell, the cell disintegrates and becomes part of the secretion. Deeper cells in the gland replace lost cells. Sebaceous (oil) glands in the skin release sebum (oil) through holocrine secretion, which can help explain the appearance of blackheads. The dark-colored material of a blackhead is sometimes mistaken for dirt, but it is actually melanin from the disintegrated cell. An interesting fact to note is that changes in hormones are the principal causes of blackhead formation, not necessarily the frequency with which a person washes their face.

ASSESS YOUR PROGRESS

20. *Distinguish between exocrine and endocrine glands. How are multicellular exocrine glands classified on the basis of their duct system? Their secretory portion shape?*

21. *Give an example of a unicellular exocrine gland. What does it secrete?*

22. *Describe three ways in which exocrine glands release secretions. Give an example of each method.*

4.4 Connective Tissue

LEARNING OUTCOMES

After reading this section, you should be able to

A. **List and describe the major functions of connective tissue.**
B. **Identify the specialized cells found in connective tissue.**
C. **Describe the three main components of the extracellular matrix of connective tissue.**
D. **Discuss the types and functions of embryonic connective tissue.**
E. **Explain how adult connective tissue is classified.**
F. **Give an example of each type of connective tissue.**
G. **Describe the characteristic functions of each type of connective tissue.**
H. **State the location of each type of connective tissue in the body.**

Connective tissue is a diverse primary tissue type that makes up part of every organ in the body. Connective tissue differs from the other three tissue types in that it consists of cells separated from each other by abundant extracellular matrix. Connective tissue is diverse in both structure and function.

Functions of Connective Tissue

Connective tissue performs the following major functions:

1. *Enclosing and separating other tissues.* Sheets of connective tissue form capsules around organs, such as the liver and kidneys. Connective tissue also forms layers that separate tissues and organs. For example, connective tissues separate muscles, arteries, veins, and nerves from one another.
2. *Connecting tissues to one another.* Strong cables, or bands, of connective tissue called tendons attach muscles to bone, whereas connective tissue bands called ligaments hold bones together.
3. *Supporting and moving parts of the body.* Bones of the skeletal system provide rigid support for the body, and the semirigid cartilage supports structures such as the nose, ears, and joint surfaces. Joints between bones allow one part of the body to move relative to other parts.
4. *Storing compounds.* Adipose tissue (fat) stores high-energy molecules, and bones store minerals, such as calcium and phosphate.
5. *Cushioning and insulating.* Adipose tissue cushions and protects the tissue it surrounds and provides an insulating layer beneath the skin that helps conserve heat.
6. *Transporting.* Blood transports the gases, nutrients, enzymes, hormones, and cells of the immune system throughout the body.
7. *Protecting.* Cells of the immune system and blood protect against toxins and tissue injury, as well as against microorganisms. Bones protect underlying structures from injury.

Cells of Connective Tissue

The specialized cells of the various connective tissues produce the extracellular matrix. The name of the cell identifies the cell functions by means of one of the following suffixes: *-blast, -cyte,* or *-clast.* (1) **Blasts** create the matrix, (2) **cytes** maintain it, and (3) **clasts** break it down for remodeling.

The connective tissue cells that form the framework of the body include bone cells, cartilage cells, and fibrous tissue cells. For bone, **osteoblasts** (*osteo-*, bone) form it, **osteocytes** maintain it, and **osteoclasts** break it down (see chapter 6). For cartilage, **chondroblasts** (*chondro-*, cartilage) form it and **chondrocytes** maintain it. For fibrous tissue, **fibroblasts** form it and **fibrocytes** maintain it.

Adipocytes (AD-i-poh-sytes), also called adipose (ADD-i-pose; fat) cells, contain large amounts of lipid. The lipid pushes the rest of the cell contents to the periphery, so that each cell appears to contain a large, centrally located lipid droplet with a thin layer of cytoplasm around it. Adipocytes are rare in some connective tissue types, such as cartilage, but abundant in others, such as loose connective tissue.

Mast cells play important roles in inflammation. They contain chemicals, such as heparin, histamine, and proteolytic enzymes, that are released in response to injury, such as trauma and infection. Mast cells commonly lie beneath membranes in loose connective tissue and along small blood vessels of organs.

White blood cells, or *leukocytes* (see chapter 19), continuously move from blood vessels into connective tissues. The rate of movement increases dramatically in response to injury or infection. In addition, accumulations of lymphocytes, a type of white blood cell, are common in some connective tissues, such as that beneath the epithelial lining of certain parts of the digestive system.

Macrophages (MAK-roh-fay-jes; *makros*, large + *phago*, to eat) are large, phagocytic cells found in some connective tissue types. They are derived from monocytes, a type of white blood cell. Macrophages are either fixed, meaning that they do not move through the connective tissue, or wandering, moving in ameboid fashion through the connective tissue. Macrophages phagocytize foreign and injured cells, and they play a major role in protecting against infections.

Platelets are fragments of hematopoietic cells containing enzymes and special proteins that function in the clotting process to reduce bleeding from a wound.

Undifferentiated mesenchymal cells are a type of **adult stem cell** that persists in connective tissue. They have the potential to form multiple cell types, such as fibroblasts or smooth muscle cells, in response to injury.

Extracellular Matrix

The extracellular matrix of connective tissue has three major components: (1) protein fibers; (2) ground substance, which consists of nonfibrous protein and other molecules; and (3) fluid. The structure of the matrix gives connective tissue types most of their functional characteristics—for example, they enable bones and cartilage to bear weight, tendons and ligaments to withstand tension, and the skin's dermis to withstand punctures, abrasions, and other abuse.

Protein Fibers of the Matrix

Three types of protein fibers help form connective tissues: (1) collagen, (2) reticular, and (3) elastic.

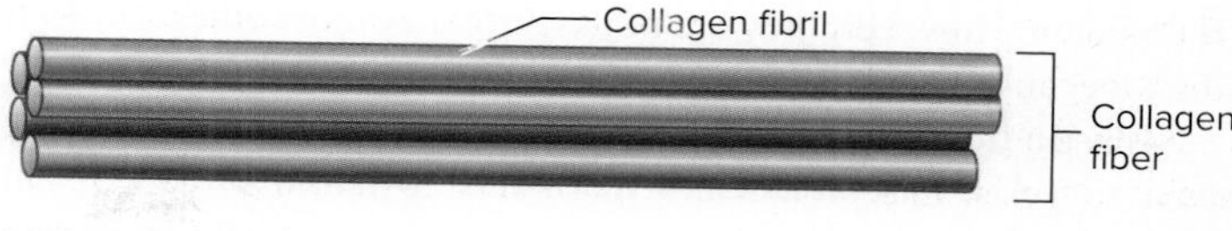

(a) Collagen fibers

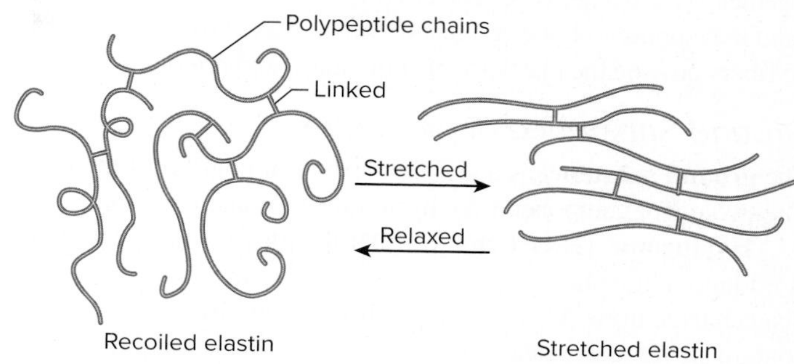

(b) Elastic fibers

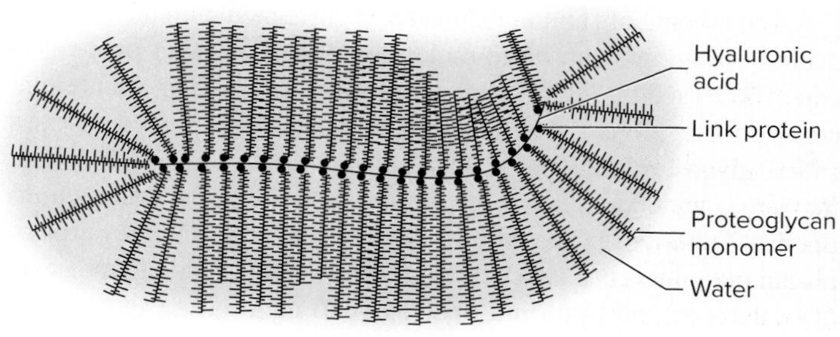

(c) Proteoglycan aggregates

FIGURE 4.5 Molecules of the Connective Tissue Matrix
(*a*) Collagen fibers. Individual collagen fibrils are joined into fibers. (*b*) Elastic fibers. The fibers can be stretched or compressed, which gives them their elastic quality. (*c*) Proteoglycan aggregates. These aggregates consist of hyaluronic acid linked to many proteoglycan monomers.

Collagen (KOL-ah-jen) **fibers** consist of the protein collagen. Collagen is the most abundant protein in the body. It accounts for one-fourth to one-third of total body protein and 6% of total body weight. Collagen is synthesized within fibroblasts and secreted into the extracellular space. After collagen molecules are secreted, they are linked together to make long collagen fibrils. The collagen fibrils are then joined together in bundles to form collagen fibers (figure 4.5*a*). Collagen fibers are very strong and flexible, like microscopic ropes, but are not very elastic.

There are at least 20 types of collagen fibers, many of which are specific to certain tissues. Type I collagen is the most abundant in the body. The flexible, ropelike strength of type I collagen fibers makes them well suited for tendons, ligaments, skin, and bone. These body structures need to resist being pulled yet have some flexibility. Type II collagen is found in cartilage, and type III is found in reticular fibers.

Reticular (re-TIK-yoo-lar; netlike) **fibers** are very short, thin fibers that branch to form a network. Networks of reticular fibers fill spaces between tissues and organs. They are composed of type

III collagen. However, they are not as strong as most other collagen fibers because they mainly play a space-filling role in the body.

Elastic fibers consist of the protein **elastin** (e-LAS-tin). As the name suggests, this protein has the ability to return to its original shape after being stretched or compressed, giving tissue an elastic quality. Fibroblasts secrete elastin polypeptide chains, which are linked together to form a network. The elastin network stretches like a rubber band in response to force and recoils when relaxed (figure 4.5*b*). Elastic fibers provide the elasticity of skin, lungs, and arteries.

Ground Substance of the Matrix

The **ground substance** is a gel-like mixture of nonfibrous molecules. The two major components are hyaluronic acid and proteoglycans.

Hyaluronic (HIGH-ah-loo-RON-ik; glassy appearance) **acid** is a long, unbranched polysaccharide chain composed of repeating disaccharide units. It gives a very slippery quality to the fluids that contain it; for that reason, it is a good lubricant for joint cavities (see chapter 8). Hyaluronic acid is also present in large quantities in connective tissue and is the major component of the vitreous humor of the eye (see chapter 15).

The amount of fluid in the matrix is correlated with the type and quantity of ground substance molecules. For example, a **proteoglycan** (PROH-tee-oh-GLYE-kan) **monomer** is a large molecule that consists of a protein core attached to many long polysaccharides called **glycosaminoglycans** (glye-kohs-am-i-noh-GLYE-kanz) that trap large quantities of water. A common glycosaminoglycan is **chondroitin** (kuhn-DROY-ten) **sulfate.** The protein cores of many proteoglycan monomers can attach through link proteins to a long molecule of hyaluronic acid to form a **proteoglycan aggregate** (figure 4.5*c*). The large quantities of water trapped by proteoglycan aggregates allow these molecules to return to their original shape when compressed or deformed. There are several types of glycosaminoglycans, and their abundance varies with each connective tissue type.

Adhesive molecules in the ground substance hold the proteoglycan aggregates together, as well as attach them to cells of the tissue. Specific adhesive molecules predominate in certain types of ground substance. For example, **chondronectin** is in the ground substance of cartilage, **osteonectin** is in the ground substance of bone, and **fibronectin** is in the ground substance of fibrous connective tissue.

ASSESS YOUR PROGRESS

23. *What is the main characteristic that distinguishes connective tissue from other tissues?*
24. *List the major functions of connective tissue, and give an example of a type of connective tissue that performs each function.*
25. *Explain the differences among -blast, -cyte, and -clast cells of connective tissue.*
26. *What are the three components of the extracellular matrix of connective tissue?*
27. *Contrast the structure and characteristics of collagen fibers, reticular fibers, and elastic fibers.*
28. *Describe the structures and functions of hyaluronic acid and proteoglycan aggregates.*
29. *What is the function of adhesive molecules? Give some specific examples.*

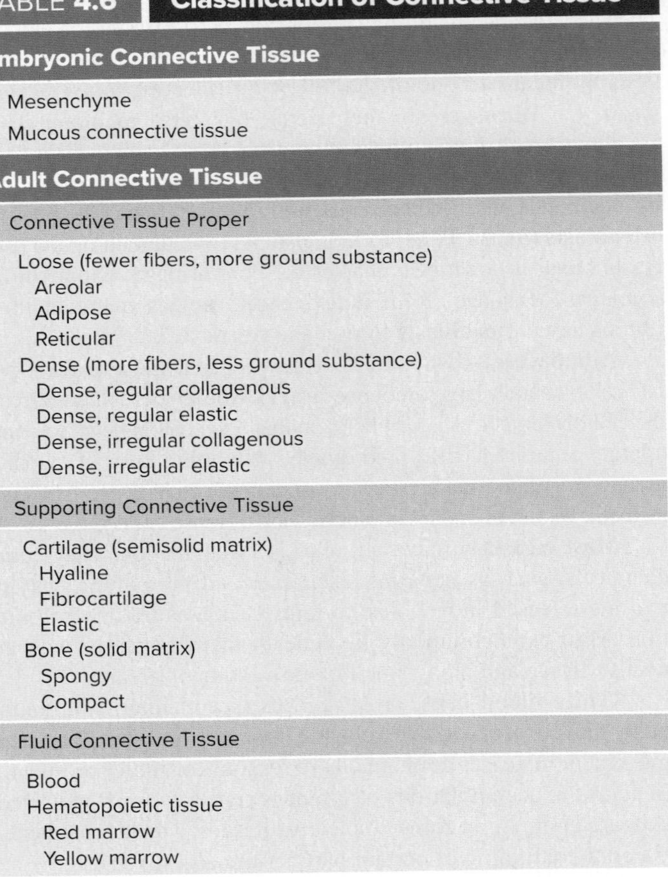

TABLE 4.6 Classification of Connective Tissue
Embryonic Connective Tissue
Mesenchyme
Mucous connective tissue
Adult Connective Tissue
Connective Tissue Proper
Loose (fewer fibers, more ground substance)
Areolar
Adipose
Reticular
Dense (more fibers, less ground substance)
Dense, regular collagenous
Dense, regular elastic
Dense, irregular collagenous
Dense, irregular elastic
Supporting Connective Tissue
Cartilage (semisolid matrix)
Hyaline
Fibrocartilage
Elastic
Bone (solid matrix)
Spongy
Compact
Fluid Connective Tissue
Blood
Hematopoietic tissue
Red marrow
Yellow marrow

Connective Tissue Classifications

Connective tissue types blend into one another, and the transition points cannot be identified precisely. As a result, connective tissue is somewhat arbitrarily classified by the type and proportions of cells and extracellular matrix components. Table 4.6 presents the classification of connective tissue used in this text.

Two major categories of connective tissue are (1) embryonic and (2) adult.

Embryonic Connective Tissue

Embryonic connective tissue is called **mesenchyme** (MEZ-en-kyme). It is composed of fibroblasts surrounded by semifluid extracellular matrix containing delicate reticular fibers (table 4.7*a*). It forms in the embryo during the third and fourth weeks of development from mesoderm and neural crest cells (see chapter 29), and all adult connective tissue types develop from it. By 8 weeks of development, most of the mesenchyme has become specialized to form the types of connective tissue seen in adults. The major source of remaining embryonic connective tissue in the newborn is in the umbilical cord, where it is called **mucous connective tissue,** or *Wharton's jelly* (table 4.7*b*). The structure of mucous connective tissue is similar to that of mesenchyme. The mucous connective tissue helps support the umbilical cord blood vessels between the mother and the child. After birth, the mucous connective tissue can also be a rich source of stem cells.

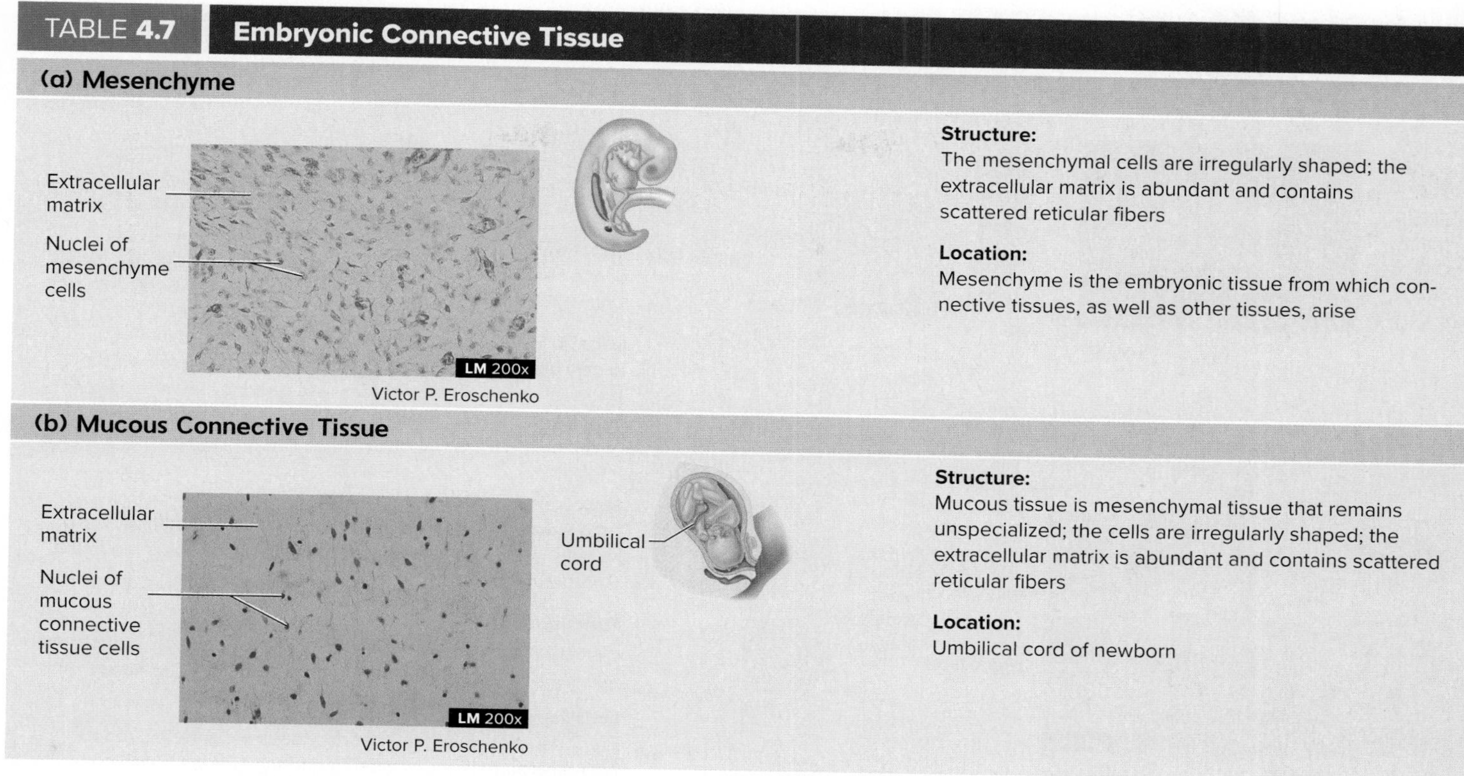

Adult Connective Tissue

Table 4.8 presents the classification of adult connective tissue used in this textbook. Adult connective tissue consists of three types: (1) connective tissue proper (loose and dense), (2) supporting connective tissue (cartilage and bone), and (3) fluid connective tissue (blood and hematopoietic tissue). Figure 4.6 summarizes the connective tissues of the body.

Connective Tissue Proper

1. **Loose connective tissue** (table 4.8) consists of relatively few protein fibers that form a lacy network, with numerous spaces filled with ground substance and fluid. Three subdivisions of loose connective tissue are areolar, adipose, and reticular.
   - **Areolar** (ah-REE-oh-lar) **tissue** cushions most organs and other tissues; it attaches the skin to underlying tissues (table 4.8*a*). It contains collagen, reticular, and elastic fibers and a variety of cells. For example, fibroblasts produce the fibrous matrix; macrophages move through the tissue, engulfing bacteria and cell debris; mast cells contain chemicals that help mediate inflammation; and lymphocytes are involved in immunity. The loose packing of areolar tissue is often associated with the other loose connective tissue types, adipose and reticular tissue.
   - **Adipose tissue** (table 4.8*b*) consists of adipocytes, which contain large amounts of lipids. Adipose tissue has special properties compared to other connective tissues; it is composed of large cells and a small amount of extracellular matrix. The matrix consists of loosely arranged collagen and reticular fibers with some scattered elastic fibers. Blood vessels form a network in the extracellular matrix. The adipocytes are usually arranged in clusters, or lobules, separated from one another by loose connective tissue. Adipose tissue functions as an insulator, a protective tissue, and a site of energy storage. Lipids take up less space per calorie than either carbohydrates or proteins and therefore are well adapted for energy storage.

     Adipose tissue exists in both yellow and brown forms. **Yellow adipose** tissue is by far the most abundant. Yellow adipose tissue appears white at birth, but it turns yellow with age because of the accumulation of pigments, such as carotene, a plant pigment that humans can metabolize as a source of vitamin A. In humans, **brown adipose** tissue is found in specific areas of the body, such as the axillae (armpits), the neck, and near the kidneys. The brown color results from the cytochrome pigments in the tissue's numerous mitochondria and its abundant blood supply. It is difficult to distinguish brown adipose from yellow adipose in babies because the color difference is not great. Brown adipose tissue is specialized to generate heat as a result of oxidative metabolism of lipid molecules in mitochondria. It can play a significant role in regulating body temperature in newborns and is now recognized to also play a role in adult metabolism (see chapter 25).
   - **Reticular tissue** has the special property of predominating in areas of the body with a high cellular content. These include lymphatic tissues (table 4.8*c*), such as in the spleen and lymph nodes, as well as in bone marrow and the liver. It is characterized by a network of reticular fibers and reticular cells. **Reticular cells** produce the reticular fibers and remain closely attached to them. The spaces between the reticular fibers can contain a wide variety of other cells, such as macrophages, blood cells, and dendritic cells,

TABLE 4.8 Connective Tissue Proper: Loose Connective Tissue

(a) Areolar Connective Tissue APR

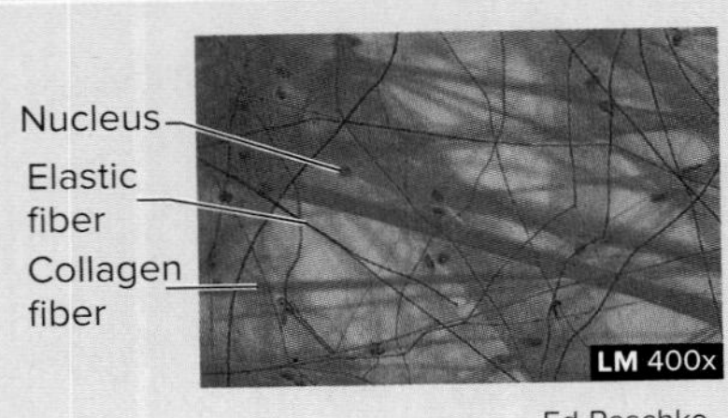

Ed Reschke

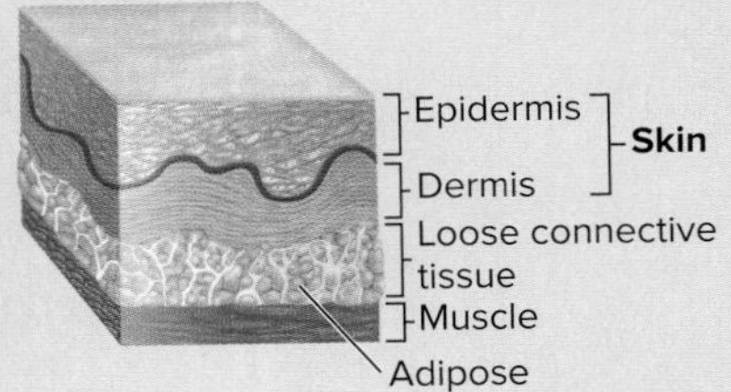

Structure:
A fine network of fibers (mostly collagen fibers with a few elastic fibers) with spaces between the fibers; fibroblasts, macrophages, and lymphocytes are located in the spaces

Function:
Loose packing, support, and nourishment for the structures with which it is associated

Location:
Widely distributed throughout the body; substance on which epithelial basement membranes rest; packing between glands, muscles, and nerves; attaches the skin to underlying tissues

(b) Adipose Tissue APR

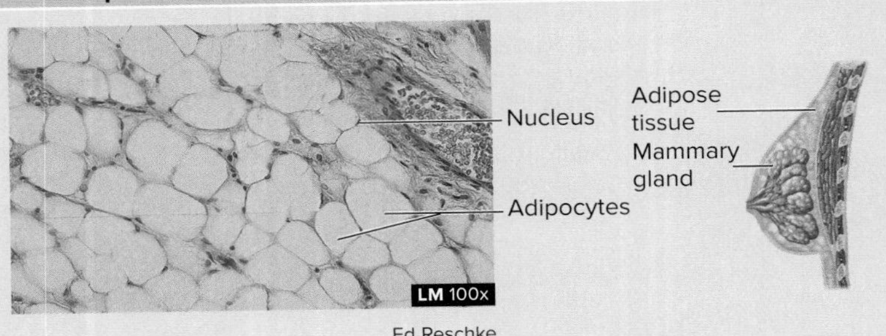

Ed Reschke

Structure:
Little extracellular matrix surrounding cells; the adipocytes, or fat cells, are so full of lipid that the cytoplasm is pushed to the periphery of the cell

Function:
Packing material, thermal insulator, energy storage, and protection of organs against injury from being bumped or jarred

Location:
Predominantly in subcutaneous areas, mesenteries, renal pelves, around kidneys, attached to the surface of the colon, mammary glands, and in loose connective tissue that penetrates into spaces and crevices

(c) Reticular Tissue APR

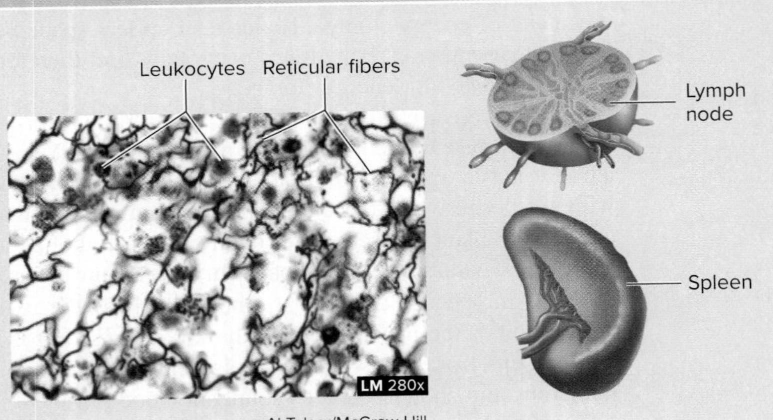

Al Telser/McGraw Hill

Structure:
Fine network of reticular fibers irregularly arranged

Function:
Provides a superstructure for lymphatic and hemopoietic tissues

Location:
Within the lymph nodes, spleen, bone marrow

which look very much like reticular cells but are cells of the immune system (see chapter 22).

2. **Dense connective tissue** has a relatively large number of protein fibers, which form thick bundles and fill nearly all of the extracellular space. Most of the cells of developing dense connective tissue are spindle-shaped fibroblasts. Once the fibroblasts become completely surrounded by matrix, they are fibrocytes. Dense connective tissue can be subdivided into two major groups: (1) dense regular and (2) dense irregular.
   - **Dense regular connective tissue** has protein fibers in the extracellular matrix that are oriented predominantly in one direction.
     - **Dense regular collagenous connective tissue** (table 4.9*a*) has abundant collagen fibers, which give this tissue a white appearance. Dense regular collagenous connective tissue forms structures such as tendons, which connect muscles to bones (see chapter 9), and most ligaments, which connect bones to bones (see chapter 8). The collagen fibers of dense connective tissue resist stretching and give the tissue considerable strength in the direction of the fiber orientation. Tendons and most ligaments consist almost entirely of thick bundles of densely packed, parallel collagen fibers with the orientation of the collagen fibers in one direction,

TABLE 4.10 Supporting Connective Tissue: Cartilage

(a) Hyaline Cartilage APR

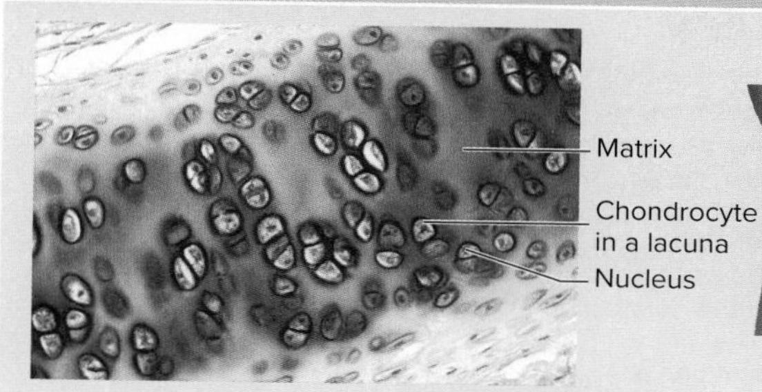

Victor P. Eroschenko

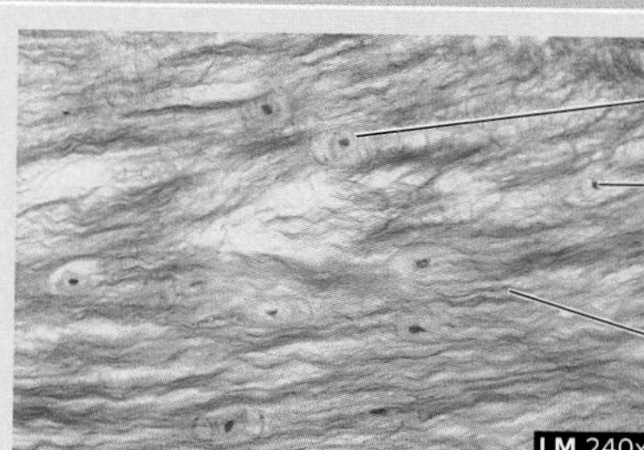

Structure:
Collagen fibers are small and evenly dispersed in the matrix, making the matrix appear transparent; the chondrocytes are found in spaces, or lacunae, within the firm but flexible matrix

Function:
Allows growth of long bones; provides rigidity with some flexibility in the trachea, bronchi, ribs, and nose; forms strong, smooth, yet somewhat flexible articulating surfaces; forms the embryonic skeleton

Location:
Growing long bones, cartilage rings of the respiratory system, costal cartilage of ribs, nasal cartilages, articulating surface of bones, and the embryonic skeleton

(b) Fibrocartilage APR

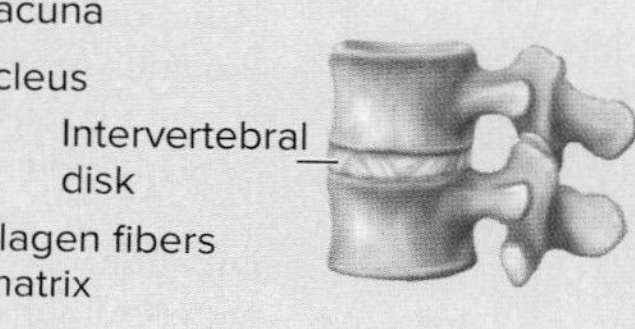

Victor P. Eroschenko

Structure:
Collagen fibers similar to those in hyaline cartilage; the fibers are more numerous than in other cartilages and are arranged in thick bundles

Function:
Somewhat flexible and capable of withstanding considerable pressure; connects structures subjected to great pressure

Location:
Intervertebral disks, pubic symphysis, and articular disks (e.g., knees and temporomandibular [jaw] joints)

(c) Elastic Cartilage APR

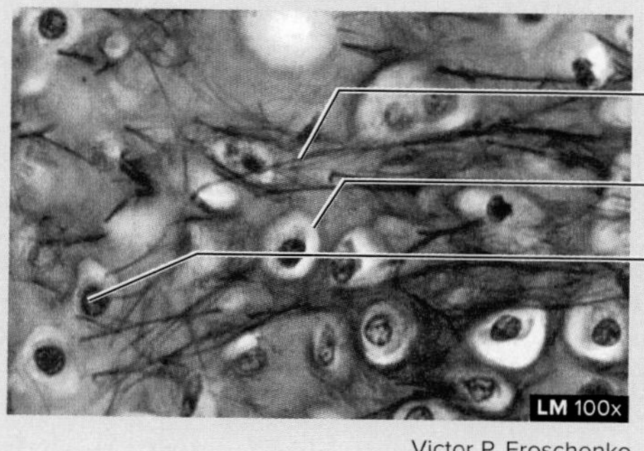

Victor P. Eroschenko

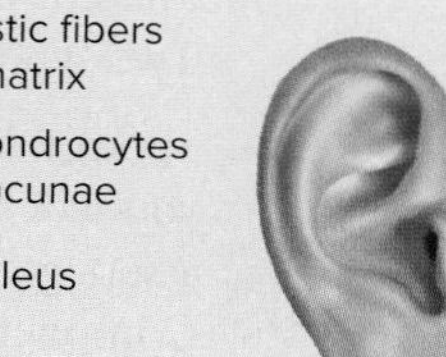

Structure:
Similar to hyaline cartilage, but matrix also contains elastic fibers

Function:
Provides rigidity with even more flexibility than hyaline cartilage because elastic fibers return to their original shape after being stretched

Location:
External ears, epiglottis, and auditory tubes

are needed, such as in the rib cage and within the trachea and bronchi (see chapter 23). It also covers the surfaces of bones that move smoothly against each other in joints. Hyaline cartilage forms most of the skeleton before it is replaced by bone in the embryo, and it is involved in growth that increases the length of bones (see chapter 6).

- **Fibrocartilage** has more collagen fibers than proteoglycans (table 4.10*b*). Compared with hyaline cartilage, fibrocartilage has much thicker bundles of collagen fibers dispersed through its matrix. Fibrocartilage is slightly compressible and very tough. It is found in areas of the body where a great deal of pressure is applied to joints, such as in the knee, in the jaw, and between the vertebrae. Some joints, such as the knee, have both hyaline and fibrocartilage connective tissue. In these joints, pads of fibrocartilage help absorb shocks and prevent bone-to-bone abrasion. Fibrocartilage injuries of the knee joint (meniscus tears) are common sports-related injuries.
- **Elastic cartilage** has numerous elastic fibers in addition to collagen and proteoglycans dispersed throughout its matrix

TABLE 4.11 Supporting Connective Tissue: Bone

(a) Spongy Bone

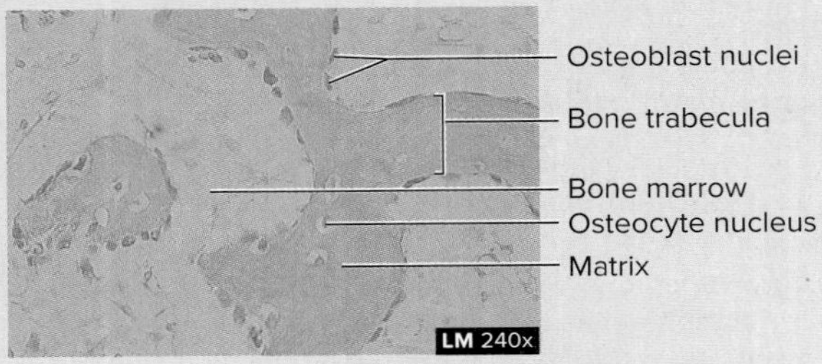

Osteoblast nuclei
Bone trabecula
Bone marrow
Osteocyte nucleus
Matrix
LM 240x
Victor P. Eroschenko

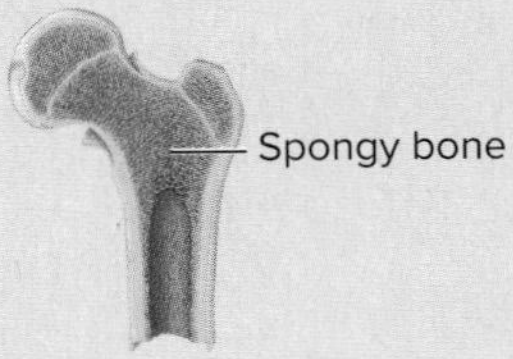

Spongy bone

Structure:
Latticelike network of scaffolding characterized by trabeculae with large spaces between them filled with hemopoietic tissue; the osteocytes, or bone cells, are located within lacunae in the trabeculae

Function:
Acts as scaffolding to provide strength and support without the greater weight of compact bone

Location:
In the interior of the bones of the skull, vertebrae, sternum, and pelvis; in the ends of the long bones

(b) Compact Bone

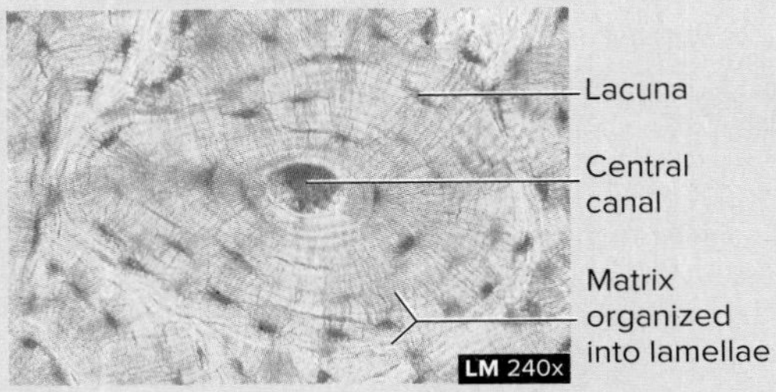

Lacuna
Central canal
Matrix organized into lamellae
LM 240x
Trent Stephens

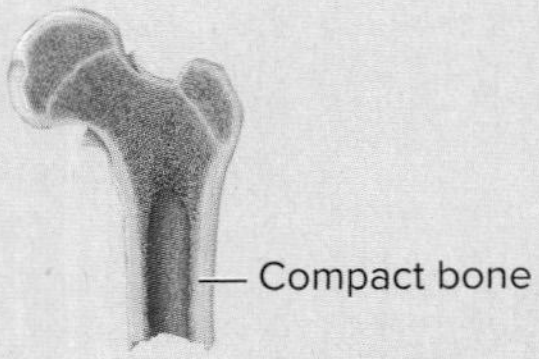

Compact bone

Structure:
Hard, bony matrix predominates; many osteocytes (not seen in this bone preparation) are located within lacunae that are distributed in a circular fashion around the central canals; small passageways connect adjacent lacunae

Function:
Provides great strength and support; forms a solid outer shell on bones that keeps them from being easily broken or punctured

Location:
Outer portions of all bones, the shafts of long bones

(table 4.10*c*). It is found in areas that have rigid but elastic properties, such as the external ears.

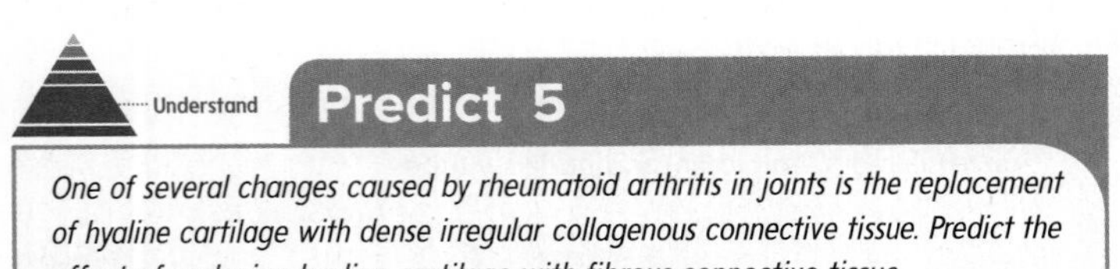

Predict 5

One of several changes caused by rheumatoid arthritis in joints is the replacement of hyaline cartilage with dense irregular collagenous connective tissue. Predict the effect of replacing hyaline cartilage with fibrous connective tissue.

2. **Bone** is a hard connective tissue that consists of living cells and mineralized matrix. Bone matrix has organic and inorganic portions. The organic portion consists of protein fibers, primarily collagen, and other organic molecules. The mineral, or inorganic, portion consists of specialized crystals called **hydroxyapatite** (hye-DROK-see-ap-ah-tyte), which contains calcium and phosphate. The strength and rigidity of the mineralized matrix allow bones to support and protect other tissues and organs. **Osteocytes** (OS-tee-oh-sites), or bone cells, are located within holes in the matrix, which are called lacunae and are similar to the lacunae of cartilage.

   Two types of bone exist:

   - **Spongy bone** has spaces between **trabeculae** (trah-BEK-yoo-lee; beams), or plates, of bone and therefore resembles a sponge (table 4.11*a*).
   - **Compact bone** is more solid, with almost no space between many thin layers, or **lamellae** (lah-MEL-ee; sing. lamella, lah-MEL-ah; thin plate) of bone (table 4.11*b*).

   Bone, unlike cartilage, has a rich blood supply. For this reason, bone can repair itself much more readily than can cartilage. Bone and bone cells are described more fully in chapter 6.

Fluid Connective Tissue

1. **Blood** is unusual among the connective tissues because the matrix between the cells is liquid (table 4.12*a*). The cells of most other connective tissues are more or less stationary within a relatively rigid matrix, but blood cells move freely within a fluid matrix. Blood's liquid matrix allows it to flow rapidly through the body, carrying nutrients, oxygen, waste products, and other materials. The matrix of

TABLE 4.12 Fluid Connective Tissue: Blood and Hematopoietic Tissue

(a) Blood APR

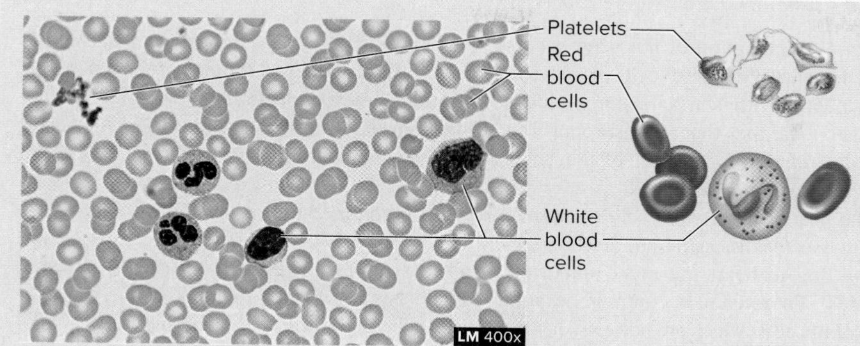

Ed Reschke/Stone/Getty Images

Structure:
Formed elements and a fluid matrix

Function:
Transports oxygen, carbon dioxide, hormones, nutrients, waste products, and other substances; protects the body from infections and is involved in temperature regulation

Location:
Within the blood vessels; white blood cells frequently leave the blood vessels and enter the extracellular spaces

(b) Bone Marrow APR

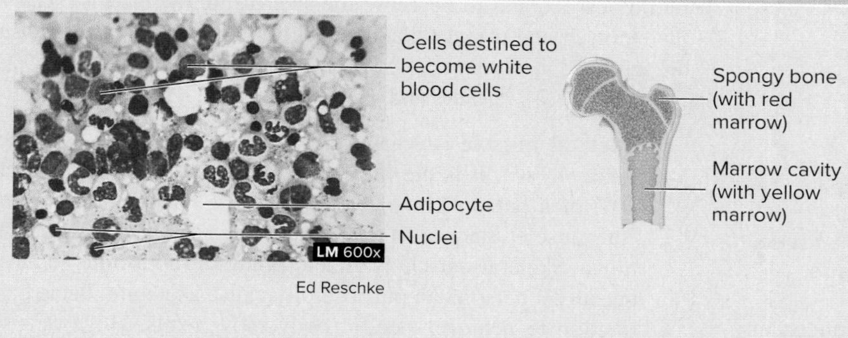

Ed Reschke

Structure:
Reticular framework with numerous blood-forming cells (red marrow)

Function:
Produces new blood cells (red marrow); stores lipids (yellow marrow)

Location:
Within marrow cavities of bone; two types: (1) red marrow (hematopoietic, or blood-forming, tissue) in the ends of long bones and in short, flat, and irregularly shaped bones and (2) yellow marrow, mostly adipose tissue, in the shafts of long bones

blood is also unusual in that most of it is produced by cells contained in other tissues, rather than by blood cells. There are three types of cellular structures: (a) red blood cells, (b) white blood cells, and (c) cell fragments called platelets. White blood cells sometimes leave the bloodstream and migrate into other tissues. Blood is discussed more fully in chapter 19.

2. **Hematopoietic** (hee-MA-toh-poy-et-ik; or hemopoietic; to make) **tissue** forms blood cells. In adults, hematopoietic tissue is found in **bone marrow** (MARE-oh; table 4.12*b*), which is the soft connective tissue in the cavities of bones. There are two types of bone marrow: (a) **red marrow** and (b) **yellow marrow** (see chapter 6). Red marrow is hematopoietic tissue surrounded by a framework of reticular fibers. Hematopoietic tissue produces red and white blood cells and platelets; it is described in detail in chapter 19. In children, the marrow of most bones is red marrow. Yellow marrow consists of yellow adipose tissue and does not produce blood cells. As children grow, yellow marrow replaces much of the red marrow in bones.

ASSESS YOUR PROGRESS

38. *Describe the cells and matrix of cartilage. What are lacunae? What is the perichondrium? Why does cartilage heal slowly?*
39. *What are the three types of cartilage? How do they differ in structure and function? Where would each type be found in the body?*
40. *Describe the cells and matrix of bone. Differentiate between spongy and compact bone.*
41. *What characteristic separates blood from other connective tissues? What are the three formed elements in blood?*
42. *Describe the function of hematopoietic tissue. Explain the difference between red marrow and yellow marrow.*

Clinical GENETICS 4.1 Marfan Syndrome

Marfan syndrome is an autosomal dominant disorder that affects approximately 1 in 5000 people. The gene for Marfan syndrome codes for a protein called fibrillin-1, which is necessary for the normal structure of the elastic fibers of connective tissue. Children of a person with Marfan syndrome have a 50% chance of inheriting the disorder because it is an autosomal dominant trait (see chapter 29). However, about 25% of the cases of Marfan syndrome occur in children whose parents do not have the disorder. In these cases, a mutation of the gene occurs during the formation of sperm cells or oocytes.

Many people with Marfan syndrome have limbs, fingers, and toes that are disproportionately long in relation to the rest of the body. Connective tissues are weakened; as a consequence, the heart valves, which are composed largely of connective tissue, do not function normally, resulting in heart murmurs (abnormal heart sounds). Poor vision is common because the lenses of the eyes, which are normally held in place by elastic fibers, are positioned abnormally. The lungs are prone to collapse, and dilation of large arteries, such as the aorta, can occur. A common cause of death in people with Marfan syndrome is rupture of the aorta. There is no cure for the condition, but treatments can reduce the danger of the symptoms. For example, drugs that lower blood pressure reduce the vascular risks.

It has been speculated that President Lincoln may have had Marfan syndrome, but some geneticists now think it more likely that he had a rare inherited form of endocrine cancer that includes physical features of Marfan syndrome.

4.5 Muscle Tissue

LEARNING OUTCOMES

After reading this section, you should be able to

A. **Describe the general structures of each of the three types of muscle tissue.**
B. **Give the locations in the body of each type of muscle tissue.**
C. **Describe the functions of each type of muscle tissue.**

The main characteristic of **muscle tissue** is that it contracts, or shortens, with a force and therefore is responsible for movement. Muscle contraction is accomplished by the interaction of contractile proteins, which are described in chapter 9. Muscles contract to move the entire body, to pump blood through the heart and blood vessels, and to decrease the size of hollow organs, such as the stomach and urinary bladder. The three types of muscle tissue are grouped according to both structure and function. They are (1) skeletal, (2) cardiac, and (3) smooth (table 4.13).

1. **Skeletal muscle** is what we normally think of as "muscle" (table 4.14*a*). It is the meat of animals and constitutes about 40% of a person's body weight. As the name implies, skeletal muscle attaches to the skeleton and enables the body to move. Skeletal muscle is under voluntary (conscious) control because a person can purposefully cause skeletal muscle contraction to achieve specific body movements. However, the nervous system can cause skeletal muscles to contract without conscious involvement, as occurs during reflex movements and the maintenance of muscle tone. Skeletal muscle cells are long, cylindrical cells, each containing many nuclei located at

TABLE **4.13** Comparison of Muscle Types

	Skeletal Muscle	Cardiac Muscle	Smooth Muscle
Location	Attached to bones	In the heart	In the walls of hollow organs, blood vessels, eyes, glands, skin
Cell Shape	Very long, cylindrical cells (1–4 cm and may extend the entire length of the muscle, 10–100 μm in diameter)	Cylindrical cells that branch (100–500 μm in length, 12–20 μm in diameter)	Spindle-shaped cells (15–200 μm in length, 5–8 μm in diameter)
Nucleus	Multinucleated, peripherally located	Single, centrally located	Single, centrally located
Striations	Yes	Yes	No
Control	Voluntary (conscious)	Involuntary (unconscious)	Involuntary (unconscious)
Ability to Contract Spontaneously	No	Yes	Yes
Function	Moves the body	Provides the major force for moving blood through the blood vessels	Moves food through the digestive tract, empties the urinary bladder, regulates blood vessel diameter, changes pupil size, contracts many gland ducts, moves hair, performs many other functions
Special Features	None	Branching fibers, intercalated disks containing gap junctions joining the cells to each other	Gap junctions

TABLE 4.14 **Muscle Tissue**

(a) Skeletal Muscle APR

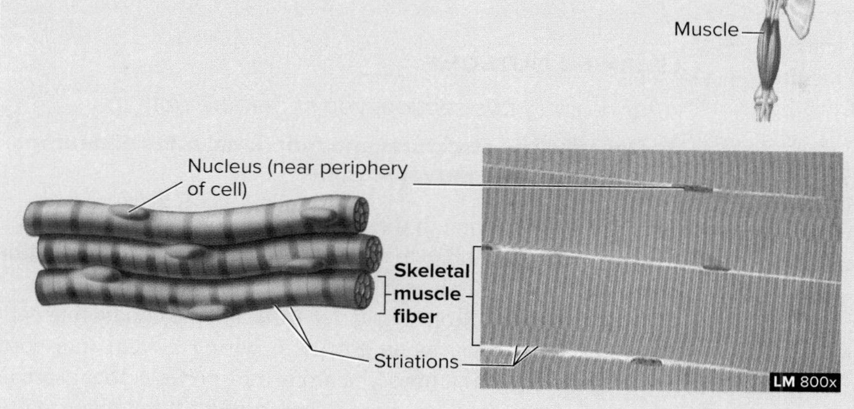

Ed Reschke

Structure:
Skeletal muscle cells or fibers appear striated (banded); cells are large, long, and cylindrical, with many nuclei

Function:
Movement of the body; under voluntary control

Location:
Attached to bone or other connective tissue

(b) Cardiac Muscle APR

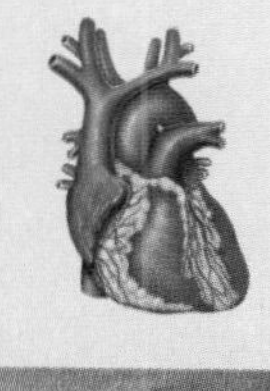

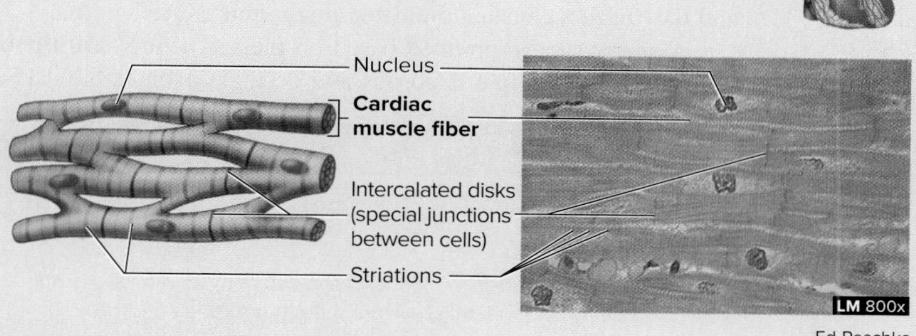

Ed Reschke

Structure:
Cardiac muscle cells are cylindrical and striated and have a single nucleus; they are branched and connected to one another by intercalated disks, which contain gap junctions

Function:
Pumps the blood; under involuntary (unconscious) control

Location:
In the heart

(c) Smooth Muscle APR

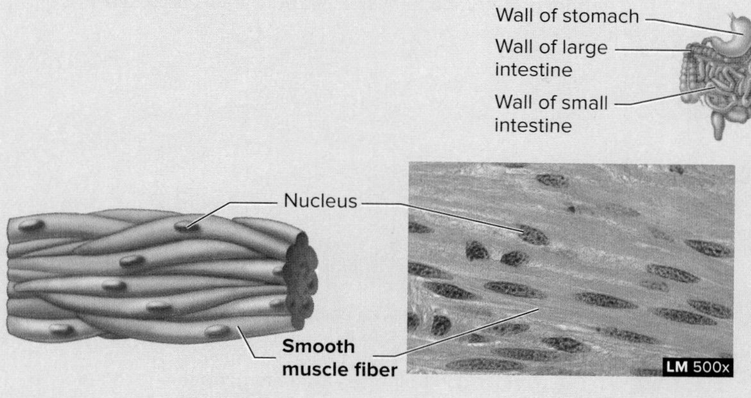

Dennis Strete/McGraw Hill

Structure:
Smooth muscle cells are tapered at each end, are not striated, and have a single nucleus

Function:
Regulates the size of organs, forces fluid through tubes, controls the amount of light entering the eye, and produces "goose bumps" in the skin; under involuntary (unconscious) control

Location:
In hollow organs, such as the stomach and intestine; skin and eyes

the periphery of the cell. Some skeletal muscle cells extend the entire length of a muscle. Skeletal muscle cells are **striated** (STRI-ate-ed), or banded, because of the arrangement of contractile proteins within the cells (see chapter 9).

2. **Cardiac muscle** is the muscle of the heart; it is responsible for pumping blood (table 4.14*b*). Cardiac muscle is under involuntary (unconscious) control, although a person can learn to influence the heart rate by using techniques such as meditation and biofeedback. Cardiac muscle cells are cylindrical but much shorter than skeletal muscle cells. Cardiac muscle cells are striated and usually have one nucleus per cell. They are often branched and connected to one another by **intercalated** (in-TER-kah-lay-ted; inserted between) **disks,** which contain specialized gap junctions and are important in coordinating cardiac muscle cell contractions (see chapter 20).
3. **Smooth muscle** forms the walls of hollow organs (except the heart); it is also found in the skin and eyes (table 4.14*c*). Smooth muscle is responsible for a number of functions, such as moving food through the digestive tract and emptying the urinary bladder. Like cardiac muscle, smooth muscle is controlled involuntarily. Smooth muscle cells are tapered at each end, have a single nucleus, and are not striated.

ASSESS YOUR PROGRESS

43. *Functionally, what is unique about muscle tissue?*
44. *Compare the structure of skeletal, cardiac, and smooth muscle cells.*
45. *Which type of muscle is under voluntary control?*
46. *Where is each type of muscle tissue found, and what tasks does each perform?*

4.6 Nervous Tissue

LEARNING OUTCOME

After reading this section, you should be able to

A. **Describe the structural and functional roles of neurons and glia in the nervous tissue.**

Nervous tissue is found in the brain, spinal cord, and nerves and is characterized by the ability to conduct electrical signals called **action potentials.** Nervous tissue consists of (1) neurons and (2) glia.

Neurons (NYUR-ons), or *nerve cells,* are the conducting cells of nervous tissue. Just as an electrical wiring system transports electricity throughout a house, neurons transport electrical signals throughout the body. A neuron is composed of three major parts: (1) a cell body, (2) dendrites, and (3) an axon. The **cell body** contains the nucleus and is the site of general cell functions. Dendrites and axons consist of projections of cytoplasm surrounded by membrane. **Dendrites** (DEN-drights) usually receive action potentials. They are much shorter than axons and have multiple branches at their ends. The **axon** (AK-son) usually conducts action potentials away from the cell body. Axons can be much longer than dendrites, and they have a constant diameter along their entire length.

Neurons can be grouped based on their structure. **Multipolar neurons** have multiple dendrites and a single axon (table 4.15*a*).

TABLE 4.15 Types of Neurons

(a) Multipolar Neuron APR

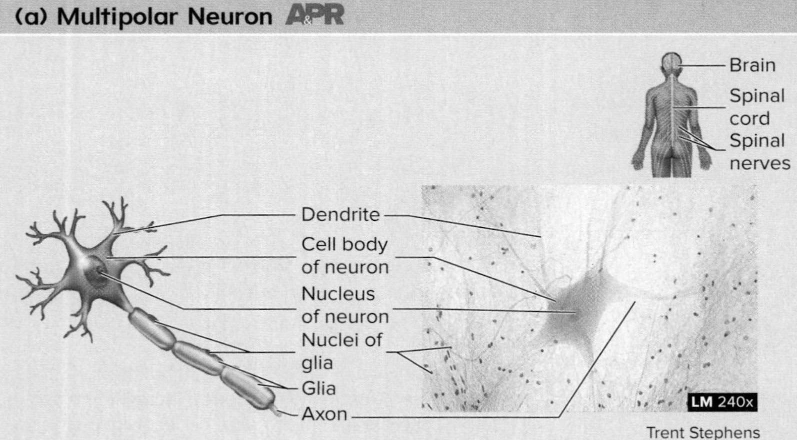

Trent Stephens

Structure:
A neuron consists of dendrites, a cell body, and a long axon; glia, or support cells, surround the neurons

Function:
Neurons transmit information in the form of action potentials, store information, and integrate and evaluate data; glia support, protect, and form specialized sheaths around axons

Location:
In the brain, spinal cord, and ganglia

(b) Pseudo-unipolar Neuron

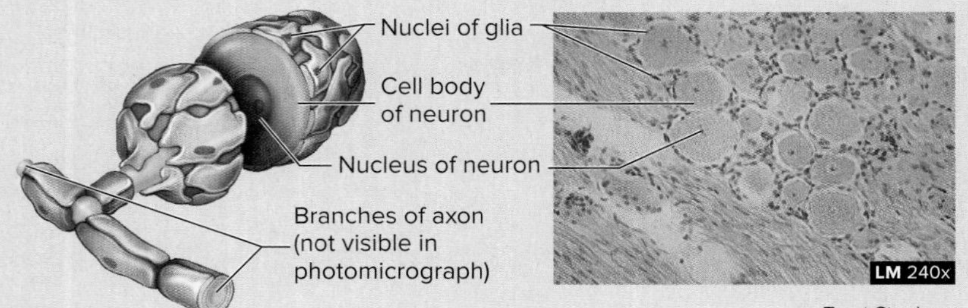

Trent Stephens

Structure:
The neuron consists of a cell body with one axon

Function:
Conducts action potentials from the periphery to the brain or spinal cord

Location:
In ganglia outside the brain and spinal cord

Bipolar neurons have a single dendrite and an axon. **Pseudo-unipolar neurons** have only a single, short process that extends from the cell body and then divides into two branches, which extend to the periphery and to the central nervous system (table 4.15*b*). The two branches function as a single axon, although there are dendritelike receptors on the peripheral branch. Within each of these subgroups are many shapes and sizes of neurons, especially in the brain and spinal cord.

Glia (GLEE-ah; glue) are the support cells of the brain, spinal cord, and peripheral nerves (table 4.15). Glia nourish, protect, and insulate neurons. Neurons and glia cells are described in greater detail in chapter 11.

ASSESS YOUR PROGRESS

47. *What is the characteristic function of nervous tissue?*
48. *Define and list the functions of the cell body, dendrites, and axon of a neuron.*
49. *Differentiate among multipolar, bipolar, and pseudo-unipolar neurons.*
50. *What are the functions of glia?*

4.7 Tissue Membranes

LEARNING OUTCOMES

After reading this section, you should be able to

A. **List the structural and functional characteristics of mucous membranes.**
B. **List the structural and functional characteristics of serous membranes.**
C. **List the structural and functional characteristics of synovial membranes.**

A tissue membrane is a thin sheet of tissue that covers a structure or lines a cavity. Most membranes are formed from a superficial epithelial tissue and the connective tissue on which it rests. There are four tissue membranes in the body, one external and three internal. The external tissue membrane is the skin, or *cutaneous* (kyu-TAY-nee-us) *membrane* (see chapter 5). The three major categories of *internal tissue membranes* are (1) mucous, (2) serous, and (3) synovial membranes.

FUNDAMENTAL **Figure**

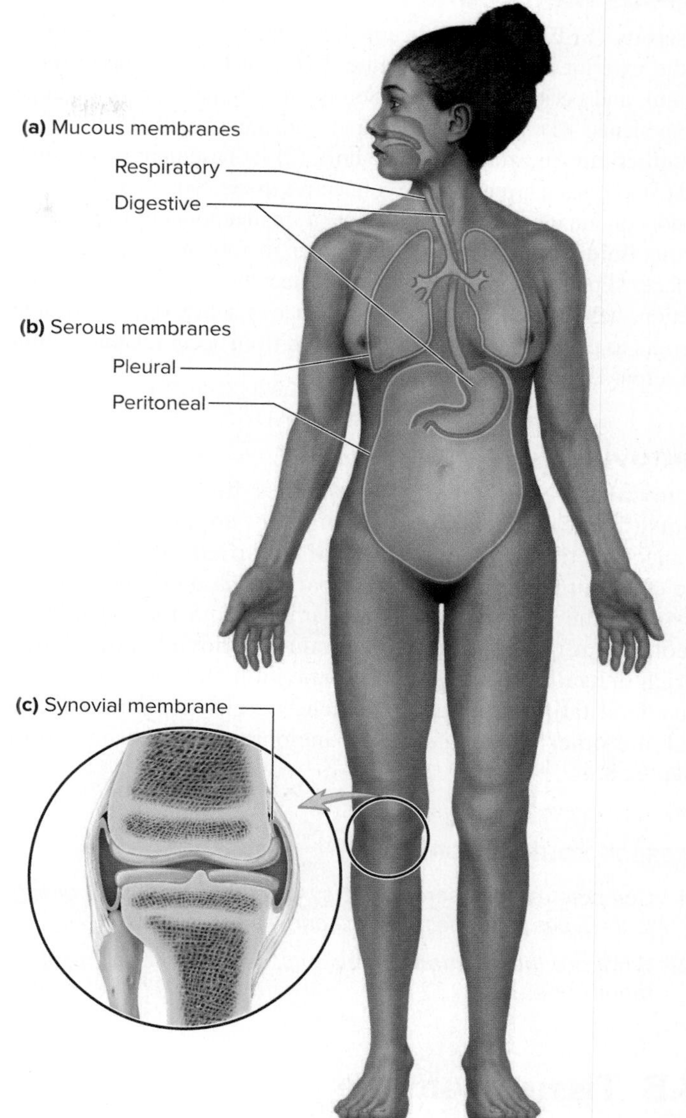

FIGURE 4.7 Internal Tissue Membranes
(*a*) Mucous membranes line cavities that open to the outside and often contain mucous glands, which secrete mucus. (*b*) Serous membranes line cavities that do not open to the exterior; they do not contain glands but do secrete serous fluid. (*c*) Synovial membranes line cavities that surround synovial joints.

Mucous Membranes

A **mucous** (MYU-kus) **membrane** lines cavities and canals that open to the outside of the body, such as the digestive, respiratory, excretory, and reproductive passages (figure 4.7*a*). Mucous membranes consist of (1) epithelial cells, (2) their basement membrane, and (3) a thick layer of loose connective tissue called the **lamina propria** (LAM-i-nah PROH-pree-ah). Some mucous membranes also contain a layer of smooth muscle cells. Many, but not all, mucous membranes contain goblet cells or multicellular mucous glands that secrete **mucus** (MYU-kus), a viscous protein substance. The functions of the mucous membranes vary, depending on their location, and include protection, absorption, and secretion. For example, the stratified squamous epithelium of the oral cavity performs a protective function, whereas the simple columnar epithelium of the small intestine absorbs nutrients and secretes digestive enzymes and mucus. Mucous membrane also lines the nasal passages. When that membrane becomes inflamed, we experience the "runny nose" characteristic of the common cold or an allergy.

Serous Membranes

A **serous** (SEER-us) **membrane** lines cavities that do not open to the exterior of the body (figure 4.7*b*), such as the pericardial, pleural, and peritoneal cavities. Serous membranes consist of three components: (1) a layer of simple squamous epithelium called **mesothelium** (me-zoh-THEE-lee-um), (2) its basement membrane, and (3) a delicate layer of loose connective tissue. Serous membranes do not contain glands, but they secrete a small amount of fluid called **serous fluid,** which lubricates the serous membranes, making their surfaces slippery. Serous membranes protect the internal organs from friction, help hold them in place, and act as selectively permeable barriers to prevent large amounts of fluid from accumulating within the serous cavities.

Synovial Membranes

Synovial (si-NOH-vee-al) **membranes** line freely movable joints (figure 4.7*c*). Synovial membranes are made up of only connective tissue. They consist of modified connective tissue cells, either intermixed with part of the dense connective tissue of the joint capsule or separated from the capsule by areolar or adipose tissue. They produce **synovial fluid,** which is rich in hyaluronic acid, making the joint fluid very slippery, thus facilitating smooth movement within the joint. Synovial and other connective tissue membranes are discussed in chapter 8.

ASSESS YOUR PROGRESS

51. *Compare mucous, serous, and synovial membranes according to the types of cavities they line and their secretions.*

52. *What are the functions of mucous, serous, and synovial membranes?*

4.8 Tissue Damage and Inflammation

LEARNING OUTCOMES

After reading this section, you should be able to

A. **Describe the process of inflammation in response to tissue damage.**
B. **Explain how inflammation protects the body.**
C. **Relate the five major signs of inflammation.**
D. **Explain how each of the five major signs of inflammation is produced.**

Inflammation (*flamma*, flame) is the response that occurs when tissues are damaged. Although many agents cause injury, such as microorganisms, cold, heat, radiant energy, chemicals, electricity, and mechanical trauma, the inflammatory response to all of them is similar. The **inflammatory response** is a defense mechanism that mobilizes the body's immune cells to isolate and destroy microorganisms and other injurious agents, and remove foreign materials and damaged cells (see chapter 22). The inflammatory response allows tissue repair to occur. Figure 4.8 illustrates the stages of the inflammatory response.

Inflammation has five major manifestations: (1) redness, (2) heat, (3) swelling, (4) pain, and (5) disturbed function. Although unpleasant, these processes usually aid recovery, and each of the symptoms can be understood in terms of events that occur during the inflammatory response.

1. After a person is injured, chemical substances called **chemical mediators** are released or activated in the tissues and the adjacent blood vessels. The mediators are histamine, kinins, prostaglandins, leukotrienes, and others.
2. Some mediators induce dilation of blood vessels and produce redness and heat. Dilation of blood vessels is beneficial because it speeds the arrival of white blood cells and other substances important for fighting infections and repairing the injury.
3. Chemical mediators also stimulate pain receptors and increase the permeability of blood vessels. The increased permeability allows materials such as clotting proteins and white blood cells to move out of the blood vessels and into the tissue, where they can deal directly with the injury. As proteins from the blood move into the tissue, they change the osmotic relationship between the blood and the tissue. Water follows the proteins by osmosis, and the tissue swells, producing **edema** (ee-DEE-mah). Edema increases the pressure in the tissue, which can also stimulate neurons and cause pain.

   Clotting proteins present in blood diffuse into the interstitial spaces and form a clot. Clotting also occurs by platelet aggregation in the injured blood vessels. Clotting isolates the injurious agent and separates it from the rest of the body. Foreign particles and microorganisms at the site of injury are "walled off" from tissues by the clotting process. Pain, limitation of movement resulting from edema, and tissue destruction all contribute to the disturbed function. This disturbance can be valuable because it warns the person to protect the injured structure from further damage.

Sometimes the inflammatory response lasts longer or is more intense than is desirable, and the patient is given drugs to suppress the symptoms. Antihistamines block the effects of histamine, aspirin prevents the synthesis of prostaglandins, and cortisone reduces the release of several chemical mediators that cause inflammation. Still, the inflammatory response by itself may not be enough to combat the effects of injury or fight off an infection, and the patient may require antibiotics.

Predict 6

In some injuries, tissues are so severely damaged that some cells die and blood vessels are destroyed. For such injuries, where do the signs of inflammation, such as redness, heat, edema, and pain, occur?

ASSESS YOUR PROGRESS

53. *What is the function of the inflammatory response?*

54. *Name the five manifestations of inflammation; explain how each is produced and the benefits of each.*

FUNDAMENTAL **Figure**

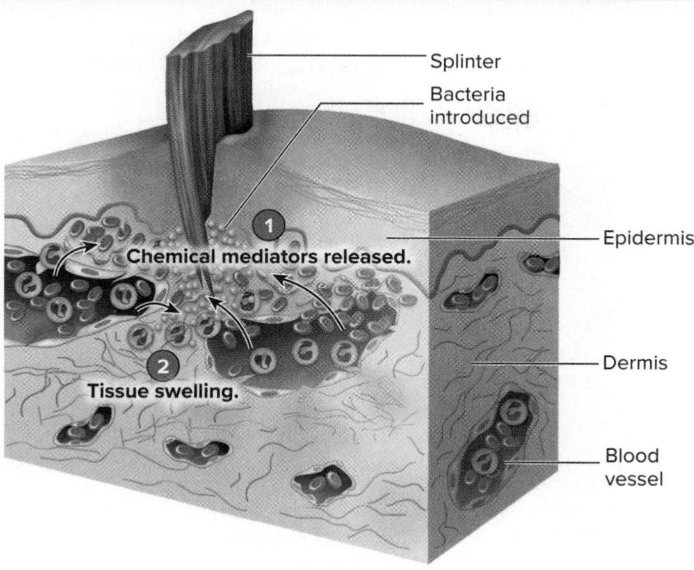

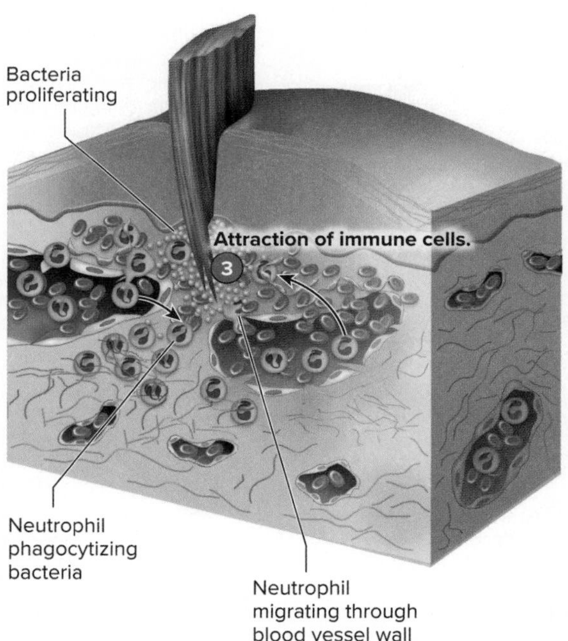

PROCESS **Figure 4.8**

Stages of the Inflammatory Response Injury to an area results in release of chemical mediators, which stimulate increased blood flow and migration of white blood cells to the site of tissue damage.

Some injuries result from internal tissue damage, such as an ankle sprain. Even though there's no break in the skin, inflammation is induced and the area becomes red, painful, and swollen. The medical treatment for such an injury is RICE: rest, ice, compression, and elevation. Explain how RICE is helpful in injury recovery.

4.9 Tissue Repair

LEARNING OUTCOMES

After reading this section, you should be able to

A. **Describe the three groups of cells based on their ability to regenerate.**

B. **Explain the major events involved in tissue repair.**

Tissue repair is the substitution of viable cells for dead cells by regeneration or replacement. In **regeneration** (ree-JEN-eh-RAY-shun), the new cells are the same type as those that were destroyed, and normal function is usually restored. In **replacement,** a new type of tissue develops, which eventually produces a scar and causes the loss of some tissue function. Most wounds heal through regeneration and replacement; which process dominates depends on the tissues involved and the nature and extent of the wound.

Cells are classified into three groups according to their ability to regenerate: (1) labile, (2) stable, or (3) permanent cells.

1. **Labile cells** continue to divide throughout life. Labile cells include undifferentiated adult stem cells in various organs of the body, such as in bone marrow, and differentiated cells in tissues that have a steady turnover of new cells replacing old cells. Differentiated labile cells can be found in the skin, mucous membranes, and hematopoietic and lymphatic tissues. Damage to these cells can be repaired completely by regeneration. The ability to engineer and transplant adult stem cells and other reprogrammed labile cells is an emerging therapeutic strategy for a number of diseases.
2. **Stable cells,** such as those of connective tissues, the liver, and endocrine glands, do not normally divide after growth ceases, but they retain the ability to divide and are capable of regeneration in response to injury.
3. **Permanent cells,** such as neurons and skeletal and cardiac muscle, are not able to replicate and, if killed, are usually replaced by a different type of cell. Permanent cells are postmitotic. For example, if damaged, neurons may recover if the cell body is not destroyed; however, if the neuron cell body is destroyed, the remainder of the neuron dies. Some undifferentiated cells of the central nervous system are stem cells that can undergo mitosis and form functional neurons in the adult. This has raised hope that damaged areas of the brain may be regenerated. Similarly, while fully differentiated skeletal and cardiac muscle cells are not able to divide, small populations of stable cells in those tissues can replace damaged muscle cells. In contrast, smooth muscle cells are considered to be stable because they can regenerate following injury. Skin repair is a good example of tissue repair (figure 4.9).

1 The basic pattern of repair is the same as for other tissues, especially those covered by epithelium. If the edges of the wound are close together, as in a surgical incision, the wound heals by a process

FUNDAMENTAL **Figure**

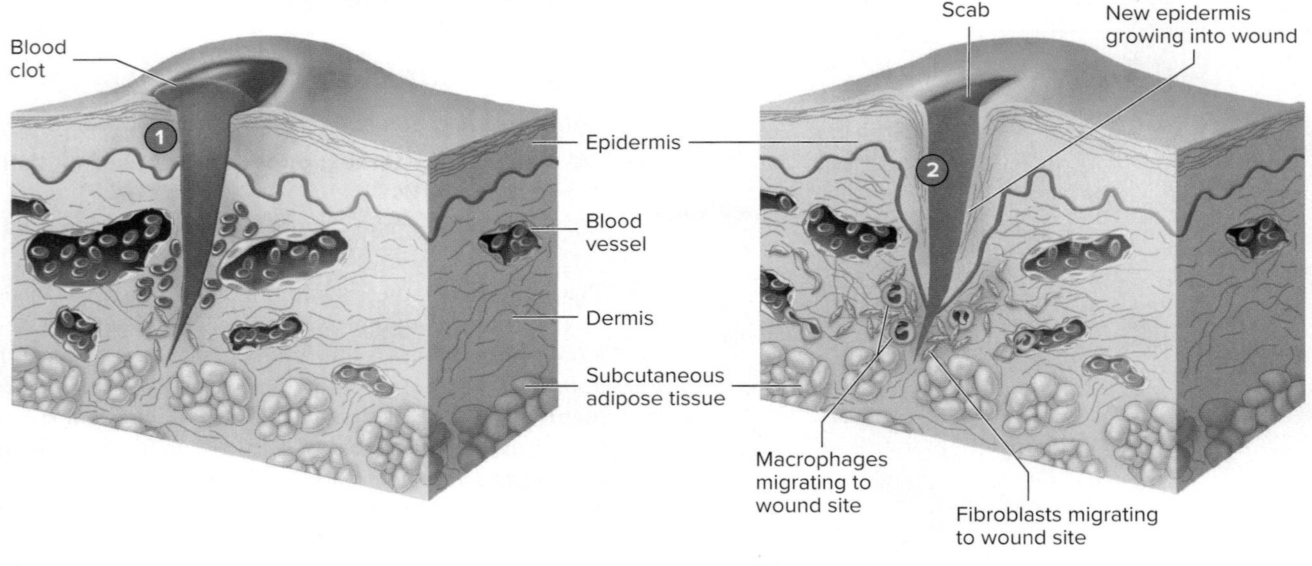

1 Clot formation.

2 Epithelial cells grow into wound.

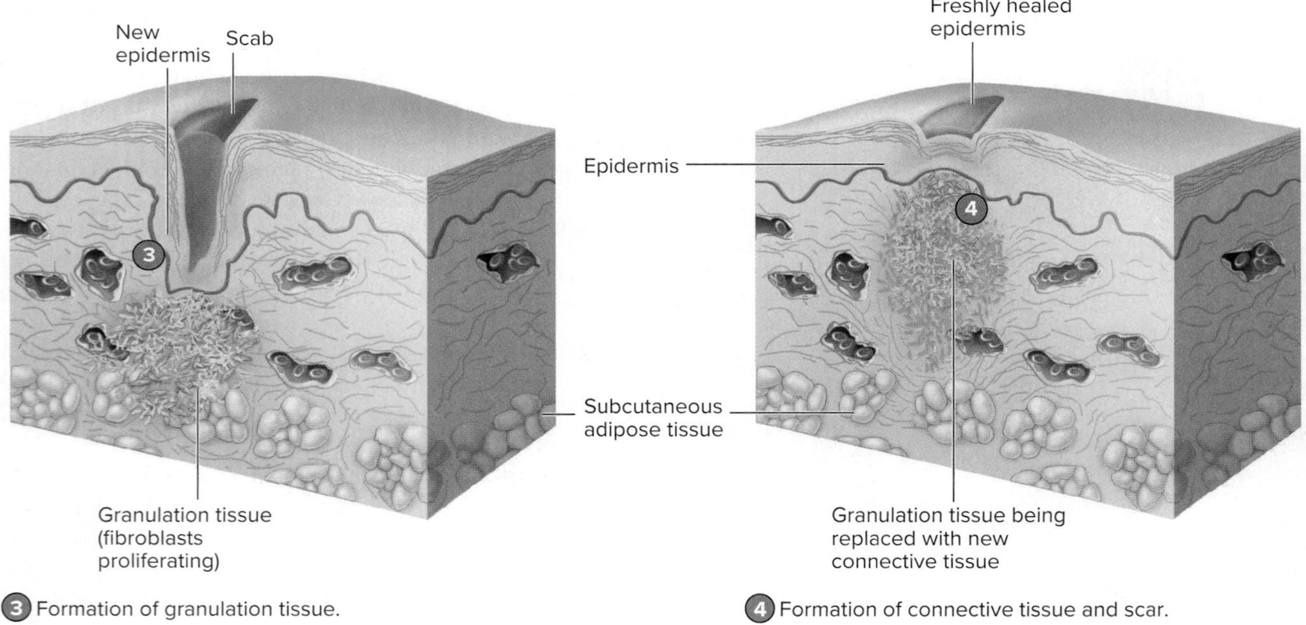

3 Formation of granulation tissue.

4 Formation of connective tissue and scar.

PROCESS **Figure 4.9**

Tissue Repair In the process that repairs tissue damage, a clot is first formed. Next, new epithelial tissue cells grow into the wound, followed by the formation of granulation tissue. Finally, the granulation tissue is replaced with new connective tissue that forms a scar.

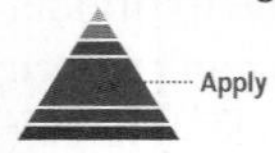

What cellular process creates the new epidermis cells in step 2?

called **primary union,** or *primary intention*. If the edges are not close together, or if tissue loss has been extensive, the process is called **secondary union,** or *secondary intention*.

In primary union, the wound first fills with blood and a clot forms (see chapter 19). The clot contains the threadlike protein **fibrin** (FIE-brin), which binds the edges of the wound together. The surface of the clot dries to form a **scab,** which seals the wound and helps prevent infection.

2 During the first week, an inflammatory response induces vasodilation and takes more blood cells and other substances to the area. Blood vessel permeability increases, resulting in edema (swelling). Fibrin and blood cells move into the wounded tissues because of the

Clinical IMPACT 4.1 Molecular Tissue Profiles of Cancer Tissue

There are many types of cancer and special names for them based on their tissue of origin. The most common types of cancer are those from epithelial tissue. A **carcinoma** (kar-sih-NOH-mah) is a cancer derived from epithelial tissue. Carcinomas include nearly all lung, breast, colon, prostate, and skin cancers. Basal cell and squamous cell carcinomas are types of skin cancer derived from epithelial tissue. **Adenocarcinomas** (AD-eh-noh-kar-si-NOH-maz) are types of carcinomas derived from glandular epithelium. Most breast cancers are adenocarcinomas. A **sarcoma** (sar-KOH-mah) is a relatively rare type of cancer derived from mesodermal tissue (muscle and connective tissue). For example, an osteosarcoma (OS-tee-oh-sar-KOH-mah) is cancer of bone, and a chondrosarcoma (KON-droh-sar-KOH-mah) is cancer of cartilage.

Identifying the tissue of origin is useful for the diagnosis and treatment of cancer. Because tumor cells have altered shapes compared with their morphology in tissues, molecular markers are commonly used to identify the type of tumor. For example, specific types of carcinomas express keratin filaments that are characteristic of different types of epithelial tissue. Other intermediate filaments are diagnostic of sarcomas and other types of cancers. Advances in gene expression profiling of cancers now can provide distinct molecular profiles that allow a more definitive diagnosis and may soon lead to targeted therapies tailored for individual patients.

increased vascular permeability. Fibrin isolates and walls off microorganisms and other foreign matter. Phagocytic white blood cells called neutrophils (NEW-troh-fills) then move into the tissue to help fight the infection (figure 4.9). They ingest bacteria and tissue debris to clear the area for repair. Neutrophils are killed in this process and can accumulate as a mixture of dead cells and fluid called **pus** (puhs). Fibroblasts from surrounding connective tissue migrate into the clot and produce collagen and other extracellular matrix components. Capillaries grow from blood vessels at the edge of the wound and revascularize the area, and fibrin in the clot is broken down and removed.

3. By two weeks, the clot has been replaced by **granulation tissue** that will eventually form a scar at the wound site. Granulation tissue is a delicate, granular-appearing connective tissue that consists of fibroblasts, collagen, and capillaries.
4. By a month, a large amount of granulation tissue is converted to a **scar,** which consists of dense irregular collagenous connective tissue. At first, a scar is bright red because numerous blood vessels are present. Later, the scar becomes white as collagen accumulates and the vascular channels are compressed.

Repair by secondary union proceeds in a similar fashion as primary union, but with some differences. Because the wound edges are far apart, the clot may not close the gap completely, and it takes the epithelial cells much longer to regenerate and cover the wound. Also, the increased tissue damage means that both the degree of inflammation and the risk of infection are greater and there is more cell debris for the phagocytes to remove. Much more granulation tissue forms, and the contraction of fibroblasts in the granulation tissue leads to **wound contracture,** resulting in disfiguring and debilitating scars. Thus, it is advisable to suture a large wound, so that it can heal by primary rather than secondary union. Healing is faster, with a lowered risk of infection and a reduced degree of scarring.

ASSESS YOUR PROGRESS

55. *Define* tissue repair. *Differentiate between repair by regeneration and repair by replacement.*
56. *Compare labile, stable, and permanent cells according to their ability to regenerate. Give examples of each type.*
57. *Describe the process of wound repair. Contrast healing by primary union and healing by secondary healing. Which process is better, and why?*
58. *What is granulation tissue? How does granulation tissue contribute to scars and wound contracture?*

EFFECTS OF AGING ON **TISSUES**

At the tissue level, age-related changes affect cells and the extracellular matrix produced by them. In general, cells divide more slowly in older people compared to younger ones. The rate of red blood cell synthesis declines in older adults. Injuries in older people heal more slowly. For example, a fracture in an adult heals slowly, and a scar, seen in radiographs of the bone, is likely to persist throughout life.

Changes in the extracellular matrix cause connective tissues with abundant collagen, such as tendons and ligaments, to become less flexible and more fragile. Elastic connective tissues become less elastic. The reduced flexibility and elasticity of connective tissue is responsible for increased wrinkling of the skin, as well as an increased tendency for older people's bones to break.

Walls of arteries also become less elastic because of changes in collagen and elastic fibers. These changes result in increased susceptibility to rupture of arteries.

Concept Check

4.1 Tissues and Histology

A. Tissues are collections of similar cells and the extracellular substances surrounding them.

B. The four primary tissue types are epithelial, connective, muscle, and nervous tissues.

4.2 Embryonic Tissue

All four of the primary tissue types are derived from each of the three germ layers (mesoderm, ectoderm, and endoderm).

1. *Which of these embryonic germ layers gives rise to muscle, bone, and blood vessels?* Remember
   - *a. ectoderm*
   - *b. endoderm*
   - *c. mesoderm*

4.3 Epithelial Tissue

A. Epithelium consists of cells with little extracellular matrix. It covers surfaces, usually has a basement membrane, and does not have blood vessels.

B. The basement membrane is secreted by the epithelial cells and attaches the epithelium to the underlying tissues.

2. *Given these characteristics:*
   (1) capable of contraction
   (2) covers free body surfaces
   (3) lacks blood vessels
   (4) composes various glands
   (5) anchored to connective tissue by a basement membrane

   Which of these are characteristics of epithelial tissue?

   - *a. 1,2,3*
   - *b. 2,3,5*
   - *c. 3,4,5*
   - *d. 1,2,3,4*
   - *e. 2,3,4,5*

Functions of Epithelial Tissues

Epithelial tissues protect underlying structures, act as barriers, permit some substances to pass through epithelial layers, secrete substances, and absorb substances.

Classification of Epithelial Tissues

Simple epithelium has a single layer of cells, stratified epithelium has two or more layers, and pseudostratified epithelium has a single layer that appears stratified. Transitional epithelium is stratified with cells that can change shape from cuboidal to flattened.

3. *A tissue that covers a surface, is one cell layer thick, and is composed of flat cells is* Remember
   - *a. simple squamous epithelium.*
   - *b. simple cuboidal epithelium.*
   - *c. simple columnar epithelium.*
   - *d. stratified squamous epithelium.*
   - *e. transitional epithelium.*

4. *Stratified epithelium is usually found in areas of the body where the principal activity is* Remember
   - *a. filtration.*
   - *b. protection.*
   - *c. absorption.*
   - *d. diffusion.*
   - *e. secretion.*

5. *Which of these characteristics do* not *describe nonkeratinized stratified squamous epithelium?* Remember
   - *a. many layers of cells*
   - *b. flat surface cells*
   - *c. living surface cells*
   - *d. found in the skin*
   - *e. outer layers covered by fluid*

6. *In parts of the body where considerable expansion occurs, such as the urinary bladder, which type of epithelium would you expect to find?* Remember
   - *a. cuboidal*
   - *b. pseudostratified*
   - *c. transitional*
   - *d. squamous*
   - *e. columnar*

7. *Epithelial cells with microvilli are most likely found*

   - *a. lining blood vessels.*
   - *b. lining the lungs.*
   - *c. lining the uterine tube.*
   - *d. lining the small intestine.*
   - *e. in the skin.*

8. *Pseudostratified ciliated columnar epithelium can be found lining the* Remember
   - *a. digestive tract.*
   - *b. trachea.*
   - *c. thyroid gland.*
   - *d. kidney tubules.*
   - *e. urinary bladder.*

9. *Given the observation that a tissue has more than one layer of cells lining a free surface, (1) list the possible tissue types that exhibit those characteristics, and (2) explain what additional observations are needed to identify the tissue type.* Understand

10. *A patient suffered from kidney failure a few days after being exposed to a toxic chemical. A biopsy of his kidney indicated that many of the thousands of epithelium-lined tubules making up the kidney had lost their simple cuboidal epithelial cells, although the basement membranes appeared mostly intact. How likely is a full recovery for this person?* Apply

11. *Humphrey has smoked for years. In the past few months, mucus has accumulated in his lungs and he coughs often. A tissue sample (biopsy) taken from the lower portion of his trachea indicated that stratified squamous epithelium has replaced the normal pseudostratified columnar epithelium lining the trachea. Humphrey's physician explained that he has bronchitis, inflammation of the respiratory airways, caused by smoking. As a result, some of the normal epithelium*

of the large respiratory passageways has been converted to stratified squamous epithelium. Explain why mucus has accumulated in Humphrey's lungs to a greater degree than normal. Apply

The Relationship Between Structure and Function of Epithelial Tissues

A. One layer of flat cells (i.e., simple squamous) allows for filtration and diffusion.

B. One layer of cubelike cells (i.e., simple cuboidal) allows for secretion.

C. One layer of tall, rectangular cells (e.g., simple columnar) provides a mechanical barrier because they are thicker than squamous and allow for secretion and absorption.

D. Multiple layers of flat cells provide a thick mechanical barrier.

E. Structures such as microvilli or cilia can occur on the apical surface, which provide increased surface area or allow for movement across the epithelium surface.

F. Epithelial cells are connected to each other or to the basement membrane. These connections provide mechanical stability, form a permeability barrier, and allow for intercellular communication.

12. *A type of cell connection whose only function is to prevent the cells from coming apart is a* Remember
    a. *desmosome.*
    b. *gap junction.*
    c. *tight junction.*

Glands

A. Glands are organs that secrete. Exocrine glands secrete through ducts, and endocrine glands release hormones that are absorbed directly into the blood.

B. Glands are classified as unicellular or multicellular. Goblet cells are unicellular glands. Multicellular exocrine glands have ducts, which are simple or compound. The ducts can be tubular or end in small sacs (acini). Tubular glands can be straight or coiled.

C. Glands are classified according to their mode of secretion. Merocrine glands (e.g., pancreas) secrete substances as they are produced, apocrine glands (e.g., mammary glands) accumulate secretions that are released when a portion of the cell pinches off, and holocrine glands (e.g., sebaceous glands) accumulate secretions that are released when the cell ruptures and dies.

13. *The glands that lose their connection with epithelium during embryonic development and secrete their cellular products into the bloodstream are called ____________ glands.* Remember
    a. *apocrine*
    b. *endocrine*
    c. *exocrine*
    d. *holocrine*
    e. *merocrine*

14. *A ____________ gland has a duct that branches repeatedly, and the ducts end in saclike structures.* Remember
    a. *simple tubular*
    b. *compound tubular*
    c. *simple coiled tubular*
    d. *simple acinar*
    e. *compound acinar*

15. *How can you distinguish between a gland that produces a merocrine secretion and a gland that produces a holocrine secretion? Assume that you have the ability to chemically analyze the composition of the secretions.* Apply

4.4 Connective Tissue

Connective tissue is distinguished by its extracellular matrix.

Functions of Connective Tissue

Connective tissues enclose and separate organs and tissues; connect tissues to one another; help support and move body parts; store compounds; cushion and insulate the body; transport substances; and protect against toxins and injury.

Cells of Connective Tissue

A. The extracellular matrix results from the activity of specialized connective tissue cells; in general, -blast cells form the matrix, -cyte cells maintain it, and -clast cells break it down. Fibroblasts form protein fibers of many connective tissues, osteoblasts form bone, and chondroblasts form cartilage.

B. Connective tissue commonly contains adipocytes, mast cells, white blood cells, macrophages, and mesenchymal cells (stem cells).

Extracellular Matrix

A. The major components of the extracellular matrix of connective tissue are protein fibers, ground substance, and fluid.

B. Protein fibers of the matrix include collagen fibers that are strong and flexible but resist stretching. Reticular fibers form a branching network that supports other cells and tissues. Elastic fibers return to their original shape after being stretched.

C. Ground substance has the following major components: (1) Hyaluronic acid that makes fluids slippery; (2) proteoglycan aggregates that trap water, which gives tissues resistance to compression; and (3) adhesive molecules that hold proteoglycans together and to plasma membranes.

Connective Tissue Classifications

Connective tissue is classified according to the type and proportions of cells and extracellular matrix fibers, ground substance, and fluid.

A. Embryonic connective tissue is called mesenchyme and gives rise to adult connective tissue.

B. Adult connective tissue consists of connective tissue proper, supporting connective tissue, and fluid connective tissue.

16. *Mesenchymal cells*

    a. *form embryonic connective tissue.*
    b. *give rise to all adult connective tissues.*
    c. *in adults produce new connective tissue cells in response to injury.*
    d. *All of these are correct.*

Connective Tissue Proper

A. Loose connective tissue includes (1) areolar connective tissue, which fills spaces around the organs and attaches the skin to underlying tissues; (2) adipose tissue, which has adipocytes filled with lipid and very little extracellular matrix (a few reticular fibers) and functions in energy storage, insulation, and protection; and (3) reticular tissue, which is a network of reticular fibers and forms the framework of lymphatic tissue, bone marrow, and the liver.

B. Dense connective tissue includes the following: (1) Dense regular connective tissue, which is composed of fibers arranged in one direction; two types of dense regular connective tissue exist: collagenous (tendons and most ligaments) and elastic (ligaments of vertebrae).

(2) Dense irregular connective tissue, which has fibers organized in many directions; two types of dense irregular connective tissue exist: collagenous (capsules of organs and dermis of skin) and elastic (large arteries).

17. *Which of these is* not *true of adipose tissue?* 

   a. *It is the site of energy storage.*
   b. *It is a type of connective tissue.*
   c. *It acts as a protective cushion.*
   d. *Brown adipose is found only in older adults.*
   e. *It functions as a heat insulator.*

18. *Which of these types of connective tissue has the smallest amount of extracellular matrix?* Remember
   a. *adipose*
   b. *bone*
   c. *cartilage*
   d. *loose connective tissue*
   e. *blood*

19. *The fibers in dense connective tissue are produced by* 

   a. *fibroblasts.*
   b. *adipocytes.*
   c. *osteoblasts.*
   d. *osteoclasts.*
   e. *macrophages.*

20. *A tissue with a large number of collagen fibers organized parallel to each other would most likely be found in* Remember
   a. *a muscle.*
   b. *a tendon.*
   c. *adipose tissue.*
   d. *a bone.*
   e. *cartilage.*

21. *Extremely delicate fibers that make up the framework for organs such as the liver, spleen, and lymph nodes are* Remember
   a. *elastic fibers.*
   b. *reticular fibers.*
   c. *microvilli.*
   d. *cilia.*
   e. *collagen fibers.*

22. *In which of these locations is dense irregular elastic connective tissue found?* Remember
   a. *ligaments*
   b. *nuchal ligament*
   c. *dermis of the skin*
   d. *large arteries*
   e. *adipose tissue*

23. *Name a tissue that has the following characteristics: abundant extracellular matrix consisting almost entirely of collagen fibers that are parallel to each other. Then state which of the following injuries results from damage to this kind of tissue: dislocated neck, dislocated vertebrae, torn tendon, or ruptured intervertebral disk.* Apply

Supporting Connective Tissue

A. Cartilage includes (1) hyaline cartilage (e.g., costal cartilage), which has evenly dispersed collagen fibers that provide rigidity with some flexibility; (2) fibrocartilage (e.g., intervertebral disks), which has collagen fibers arranged in thick bundles and can withstand great pressure; and (3) elastic cartilage (e.g., outer ear), which is similar to hyaline cartilage but contains elastin and is more flexible than hyaline cartilage.

B. Bone contains osteocytes surrounded by a mineralized matrix (hydroxyapatite) that makes bone very hard. Spongy bone has spaces between bony trabeculae; compact bone is more solid.

24. *Fibrocartilage is found* 

   a. *in the cartilage of the trachea.*
   b. *in the rib cage.*
   c. *in the external ear.*
   d. *on the surface of bones in movable joints.*
   e. *between vertebrae.*

25. *A tissue composed of cells located in lacunae surrounded by a hard matrix of hydroxyapatite is* Remember
   a. *hyaline cartilage.*
   b. *bone.*
   c. *nervous tissue.*
   d. *dense regular collagenous connective tissue.*
   e. *fibrocartilage.*

Fluid Connective Tissue

A. Blood contains cells that are suspended in a fluid matrix.

B. Hematopoietic tissue forms blood cells.

4.5 Muscle Tissue

A. Muscle tissue has the ability to contract.

B. Skeletal (striated voluntary) muscle attaches to bone and is responsible for body movement. Skeletal muscle cells are long and cylindrically shaped with many peripherally located nuclei.

C. Cardiac (striated involuntary) muscle cells are cylindrical, branching cells with a single, central nucleus. Cardiac muscle is found in the heart and is responsible for pumping blood through the circulatory system.

D. Smooth (nonstriated involuntary) muscle forms the walls of hollow organs, the iris of the eye, and other structures. Its cells are spindle-shaped with a single, central nucleus.

26. *Which of these characteristics apply to smooth muscle?* Remember
   a. *striated, involuntary*
   b. *striated, voluntary*
   c. *nonstriated, involuntary*
   d. *nonstriated, voluntary*

4.6 Nervous Tissue

A. Nervous tissue is able to conduct electrical impulses and is composed of neurons (conductive cells) and glia (support cells).

B. Neurons have cell processes called dendrites and axons. Dendrites receive electrical impulses, and axons conduct them. Neurons can be multipolar (several dendrites and an axon), bipolar (one dendrite and one axon), or pseudo-unipolar (one axon).

27. *Which of these statements about nervous tissue is* not *true?*
   a. *Neurons have cytoplasmic extensions called axons.* 

   b. *Electrical signals (action potentials) are conducted along axons.*
   c. *Bipolar neurons have two axons.*
   d. *Neurons are nourished and protected by glia.*
   e. *Dendrites receive electrical signals and conduct them toward the cell body.*

4.7 Tissue Membranes

A. There are four tissue membranes in the body, one external (skin) and three internal (mucous, serous, synovial).

B. Mucous membranes line cavities that open to the outside and often contain mucous glands, which secrete mucus.

C. Serous membranes line cavities that do not open to the exterior and do not contain glands but do secrete serous fluid.

D. Synovial membranes are formed by connective tissue, line joint cavities, and secrete a lubricating fluid.

28. *The linings of the digestive, respiratory, excretory, and reproductive passages are composed of* Remember

    a. serous membranes.
    b. mucous membranes.
    c. mesothelium.
    d. synovial membranes.
    e. endothelium.

4.8 Tissue Damage and Inflammation

A. Inflammation involves a response that isolates injurious agents from the rest of the body and destroys the injurious agent.

B. Inflammation produces five symptoms: redness, heat, swelling, pain, and disturbed function.

29. *Chemical mediators*

    a. cause blood vessels to constrict.
    b. decrease the permeability of blood vessels.
    c. initiate processes that lead to edema.
    d. help prevent clotting.
    e. decrease pain.

30. *Antihistamines block the effect of a chemical mediator called histamine, which is released during the inflammatory response. What effect does administering antihistamines have on the inflammatory response, and is the use of an antihistamine beneficial?*

4.9 Tissue Repair

A. Tissue repair is the substitution of viable cells for dead ones. Tissue repair occurs by regeneration (labile cells and stable cells) or replacement (permanent cells).

B. Tissue repair by primary union occurs when the edges of the wound are close together. Secondary union occurs when the edges are far apart.

31. *Which of these types of cells is labile?*

    a. neuron
    b. skin
    c. liver
    d. pancreas

32. *Permanent cells* Remember

    a. divide and replace damaged cells in replacement tissue repair.
    b. form granulation tissue.
    c. are responsible for removing scar tissue.
    d. are usually replaced by a different cell type if they are destroyed.
    e. are replaced during regeneration tissue repair.

Answers to this chapter's odd-numbered Concept Check questions appear in Appendix F.

5

CHAPTER

Integumentary System

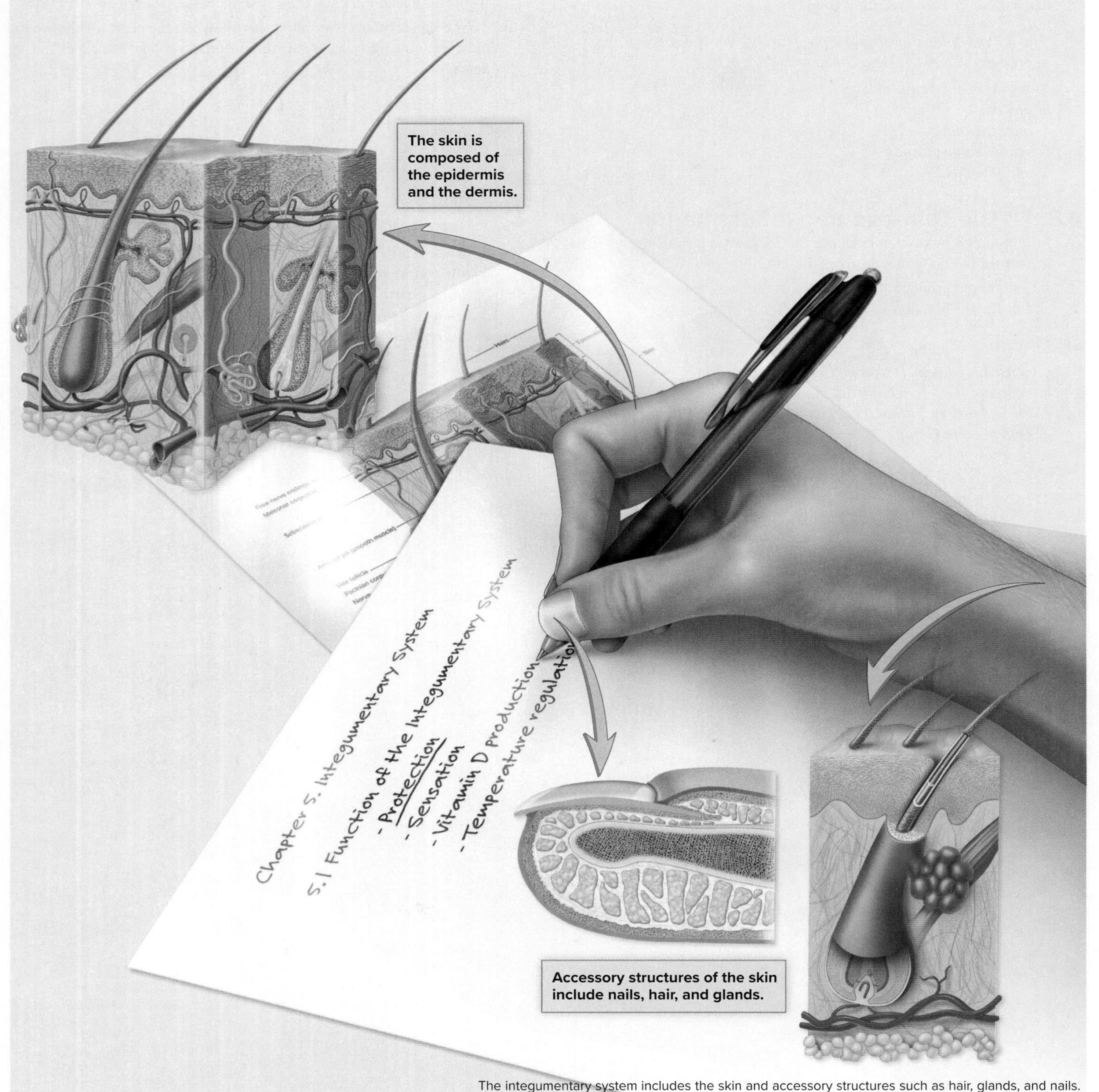

The integumentary system includes the skin and accessory structures such as hair, glands, and nails.

It is the morning of "the big day." You look in the mirror and, much to your dismay, there is a big, red bump on your chin. Just when you needed to look your best, this had to happen! For most people, blemish-free skin is highly desirable, and any sign of acne is cause for embarrassment. Hair loss and crows' feet also cause consternation in some people. It goes without saying that much time, effort, and money are spent on changing the appearance of the integumentary system. Think about the amount of counter space dedicated to skin care products, hair care products, and cosmetics in a typical discount store. People apply lotion to their skin, color their hair, and trim their nails. They try to prevent sweating by using antiperspirants and reduce or even mask body odor by washing and using deodorants and perfumes.

The **integumentary** (in-teg-you-MEN-tah-ree) **system** consists of the skin and accessory structures such as hair, glands, and nails. Although people are concerned about the appearance of their integumentary system for vanity's sake, its appearance can also indicate physiological imbalances. Some disorders, such as acne or warts, affect only the integumentary system. Other disorders affect different body parts but are reflected in the integumentary system, which provides useful signs for diagnosis. For example, reduced blood flow through the skin during a heart attack can cause a person to look pale, whereas increased blood flow as a result of fever can cause a flushed appearance. Some diseases cause skin rashes such as those characteristic of measles, chickenpox, and allergic reactions.

Understand

Learn to Predict

It was a dream job—summer days spent poolside, soaking up the sun. Following her first year at college, Laura worked as a lifeguard at the country club in her hometown. By the end of summer, she had a golden tan and was eager to show off her new look on campus. However, after returning to school in the fall, she was disappointed to see that her skin kept getting lighter, and in only a few weeks it had returned to its normal paler tone.

By combining your understanding of epithelial tissue from chapter 4 with further information about skin structure and pigmentation in this chapter, explain how and why Laura's tan faded in the fall.

Answers to this question and the chapter's odd-numbered Predict questions can be found in Appendix E.

5.1 Functions of the Integumentary System

LEARNING OUTCOME

After reading this section, you should be able to

A. **Describe the general functions of the integumentary system.**

Although we are often concerned with how the integumentary system looks, it has many important functions that go beyond appearance. The integumentary system includes the skin and accessory structures such as hair, nails, and glands. It forms the boundary between the body and the external environment, thereby separating us from the external environment while allowing us to interact with it. The major functions of the integumentary system are:

1. *Protection.* The skin is the covering of the body. Though exposed to the external environment, the skin's structure reduces the negative and harmful effects of ultraviolet light. Acting as a barrier, the skin also keeps microorganisms from entering the body and prevents dehydration by reducing water loss.
2. *Sensation.* The integumentary system has sensory receptors that can detect heat, cold, touch, pressure, and pain.
3. *Temperature regulation.* The skin plays a major role in regulating body temperature through the modulation of blood flow through the skin and the activity of sweat glands.
4. *Vitamin D production.* When exposed to ultraviolet light, the skin produces a molecule that can be transformed into the hormonal form of vitamin D, an important regulator of calcium homeostasis.
5. *Excretion.* Small amounts of waste products are excreted through the skin and glands.

ASSESS YOUR PROGRESS

Answers to these questions are found in the section you have just completed. Re-read the section if you need help in answering these questions.

1. *Provide an example for each function of the integumentary system.*

Module 4
Integumentary System

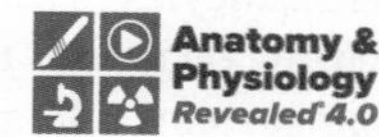

5.2 Skin

LEARNING OUTCOMES

After reading this section, you should be able to

A. **Describe the structure of the epidermis.**
B. **Describe the function of the epidermis.**
C. **Discuss the epidermal strata and relate them to the process of keratinization.**
D. **Differentiate between thick and thin skin as to the layers present and their locations.**
E. **Explain the major factors affecting skin color.**
F. **Describe the structure of the dermis.**
G. **Describe the functions of the dermis.**

The skin is made up of two major tissue layers, the epidermis and the dermis (figure 5.1). The **epidermis** (ep-ih-DER-miss; upon the dermis) is the superficial layer of the skin, consisting of stratified squamous epithelial tissue. The multiple cell layers of the epidermis protect against the potential damage from abrasion on the skin's surface. In addition, the epidermis reduces water loss through the skin. The epidermis rests on the **dermis** (DER-miss; skin), a layer of connective tissue. The structure of the dermis is responsible for most of the strength of the skin. Leather is a durable material used to make items such as furniture coverings. Leather is produced from the skin of an animal by removing the epidermis and preserving the dermis in a process called tanning.

The skin rests on the **subcutaneous tissue,** or *hypodermis* (high-poh-DER-miss), a layer of loose connective tissue (figure 5.1). The subcutaneous tissue is not part of the skin or the integumentary system, but it does connect the skin to underlying muscle or bone. Table 5.1 summarizes the structures and functions of the skin and subcutaneous tissue.

Epidermis

The epidermis is stratified squamous epithelium and as such has many of the characteristics described in chapter 4. It is separated from the underlying dermis by a basement membrane. The epidermis contains no blood vessels. The living cells of the epidermis receive nutrients and excrete waste products by the diffusion of substances between the epidermis and the capillaries of the dermis (figure 5.1*a*). Though the epidermis is stratified, it is not as thick as the dermis.

The epidermis is composed of several types of cells. Most cells of the epidermis are called **keratinocytes** (ke-RAT-i-noh-sytes) because they produce a protein mixture called **keratin** (KER-ah-tin), which makes the cells more durable. It is the durability of the keratinocytes that gives the epidermis its ability to resist abrasion and reduce water loss. Other cells of the epidermis include melanocytes, Langerhans cells, and Merkel cells.

- **Melanocytes** (MEL-an-oh-sytes) produce the pigment melanin, which contributes to skin color.
- **Langerhans cells** are part of the immune system (see chapter 22).
- **Merkel cells** are specialized epidermal cells associated with the nerve endings responsible for detecting light touch and superficial pressure (see figure 5.1 and chapter 14).

The keratinocytes of the epidermis are constantly lost at its surface but are also constantly replaced by new keratinocytes moving from deeper layers. These new keratinocytes are produced when keratinocyte stem cells undergo mitosis in the deepest layer of the epidermis. As new cells form, they push older cells to the surface, where they slough off. The outermost cells in this stratified arrangement protect the cells underneath, and the deeper, replicating cells replace cells lost from the surface. (*Note*: This information will be useful when answering the Learn to Predict question at the beginning of the chapter.)

As keratinocytes move from the deeper epidermal layers to the surface, the cells change shape and chemical composition, through the process called **keratinization** (KER-ah-tin-i-ZAY-shun), where the cells accumulate keratin. During keratinization, the cells eventually die and produce an outer layer of dead, hard cells that resists abrasion and forms a permeability barrier. The study of keratinization is important because many skin diseases result from malfunctions in this process. For example, large scales of epidermal tissue are sloughed off in **psoriasis** (soh-RYE-ah-sis; table 5.2). By comparing normal and abnormal keratinization, scientists may be able to develop effective therapies for psoriasis.

Although keratinization is a continual process, distinct transitional stages can be recognized as the cells change. On the basis of these stages, the many layers of cells in the epidermis are divided into regions, or **strata** (sing. stratum; figure 5.2). From the deepest to the most superficial, the five strata are the (1) stratum basale, (2) stratum spinosum, (3) stratum granulosum, (4) stratum lucidum, and (5) stratum corneum. The number of cell layers in each stratum and even the number of strata in the skin vary, depending on the location in the body.

Stratum Basale

The **stratum basale** (ba-SAL-eh), or *stratum germinativum* (JER-mi-nah-TYVE-um; see figure 5.2) is the deepest portion of the epidermis. It is a single layer of cuboidal or columnar cells. At the stratum basale, the epidermis is anchored to the basement membrane by hemidesmosomes. In addition, desmosomes hold the keratinocytes together (see chapter 4). The connections formed by the hemidesmosomes and desmosomes provide structural strength to the epidermis. Keratinocytes are strengthened internally by keratin fibers (intermediate filaments) that insert into the desmosomes.

Keratinocyte stem cells of the stratum basale undergo mitotic divisions approximately every 19 days. One daughter cell remains a stem cell in the stratum basale and divides again, but the other daughter cell is pushed toward the surface and becomes keratinized. It takes approximately 40–56 days for the cell to reach the epidermal surface and slough off.

Stratum Spinosum

Superficial to the stratum basale is the **stratum spinosum** (spye-NOH-sum), consisting of 8–10 layers of many-sided cells

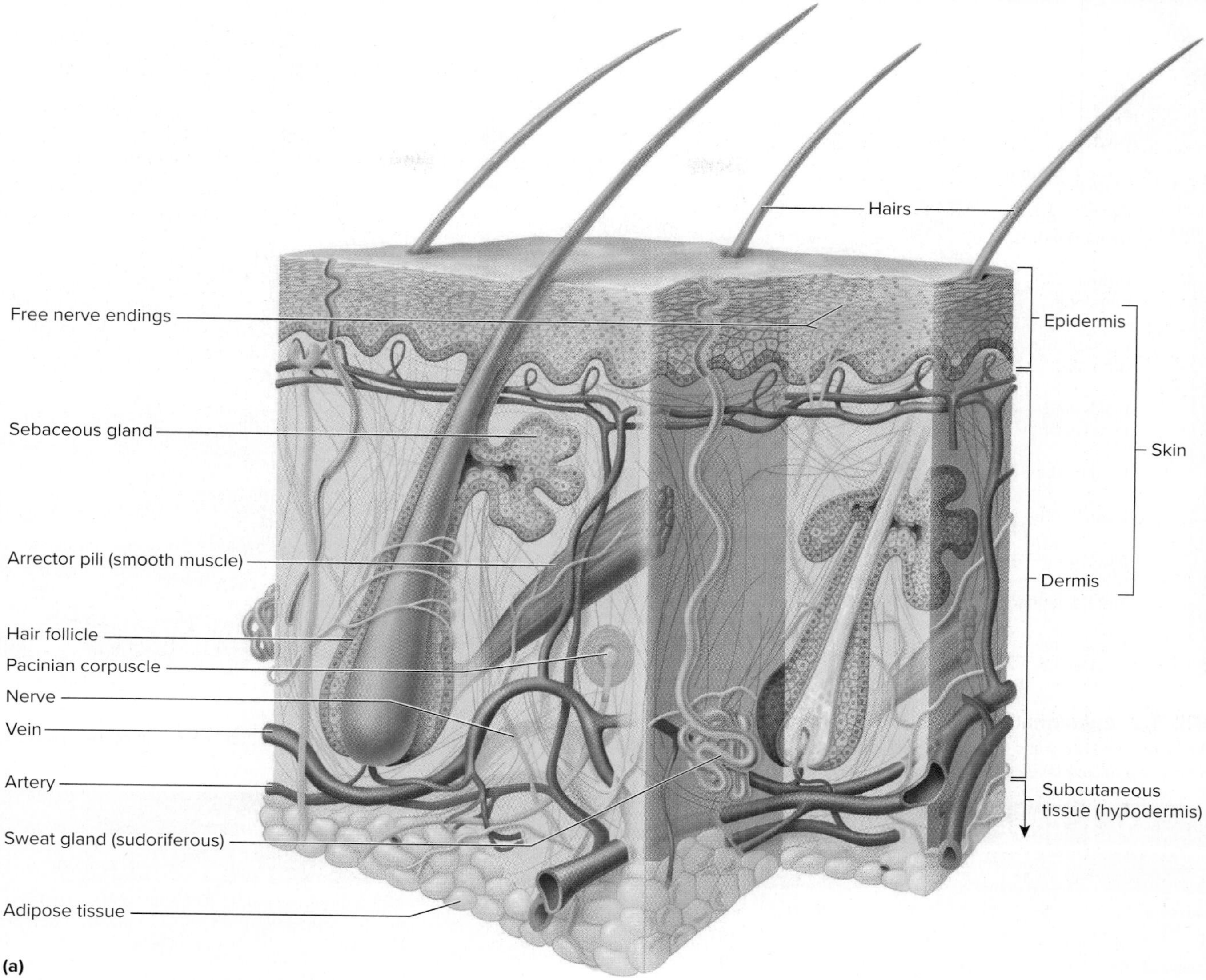
Hairs
Free nerve endings
Sebaceous gland
Arrector pili (smooth muscle)
Hair follicle
Pacinian corpuscle
Nerve
Vein
Artery
Sweat gland (sudoriferous)
Adipose tissue
Epidermis
Skin
Dermis
Subcutaneous tissue (hypodermis)

(a)

Epidermis
Dermis
LM 40x

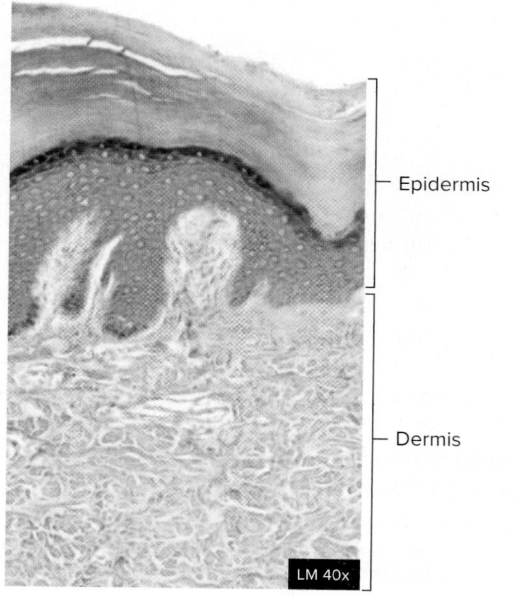

(b)

FIGURE 5.1 Skin and Subcutaneous Tissue

(*a*) The skin, consisting of the epidermis and the dermis, is connected by the subcutaneous tissue to underlying structures. Note the accessory structures (hairs, glands, sensory receptor, and arrector pili), some of which project into the subcutaneous tissue, as well as the large amount of adipose tissue in the subcutaneous tissue. (*b*) Photomicrograph of the skin showing the dermis covered by the epidermis.
(b) Victor P. Eroschenko APR

FUNDAMENTAL Figure

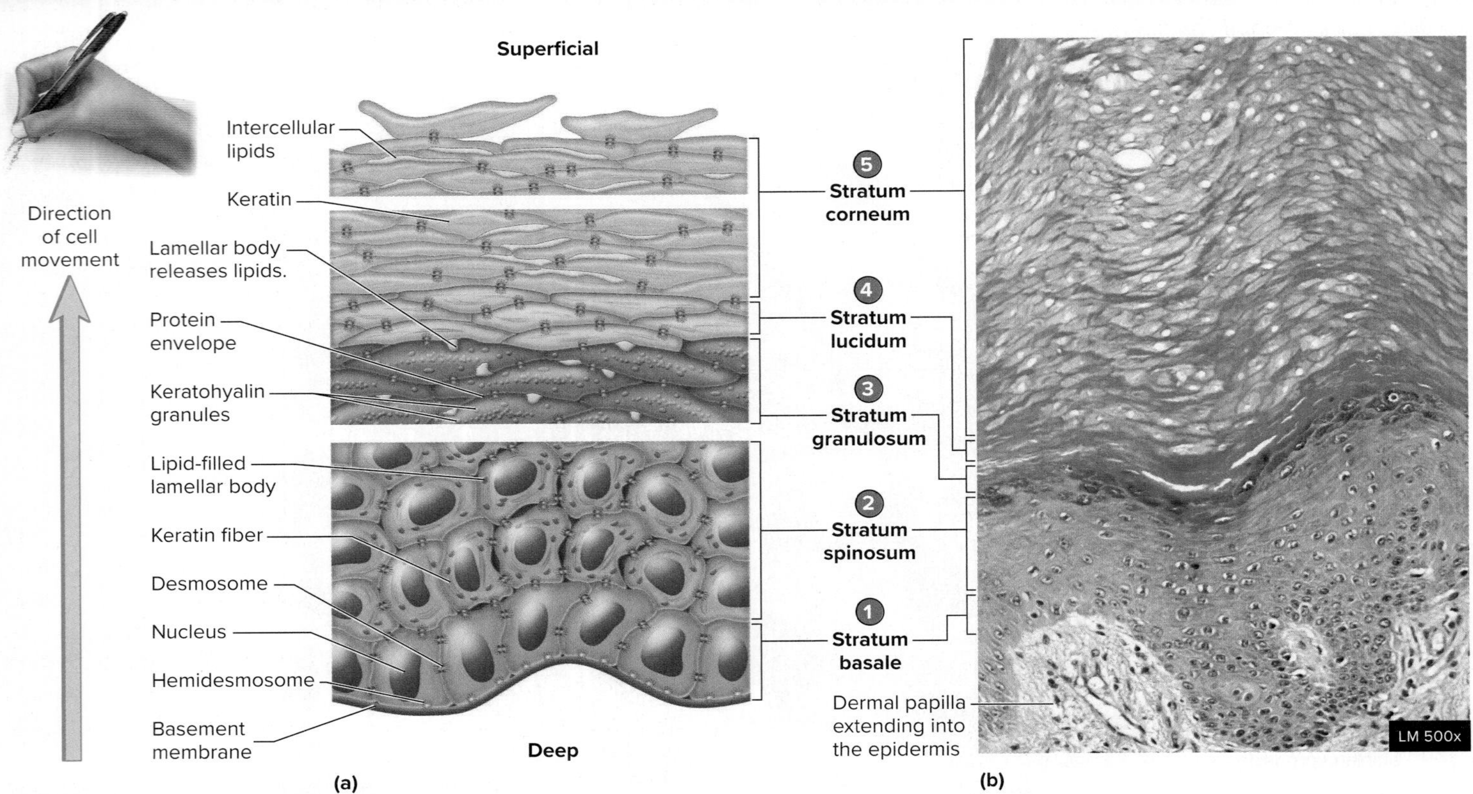

FIGURE 5.2 Epidermal Layers and Keratinization
(*a*) As keratinocytes progress from one stratum to the next, they undergo a series of changes called keratinization. (*b*) Photomicrograph of the epidermis resting on the papillary layer of the dermis (b) Alvin Telser/McGraw Hill Education.

TABLE 5.1 Comparison of the Skin (Epidermis and Dermis) and Subcutaneous Tissue

Part	Structure	Function
Epidermis	Superficial part of skin; stratified squamous epithelium; composed of four or five strata	Prevents water loss and the entry of chemicals and microorganisms; protects against abrasion and harmful effects of ultraviolet light; produces vitamin D; gives rise to hair, nails, and glands
Stratum corneum	Most superficial stratum of the epidermis; 25 or more layers of dead squamous cells	Provides structural strength due to keratin within cells; prevents water loss due to lipids surrounding cells; sloughing off of most superficial cells resists abrasion
Stratum lucidum	Three to five layers of dead cells; appears transparent; present in thick skin, absent in most thin skin	Disperses keratohyalin around keratin fibers
Stratum granulosum	Two to five layers of flattened, diamond-shaped cells	Produces keratohyalin granules; lamellar bodies release lipids from cells; cells die
Stratum spinosum	A total of 8–10 layers of many-sided cells	Produces keratin fibers; lamellar bodies form inside keratinocytes
Stratum basale	Deepest stratum of the epidermis; single layer of cuboidal or columnar cells; basement membrane of the epidermis attaches to the dermis	Produces cells of the most superficial strata; melanocytes produce and contribute melanin, which protects against ultraviolet light
Dermis	Deep part of skin; connective tissue composed of two layers	Is responsible for the structural strength and flexibility of the skin; the epidermis exchanges gases, nutrients, and waste products with blood vessels in the dermis
Papillary layer	Papillae project toward the epidermis; loose connective tissue	Brings blood vessels close to the epidermis; dermal papillae form fingerprints and footprints
Reticular layer	Mat of collagen and elastic fibers; dense irregular connective tissue	Is the main fibrous layer of the dermis; strong in many directions; forms cleavage lines
Subcutaneous tissue	Not part of the skin; loose connective tissue with abundant deposits of adipose tissue	Attaches the dermis to underlying structures; adipose tissue provides energy storage, insulation, and padding; blood vessels and nerves from the subcutaneous tissue supply the dermis

(see figure 5.2). As the cells in this stratum are pushed to the surface, they flatten; desmosomes break apart, and new desmosomes form. During preparation for microscopic observation, the cells usually shrink from one another, except where they are attached by desmosomes, causing the cells to appear spiny—hence the name stratum spinosum. As keratinocytes progress through this stratum, additional keratin fibers and lipid-filled, membrane-bound organelles called **lamellar** (LAM-eh-lar, lah-MEL-ar) **bodies** form inside the cells.

Stratum Granulosum

The **stratum granulosum** (gran-yoo-LOH-sum) consists of two to five layers of somewhat flattened, diamond-shaped cells. The long axes of these cells are oriented parallel to the surface of the skin (see figure 5.2). This stratum derives its name from the presence of protein granules of **keratohyalin** (KER-ah-toh-HIGH-ah-lin), which accumulate in the cytoplasm of the keratinocytes. The lamellar bodies, formed as the cells pass through the stratum spinosum, move to the plasma membrane and release their lipid contents into the extracellular space. Inside the keratinocyte, a protein envelope forms beneath the plasma membrane. In the most superficial layers of the stratum granulosum, the nucleus and other organelles degenerate, and the keratinocyte dies. Unlike the other organelles and the nucleus, however, the keratin fibers and keratohyalin granules within the cytoplasm do not degenerate.

Stratum Lucidum

The **stratum lucidum** (LOO-see-dum) is a thin, clear zone above the stratum granulosum (see figure 5.2). It consists of several layers of dead keratinocytes with indistinct boundaries. Keratin fibers are present, but the keratohyalin, which was evident as granules in the stratum granulosum, has dispersed around the keratin fibers, and the cells appear somewhat transparent. The stratum lucidum is present in only a few areas of the body (see the section "Thick and Thin Skin").

Stratum Corneum

The last, and most superficial, stratum of the epidermis is the **stratum corneum** (COR-nee-um; see figure 5.2). This stratum is composed of 25 or more layers of dead, overlapping squamous cells joined by desmosomes. Eventually, the desmosomes break apart, and the cells are shed from the surface of the skin. Excessive shedding of the stratum corneum of the scalp results in dandruff. Less noticeably, skin cells are continually shed from other areas as clothes rub against the body or as the skin is washed.

The stratum corneum consists of **cornified cells,** which are dead keratinocytes, with a hard protein envelope, filled with the protein keratin. Keratin is a mixture of keratin fibers and keratohyalin. The envelope and the keratin are responsible for the structural strength of the stratum corneum. The type of keratin found in the skin is soft keratin. Another type of keratin, hard keratin, is found in nails and the external parts of hair. Cells containing hard keratin are more durable than cells with soft keratin, and they are not shed.

Lipids are released from lamellar bodies surrounding the skin cells. The lipids are responsible for many of the skin's permeability characteristics.

Predict 1

Some drugs are administered by applying them to the skin (e.g., a nicotine skin patch to help a person stop smoking). The drug diffuses through the epidermis to blood vessels in the dermis. What kinds of substances can pass easily through the skin by diffusion? What kinds of substances have difficulty diffusing through the skin?

Thick and Thin Skin

When we say a person has thick or thin skin, we are usually referring metaphorically to the person's ability to take criticism. However, in a literal sense all of us have both thick and thin skin. Skin is classified as thick or thin based on the structure of the epidermis. **Thick skin** has all five epithelial strata, and the stratum corneum has many layers of cells. Thick skin is found in areas subject to pressure or friction, such as the palms of the hands, the soles of the feet, and the fingertips.

Thin skin covers the rest of the body and is more flexible than thick skin. The stratum lucidum is generally absent in thin skin. Additionally, each stratum in thin skin consists of fewer layers of cells than are found in thick skin. For example, the stratum granulosum frequently has only one or two layers of cells, as opposed to the three to five layers of cells in thick skin. Another important difference between thick and thin skin is that hair is found only in thin skin. Recall the first key concept of anatomy and physiology is the relationship between structure and function. This variation in the structure of skin relative to degree of exposure to pressure and friction is a good example of this relationship.

The entire skin, including both the epidermis and the dermis, varies in thickness from 0.5 mm in the eyelids to 5.0 mm on the back and shoulders. The terms *thin* and *thick* refer only to the epidermis and should not be used when total skin thickness is considered. It is actually variation in the thickness of the dermis that accounts for most of the difference in total skin thickness. For example, the skin of the back is thin skin, whereas that of the palm of the hand is thick skin; however, because the dermis of the skin of the back is thicker, the total skin thickness of the back is greater than that of the palm.

In skin subjected to friction or pressure, an area called a **callus** (KAL-us) often forms when the stratum corneum of the epidermis increases in thickness. The increased number of cell layers provides added protection in the area that experiences more mechanical stress. The skin over bony prominences develop a cone-shaped structure called a **corn.** The base of the cone is at the surface, but the apex extends deep into the epidermis, and pressure on the corn may be quite painful. Calluses and corns can develop in both thin and thick skin.

Skin Color

The factors that determine skin color include (1) pigments in the skin, (2) blood circulating through the skin, and (3) the thickness of the stratum corneum.

Melanin (MEL-ah-nin) is the group of pigments primarily responsible for skin, hair, and eye color. Melanin also provides protection against ultraviolet light from the sun. Large amounts of melanin are found in certain regions of the skin, such as freckles, moles, the nipples, the areolae of the breasts, the axillae, and the genitalia. Other areas of the body, such as the lips, palms of the hands, and soles of the feet, contain less melanin.

Melanin is produced by **melanocytes** (MEL-an-oh-sytes), irregularly shaped cells with many long processes that extend between the keratinocytes of the stratum basale and the stratum spinosum. Figure 5.3 illustrates how melanin, produced by melanocytes, is transferred to keratinocytes, resulting in a relatively consistent skin tone across the body.

1. Melanocytes produce and package melanin into vesicles called **melanosomes** (MEL-ah-no-sohms).
2. These melanosomes move into cell processes of the melanocytes.
3. Keratinocytes phagocytize (see chapter 3) the tips of the melanocyte cell processes, thereby acquiring melanosomes.

Melanin production involves the enzymatic modification of the amino acid tyrosine to an intermediate. This intermediate may be modified in different ways producing pigments that can be brown, black, yellow, or red. The types of melanin produced are determined by genetic factors. The degree to which melanin is produced is influenced by exposure to light and hormones. The number of melanocytes in the skin is relatively the same for all humans, regardless of race. Racial variations in skin color are determined by several major factors:

- types of melanin produced
- amount of melanin produced
- size of melanosomes (melanin-filled vesicles in cells)
- number of melanosomes
- distribution of melanosomes

Although many genes are responsible for skin color, a single mutation (see chapter 29) can prevent the manufacture of melanin. **Albinism** (AL-bi-niz-em) is usually a recessive genetic trait that results from an inability to produce tyrosinase. The result is a deficiency or an absence of pigment in the skin, the hair, and the irises of the eyes. For those individuals who are able to produce melanin, exposure to ultraviolet light darkens the melanin already present in the skin and stimulates melanin production, resulting in tanning. (*Note*: This information will be helpful when answering the Learn to Predict question at the beginning of the chapter.)

Certain conditions may cause increases in melanin production and therefore changes in pigmentation in areas of the body. During pregnancy, certain hormones, such as estrogen and melanocyte-stimulating hormone, cause the mother's body to increase melanin production, which causes darkening of the nipples, areolae, and genitalia. The cheekbones, forehead, and chest also may darken, resulting in the "mask of pregnancy." In addition, a dark line of pigmentation may appear on the midline of the abdomen. Diseases that cause increased secretion of adrenocorticotropic hormone and melanocyte-stimulating hormone, such as Addison disease, also cause increased pigmentation.

Skin color can also show variation due to changes in blood flow. These changes in skin color are not as long lasting and often dissipate in a few minutes or hours. Erythema and cyanosis are examples of these types of skin color changes. **Erythema** (er-ih-THEE-mah) is a condition in which the skin turns a reddish hue when the amount of blood flowing through the skin increases. An inflammatory response (see section 4.8, "Tissue Damage and Inflammation") stimulated by infection, sunburn, allergic reactions, insect bites, or other causes can produce erythema. Exposure to the cold and blushing or flushing when angry or hot can also produce erythema. A decrease in blood flow, as occurs in shock, can make the skin appear pale, and a decrease in the blood O_2 content produces **cyanosis** (sigh-ah-NOH-sis), a bluish skin color (see Clinical Impact 5.2).

Carotene (KAIR-oh-teen) is a yellow pigment found in plants, such as carrots and corn. Humans normally ingest carotene and use it as a source of vitamin A. Carotene is lipid-soluble and, when large amounts of carotene are consumed, the excess accumulates in the stratum corneum and in adipocytes of the dermis and subcutaneous tissue, causing the skin to develop a yellowish tint. The yellowish tint slowly disappears once carotene intake is reduced.

PROCESS **Figure**

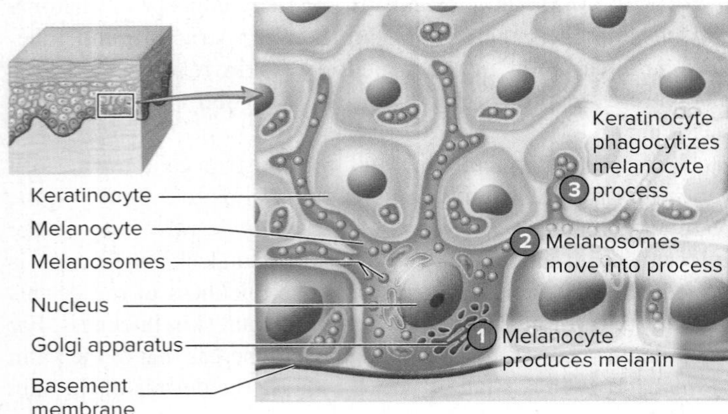

PROCESS **Figure 5.3**

Melanin Transfer to Keratinocytes

Melanocytes make melanin, which is packaged into melanosomes and transferred to many keratinocytes. Melanin protects a cell's DNA from UV damage. APR

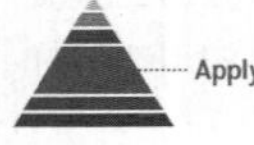

Based on this information, around which cellular structures would you expect the melanosomes to congregate?

Clinical IMPACT 5.1 Skin Cancer

Skin cancer is the most common type of cancer. Most skin cancers result from damage caused by the ultraviolet (UV) radiation in sunlight. Some skin cancers are induced by chemicals, x-rays, depression of the immune system, or inflammation, whereas others are inherited.

UV radiation damages the genes (DNA) in epidermal cells, producing mutations. If a mutation is not repaired, the mutation is passed to one of the two daughter cells when a cell divides by mitosis. If the mutations affect genes that regulate the cell cycle, uncontrolled cell division and skin cancer can result.

The amount of protective melanin in the skin affects the likelihood of developing skin cancer. Fair-skinned individuals, who have less melanin, are at an increased risk of developing skin cancer compared with dark-skinned individuals, who have more melanin. Long-term or intense exposure to UV radiation also increases the risk. Thus, individuals who are older than 50, who have engaged in repeated recreational or occupational exposure to the sun, or who have experienced sunburn are at increased risk. Most skin cancers develop on the parts of the body that are frequently exposed to sunlight, such as the face, neck, ears, and dorsum of the forearm and hand. A physician should be consulted if skin cancer is suspected.

There are three types of skin cancer: (1) basal cell carcinoma, (2) squamous cell carcinoma, and (3) melanoma (figure 5.4). **Basal cell carcinoma,** the most common type, affects cells in the stratum basale. Basal cell carcinomas have a varied appearance. Some are open sores that bleed, ooze, or crust for several weeks. Others are reddish patches; shiny, pearly, or translucent bumps; or scarlike areas of shiny, taut skin. Removal or destruction of the tumor cures most cases.

Squamous cell carcinoma is the second most common type of skin cancer. Squamous cell carcinoma affects cells in the stratum spinosum and can appear as a wartlike growth; a persistent, scaly red patch; an open sore; or an elevated growth with a central depression. These lesions may bleed. Removal or destruction of the tumor cures most cases.

Melanoma (MEL-ah-NOH-mah) is the least common, but most deadly, type of skin cancer, accounting for over 77% of the skin cancer deaths in the United States. Because they arise from melanocytes, most melanomas are black or brown, but occasionally a melanoma stops producing melanin and appears skin-colored, pink, red, or purple. About 40% of melanomas develop in preexisting moles. Treatment of melanomas when they are confined to the epidermis is almost always successful. However, if a melanoma invades the dermis and metastasizes (spreads) to other parts of the body, it is difficult to treat and can be deadly.

Early detection and treatment of melanoma before it metastasizes can prevent death. Melanoma can be detected by routine examination of the skin and application of the **ABCDE rule,** which states the signs of melanoma:

- *A* stands for asymmetry (one side of the lesion does not match the other side),
- *B* is for border irregularity (the edges are ragged, notched, or blurred),
- *C* is for color (pigmentation is not uniform),
- *D* is for diameter (greater than 6 mm), and
- *E* is for evolving (lesion changes over time). Evolving lesions change size, shape, elevation, or color; they may bleed, crust, itch, or become tender.

Limiting exposure to the sun and using sunscreens can reduce everyone's likelihood of developing skin cancer, especially those who have a genetic susceptibility. Two types of UV radiation play a role. Ultraviolet-B (UVB; 290–320 nm) radiation is the most potent for causing sunburn; it is also the main cause of basal and squamous cell carcinomas and a significant cause of melanoma. Ultraviolet-A (UVA; 320–400 nm) also contributes to skin cancer development, especially melanoma. It, too, penetrates the dermis, causing wrinkling and leathering of the skin. The Skin Cancer Foundation recommends using a broad-spectrum sunscreen that protects against both UVB and UVA, with a sun protection factor (SPF) of at least 15.

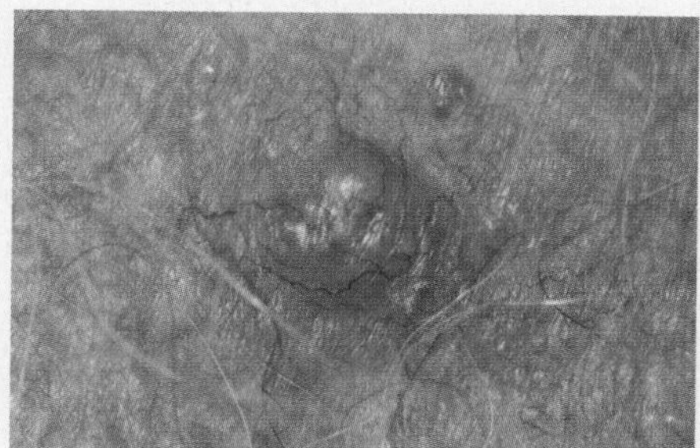

(a) Basal cell carcinoma

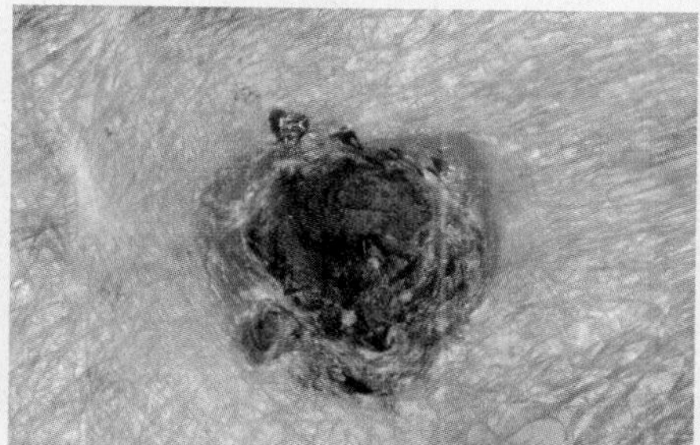

(b) Squamous cell carcinoma

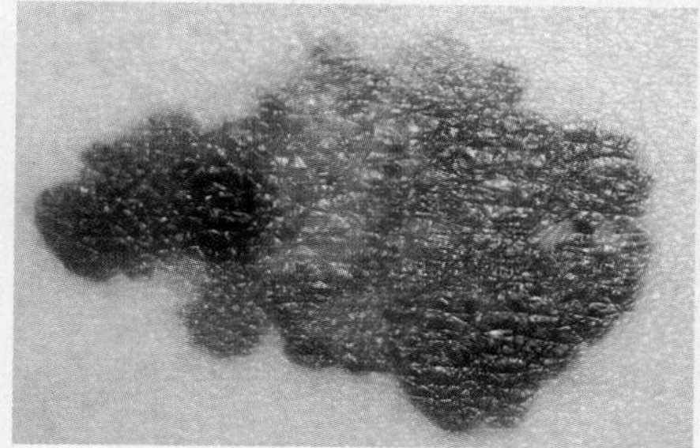

(c) Melanoma

FIGURE 5.4 Cancer of the Skin

There are three types of skin cancer: (*a*) basal cell carcinoma, (*b*) squamous cell carcinoma, (*c*) melanoma. (a) Dr. P. Marazzi/Science Photo Library/Getty Images; (b) Dr. P. Marazzi/Science Source; (c) National Cancer Institute (NCI)

The location of pigments and other substances in the skin affects the color produced. For example, light reflected off dark pigment in the dermis or subcutaneous tissue can be scattered by collagen fibers of the dermis to produce a blue color. The same effect produces the blue color of the sky as light is reflected from dust particles in the air. The deeper within the dermis or subcutaneous tissue any dark pigment is located, the bluer the pigment appears because of the light-scattering effect of the overlying tissue. This effect causes the blue color of tattoos, bruises, and some superficial blood vessels.

ASSESS YOUR PROGRESS

2. *From deepest to most superficial, name and describe the five strata of the epidermis. In which stratum are new cells formed by mitosis? Which strata have live cells, and which strata have dead cells?*
3. *Describe the structural features resulting from keratinization that make the epidermis structurally strong and resistant to water loss.*
4. *Compare the structure and location of thick and thin skin. Is hair in thick or thin skin?*
5. *Which cells of the epidermis produce melanin? What happens to the melanin once it is produced?*
6. *How do genetic factors, exposure to sunlight, and hormones determine the amount of melanin in the skin?*
7. *How do carotene, blood flow, blood O_2 content, and collagen affect skin color?*

Dermis

The dermis is connective tissue. Recall from chapter 4 that connective tissue consists of cells distributed widely in an extensive extracellular matrix, which includes protein fibers. The cells of the dermis include fibroblasts, a few adipocytes, and macrophages. Collagen is the main type of protein fiber of the extracellular matrix, but elastic and reticular fibers are also present. The dermis contains blood vessels that allow for nutrient and waste exchange to the cells of the dermis and the living cells of the epidermis. The dermis also contains nerve endings, hair follicles, smooth muscles, glands, and lymphatic vessels (figure 5.5). The nerve endings are varied in structure and function. They include (1) free nerve endings for pain, itch, tickle, and temperature sensations; (2) hair follicle receptors for light touch; (3) Pacinian corpuscles for deep pressure; (4) Meissner corpuscles for detecting simultaneous stimulation at two points on the skin; and (5) Ruffini end organs for sensing continuous touch or pressure (see figure 5.5).

The dermis is composed of two tissue layers (see figure 5.5): the superficial **papillary** (PAP-i-lar-ee) **layer** and the deeper **reticular** (re-TIK-yoo-lar) **layer.** The papillary layer derives its name from projections, called **dermal papillae** (pah-PIL-ee), that extend toward the epidermis. The papillary layer is loose connective tissue with thin fibers that are somewhat loosely arranged. The papillary layer also contains blood vessels that supply the overlying epidermis with O_2 and nutrients, remove waste products, and aid in regulating body temperature.

The dermal papillae under the thick skin of the palms of the hands and soles of the feet lie in parallel, curving ridges. These ridges shape the overlying epidermis into patterns called **friction ridges.** The impressions left on surfaces by these friction ridges form fingerprints and footprints. The friction ridges improve the grip of the hands and feet. Everyone has unique friction ridge patterns, even identical twins.

The reticular layer, which is composed of dense irregular connective tissue, is the main layer of the dermis. It is continuous with the subcutaneous tissue and forms a mat of irregularly arranged fibers that are resistant to stretching in many directions. The elastic and collagen fibers are oriented more in some directions than in others and produce **cleavage lines,** or *tension lines,* in the skin (figure 5.6). It is important for health professionals to understand cleavage line directions because an incision made

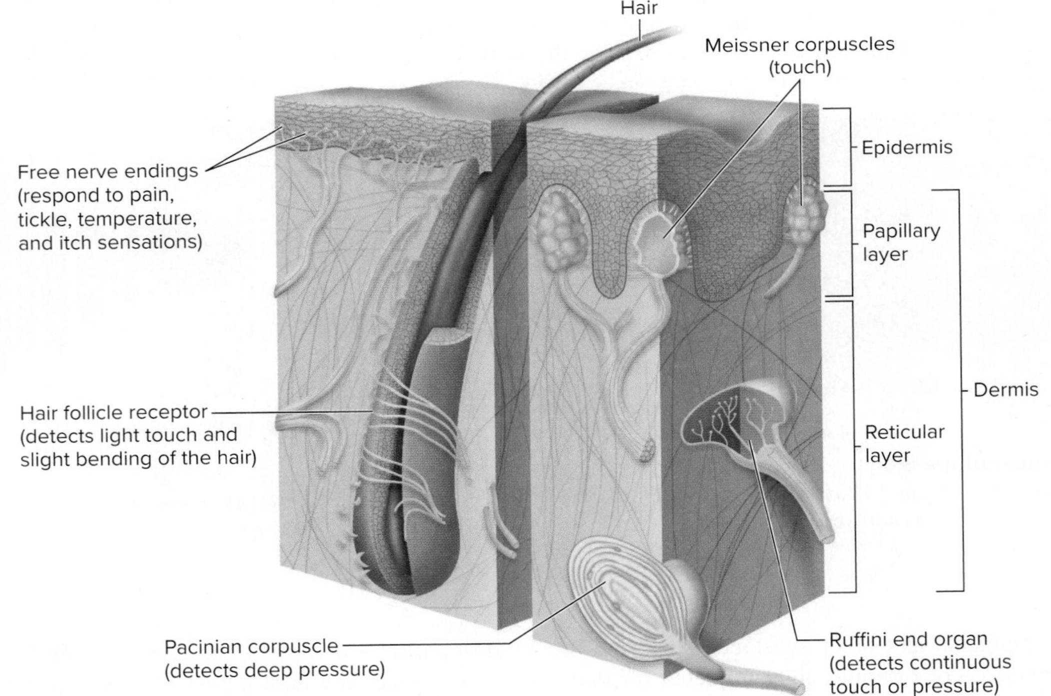

FIGURE 5.5 Dermis
The dermis is the deep layer of the skin, composed of two layers: the papillary layer and the reticular layer. Sensory receptors of the dermis include free nerve endings, hair follicle receptors, Pacinian corpuscles, Meissner corpuscles, and Ruffini end organs.

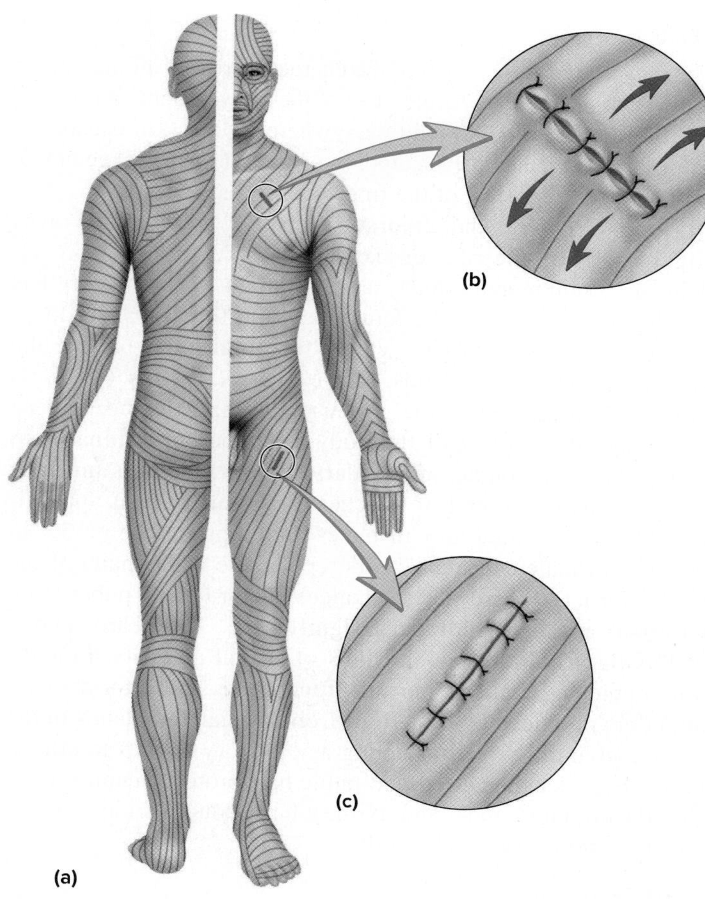

FIGURE 5.6 Cleavage Lines

(*a*) The orientation of collagen fibers produces cleavage lines, or tension lines, in the skin. The left half of the image illustrates cleavage lines of the posterior surface of the body. The right half of the image illustrates cleavage lines of the anterior surface of the body. (*b*) An incision made across cleavage lines can gap, increasing the time needed for healing and resulting in increased scar tissue formation. (*c*) An incision made parallel to cleavage lines results in less gapping, faster healing, and less scar tissue.

parallel to the cleavage lines is less likely to gap than an incision made across them. The development of infections and the formation of scar tissue are reduced in wounds where the edges are closer together.

If the skin is overstretched, the dermis may rupture and leave lines that are visible through the epidermis. These lines of scar tissue, called **stretch marks,** can develop in the skin of individuals who have experienced rapid growth. For example, stretch marks commonly form on the abdomen and breasts of a woman during pregnancy or on the skin of athletes who have quickly increased muscle size by intense weight training.

ASSESS YOUR PROGRESS

8. *Name and compare the two layers of the dermis. Which layer is responsible for most of the structural strength of the skin?*
9. *What are formed by the dermal papillae in thick skin? What roles do they have?*
10. *What are cleavage lines, and how are they related to the healing of a cut?*

5.3 Subcutaneous Tissue

LEARNING OUTCOMES

After reading this section, you should be able to

A. **Describe the structure of the subcutaneous tissue.**
B. **Describe the functions of the subcutaneous tissue.**

Deep to the skin is the subcutaneous tissue. The subcutaneous tissue attaches the skin to underlying bone and muscle and supplies the skin with blood vessels and nerves (see figure 5.1). The subcutaneous tissue consists of loose connective tissue with collagen and elastic fibers. The main types of cells within the subcutaneous tissue are fibroblasts, adipocytes, and macrophages. The subcutaneous tissue, which is not part of the skin, is sometimes called the *hypodermis*.

Approximately half the body's stored lipids are in the subcutaneous tissue, where they function in insulation and padding and as a source of energy. The subcutaneous tissue can be used to estimate total body fat by pinching the skin at selected locations and measuring the thickness of the skin fold and underlying subcutaneous tissue. The thicker the fold, the greater the amount of total body fat.

The amount of adipose tissue in the subcutaneous tissue varies with age, sex, and diet. Most infants have a chubby appearance because they have proportionately more adipose tissue than adults. Females have proportionately more adipose tissue than males, especially over the thighs, buttocks, and breasts. This accounts for some of the differences in body shape between the sexes and is also responsible for some of the differences in body shape between individuals of the same sex.

Injections are used to introduce certain substances, such as medication and vaccines, into the body by puncturing the skin. There are three types of injections (figure 5.7). (1) An

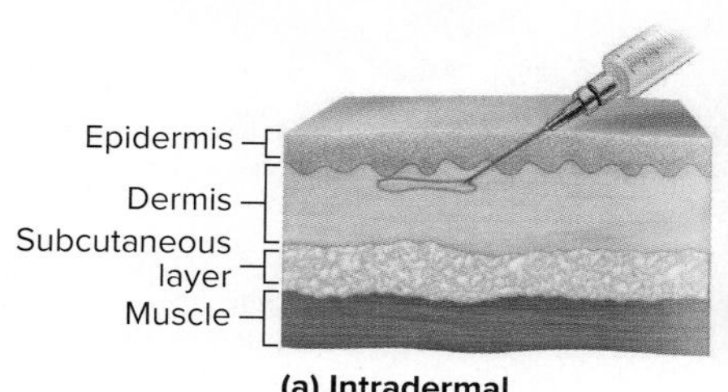

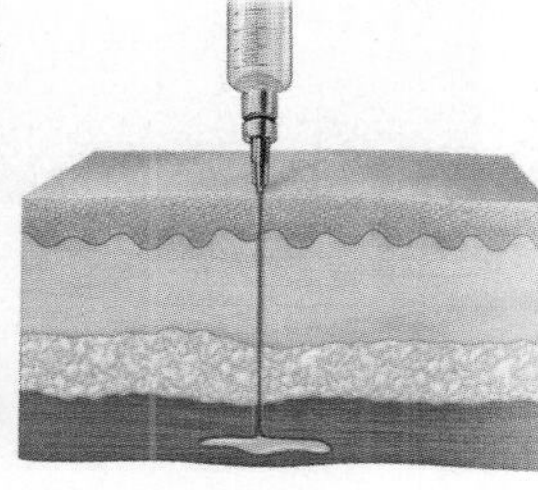

(c) Intramuscular

FIGURE 5.7 Injection

(*a*) An intradermal injection introduces substances to the dermis. (*b*) A subcutaneous injection introduces substances into the subcutaneous tissue. (*c*) An intramuscular injection introduces substances into a muscle deep to the subcutaneous tissue.

intradermal injection (figure 5.7*a*), as is used for the tuberculin skin test, goes into the dermis. It is administered by drawing the skin taut and inserting a small needle at a shallow angle into the skin. (2) A **subcutaneous injection** (figure 5.7*b*) extends into the subcutaneous tissue; an insulin injection is one example. A subcutaneous injection is achieved by pinching the skin to form a "tent," into which a short needle is inserted. (3) An **intramuscular injection** (figure 5.7*c*) reaches a muscle deep to the subcutaneous tissue. It is accomplished by inserting a long needle at a 90-degree angle to the skin. Intramuscular injections are used for injecting most vaccines and certain antibiotics.

ASSESS YOUR PROGRESS

11. *Name the types of tissue forming the subcutaneous tissue layer.*
12. *How is the subcutaneous tissue related to the skin?*
13. *List the functions of the adipose tissue within the subcutaneous tissue.*

5.4 Accessory Skin Structures

LEARNING OUTCOMES

After reading this section, you should be able to

A. **Describe the structure of a hair.**
B. **Discuss the phases of hair growth.**
C. **Explain the function of the arrector pili muscle.**
D. **List the glands of the skin and describe the secretions they produce.**
E. **Describe the parts of a nail.**
F. **Explain how nails grow.**

The skin includes several types of structures that are embedded in or otherwise associated with the epidermis and dermis and are therefore referred to as accessory structures. The accessory skin structures include the hair, glands, and nails.

Hair

The presence of **hair** is one of the characteristics of all mammals; if the hair is dense and covers most of the body surface, it is called fur. In humans, hair is found everywhere on the skin except the palms, the soles, the lips, the nipples, parts of the external genitalia, and the distal segments of the fingers and toes.

Hair structure and coloration change as a person ages (figure 5.8). By the fifth or sixth month of fetal development, delicate, unpigmented hair called **lanugo** (la-NYU-go) has developed and covered the fetus. Near the time of birth, long, coarse, and pigmented hairs called **terminal hairs** replace the lanugo of the scalp, eyelids, and eyebrows. **Vellus** (VEL-us) **hairs,** which are short, fine, and usually unpigmented, replace the lanugo on the rest of the body. At puberty, terminal hair, especially in the pubic and axillary regions, replaces much of the vellus hair. The hair of the chest, legs, and arms is approximately 90% terminal hair in males and approximately 35% in females. In males, terminal hairs replace the vellus hairs of the face to form the beard. These changes in hair type at puberty are universal and have biological significance. The beard, pubic, and axillary hair are visible signs of sexual maturity. In addition, pubic and axillary hair may function as wicks for dispersing odors produced by secretions from specialized glands in the pubic and axillary regions acting as olfactory signals to others. It also has been suggested that pubic hair protects against abrasion during intercourse and axillary hair reduces friction when the arms move against the body.

Hair Structure

A hair is divided into the **shaft,** which protrudes above the surface of the skin, and the **root,** located below the surface (figure 5.9*a*). The base of the root is expanded to form the **hair bulb.** Most of the root and the shaft are composed of columns of dead, keratinized epithelial cells arranged in three concentric layers: (1) the medulla, (2) the cortex, and (3) the cuticle (figure 5.9*c, d*). The **medulla** (meh-DULL-ah) is the central axis of the hair, and it consists of two or three layers of cells containing soft keratin. The **cortex** surrounds the medulla and forms the bulk of the hair. The cells of the cortex contain hard keratin. The cortex is

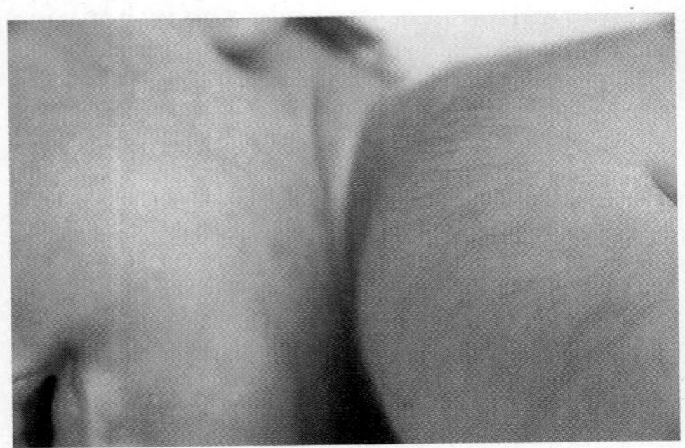
(a) Lanugo

(b) Vellus hair

(c) Terminal hair

FIGURE 5.8 Types of Hair
(*a*) An infant with lanugo (*b*) Vellus hair (*c*) Terminal hair of the scalp, eyebrows, eyelashes, and beard (a) Ivan Lonan/Shutterstock; (b) Bele Olmez/Getty Images; (c) Diego Cervo/Shutterstock

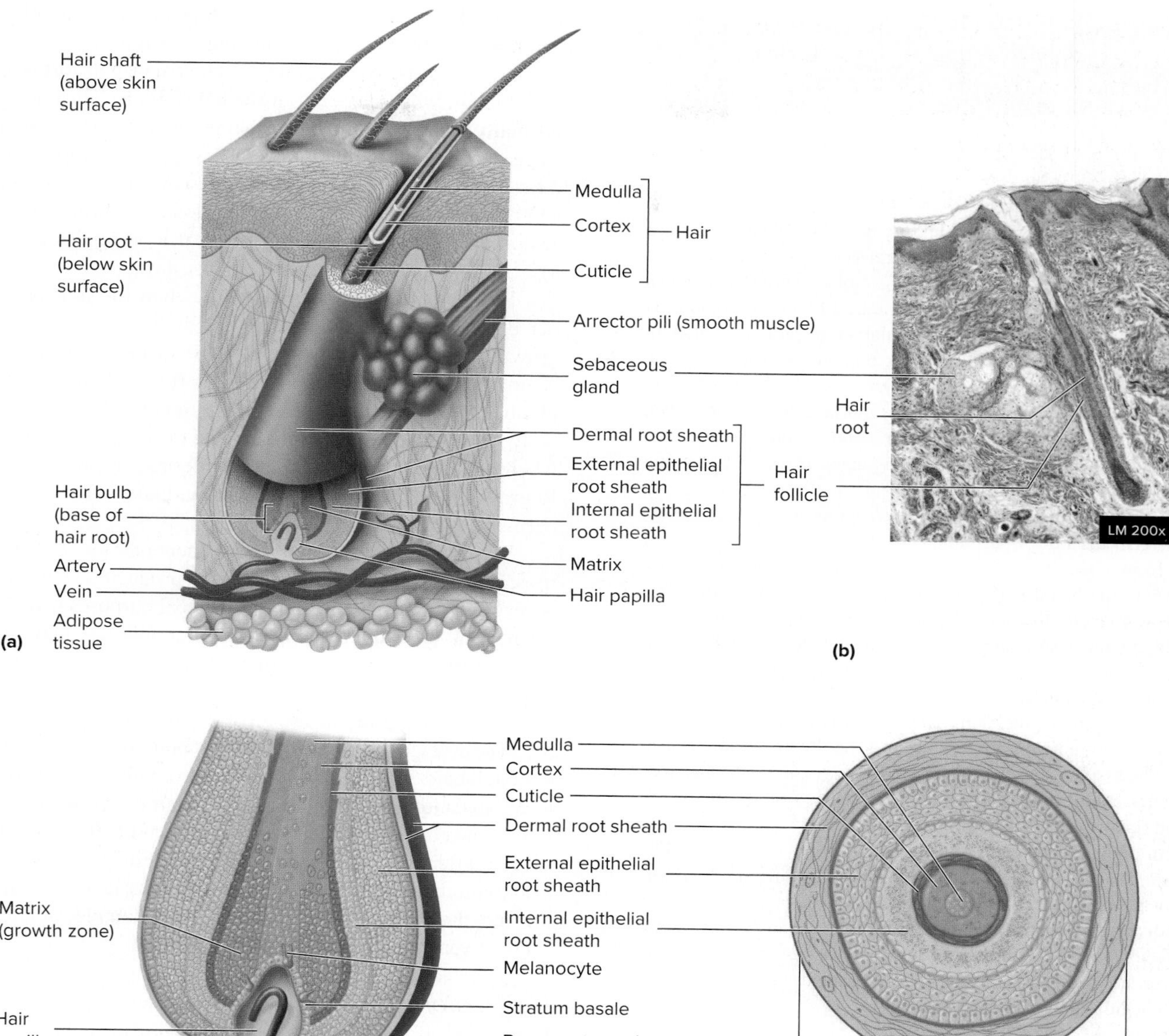

FIGURE 5.9 Hair Follicle

(*a*) The hair follicle contains the hair and consists of a dermal and an epithelial root sheath. (*b*) Photomicrograph of hair follicle with associated sebaceous gland. (*c*) Enlargement of the hair follicle wall and hair bulb. (*d*) Cross section of a hair within a hair follicle. (b) Al Telser/McGraw Hill APR

covered by the **cuticle** (KEW-tih-cul), a single layer of cells also containing hard keratin. The edges of the cuticle cells overlap like shingles on a roof.

The **hair follicle** is a tubelike invagination of the epidermis that extends into the dermis. A hair develops and grows within each hair follicle. A hair follicle consists of a **dermal root sheath** and an **epithelial root sheath.** The dermal root sheath is the portion of the dermis that surrounds the epithelial root sheath. The epithelial root sheath is divided into external and internal parts (figure 5.9*c, d*). At the opening of the follicle, the external epithelial root sheath has all the strata found in thin skin. Deeper in the hair follicle, the number of cells decreases until, at the hair bulb, only the stratum basale is present. This arrangement of epidermal cells has important consequences for skin repair. If the epidermis and the superficial part of the dermis are damaged, the keratinocyte stem cells located in the stratum basale of the undamaged part of the hair follicle can be a source of new epithelium.

Clinical IMPACT 5.2

The Integumentary System as a Diagnostic Aid

The integumentary system can be used in diagnosis because it is easily observed and often reflects events occurring in other parts of the body. For example, **cyanosis,** a bluish color to the skin that results from decreased blood O_2 content, is an indication of impaired cardiovascular or respiratory function. When red blood cells wear out, they are broken down, and the liver excretes part of their contents as bile pigments into the small intestine. **Jaundice** (JAWN-dis), a yellowish skin color, occurs when excess bile pigments accumulate in the blood. If a disease, such as viral hepatitis, damages the liver, bile pigments are not excreted and accumulate in the blood.

Rashes and lesions in the skin can be symptomatic of problems elsewhere in the body (see table 5.2). For example, scarlet fever results from a bacterial infection in the throat. The bacteria release a toxin into the blood that causes the pink-red rash for which this disease was named. In allergic reactions (see chapter 22), histamine released into the tissues produces swelling and reddening. Development of the skin rash called hives can indicate an allergy to foods or drugs, such as penicillin.

The condition of the skin, hair, and nails is affected by nutritional status. Vitamin A deficiency causes the skin to produce excess keratin and assume a characteristic sandpaper texture, whereas iron-deficiency anemia causes the nails to lose their normal contour and become flat or concave (spoon-shaped).

Hair concentrates many substances, which can be detected by laboratory analysis, and comparing a patient's hair with "normal" hair can be useful in certain diagnoses. For example, lead poisoning results in high levels of lead in the hair. Forensic analyses can also be conducted on hair samples to test for drug use and poisoning. However, hair analyses are not reliable for determining a person's general health or nutritional status.

The internal epithelial root sheath of the hair follicle has raised edges that mesh closely with the raised edges of the hair cuticle, and this arrangement holds the hair in place. When a hair is pulled out, the internal epithelial root sheath usually comes out as well and is plainly visible as whitish tissue around the root of the hair.

The hair bulb is an expanded knob at the base of the hair root (figure 5.9*a*, *c*). Inside the hair bulb is a mass of undifferentiated epithelial cells called the **matrix.** The matrix produces both the hair and the internal epithelial root sheath. The dermis of the skin projects into the hair bulb as a **hair papilla.** Within the hair papilla are blood vessels that provide nourishment to the cells of the matrix.

Hair Growth

Hair is produced in cycles that involve a **growth stage** and a **resting stage.** During the growth stage, a hair increases in length as new matrix cells are produced, differentiate, become keratinized, and die. The hair grows longer as cells are added at the base of the hair root. Eventually, hair growth stops; the hair follicle shortens and holds the hair in place. A resting period follows, after which a new cycle begins. With this new cycle, a new hair forms to replace the old hair, which falls out of the hair follicle. Thus, losing a hair normally means that the hair is being replaced. The length of each stage depends on the hair—eyelashes grow for approximately 30 days and rest for 105 days, whereas scalp hairs grow for 3 years and rest for 1–2 years. At any given time, an estimated 90% of the scalp hairs are in the growing stage. It is normal for a person to lose approximately 100 scalp hairs per day.

Hair loss can be more extensive than the normal 100 hairs per day. In some cases, extensive hair loss may occur, but hair growth may return, such as occurs in patients receiving certain chemotherapies. **Alopecia areata,** often called spot baldness, involves varying degrees of hair loss and can affect all areas of the body. The condition is most likely due to an autoimmune response, where the defense cells of the body destroy normal, healthy cells. Regrowth of hair occurs in many individuals, but some experience permanent hair loss.

The most common kind of permanent hair loss is "pattern baldness." Hair follicles shrink and revert to producing vellus hair, which is very short, transparent, and for practical purposes invisible. Eventually, hair production in these smaller follicles may completely cease. Although baldness is more common and more pronounced in certain males, it can also occur in females. Genetic factors and the hormone testosterone are involved in causing pattern baldness.

The average rate of hair growth is approximately 0.3 mm per day, although hairs grow at different rates, even in the same approximate location. Cutting, shaving, or plucking hair does not alter the growth rate or the character of the hair, but hair can feel coarse and bristly shortly after shaving because the short hairs are less flexible. Maximum hair length is determined by the rate of hair growth and the length of the growing phase. For example, scalp hair can become very long, but eyelashes stay short.

Hair Color

Hair color is the result of melanin production by melanocytes and the distribution of melanin to the cells of the hair. Similar to how melanocytes of the epidermis produce melanin and pass it to the keratinocytes of the skin, melanocytes within the hair bulb matrix (see figure 5.9*c*) produce melanin and pass it to keratinocytes in the hair cortex and medulla. As with the skin, varying amounts and types of melanin cause different shades of hair color. Blonde hair has little black-brown melanin, whereas jet black hair has the most. Intermediate amounts of melanin account for different shades of brown. Red hair is caused by varying amounts of a red type of melanin. Hair sometimes contains both black-brown and red melanin. Hair color is controlled by several genes, and dark hair color is not necessarily dominant over light. With age, the amount of melanin in hair can decrease, causing hair color to fade or become white (i.e., no melanin). Gray hair is usually a mixture of unfaded, faded, and white hairs.

Muscles

Associated with each hair follicle are smooth muscle cells called the **arrector pili** (ah-REK-tor PIE-lee). The arrector pili extend from the dermal root sheath of the hair follicle to the papillary layer of the dermis (see figure 5.9*a*). Normally, the hair follicle and the hair inside it are at an oblique angle to the surface of the skin. When the arrector pili muscles contract, however, they pull the follicle into a more perpendicular position, causing the hair to "stand on end." Movement of the hair follicles produces raised areas called "goose bumps." This is a common response to cold temperatures as well as strong emotional responses. In other mammals, arrector pili muscle contractions are important for warmth as well as communication of aggression or fear.

ASSESS YOUR PROGRESS

14. *When and where are lanugo, vellus, and terminal hairs found in the skin?*
15. *What are the regions of a hair? What type of cells make up most of a hair?*
16. *Describe the three layers of a hair seen in cross section.*
17. *Describe the parts of a hair follicle. How is the epithelial root sheath important in skin repair?*
18. *In what part of a hair does growth take place? What are the stages of hair growth? Do all hairs grow at the same rate?*
19. *What determines the different shades of hair color?*
20. *Explain the location and action of arrector pili muscles.*

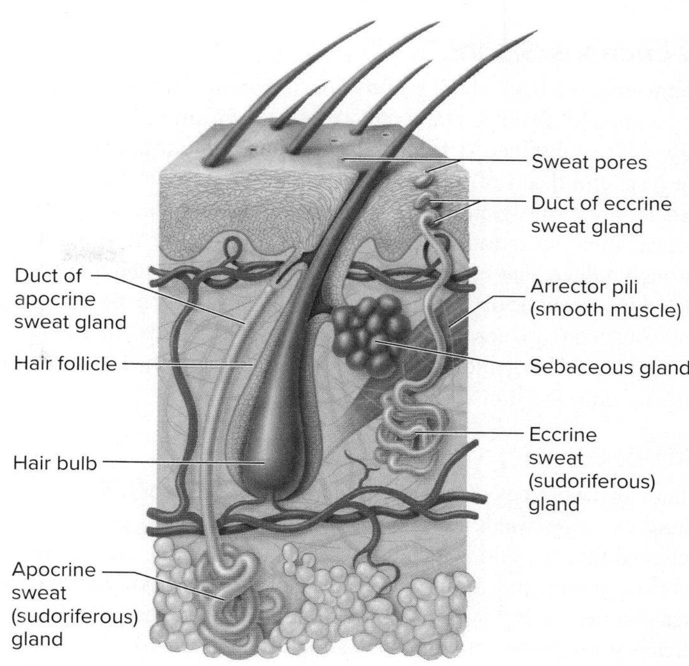

FIGURE 5.10 Glands of the Skin
Sebaceous glands and apocrine sweat glands empty into a hair follicle. Eccrine sweat glands empty onto the surface of the skin.

Glands

The skin has several types of glands that secrete materials onto its surface; however, not all are functional in all individuals. For example, mammary glands are a type of skin gland that are normally only functional in lactating women. The major glands of the skin are the sebaceous glands and the sweat glands (figure 5.10).

MICROBES In Your Body 5.1 — Using Bacteria to Fight Bacteria

Acne (acne vulgaris) is the most common skin condition in the United States. Though 80% of all American adolescents develop acne, adults can also be affected by it. When considering all age groups, approximately 40 to 50 million Americans suffer from acne. Unfortunately, there is not a tried-and-true cure for acne; however, new research examining the skin microbiome may have found a natural and effective treatment to get healthy, clear skin.

Unique species of bacteria, *Cutibacterium acnes (C. acnes)*, formerly *Propionibacterium acnes* are found in sebum-rich areas of the skin, such as the forehead, side of the nose, and back. There, these bacteria feed on lipids found in sebum. Although it has been difficult to study these bacteria (see Microbes in Your Body 1.1), scientists have now determined specific genetic traits of skin microbiome bacteria and have identified three unique strains of *C. acnes*. Of the three strains, one is more dominant in people with acne-free skin. Research has shown that this strain of *C. acnes* does not adversely affect the host. However, the other two strains of *C. acnes* are pathogenic to humans. So how does this information help scientists learn how to prevent acne? It seems that the "good" *C. acnes* prevents invasion of the skin by certain bacteria through a natural metabolic process. When *C. acnes* breaks down lipids, the skin pH is lowered to a level not tolerated by the invading bacteria. Scientists have proposed that the strain of *C. acnes* in healthy skin ("good" *C. acnes*) kills off the pathogenic strains of *C. acnes* ("bad" *C. acnes*) in a similar fashion. Because acne-affected people do not host the "good" strain, the "bad" strain can take over and cause the annoying skin eruptions of acne. Thus, perhaps in the future, to prevent acne, affected people can apply the "good" *C. acnes* or similar bacteria to their skin to prevent the "bad" *C. acnes* from taking over; so-called skin probiotics.

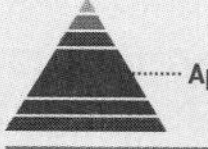

Predict 2

You just learned that acne-causing bacteria tend to live in areas of the skin with many sebaceous glands. However, in section 5.4, it states that sebum protects against certain bacteria.

a. *Based on what you've learned about bacteria in the Microbes in Your Body 1.1 and 3.1, why do you think* C. acnes *are able to survive the antibacterial effects of sebum?*
b. *Why do you think certain acne medications are so effective simply by inhibiting sebum production?*

Sebaceous Glands

Sebaceous (se-BAY-shus) **glands,** located in the dermis, are simple or compound alveolar glands that produce **sebum** (SEE-bum), an oily, white substance rich in lipids. Because sebum is released by the lysis and death of secretory cells, sebaceous glands are classified as holocrine glands (see chapter 4). Most sebaceous glands release their secretions into the upper part of the hair follicles through a duct. The secretion of sebum onto the hair and surrounding skin prevents drying and protects against some bacteria. A few sebaceous glands located in the lips, the eyelids (meibomian glands), and the genitalia are not associated with hairs but open directly onto the skin surface.

Sweat Glands

There are two types of **sweat,** or *sudoriferous* (soo-doh-RIF-er-us) **glands:** eccrine glands and apocrine glands. At one time, physiologists believed that secretions were released in a merocrine fashion from eccrine glands and in an apocrine fashion from apocrine glands (see chapter 4). But we now know that apocrine sweat glands also release some of their secretions in a merocrine fashion, and possibly some in a holocrine fashion. Traditionally, they are still referred to as apocrine sweat glands.

Eccrine (EK-rin) **sweat glands** (sometimes called *merocrine* (MARE-oh-krin) *sweat glands*) are the most common type of sweat gland. They are simple, coiled, tubular glands that open directly onto the surface of the skin through sweat pores (see figure 5.10). Eccrine sweat glands can be divided into two parts: (1) the deep, coiled portion, which is located mostly in the dermis; and (2) the duct, which passes to the skin surface. The coiled part of the gland produces an isotonic fluid that is mostly water but also contains some salts (mainly sodium chloride) and small amounts of ammonia, urea, uric acid, and lactic acid. As this fluid moves through the duct, sodium chloride moves by active transport from the duct back into the body, thereby conserving salts. The resulting hyposmotic fluid that leaves the duct is called **sweat.** When the body temperature starts to rise above normal, the sweat glands produce sweat, which evaporates and cools the body. Sweat also can be released in the palms, soles, and axillae as a result of emotional stress.

Eccrine sweat glands are distributed over the majority of the areas of the body but are most numerous in the palms of the hands and soles of the feet. Eccrine sweat glands are not found on the margin of the lips, the labia minora, and the tips of the penis and clitoris.

Apocrine (AP-oh-krin) **sweat glands** are simple, coiled, tubular glands that usually open into hair follicles superficial to the opening of the sebaceous glands (see figure 5.10). Apocrine sweat glands are found in the axillae and genitalia (scrotum and labia majora) and around the anus. Unlike eccrine sweat glands, apocrine sweat glands do not help regulate temperature in humans. Apocrine sweat glands become active at puberty as a result of sex hormones. Their secretions contain organic substances that are essentially odorless when first released but are quickly metabolized by bacteria to cause what is commonly known as body odor. Many mammals use scent as a means of communication, and physiologists have suggested that the activity of apocrine sweat glands may signal sexual maturity.

Other Glands

Other skin glands are the ceruminous glands and the mammary glands. The **ceruminous** (se-ROO-mi-nus) **glands** are modified eccrine sweat glands located in the ear canal (external auditory canal). **Cerumen,** or earwax, is composed of the combined secretions of ceruminous glands and sebaceous glands. Cerumen and hairs in the ear canal protect the tympanic membrane by preventing dirt and small insects from moving too deeply into the ear canal. However, an accumulation of cerumen can block the ear canal and make hearing more difficult.

The **mammary glands** are modified apocrine sweat glands located in the breasts. They produce milk. The structure and regulation of mammary glands are discussed in chapters 28 and 29.

Nails

A **nail** is a thin plate consisting of layers of dead stratum corneum cells that contain a very hard type of keratin. Nails are located on the distal ends of the digits (fingers and toes). A nail consists of the proximal **nail root** and the distal **nail body** (figure 5.11*a*). The nail root is covered by skin, and the nail body is the visible portion of the nail. The lateral and proximal edges of the nail are covered by skin called the **nail fold,** and the edges of the nail are held in place by the **nail groove** (figure 5.11*a, b*). The stratum corneum of the nail fold grows onto the nail body as the **cuticle,** or *eponychium* (ep-oh-NIK-ee-um). Beneath the free edge of the nail body is the **hyponychium** (HIGH-poh-NIK-ee-um), a thickened region of the stratum corneum (figure 5.11*c*).

The nail root extends distally from the **nail matrix.** The nail also attaches to the underlying **nail bed,** which is located between the nail matrix and the hyponychium. The nail matrix and bed are composed of epithelial tissue, with a stratum basale that gives rise to the cells that form the nail. Though both contribute to the growth of the nail, the nail matrix is thicker than the nail bed and produces nearly all of the nail. The nail bed is visible through the clear nail and appears pink because of blood vessels in the underlying dermis. A small part of the nail matrix, the **lunula** (LOO-noo-lah), is seen through the nail body as a whitish, crescent-shaped area at the base of the nail. The lunula, seen best on the thumb, appears white because the blood vessels do not show through the thicker nail matrix.

As the nail forms in the nail matrix and bed, it slides over the nail bed toward the distal end of the digit. Nails grow at an average rate of 0.5–1.2 mm per day, and fingernails grow more rapidly than toenails. Unlike hair, they grow continuously throughout life and do not have a resting phase.

Predict 3

While trying to fix some loose boards on his deck, Bob hit his left thumb with his hammer. The hammer struck his thumbnail distal to the lunula and proximal to the hyponychium. After a short period, a dark area appeared in the area of the nail bed. The injury was very painful until a physician drilled a small hole through Bob's nail, releasing bloody fluid. After nearly 2 months, the dark area moved to the free edge of the nail. Explain why a dark area developed in the nail. What caused Bob's pain, and why did drilling a hole in his nail relieve it? Why did the dark area move distally over time?

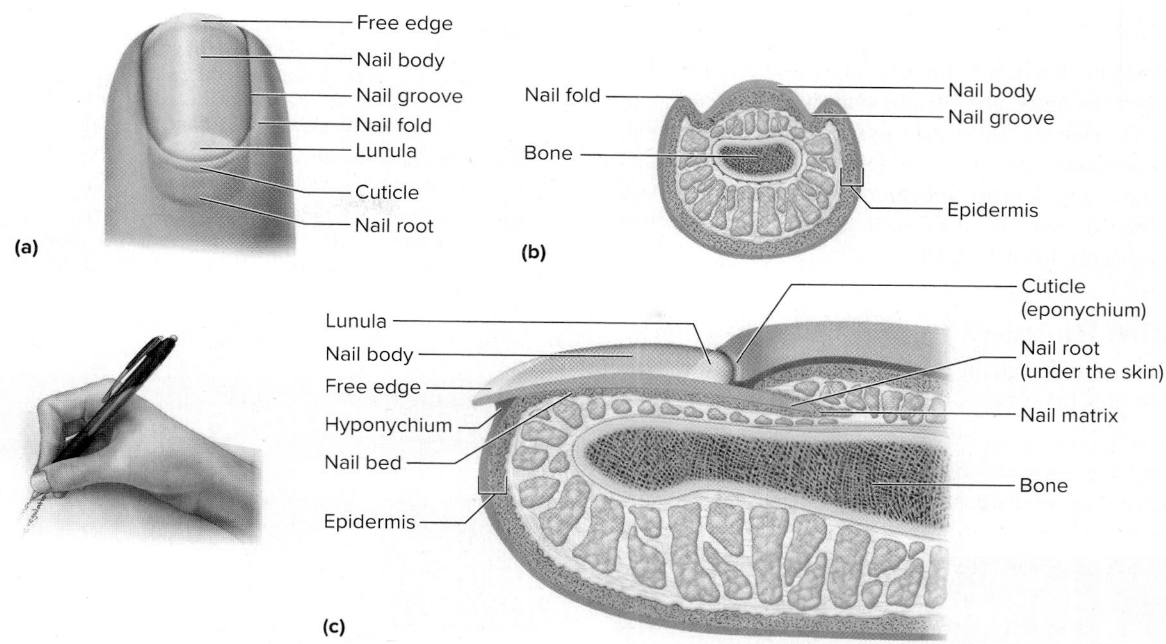

FIGURE 5.11 Nail
(*a*) Dorsal view of the exterior nail. (*b*) Cross section of the nail. (*c*) Longitudinal section of the nail. APR

ASSESS YOUR PROGRESS

21. *What do sebaceous glands secrete? What is the function of the secretion?*

22. *Which glands of the skin are responsible for cooling the body? Where are they located? Which glands are involved with producing body odor? Where are they located?*

23. *Name the parts of a nail. Which part produces most of the nail? What is the lunula?*

24. *What makes a nail hard? Do nails have growth stages?*

5.5 Physiology of the Integumentary System

LEARNING OUTCOMES

After reading this section, you should be able to

A. **Relate the protective functions of the skin, hair, glands, and nails.**
B. **Explain how the skin acts as a sense organ.**
C. **Discuss the importance of the skin in temperature regulation.**
D. **Describe the involvement of the skin in vitamin D production and in excretion.**

Protection

The integumentary system is the body's outer barrier, defending it from harm:

1. The skin protects underlying structures from mechanical damage. Both the dermis and the epidermis play roles in this line of defense, but in different ways. The dermis, particularly the irregular dense connective tissue of the reticular layer, provides structural strength, preventing tearing of the skin. The stratified epithelium of the epidermis protects against abrasion. As the outer cells of the stratum corneum slough off, they are replaced by cells from the stratum basale. Calluses develop in areas subject to heavy friction or pressure.
2. The skin prevents microorganisms and other foreign substances from entering the body. Secretions from skin glands produce an environment unsuitable for some microorganisms. The skin also contains components of the immune system that act against microorganisms (see chapter 22).
3. Melanin absorbs ultraviolet light and protects underlying structures from its damaging effects.
4. Hair provides protection in several ways. The hair on the head acts as a heat insulator and protects against ultraviolet light and abrasion. The eyebrows keep sweat out of the eyes, the eyelashes protect the eyes from foreign objects, and hair in the nose and ears prevents dust and other materials from entering. Axillary and pubic hair protect against abrasion.
5. Nails protect the ends of the fingers and toes from damage and can be used in defense.
6. The intact skin plays an important role in reducing water loss because its lipids act as a barrier to the diffusion of water.

Though the skin acts as a barrier, it is interesting to note that some lipid-soluble substances readily pass through the epidermis. Lipid-soluble medications can be administered by applying them to the skin, after which the medication slowly diffuses through the skin into the blood. For example, nicotine patches are applied to help reduce withdrawal symptoms in people attempting to quit smoking.

Sensation

Receptors in the skin can detect pain, heat, cold, and pressure. For example, the epidermis and dermal papillae are well supplied with touch receptors. The dermis and deeper tissues contain pain, heat, cold, touch, and pressure receptors. Hair follicles (but not the hair) are well innervated, and sensory receptors surrounding the base of hair follicles can detect hair movement. Sensory receptors are discussed in more detail in chapter 14.

Temperature Regulation

Body temperature is affected by blood flow through the skin. Figure 5.12 illustrates the process of heat exchange in the skin.

1. When blood vessels (arterioles) in the dermis dilate, more warm blood flows from deeper structures to the skin.
2. Heat loss increases, resulting in a reduction in body temperature.
3. Body temperature tends to increase as a result of exercise, fever, or a rise in environmental temperature. In order to maintain homeostasis, this excess heat must be lost. The body accomplishes this by producing sweat. The sweat spreads over the surface of the skin; as it evaporates, the body loses heat.
4. When blood vessels in the dermis constrict, less warm blood flows from deeper structures to the skin.
5. As a result of reduced blood flow through the skin, heat loss decreases. If body temperature begins to drop below normal, heat can be conserved by a decrease in the diameter of dermal blood vessels.

Case STUDY 5.1 Frostbite

Billy was hiking in the mountains one autumn day. Unexpectedly, a cold front moved in and the temperature dropped to well below freezing. Billy was unprepared for the temperature change, and he did not have a hat or earmuffs. As the temperature dropped, his ears and nose became pale in color. After continued exposure to the dropping temperatures, every 15–20 minutes, his ears and nose turned red for 5–10 minutes and then became pale again. After several hours, Billy managed to hike back to the trail head. By then, he was very chilled and had no sensation in his ears or nose. As he looked in the rearview mirror of his car, he could see that the skin of his ears and nose had turned white. It took Billy 2 hours to drive to the nearest emergency room, where he learned that the white skin meant he had frostbite of his ears and nose. About 2 weeks later, the frostbitten skin peeled. Despite treatment with an antibiotic, the skin of his right ear became infected. Eventually, Billy recovered, but he lost part of his right ear.

Predict 4

Frostbite is the most common type of freezing injury. When skin temperature drops below 0°C (32°F), the skin freezes and ice crystal formation damages tissues.

a. Using figure 5.12, describe the mechanism that caused Billy's ears and nose to become pale. How is this mechanism beneficial when the ambient temperature is decreasing?

b. Explain what happened when Billy's ears and nose periodically turned red. How is this beneficial when the ambient temperature is very cold?

c. What is the significance of Billy's ears and nose turning and staying white?

d. Why is a person with frostbite likely to develop an infection of the affected part of the body?

FUNDAMENTAL **Figure**

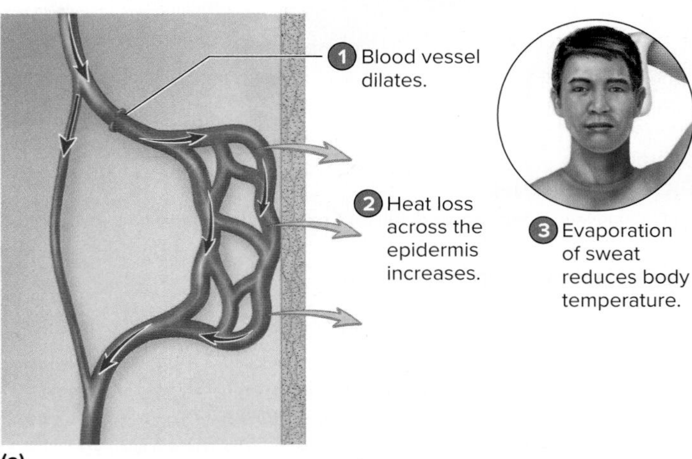

(a)

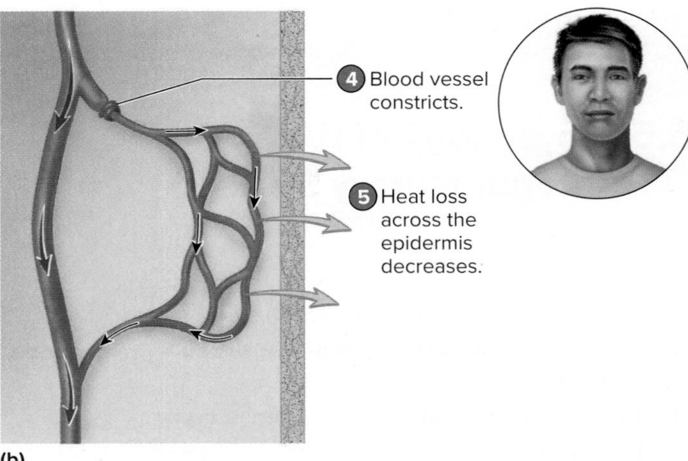

(b)

PROCESS **Figure 5.12**

Heat Exchange in the Skin

(*a*) Blood transfers heat from deeper tissues to the surface of the skin, where the heat is lost. Alteration of blood vessel diameter, and therefore blood flow, allows for regulation of heat loss at the skin. (*b*) Constriction of blood vessels reduces heat loss across the epidermis. APR

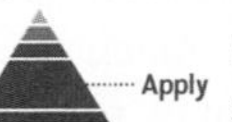

Explain why placing an ice pack on an area of skin results in the area appearing red.

Concept Check

The integumentary system consists of the skin, hair, glands, and nails.

5.1 Functions of the Integumentary System

The integumentary system separates and protects us from the external environment. Other functions include sensation, temperature regulation, vitamin D production, and excretion of small amounts of waste products.

5.2 Skin

Epidermis

A. The epidermis is stratified squamous epithelium divided into five strata, from deep to superficial: stratum basale, stratum spinosum, stratum granulosum, stratum lucidum, and stratum corneum.

B. Keratinization is the transformation of the living cells of the stratum basale into the dead squamous cells of the stratum corneum.

- Keratinized cells are filled with keratin and have a protein envelope, both of which contribute to structural strength. The cells are also held together by many desmosomes.

C. Soft keratin is present in skin and the inside of hairs, whereas hard keratin occurs in nails and the outside of hairs. Hard keratin makes cells more durable, and these cells are not shed.

1. *If a splinter penetrates the skin of the palm of the hand to the second epidermal layer from the surface, the last layer damaged is the*
   a. stratum granulosum.
   b. stratum basale.
   c. stratum corneum.
   d. stratum lucidum.
   e. stratum spinosum.

   Understand

For questions 2–6, match the layer of the epidermis with the correct description or function:

a. stratum basale
b. stratum corneum
c. stratum granulosum
d. stratum lucidum
e. stratum spinosum

2. *Production of keratin fibers; formation of lamellar bodies; limited amount of cell division* Remember
3. *Sloughing occurs; 25 or more layers of dead squamous cells* Remember
4. *Production of cells; melanocytes produce and contribute melanin; hemidesmosomes present* 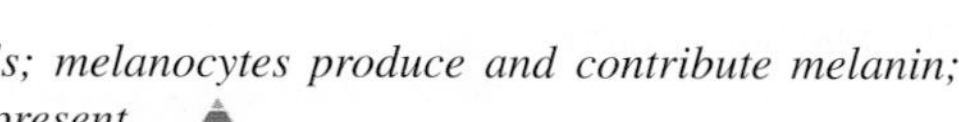

5. *Production of keratohyalin granules; lamellar bodies release lipids; cells die* Remember
6. *Dispersion of keratohyalin around keratin fibers; layer appears transparent; cells dead* Remember
7. *The skin of infants is more easily penetrated and injured by abrasion than is the skin of adults. Based on this fact, which stratum of the epidermis is probably much thinner in infants than in adults?* Understand

Thick and Thin Skin

A. Thick skin has all five epithelial strata.

B. Thin skin contains fewer cell layers per stratum, and the stratum lucidum is usually absent. Hair is found only in thin skin.

Skin Color

A. Melanocytes produce melanin inside melanosomes and then transfer the melanin to keratinocytes. The size and distribution of melanosomes determine skin color. Melanin production is determined genetically but can be influenced by ultraviolet light (tanning) and hormones.

B. Carotene, an ingested plant pigment, can cause the skin to appear yellowish.

C. Increased blood flow produces a red skin color, whereas decreased blood flow causes pale skin. Decreased oxygen content in the blood results in a bluish color, a condition called cyanosis.

8. *The function of melanin in the skin is to* 

   a. lubricate the skin.
   b. prevent skin infections.
   c. protect the skin from ultraviolet light.
   d. reduce water loss.
   e. help regulate body temperature.
9. *Concerning skin color, which pair of statements is* not *correctly matched?* Remember
   a. skin appears yellow—carotene present
   b. no skin pigmentation (albinism)—genetic disorder
   c. skin tans—increased melanin production
   d. skin appears blue (cyanosis)—oxygenated blood
   e. Blacks darker than Caucasians—more melanin in Black skin
10. *Melanocytes are found primarily in the stratum basale of the epidermis. In reference to their function, why does this location make sense?* Apply

Dermis

A. The dermis is connective tissue divided into two layers.

B. The papillary layer has projections called dermal papillae and is composed of loose connective tissue that is well supplied with capillaries.

C. The reticular layer is the main layer. It is dense irregular connective tissue consisting mostly of collagen.

For questions 11–13, match the layer of the dermis with the correct description or function:

a. papillary layer
b. reticular layer

11. *Layer of dermis responsible for most of the structural strength of the skin* Remember
12. *Layer of dermis responsible for fingerprints and footprints* 

13. *Layer of dermis responsible for cleavage lines and stretch marks* 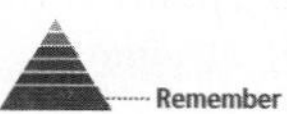

14. *The rate of water loss from the skin of a hand was measured. Following the measurement, the hand was soaked in alcohol for 15 minutes. After all the alcohol had been removed from the hand, the rate of water loss was again measured. Compared with the rate of water loss before soaking, what difference, if any, would you expect in the rate of water loss after soaking the hand in alcohol?* Apply

15. *It has been several weeks since George has competed in a tennis match. After a match, he discovers that a blister has formed beneath an old callus on his foot, and the callus has fallen off. When he examines the callus, it appears yellow. Can you explain why?* Apply

16. *A woman has stretch marks on her abdomen, yet she states that she has never been pregnant. Is this possible?* Understand

5.3 Subcutaneous Tissue

A. Located beneath the dermis, the subcutaneous tissue is loose connective tissue that contains collagen and elastic fibers.

B. The subcutaneous tissue attaches the skin to underlying structures and is a site of lipid storage.

5.4 Accessory Skin Structures

Hair

A. Lanugo (fetal hair) is replaced near the time of birth by terminal hairs (scalp, eyelids, and eyebrows) and vellus hairs. At puberty, vellus hairs can be replaced with terminal hairs.

B. A hair has three parts: shaft, root, and hair bulb.

C. The root and shaft of a hair are composed of dead keratinized epithelial cells. In the center, a cortex of cells containing hard keratin surrounds a medulla composed of cells containing soft keratin. The cortex is covered by the cuticle, a single layer of cells filled with hard keratin.

D. The hair bulb produces the hair in cycles, with a growth stage and a resting stage.

E. Hair color is determined by the amount and kind of melanin present.

F. Contraction of the arrector pili muscles, which are smooth muscles, causes hair to "stand on end" and produces "goose bumps."

17. *After birth, the type of hair on the scalp, eyelids, and eyebrows is* Remember
    a. lanugo.
    b. terminal hair.
    c. vellus hair.

18. *Hair*

    a. is produced by the dermal root sheath.
    b. consists of living, keratinized epithelial cells.
    c. is colored by melanin.
    d. contains mostly soft keratin.
    e. grows from the tip.

19. *Given these parts of a hair and hair follicle:*

    (1) cortex
    (2) cuticle
    (3) dermal root sheath
    (4) epithelial root sheath
    (5) medulla

    Arrange the structures in the correct order from the outside of the hair follicle to the center of the hair.
    a. 1,4,3,5,2
    b. 2,1,5,3,4
    c. 3,4,2,1,5
    d. 4,3,1,2,5
    e. 5,4,3,2,1

20. *Concerning hair growth,*
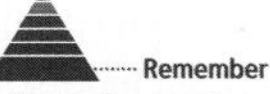

    a. hair falls out of the hair follicle at the end of the growth stage.
    b. most of the hair on the body grows continuously.
    c. cutting or plucking the hair increases its growth rate and thickness.
    d. genetic factors and the hormone testosterone are involved in "pattern baldness."
    e. eyebrows have a longer growth stage and resting stage than scalp hair.

21. *Smooth muscles that are attached to hair follicles and produce "goose bumps" when they contract are called* Remember
    a. external root sheaths.
    b. arrector pili.
    c. dermal papillae.
    d. internal root sheaths.
    e. hair bulbs.

22. *Why are your eyelashes not a foot long? Your fingernails?*
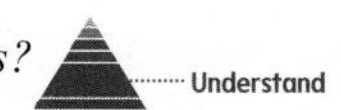

23. *Pulling on hair can be quite painful, yet cutting hair is not painful. Explain.* Understand

Glands

A. Sebaceous glands produce sebum, which oils the hair and the surface of the skin.

B. Eccrine sweat glands produce sweat, which cools the body. Apocrine sweat glands produce an organic secretion that can be broken down by bacteria to cause body odor.

C. Other skin glands are ceruminous glands, which make cerumen (earwax), and mammary glands, which produce milk.

For questions 24–26, match the type of gland with the correct description or function:

a. apocrine sweat gland
b. eccrine sweat gland
c. sebaceous gland

24. *Alveolar gland that produces a white, oily substance; usually open into hair follicles* Remember

25. *Coiled, tubular gland that secretes a hyposmotic fluid that cools the body; most numerous in the palms of the hands and soles of the feet* Remember

26. *Secretions from this coiled, tubular gland are broken down by bacteria to produce body odor; found in the axillae, in the genitalia, and around the anus* Remember

Nails

A. The nail root is covered by skin, and the nail body is the visible part of the nail.

B. Nearly all of the nail is formed by the nail matrix, but the nail bed contributes.

C. The lunula is the part of the nail matrix visible through the nail body.

D. The nail is stratum corneum containing hard keratin.

27. *The lunula of the nail appears white because*

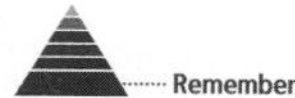

   a. *it lacks melanin.*
   b. *blood vessels cannot be seen through the thick nail matrix.*
   c. *the cuticle decreases blood flow to the area.*
   d. *the nail root is much thicker than the nail body.*
   e. *the hyponychium is thicker than the cuticle.*

28. *Most of the nail is produced by the*

   a. *cuticle.*
   b. *hyponychium.*
   c. *nail bed.*
   d. *nail matrix.*
   e. *dermis.*

29. *A patient has an ingrown toenail, in which the nail grows into the nail fold. Would cutting the nail away from the nail fold permanently correct this condition? Why or why not?* Apply

30. *Harry, age 55, went to a health fair and had a PSA test. The test results and subsequent examinations indicated prostate cancer. Harry was given radiation treatments and chemotherapeutic drugs. These drugs adversely affect cancer cells by interrupting mitosis, but they also interrupt mitosis in normal cells. Describe the probable effect of chemotherapy on Harry's epidermis, hair, nails, skin pigmentation, and sebaceous glands.* Apply

5.5 Physiology of the Integumentary System

Protection

A. The skin protects against abrasion and ultraviolet light, prevents the entry of microorganisms, helps regulate body temperature, and prevents water loss.

B. Hair protects against abrasion and ultraviolet light and is a heat insulator.

C. Nails protect the ends of the digits.

Sensation

The skin contains sensory receptors for pain, touch, hot, cold, and pressure, which allow for proper responses to the environment.

Temperature Regulation

A. Through dilation and constriction of blood vessels, the skin controls heat loss from the body.

B. Sweat glands produce sweat, which evaporates and lowers body temperature.

Vitamin D Production

A. Skin exposed to ultraviolet light produces cholecalciferol, which is modified in the liver and then in the kidneys to form active vitamin D.

B. Active vitamin D, also called calcitriol, increases blood calcium levels by promoting calcium uptake from the small intestine.

Excretion

Skin glands remove small amounts of waste products (e.g., urea, uric acid, and ammonia) but are not important in excretion.

31. *The skin helps maintain optimum calcium and phosphate levels in the body by participating in the production of* Remember
   a. *vitamin A.*
   b. *vitamin B.*
   c. *vitamin D.*
   d. *melanin.*
   e. *keratin.*

32. *Which of these processes increase(s) heat loss from the body?* Understand
   a. *dilation of dermal arterioles*
   b. *constriction of dermal arterioles*
   c. *increased sweating*
   d. *Both a and c are correct.*
   e. *Both b and c are correct.*

33. *Defend or refute the following statement: Dark-skinned children are more susceptible to rickets (insufficient calcium in the bones) than fair-skinned children.* Apply

Answers to this chapter's odd-numbered Concept Check questions appear in Appendix F.

6

CHAPTER

Skeletal System

BONES AND BONE TISSUE

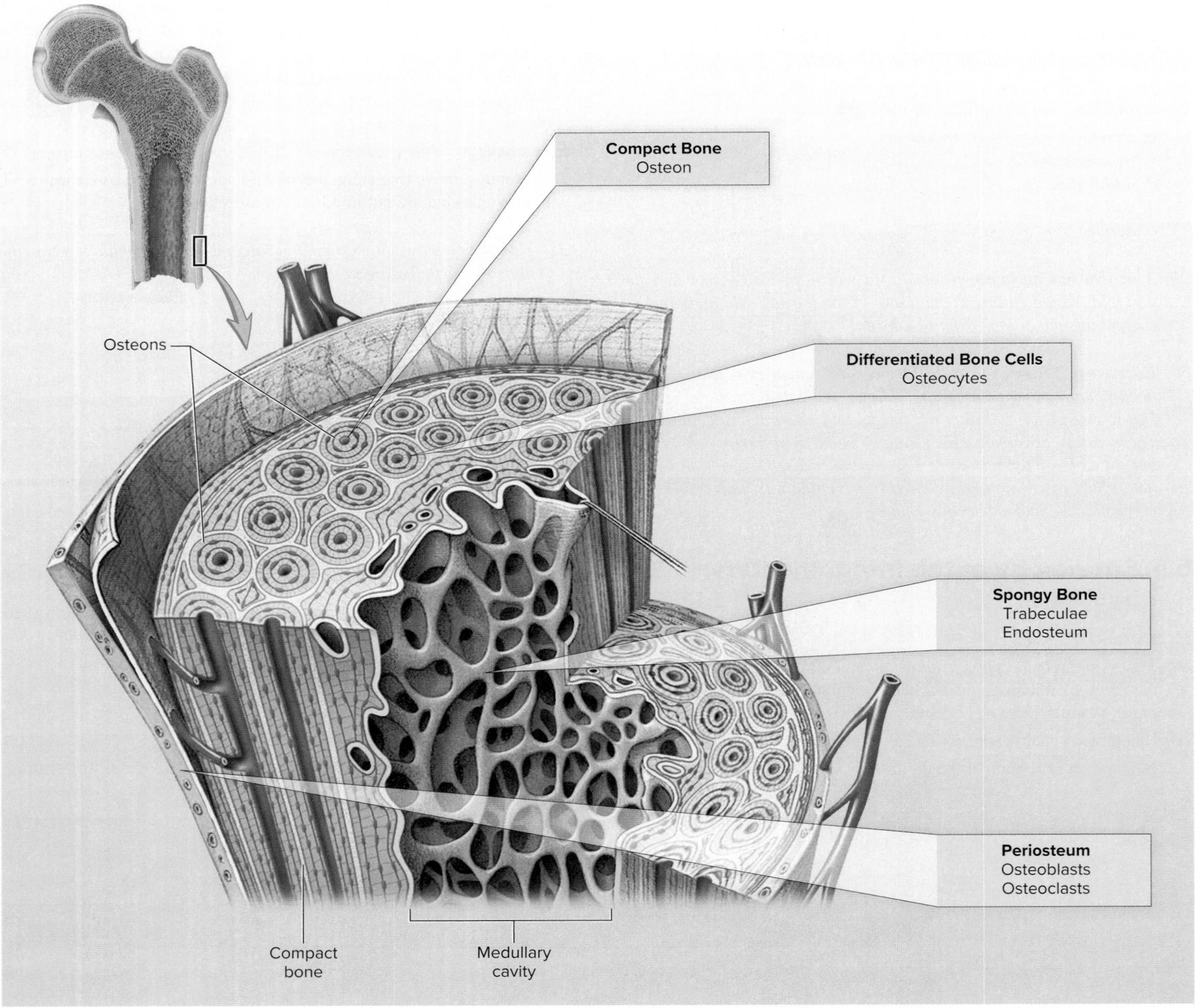

Compact Bone
Osteon
Differentiated Bone Cells
Osteocytes
Osteons
Spongy Bone
Trabeculae
Endosteum
Periosteum
Osteoblasts
Osteoclasts
Compact bone
Medullary cavity

The skeletal system is the framework that helps maintain the body's shape and enables us to move. The skeletal system is composed of bones, cartilage, and ligaments.

One of the most iconic symbols of the human form, the skeleton, is essential for our day-to-day activities. Sitting, standing, walking, picking up a pencil, and taking a breath all involve the skeletal system. Besides helping the body move and breathe, the skeleton is the structural framework that gives the body its shape and protects the internal organs and soft tissues. Although the skeleton consists of the mineralized material left after the flesh and organs have been removed and is often associated with death, it is composed of dynamic, living tissues that are able to grow, adapt to stress, and undergo repair after injury.

Learn to Predict

Amir, a 48-year-old hospital nurse, had started to dread 12-hour shifts. This was very unusual for Amir, who loved his job, most of all helping his patients get well so they could go home from the hospital. However, over the last several months, his left knee had been bothering him. He figured it was just arthritis. But after assisting on one particularly long surgery, he tripped, fell, and broke his femur just above the knee. When the doctor x-rayed his leg, another deformity was just beginning to be visible in his left femur. After more testing, Amir was eventually diagnosed with Paget (PAJ-it) disease. Paget disease is typified by random, excessive bone breakdown by osteoclasts followed by disorderly formation of new bone. The new bone has a much higher amount of spongy bone compared to compact bone. The classic hallmark of Paget disease is an overall bone demineralization and weakening. The cause of Paget disease is still unclear; however, it usually affects people past 40 years of age and responds reasonably well to medical treatment.

Why would treatment with medications used to prevent osteoporosis also be effective for treatment of Paget disease?

Answers to this question and the chapter's odd-numbered Predict questions can be found in Appendix E.

6.1 Functions of the Skeletal System

LEARNING OUTCOMES

After reading this section, you should be able to

A. **List the components of the skeletal system.**
B. **Explain the functions of the skeletal system.**

The skeletal system has four components: bones, cartilage, tendons, and ligaments. The skeleton is usually thought of as the framework of the body, but the skeletal system has many other functions as well, including the following:

1. *Body support.* Rigid, strong bone is well suited for bearing weight and is the major supporting tissue of the body. Cartilage provides a firm yet flexible support within certain structures, such as the nose, external ear, thoracic cage, and trachea. **Ligaments,** strong bands of fibrous connective tissue, hold bones together.
2. *Organ protection.* Bone is hard and protects the organs it surrounds. For example, the skull encloses and protects the brain, and the vertebrae surround the spinal cord. The rib cage protects the heart, lungs, and other organs of the thorax.
3. *Body movement.* Skeletal muscles attach to bones by **tendons,** which are strong bands of connective tissue. Contraction of the skeletal muscles moves the bones, producing body movements. Joints, which are formed where two or more bones come together, allow movement between bones. Smooth cartilage covers the ends of bones within some joints, allowing the bones to move freely. Ligaments allow some movement between bones but prevent excessive movements.
4. *Mineral storage.* Some minerals in the blood are stored in bone. If blood levels of these minerals decrease, the minerals are released from bone into the blood. The principal minerals stored are calcium and phosphorus, two minerals essential for many physiological processes. Adipose tissue is also stored within bone cavities. If needed, the lipids are released into the blood and used by other tissues as a source of energy.
5. *Blood cell production.* Many bones contain cavities filled with red bone marrow, which gives rise to blood cells and platelets (see chapter 19).

ASSESS YOUR PROGRESS

Answers to these questions are found in the section you have just completed. Re-read the previous section if you need help in answering these questions.

1. *Name the four components of the skeletal system.*
2. *Describe the five major functions of the skeletal system.*

Module 5
Skeletal System

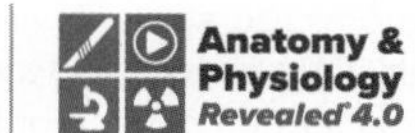

6.2 Cartilage

LEARNING OUTCOMES

After reading this section, you should be able to

A. **Relate the importance of cartilage to the structure of the skeletal system.**
B. **Describe the structure of hyaline cartilage.**
C. **Explain the types of cartilage growth.**

There are three types of cartilage: (1) hyaline cartilage, (2) fibrocartilage, and (3) elastic cartilage (see chapter 4). Although each type of cartilage can provide support, hyaline cartilage is most intimately associated with bone. An understanding of hyaline cartilage structure is important because most bones in the body start out as a hyaline cartilage model. In addition, growth in bone length and bone repair often involve making hyaline cartilage first, then replacing it with bone.

Recall from chapter 1 that most human cells start out in an undeveloped state and then differentiate into their final form. Undifferentiated cell names often end with the suffix *-blast,* which means "seed" or "bud." Once the undifferentiated cell has grown and developed into its final form, the suffix *-cyte* replaces *-blast* in the name.

Specifically, hyaline cartilage **chondroblasts** (KON-droh-blasts; cartilage) secrete a matrix, which surrounds the chondroblasts (figure 6.1). Once the matrix has surrounded the chondroblast, it has differentiated into a **chondrocyte** (KON-droh-site). Chondrocytes are rounded cells that occupy a space called a **lacuna** (la-KOO-nah) within the matrix. The matrix contains collagen, which provides strength, and proteoglycans, which make cartilage resilient by trapping water.

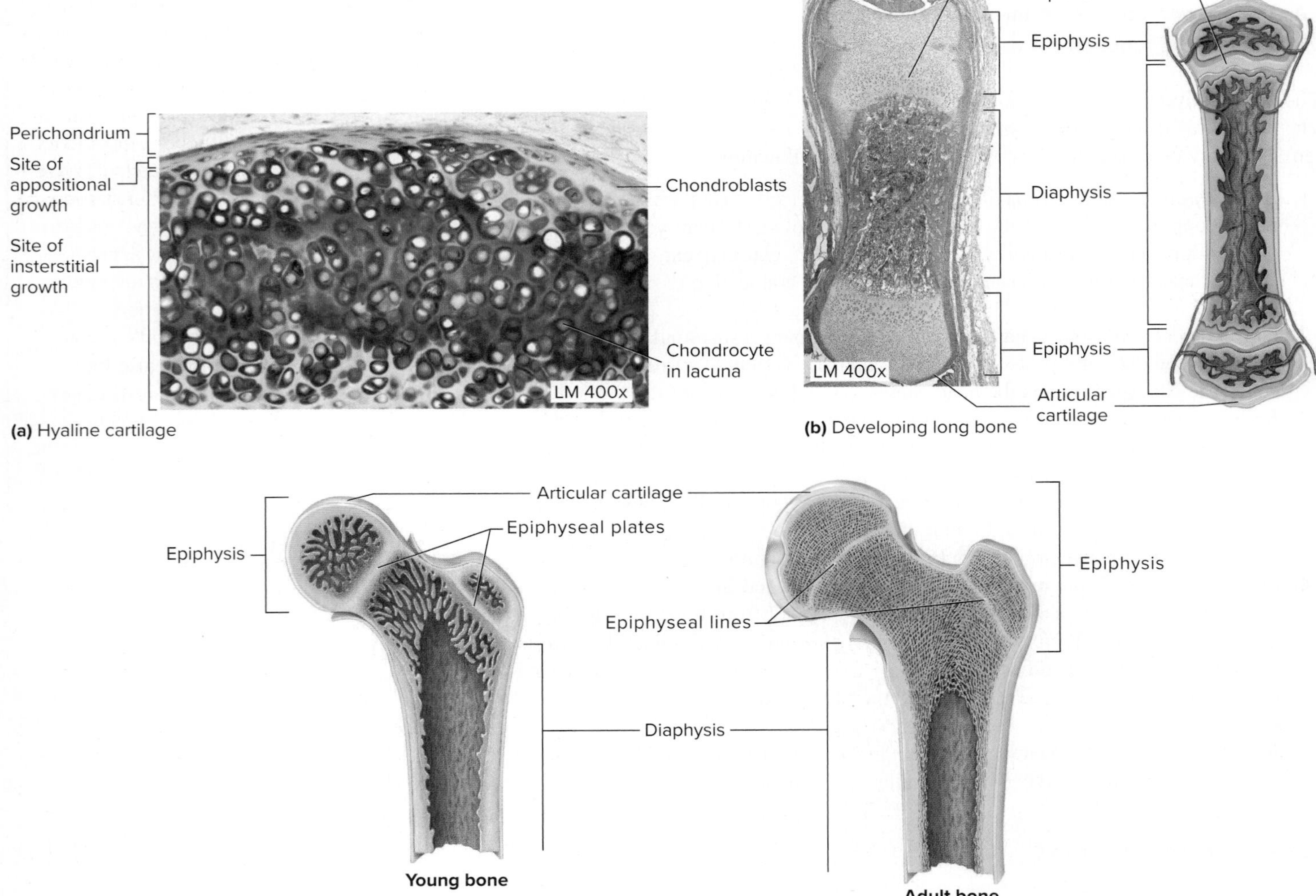

FIGURE 6.1 Location of Hyaline Cartilage in Bone

(*a*) Photomicrograph of hyaline cartilage covered by perichondrium. Appositional growth occurs when new cartilage is added to the surface by chondroblasts. Interstitial growth occurs when chondrocytes divide. (*b*) Photomicrograph of developing long bone demonstrating the initial structure is composed of hyaline cartilage. (*c*) Comparison of the location in hyaline cartilage in young bone to adult bone. The articular cartilage is the only remaining hyaline cartilage in adult bone. (a) J M Barres/agefotostock/Alamy Stock Photo; (b) JOSE CALVO/Science Source

Most cartilage is covered by a protective connective tissue sheath called the **perichondrium** (per-i-KON-dree-um; figure 6.1). The perichondrium is a double-layered outer layer of dense irregular connective tissue containing fibroblasts. The inner, more delicate layer has fewer fibers and contains chondroblasts. Blood vessels and nerves penetrate the outer layer of the perichondrium but do not enter the cartilage matrix, so nutrients must diffuse through the cartilage matrix to reach the chondrocytes. **Articular** (ar-TIK-yoo-lar) **cartilage,** which is hyaline cartilage that covers the ends of bones where they come together to form joints, has no perichondrium, blood vessels, or nerves.

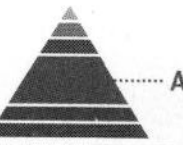

Predict 1

Explain why damaged cartilage takes a long time to heal. What are the advantages of articular cartilage having no perichondrium, blood vessels, or nerves?

There are two types of cartilage growth: (1) appositional growth and (2) interstitial growth. In **appositional growth,** chondroblasts in the perichondrium add new cartilage to the outside edge of the existing cartilage. In **interstitial growth,** chondrocytes in the center of the tissue divide and add more matrix in between the existing cells (figure 6.1).

ASSESS YOUR PROGRESS

3. *What are the three types of cartilage? Which type is more closely associated with bone?*
4. *Describe the structure of hyaline cartilage. Name the two types of cartilage cells. What is a lacuna?*
5. *Differentiate between appositional and interstitial growth of cartilage.*

6.3 Bone Histology

LEARNING OUTCOMES

After reading this section, you should be able to

A. **Describe the components of the extracellular bone matrix and state the function of each.**
B. **List each type of bone cell.**
C. **Give the function of each type of bone cell.**
D. **Give the origin of each type of bone cell.**
E. **Describe the structure of woven and lamellar bone.**
F. **Explain the structural differences between compact and spongy bone.**

In chapter 4, you learned that bone is a type of connective tissue. Recall that connective tissue is characterized by having spread-out cells separated by a nonliving material called matrix. In bone, as in other connective tissues, the bone cells produce the bone matrix and become entrapped within it. The cells also break down old matrix so that new matrix can replace it. Bone matrix composition is responsible for the characteristics of bone.

Bone Matrix

By weight, mature bone matrix is normally about 35% organic and 65% inorganic material. The organic material consists primarily of collagen and proteoglycans. The inorganic material consists primarily of a calcium phosphate crystal called **hydroxyapatite** (high-DROK-see-ap-ah-tyte), which has the molecular formula $Ca_{10}(PO_4)_6(OH)_2$.

The collagen and mineral components are responsible for the major functional characteristics of bone. Bone matrix can be compared to reinforced concrete. Like reinforcing steel bars, the collagen fibers lend flexible strength to the matrix; like concrete, the mineral components give the matrix weight-bearing strength.

If mineral in a long bone is reduced, collagen becomes the primary constituent and the bone is overly flexible. On the other hand, if the amount of collagen is reduced in the bone, the mineral component becomes the primary constituent and the bone is very brittle (figure 6.2). Try this: Soak a small chicken bone in white vinegar for 3–5 days. Do you think the bone will change? Which matrix component could be altered?

Bone Cells

There are three types of bone cells—(1) osteoblasts, (2) osteocytes, and (3) osteoclasts—each with different functions and a unique origin.

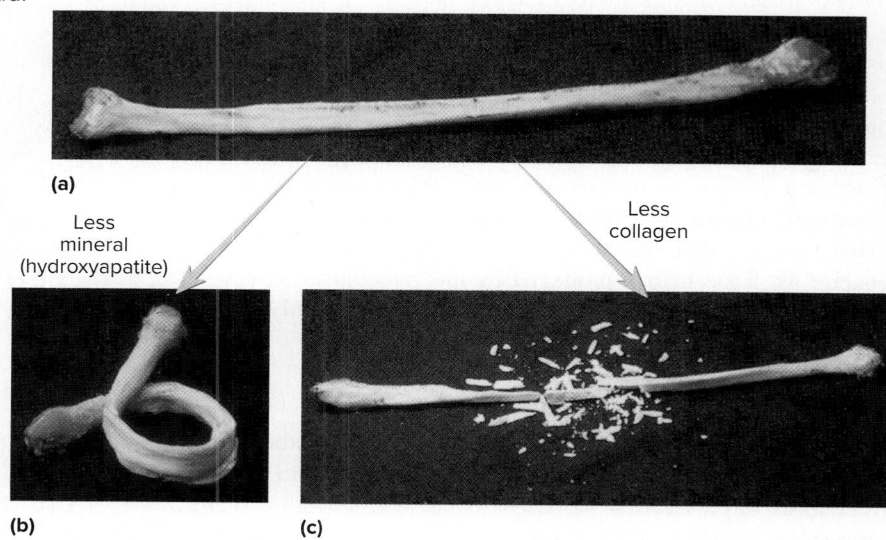

FIGURE 6.2 Effects of Changing the Bone Matrix
(*a*) Normal bone. (*b*) Demineralized bone, soaked in acid, in which collagen is the primary remaining component, can be bent without breaking. (*c*) When collagen is denatured, mineral is the primary remaining component, making the bone so brittle that it is easily shattered. Trent Stephens

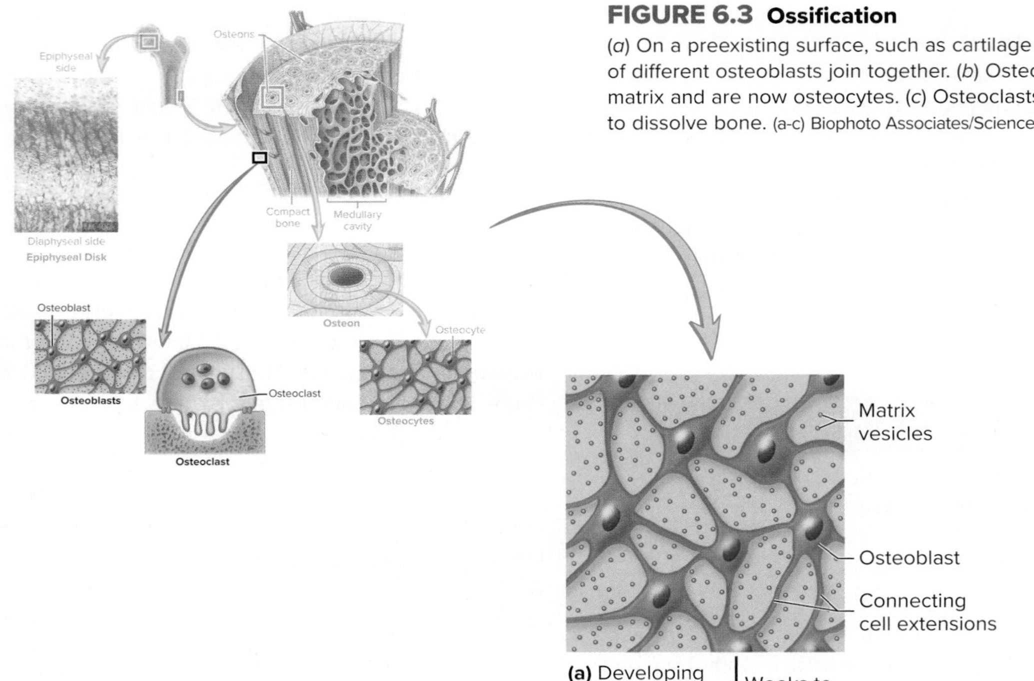

FIGURE 6.3 Ossification

(*a*) On a preexisting surface, such as cartilage or bone, the cell extensions of different osteoblasts join together. (*b*) Osteoblasts have produced bone matrix and are now osteocytes. (*c*) Osteoclasts form sealed compartments to dissolve bone. (a-c) Biophoto Associates/Science Source

(a) Developing bone

(b) Newly formed bone

Photomicrograph of an osteocyte

(c)

Osteoblasts

Osteoblasts (OS-tee-oh-blasts) are bone-building cells. These cells have an extensive endoplasmic reticulum and numerous ribosomes. Osteoblasts produce collagen and proteoglycans, which are packaged into vesicles by the Golgi apparatus and secreted by exocytosis. Osteoblasts also secrete **matrix vesicles.** Matrix vesicles contain high concentrations of Ca^{2+} and PO_4^{3-}. When the concentrations of Ca^{2+} and PO_4^{3-} reach a certain level, hydroxyapatite crystals form. The hydroxyapatite crystals act as templates that stimulate further hydroxyapatite formation and mineralization of the matrix.

The formation of new bone by osteoblasts is called **ossification** (OS-ih-fih-KAY-shun), or *osteogenesis* (OS-tee-oh-JEN-eh-sis). Ossification occurs by appositional growth on the surface of previously existing material, either bone or cartilage. For example, osteoblasts beneath the periosteum cover the surface of preexisting bone (figure 6.3*a*). Elongated cell extensions from osteoblasts connect to the cell extensions of other osteoblasts through gap junctions (see chapter 4). Bone matrix produced by the osteoblasts covers the older bone surface and surrounds the osteoblast cell bodies and extensions. The result is a new layer of bone.

Osteocytes

Just as with the chondroblast conversion to chondrocyte, osteoblasts become **osteocytes** (OS-tee-oh-sites) once the osteoblasts have secreted sufficient bone matrix (figure 6.3*b*). Osteocytes account for 90–95% of bone cells and are very long-lived, with a life span of up to 25 years. Osteocytes are connected to neighboring osteocytes through their cell extensions. Osteocytes become relatively inactive, compared with most osteoblasts, but it is possible for them to produce the components needed to maintain the bone matrix.

Osteocyte cell bodies are housed within the bone matrix in spaces called **lacunae** (la-KOO-nee). Osteocyte cell extensions are housed in narrow, long spaces called **canaliculi** (kan-ah-LIK-yoo-lye; little canals; figure 6.3*b*). In a sense, the cells and their extensions form a "mold" around which the matrix is formed. Bone differs from cartilage in that the extensions of bone cells are in contact with one another through the canaliculi. Instead of

6.4 Bone Anatomy

LEARNING OUTCOMES

After reading this section, you should be able to

A. **Classify bones according to their shape.**
B. **Label the parts of a typical long bone.**
C. **Explain the differences in structure between long bones and flat, short, and irregular bones.**

Structure of a Long Bone

A long bone is the traditional model for overall bone structure (figure 6.8; table 6.1). The **diaphysis** (die-AF-ih-sis) is the center portion of the bone. It is composed primarily of compact bone, surrounding a hollow center called the **medullary cavity.** Some spongy bone can be found lining the medullary cavity. The ends of a long bone are called **epiphyses** (eh-PIF-ih-seez; sing. epiphysis). The epiphyses are mostly spongy bone, with an outer layer of compact bone. Within joints, the end of a long bone is covered with hyaline cartilage called **articular cartilage** (figure 6.8*a,b*).

During bone formation and growth, bones develop from centers of ossification (see section 6.5). The primary ossification center is in the diaphysis. The epiphysis develops from different centers of ossification from the diaphysis. Each long bone of the arm, forearm, thigh (figure 6.8*a,b*), and leg has one or more epiphyses on each end of the bone. Each long bone of the hand and foot has one epiphysis, which is located on the proximal or distal end of the bone.

The **epiphyseal** (ep-i-FIZ-ee-al) **plate,** or *growth plate,* is located between the epiphysis and the diaphysis (figure 6.8*b*). Growth in bone length (discussed in section 6.6) occurs at the epiphyseal plate. Consequently, growth in length of the long bones of the arm, forearm, thigh, and leg occurs at both ends of the diaphysis, whereas growth in length of the hand and foot bones occurs at one end of the diaphysis. When bone stops growing in length, the epiphyseal plate becomes ossified and is called the **epiphyseal line.**

The cavities of spongy bone and the medullary cavity are filled with marrow. **Red marrow** is the site of blood cell formation, and **yellow marrow** is mostly adipose tissue. In the fetus, the spaces within bones are filled with red marrow. The conversion

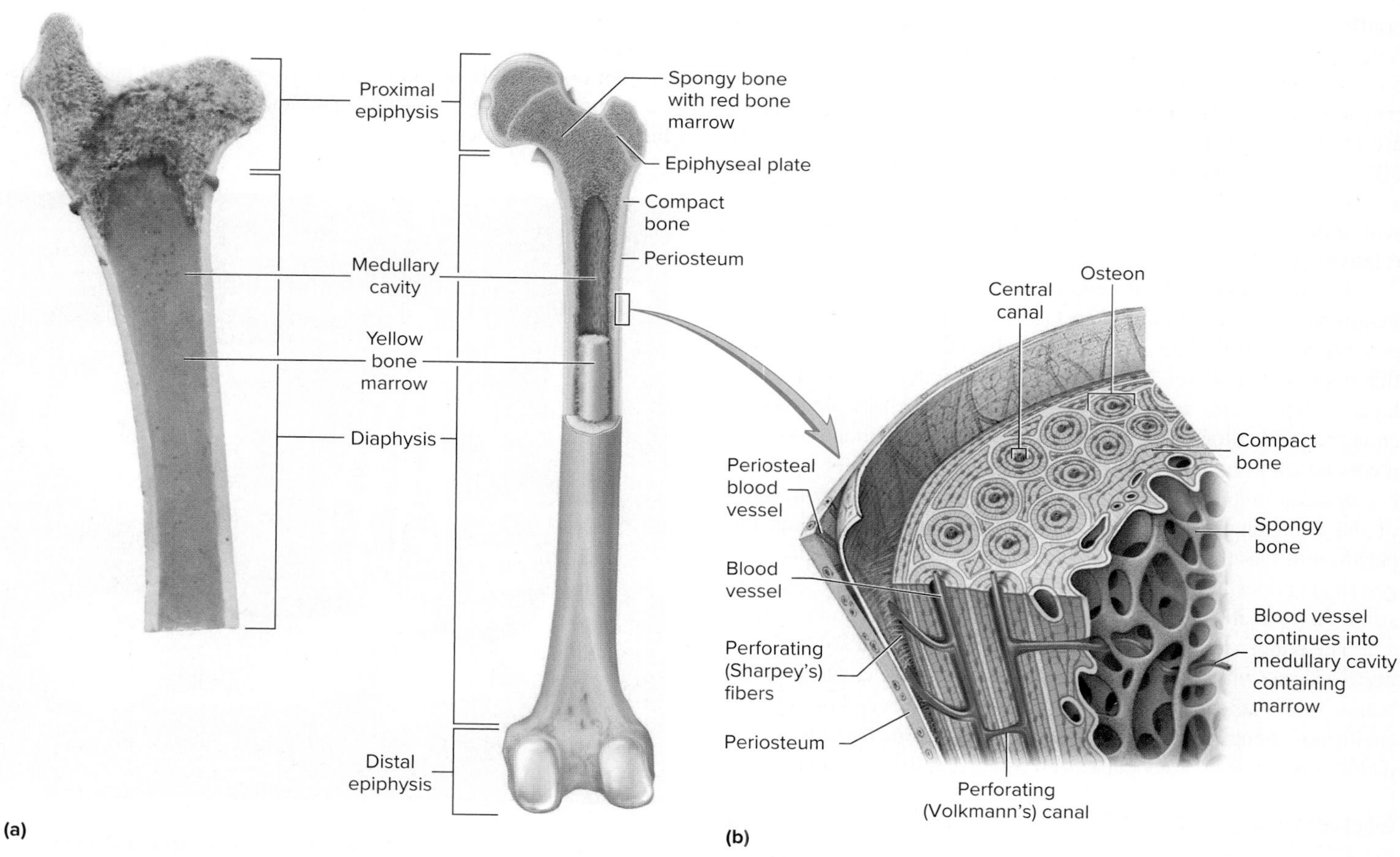

FIGURE 6.8 Long Bone

The femur (thighbone) serves as a model of the parts of a long bone. (*a*) This longitudinal section shows the location of the epiphyseal plate as well as the medullary cavity. The femur is unusual in that it has two epiphyses at its proximal end. (*b*) Detailed structure of the compact bone along the diaphysis of a long bone. (a) B Christopher/Alamy Stock Photo

TABLE 6.1 Gross Anatomy of a Long Bone

Part	Description
Diaphysis	Shaft of the bone
Epiphysis	End of the bone; develops from its own center of ossification
Periosteum	Outer, double-layered connective tissue membrane with ligaments and tendons attached to bone through the periosteum; blood vessels and nerve pathways; the periosteum is where bone grows in diameter
Endosteum	Thin connective tissue membrane lining the inner cavities of bone
Articular cartilage	Thin layer of hyaline cartilage covering a bone where it forms a joint (articulation) with another bone
Epiphyseal plate	Hyaline cartilage between the diaphysis and epiphysis; its growth allows for growth in bone length
Spongy bone	Bone having many small spaces; found mainly in the epiphysis; arranged into trabeculae
Compact bone	Dense bone with few internal spaces organized into osteons; forms the diaphysis and covers the spongy bone of the epiphyses
Medullary cavity	Large cavity within the diaphysis
Red marrow	Connective tissue in the spaces of spongy bone or in the medullary cavity; the site of blood cell production
Yellow marrow	Fat stored within the medullary cavity or in the spaces of spongy bone

of red marrow to yellow marrow begins just before birth and continues well into adulthood. Yellow marrow completely replaces the red marrow in the long bones of the limbs, except for some red marrow in the proximal part of the arm bones and thighbones. Elsewhere, varying proportions of yellow and red marrow are found. For example, part of the hipbone (ilium) may contain 50% red marrow and 50% yellow marrow. The hipbone is used as a source of donated red bone marrow because it is a large bone with more red marrow than smaller bones and it can be accessed relatively easily.

The **periosteum** (PER-ee-OSS-tee-um) is a connective tissue membrane covering the outer surface of a bone (figure 6.8*b*). The outer fibrous layer is dense irregular collagenous connective tissue that contains blood vessels and nerves. The inner layer is a single layer of bone cells, including osteoblasts, osteoclasts, and osteochondral progenitor cells (see section 6.3). Where tendons and ligaments attach to bone, the collagen fibers of the tendon or ligament become continuous with those of the periosteum. In addition, some of the collagen fibers of the tendons or ligaments penetrate the periosteum into the outer part of the bone. These bundles of collagen fibers are called **perforating fibers,** or *Sharpey fibers,* and they strengthen the attachment of the tendons or ligaments to the bone.

The **endosteum** (en-DOSS-tee-um) is a single cell layer of connective tissue that lines the internal surfaces of all cavities within bones, such as the medullary cavity of the diaphysis and the smaller cavities in spongy and compact bone (figure 6.8*b*). The endosteum includes osteoblasts, osteoclasts, and osteochondral progenitor cells.

Structure of Flat, Short, and Irregular Bones

Flat bones contain an interior framework of spongy bone sandwiched between two layers of compact bone (see figure 6.5). Short and irregular bones have a composition similar to the epiphyses of long bones—compact bone surfaces surrounding a spongy bone center with small spaces that are usually filled with marrow. Short and irregular bones are not elongated and have no diaphyses. However, certain regions of these bones, such as the processes (projections), have epiphyseal growth plates and therefore small epiphyses (figure 6.9).

Sinuses (SIGH-nus-ez) within some of the flat and irregular bones of the skull are air-filled spaces (see chapter 7). Sinuses are lined by mucous membranes.

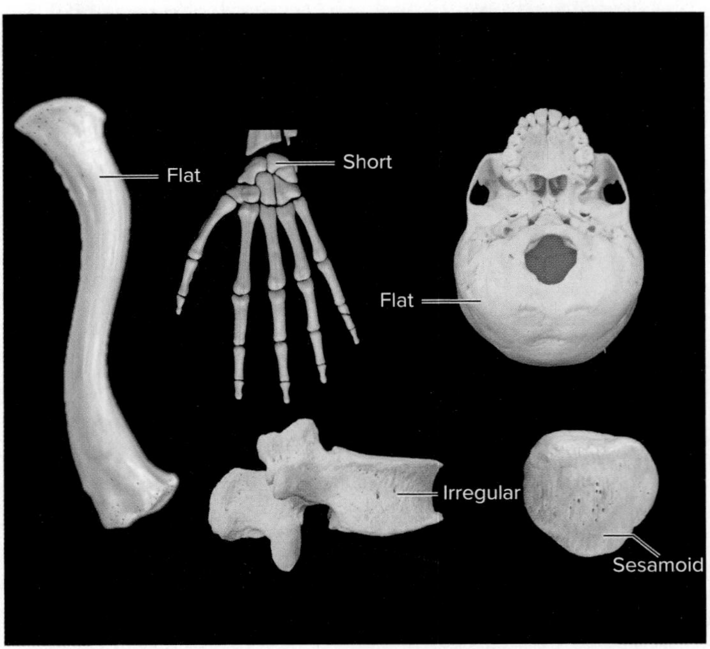

FIGURE 6.9 Structure of Flat, Short, and Irregular Bones
There are three primary bone shapes, which include flat, short, and irregular bones. There are a few examples of rounded bones, called sesamoid bones, such as the patella shown here. (a) Christine Eckel/McGraw Hill Education; (b) David Marchal/Alamy Stock Photo; (c) Christine Eckel/McGraw Hill Education; (d) Christine Eckel/McGraw Hill Education; (e) Jesada Sabai/Shutterstock

ASSESS YOUR PROGRESS

14. *List the four basic shapes of bones, and give an example of each.*
15. *Sketch and label the parts of a typical long bone.*
16. *Where are the periosteum and endosteum located, and what types of cells are found in each? What is the function of perforating (Sharpey) fibers?*
17. *What are red and yellow bone marrows? Where are they located in a child and in an adult?*
18. *Compare the structure of a long bone with those of flat, short, and irregular bones. Explain where compact and spongy bones are found in each type.*

6.5 Bone Development

LEARNING OUTCOMES

After reading this section, you should be able to

A. **Outline the process of intramembranous ossification.**
B. **Describe the steps of endochondral ossification.**
C. **List the bones, or parts of bones, that develop from each type of ossification.**

Bone formation in the fetus follows two patterns: (1) **intramembranous ossification** and (2) **endochondral ossification.** Intramembranous ossification starts within embryonic connective tissue membranes. Endochondral ossification starts with a cartilage model. No matter the type of bone formation, bone is first formed into woven bone, and is then remodeled into lamellar bone. Table 6.2 compares the two types of ossification.

Intramembranous Ossification

Many skull bones, part of the mandible (lower jaw), and the diaphyses of the clavicles (collarbones) develop by intramembranous ossification (figure 6.10). At approximately the fifth week of development in an embryo, embryonic mesenchyme condenses around the developing brain to form a membrane of connective tissue with delicate, randomly oriented collagen fibers. This membrane will eventually become cranial bones of the skull. Intramembranous ossification of the membrane begins at approximately the eighth week of embryonic development and is completed by approximately 2 years of age.

The locations in the membrane where intramembranous ossification begins are called **centers of ossification.** The centers of ossification expand to form a bone by gradually ossifying the membrane. Thus, the centers have the oldest bone, and the expanding edges the youngest bone. **Fontanels,** or soft spots, are the larger, membrane-covered spaces between the developing skull bones that have not yet been ossified (figure 6.10; see chapter 8). The bones eventually grow together, and all the fontanels

Clinical IMPACT 6.1

Cleft Lip or Palate

During fetal development, the facial bones sometimes fail to fuse with one another. A **cleft lip** results if the maxillae do not form normally, and a **cleft palate** occurs when the palatine processes of the maxillae do not fuse with one another. A cleft palate produces an opening between the nasal and oral cavities, making it difficult to eat or drink or to speak distinctly. An artificial palate may be inserted into a newborn's mouth until the palate can be repaired. A cleft lip alone, or both cleft lip and palate, occurs approximately once in every 1000 births and is more common in males. A cleft palate alone occurs approximately once in every 2000 births and is more common in females. For more information on fetal development, see chapter 29.

TABLE 6.2 Comparison of Intramembranous and Endochondral Ossification

Characteristic	Intramembranous	Endochondral
Starting material	Embryonic mesenchyme membrane	Hyaline cartilage model surrounded by a perichondrium
Periosteum formation	Osteochondral progenitor cells differentiate into osteoblasts Osteochondral progenitor cells surrounding developing bone form the periosteum	Chondrocytes hypertrophy; the cartilage calcifies and is removed Osteochondral progenitor cells differentiate into osteoblasts and secrete bony matrix Perichondrium now called periosteum
Centers of ossification	Ossification begins in centers of ossification Spongy bone formed by internal osteoblasts Compact bone formed by periosteal osteoblasts	Osteoblasts invade the calcified cartilage in centers of ossification Primary ossification centers form spongy bone in diaphysis Secondary ossification centers form spongy bone in epiphyses Compact bone formed by periosteal osteoblasts
Remodeling	Woven bone is remodeled into lamellar bone and is indistinguishable from endochondral bone.	Woven bone is remodeled into lamellar bone and is indistinguishable from intramembranous bone.

FUNDAMENTAL **Figure**

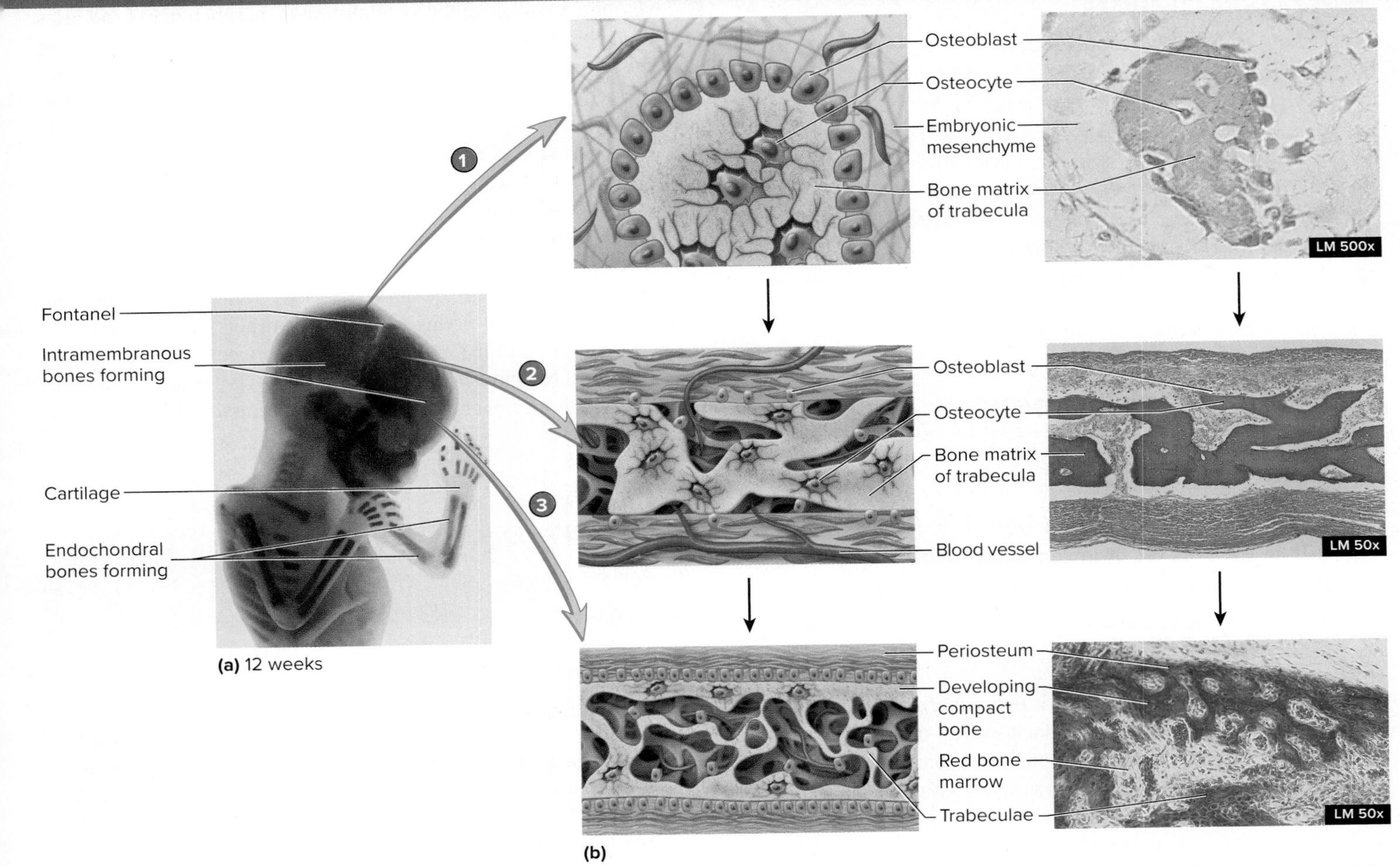

Fontanel

Intramembranous bones forming

Cartilage

Endochondral bones forming

(a) 12 weeks

Osteoblast

Osteocyte

Embryonic mesenchyme

Bone matrix of trabecula

LM 500x

Osteoblast

Osteocyte

Bone matrix of trabecula

Blood vessel

LM 50x

Periosteum

Developing compact bone

Red bone marrow

Trabeculae

LM 50x

(b)

PROCESS **Figure 6.10**

Intramembranous Ossification

(*a*) Twelve-week-old fetus showing intramembranous and endochondral ossification. Intramembranous ossification occurs at ossification centers in the flat bones of the skull. Endochondral ossification has formed bones in the diaphyses of long bones. The ends of the long bones are still cartilage at this stage of development. Therefore, the youngest bone is at the edge of the expanding bone and the oldest bone is at the center of ossification. (*b*) Steps 1–3 show intramembranous ossification of progressively older bone as the skull develops. (a) Biophoto Associates/Science Source; (b, 1) Victor Eroschenko; (b, 2) Ed Reschke/Stone/Getty Images; (b, 3) Victor Eroschenko

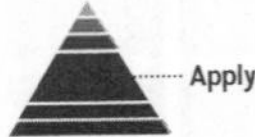

What type of cellular process is most likely the mechanism employed by osteoblasts to release bone matrix until they are surrounded by it?

have usually closed by 2 years of age. Figure 6.10 shows the steps in intramembranous ossification.

1. *Osteoblast formation:* Some embryonic mesenchymal cells in the connective tissue membrane differentiate into osteochondral progenitor cells. The osteochondral progenitor cells then form osteoblasts. The osteoblasts produce bone matrix. The bone matrix will surround the collagen fibers of the connective tissue membrane. Once they are embedded in bone matrix, the osteoblasts become osteocytes. As a result of this process, many tiny trabeculae of woven bone develop.
2. *Spongy bone formation:* Additional osteoblasts gather on the surfaces of the trabeculae and produce more bone, thereby causing the trabeculae to become larger and longer. Spongy bone forms as the trabeculae join together, resulting in an interconnected network of trabeculae separated by spaces.
3. *Compact bone formation:* Cells within the spaces of the spongy bone specialize to form red bone marrow, and cells surrounding the developing bone specialize to form the periosteum. Osteoblasts from the periosteum lay down bone matrix to form an outer surface of compact bone.

Thus, the end products of intramembranous bone formation are bones with outer compact bone surfaces and spongy centers (see figure 6.5). Remodeling converts woven bone to lamellar bone and contributes to the final shape of the bone.

Endochondral Ossification

The formation of cartilage begins at approximately the end of the fourth week of embryonic development. Endochondral

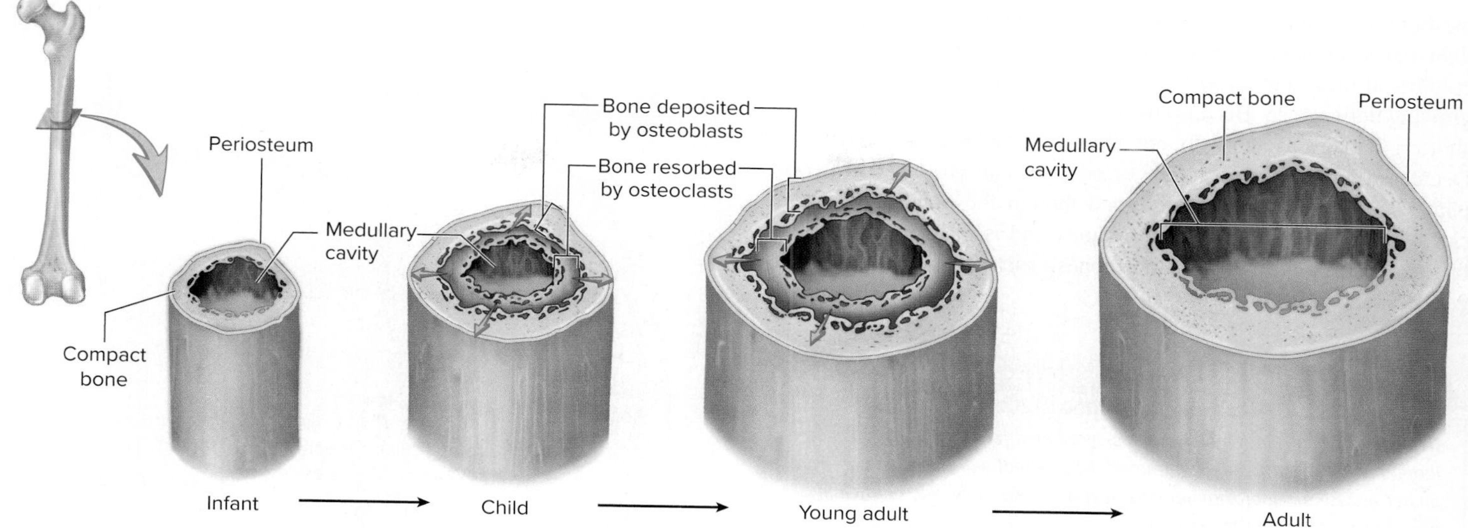

FIGURE 6.14 Bone Growth in Width
Bones can increase in width by the formation of new bone beneath the periosteum. APR

Insufficient vitamin D in children causes **rickets,** a disease resulting from reduced mineralization of the bone matrix. Children with rickets may have bowed bones and inflamed joints. During the winter in northern climates, children who are not exposed to sufficient sunlight can take supplementary vitamin D to prevent rickets. The body's inability to absorb lipids in which vitamin D is soluble can also result in vitamin D deficiency. This condition sometimes occurs in adults who have digestive disorders. Low vitamin D levels can be one cause of "adult rickets," or **osteomalacia** (OS-tee-oh-mah-LAY-shee-ah), a softening of the bones due to calcium depletion.

Vitamin C is necessary for osteoblasts to synthesize collagen. Normally, as old collagen breaks down, new collagen is synthesized to replace it. Vitamin C deficiency results in bones and cartilage with fewer collagen fibers because collagen synthesis is impaired. In children, vitamin C deficiency can retard growth. In both children and adults, vitamin C deficiency can result in **scurvy,** which is marked by ulceration and hemorrhage in almost any area of the body because normal collagen synthesis is not occurring in connective tissues. Wound healing, which requires collagen synthesis, is hindered in patients with vitamin C deficiency. In extreme cases, the teeth fall out because the ligaments that hold them in place break down.

Hormones

Hormones are very important in bone growth. **Growth hormone** from the anterior pituitary increases general tissue growth (see chapters 17 and 18), including overall bone growth, by stimulating interstitial cartilage growth and appositional bone growth. Disruptions in normal growth hormone can cause dramatic changes in an individual's height. Excessive growth hormone secretion results in pituitary gigantism, whereas insufficient growth hormone secretion results in pituitary dwarfism (figure 6.15). **Thyroid hormones** are also required for normal growth of all tissues, including cartilage; therefore, a decrease in this hormone can result in a smaller individual. **Reproductive hormones** also regulate bone growth. Estrogen is the primary female reproductive hormone and testosterone is the primary male reproductive hormone. During puberty, the levels of these hormones increase dramatically. The increased hormone levels stimulate significant growth spurts in the beginning. Toward the end of puberty, both estrogen and testosterone stop bone growth. They both cause

FIGURE 6.15 Effect of Growth Hormone on Stature
The taller man (giant) has excessive growth hormone secretion, whereas the shorter man (dwarf) has insufficient growth hormone secretion.
Hulton Archive/Getty Images

ossification of epiphyseal plates. Females usually stop growing earlier than males, around age 18. Estrogens are more effective at closing the epiphyseal plate than testosterone is. Males can potentially continue growing until age 25. Because their entire growth period is somewhat shorter, females usually do not reach the same height as males. Decreased levels of testosterone or estrogen can prolong the growth phase of the epiphyseal plates, even though the bones grow more slowly. Overall, growth is very complex and is influenced by many factors besides reproductive hormones, such as other hormones, genetics, and nutrition.

Predict 7

Nellie is a 12-year-old female who has an adrenal tumor that is producing a large amount of estrogen. If untreated, what effect will this condition have on her growth for approximately the next 6 months? How will her height have been affected by the time she is 18?

ASSESS YOUR PROGRESS

23. *Name and describe the events occurring in the four zones of the epiphyseal plate. Explain how the epiphyseal plate remains the same thickness while the bone increases in length.*
24. *Explain the process of growth at the articular cartilage. What happens to the epiphyseal plate and the articular cartilage when bone growth ceases?*
25. *Describe how new osteons are produced as a bone increases in width.*
26. *Explain how illness or malnutrition can affect bone growth. How do vitamins D and C affect bone growth?*
27. *Bone growth is greatly affected by growth hormone and thyroid hormone. Explain these effects.*
28. *How do estrogen and testosterone affect bone growth? How do these effects account for the average height difference observed in men and women?*

6.7 Bone Remodeling

LEARNING OUTCOMES

After reading this section, you should be able to

A. **Explain the need for bone remodeling, particularly in long bones.**
B. **Describe the role of a basic multicellular unit (BMU) in the remodeling process.**
C. **Discuss how mechanical stress affects bone remodeling and bone strength.**

Just as our homes must be remodeled when they fall into disrepair, bone that becomes old is replaced with new bone in a process called **bone remodeling.** In this process, osteoclasts remove old bone and osteoblasts deposit new bone. Bone remodeling converts woven bone into lamellar bone and is involved in several important functions, including bone growth, changes in bone shape, adjustment of the bone to stress, bone repair, and calcium ion (Ca^{2+}) regulation in the body.

The structure of a long bone—a hollow cylinder with a medullary cavity in the center—has two mechanical advantages: (1) A hollow cylinder is lighter in weight than a solid rod and (2) a hollow cylinder with the same height, weight, and composition as a solid rod, but with a greater diameter, can support much more weight without bending. As a long bone increases in length and diameter, the size of the medullary cavity also increases (figure 6.16), keeping the bone from becoming very heavy. In addition, as the bone grows in diameter, the relative thickness of compact bone is maintained as osteoclasts remove bone on the inside and osteoblasts add bone to the outside.

Bone remodeling involves a **basic multicellular unit (BMU).** A BMU is a temporary assembly of osteoclasts and osteoblasts that travels through or across the surface of bone. These cells remove old bone matrix and replace it with new bone matrix. The

PROCESS **Figure**

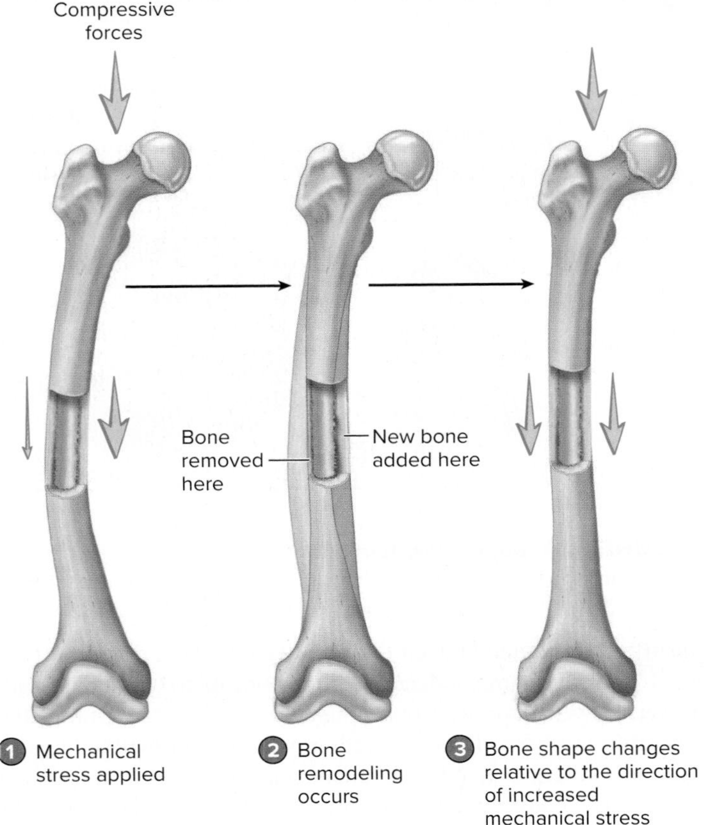

PROCESS **Figure 6.16**

Remodeling of a Long Bone

Stimulation of osteoblasts, such as during maturation or with increased mechanical stimuli, increases the amount of bone present.

Under conditions of reduced mechanical stress, such as when a person is bedridden or paralyzed, their bones experience a loss in density. Predict the activity of the osteoblasts in these conditions.

average life span of a BMU is approximately 6 months, and BMU activity renews the entire skeleton every 10 years. In compact bone, the osteoclasts of a BMU break down bone matrix, forming a tunnel. Interstitial lamellae (see figure 6.7*a*) are remnants of osteons that were not completely removed when a BMU formed a tunnel. Blood vessels grow into the tunnel, and osteoblasts of the BMU move in and lay down a layer of bone on the tunnel wall, forming a concentric lamella. Additional concentric lamellae are produced, filling in the tunnel from the outside to the inside, until an osteon is formed, with the center of the tunnel becoming a central canal containing blood vessels. In spongy bone, the BMU removes bone matrix from the surface of a trabecula, forming a cavity, which the BMU then fills in with new bone matrix.

Mechanical Stress and Bone Strength

The amount of mechanical stress, such as when weightlifting, applied to a bone can modify the bone's strength. This modification occurs through several mechanisms including (1) remodeling, (2) the formation of additional bone, or (3) alteration in trabecular alignment to reinforce the scaffolding. Figure 6.16 shows the steps in bone remodeling.

1. Mechanical stress, such as starting a weight-lifting program, applied to bone increases osteoblast activity in bone tissue.
2. In addition, increased physical pressure in bone initiates electrical changes that stimulate osteoblast activity. Therefore, applying weight (pressure) to a broken bone can speed the healing process. Weak pulses of electric current are sometimes applied to a broken bone to speed healing.
3. Bone becomes thicker and has more strength upon being exposed to greater mechanical stimuli.

Under conditions of reduced stress, as when a person is bedridden or paralyzed, osteoclast activity continues at a nearly normal rate but osteoblast activity decreases, resulting in less bone density.

ASSESS YOUR PROGRESS

29. *Why is it important for bone remodeling to occur?*
30. *What is a basic multicellular unit (BMU)? Explain how a BMU directs remodeling in compact bone and in spongy bone.*
31. *How does bone adjust to mechanical stress? Describe the roles of osteoblasts and osteoclasts in this process. What happens to bone that is not subject to mechanical stress?*

6.8 Bone Fracture Classification and Repair

LEARNING OUTCOMES

After reading this section, you should be able to

A. **List the main bone fracture types.**
B. **List the characteristics of bone fracture types.**
C. **Outline and explain the steps in bone repair.**

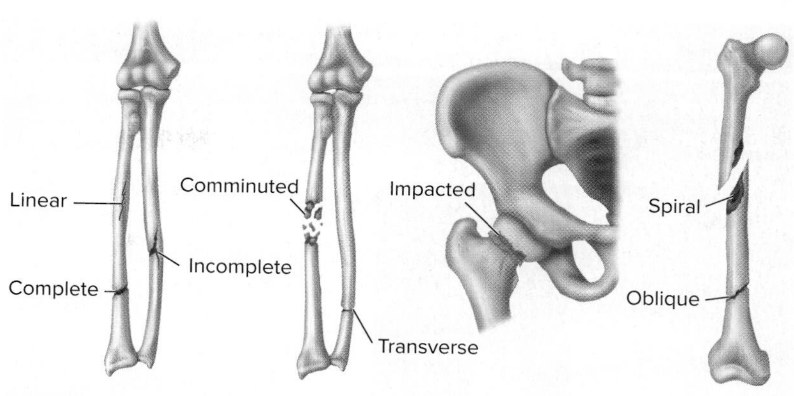

FIGURE 6.17 Types of Bone Fractures

Bone Fracture Classification

Classification of bone fractures is surprisingly complex. There are five main categories of bone fractures discussed in this text: (1) mechanism of fracture, (2) soft-tissue damage, (3) displacement vs. nondisplacement, (4) fracture pattern, and (5) number of fragments in the fractured bone (figure 6.17). Table 6.3 contains representative x-ray images of several categories of fractures.

Mechanism of Fracture

The first criterion for bone fracture type falls under the category of the mechanism by which the fracture occurred. There are three primary ways fractures can occur: (1) through a trauma to the bone (traumatic), (2) through a pathology (disease) of the bone (pathologic), or (3) at a location of an implant on the bone (periprosthetic).

Soft-Tissue Damage

The next criterion by which bone fractures are classified is by the amount of soft-tissue damage. There are two main types: (1) Closed (stable or simple): In a closed fracture, there is no visible damage to the skin at the injury site. (2) Open (compound): In an open fracture, there is visible damage to the skin at the trauma site, possibly including a fragment of the fractured bone protruding from the skin.

Displaced vs. Nondisplaced

Two possibilities exist for the position of the fractured bone ends after the fracture has occurred: (1) displaced, where the ends of the bones are offset from each other and are not aligned anatomically, and (2) nondisplaced, where the ends of the bone remain in anatomical alignment.

Fracture Pattern

This classification is based on the pattern of the fracture on the bone. These include:

1. Linear Fracture—runs parallel to the length of the bone
2. Spiral Fracture—results from twisting of one part of the bone
3. Avulsion Fracture—separation of a bone fragment from the rest of the bone
4. Stress (hairline) Fracture—incomplete fracture resulting from overuse of the bone

TABLE 6.3 Types of Bone Fractures

Type of Fracture	Images	Characteristics	Possible Locations	Possible Causes	Treatments
Open Fracture	Prakaymas vitchitchalao/Alamy Stock Photo	End of fractured bone protrudes through open wound in skin; increases risk of infection	Phalanges of fingers, tibia, distal radius are most common	Falls from standing height, automobile accidents	Therapeutic irrigation and wound debridement; treatment with antibiotics followed by surgical intervention for internal or external fixation of the bone
Displaced Fracture	MossStudio/Shutterstock	Ends of fractured bone move so that they are no longer aligned; more painful than other fracture types and may cause internal damage from the bone ends	Surgical neck of humerus, radius and ulna, tibia and fibula	Hard blow, falls, or other trauma	Reduction of the broken bones ("set" the bones); splinting for a day or two followed by immobilization with a cast for 4–6 weeks
Spiral Fracture	Sutthaburawonk/Getty Images	A helical fracture from twisting of the bone	Tibia, humerus	Common in snow skiers whose feet and ankles are locked into ski boots	Immobilization with a cast for 4–6 weeks
Comminuted Fracture	Robert Destefano/Alamy Stock Photo	Results in at least three bone fragments	Tibia, radius, ulna	Occurs in patients with weakened bones or from a severe accident	Often necessary to surgically place a pin in the bone followed by immobilization in a cast for 4–6 weeks
Greenstick Fracture	Scott Camazine/Alamy Stock Photo	Fracture with break on one side and bend on the other side of bone	Typical in young children due to increased collagen percentage in bone	Falls, motor vehicle accidents	Immobilization with a cast or splint for 4–6 weeks

PROCESS **Figure**

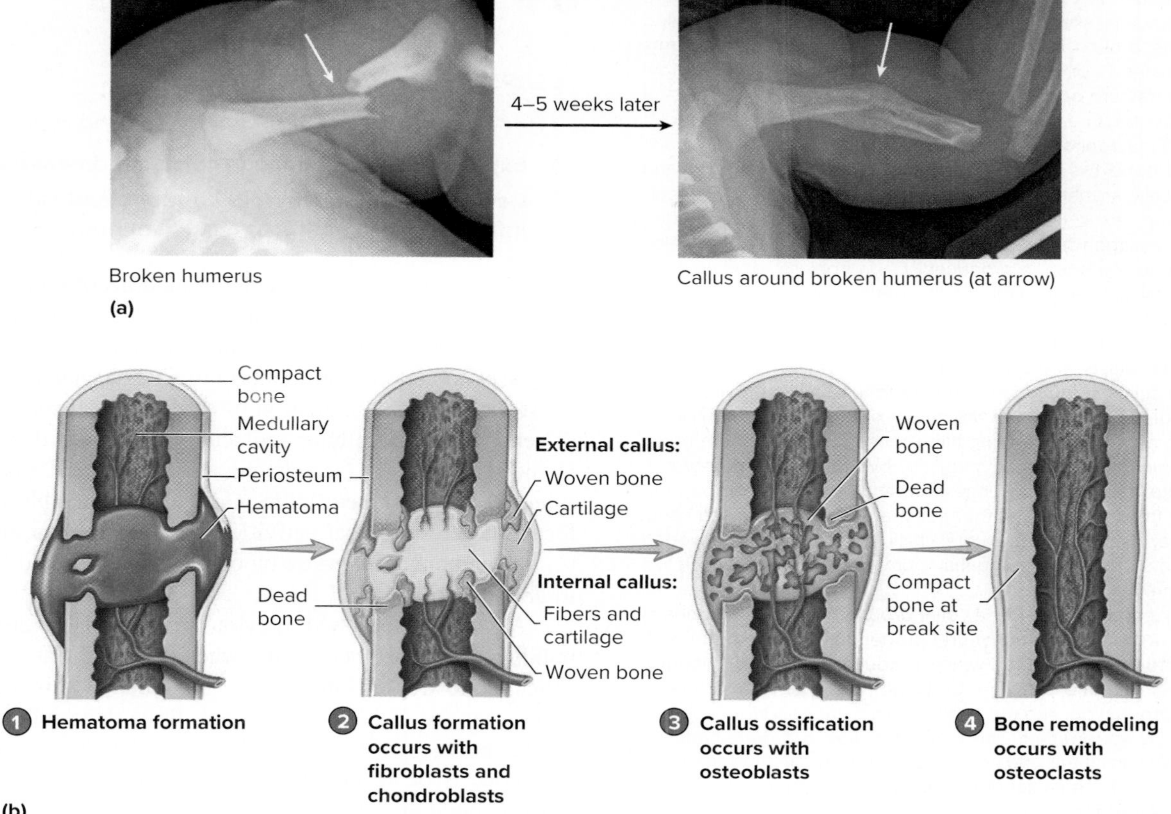

PROCESS **Figure 6.18**

Bone Repair

(*a*) On the top is a radiograph of the broken humerus of author A. Russo's granddaughter, Viviana. On the bottom is the same humerus a few weeks later, with a callus now formed around the break. (*b*) The steps in bone repair. (a,1-2) Andrew F. Russo

Suppose an astronaut who currently lives in the International Space Station fractured a bone. The doctor in the space station told her to expect bone repair to take 8 weeks. If the astronaut experienced the same bone fracture while living on Earth, do you think the expected bone repair time would be shorter or longer than 8 weeks?

5. Compression Fracture—the bone collapses; common in spongy bone, often due to weakening of the bone such as in osteoporosis

Number and Arrangement of Bone Fragments

Fractures are categorized by the completeness of the break and its alignment relative to the bone. This category includes:

1. Incomplete Fracture—a fracture that traverses only part of the bone
2. Complete Fracture—a fracture that completely separates the bone into at least two fragments
3. Comminuted Fracture—a fracture where the bone breaks into multiple fragments

Age-Specific

Some fracture types occur mainly in children because their bones contain more organic matrix relative to inorganic matrix. These include (1) greenstick fractures, where only one side of the bone breaks and the opposite side just bends (such as when trying to break a green branch from a tree), and (2) epiphyseal fractures, where the epiphysis separates from the diaphysis within the epiphyseal plate. These can result in differing lengths of adult bones due to uneven growth of the two limbs.

Bone Repair

Bone is a living tissue that can undergo repair if it is damaged (figure 6.18*a*). Figure 6.18*b* shows the four major steps in bone repair.

1 *Hematoma formation.* A **hematoma** (hee-mah-TOH-mah) is a localized mass of blood released from blood vessels but confined within an organ or a space. When a bone is fractured, the blood vessels in the bone and surrounding periosteum are damaged and a hematoma forms. Usually, the blood in a hematoma forms a clot, which consists of fibrous proteins that stop the bleeding. Disruption of blood vessels in the central canals results in inadequate blood delivery to osteocytes, and bone tissue adjacent to the fracture site dies. Tissues around the bone often become inflamed and swollen following the injury.

2. *Callus formation.* A **callus** (KAL-us) is a mass of bone tissue that forms at a fracture site. An **external callus** encircles the break and connects the broken ends of the bone. An **internal callus** forms *between* the ends of the broken bone, as well as in the marrow cavity if the fracture occurs in the diaphysis of a long bone. Several days after the fracture, blood vessels grow into the clot. As the clot dissolves, (1) macrophages clean up cell debris, (2) osteoclasts break down dead bone tissue, and (3) fibroblasts produce collagen and other extracellular materials to form granulation tissue, the precursor to healed tissue (see chapter 4). As the fibroblasts continue to produce collagen fibers, a denser fibrous network, which helps hold the bone together, is produced. Chondroblasts derived from osteochondral progenitor cells of the periosteum and endosteum begin to produce cartilage in the fibrous network. As these events are occurring, osteochondral progenitor cells in the endosteum become osteoblasts and produce new bone, which contributes to the internal callus. If formation of the internal callus is prevented by infection, bone movements, or the nature of the injury, the two ends of the bone do not rejoin—a condition called nonunion of the bone. This condition can be treated surgically by implanting an appropriate substrate, such as living bone from another site in the body or dead bone from a cadaver. Other substrates have also been used. For example, a specific marine coral calcium phosphate is converted into a predominantly hydroxyapatite biomatrix that is very much like spongy bone.

   The external callus forms a collar *around* the opposing ends of the bone fragments. Osteochondral progenitor cells from the periosteum become osteoblasts, which produce bone, and chondroblasts, which produce cartilage. Cartilage production is more rapid than bone production, and the cartilage from each side of the break eventually grows together. The external callus is a bone-cartilage collar that stabilizes the ends of the broken bone. In modern medical practice, applying a cast or surgically implanting metal supports can help stabilize the bone.

3. *Callus ossification.* Like the cartilage models formed during fetal development, the cartilage in the external callus is replaced by woven spongy bone through endochondral ossification. The result is a stronger external callus. Even as the internal callus is forming and replacing the hematoma, osteoblasts from the periosteum and endosteum enter the internal callus and begin to produce bone. Eventually, the fibers and cartilage of the internal callus are replaced by woven spongy bone, which further stabilizes the broken bone.

4. *Bone remodeling.* Filling the gap between bone fragments with an internal callus of woven bone is not the end of the repair process because woven bone is not as structurally strong as the original lamellar bone. Repair is complete only when the woven bone of the internal callus and the dead bone adjacent to the fracture site have been replaced by compact bone. In this compact bone, osteons from both sides of the break extend across the fracture line to "peg" the bone fragments together. This remodeling process takes time—as much as a year or more. As the internal callus is remodeled and becomes stronger, the external callus is reduced in size by osteoclast activity. Eventually, repair may be so complete that no evidence of the break remains; however, the repaired zone usually remains slightly thicker than the adjacent bone. If the fracture has occurred in the diaphysis of a long bone, remodeling also restores the medullary cavity.

ASSESS YOUR PROGRESS

32. *What are the four steps of bone repair?*

33. *How does breaking a bone result in hematoma formation?*

34. *Distinguish between the location and composition of the internal callus and those of the external callus.*

35. *Why is remodeling of the ossified callus necessary?*

6.9 Calcium Homeostasis

LEARNING OUTCOMES

After reading this section, you should be able to

A. **Explain the role of bone in calcium homeostasis.**

B. **Describe how parathyroid hormone and calcitonin influence bone health and calcium homeostasis.**

One of the most underappreciated functions of bone is Ca^{2+} storage. Calcium is an important physiological regulator of many processes required to achieve and maintain homeostasis. These processes include (1) stimulation of skeletal muscle contraction, (2) stimulation and regulation of cardiac muscle contraction, and (3) exocytosis of cellular molecules, including those important for neural signaling (see chapters 9, 11, and 20). Osteoclast and osteoblast activity determines Ca^{2+} levels available in the blood for these physiological activities. These cells can either release Ca^{2+} from bone to *increase* blood Ca^{2+} levels or add Ca^{2+} to bone to *decrease* blood Ca^{2+} levels.

As we've discussed previously, osteoblasts are the bone-building cells. In other words, when they add Ca^{2+} to bone, it is called **bone deposition.** You might think of this as "making a deposit" in the Ca^{2+} "bank" (bone). Bone deposition is necessary during bone growth, repair, and remodeling—processes where new bone is being produced. Osteoblasts remove Ca^{2+} from the blood to build the new bone, which decreases blood Ca^{2+} levels. In contrast, osteoclasts are the "bone-destroying" cells; they remove Ca^{2+} from bone, which, you may remember, is called **bone reabsorption.** You might think of this as "making a withdrawal" from the Ca^{2+} "bank." Bone reabsorption occurs when bone is broken down, which increases blood Ca^{2+} levels. This is also important during bone growth, repair, and remodeling, but can also be activated simply when Ca^{2+} is needed elsewhere. If bone reabsorption occurred for an abnormal length of time, bone would become overly demineralized and weak. This can be seen in conditions such as osteomalacia and osteoporosis. Think back to the activity at the beginning of this chapter with the chicken bone soaking in vinegar. The vinegar causes demineralization of the bone and it becomes rubbery. Osteoclast and osteoblast activity is regulated by hormones to achieve homeostasis. If blood Ca^{2+} levels are too low, osteoclast activity is stimulated. On the other hand, if blood Ca^{2+} levels are too high, osteoclast activity is inhibited. Manipulation of these hormones is a common action of medications used to slow the progression of osteoporosis.

Calcium homeostasis is regulated by three hormones (chemical messengers delivered via the blood): (1) parathyroid hormone (PTH); (2) calcitriol, a biologically active form of vitamin D_3; and (3) calcitonin (table 6.4).

Parathyroid Hormone

Parathyroid hormone is secreted by cells in the parathyroid gland and is essential for the maintenance of blood Ca^{2+} levels within the homeostatic limits. PTH production and secretion are controlled by Ca^{2+}-sensing receptors in the parathyroid

TABLE **6.4** **Hormonal Regulation of Calcium Homeostasis**

Hormone	Site of Action	Hormonal Action
PTH	Kidney tubules Bone cells	Activate calcitriol ↑ Blood Ca^{2+} levels
Calcitriol	Kidney tubules Small intestine Bone cells	↑ Blood Ca^{2+} levels
Calcitonin	Bone cells	↓ Blood Ca^{2+} levels

gland. The key signal for PTH secretion is a reduction in blood Ca^{2+} levels (see figure 18.11). PTH works through two general mechanisms: (1) direct effects on bone cells and in the kidney and (2) indirect effects on the small intestine.

1. Direct Effects of PTH
   a. Bone Cells
   PTH increases blood Ca^{2+} levels by exerting direct regulatory control of osteoblasts and osteocytes to increase formation and activation of osteoclasts, the principal bone-reabsorbing cells. Recall from section 6.3 that osteoblasts produce factors that induce development of osteoclasts.

   Specifically, the membranes of osteoblasts and osteocytes express a regulatory molecule called **receptor activator of nuclear factor kappaβ ligand (RANKL).** RANKL exists in two forms: (1) membrane-bound and (2) soluble; however, it is the soluble form of RANKL that is more potent in triggering osteoclast formation. RANKL belongs to a family of inflammatory signals called cytokines (see chapter 22). Additionally, it has been demonstrated that RANKL production and function are regulated by molecules called *toll-like receptors (TLRs).* TLRs are membrane-bound proteins found in immune cells such as macrophages that recognize microbe-specific molecules (see chapter 22). Understanding these interrelationships becomes very significant when you remember that osteoclasts are derived from the same precursor cells as macrophages. It is interactions between TLRs and RANKL that are linked to the mechanisms governing the pathology of bacteria-driven bone loss in diseases such as osteomyelitis and periodontal disease in the oral cavity (see Microbes in Your Body: "Disruption of Bone Homeostasis by Bacteria").

   RANKL binds to its receptor to activate differentiation of precursor cells into active osteoclasts. The receptor for RANKL is called **receptor activator of nuclear factor kappaβ (RANK).** RANK is located in the plasma membrane of both undifferentiated and differentiated osteoclasts. RANKL also stimulates mature osteoclasts to begin bone reabsorption.

   PTH stimulates synthesis and secretion of RANKL by osteoblasts and osteocytes, which in turn activates osteoclasts. It is through the stimulation of RANKL that PTH exerts its direct effects. Further, PTH increases blood Ca^{2+} levels by continuing to stimulate osteoclast formation. Normally, a RANKL decoy receptor, called **osteoprotegerin** (OS-tee-oh-proh-TEJ-er-in; **OPG**), prevents osteoclast differentiation. OPG does this by blocking RANKL from binding to RANK. This system helps keep the number of osteoclasts in check and prevents overdestruction of bone. However, if blood Ca^{2+} levels are too low, PTH can override the function of OPG. PTH does so by inhibiting the secretion of OPG by osteoblasts and osteocytes. Without OPG, the number of activated osteoclasts can continue to increase. It is the balance between the levels of RANKL and OPG that regulates active osteoclast formation.

   It is interesting to note that PTH has been found to also promote bone deposition. Although contradictory to PTH's known bone reabsorption function, giving patients PTH intermittently rather than continuously helps prevent osteoporosis (bone demineralization) from progressing. However, the exact mechanism for PTH stimulation of bone formation is yet unclear. This information may help you answer this chapter's Learn to Predict question.

   b. Kidney Tubules
   PTH stimulates the reabsorption of Ca^{2+} from urine in the kidney tubules, which reduces the amount of Ca^{2+} excreted in the urine.
2. Indirect Effects of PTH in the Small Intestine
   PTH promotes the activation of calcitriol in the kidneys. Calcitriol increases absorption of Ca^{2+} in the small intestine. Thus, PTH indirectly increases Ca^{2+} uptake from the small intestine via calcitriol (figure 6.19).

Calcitriol

Calcitriol increases blood Ca^{2+} levels. It is a steroid hormone derived from vitamin D_3. Recall from chapter 5 that vitamin D_3 production is initiated in the skin and continued in the liver and then in the kidney, where calcitriol activation occurs. PTH stimulates calcitriol activation in the kidney, which contributes to PTH-induced increases in blood Ca^{2+} levels. In addition to calcitriol stimulating intestinal Ca^{2+} absorption, it is one of the most potent stimulators of RANKL production by osteoblasts. Thus, calcitriol and PTH work together to increase osteoclast activity for bone reabsorption. In addition, calcitriol assists PTH in the kidney tubules by preventing Ca^{2+} removal through urine. These actions of calcitriol increase blood Ca^{2+} levels.

Calcitonin

Calcitonin (KAL-si-TOH-nin) is secreted from C cells in the thyroid gland when blood Ca^{2+} levels are too high (see figure 18.8). Calcitonin rapidly lowers blood Ca^{2+} levels by inhibiting osteoclast activity (figure 6.19). However, the exact role of calcitonin, especially in adult bone remodeling, is still under investigation. PTH and calcitonin are described more fully in chapters 18 and 27.

FUNDAMENTAL **Figure**

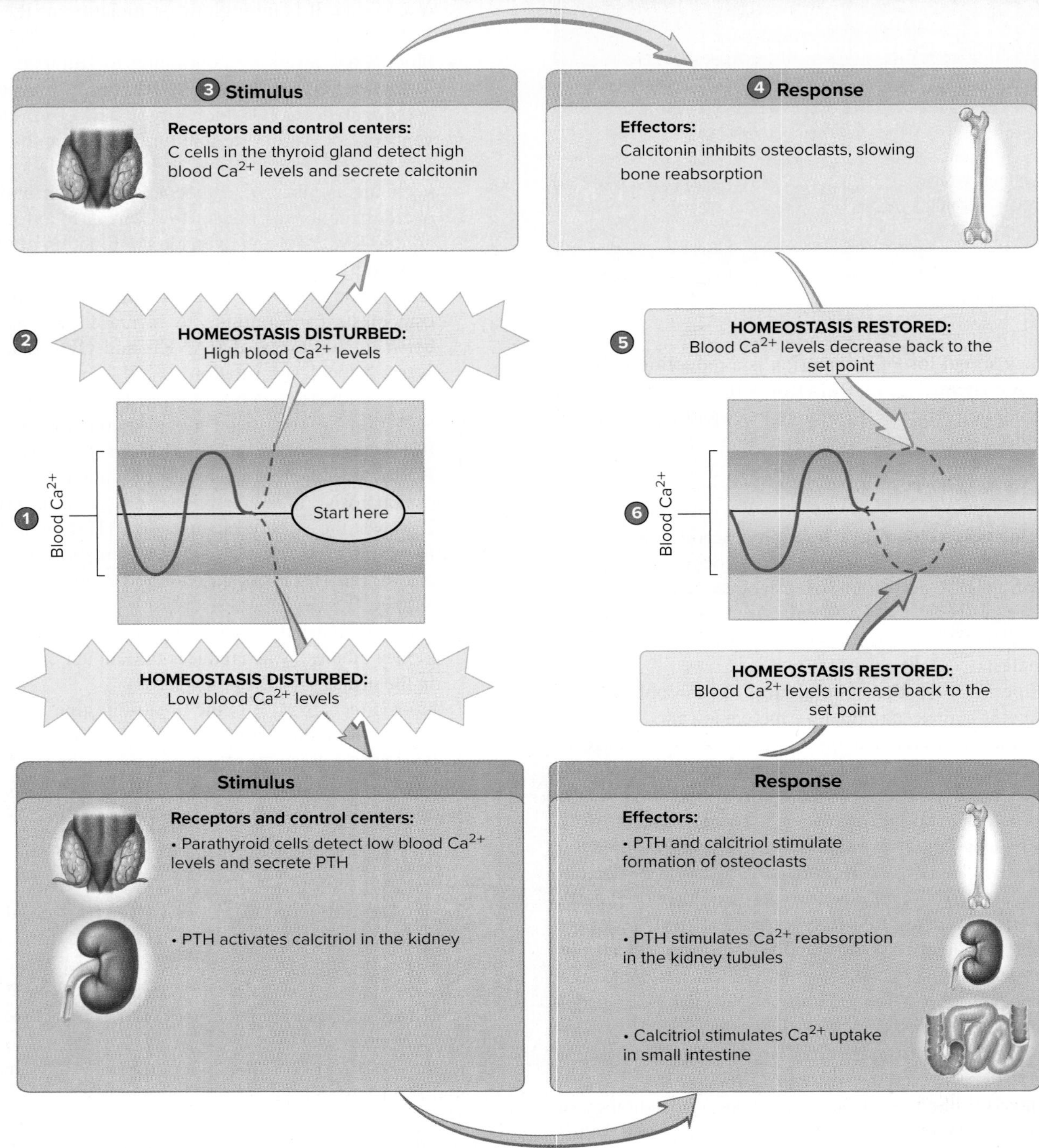

HOMEOSTASIS FIGURE 6.19 Regulation of Blood Ca^{2+} Levels

(1) Blood Ca^{2+} levels are in the normal range. (2) Blood Ca^{2+} levels increase outside their normal range, which causes homeostasis to be disturbed. (3) The control centers respond to the change in blood levels. (4) The control center releases calcitonin, which inhibits osteoclasts. (5) Reduced osteoclast activity causes blood Ca^{2+} levels to decrease. (6) Ca^{2+} levels return to their normal range and homeostasis is restored. Observe the responses to a decrease in blood Ca^{2+} levels outside the normal range by following the lower, *pink arrows*.

ASSESS YOUR PROGRESS

36. *How is calcium moved into and out of bone? What happens in bone when blood calcium levels decrease? When blood calcium levels increase?*

37. *Name the hormone that is the major regulator of Ca^{2+} levels in the body. What stimulates the secretion of this hormone?*

38. *Describe how PTH controls the number of osteoclasts. What are the effects of PTH on the formation of calcitriol, Ca^{2+} uptake in the small intestine, and reabsorption of Ca^{2+} from the urine?*

39. *What stimulates calcitonin secretion? How does calcitonin affect osteoclast activity?*

MICROBES In Your Body 6.1 Disruption of Bone Homeostasis by Bacteria

Osteomyelitis is a bacterial infection in bone. Usually, the aggressive pathogen *Staphylococcus aureus* is the causative organism. This bacterium is more commonly found on our skin but can move into bone in three major ways: (1) The bacterium spreads to the bone through the bloodstream from another infected location in the body, such as an abscessed tooth; (2) it penetrates the bone through an open wound on the skin, which may occur in severe cases of diabetes; and (3) it is introduced into a joint or bone during surgery—for example, while putting a pin in a broken bone. Once bacteria are in the bone, their presence induces a severe inflammatory response, which is then followed by progressive bone loss. Unfortunately, osteomyelitis can be difficult to treat. This difficulty is due to the bacteria simultaneously initiating three responses in the bone, which together result in devastating bone loss. These responses are (1) increased development of osteoclasts, (2) stimulation of the secretion of inflammation-causing chemicals, and (3) disruption of the chemical signaling between osteoblasts and osteoclasts.

In order to understand how these three responses are activated, we need a brief overview of interactions between pathogens and immune cells. For a more detailed description, see Microbes in Your Body 22.1. Bacterial cell walls possess unique combinations of marker proteins (see chapter 3) that our immune cells recognize and respond to. Our immune cells use cell membrane receptors to bind the marker proteins. As it turns out, both osteoblasts and osteoclasts have these receptors, called toll-like receptors (TLRs). This is not too surprising when you recall that both cell types are formed from the same precursor cells that form certain immune cells. Because of this, bacteria can induce bone cells to produce chemicals that damage the bone. During infection, osteoblasts are co-opted to overactivate osteoclasts, the bone-destroying cells. However, the exact mechanism underlying the induction of osteoclasts and TLRs has not yet been fully elucidated.

S. aureus cell walls contain a certain cell marker that alters signaling dynamics in such a way that the production of osteoclasts increases but the production of osteoblasts decreases. Bacterial infection prevents normal functioning of the bone-forming osteoblasts.

Thus, osteoclast bone reabsorption occurs without inhibition, while the osteoblast apoptosis decreases the amount of new bone formation. Osteoblast-specific secretion of pro-inflammatory chemicals directly damages bone and stimulates osteoclast formation. The final result is that although the host's immune response is designed to remove the infection, it results in massive damage of the host's own tissues.

The most common treatment for osteomyelitis is a 4- to 8-week course of antibiotics. The doctor may prescribe intravenous dosing with the antibiotics; thus, patients are often fitted with a peripherally inserted central catheter (PICC) line. If the infection persists, it may be necessary to perform surgery in which the infected tissue is removed, in a process called debridement. In cases of severe tissue damage, a bone graft is necessary. Fortunately, the incidence of osteomyelitis is low, 2 in 10,000 people, and the majority of osteomyelitis cases are successfully resolved.

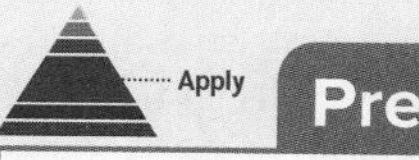

Predict 8

In addition to targeting the bacteria for death, what is one theoretical medical approach that could help reduce the amount of bone loss during osteomyelitis?

Case STUDY 6.1 Bone Density

Henry is a 65-year-old man who was admitted to the emergency room after a fall. A radiograph confirmed that he had fractured the proximal part of his arm bone (surgical neck of the humerus). The radiograph also revealed that his bone matrix was not as dense as it should be for a man his age. A test for blood Ca^{2+} was normal. On questioning, Henry confessed that he is a junk food addict who eats few vegetables and never consumes dairy products. In addition, Henry never exercises and seldom goes outdoors except at night.

Understand

Predict 9

Use your knowledge of bone physiology and figure 6.19 to answer the following questions.

A. Why is Henry more likely to break a bone than are most men his age?

B. How have Henry's eating habits contributed to his low bone density?

C. Would Henry's PTH levels be lower than normal, normal, or higher than normal?

D. What effect has Henry's nocturnal lifestyle had on his bone density?

E. How has lack of exercise affected his bone density?

Systems PATHOLOGY | Osteoporosis

Background Information

Betty has smoked heavily for at least 50 years. She does not exercise, seldom goes outdoors, has a poor diet, and is slightly underweight. Betty fell and radiographs revealed significant loss of bone density and a fractured femur (figure 6.20).

Osteoporosis (OS-tee-oh-poh-ROH-sis), or porous bone, is a loss of bone matrix. The loss of bone mass makes bones so porous and weakened that they become deformed and prone to fracture (figure 6.20). The occurrence of osteoporosis increases with age. In both men and women (although it is 2.5 times more common in women), bone mass starts to decrease at about age 40 and continually decreases thereafter. Women can eventually lose approximately one-half, and men one-quarter, of their spongy bone.

The most common causes of osteoporosis include decreased reproductive hormone production, inadequate dietary intake or too little absorption of calcium, and too little exercise or disuse from injury.

Women are more susceptible to reproductive hormone (estrogen) declines because they tend to enter menopause in their midlife years (40s to late 50s); men's testosterone levels do not decrease significantly until after age 65. The decrease in estrogen can lead to osteoporosis, mostly in spongy bone, especially in the vertebrae of the spine and the bones of the forearm. Collapse of the vertebrae can cause a decrease in height or, in more severe cases, kyphosis in the upper back (figure 6.21). Estrogen levels also decline in women who have had their ovaries removed and due to cigarette smoking. However, men are also prone to bone loss if they have a sedentary lifestyle, have a poor diet, or have had a broken bone immobilized. Significant amounts of bone are lost after 8 weeks of immobilization (figure 6.22).

Early diagnosis of osteoporosis can lead to more preventive treatments. Instruments that measure the absorption of photons (particles of light) by bone are used; of these, dual-energy x-ray absorptiometry (DEXA) is considered the best. Doctors recommend consuming at least 1000 mg of calcium per day (1200 mg/day for people over age 50). Calcium-rich foods include milk, yogurt, broccoli, cauliflower, salmon, tofu, and leafy green vegetables. However, most people consume only about one-third of their needed calcium, so physicians suggest taking a calcium supplement in combination with an 800–1000 IU vitamin D supplement to help absorb the calcium. Patients should also avoid high phosphorus foods such as red meat and soft drinks. In addition, doctors also suggest avoiding excess alcohol and caffeine because they decrease the amount of calcium that is absorbed. Regular weight-bearing exercises such as running, walking, and weight lifting for 30–45 minutes three times a week can also help prevent bone loss or help regain mild bone loss. However, if bone loss has been excessive, there are medications that can prevent further loss from occurring. There are four classes of anti-osteoporosis medications: bisphosphonates, estrogen-like medications, antibodies that inactivate the bone-breakdown mechanism, and calcitonin-replacement medications. Bisphosphonates are osteoclast inhibitors and include alendronate (Fosamax) and riseadronate (Actonel), which are taken once a week. Ibandronate (Boniva) is taken once a month. The newest medication, zoledronic acid (Reclast), is a once-per-year injection. The estrogen-like medicine is called raloxifene (Evista) and has not

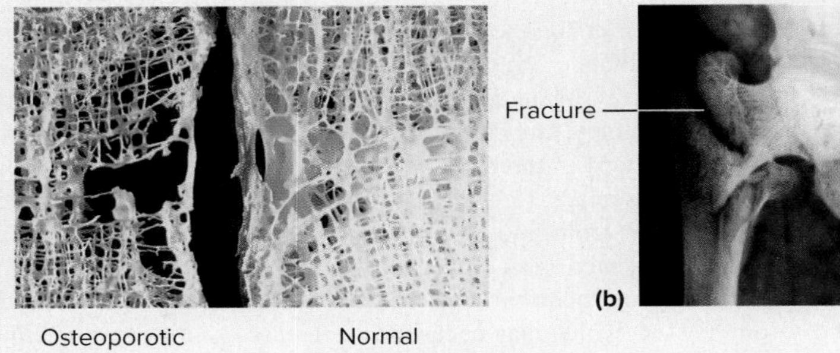

FIGURE 6.20 Imaging of Osteoporotic Bone Tissue
(*a*) Photo of osteoporotic bone (left) and normal bone (right). Osteoporosis causes depletion in the mineral content of bone, leaving it thin and fragile compared to normal bone. (*b*) Radiograph of femur head showing fracture, most likely due to osteoporosis. (a) Michael Klein/Photolibrary/Getty Images; (b) Princess Margaret Rose Orthopaedic Hospital/SPL/Science Source

FIGURE 6.21 Kyphosis of Upper Back
As people with osteoporosis continue to age, the thinning of bone matrix can cause vertebrae to collapse, which creates a "hump" on the upper thorax region of the vertebral column. Larry Mulvehill/Science Source

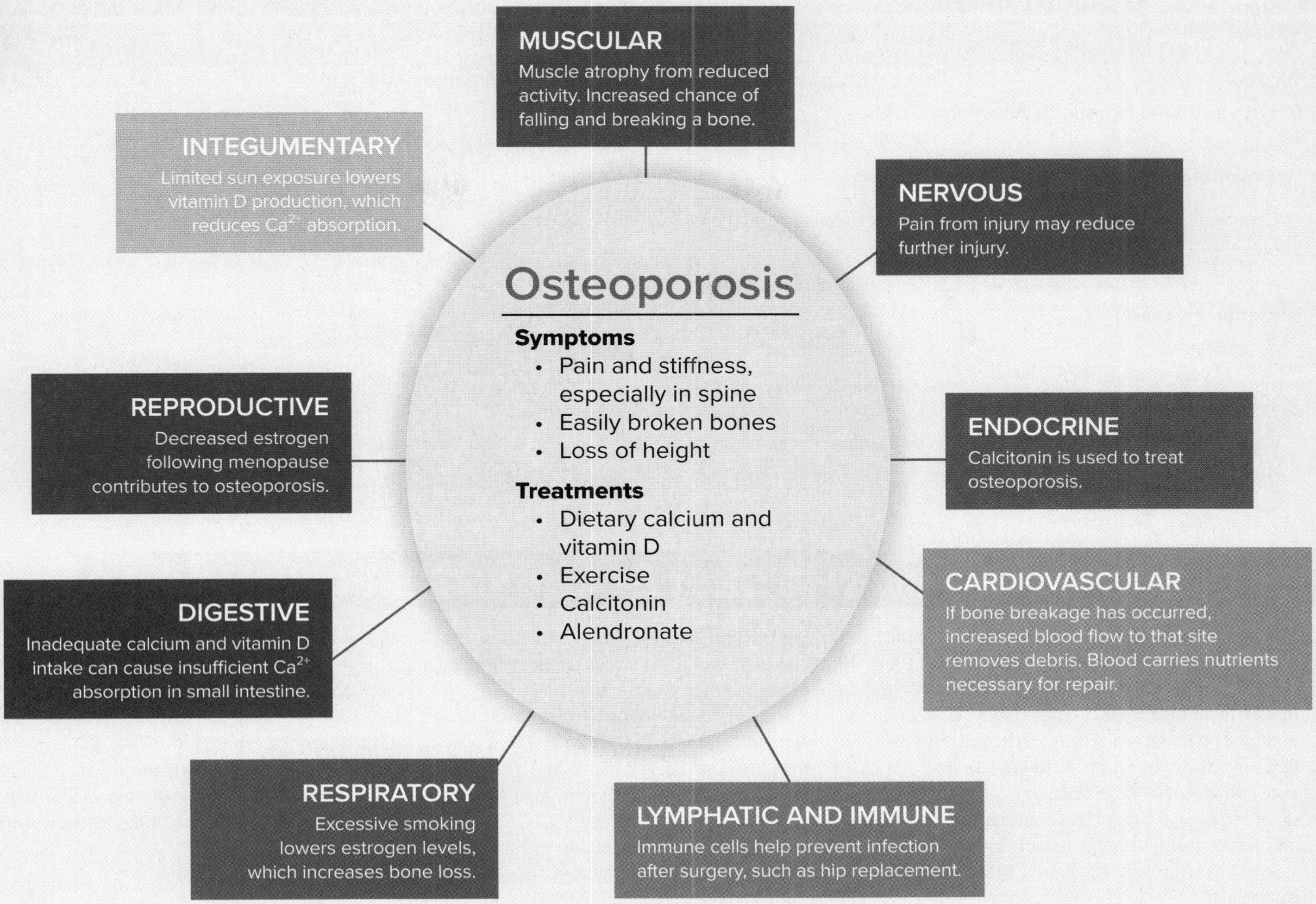

MUSCULAR
Muscle atrophy from reduced activity. Increased chance of falling and breaking a bone.

INTEGUMENTARY
Limited sun exposure lowers vitamin D production, which reduces Ca^{2+} absorption.

NERVOUS
Pain from injury may reduce further injury.

Osteoporosis

Symptoms
- Pain and stiffness, especially in spine
- Easily broken bones
- Loss of height

Treatments
- Dietary calcium and vitamin D
- Exercise
- Calcitonin
- Alendronate

REPRODUCTIVE
Decreased estrogen following menopause contributes to osteoporosis.

ENDOCRINE
Calcitonin is used to treat osteoporosis.

DIGESTIVE
Inadequate calcium and vitamin D intake can cause insufficient Ca^{2+} absorption in small intestine.

CARDIOVASCULAR
If bone breakage has occurred, increased blood flow to that site removes debris. Blood carries nutrients necessary for repair.

RESPIRATORY
Excessive smoking lowers estrogen levels, which increases bone loss.

LYMPHATIC AND IMMUNE
Immune cells help prevent infection after surgery, such as hip replacement.

FIGURE 6.22 Interactions Between Osteoporosis and Organ Systems of the Body
Osteoporosis results in a reduction in bone matrix.

been associated with either breast or uterine cancer. The most common antibody medication is denosumab (Prolia) and is taken once every 6 months. Calcitonin-like medicines such as Calcimar and Miacalcin also inhibit osteoclasts.

A relatively new area of concern for patients with osteoporosis is for those who take proton pump inhibitors (PPIs) for acid reflux. Some studies have shown that long-term (after 5 years) use of PPIs is associated with increased risk of fractures, especially if other fracture risk factors are present. However, for the majority of people, the risk of PPI use causing fractures is low. Because PPIs reduce stomach acid production, it is thought they may contribute to reduced calcium absorption. Table 6.5 describes other skeletal diseases and disorders.

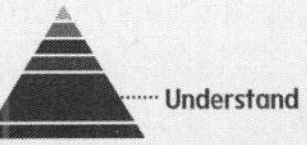

Predict 10

What advice should Betty give her granddaughter, so that the granddaughter will be less likely to develop osteoporosis when she is Betty's age?

TABLE 6.5 Representative Diseases and Disorders of the Skeletal System

Condition	Description
Tumors	May be malignant or benign and cause a range of bone defects
Growth and Developmental Disorders	
Gigantism	Abnormally increased body size due to excessive growth at the epiphyseal plates
Dwarfism	Abnormally small body size due to improper growth at the epiphyseal plates
Osteogenesis imperfecta	See Clinical Genetics 6.1
Rickets	Growth retardation due to nutritional deficiencies in minerals (Ca^{2+}) or vitamin D; results in bones that are soft, weak, and easily broken
Bacterial Infections	
Osteomyelitis	See Microbes in Your Body 6.1
Tuberculosis	Typically, a lung bacterium that can also affect bone
Decalcification	
Osteomalacia	Softening of adult bones due to calcium depletion; often caused by vitamin D deficiency
Osteoporosis	See Systems Pathology

EFFECTS OF AGING ON THE SKELETAL SYSTEM AND JOINTS

The most significant age-related changes in the skeletal system affect the joints as well as the quality and quantity of bone matrix. The bone matrix in an older bone is more brittle than in a younger bone because decreased collagen production results in relatively more mineral and less collagen fibers. With aging, the amount of matrix also decreases because the rate of matrix formation by osteoblasts becomes slower than the rate of matrix breakdown by osteoclasts.

Significant loss of bone increases the likelihood of bone fractures. For example, loss of trabeculae greatly increases the risk of fractures of the vertebrae. In addition, loss of bone and the resulting fractures can cause deformity, loss of height, pain, and stiffness. Loss of bone from the jaws can also lead to tooth loss.

A number of changes occur within many joints as a person ages. Changes in synovial joints have the greatest effect and often present major problems for older people. With use, the cartilage covering articular surfaces can wear down and the rate of replacement declines. Many people also experience arthritis, an inflammatory degeneration of the joints, with advancing age. In addition, the ligaments and tendons surrounding a joint shorten and become less flexible with age, resulting in decreased range of motion.

Concept Check

6.1 Functions of the Skeletal System

A. The skeletal system consists of bones, cartilage, tendons, and ligaments.

B. The skeletal system supports the body, protects the organs it surrounds, allows body movements, stores minerals and lipids, and is the site of blood cell production.

1. *Which of these is* not *a function of bone?* Remember
    - *a. internal support and protection*
    - *b. attachment for the muscles*
    - *c. calcium and phosphate storage*
    - *d. blood cell production*
    - *e. vitamin D storage*

6.2 Cartilage

A. Chondroblasts produce cartilage and become chondrocytes. Chondrocytes are located in lacunae surrounded by matrix.

B. The matrix of cartilage contains collagen fibers (for strength) and proteoglycans (to trap water).

C. The perichondrium surrounds cartilage. The outer layer contains fibroblasts, while the inner layer contains chondroblasts.

D. Cartilage grows by both appositional and interstitial growth.

2. *Chondrocytes are mature cartilage cells within the __________, and they are derived from __________.* Remember
    - *a. perichondrium, fibroblasts*
    - *b. perichondrium, chondroblasts*
    - *c. lacunae, fibroblasts*
    - *d. lacunae, chondroblasts*

3. *Which of these statements concerning cartilage is correct?*

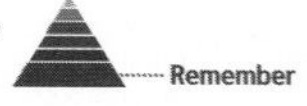

    - *a. Cartilage often occurs in thin plates or sheets.*
    - *b. Chondrocytes receive nutrients and oxygen from blood vessels in the matrix.*

c. Articular cartilage has a thick perichondrium layer.
d. The perichondrium contains both chondrocytes and osteocytes.
e. Appositional growth of cartilage occurs when chondrocytes within the tissue add more matrix from the inside.

6.3 Bone Histology

Bone Matrix

A. Collagen provides flexible strength.

B. Hydroxyapatite provides compressional strength.

4. *Which of these substances make(s) up the major portion of bone?*

   Remember

   a. collagen
   b. hydroxyapatite
   c. proteoglycan aggregates
   d. osteocytes
   e. osteoblasts

5. *The flexible strength of bone occurs because of*

   a. osteoclasts.
   b. ligaments.
   c. hydroxyapatite.
   d. collagen fibers.
   e. periosteum.

6. *When a person develops Paget disease, for unknown reasons the collagen fibers in the bone matrix run randomly in all directions. In addition, the amount of spongy bone decreases. What symptoms would you expect to observe?*

   Understand

Bone Cells

A. Osteoblasts produce bone matrix and become osteocytes. Osteocytes are located in lacunae and are connected to one another through canaliculi.

B. Osteoclasts break down bone (with assistance from osteoblasts).

C. Osteoblasts originate from osteochondral progenitor cells, whereas osteoclasts originate from monocyte/macrophage lineage stem cells in red bone marrow.

D. Ossification, the addition of bone to preexisting bone, occurs through appositional growth.

7. *The primary function of osteoclasts is to*

   a. prevent osteoblasts from forming.
   b. become osteocytes.
   c. break down bone.
   d. secrete calcium salts and collagen fibers.
   e. form the periosteum.

Woven and Lamellar Bone

A. Woven bone has collagen fibers oriented in many directions. It is remodeled to form lamellar bone.

B. Lamellar bone is arranged in thin layers, called lamellae, which have collagen fibers oriented parallel to one another.

Spongy and Compact Bone

A. Spongy bone has many spaces. Lamellae combine to form trabeculae containing spaces filled with bone marrow and blood vessels. The trabeculae are oriented along lines of stress and provide structural strength.

B. Compact bone is dense, with few spaces and consists of organized lamellae. Circumferential lamellae form the outer surface of compact bones; concentric lamellae surround central canals, forming osteons; interstitial lamellae are remnants of lamellae left after bone remodeling. Canals within compact bone provide a means for exchanging gases, nutrients, and waste products.

8. *Central canals*

   a. connect perforating canals to canaliculi.
   b. connect spongy bone to compact bone.
   c. are where blood cells are produced.
   d. are found only in spongy bone.
   e. are lined with periosteum.

9. *The lamellae found in osteons are __________ lamellae.*

   Remember

   a. circumferential
   b. concentric
   c. interstitial

10. *Spongy bone consists of interconnecting rods or plates of bone called*

    Remember

    a. osteons.
    b. canaliculi.
    c. circumferential lamellae.
    d. a haversian system.
    e. trabeculae.

6.4 Bone Anatomy

Structure of a Long Bone

A. The diaphysis is the shaft of a long bone, and the epiphyses are distinct from the diaphysis and house the epiphyseal plate.

B. The epiphyseal plate is the site of lengthwise bone growth.

C. The medullary cavity is a space within the diaphysis and, in juveniles, contains red marrow, which is the site of blood cell production; in adults it contains yellow marrow, which consists of fat.

D. The periosteum covers the outer surface of bone.

E. The endosteum lines cavities inside bone and contains osteoblasts, osteoclasts, and osteochondral progenitor cells.

11. *Yellow marrow is*

    a. found mostly in children's bones.
    b. found in the epiphyseal plate.
    c. important for blood cell production.
    d. mostly adipose tissue.

12. *The periosteum*

    a. is an epithelial tissue membrane.
    b. covers the outer and internal surfaces of bone.
    c. contains only osteoblasts.
    d. becomes continuous with collagen fibers of tendons or ligaments.
    e. has a single fibrous layer.

Structure of Flat, Short, and Irregular Bones

Flat, short, and irregular bones have an outer covering of compact bone surrounding spongy bone.

6.5 Bone Development

Intramembranous Ossification

A. Some skull bones, part of the mandible, and the diaphyses of the clavicles develop from membranes.

B. Within the membrane at centers of ossification, osteoblasts produce bone along the membrane fibers to form spongy bone.

C. Beneath the periosteum, osteoblasts lay down compact bone to form the outer surface of the bone.

13. *Given these events:*

(1) Osteochondral progenitor cells become osteoblasts.
(2) Connective tissue membrane is formed.
(3) Osteoblasts produce woven bone.

Which sequence best describes intramembranous bone formation?

a. 1,2,3
b. 1,3,2
c. 2,1,3
d. 2,3,1
e. 3,2,1

14. *Intramembranous bone formation*

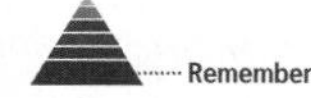

a. occurs at the epiphyseal plate.
b. is responsible for growth in diameter of a bone.
c. gives rise to the flat bones of the skull.
d. occurs within a hyaline cartilage model.
e. produces articular cartilage in the long bones.

15. *The ossification regions formed during early fetal development*

a. are secondary ossification centers.
b. become articular cartilage.
c. become medullary cavities.
d. become the epiphyses.
e. are primary ossification centers.

Endochondral Ossification

A. Most bones develop from a cartilage model.

B. The cartilage matrix is calcified, and chondrocytes die. Osteoblasts form bone on the calcified cartilage matrix, producing spongy bone.

C. Osteoblasts build an outer surface of compact bone beneath the periosteum.

D. Primary ossification centers form in the diaphysis during fetal development. Secondary ossification centers form in the epiphyses. Articular cartilage on the ends of bones and the epiphyseal plate does not ossify.

16. *Given these processes:*

(1) Chondrocytes die.
(2) Cartilage matrix calcifies.
(3) Chondrocytes hypertrophy.
(4) Osteoblasts deposit bone.
(5) Blood vessels grow into lacunae.

Which sequence best represents the order in which these processes occur during endochondral bone formation?

a. 3,2,1,4,5
b. 3,2,1,5,4
c. 5,2,3,4,1
d. 3,2,5,1,4
e. 3,5,2,4,1

6.6 Bone Growth

A. Bones increase in size only by appositional growth, the addition of new bone to the surface of older bone or cartilage.

B. Trabeculae grow by appositional growth.

Growth in Bone Length

A. Epiphyseal plate growth involves the interstitial growth of cartilage followed by appositional bone growth on the cartilage.

B. Epiphyseal plate growth results in increased length of the diaphysis and bony processes. Bone growth in length ceases when the epiphyseal plate becomes ossified and forms the epiphyseal line.

17. *Growth in the length of a long bone occurs*

a. at the primary ossification center.
b. beneath the periosteum.
c. at the center of the diaphysis.
d. at the epiphyseal plate.
e. at the epiphyseal line.

18. *During growth in length of a long bone, cartilage forms and then ossifies. The location of the ossification is the zone of*

Remember

a. calcification.
b. hypertrophy.
c. proliferation.
d. resting cartilage.

Growth at Articular Cartilage

A. Articular cartilage growth involves the interstitial growth of cartilage followed by appositional bone growth on the cartilage.

B. Articular cartilage growth results in larger epiphyses and an increase in the size of bones that do not have epiphyseal plates.

Growth in Bone Width

A. Appositional bone growth beneath the periosteum increases the diameter of long bones and the size of other bones.

B. Bone reabsorption by osteoclasts occurs along the medullary cavity.

Factors Affecting Bone Growth

A. Genetic factors determine bone shape and size. The expression of genetic factors can be modified.

B. Factors that alter the mineralization process or the production of organic matrix, such as deficiencies in vitamins D and C, can affect bone growth.

C. Growth hormone, thyroid hormone, estrogen, and testosterone stimulate bone growth.

D. Estrogen and testosterone cause increased bone growth and closure of the epiphyseal plate.

19. *Chronic vitamin D deficiency results in which of these consequences?*

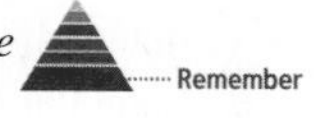

a. Bones become brittle.
b. The percentage of bone composed of hydroxyapatite increases.
c. Bones become soft and pliable.
d. Scurvy occurs.
e. Both a and b are correct.

20. *Estrogen*
    a. stimulates a burst of growth at puberty.
    b. causes a later closure of the epiphyseal plate than testosterone does.
    c. causes a longer growth period in females than testosterone causes in males.
    d. tends to prolong the growth phase of the epiphyseal plates.
    e. All of these are correct.

21. *In some cultures, eunuchs were responsible for guarding harems, which are the collective wives of one male. Eunuchs are males who were castrated as boys. Castration removes the testes, the major site of testosterone production in males. Because testosterone is responsible for the sex drive in males, the reason for castration is obvious. As a side effect of this procedure, the eunuchs grew to above-normal heights. Can you explain why?*

6.7 Bone Remodeling

A. Remodeling converts woven bone to lamellar bone and allows bone to change shape, adjust to stress, repair itself, and regulate body calcium levels.

B. Bone adjusts to stress by adding new bone and by realigning bone through remodeling.

22. *Bone remodeling can occur* 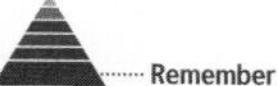
    a. when woven bone is converted into lamellar bone.
    b. as bones are subjected to varying patterns of stress.
    c. as a long bone increases in diameter.
    d. when new osteons form in compact bone.
    e. All of these are correct.

23. *Explain why running helps prevent osteoporosis in older people. Does the benefit include all bones or mainly those of the lower limbs and spine?*

24. *Astronauts can experience a dramatic decrease in bone density while in a weightless environment. Explain how this happens, and suggest a way to slow the loss of bone tissue.*

6.8 Bone Fracture Classification and Repair

A. Fractures are classified by several criteria.

B. Fractures can be due to trauma, disease, or medical implants.

C. The ends of the bone may either align anatomically or be apart, even possibly protruding from the skin.

D. Other classes depend on the number of fragments, such as comminuted, or age-specific injuries such as an epiphyseal fracture.

E. Fracture repair begins with the formation of a hematoma.

F. The hematoma is replaced by an internal callus consisting of fibers and cartilage.

G. The external callus is a bone-cartilage collar that stabilizes the ends of the broken bone.

H. The internal and external calluses are ossified to become woven bone. The woven bone is replaced by compact bone.

25. *Given these processes:* 
    (1) cartilage ossification
    (2) external callus formation
    (3) hematoma formation
    (4) internal callus formation
    (5) remodeling of woven bone into compact bone

    Which sequence best represents the order in which the processes occur during repair of a fracture?
    a. 1,2,3,4,5
    b. 2,4,3,1,5
    c. 3,4,2,1,5
    d. 4,1,5,2,3
    e. 5,3,4,2,1

26. *Which of these processes during bone repair requires the longest period of time?*
    a. cartilage ossification
    b. external callus formation
    c. hematoma formation
    d. internal callus formation
    e. remodeling of woven bone into compact bone

27. *When a long bone breaks, blood vessels at the fracture line are severed. The formation of blood clots stops the bleeding. Within a few days, bone tissue on both sides of the fracture site dies. However, the bone dies back only a certain distance from the fracture line. Explain.*

6.9 Calcium Homeostasis

PTH increases blood Ca^{2+} by increasing bone reabsorption and promoting calcitriol activation, which increases Ca^{2+} absorption from the small intestine and the reabsorption of Ca^{2+} from the urine. Calcitonin decreases blood Ca^{2+} by decreasing bone breakdown.

28. *If the secretion of parathyroid hormone (PTH) increases, osteoclast activity ________ and blood Ca^{2+} levels _______.*
    a. decreases, decrease
    b. decreases, increase
    c. increases, decrease
    d. increases, increase

29. *A patient has hyperparathyroidism because a tumor in the parathyroid gland is producing excessive amounts of PTH. How does this hormone affect bone? Would the administration of large doses of vitamin D help the situation? Explain.*

Answers to this chapter's odd-numbered Concept Check questions appear in Appendix F.

7

CHAPTER

Skeletal System

GROSS ANATOMY

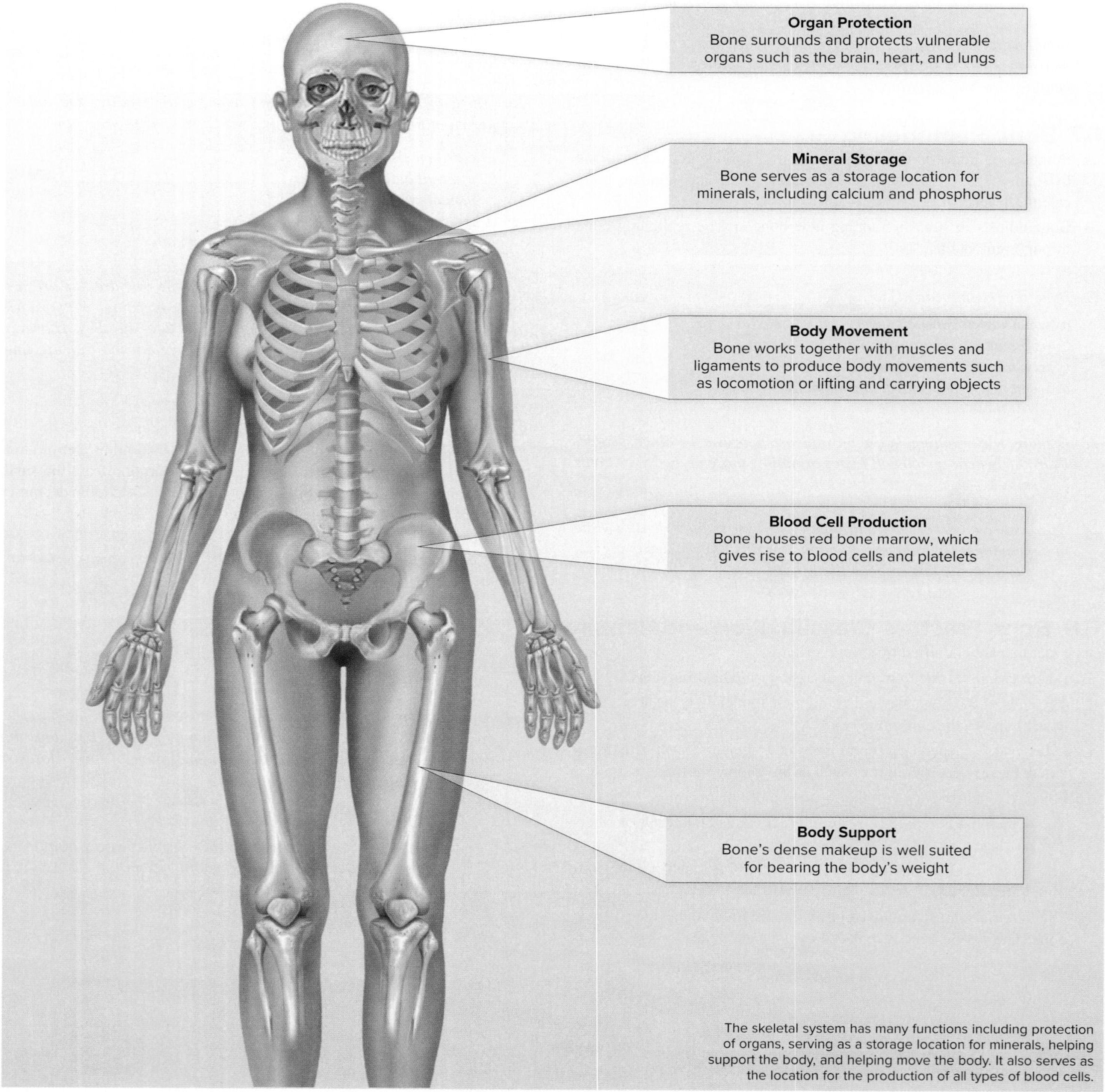

Organ Protection
Bone surrounds and protects vulnerable organs such as the brain, heart, and lungs

Mineral Storage
Bone serves as a storage location for minerals, including calcium and phosphorus

Body Movement
Bone works together with muscles and ligaments to produce body movements such as locomotion or lifting and carrying objects

Blood Cell Production
Bone houses red bone marrow, which gives rise to blood cells and platelets

Body Support
Bone's dense makeup is well suited for bearing the body's weight

The skeletal system has many functions including protection of organs, serving as a storage location for minerals, helping support the body, and helping move the body. It also serves as the location for the production of all types of blood cells.

The skeletal system is the framework that helps maintain the body's shape and enables us to move normally. Muscles and bones work together to move our bodies. When the muscles contract, they pull on the bones, often with considerable force. Human bones are very strong and can resist tremendous bending and compression forces without breaking. Nonetheless, each year approximately 6.8 million Americans break a bone.

The skeletal system is composed of bones, cartilage, and ligaments. However, to study skeletal gross anatomy, anatomists use dried, prepared bones so that they can view the major features of individual bones unobstructed by associated soft tissues. As you study the bones depicted in this chapter, keep in mind that living bones not only contain soft tissue, such as the periosteum (see chapter 6), but also have important relationships with many soft tissues, including muscles, tendons, ligaments, cartilage, nerves, and blood vessels.

Understand

Learn to Predict

Dave Plummer loves telling people around the pool that he has a pig valve in his heart. At the age of 70, Dave required replacement of a heart valve. The surgeon opened Dave's thoracic cavity by making a longitudinal midline incision from the superior to the inferior margin of his sternum through the skin and underlying soft tissue. Then he cut the sternum with a bone saw along the same line, so that the right and left halves of the sternum could be spread apart enough to expose the heart. After the defective valve had been replaced, the surgeon wired the two halves of the sternum back together. For several days after the surgery, Dave experienced significant discomfort in his back, and although he started walking within a few days, he could not resume his normal swimming routine until 2 months later.

Name the specific parts of the skeletal system and the tissue layers of the bone that the surgeon cut. Also, explain Dave's back discomfort and why he could not resume swimming sooner.

Answers to this question and the chapter's odd-numbered Predict questions can be found in Appendix E.

7.1 Skeletal Anatomy Overview

LEARNING OUTCOMES

After reading this section, you should be able to

A. **Define the anatomical terms for bone features.**
B. **List the two anatomical portions of the skeleton.**
C. **List the bone shapes.**

The average adult has 206 bones (table 7.1; figure 7.1). However, the actual number of bones varies between people and decreases with age as bones become fused. Bones are segregated into the **axial skeleton** and the **appendicular skeleton** (see figure 7.1). The axial skeleton consists of the bones of the skull, the auditory ossicles, the hyoid bone, the vertebral column, and the thoracic cage (rib cage). The appendicular skeleton consists of the bones of the **upper limbs,** the **lower limbs,** and the two **girdles.** The term *girdle,* which means "belt" or "zone," refers to the two zones where the limbs are attached to the body. These two zones are the **pectoral girdle** and the **pelvic girdle.**

Bone Shapes

Individual bones are classified according to shape: long, flat, short, or irregular (figure 7.2). **Long bones** are longer than they are wide. Most of the bones of the upper and lower limbs are long bones. **Flat bones** have a relatively thin, flattened shape and are usually curved. Examples of flat bones include certain skull bones, the ribs, the breastbone (sternum), and the shoulder blades (scapulae). **Short bones** are round or nearly cube-shaped, as exemplified by the bones of the wrist (carpal bones) and ankle (tarsal bones). **Irregular bones,** such as the vertebrae and facial bones, have shapes that do not readily fit into the other three categories.

Skeletal Terminology

Anatomists use several common terms to describe the features, or surface markings, of bones (table 7.2). Most of these features involve the relationship between the bones and associated soft tissues. If a bone possesses a **tubercle** (TOO-ber-kul) (rounded projection) or a **process** (sharp projection), most likely a ligament or tendon was attached to that tubercle or process during life. If a bone has a smooth, articular surface, that surface was part of a joint and was covered with articular cartilage. If the bone has a **foramen** (foh-RAY-men) (hole; pl. foramina; foh-RAM-i-nah) in it, that foramen was the opening through which a nerve or blood vessel passed. Some skull bones contain mucous membrane–lined air spaces called **sinuses.** Use table 7.2 as you

Module 5
Skeletal System

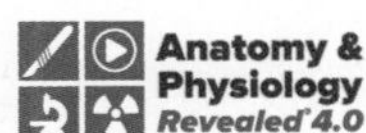

TABLE 7.1 Number of Named Bones Listed by Category

Bones		Number
Axial Skeleton		
Skull (Cranium)		
Cranial bones		
Paired (left and right)	Parietal	2
	Temporal	2
Unpaired (single)	Frontal	1
	Sphenoid	1
	Occipital	1
	Ethmoid	1
Facial bones		
Paired	Maxilla	2
	Zygomatic	2
	Palatine	2
	Lacrimal	2
	Nasal	2
	Inferior nasal concha	2
Unpaired	Mandible	1
	Vomer	1
	Total skull bones	22
Bones Associated with the Skull		
Auditory ossicles		
Malleus		2
Incus		2
Stapes		2
Hyoid		1
	Total associated bones	7
Vertebral Column		
Cervical vertebrae		7
Thoracic vertebrae		12
Lumbar vertebrae		5
Sacrum		1
Coccyx		1
	Total vertebral column bones	26
Thoracic Cage		
Ribs		24
Sternum		1
	Total thoracic cage bones	25
	Total axial skeleton bones	80

Bones		Number
Appendicular Skeleton		
Pectoral Girdle		
Scapula		2
Clavicle		2
Upper Limb		
Humerus		2
Ulna		2
Radius		2
Carpal bones		16
Metacarpal bones		10
Phalanges		28
	Total girdle and upper limb bones	64
Pelvic Girdle		
Hip bone		2
Lower Limb		
Femur		2
Tibia		2
Fibula		2
Patella		2
Tarsal bones		14
Metatarsal bones		10
Phalanges		28
	Total girdle and lower limb bones	62
	Total appendicular skeleton bones	126
	Total axial skeleton bones	80
	Total appendicular skeleton bones	126
	Total bones	206

progress through this chapter to help you learn skeletal anatomy; the name of the structure can provide some important clues and means of remembering it. Consider the structure *foramen ovale,* in the skull. Because this structure includes the term *foramen,* then you know you're looking for a "hole" in the skull. Then, consider the next part of the structure's name, *ovale*. This opening is, indeed, shaped like an oval; this structure is an "oval-shaped hole" in the skull. Using the names of the structures can provide a helpful aid for learning. There are more tips throughout this chapter that you can use when learning skeletal anatomy.

FUNDAMENTAL **Figure**

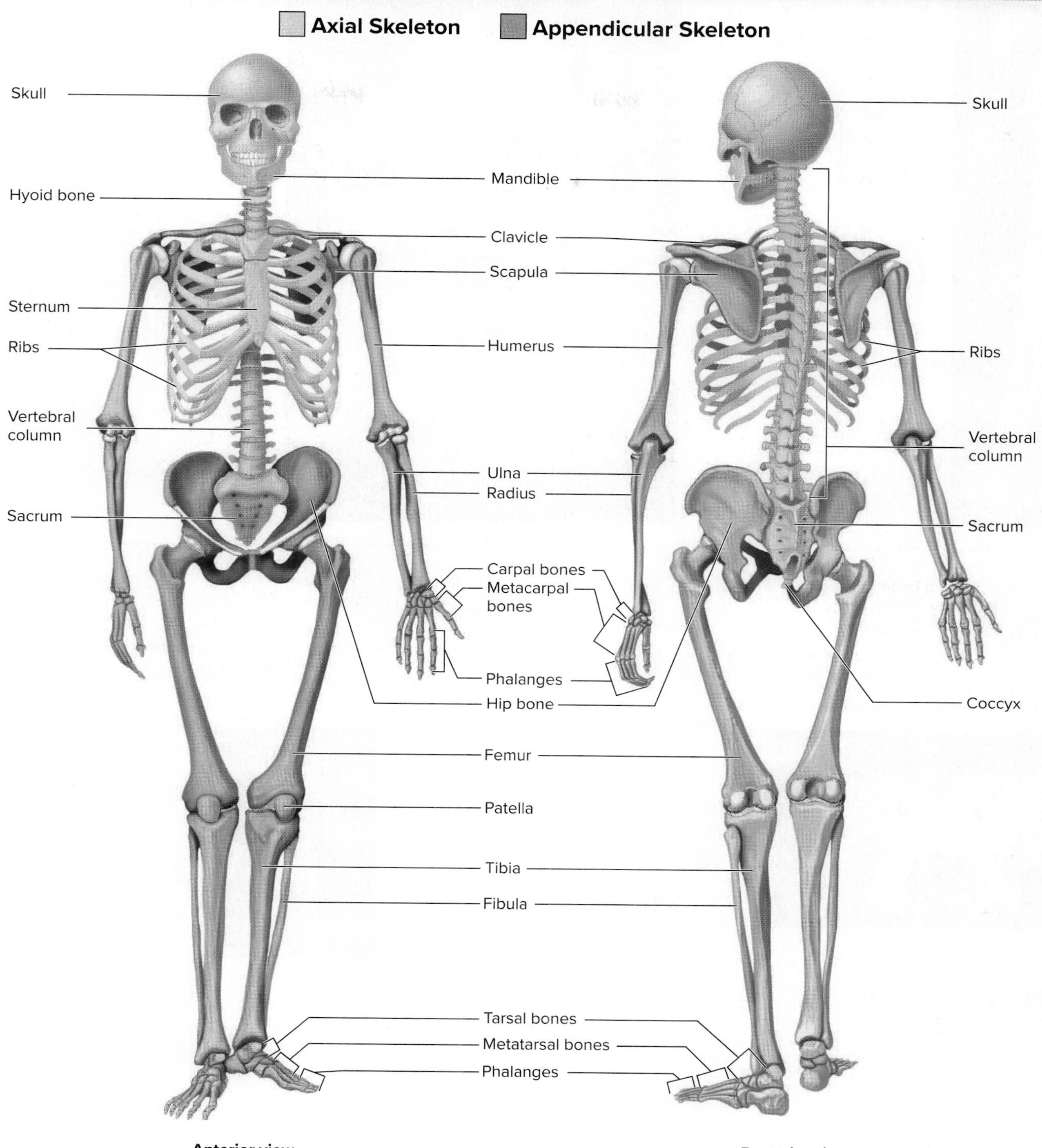

FIGURE 7.1 Complete Skeleton
Bones of the axial skeleton are listed in the columns on each side of the figure; bones of the appendicular skeleton are listed in the center of the two skeleton views. (The skeleton is not shown in the anatomical position.) APR

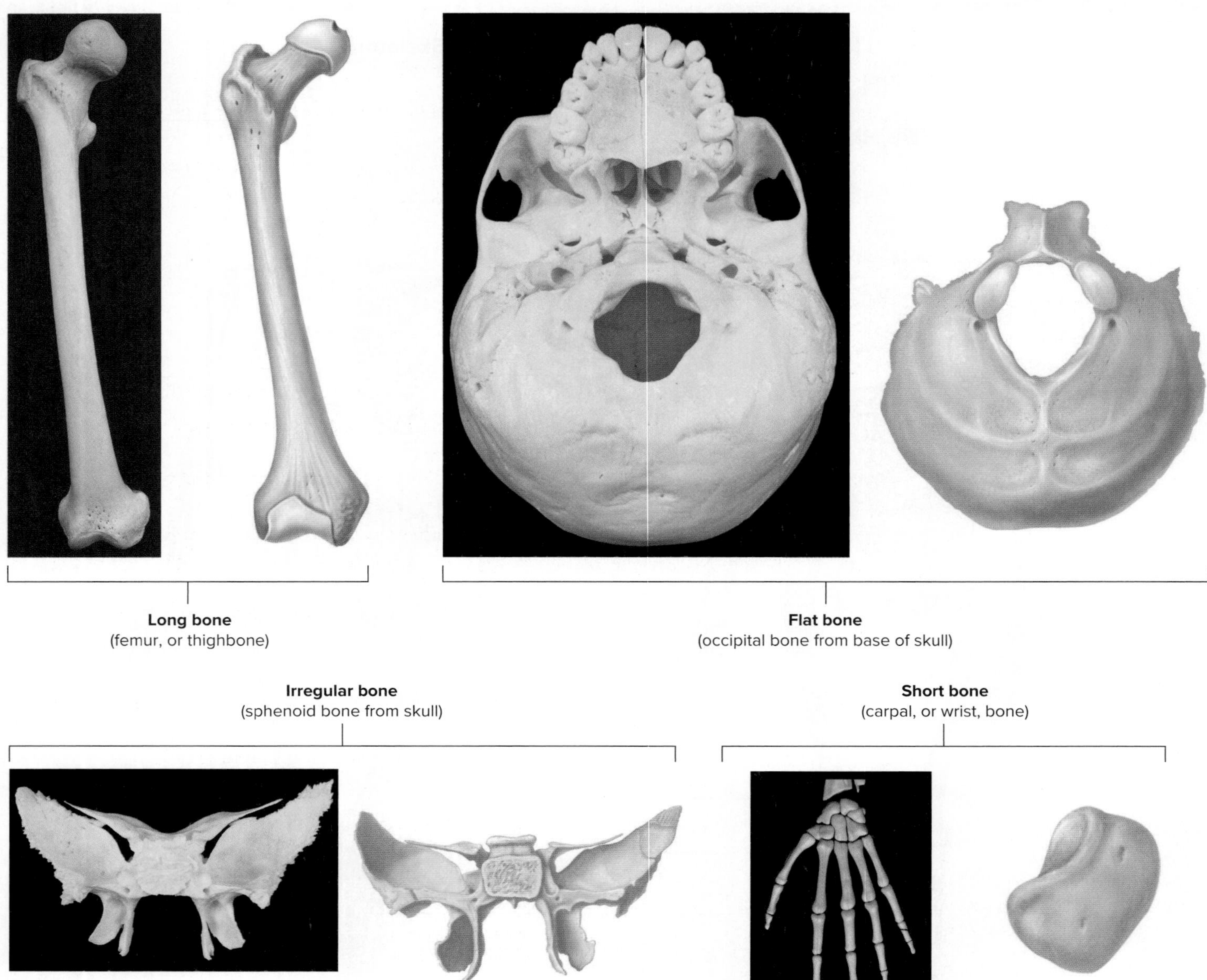

FIGURE 7.2 Bone Shapes
There are four main bone shapes: long, flat, irregular, and short. Christine Eckel/McGraw Hill Education

TABLE 7.2 Anatomical Terms for Bone Features (Surface Markings)

Term	Description	Example
Body	Main part	Body of femur
Head	Enlarged, often rounded end	Head of femur
Neck	Constriction between head and body	Neck of femur
Margin, border	Edge	Lateral border of scapula
Angle	Bend	Mandibular angle
Ramus	Branch off the body beyond the angle	Mandibular ramus
Condyle	Smooth, rounded articular surface	Lateral condyle of tibia
Facet	Small, flattened articular surface	Superior articular facet of atlas
Ridges		
Line, linea	Low ridge	Intertrochanteric line of femur
Crest, crista	Prominent ridge	Iliac crest
Spine	Very high ridge	Scapular spine
Projections		
Process	Prominent projection	Acromion process of scapula
Tubercle	Small, rounded projection	Greater tubercle of humerus
Tuberosity, tuber	Rounded projection; larger than a tubercle	Deltoid tuberosity of humerus
Trochanter	Tuberosity on the proximal femur	Greater trochanter of femur
Epicondyle	Upon a condyle	Lateral epicondyle of femur
Lingula	Flat, tongue-shaped process	Lingula of mandible
Hamulus	Hook-shaped process	Pterygoid hamulus of sphenoid bone
Horn	Horn-shaped process	Greater horn of hyoid bone
Openings		
Foramen	Hole	Foramen magnum of occipital bone
Canal, meatus	Tunnel	Hypoglossal canal of occipital bone
Fissure	Cleft	Superior orbital fissure of sphenoid bone
Sinus, labyrinth	Cavity	Ethmoid labyrinth
Depressions		
Fossa	General term for a depression	Coronoid fossa of humerus
Notch	Depression in the margin of a bone	Mandibular notch
Fovea	Little pit	Fovea capitis of femur
Groove, sulcus	Deep, narrow depression	Intertubercular groove of humerus

ASSESS YOUR PROGRESS

Answers to these questions are found in the section you have just completed. Re-read the section if you need help in answering these questions.

1. *How are rounded and sharp projections, and openings in bones, related to soft tissues?*
2. *What are the two anatomical portions of the skeleton?*
3. *What does each of the following terms mean:* tubercle, condyle, spine, foramen, fossa?

7.2 Axial Skeleton

LEARNING OUTCOMES

After reading this section, you should be able to

A. **Describe the general functions of the axial skeleton and list its parts.**
B. **List the major sutures of the skull and the bones they connect.**
C. **Name the bones of the skull and describe their features as seen from the superior, posterior, lateral, anterior, and inferior views.**
D. **Name the bones that compose the orbit of the eye.**
E. **List the bones and cartilage that form the nasal septum.**
F. **Describe the locations and functions of the paranasal sinuses.**
G. **List the bones of the cranium and face.**
H. **Explain the unique structure of the hyoid bone.**
I. **Describe the shape of the vertebral column, list its divisions, and state its functions.**
J. **Discuss the common features of the vertebrae and contrast the structure of vertebrae from each region.**
K. **List the bones and cartilage of the thoracic cage, including the three types of ribs.**

The axial skeleton forms the central axis of the body. It protects the brain, the spinal cord, and the vital organs housed within the thorax.

Skull

The skull consists of 8 cranial bones and 14 facial bones, a total of 22 bones (table 7.3 and figures 7.3–7.13). The cranial bones, or cranium (KRAY-nee-um), house and protect the brain. Both the exterior and the interior of the skull have visible ridges and lines. Most of these are locations where head and neck muscles attach to the cranium. The cranial bones are connected by immovable joints called **sutures** (see chapter 8). There are four principal sutures: (1) **coronal,** (2) **sagittal,** (3) **lambdoid,** and (4) **squamous.** The specific sutures will be discussed along with the bones they connect. All other skull bones are held together by sutures as well and are named according to the bones they connect. The top of

TABLE 7.3 Processes and Other Features of the Skull

Feature	Bone on Which Feature Is Found	Description
External Features		
Temporal lines	Parietal	Attachment site for the temporalis muscle, which closes the jaw (shown in figure 7.5)
Mandibular fossa	Temporal	Depression where the mandible articulates with the skull (shown in figure 7.10)
Mastoid process	Temporal	Enlargement posterior to the ear; attachment site for several muscles that move the head (shown in figures 7.4, 7.5, and 7.10)
Styloid process	Temporal	Attachment site for three muscles (to the tongue, pharynx, and hyoid bone) and some ligaments (shown in figure 7.5)
Nuchal lines	Occipital	Attachment points for several posterior neck muscles (shown in figures 7.4 and 7.10)
Occipital condyle	Occipital	Point of articulation between the skull and the vertebral column (shown in figures 7.4 and 7.10)
Pterygoid hamulus	Sphenoid	Hooked process on the inferior end of the medial pterygoid plate, around which the tendon of one palatine muscle passes; an important dental landmark (shown in table 7.7*e*)
Pterygoid plates (medial and lateral)	Sphenoid	Bony plates on the inferior aspect of the sphenoid bone; the lateral pterygoid plate is the site of attachment for two muscles of mastication (chewing; shown in figures 7.10 and 7.12)
Palatine process	Maxilla	Anterior two-thirds of the hard palate (shown in figures 7.10 and 7.12)
Alveolar process	Mandible, maxilla	Ridges on the mandible and maxilla containing the teeth (shown in figure 7.7)
Horizontal plate	Palatine	Posterior third of the hard palate (shown in figure 7.12)
Angle	Mandible	Posterior, inferior corner of the mandible (shown in figure 7.5)
Coronoid process	Mandible	Attachment point for the temporalis muscle (shown in figure 7.5)
Mental protuberance	Mandible	Chin (resembles a bent knee; shown in figures 7.5 and 7.7)
Mandibular condyle	Mandible	Region where the mandible articulates with the skull (shown in figure 7.5)
Ramus	Mandible	Portion of the mandible superior to the angle (shown in figure 7.5)
Internal Features		
Crista galli	Ethmoid	Process in the anterior part of the cranium to which one of the connective tissue coverings of the brain (dura mater) connects (shown in figures 7.9 and 7.12)
Petrous part	Temporal	Thick, interior part of temporal bone containing the middle and inner ears and the auditory ossicles (shown in figure 7.9)
Sella turcica	Sphenoid	Bony structure, resembling a saddle, in which the pituitary gland is located (shown in figure 7.9)

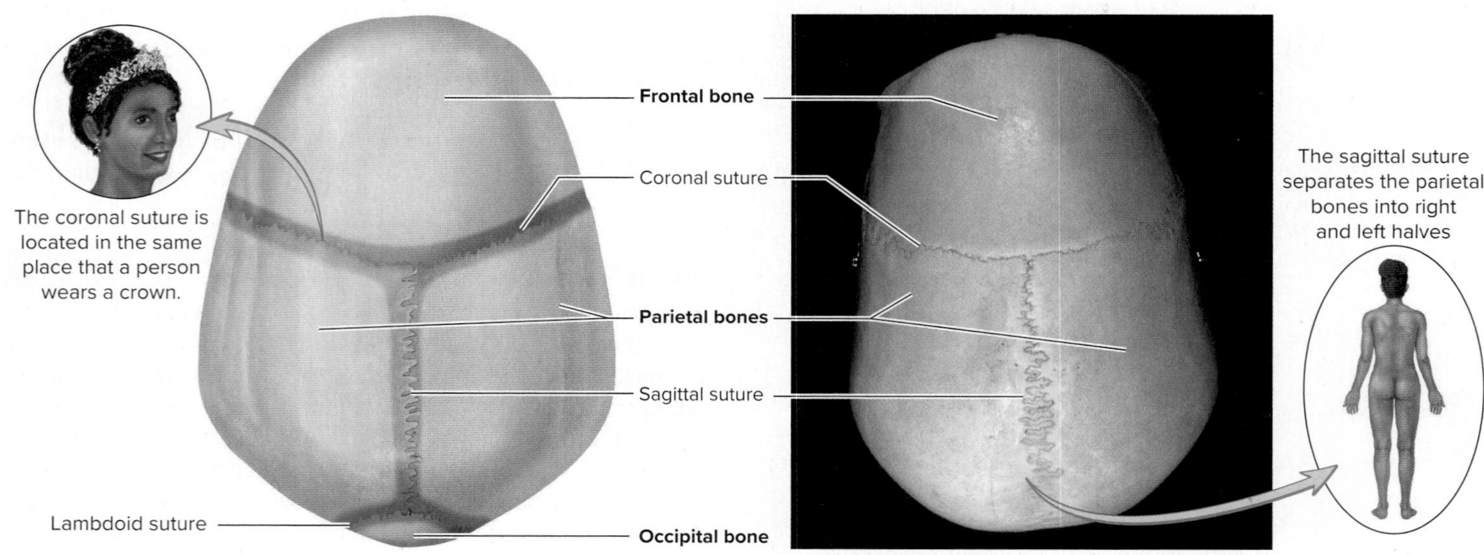

FIGURE 7.3 Superior View of the Skull

Only four skull bones are visible from a superior view: the frontal bone, the two parietal bones, and a small portion of the occipital bone. (The names of the bones are in bold.) (b) Biology Pics/Science Source

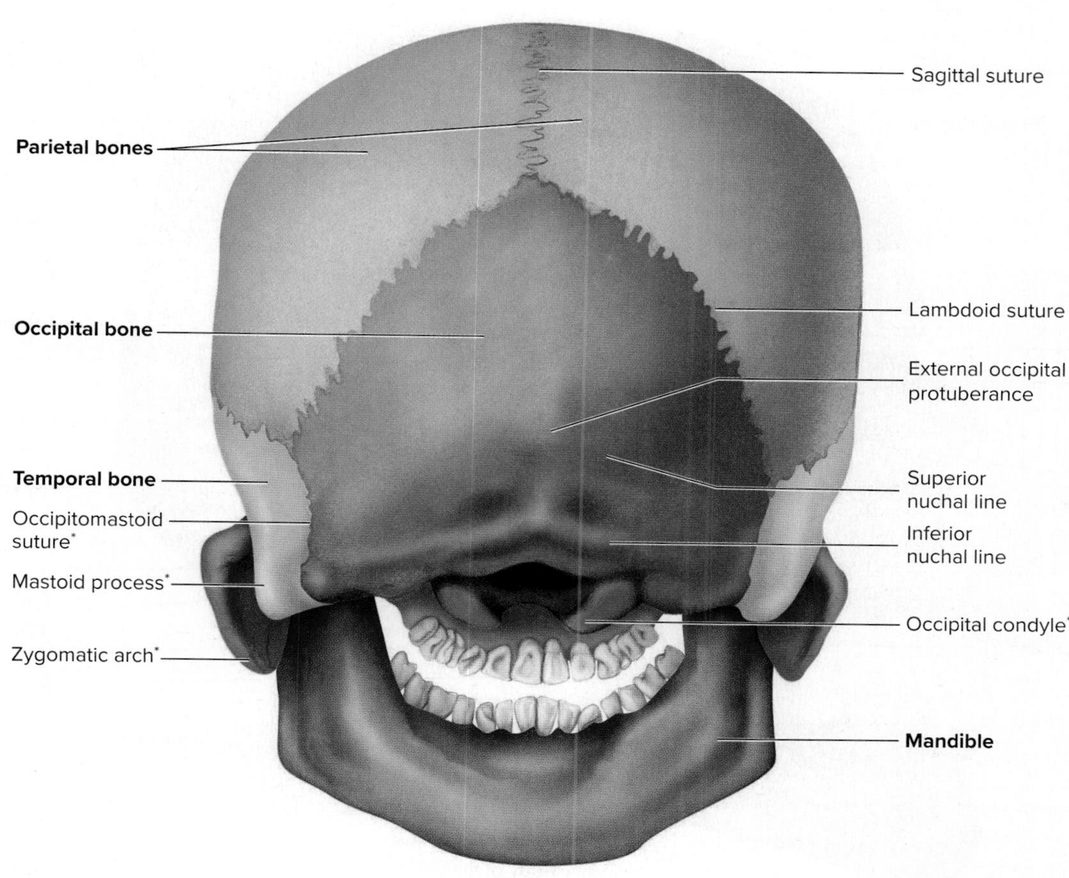

FIGURE 7.4 Posterior View of the Skull
The parietal and occipital bones are the major structures visible in the posterior view of the skull. (The names of the bones are in bold. Structures marked with an asterisk (*) are symmetrical. There is one of each on both the right and the left halves of the skull.)

the skull, called the **calvaria** (kal-VAY-ree-ah), is often removed to view the interior of the skull. The facial bones form the basis of the face; contain cavities for the eyes, nose, and mouth; and are the attachment sites for our facial expression muscles. We discuss the fetal skull in chapter 8. Tables 7.4–7.8 list key features of the skull. A good first step when learning skull anatomy is to begin by learning only the names of the individual bones. To help you with that, this section lists each skull bone separately. Next, focus on the features associated with each bone, using the names of the individual features as descriptors.

Cranial Bones

The 8 bones of the cranium include (1) the frontal bone, (2) the 2 parietal bones, (3) the 2 temporal bones, (4) the occipital bone, (5) the sphenoid bone, and (6) the ethmoid bone.

Frontal Bone

The **frontal bone** is connected to the two parietal bones by the **coronal suture** (figures 7.3, 7.5, and 7.7). The term *coronal* is derived from the Latin term meaning "crown"; the coronal suture is located where a person would wear a crown or a tiara. The frontal bone is most well known at the "forehead." It forms the roof of both the orbit of the eye and the nasal cavity (tables 7.4 and 7.5). The superior border of each of the orbits contains a **supraorbital foramen,** or **notch,** which allows passage of a blood vessel and nerve for the eyelid and eye. Between the two orbits is the **glabella** (smooth), a smooth region of bone. The frontal bone also contains the **frontal sinus,** one of the **paranasal sinuses** (figure 7.13). Internally, the frontal bone forms the **anterior cranial fossa,** which supports the frontal lobes of the brain.

Parietal Bones

The paired parietal bones form nearly half of the superior portion of the skull (see figure 7.3). The two parietal bones are joined medially by the **sagittal suture** (*sagittal* refers to "left and right halves of a structure") and are connected to the occipital bone by the **lambdoid suture** (this suture looks like the Greek letter lambda, "Λ," when viewed from the posterior). Occasionally, extra, small bones called **sutural** (SOO-choor-al) **bones,** or wormian bones, form along the lambdoid suture. Along with the temporal bones, the parietal bones make up the majority of the lateral portion of the skull.

Two sets of muscle attachment sites, the **superior temporal line** and the **inferior temporal line,** arch across the lateral surface of the parietal bone. These lines serve as attachment sites for the temporalis muscle, a major mastication (chewing) muscle.

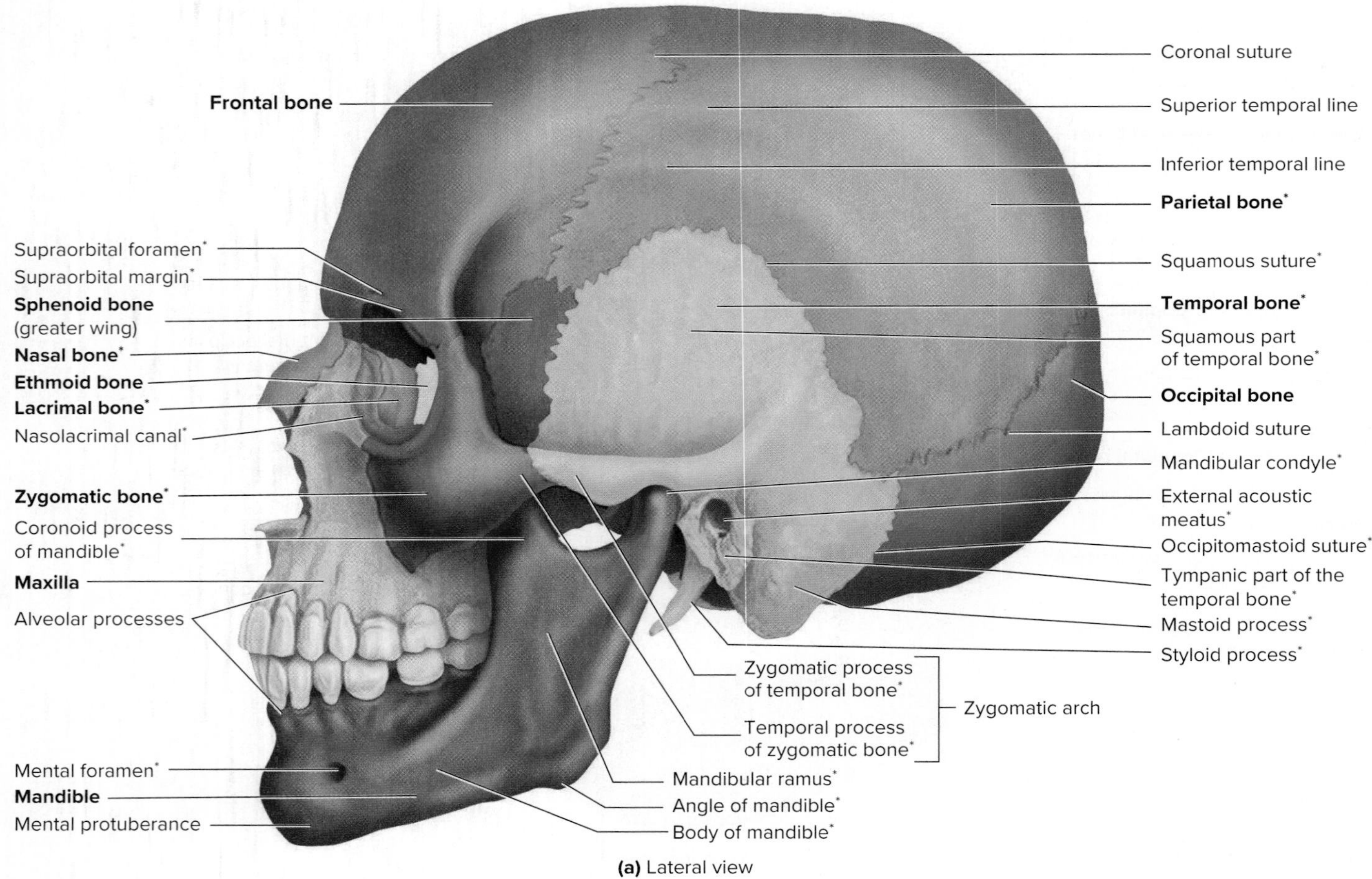

FIGURE 7.5 Left Lateral View of the Skull

(*a*) The parietal bone and the squamous part of the temporal bone form a major portion of the side of the head. (*b*) Photo of the same view in (*a*). (The names of the bones are in bold. Structures marked with an asterisk (*) are symmetrical. There is one of each on both the right and the left halves of the skull.) (b) Christine Eckel/McGraw Hill APR

Temporal Bones

The **temporal bones** are connected to the skull by the **squamous sutures** (*squamous* means "scale" as in scales on a fish that slightly overlap each other; see figure 7.5). The term *temporal* means "related to time"; the temporal bone's name is derived from the observation that the hair on the temples turns gray as a person ages. The temporal bone is subdivided into three main regions: (1) the squamous part, (2) the tympanic part, and (3) the petrous part.

1. The **squamous part** of each temporal bone meets the parietal bone superiorly. The **zygomatic** (zie-goh-MAT-ik) **process** extends from the squamous part anteriorly toward the zygomatic bone of the face. It joins with the temporal process of the zygomatic bone to form the **zygomatic arch,** a bridge across the side of the skull (see figure 7.5). Note that bone processes are named for the bones to which they extend. The zygomatic process has an oval-shaped fossa on the inferior side, called the **mandibular fossa.** The mandibular fossa is the articulation site of the mandible. When chewing, the zygomatic arch is quite evident to the touch (figure 7.6). Occasionally, a person will experience intense pain in the jaw while eating and may have trouble fully opening and closing their mouth. This can be due to **temporomandibular joint disorder (TMJ),** inflammation to the joint at the mandibular fossa (see chapter 8).
2. The **tympanic part** of the temporal bone has the prominent **external acoustic meatus** (*external auditory canal*), which transmits sound waves toward the eardrum, or tympanic membrane. The external ear surrounds the external acoustic meatus.
3. The **petrous part** of the temporal bone extends posterolaterally from the center of the sphenoid bone (see figures 7.9 and 7.10). The petrous part, together with the sphenoid bone, makes up the **middle cranial fossa** (see figure 7.9), which contains the temporal lobes of the brain. The petrous part is a thick, bony ridge (petrous; rocky); is hollow; and houses the middle and inner ears. The **internal acoustic meatus** (see figure 7.9) is located on the posteromedial surface of the petrous part and is the opening for a nerve controlling hearing and balance.

Externally, the **mastoid** (MASS-toyd) **process** (see figures 7.4, 7.5, and 7.10) is a large, bony inferior projection that can be seen and felt just posterior to the external ear. This process is not solid bone, but is filled with cavities called **mastoid air cells,** which are connected to the middle ear and can sometimes become infected, causing **mastoiditis.** Neck muscles that rotate the head attach to the mastoid process.

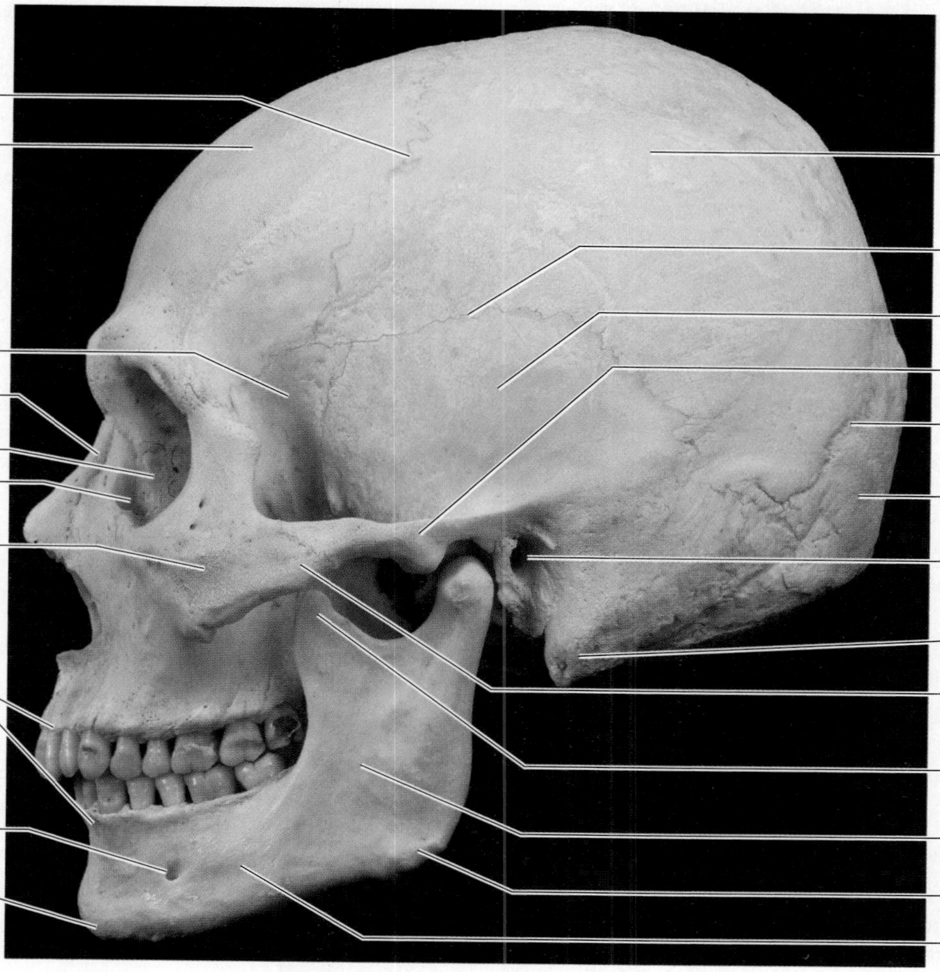
Coronal suture
Frontal bone
Sphenoid bone (greater wing)
Nasal bone*
Lacrimal bone*
Nasolacrimal canal*
Zygomatic bone*
Alveolar processes
Mental foramen*
Mental protuberance
Parietal bone*
Squamous suture*
Temporal bone*
Zygomatic process of Temporal bone
Lambdoid suture
Occipital bone
External acoustic meatus*
Mastoid process*
Temporal process of zygomatic bone*
Coronoid process of mandible
Mandibular ramus*
Angle of mandible*
Body of mandible*
(b) Lateral view

FIGURE 7.5 **(continued)**

Frontal bone
Supraorbital margin
Zygomatic arch
Nasal bone
Zygomatic bone
Maxilla
Mastoid process
Mandible
Mental protuberance
Angle of mandible

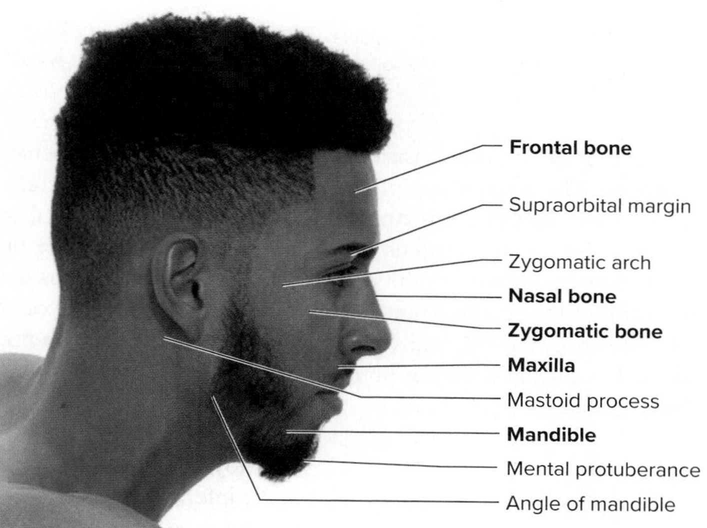

FIGURE 7.6 **Lateral View of the Face**

View of bony landmarks on the lateral surface of the face. Aaron Roeth/ McGraw Hill Education

The **styloid** (STY-loyd; stylus, or pen-shaped) **process** (see figures 7.5 and 7.10) projects from the inferior of the petrous part of the temporal bone. The styloid process serves as an attachment site for three muscles necessary for movement of the tongue, hyoid bone, and pharynx. The **stylomastoid foramen** (see figure 7.10) is located between the styloid process and mastoid process and allows for passage of a nerve controlling facial muscles.

There are three additional important foramina on the inferior side of the petrous part (see figures 7.9 and 7.10). The **jugular** (JUG-you-lar) **foramina** allow the jugular veins to carry the majority of the blood away from the brain. The **carotid** (kah-ROT-id) **canals** are the major entry point for blood delivery to the brain. The carotid arteries enter the brain at the inferior opening of each carotid canal (see figure 7.9) and then pass through each carotid canal, which run anteromedially through the petrous part (*carotid* is the Greek term meaning "to put into a stupor" because compression of the carotid arteries can cause a person to pass out). A thin plate of bone separates the carotid canal from the middle ear, allowing us to hear our own pulse, usually when frightened or during exercise. The **foramen lacerum** (lah-SER-um; torn) is an easily noticeable opening in a dried skull at the border of the petrous part and the sphenoid bone. However, this foramen is only an artifact of the dried skull; in life, this opening is closed off by cartilage.

FUNDAMENTAL **Figure**

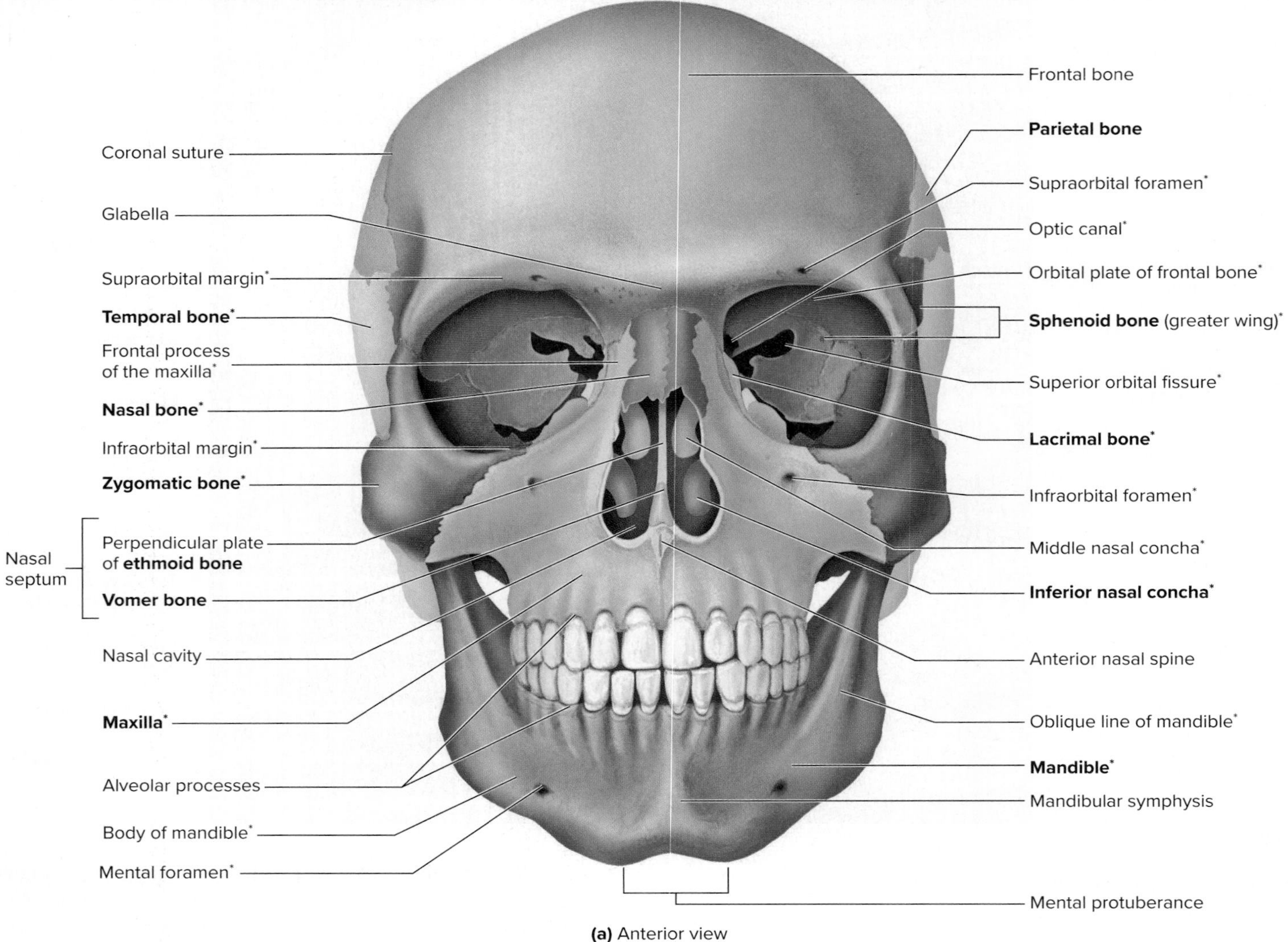

(a) Anterior view

FIGURE 7.7 Anterior View of the Skull

(*a*) The major structures seen from the anterior view are the frontal bone, the zygomatic bones, the maxilla, and the mandible. (*b*) Photo of the same view in (*a*). (The names of the bones are in bold. Structures marked with an asterisk (*) are symmetrical. There is one of each on both the right and the left halves of the skull.)

(b) Chanon saguansak/Shutterstock APR

Occipital Bone

The **occipital bone** makes up the majority of the skull's posterior wall and base (see figures 7.4, 7.9, and 7.10) (*occipital* means back of the head). Its most prominent feature is the **foramen magnum** (large hole), the opening where the brainstem connects to the spinal cord (see figures 7.9 and 7.10). This region also forms the **posterior cranial fossae** that support the cerebellum of the brain. Externally, two rounded projections on either side of the foramen magnum are the **occipital condyles** (see figure 7.10). The occipital condyles are the points of articulation between the skull and the first cervical vertebra. This articulation partly allows for nodding "yes" (as in "Yes, I love learning skeletal anatomy!"). In the anteromedial region of each occipital condyle are the **hypoglossal canals** where the nerve innervating the tongue exits the skull.

Posteriorly, an **external occipital protuberance** (see figure 7.4) is present on the occipital bone. It can be felt through the scalp at the base of the head and varies considerably in size from person to person. The external occipital protuberance is the site of attachment of the **ligamentum nuchae** (NOO-kee; nape of neck), an elastic ligament that extends down the neck and helps keep the head erect by pulling on the occipital bone. Also, visible on the posterior of the occipital bone are a set of small ridges that extend laterally from the external occipital protuberance, called **nuchal lines.** The nuchal lines are points of attachment for several neck muscles that move the head.

Sphenoid Bone

Although appearing to be two bones, one on each side of the skull anterior to the temporal bone, the **sphenoid** (SFEE-noyd) **bone** is actually a single bone that extends completely across the skull (see figure 7.5). When viewed as a whole, the sphenoid bone somewhat resembles a bat with four distinct parts: (1) a central **body,** (2) a

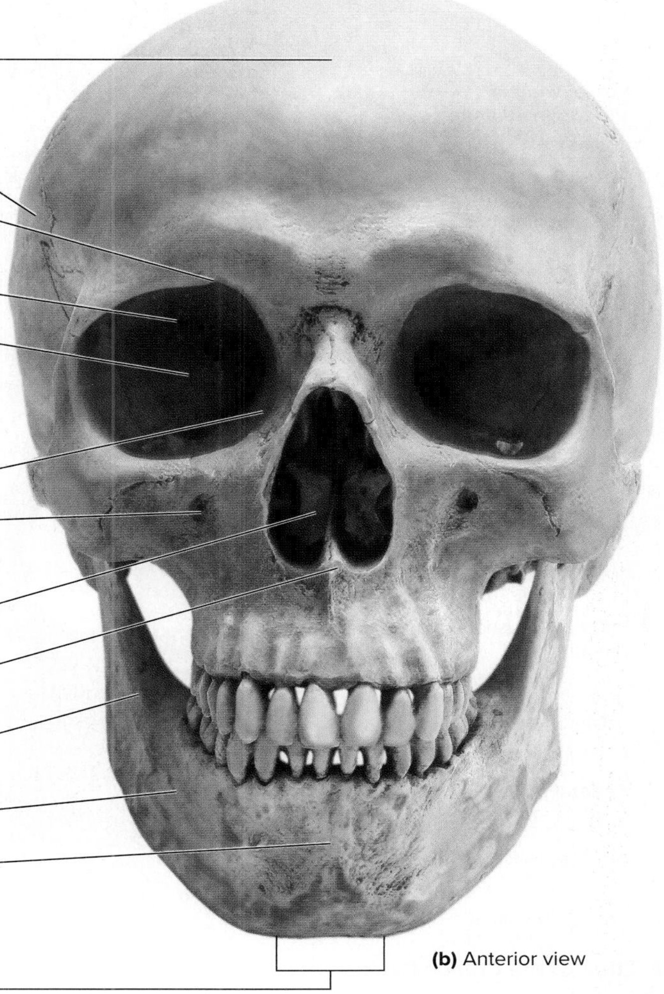
Frontal bone
Parietal bone
Supraorbital foramen*
Orbital plate of frontal bone*
Sphenoid bone (greater wing)*
Lacrimal bone*
Infraorbital foramen*
Inferior nasal concha*
Anterior nasal spine
Oblique line of mandible*
Mandible*
Mandibular symphysis
Mental protuberance
(b) Anterior view

FIGURE 7.7 (continued)

Glabella
Supraorbital margin
Zygomatic bone
Maxilla
Frontal bone
Mandible
Mental protuberance

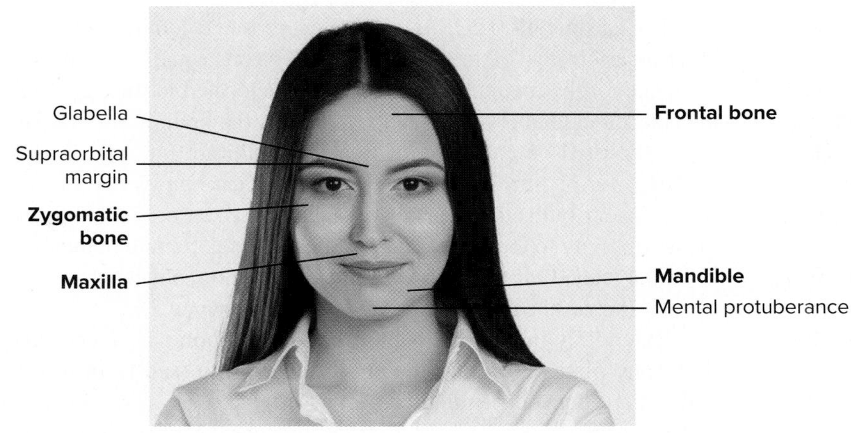

FIGURE 7.8 Anterior View of the Face

View of bony landmarks on the anterior of the face. (The names of the bones are in bold.) FabrikaSimf/Shutterstock

pair of processes called the **greater wings,** (3) a pair of processes called the **lesser wings,** and (4) inferior processes called the **pterygoid** (TER-ih-goyd; wing-shaped) **processes.**

The body of the sphenoid bone forms a central prominence within the floor of the cranial cavity. The shape of this prominence resembles a saddle, called the **sella turcica** (SEL-ah TUR-sih-kah; Turkish saddle) (see figure 7.9). In life, the sella turcica surrounds and protects the pituitary gland. Within the body of the sphenoid bone are the **sphenoidal sinuses** (see figure 7.13). An **optic canal** is located on each side of the sphenoid bone just anterior to the sella turcica. The optic canal is the passageway for the optic nerve to enter the brain from the eyes. Three additional paired foramina are located on either side of the sella turcica: (1) the **foramen rotundum** (round), (2) the **foramen**

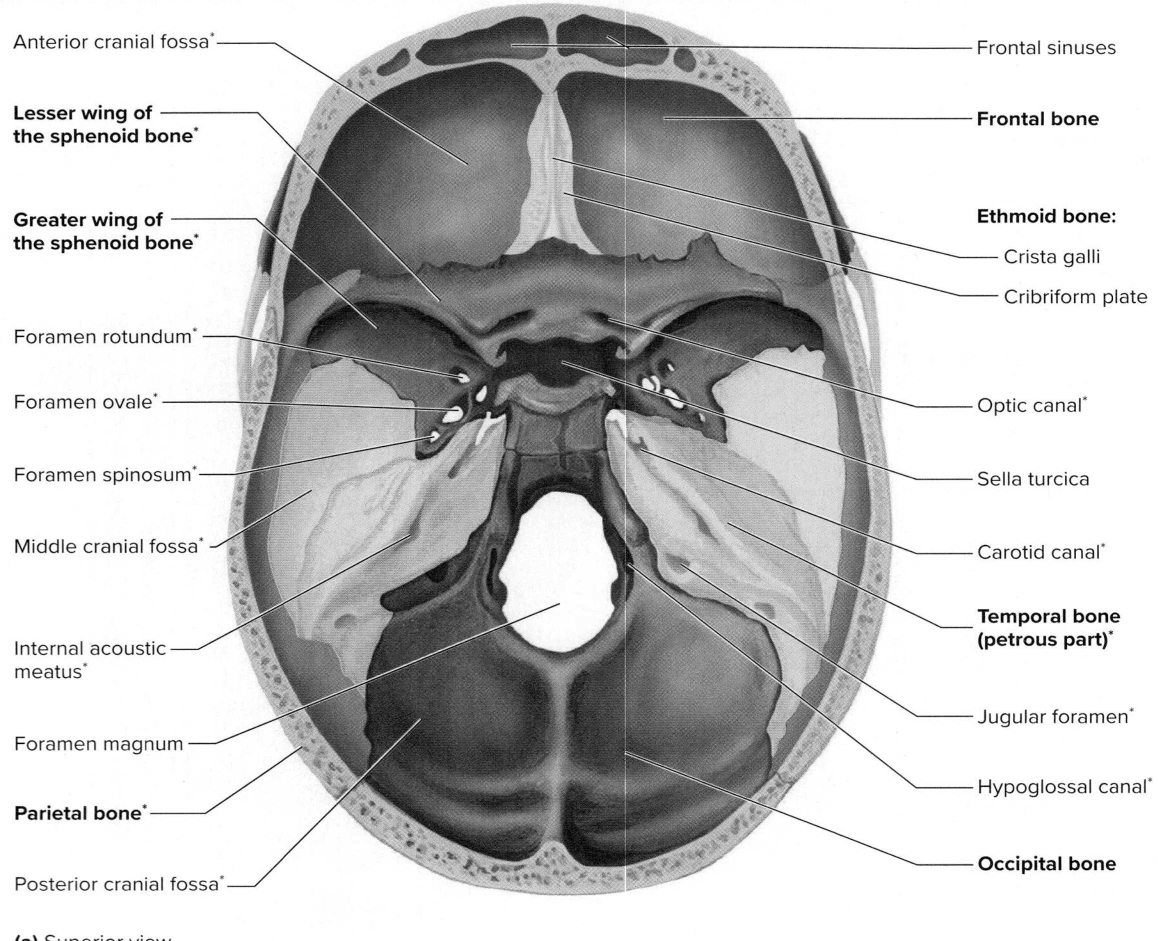

(a) Superior view

FIGURE 7.9 Floor of the Cranial Cavity

(*a*) Drawing of the floor of the cranial cavity. The calvaria has been removed, and the floor is viewed from above. (*b*) Photo of the same view in (*a*). (The names of the bones are in bold. Structures marked with an asterisk (*) are symmetrical. There is one of each on both the right and the left halves of the skull.) (b) Christine Eckel/McGraw Hill Education APR

ovale (oh-VAL-ee; oval), and (3) the **foramen spinosum** ('to bore through") (see figures 7.9 and 7.10). The foramen rotundum and foramen ovale are passageways for blood vessels and nerves that supply structures of the face, while the foramen spinosum allows passage of a meningeal artery.

The greater wings of the sphenoid bone (1) form the floor of the **middle cranial fossa,** (2) are a part of the lateral skull wall, and (3) form the posterior wall of the orbits. The lesser wings of the sphenoid bone form a ridge on each side of the optic canals. This ridge separates the anterior cranial fossa from the middle cranial fossa. Additionally, the lesser wings are the superior border of the **superior orbital fissure,** where cranial nerves controlling eye movement enter the orbit (see figure 7.11). The pterygoid processes, which extend inferiorly, are attachment sites for muscles of mastication (see figure 7.10).

Ethmoid Bone

The **ethmoid** (ETH-moid; *ethmos,* sieve) **bone** is appropriately named because it is a very porous, fragile bone. It is centrally located in the skull, forming the **nasal septum** (wall), a large portion of the nasal cavity, as well as the medial wall of the orbits. The sinuses within the ethmoid bone form a maze of interconnected ethmoidal air cells, collectively called the **ethmoidal labyrinth,** or the **ethmoidal sinuses** (see figure 7.13 and table 7.7*f*).

The **crista galli** (KRIS-tah- GAL-ee; rooster's comb) is a prominent superior ridge of the ethmoid bone. The crista galli is an attachment site for the meninges of the brain. It is located in the center of the anterior cranial fossa and helps to anchor the brain in the cranial cavity. Located on each side of the crista galli are the **cribriform** (KRIB-ri-form; sievelike) **plates,** each of which houses one of the two olfactory bulbs that transmit signals for the sense of smell from the nasal cavity to the brain. The cribriform plates contain numerous foramina, called **olfactory foramina,** which allow olfactory nerves to enter the nasal cavity (see figure 7.12*a* and chapter 15).

Extending inferiorly from the ethmoid bone is a central, thin bony plate called the **perpendicular plate** (see figures 7.7 and 7.12). The perpendicular plate forms the superior portion of the nasal septum, which divides the nasal cavity into right and left halves. Protruding medially from the ethmoid bone are two scroll-shaped bones called the **superior** and **middle nasal conchae** (KON-kee) (see figures 7.7 and 7.12). The **inferior**

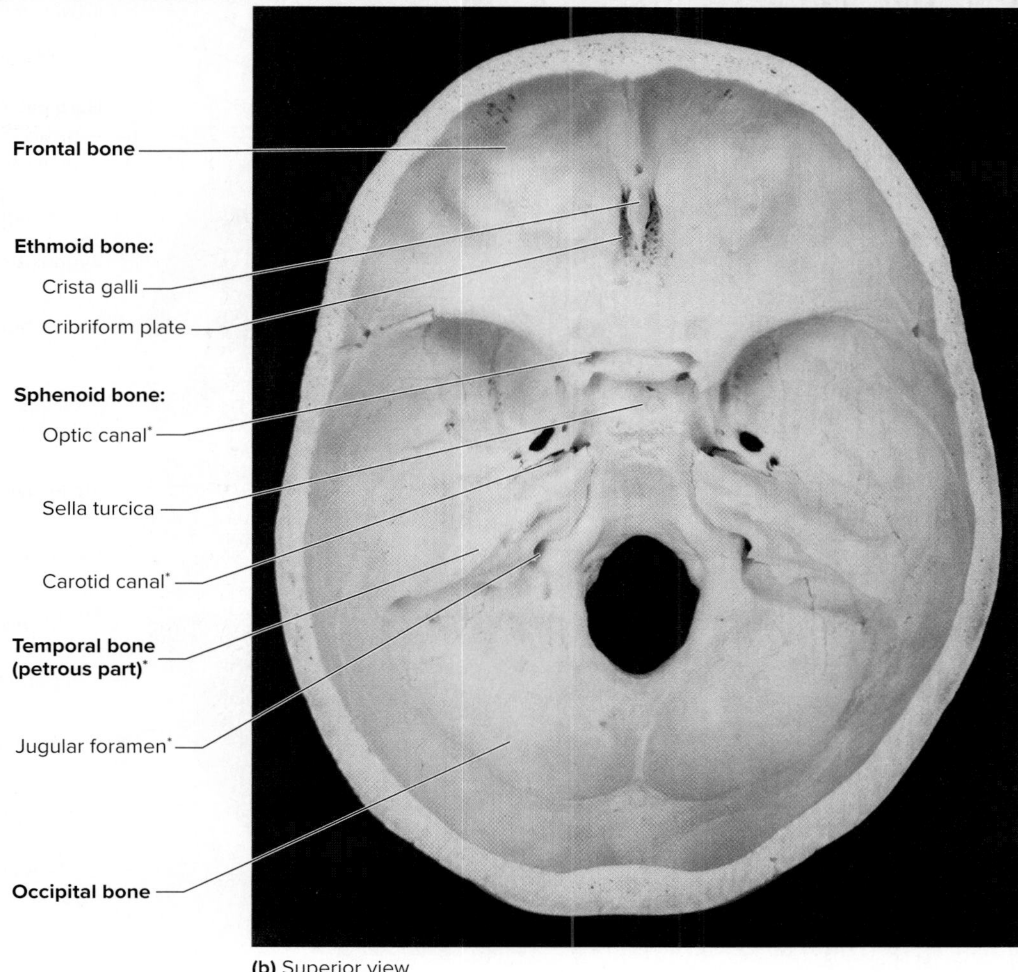

(b) Superior view

FIGURE 7.9 (continued)

nasal concha is a separate bone, which will be discussed later. Together, the three nasal conchae increase the surface area in the nasal cavity, thereby facilitating moistening of and removal of particles from air in the nasal cavity, and warming of the air inhaled through the nose.

Specialized Regions in the Skull

Cranial Fossae

As we've described, the cranial cavity houses and protects the brain within shallow depressions. When the calvaria is removed and the floor of the cranial cavity is visible, these depressions, the cranial fossae, become evident. There are three fossae that are formed as the developing cranium conforms to the shape of the brain. The three fossae include:

1. The anterior cranial fossa, which is formed by regions of the frontal bone, the ethmoid bone, and the lesser wings of the sphenoid bone. The anterior cranial fossa houses the frontal lobes of the brain.
2. The middle cranial fossa encompasses the area from the posterior portion of the lesser wings of the sphenoid bone to the petrous part of the temporal bone. It is bordered laterally by the parietal bones. The temporal lobes of the brain rest in this fossa.
3. The posterior cranial fossa is bordered anteriorly by the posterior portion of the petrous part of the temporal bone, posteriorly by the occipital bone, and laterally by the parietal bone. The cerebellum and a portion of the brainstem are located in this fossa.

TABLE 7.4 Bones Forming the Orbit (see figures 7.7 and 7.11)

Bone	Part of Orbit
Frontal	Roof
Sphenoid	Roof and posterolateral wall
Zygomatic	Lateral wall
Maxilla	Floor
Lacrimal	Medial wall
Ethmoid	Medial wall
Palatine	Medial wall

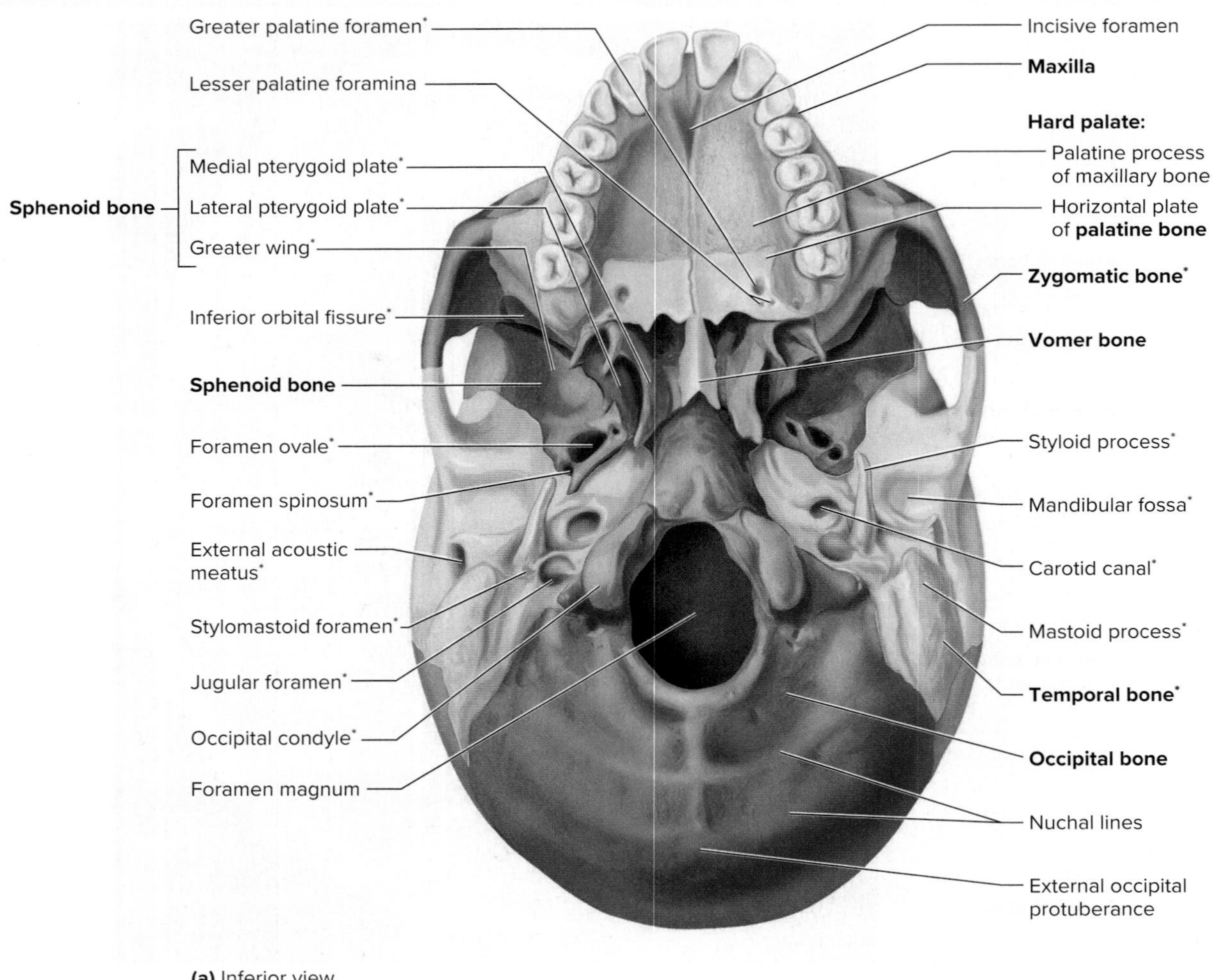

FIGURE 7.10 Inferior View of the Skull

(*a*) Drawing of an inferior view of the skull with the mandible removed. The base of the skull is complex, with a number of foramina and specialized surfaces. (*b*) Photo of the same view in (*a*). (The names of the bones are in bold. Structures marked with an asterisk (*) are symmetrical. There is one of each on both the right and the left halves of the skull.) (b) Christine Eckel/McGraw Hill Education

Paranasal Sinuses

Considered together, the sinuses found in the frontal bone, the ethmoid bone, the sphenoid bone, and the maxilla are called the paranasal sinuses (see figure 7.13). The paranasal sinuses are openings within particular bones that open into the nasal cavity. The sinuses have two major functions: (1) they decrease the weight of the skull and (2) they act as a resonating chamber when speaking. Compare the sound of your voice during a head cold to its sound normally.

Orbits

Table 7.4 lists all the bones that converge to form the orbits. The orbits (see figures 7.6 and 7.11) are cone-shaped fossae, each with a posterior-facing apex. They are called the orbits because the eyes rotate within the fossae. Portions of multiple bones converge to form the orbits. The orbits protect the eyes and are the locations

TABLE 7.5 Bones Forming the Nasal Cavity (see figures 7.7 and 7.12)

Bone	Part of Nasal Cavity
Frontal	Roof
Nasal	Roof
Sphenoid	Roof
Ethmoid	Roof, septum, lateral wall
Inferior nasal concha	Lateral wall
Lacrimal	Lateral wall
Maxilla	Floor
Palatine	Floor and lateral wall
Vomer	Septum

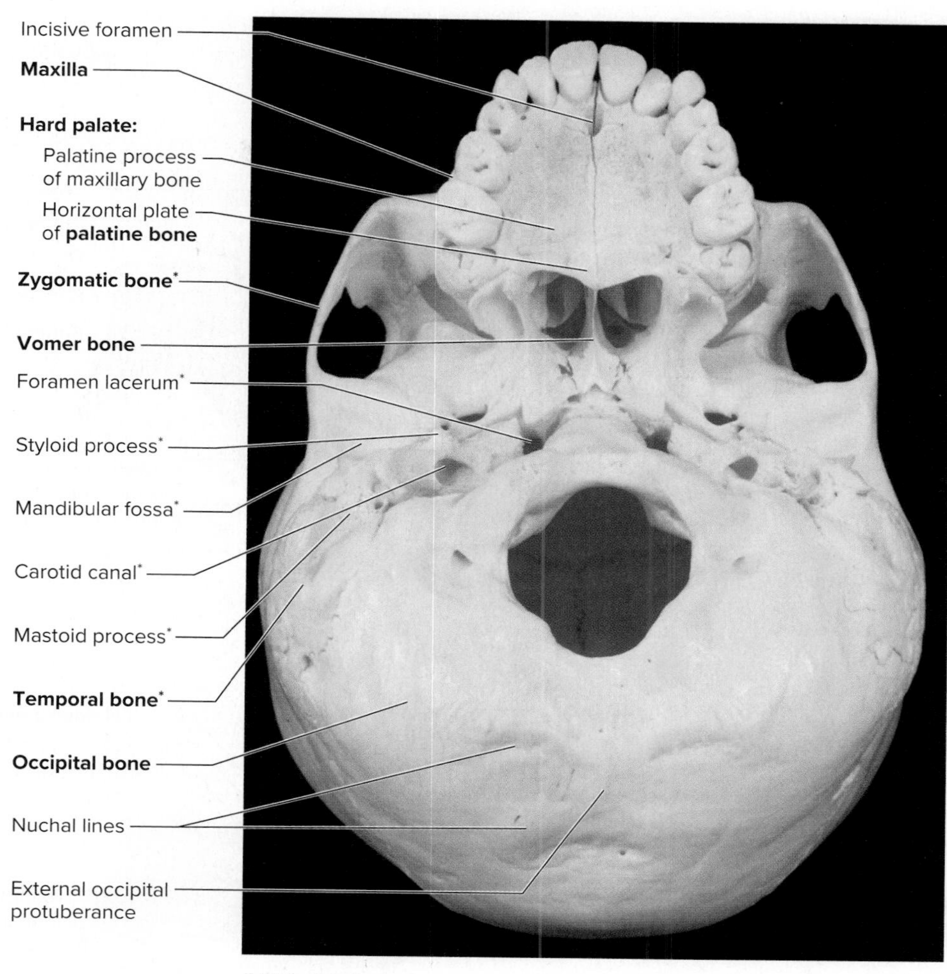

(b) Inferior view

FIGURE 7.10 (continued)

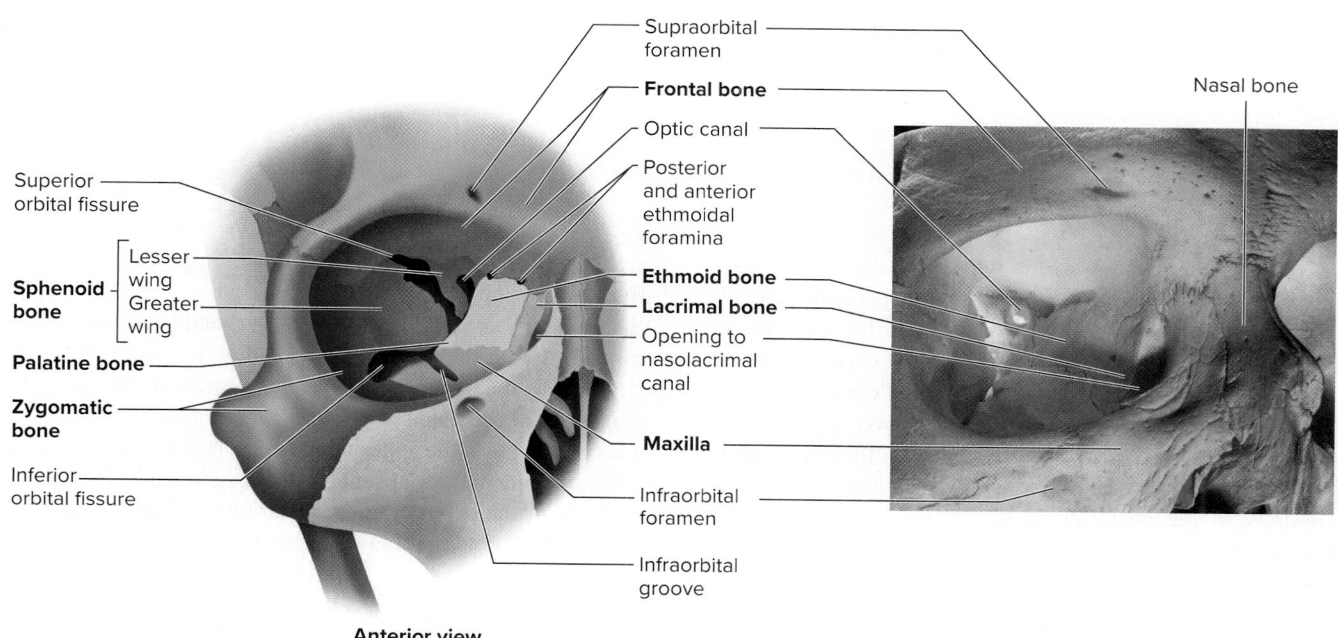

FIGURE 7.11 Bones of the Right Orbit

Multiple bones converge to form the orbits of the eyes. (The names of the bones are in bold.) VideoSurgery/Science Source

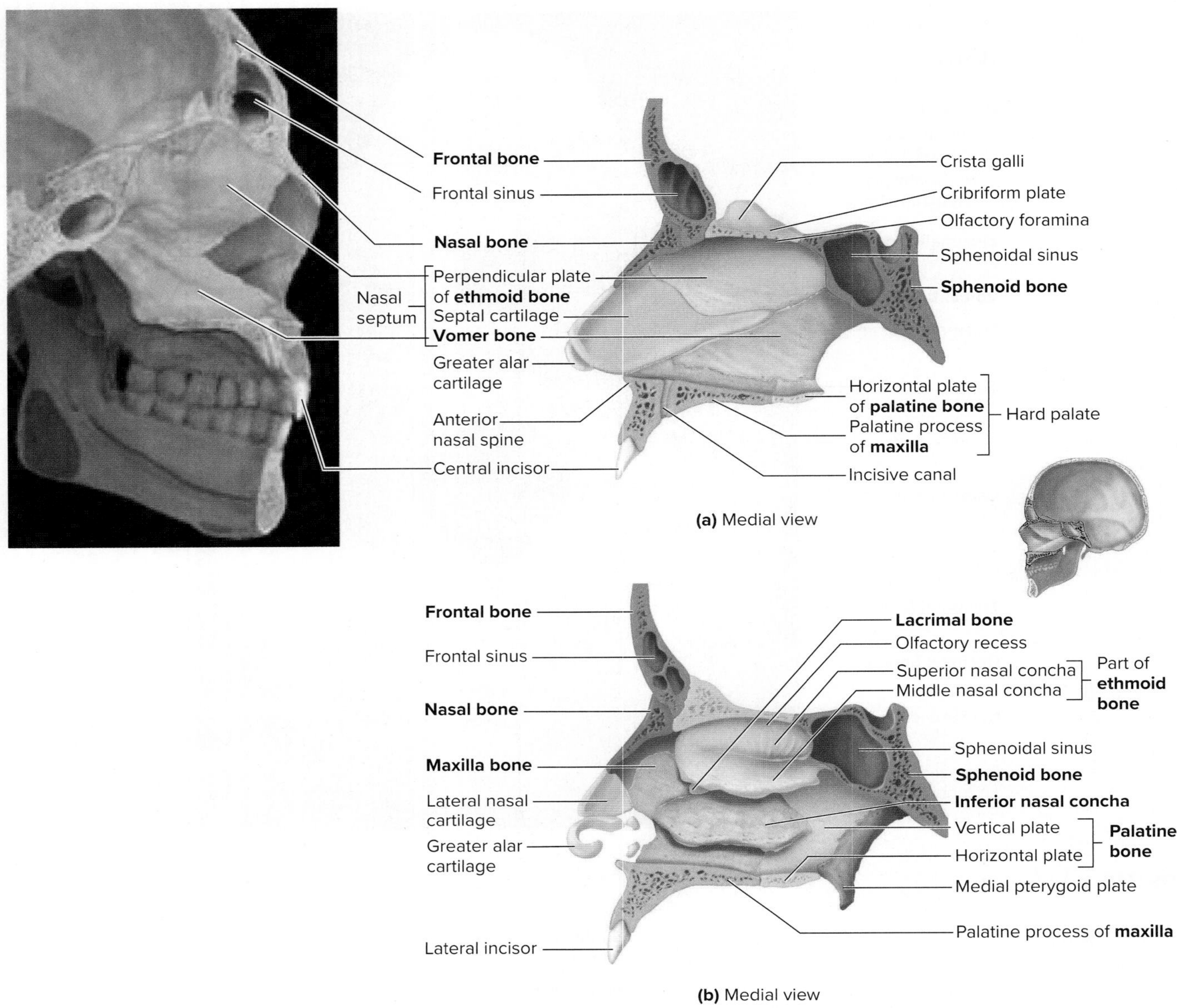

FIGURE 7.12 Bones of the Nasal Cavity

(*a*) Nasal septum as seen from the nasal cavity. (*b*) Right lateral nasal wall as seen from inside the nasal cavity with the nasal septum removed. (The names of the bones are in bold.) (a) APR/McGraw Hill

where the muscles controlling eye movements attach. The orbits have several openings through which structures communicate between the orbit and other cavities. The nasolacrimal duct passes from the orbit into the nasal cavity through the **nasolacrimal canal,** carrying tears from the eyes to the nasal cavity, which is why you often need to blow your nose when you cry (see figure 7.11). The optic nerve for vision passes from the eye through the optic canal and enters the cranial cavity. Superior and inferior orbital fissures in the posterior of the orbits provide openings through which nerves and blood vessels communicate with structures in the orbit or pass to the face.

Nasal Cavity

Table 7.5 lists the bones that converge to form the nasal cavity. The cavity has a rounded opening anteriorly and is separated into right and left halves by the nasal septum. The posterior part of the nasal septum consists primarily of the perpendicular plate of the ethmoid bone, as discussed earlier, and the vomer bone, to be discussed with the facial bones. Hyaline cartilage forms the anterior part of the nasal septum. The entrances to the nasal cavity in a dried skull are much larger than the openings in a living person. This is because the external nose is formed mostly of hyaline cartilage and will be absent from a dried skull. The only visible portions of the external nose in a dried skull are (1) the two nasal bones and (2) the maxilla (see figure 7.7).

Facial Bones

The 14 facial bones of the skull include (1) the 2 zygomatic bones, (2) the 2 maxilla bones, (3) the 2 palatine bones, (4) the 2 lacrimal bones, (5) the 2 nasal bones, (6) the mandible,

TABLE **7.6** **Skull Foramina, Fissures, and Canals (see figures 7.9 and 7.10)**

Opening	Bones Containing the Opening	Structures Passing Through Openings
Supraorbital foramen or notch	Frontal	Supraorbital nerve and vessels
Carotid canal	Temporal	Carotid artery and carotid sympathetic nerve plexus
External acoustic meatus	Temporal	Sound waves passing to the eardrum
Internal acoustic meatus	Temporal	Facial nerve and vestibulocochlear nerve
Stylomastoid foramen	Temporal	Facial nerve
Jugular foramen	Between temporal and occipital	Internal jugular vein, glossopharyngeal nerve, vagus nerve, and accessory nerve
Foramen magnum	Occipital	Spinal cord, accessory nerves, and vertebral arteries
Hypoglossal canal	Occipital	Hypoglossal nerve
Foramen lacerum	Between temporal, occipital, and sphenoid	Filled with cartilage in life
Foramen rotundum	Sphenoid	Maxillary division of trigeminal nerve
Foramen ovale	Sphenoid	Mandibular division of trigeminal nerve
Foramen spinosum	Sphenoid	Middle meningeal artery
Optic canal	Sphenoid	Optic nerve and ophthalmic artery
Pterygoid canal	Sphenoid	Sympathetic and parasympathetic nerves to the face
Superior orbital fissures	Sphenoid	Oculomotor nerve, trochlear nerve, ophthalmic division of trigeminal nerve, abducens nerve, and ophthalmic veins
Inferior orbital fissures	Between sphenoid and maxilla	Infraorbital nerve and blood vessels and zygomatic nerve
Ethmoidal foramina, anterior and posterior	Between ethmoid and frontal	Anterior and posterior ethmoidal nerves
Olfactory foramina	Ethmoid	Olfactory nerves
Zygomaticofacial foramen	Zygomatic	Zygomaticofacial nerve
Zygomaticotemporal foramen	Zygomatic	Zygomaticotemporal nerve
Incisive foramen	Between maxillae	Incisive nerve
Infraorbital foramen	Maxilla	Infraorbital nerve
Sphenopalatine foramen	Between palatine and sphenoid	Nasopalatine nerve and sphenopalatine blood vessels
Palatine foramina, anterior and posterior	Palatine	Palatine nerves
Nasolacrimal canal	Between lacrimal and maxilla	Nasolacrimal (tear) duct
Mandibular foramen	Mandible	Inferior alveolar nerve to the mandibular teeth
Mental foramen	Mandible	Mental nerve

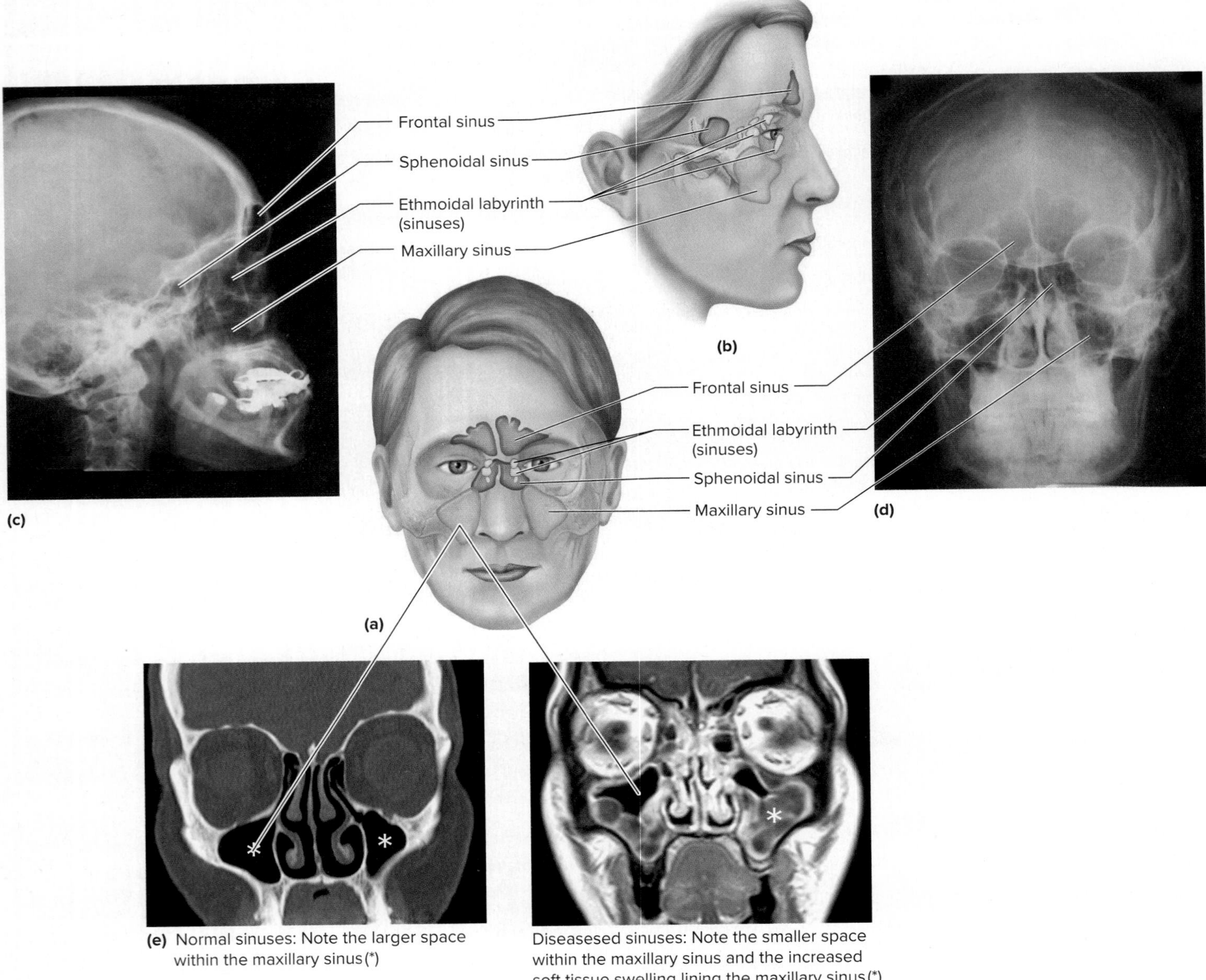

(e) Normal sinuses: Note the larger space within the maxillary sinus(*)

Diseased sinuses: Note the smaller space within the maxillary sinus and the increased soft tissue swelling lining the maxillary sinus(*)

FIGURE 7.13 Paranasal Sinuses
(*a*) Anterior view. (*b*) Lateral view. (*c*) X-ray of the sinuses, lateral view. (*d*) X-ray of the sinuses, anterior view. (*e*) MRI showing a larger space present in maxillary sinuses of a healthy patient (left) in comparison with smaller space present in maxillary sinuses of a non-healthy patient (right). (c, d) Hemera Technologies/Able-Stock.com/Getty Images (e 1, 2) Living Art Enterprises, LLC/Science Source

(7) the vomer bone, and (8) the 2 inferior nasal conchae (figure 7.8; see table 7.8). These bones, in addition to two cranial bones (the frontal and ethmoid bones), form the structure of the face in the anterior of the skull. The facial bones protect the major sensory organs located in the face: the eyes, nose, and tongue. These bones also provide attachment point for muscles controlling mastication, facial expressions associated with our emotions, and eye movements. Table 7.6 lists many of the unique features of the skull, including muscle attachment points and openings for nerve and blood vessel passage. The jaws (mandible and maxillae) possess **alveolar** (al-VEE-oh-lar) **processes** with sockets for tooth attachment. It is the bones of the face and their soft tissues that determine the uniqueness of each individual's facial appearance.

Zygomatic Bones

The **zygomatic** (zie-goh-MAT-ik) **bones,** commonly known as the cheekbones, are anterior to the sphenoid bone (see figure 7.6).

TABLE 7.7 Cranial Bones of the Skull

(a) Frontal Bone—Anterior View

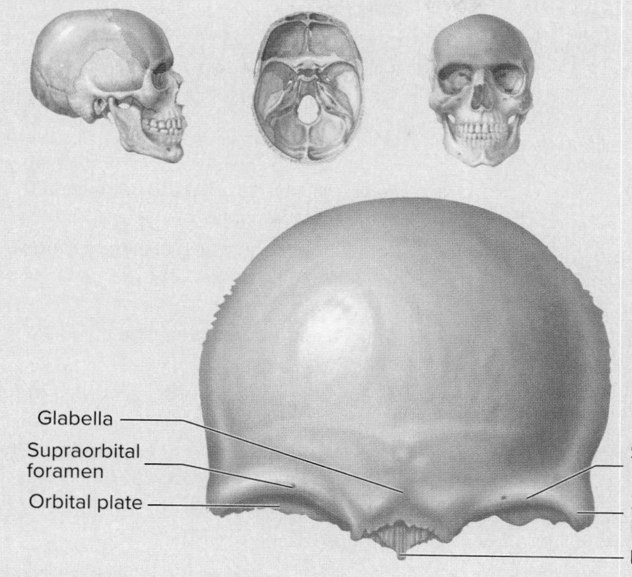

Landmark	Description
Glabella	Area between the supraorbital margins
Nasal spine	Superior part of the nasal bridge
Orbital plate	Roof of the orbit
Supraorbital foramen	Opening through which nerves and vessels exit the skull to the skin of the forehead
Supraorbital margin	Ridge forming the anterior superior border of the orbit
Zygomatic process	Connects to the zygomatic bone; helps form the lateral margin of the orbit

Special Features

Forms the forehead and roof of the orbit

Contains the frontal sinus

(b) Parietal Bone (Right)—Lateral View

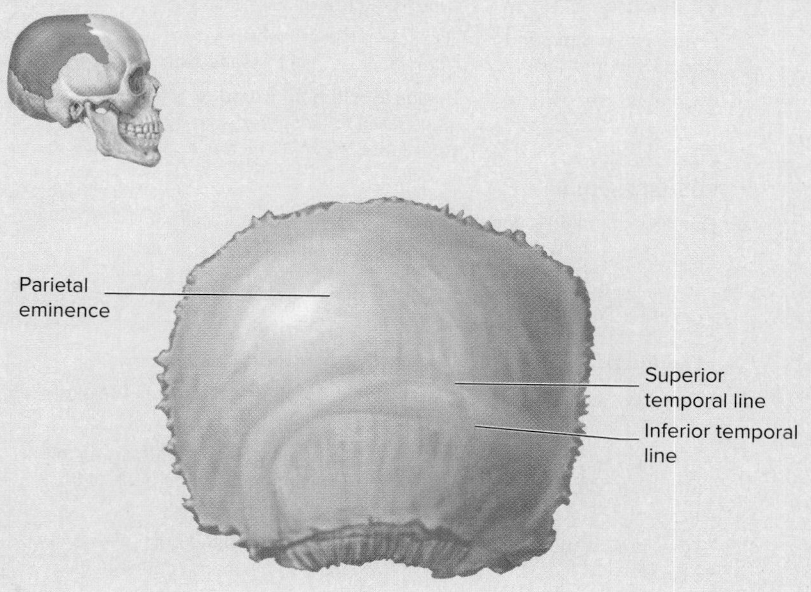

Landmark	Description
Parietal eminence	The widest part of the head is from one parietal eminence to the other.
Superior and inferior temporal lines	Attachment point for temporalis muscle

Special Feature

Forms lateral wall of skull

TABLE 7.7 Cranial Bones of the Skull—Continued

(c) Temporal Bone (Right)—Lateral and Medial Views

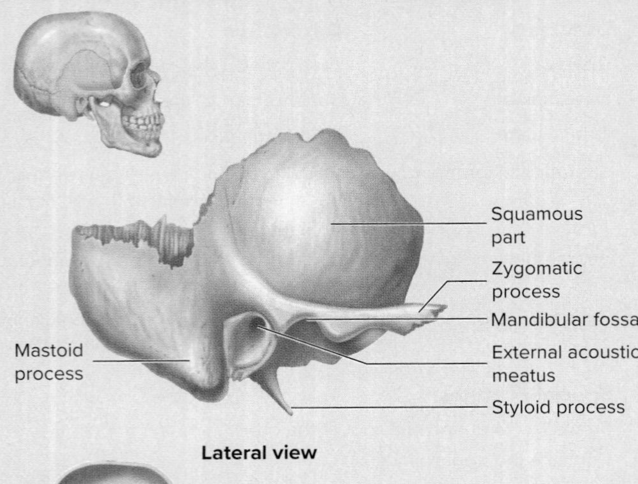

Lateral view

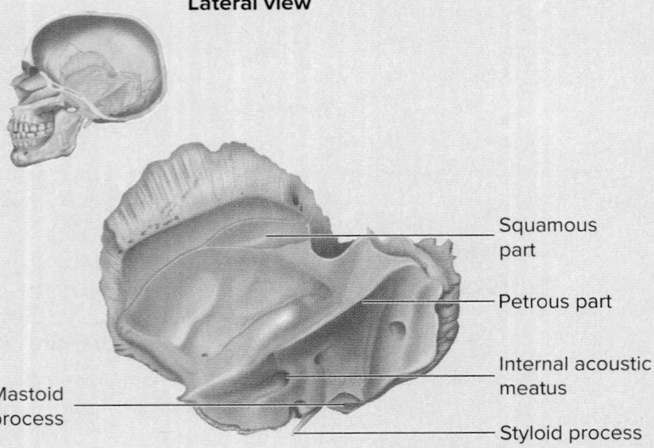

Medial view

Landmark	Description
Carotid canal (shown in figures 7.9 and 7.10)	Canal through which the internal carotid artery enters the cranial cavity
External auditory canal	External canal of the ear; carries sound to the ear
Internal auditory canal (shown in figure 7.9)	Opening through which the facial (cranial nerve VII) and vestibulocochlear (cranial nerve VIII) nerves enter the petrous part of the temporal bone
Forms one side of jugular foramen (shown in figures 7.9 and 7.10)	Foramen through which the internal jugular vein exits the cranial cavity
Mandibular fossa	Articulation point between the mandible and skull
Mastoid process	Attachment point for muscles moving the head and for a hyoid muscle
Middle cranial fossa (shown in figure 7.9)	Depression in the floor of the cranial cavity formed by the temporal lobes of the brain
Petrous part (shown in figure 7.9)	Thick portion of the temporal bone
Squamous part (shown in figure 7.9)	Flat, lateral portion of the temporal bone
Styloid process	Attachment for muscles of the tongue, throat, and hyoid bone
Stylomastoid foramen (shown in figure 7.10)	Foramen through which the facial nerve (cranial nerve VII) exits the skull
Zygomatic process	Helps form the bony bridge extending from the cheek to just anterior to the ear; attachment for a muscle that moves the mandible

Special Features

Contains the middle and inner ear and the mastoid air cells

Place where the mandible articulates with the rest of the skull

(d) Occipital Bone—Inferior View

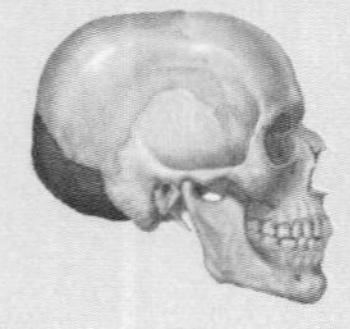

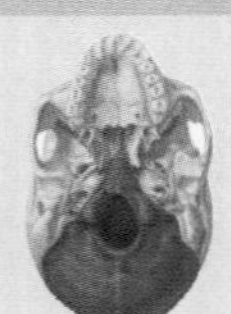

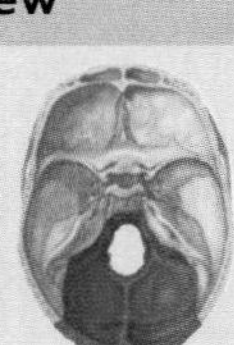

Anterior

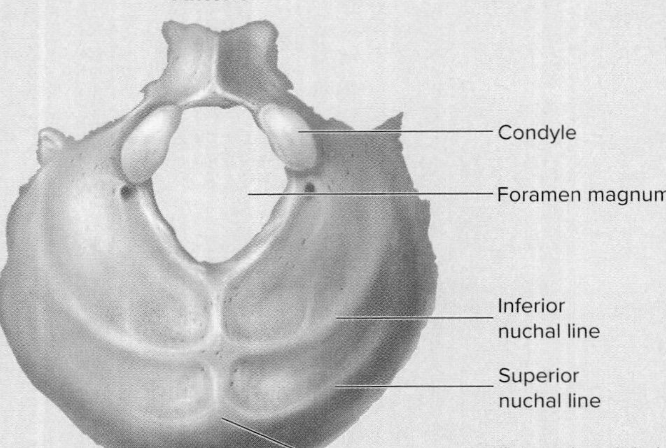

Posterior

Landmark	Description
Condyle	Articulation point between the skull and first vertebra
External occipital protuberance	Attachment point for a strong ligament (nuchal ligament) in the back of the neck
Foramen magnum	Opening around the point where the brain and spinal cord connect
Hypoglossal canal (shown in figure 7.9)	Opening through which the hypoglossal nerve (cranial nerve XII) passes
Inferior nuchal line	Attachment point for neck muscles
Posterior cranial fossa (shown in figure 7.9)	Depression in the posterior of the cranial cavity formed by the cerebellum
Superior nuchal line	Attachment point for neck muscles

Special Feature

Forms the base of the skull

TABLE 7.7 Cranial Bones of the Skull—Continued

(e) Sphenoid Bone—Superior and Posterior Views

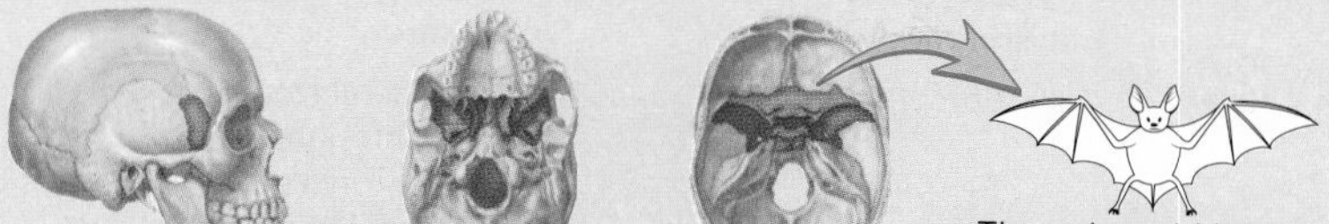

The sphenoid bone is somewhat shaped like a bat.

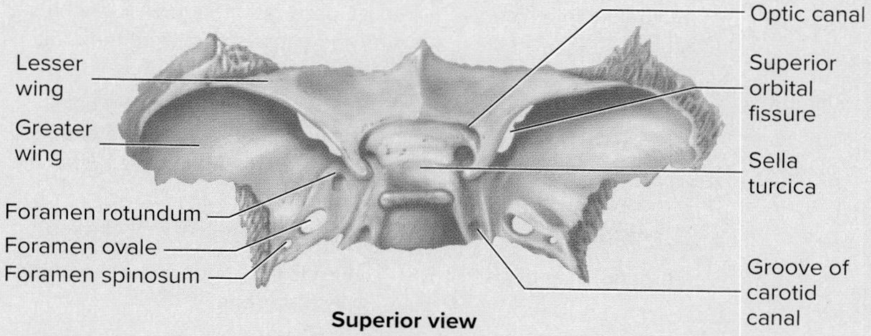

Lesser wing
Greater wing
Foramen rotundum
Foramen ovale
Foramen spinosum
Optic canal
Superior orbital fissure
Sella turcica
Groove of carotid canal

Superior view

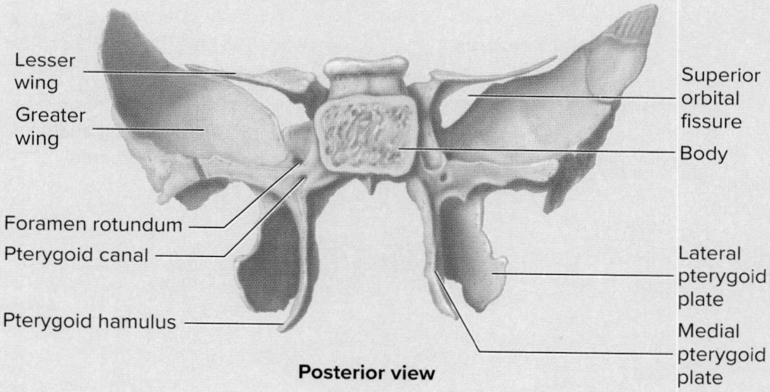

Lesser wing
Greater wing
Foramen rotundum
Pterygoid canal
Pterygoid hamulus
Superior orbital fissure
Body
Lateral pterygoid plate
Medial pterygoid plate

Posterior view

Landmark	Description
Body	Thickest part of the bone; articulates with the occipital bone
Foramen ovale	Opening through which a branch of the trigeminal nerve (cranial nerve V) exits the cranial cavity
Foramen rotundum	Opening through which a branch of the trigeminal nerve (cranial nerve V) exits the cranial cavity
Foramen spinosum	Opening through which a major artery to the meninges (membranes around the brain) enters the cranial cavity
Greater wing	Forms the floor of the middle cranial fossa; several foramina pass through this wing
Lateral pterygoid plate	Attachment point for muscles of mastication (chewing)
Lesser wing	Superior border of the superior orbital fissure
Medial pterygoid plate	Posterolateral walls of the nasal cavity
Optic canal	Opening through which the optic nerve (cranial nerve II) passes from the orbit to the cranial cavity
Pterygoid canal	Opening through which nerves and vessels exit the cranial cavity
Pterygoid hamulus	Process around which the tendon passes from a muscle to the soft palate
Sella turcica	Fossa containing the pituitary gland
Superior orbital fissure	Opening through which nerves and vessels enter the orbit from the cranial cavity

Special Feature

Contains the sphenoidal sinus

TABLE 7.7 Cranial Bones of the Skull—Continued

(f) Ethmoid Bone—Superior, Lateral, and Anterior Views

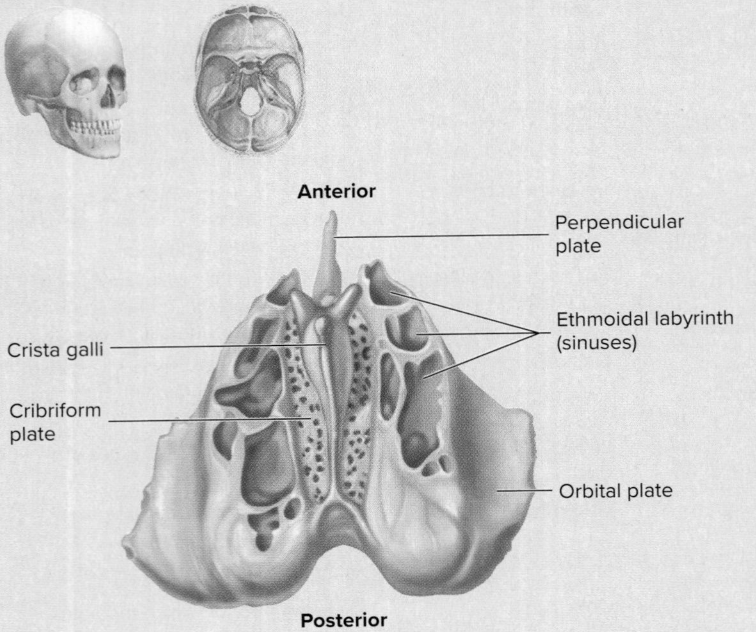

Superior view

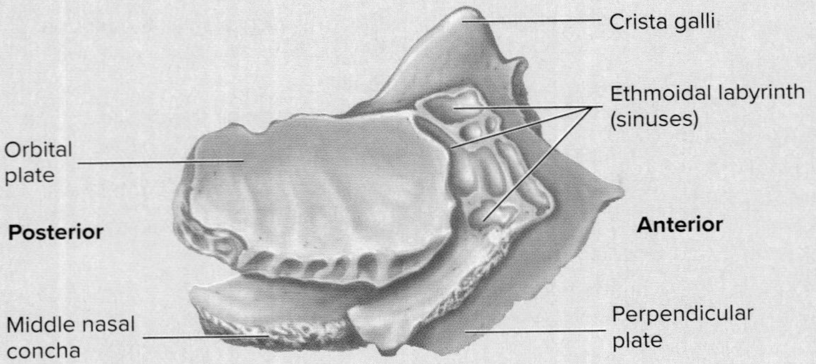

Lateral view

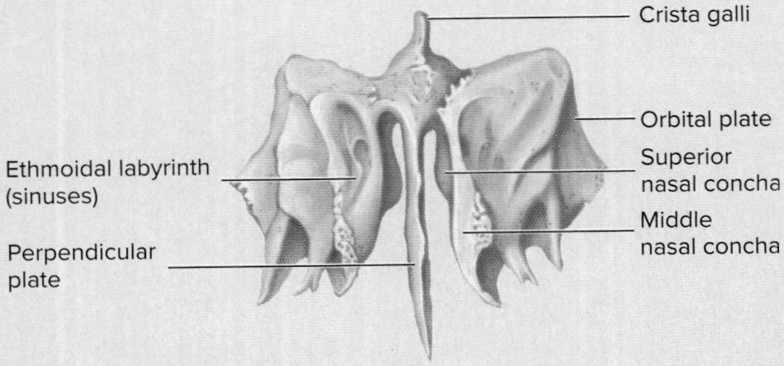

Anterior view

Landmark	Description
Cribriform plate	Contains numerous olfactory foramina through which branches of the olfactory nerve (cranial nerve I) enter the cranial cavity from the nasal cavity
Crista galli	Attachment for meninges (membranes around brain)
Ethmoidal foramina (shown in figure 7.11)	Openings through which nerves and vessels pass from the orbit to the nasal cavity
Middle nasal concha	Ridge extending into the nasal cavity; increases surface area, helps warm and moisten air in the cavity
Orbital plate	Forms the medial wall of the orbit
Perpendicular plate	Forms the superior portion of the nasal septum
Superior nasal concha	Ridge extending into the nasal cavity; increases surface area, helps warm and moisten air in the cavity

Special Features

Forms part of the nasal septum and part of the lateral walls and roof of the nasal cavity

Contains the ethmoidal labyrinth, or ethmoidal sinuses; the labyrinth is divided into anterior, middle, and posterior ethmoidal cells

There they form part of the inferiolateral border of the orbits (see table 7.4). As previously discussed, the temporal process of the zygomatic bone articulates with the zygomatic process of the temporal bone to form the **zygomatic arch.**

Maxillae

Each **maxilla** (mak-SIL-ah; pl. maxillae, upper jaw) is anterior and inferior to the zygomatic bones and the two maxillae are fused medially (see figures 7.7 and 7.10). The maxillae are two of the three jaw bones, and form (1) the upper jaw, (2) the majority of the roof of the mouth, and (3) the center portion of the face.

Each of the two maxillary bones has a **palatine process.** These join medially to form the anterior two-thirds of the **hard palate,** or the roof of the mouth. The **incisive foramen** is located just posterior to the incisor teeth and allows passage of blood vessels and nerves. The posterior one-third is formed by two other facial bones, the palatine bones, to be discussed later. Extending posteriorly from the hard palate are soft tissues, which collectively form the soft palate. The hard and soft palates separate the nasal cavity from the mouth, enabling humans to chew and breathe at the same time.

Alveolar processes in the maxilla anchor the upper teeth of the jaw (see figure 7.7). Just inferior to the nasal cavity, the two maxillae fuse medially, forming the **anterior nasal spine;** superiorly, the **frontal processes** of the maxilla help form a portion of the bridge of the nose (see figure 7.7). Inferior to the orbits, within each maxilla, is an **infraorbital foramen** for passage of a facial nerve and artery (see figure 7.11). At the junction of the maxilla with the greater wing of the sphenoid bone is the **inferior orbital fissure** (see figure 7.11). This fissure allows the passage of several nerves and blood vessels to the face.

Palatine Bones

The **palatine bones** have **horizontal plates** that fuse medially to form the posterior portion of the hard palate, as described earlier with the maxillae. The **vertical plates** project superiorly to form a small portion of the orbit and nasal cavity (see figures 7.11 and 7.12).

Lacrimal Bones

The **lacrimal** (LAK-rih-mal; tears) **bones** are the smallest of the skull bones and house the depression through which the nasolacrimal duct enters the nasolacrimal canal, joining the orbits and nasal cavity (see figure 7.11 and chapter 15).

Nasal Bones

The **nasal bones,** along with the frontal processes of the maxillae, form the bridge of the nose where eyeglasses rest.

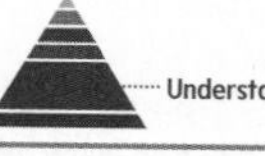

Predict 1

A direct blow to the nose may result in a "broken nose." List at least three bones that may be broken.

Mandible

The **mandible** (lower jaw) is the only skull bone that is freely movable relative to the other skull bones. It is inferior to the maxillae and attaches posteriorly to the temporal bone via the **mandibular fossae** (see figure 7.5 and table 7.8). The mandible has two main parts: (1) the **body** and (2) the **ramus** (branch). The body, where the "chin" is located, is U-shaped and extends both anteriorly and posteriorly. The ramus branches from the body at the **mandibular angle** and projects superiorly toward the temporal bone. The ramus joins the temporal bone by way of the articulation of the **mandibular condyle** with the mandibular fossa. The **coronoid** (KOHR-oh-noyd) **process** is anterior to the mandibular condyle on the ramus. The powerful muscle of mastication, the temporalis muscle, attaches to the coronoid process. Alveolar processes of the mandible contain the lower teeth.

Anteriorly, the two halves of the mandible are fused, forming a pointed **mental protuberance,** which is commonly referred to as the chin. On each anterolateral surface of the body is the **mental foramen** for passage of nerves and blood vessels to the chin.

Vomer

The **vomer** forms most of the posterior portion of the nasal septum and can be seen between the medial pterygoid plates of the sphenoid bone in the center of the nasal cavity (see figure 7.10).

Inferior Nasal Conchae

The **inferior nasal concha,** as discussed with the ethmoid bone, is one of the three conchae in the nasal cavity that provide increased surface area (see figures 7.7 and 7.12).

ASSESS YOUR PROGRESS

4. *What are the parts and general functions of the axial skeleton?*
5. *Name the four major sutures of the skull and the bones they connect.*
6. *List the seven bones that form the orbit of the eye.*
7. *What is a sinus? What are the functions of sinuses? Give the locations of the paranasal sinuses.*
8. *Name the bones and cartilage that compose the nasal septum.*
9. *What bones form the hard palate, and what is the function of the hard palate?*
10. *What structure allows the brainstem to connect to the spinal cord?*
11. *Name the foramina that allow the passage of the following nerves and blood vessels: optic nerve, olfactory nerve, vestibulocochlear nerve, incisive nerve, facial nerve, carotid artery, and internal jugular vein.*
12. *What structure allows sound waves to reach the eardrum?*
13. *List the bones that make up the floor of the cranium.*
14. *State the bone features where the following muscles attach to the skull: neck muscles, throat muscles, muscles of mastication, muscles of facial expression, and muscles that move the eyeballs.*
15. *Name the bones of the cranium and face. What are the functions accomplished by each group?*

Hyoid Bone

The **hyoid bone** (Gr., shaped like the lowercase letter upsilon, υ; table 7.9) is important for speech and swallowing. Some tongue muscles as well as neck muscles that elevate the larynx attach to the hyoid. The hyoid bone is unpaired, and is often listed as part of the facial bones. However, it is not part of the adult skull (see table 7.1). The hyoid bone has the unique distinction of being the only bone in the body not directly attached to another bone. It has no direct bony attachment to the skull. Instead, muscles and ligaments attach it to the skull, so the hyoid is embedded in soft tissue in the neck just below the mandible.

Vertebral Column

The **vertebral column** performs five major functions: (1) It supports the weight of the head and trunk, (2) it protects the spinal cord, (3) it allows spinal nerves to exit the spinal cord, (4) it provides a site for muscle attachment, and (5) it permits movement of the head and trunk.

The vertebral column usually consists of 26 bones, called **vertebrae** (VER-teh-bray), which can be divided into five regions: 7 **cervical vertebrae,** 12 **thoracic vertebrae,** 5 **lumbar vertebrae,** 1 **sacral bone,** and 1 **coccygeal** (kok-SIJ-ee-al) **bone** (figure 7.14). For convenience, each of the five regions is identified by a letter, and the vertebrae within each region are numbered: C1–C7, T1–T12, L1–L5, S, and CO. You can remember the number of vertebrae in the nonfused regions of the vertebral column by remembering mealtimes: 7, 12, and 5. The developing embryo has about 33 or 34 vertebrae, but by adulthood the 5 sacral vertebrae have fused to form 1 bone, and the 4 or 5 coccygeal bones usually have fused to form 1 bone.

The adult vertebral column has four major curvatures (figure 7.14): (1) The cervical region curves anteriorly, (2) the thoracic region curves posteriorly, (3) the lumbar region curves anteriorly, and (4) the sacral and coccygeal regions together curve posteriorly. The curves form during embryonic development. Because the embryo and fetus are C-shaped within the uterus, the vertebral column is naturally curved from the beginning. After birth, when the infant raises its head, a secondary curve, which curves anteriorly, develops in the cervical region. Later, when the infant learns to sit and then walk, the lumbar portion of the column also becomes curved anteriorly. These spinal curvatures help accommodate our upright posture by aligning our body weight with our pelvis and lower limbs.

General Features of the Vertebrae

Each vertebra consists of (1) a body, (2) a vertebral arch, and (3) several processes (table 7.10). Two specific portions of the vertebrae help support the body's weight and protect the spinal cord. The **vertebral body,** the solid bony disk of each vertebra, supports the body's weight. The **vertebral arch,** along with the body, protects the spinal cord. The vertebral arch projects posteriorly from the body. Together, the vertebral arch and the body form a complete bony circle enclosing the **vertebral foramen,** which is occupied by the spinal cord in a living person. The vertebral foramina of adjacent vertebrae combine to form the **vertebral canal,** which contains the entire spinal cord and cauda equina (see figure 12.1).

The vertebral arch is divided into left and right halves, and each half has two parts: (1) the **pedicle** (PED-ih-kul; foot), which is attached to the body, and (2) the **lamina** (LAM-i-na; thin plate), which forms the posterior portion of the vertebral foramen.

TABLE 7.8 Facial Bones of the Skull

(a) Zygomatic Bone (Right)—Lateral View

Landmark	Description
Frontal process	Connection to the frontal bone; helps form the lateral margin of the orbit
Infraorbital margin	Ridge forming the inferior border of the orbit
Temporal process	Helps form the bony bridge from the cheek to just anterior to the ear
Zygomaticofacial foramen	Opening through which a nerve and vessels exit the orbit to the face

Special Features

Forms the prominence of the cheek

Forms the anterolateral wall of the orbit

TABLE 7.8 Facial Bones of the Skull—Continued

(b) Maxilla (Right)—Anterior, Medial, and Lateral Views

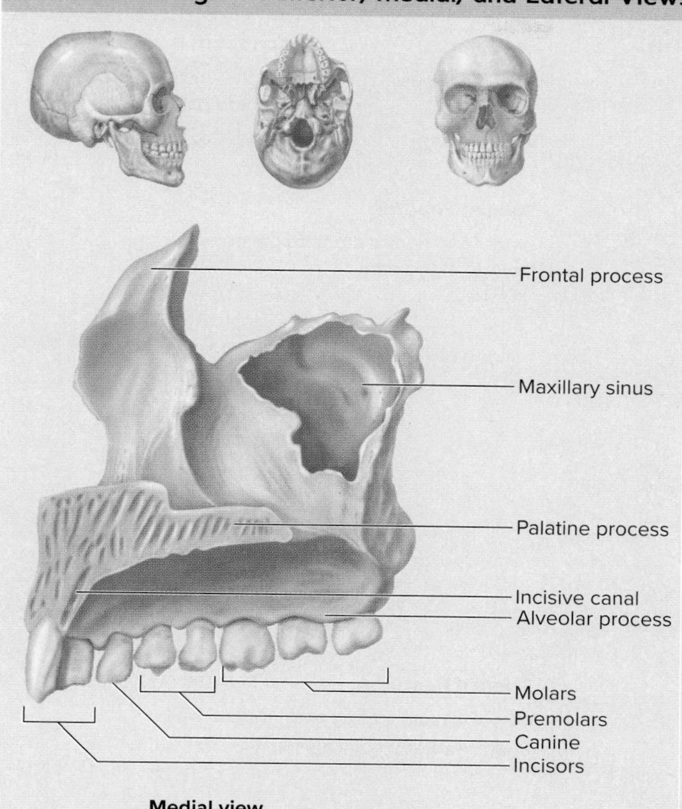

Medial view

Landmark	Description
Alveolar process	Ridge containing the teeth
Anterior nasal spine	Forms part of the nasal septum
Frontal process	Forms the sides of the nasal bridge
Incisive canal	Opening through which a nerve exits the nasal cavity to the roof of the oral cavity
Infraorbital foramen	Opening through which a nerve and vessels exit the orbit to the face
Maxillary tuberosity	Rounded projection posterior to the last maxillary molar tooth
Orbital surface	Forms the floor of the orbit
Palatine process	Forms the anterior two-thirds of the hard palate
Zygomatic process	Connection to the zygomatic bone; helps form the interior margin of the orbit

Special Features

Contains the maxillary sinus and maxillary teeth

Forms part of nasolacrimal canal

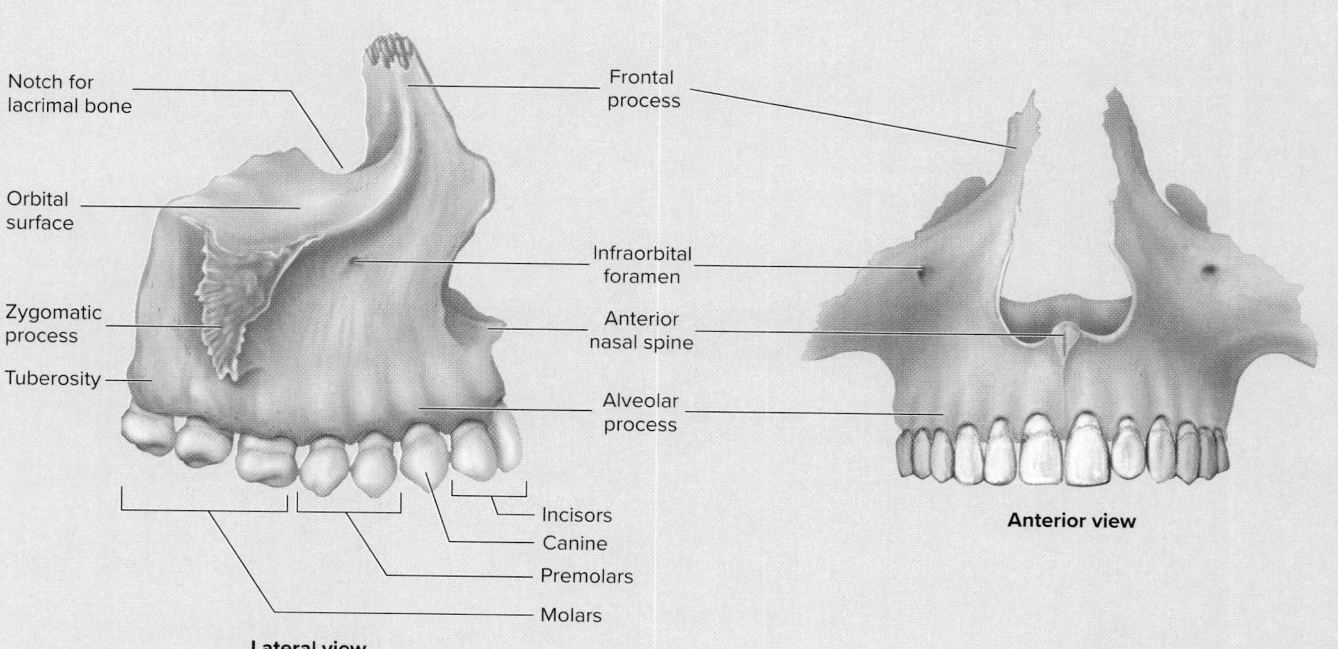

Lateral view

Anterior view

TABLE 7.8 Facial Bones of the Skull—Continued

(c) Palatine Bone (Right)—Medial and Anterior Views

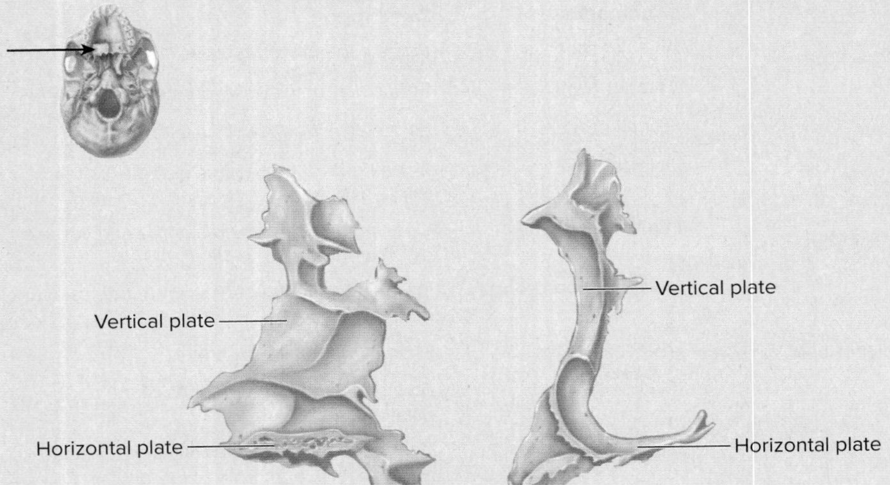

Landmark	Description
Horizontal plate	Forms the posterior one-third of the hard palate
Vertical plate	Forms part of the lateral nasal wall

Special Feature

Helps form part of the hard palate and a small part of the wall of the orbit

(d) Lacrimal Bone (Right)—Anterolateral View

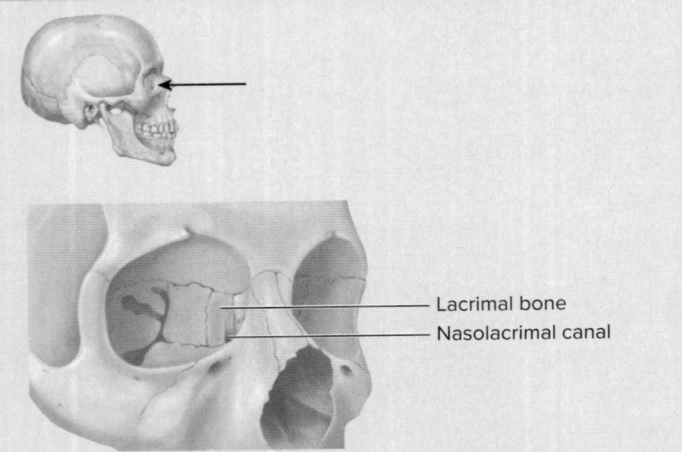

Special Features

Forms a small portion of the orbital wall

Forms part of the nasolacrimal canal

(e) Nasal Bone (Right)—Anterolateral View

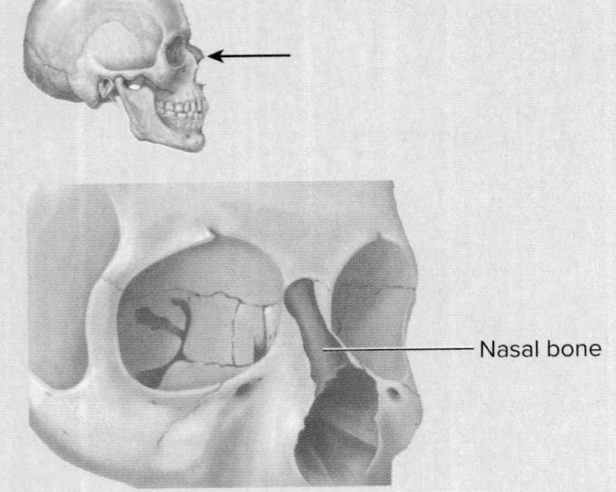

Special Feature

Forms the bridge of the nose

TABLE 7.8 Facial Bones of the Skull—Continued

(f) Mandible (Right Half)—Anterior, Medial, and Lateral Views

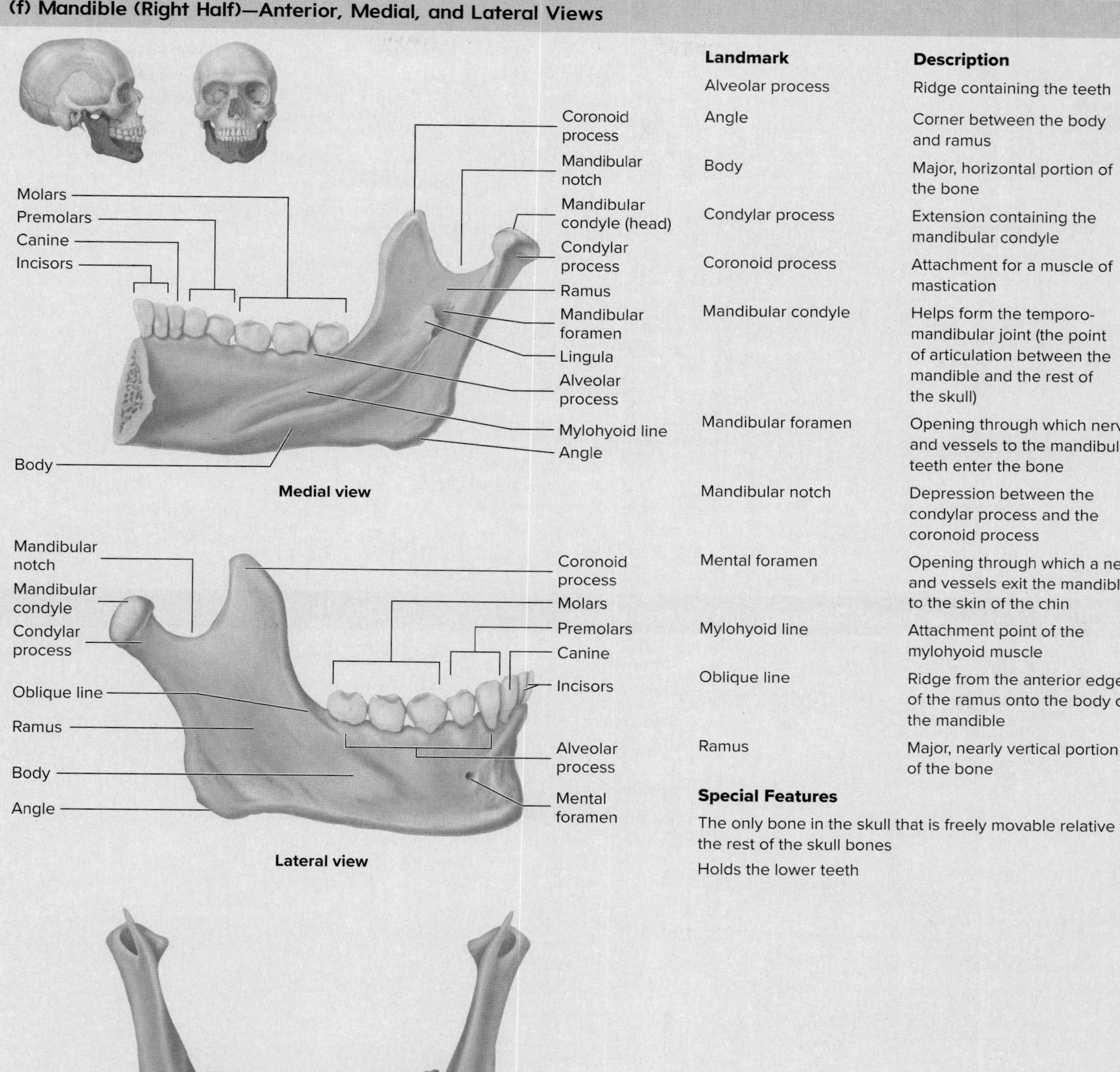

Landmark	Description
Alveolar process	Ridge containing the teeth
Angle	Corner between the body and ramus
Body	Major, horizontal portion of the bone
Condylar process	Extension containing the mandibular condyle
Coronoid process	Attachment for a muscle of mastication
Mandibular condyle	Helps form the temporomandibular joint (the point of articulation between the mandible and the rest of the skull)
Mandibular foramen	Opening through which nerves and vessels to the mandibular teeth enter the bone
Mandibular notch	Depression between the condylar process and the coronoid process
Mental foramen	Opening through which a nerve and vessels exit the mandible to the skin of the chin
Mylohyoid line	Attachment point of the mylohyoid muscle
Oblique line	Ridge from the anterior edge of the ramus onto the body of the mandible
Ramus	Major, nearly vertical portion of the bone

Special Features

The only bone in the skull that is freely movable relative to the rest of the skull bones

Holds the lower teeth

TABLE 7.8 Facial Bones of the Skull—Continued

(g) Vomer—Anterior and Lateral Views

Alae
Vertical plate
Anterior view

Alae
Vertical plate
Lateral view

Landmark	Description
Alae	Attachment points between the vomer and sphenoid
Vertical plate	Forms part of the nasal septum

Special Feature

Forms most of the posterior and inferior portions of the nasal septum

TABLE 7.9 Hyoid Bone—Anterior and Lateral Views

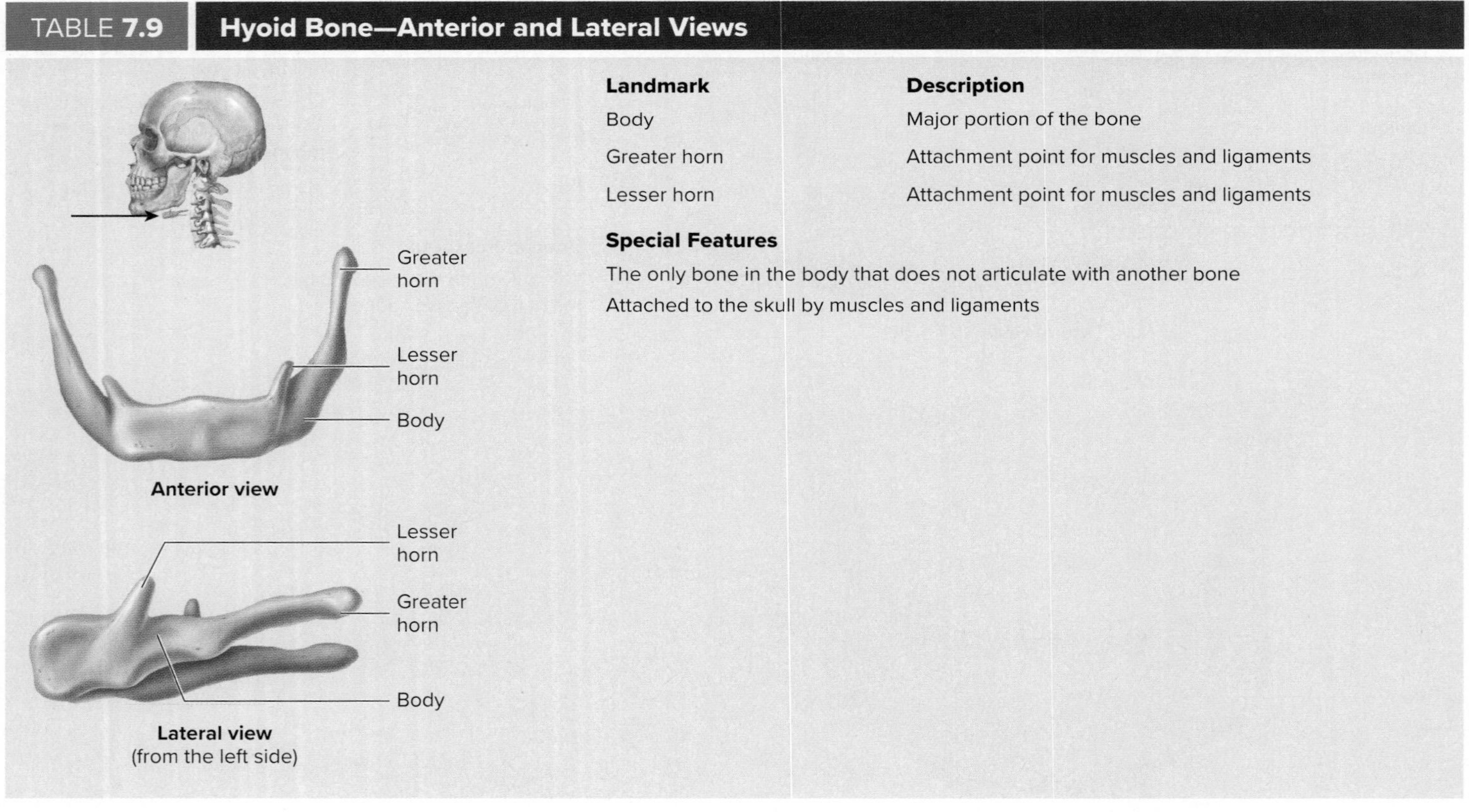

Anterior view

Lateral view (from the left side)

Landmark	Description
Body	Major portion of the bone
Greater horn	Attachment point for muscles and ligaments
Lesser horn	Attachment point for muscles and ligaments

Special Features

The only bone in the body that does not articulate with another bone

Attached to the skull by muscles and ligaments

FUNDAMENTAL **Figure**

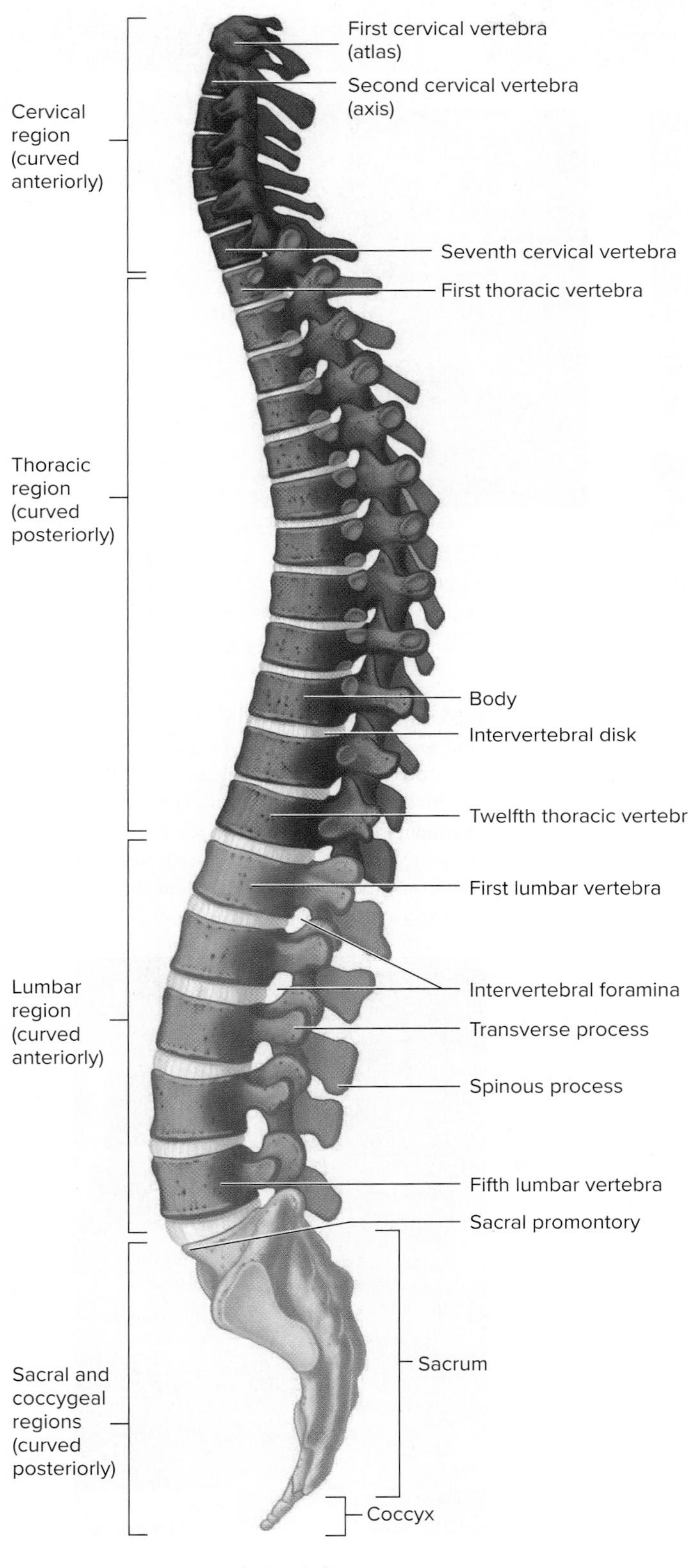

FIGURE 7.14 Vertebral Column

The complete vertebral column is viewed from the left side. 

Sometimes a **laminectomy** is performed to relieve pain from a compressed spinal nerve root due to a herniated intervertebral disk or other vertebral injuries. A surgeon removes the lamina from the injured vertebra.

A **transverse process** extends laterally from each side of the arch between the lamina and the pedicle, and a single **spinous process** lies at the junction between the two laminae. The spinous processes can be seen and felt as a series of rounded projections down the midline of the back (figure 7.19). Much vertebral movement is accomplished by the contraction of the skeletal muscles attached to the transverse and spinous processes (see chapter 10).

The **intervertebral foramina** are the locations where two vertebrae meet (table 7.10*d*; see figure 7.14). Each intervertebral foramen is formed by **intervertebral notches** in the pedicles of adjacent vertebrae. These foramina are where spinal nerves exit the spinal cord.

Movement and additional support of the vertebral column are made possible by the vertebral processes. Each vertebra has two **superior** and two **inferior articular processes,** with the superior processes of one vertebra articulating with the inferior processes of the next superior vertebra (table 7.10*c,d*). Overlap of these processes increases the rigidity of the vertebral column. The region of overlap and articulation between the superior and inferior articular processes creates a smooth **articular facet** (FAS-et; little face) on each articular process.

Intervertebral Disks

In a living person, vertebrae are separated by **intervertebral disks.** Intervertebral disks are composed of fibrocartilage and are located between the bodies of adjacent vertebrae (figure 7.20 and table 7.10; see figure 7.14). The intervertebral disks provide support and cushion the vertebral bodies. The intervertebral disks consist of an external **annulus fibrosus** (AN-yoo-lus fye-BROH-sus; fibrous ring) and an internal, gelatinous **nucleus pulposus** (pul-POH-sus; pulp). As a person ages, the disk becomes more compressed, which decreases distance between vertebrae. The reduction in thickness of the intervertebral disks actually decreases the height of a person. So, we really can shrink as we age! In addition, the annulus fibrosus becomes weaker with age and thus more susceptible to herniation.

Regional Differences in Vertebrae

Each of the five regions of the vertebral column has uniquely shaped vertebrae that contribute to the particular function of each region of the vertebral column. As one region gives way to another region, the characteristics between regional vertebrae become less distinct (table 7.11).

Cervical Vertebrae

Cervical vertebrae are located in the vertebral column region with the greatest range of motion. These vertebrae support and move the head (figure 7.14). However, because the cervical vertebrae support only the weight of the head, they have very small bodies, making dislocations and fractures in this area of the vertebral column more common than in other regions. Most cervical vertebrae have **bifid** (BYE-fid; split) **spinous processes.** Cervical

Clinical IMPACT 7.1

Abnormal Spinal Curvatures

In some people, the normal spinal curvature becomes distorted due to disease or a congenital defect. Figure 7.15 shows a healthy spine's curvature. The three most common spinal curvatures are lordosis, kyphosis, and scoliosis. **Lordosis** (lore-DOH-sis; hollow back) is an exaggeration of the convex curve of the lumbar region (figure 7.16). **Kyphosis** (kie-FOH-sis; hump back) is an exaggeration of the concave curve of the thoracic region (figure 7.17). It is most common in postmenopausal females but can also occur in males and becomes more prevalent as people age. **Scoliosis** (skoh-lee-OH-sis) is an abnormal lateral and rotational curvature of the vertebral column (figure 7.18). Contrary to popular belief, scoliosis in school-age children is not associated with carrying overly heavy backpacks. Studies have shown that, although back pain is common in backpack-bearing school kids, structural changes in the vertebral column are not. Treatments for abnormal spinal curvature depend on the age and overall medical condition of the person. However, most treatments include repeated examinations to monitor the status of the curvature, a back brace, and surgery when the curving is not slowed by bracing.

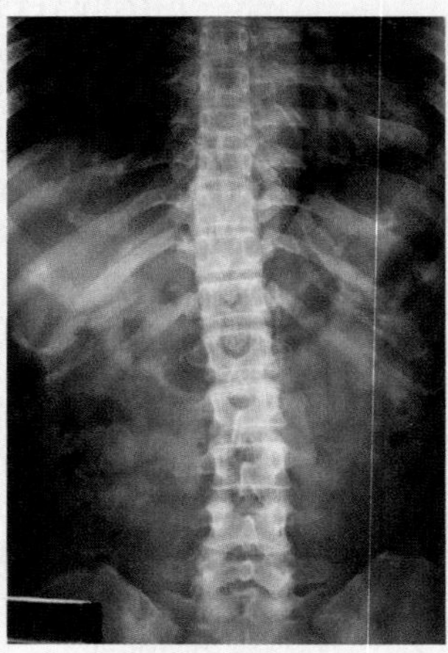

FIGURE 7.15 Healthy Spine
A healthy spine has normal anterior and posterior curves. stockdevil/Getty Images

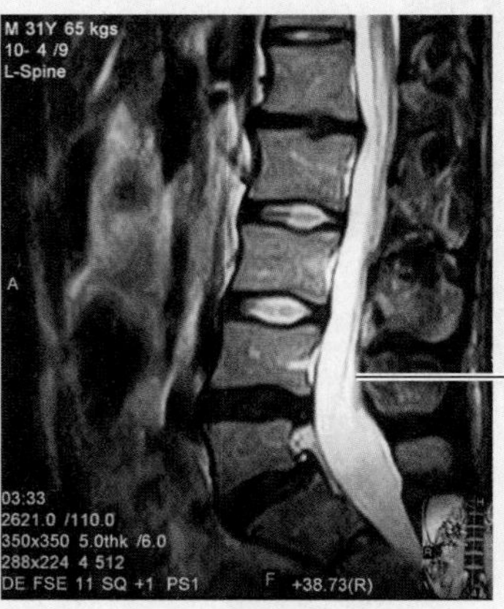

FIGURE 7.16 Lordosis
A spine with lordosis has an exaggerated convex curve of the lumbar region. Marko Rupena/Alamy Stock Photo

Excessive concave curvature of thoracic spine

FIGURE 7.17 Kyphosis
A spine with kyphosis has an exaggerated concave curve of the thoracic region. Apogee/Science Source

Posterior view

FIGURE 7.18 Scoliosis
A spine with scoliosis has lateral curves. Princess Margaret Rose Orthopaedic Hospital/Science Source

TABLE 7.10 General Structure of a Vertebra

Feature	Description
Body	Disk-shaped; usually the largest part with flat surfaces directed superiorly and inferiorly; forms the anterior wall of the vertebral foramen; intervertebral disks are located between the bodies
Vertebral foramen	Hole in each vertebra through which the spinal cord passes; adjacent vertebral foramina form the vertebral canal
Vertebral arch	Forms the lateral and posterior walls of the vertebral foramen; possesses several processes and articular surfaces
Pedicle	Foot of the arch with one on each side; forms the lateral walls of the vertebral foramen
Lamina	Posterior part of the arch; forms the posterior wall of the vertebral foramen
Transverse process	Process projecting laterally from the junction of the lamina and pedicle; a site of muscle attachment
Spinous process	Process projecting posteriorly at the point where the two laminae join; a site of muscle attachment; strengthens the vertebral column and allows for movement
Articular processes	Superior and inferior projections containing articular facets where vertebrae articulate with each other; strengthen the vertebral column and allow for movement
Intervertebral notches	Form intervertebral foramina between two adjacent vertebrae through which spinal nerves exit the vertebral canal

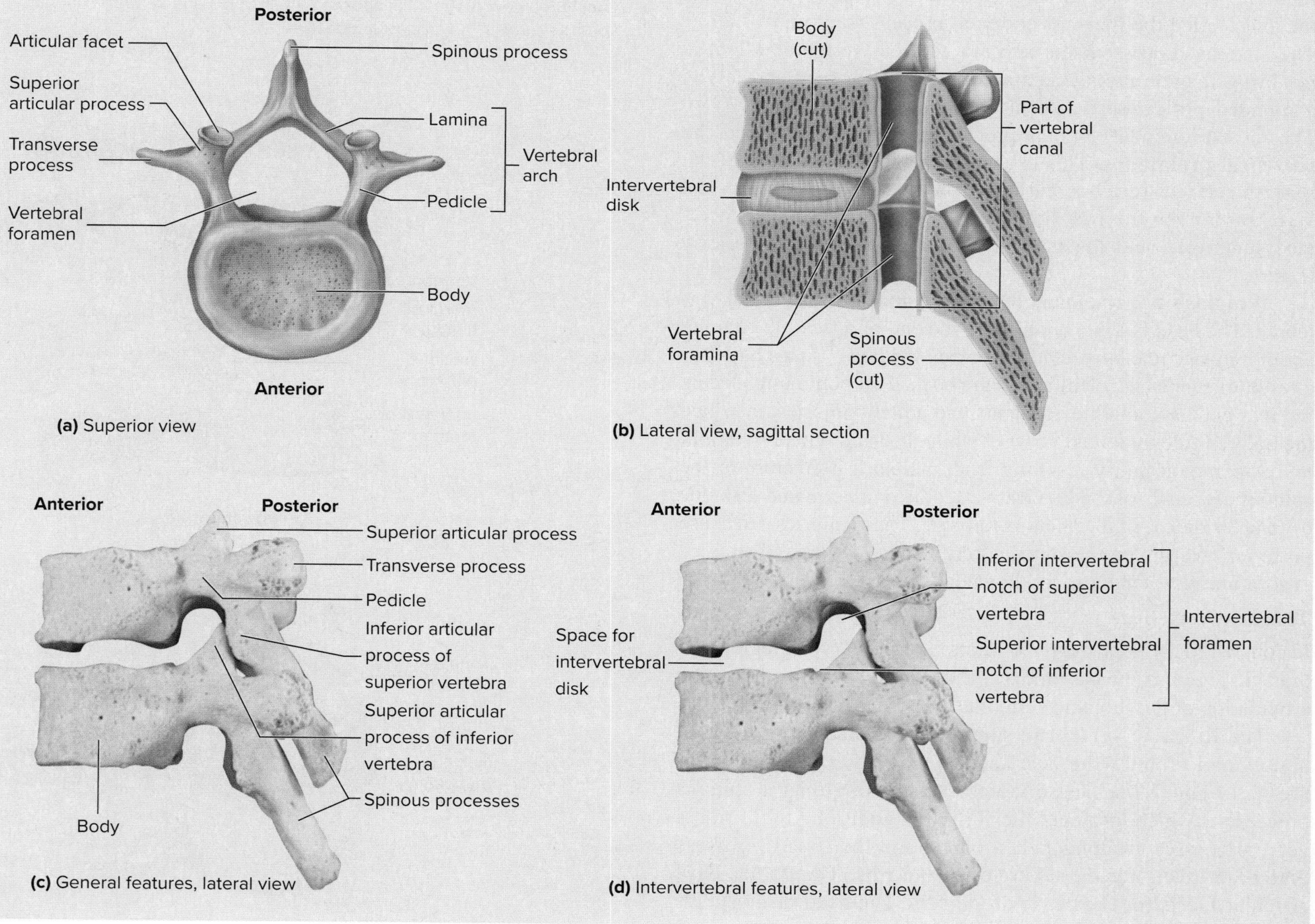

(a) Superior view

(b) Lateral view, sagittal section

(c) General features, lateral view

(d) Intervertebral features, lateral view

vertebrae are also unique in that the transverse processes possess **transverse foramina** through which the vertebral arteries extend toward the head.

The first two cervical vertebrae include (1) the **atlas** (C1) and (2) the **axis** (C2) (figure 7.23). The atlas and axis are heftier than the other five cervical vertebrae because they directly support the weight of the head and control its movements. The atlas derives its name from the Greek mythology character, Atlas, who held the world (the head) on his shoulders. The atlas does not have a body or a spinous process. However, it has large, flattened areas on its superior surface called the **superior articular facets** where the occipital condyles of the skull rest. The connection between the occipital condyles and the superior articular facets forms a joint that allows you to nod your head "yes" (see chapter 8).

The axis is so named because the joint between the atlas and the axis allows for a significant amount of head rotation. Shaking your head "no" occurs when the atlas rotates on the axis. This rotation occurs around the highly modified superior process of the axis, called the **dens,** or odontoid process (see figure 7.23*b*). The spinous process of the seventh cervical vertebra, which is not bifid, is quite pronounced and often can be seen and felt as a rounded projection between the shoulders (see figure 7.19). The most prominent spinous process in this area is called the **vertebral prominens.** This is usually the spinous process of the seventh cervical vertebra, but it may be that of the sixth cervical vertebra or even the first thoracic. The superior articular facets face superiorly, and the inferior articular facets face inferiorly (figure 7.24).

Whiplash is a traumatic hyperextension of the cervical vertebrae. The head is a heavy object at the end of a flexible column, and it may become hyperextended when the head "snaps back" as a result of sudden acceleration of the body. This commonly occurs in "rear-end" automobile accidents and athletic injuries, in which the body is quickly forced forward while the head remains stationary. A common injury resulting from whiplash is fracture of the spinous processes of the cervical vertebrae or a herniated disk due to an anterior tear of the annulus fibrosus. These injuries can cause posterior pressure on the spinal cord or spinal nerves and strained or torn muscles, tendons, and ligaments.

Thoracic Vertebrae

In contrast to the large degree of motion of the cervical region, the thoracic region is the least moveable of the five regions due to the articulation of the thoracic vertebrae with the ribs.

The **thoracic vertebrae** support the thoracic cage, which houses and protects the heart and lungs (figure 7.25; see figures 7.14 and 7.28). These vertebrae have the longest spinous processes, which project inferiorly. In addition, their transverse processes are longer than others and the first 10 possess **articular facets** for the tubercles of the ribs. The bodies have articular facets for the heads of the ribs. The head of most ribs articulates with the inferior articular facet of one vertebra and with the superior articular facet for the rib head on the next vertebra down. One way to recognize thoracic vertebrae is that they resemble a giraffe's head when viewed posteriolaterally (see figure 7.25).

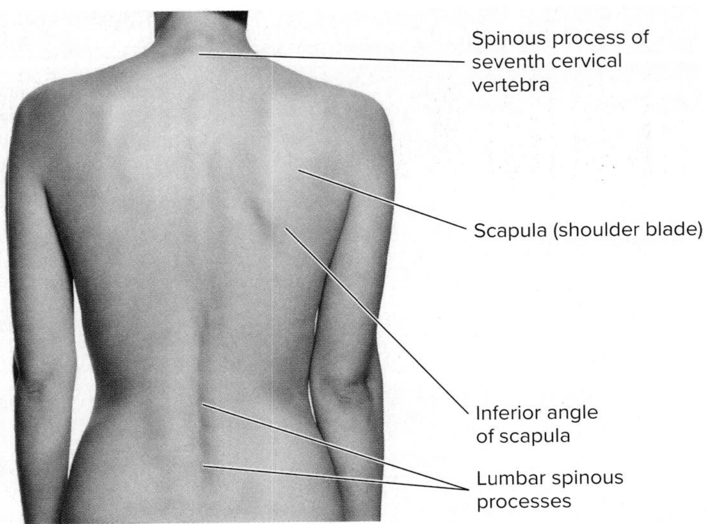

FIGURE 7.19 Surface View of the Back
A posterior view of the back showing the scapula and vertebral spinous processes. Brand New Images/Getty Images

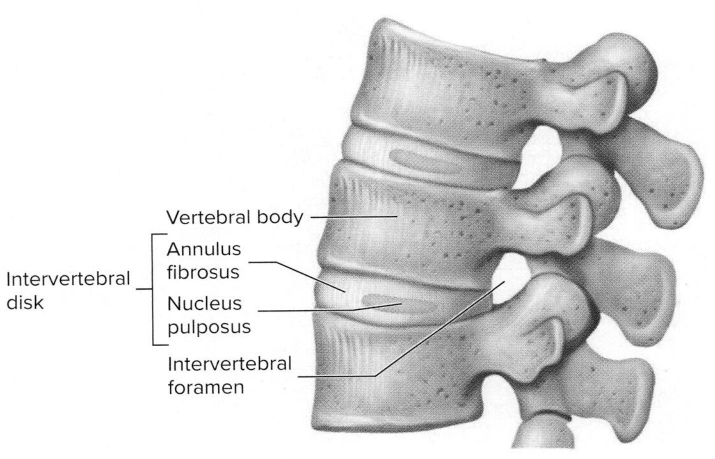

(a) Lateral view

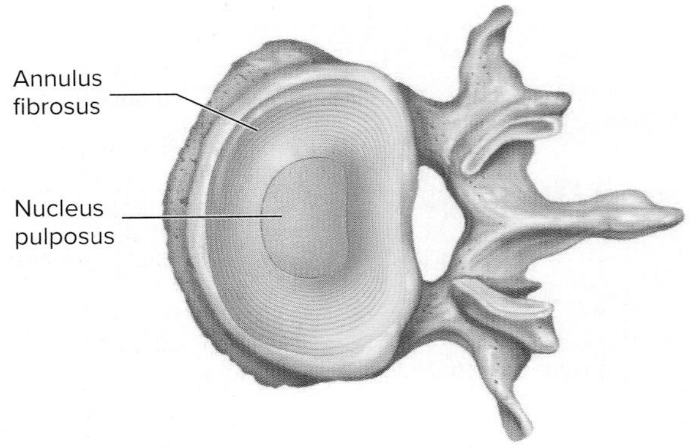

(b) Superior view

FIGURE 7.20 Intervertebral Disk
(*a*) Lateral view. (*b*) Superior view. APR

Clinical IMPACT 7.2 Herniated Intervertebral Disk

A **herniated disk** (*ruptured disk*) results when the annulus fibrosus breaks or balloons, releasing all or part of the nucleus pulposus (figure 7.21; see figure 7.20 for normal disk). The herniated part of the disk may push against and compress the spinal cord, cauda equina, or spinal nerves. The compression compromises the normal function of this nervous tissue and produces pain and numbness in the limb it supplies. The inferior lumbar and inferior cervical intervertebral disks are the most common disks to become herniated because the vertebral column has a lot of mobility in these areas. In addition, the lumbar region bears a significant amount of the body's weight.

Herniated disks can be repaired in one of several ways. One procedure is prolonged bed rest, based on the tendency for the herniated part of the disk to recede and the annulus fibrosus to repair itself. However, many cases require surgery. A **laminectomy** is the removal of a vertebral lamina, or vertebral arch. A **hemilaminectomy** is the removal of a portion of a vertebral lamina. These procedures reduce the compression of the spinal nerve or spinal cord. **Fenestration** involves removal of the nucleus pulposus, leaving the annulus fibrosus intact. In extreme cases, the entire damaged disk is removed and a metal cage is inserted into the space previously occupied by the disk. Red bone marrow stem cells harvested from the hip are then injected into the space to allow for new bone growth. The bone marrow technique is one of the newest forms of vertebral fusion surgery. Previously, a piece of hip bone from either the patient or a donor was inserted into the space vacated by the damaged disk. The vertebrae adjacent to the removed disk are usually further anchored together with a titanium plate held in place with titanium screws inserted into the vertebral bodies. Eventually, the adjacent vertebrae become fused by new bone growth across the gap. In figure 7.22, a post-surgery x-ray shows a cervical fusion after new bone has formed. The bright white structures are the screws and the plate that were added for stability. This is the type of surgery performed on author C. VanPutte.

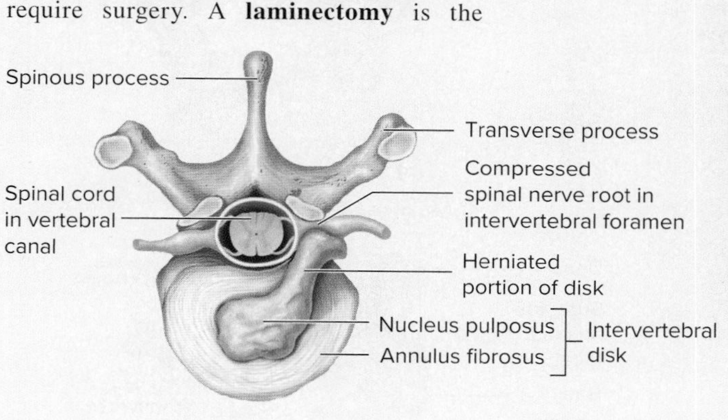

FIGURE 7.21 Herniated Disk
The nucleus pulposus is forced out of the annulus fibrosus in a herniated disk.

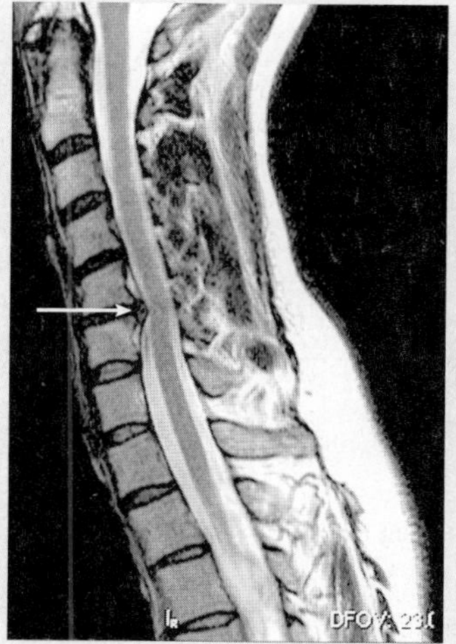

(a) Site of herniated intervertebral disk; note compression of spinal cord (arrow)

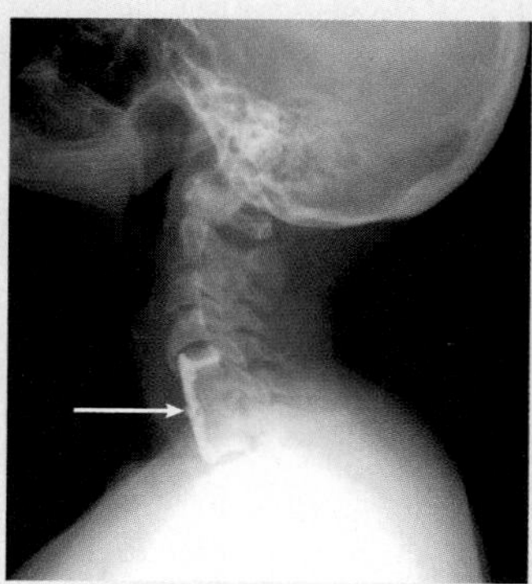

(b) Site of surgical fusion of vertebrae. Note metal bracket on the anterior of the spinal column (arrow)

FIGURE 7.22 Cervical Fusion
(*a*) X-ray showing extension of the neck after cervical fusion surgery.
(*b*) X-ray showing flexion of the neck after cervical fusion surgery.
Medical Body Scans/Science Source

Lumbar Vertebrae

The **lumbar vertebrae** support the majority of the body's weight (figure 7.26; see figure 7.14). Consequently, they have massive bodies and heavy, rectangular transverse and spinous processes. The thickness of the bodies makes fractures of the lumbar vertebrae less common, but ruptured intervertebral disks are more common in this area than in other regions of the vertebral column. The fifth lumbar vertebra or first coccygeal vertebra may become fused into the sacrum. Conversely, the first sacral vertebra may fail to fuse with the rest of the sacrum, resulting in six lumbar vertebrae. The superior articular facets face medially, and the inferior articular facets face laterally. When the superior articular surface of one lumbar vertebra joins the inferior articulating surface of another lumbar vertebra, the resulting arrangement adds strength to the inferior portion of the vertebral column and limits rotation of the lumbar vertebrae. A way to recognize lumbar vertebrae is that they somewhat resemble a moose head when viewed from a posteriolateral angle (see figure 7.28).

Predict 2

Why are the lumbar vertebrae more massive than the cervical vertebrae? Describe some expected differences between the vertebrae of a person who engages in regular vigorous physical exercise and those of a person who never exercises.

TABLE 7.11 Comparison of Vertebral Regions

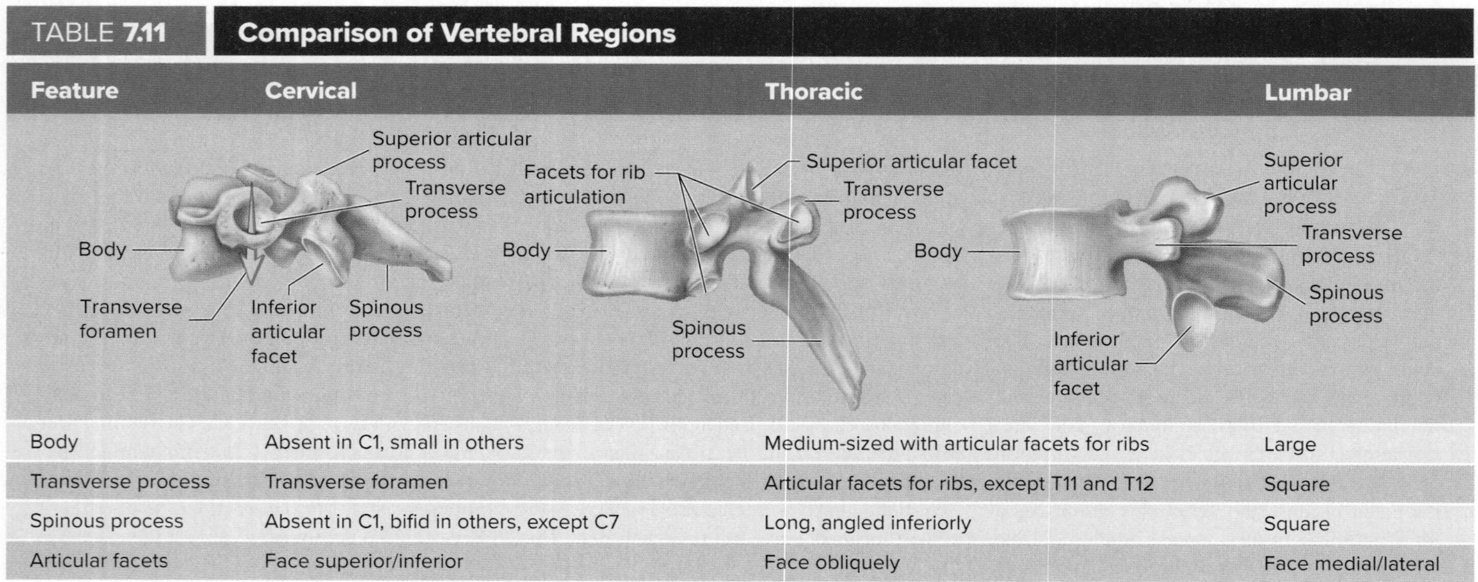

Feature	Cervical	Thoracic	Lumbar
Body	Absent in C1, small in others	Medium-sized with articular facets for ribs	Large
Transverse process	Transverse foramen	Articular facets for ribs, except T11 and T12	Square
Spinous process	Absent in C1, bifid in others, except C7	Long, angled inferiorly	Square
Articular facets	Face superior/inferior	Face obliquely	Face medial/lateral

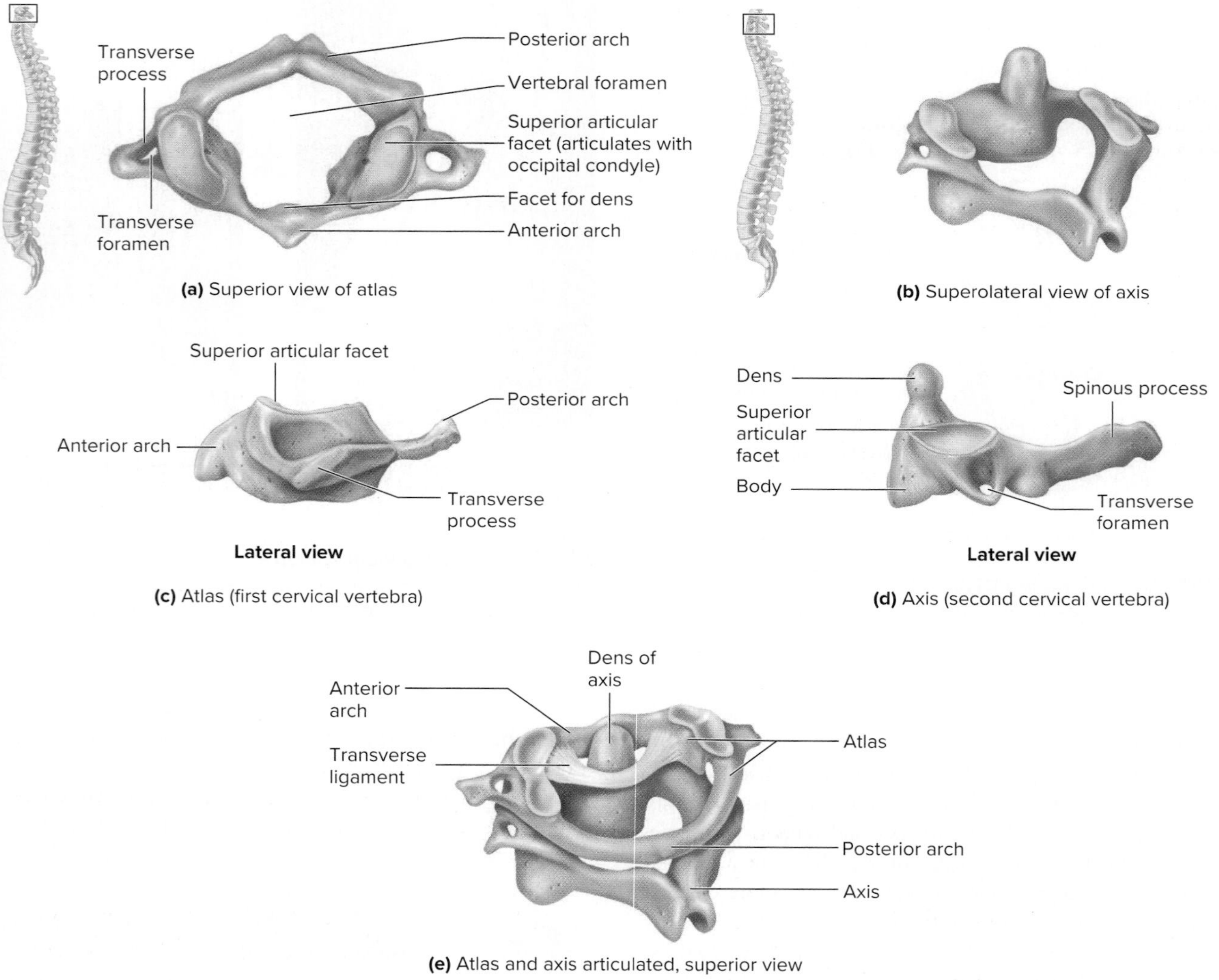

(a) Superior view of atlas

(b) Superolateral view of axis

Lateral view

(c) Atlas (first cervical vertebra)

Lateral view

(d) Axis (second cervical vertebra)

(e) Atlas and axis articulated, superior view

FIGURE 7.23 Cervical Vertebrae: Atlas and Axis

The posterior portion lies at the top of each superior view illustration. (*a*) Atlas (first cervical vertebra), superior view. (*b*) Axis (second cervical vertebra), superior view. (*c*) Lateral view of atlas. (*d*) Lateral view of axis. (*e*) Atlas and axis articulated, superior view.

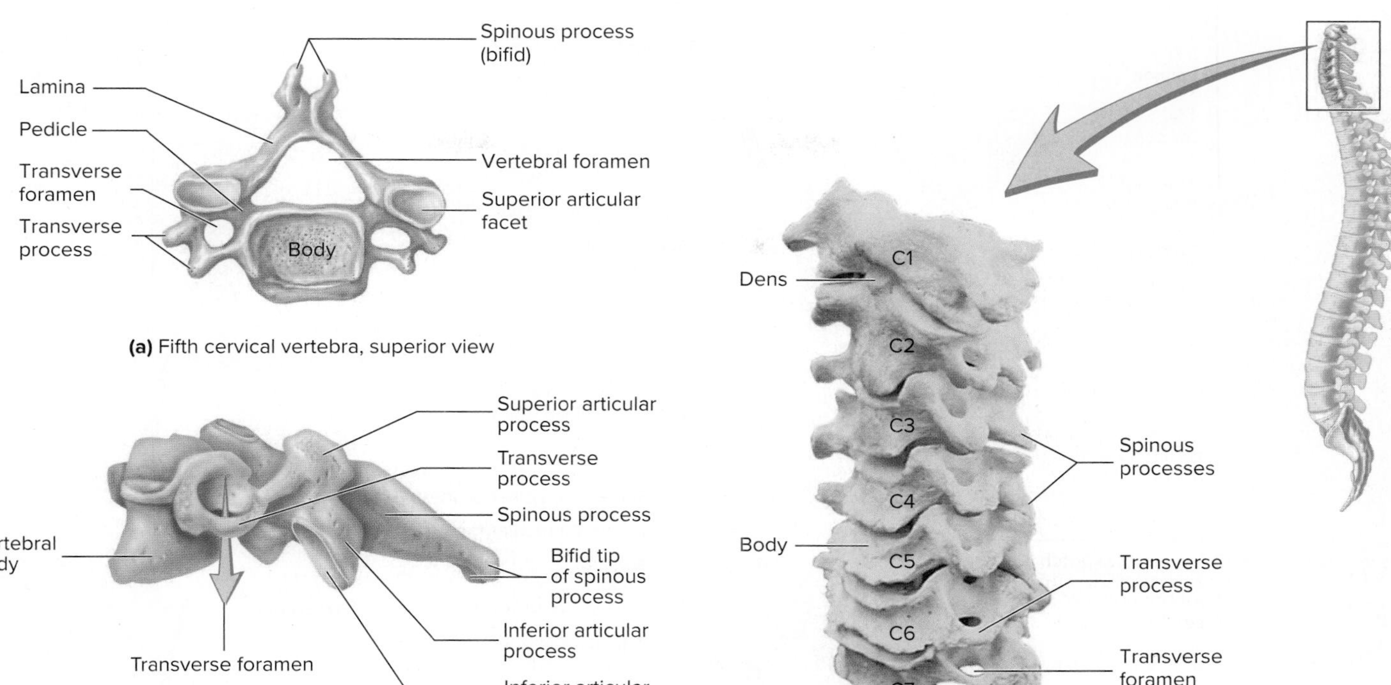

(a) Fifth cervical vertebra, superior view

(b) Fifth cervical vertebra, lateral view

(c) Anterolateral view

FIGURE 7.24 Cervical Vertebrae

The posterior portion lies at the top of each superior view illustration. (*a*) Fifth cervical vertebra, superior view. (*b*) Fifth cervical vertebra, lateral view. (*c*) Cervical vertebrae together from an anterolateral view. (c) Trent Stephens

Sacrum

The **sacrum** is located between the two hip bones (figure 7.27; see figures 7.14 and 7.37). It articulates with each hip bone by way of the **auricular surfaces,** forming the **sacroiliac joint.** The sacrum is formed from five separate sacral vertebrae that begin to fuse during adolescence, resulting in a solid bony plate by the mid-20s. The sacrum is part of the pelvic girdle, which provides stable support for our lower limbs. The pelvic girdle will be described more fully with the appendicular skeleton.

At the superior surface of the sacrum, the lateral portions (the former transverse processes) flare out like wings and are called the **alae** (AY-lee; wings). The former spinous processes, now partially fused, form a ridge along the posteriomedial surface called the **median sacral crest.** At the inferior surface of the sacrum, there is an opening, called the **sacral hiatus** (high-AYE-tus; gap), which is the termination of the vertebral canal. The vertebral canal is called the **sacral canal** through the sacrum. The sacral hiatus is a common anesthesia injection site. Spinal nerves exit the sacral canal through the **sacral foramina,** both posteriorly and anteriorly.

On the anterior surface, **transverse lines** remain visible where the individual vertebrae fused. The first sacral vertebra bulges anteriorly into the pelvic cavity. This bulge is called the **sacral promontory** (see figure 7.14). It is used as a clinical landmark for separation of the abdominal cavity and the pelvic cavity.

Coccyx

The **coccyx** (KOK-siks) is commonly referred to as the tailbone (figure 7.27; see figure 7.14). It is the terminal portion of the vertebral column. It can be formed from three to five semifused vertebrae. In males, the coccyx may project anteriorly, but in females, it often projects more inferiorly. The coccygeal vertebrae are much smaller than the other vertebrae and have neither vertebral foramina nor well-developed processes. The coccyx is easily broken when a person falls by sitting down hard on a solid surface.

Thoracic Cage

The **thoracic cage,** commonly called the rib cage, protects the heart and lungs within the thorax. It forms a semirigid chamber, which can increase and decrease in volume during respiration. It consists of (1) the thoracic vertebrae, (2) the ribs with their associated costal (rib) cartilages, and (3) the sternum (figure 7.28*a*).

Ribs and Costal Cartilages

There are 12 pairs of **ribs.** Ribs are classified as either true ribs or false ribs. Ribs 1–7 are called **true ribs.** True ribs attach directly through **costal cartilage** to the sternum. Ribs 8–12 are called **false ribs** because they do not attach directly to the sternum. The false ribs consist of two groups. Ribs 8–10 are joined by a common cartilage to the costal cartilage of rib 7, which in turn is attached to the

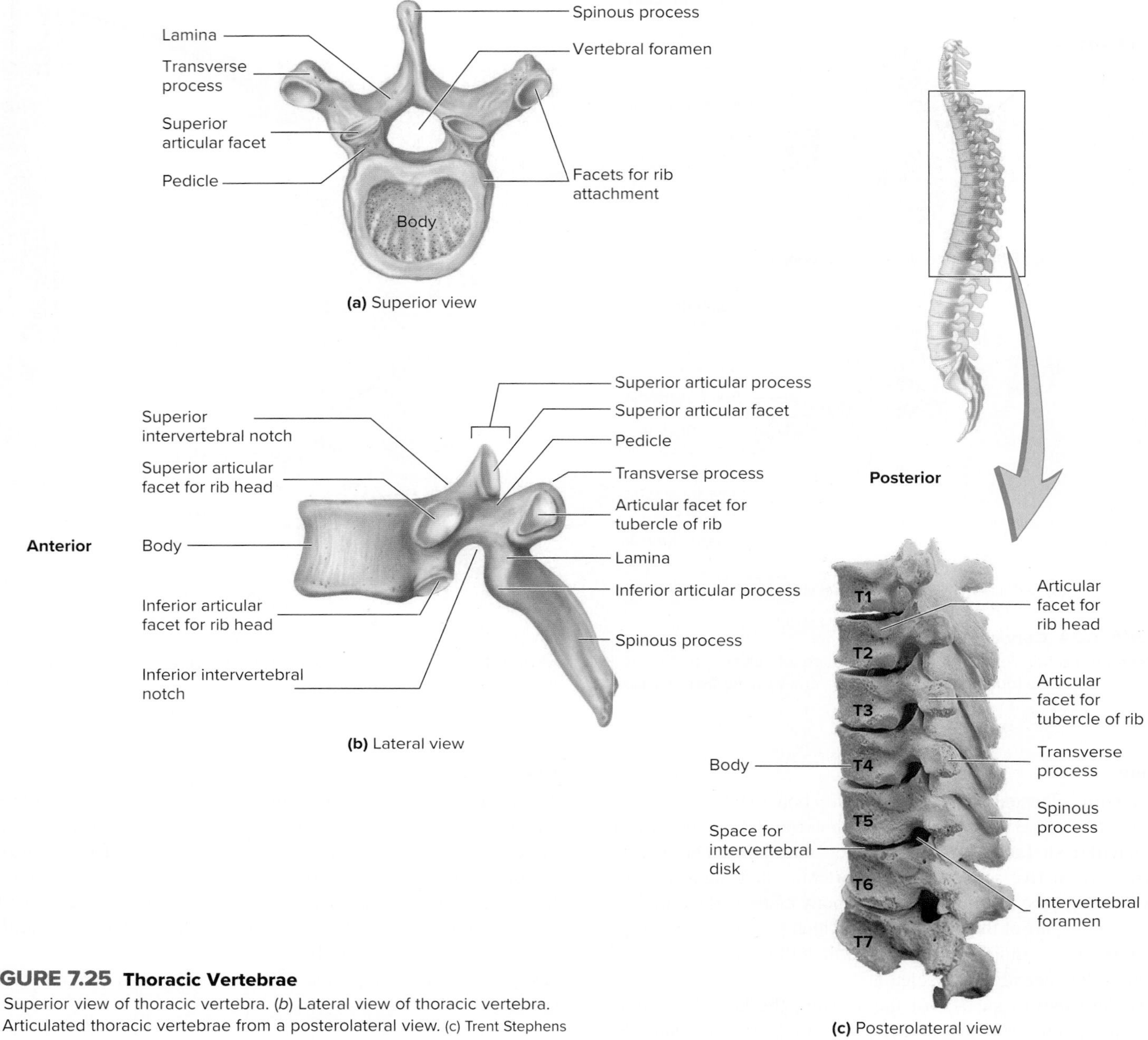

FIGURE 7.25 Thoracic Vertebrae

(*a*) Superior view of thoracic vertebra. (*b*) Lateral view of thoracic vertebra. (*c*) Articulated thoracic vertebrae from a posterolateral view. (c) Trent Stephens

sternum. Two of the false ribs, ribs 11 and 12, are also called **floating ribs** because they do not attach to the sternum. The costal cartilages are flexible and permit the thoracic cage to expand during respiration. A dislocation between a rib and its costal cartilage is called a **separated rib.** A separated rib is very painful because it can move, and overlap adjacent ribs. Separation of rib 10 is the most common.

Most ribs attach to the thoracic vertebrae in two locations (figure 7.28*b,c*). First, the **head** of the rib articulates with the bodies and intervertebral disks of two adjacent vertebrae. These sites of articulation are called the inferior articular facet on the superior vertebra and the superior articular facet on the inferior vertebra. Second, the **tubercle** of the rib articulates with the transverse process of the inferior vertebra. The **neck** of the rib is between the head and tubercle, and the **body** is the main part of the rib. The **angle** of the rib is located just lateral to the tubercle and is the point of greatest curvature. The angle is the weakest part of the rib and can be fractured in a crushing injury, as may occur in an automobile accident. Sometimes the transverse processes of the seventh cervical vertebra form separate bones called **cervical ribs.** These ribs may be tiny pieces of bone or may be long enough to reach the sternum. In addition, the first lumbar vertebra may develop lumbar ribs.

Sternum

The **sternum,** or breastbone, has been described as sword-shaped and has three parts (figure 7.28*a*): (1) The **manubrium**

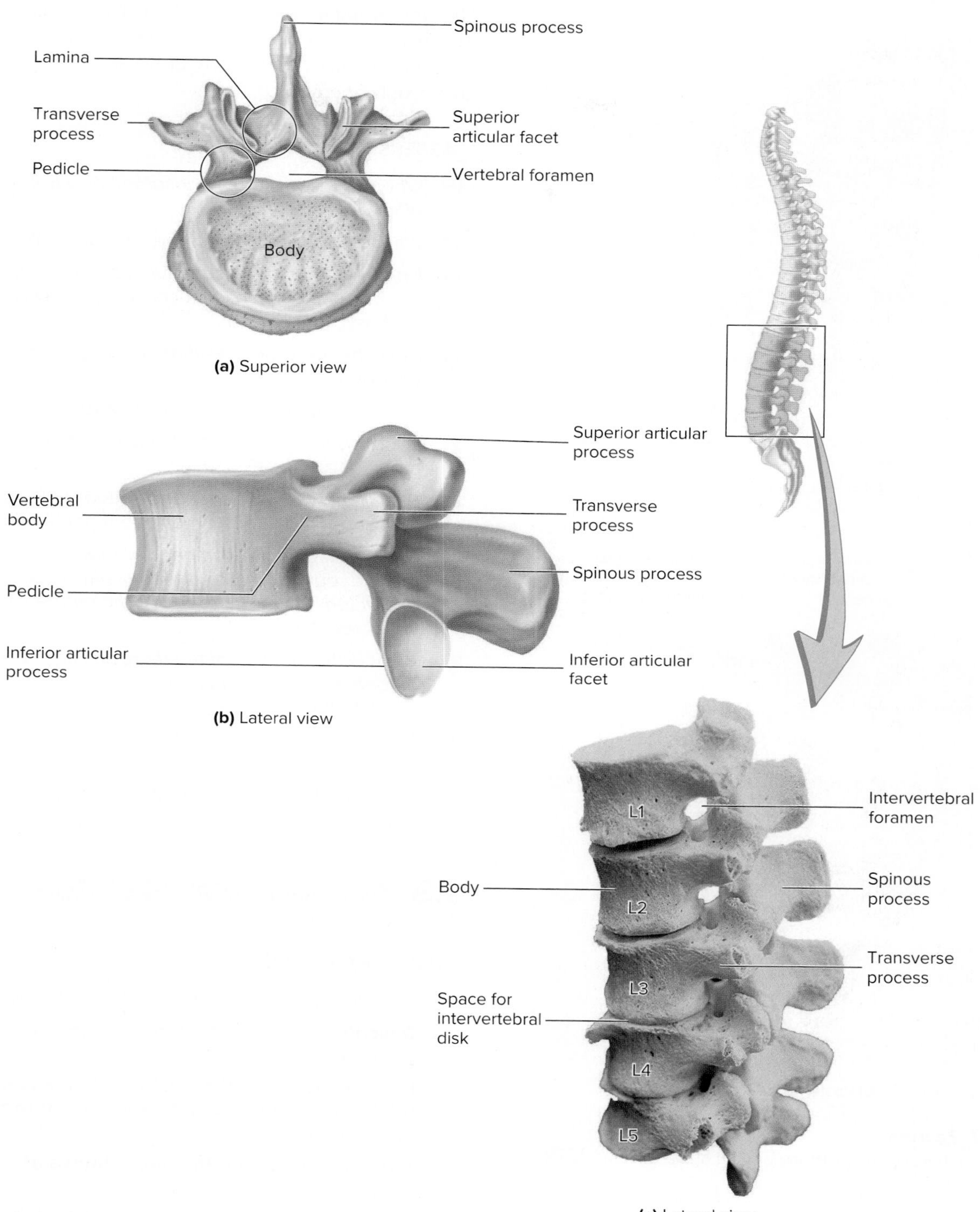

FIGURE 7.26 Lumbar Vertebrae

(*a*) Superior view of a lumbar vertebra. (*b*) Lateral view of a lumbar vertebra. (*c*) Articulated lumbar vertebrae from a lateral view. (c) Trent Stephens

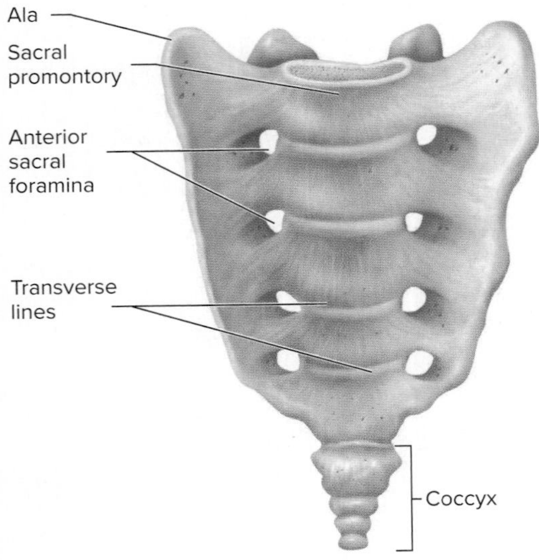

(a) Anterior view

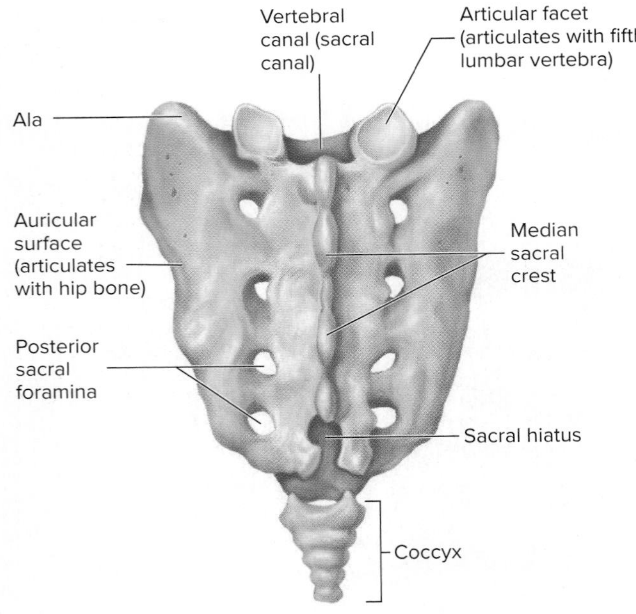

(b) Posterior view

FIGURE 7.27 Sacrum
(*a*) Anterior view of the sacrum. (*b*) Posterior view of the sacrum. APR

(mah-NOO-bree-um; handle) is the "sword handle"; (2) the **body,** or gladiolus (sword), is the "blade"; and (3) the **xiphoid** (ZI-foyd; sword) **process** is the "sword tip." The superior margin of the manubrium has a **jugular** (suprasternal) **notch** in the midline, which can be easily felt at the anterior base of the neck (figure 7.29). The first rib and the clavicle articulate with the manubrium. The point at which the manubrium joins the body of the sternum can be felt as a prominence on the anterior thorax called the **sternal angle** (see figure 7.28*a*). The cartilage of the second rib attaches to the sternum at the sternal angle, the third through seventh ribs attach to the body of the sternum, and no ribs attach to the xiphoid process.

ASSESS YOUR PROGRESS

16. *Where is the hyoid bone located? Why is it a unique bone? What are its functions?*
17. *What are the functions of the vertebral column?*
18. *Name the four major curvatures of the adult vertebral column, and explain what causes them. Describe scoliosis, kyphosis, and lordosis.*
19. *Describe the structures that are common to most vertebrae.*
20. *Where do spinal nerves exit the vertebral column?*
21. *Describe the structure and function of the intervertebral disks.*
22. *Explain how the superior and inferior articular processes help support and allow movement of the vertebral column.*
23. *Name and give the number of vertebrae in each of the five regions of the vertebral column. Describe the characteristics that distinguish the different regions of vertebrae.*
24. *What is the function of the thoracic cage? Distinguish among true, false, and floating ribs, and give the number of each type.*
25. *Describe the articulation of the ribs with thoracic vertebrae.*
26. *What are the parts of the sternum? Name the structures that attach to the sternum.*

7.3 Appendicular Skeleton

LEARNING OUTCOMES

After reading this section, you should be able to

A. **Describe the girdles that make up the appendicular skeleton.**
B. **Identify the bones that make up the pectoral girdle and relate their structure and arrangement to the function of the girdle.**
C. **Name and describe the major bones of the upper limb.**
D. **List the bones that make up the pelvic girdle and explain why the pelvic girdle is more stable than the pectoral girdle.**
E. **Name the bones that make up the hip bone. Distinguish between the male and the female pelvis.**
F. **Identify and describe the bones of the lower limb.**

The appendicular skeleton allows movement of our appendages and supports our weight in an upright position.

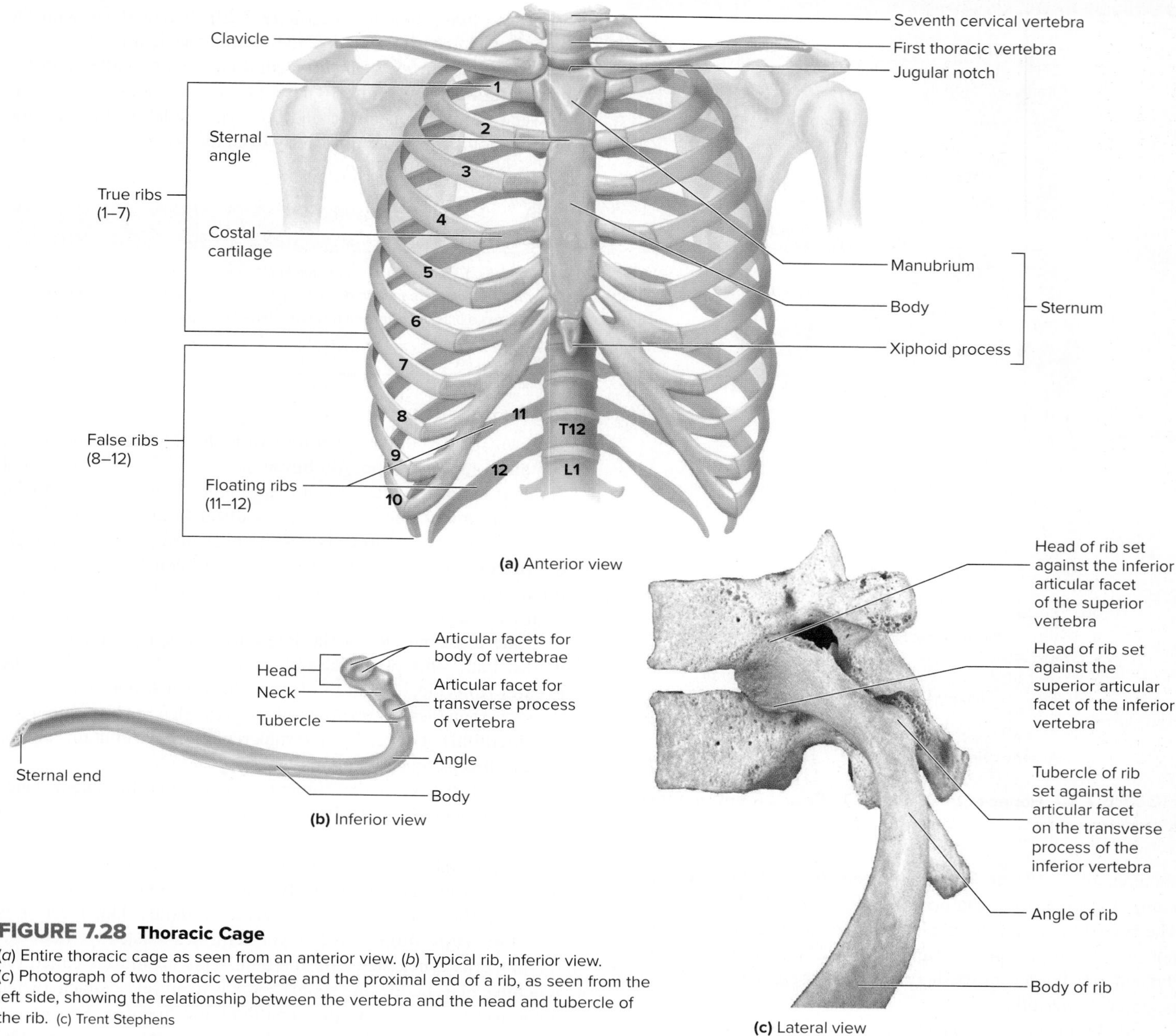

FIGURE 7.28 Thoracic Cage

(*a*) Entire thoracic cage as seen from an anterior view. (*b*) Typical rib, inferior view. (*c*) Photograph of two thoracic vertebrae and the proximal end of a rib, as seen from the left side, showing the relationship between the vertebra and the head and tubercle of the rib. (c) Trent Stephens

Acromial end of clavicle
Acromion process
Jugular notch
Clavicle
Sternum

FIGURE 7.29 Upper Thorax

Surface anatomy of the upper thorax. ©Eric A. Wise

Pectoral Girdle and Upper Limb

Picture a baseball pitcher winding up to throw a fastball and you have a great demonstration of the mobility of your upper limb (figure 7.30). This mobility is possible because muscles attach the upper limb and its girdle rather loosely to the rest of the body. Thus, the upper limb is capable of a wide range of movements, including throwing, lifting, grasping, pulling, and touching.

Pectoral Girdle: Scapula and Clavicle

The **pectoral** (PEK-toh-ral) **girdle** consists of two pairs of bones that attach each of the upper limbs to the body: Each pair is composed of a **scapula** (SKAP-you-lah), commonly known as the

FUNDAMENTAL **Figure**

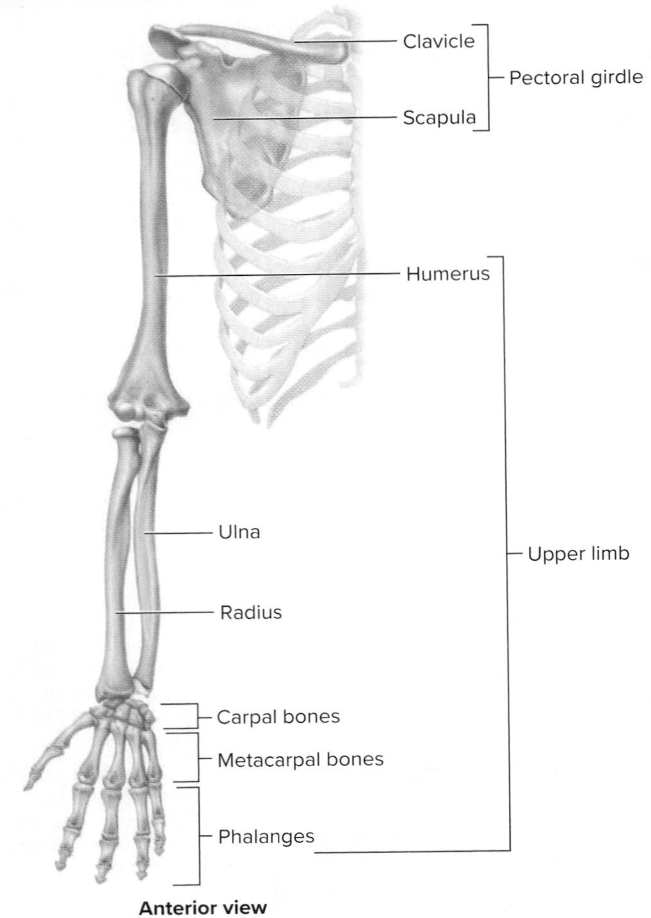

FIGURE 7.30 Bones of the Pectoral Girdle and Right Upper Limb
Anterior view of the bones of the pectoral girdle and upper limb.

shoulder blade (figure 7.31), and a **clavicle** (KLAV-i-kul), commonly known as the collarbone (see figures 7.28, 7.30, and 7.31). The scapula is a flat, triangular bone that can easily be seen and felt in a living person (see figure 7.19). The base of the triangle, the superior border, faces superiorly; the apex, the inferior angle, is directed inferiorly.

At the tip of the shoulder, there is the large **acromion** (ah-CROH-mee-on; shoulder tip) **process** of the scapula. The acromion process has three functions: (1) to form a protective cover for the shoulder joint, (2) to form the attachment site for the clavicle, and (3) to provide attachment points for some of the shoulder muscles. The **scapular spine** extends from the acromion process across the posterior surface of the scapula. The scapular spine divides the posterior of the scapula into (1) a small **supraspinous fossa** superior to the spine and (2) a larger **infraspinous fossa** inferior to the spine. The deep, anterior surface of the scapula constitutes the **subscapular fossa.** The smaller **coracoid** (crow's beak) **process** provides attachments for some shoulder and arm muscles. A **glenoid** (GLEE-noyd, GLEN-oyd) **cavity,** located in the superior lateral portion of the bone, articulates with the head of the humerus.

The clavicle (see figures 7.28, 7.30, and 7.31*c*) is a long bone with a slight sigmoid (S-shaped) curve. It is easily seen and felt in the living human (see figure 7.29). It articulates with the scapula and the sternum. On the lateral end it articulates with the acromion process. On the medial end it articulates with the manubrium of the sternum. These are the only bony connections between the pectoral girdle and the axial skeleton. Because the clavicle holds the upper limb away from the body, it facilitates the limb's mobility.

Predict 3

Sarah fell off the trampoline in her backyard. She was crying and holding her right shoulder, so her mother took her to the emergency room. Dr. Smart diagnosed a broken collarbone (clavicle), based on the position of Sarah's right upper limb. Explain.

Arm: Humerus

The arm, the part of the upper limb from the shoulder to the elbow, contains only one bone, the **humerus** (figure 7.32). The medial humeral **head** articulates with the glenoid cavity of the scapula. The **anatomical neck,** immediately distal to the head, is almost nonexistent; thus, a surgical neck has been designated. The **surgical neck** is so named because it is a common fracture site that often requires surgical repair. Removal of the humeral head due to disease or injury occurs down to the level of the surgical neck.

The proximal end of the humerus has two prominent landmarks, both sites of muscle attachment: (1) Laterally, it is the **greater tubercle.** (2) Anteriorly, it is the **lesser tubercle.** Between the greater and lesser tubercle is a groove called the **intertubercular (bicipital) groove.** The intertubercular groove contains one of the two biceps brachii tendons.

The diaphysis of the humerus has a noticeable lateral landmark. The **deltoid tuberosity** is the site of attachment of the deltoid muscle.

The distal end of the humerus has several unique features where it articulates with the two forearm bones at the elbow. Laterally, the humerus articulates with the radius. This location is called the **capitulum** (kah-PIT-you-lum; head-shaped). Medially, the humerus articulates with the ulna. This location is called the **trochlea** (TROK-lee-ah; spool). Forearm muscles attach to the humerus just superior to the capitulum and trochlea. The attachment sites are the **medial epicondyle** and the **lateral epicondyle.**

Anteriorly, on the distal end, just superior to the trochlea, is a fossa called the **coronoid** (KOR-oh-noyd; crow's beak) **fossa,** which accommodates a portion of the ulna. Posteriorly, on the distal end, is another large fossa called the **olecranon** (oh-LEK-rah-non; elbow) **fossa,** which accommodates a portion of the ulna that is easily felt as the point of the elbow.

Forearm: Ulna and Radius

The forearm has two bones: (1) the **ulna** and (2) the **radius** (figure 7.33). The ulna is medial, the same side as the little finger, and the radius is lateral, the same side as the thumb. The ulna and radius articulate with the humerus at the elbow joint. There are several unique features of these two bones at the site of attachment to the humerus.

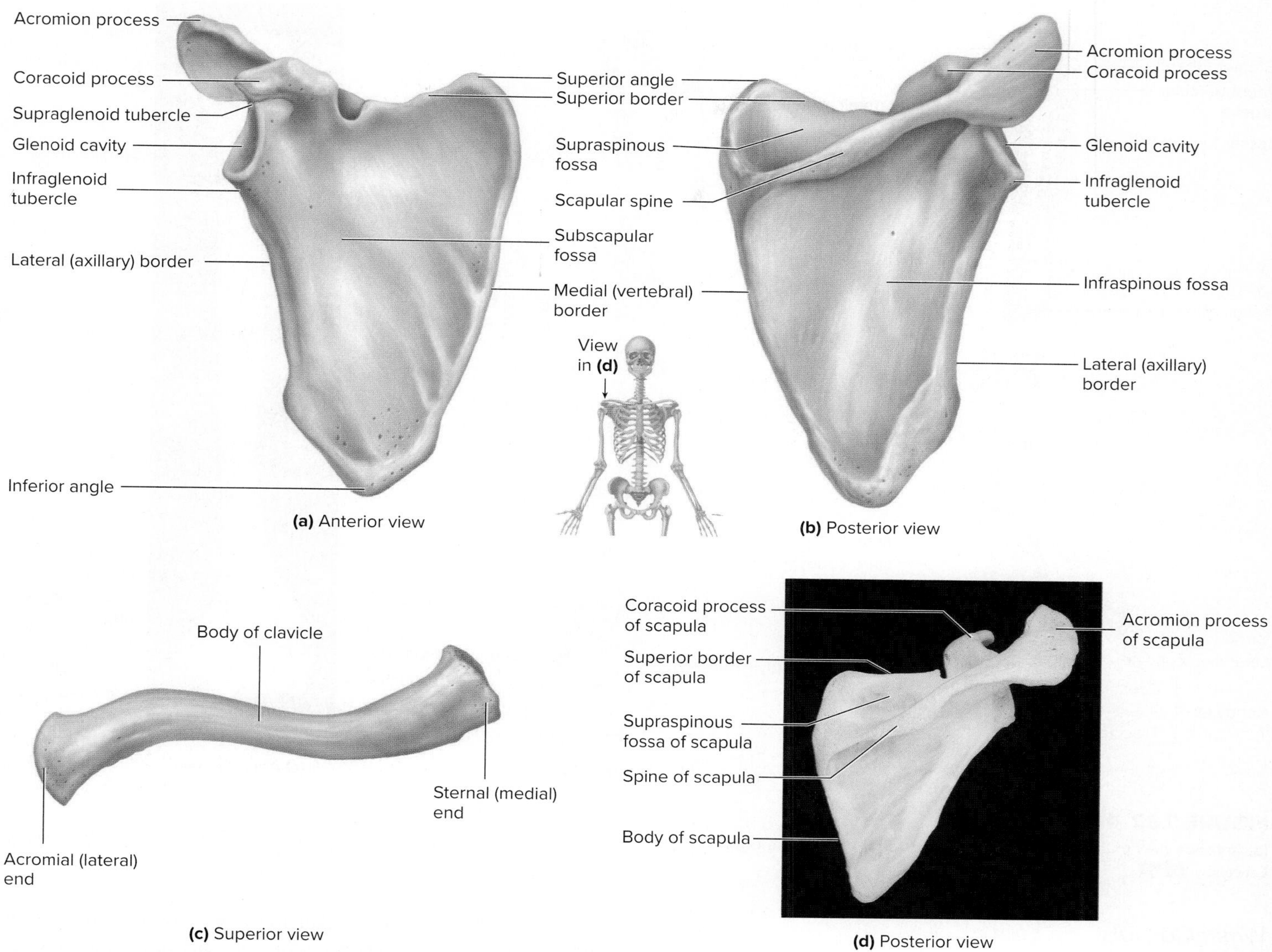

FIGURE 7.31 Right Scapula and Clavicle

(*a*) Right scapula, anterior view. (*b*) Right scapula, posterior view. (*c*) Right clavicle, superior view. (*d*) Photograph of the right scapula from a posterior view.
(d) Christine Eckel/McGraw Hill Education photographer APR

Ulna

The portion of the ulna that articulates with the humerus is the C-shaped **trochlear notch.** The trochlear notch rotates over the trochlea of the humerus when bending the elbow. The anterior surface of the proximal end of the ulna has a process called the **coronoid process.** The coronoid process inserts into the coronoid fossa of the humerus when the elbow is bent. The posterior surface of the proximal end of the ulna has a much larger process called the **olecranon process.** The olecranon process inserts into the olecranon fossa of the humerus when the elbow is straightened. On the medial side of the proximal end of the ulna is the **radial notch** where the head of the radius rotates (see figure 7.33).

On the distal end of the ulna, on the medial side, is the **head** of the ulna. The head of the ulna articulates with both the radius and the wrist bones (see figures 7.33 and 7.35). On the distal end of the ulna, on the lateral side, there is a small process called the **styloid** (STY-loyd; stylus) **process.** Ligaments of the wrist attach to the styloid process.

Radius

The portion of the radius that articulates with the humerus is the **head.** The head of the radius rotates over the capitulum of the humerus when bending the elbow. The head is concave and is formed into a smooth cylinder of bone. The radial head rotates against the radial notch of the ulna when the forearm supinates (turn the hand "palm up") and pronates (turn the hand "palm down"; see chapter 8). Just inferior to the radial head on the medial side is the **radial tuberosity,** the site of attachment for the biceps brachii muscle of the arm.

The distal end of the radius also has a **styloid process.** The styloid process of the radius is lateral and also serves as an attachment location for wrist ligaments.

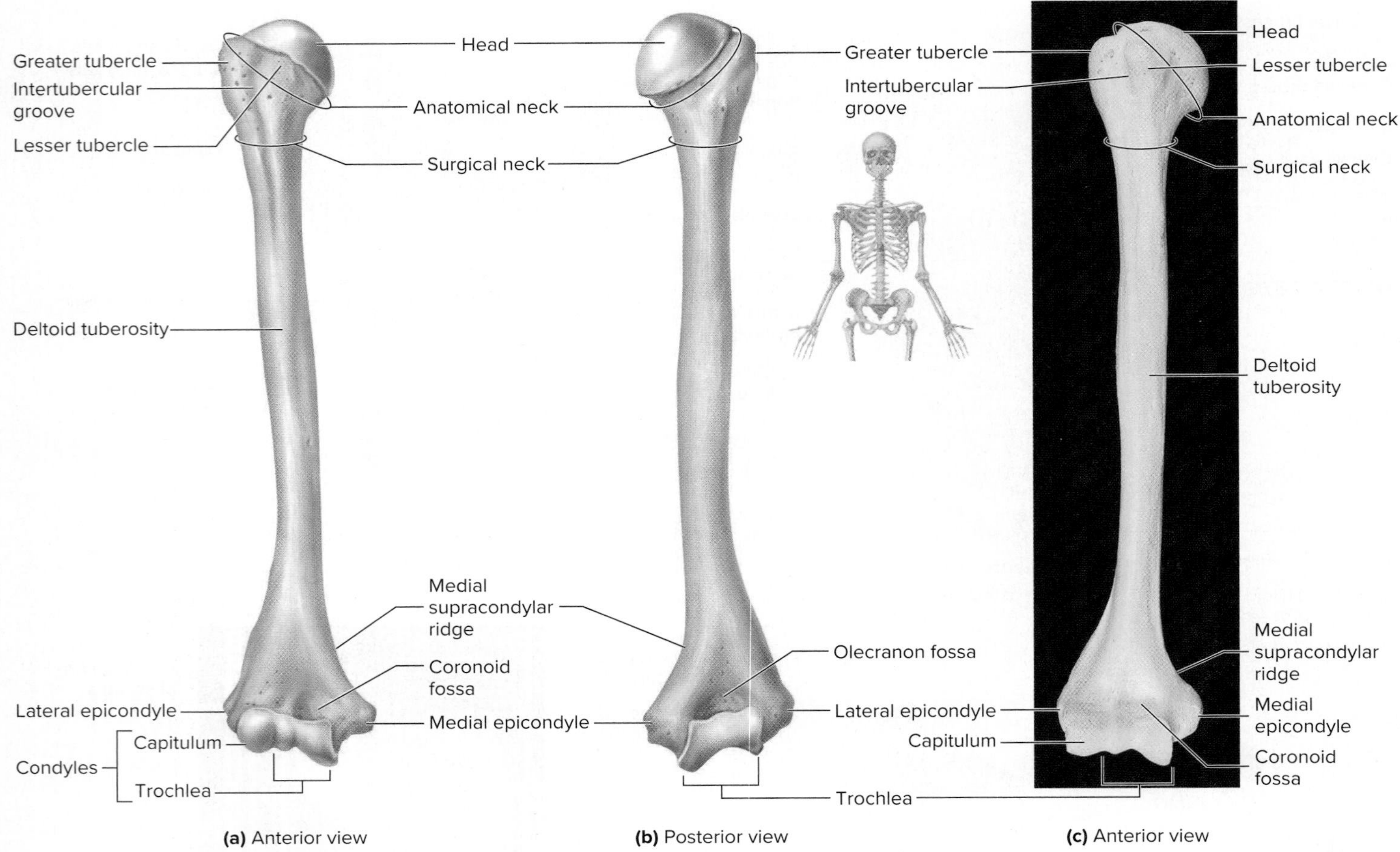

FIGURE 7.32 Right Humerus
(*a*) Anterior view of the right humerus. (*b*) Posterior view of the right humerus. (*c*) Photo of the anterior view of the right humerus. (c) Christine Eckel/McGraw Hill Education APR

Wrist: Carpals

The wrist is a relatively short region between the forearm and the hand; it is composed of eight **carpal** (KAR-pal) **bones** arranged into two rows of four each (figure 7.35). The proximal row of carpal bones, lateral to medial, includes (1) the **scaphoid** (SKAF-oyd), which is boat-shaped; (2) the **lunate** (LOO-nayt), which is moon-shaped; (3) the three-cornered **triquetrum** (try-KWEE-trum, try-KWET-rum); and (4) the pea-shaped **pisiform** (PIS-i-form), which is located on the palmar surface of the triquetrum. The distal row of carpal bones, from medial to lateral, includes (1) the **hamate** (HA-meyt), which has a hooked process on its palmar side, called the hook of the hamate; (2) the head-shaped **capitate** (KAP-i-tate); (3) the **trapezoid** (TRAP-e-zoid), which is named for its resemblance to a four-sided geometric form with two parallel sides; and (4) the **trapezium** (tra-PEE-zee-um), which is named after a four-sided geometric form with no two sides parallel. A number of mnemonics have been developed to help students remember the carpal bones. The following one represents them in order from lateral to medial for the proximal row (top) and from medial to lateral (by the thumb) for the distal row: **S**traight **L**ine **T**o **P**inky, **H**ere **C**omes **T**he **T**humb—that is, **S**caphoid, **L**unate, **T**riquetrum, **P**isiform, **H**amate, **C**apitate, **T**rapezoid, and **T**rapezium.

The eight carpal bones, taken together, are convex posteriorly and concave anteriorly. The anterior concavity of the carpal bones is accentuated by the tubercle of the trapezium at the base of the thumb and the hook of the hamate at the base of the little finger. A ligament stretches across the wrist from the tubercle of the trapezium to the hook of the hamate to form a tunnel on the anterior surface of the wrist called the **carpal tunnel.** Tendons, nerves, and blood vessels pass through this tunnel to enter the hand.

Hand: Metacarpals and Phalanges

Five **metacarpal bones** are attached to the carpal bones and make up the central portion of the hand (figure 7.35). They are numbered one to five, starting with the most lateral metacarpal bone, at the base of the thumb. The metacarpal bones form a curve so that, in the resting position, the palm of the hand is concave. The distal ends of the metacarpal bones help form the knuckles of the hand (see figure 7.34). The spaces between the metacarpal bones are occupied by soft tissue.

The five **digits** of each hand include one thumb (**pollex**) and four fingers. Each digit consists of small long bones called **phalanges** (fah-LAN-jeez; sing. phalanx). The thumb has two phalanges, called proximal and distal. Each finger has three phalanges, designated proximal, middle, and distal. One or two **sesamoid** (SES-ah-moyd)

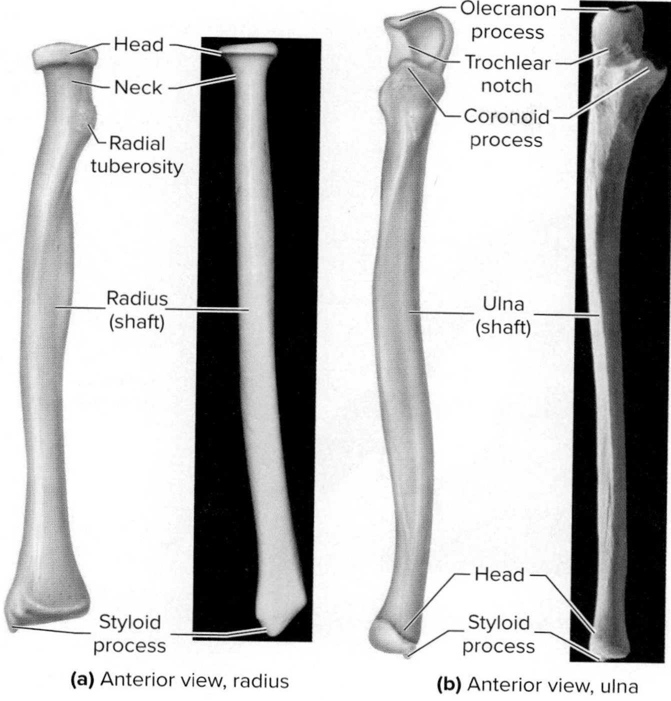

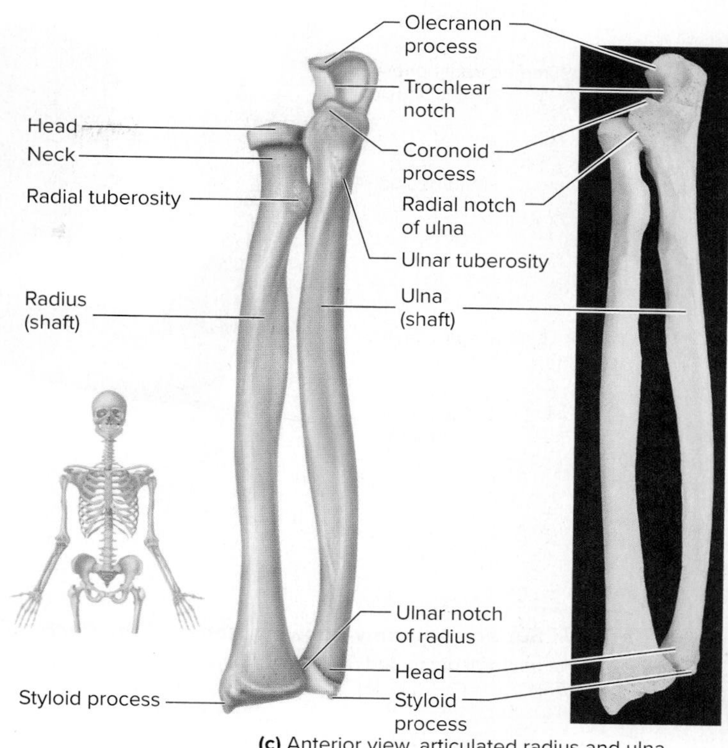

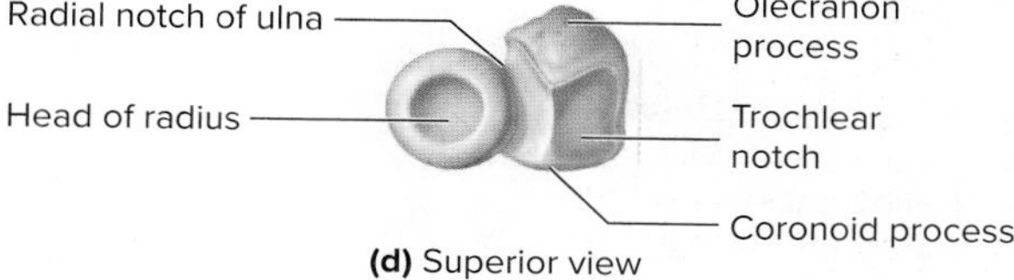

FIGURE 7.33 Right Ulna and Radius
(*a*) Anterior view of the right radius. (*b*) Anterior view of the right ulna. (*c*) Anterior view of articulated right radius and ulna. (*d*) Proximal ends of the right ulna and radius. (a) MedicalRF/Science Source; (b) James Stevenson/Science Source; (c2) Christine Eckel/McGraw Hill Education

bones (not shown in figure 7.35) often form near the junction between the proximal phalanx and the metacarpal bone of the thumb. Sesamoid bones are small bones located within some tendons that increase the mechanical advantage of tendons where they cross joints.

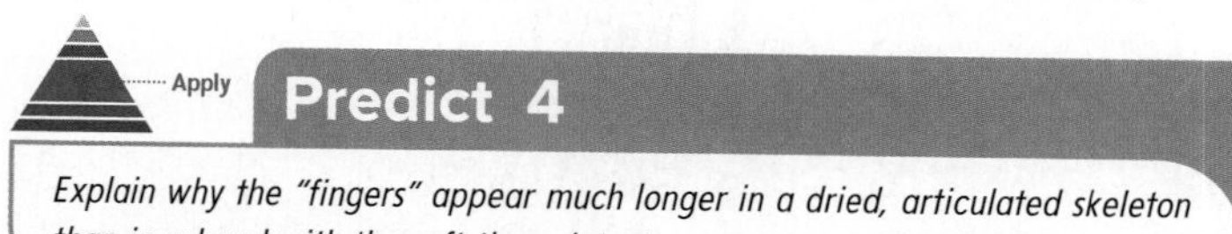

Explain why the "fingers" appear much longer in a dried, articulated skeleton than in a hand with the soft tissue intact.

ASSESS YOUR PROGRESS

27. *Describe how the upper and lower limbs are attached to the axial skeleton.*
28. *Name the bones that make up the pectoral girdle. Describe their functions.*
29. *What are the functions of the acromion process and the coracoid process of the scapula?*
30. *Identify the bones of the upper limb, and describe their arrangement.*
31. *Name the important sites of muscle attachment on the humerus.*
32. *What is the function of the radial tuberosity? The styloid processes? Name the part of the ulna commonly referred to as the elbow.*
33. *List the eight carpal bones. What is the carpal tunnel?*
34. *What bones form the hand? How many phalanges are in each finger and in the thumb?*

Pelvic Girdle and Lower Limb

The lower limbs support the body and are essential for normal standing, walking, and running. The general pattern of the lower limb (figure 7.36) is very similar to that of the upper limb, except that the pelvic girdle is attached much more firmly to the body than the pectoral girdle is and the bones in general are thicker, heavier, and longer than those of the upper limb. These structures reflect the function of the lower limb in supporting and moving the body.

Pelvic Girdle: Hip Bones and Sacrum

Hip Bones

The **pelvic girdle** is formed by the two **hip bones** (*coxal bones*) and the sacrum (see figure 7.36). The hip bones join each other anteriorly and connect with the sacrum posteriorly forming a

Heads of metacarpal bones (knuckles)
Head of ulna
Lateral epicondyle
Olecranon process
Acromion process
Olecranon process
Medial epicondyle
Medial border of scapula

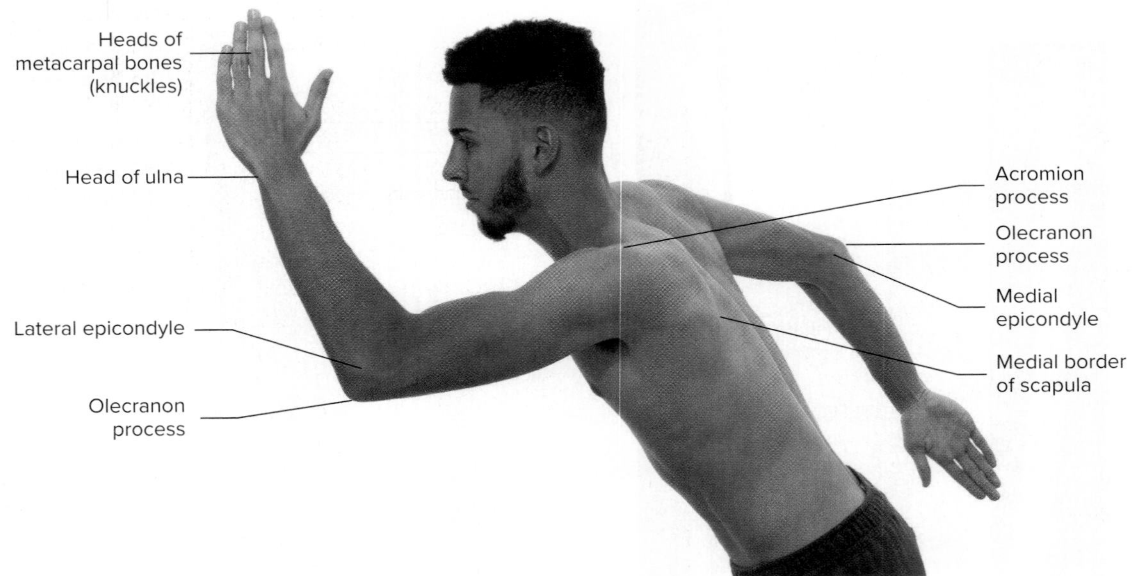

FIGURE 7.34 Surface Anatomy Showing Bones of the Pectoral Girdle and Upper Limb
Lateral view of the pectoral girdle and upper limb. Aaron Roeth/McGraw Hill Education

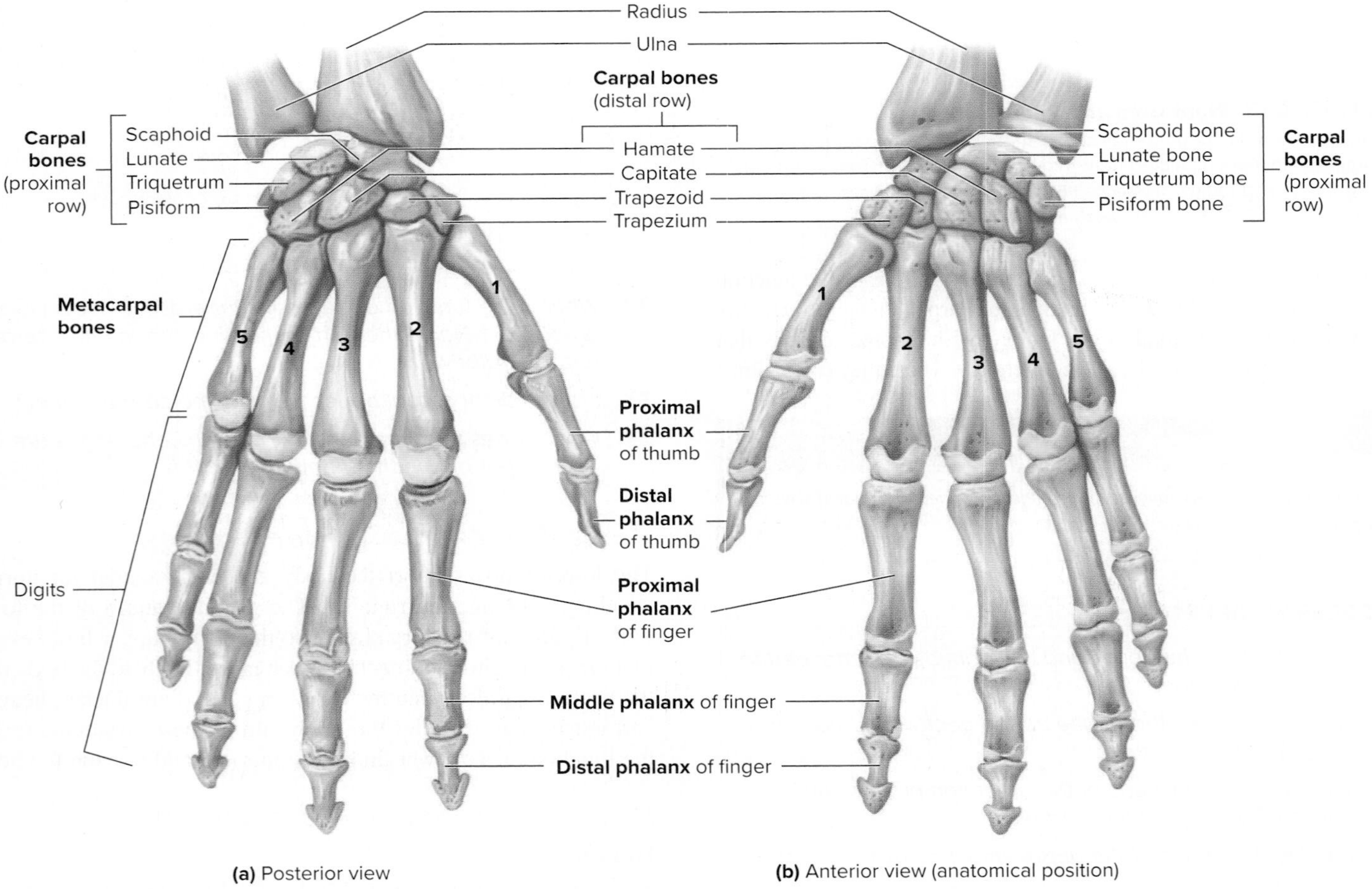

Radius
Ulna
Carpal bones (distal row)
Carpal bones (proximal row)
Scaphoid
Lunate
Triquetrum
Pisiform
Hamate
Capitate
Trapezoid
Trapezium
Scaphoid bone
Lunate bone
Triquetrum bone
Pisiform bone
Carpal bones (proximal row)
Metacarpal bones
1
2
3
4
5
Proximal phalanx of thumb
Distal phalanx of thumb
Proximal phalanx of finger
Middle phalanx of finger
Distal phalanx of finger
Digits
(a) Posterior view
(b) Anterior view (anatomical position)

FIGURE 7.35 Bones of the Right Wrist and Hand
(*a*) Posterior view. (*b*) Anterior view. APR

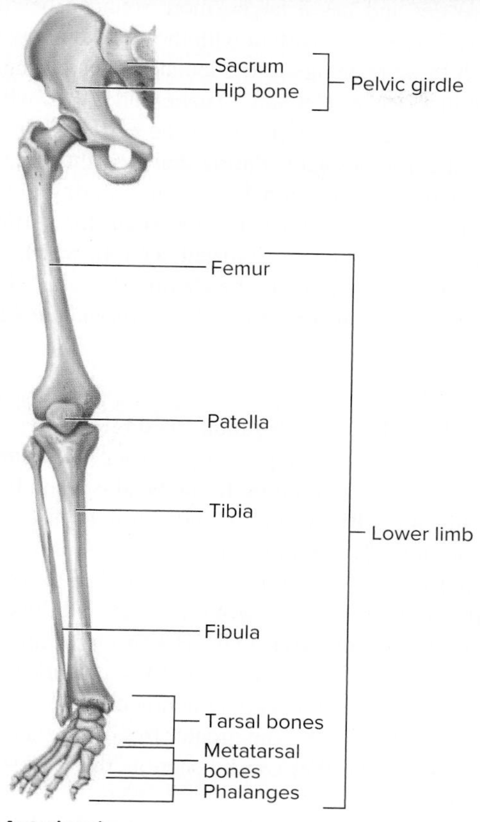

FIGURE 7.36 Bones of the Right Half of the Pelvic Girdle and the Right Lower Limb

complete circle of bone. The **pelvis** (pel′vis; basin) includes the pelvic girdle and the coccyx (figure 7.37).

Each hip bone is formed from three separate bones fused into a large bony plate: (1) the **ilium** (IL-ee-um; groin), (2) the **ischium** (IS-kee-um; hip), and (3) the **pubis** (PYOO-bis; genital hair) (figure 7.39). The three individual bones converge near the center of the hip socket, called the **acetabulum** (as-eh-TAB-you-lum; vinegar cup). The lower limbs articulate with the pelvic girdle in the acetabulum.

The articular surface of the acetabulum is crescent-shaped and occupies only the superior and lateral aspects of the fossa. The pelvic girdle serves as the place of attachment for the lower limbs, supports the weight of the body, and protects internal organs. Because the pelvic girdle is a complete bony ring, it provides more stable support but less mobility than the incomplete ring of the pectoral girdle. In addition, the pelvis in a female protects a developing fetus and forms a passageway through which the fetus passes during delivery.

Ilium

The largest of the three hip bones is the ilium. The **iliac crest** forms the most superior border of the ilium (see figure 7.39). The crest ends anteriorly as the **anterior superior iliac spine** and posteriorly as the **posterior superior iliac spine.** The crest and anterior spine can be felt and even seen in thin individuals (figure 7.40). The anterior superior iliac spine is an important anatomical landmark used, for example, to find the correct location for giving gluteal injections into the hip (see Clinical Impact 7.3). A dimple overlies the posterior superior iliac spine just superior to the buttocks. The **greater sciatic** (sigh-AT-ik) **notch** is on the posterior side of the ilium, just inferior to the posterior inferior iliac spine. The sciatic nerve passes through the greater sciatic notch. The **auricular surface** of the ilium joins the sacrum to form the **sacroiliac joint** (see figure 7.37). The medial side of the ilium consists of a large depression called the **iliac fossa.**

Ischium

Of the two inferior hip bones, the ischium is more posterior than the pubis. The ischium has a thick **ischial** (IS-kee-ul) **tuberosity.** Posterior thigh muscles attach to the ischial tuberosity, and it's the portion of the pelvis on which a person sits (see figure 7.39*a*). The ischium also has a posterior **ischial spine,** a site of ligament attachment.

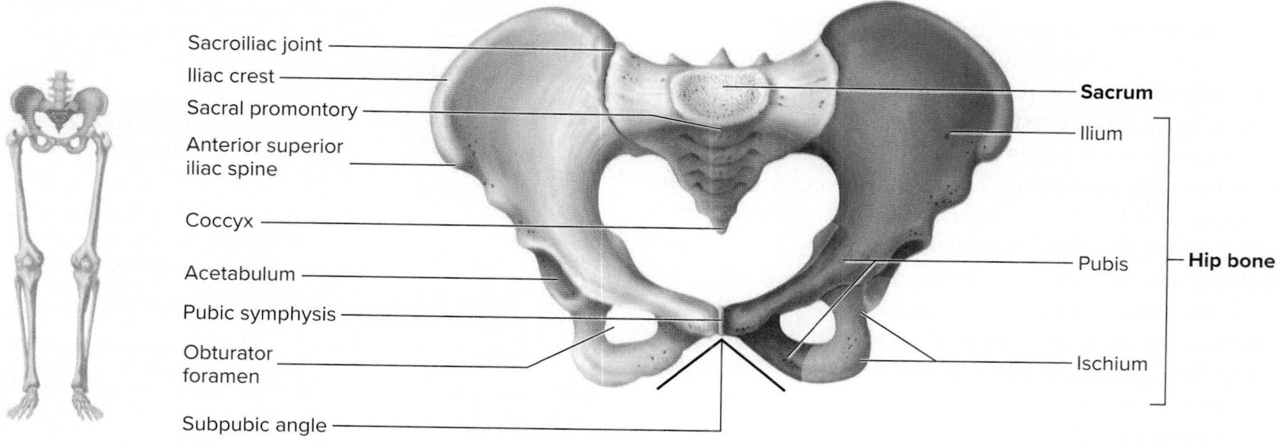

FIGURE 7.37 Pelvis
Anterosuperior view of the bones of the articulated pelvis.

Clinical IMPACT 7.3

Gluteal Injections

The large gluteal muscles (hip muscles; see chapter 10) are a common site for intramuscular injections. Gluteal injections are made in the superolateral region of the hip (figure 7.38) because a large nerve (the sciatic nerve; see chapter 12) lies deep to the other gluteal regions. The landmarks for such an injection are the anterior superior iliac spine and the tubercle of the iliac crest, which lies about one-third of the way along the iliac crest from anterior to posterior.

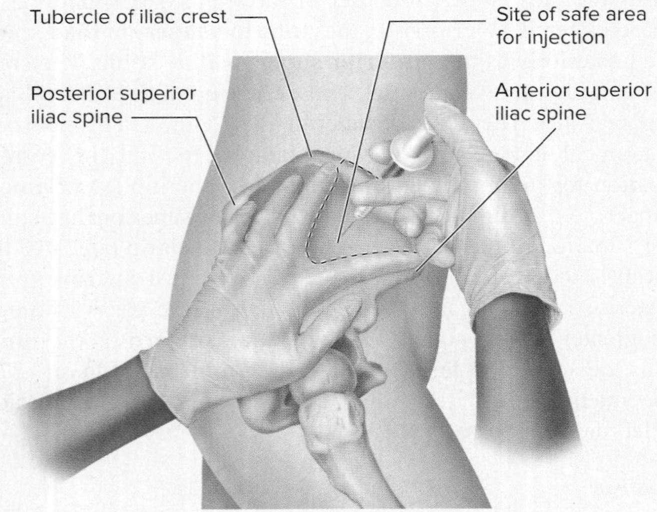

FIGURE 7.38 Gluteal Injection Site
Injections into the gluteal muscles should avoid hitting the sciatic nerve.

Pubis

The pubis forms the anterior portion of the pelvic girdle (see figure 7.39). The two pubic bones are joined by the **pubic symphysis** (SIM-fi-sis; joined), a thick pad of fibrocartilage. Abdominal muscles attach to the **pubic crest,** a medial ridge. Laterally, where the pubic crest ends, is the **pubic tubercle,** the attachment site of the inguinal ligament (see figure 7.39*b*). At the point of fusion with the ischium, the two bones surround the noticeable **obturator** (OB-tour-ate-or; closed up) **foramen** (see figure 7.39). However, in a living person, only a few nerves and blood vessels pass through; it is otherwise closed by a ligament.

The pelvis is subdivided into a **true pelvis** and a **false pelvis** (figure 7.41). The opening to the true pelvis is the **pelvic inlet,** and the inferior opening of the true pelvis is the **pelvic outlet.** The false pelvis is formed by muscle overlying bone of the true pelvis.

Comparison of the Male Pelvis and the Female Pelvis

The male pelvis is usually more massive than the female pelvis as a result of the greater weight and size of the male body. The female pelvis is broader and has a larger, more rounded pelvic inlet and outlet (figure 7.41*a,b*), consistent with the need to allow the fetus to pass through these openings in the female pelvis during childbirth. A wide, circular pelvic inlet and a pelvic outlet with widely spaced ischial spines can facilitate delivery of the newborn. A smaller pelvic outlet can cause problems during delivery; thus, the size of the pelvic inlet and outlet is routinely measured during prenatal pelvic examinations. If the pelvic outlet is too small for normal delivery, the physician may perform a **cesarean section,** which is the surgical removal of the fetus through the abdominal wall. Table 7.12 lists additional differences between the male pelvis and the female pelvis.

Thigh: Femur

The thigh, like the arm, contains a single bone, the **femur.** Medially, the femur has a prominent, rounded **head,** where it articulates with the acetabulum. In the head is a small indentation called the **fovea capitis,** where a ligament helps secure the femur to the acetabulum. The femur also has a well-defined **neck.** Both the head and neck of the femur are located at an oblique angle to its shaft (figure 7.42). The proximal shaft exhibits two projections: a **greater trochanter** (TROH-kan-ter; runner) lateral to the neck and a smaller, **lesser trochanter** inferior and posterior to the neck. Both trochanters are attachment sites for muscles that fasten the hip to the thigh. The greater trochanter and its attached muscles form a bulge that can be seen as the widest part of the hips (see figure 7.40).

The femur articulates with the tibia to form the knee. There are two smooth rounded projections that rotate on the superior surface of the tibia when we bend our knee. These two rounded projections are (1) the **medial condyle** and (2) the **lateral condyle** (figure 7.42). Just superior to the medial and lateral condyles are two large ligament attachment sites. These are (1) the **medial epicondyle** and (2) the **lateral epicondyle.** Additionally, on the

TABLE 7.12 Differences Between the Male Pelvis and the Female Pelvis (see figure 7.41)

Area	Description
General	In females, somewhat lighter in weight and wider laterally but shorter superiorly to inferiorly and less funnel-shaped; less obvious muscle attachment points in females
Sacrum	Broader in females, with the inferior part directed more posteriorly; the sacral promontory does not project as far anteriorly in females
Pelvic inlet	Heart-shaped in males; oval in females
Pelvic outlet	Broader and more shallow in females
Subpubic angle	Less than 90 degrees in males; 90 degrees or more in females
Ilium	More shallow and flared laterally in females
Ischial spines	Farther apart in females
Ischial tuberosities	Turned laterally in females and medially in males

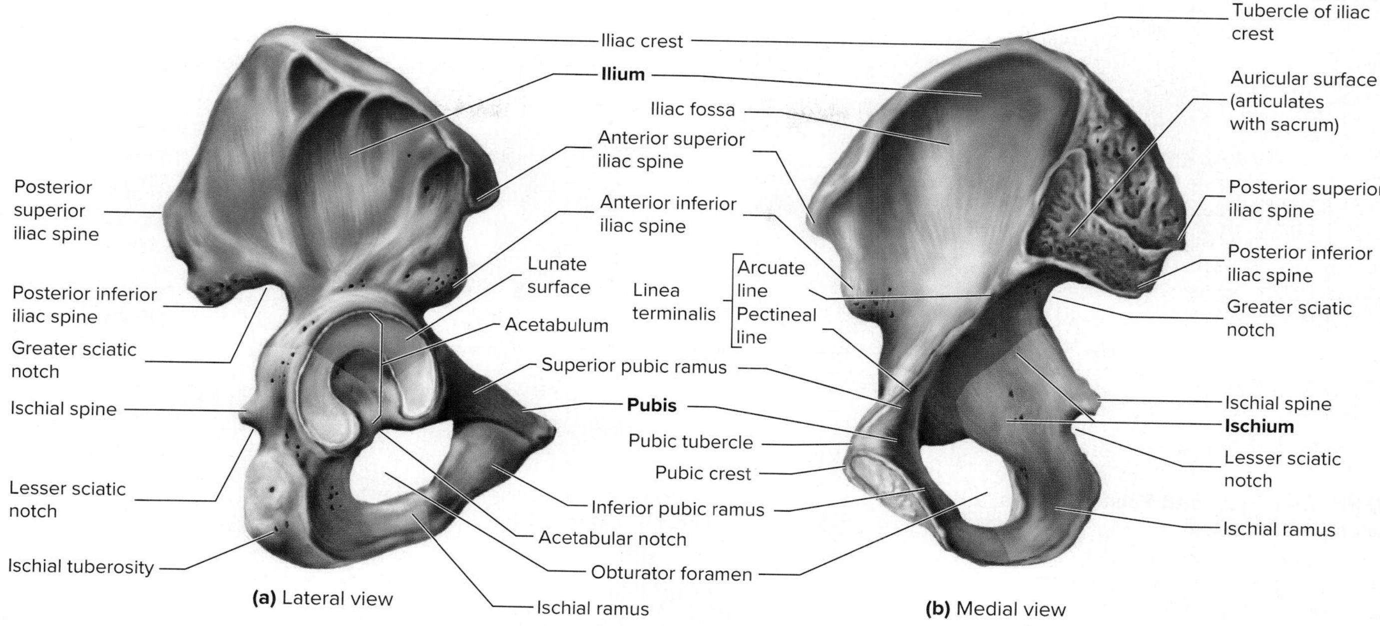

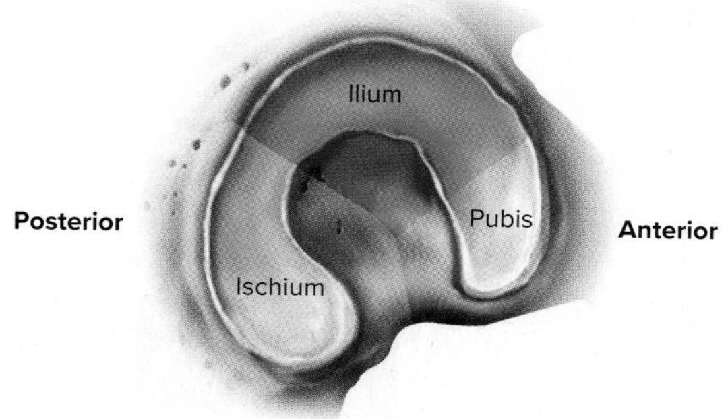

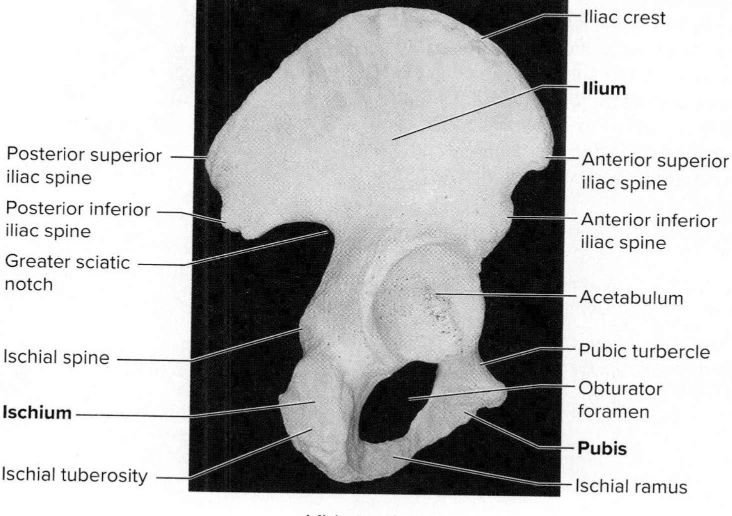

FIGURE 7.39 Hip Bone
(*a*) Right hip bone, lateral view. Each hip bone is formed by fusion of the ilium, ischium, and pubis. The three bones can be seen joining near the center of the acetabulum, separated by lines of cartilage. (*b*) Right hip bone, medial view. (*c*) Focused view of acetabulum and the convergence site of the three hip bones. (*d*) Right hip bone, lateral view. (The names of the three bones forming the hip bone are in bold.) (c) Christine Eckel/McGraw Hill Education APR

medial side superior to the medial epicondyle is the **adductor tubercle,** a muscle attachment site.

On the posterior surface of the femur, the **gluteal tuberosity** is visible inferior to the lesser trochanter (see figure 7.42). The gluteal tuberosity is the location of attachment of the buttock muscle, the gluteus maximus. Extending inferiorly from the gluteal tuberosity is the **linea aspera** (LI-nee-ah AS-peer-ah), a site of attachment of many thigh muscles.

The **patella,** or kneecap, is a large sesamoid bone located within the tendon of the quadriceps femoris muscle group, which is the major muscle group of the anterior thigh (figure 7.43). The patella articulates with the patellar groove of the femur to create a smooth articular surface over the anterior distal end of the femur. The patella holds the tendon away from the distal end of the femur.

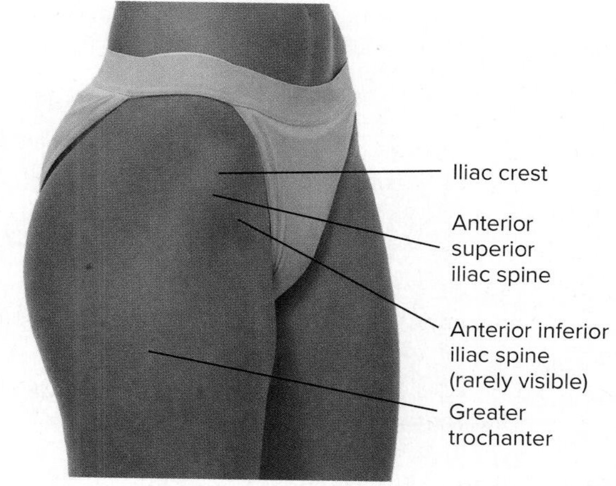

FIGURE 7.40 Surface Anatomy of the Hip Bone and Femur: Anterolateral View Aaron Roeth, photogrpaher/McGraw Hill Education

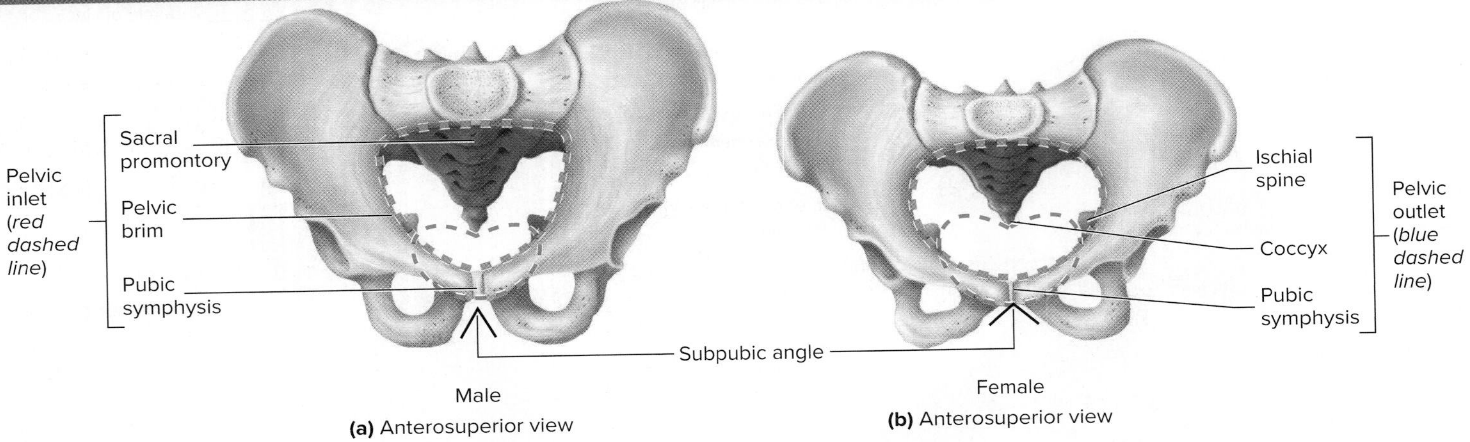

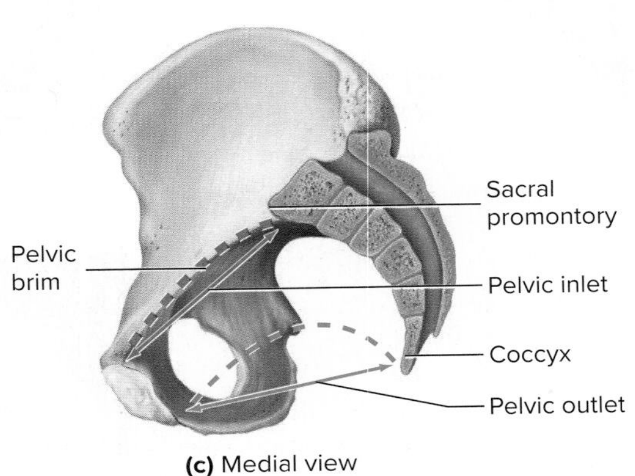

FIGURE 7.41 True and False Pelvises in Males and Females
(*a*) In a male, the pelvic inlet (*red dashed line*) and outlet (*blue dashed line*) are small and the subpubic angle is less than 90 degrees. The true pelvis is shown as *blue*. The false pelvis is shown as *natural bone color*. (*b*) In a female, the pelvic inlet (*red dashed line*) and outlet (*blue dashed line*) are larger and the subpubic angle is 90 degrees or greater. (*c*) Midsagittal section through the pelvis to show the pelvic inlet (*red arrow and red dashed line*) and the pelvic outlet (*blue arrow and blue dashed line*).

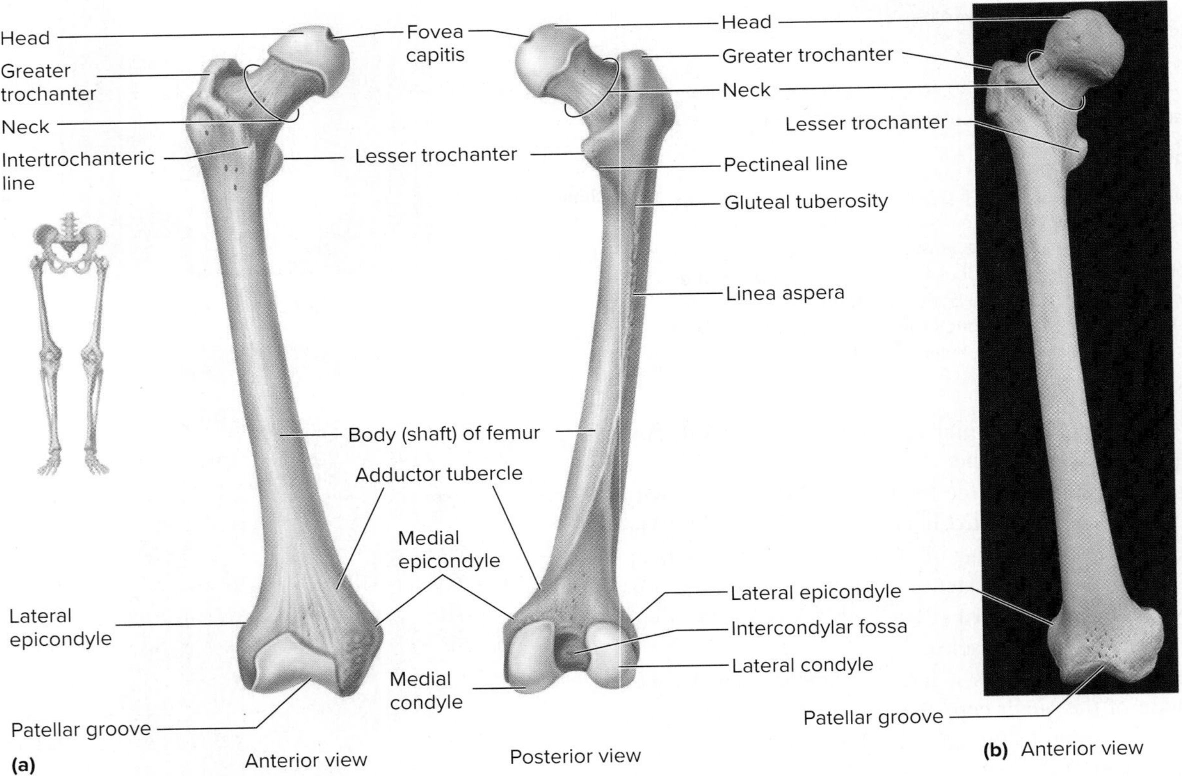

FIGURE 7.42 Right Femur
(*a*) Anterior and posterior views of the right femur. (*b*) Photo of anterior view of the right femur. (b) Christine Eckel/McGraw Hill Education

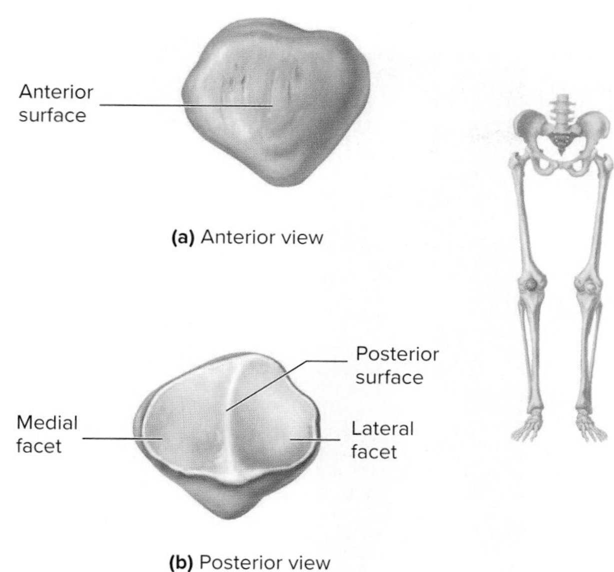

FIGURE 7.43 Right Patella
(*a*) Anterior view. (*b*) Posterior view.

If the patella is severely fractured, the tendon from the quadriceps femoris muscle group may be torn, severely reducing muscle function. In extreme cases, it may be necessary to remove the patella to repair the tendon, which reduces the amount of power the quadriceps femoris muscle can generate. Abnormal tracking of the patella can become a problem in some teenagers, especially females. As a young female's hips widen during puberty, the angles at the joints between the hips and the tibia may change considerably, forcing the patella to track more laterally than normal and causing pain, especially in physically active females.

Leg: Tibia and Fibula

The leg is the part of the lower limb between the knee and the ankle. Like the forearm, it consists of two bones: (1) the medial **tibia** (TIB-ee-ah), or shinbone, and (2) the lateral **fibula** (FIB-you-lah; figure 7.44). The tibia is the larger of the two and is the major weight-bearing bone of the leg.

The rounded condyles of the femur rest on flat condyles on the proximal end of the tibia. The condyles are called the **medial condyle** and the **lateral condyle** (figure 7.44). Projecting superiorly between the condyles is the **intercondylar eminence** (jut, project), which separates the intercondylar area into anterior and posterior regions. The anterior cruciate ligament and the posterior cruciate ligament attach in the anterior and posterior intercondylar regions (see chapter 8). Just distal to the condyles of the tibia, on its anterior surface, is the easily felt **tibial tuberosity** (see figure 7.44). The tibial tuberosity is the point of attachment for the quadriceps femoris muscle group. The fibula does not articulate with the femur, but its **head** articulates with the proximal end of the tibia.

Ankle

The **ankle** consists of the distal ends of the tibia and fibula forming a partial socket that articulates with a bone of the foot (the talus) (figure 7.46). A prominence can be seen on each side of the ankle (see figure 7.45). These are the **medial malleolus** of the distal tibia and the **lateral malleolus** of the distal fibula.

Foot: Tarsals, Metatarsals, and Phalanges

There are seven **tarsal** (TAR-sahl; foot) **bones** (see figure 7.46). The tarsal bones include (1) the **talus** (TAY-lus; ankle), (2) the **calcaneus** (kal-KAY-nee-us; heel), (3) the **navicular** (nah-VIK-you-lar), (4–6) the medial, intermediate, and lateral **cuneiforms** (KYOO-nee-ih-forms), and (7) the **cuboid** (KYOO-boyd) (see figure 7.46). A mnemonic used for the tarsal bones is **T**iger **C**ub **N**eeds **MILC** (**T**alus, **C**alcaneus, **N**avicular, **M**edial cuneiform, **I**ntermediate cuneiform, **L**ateral cuneiform, and **C**uboid).

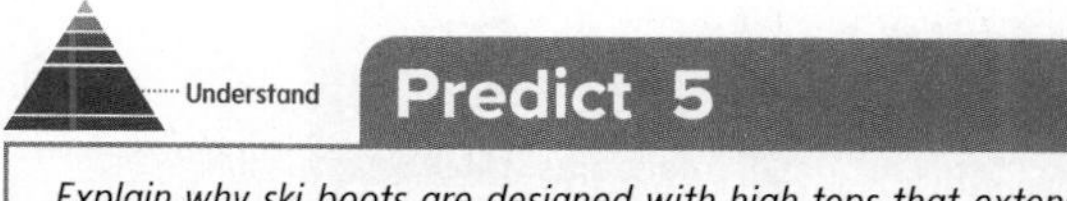

Predict 5

Explain why ski boots are designed with high tops that extend partway up the leg.

The **metatarsal bones** and **phalanges** of the foot are arranged in a manner very similar to that of the metacarpal bones and phalanges of the hand, with the great toe (**hallux**) comparable to the thumb (figure 7.46). Small sesamoid bones often form in the tendons of muscles attached to the great toe. The ball of the foot is the junction between the metatarsal bones and the phalanges.

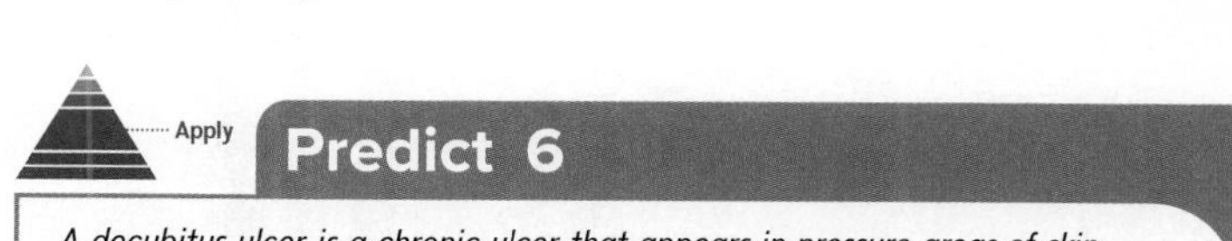

Predict 6

A decubitus ulcer is a chronic ulcer that appears in pressure areas of skin overlying a bony prominence in bedridden or otherwise immobilized patients. Where are decubitus ulcers likely to occur?

There are three primary **arches** in the foot formed by the positions of the tarsal bones and metatarsal bones and held in place by ligaments. Two **longitudinal arches** extend from the heel to the ball of the foot, and a **transverse arch** extends across the foot. The transverse arch is located at the connection between the five metatarsals, the three cuneiforms, and the cuboid. The arches serve as an adjustable lever to assist in the two main functions of the foot: (1) to support the body in its upright position both while standing and in forward movement during walking and (2) to push the body forward during walking and to absorb shock when the foot contacts the ground. The arches function similarly to the springs of a car, allowing the foot to give and spring back (see chapter 8).

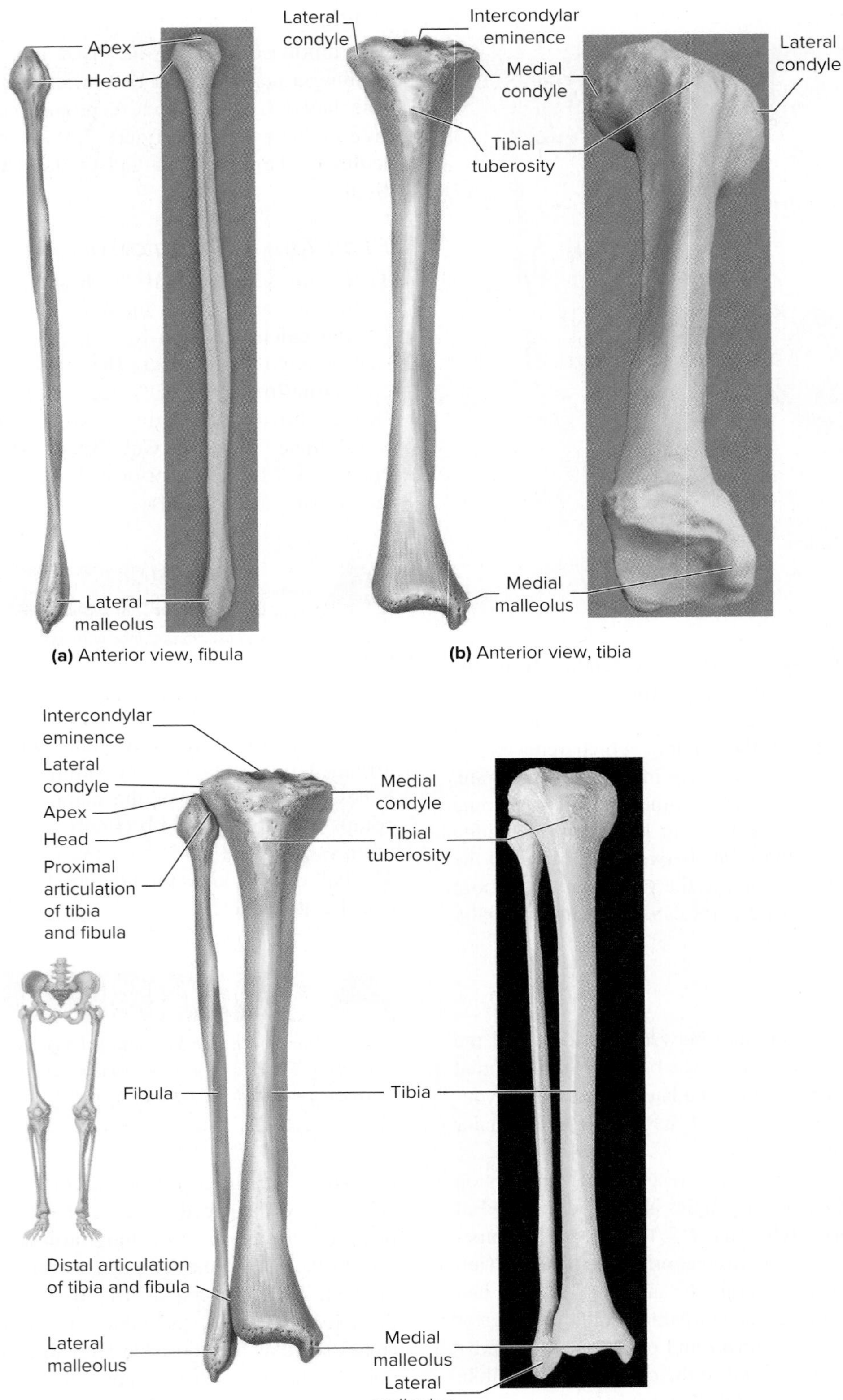

FIGURE 7.44 Right Tibia and Fibula

(*a*) Anterior view of right fibula. (*b*) Anterior view of right tibia. (*c*) Anterior view of the articulated right tibia and fibula. (a, b) ©Bone Clones, www.boneclones.com; (c2) Christine Eckel/McGraw Hill Education

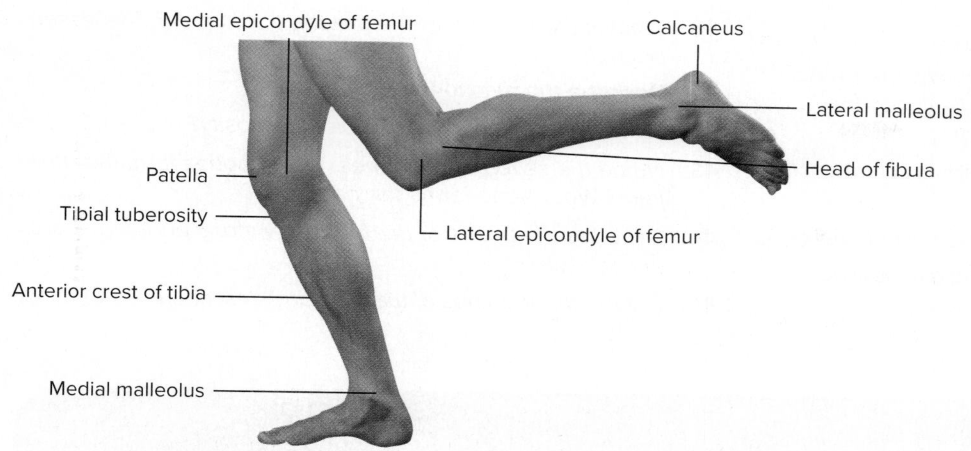

FIGURE 7.45 Lower Limb
Surface anatomy of the bones in the lower limb. ©Eric A. Wise

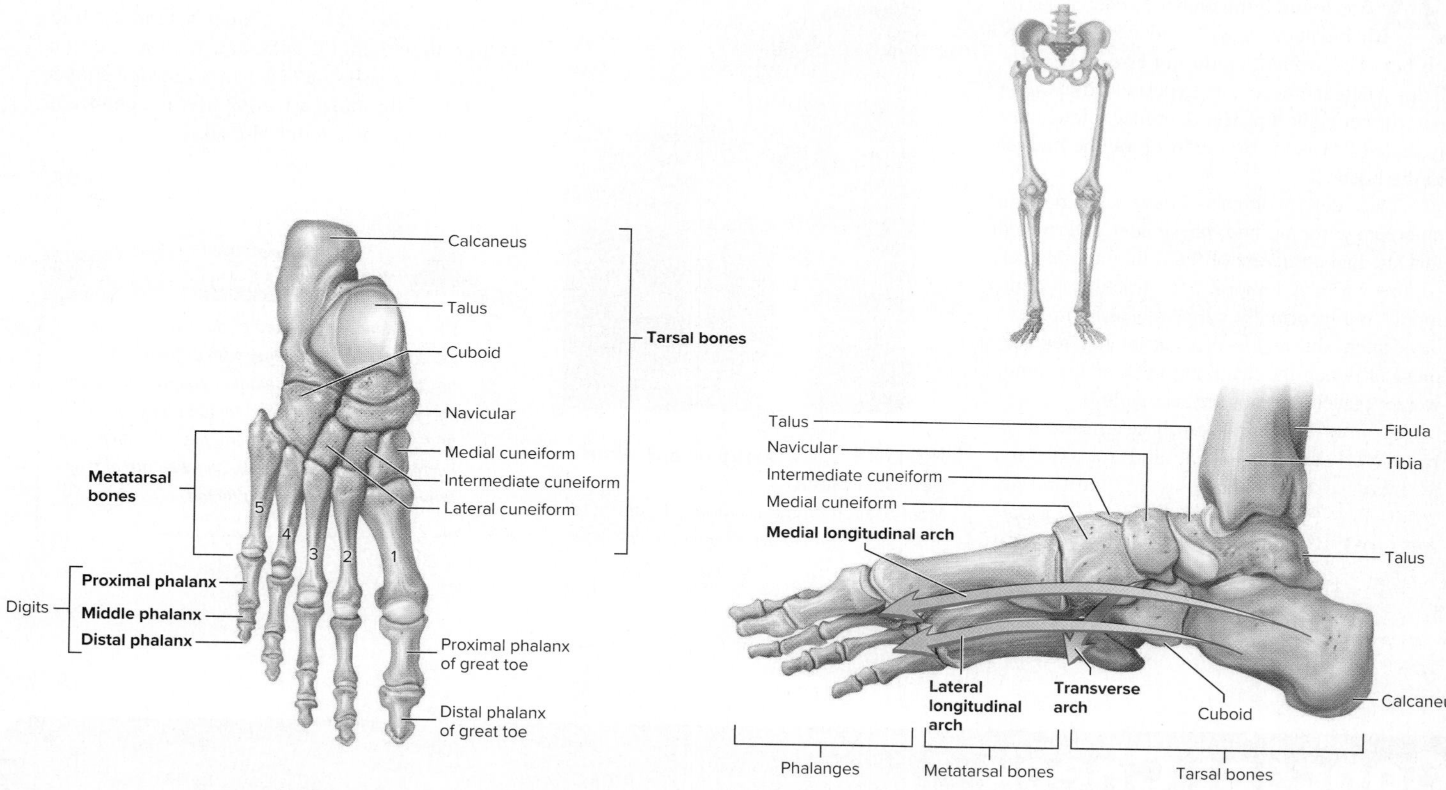

Calcaneus
Talus
Cuboid
Navicular
Medial cuneiform
Intermediate cuneiform
Lateral cuneiform
Tarsal bones
Metatarsal bones
5 4 3 2 1
Digits
Proximal phalanx
Middle phalanx
Distal phalanx
Proximal phalanx of great toe
Distal phalanx of great toe

(a) Superior view

Talus
Navicular
Intermediate cuneiform
Medial cuneiform
Medial longitudinal arch
Fibula
Tibia
Talus
Lateral longitudinal arch
Transverse arch
Cuboid
Calcaneus
Phalanges
Metatarsal bones
Tarsal bones

(b) Medial inferior view

FIGURE 7.46 Bones of the Right Foot
(*a*) Superior view of the bones of the foot. (*b*) The medial longitudinal arch is formed by the calcaneus, the talus, the navicular, the cuneiforms, and three medial metatarsal bones. The lateral longitudinal arch is formed by the calcaneus, the cuboid, and two lateral metatarsal bones. The transverse arch is formed by the cuboid and the cuneiforms. APR

ASSESS YOUR PROGRESS

35. *What bones form the pelvic girdle? Explain why the pelvic girdle is more stable than the pectoral girdle. How does this stability affect movement?*
36. *Describe the structure of the hip bone. What articulations does the hip bone make?*
37. *Name the important sites of muscle attachment on the pelvis.*
38. *Describe the differences between a male and a female pelvis.*
39. *Distinguish between the lower limb and the leg.*
40. *What is the function of the greater trochanter? The lesser trochanter?*
41. *Describe the function of the patella.*
42. *What is the function of the tibial tuberosity?*
43. *Name the seven tarsal bones. Which bones form the ankle joint? What bone forms the heel?*
44. *Describe the bones of the foot. How many phalanges are in each toe?*
45. *List the three arches of the foot, and describe their function.*

Case STUDY 7.1 A "Broken Hip"

An 85-year-old woman who lived alone was found lying on her kitchen floor by her daughter, who had gone to check on her. The woman could not rise, even with help; when she tried, she experienced extreme pain in her right hip. Her daughter immediately dialed 911, and paramedics took the mother to the hospital.

The elderly woman's hip was x-rayed in the emergency room, and physicians determined that she had a fracture of the right femoral neck (figure 7.47). A femoral neck fracture is commonly, but incorrectly, called a broken hip. Two days later, she received a partial hip replacement in which the head and neck of the femur were replaced, but not the acetabulum.

Approximately 1.6 million femoral neck fractures occur worldwide and are expected to increase to as many as 6.3 million by 2050. This type of fracture increases a person's risk of death during the first several months by 8-fold. The risk of suffering a femoral neck fracture doubles each decade of life after age 50. Females tend to fracture their femoral neck at a higher rate than males. Females have a 1 in 3 lifetime chance while males have a 1 in 12 lifetime chance of fracturing their femoral neck.

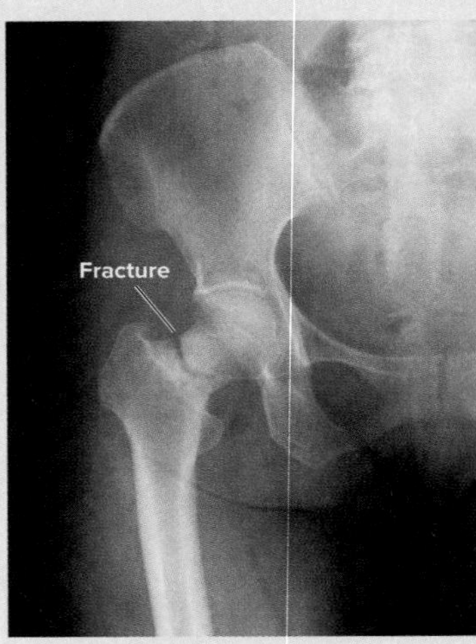

FIGURE 7.47 X-ray of a Broken Femoral Neck
Most broken hips are actually fractures of the femoral neck. Sutthaburawonk/Getty Images

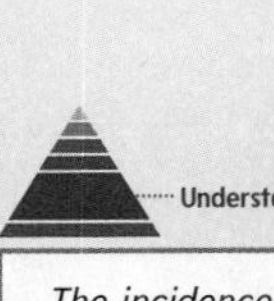

Predict 7

The incidence of fracture of the femoral neck increases as patients age, with a greater number of patients being females. The overall risk of injury is 86% in males and females 65 years old and older. Why is the femoral neck so commonly injured (hint: see figure 7.1), and why are elderly females most commonly affected?

Concept Check

7.1 Skeletal Anatomy Overview

Bones have processes, smooth surfaces, and holes that are associated with ligaments, muscles, joints, nerves, and blood vessels.

1. *Which of these is part of the appendicular skeleton?*

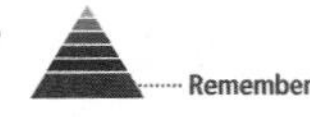

   a. cranium
   b. ribs
   c. clavicle
   d. sternum
   e. vertebra

2. *A knoblike projection on a bone is called a________* (Remember)
   a. spine.
   b. facet.
   c. tuberosity.
   d. sulcus.
   e. ramus.

7.2 Axial Skeleton

The axial skeleton consists of the skull, auditory ossicles, hyoid bone, vertebral column, and thoracic cage.

Skull

A. The skull, or cranium, can be thought of as a single unit.

B. The parietal bones are joined at the midline by the sagittal suture; they are joined to the frontal bone by the coronal suture, to the occipital bone by the lambdoid suture, and to the temporal bone by the squamous suture.

C. Nuchal lines are the points of attachment for neck muscles.

D. The skull is composed of 22 bones.
- The auditory ossicles, which function in hearing, are located inside the temporal bones.
- The cranial bone protects the brain.
- The facial bones protect the sensory organs of the head and are muscle attachment sites (mastication, facial expression, and eye muscles).
- The mandible and maxillae possess alveolar processes with sockets for the attachment of the teeth.

E. Frontal Bone
- The orbits contain the eyes.

F. Parietal Bones
- The temporal lines are attachment points of the temporalis muscle.

G. Temporal Bones
- The external auditory canal transmits sound waves toward the eardrum.
- Important neck muscles attach to the mastoid process.
- The zygomatic arch, from the temporal and zygomatic bones, forms a bridge across the side of the skull.
- The mandible articulates with the temporal bone.
- Blood reaches the brain through the internal carotid arteries, which pass through the carotid canals, and through the vertebral arteries, which pass through the foramen magnum.
- Most blood leaves the brain through the internal jugular veins, which exit through the jugular foramina.
- Styloid processes provide attachment points for three muscles involved in moving the tongue, hyoid bone, and pharynx.

H. Occipital Bone
- The spinal cord and brain are connected through the foramen magnum.
- Occipital condyles are points of articulation between the skull and the vertebral column.

I. Sphenoid Bone
- Sinuses within bone are air-filled cavities. The paranasal sinuses, which connect to the nasal cavity, are the frontal, sphenoidal, and maxillary sinuses and the ethmoidal labyrinth.
- The sella turcica is occupied by the pituitary gland.

J. Ethmoid Bone
- The nasal cavity is divided by the nasal septum, and the hard palate separates the nasal cavity from the oral cavity.
- The crista galli is a point of attachment for one of the meninges.
- The olfactory nerves extend into the roof of the nasal cavity through the cribriform plate.

3. *The perpendicular plate of the ethmoid and the_________ form the nasal septum.* Remember
   a. palatine process of the maxilla
   b. horizontal plate of the palatine
   c. vomer
   d. nasal bone
   e. lacrimal bone

4. *Which of these bones does* not *contain a paranasal sinus?*

   a. ethmoid
   b. sphenoid
   c. frontal
   d. temporal
   e. maxilla

5. *The mandible articulates with the skull at the* Remember
   a. styloid process.
   b. occipital condyle.
   c. mandibular fossa.
   d. zygomatic arch.
   e. medial pterygoid.

6. *The nerves for the sense of smell pass through the________* Remember
   a. cribriform plate.
   b. nasolacrimal canal.
   c. internal auditory canal.
   d. optic canal.
   e. orbital fissure.

7. *The major blood supply to the brain enters through the________* Remember
   a. foramen magnum.
   b. carotid canals.
   c. jugular foramina.
   d. Both a and b are correct.
   e. All of these are correct.

8. *The site of the sella turcica is the__________*

   a. sphenoid bone.
   b. maxillae.
   c. frontal bone.
   d. ethmoid bone.
   e. temporal bone.

9. *Which of these bones is* not *in contact with the sphenoid bone?* Remember
   a. maxilla
   b. inferior nasal concha
   c. ethmoid
   d. parietal
   e. vomer

10. *A patient has an infection in the nasal cavity. Name seven adjacent structures to which the infection could spread.* Understand

Hyoid Bone

The hyoid bone, which is not attached to other bones, is the attachment site for the throat and tongue muscles.

Vertebral Column

A. The vertebral column provides flexible support and protects the spinal cord.

B. The vertebral column has four major curvatures: cervical, thoracic, lumbar, and sacral/coccygeal. Abnormal curvatures include lordosis in the lumbar region, kyphosis in the thoracic region, and scoliosis, an abnormal lateral curvature.

C. A typical vertebra consists of a body, a vertebral arch, and various processes.
- Part of the body and the vertebral arch (pedicle and lamina) form the vertebral foramen, which contains and protects the spinal cord.
- Spinal nerves exit through the intervertebral foramina.
- The transverse and spinous processes are points of muscle and ligament attachment.
- Vertebrae articulate with one another through the superior and inferior articular processes.

D. Adjacent bodies are separated by intervertebral disks. Each disk has a fibrous outer covering (annulus fibrosus) surrounding a gelatinous interior (nucleus pulposus).

E. Vertebrae can be distinguished by region.
- All seven cervical vertebrae have transverse foramina, and most have bifid spinous processes.
- The 12 thoracic vertebrae are characterized by long, downward-pointing spinous processes and demifacets.
- The five lumbar vertebrae have thick, heavy bodies and processes.
- The sacrum consists of five fused vertebrae and attaches to the hip bones to form the pelvis.
- The coccyx consists of four fused vertebrae attached to the sacrum.

11. A herniated disk occurs when________

a. the annulus fibrosus ruptures.
b. the intervertebral disk slips out of place.
c. the spinal cord ruptures.
d. too much fluid builds up in the nucleus pulposus.
e. All of these are correct.

12. The weight-bearing portion of a vertebra is the________ Remember

a. vertebral arch.
b. articular process.
c. body.
d. transverse process.
e. spinous process.

13. Transverse foramina are found only in________ Remember

a. cervical vertebrae.
b. thoracic vertebrae.
c. lumbar vertebrae.
d. the sacrum.
e. the coccyx.

14. A patient is unconscious. X-rays reveal that the superior articular facet of the atlas has been fractured. Would this condition result from falling on the top of the head or being hit in the jaw with an uppercut? Explain. Apply

15. If the vertebral column is forcefully rotated, what part of a vertebra is most likely to be damaged? In what area of the vertebral column is such damage most likely? Apply

Thoracic Cage

A. The thoracic cage (consisting of the ribs, their associated costal cartilages, and the sternum) protects the thoracic organs and changes volume during respiration.

B. Twelve pairs of ribs attach to the thoracic vertebrae. They are divided into seven pairs of true ribs and five pairs of false ribs. Two pairs of false ribs are floating ribs.

C. The sternum is composed of the manubrium, the body, and the xiphoid process.

16. Which of these statements concerning ribs is correct?

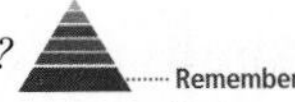

a. The true ribs attach directly to the sternum with costal cartilage.
b. There are five pairs of floating ribs.
c. The head of the rib attaches to the transverse process of the vertebra.
d. Ribs 8–10 are classified as true ribs.
e. Floating ribs do not attach to vertebrae.

17. The point where the scapula and clavicle connect is the ________ Remember

a. coracoid process.
b. styloid process.
c. glenoid cavity.
d. acromion process.
e. capitulum.

7.3 Appendicular Skeleton

The appendicular skeleton consists of the upper and lower limbs and the girdles that attach the limbs to the body.

Pectoral Girdle and Upper Limb

A. The upper limb is attached loosely and functions in grasping and manipulation.

B. The pectoral girdle consists of the scapulae and clavicles.
- The scapula articulates with the humerus and the clavicle. It is an attachment site for shoulder, back, and arm muscles.
- The clavicle holds the shoulder away from the body, permitting the arm to move freely.

C. The arm bone is the humerus.
- The humerus articulates with the scapula (head), the radius (capitulum), and the ulna (trochlea).
- Sites of muscle attachment are the greater and lesser tubercles, the deltoid tuberosity, and the epicondyles.

D. The forearm contains the ulna and the radius.
- The ulna and the radius articulate with each other and with the humerus and the wrist bones.
- The wrist ligaments attach to the styloid processes of the radius and the ulna.

E. Eight carpal bones, or wrist bones, are arranged in two rows.

F. The hand consists of five metacarpal bones.

G. The phalanges are digital bones. Each finger has three phalanges, and the thumb has two phalanges.

18. The distal medial process of the humerus to which the ulna joins is the _____

a. epicondyle.
b. deltoid tuberosity.
c. malleolus.
d. capitulum.
e. trochlea.

19. Which of these is not *a point of muscle attachment on the pectoral girdle or upper limb?* Remember

a. epicondyles
b. mastoid process
c. radial tuberosity
d. spine of scapula
e. greater tubercle

20. *What might be the consequences of breaking both the ulna and the radius if the two bones fuse to each other during repair of the fracture?* Understand

Pelvic Girdle and Lower Limb

A. The lower limb is attached solidly to the hip bone and functions in support and movement.

B. The pelvic girdle consists of the right and left hip bones and the sacrum. Each hip bone is formed by the fusion of the ilium, the ischium, and the pubis.
   - The hip bones articulate with each other (symphysis pubis) and with the sacrum (sacroiliac joint) and the femur (acetabulum).
   - Important sites of muscle attachment are the iliac crest, the iliac spines, and the ischial tuberosity.
   - The female pelvis has a larger pelvic inlet and outlet than the male pelvis.

C. The bone in the thigh is the femur.
   - The femur articulates with the hip bone (head), the tibia (medial and lateral condyles), and the patella (patellar groove).
   - Sites of muscle attachment are the greater and lesser trochanters and the adductor tubercle.
   - Sites of ligament attachment are the lateral and medial epicondyles.

D. The leg consists of the tibia and the fibula.
   - The tibia articulates with the femur, the fibula, and the talus. The fibula articulates with the tibia and the talus.
   - Tendons from the thigh muscles attach to the tibial tuberosity.

E. Seven tarsal bones form the proximal portion of the foot.

F. The foot consists of five metatarsal bones.

G. The toes have three phalanges each, except for the big toe, which has two.

H. The bony arches transfer weight from the heels to the toes and allow the foot to conform to many different positions.

21. *The bone(s) of the foot on which the tibia rests is (are) the* _____ Remember
    a. talus.
    b. calcaneus.
    c. metatarsal bones.
    d. navicular.
    e. phalanges.

22. *The projection on the hip bone of the pelvic girdle that is used as a landmark for finding an injection site is the*________ Remember
    a. ischial tuberosity.
    b. iliac crest.
    c. anterior superior iliac spine.
    d. posterior inferior iliac spine.
    e. ischial spine.

23. *When comparing the pectoral girdle with the pelvic girdle, which of these statements is correct?* Remember
    a. The pectoral girdle has greater mass than the pelvic girdle.
    b. The pelvic girdle is more firmly attached to the body than the pectoral girdle.
    c. The pectoral girdle has the limbs more securely attached than the pelvic girdle.
    d. The pelvic girdle allows greater mobility than the pectoral girdle.

24. *When comparing a male pelvis with a female pelvis, which of these statements is correct?* Remember
    a. The pelvic inlet in males is larger and more circular.
    b. The subpubic angle in females is less than 90 degrees.
    c. The ischial spines in males are closer together.
    d. The sacrum in males is broader and less curved.

25. *A site of muscle attachment on the proximal end of the femur is the* _______ Remember
    a. greater trochanter.
    b. epicondyle.
    c. greater tubercle.
    d. intercondylar eminence.
    e. condyle.

26. *A person with paraplegia develops decubitus ulcers (pressure sores) on the buttocks from sitting in a wheelchair for extended periods. Name the bony protuberance responsible.* Understand

27. *Why do females tend to suffer more knee pain and injuries than males?* Apply

28. *On the basis of the bone structure of the lower limb, explain why it is easier to turn the foot medially (sole of the foot facing toward the midline of the body) than laterally. Why is it easier to bend the wrist medially than laterally?* Apply

29. *Justin leaped from his hotel room to avoid burning to death in a fire. If he landed on his heels, what bone was likely to fracture? Unfortunately for Justin, an iron beam fell on the distal part of Justin's foot (not the toes). What bones could now be fractured?* Understand

Answers to this chapter's odd-numbered Concept Check questions appear in Appendix F.

8 CHAPTER Joints and Movement

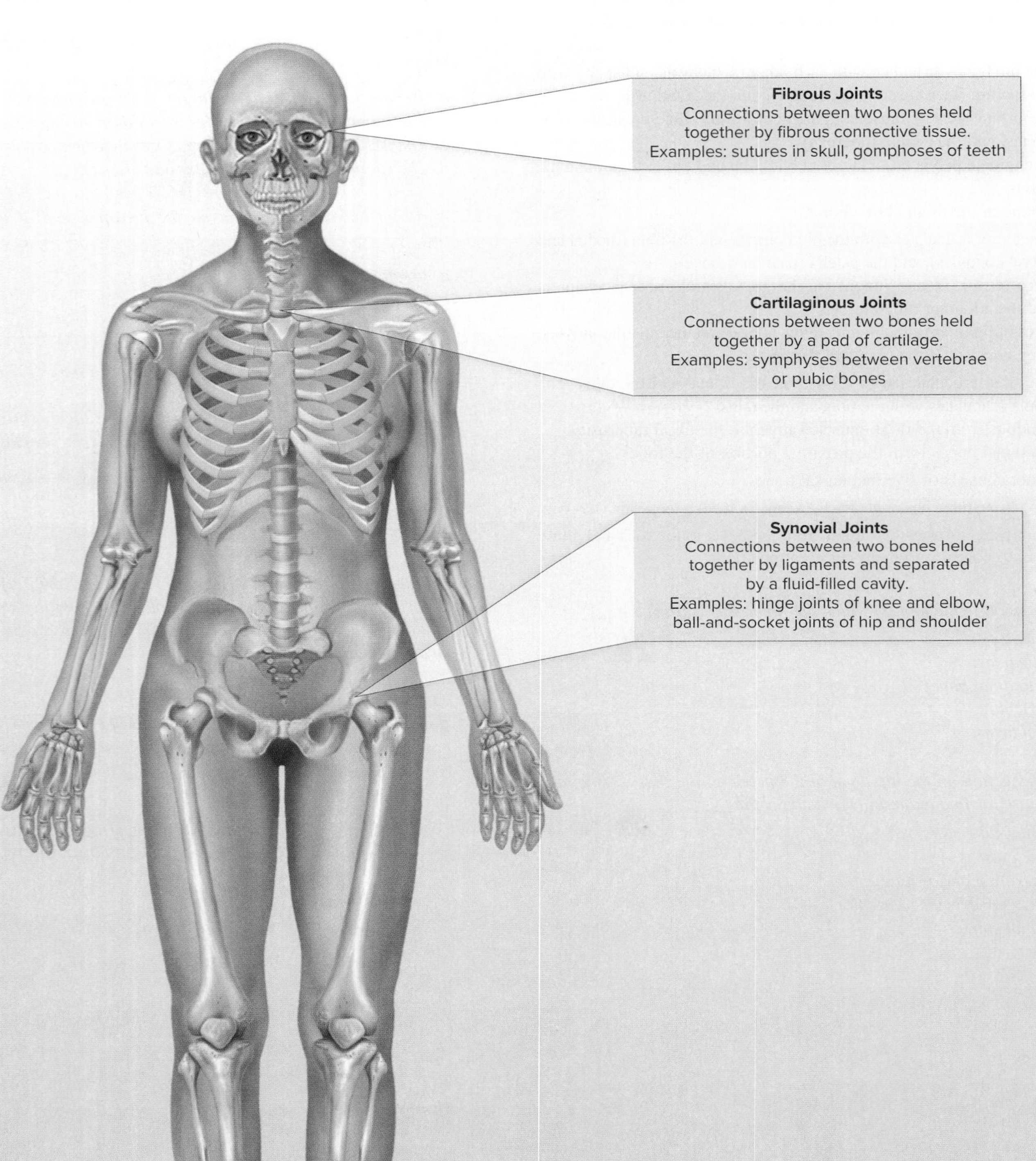

Joints are part of the musculoskeletal system and are integral to the body's structural stability as well as its ability to move.

Watch a skier attack moguls on a mountain, or a player dribble a ball past defenders, and you are watching joints in action. Muscles pull on bones to make them move, but movement would not be possible without the joints between the bones. A joint is a place where two or more bones come together. Although we usually think of joints as movable, that is not always the case. Many joints allow only limited movement, and others allow no apparent movement at all. The structure of a given joint is directly correlated with its degree of movement.

Movable joints are places in the body where the bones move in close contact with each other. When working with machines, we know that the parts that make contact require the most maintenance. But in our bodies we tend to pay little attention to the movable joints until disease or damage makes movement very difficult. In this chapter, we will discuss types of joints, movements possible at joints, as well as aspects of the health of our joints.

Learn to Predict

Andy was excited as he started his last ski run down the mountain. Then his ski caught the edge of a mogul, and he heard and felt a pop in his left knee. When he tried to stand up, the pain immediately convinced him to wait for the ski patrol. In the emergency clinic, x-rays showed that bones were not broken. However, based on a clinical mobility examination called the anterior drawer test, it was apparent that ligaments of Andy's left knee were damaged. In the test, his leg was moved in an anterior direction relative to the thigh, while his knee was flexed at a 90-degree angle. Andy's results showed a greater mobility than normally expected. A subsequent magnetic resonance image confirmed that ligaments were torn. Fortunately, after reconstructive surgery and physical therapy to maintain range of motion and rebuild strength, Andy was soon able to play sports and ski again.
In chapters 6 and 7 you learned about bone anatomy, growth, and repair.
After focusing on the structure and function of joints in chapter 8, describe the likely injury to Andy's knee and how this ligament damage would affect mobility of the tibia relative to the femur.

Answers to this question and the chapter's odd-numbered Predict questions can be found in Appendix E.

8.1 Classes of Joints

LEARNING OUTCOMES

After reading this section, you should be able to

A. **Describe the two systems for classifying joints.**
B. **Explain the structure of a fibrous joint.**
C. **List the three types of fibrous joints and give an example of each type.**
D. **Contrast the two types of cartilaginous joints and give examples of each type.**
E. **Illustrate the structure of a synovial joint.**
F. **Explain the roles of the components of a synovial joint.**
G. **Classify synovial joints based on the shape of the bones in the joint and give an example of each type.**
H. **Distinguish among uniaxial, biaxial, and multiaxial synovial joints.**

Joints, or *articulations,* are commonly named according to the bones or portions of bones that join together; for example, the temporomandibular joint is between the temporal bone and the mandible. Some joints are given the Greek or Latin equivalent of the common name, such as cubital (KYOO-bi-tal; cubit, elbow or forearm) joint for the elbow joint.

Joints are classified structurally as (1) **fibrous,** (2) **cartilaginous,** or (3) **synovial,** according to the major connective tissue type that binds the bones together and whether a fluid-filled joint capsule is present.

Joints can also be classified in functional categories according to their degree of motion as (1) **synarthroses** (SIN-ahr-THRO-sez), which are nonmovable joints; (2) **amphiarthroses** (AM-fee-ahr-THRO-sez), which are slightly movable joints; or (3) **diarthroses** (DI-ahr-THRO-sez), which are freely movable joints. In general, fibrous and cartilaginous joints have little or no movement and are synarthroses and amphiarthroses joints; synovial joints have considerable movement and are mostly diarthroses joints. Because this functional classification is somewhat limited, our discussions are based on the more precise structural classification scheme of joints as fibrous, cartilaginous, and synovial.

Fibrous Joints

Fibrous joints are the connections between two bones that are held together by fibrous connective tissue. They have no joint cavity and exhibit little or no

Module 5
Skeletal System

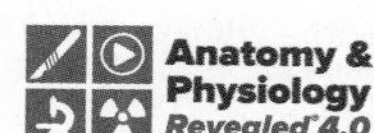

movement. Fibrous joints are subdivided on the basis of structure as (1) sutures, (2) syndesmoses, and (3) gomphoses (table 8.1).

Sutures

Sutures (SOO-churz) are seams found only between the bones of the skull (figure 8.1). Some sutures may become completely immovable in older adults. Few sutures are smooth, and the opposing bones often interdigitate (have interlocking, fingerlike processes). This interdigitation adds considerable stability to sutures. The tissue between the bones is dense regular collagenous connective tissue, and the periosteum on the inner and outer surfaces of the adjacent bones continues over the joint. The two layers of periosteum plus the dense fibrous connective tissue in between form a **sutural ligament.**

TABLE 8.1 Fibrous Joints

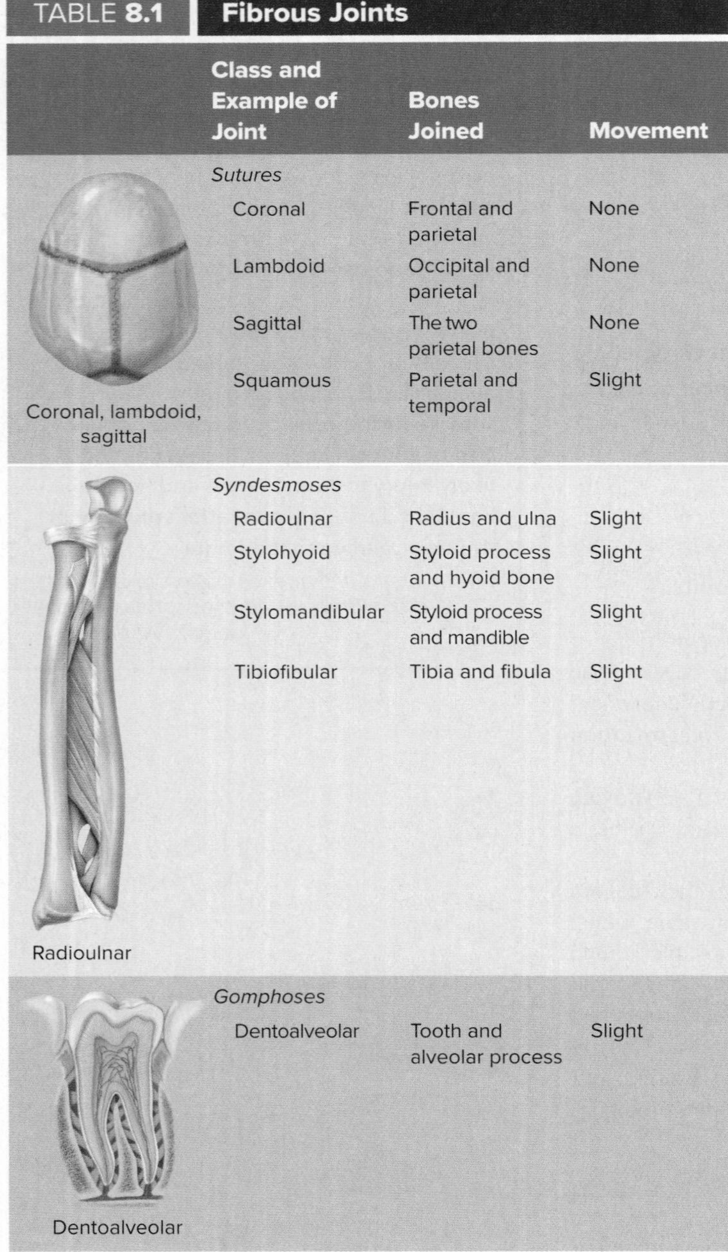

Class and Example of Joint	Bones Joined	Movement
Sutures		
Coronal	Frontal and parietal	None
Lambdoid	Occipital and parietal	None
Sagittal	The two parietal bones	None
Squamous	Parietal and temporal	Slight
Syndesmoses		
Radioulnar	Radius and ulna	Slight
Stylohyoid	Styloid process and hyoid bone	Slight
Stylomandibular	Styloid process and mandible	Slight
Tibiofibular	Tibia and fibula	Slight
Gomphoses		
Dentoalveolar	Tooth and alveolar process	Slight

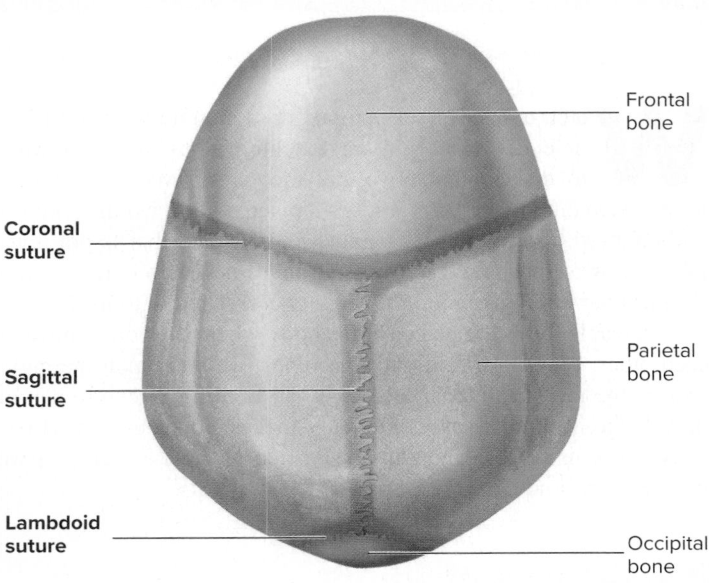

FIGURE 8.1 Sutures of the Skull
Superior view of the sutures of the adult skull.

In a newborn, some of the sutures have a membranous area called a **fontanel** (FON-tah-nel; little fountain, so named because the membrane can be seen to move with the pulse; soft spot). The fontanels make the skull flexible during the birth process and allow for growth of the head after birth (figure 8.2).

The margins of bones within sutures are sites of continuous intramembranous bone growth, and many sutures eventually become ossified. For example, ossification of the suture between the two frontal bones occurs shortly after birth, so that they usually form a single frontal bone in the adult skull. In most normal adults, the coronal, sagittal, and lambdoid sutures are not fused. However, in some very old adults, even these sutures ossify. When a suture becomes fully ossified, it becomes a **synostosis** (sin-os-TOH-sis). A synostosis results when two bones grow together across a joint to form a single bone.

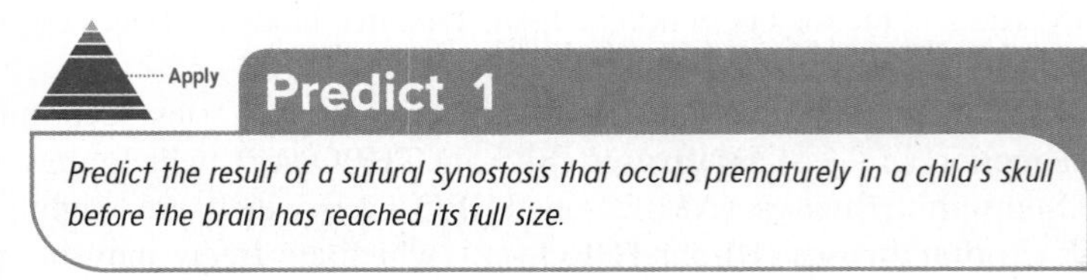
Apply

Predict 1

Predict the result of a sutural synostosis that occurs prematurely in a child's skull before the brain has reached its full size.

Syndesmoses

A **syndesmosis** (SIN-dez-MOH-sis) is a slightly movable type of fibrous joint. The bones are farther apart than in a suture and are joined by ligaments. Some movement may occur at syndesmoses because the ligaments are flexible; this occurs in the radioulnar syndesmosis, for example, which binds the radius and ulna together (figure 8.3).

Gomphoses

Gomphoses (gom-FOH-seez) are specialized joints consisting of pegs that fit into sockets and are held in place by fine bundles of regular collagenous connective tissue. The only gomphoses in the human body are the joints between the teeth and the sockets (alveoli) of the mandible and maxillae (figure 8.4). The connective tissue bundles between the teeth and their sockets are called **periodontal** (PER-ee-oh-DON-tal) **ligaments;** they allow a slight amount of "give" to the teeth during mastication. This small amount of movement also allows teeth to be gradually realigned by braces. However, the accumulation of plaque and bacteria, called a biofilm, in periodontal disease can destroy the periodontal ligaments and the bone. A biofilm consists of a group of microbes embedded within a slime-based extracellular matrix. Inflammation caused by the bioflim may cause teeth to become so loose that they come out of their sockets. Periodontal disease is the leading cause of tooth loss for adults in the United States.

Cartilaginous Joints

Cartilaginous joints hold two bones together by a pad of cartilage. Like fibrous joints, these joints exhibit little or no movement. Cartilaginous joints are subdivided on the basis of the type of cartilage as (1) synchondroses, which contain hyaline cartilage, and (2) symphyses, which contain fibrocartilage (table 8.2).

Synchondroses

A **synchondrosis** (SIN-kon-DROH-sis) consists of two bones joined by hyaline cartilage where little or no movement occurs (figure 8.5*a*). Most synchondroses are temporary. An example of a temporary synchondrosis is the epiphyseal plates of growing bones (figure 8.5*b*). In the case of epiphyseal plates, the synchondrosis is converted to a synostosis as bone replaces the existing cartilage (see section 6.6). Other synchondroses can be converted to synovial joints. An example is the majority of **costochondral joints** between the ribs and the costal cartilages (figure 8.5*c*). These joints begin as synchondroses but, because movement occurs between them and the sternum, all but the first usually develop synovial joints at those junctions. Some synchondroses persist in the adult. An example is the sternocostal synchondrosis between the first rib and the sternum (figure 8.5*c*).

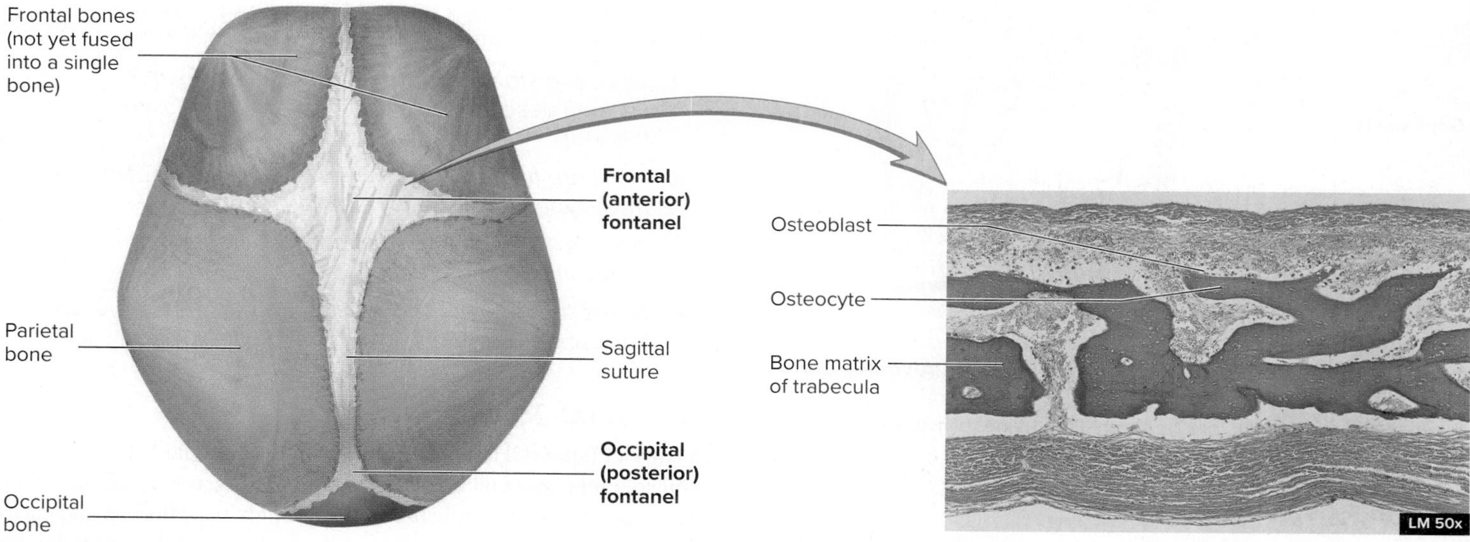

FIGURE 8.2 Fetal Skull Showing Fontanels and Sutures

(*a*) Lateral view of the fetal skull fontanels and sutures. (*b*) Superior view of the fetal skull fontanels and sutures. (*c*) Photomicrograph of a fontanel undergoing intramembranous ossification. (c) Ed Reschke/Stone/Getty Images

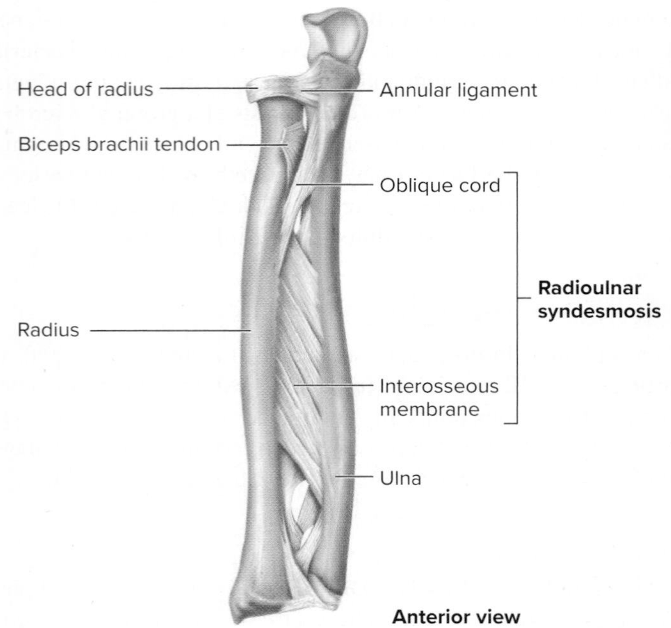

FIGURE 8.3 Radioulnar Syndesmosis
Anterior view of the right radioulnar syndesmosis.

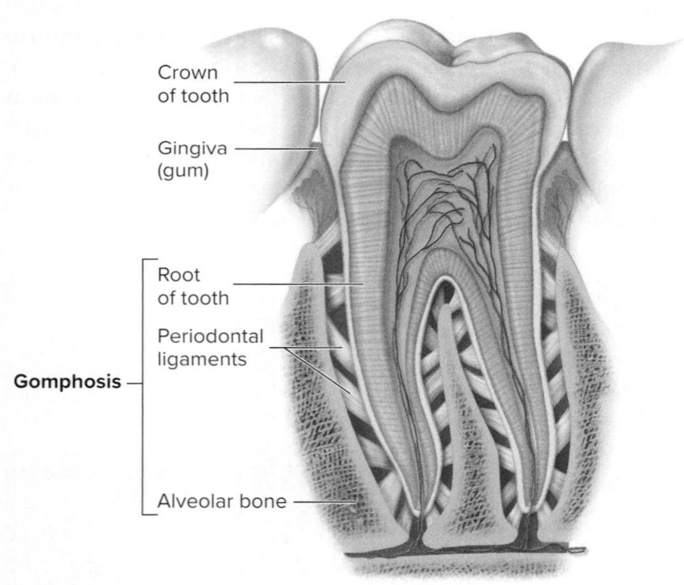

FIGURE 8.4 Gomphosis Between a Tooth and Alveolar Bone of the Mandible
Cross section view of the joint between a tooth and mandibular bone.

Symphyses

A **symphysis** (SIM-fi-sis) consists of two bones joined by a pad of fibrocartilage. Examples of symphyses include the intervertebral disks (see figures 7.10 and 7.15), the junction between the manubrium and the body of the sternum (figure 8.5*c*), and the pubic symphysis (figure 8.6). Some of these joints are slightly movable because of the somewhat flexible nature of fibrocartilage. This is especially important for the intervertebral disks because the disk also acts as a shock absorber between the vertebrae.

TABLE 8.2 Cartilaginous Joints

	Class and Example of Joint	Bones Joined	Movement
	Synchondroses (hyaline cartilage)		
	Epiphyseal plate	Diaphysis and epiphysis of a long bone	None
	Sternocostal	Anterior cartilaginous part of first rib; between rib and sternum	Slight
Epiphyseal plate	Sphenooccipital	Sphenoid and occipital	None
	Symphyses (fibrocartilage)		
	Intervertebral	Bodies of adjacent vertebrae	Slight
	Manubriosternal	Manubrium and body of sternum	None
Intervertebral	Pubic symphysis	The two hip bones	Slight except during childbirth
	Xiphisternal	Xiphoid process and body of sternum	None

ASSESS YOUR PROGRESS

Answers to these questions are found in the section you have just completed. Re-read the section if you need help in answering these questions.

1. *What two standards are used to classify joints? List and describe the classification system used in this text.*
2. *What are the characteristics of a fibrous joint? Name the three types, and give an example of each.*
3. *What is a synostosis? How does it differ from a syndesmosis or a gomphosis?*
4. *Name the two types of cartilaginous joints, tell the type of cartilage present, and give an example of each.*

Synovial Joints

Synovial (sih-NOH-vee-al) **joints** contain synovial fluid and allow considerable movement between articulating bones (figure 8.7). These joints are anatomically more complex than fibrous and cartilaginous joints. Most joints that unite the bones of the appendicular skeleton are synovial joints, reflecting the far greater mobility of the appendicular skeleton compared with the axial skeleton.

The articular surfaces of bones within synovial joints are covered with a thin layer of hyaline cartilage called **articular cartilage.** The articular cartilage provides a smooth surface where

TABLE 8.4 Synovial Joints

	Class and Example of Joint	Bones Joined	Movement
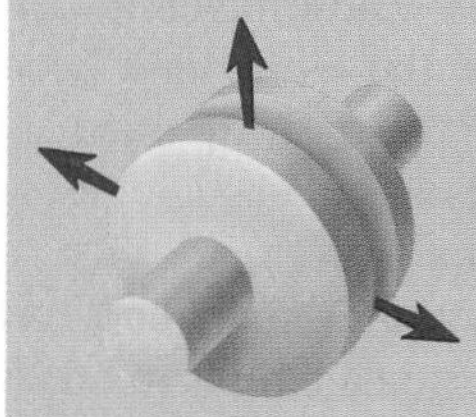 Plane; 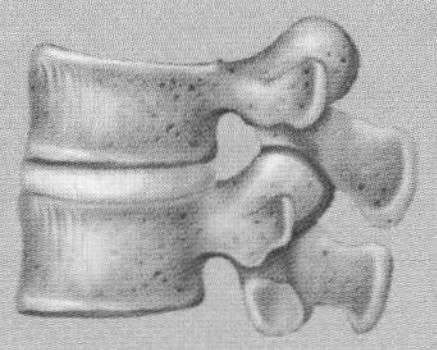 Intervertebral	*Plane*		
	Intervertebral	Between articular processes of adjacent vertebrae	Uniaxial; slight
	Acromioclavicular	Acromion process of scapula and clavicle	Uniaxial; slight
	Carpometacarpal	Carpals and metacarpals 2–5	Uniaxial; slight
	Costovertebral	Ribs and vertebrae	Uniaxial; slight
	Intercarpal	Between carpal bones	Uniaxial; slight
	Intermetatarsal	Between metatarsal bones	Uniaxial; slight
	Intertarsal	Between tarsal bones	Uniaxial; slight
	Sacroiliac	Between sacrum and hip bone (complex joint with several planes and synchondroses)	Uniaxial; slight
	Tarsometatarsal	Tarsal bones and metatarsal bones	Uniaxial; slight
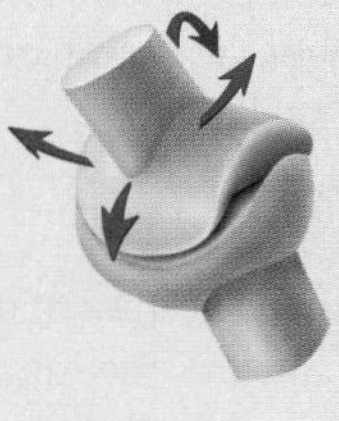 Saddle; 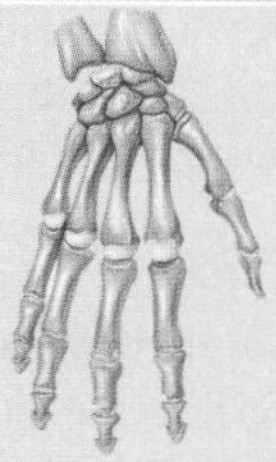 Carpometacarpal pollicis	*Saddle*		
	Carpometacarpal pollicis	Carpal and metacarpal of thumb	Biaxial
	Sternoclavicular	Manubrium of sternum and clavicle	Multiaxial; slight
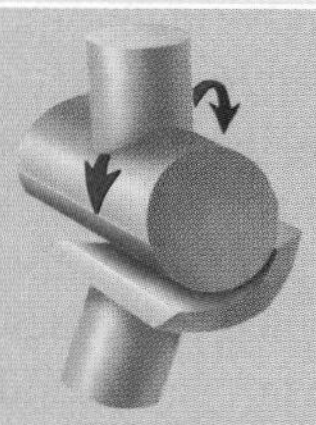 Hinge; 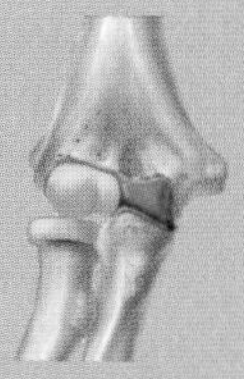 Cubital	*Hinge*		
	Cubital (elbow)	Humerus, ulna, and radius	Uniaxial
	Knee	Femur and tibia	Uniaxial
	Interphalangeal	Between phalanges	Uniaxial
	Talocrural (ankle)	Talus, tibia, and fibula	Multiaxial; one predominates
 Pivot; 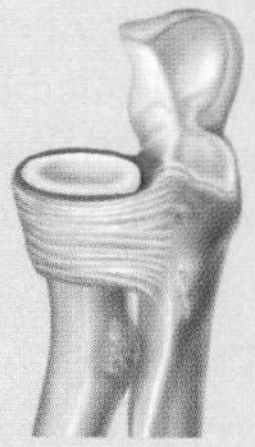 Proximal radioulnar	*Pivot*		
	Atlantoaxial	Atlas and axis	Uniaxial rotation
	Proximal radioulnar	Radius and ulna	Uniaxial rotation
	Distal radioulnar	Radius and ulna	Uniaxial rotation
 Ball-and-socket; 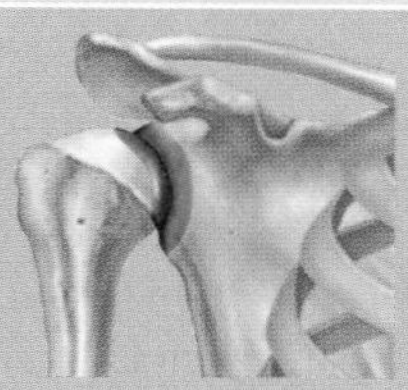 Glenohumeral	*Ball-and-Socket*		
	Glenohumeral (shoulder)	Scapula and humerus	Multiaxial
	Hip	Hip bone and femur	Multiaxial
 Ellipsoid; 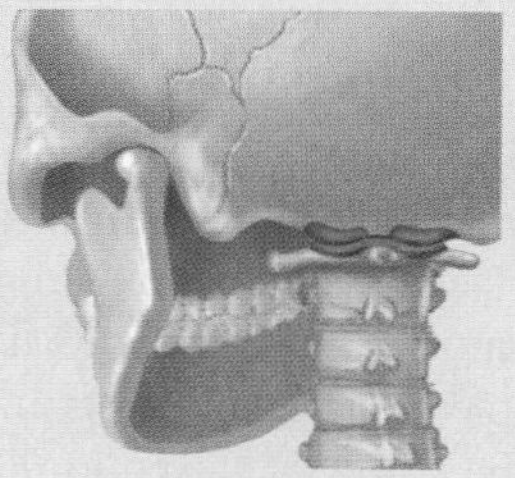 Atlantooccipital	*Ellipsoid*		
	Atlantooccipital	Atlas and occipital bone	Biaxial
	Metacarpophalangeal (knuckles)	Metacarpal bones and phalanges	Biaxial
	Metatarsophalangeal (ball of foot)	Metatarsal bones and phalanges	Biaxial
	Radiocarpal (wrist)	Radius and carpal bones	Multiaxial
	Temporomandibular	Mandible and temporal bone	Multiaxial; one predominates

An **ellipsoid joint** (condyloid joint) is a modified ball-and-socket joint (table 8.4). The articular surfaces are ellipsoid in shape, rather than spherical as in regular ball-and-socket joints. Ellipsoid joints are biaxial because the shape of the joint limits its range of movement almost to a hinge motion in two axes and restricts rotation. The atlantooccipital joint of the neck is an example.

ASSESS YOUR PROGRESS

5. *Describe the structure of a synovial joint. How do the different parts of the joint contribute to joint movement?*
6. *What are articular disks, and where are they found?*
7. *What are bursae and tendon sheaths? What is the function of each?*
8. *On what basis are synovial joints classified? List and describe the six types of synovial joints, and give an example of each.*
9. *What directional movements are permitted at each type of synovial joint?*

8.2 Types of Movement

LEARNING OUTCOMES

After reading this section, you should be able to

A. **Categorize movements as gliding, angular, circular, special, or a combination of types.**
B. **Demonstrate the difference between the following pairs of movements: flexion and extension; plantar flexion and dorsiflexion; abduction and adduction; supination and pronation; elevation and depression; protraction and retraction; opposition and reposition; inversion and eversion.**
C. **Distinguish between rotation and circumduction. What is excursion?**

There are three general types of movement: (1) gliding, (2) angular, and (3) circular. In addition, there are special movements that are unique to a small number of joints, as well as combination movements that are the composite of specific movements. The type of movement is dictated by the joint's structure. Some joints are limited to only one type of movement; others can move in several directions. With few exceptions, movement is best described in relation to the anatomical position. Because most movements are also possible in the opposite direction, they are often illustrated in pairs.

Gliding Movements

Gliding movements are the simplest of all the types of movement. These movements occur in plane joints between two flat or nearly flat surfaces that slide or glide over each other. These joints often allow only slight movement, as occurs between carpal bones.

Angular Movements

Angular movements involve changes in the angle between the bones at the joint. In angular movement, the trunk or a limb bends relative to another part of the body. The most common angular movements are flexion and extension and abduction and adduction.

Flexion and Extension

Flexion and extension are common opposing movements (figure 8.9A). **Flexion** is a bending movement that *decreases* the angle of the joint to bring the articulating bones closer together. **Extension** is a straightening movement that *increases* the angle of the joint to straighten the articulating bones. These bending and extending movements can easily be seen at the elbow and knee joints (figure 8.9A*b,d*). **Hyperextension** is usually defined as extension of a joint beyond the anatomical position (180 degrees) (figure 8.9A). Hyperextension can be a normal movement, such as the movement of the neck when looking up at the stars, but it can also result in injury. For example, when a person attempts to break a fall by putting out a hand, the force of the fall can result in hyperextension of the wrist, resulting in a sprained joint or broken bone.

There are special cases of flexion when describing the movement of the foot. Movement of the foot toward the plantar surface, as when standing on the toes, is commonly called **plantar flexion;** movement of the foot toward the shin, as when walking on the heels, is called **dorsiflexion** (figure 8.9A*e*).

Abduction and Adduction

Abduction (to take away) is movement away from the midline; **adduction** (to bring together) is movement toward the midline. Moving the upper limbs away from the body, as is done in the outward step of jumping jacks, is abduction, and bringing the upper limbs back toward the body is adduction (figure 8.9A*f*). In the hand, abduction spreads the fingers apart, away from the midline of the hand, and adduction brings them back together (figure 8.9A*g*). Abduction of the thumb moves it anteriorly, away from the palm. Abduction of the wrist, which is sometimes called radial deviation, moves the hand away from the midline of the body, and adduction of the wrist, sometimes called ulnar deviation, moves the hand toward the midline. Abduction of the head, which involves tilting the head to one side, is commonly called lateral flexion of the neck. Bending at the waist to one side is usually called **lateral flexion** of the vertebral column, rather than abduction.

Circular Movements

Circular movements involve rotation around an axis in a circular pattern or an arc.

Rotation

Rotation is the turning of a structure around its long axis, as in rotating the head to shake the head "no" or rotating the arm or the entire body (figure 8.9B*a*). Medial rotation of the humerus with the forearm flexed brings the hand toward the body. Lateral rotation of the humerus moves the hand away from the body.

Pronation and Supination

Pronation (proh-NAY-shun) and **supination** (soo-pih-NAY-shun) refer to the unique rotation of the forearm (figure 8.9B*c*). The word *prone* means lying facedown; the word *supine* means lying faceup. Pronation is rotation of the forearm so that the palm faces posteriorly in relation to the anatomical position. The palm of the hand faces inferiorly if the elbow is flexed to 90 degrees. Supination is

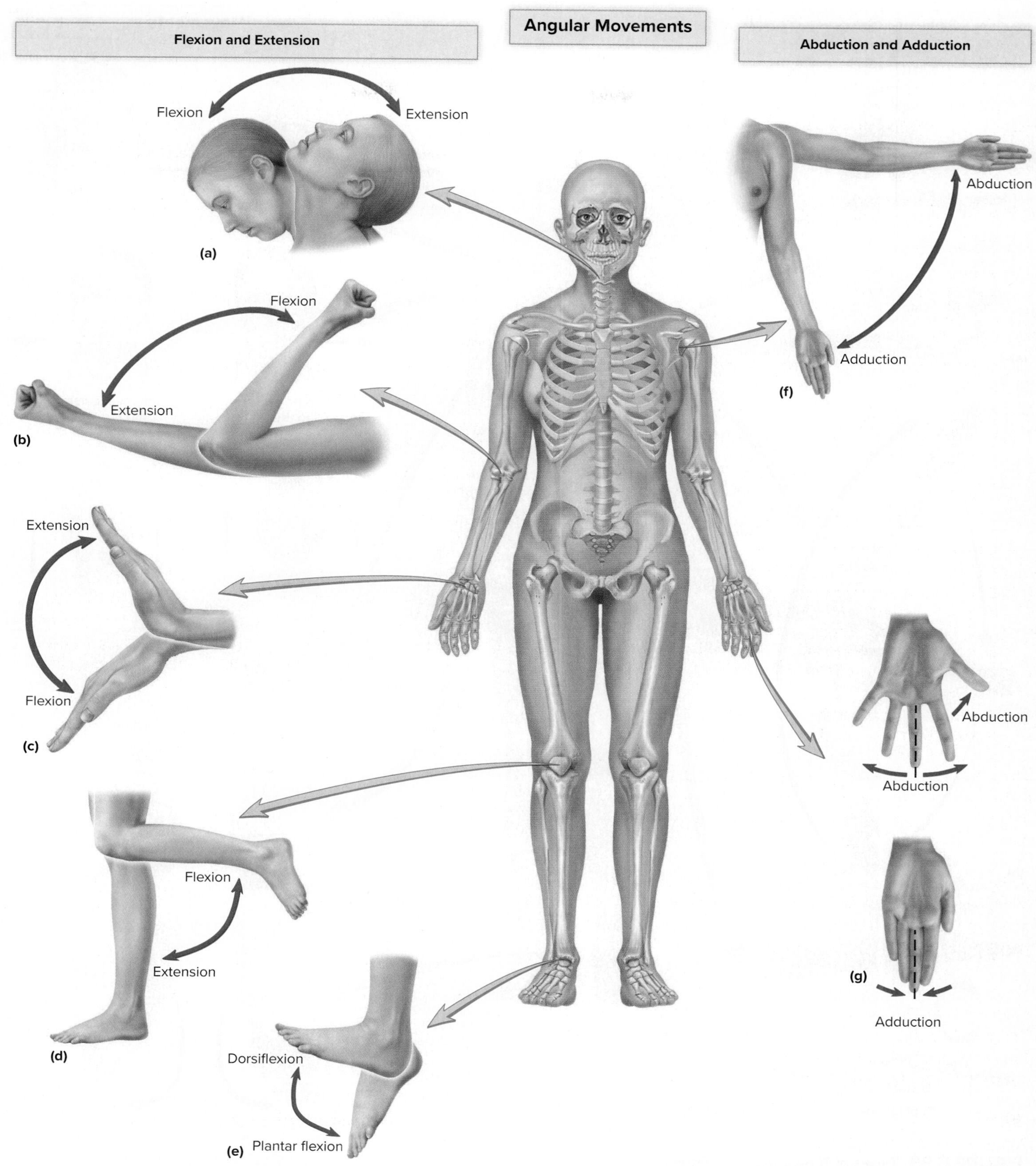

FIGURE 8.9A Types of Movement
Flexion, extension, and hypertension of (*a*) the neck, (*b*) the elbow, (*c*) the wrist, and (*d*) the knee. (*e*) Dorsiflexion allows walking on the heels while plantar flexion allows standing on the toes. Abduction and adduction of (*f*) the upper limb and (*g*) the fingers.

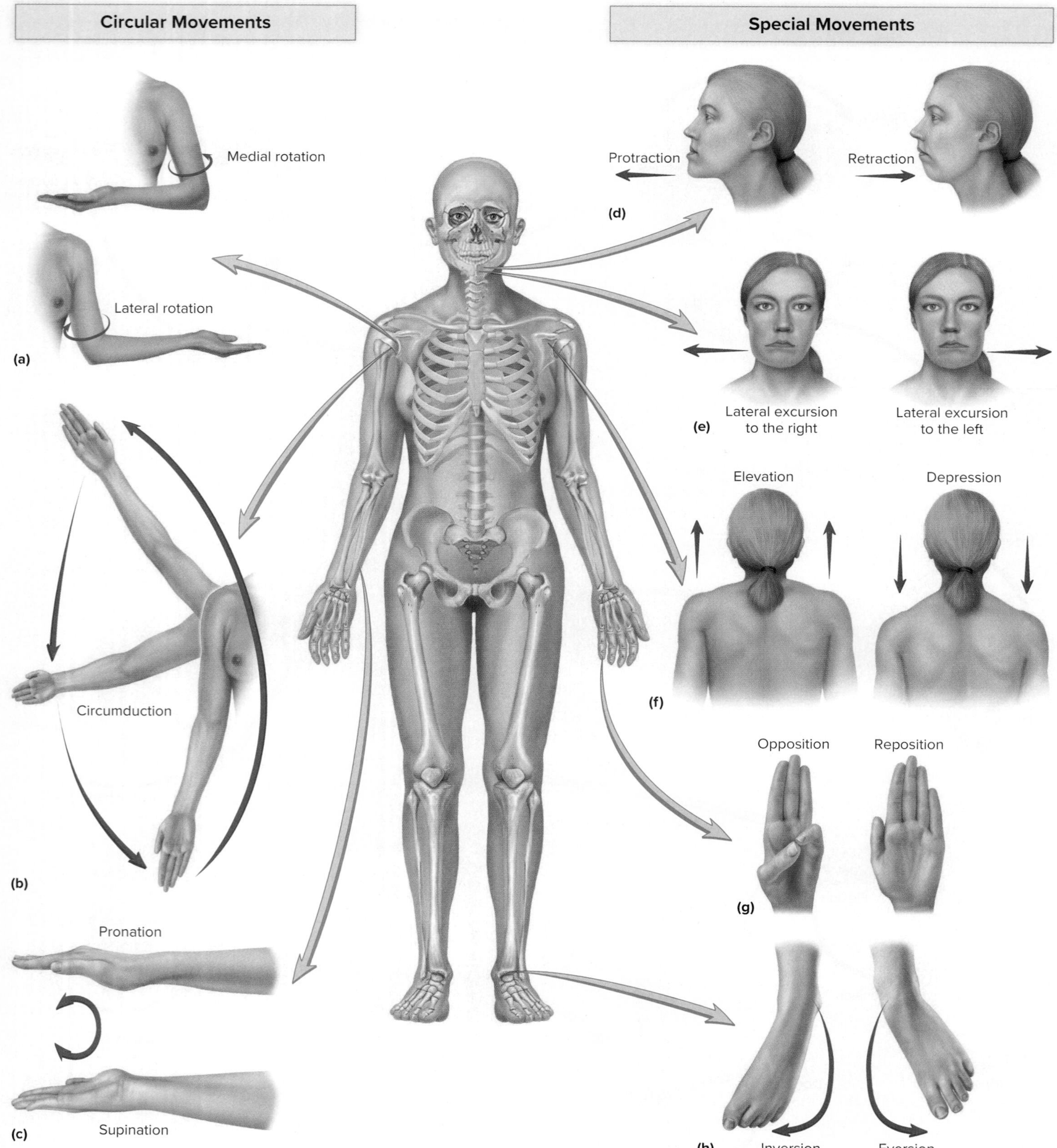

FIGURE 8.9B Types of Movement (continued)

(*a*) Medial and lateral rotation of the arm toward and away from the body. (*b*) Circular movement of the arm allows throwing of a ball. (*c*) Rotation of the forearm allows the position of the palm of the hand to move relative to the anatomical position. (*d*) Specialized gliding motions allow jutting and pulling back motions of the jaw. (*e*) Lateral excursion of the mandible to the right or left allows grinding of teeth while chewing. (*f*) Specialized movements allow shrugging and lowering of the shoulders. (*g*) This movement allows touching of the thumb and fingers. (*h*) Inversion allows rolling out and eversion allows rolling in of the foot.

rotation of the forearm so that the palm faces anteriorly in relation to the anatomical position. The palm of the hand faces superiorly if the elbow is flexed to 90 degrees. Thus, pronation and supination move the palm to the corresponding position as a prone or supine subject, respectively. In pronation, the radius and ulna cross; in supination, they are parallel. The head of the radius rotates against the radial notch of the ulna during supination and pronation (see chapter 7).

Circumduction

Circumduction is a combination of flexion, extension, abduction, and adduction (figure 8.9B*b*). It occurs at freely movable joints, such as the shoulder. In circumduction, the arm moves in an arc so that it traces a cone, with the shoulder joint at the apex of the cone, as occurs when pitching a baseball.

Special Movements

Special movements are those movements that are unique to only one or two joints and do not fit neatly into any of the other categories.

Elevation and Depression

Elevation moves a structure superiorly; **depression** moves it inferiorly (figure 8.9B*f*). Shrugging the shoulders is an example of scapular elevation. Depression of the mandible opens the mouth, and elevation closes it.

Protraction and Retraction

Protraction is a gliding motion that moves a structure in an anterior direction (figure 8.9B*d*). Jutting out the jaw and hunching the shoulders are examples of protraction. **Retraction** is a gliding motion that moves a structure in a posterior direction (figure 8.9B*d*). Pulling the jaw back and pinching or pulling the scapulae back toward the vertebral column illustrate retraction.

Excursion

Lateral excursion is moving the mandible to either the right or the left of the midline (figure 8.9B*e*), as occurs when grinding the teeth or chewing. **Medial excursion** returns the mandible to the midline position.

Opposition and Reposition

Opposition is a movement unique to the thumb (figure 8.9B*g*). It occurs when the thumb and the tip of a finger on the same hand are brought toward each other across the palm. **Reposition** returns the thumb to the neutral, anatomical position.

Inversion and Eversion

Inversion turns the ankle so that the plantar surface of the foot faces medially, toward the opposite foot, with the weight on the outside edge of the foot (rolling out). **Eversion** turns the ankle so that the plantar surface faces laterally, with the weight on the inside edge of the foot (rolling in; figure 8.9B*h*). Sometimes inversion of the foot is called supination and eversion is called pronation. Although commonly used as clinical terms, *supination* and *pronation* of the feet are more complex than just inversion and eversion, and they involve movements at multiple joints of the ankle and foot. Some supination and pronation are normal, but excessive pronation is a common cause of injury among runners.

Combination Movements

Most movements that we perform in the course of normal activities are combinations of the movements named previously. These combined movements are described by naming the individual movements involved. For example, when a person steps forward and to the side at a 45-degree angle, the movement at the hip is a combination of flexion and abduction.

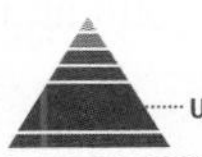
Understand

Predict 3

What combination of movements at the shoulder and elbow joints allows a person to move the right upper limb from the anatomical position to touch the right side of the head with the fingertips?

ASSESS YOUR PROGRESS

10. *Describe flexion and extension. How are they different for the upper and lower limbs? What is hyperextension?*
11. *Contrast abduction and adduction. Describe these movements for the head, upper limbs, wrist, fingers, waist, lower limbs, and toes. For what part of the body is the term* lateral flexion *used?*
12. *Distinguish among rotation, circumduction, pronation, and supination. Give an example of each.*
13. *Explain the following jaw movements: protraction, retraction, lateral excursion, medial excursion, elevation, and depression.*
14. *Describe opposition and reposition of the thumb.*
15. *What terms are used for turning the side of the foot medially or laterally?*

8.3 Range of Motion

LEARNING OUTCOMES

After reading this section, you should be able to

A. **Explain the difference between active and passive range of motion.**
B. **Describe the consequences of movement beyond the normal range.**
C. **List the factors that affect normal range of motion.**

Range of motion describes the amount of mobility that can be demonstrated in a given joint. **Active range of motion** is the amount of movement that can be accomplished by contracting the muscles that normally act across a joint. **Passive range of motion** is the amount of movement that can be accomplished when the structures that meet at the joint are moved by an outside force, as when a therapist holds on to a patient's forearm and moves it toward the arm, flexing the elbow joint. Passive range of motion for normal joints is somewhat greater than active range of motion. However, when comparing range of motion of a normal joint to that of an injured joint, such as a dislocation, passive and active ranges of motion are not dramatically different.

In fact, movement of joints beyond the normal range of motion can cause dislocations and sprains. A **dislocation,** or *luxation,* of a joint occurs when the articulating surfaces of the bones are moved out of proper alignment. A *subluxation* is a partial dislocation. Dislocations are often accompanied by painful damage to the supporting ligaments and articular cartilage. A **sprain** occurs when ligaments are damaged. The degree of damage can range from stretched to completely torn ligaments. Sprains often result in inflammation, swelling, and pain. Dislocations and sprains are common sports injuries.

The range of motion for a given joint is influenced by a number of factors that are determined by the properties of the joint and surrounding tissue:

1. Shape of the articular surfaces of the bones forming the joint
2. Amount and shape of cartilage covering those articular surfaces
3. Strength and location of ligaments, tendons, and muscles associated with the joint
4. Bulk of surrounding tissues, such as muscle and adipose tissue
5. Amount of fluid in and around the joint
6. Amount of pain in and around the joint
7. Amount of use or disuse the joint has received over time

Abnormalities in the range of motion can occur when any of those components change. For example, damage to a ligament associated with a given joint may increase that joint's range of motion. A torn piece of cartilage within a joint can limit its range of motion. If the nerve supply to a muscle is damaged so that the muscle is weakened, the active range of motion for the joint acted on by that muscle may decrease, but the joint's passive range of motion should remain unchanged. Fluid buildup and/or pain in or around a joint (as occurs when the soft tissues around the joint develop edema following an injury) can severely limit both the active and passive ranges of motion for that joint. With disuse, both the active and passive ranges of motion for a given joint decrease.

ASSESS YOUR PROGRESS

16. *What is range of motion? Contrast active and passive range of motion and the factors that may influence normal range of motion.*

17. *Discuss some examples of the changes that may occur with movement beyond the normal range.*

8.4 Description of Selected Joints

LEARNING OUTCOMES

After reading this section, you should be able to

A. **Describe the structure and movements of the TMJ.**
B. **Compare and contrast the ball-and-socket joints of the shoulder and hip.**
C. **Compare and contrast the hinge joints of the elbow, knee, and ankle.**
D. **Describe the ligaments that support the complex ellipsoid joint of the knee.**
E. **Explain the structure and functions of the arches of the foot.**
F. **Discuss the common disorders that affect these major joints.**

It is impossible in a limited space to describe all the joints of the body; therefore, we have chosen to describe only selected joints, based on their representative structure, important function, or clinical significance.

Temporomandibular Joint

The mandible articulates with the temporal bone to form the **temporomandibular joint (TMJ).** The mandibular condyle fits into the mandibular fossa of the temporal bone. A fibrocartilage articular disk is located between the mandible and the temporal bone, dividing the joint into superior and inferior joint cavities (figure 8.10). The joint is surrounded by a fibrous capsule, to which the articular disk is attached at its margin, and is strengthened by lateral and accessory ligaments.

The temporomandibular joint is a combination plane and ellipsoid joint, with the ellipsoid portion predominating. Opening of the jaw first involves the inferior cavity of the TMJ below the articular disk. The mandibular condyle rotates anteriorly on the disk in the familiar hingelike movement of the jaw. The second portion of jaw opening occurs in the superior cavity of the TMJ. The articular disk

Clinical IMPACT 8.3

TMJ Disorders

TMJ disorders are the most common cause of chronic orofacial pain. The primary symptom is pain in the jaw muscles and/or joint. Other symptoms include radiating pain in the face, head, and neck; reduced range of motion or locking of the jaw; and painful clicking or grating when moving the jaw. Ear pain is another symptom, which often leads patients to their physicians, who then refer them to a dentist. It is estimated that 5–12% of the population experience TMJ pain. It is at least twice as prevalent among women.

TMJ disorders often have no obvious cause or trigger. However, a consistent cause of TMJ disorders is bruxism, the unconscious grinding and clenching of the teeth. Bruxism can occur at any time, but that which occurs during sleep typically causes more damage than bruxism that occurs while awake. Many TMJ cases can improve with treatment, although for some patients the pain is persistent or continues to recur. A physical therapist or other specialist can sometimes help relax and restore function to involved muscles, as well as identify habits that may be contributing to the condition, such as forward head posture or biting fingernails. Reducing stress and anxiety and avoiding hard food or chewing gum can help. Certain analgesic and anti-inflammatory medications and oral splints at night may also be helpful. Injections of botulinum toxin, or BOTOX®, have been shown to treat TMJ pain and bruxism for up to 4 months at a time. BOTOX prevents the release of the neurotransmitter that stimulates skeletal muscle contraction, which allows muscles of the face and jaw to relax. The relaxation of these muscles can relieve pain caused by TMJ disorders. Patients need to receive injections regularly to continue receiving the benefits of BOTOX therapy.

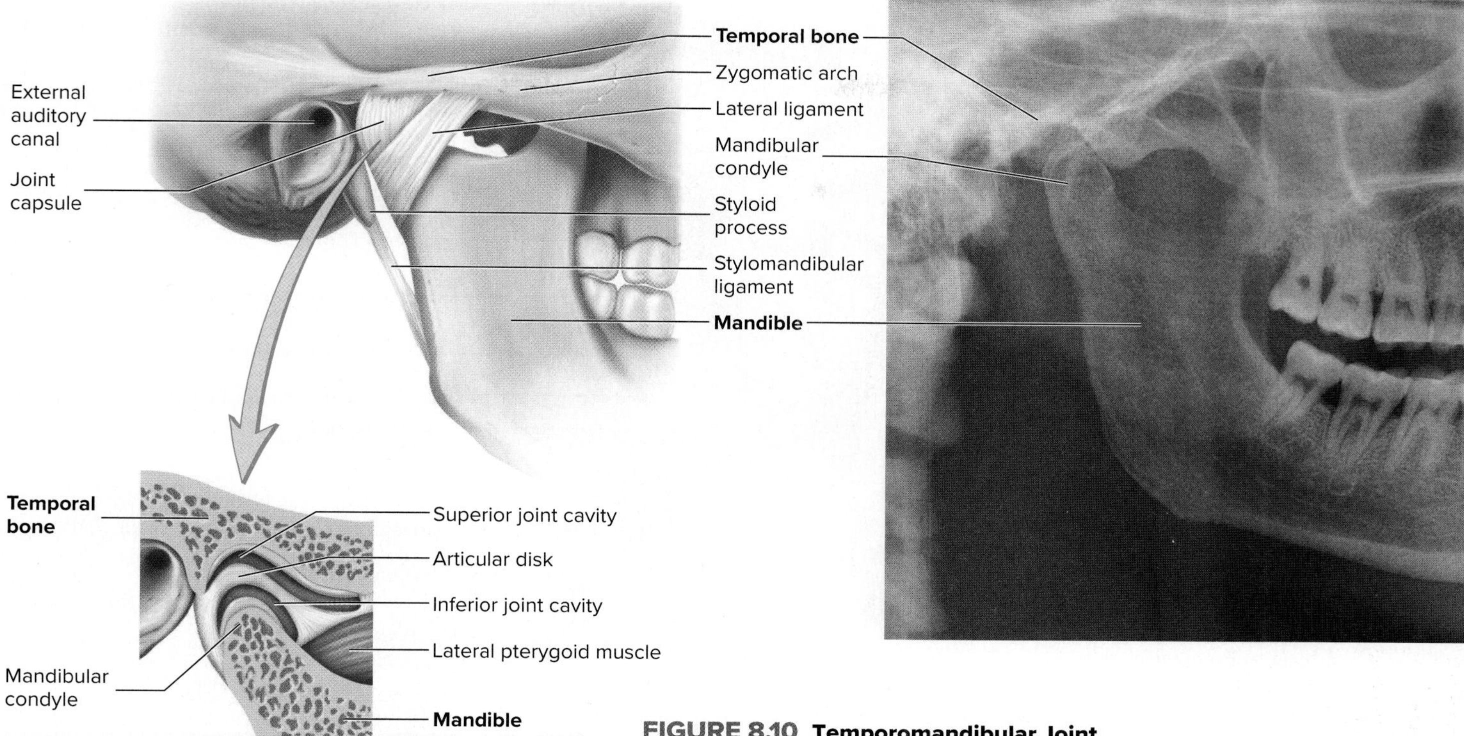

FIGURE 8.10 Temporomandibular Joint
Lateral view of the right temporomandibular joint (left), x-ray of lateral view of the same joint (right). A sagittal view of the joint is magnified. (X-ray image): Dr. Debra Dixon APR

and condyle together glide anteriorly. This is similar to the motion that occurs in protraction of the mandible. In addition, mediolateral movements of the mandibular condyle allow lateral excursion, or side-to-side, motions of the jaw. Together, these movements allow chewing and grinding in mastication.

Shoulder Joint

The **shoulder joint,** or *glenohumeral joint,* is a ball-and-socket joint (figure 8.11) that has less stability but more mobility than the other ball-and-socket joint, the hip. Flexion, extension, abduction, adduction, rotation, and circumduction can all occur at the shoulder joint. The rounded head of the humerus articulates with the shallow glenoid cavity of the scapula. The rim of the glenoid cavity is built up slightly by the **glenoid labrum,** a fibrocartilage ring to which the joint capsule is attached. There are two bursae in the shoulder joint: (1) a **subscapular bursa** (not shown in figure 8.11), which opens into the joint cavity, and (2) a **subacromial bursa** near the joint cavity, but separated from the cavity by the joint capsule (figure 8.11).

The stability of the shoulder joint is maintained primarily by four sets of ligaments and four muscles. The ligaments are listed in table 8.5. The four muscles are referred to collectively as the **rotator cuff.** The rotator cuff holds the humeral head tightly within the glenoid cavity (see chapter 10). The head of the humerus is also supported against the glenoid cavity by the tendon from the biceps brachii muscle in the anterior part of the arm. This tendon is unusual in that it passes through the articular capsule of the shoulder joint before crossing the head of the humerus and attaching to the scapula at the supraglenoid tubercle (see figure 7.31*a*).

TABLE 8.5 Ligaments of the Shoulder Joint (see figure 8.11)

Ligament	Description
Glenohumeral (superior, middle, and inferior)	Three slightly thickened longitudinal sets of fibers on the anterior side of the capsule; extend from the humerus to the margin of the glenoid cavity
Transverse humeral	Lateral, transverse, fibrous thickening of the joint capsule; crosses between the greater and lesser tubercles and holds down the tendon from the long head of the biceps brachii muscle
Coracohumeral	Crosses from the root of the coracoid process to the humeral neck
Coracoacromial	Crosses above the joint between the coracoid process and the acromion process; an accessory, protective ligament

The most common traumatic shoulder disorders are dislocation of bones and tears in muscles or tendons. The shoulder

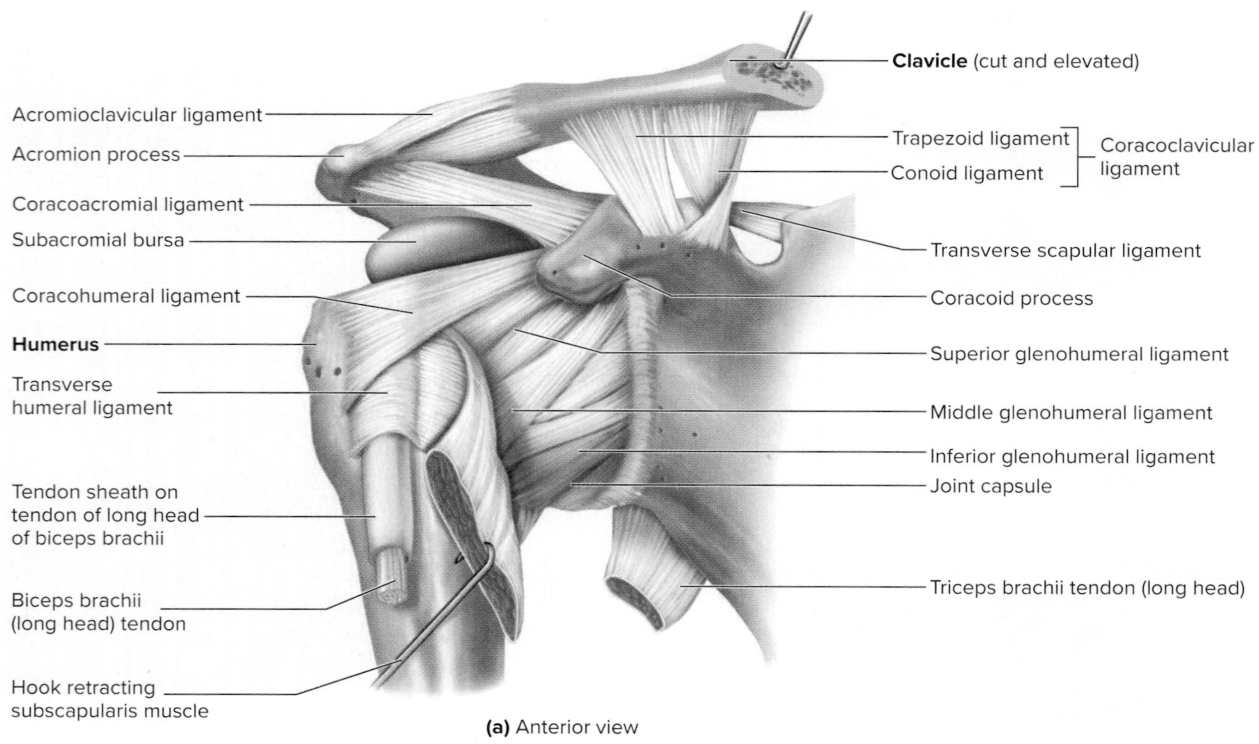

(a) Anterior view

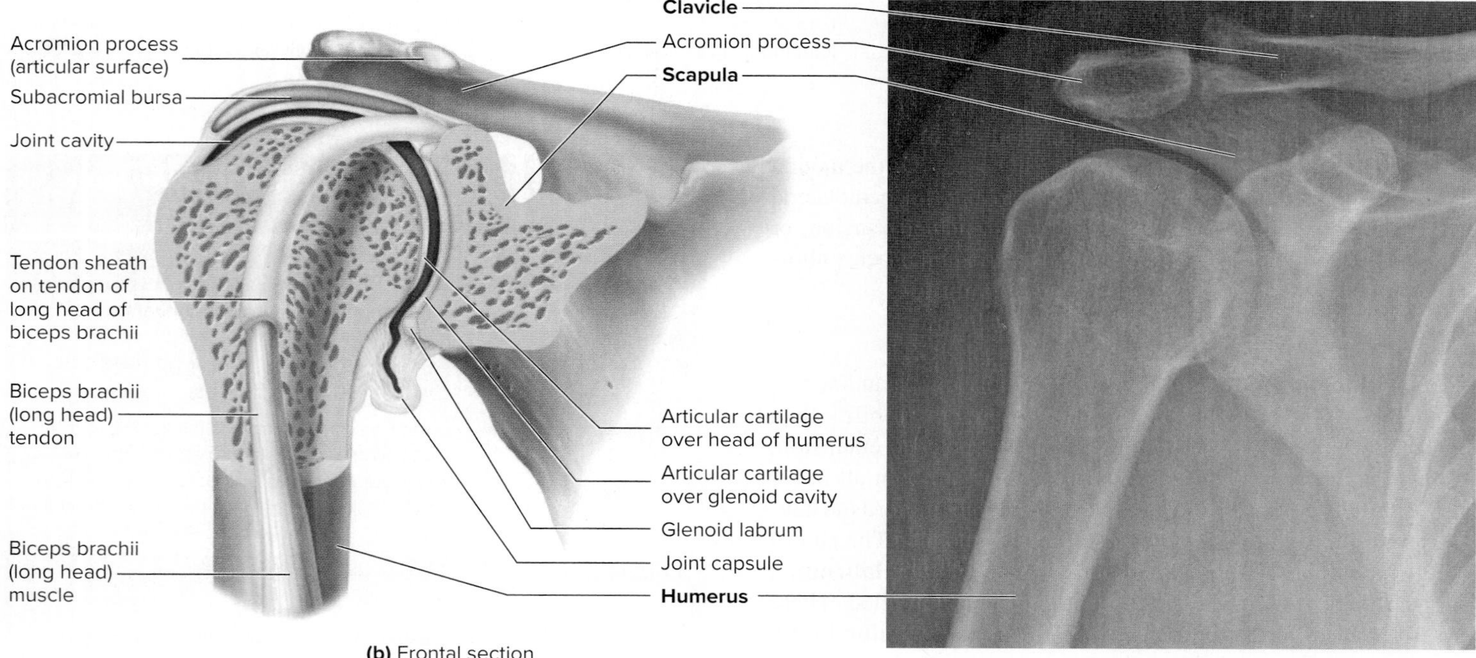

(b) Frontal section

FIGURE 8.11 Shoulder Joint
(*a*) Anterior view of the right shoulder joint. (*b*) Frontal section of the same joint (left), x-ray of right shoulder joint (right). (b) Ivan Smuk/Alamy Stock Photo APR

is the most commonly dislocated joint in the body. Major ligaments cross the superior part of the shoulder joint, and no major ligaments or muscles are associated with the inferior side. As a result, the humerus is most likely to become dislocated inferiorly into the axilla. Because the axilla contains very important nerves and arteries, severe and permanent damage may occur when the humeral head dislocates inferiorly. The axillary nerve is the most commonly damaged nerve (see chapter 12). Chronic shoulder disorders include tendinitis (inflammation of tendons), bursitis (inflammation of bursae), and arthritis (inflammation of joints).

Bursitis of the subacromial bursa can become very painful when the large shoulder muscle, called the deltoid muscle, compresses the bursa during shoulder movement.

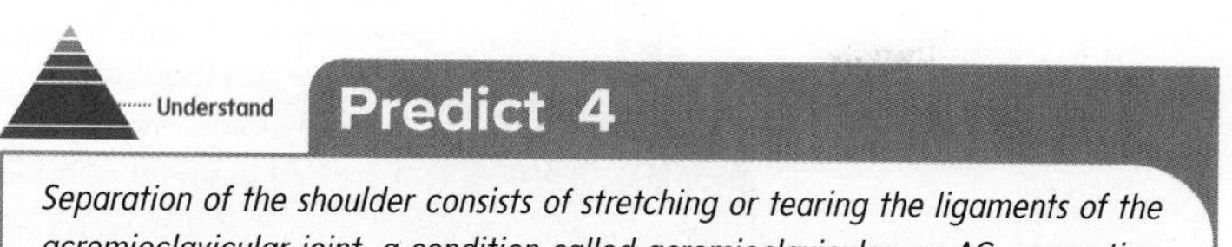

Predict 4

Separation of the shoulder consists of stretching or tearing the ligaments of the acromioclavicular joint, a condition called acromioclavicular, or AC, separation. Using figure 8.11 (anterior view) and your knowledge of the articulated skeleton, explain the nature of a shoulder separation and predict the problems that may follow a separation.

Elbow Joint

The **elbow joint,** or *cubital joint,* is a compound hinge joint (figure 8.12). It consists of the **humeroulnar joint,** between the humerus and ulna, and the **humeroradial joint,** between the humerus and radius. The **proximal radioulnar joint,** between the proximal radius and ulna, is also closely related. Recall that the elbow has two types of movement: flexion/extension and pronation/supination. Flexion/extension occurs at the humeroulnar and humeroradial joints. These joints are limited to flexion and extension because of the shape of the trochlear notch and its association with the trochlea of the humerus (figure 8.12*a*). In contrast, pronation/supination occurs at the proximal radioulnar joint. The rounded head of the radius rotates in the radial notch of the ulna and against the capitulum of the humerus (figure 8.12*b*), allowing these circular movements of the hand.

The elbow joint is surrounded by a joint capsule. The humeroulnar joint is reinforced by the **ulnar collateral ligament** (figure 8.12*d*). The humeroradial and proximal radioulnar joints are reinforced by the **radial collateral ligament** and the **radial annular ligament** (figure 8.12*c*). A subcutaneous **olecranon bursa** covers the proximal and posterior surfaces of the olecranon process.

Elbow problems are commonly caused by excessive use or stress placed on the joint. Overuse of a joint can cause tendinitis, an inflammation or injury to the tendons that attach muscle to bone. A classic example is *tennis elbow,* although it can be caused by many repetitive activities in addition to tennis and other sports. **Olecranon bursitis** is inflammation of the olecranon bursa. It can be caused by excessive pressure of the elbow against a hard surface and is sometimes referred to as *student's elbow*. This condition typically develops over a period of months, but it can also

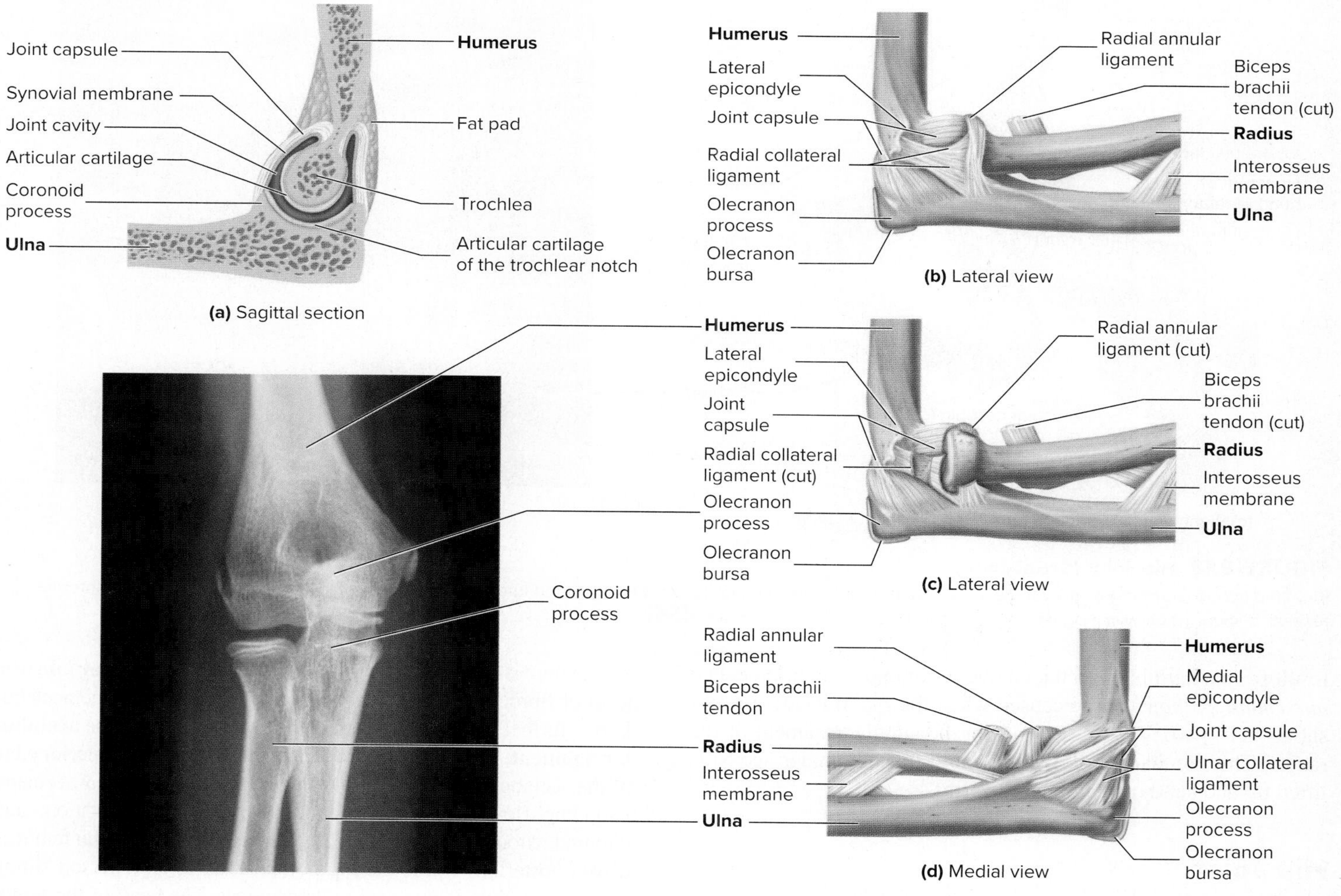

FIGURE 8.12 Right Elbow Joint

(*a*) Sagittal section showing the relationship between the ulna and the humerus. (*b*) Lateral view with ligaments cut to show the relationships among the radial head, ulna, and humerus. (*c*) Lateral view. (*d*) Medial view (right), compared to x-ray of anterior view (left). (c, d) Puwadol Jaturawutthichai/Alamy Stock Photo

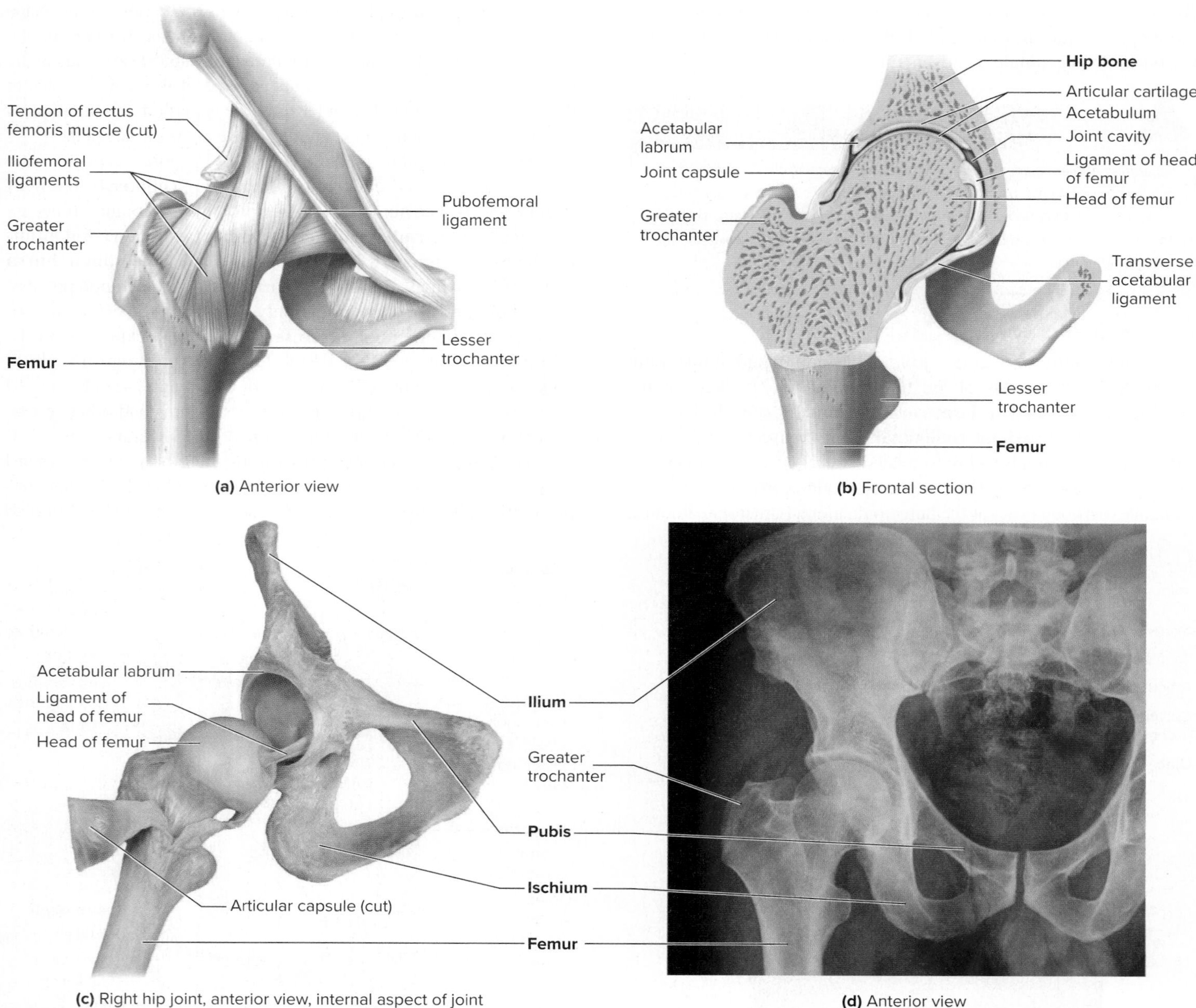

FIGURE 8.13 Hip Joint (Coxal Joint)
Right hip joint seen from (*a*) anterior view, (*b*) frontal section, and (*c*) anterior view with just the internal aspects shown. (*d*) x-ray, anterior view, no internal aspects shown. (c) Christine Eckel/McGraw Hill Education; (d) temet/Getty Images APR

result from a hard blow to the elbow. A common condition called *nursemaid's elbow* can be caused when the radial head becomes subluxated (partially separated) from the annular ligament of the radius. This can happen if a young child (usually under age 5) is lifted by one hand or swung by the arms.

Hip Joint

The femoral head articulates with the relatively deep, concave acetabulum of the hip bone to form the **hip joint,** or *coxal joint* (figure 8.13). The head of the femur is more nearly a complete ball than the articulating surface of any other bone of the body. The acetabulum is deepened and strengthened by the **acetabular labrum,** a lip of fibrocartilage, which is incomplete inferiorly. The acetabulum is further deepened and strengthened by a **transverse acetabular ligament,** which crosses the acetabular notch on the inferior edge of the acetabulum. The hip is capable of a wide range of movement, including flexion, extension, abduction, adduction, rotation, and circumduction. Dislocation of the hip may occur when the femur is driven posteriorly while the hip is flexed, as when a person sitting in an automobile is involved in an accident. The head of the femur usually dislocates posterior to the acetabulum, tearing the acetabular labrum, the fibrous capsule, and the ligaments. Fracture of the femur and the hip bone often accompanies hip dislocation.

TABLE 8.6 Ligaments of the Hip Joint (see figure 8.13)

Ligament	Description
Transverse acetabular	Bridges gap in the inferior margin of the fibrocartilaginous acetabular labrum
Iliofemoral	Strong, thick band between the anterior inferior iliac spine and the intertrochanteric line of the femur
Pubofemoral	Extends from the pubic portion of the acetabular rim to the inferior portion of the femoral neck
Ischiofemoral	Bridges the ischial acetabular rim and the superior portion of the femoral neck; less well defined
Ligament of the head of the femur	Weak, flat band from the margin of the acetabular notch and the transverse ligament to a fovea in the center of the femoral head

An extremely strong joint capsule, reinforced by several ligaments, extends from the rim of the acetabulum to the neck of the femur (table 8.6). The **iliofemoral ligament** is especially strong. When standing, most people tend to thrust the hips anteriorly. This position is relaxing because the iliofemoral ligament supports much of the body's weight. The **ligament of the head of the femur** (round ligament of the femur) is located inside the hip joint between the femoral head and the acetabulum. This ligament does not contribute much toward strengthening the hip joint; however, it does carry a small nutrient artery to the head of the femur in about 80% of the population. The deepened acetabular labrum, ligaments of the hip, and surrounding muscles make the hip joint much more stable but less mobile than the shoulder joint.

Knee Joint

The **knee joint** is a modified hinge joint located between the femur and the tibia (figure 8.14). Functionally, the knee forms a complex ellipsoid union that allows flexion, extension, and a small amount of rotation of the leg. The distal end of the femur has two large, ellipsoid surfaces with a deep fossa between them. The femur articulates with the tibia, not with the fibula. The fibula articulates only with the lateral side of the tibia. The proximal end of the tibia is flattened and smooth laterally, with a crest called the intercondylar eminence in the center (see figure 7.42). The margins of the tibia are built up by menisci (figure 8.14*b,d*). The menisci are thick, articular disks of fibrocartilage that deepen the articular surface.

The knee joint is stabilized by a combination of ligaments and tendons. The four major ligaments that provide knee joint stability are the (1) anterior cruciate, (2) posterior cruciate, (3) medial collateral, and (4) lateral collateral ligaments. The two **cruciate** (KROO-shee-ate; crossed) **ligaments** extend between the intercondylar eminence of the tibia and the fossa of the femur (figure 8.14*b,d,e*). The **anterior cruciate ligament** prevents anterior displacement of the tibia relative to the femur, and the **posterior cruciate ligament** prevents posterior displacement of the tibia. The **medial** (tibial) and **lateral** (fibular) **collateral ligaments** stabilize the medial and lateral sides, respectively, of the knee. Joint strength is also provided by popliteal ligaments and tendons of the thigh muscles that extend around the knee (table 8.7).

A number of bursae surround the knee (figure 8.14*f*). The largest is the **suprapatellar bursa,** a superior extension of the joint capsule that allows the anterior thigh muscles to move over the distal end of the femur. Other knee bursae include the subcutaneous prepatellar bursa and the deep infrapatellar bursa, as well as the popliteal bursa, the gastrocnemius bursa, and the subcutaneous infrapatellar bursa (not shown in figure 8.14). This information may help you answer the Learn to Predict at the beginning of this chapter.

Ankle Joint and Arches of the Foot

The **ankle joint,** or *talocrural* (TAH-loh-KROO-ral) joint, is a highly modified hinge joint formed by two articulations between the distal tibia and fibula with the talus in one joint capsule (figure 8.16). The medial and lateral malleoli of the tibia and fibula, which form the medial and lateral margins of the ankle, are rather extensive, whereas the anterior and posterior margins are almost nonexistent. As a result, a hinge joint is created. A fibrous capsule surrounds the joint, with the medial and lateral parts thickened to form ligaments. Other ligaments also help stabilize the joint (table 8.8). Movements at the ankle joint are dorsiflexion, plantar flexion, and limited inversion and eversion.

The arches (see figure 7.46) have ligaments that serve two major functions: to hold the bones in their proper relationship as segments of the arch and to provide ties across the arch somewhat like a bowstring. As weight is transferred through the arch system, some of the ligaments are stretched, giving the foot more flexibility and allowing it to adjust to uneven surfaces. When weight is removed from the foot, the ligaments recoil and restore the arches to their unstressed shape.

The arches of the foot normally form early in fetal life. Failure to form results in congenital **flat feet,** or fallen arches, in which the arches, primarily the medial longitudinal arch, are depressed or collapsed (see figure 7.46). This condition is sometimes, but not always, painful. Flat feet may also occur when the muscles and ligaments supporting the arch fatigue and allow the arch, usually the medial longitudinal arch, to collapse. During prolonged standing, the plantar calcaneonavicular ligament may stretch, flattening the medial longitudinal arch. The transverse arch may also become flattened. The strained ligaments can become painful. The plantar fascia is composed of the deep connective tissue superficial to the ligaments in the central plantar surface of the foot and the thinner fascia on the medial and lateral sides of the plantar surface (see figure 8.16). **Plantar fasciitis,** an inflammation of the plantar fascia, can be a problem for distance runners.

Predict 5

Ford hurt his knee in an auto accident when his knee was rammed into the dashboard. The doctor tested the knee for ligament damage by having Ford sit on the edge of a table with his knee flexed at a 90-degree angle. The doctor attempted to pull the tibia in an anterior direction (anterior drawer test) and then tried to push the tibia in a posterior direction (posterior drawer test). Results of the anterior drawer test were normal, but unusual movement did occur during the posterior drawer test. Explain the purpose of each test, and describe which ligament was damaged.

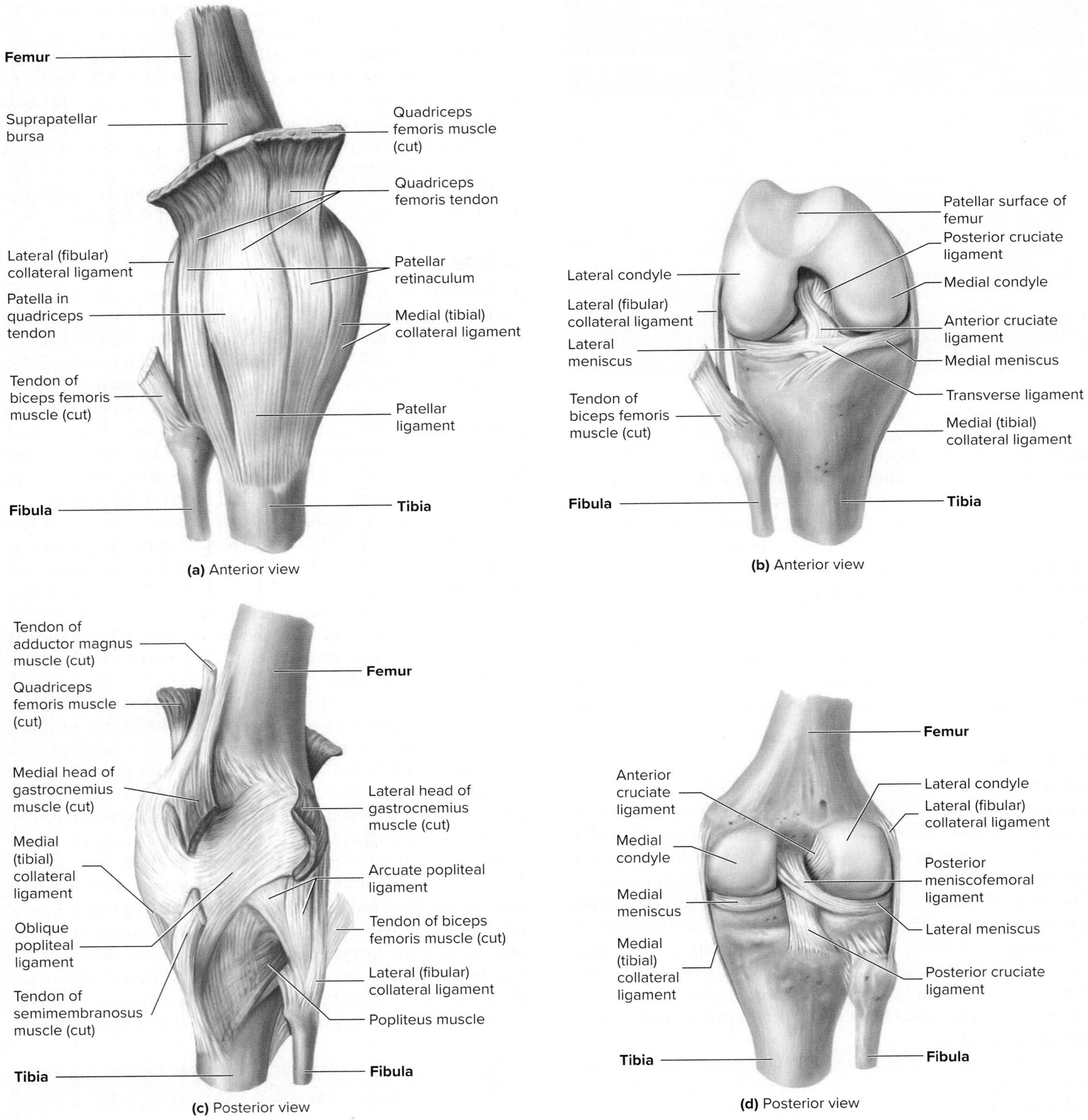

Femur
Suprapatellar bursa
Quadriceps femoris muscle (cut)
Quadriceps femoris tendon
Lateral (fibular) collateral ligament
Patellar retinaculum
Patella in quadriceps tendon
Medial (tibial) collateral ligament
Tendon of biceps femoris muscle (cut)
Patellar ligament
Fibula
Tibia

(a) Anterior view

Patellar surface of femur
Posterior cruciate ligament
Lateral condyle
Medial condyle
Lateral (fibular) collateral ligament
Anterior cruciate ligament
Lateral meniscus
Medial meniscus
Transverse ligament
Tendon of biceps femoris muscle (cut)
Medial (tibial) collateral ligament
Fibula
Tibia

(b) Anterior view

Tendon of adductor magnus muscle (cut)
Femur
Quadriceps femoris muscle (cut)
Medial head of gastrocnemius muscle (cut)
Lateral head of gastrocnemius muscle (cut)
Medial (tibial) collateral ligament
Arcuate popliteal ligament
Oblique popliteal ligament
Tendon of biceps femoris muscle (cut)
Lateral (fibular) collateral ligament
Tendon of semimembranosus muscle (cut)
Popliteus muscle
Tibia
Fibula

(c) Posterior view

Femur
Lateral condyle
Anterior cruciate ligament
Lateral (fibular) collateral ligament
Medial condyle
Posterior meniscofemoral ligament
Medial meniscus
Lateral meniscus
Medial (tibial) collateral ligament
Posterior cruciate ligament
Tibia
Fibula

(d) Posterior view

FIGURE 8.14 Right Knee Joint

(*a*) Anterior superficial view. (*b*) Anterior deep view (knee flexed). (*c*) Posterior superficial view. (*d*) Posterior deep view. 

Concept Check

8.1 Classes of Joints

A. A joint, or an articulation, is a place where two bones come together.

B. Joints are named according to the bones or parts of bones involved.

C. Joints are classified structurally according to the type of connective tissue that binds them together and whether fluid is present between the bones.

1. *Which of these joints is* not *matched with the correct joint type?*

   a. parietal bone to occipital bone—suture
   b. between the hip bones—symphysis
   c. humerus and scapula—synovial
   d. shafts of the radius and ulna—synchondrosis
   e. teeth in alveolar process—gomphosis

2. *Which type of joint is the most movable?*

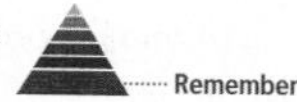

   a. sutures
   b. syndesmoses
   c. symphyses
   d. synovial
   e. gomphoses

Fibrous Joints

A. Fibrous joints, in which bones are connected by fibrous tissue with no joint cavity, are capable of little or no movement.

B. Sutures involve interdigitating bones held together by dense fibrous connective tissue. They occur between most skull bones.

C. Syndesmoses are joints consisting of fibrous ligaments.

D. Gomphoses are joints in which pegs fit into sockets and are held in place by periodontal ligaments (teeth in the jaws).

E. Some sutures and other joints can become ossified (synostoses).

Cartilaginous Joints

A. Synchondroses are immovable joints in which bones are joined by hyaline cartilage. Epiphyseal plates are examples.

B. Symphyses are slightly movable joints made of fibrocartilage.

3. *The intervertebral disks are examples of*

   a. sutures.
   b. syndesmoses.
   c. symphyses.
   d. synovial joints.
   e. gomphoses.

4. *Joints containing hyaline cartilage are called ________, and joints containing fibrocartilage are called ________.*

   Remember

   a. sutures, synchondroses
   b. syndesmoses, symphyses
   c. symphyses, syndesmoses
   d. synchondroses, symphyses
   e. gomphoses, synchondroses

5. *How would body function be affected if the sternal synchondroses and the sternocostal synchondrosis of the first rib were to become synostoses?*

   Understand

Synovial Joints

A. Synovial joints are capable of considerable movement. They consist of the following:
   - Articular cartilage on the ends of bones that provides a smooth surface for articulation. Articular disks can provide additional support.
   - A joint cavity is surrounded by a joint capsule of fibrous connective tissue, which holds the bones together while permitting flexibility. A synovial membrane produces synovial fluid, which lubricates the joint.

B. Bursae are extensions of synovial joint cavities that protect skin, tendons, or bone from structures that could rub against them.

C. Synovial joints are classified according to the shape of the adjoining articular surfaces: plane (two flat surfaces), saddle (two saddle-shaped surfaces), hinge (concave and convex surfaces), pivot (cylindrical projection inside a ring), ball-and-socket (rounded surface into a socket), and ellipsoid (ellipsoid concave and convex surfaces).

6. *The inability to produce the fluid that keeps most joints moist would likely be caused by a disorder of the*

   Remember

   a. cruciate ligaments.
   b. synovial membrane.
   c. articular cartilage.
   d. bursae.
   e. tendon sheath.

7. *Assume that a sharp object penetrated a synovial joint. Given these structures:*

   Remember

   (1) tendon or muscle
   (2) ligament
   (3) articular cartilage
   (4) fibrous capsule (of joint capsule)
   (5) skin
   (6) synovial membrane (of joint capsule)

   Choose the order in which they would most likely be penetrated.

   a. 5,1,2,6,4,3
   b. 5,2,1,4,3,6
   c. 5,1,2,6,3,4
   d. 5,1,2,4,3,6
   e. 5,1,2,4,6,3

8. *Which of these joints is correctly matched with the type of joint?*

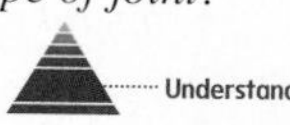

   a. atlas to occipital condyle—pivot
   b. tarsal bones to metatarsal bones—saddle
   c. femur to hip bone—ellipsoid
   d. tibia to talus—hinge
   e. scapula to humerus—plane

8.2 Types of Movement

A. Gliding movements occur when two flat surfaces glide over one another.

B. Angular movements include flexion and extension, plantar flexion and dorsiflexion, and abduction and adduction.

C. Circular movements include rotation, pronation and supination, and circumduction.

D. Special movements include elevation and depression, protraction and retraction, excursion, opposition and reposition, and inversion and eversion.

E. Combination movements involve two or more of the previously mentioned movements.

9. *When you grasp a doorknob, what movement of your forearm is necessary to unlatch the door—that is, to turn the knob in a clockwise direction? (Assume using the right hand.)* Remember
   - *a. pronation*
   - *b. rotation*
   - *c. supination*
   - *d. flexion*
   - *e. extension*

10. *After the door is unlatched, what movement of the elbow is necessary to open it? (Assume the door opens in and you are on the inside.)* Remember
    - *a. pronation*
    - *b. rotation*
    - *c. supination*
    - *d. flexion*
    - *e. extension*

11. *After the door is unlatched, what movement of the shoulder is necessary to open it? (Assume the door opens in and you are on the inside.)* Remember
    - *a. pronation*
    - *b. rotation*
    - *c. supination*
    - *d. flexion*
    - *e. extension*

12. *When grasping a doorknob, the thumb and finger undergo* Remember
    - *a. opposition.*
    - *b. reposition.*
    - *c. lateral excursion.*
    - *d. medial excursion.*
    - *e. dorsiflexion.*

13. *A runner notices that the lateral side of her right shoe is wearing much more than the lateral side of her left shoe. This could mean that her right foot undergoes more _____________ than her left foot.* Remember
    - *a. eversion*
    - *b. inversion*
    - *c. plantar flexion*
    - *d. dorsiflexion*
    - *e. lateral excursion*

14. *For a ballet dancer to stand on her toes, her feet must*

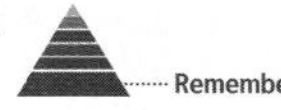

   - *a. evert.*
   - *b. invert.*
   - *c. plantar flex.*
   - *d. dorsiflex.*
   - *e. abduct.*

15. *Using an articulated skeleton, describe the type of joint and the movement(s) possible for each of the following joints:* Remember
    - *a. joint between the zygomatic bone and the maxilla*
    - *b. ligamentous connection between the coccyx and the sacrum*
    - *c. elbow joint*

16. *For each of the following muscles, describe the motion(s) produced when the muscle contracts. It may be helpful to use an articulated skeleton.* Remember
    - *a. The biceps brachii muscle attaches to the coracoid process of the scapula (one head) and to the radial tuberosity of the radius. Name two movements that the muscle accomplishes in the forearm.*
    - *b. The rectus femoris muscle attaches to the anterior inferior iliac spine and the tibial tuberosity. How does contraction move the thigh? The leg?*
    - *c. The supraspinatus muscle is located in and attached to the supraspinatus fossa of the scapula. Its tendon runs over the head of the humerus to the greater tubercle. When it contracts, what movement occurs at the glenohumeral (shoulder) joint?*
    - *d. The gastrocnemius muscle attaches to the medial and lateral condyles of the femur and to the calcaneus. What movement of the leg results when this muscle contracts? Of the foot?*

8.3 Range of Motion

A. Range of motion is the amount of movement, active or passive, that can occur at a joint.

B. Range of motion can be affected by the several properties of the joint and surrounding tissues.

8.4 Description of Selected Joints

A. The temporomandibular joint is a complex hinge and gliding joint between the temporal and mandibular bones.

B. The shoulder joint is a ball-and-socket joint between the head of the humerus and the glenoid cavity of the scapula that permits a wide range of motion.

C. The elbow joint is a compound hinge joint between the humerus, the ulna, and the radius.

D. The hip joint is a ball-and-socket joint between the head of the femur and the acetabulum of the hip bone.

E. The knee joint is a hinge joint between the femur and the tibia that is supported by many ligaments.

F. The ankle joint is a special hinge joint of the tibia, the fibula, and the talus that allows dorsiflexion and plantar flexion and inversion and eversion.

17. *A meniscus is found in the*

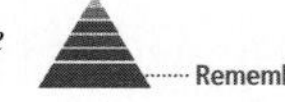

   - *a. shoulder joint.*
   - *b. elbow joint.*
   - *c. hip joint.*
   - *d. knee joint.*
   - *e. ankle joint.*

18. *A lip (labrum) of fibrocartilage deepens the joint cavity of the* Remember
    - *a. temporomandibular joint.*
    - *b. shoulder joint.*
    - *c. elbow joint.*
    - *d. knee joint.*
    - *e. ankle joint.*

19. *Which of these joints has a tendon inside the joint cavity?*
    a. *temporomandibular joint*
    b. *shoulder joint*
    c. *elbow joint*
    d. *knee joint*
    e. *ankle joint*

20. *Which of these structures help stabilize the shoulder joint?*
    a. *rotator cuff muscles*
    b. *cruciate ligaments*
    c. *medial and lateral collateral ligaments*
    d. *articular disks*
    e. *All of these are correct.*

21. *Bursitis of the subacromial bursa could result from*

    a. *flexing the wrist.*
    b. *kneeling.*
    c. *overusing the shoulder joint.*
    d. *running a long distance.*
    e. *extending the elbow.*

22. *At first, Donnie's wife accused her once-active 25-year-old husband of trying to get out of housework by constantly complaining about pain and stiffness in his lower back. But over the next 5 months, the pain and stiffness increased and seemed to be spreading up his vertebral column. The family doctor referred Donnie to a rheumatologist, who diagnosed ankylosing spondylitis (AS). AS, a chronic inflammation of joints at points where ligaments, tendons, and joint capsule insert into bone, causes fibrosis (the development of scar tissue), ossification, and fusion of joints. Combine your knowledge about bone growth, repair, and anatomy from chapters 6 and 7 and joint structure and function from this chapter to identify the category of joints primarily affected by AS, and explain how chronic inflammation of Donnie's joints led to their fusion.*

Answers to this chapter's odd-numbered Concept Check questions appear in Appendix F.

9

CHAPTER

Muscular System

HISTOLOGY AND PHYSIOLOGY

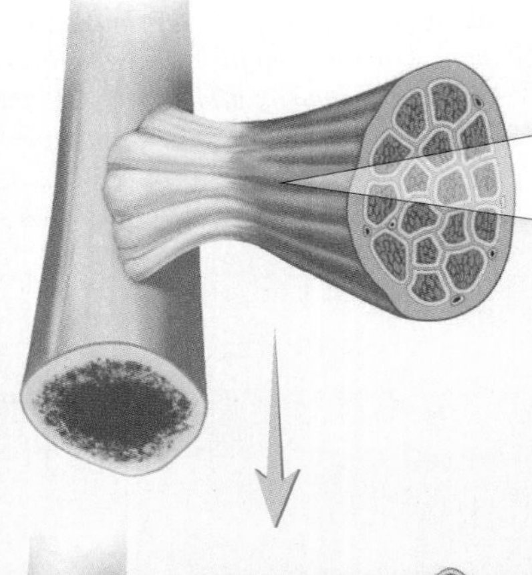

Whole Muscle
A complete organ surrounded by muscular fascia and epimysium; has many blood vessels and nerves, including motor neurons that stimulate contraction.

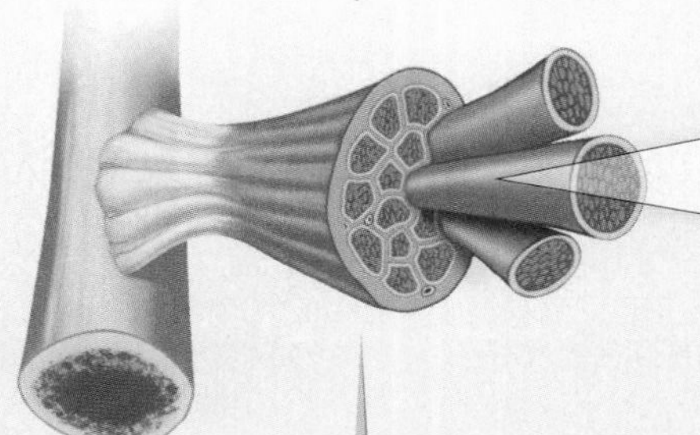

Muscle Fascicle
Bundle of muscle fibers within the entire muscle; surrounded by the connective tissue layer, perimysium.

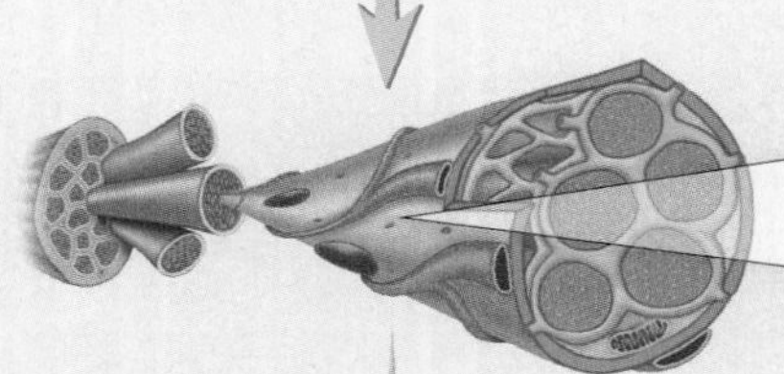

Muscle Fiber
Individual muscle cell within a fascicle; surrounded by the connective tissue layer, endomysium.

Myofibril
Groups of contractile proteins within individual muscle fibers; surrounded by specialized endoplasmic reticulum, called sarcoplasmic reticulum.

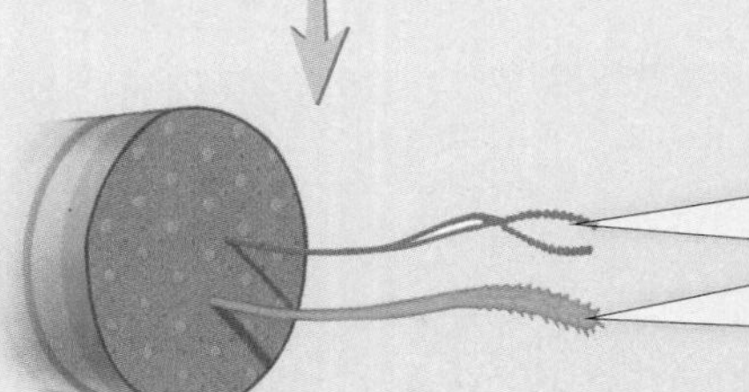

Myofilament
Protein filaments, either myosin or actin; interact to shorten the muscle fiber during contraction.

The hierarchical organization of a muscle is an excellent illustration of the relationship between form and function.

In order to turn the pages of this chapter, move your eyes across the page, and continue breathing, electrical impulses must travel to millions of tiny motors throughout your body. These "motors" are really your muscle cells, which, on receiving a nerve impulse, convert chemical ATP energy into the mechanical energy of moving cell parts. The body has three types of muscle tissue, each with a different purpose. The muscles you voluntarily control are called skeletal muscles, and they work with the skeletal system to produce coordinated movements of your limbs. The digestive, cardiovascular, urinary, and reproductive systems all use smooth muscle to propel materials through the body. The heart contains specialized cardiac muscle tissue to pump blood. No matter where muscle tissues are in the body, they all share the same feature: contraction.

Learn to Predict

Winning a 1-month membership to a health club changed Bob's life. He gave up junk food and now works out daily. In one of his aerobic exercises, he slowly flexes his elbow and supinates his right hand while lifting a 35-pound weight; then he lowers the weight back to its starting position. He repeats this process several times.

Explain how Bob's muscles are able to lift and lower the weight slowly.

Answers to this question and the chapter's odd-numbered Predict questions can be found in Appendix E.

9.1 Functions of the Muscular System

LEARNING OUTCOMES

After reading this section, you should be able to

A. **Summarize the major characteristics of skeletal, smooth, and cardiac muscle.**

B. **Summarize the functions of the muscular system.**

Movements of the body result from muscle contractions. The movements include the heart beating, running a marathon, and moving food through the intestines. As described in chapter 4, there are three types of muscle tissue: (1) skeletal, (2) smooth, and (3) cardiac (table 9.1). Because skeletal muscle is the most abundant and most studied type, this chapter examines the physiology of skeletal muscle in greatest detail. Chapter 10 focuses on the anatomy of the skeletal muscle system.

Types of Muscle Tissue

Skeletal muscle is voluntary muscle and constitutes about 40% of the body's weight. Locomotion, facial expressions, posture, respiratory functions, speech, and other body movements are due to skeletal muscle contraction. The nervous system controls the voluntary aspects of skeletal muscle.

Smooth muscle is involuntary muscle and is the most widely distributed type of muscle in the body. It is found in the walls of hollow organs, such as the stomach and uterus, and tubes, such as blood vessels and ducts of certain glands. Smooth muscle contraction propels urine through the urinary tract, mixes food in the stomach and the small intestine, regulates the flow of blood through blood vessels, and controls the size of the pupil of the eye.

Cardiac muscle is also involuntary and is found only in the heart. Its contractions provide the major force for moving blood through the circulatory system. Cardiac muscle and many smooth muscles are autorhythmic. Autorhythmicity allows these cells to contract spontaneously and rhythmically.

The following list summarizes the major functions of all three types of muscle:

1. *Movement of the body.* Most skeletal muscles are attached to bones and are responsible for the majority of body movements, including walking, running, chewing, and manipulating objects with the hands.
2. *Maintenance of posture.* Skeletal muscles constantly maintain tone, which keeps us sitting or standing erect.
3. *Respiration.* Contraction of the skeletal muscles of the thorax and the diaphragm helps us breathe.

Module 6
Muscular System

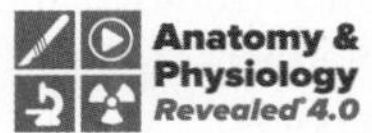

TABLE 9.1 **Comparison of Muscle Types**

	Skeletal Muscle	Smooth Muscle	Cardiac Muscle
Location	Attached to bones	Walls of hollow organs, blood vessels, eyes, glands, and skin	Heart
Appearance	LM 800x Ed Reschke	LM 800x Victor P. Eroschenko	LM 400x Ed Reschke
Cell Shape	Very long and cylindrical (1 mm–4 cm, or as much as 30 cm in length, 10 μm–100 μm in diameter)	Spindle-shaped (15–200 μm in length, 5–8 μm in diameter)	Cylindrical and branched (100–500 μm in length, 12–20 μm in diameter)
Nucleus	Multiple nuclei, peripherally located	Single, centrally located	Single, centrally located
Special Cell-to-Cell Attachments	None	Gap junctions join some visceral smooth muscle cells together	Intercalated disks join cells to one another
Striations	Yes	No	Yes
Control	Voluntary and involuntary (reflexes)	Involuntary	Involuntary
Capable of Spontaneous Contraction	No	Yes (some smooth muscle)	Yes
Function	Controlling body movement	Moving food through the digestive tract, emptying the urinary bladder, regulating blood vessel diameter, changing pupil size, contracting many gland ducts, moving hair, and many other functions	Pumping blood; contractions provide the major force for propelling blood through blood vessels

4. *Production of body heat.* When skeletal muscles contract, heat is given off as a by-product. This released heat is critical for maintaining body temperature.
5. *Communication.* Skeletal muscles are involved in all aspects of communication, including speaking, writing, typing, gesturing, and smiling or frowning.
6. *Constriction of organs and vessels.* The contraction of smooth muscle within the walls of internal organs and vessels causes those structures to constrict. This constriction can help propel and mix food and water in the digestive tract; remove materials from organs, such as the urinary bladder or sweat glands; and regulate blood flow through vessels.
7. *Contraction of the heart.* The contraction of cardiac muscle causes the heart to beat, propelling blood to all parts of the body.

ASSESS YOUR PROGRESS

Answers to these questions are found in the section you have just completed. Re-read the section if you need help in answering these questions.

1. *List and describe the functions performed by skeletal muscle tissue.*
2. *State the functions of smooth and cardiac muscle tissues.*
3. *Using table 9.1, distinguish among skeletal, smooth, and cardiac muscle tissues as to their locations, appearance, cell shape, and cell-to-cell attachments.*

9.2 General Properties of Muscle Tissue

LEARNING OUTCOME

After reading this section, you should be able to

A. **Explain the four functional properties of muscle tissue.**

Muscle tissue is highly specialized. It has four major functional properties:

1. **Contractility** is the ability of muscle to shorten forcefully, or contract. For example, lifting this textbook requires certain muscles to contract. When muscle contracts, it either causes the structures to which it is attached (such as a bone) to move or increases pressure inside a blood vessel or a hollow organ, such as the intestine. On the other hand, it lengthens passively. Forces that oppose contraction cause muscles to lengthen. Examples of this type of force include gravity pulling on a limb and the pressure of fluid in a hollow organ, such as urine in the bladder. Thus, muscle shortening is forceful and muscle lengthening is passive.
2. **Excitability** is the capacity of muscle to respond to an electrical stimulus. Normally, the stimulus is from nerves that we consciously control. For instance, if you decide to wave to a friend, the conscious decision to lift your arm is sent via nerves. Smooth muscle and cardiac muscle also respond to stimulation by nerves and hormones but can sometimes contract spontaneously.
3. **Extensibility** means a muscle can be stretched beyond its normal resting length and still be able to contract. If you stretch to reach a dropped pencil, your muscles are longer than they are normally, but you can still retrieve the pencil.
4. **Elasticity** is the ability of muscle to spring back to its original resting length after it has been stretched. Taking a deep breath demonstrates elasticity because exhalation is simply the recoil of your respiratory muscles back to the resting position, similar to releasing a stretched rubberband.

ASSESS YOUR PROGRESS

4. *Identify the four specialized functional properties of muscle tissue, and give an example of each.*
5. *Outline the differences in control and function for skeletal, smooth, and cardiac muscle.*

9.3 Skeletal Muscle Anatomy

LEARNING OUTCOMES

After reading this section, you should be able to

A. **Describe the connective tissue components of skeletal muscle.**
B. **Explain the blood supply and innervation of skeletal muscle.**
C. **Discuss the origin of muscle fibers and explain how muscle hypertrophy occurs.**
D. **Describe the components of a muscle fiber.**
E. **Relate the types of myofilaments and describe their structures.**
F. **Produce diagrams that illustrate the arrangement of myofilaments in a sarcomere.**
G. **Describe how the sliding filament model explains the contraction of muscle fibers.**
H. **Explain what happens to the length of the A band, I band, and H zone during contraction.**

Whole Skeletal Muscle Anatomy

Individual skeletal muscles, such as the biceps brachii, are complete organs. Recall from chapter 1 that an organ consists of two or more tissue types working together for a common function. A skeletal muscle consists of skeletal muscle tissue, nervous tissue, connective tissue, and adipose tissue. For our purposes, we will start our discussion of skeletal muscle anatomy and physiology at the whole muscle (organ) level and conclude at the cellular level. Each muscle cell is called a **muscle fiber.**

Connective Tissue Coverings

Each skeletal muscle is surrounded by several connective tissue layers that support the muscle during contraction. A skeletal muscle has three layers of connective tissue: (1) the epimysium, (2) the perimysium, and (3) the endomysium.

The **epimysium** (ep-ih-MIS-ee-um; *mys,* muscle) forms a connective tissue sheath that surrounds each skeletal muscle. It is a layer of dense irregular connective tissue, whose protein fibers gradually merge with the **muscular fascia** (FASH-ee-ah), the layer of connective tissue between adjacent muscles and between muscles and the skin. These outer layers of connective tissue keep the muscles separate from surrounding tissues and organs.

The **perimysium** (PER-ih-MIS-ee-um, PER-i-MIZ-ee-um) subdivides each whole muscle into numerous, visible bundles of muscle fibers (cells) called **fascicles** (FAS-i-kuhls). The perimysium is a loose connective tissue serving as passageways for blood vessels and nerves that supply each fascicle.

The **endomysium** (EN-doh-MIS-ee-um) is a delicate layer of connective tissue that separates the individual muscle fibers within each fascicle. The endomysium serves as passageways for nerve fibers and blood vessels that supply each separate muscle fiber.

The protein fibers of the three layers of connective tissue are interwoven and blend into one another. The collagen fibers of the three layers converge at the ends of the muscle and together form **tendons** or **aponeuroses,** which attach muscle to bone. Sometimes the epimysium of one muscle will directly attach to the tendon or fascia of another muscle. These attachments serve to move the bones or skin for locomotion, facial expression, and other types of movements.

Nerves and Blood Vessels

Skeletal muscles have a rich supply of blood vessels and nerves (figure 9.1). The specialized nerve cells responsible for stimulating skeletal muscle contraction are called **motor neurons.** Motor neurons originate in the brain and spinal cord and extend to skeletal

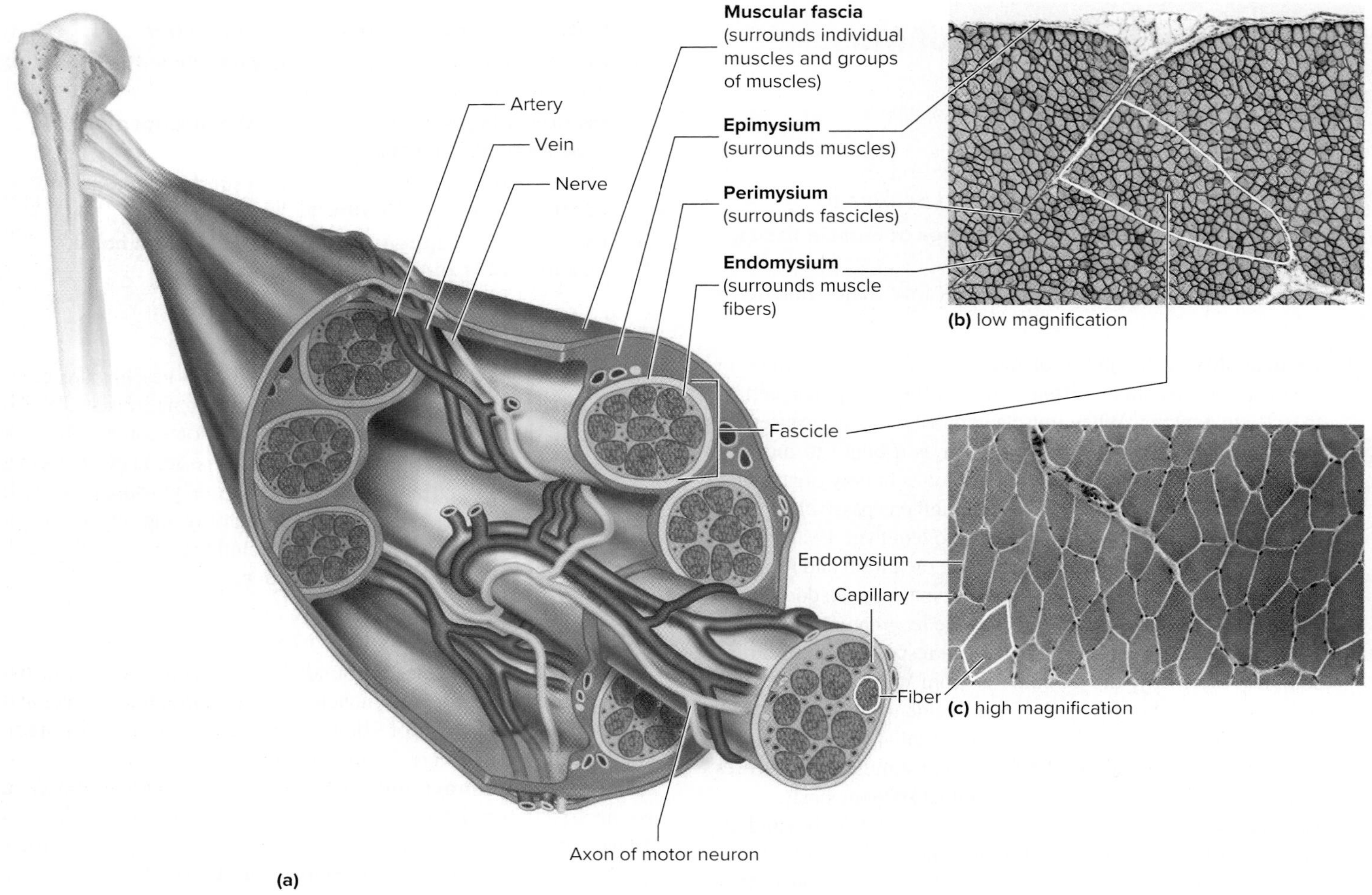

FIGURE 9.1 Whole Skeletal Muscle Structure: Connective Tissue, Innervation, and Blood Supply
(*a*) A muscle is composed of muscle fascicles, each surrounded by perimysium. The fascicles are composed of bundles of individual muscle fibers (muscle cells), each surrounded by endomysium. This figure shows the relationship among muscles, muscle fascicles, muscle fibers, and associated connective tissue layers: the epimysium, perimysium, and endomysium. Arteries, veins, and nerves course together through the connective tissue of muscles. They branch frequently as they approach individual muscle fibers. At the level of the perimysium, axons of neurons branch, and each branch extends to a muscle fiber. (*b*) Photomicrograph of whole muscle cross section (10x). (*c*) Photomicrograph of cross section of individual muscle fibers showing the endomysium (100x).
(*b*) Alvin Telser/Science Source; (*c*) Biophoto Associates/Science Source APR

muscle fibers through nerves. Whole muscles are generally supplied by several motor neurons. Each motor neuron, in turn, controls several muscle fibers, with each fiber being supplied by a branch of the motor neuron. At the fascicles, the axons branch repeatedly, each branch innervating one muscle fiber. Every skeletal muscle fiber in the body is controlled by a branch of a motor neuron. The contact points between the axons and the muscle fibers, called synapses or neuromuscular junctions, are described later in this section.

An artery and either one or two veins extend together with a nerve through the connective tissue layers of skeletal muscles. Numerous branches of the arteries supply the extensive capillary networks surrounding the muscle fibers, and blood is carried away from the capillary beds by branches of the veins.

Skeletal Muscle Fiber Anatomy

Skeletal muscle fibers are very unique cells. They develop from the fusion of several hundred embryonic cells called **myoblasts** (MY-oh-blasts). Each myoblast contains its own nucleus. Thus, the result of skeletal muscle fiber formation is an enormous cell with several hundred nuclei just under the plasma membrane. Most skeletal muscle fibers range in size from about 1 millimeter (mm) long to about 4 centimeters (cm) in length, but there are some skeletal muscle fibers that are as much as 30 cm (almost 1 foot) in length. For comparison, the typical skin cell is about a 30-micrometer (μm; 0.003 cm) oval-shaped cell and a red blood cell is only about an 8 μm diameter oval. The diameter of most muscle fibers ranges from 10 μm to around 100 μm, but can be as much as 500 μm wide.

Large muscles contain many large-diameter muscle fibers, whereas small, delicate muscles contain many small-diameter muscle fibers. However, most muscles contain a mixture of small- and large-diameter muscle fibers. As seen in a longitudinal section, alternating light and dark bands give the muscle fiber a **striated** (STRY-ate-ed; banded), or striped, appearance (figure 9.2).

The number of skeletal muscle fibers remains relatively constant after birth. Enlargement, or **hypertrophy,** of muscles in children and adults results from an increase in the *size* of each

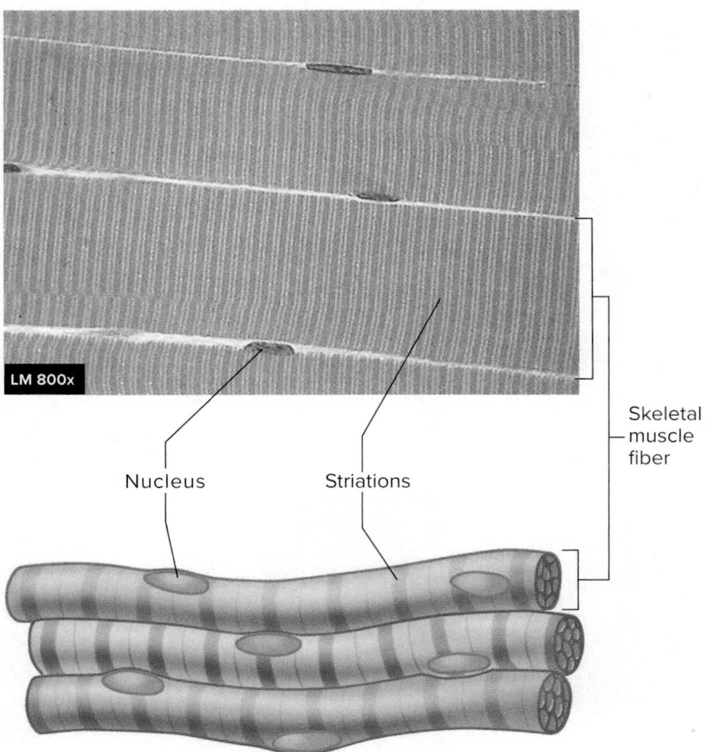

FIGURE 9.2 Skeletal Muscle Fibers
Skeletal muscle fibers in longitudinal section. Ed Reschke APR

muscle fiber, not from a substantial increase in the *number* of muscle fibers. Similarly, hypertrophy of muscles in response to exercise is due mainly to an increase in muscle fiber size, rather than an increase in number.

Histology of Muscle Fibers

Muscle contraction is much easier to understand when we consider the structure of a muscle fiber (figure 9.3). There are two main aspects to muscle contraction: (1) an electrical component and (2) a mechanical component. The parts of a skeletal muscle fiber can be categorized based on their specific role in muscle contraction.

Electrical Component Structures

Recall that excitability is one of the four major functional properties of skeletal muscle. There are three muscle fiber components that respond to and transmit electrical signals: (1) the sarcolemma, (2) transverse tubules, and (3) the sarcoplasmic reticulum.

1. The **sarcolemma** (SAR-koh-LEM-ah; *sarco,* flesh + *lemma,* husk; figure 9.3) is the plasma membrane of muscle fibers. We will discuss its specific role in transmitting electrical impulses to the interior of the muscle fiber in section 9.4.
2. **Transverse tubules,** or **T tubules,** are tubelike inward folds of the sarcolemma (figure 9.3). At regular intervals along the muscle fiber, the sarcolemma forms T tubules by projecting and extending into the interior of the muscle fiber. The T tubules carry electrical impulses into the center of the muscle fiber so that every contractile unit of the muscle fiber contracts in unison.

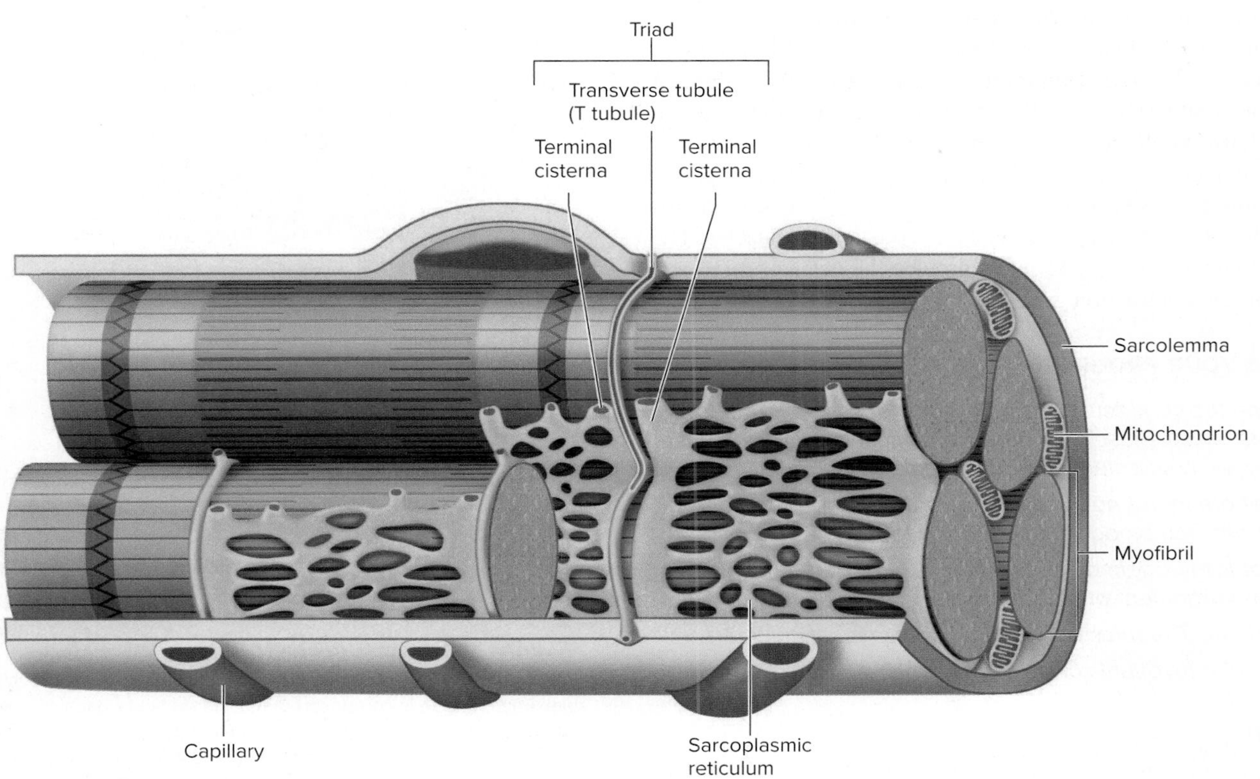

FIGURE 9.3 Structure of the Triad
T tubule and the sarcoplasmic reticulum on each side of the T tubule form a triad.

3. The **sarcoplasmic reticulum** (SAR-koh-PLAZ-mik re-TIK-you-lum) is a highly specialized smooth endoplasmic reticulum in skeletal muscle fibers that stores high levels of Ca^{2+} (figure 9.3). Release of Ca^{2+} from the sarcoplasmic reticulum is a "switch" for muscle contraction. T tubules lie next to enlarged portions of the sarcoplasmic reticulum called **terminal cisternae** (sis-TER-nee). Two terminal cisternae and their associated T tubule form a critical structure for muscle contraction called a **triad** (TRY-ad) (figure 9.3). We will continue our discussion of the triad in section 9.4.

Muscle fibers also contain other organelles such as numerous mitochondria and energy-storing glycogen granules. Together these organelles constitute the cytoplasm, called the **sarcoplasm** (SAR-koh-plazm) in muscle fibers.

Mechanical Component Structures

The general muscle property of contractility is due to two main structures in muscle fibers: (1) myofibrils and (2) myofilaments.

1. **Myofibrils** (my-oh-FIE-brillz) are bundles of protein filaments (figure 9.3). Each muscle fiber has numerous myofibrils in its sarcoplasm. The myofibrils are long threadlike structures extending the entire length of the muscle fiber. Each myofibril is 1–3 μm in diameter, approximately 6 times smaller than a human hair, which is about 17 μm in diameter. It is the protein filaments in the myofibrils that interact to shorten the muscle fiber during contraction.
2. There are two types of **myofilaments** (my-oh-FIL-ah-ments) in each myofibril: (1) **actin** (AK-tin) **myofilaments** and (2) **myosin** (MY-oh-sin) **myofilaments** (figure 9.4). Actin myofilaments, or **thin filaments,** are approximately 8 nanometers (nm) in diameter and 1000 nm in length. Myosin myofilaments, or **thick filaments,** are approximately 12 nm in diameter and 1800 nm in length. In comparison, the common cold virus is about 30 nm in diameter. The actin and myosin myofilaments are arranged into highly ordered units called **sarcomeres** (SAR-koh-meerz; figure 9.5). The sarcomeres are the structural and functional units of skeletal muscles. The myofilaments in the sarcomere provide the mechanical aspect of muscle contraction.

ASSESS YOUR PROGRESS

6. *Name the connective tissue layers that surround muscle fibers, muscle fascicles, and whole muscles. Distinguish between a sarcolemma and muscular fascia.*
7. *What are motor neurons? How do the axons of motor neurons and blood vessels extend to muscle fibers?*
8. *What is the origin of muscle fibers? How do you explain the enlargement of muscle fibers?*
9. *What are T tubules and the sarcoplasmic reticulum?*
10. *Describe myofibrils and myofilaments.*

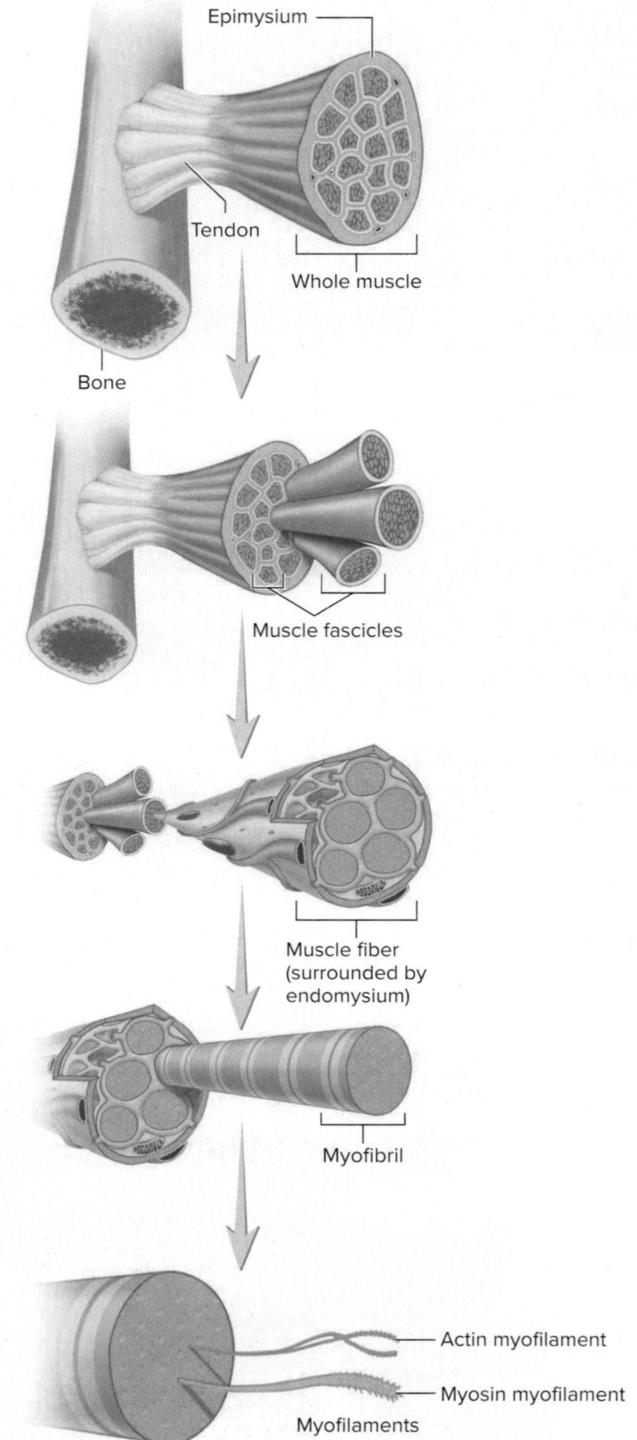

FIGURE 9.4 Structure of a Muscle

A whole muscle is surrounded by a connective tissue sheath called epimysium. Each muscle is composed of muscle fascicles, each of which is surrounded by a connective tissue layer called perimysium. The fascicles are composed of individual muscle fibers (cells). Each fiber is surrounded by a connective tissue layer called endomysium. Muscle fibers contain groups of protein fibers called myofibrils. Myofibrils are composed of protein filaments called myofilaments.

Sarcomeres

Sarcomeres join end to end forming the myofibrils. The sarcomere is the smallest portion of a muscle that can contract. Each sarcomere has a precise boundary. Filamentous networks of proteins, called **Z disks,** form a stationary anchor for actin myofilaments (see figures 9.4 and 9.5). One sarcomere extends from one Z disk to the next Z disk. It is the arrangement of the actin and myosin myofilaments within sarcomeres that gives skeletal muscle its striated appearance.

Each sarcomere has three regions: two lighter-staining regions, called **I bands,** and a central darker-staining region, called an A band. Each of the two I bands includes a Z disk and extend to the ends of the myosin myofilaments. The I bands contain only actin myofilaments (thin filaments) and thus appear lighter staining.

The darker-staining band in the center of each sarcomere is called an **A band.** Each A band contains both actin and myosin myofilaments overlapping, except in the center of the A band. The center of each A band has a smaller band, called the **H zone,** and contains only myosin myofilaments (thick filaments). Each myosin molecule in the A band is surrounded by six actin myofilaments (figure 9.5). The middle of each H zone has a dark line, called the **M line.** The M line consists of delicate filaments that hold the myosin myofilaments in place (figure 9.5).

The numerous myofibrils are oriented within each muscle fiber so that A bands and I bands of parallel myofibrils are aligned and thus produce the striated pattern seen through a microscope. In addition to actin and myosin, there are other, less visible proteins within sarcomeres. These proteins help hold actin and myosin in place. In particular, the protein **titin** (TIE-tin; figure 9.5) gives muscle the ability to stretch (extensibility) and recoil (elasticity). Titin is one of the largest known proteins and is the largest protein in humans, consisting of a single chain of nearly 27,000 amino acids. Each titin molecule extends from the M line to the Z disk. The titin anchors the myosin myofilaments to the M line, keeping them centered in the sarcomere. At the point of attachment to the Z disks, the titin molecule functions as a spring, which allows the sarcomeres to recoil back to their resting length after being stretched.

Actin and Myosin Myofilament Structure

Actin Myofilaments

Each actin myofilament is composed of three separate proteins: (1) globular (G) actin, (2) tropomyosin, and (3) troponin (figure 9.5).

G actin molecules are globular subunits that form a long chain of about 200 subunits. The chain of 200 G actin subunits forms into a strand called **fibrous (F) actin.** Each G actin subunit has an active site for myosin myofilament binding during muscle contraction. In a sense, we can think of the active sites on the G actin as receptor sites for a portion of the myosin myofilament, the myosin head.

Tropomyosin (troh-poh-MY-oh-sin) is a long, fibrous protein that lies in the groove along the fibrous actin strand. In a relaxed muscle, tropomyosin is covering the active sites on the G actin subunits. A muscle cannot contract until the tropomyosin moves to uncover the active sites.

Troponin (TROH-poh-nin) consists of three subunits: (1) a subunit that anchors the troponin to the actin, (2) a subunit that prevents the tropomyosin from uncovering the G actin active sites in a relaxed muscle, and (3) a subunit that binds Ca^{2+}.

It is the relationship among troponin and tropomyosin that dictates when the skeletal muscle will contract. We will describe the specific process in section 9.4.

Myosin Myofilaments

Myosin myofilaments are composed of many elongated **myosin molecules** shaped like golf clubs (figure 9.5). Each myosin molecule consists of two **myosin heavy chains** wound together to form a **rod portion** lying parallel to the myosin myofilament and two **myosin heads** that extend laterally (figure 9.5). Four light myosin chains are attached to the heads of each myosin molecule. Each myosin myofilament consists of about 300 myosin molecules arranged so that about 150 of them have their heads projecting toward each end. The centers of the myosin myofilaments consist of only the rod portions of the myosin molecules. The myosin heads have three important properties: (1) The heads bind to active sites on the actin molecules to form **cross-bridges** to contract the muscle; (2) the heads are attached to the rod portion by a hinge region that bends and straightens during contraction; and (3) the heads are ATPase enzymes, which break down adenosine triphosphate (ATP), releasing energy. Part of the energy is used to bend the hinge region of the myosin molecule during contraction.

Neuromuscular Junction Structure

Recall that each muscle fiber is in contact with a branch of a motor neuron axon from the brain or spinal cord (see figure 9.1). The motor neurons carry electrical signals called **action potentials,** which cause action potentials in the muscle fiber. The point of contact of motor neuron axon branches with the muscle fiber is called the **neuromuscular junction,** or **synapse** (figure 9.5).

The neuromuscular junction consists of a group of enlarged axon terminals that rests in an invagination of the sarcolemma. Therefore, a neuromuscular junction consists of (1) the axon terminals and (2) the area of the muscle fiber sarcolemma they innervate. Each axon terminal is called the **presynaptic** (PREE-si-NAP-tik) **terminal.** The space between the presynaptic terminal and the muscle fiber is the **synaptic** (si-NAP-tik) **cleft.** The muscle plasma membrane in the area of the junction is called the **motor end-plate,** or the **postsynaptic** (post-si-NAP-tik) **membrane** (figure 9.5). Each presynaptic terminal contains numerous mitochondria and many small, spherical sacs, called **synaptic vesicles.** The synaptic vesicles contain the neurotransmitter **acetylcholine** (AS-eh-til-KOH-leen; **ACh**). A **neurotransmitter** (NOOR-oh-trans-MIT-er) is a molecule that allows a neuron to communicate with its target. They are released from a presynaptic membrane and diffuse across the synaptic cleft to alter the activity of the muscle fiber. Neurotransmitters can stimulate or inhibit the production of an action potential in the motor end-plate (the sarcolemma) by binding to **ligand-gated ion channels.** Recall from chapter 3 that gated ion channels limit ion movement across the plasma membrane by opening and closing. Ligand-gated ion channels are specialized membrane transport proteins that are opened or closed by specific molecules, such as neurotransmitters. The generic term for these specific molecules is **ligand** (LIG-and, LIH-gand). When opened, the ligand-gated ion channels allow ions to cross the plasma membrane (see section 9.4).

Sliding Filament Model

The primary function of skeletal muscle fibers is to generate force by contracting, or shortening. The parallel arrangement of myofilaments in a sarcomere allows them to interact, which causes

FUNDAMENTAL Figure

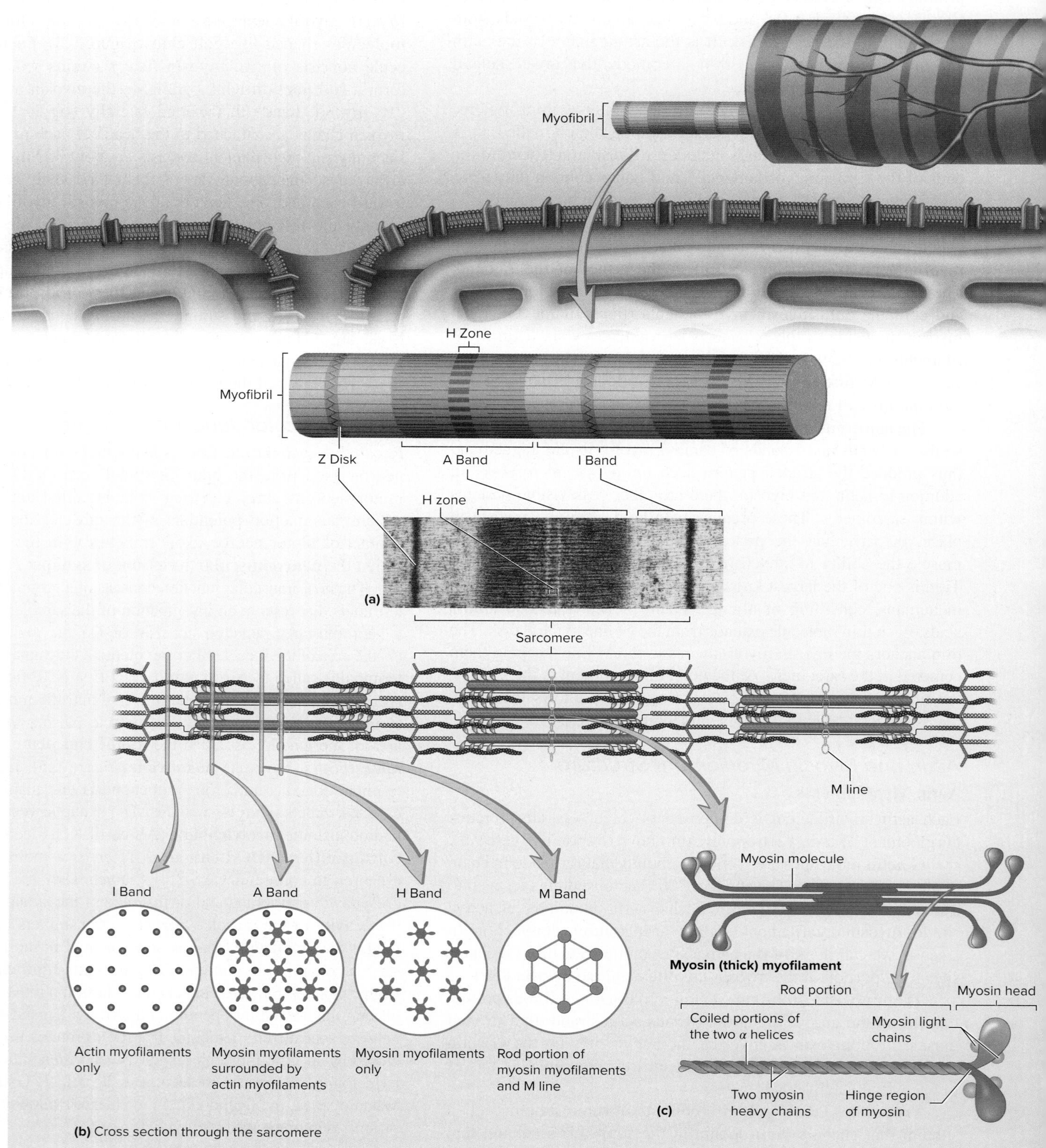

(b) Cross section through the sarcomere

FIGURE 9.5 Structure of Muscle Fibers and Organization of Sarcomeres

(*a*) A sarcomere consists of actin (thin) myofilaments, attached to Z disks, and myosin (thick) myofilaments, suspended between the actin myofilaments. An electron micrograph of a sarcomere shows a myofibril of a muscle fiber. (*b*) Diagram of adjacent sarcomeres, depicting structures responsible for the banding pattern. The I band is between the ends of myosin myofilaments on each side of a Z disk. The A band is formed by the myosin myofilaments within a sarcomere. The H zone is between the ends of the actin myofilaments within a sarcomere. Myosin myofilaments are attached to the M line. Cross sections through regions of the sarcomeres show the arrangement of proteins in three dimensions. (*c*) Myosin myofilaments (*green*, on right) are made up of many golf-club-shaped myosin molecules, with all the heads pointing in one direction at one end and the opposite direction at the other end. Myosin molecules are composed of two molecules of heavy

The resting membrane potential is established once the movement of K^+ out of the cell by diffusion is in equilibrium with the movement of K^+ into the cell by the sodium-potassium pump. The details of the resting membrane potential are described more fully in chapter 11.

The resting membrane potential can be measured in units called **millivolts** (mV; mV = 1/1000 volt). The potential differences across the plasma membranes of neurons and muscle fibers are between −70 and −90 mV. In comparison, a "AA" battery is about 1.5 V. The potential difference is reported as a negative number because the inner surface of the plasma membrane is negative compared with the outside.

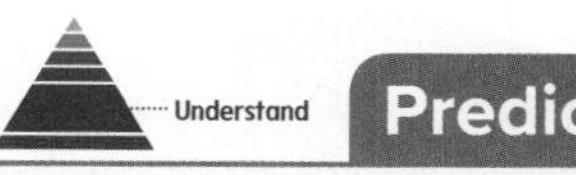

Predict 1

If ligand-gated K^+ channels were to open in an unstimulated muscle fiber, how would this affect the resting membrane potential?

ASSESS YOUR PROGRESS

18. *What type of ion channel contributes to the resting membrane potential? Describe the permeability characteristics of the plasma membrane.*
19. *What are the two types of gated ion channels in the plasma membrane? Explain what causes each type to open and close.*
20. *What is the resting membrane potential? What three factors create the resting membrane potential?*
21. *How does the sodium-potassium pump help maintain the polarized nature of the resting membrane?*

Action Potentials

An action potential occurs when the excitable cell is stimulated. The action potential is a reversal of the resting membrane potential such that the inside of the plasma membrane becomes positively charged compared with the outside. This charge reversal occurs because ion channels open when a cell is stimulated. The diffusion of ions through these channels changes the charge across the plasma membrane and produces an action potential.

An action potential lasts from approximately 1 millisecond to a few milliseconds, and it has two phases: (1) depolarization and (2) repolarization. Figure 9.8 shows the changes that occur in the membrane potential during an action potential. Stimulation of a cell causes depolarization. Depolarization occurs when the inside of the plasma membrane becomes more positive (figure 9.8). If the depolarization causes the membrane potential to reach **threshold,** an action potential is triggered. Threshold is the membrane potential at which voltage-gated Na^+ channels open. The **depolarization phase** of the action potential is a brief period during which further depolarization occurs and the inside of the cell becomes even more positively charged (figure 9.8). The charge difference across the plasma membrane is said to be reversed when the membrane potential becomes a positive value. The **repolarization phase** is the return of the membrane potential to its resting value.

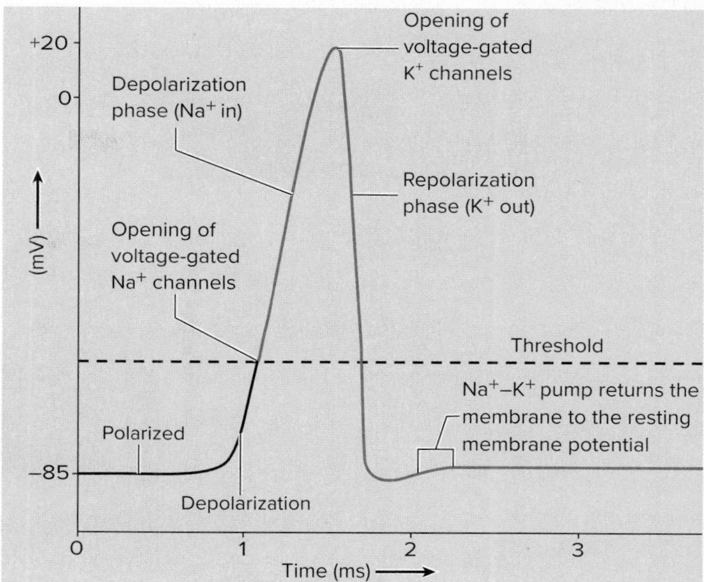

Depolarization is a change in the charge difference across the plasma membrane, which makes the charge inside the cell more positive relative to the outside and the charge outside the plasma membrane less positive than before. Once threshold is reached, an action potential is produced. During the depolarization phase of the action potential, the membrane potential changes from approximately −85 mV to approximately +20 mV. During the repolarization phase, the inside of the plasma membrane changes from approximately +20 mV back to −85 mV.

FIGURE 9.8 Depolarization and the Action Potential in Skeletal Muscle

Depolarization brings the membrane potential closer to threshold. An action potential is generated along the sarcolemma of a skeletal muscle fiber.

Figure 9.9 shows the changes that occur in the membrane during an action potential.

1. The depolarization and repolarization phases are due to the opening and closing of voltage-gated ion channels. Before a neuron or a muscle fiber is stimulated, the Na^+ and K^+ voltage-gated ion channels are closed.
2. When the cell is stimulated, either voltage-gated or ligand-gated Na^+ channels open, depending on the stimulus. In either case, Na^+ diffuses into the cell. The positively charged Na^+ makes the inside of the plasma membrane depolarized (more positive). If this depolarization reaches threshold, many voltage-gated Na^+ channels are stimulated to open rapidly, causing Na^+ to diffuse into the cell until the inside of the plasma membrane becomes positive for a brief time.
3. As the inside of the cell becomes positive, this voltage change causes additional permeability changes in the plasma membrane, which stop depolarization and start repolarization. Repolarization occurs when voltage-gated Na^+ channels close and voltage-gated K^+ channels open. When K^+ moves out of the cell, the inside of the plasma membrane becomes more negative and the outside becomes more positive. The action potential ends, and the resting membrane potential is reestablished by the sodium-potassium pump.

Action potentials occur according to the **all-or-none principle,** which means that all action potentials are identical for a given excitable cell. If a stimulus is strong enough to produce a depolarization that reaches threshold, or even if it exceeds threshold by a substantial amount, all of the permeability changes

PROCESS **Figure**

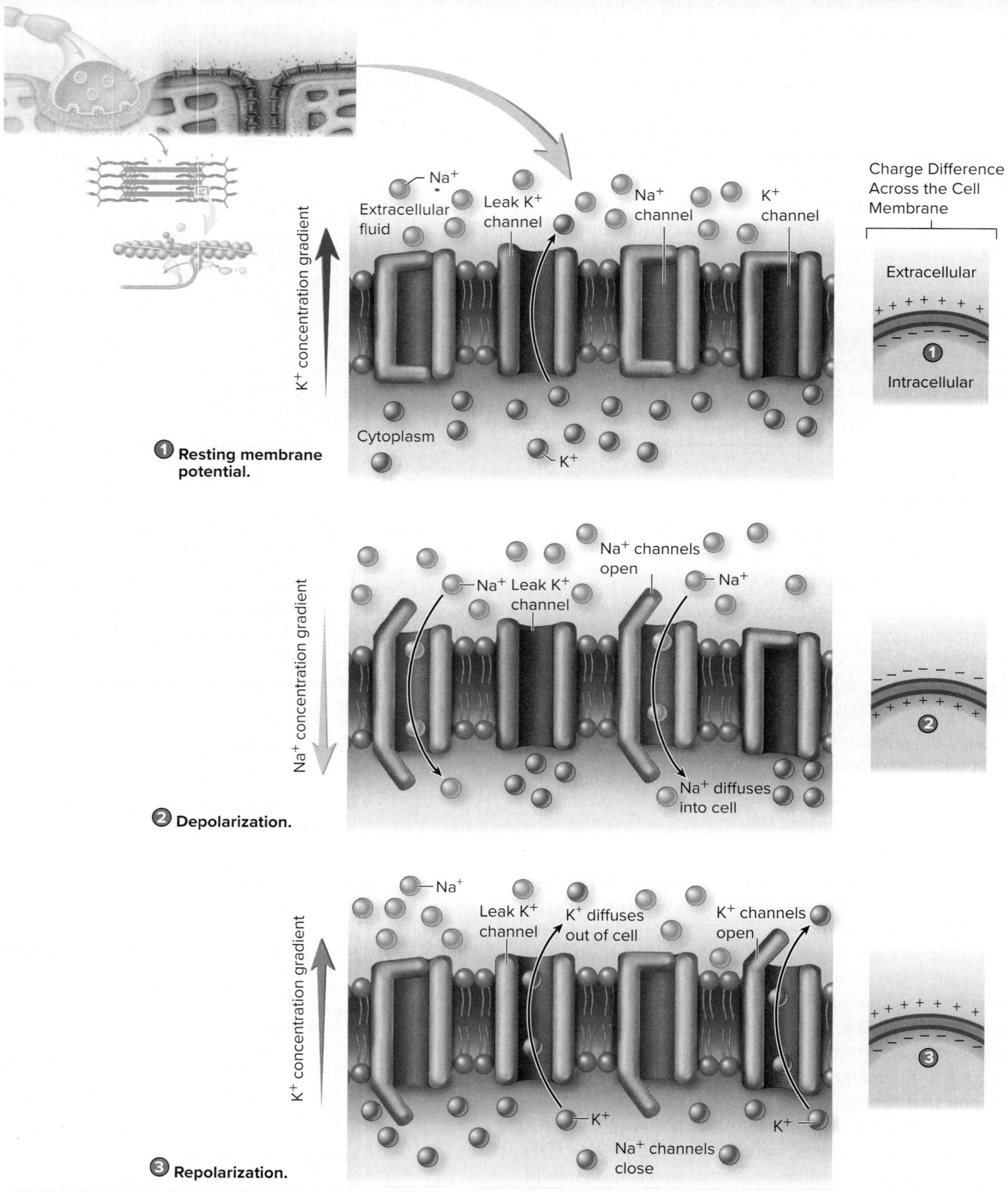

Na+
Extracellular fluid
Leak K+ channel
Na+ channel
K+ channel
Charge Difference Across the Cell Membrane
Extracellular
Intracellular
K+ concentration gradient
Cytoplasm
K+

1 **Resting membrane potential.**

Na+ channels open
Na+
Leak K+ channel
Na+ concentration gradient
Na+ diffuses into cell

2 **Depolarization.**

Na+
Leak K+ channel
K+ diffuses out of cell
K+ channels open
K+ concentration gradient
K+
Na+ channels close

3 **Repolarization.**

PROCESS **Figure 9.9**

Voltage-Gated Ion Channels and the Action Potential

Step 1 illustrates the status of voltage-gated Na^+ and K^+ channels in a resting cell. Steps 2 and 3 show how the channels open and close to produce an action potential. At the far right, the charge difference across the plasma membrane at each stage is illustrated.

What type of transport mechanism is demonstrated by Na^+ movement through the open voltage-gated Na^+ channels? APR

responsible for an action potential proceed without stopping. Consequently, all of the action potentials in a given cell are alike (the "all" part). If a stimulus is so weak that the depolarization does not reach threshold, few of the permeability changes occur. The membrane potential returns to its resting level after a brief period without producing an action potential (the "none" part). An action potential can be compared to the starter in a car. Once the ignition switch is pressed (reaches threshold), the car starts (an action potential is produced), and each time, the engine runs the same as the previous time the car started (the "all" part). If the ignition switch is pressed but not fully (does not reach threshold), the car does not start (the "none" part). Figure 9.10 summarizes the events in an action potential along the sarcolemma.

1. Before initiation of an action potential, the muscle fiber is in its resting membrane potential.
2. Depolarization occurs upon opening of voltage-gated Na^+ channels.
3. Repolarization occurs when the Na^+ channels close and the voltage-gated K^+ channels open.
4. A period of hyperpolarization, also called the after-potential, occurs because the voltage-gated K^+ channels stay open longer than required to reach resting membrane potential. The Na^+-K^+ pump restores the resting ion balance.

Action potentials occur in one area of the plasma membrane and then travel, or **propagate,** along the plasma membrane. An action potential produced at one location in the plasma membrane stimulates the production of an action potential in the neighboring section of plasma membrane (figure 9.11).

1. An action potential in a local area of the plasma membrane is indicated by the *green band*. Note the reversal of charge across the plasma membrane.
2. The depolarization of the membrane in one action potential location triggers the opening of nearby voltage-gated Na+ channels.
3. The action potential propagates along the plasma membrane (*green arrow*).

Note that a single action potential does not actually move along the plasma membrane. Rather, an action potential at one location stimulates the production of a second action potential in an adjacent location, which in turn stimulates the production of another, and so on. It is like a long row of dominoes in which each domino knocks down the next. Each domino falls, but no single domino actually travels the length of the row.

If all action potentials are identical, how does the brain distinguish between a strong stimulus, such as a loud noise, and a weaker stimulus, such as a quiet noise? A stronger stimulus causes more action potentials to be sent. This is called the **action potential frequency.**

The action potential frequency is the number of action potentials produced in a certain amount (usually per second) of time. As the strength of the stimulus applied to a neuron or a muscle fiber increases, the number of action potentials fired increases. The action potential frequency can affect the strength of a muscle contraction (see section 9.5).

In summary, the resting membrane potential results from a charge difference across the plasma membrane. An action potential, which is a reversal of that charge difference, stimulates cells to respond. The nervous system controls muscle contractions by sending action potentials along axons, which then cause action potentials in the muscle fibers. An increased frequency of action potentials sent to the muscle fibers can result in stronger muscle contraction. Next, we consider the specific communication between a motor neuron and the skeletal muscle fiber.

ASSESS YOUR PROGRESS

22. *List the two types of voltage-gated channels that play important roles in the production of action potentials.*
23. *What value must depolarization reach in an electrical cell to trigger an action potential?*
24. *Describe the changes that occur during the depolarization and repolarization phases of an action potential.*
25. *Describe the propagation of an action potential.*
26. *How does the frequency of action potentials affect muscle contractions?*

The Function of the Neuromuscular Junction

Recall that each muscle fiber is innervated by a branch of a motor neuron at the neuromuscular junction. This point of contact between the axon terminal and the sarcolemma results in an action potential in the muscle fiber. The primary stimulus for this action potential is the release of acetylcholine from the motor neuron.

Figure 9.12 outlines the steps that occur at the neuromuscular junction to generate muscle contraction.

1. When an action potential reaches the presynaptic terminal of a motor neuron, it causes voltage-gated calcium ion (Ca^{2+}) channels in the plasma membrane of the axon to open; as a result, Ca^{2+} diffuses into the axon terminal.
2. Once inside the cell, the Ca^{2+} causes a few synaptic vesicles to migrate to the presynaptic terminal, where they fuse with the plasma membrane.
3. The acetylcholine molecules are released from the synaptic vesicles.
4. The acetylcholine molecules diffuse across the synaptic cleft and bind to ligand-gated Na^+ channels in the motor end-plate, causing them to open.
5. Sodium ions then diffuse into the muscle fiber, causing depolarization. In skeletal muscle, each action potential in the motor neuron causes a depolarization in the muscle fiber that exceeds threshold. This will produce an action potential in the muscle fiber.
6. Next, acetylcholine detaches from the ligand-gated Na^+ channels, which then close.

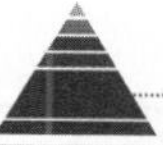

Predict 2

Predict the consequence if presynaptic action potentials in an axon release insufficient acetylcholine to depolarize a skeletal muscle fiber to threshold.

7. The enzyme **acetylcholinesterase** (AS-eh-til-KOH-leen-ESS-ter-ase) rapidly breaks down acetylcholine in the synaptic cleft into acetic acid and choline. Acetylcholinesterase keeps acetylcholine from accumulating within the synaptic cleft, where it would act as a constant stimulus at the motor end-plate, producing continuous contraction in the muscle fiber. The release of acetylcholine and its rapid degradation in the synaptic cleft ensure that one presynaptic action potential yields only one action potential at the motor end-plate.

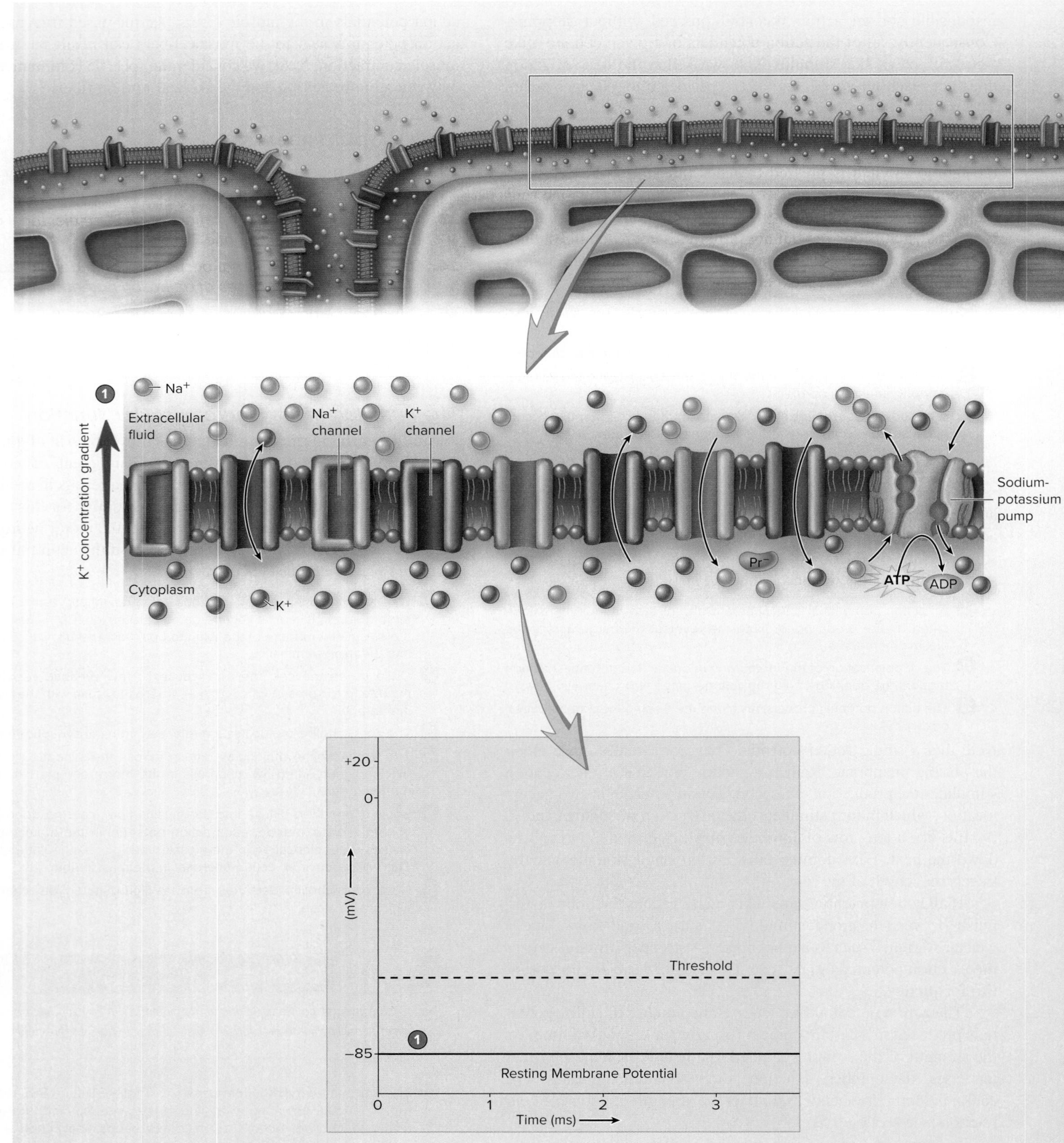

FIGURE 9.10 Summary of Action Potential Generation

The plasma membrane of a skeletal muscle fiber is at rest before it receives a stimulus to contract. During the resting membrane potential, the gated channels are closed and the Na^+–K^+ pump helps maintain the uneven distribution of ions across the plasma membrane. When an action potential arrives at the neuromuscular junction, voltage-gated Na^+ channels are stimulated to open, which depolarizes the muscle fiber to about +20 mV. At this point, voltage-gated K^+ channels open and the membrane potential returns to the resting membrane potential after initially becoming even more negative. This cycle is repeated along the sarcolemma and eventually results in contraction of the muscle.

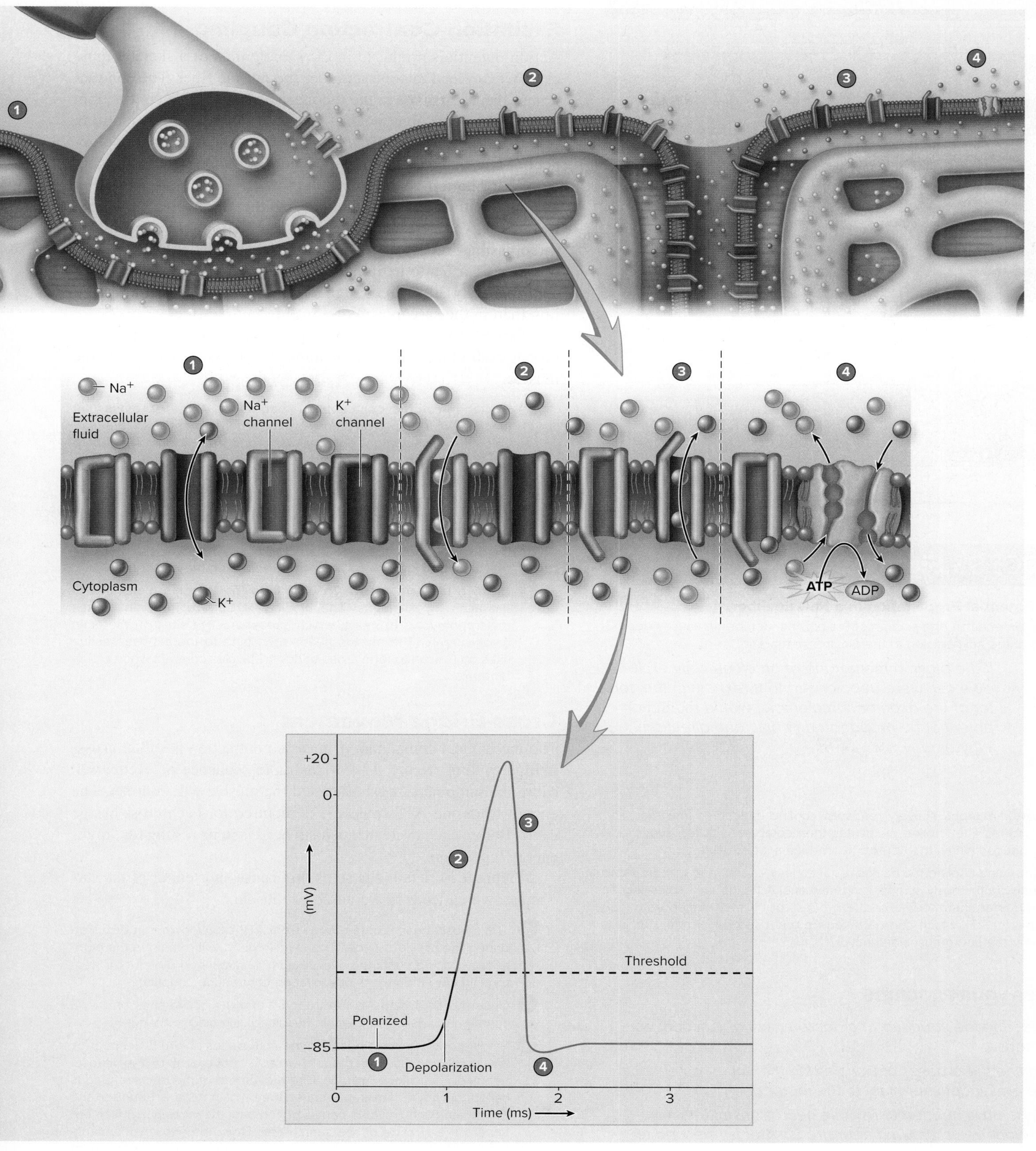
1
2
3
4
Na+
Extracellular fluid
Na+ channel
K+ channel
Cytoplasm
K+
ATP
ADP
+20
0
–85
(mV)
Threshold
Polarized
Depolarization
0
1
2
3
Time (ms)

PROCESS Figure

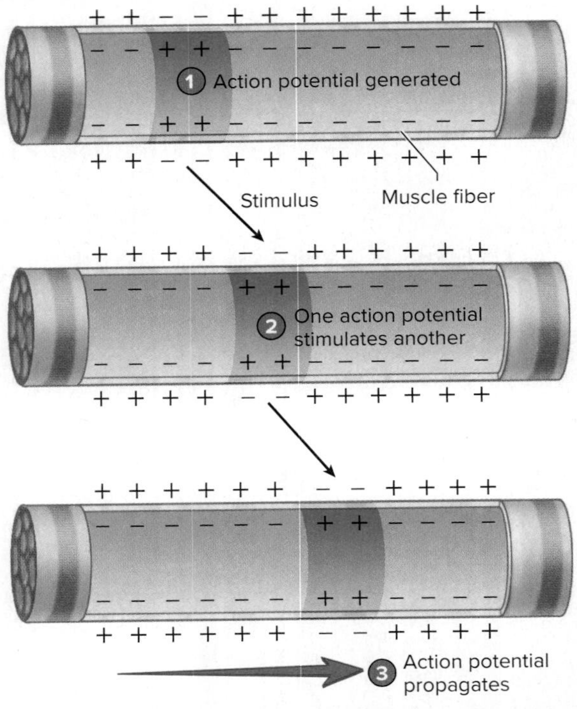

PROCESS Figure 9.11

Action Potential Propagation in a Muscle Fiber.

An action potential in one section of the plasma membrane causes depolarization of the next section of the plasma membrane.

If the plasma membrane of an electrically excitable cell were depolarized to threshold in the center of the axon or sarcolemma, would the action potential be propagated in only one direction? Why or why not? APR

8. Motor neurons actively reabsorb choline molecules into the axon terminal. The choline molecules then combine with the acetic acid produced within the neuron to produce acetylcholine.
9. Recycling choline molecules requires less energy and is more rapid than continuously synthesizing new acetylcholine molecules. Acetic acid is an intermediate in the process of glucose metabolism (see chapter 25), which can be taken up and used by a variety of cells near the neuromuscular junction.

ASSESS YOUR PROGRESS

27. *Describe the structure of a neuromuscular junction, or synapse.*
28. *Outline the process of transferring the action potential in the presynaptic terminal to the motor end-plate.*
29. *What ion is needed to release neurotransmitters from the synaptic vesicle? What neurotransmitter is released to skeletal muscle fibers?*
30. *What is the importance of acetylcholinesterase in the synaptic cleft? What would occur if acetylcholinesterase were not present?*

Excitation-Contraction Coupling

Action potentials produced in the sarcolemma of a skeletal muscle fiber can lead to contraction of the muscle fiber. The contraction of the fiber is due to the second aspect of muscle contraction, the mechanical component. Excitation-contraction coupling occurs at the triad (see figure 9.3). It links the electrical component of muscle contraction to the mechanical component. In other words, excitation-contraction coupling is the link between an action potential on the sarcolemma and the sarcomere shortening. Recall that Ca^{2+}, which is key for contraction, is stored in the sarcoplasmic reticulum. The sarcoplasmic reticulum actively transports Ca^{2+} into its lumen; thus, the concentration of Ca^{2+} is approximately 2000 times higher within the sarcoplasmic reticulum than in the sarcoplasm of a resting muscle fiber.

Figure 9.13 explains the steps linking an action potential propagated along the sarcolemma to the shortening of the muscle.

1. Excitation-contraction coupling begins at the neuromuscular junction with the production of an action potential in the sarcolemma. The action potential is propagated along the entire sarcolemma of the muscle fiber and into the T tubules. The T tubules wrap around sarcomeres, where actin and myosin overlap and carry action potentials into the interior of the muscle fiber.
2. There, the action potentials cause voltage-gated Ca^{2+} channels in the terminal cisternae of the sarcoplasmic reticulum to open. When the Ca^{2+} channels open, Ca^{2+} rapidly diffuses out of the sarcoplasmic reticulum and into the sarcoplasm surrounding the myofibrils.
3. Once in the sarcoplasm, Ca^{2+} binds to the troponin molecules of the actin myofilaments. The binding of Ca^{2+} to troponin causes the tropomyosin to move, which exposes active sites on the actin myofilaments. The myosin heads then bind to the exposed active sites on G actin to form cross-bridges. Muscles contract when cross-bridges move.

Cross-Bridge Movement

The mechanical component of muscle contraction is called **cross-bridge cycling** (figure 9.14). This rapid sequence of events will cause the sarcomeres to shorten and the muscle will contract. The energy from one ATP molecule is required for each cross-bridge cycle. Before each cycle, the myosin head is in its resting (or "high-energy") position.

Figure 9.14 details the steps that cause shortening of the sarcomere, which leads to a contracted muscle.

1. The myosin head stores energy from ATP breakdown that occurred during the previous cycle. The myosin head will remain in the high-energy position until the muscle fiber is stimulated by a motor neuron initiating the events of excitation-contraction coupling.
2. Once the Ca^{2+} binds to the troponin and the active sites on the G actin are exposed, the myosin heads quickly bind to them.
3. Binding of the myosin heads to the active sites on the G actin forms the cross-bridges and triggers a rapid movement of the myosin heads at their hinged region. The movement of the myosin head is called the **power stroke.** Because the myosin head is bound to the G actin, the actin myofilament is pulled past the myosin myofilament toward the H zone of the sarcomere. Thus, the two myofilaments are "sliding" past each other. However, the myosin myofilament doesn't move; it is the actin myofilament that moves. Compare the myosin head to the wire of a traditional mouse trap. Which position of the myosin head would be equivalent to a mouse trap that has been set?

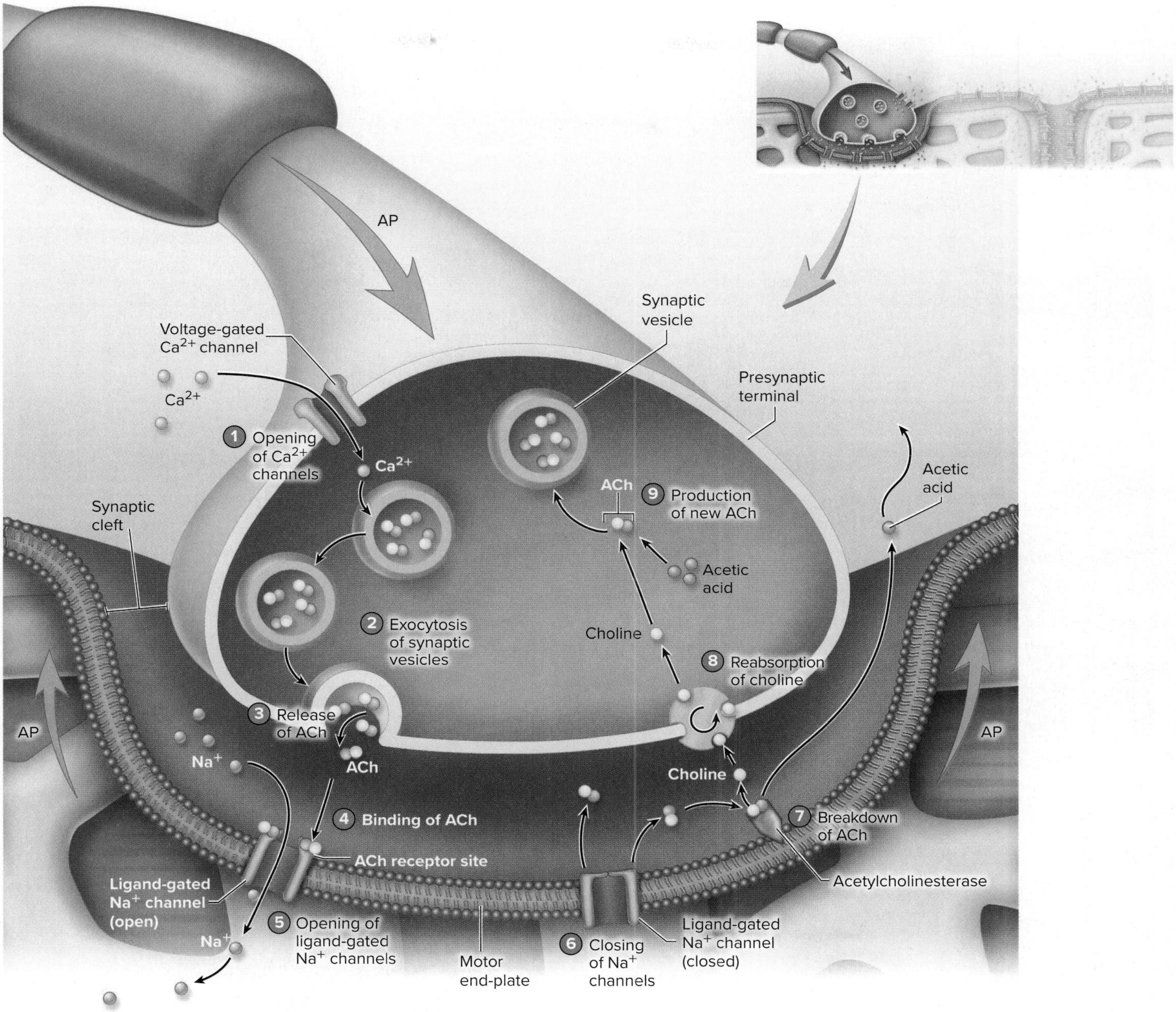

AP
Voltage-gated Ca^{2+} channel
Ca^{2+}
1 Opening of Ca^{2+} channels
Ca^{2+}
Synaptic cleft
Synaptic vesicle
Presynaptic terminal
ACh
9 Production of new ACh
Acetic acid
Acetic acid
Choline
2 Exocytosis of synaptic vesicles
8 Reabsorption of choline
3 Release of ACh
AP
AP
Na^+
ACh
Choline
4 Binding of ACh
7 Breakdown of ACh
ACh receptor site
Acetylcholinesterase
Ligand-gated Na^+ channel (open)
Na^+
5 Opening of ligand-gated Na^+ channels
Motor end-plate
6 Closing of Na^+ channels
Ligand-gated Na^+ channel (closed)

PROCESS **Figure 9.12**

Function of the Neuromuscular Junction

In the autoimmune disorder myasthenia gravis, antibodies are formed against acetylcholine receptors, reducing the number of receptors in the neuromuscular junction. How would prescribing a medication that is an acetylcholinesterase inhibitor help?

PROCESS **Figure**

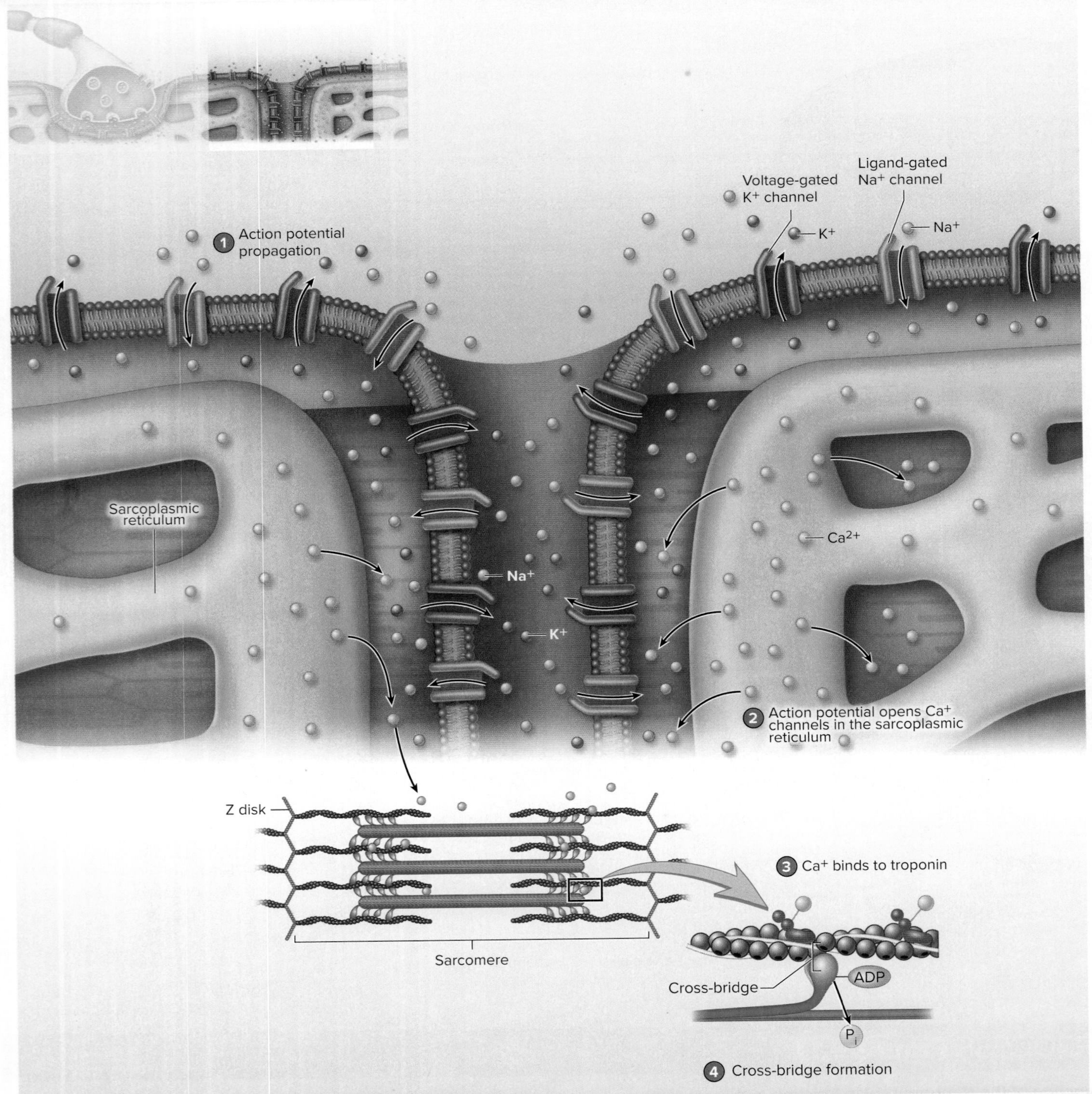

PROCESS **Figure 9.13**

Action Potentials and Muscle Contraction

Action potentials are propagated down the T tubules and stimulate Ca^{2+} release from the sarcoplasmic reticulum.

Apply *Recently, it has been observed that several muscle diseases and disorders are linked to problems with triad structure and function. One such disorder is called malignant hyperthermia, a dire hypermetabolic response to certain inhaled anesthetics such as halothane. Muscles become very rigid due to excessive contraction (especially the masseter muscle), the body temperature spikes, and muscles break down. Death is certain if not treated. Given the principal symptoms of malignant hyperthermia, what is its likely cause? Propose a theoretical mechanism for a treatment that would dampen the deleterious effects of this disorder.* APR

PROCESS Figure

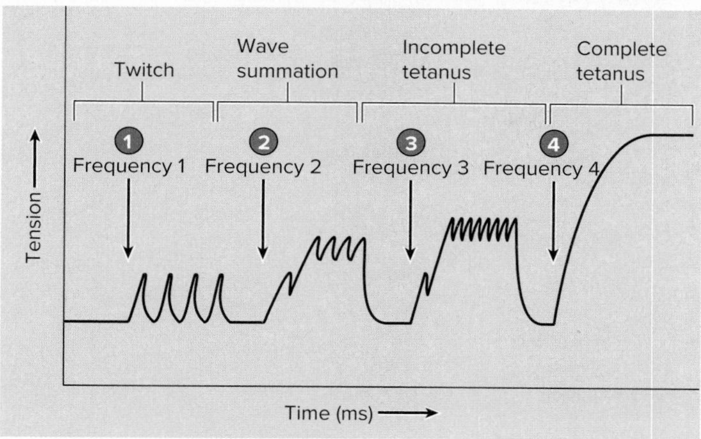

PROCESS Figure 9.20

Wave Summation

Stimuli 1–4 increase in frequency. For each stimulus, the arrow indicates the start of stimulation. As the frequency of the stimuli increase, the muscle fiber eventually does not relax at all and the muscle fiber contracts continuously in complete tetanus

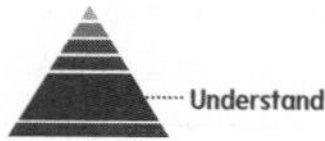

What characteristic of the skeletal muscle fiber action potential makes it possible for skeletal muscle fibers to exhibit wave summation and consequently complete tetanus?

cross-bridges and so the muscle fiber is unable to relax between twitches. The twitches merge together more and more (incomplete tetanus, figure 9.20, *frequency 2*) until the muscle fiber stays completely contracted with no relaxation (complete tetanus, figure 9.20, *frequency 4*).

A significant factor in wave summation is the fact that the sarcoplasm and the connective tissue components of muscle have some elasticity. During each separate muscle twitch, some of the tension produced by the contracting muscle fibers is used to stretch those elastic elements, and the remaining tension is applied to the load to be lifted. In a single muscle twitch, relaxation begins before the elastic components are totally stretched. The maximum tension produced during a single muscle twitch is therefore not applied to the load to be lifted. However, in a muscle stimulated at a high frequency, the elastic elements stretch during the very early part of the prolonged contraction. After that, all the tension produced by the muscle is applied to the load to be lifted, and the observed tension produced by the muscle increases.

Muscle Fiber Diameter

The greater the muscle fiber diameter, the greater the force the muscle fiber can generate. In general, larger diameter fibers have more myofibrils than smaller diameter muscle fibers and thus have a greater number of cross-bridges that can be formed. This is the same idea we've already discussed: If more people work together, a heavier object can be lifted than what a single person can lift. The more cross-bridges that get formed, the more force a muscle can generate.

Muscle Fiber Length at the Time of Contraction

The initial length of a muscle fiber has a strong influence on the amount of tension it produces. The force applied to an object to be lifted when a muscle contracts is called **active tension.** As the length of a muscle fiber increases, its active tension also increases, to a point. If the muscle fiber stretches farther than its optimum length, the active tension it produces begins to decline. The muscle fiber length plotted against the tension produced by the muscle fiber in response to maximal stimuli is the **active tension curve** (figure 9.21).

If a muscle fiber stretches so that the actin and myosin myofilaments within the sarcomeres do not overlap—or overlap to a

Case STUDY 9.1 | Organophosphate Poisoning

John has a number of prize apple trees in his backyard. To prevent them from becoming infested with insects, he sprayed them with an organophosphate insecticide. Being in a rush to spray the trees before leaving town on vacation, he failed to pay attention to the safety precautions on the packaging and sprayed the trees without using any skin or respiratory protection. Soon he experienced severe stomach cramps, double vision, difficulty breathing, and spastic contractions of his skeletal muscles. John's wife took him to the emergency room, where he was diagnosed with organophosphate poisoning and given medication. Soon many of John's symptoms subsided.

Organophosphate insecticides exert their effects by binding to the enzyme acetylcholinesterase within synaptic clefts, rendering it ineffective. Thus, the organophosphate poison and acetylcholine "compete" for the acetylcholinesterase and, as the organophosphate poison increases in concentration, the enzyme is less effective in degrading acetylcholine. Organophosphate poisons affect synapses in which acetylcholine is the neurotransmitter, including skeletal muscle synapses and smooth muscle synapses, such as those in the walls of the stomach, intestines, and air passageways.

Predict 4

Organophosphate insecticides exert their effects by binding to the enzyme acetylcholinesterase within synaptic clefts, rendering it ineffective. Use figures 9.12 and 9.20 to help answer the following questions.

a. Explain the spastic contractions that occurred in John's skeletal muscles.

b. Propose as many mechanisms as you can by which a drug could counteract the effects of organophosphate poisoning.

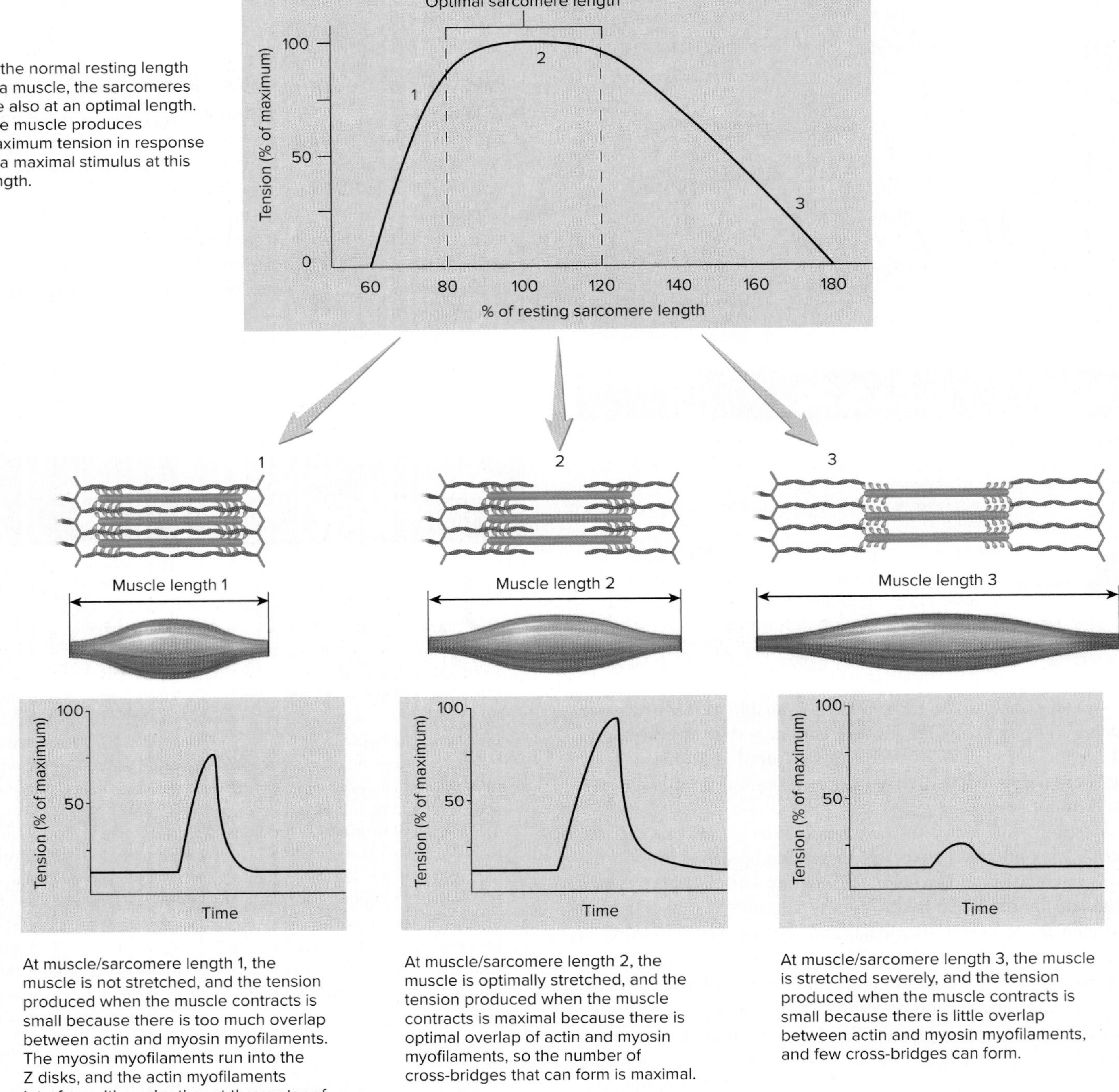

FIGURE 9.21 Muscle Length and Tension
The length of a muscle before it is stimulated influences the muscle's force of contraction. As the muscle changes length, the sarcomeres also change length.

very small extent—the muscle fiber produces very little active tension when it is stimulated. Also, if the muscle fiber does not stretch at all, the myosin myofilaments touch each of the Z disks in each sarcomere, and very little contraction of the sarcomeres can occur. If the muscle fiber stretches to its optimum length, optimal overlap of the actin and myosin myofilaments takes place. When the muscle fiber is stimulated, cross-bridge formation results in maximal contraction.

This relationship between muscle fiber length and tension can also be applied to a whole muscle. For example, before lifting heavy objects, weight lifters and others usually assume positions in which their muscles are stretched close to their optimum length. Consider the position a weight lifter assumes before power lifting. The weight lifter's position stretches the upper limb and lower limb muscles to a near-optimum length for muscle contraction. Before the ball is snapped, a football lineman's stance stretches most muscle groups in the lower limbs so that they are near their optimum length for suddenly moving the body forward.

Passive tension is the tension applied to the load when a muscle stretches but is not stimulated. It is similar to the tension that would be produced if the muscle were replaced with an elastic band. Passive tension exists because the muscle and its connective tissue have some elasticity. The sum of active and passive tension is called **total tension.**

Force of Contraction in Whole Muscles

The increase in muscle force by individual muscle fibers is only about 5 times higher than that of a single twitch. However, muscles are capable of generating increased tension of at least 100,000 times that of a single twitch. Thus, increases in action potential frequency only account for a very small fraction of the force muscles can exert. Force generation is much more dependent on the total number of muscle fibers contracting together.

Recruitment

The nervous system regulates muscle force by increasing the number of contracting motor units. Recall that some motor units may contain hundreds of muscle fibers. An increase in the number of motor units contracting means many muscle fibers are contracting. This response to a stronger stimulus from the nervous system is called **multiple-motor-unit recruitment** (figure 9.22).

Multiple-motor-unit recruitment resulting in graded responses can be demonstrated by applying brief electrical stimuli of increasing strength to the nerve supplying a muscle (figure 9.22). Various results are possible, depending on the strength of the stimulus:

1. A **subthreshold stimulus** is not strong enough to cause an action potential in any of the axons in a nerve and does not cause a contraction.
2. As the stimulus strength increases, it eventually becomes a **threshold stimulus,** which is strong enough to produce an action potential in a single motor unit axon, causing all the muscle fibers of the motor unit to contract.
3. Progressively stronger stimuli, called **submaximal stimuli,** produce action potentials in axons of additional motor units.
4. A **maximal stimulus** produces action potentials in the axons of all the motor units of that muscle. Consequently, even greater stimulus strengths (called *supramaximal stimuli*) have no additional effect.

The Size Principle

Recall that motor units vary in the number of muscle fibers each contains. In general, small motor units (those with few muscle fibers) perform more delicate tasks and large motor units (those with many muscle fibers) perform more coarse tasks. During recruitment, small motor units are recruited first, followed by large motor units. This connection between the order of recruitment and the size of motor unit is called the **size principle.**

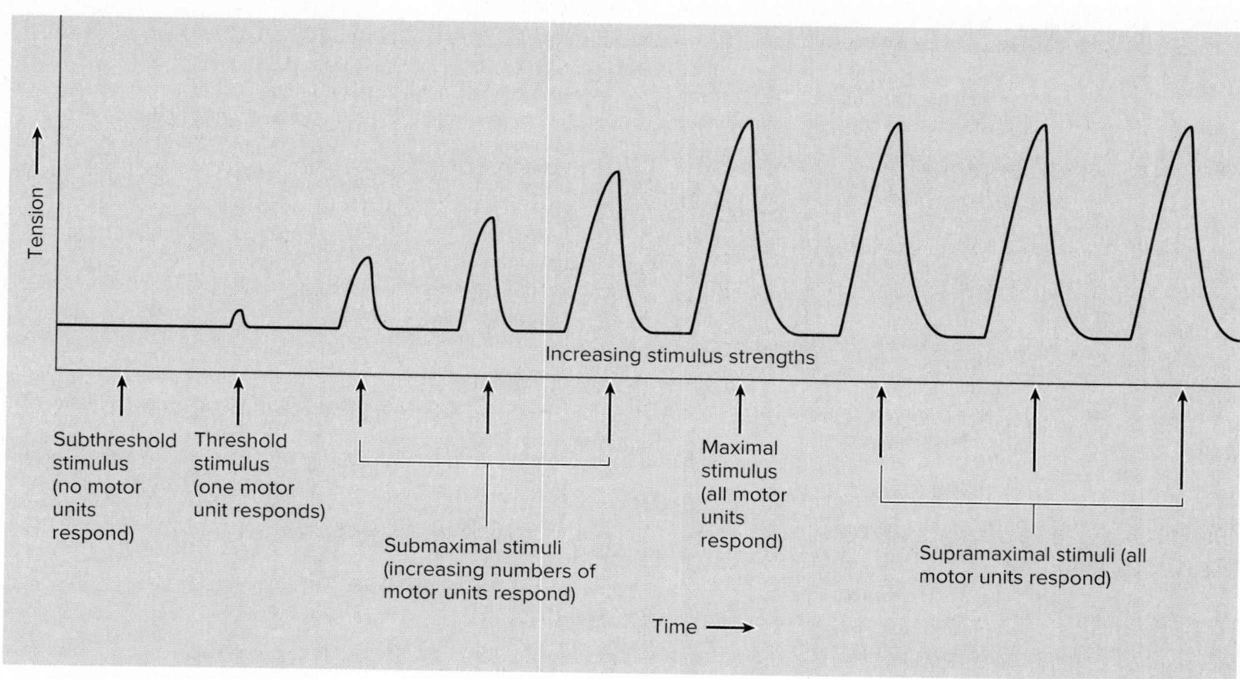

FIGURE 9.22 Multiple-Motor-Unit Recruitment in a Whole Muscle
Multiple-motor-unit recruitment occurs as stimuli of increasing strength are applied to a nerve that innervates a muscle. The amount of tension (height of peaks) is influenced by the number of motor units responding. Once all motor units respond, tension cannot increase any further.

There are also variations in motor unit recruitment when muscles stay contracted for long periods of time. This constant tension is called **muscle tone.** Muscle tone is responsible for keeping the back and lower limbs straight, the head upright, and the abdomen flat. Muscle tone depends on a small percentage of all the motor units contracting out of phase with one another at any point in time. The frequency of nerve impulses causes incomplete tetanus for short periods, but the contracting motor units are stimulated in such a way that the tension produced by the whole muscle remains constant.

Movements of the body are usually smooth and occur at widely differing rates—some very slowly and others quite rapidly. Very few body movements resemble the rapid contractions of individual muscle twitches. Rather, smooth, slow contractions result from an increasing number of motor units contracting out of phase as the muscles shorten, as well as from a decreasing number of motor units contracting out of phase as muscles lengthen. Each motor unit exhibits either incomplete or complete tetanus, but, because the contractions are out of phase and because the number of motor units activated varies at each point in time, a smooth contraction results. Consequently, muscles are capable of contracting either slowly or rapidly, depending on the number of motor units stimulated and the rate at which that number increases or decreases. A summary of physiological muscle responses is presented in table 9.3.

Types of Isotonic and Isometric Contractions

Concentric (kon-SEN-trik) **contractions** are isotonic contractions in which tension in the muscle is great enough to overcome the opposing resistance, and the muscle shortens. Concentric contractions result in an increasing tension as the muscle shortens. Many of the movements performed by muscles require concentric contractions—for example, lifting a loaded backpack from the floor to a table top. **Eccentric** (ek-SEN-trik) **contractions** are isotonic contractions in which tension is maintained in a muscle, but the opposing resistance is great enough to cause the muscle to increase in length. For example, eccentric contractions occur when a person slowly lowers a heavy weight. Eccentric contractions produce substantial force—in fact, eccentric contractions during exercise often produce greater tension than concentric contractions do. Eccentric contractions are of clinical interest because repetitive eccentric contractions, as occur in the lower limbs of people who run downhill for long distances, tend to injure muscle fibers and muscle connective tissue.

Predict 5

Mary overheard an argument between two students who could not decide if a weight lifter who lifts a weight above the head and then holds it there before lowering it is using isometric, concentric, or eccentric muscle contractions. Mary is an expert on muscle contractions, so she settles the debate. What is her explanation?

TABLE 9.3 Types of Physiological Muscle Responses

Physiological Response	Characteristics
Treppe	Tension produced increases for the first few contractions in response to a maximal stimulus at a *low frequency* in a muscle that has been at rest for some time. Increased tension may result from the accumulation of small amounts of Ca^{2+} in the sarcoplasm for the first few contractions or from an increasing rate of enzyme activity.
Wave summation	Summation results when many action potentials are produced in a muscle fiber. ■ Contraction occurs in response to the first action potential, but there is not enough time for relaxation to occur between action potentials. ■ Because each action potential causes the release of Ca^{2+} from the sarcoplasmic reticulum, the ion levels remain elevated in the sarcoplasm to produce a tetanic contraction. ■ The tension produced as a result of wave summation is greater than the tension produced by a single muscle twitch. The increased tension results from the greater concentration of Ca^{2+} in the sarcoplasm and the stretch of the elastic components of the muscle early in contraction.
Tetanus of muscles	Tetanus of muscles results from wave summation; frequency of stimulus is higher than for treppe. ■ Incomplete tetanus occurs when the action potential frequency is low enough to allow partial relaxation of the muscle fibers. ■ Complete tetanus occurs when the action potential frequency is high enough that no relaxation of the muscle fibers occurs.
Multiple-motor-unit recruitment	Each motor unit responds in an all-or-none fashion. A whole muscle is capable of producing an increasing amount of tension as the number of motor units stimulated increases.
Isometric contractions	A muscle produces increasing tension as it remains at a constant length; this is characteristic of postural muscles that maintain a constant tension without changing their length.
Isotonic contractions	A muscle produces a constant tension and shortens during contraction; this is characteristic of finger and hand movements. ■ In concentric contractions, a muscle produces tension as it shortens; this is characteristic of biceps brachii curl exercises. ■ In eccentric contractions, a muscle produces tension as it resists lengthening; this is characteristic of slowly descending a flight of stairs.

ASSESS YOUR PROGRESS

36. *What is a motor unit? Explain why the size of motor units can be different in different muscles.*
37. *What does it mean to say that a whole muscle responds to stimuli in a graded fashion? What are the two ways to increase the force of contraction?*
38. *What is treppe? Explain the physiological reason for it.*
39. *What is multiple-motor-unit recruitment? Explain the five possible results of multiple-motor-unit recruitment.*
40. *How does the lack of an unresponsive period in skeletal muscle fiber contraction explain wave summation? What is the relationship to incomplete tetanus and complete tetanus?*
41. *Distinguish between active tension and passive tension of a muscle.*
42. *Explain how the initial length of the muscle affects actin and myosin overlap, and therefore the amount of contraction that occurs.*
43. *Describe isometric, isotonic, concentric, and eccentric contractions, and give an example of each.*
44. *What is muscle tone, and how is it maintained?*

9.6 Muscle Fiber Types

LEARNING OUTCOMES

After reading this section, you should be able to

A. **Distinguish between fast-twitch and slow-twitch muscle fibers.**
B. **Explain the functions for which each type is best adapted.**
C. **Describe how training can increase the size and efficiency of both types of muscle fibers.**
D. **Explain how muscle metabolism causes normal body temperature.**
E. **Describe how muscles respond to changes from normal body temperature.**

There are two major types of skeletal muscle fibers: slow-twitch and fast-twitch. Not all skeletal muscles have identical functional capabilities. They differ in several respects, including the composition of their muscle fibers, which may contain slightly different forms of myosin. The form of myosin in slow-twitch muscle fibers causes the muscle fibers to contract more slowly and to be more resistant to fatigue, whereas the form of myosin in fast-twitch muscle fibers causes the muscle fibers to contract quickly and to fatigue quickly (table 9.4). The proportion of muscle fiber types differs within individual muscles.

Slow-Twitch Muscle Fibers

Slow-twitch muscle fibers (type I) contract more slowly, have a better-developed blood supply, have more mitochondria, and are more fatigue-resistant than fast-twitch muscle fibers. Slow-twitch muscle fibers respond relatively slowly to nervous stimulation. The enzymes on the myosin heads responsible for the breakdown of ATP are called **myosin ATPase.** Slow-twitch muscle fibers break down ATP slowly because their myosin heads have a slow form of myosin ATPase. The relatively slow breakdown of ATP means that cross-bridge movement occurs slowly, which causes the muscle to contract slowly. Aerobic respiration is the primary source for ATP synthesis in slow-twitch muscles, and their capacity to perform aerobic respiration is enhanced by a plentiful blood supply and the presence of numerous mitochondria. They are called oxidative muscle fibers because of their enhanced capacity to carry out aerobic respiration. Slow-twitch muscle fibers also contain large amounts of **myoglobin** (my-oh-GLOH-bin). Myoglobin is similar to hemoglobin, the protein that transports O_2 in red blood cells. Myoglobin binds O_2 in muscle fibers and serves as an O_2 reservoir during increased muscle activity. Myoglobin thus enhances the capacity of the muscle fibers to perform for a longer period of time. Because myoglobin is a dark-colored pigment, muscles with more myoglobin appear dark ("dark meat").

Fast-Twitch Muscle Fibers

Fast-twitch muscle fibers (type II) respond rapidly to nervous stimulation. Their myosin heads have a fast form of the enzyme myosin ATPase. The fast ATPase allows them to break down ATP

TABLE 9.4 Characteristics of Skeletal Muscle Fiber Types

Characteristic	Slow-Twitch Oxidative (SO) (Type I)	Fast-Twitch Oxidative Glycolytic (FOG) (Type IIa)	Fast-Twitch Glycolytic (FG) (Type IIx)
Myoglobin Content	High	High	Low
Mitochondria	Many	Many	Few
Capillaries	Many	Many	Few
Metabolism	High aerobic capacity, low anaerobic capacity	Intermediate aerobic capacity, high anaerobic capacity	Low aerobic capacity, highest anaerobic capacity
Fatigue Resistance	High	Intermediate	Low
Myosin ATPase Activity	Slow	Fast	Fast
Glycogen Concentration	Low	High	High
Location Where Fibers Are Most Abundant	Generally in postural muscles and more in lower limbs than upper limbs	Generally in lower limbs	Generally in upper limbs
Functions	Maintenance of posture and performance of endurance activities	Endurance activities in endurance-trained muscles	Rapid, intense movements of short duration

more rapidly than slow-twitch muscle fibers. This allows their cross-bridges to release and form more rapidly than those in slow-twitch muscle fibers. Muscles containing a high percentage of fast-twitch muscle fibers have a less-well-developed blood supply than muscles containing a high percentage of slow-twitch muscle fibers. In addition, fast-twitch muscle fibers have very little myoglobin and fewer and smaller mitochondria. Fast-twitch muscle fibers have large deposits of glycogen and are well adapted to perform anaerobic respiration. However, the anaerobic respiration of fast-twitch muscle fibers is not adapted for supplying a large amount of ATP for a prolonged period. The muscle fibers tend to contract rapidly for a shorter time and to fatigue relatively quickly. Fast-twitch muscle fibers come in three subtypes depending on the form of the myosin heavy chain that is expressed: type IIa, IIb, and IIx. Humans primarily have type IIx fibers, however some specialized muscles have been shown to have type IIb fibers. Type IIa have historically been referred to as fast-twitch oxidative glycolytic (FOG) muscle fibers, while type IIx have been called fast-twitch glycolytic (FG) muscle fibers (table 9.4). Type IIa muscle fibers rely on both anaerobic and aerobic ATP production, whereas type IIb/IIx muscle fibers rely almost exclusively on anaerobic glycolysis for ATP production.

Distribution of Fast-Twitch and Slow-Twitch Muscle Fibers

The muscles of many animals are composed primarily of either fast-twitch or slow-twitch muscle fibers. Muscles that consist mainly of fast-twitch muscle fibers will appear whitish. This is because this type of muscle has a relatively poor blood supply and very little of the dark-colored myoglobin. Chicken breast is an example of a muscle that has primarily fast-twitch muscle fibers. These muscles are adapted to contract rapidly for a short time, but will fatigue quickly. Chickens fly only very short distances.

However, muscles that consist mainly of slow-twitch muscle fibers are darker, or reddish, in color. These muscles have a well-developed blood supply and a large amount of myoglobin. Duck breast is an example of a muscle that has mainly slow-twitch muscle fibers. Muscles that have mostly slow-twitch muscle fibers are adapted to contract slowly for a long time and will fatigue very slowly. Ducks fly long distances when they migrate for the winter.

Human muscles exhibit no clear separation of slow-twitch and fast-twitch muscle fibers. Most muscles have both types of muscle fibers, although the number of each varies for each muscle. The large postural muscles of the back and lower limbs contain more slow-twitch muscle fibers, whereas the muscles of the upper limbs contain more fast-twitch muscle fibers.

The distribution of slow-twitch and fast-twitch muscle fibers in a given muscle is fairly constant for each individual and is established during early development. Sprinters have a greater percentage of fast-twitch muscle fibers, whereas long-distance runners have a higher percentage of slow-twitch muscle fibers in their lower limb muscles. Athletes who perform a variety of anaerobic and aerobic exercises tend to have a more balanced mixture of fast-twitch and slow-twitch muscle fibers.

Effects of Exercise

Neither fast-twitch nor slow-twitch muscle fibers can be easily converted to muscle fibers of the other type without specialized training. Training can increase the size and capacity of both types of muscle fibers so that they perform more efficiently. Intense exercise that requires anaerobic respiration, such as weight lifting, increases muscular strength and mass and causes fast-twitch muscle fibers to enlarge more than slow-twitch muscle fibers. Conversely, aerobic exercise increases the vascularity of muscle and causes slow-twitch muscle fibers to enlarge more. Aerobic exercise training can convert some fast-twitch muscle fibers that fatigue readily (type IIx) to fast-twitch muscle fibers that resist fatigue (type IIa). In addition to changes in myosin, increases occur in both the number of mitochondria in the muscle fibers and their blood supply. Weight training followed by periods of rest can convert some muscle fibers from type IIa to type IIx. Through specific training, a person with more fast-twitch muscle fibers can run long distances, and a person with more slow-twitch muscle fibers can increase the speed at which he or she runs.

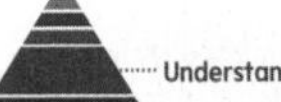

Predict 6

Susan recently began racing her bicycle. Her training consists entirely of long rides at a steady pace. When she entered her first race, she was excited that she was able to keep pace with the rest of the riders. However, during the final sprint to the finish line, the other riders left her in their dust, and she finished in last place. Why was she unable to keep pace during the finishing sprint? As her coach, what advice would you give Susan about training for her next race?

In response to exercise, a muscle increases in size, or hypertrophies (high-PER-troh-fees), and increases in strength and endurance. Conversely, a muscle that is not used decreases in size, or atrophies (AT-roh-fees). For example, muscular atrophy occurs in an arm or a leg that is placed in a cast for several weeks. Because muscle fiber numbers do not change appreciably during most of a person's life, atrophy and hypertrophy result from changes in the size of individual muscle fibers. As a muscle fiber increases in size, the number of myofibrils and sarcomeres increases. The number of nuclei in each muscle fiber increases in response to exercise, but the nuclei of muscle fibers cannot divide. New nuclei are added to muscle fibers because small satellite cells near skeletal muscle fibers increase in number in response to exercise and then fuse with the skeletal muscle fibers. Other elements, such as blood vessels, connective tissue, and mitochondria, also increase in number. Atrophy due to lack of exercise results from a decrease in all these elements without a decrease in muscle fiber number. However, severe atrophy, as occurs in older people who cannot readily move their limbs, does involve an irreversible decrease in the number of muscle fibers and can lead to paralysis.

There are two reasons athletic training increases muscle strength: (1) increased muscle size and (2) an increase in the number of motor units recruited simultaneously by the nervous system. In addition, trained muscles are usually less restricted by excess adipose tissue. Metabolic enzymes increase in hypertrophied muscle fibers, resulting in a greater capacity to take in nutrients and produce ATP. Improved endurance in trained muscles is in part due to improved metabolism, increased circulation to the exercising muscles, increased numbers of capillaries, more efficient respiration, and a greater capacity of the heart to pump blood.

ASSESS YOUR PROGRESS

45. *Contrast the structural and physiological differences between slow-twitch and fast-twitch muscle fibers.*
46. *Explain the functions for which each type of muscle fiber is best adapted and how slow-twitch and fast-twitch muscle fibers are distributed.*
47. *How does anaerobic versus aerobic exercise affect muscles?*
48. *What factors contribute to increases in muscle size, strength, and endurance?*

Heat Production

The rate of metabolism in skeletal muscle differs before, during, and after exercise. As chemical reactions occur within cells, some energy is released in the form of heat. Normal body temperature results primarily from this heat. Because the rate of chemical reactions increases in muscle fibers during contraction, the rate of heat production also increases, causing a rise in body temperature. After exercise, increased metabolism resulting from recovery oxygen consumption helps keep the body temperature elevated, but sweating and vasodilation of blood vessels in the skin speed heat loss and keep body temperature within its normal range (see chapter 25).

When body temperature declines below a certain level, the nervous system responds by inducing shivering, rapid skeletal muscle contractions that produce shaking rather than coordinated movements. During shivering, the muscle movement increases heat production up to 18 times that of resting levels, and the heat produced can exceed the amount produced during moderate exercise. Thus, shivering helps raise body temperature to its normal range.

ASSESS YOUR PROGRESS

49. *How do muscles contribute to body temperature before, during, and after exercise?*
50. *What is accomplished by shivering?*

9.7 Energy Sources for Muscle Contraction

LEARNING OUTCOMES

After reading this section, you should be able to

A. **Describe four sources of energy for ATP production in muscles.**
B. **Distinguish between oxygen deficit and excess postexercise oxygen consumption.**
C. **Compare the mechanisms involved in the major types of muscle fatigue.**
D. **Contrast physiological contracture and rigor mortis.**

Skeletal muscle fibers have three major ATP-dependent enzymes: (1) the myosin head, (2) the Na^+–K^+ pump to maintain the resting membrane potential, and (3) the Ca^{2+} reuptake pump in the sarcoplasmic reticulum. You learned in section 9.4 that both skeletal muscle contraction and relaxation require ATP in order to take place. Muscle fibers store only enough ATP to contract for about 5–6 seconds. After that, muscle fibers must synthesize additional ATP very quickly, eventually producing one ATP at the same rate one ATP is used. Skeletal muscle fibers produce ATP through four processes:

1. Conversion of two ADP to one ATP and one adenosine monophosphate (AMP) by the enzyme adenylate kinase
2. Transfer of a phosphate from a molecule called creatine (KREE-a-teen) phosphate by the enzyme creatine kinase from ADP to form ATP
3. Anaerobic production of ATP during intensive short-term exercise
4. Aerobic production of ATP during most exercise and normal conditions

We will first describe the steps in each of the four ATP-producing pathways. Then, we will discuss the timeframe for each pathway: (1) immediately upon contraction, (2) when muscle contraction is short term, and (3) if the muscle contraction is continued for several hours.

Adenylate Kinase and Creatine Kinase

Muscle fibers have two enzymes that help quickly produce small amounts of ATP. The ATP produced by these enzymes is sufficient for an additional 15 seconds of contraction beyond the initial 5–6 seconds from stored ATP. These two enzymes are (1) adenylate kinase and (2) creatine kinase.

Adenylate Kinase

Adenylate kinase, or *myokinase,* transfers one phosphate from one ADP to a second ADP, resulting in one ATP and one AMP (figure 9.23*a*).

Creatine Kinase

During periods of rest, muscle fibers accumulate extra ATP. This extra ATP is utilized in muscle fibers to transfer a phosphate from the ATP to a small protein synthesized by muscle fibers called **creatine.** The transfer of the phosphate creates the molecule **creatine phosphate.** This molecule acts like a "bank" for "high-energy" phosphate. When ATP levels start to drop in a contracting muscle fiber, the enzyme **creatine kinase** will transfer a phosphate from creatine phosphate to ADP, immediately producing ATP (figure 9.23*b*).

Anaerobic Respiration

Anaerobic (an-uh-ROH-bik) **respiration** does not require O_2 and involves the breakdown of glucose to produce ATP and lactate. Anaerobic respiration produces only enough ATP to power muscle contractions for 30–40 seconds. It's important to note that exercise is not usually exclusively limited to one type of ATP production, such as anaerobic respiration. Later, we will discuss the blending of the four ATP production pathways under typical muscle contraction conditions. Anaerobic respiration produces far less ATP than other pathways, but can produce ATP in a matter of a few seconds. The

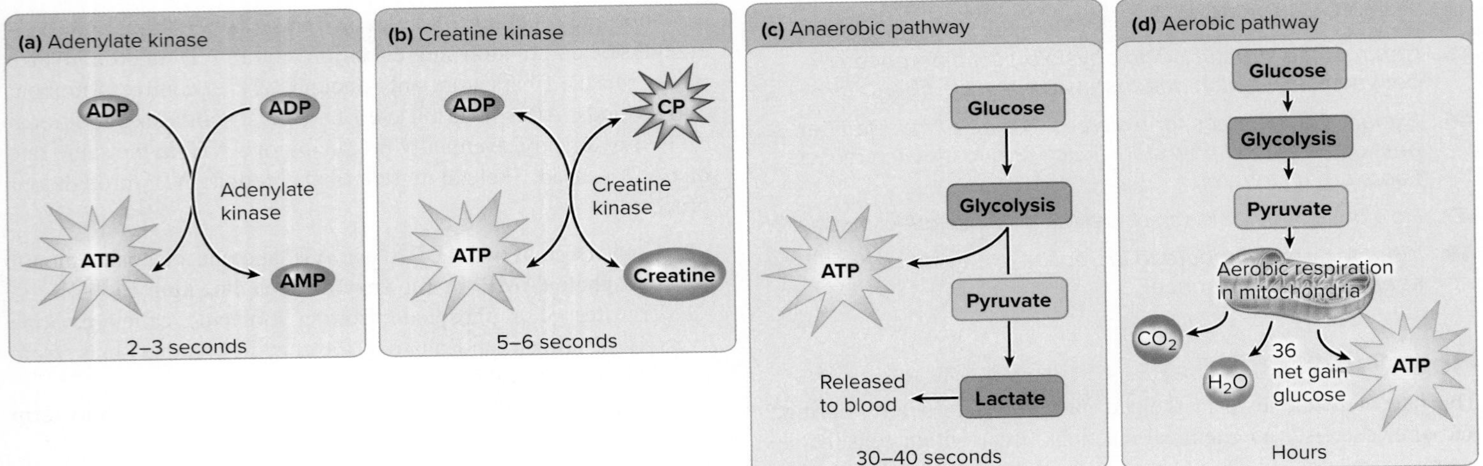

FIGURE 9.23 Production of ATP in Skeletal Muscle

There are four main pathways for ATP production in skeletal muscle. (*a*) Adenylate kinase quickly converts ADP to ATP. This produces only a few seconds of ATP. (*b*) Creatine kinase uses banked phosphate from creatine phosphate for immediate ATP, but is depleted within 5–6 seconds. (*c*) Anaerobic respiration is used for short-term, intense exercise and can provide up to an additional 40 seconds of ATP. (*d*) Aerobic respiration produces ATP for hours of exercise.

first step of anaerobic respiration is the enzymatic pathway, called **glycolysis** (glye-KOHL-ih-sis). In glycolysis, one glucose molecule is broken down into two molecules of **pyruvate,** producing a net gain of two ATP molecules. In anaerobic respiration, the pyruvate is then converted to a molecule called **lactate** (figure 9.23*c*).

Historically, ATP production in skeletal muscle was thought to be clearly delineated into purely aerobic activities versus purely anaerobic activities and that the product of anaerobic respiration was principally lactic acid. Lactic acid was considered to be a harmful waste product that must be removed from the body. However, it is now widely recognized that anaerobic respiration ultimately gives rise to lactic acid's alternate chemical form, the conjugate base lactate. Moreover, it is now known that lactate is a critical metabolic intermediate that is formed and used continuously even under fully aerobic conditions. Lactate is produced by skeletal muscle cells at all times, but particularly during exercise, and is subsequently broken down (65–70%) or used to make new glucose (30–35%). Thus, the aerobic and anaerobic mechanisms of ATP production are linked through lactate.

Aerobic Respiration

Aerobic (ai-ROH-bik) **respiration** requires O_2 and breaks down glucose to produce ATP, CO_2, and H_2O (figure 9.23*d*). Although glucose breakdown pathways produce the maximum number of ATP, lipids and amino acids as well as other nutrients can also be used to produce ATP. The ATP from aerobic respiration supplies 95% of the total ATP required by a cell and provides enough ATP for hours of muscle contraction as long as O_2 is readily available.

Aerobic respiration occurs mostly in the mitochondria and is much more efficient than anaerobic respiration. With aerobic respiration pathways, the breakdown of a single glucose molecule produces up to 36 ATP, 18 times more than anaerobic respiration.

The first step in aerobic respiration is also glycolysis. However, instead of converting the two pyruvate molecules into lactate as in anaerobic respiration, the two pyruvate molecules are transported into the mitochondria. There, pyruvate is processed through the **citric acid cycle,** followed by the **electron-transport chain.** The details of these two pathways are discussed in chapter 25. It is the electron-transport chain that produces the bulk of ATP for aerobic respiration and is the oxygen-dependent pathway of aerobic respiration.

ATP Production as Exercise Progresses

At the onset of exercise, the small ATP reserve in muscle fibers is quickly depleted. It is at this point that direct phosphorylation of ADP by adenylate kinase and creatine kinase occurs, but it is also rapidly depleted after about 15 seconds.

When a muscle fiber is working too strenuously for ATP stores and creatine phosphate to be able to provide enough ATP, anaerobic respiration predominates. Typically, the type II muscle fibers are the primary anaerobic muscle fibers. The type II muscle fibers break down glucose into the intermediate lactate, which can be shuttled to adjacent type I muscle fibers to make ATP or secreted into the blood for uptake by other tissues, such as the liver, to make new glucose. Thus, in skeletal muscle, the type II muscle fiber anaerobic pathways and the type I muscle fiber aerobic pathways are not mutually exclusive. Rather, they work together, with lactate being the product of the type II muscle fiber anaerobic pathways, which then serves as the starting point of the type I muscle fiber aerobic pathways.

Although aerobic respiration produces many more ATP molecules than anaerobic respiration does, the rate at which the ATP molecules are produced is slower. Resting muscles or muscles involved in long-term exercise, such as long-distance running or other endurance activities, use aerobic respiration for ATP synthesis. Aerobic respiration can provide enough ATP for hours of exercise. Table 9.5 provides a summary of ATP production in skeletal muscle.

TABLE 9.5 Sources of ATP in Skeletal Muscle

Pathway	Myokinase	Creatine Kinase	Anaerobic Respiration	Aerobic Respiration
Energy source	ADP	Creatine phosphate	Glucose	Glucose, fatty acids, amino acids
Oxygen required	No	No	No	Yes
ATP yield	1 per ADP	1 per creatine phosphate	2 per glucose molecule	Up to 36 per glucose molecule
Duration of energy supply	Up to 10 seconds	Up to 10 seconds	Up to 3 minutes	Hours
Type of work supported	Moderate exercise and extreme exercise	Moderate exercise and extreme exercise	Extreme exercise	Resting and all exercise

Understand

Predict 7

A condition called McArdle disease is due to a deficiency of an enzyme necessary for the breakdown of the stored form of glucose, called glycogen. Predict how the disease affects a person's ability to exercise.

Muscle Fatigue

Fatigue (fah-TEEG) is a temporary state of reduced work capacity. Without fatigue, muscle fibers would be worked to the point of structural damage to them and their supportive tissues. Historically, it was thought that buildup of lactate and the corresponding drop in pH (acidosis) was the major cause of fatigue. However, it is now established that there are multiple mechanisms underlying muscular fatigue:

1. Acidosis and ATP depletion due to either an increased ATP consumption or a decreased ATP production
2. Oxidative stress, which is characterized by the buildup of excess reactive oxygen species (ROS; free radicals)
3. Local inflammatory reactions

Acidosis and ATP Depletion

Anaerobic respiration results in the breakdown of glucose to lactate and protons accounting for lowered pH. Lowered pH has several cellular effects, including weak cross-bridge formation by interfering with Ca^{2+} binding to troponin and overall less Ca^{2+} release from the sarcoplasmic reticulum. Lactic acidosis can also result when liver dysfunction results in reduced clearance of lactate (such as using it to produce glucose). Usually, increased lactate levels are due to increased anaerobic respiration production of ATP when aerobic respiration production of ATP is reduced. Increases in lactate are also seen in patients with mitochondrial disorders and chronic obstructive pulmonary disease (COPD).

However, to what extent ATP reductions are responsible for muscular fatigue is still not clear. Recent studies have demonstrated that sarcoplasmic ATP levels stay relatively constant even in the face of decreasing muscle force production. But decreased ATP does cause fatigue. More specifically, it is the *localized* decreases in ATP levels or those associated with specific transport systems that are correlated with muscle fatigue.

Oxidative Stress

ROS are a natural by-product of metabolism and include molecules such as peroxides. They can result in damage to cells. During intense exercise, increases in ROS production cause the breakdown of proteins, lipids, or nucleic acids. In addition, ROS trigger an immune system chemical called interleukin-6 (IL-6). IL-6 is a mediator of inflammation, which is the most likely cause of muscle soreness.

Inflammation

In addition to the stimulation of IL-6 by ROS, which causes inflammation, the immune system is directly activated by exercise. T-lymphocytes, a type of white blood cell, migrate into heavily worked muscles. The presence of immune system intermediates increases the perception of pain, which most likely serves as a signal to protect those tissues from further damage.

An example of muscle fatigue occurs when a runner collapses on the track and must be helped off. The runner's muscle can no longer function, regardless of how determined the runner is. Under conditions of extreme muscular fatigue, muscle may become incapable of either contracting or relaxing. This condition, called **physiological contracture** (kon-TRAK-chur), occurs when there is too little ATP to bind to myosin myofilaments. Because binding of ATP to the myosin heads is necessary for cross-bridge release between the actin and myosin, the cross-bridges between the actin and myosin myofilaments cannot be broken, and the muscle cannot relax.

Rigor mortis (see figure 9.14), the development of rigid muscles several hours after death, is similar to physiological contracture. Recall that ATP is required for both muscle contraction and relaxation. In the absence of ATP, the myosin heads cannot release and muscles remain very rigid for hours.

The most common type of fatigue, **psychological fatigue,** involves the central nervous system rather than the muscles themselves. The muscles are still capable of contracting, but the individual "perceives" that continued muscle contraction is impossible. A determined burst of activity in a tired runner in response to pressure from a competitor is an example of how psychological fatigue can be overcome.

Although fatigue reduces power output, the overall benefit is that it prevents complete exhaustion of ATP reserves, which could otherwise lead to severe damage of the muscle fibers.

Muscle Soreness

Following vigorous exercise, people sometimes experience muscle pain, which can last for several days. The pain is more common in untrained people. In addition, highly repetitive eccentric muscle contractions produce pain more readily than concentric contractions do. The pain is related to inflammatory chemical influx into the muscle fibers. In people with exercise-induced muscle soreness, enzymes that are normally found inside muscle fibers can be detected in the extracellular fluid. These enzymes are able to leave the muscle fibers because injury has increased the permeability of plasma membranes, or has even ruptured them. Also found in the extracellular fluid of muscles are fragments of collagen, indicating that both muscle fibers and the connective tissue of muscles have been injured. Exercise schedules that alternate exercise with periods of rest, such as lifting weights every other day, provide time for the repair of muscle tissue.

ASSESS YOUR PROGRESS

51. *What is fatigue? List the three locations where fatigue can develop.*

52. *Describe what occurs to produce each type of fatigue.*

53. *Explain the causes of physiological contracture and rigor mortis.*

Oxygen Deficit and Excess Postexercise Oxygen Consumption

When a person exercises, there are two distinct phases of O_2 use: (1) at the onset of exercise or increase in exercise intensity, called the oxygen deficit, and (2) after exercise has ended, called excess post-exercise oxygen consumption. **Oxygen deficit** is the lag time between when a person begins to exercise and when he or she begins to breathe more heavily because of the exercise. **Excess postexercise oxygen consumption** is the lag time before breathing returns to its preexercise rate once exercise stops. These changes in breathing patterns reflect muscles' need for more oxygen to produce ATP through aerobic respiration. The oxygen deficit is the insufficient oxygen consumption relative to increased activity at the onset of exercise. This deficit must be repaid during and after exercise once oxygen consumption catches up with the increased activity level. At the onset of exercise, muscles primarily acquire the ATP they need from the creatine kinase and myokinase systems, as well as anaerobic respiration—three systems that can supply ATP relatively quickly and without requiring oxygen (table 9.5). The ability of aerobic respiration to supply ATP at the onset of exercise lags behind that of the creatine kinase system and anaerobic respiration. This explains the lag between the onset of exercise and the need for increased oxygen.

Excess postexercise oxygen consumption is the elevated oxygen consumption that occurs after exercise has ended. A small part of the excess postexercise oxygen is used to "repay" the oxygen deficit incurred at the onset of exercise, but most of the excess postexercise oxygen is used to support metabolic processes that restore homeostasis after it was disturbed during exercise. Such disturbances include exercise-related increases in body temperature, changes in intra- and extracellular ion concentrations, and changes in metabolite and hormone levels. Excess postexercise oxygen consumption generally lasts minutes to hours, depending on the individual's physical conditioning and on the length and intensity of the exercise session. In extreme cases, such as following a marathon, excess postexercise oxygen consumption can last as long as 15 hours.

Understand

Predict 8

Eric is a highly trained cross-country runner, and his brother John is a computer programmer who almost never exercises. While the two brothers were working on a remodeling project in the basement of their house, the doorbell rang upstairs: A package they were both very excited about was being delivered. They raced each other up the stairs to the front door to see who could get the package first. When they reached the door, both were breathing heavily. However, John continued to breathe heavily for several minutes while Eric was opening the package. Why did John breathe heavily longer than Eric, even though they had both run the same distance?

ASSESS YOUR PROGRESS

54. *List the energy sources used to synthesize ATP for muscle contraction.*

55. *What is the function of creatine phosphate, and when is it used?*

56. *Contrast the efficiency of anaerobic and aerobic respiration. When is each type used by cells?*

57. *When does lactate increase in a muscle fiber?*

58. *What is the difference between oxygen deficit and excess postexercise oxygen consumption? Explain the factors that contribute to an oxygen deficit.*

9.8 Smooth Muscle

LEARNING OUTCOMES

After reading this section, you should be able to

A. **Describe the structural features of smooth muscle cells and contrast them with skeletal muscle fibers.**
B. **Explain the steps of smooth muscle contraction.**
C. **Explain how smooth muscle contraction differs from skeletal muscle contraction.**
D. **Compare the two types of smooth muscle as to their action and locations.**
E. **Describe the electrical and functional properties of smooth muscle.**
F. **Explain how smooth muscle activities are regulated.**

Smooth muscle is distributed widely throughout the body and is more variable in function than other muscle types. Smooth muscle cells (figure 9.24) are smaller than skeletal muscle fibers, ranging from 15 to 200 μm in length and from 5 to 8 μm in diameter. They are spindle-shaped, with a single nucleus in the middle

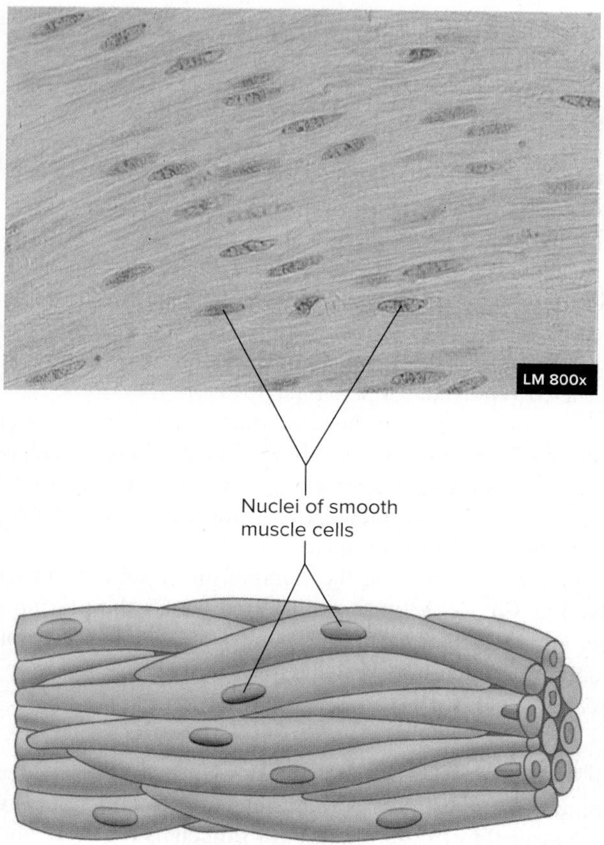

FIGURE 9.24 Smooth Muscle Histology
Smooth muscle tissue is made up of sheets or bundles of spindle-shaped cells, with a single nucleus in the middle of each cell. ©Victor Eroschenko APR

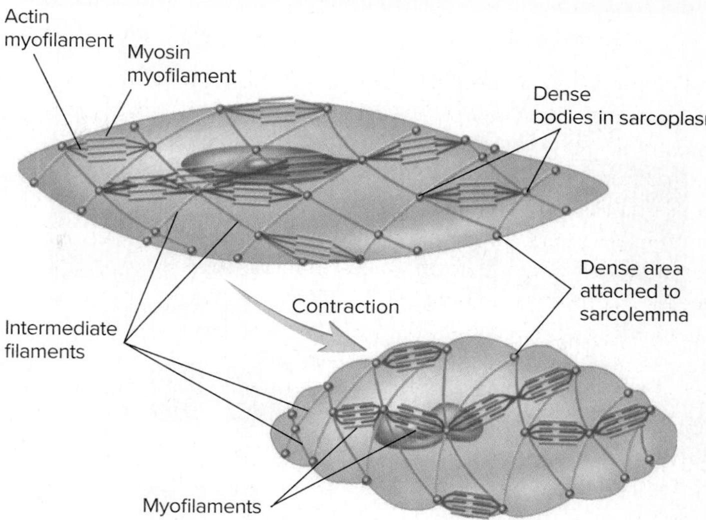

FIGURE 9.25 Actin and Myosin Proteins in a Smooth Muscle Cell
Bundles of contractile myofilaments containing actin and myosin are anchored at one end to dense areas in the plasma membrane and at the other end, through dense bodies, to intermediate filaments. The contractile myofilaments are oriented with the long axis of the cell; when actin and myosin slide over one another during contraction, the cell shortens.

of the cell. Compared with skeletal muscle, fewer total myofilaments are present, but, in smooth muscle, there are more actin than myosin myofilaments. The actin and myosin myofilaments overlap, but they are organized as loose bundles instead of sarcomeres. Consequently, smooth muscle does not have a striated appearance. Actin myofilaments are attached to structures called **dense bodies,** which are scattered through the muscle fiber sarcoplasm, and to **dense areas,** which are in the plasma membrane. Dense bodies and dense areas are considered equivalent to the Z disks in skeletal muscle. Noncontractile **intermediate filaments** also attach to the dense bodies. The intermediate filaments and dense bodies form an intracellular cytoskeleton, which has a longitudinal or spiral organization. The smooth muscle cells shorten when the actin and myosin slide over one another during contraction (figure 9.25).

Sarcoplasmic reticulum is present in smooth muscle cells, but no T tubule system exists. Some shallow, invaginated areas called **caveolae** (kav-ee-OH-lee) lie along the surface of the plasma membrane. The function of caveolae is not well known, but it may be similar to that of both the T tubules and the sarcoplasmic reticulum of skeletal muscle.

Other differences exist between smooth muscle and skeletal muscle. In particular, smooth muscle has a slower contraction speed than skeletal muscle. This difference is due to several factors. In smooth muscle, some of the Ca^{2+} required to initiate contractions enters the cell from the extracellular fluid and from the sarcoplasmic reticulum. Therefore, it is the greater distance that Ca^{2+} must diffuse, the slower rate at which action potentials are propagated between smooth muscle cells, and the slower rate of cross-bridge formation between actin and myosin myofilaments that are all responsible for the slower contraction of smooth muscle.

Figure 9.26 outlines the steps in smooth muscle contraction.

1. Smooth muscle contraction is stimulated both neurally and hormonally. Recall from chapter 3 that many ligands, such as hormones, can activate a G protein mechanism that opens an ion channel. Regardless of the stimulus source, however, Ca^{2+} is the key to smooth muscle contraction.
2. Just as in skeletal muscle, Ca^{2+} also regulates contraction in smooth muscle. However, the role of Ca^{2+} in smooth muscle differs from that in skeletal muscle fibers. In smooth muscle fibers, there are no troponin molecules bound to actin. Instead, Ca^{2+} that enters the sarcoplasm binds to a protein called **calmodulin** (kal-MOD-yoo-lin).
3. Once calmodulin is bound to Ca^{2+}, the calcium-calmodulin complex activates an enzyme called **myosin kinase** (KYE-nays).
4. Myosin kinase transfers a phosphate group from ATP to the heads of myosin molecules.
5. Cross-bridge formation occurs when myosin myofilaments have phosphate groups bound to them. The enzymes responsible for cross-bridge cycling are slower than the enzymes in skeletal muscle, resulting in slower cross-bridge formation. Once activated, cross-bridge formation has energy requirements very similar to those of cross-bridge formation in skeletal muscle fibers.
6. Relaxation of smooth muscle results because of the activity of another enzyme, called **myosin phosphatase** (FOS-fah-tays). This enzyme removes the phosphate group from the myosin molecules.

PROCESS **Figure**

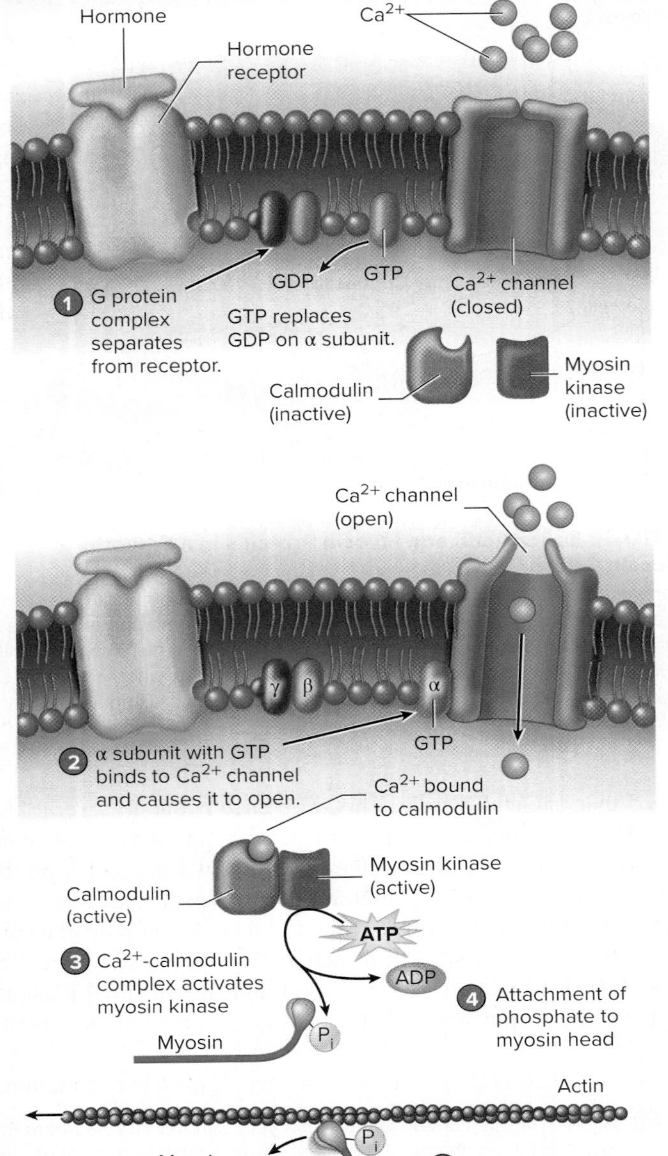

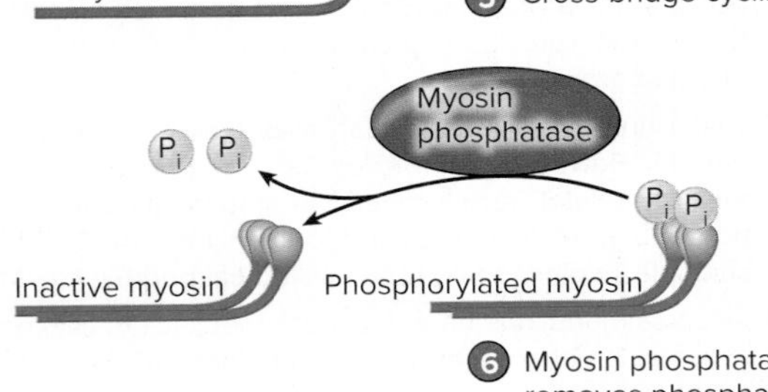

PROCESS **Figure 9.26**

Smooth Muscle Contraction

Calcium binds to calmodulin to activate cross-bridge formation.

What is the major difference between smooth muscle and skeletal muscle regarding the relaxation phase?

If the phosphate is removed from myosin while the cross-bridges are attached to actin, the cross-bridges release very slowly. This explains how smooth muscle is able to sustain tension for long periods and without extensive energy expenditure. This period of sustained tension is often called the **latch state** of smooth muscle contraction. If myosin phosphatase removes the phosphate from myosin molecules while the cross-bridges are not attached, relaxation occurs much more rapidly.

In summary, elevated Ca^{2+} levels in the sarcoplasm of smooth muscle cells result in the activation of myosin molecules and the formation of cross-bridges. Also, the action of myosin phosphatase results in a high percentage of myosin molecules having their phosphates removed while bound to actin. This process favors sustained contractions, or the latch state, and a low rate of energy consumption because of the slow release of cross-bridges. As long as Ca^{2+} is present, cross-bridges re-form quickly after being released. Consequently, many cross-bridges are intact at any given time in contracted smooth muscle.

Calcium ion levels in the sarcoplasm of smooth muscle are reduced as Ca^{2+} is actively transported across the plasma membrane, including the plasma membrane of caveolae, and into the sarcoplasmic reticulum. Muscles relax in response to lower intracellular levels of Ca^{2+}.

Types of Smooth Muscle

There are two types of smooth muscle, (1) visceral and (2) multiunit. **Visceral** (VISS-er-al) **smooth muscle** is the more common of the two types. It occurs in sheets and includes the smooth muscle of the digestive, reproductive, and urinary tracts. Visceral smooth muscle has numerous gap junctions (see chapter 4), which allow action potentials to pass directly from one cell to another. As a consequence, sheets of smooth muscle cells function as a unit, and a wave of contraction traverses the entire smooth muscle sheet. Visceral smooth muscle is often autorhythmic, but in some areas it contracts only when stimulated. For example, visceral smooth muscle in the digestive tract contracts spontaneously and at relatively regular intervals, whereas visceral smooth muscle in the urinary bladder contracts only when stimulated by the nervous system.

Multiunit smooth muscle occurs in various configurations: sheets, as in the walls of blood vessels; small bundles, as in the arrector pili muscles and the iris of the eye; and single cells, as in the capsule of the spleen. Multiunit smooth muscle has fewer gap junctions than visceral smooth muscle, and cells or groups of cells act as independent units. It normally contracts only when stimulated by nerves or hormones.

In visceral smooth muscle tissue, the arrangement between neurons and smooth muscle fibers differs from that in skeletal muscle tissue. The synapses are more diffuse than in skeletal muscle. Axons of neurons terminate in a series of dilations along the branching axons within the connective tissue among the smooth muscle cells. These dilations have vesicles containing neurotransmitter molecules that, once released, diffuse among the smooth muscle cells and bind to receptors on their surfaces. Multiunit smooth muscle has synapses more like those found in skeletal muscle tissue.

Electrical Properties of Smooth Muscle

The resting membrane potential of smooth muscle cells is usually not as negative as that of skeletal muscle fibers. It normally ranges between –55 and –60 mV, compared with approximately –85 mV in skeletal muscle fibers. Furthermore, the resting membrane potential of many visceral smooth muscle cells fluctuates, with slow depolarization and repolarization phases. These slow waves of depolarization and repolarization are propagated from cell to cell for short distances (figure 9.27*a*). More "classic" action potentials can be triggered by the slow waves of depolarization and usually are propagated for longer distances (figure 9.27*b*). In addition, some smooth muscle types have action potentials with a plateau, or prolonged depolarization (figure 9.27*c*). The slow waves in the resting membrane potential may result from a spontaneous and progressive increase in the permeability of the plasma membrane to Na^+ and Ca^{2+}, or they may be controlled by neurons. Sodium ions and Ca^{2+} diffuse into the cell through their respective channels and produce the depolarization.

Smooth muscle does not respond in an all-or-none fashion to action potentials. A series of action potentials in smooth muscle can result in a single, slow contraction followed by slow relaxation instead of individual contractions in response to each action potential, as occurs in skeletal muscle. A slow wave of depolarization that has one to several more classic-appearing action potentials superimposed on it is common in many types of smooth muscle. After the wave of depolarization, the smooth muscle contracts. Action potentials with plateaus are common in smooth muscle that exhibits periods of sustained contraction.

Spontaneously generated action potentials that lead to contractions are characteristic of visceral smooth muscle in the uterus, the ureter, and the digestive tract. Certain smooth muscle cells in these organs function as **pacemaker cells,** which tend to develop action potentials more rapidly than other cells.

The nervous system can regulate smooth muscle contractions by increasing or decreasing action potentials carried by neuron axons to smooth muscle. Responses of smooth muscle cells result in depolarization and increased contraction or hyperpolarization and decreased contraction. The nervous system can also regulate the pacemaker cells.

Hormones and ligands produced locally in tissues can bind to receptors on some smooth muscle plasma membranes. The combination of a hormone or other ligands with a receptor causes ligand-gated Ca^{2+} channels in the plasma membrane to open (see figure 9.26). Calcium ions then enter the cell and cause smooth muscle contractions to occur without a major change in the membrane potential. For example, some smooth muscles contract when exposed to the hormone epinephrine, which binds to epinephrine receptors to activate G proteins in the plasma membrane (see figure 9.26). The α subunit of the G complex can produce intracellular mediator molecules, which open the ligand-gated Ca^{2+} channels in the plasma membrane or sarcoplasmic reticulum.

Predict 9

Explain how a ligand can bind to a membrane-bound receptor in a smooth muscle cell and cause sustained contraction for a prolonged period without a large increase in ATP breakdown.

Functional Properties of Smooth Muscle

Smooth muscle has four functional properties not seen in skeletal muscle:

1. Some visceral smooth muscle exhibits autorhythmic contractions.
2. Smooth muscle tends to contract in response to being stretched, but a slow increase in length produces less response than a more rapid increase in length.
3. Smooth muscle exhibits a relatively constant tension, called **smooth muscle tone,** over a long period and maintains that tension in response to a gradual increase in the smooth muscle length.
4. The amplitude of contraction produced by smooth muscle also remains constant, although the muscle length varies.

Smooth muscle is therefore well adapted for lining the walls of hollow organs, such as the stomach and the urinary bladder. As the volume of the stomach or urinary bladder increases, the

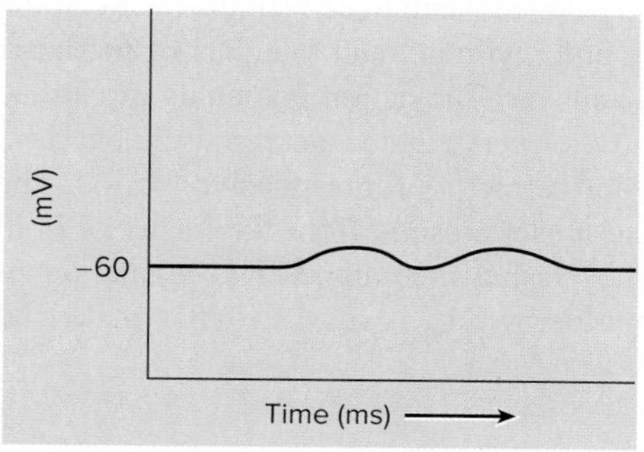

(a) Slow waves of depolarization

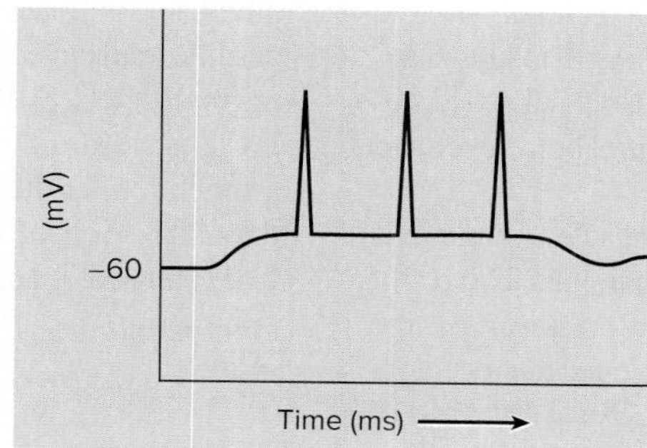

(b) Action potentials in smooth muscle superimposed on a slow wave of depolarization

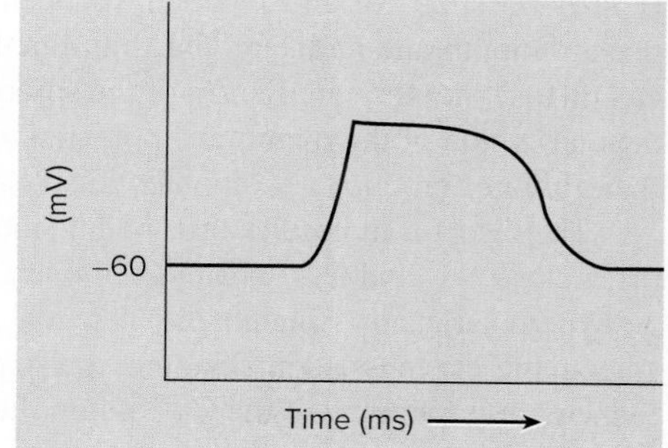

(c) Action potential with prolonged depolarization (plateau)

FIGURE 9.27 Membrane Potentials in Smooth Muscle
Smooth muscle exhibits three patterns of action potentials.

tension applied to its contents increases only slightly. Also, as the volume of the large and small intestines increases, the contractions that move food through them do not dramatically change in amplitude.

Regulation of Smooth Muscle

The autonomic nervous system innervates smooth muscle, whereas the somatic motor nervous system innervates skeletal muscle (see chapter 11). The regulation of smooth muscle is therefore involuntary, and the regulation of skeletal muscle is voluntary.

The most important neurotransmitters released from the nerves that innervate smooth muscle cells are **acetylcholine** and **norepinephrine.** Acetylcholine stimulates some smooth muscle types to contract but inhibits others.

Hormones are also important in regulating smooth muscle. Epinephrine, a hormone from the adrenal medulla, stimulates some smooth muscles, such as those in the blood vessels of the small intestine, and inhibits other smooth muscles, such as those in the intestinal wall. Oxytocin stimulates contractions of uterine smooth muscle, especially during childbirth. These and other hormones are discussed more thoroughly in chapters 17 and 18. Other chemical substances produced locally by surrounding tissues—such as histamine, prostaglandins, and by-products of metabolism—also influence smooth muscle function. For example, blood flow through capillaries is dramatically influenced by these substances (see chapter 21).

The type of receptors present on the plasma membrane to which the neurotransmitters or hormones bind determines the response of the smooth muscle. Some smooth muscle types have receptors to which acetylcholine binds, and the receptor responds by stimulating contractions; other smooth muscle types have receptors to which acetylcholine binds, and the receptor responds by inhibiting contractions. A similar relationship exists for smooth muscle receptors for norepinephrine and certain hormones. In some smooth muscle fibers, norepinephrine stimulates contraction, while in others, it inhibits contraction.

The receptor molecules that stimulate smooth muscle contractions often open either Na^+ or Ca^{2+} channels. When these channels open, Na^+ and Ca^{2+} pass through their respective channels into the cell and cause depolarization of the plasma membrane. It is also possible for the receptor to open Ca^{2+} channels in the plasma membrane and sarcoplasmic reticulum. As a result, Ca^{2+} can diffuse into the sarcoplasm of the smooth muscle cells without depolarization of the membrane potential to its threshold level and therefore not produce action potentials.

The receptor molecules that inhibit smooth muscle contractions often close Na^+ and Ca^{2+} channels or open K^+ channels. The result is hyperpolarization (membrane potential below resting) of the smooth muscle cells and inhibition. It is also possible for the receptors to increase the activity of the Ca^{2+} pump that transports Ca^{2+} out of the cell or into the sarcoplasmic reticulum. As a result, relaxation may occur without a change in the resting membrane potential.

Receptors in specific smooth muscle types for neurotransmitters and hormones are presented in the chapters discussing smooth muscle types.

ASSESS YOUR PROGRESS

59. *Describe a typical smooth muscle cell. How do its structure and its contraction process differ from those of skeletal muscle fibers?*
60. *What ion is key to smooth muscle contraction? What are the functions of this ion?*
61. *What is the role of calmodulin? Of myosin phosphatase?*
62. *Compare visceral smooth muscle and multiunit smooth muscle as to locations and structure.*
63. *Explain why visceral smooth muscle contracts as a single unit.*
64. *How do smooth muscle cells differ from skeletal muscle fibers in their electrical properties?*
65. *How are spontaneous contractions produced in smooth muscle?*
66. *List four functional properties of smooth muscle that are not seen in skeletal muscle. Can smooth muscle develop an oxygen deficit?*
67. *How do the nervous system and hormones regulate smooth muscle contraction?*
68. *How are ion channels affected by receptors that stimulate smooth muscle contractions? That inhibit smooth muscle contractions?*

9.9 Cardiac Muscle

LEARNING OUTCOME

After reading this section, you should be able to

A. **Discuss the structural and functional characteristics of cardiac muscle.**

Cardiac muscle, which is found only in the heart, is discussed in detail in chapter 20. Like skeletal muscle tissue, cardiac muscle tissue is striated, but each cell usually contains one nucleus located near the center. Adjacent cells join to form branching muscle fibers by specialized cell-to-cell attachments called **intercalated** (in-TER-kah-lay-ted) **disks,** which have gap junctions that allow action potentials to pass from cell to cell (figure 9.28). Some cardiac muscle cells are autorhythmic, and one part of the heart normally acts as the pacemaker. The action potentials of cardiac muscle are similar to those of nerve and skeletal muscle but have a much longer duration and refractory (unresponsive) period. The depolarization of cardiac muscle results from the influx of both Na^+ and Ca^{2+} across the plasma membrane. The regulation of contraction in cardiac muscle by Ca^{2+} is similar to that of skeletal muscle.

ASSESS YOUR PROGRESS

69. *Compare the structural and functional characteristics of cardiac muscle with those of skeletal muscle.*
70. *How is cardiac muscle similar to smooth muscle?*

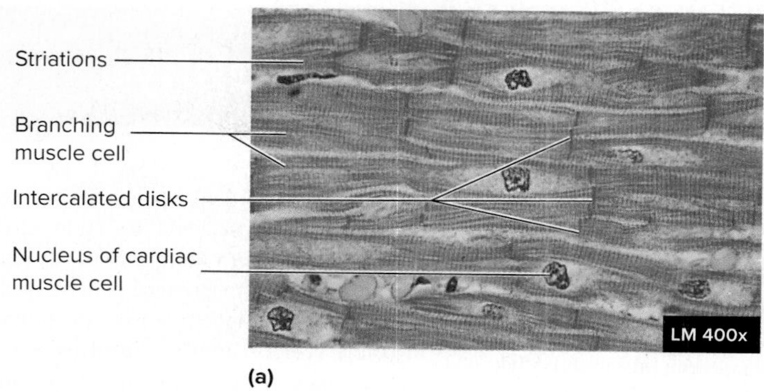

(a)

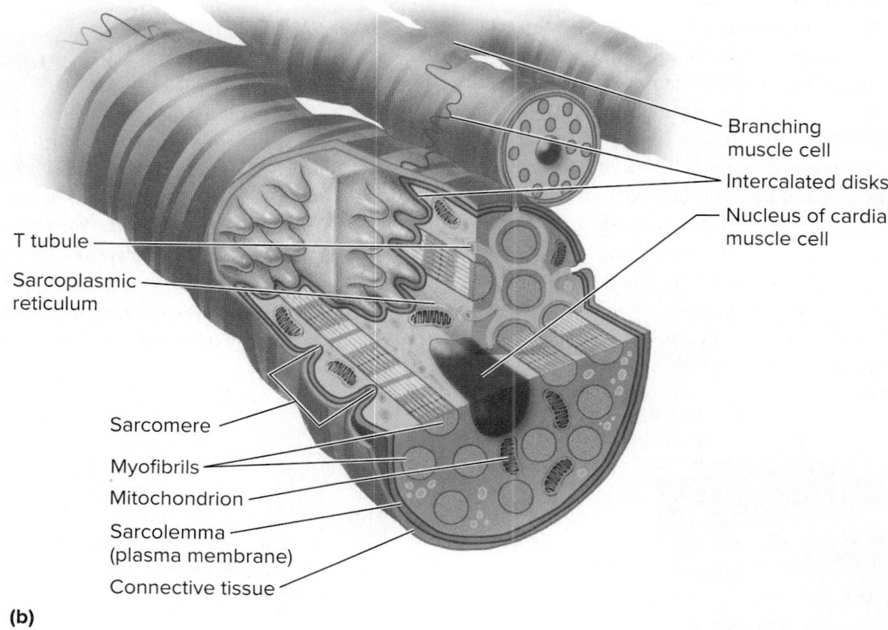

(b)

FIGURE 9.28 Cardiac Muscle Fibers
Longitudinal section of cardiac muscle fibers. (*a*) Photomicrograph of cardiac muscle fibers. (*b*) Drawing of cardiac muscle fibers. (a) Ed Reschke

EFFECTS OF AGING ON **SKELETAL MUSCLE**

Aging skeletal muscle undergoes several changes: reduction in muscle mass, slower response time for muscle contraction, reduction in stamina, and increased recovery time. Loss of muscle fibers begins as early as 25 years of age, and by age 80 the muscle mass has been reduced by approximately 50%. Most of the loss of strength and speed is due to the loss of muscle fibers, particularly fast-twitch muscle fibers.The surface area of the neuromuscular junction decreases, and as a result, action potentials in neurons stimulate action potentials in muscle cells more slowly; thus, fewer action potentials are produced in muscle fibers. There is also a decrease in the density of capillaries in skeletal muscles so that a longer recovery period is required after exercise.

Systems PATHOLOGY | Duchenne Muscular Dystrophy

Background Information

A couple became concerned about their 3-year-old son, Greger, when they noticed that he was much weaker than other boys his age and his muscles appeared poorly developed. Eventually, it was readily apparent that Greger had difficulty sitting, standing, climbing stairs, and even walking. When Greger tried to stand, he would use his hands and arms to climb up his legs. Finally, the couple took Greger to his pediatrician, who, after several tests, informed them that Greger had Duchenne muscular dystrophy. **Duchenne muscular dystrophy (DMD)** is usually identified in children around 3 years of age, when their parents notice slow motor development with progressive weakness and muscle wasting (atrophy). Typically, muscular weakness begins in the hip muscles, which causes a waddling gait. Temporary enlargement of the calf muscles is apparent in 80% of cases. The enlargement is paradoxical because the muscle fibers are actually getting smaller, but the amount of fibrous connective tissue and fat between the muscle fibers is increasing (figure 9.29*a*,*b*). The protein that normally protects muscle against mechanical stress is not functional in patients with DMD. This is thought to be the primary cause of the muscle weakness and other symptoms. Rising from the floor by using the hands and arms is characteristic and is caused by weakness of the lumbar and hip muscles (figure 9.29*c*). Within 3 to 5 years, the muscles of the shoulder girdle become involved. The replacement of muscle with connective tissue contributes to muscular atrophy and shortened, inflexible muscles called contractures. The contractures limit movements and can cause severe deformities of the skeleton. By 10 to 12 years of age, people with DMD are usually unable to walk, and few live beyond age 20. DMD is genetic, but because of its inheritance pattern, mostly males are affected. There is no effective treatment to prevent the progressive deterioration of muscles in DMD. Therapy primarily involves exercises to help strengthen muscles and prevent contractures. Figure 9.30 demonstrates the impact DMD has on other organ systems. Table 9.6 lists other diseases and disorders of the muscular system.

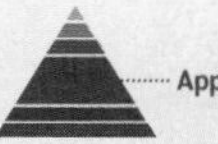

Predict 10

A boy with advanced Duchenne muscular dystrophy developed pulmonary edema (accumulation of fluid in the lungs) and pneumonia caused by a bacterial infection. His physician diagnosed the condition in the following way: The pulmonary edema was the result of heart failure, and the increased fluid in the lungs provided a site where bacteria could invade and grow. The fact that the boy could not breathe deeply or cough effectively made the condition worse. How would the muscle tissues in a boy with advanced DMD differ from the muscle tissues in a boy with less-advanced DMD?

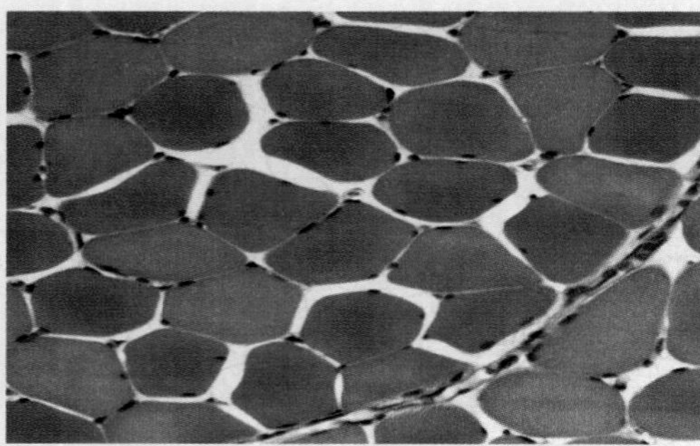

(a) Normal muscle tissue

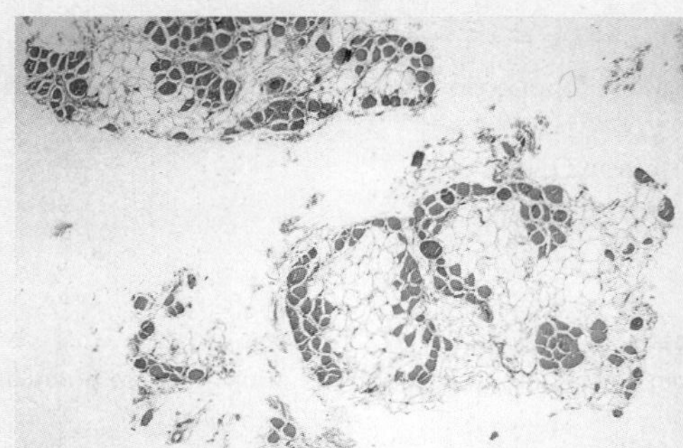

(b) DMD muscle tissue

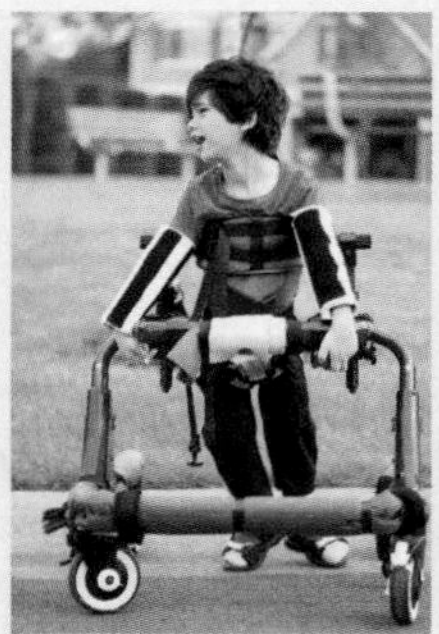

(c) A DMD patient

FIGURE 9.29 Effects of DMD on Skeletal Muscle Tissue

(*a*) Cross section of normal skeletal muscle tissue. Note the lesser amount of adipose and connective tissue between muscle fibers than seen in (*b*). (*b*) Cross section of DMD skeletal muscle tissue. Skeletal muscle fibers decrease in size and have increased amount of adipose and connective tissue distributed among the muscle fibers. (c) Patients with DMD must support themselves whether sitting or standing on the ground. (a) Biophoto Associates/Science Source; (b) Dr. Edwin P. Ewing, Jr./Centers for Disease Control and Prevention; (c) Jaren Jai Wicklund/Shutterstock

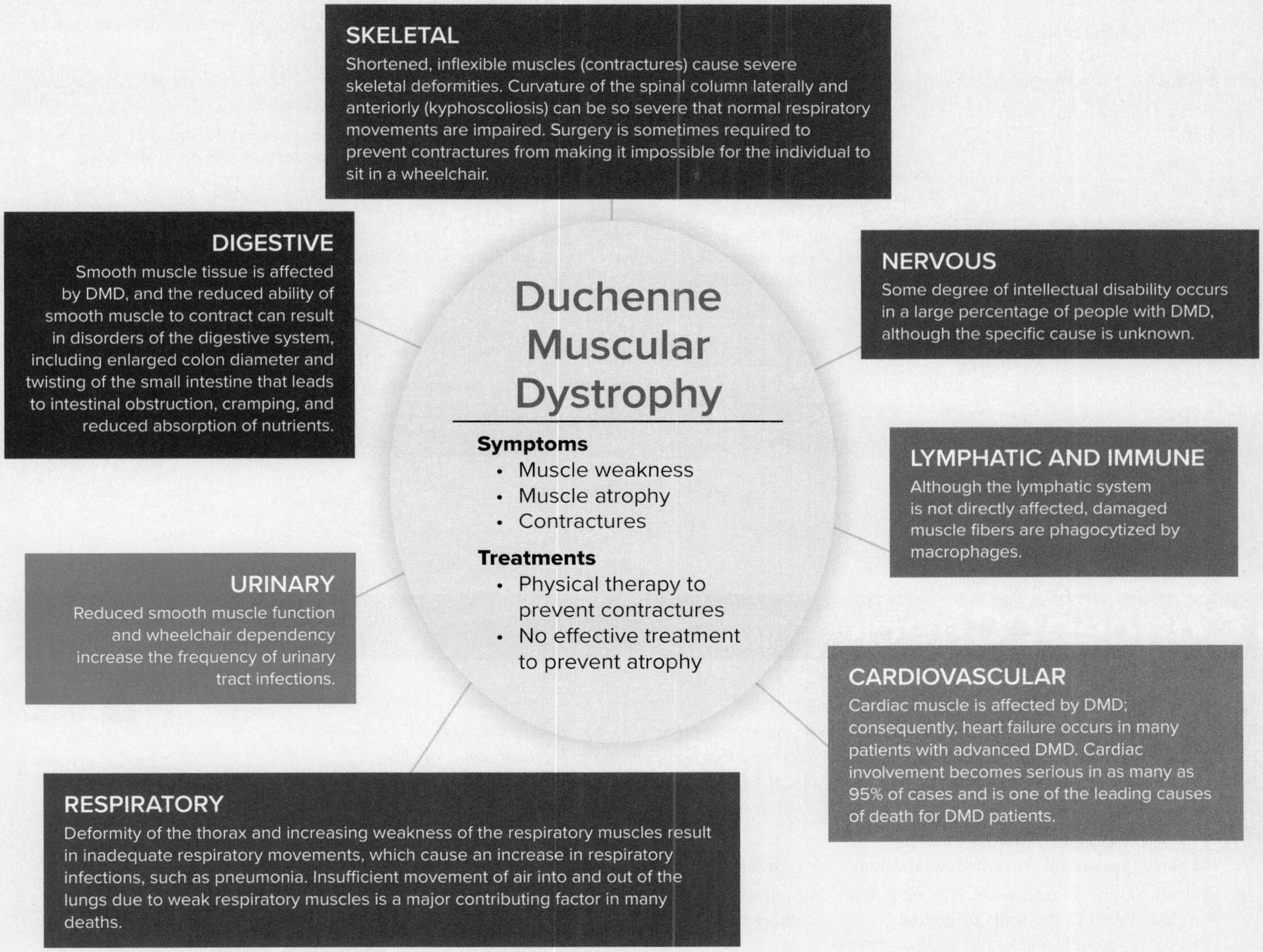

FIGURE 9.30 Interactions Between DMD and Other Organ Systems

DMD affects most systems of the body because muscle tissue is used for many body functions.

TABLE 9.6 Representative Diseases and Disorders of the Muscular System

Condition	Description
Cramps	Painful, spastic contractions of skeletal muscle; due to multiple causes such as dehydration and ion imbalance
Fibromyalgia (FIE-broh-my-AL-jee-uh)	Non-life-threatening, chronic, widespread pain in skeletal muscles with no known cure; also known as chronic muscle pain syndrome
Hypertrophy	Enlargement of skeletal muscle due to an increased number of myofibrils, as occurs with increased muscle use; in cardiac muscle, usually a result of other dieases, commonly hypertension
Atrophy	Decrease in muscle size due to a decreased number of myofilaments; can occur due to disuse of a muscle, as in paralysis; can also occur in cardiac muscle due to certain pathologies such as chronic heart failure
Muscular dystrophy	Group of genetic disorders in which muscles degenerate and atrophy; usually affects skeletal muscle and sometimes cardiac muscle
Duchenne muscular dystrophy	See Systems Pathology
Myotonic muscular dystrophy	Skeletal muscles are weak and fail to relax following forceful contractions; affects the hands most severely; dominant trait in 1/20,000 births
Myasthenia gravis	See Clinical Impact 9.1
Tendinitis (ten-di-NY-tis)	Inflammation of a tendon or its attachment point due to overuse of a skeletal muscle
Fibrosis	Scarring of damaged cardiac or skeletal muscle due to deposition of connective tissue
Fibrositis	Inflammation of fibrous connective tissue, resulting in soreness after prolonged skeletal muscle tension; not progressive

Concept Check

9.1 Functions of the Muscular System

Muscles are responsible for movement of the arms, legs, heart, and other parts of the body; maintenance of posture; respiration; production of body heat; communication; constriction of organs and vessels; and heartbeat.

Types of Muscle Tissue

A. The three types of muscle are skeletal, smooth, and cardiac.

B. Skeletal muscle is responsible for most body movements; smooth muscle is found in the walls of hollow organs and tubes and moves substances through them; and cardiac muscle is in the heart and pumps blood.

1. *Which of these is true of skeletal muscle?*

   a. spindle-shaped cells
   b. under involuntary control
   c. many peripherally located nuclei per muscle fiber
   d. forms the walls of hollow internal organs
   e. may be autorhythmic

9.2 General Properties of Muscle Tissue

A. Muscle exhibits contractility (shortens forcefully), excitability (responds to stimuli), extensibility (can be stretched and still contract), and elasticity (recoils to resting length).

B. Muscle tissue shortens forcefully but lengthens passively.

2. *Which of these is* not *a major property of muscle?*

   a. contractility
   b. elasticity
   c. excitability
   d. extensibility
   e. secretability

9.3 Skeletal Muscle Anatomy

Skeletal muscle fibers are associated with connective tissue, blood vessels, and nerves.

Whole Skeletal Muscle Anatomy

A. The entire muscle is surrounded by a connective tissue layer called the epimysium.

B. Muscle fascicles, bundles of muscle fibers, are covered by the connective tissue layer called the perimysium.

C. At the level of the perimysium, axons of motor neurons branch, and each branch projects to a muscle fiber to form a neuromuscular junction.

3. *Given these structures:*

   (1) whole muscle
   (2) muscle fiber (cell)
   (3) myofilament
   (4) myofibril
   (5) muscle fasciculus

Choose the arrangement that lists the structures in the correct order from largest to smallest.

a. 1,2,5,3,4
b. 1,2,5,4,3
c. 1,5,2,3,4
d. 1,5,2,4,3
e. 1,5,4,2,3

Skeletal Muscle Fiber Anatomy

A. A muscle fiber is a single cell consisting of a plasma membrane (sarcolemma), cytoplasm (sarcoplasm), several nuclei, and myofibrils.

B. Myofibrils are composed of two major protein fibers: actin and myosin. Actin myofilaments consist of F actin, tropomyosin, and troponin. Myosin molecules constitute myosin myofilaments.

C. Actin and myosin are organized to form sarcomeres. Myofibrils appear striated because of A bands and I bands of sarcomeres.

4. *Each myofibril* 

   a. is made up of many muscle fibers.
   b. contains sarcoplasmic reticulum.
   c. is made up of many sarcomeres.
   d. contains T tubules.
   e. is the same thing as a muscle fiber.

5. *Myosin myofilaments are* 

   a. attached to the Z disk.
   b. found primarily in the I band.
   c. thinner than actin myofilaments.
   d. absent from the H zone.
   e. attached to filaments that form the M line.

6. *Which of these statements about the molecular structure of myofilaments is true?* Remember
   a. Tropomyosin has a binding site for Ca^{2+}.
   b. The head of the myosin molecule binds to an active site on G actin.
   c. ATPase is found on troponin.
   d. Troponin binds to the rodlike portion of myosin.
   e. Actin molecules have a hingelike portion, which bends and straightens during contraction.

9.4 Skeletal Muscle Fiber Physiology

Excitability of Muscle Fibers

A. Plasma membranes are polarized, which means that a charge difference, called the resting membrane potential, exists across the plasma membrane.

B. The plasma membrane becomes polarized because the tendency for K^+ to diffuse out of the cell is resisted by the negative charges of ions and molecules inside the cell.

C. Two types of membrane channels produce action potentials: ligand-gated and voltage-gated channels.

7. *The part of the sarcolemma that invaginates into the interior of skeletal muscle fibers is the* Remember
   a. T tubule system.
   b. sarcoplasmic reticulum.
   c. myofibrils.
   d. terminal cisternae.
   e. mitochondria.

Action Potentials

A. Depolarization results from an increase in the permeability of the plasma membrane to Na^+.

B. The repolarization phase of the action potential occurs when the Na^+ channels close and the K^+ channels open briefly.

C. Action potentials propagate along the plasma membranes of neurons and skeletal muscle fibers in an all-or-none fashion.

D. Acetylcholine released from the presynaptic terminal of a motor neuron produces an action potential.

E. After an action potential occurs, acetylcholinesterase splits acetylcholine into acetic acid and choline.

8. *During the depolarization phase of an action potential, the permeability of the plasma membrane to* Remember
   a. Ca^{2+} increases.
   b. Na^+ increases.
   c. K^+ increases.
   d. Ca^{2+} decreases.
   e. Na^+ decreases.

9. *During repolarization of the plasma membrane* 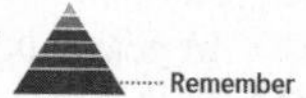

   a. Na^+ moves to the inside of the cell.
   b. Na^+ moves to the outside of the cell.
   c. K^+ moves to the inside of the cell.
   d. K^+ moves to the outside of the cell.

10. *Given these events:* Remember
   (1) Acetylcholine is broken down into acetic acid and choline.
   (2) Acetylcholine diffuses across the synaptic cleft.
   (3) An action potential reaches the terminal branch of the motor neuron.
   (4) Acetylcholine combines with a ligand-gated ion channel.
   (5) An action potential is produced on the muscle fiber's plasma membrane.

   Choose the arrangement that lists the events in the order they occur at a neuromuscular junction.

   a. 2,3,4,1,5
   b. 3,2,4,5,1
   c. 3,4,2,1,5
   d. 4,5,2,1,3
   e. 5,1,2,4,3

11. *Acetylcholinesterase is an important molecule in the neuromuscular junction because it* Remember
   a. stimulates receptors on the presynaptic terminal.
   b. synthesizes acetylcholine from acetic acid and choline.
   c. stimulates receptors within the motor end-plate.
   d. breaks down acetylcholine.
   e. causes the release of Ca^{2+} from the sarcoplasmic reticulum.

12. *Bob improperly canned some homegrown vegetables. After eating the vegetables, he contracted botulism poisoning with symptoms that included difficulty swallowing and breathing. Eventually, he died of respiratory failure (his respiratory muscles relaxed and would not contract). Assuming that botulism toxin affects the neuromuscular junction, propose the ways that the toxin produces the observed symptoms.* Apply

13. *A patient is thought to be suffering from either muscular dystrophy or myasthenia gravis. How would you distinguish between the two conditions?* Apply

Excitation-Contraction Coupling

A. A triad is a T tubule (an invagination of the sarcolemma) and two terminal cisternae (an enlarged area of sarcoplasmic reticulum).
B. Action potentials move into the T tubule system, causing Ca^{2+} channels to open and release Ca^{2+} from the sarcoplasmic reticulum.
C. Calcium ions diffuse from the sarcoplasmic reticulum to the myofilaments and bind to troponin. Contraction occurs when myosin heads bind to active sites on actin, myosin changes shape, and actin is pulled past the myosin.
D. Relaxation occurs when calcium is taken up by the sarcoplasmic reticulum.

14. *Given these events:*

(1) The sarcoplasmic reticulum releases Ca^{2+}.
(2) The sarcoplasmic reticulum takes up Ca^{2+}.
(3) Calcium ions diffuse into the sarcoplasm.
(4) An action potential moves down the T tubule.
(5) The sarcomere shortens.
(6) The muscle relaxes.

Choose the arrangement that lists the events in the order they occur following a single stimulation of a skeletal muscle fiber.

a. 1,3,4,5,2,6
b. 2,3,5,4,6,1
c. 4,1,3,5,2,6
d. 4,2,3,5,1,6
e. 5,1,4,3,2,6

15. *Given these events:* Remember
(1) Calcium ions combine with tropomyosin.
(2) Calcium ions combine with troponin.
(3) Tropomyosin pulls away from actin.
(4) Troponin pulls away from actin.
(5) Tropomyosin pulls away from myosin.
(6) Troponin pulls away from myosin.
(7) Myosin binds to actin.

Choose the arrangement that lists the events in the order they occur during muscle contraction.

a. 1,4,7
b. 2,5,6
c. 1,3,7
d. 2,4,7
e. 2,3,7

16. *Predict and explain the response if the ATP concentration in a muscle that was exhibiting rigor mortis could be instantly increased.*

Cross-Bridge Movement

ATP is required for the cycle of cross-bridge formation, movement, and release.

Muscle Relaxation

Calcium ions are transported into the sarcoplasmic reticulum.

9.5 Whole Skeletal Muscle Physiology

The Muscle Twitch

A muscle twitch is the contraction of a single muscle fiber or a whole muscle in response to a stimulus. It consists of lag, contraction, and relaxation phases.

Force of Contraction in Individual Muscle Fibers

A. A stimulus of increasing magnitude results in graded contractions of increased force through either summation or recruitment.
B. A motor unit is one motor neuron and all the muscle fibers it controls. Precise movements use small motor units. Gross movements use large motor units.
C. Isometric contractions cause a change in muscle tension but no change in muscle length.
D. Isotonic contractions cause a change in muscle length but no change in muscle tension.
E. Treppe is an increase in the force of contraction during the first few contractions of a rested muscle.
F. Incomplete tetanus is partial relaxation between contractions; complete tetanus is no relaxation between contractions.
G. A stimulus of increasing frequency increases the force of contraction (wave summation).

17. *With stimuli of increasing strength, which of these is capable of a graded response?* Remember
a. neuron axon
b. muscle fiber
c. motor unit
d. whole muscle

18. *Considering the force of contraction of a skeletal muscle fiber, wave summation occurs because of* Remember
a. increased strength of action potentials on the plasma membrane.
b. a decreased number of cross-bridges formed.
c. an increase in Ca^{2+} concentration around the myofibrils.
d. an increased number of motor units recruited.
e. increased permeability of the sarcolemma to Ca^{2+}.

19. *Which of these events occurs during the lag (latent) phase of muscle contraction?* Remember
a. cross-bridge movement
b. active transport of Ca^{2+} into the sarcoplasmic reticulum
c. Ca^{2+} binding to troponin
d. sarcomere shortening
e. breakdown of ATP to ADP

20. *Explain what is happening at the level of individual sarcomeres when a person is using his or her biceps brachii muscle to hold a weight in a constant position. Contrast this with what is happening at the level of individual sarcomeres when a person lowers the weight, as well as when he or she raises the weight.* Understand

Force of Contraction in Whole Muscles

A. Multiple-motor-unit recruitment results in more motor units responding to greater stimuli.
B. Concentric contractions cause muscles to shorten and tension to increase.
C. Eccentric contractions cause muscles to lengthen and tension to decrease gradually.

D. Muscle tone is the maintenance of steady tension for long periods.
E. Asynchronous contractions of motor units produce smooth, steady muscle contractions.

21. *A weight lifter attempts to lift a weight from the floor, but the weight is so heavy that he is unable to move it. The type of muscle contraction the weight lifter is using is mostly*

Remember

a. isometric.
b. isotonic.
c. isokinetic.
d. concentric.
e. eccentric.

22. *Design an experiment to test the following hypothesis: Muscle A has the same number of motor units as muscle B. (Assume that you can stimulate the nerves that innervate skeletal muscles with an electronic stimulator and monitor the tension produced by the muscles.)*

Apply

9.6 Muscle Fiber Types

Slow-Twitch Muscle Fibers

Slow-twitch muscle fibers break down ATP slowly and have a well-developed blood supply, many mitochondria, and myoglobin.

Fast-Twitch Muscle Fibers

Fast-twitch muscle fibers break down ATP rapidly.

A. Type IIa muscle fibers have a well-developed blood supply, more mitochondria, and more myoglobin.
B. Type IIx muscle fibers have large amounts of glycogen, a poor blood supply, fewer mitochondria, and little myoglobin.

Distribution of Fast-Twitch and Slow-Twitch Muscle Fibers

People who are good sprinters have a greater percentage of fast-twitch muscle fibers in their leg muscles, and people who are good long-distance runners have a higher percentage of slow-twitch muscle fibers.

23. *Which of these conditions would you expect to find within the leg muscle fibers of a world-class marathon runner?*

Remember

a. myoglobin-poor
b. contract very quickly
c. primarily anaerobic
d. numerous mitochondria

24. *A researcher is investigating the composition of muscle tissue in the gastrocnemius muscles (in the calf of the leg) of athletes. She takes a needle biopsy from the muscle and determines the concentration (or enzyme activity) of several substances. Describe the major differences this researcher sees when comparing the muscles of athletes who perform in the following events: 100-meter dash, weight lifting, and 10,000-meter run.*

Understand

25. *After learning about muscle fiber types in his anatomy and physiology class, Alex started to notice differences in the color of the turkey meat he ate for lunch. Some of the meat was very white and some of it was much darker. From the color of the meat, Alex guessed which muscles the bird used for maintenance of posture and/or slow movements, such as walking, and which muscles it used for quicker movements, such as running or flying. What type of muscle fiber predominates in white meat? In dark meat? Explain how the color of the meat relates to the function of the muscle.*

Apply

Effects of Exercise

A. Muscles increase (hypertrophy) or decrease (atrophy) in size because of a change in the size of muscle fibers.
B. Anaerobic exercise develops type IIx muscle fibers. Aerobic exercise develops type I muscle fibers and changes type IIx muscle fibers into type IIa fast-twitch muscle fibers.

26. *Which of these increases the* least *as a result of muscle hypertrophy?*

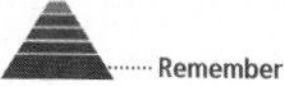

a. number of sarcomeres
b. number of myofibrils
c. number of muscle fibers
d. blood vessels and mitochondria
e. connective tissue

Heat Production

Heat is a by-product of chemical reactions in muscles. Shivering produces heat to maintain body temperature.

9.7 Energy Sources for Muscle Contraction

Energy for muscle contraction comes from ATP.

Adenylate Kinase and Creatine Kinase

A. Two ADP are converted by adenylate kinase to one ATP and one AMP during intense exercise.
B. ATP synthesized when ADP reacts with creatine phosphate provides energy for a short time during intense exercise.

Anaerobic Respiration

The ATP synthesized by anaerobic respiration provides energy for a short time during intense exercise. Anaerobic respiration produces ATP less efficiently but more rapidly than aerobic respiration. Lactate levels increase because of anaerobic respiration.

Aerobic Respiration

The ATP synthesized by aerobic respiration produces energy for muscle contractions under resting conditions or during exercises such as long-distance running. Although ATP is produced more efficiently, it is produced more slowly.

ATP Production as Exercise Progresses

Aerobic respiration produces more ATP than anaerobic respiration, but at a slower rate.

27. *Jerry Jogger's 3-mile run every morning takes about 30 minutes. Which of these sources provides most of the energy for his run?*

Remember

a. aerobic respiration
b. anaerobic respiration
c. creatine phosphate
d. stored ATP

Muscle Fatigue

A. Fatigue, the decreased ability to do work, can be caused by the central nervous system, depletion of ATP in muscles, or depletion of acetylcholine in the neuromuscular junction.
B. Physiological contracture (the inability of muscles to contract or relax) and rigor mortis (stiff muscles after death) result from inadequate amounts of ATP.

28. *Which of these types of fatigue is the most common?* Remember
    a. *muscular fatigue*
    b. *psychological fatigue*
    c. *synaptic fatigue*
    d. *army fatigue*

29. *Given these conditions:*
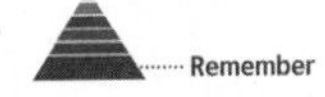

    (1) *low ATP levels*
    (2) *little or no transport of* Ca^{2+} *into the sarcoplasmic reticulum*
    (3) *release of cross-bridges*
    (4) Na^{+} *accumulation in the sarcoplasm*
    (5) *formation of cross-bridges*

    Choose the conditions that occur in both physiological contracture and rigor mortis.
    a. *1,2,3*
    b. *1,2,5*
    c. *1,2,3,4*
    d. *1,2,4,5*
    e. *1,2,3,4,5*

Muscle Soreness

Soreness is caused by inflammation in the muscle.

Oxygen Deficit and Excess Postexercise Oxygen Consumption

After anaerobic respiration, aerobic respiration is higher than normal, as the imbalances of homeostasis that occurred during exercise become rectified.

30. *Seth noticed that his rate of respiration was elevated after running a 100-meter race but was not as elevated after running slowly for a much longer distance. How would you explain this?* Understand

31. *Experiments were performed in an anatomy and physiology laboratory. First, the rate and depth of respiration for a resting student were determined. In experiment A, students ran in place for 30 seconds, immediately sat down and relaxed, and then had their respiration rate and depth measured. Experiment B was conducted in the same manner as experiment A, except that the students held their breath while running in place. What differences in respiration would you expect for the two experiments? Explain the basis for your predictions.* Apply

9.8 Smooth Muscle

A. Smooth muscle cells are spindle-shaped with a single nucleus but are not striated.

B. Calcium ions enter the cell to initiate contraction; calmodulin binds to Ca^{2+} and activates an enzyme that transfers a phosphate group from ATP to myosin to form cross-bridges.

C. Relaxation results when myosin phosphatase removes a phosphate group from the myosin molecule.

32. *Relaxation in smooth muscle occurs when*
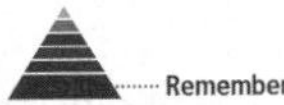

    a. *myosin kinase attaches phosphate to the myosin head.*
    b. Ca^{2+} *binds to calmodulin.*
    c. *myosin phosphatase removes phosphate from myosin.*
    d. Ca^{2+} *channels open.*
    e. Ca^{2+} *is released from the sarcoplasmic reticulum.*

Types of Smooth Muscle

A. Visceral smooth muscle fibers contract slowly, have gap junctions (and thus function as a single unit), and can be autorhythmic.

B. Multiunit smooth muscle fibers contract rapidly in response to stimulation by neurons and function independently.

33. *Compared with skeletal muscle, visceral smooth muscle*

    a. *has the same ability to be stretched.*
    b. *loses the ability to contract forcefully when stretched.*
    c. *maintains about the same tension, even when stretched.*
    d. *cannot maintain long, steady contractions.*
    e. *can accumulate a substantial oxygen deficit.*

Electrical Properties of Smooth Muscle

A. Spontaneous contractions result from Na^{+} and Ca^{2+} leakage into cells; Na^{+} and Ca^{2+} movement into the cell is involved in depolarization.

B. The autonomic nervous system, hormones, and chemicals produced locally can inhibit or stimulate action potentials (and thus contractions).

34. *High blood* K^{+} *concentrations cause depolarization of the resting membrane potential. Predict and explain the effect of high blood* K^{+} *levels on smooth muscle function.* Apply

Functional Properties of Smooth Muscle

A. Smooth muscle can contract autorhythmically in response to stretch or when stimulated by the autonomic nervous system or hormones.

B. Smooth muscle maintains a steady tension for long periods.

35. *Predict the shape of an active tension curve for visceral smooth muscle. How does it differ from the active tension curve for skeletal muscle?* Apply

Regulation of Smooth Muscle

A. Smooth muscle is innervated by the autonomic nervous system and is involuntary.

B. Hormones are important in regulating smooth muscle. Certain hormones can increase the Ca^{2+} permeability of some smooth muscle membranes and therefore cause contraction without a change in the resting membrane potential.

36. *A hormone stimulates the smooth muscle of a blood vessel to contract. Although the hormone causes a small change in membrane potential, the smooth muscle contracts substantially. Explain.* Apply

9.9 Cardiac Muscle

Cardiac muscle fibers are striated, have a single nucleus, are connected by intercalated disks (and thus function as a single unit), and are capable of autorhythmicity.

Answers to this chapter's odd-numbered Concept Check questions appear in Appendix F.

10

CHAPTER

Muscular System

GROSS ANATOMY

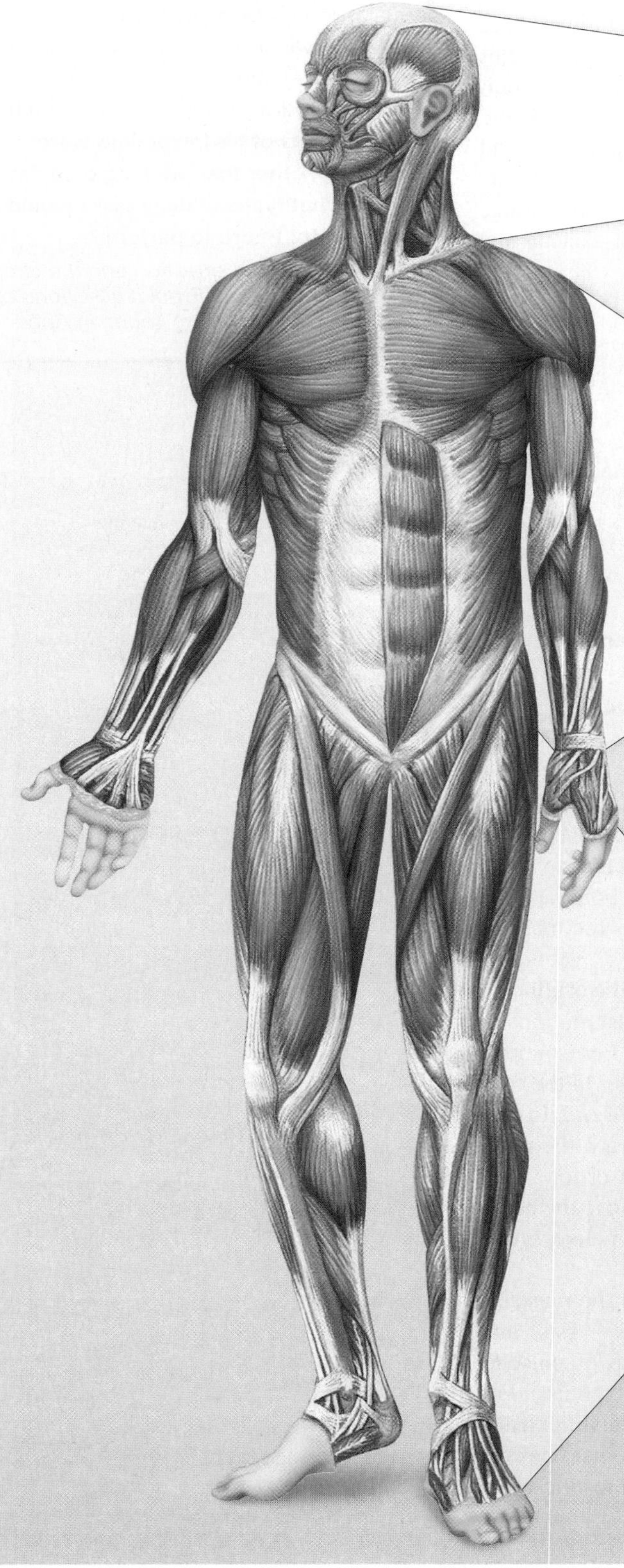

Head and Neck Muscles
The head muscles include muscles of facial expression. The neck muscles include muscles that rotate and allow side-to-side movement of the head.

Trunk and Upper Limb Muscles
The trunk muscles include muscles that aid in breathing and flexing the trunk (i.e., "bend at the waist") while the upper limb muscles include muscles that allow you to raise your hand in class to ask a question or to throw a pitch.

Lower Limb Muscles
The lower limb muscles include muscles that help you stand upright, walk to class, or go for a run.

Throughout this chapter, you will learn the names of head, neck, trunk, upper limb, and lower limb muscles. You will also be able to explain which muscles are important for various movements of the body.

Without muscles, we humans would be little more than department store mannequins—unable to walk, talk, blink our eyes, or even hold this textbook. But none of these inconveniences would bother us for long because we would also not be able to breathe.

One of the major characteristics of living human beings is our ability to move about. But we also use our skeletal muscles when we are not "moving." Postural muscles are constantly contracting to keep us sitting or standing upright. Respiratory muscles are constantly functioning to keep us breathing, even while we are asleep. Communication of all kinds requires skeletal muscles, whether for writing, typing, or speaking. Even silent communication using hand signals or facial expressions requires skeletal muscle function.

This chapter focuses on the anatomy of the major named skeletal muscles; cardiac muscle is considered in more depth in later chapters. The physiology of skeletal and smooth muscle is described in chapter 9.

Learn to Predict

While weight training, Pedro strained his back injuring the following muscles: psoas major, iliacus, pectineus, sartorius, vastus lateralis, vastus medius, vastus intermedius, and rectus femoris.

Predict Pedro's symptoms and which movements of his lower limb were affected, other than walking on a flat surface. What types of daily tasks would be difficult for Pedro to perform?

Answers to this question and the chapter's odd-numbered Predict questions can be found in Appendix E.

10.1 General Principles of Skeletal Muscle Anatomy

LEARNING OUTCOMES

After reading this section, you should be able to

A. **Define the following and give an example of each: *origin, insertion, agonist, antagonist, synergist, fixator,* and *prime mover*.**
B. **Explain how fasciculus orientation determines muscle shape and list examples of muscles that demonstrate each shape.**
C. **Recognize muscle names based on specific nomenclature rules.**
D. **Explain each of the three classes of levers in the body and give a specific example of each class.**

Most skeletal muscles are attached to bones. They extend from bone to bone across the linking joint. Everyday movements involve skeletal muscles contracting to move bones connected by joints. However, not all muscles are attached to bone at both ends. For example, some facial muscles attach to the skin, moving it as the muscles contract. One such movement is easily recognized as a smile.

The two points of attachment of each muscle to the bone are called the origin and the insertion. The **origin,** also called the *fixed end,* is usually the most stationary, proximal end of the muscle. Some muscles have more than one origin. For example, the triceps brachii has three origins that join together to form one muscle. In the case of multiple origins, each origin is called a **head.** The **insertion,** or *mobile end,* is usually the distal end of the muscle attached to the bone being pulled toward the other bone of the joint. The part of the muscle between the origin and the insertion is the **belly** (figure 10.1). At the attachment point, **tendons** connect each muscle to the bone. Tendons are composed of dense connective tissue and can be long and ropelike, broad and sheetlike (called **aponeuroses;** ap-uh-noo-ROH-sis), or very short.

The specific body movement a muscle contraction causes is called the muscle's **action.** Muscles are typically studied in groups called **agonists** (AG-on-ists) and **antagonists** (an-TAG-on-ists). The action of a single muscle or group of muscles (agonist) is opposed by that of another muscle or group of muscles (antagonist). For example, the biceps brachii flexes (bends) the elbow, and the triceps brachii extends the elbow. In the example of elbow flexion, the biceps brachii is the agonist (flexes), whereas the triceps brachii is the antagonist (extends). When extending the elbow, the

Module 6
Muscular System

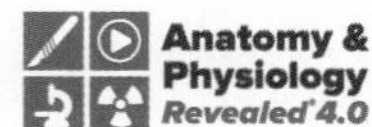

TABLE 10.4 Muscles of Mastication (see figures 10.8 and 10.9)

Muscle	Origin	Insertion	Nerve	Action
Temporalis	Temporal fossa	Anterior portion of mandibular ramus and coronoid process	Mandibular division of trigeminal	Elevates and retracts (moves posteriorly) mandible; involved in excursion (see chapter 8)
Masseter	Zygomatic arch	Lateral side of mandibular ramus	Mandibular division of trigeminal	Elevates and protracts (moves anteriorly) mandible; involved in excursion
Pterygoids				
Lateral	Lateral side of lateral pterygoid plate and greater wing of sphenoid	Condylar process of mandible and articular disk	Mandibular division of trigeminal	Depresses and protracts mandible; involved in excursion; side-to-side movements
Medial	Medial side of lateral pterygoid plate and tuberosity of maxilla	Medial surface of mandible	Mandibular division of trigeminal	Elevates and protracts mandible; involved in excursion; side-to-side movements

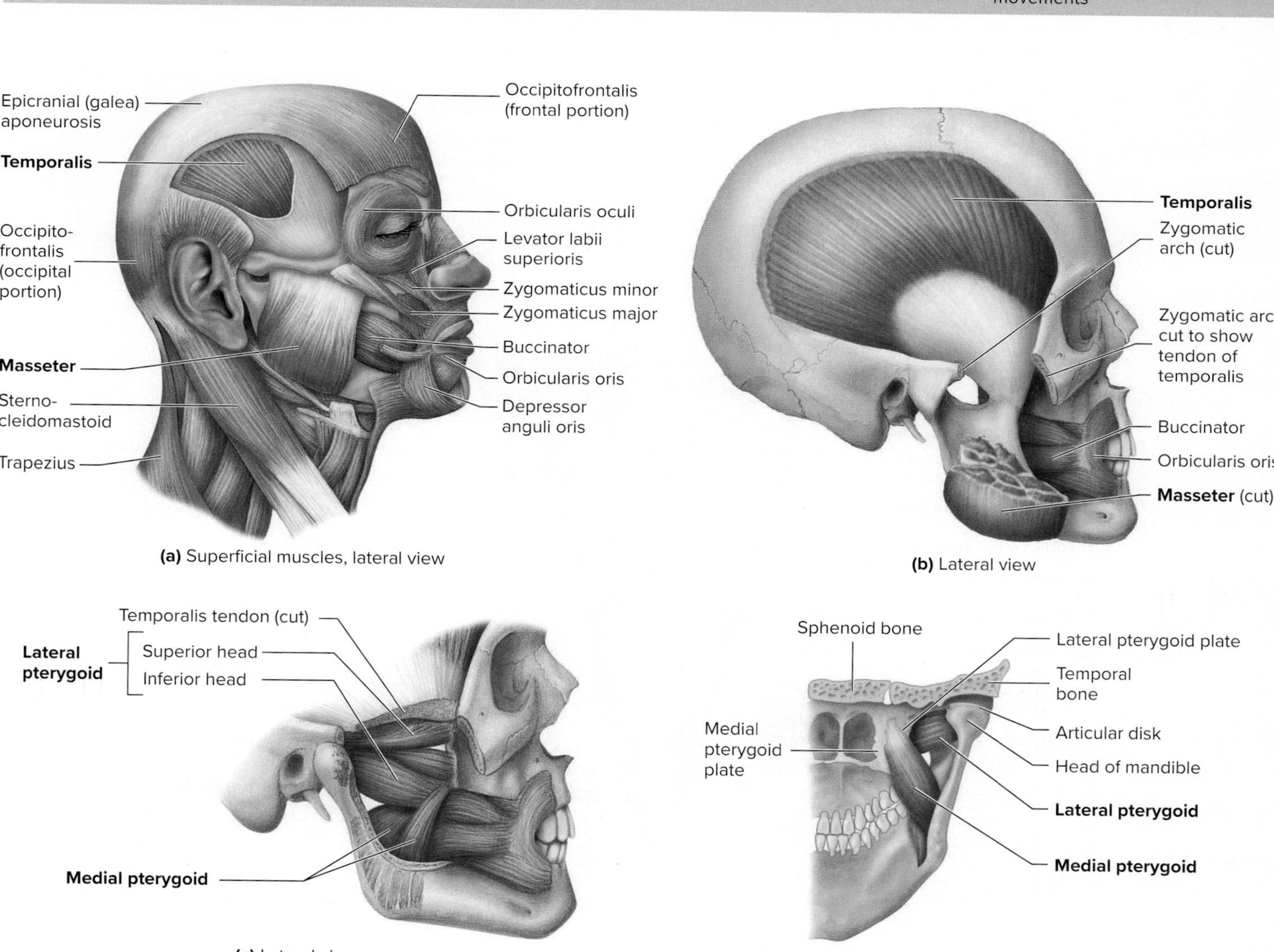

FIGURE 10.9 Muscles of Mastication

(*a*) Lateral view of muscles of mastication. (*b*) The masseter and zygomatic arch are cut away to expose the temporalis. (*c*) The masseter and temporalis muscles are removed, and the zygomatic arch and part of the mandible are cut away to reveal the deeper muscles. (*d*) Frontal section of the skull, showing the pterygoid muscles. (Muscle names in bold are those involved in mastication.) APR

TABLE 10.5 Hyoid Muscles (see figure 10.10)

Muscle	Origin	Insertion	Nerve	Action
Suprahyoid Muscles				
Digastric	Mastoid process (posterior belly)	Mandible near midline (anterior belly)	Posterior belly—facial; anterior belly—mandibular division of trigeminal	Depresses and retracts mandible; elevates hyoid
Geniohyoid	Mental protuberance of mandible	Body of hyoid	Fibers of C1 and C2 with hypoglossal	Protracts hyoid; depresses mandible
Mylohyoid	Body of mandible	Hyoid	Mandibular division of trigeminal	Elevates floor of mouth and tongue; depresses mandible when hyoid is fixed
Stylohyoid	Styloid process	Hyoid	Facial	Elevates hyoid
Infrahyoid Muscles				
Omohyoid	Superior border of scapula	Hyoid	Upper cervical through ansa cervicalis	Depresses hyoid; fixes hyoid when opening mouth
Sternohyoid	Manubrium and first costal cartilage	Hyoid	Upper cervical through ansa cervicalis	Depresses hyoid; fixes hyoid when opening mouth
Sternothyroid	Manubrium and first or second costal cartilage	Thyroid cartilage	Upper cervical through ansa cervicalis	Depresses larynx; fixes hyoid when opening mouth
Thyrohyoid	Thyroid cartilage	Hyoid	Upper cervical, passing with hypoglossal	Depresses hyoid and elevates thyroid cartilage of larynx; fixes hyoid when opening mouth

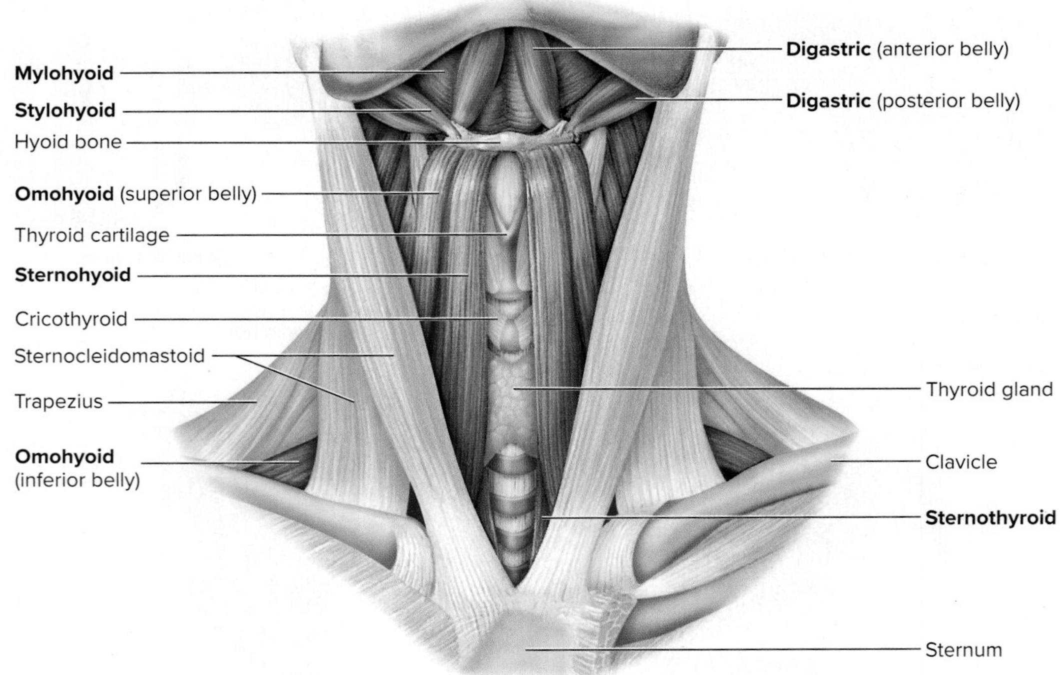

(a) Anterior superficial view

FIGURE 10.10 Hyoid Muscles
(*a*) Anterior superficial hyoid muscles. Hyoid muscles are shown in dark red, and the muscle names are in bold.

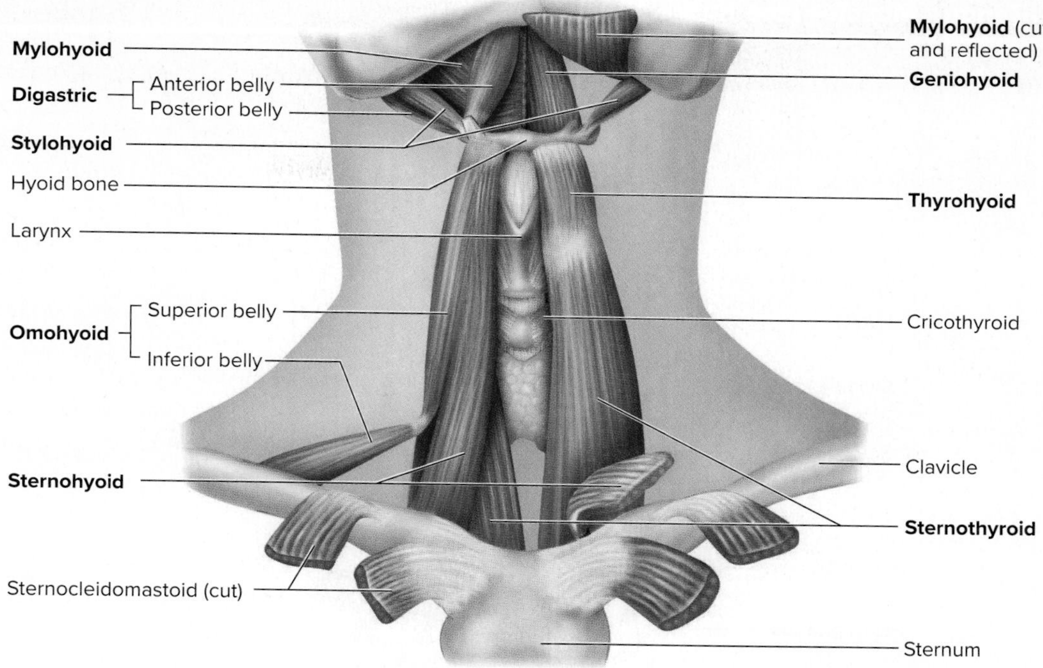

(b) Anterior deep view

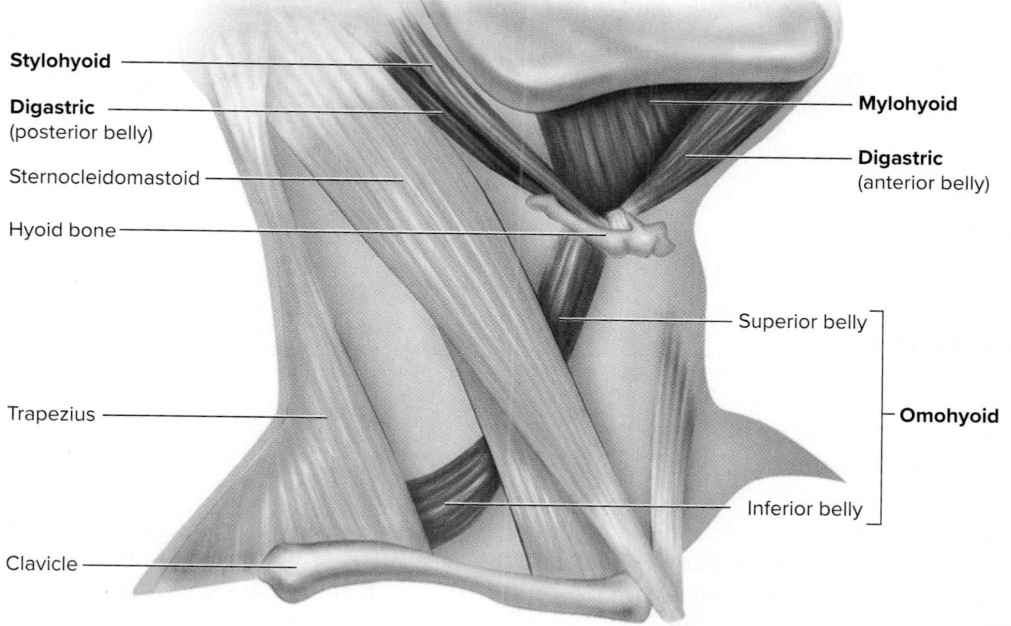

(c) Anterolateral view

FIGURE 10.10 (continued)

(*b*) Anterior deep hyoid muscles. (*c*) Lateral view of hyoid muscles. Both suprahyoid and infrahyoid muscles are included in this image. Hyoid muscles are shown in dark red, and the muscle names are in bold.

TABLE 10.6 Tongue Muscles (see figure 10.11)

Muscle	Origin	Insertion	Nerve	Action
Intrinsic Muscles				
Longitudinal, transverse, and vertical (not illustrated)	Within tongue	Within tongue	Hypoglossal	Change tongue shape
Extrinsic Muscles				
Genioglossus	Mental protuberance of mandible	Tongue	Hypoglossal	Depresses and protrudes tongue
Hyoglossus	Hyoid	Side of tongue	Hypoglossal	Retracts and depresses side of tongue
Styloglossus	Styloid process of temporal bone	Tongue (lateral and inferior)	Hypoglossal	Retracts tongue
Palatoglossus	Soft palate	Tongue	Pharyngeal plexus	Elevates posterior tongue

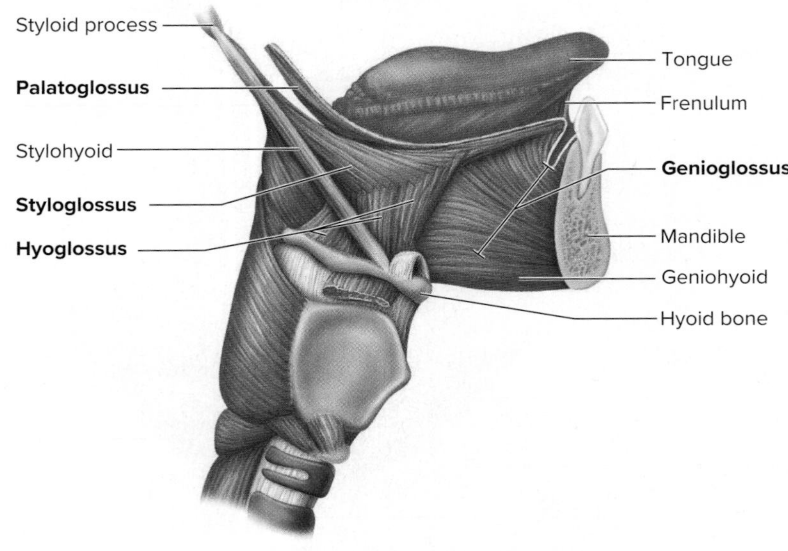

FIGURE 10.11 Tongue Muscles
Right lateral view of tongue muscles. (Muscle names in bold are tongue muscles.)

The muscles of the larynx are listed in table 10.7 and illustrated in figure 10.12*b*. Most of the laryngeal muscles help narrow or close the laryngeal opening so that food does not enter the larynx when a person swallows. A speech therapist spends much of their time helping patients with swallowing to avoid choking. The remaining muscles shorten (relax) the vocal cords to lower the pitch of the voice or lengthen (tense) the vocal cords to raise the pitch of the voice.

Movements of the Eyeball

The eyeball rotates within the orbit to allow vision in a wide range of directions. The movements of each eye are accomplished by six muscles, which are named for the arrangement of their fascicles relative to the eye (table 10.8; figure 10.13).

Each of the four rectus (straight) muscles attaches to the eyeball anterior to the center of the sphere.

1. The superior rectus rotates the anterior portion of the eyeball superiorly, so that the pupil, and thus the gaze, is directed superiorly (looking up).
2. The inferior rectus depresses the gaze.
3. The lateral rectus laterally deviates (abducts) the gaze (looking to the side).
4. The medial rectus medially deviates (adducts) the gaze (looking toward the nose).

TABLE 10.7 Muscles of Swallowing and the Larynx (see figures 10.11 and 10.12)

Muscle	Origin	Insertion	Nerve	Action
Larynx				
Arytenoids				
Oblique (not illustrated)	Arytenoid cartilage	Opposite arytenoid cartilage	Recurrent laryngeal	Narrows opening to larynx
Transverse (not illustrated)	Arytenoid cartilage	Opposite arytenoid cartilage	Recurrent laryngeal	Narrows opening to larynx
Cricoarytenoids				
Lateral (not illustrated)	Lateral side of cricoid cartilage	Arytenoid cartilage	Recurrent laryngeal	Narrows opening to larynx
Posterior (not illustrated)	Posterior side of cricoid cartilage	Arytenoid cartilage	Recurrent laryngeal	Widens opening of larynx
Cricothyroid	Anterior cricoid cartilage	Thyroid cartilage	Superior laryngeal	Lengthens (tenses) vocal cords
Thyroarytenoid (not illustrated)	Thyroid cartilage	Arytenoid cartilage	Recurrent laryngeal	Shortens (relaxes) vocal cords
Vocalis (not illustrated)	Thyroid cartilage	Arytenoid cartilage	Recurrent laryngeal	Shortens (relaxes) vocal cords
Soft Palate				
Levator veli palatini	Temporal bone and pharyngotympanic	Soft palate	Pharyngeal plexus	Elevates soft palate during swallowing
Palatoglossus	Soft palate	Tongue	Pharyngeal plexus	Narrows fauces; elevates posterior tongue
Palatopharyngeus	Soft palate	Pharynx	Pharyngeal plexus	Narrows fauces; depresses palate; elevates pharynx
Tensor veli palatini	Sphenoid and auditory tube	Soft palate division of auditory tube	Mandibular, division of trigeminal	Tenses soft palate; opens auditory tube
Uvulae	Posterior nasal spine	Uvula	Pharyngeal plexus	Elevates uvula
Pharynx				
Pharyngeal constrictors				
Inferior	Thyroid and cricoid cartilages	Pharyngeal raphe	Pharyngeal plexus and external laryngeal nerve	Narrows inferior portion of pharynx in swallowing
Middle	Stylohyoid ligament and hyoid	Pharyngeal raphe	Pharyngeal plexus	Narrows pharynx in swallowing
Superior	Medial pterygoid plate, mandible, floor of mouth, and side of tongue	Pharyngeal raphe	Pharyngeal plexus	Narrows superior portion of pharynx in swallowing
Salpingopharyngeus	Auditory tube	Pharynx	Pharyngeal plexus	Elevates pharynx; opens auditory tube in swallowing
Stylopharyngeus	Styloid process	Pharynx	Glossopharyngeus	Elevates pharynx

The superior rectus and inferior rectus are not completely straight in their orientation to the eye; thus, they also medially deviate the gaze as they contract.

The oblique (at an angle) muscles insert onto the posterolateral margin of the eyeball, so that both muscles laterally deviate the gaze as they contract (see chapter 15, figure 15.9). (1) The superior oblique elevates the posterior part of the eye, thus directing the pupil inferiorly and depressing the gaze. (2) The inferior oblique elevates the gaze.

Predict 2

Strabismus (stra-BIZ-muss) is a condition in which one or both eyes deviate in a medial or lateral direction. In some cases, strabismus is caused by a weakness in either the medial or the lateral rectus muscle. If the lateral rectus of the right eye is weak, in which direction does the eye deviate?

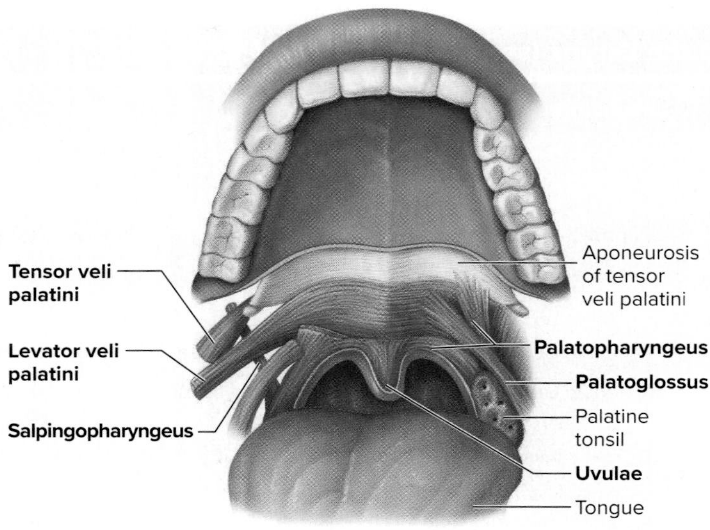

(a) Anterior view

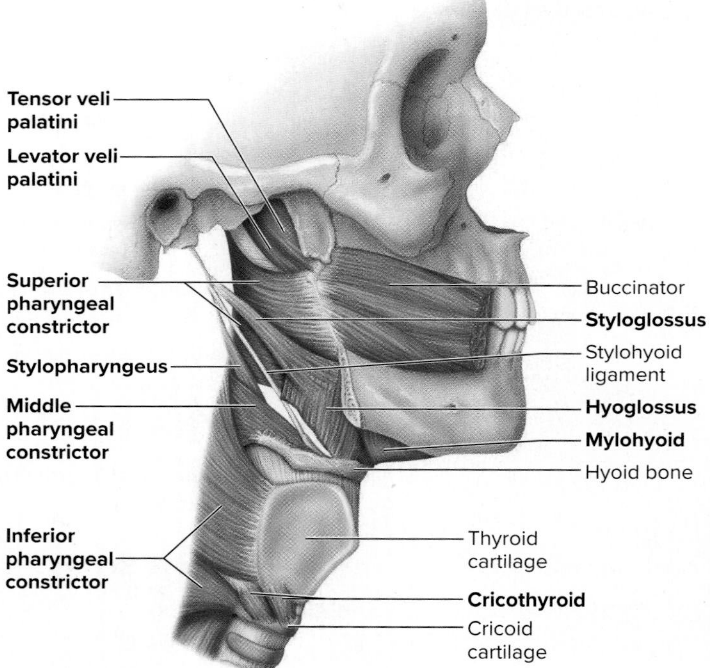

(b) Lateral view

FIGURE 10.12 Muscles of the Palate, Pharynx, and Larynx
(*a*) Anterior-inferior view of the palate. The palatoglossus and part of the palatopharyngeus muscles are cut on one side to reveal the deeper muscles. (*b*) Lateral view of the palate, pharynx, and larynx. Part of the mandible has been removed to reveal the deeper structures. (Muscle names in bold are muscles of swallowing and tongue movement.)

TABLE 10.8 Muscles Moving the Eye (see figure 10.13)

Muscle	Origin	Insertion	Nerve	Action
Oblique				
Inferior	Orbital plate of maxilla	Sclera of eye	Oculomotor	Elevates and laterally moves eye
Superior	Common tendinous ring	Sclera of eye	Trochlear	Depresses and laterally moves eye
Rectus				
Inferior	Common tendinous ring	Sclera of eye	Oculomotor	Depresses and medially moves eye
Lateral	Common tendinous ring	Sclera of eye	Abducens	Laterally moves eye
Medial	Common tendinous ring	Sclera of eye	Oculomotor	Medially moves eye
Superior	Common tendinous ring	Sclera of eye	Oculomotor	Elevates and medially moves eye

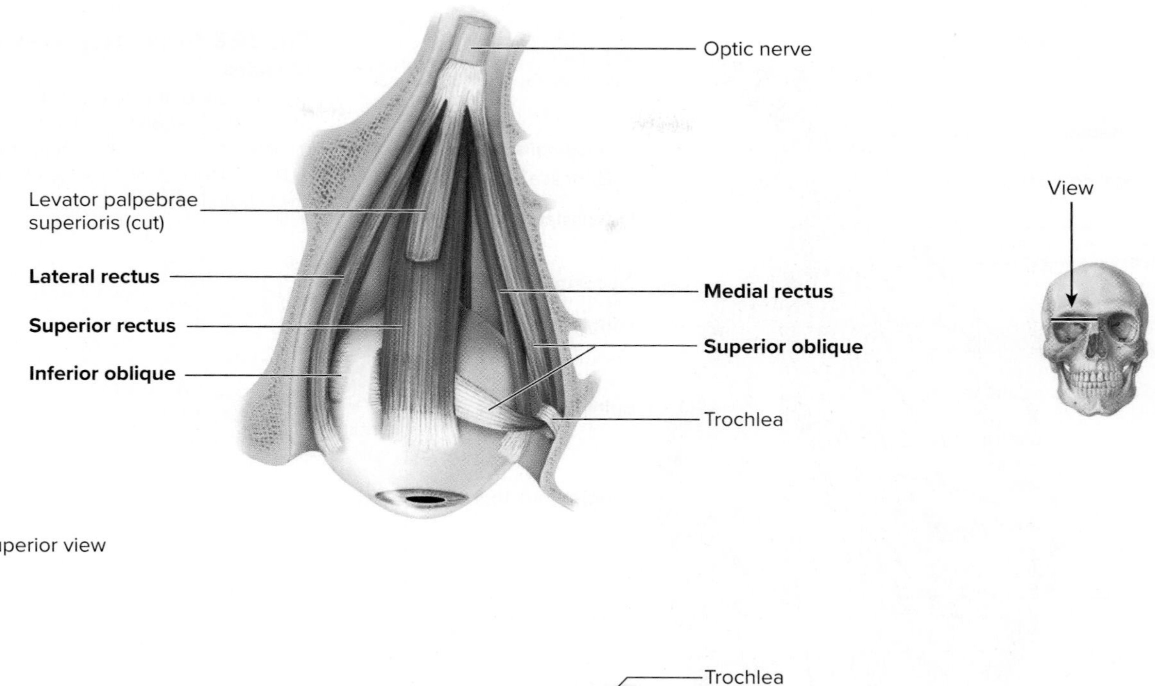

(a) Superior view

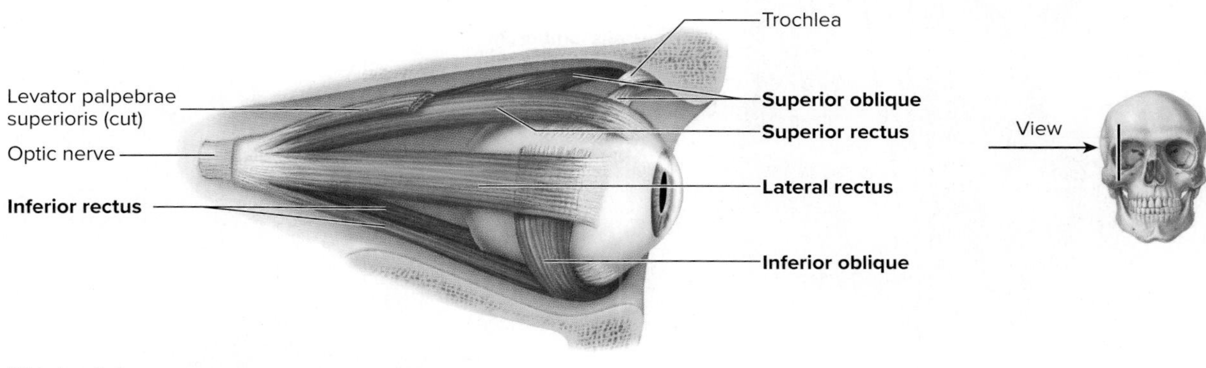

(b) Lateral view

FIGURE 10.13 Muscles That Move the Right Eyeball
(*a*) Superior view of muscles in the eye orbit. (*b*) Lateral view of muscles in the eye orbit. (Names of muscles of eye movement are in bold.)

ASSESS YOUR PROGRESS

12. *Name the muscles responsible for opening and closing the jaw.*
13. *What muscles are used to cause lateral and medial excursion of the jaw?*
14. *Contrast the movements produced by the extrinsic and intrinsic tongue muscles.*
15. *Explain the interaction of the suprahyoid and infrahyoid muscles in swallowing.*
16. *Which muscles open and close the openings to the auditory tube and to the larynx?*
17. *Describe the muscles of the eye and the movements they produce.*

10.3 Trunk Muscles

LEARNING OUTCOMES

After reading this section, you should be able to

A. **Describe the muscles of the vertebral column and the actions they accomplish.**
B. **List the muscles of the thorax and give each of their actions.**
C. **Describe the muscles of the abdominal wall and explain their actions.**
D. **List and describe the muscles of the pelvic diaphragm and perineum.**

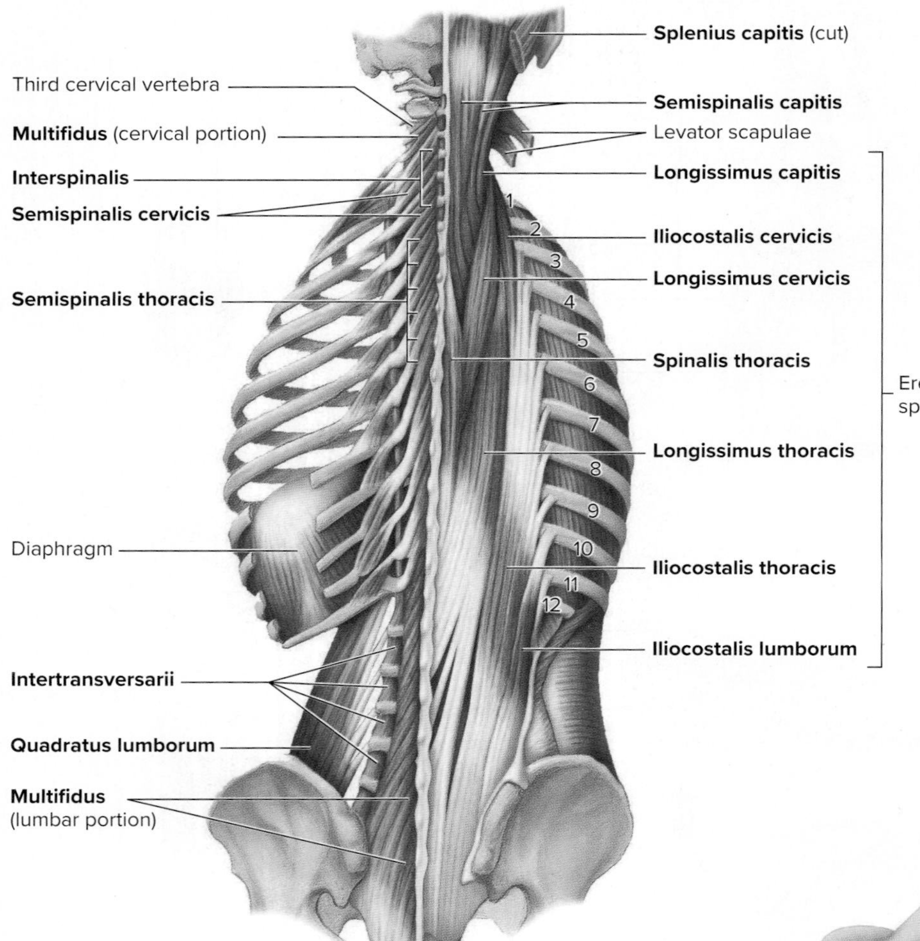

FIGURE 10.14 Deep Neck and Back Muscles

On the right of this figure, the erector spinae group of muscles is shown. On the left of this figure, these muscles are removed to reveal the deeper back muscles. (Names of muscles of the neck and back are in bold.) APR

Muscles Moving the Vertebral Column

The muscles that extend, laterally flex, and rotate the vertebral column are divided into superficial and deep groups (table 10.9). In general, the muscles of the superficial group connect the vertebrae to the ribs, whereas the muscles of the deep group connect vertebrae together. These back muscles are very strong to maintain erect posture. The **erector spinae** (ee-REK-tor SPEE-nee) group of muscles on each side of the back consists of three subgroups: (1) the **iliocostalis** (IL-ee-oh-kos-TAH-lis), (2) the **longissimus** (lon-GIS-i-mus), and (3) the **spinalis** (spy-NAY-lis). The longissimus group accounts for most of the muscle mass in the lower back (figure 10.14). The deepest muscles of the back attach between the spinous and transverse processes of individual vertebrae (figure 10.15).

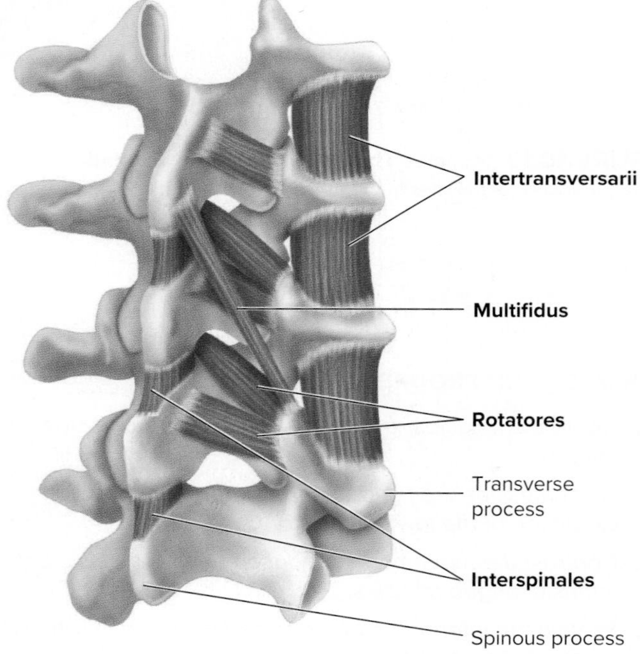

FIGURE 10.15 Vertebral Muscles

Deep muscles associated with the vertebrae are shown. (Muscle names are in bold.)

Thoracic Muscles

The muscles of the thorax are mainly involved in the control of breathing (see chapter 23). Four major groups of thoracic muscles

TABLE 10.9 Muscles Acting on the Vertebral Column (see figures 10.5, 10.6, 10.14, and 10.15)

Muscle	Origin	Insertion	Nerve	Action
Superficial				
Erector spinae (divides into three columns)				
Iliocostalis				
Cervicis	Superior six ribs	Transverse processes of middle cervical vertebrae	Dorsal rami of thoracic nerves	Extends, laterally flexes, and rotates vertebral column
Thoracis	Inferior six ribs	Superior six ribs	Dorsal rami of thoracic nerves	Extends, laterally flexes, and rotates vertebral column
Lumborum	Sacrum, ilium, and lumbar vertebrae	Inferior six ribs	Dorsal rami of thoracic and lumbar nerves	Extends, laterally flexes, and rotates vertebral column
Longissimus				
Capitis	Upper thoracic and lower cervical vertebrae	Mastoid process	Dorsal rami of cervical nerves	Extends head
Cervicis	Upper thoracic vertebrae	Transverse processes of upper cervical vertebrae	Dorsal rami of cervical nerves	Extends neck
Thoracis	Ribs and lower thoracic vertebrae	Transverse processes of upper lumbar vertebrae and ribs	Dorsal rami of thoracic and lumbar nerves	Extends vertebral column
Spinalis				
Cervicis (not illustrated)	C6–C7	Spinous processes of C2–C3	Dorsal rami of cervical nerves	Extends neck
Thoracis	T11–L2	Spinous processes of middle and upper thoracic vertebrae	Dorsal rami of thoracic nerves	Extends vertebral column
Semispinalis				
Cervicis	Transverse processes of T2–T5	Spinous processes of C2–C5	Dorsal rami of cervical nerves	Extends neck
Thoracis	Transverse processes of T5–T11	Spinous processes of C5–T4	Dorsal rami of thoracic nerves	Extends vertebral column
Splenius cervicis	Spinous processes of C3–C5	Transverse processes of C1–C3	Dorsal rami of cervical nerves	Rotates and extends neck
Deep				
Interspinales	Spinous processes of all vertebrae	Next superior spinous process	Dorsal rami of spinal nerves	Extends back and neck
Intertransversarii	Transverse processes of all vertebrae	Next superior transverse process	Dorsal rami of spinal nerves	Laterally flexes vertebral column
Multifidus	Transverse processes of vertebrae; posterior surface of sacrum and ilium	Spinous processes of superior vertebrae	Dorsal rami of spinal nerves	Extends and rotates vertebral column
Quadratus lumborum	Iliac crest and lower lumbar vertebrae	Twelfth rib and upper lumbar vertebrae	Upper lumbar	Laterally flexes vertebral column and depresses twelfth rib
Rotatores	Transverse processes of all vertebrae	Base of spinous process of superior vertebrae	Dorsal rami of spinal nerves	Extends and rotates vertebral column

TABLE 10.10 Muscles of the Thorax (see figure 10.16)

Muscle	Origin	Insertion	Nerve	Action
Diaphragm	Interior of ribs, sternum, and lumbar vertebrae	Central tendon of diaphragm	Phrenic	Inspiration depresses floor of thorax
Intercostals				
External	Inferior margin of each rib	Superior border of next rib below	Intercostal	Quiet inspiration elevates ribs
Internal	Superior margin of each rib	Inferior border of next rib above	Intercostal	Forced expiration depresses ribs
Scalene muscles				
Anterior	Transverse processes of C3–C6	First rib	Cervical plexus	Elevates first rib
Medial	Transverse processes of C2–C6	First rib	Cervical plexus	Elevates first rib
Posterior	Transverse processes of C4–C6	Second rib	Cervical and brachial plexuses	Elevates second rib

are associated with the rib cage, which helps air flow into the lungs. Changes in the diameter of the rib cage are important for determining airflow into and out of the lungs. (table 10.10; figure 10.16). The **scalene** (SKAY-leen) muscles elevate the first two ribs during more forceful inspiration. The **external intercostals** (IN-ter-KOS-tulz; between ribs) elevate the ribs during quiet, resting inspiration. The **internal intercostals** and **transversus thoracis** (thoh-RAH-sis) muscles depress the ribs during forced expiration.

The **diaphragm** (DIE-ah-fram; figure 10.16*a*) is the muscle responsible for normal, quiet breathing. It is a dome-shaped muscle; when it contracts, the dome flattens slightly, causing the volume of the thoracic cavity to increase and resulting in inspiration. If this dome of skeletal muscle or the phrenic nerve controlling it is severely damaged, the amount of air moving into and out of the lungs may be so small that the individual cannot survive without the aid of an artificial respirator.

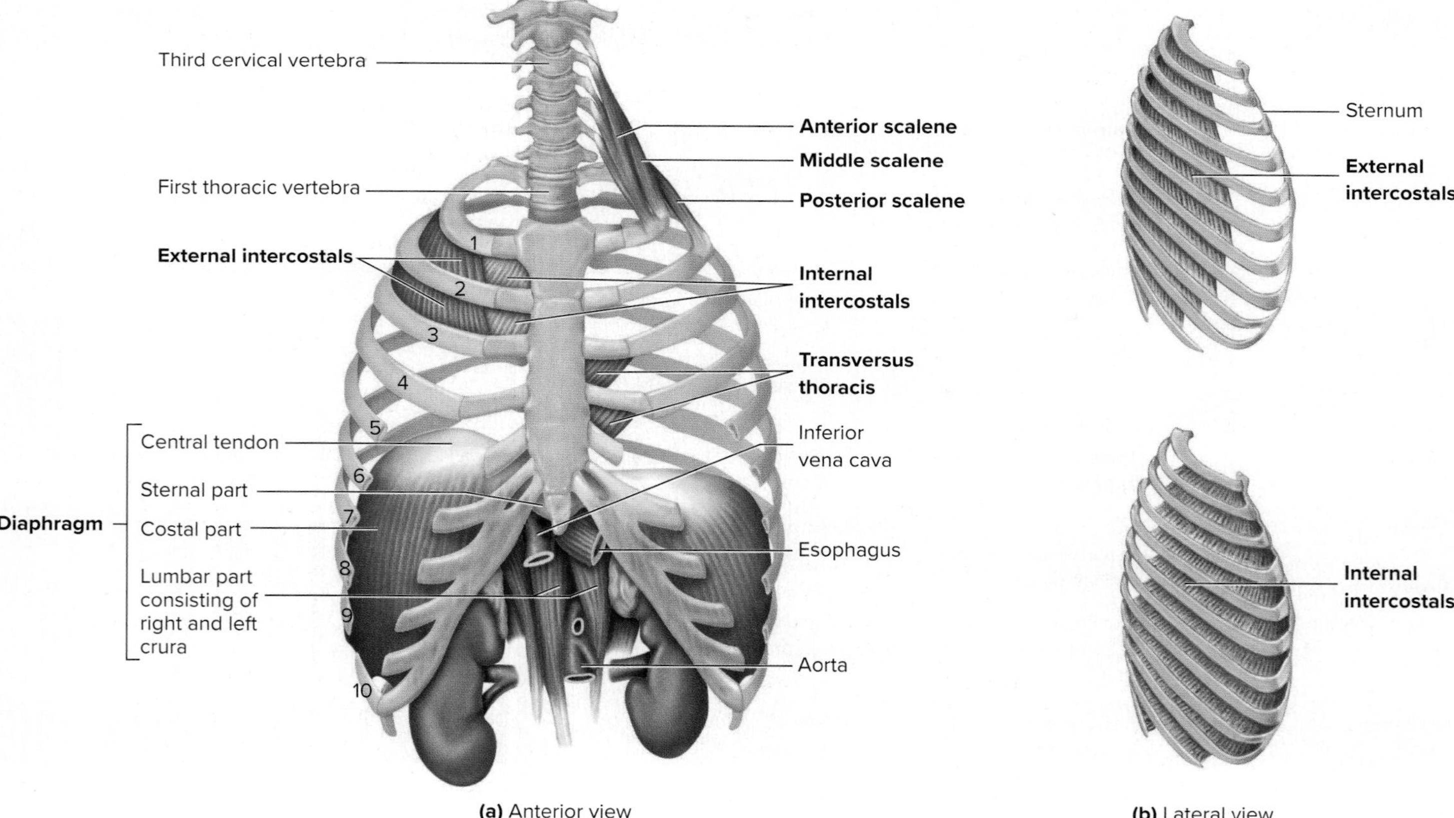

FIGURE 10.16 Muscles of the Thorax
The muscles of the thorax are important for respiration. (Muscle names are in bold.) APR

Abdominal Wall

The muscles of the anterior abdominal wall include the (1) rectus abdominis, (2) external abdominal oblique, (3) internal abdominal oblique, and (4) transversus abdominis (table 10.11; figures 10.17 and 10.18). These muscles flex and rotate the vertebral column. Contraction of the abdominal muscles when the vertebral column is stationary decreases the volume of the abdominal cavity and the thoracic cavity and can aid in such

TABLE 10.11 Muscles of the Abdominal Wall (see figures 10.3a, 10.14, 10.17, and 10.18)

Muscle	Origin	Insertion	Nerve	Action
Anterior				
Rectus abdominis	Pubic crest and symphysis pubis	Xiphoid process and inferior ribs	Branches of lower thoracic	Flexes vertebral column; compresses abdominal wall
External abdominal oblique	Fifth to twelfth ribs	Iliac crest, inguinal ligament, and rectus sheath	Branches of lower thoracic	Flexes and rotates vertebral column; compresses abdominal wall; depresses thorax
Internal abdominal oblique	Iliac crest, inguinal ligament, and lumbar fascia	Tenth to twelfth ribs and rectus sheath	Lower thoracic	Flexes and rotates vertebral column; compresses abdominal wall; depresses thorax
Transversus abdominis	Seventh to twelfth costal cartilages, lumbar fascia, iliac crest, and inguinal ligament	Xiphoid process, linea alba, and pubic tubercle	Lower thoracic	Compresses abdominal wall

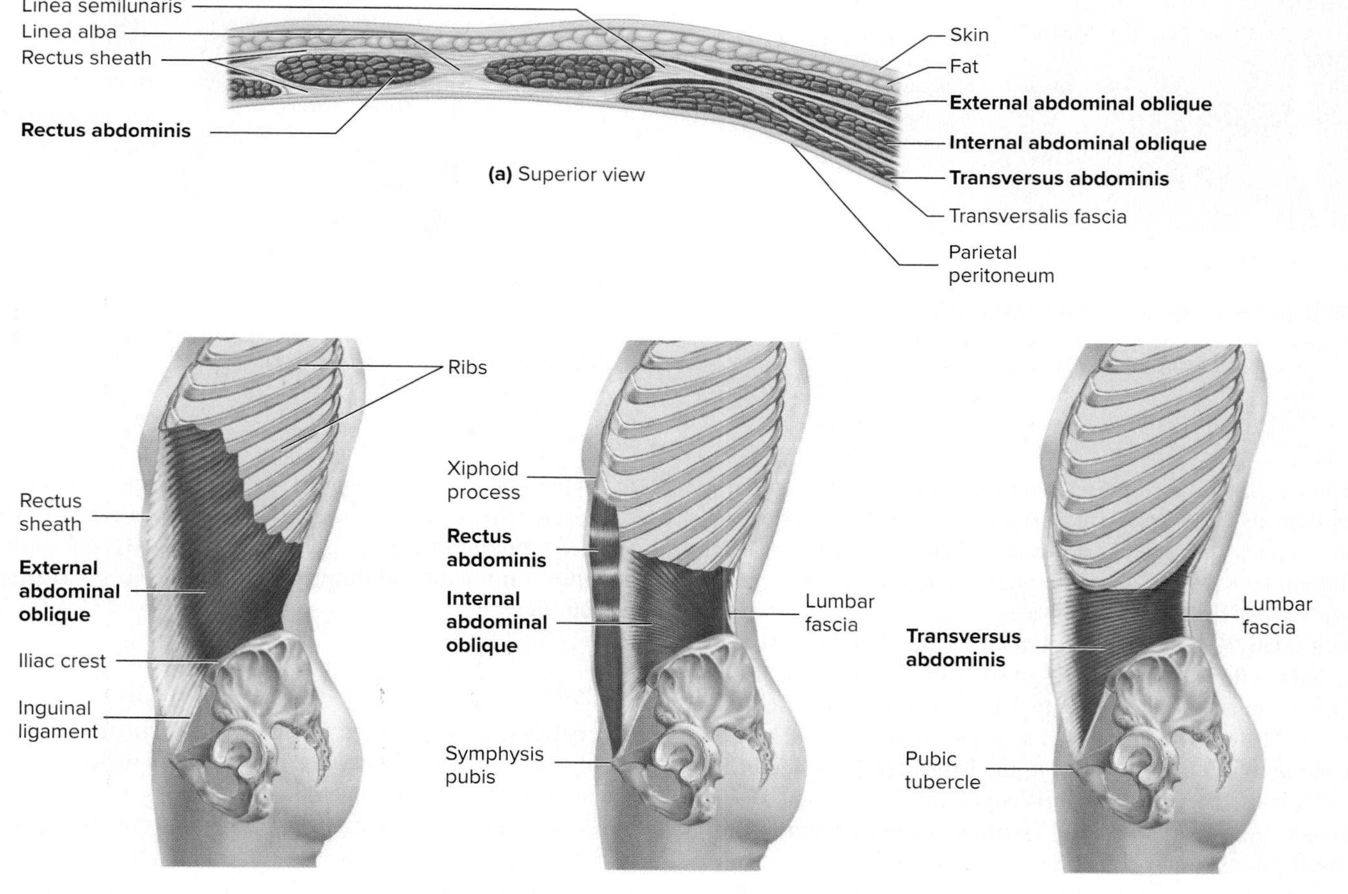

FIGURE 10.17 Anterior Abdominal Wall Muscles
(*a*) Cross section superior to the umbilicus. (*b*) Abdominal muscles shown individually. (Muscle names are in bold.) APR

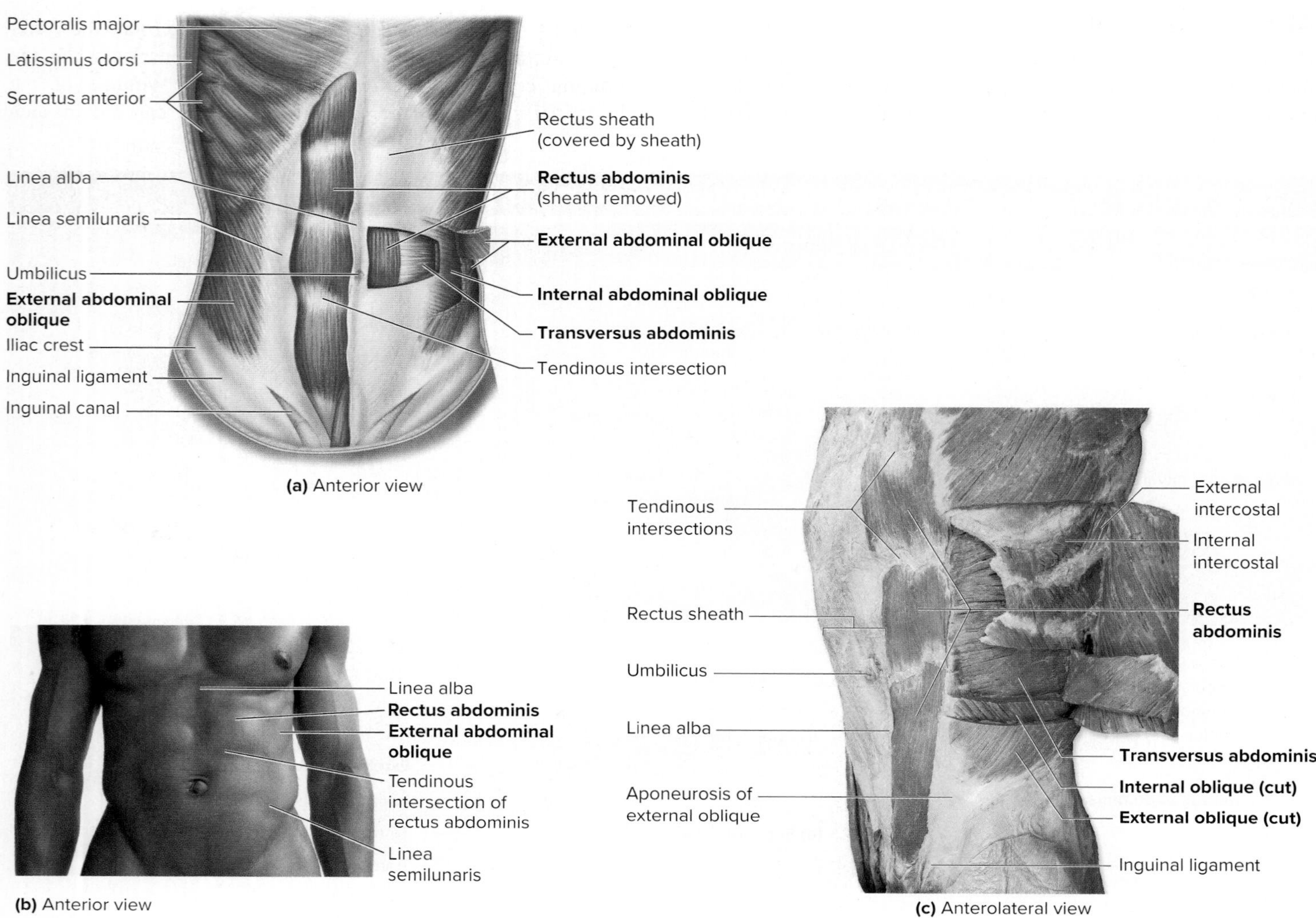

FIGURE 10.18 Anterior Abdominal Wall Muscles
(*a*) Windows in the side reveal the various muscle layers. (*b*) Surface anatomy of anterior abdominal muscle. (*c*) Muscles of the abdomen as viewed in a cadaver. (Muscles of the abdominal wall are in bold.) (b) Jill Braaten/McGraw Hill Education; (c) Christine Eckel/McGraw Hill Education

functions as forced expiration, vomiting, defecation, coughing, and childbirth. The criss-cross layering of all the abdominal muscles creates a strong anterior wall, which holds in and protects the abdominal viscera. This is especially important because the anterior wall is not supported by bone.

In a relatively muscular person with little body fat, a vertical line called the **linea alba** (LIN-ee-ah AL-bah), or *white line,* is visible. It is an area consisting of only dense regular connective tissue (see figure 10.18). The linea alba extends from the xiphoid process of the sternum through the navel to the pubis. On each side of the linea alba is the **rectus abdominis** (see figures 10.17 and 10.18), surrounded by a **rectus sheath. Tendinous intersections** (tendinous inscriptions) transect the rectus abdominis at three, or sometimes more, locations, causing the abdominal wall of a lean, well-muscled person to appear segmented (a "six-pack"). Lateral to the rectus abdominis is the **linea semilunaris** (sem-ee-loo-NAR-is; a crescent- or half-moon-shaped line); lateral to it are three layers of muscle (figures 10.17 and 10.18). From superficial (outermost) to deep (innermost), these muscles are the **external abdominal oblique, internal abdominal oblique,** and **transversus abdominis.**

Pelvic Diaphragm and Perineum

The pelvis is a ring of bone (see chapter 7) with an inferior opening that is closed by a muscular wall, through which the anus and the urogenital openings penetrate (table 10.12). The pelvic floor is called the **pelvic diaphragm.** It consists of the **coccygeus** (kok-SIH-jee-us) muscle and the **levator ani** (AN-eye) muscle. Just inferior to (beneath) the pelvic diaphragm is a diamond-shaped area called the **perineum** (PER-ih-NEE-um; figure 10.19). The anterior half of the perineum is the **urogenital triangle,** and the

TABLE 10.12 Muscles of the Pelvic Diaphragm and Perineum (see figure 10.19)

Muscle	Origin	Insertion	Nerve	Action
Pelvic Diaphragm				
Coccygeus	Ischial spine	Coccyx	S3 and S4	Forms pelvic floor; supports pelvic organs
Levator ani	Posterior pubis and ischial spine	Sacrum and coccyx	Fourth sacral	Elevates anus; supports pelvic organs
Perineum				
Urogenital triangle				
Bulbospongiosus	Male—central tendon of perineum and median raphe of penis	Dorsal surface of penis and bulb of penis	Pudendal	Compresses base of penis; ejects urine or semen; erects penis
	Female—central tendon of perineum	Base of clitoris	Pudendal	Erects clitoris
Ischiocavernosus	Ischial ramus	Corpus cavernosum	Perineal	Compresses base of penis or clitoris
External urethral sphincter (not illustrated)	Pubic ramus	Median raphe	Pudendal	Constricts urethra to stop urine flow
Transverse perineal muscle				
Deep	Ischial ramus	Median raphe	Pudendal	Supports pelvic floor
Superficial	Ischial ramus	Central perineal	Pudendal	Fixes central tendon
Anal triangle				
External anal sphincter	Coccyx	Central tendon of perineum	Fourth sacral and pudendal	Keeps orifice of anal canal closed; relaxes during defecation

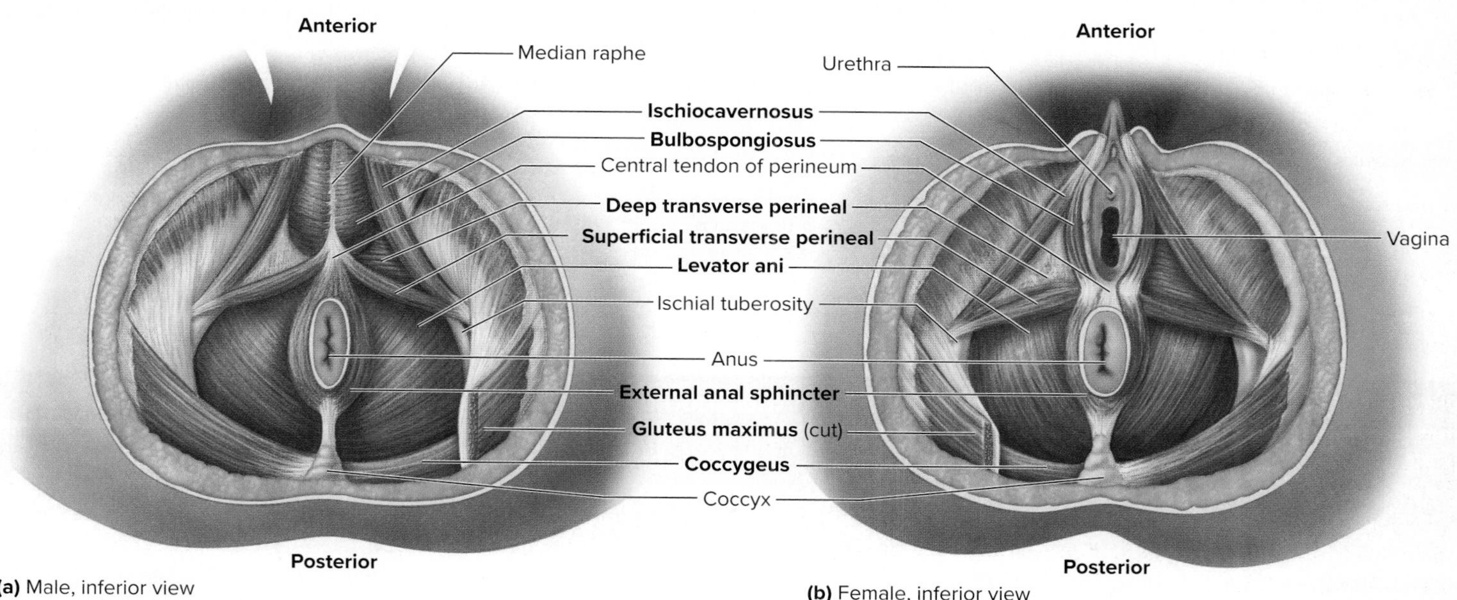

FIGURE 10.19 Muscles of the Pelvic Diaphragm and Perineum
(*a*) Male pelvic diaphragm and perineum. (*b*) Female pelvic diaphragm and perineum. (Muscle names are in bold.)

posterior half of the perineum is the **anal triangle** (see chapter 28). During pregnancy, the muscles of the pelvic diaphragm and urogenital triangle may be stretched by the extra weight of the fetus, and specific exercises are designed to strengthen them.

ASSESS YOUR PROGRESS

18. *List the actions of the group of back muscles that attaches to the vertebrae or ribs (or both). What is the name of the superficial subgroup?*

19. *Name the muscle that is mainly responsible for respiratory movements. What other muscles aid this movement?*

20. *Explain the anatomical basis for the segments ("cuts") seen on a well-muscled individual's abdomen. What are the functions of the abdominal muscles? List the muscles of the anterior abdominal wall.*

21. *What openings penetrate the pelvic diaphragm muscles? Name the area inferior to the pelvic diaphragm.*

10.4 Upper Limb Muscles

LEARNING OUTCOMES

After reading this section, you should be able to

A. **Describe the movements of the scapula and list the muscles associated with it.**
B. **Name and locate the muscles acting on the shoulder and arm and explain their movements.**
C. **List and describe the muscles and movements of the forearm, wrist, hand, and fingers.**
D. **Distinguish between extrinsic and intrinsic hand muscles.**

The major connection of the upper limb to the body is accomplished by muscles (tables 10.13 and 10.14; figure 10.20). The muscles of the upper limb include those that move the scapula and those that move the arm, forearm, and hand.

TABLE 10.13 Muscles Acting on the Scapula (see figure 10.20)

Muscle	Origin	Insertion	Nerve	Action
Levator scapulae	Transverse processes of C1–C4	Superior angle of scapula	Dorsal scapular	Elevates, retracts, and rotates scapula; laterally flexes neck
Pectoralis minor	Third to fifth ribs	Coracoid process of scapula	Medial pectoral	Depresses scapula or elevates ribs
Rhomboideus				
Major	Spinous processes of T1–T4	Medial border of scapula	Dorsal scapular	Retracts, rotates, and fixes scapula
Minor	Spinous processes of C6–C7	Medial border of scapula	Dorsal scapular	Retracts, slightly elevates, rotates, and fixes scapula
Serratus anterior	First to eighth or ninth ribs	Medial border of scapula	Long thoracic	Rotates and protracts scapula; elevates ribs
Subclavius	First rib	Clavicle	Subclavian	Fixes clavicle or elevates first rib
Trapezius	External occipital protuberance, ligamentum nuchae, and spinous processes of C7–T12	Clavicle, acromion process, and scapular spine	Accessory and cervical plexus	Elevates, depresses, retracts, rotates, and fixes scapula; extends neck

TABLE 10.14 Overview of Muscle Actions on the Shoulder and Arm

Flexion	Extension	Abduction	Adduction	Medial Rotation	Lateral Rotation
Deltoid	Deltoid	Deltoid	Pectoralis major	Pectoralis major	Deltoid
Pectoralis major	Teres major	Supraspinatus	Latissimus dorsi	Teres major	Infraspinatus
Coracobrachialis	Latissimus dorsi		Teres major	Latissimus dorsi	Teres minor
Biceps brachii	Pectoralis major		Teres minor	Deltoid	
	Triceps brachii		Triceps brachii	Subscapularis	
			Coracobrachialis		

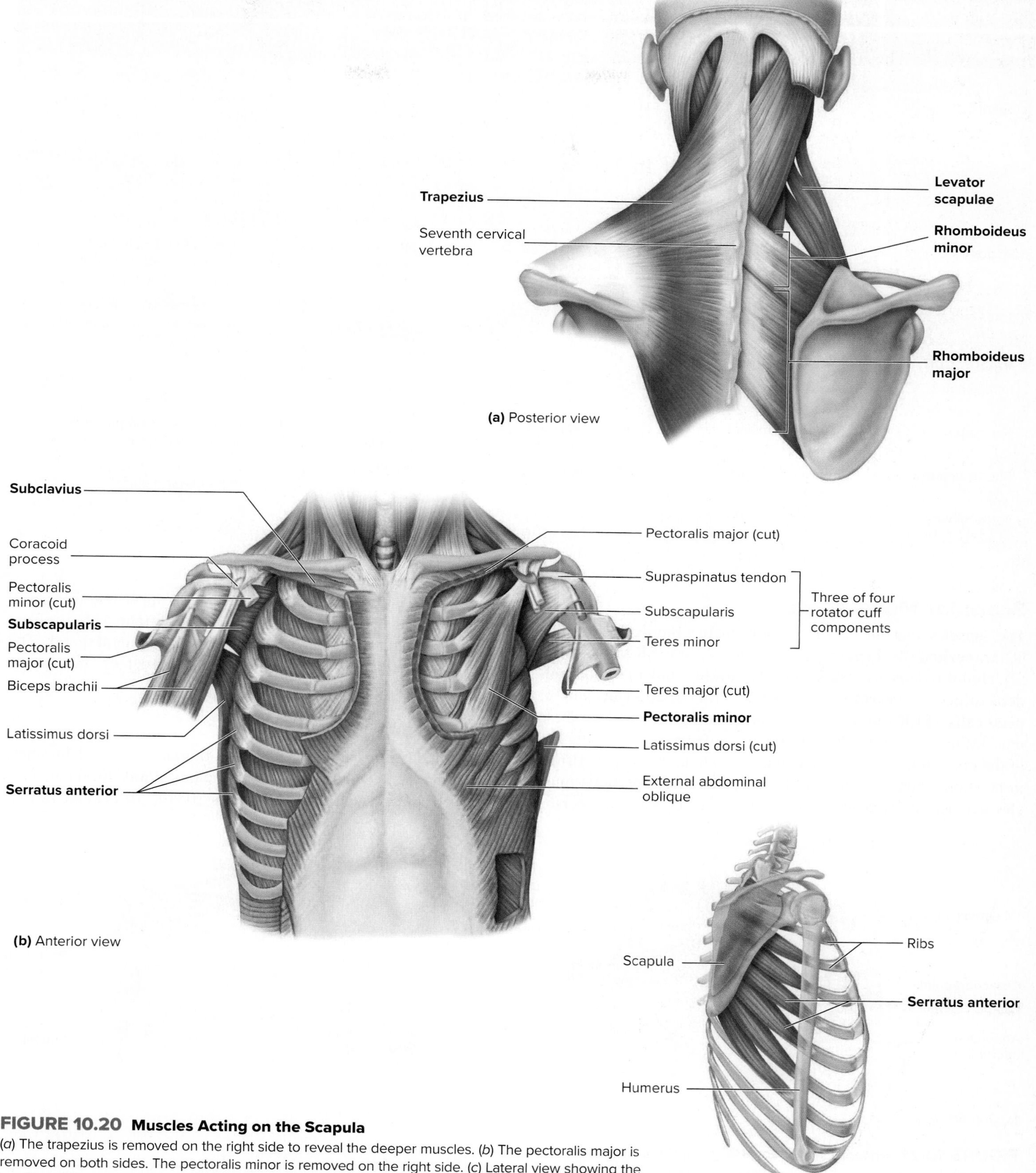

FIGURE 10.20 Muscles Acting on the Scapula
(*a*) The trapezius is removed on the right side to reveal the deeper muscles. (*b*) The pectoralis major is removed on both sides. The pectoralis minor is removed on the right side. (*c*) Lateral view showing the location of the serratus anterior. (The bold terms denote muscles that act on the scapula.) APR

TABLE 10.15 Muscles Acting on the Arm (see figures 10.20–10.23)

Muscle	Origin	Insertion	Nerve	Action
Coracobrachialis	Coracoid process of scapula	Midshaft of humerus	Musculocutaneous	Adducts arm and flexes shoulder
Deltoid	Clavicle, acromion process, and scapular spine	Deltoid tuberosity	Axillary	Flexes and extends shoulder; abducts and medially and laterally rotates arm
Latissimus dorsi	Spinous processes of T7–L5; sacrum and iliac crest; inferior angle of scapula in some people	Medial crest of intertubercular groove	Thoracodorsal	Adducts and medially rotates arm; extends shoulder
Pectoralis major	Clavicle, sternum, superior six costal cartilages, and abdominal aponeurosis	Lateral crest of intertubercular groove	Medial and lateral pectoral	Flexes shoulder; adducts and medially rotates arm; extends shoulder from flexed position
Teres major	Lateral border of scapula	Medial crest of intertubercular groove	Lower subscapular C5 and C6	Extends shoulder; adducts and medially rotates arm
Rotator Cuff				
Infraspinatus	Infraspinous fossa of scapula	Greater tubercle of humerus	Suprascapular C5 and C6	Laterally rotates arm; holds head of humerus in place
Subscapularis	Subscapular fossa	Lesser tubercle of humerus	Upper and lower subscapular C5 and C6	Medially rotates arm; holds head of humerus in place
Supraspinatus	Supraspinous fossa	Greater tubercle of humerus	Suprascapular C5 and C6	Abducts arm; holds head of humerus in place
Teres minor	Lateral border of scapula	Greater tubercle of humerus	Axillary C5 and C6	Laterally rotates and adducts arm; holds head of humerus in place

Scapular Movements

The muscles that attach the scapula to the thorax include the (1) **trapezius,** (2) **levator scapulae** (le-VAY-tor SKAP-you-lee), (3) **rhomboideus** (rom-BOY-dee-us) **major** and (4) **rhomboideus minor,** (5) **serratus** (ser-AH-tus; serrated) **anterior,** and (6) **pectoralis** (PEK-toh-RA-lis) **minor** (see figure 10.22). These muscles move the scapula, permitting a wide range of movements of the upper limb, or they act as fixators to hold the scapula firmly in position when the arm muscles contract. The superficial muscles that act on the scapula can easily be seen on a living person (see figure 10.5*b*): The trapezius forms the upper line from each shoulder to the neck, and the origin of the serratus anterior from the first eight or nine ribs can be seen along the lateral thorax. The serratus anterior inserts onto the medial border of the scapula (figure 10.20*c*).

Arm Movements

Each of our arms is attached to the thorax by several muscles, including the **pectoralis major** and the **latissimus dorsi** (lah-TIS-i-mus DOR-sigh; table 10.15; figures 10.20*b*, 10.21, and 10.22).

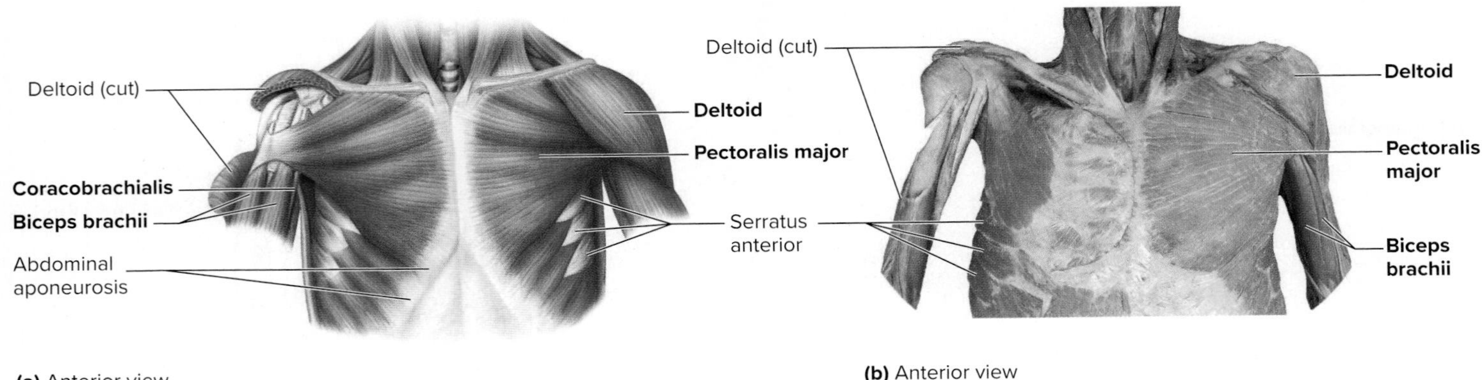

FIGURE 10.21 Anterior Muscles Attaching the Upper Limb to the Body
(*a*) Anterior pectoral muscles. (Names of muscles attaching the upper limb to the body are in bold.) (*b*) Cadaver photo showing anterior pectoral muscles.
(b) Christine Eckel/McGraw Hill Education APR

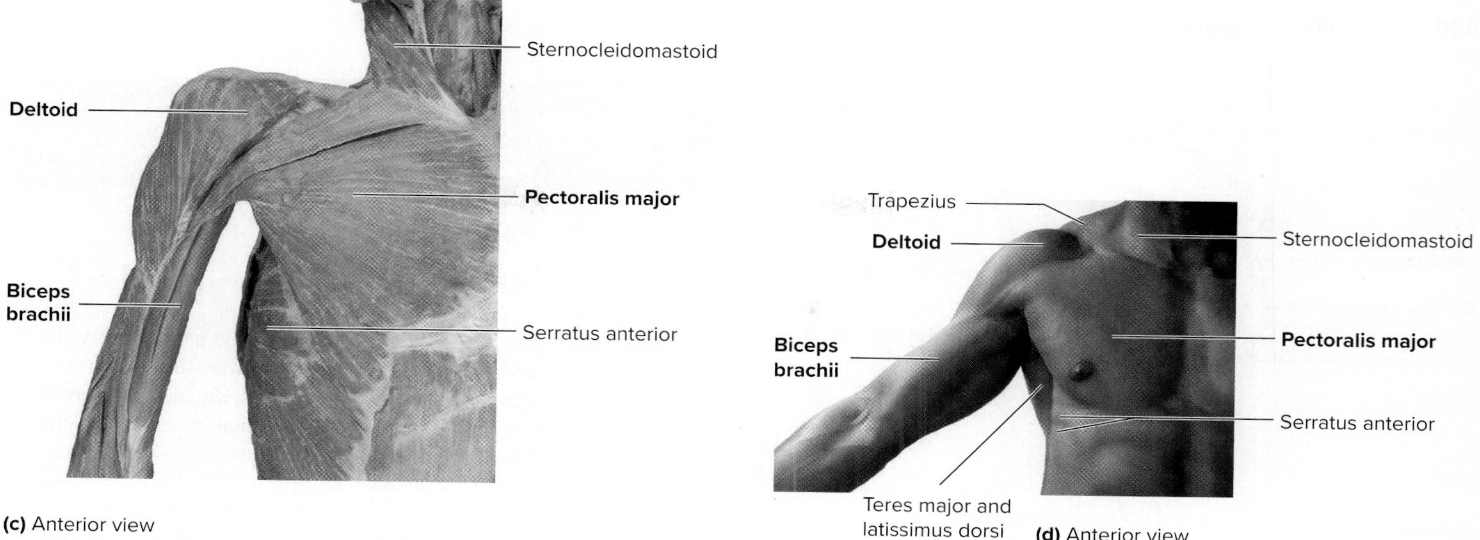

FIGURE 10.21 (continued)

(*c*) Right pectoral region of a cadaver. (*d*) Surface anatomy of the right anterior pectoral region. (Names of the upper limb muscles are in bold.)
(c) Rebecca Gray/McGraw Hill Education; (d) Jill Braaten/McGraw Hill Education

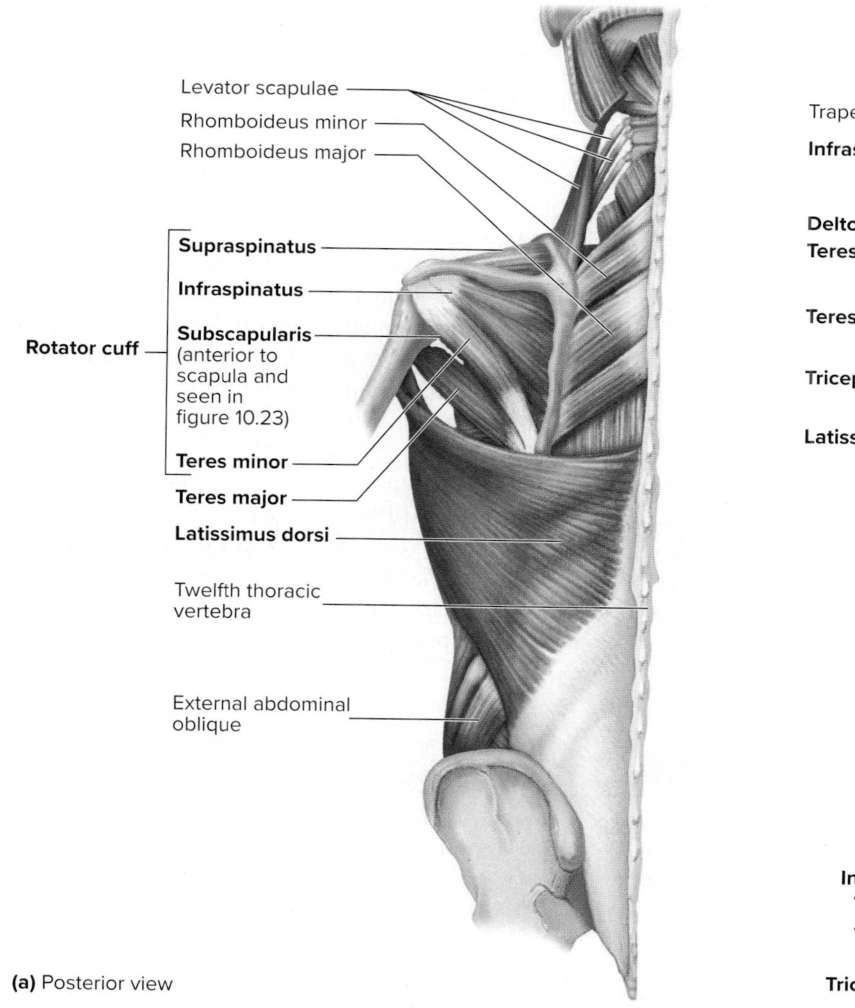

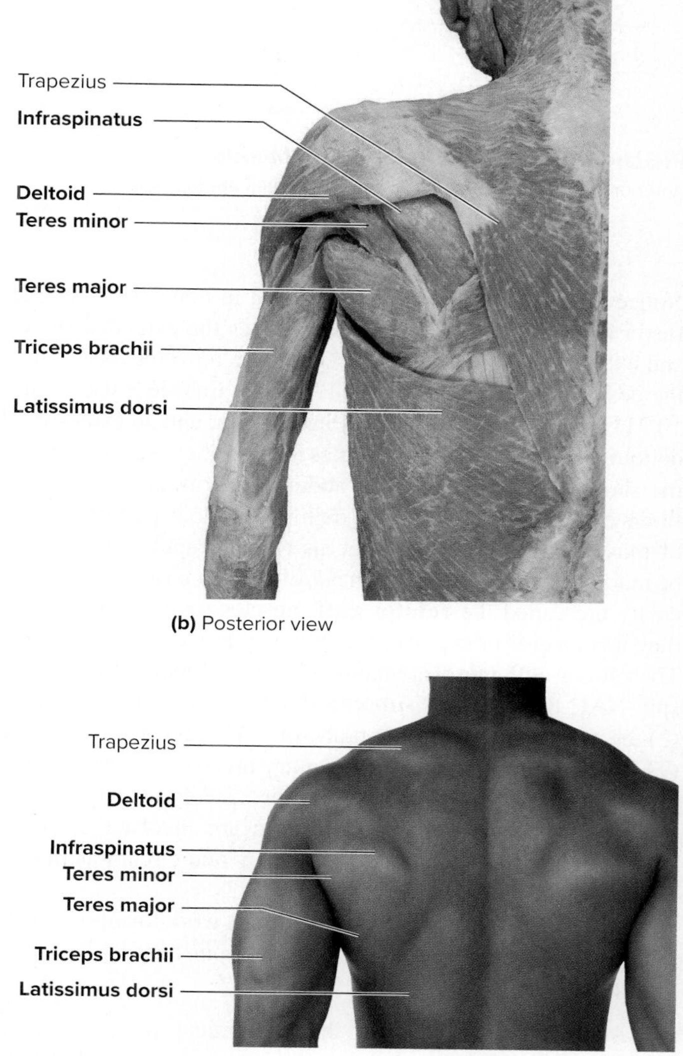

FIGURE 10.22 Posterior Muscles Attaching the Upper Limb to the Body

(*a*) Posterior view of muscles of the left posterior pectoral region. (*b*) Posterior view of a cadaver. (*c*) Surface anatomy. (Names of muscles for upper limb attachment are in bold.) (b) Christine Eckel/McGraw Hill Education; (c) Jill Braaten/McGraw Hill Education

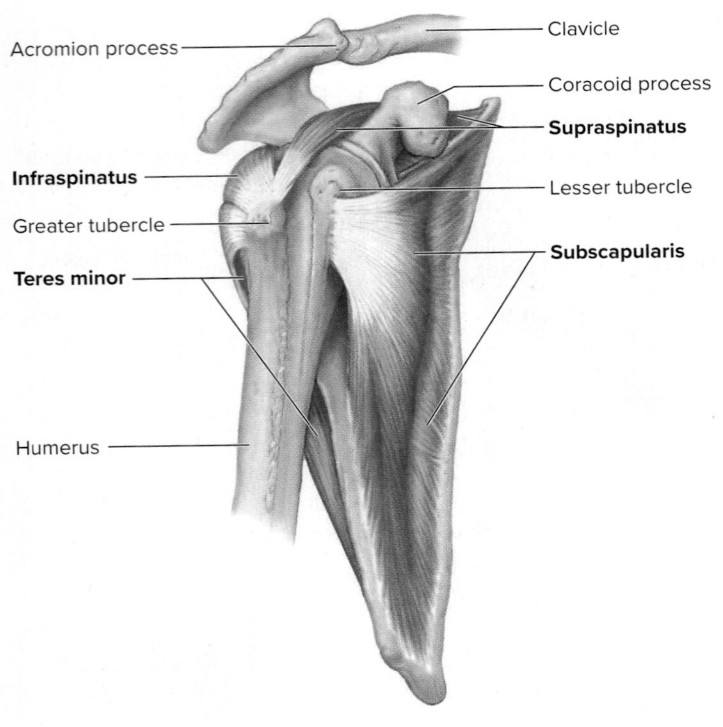

FIGURE 10.23 Right Rotator Cuff Muscles
Anterior view of the rotator cuff. (Muscle names are in bold.)

Clinical IMPACT 10.1

Shoulder Pain and Torn Rotator Cuff

Baseball pitchers, because they throw very hard, may tear their rotator cuffs. Such tears result in pain in the anterosuperior part of the shoulder. Older people may also develop such pain because of **degenerative tendinitis** of the rotator cuff. The supraspinatus tendon is the most commonly affected part of the rotator cuff in either trauma or degeneration, probably because it has a relatively poor blood supply. If the damage is severe, surgery is required to repair the area. During surgery, the loose tissue debris is removed, and the scapula is shaved or smoothed to make more room for the supraspinatus tendon. Finally, the torn edges of the supraspinatus tendon are sewn together and to the top of the humerus.

Pain in the shoulder can also result from **subacromial bursitis,** which is inflammation of the subacromial bursa. **Biceps tendinitis,** inflammation of the biceps brachii long head tendon, can also cause shoulder pain. This inflammation is also commonly caused by throwing a baseball or football.

Notice that the pectoralis major is listed in table 10.15 as both a flexor and an extensor. This muscle flexes the extended shoulder and extends the flexed shoulder. Try these movements and notice the position and action of the muscle. The **deltoid** muscle (figure 10.21) is also listed in table 10.15 as a flexor and an extensor. The deltoid muscle is like three muscles in one: The anterior fibers flex the shoulder, the lateral fibers abduct the arm, and the posterior fibers extend the shoulder. The deltoid muscle is part of the group of muscles that binds the humerus to the scapula. However, the primary muscles holding the head of the humerus in the glenoid cavity are called the **rotator cuff** muscles (table 10.15) because they form a cuff or cap over the proximal humerus (figure 10.23). The rotator cuff muscles include (1) the **infraspinatus** (IN-frah-spih-NAH-tus), (2) the **subscapularis** (SUB-skap-you-LAR-is), (3) the **supraspinatus** (SOO-prah-spi-NAH-tus), and (4) the **teres** (TER-ees) **minor.** A rotator cuff injury involves damage to one or more of these muscles or their tendons, usually the supraspinatus muscle. The muscles moving the arm are involved in flexion, extension, abduction, adduction, rotation, and circumduction (see chapter 8; see table 10.14).

To visualize how these muscle groups work together, imagine that you want to raise your arm so that your hand is high above your head.

1. Abduct your arm from the anatomical position through 90 degrees (to the point at which the hand is level with the shoulder); this involves moving the humerus and is accomplished by the deltoid muscle assisted by the rotator cuff muscles, which hold the head of the humerus tightly in place. In the initial phase of abduction, the deltoid is assisted by the supraspinatus. Place your hand on your deltoid, and feel it contract as you abduct 90 degrees.
2. Next, move your arm from 90 degrees to 180 degrees, so that your hand is high above your head; this movement primarily involves rotation of the scapula, which is accomplished by the trapezius and serratus anterior muscles.

Feel the inferior angle of your scapula as you abduct your arm to 90 degrees and then rotate to 180 degrees. Do you notice a big difference? Bear in mind that your arm cannot move from 90 degrees to 180 degrees unless the head of the humerus is held tightly in the glenoid cavity by the rotator cuff muscles, especially the supraspinatus. Damage to the supraspinatus muscle can prevent abduction past 90 degrees.

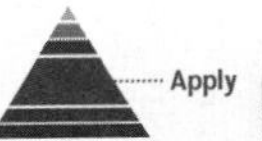

Predict 3

A tennis player complains of pain in the shoulder when she abducts her arm while serving or reaching for an overhead volley (extreme abduction). In extreme abduction, the supraspinatus muscle rises superiorly and may be damaged by compression against what bony structure?

Several muscles that act on the arm can be seen very clearly in the living individual (see figures 10.21*d* and 10.22*c*). The pectoralis major forms the upper chest, and the deltoids are prominent over the shoulders. The deltoid is a common site for administering injections.

Forearm Movements

Extension and Flexion of the Elbow

The muscles of elbow extension are the **triceps brachii** (TRY-seps BRAY-kee-eye) and the **anconeus** (ang-KOH-nee-us) muscles. The prime mover of elbow flexion is the **brachialis** (BRAY-kee-AL-is) muscle. The **biceps brachii** and the **brachioradialis** (BRAY-kee-oh-RAY-dee-AL-is) muscles assist the brachialis in elbow flexion (table 10.16; figure 10.24; see figure 10.26*a*). The triceps brachii constitutes the main mass visible on the posterior aspect of the arm (see figures 10.22*c* and 10.24*c*). The biceps brachii is readily visible on the anterior aspect of the arm (see figures 10.21*d* and 10.24*d*). The brachialis lies deep to the biceps brachii and can be seen only as a mass on the medial and lateral sides of the arm. The brachioradialis forms a bulge on the anterolateral side of the forearm just distal to the elbow (figures 10.24*b* and 10.25*b*,*d*). If the elbow is forcefully flexed in the midprone position (midway between pronation and supination), the brachioradialis stands out clearly on the forearm (figure 10.25*d*).

Supination and Pronation

The muscles that supinate (turn palm up) the forearm and hand are (1) the **supinator** and (2) the **biceps brachii** (see figures 10.24, 10.25*c*, and 10.26*b*). The muscles that pronate (turn palm down) the forearm and hand are (1) the **pronator quadratus** (proh-NAY-ter kwah-DRAH-tus) and (2) the **pronator teres** (TER-eez, TEER-eez; see figures 10.24*a* and 10.25*a*,*c*).

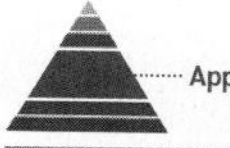

Predict 4

Explain the difference between doing chin-ups with the forearm supinated and doing them with it pronated. The action of which muscle predominates in each type of chin-up? Which type is easier? Why?

Wrist, Hand, and Finger Movements

The forearm muscles are divided into anterior and posterior groups (table 10.17; see figures 10.25 and 10.26). Flexion of the wrist and fingers, such as when making a fist, is accomplished by most of the anterior forearm muscles. Extension of the wrist and fingers, such as when opening a fist, is accomplished by most of the posterior forearm muscles.

Extrinsic Hand Muscles

The **extrinsic hand muscles** are located in the posterior forearm and have tendons that extend into the hand. These muscles extend the wrist and fingers. A strong ring of fibrous connective tissue, the **extensor retinaculum** (ret-ih-NAK-you-lum; bracelet), encircles the flexor and extensor tendons to hold them in place around the wrist, so that they do not "bowstring" (pull away from the bone) during muscle contraction (figure 10.26*a*,*c*).

Flexion of the wrist is accomplished by two major anterior forearm muscles, (1) the **flexor carpi radialis** (KAR-pye ray-dee-AH-lis) and (2) the **flexor carpi ulnaris** (KAR-pye ul-NAR-is). Extension of the wrist is through the action of three posterior forearm muscles, (1) the **extensor carpi radialis longus,** (2) the **extensor carpi radialis brevis,** and (3) the **extensor carpi ulnaris.** The tendon of the flexor carpi radialis serves as a landmark for locating the radial pulse, which is lateral to the tendon (see figure 10.25*d*). The wrist flexors and extensors are visible on the anterior and posterior surfaces of the forearm (see figures 10.25*d* and 10.26*d*).

Flexion of the four medial digits is a function of (1) the **flexor digitorum superficialis** (SOO-per-FISH-ee-AY-lis) and (2) the **flexor digitorum profundus** (DIJ-ih-TOR-um proh-FUN-dus; deep). Extension is accomplished by the **extensor digitorum.** The tendons of this muscle are very visible on the dorsum of the hand (figure 10.26*d*). The little finger has an additional extensor, the **extensor digiti minimi** (DIJ-i-tie MIN-i-mye). The index finger also has an additional extensor, the **extensor indicis** (IN-di-sis).

Movement of the thumb is caused in part by three muscles: (1) the **abductor pollicis** (POL-i-sis) **longus,** (2) the **extensor**

TABLE 10.16 Muscles Acting on the Arm (see figure 10.24)

Muscle	Origin	Insertion	Nerve	Action
Arm				
Biceps brachii	Long head—supraglenoid tubercle	Radial tuberosity and aponeurosis of biceps brachii	Musculocutaneous	Flexes shoulder and elbow; supinates forearm and hand
	Short head—coracoid process			
Brachialis	Anterior surface of humerus	Ulnar tuberosity and coronoid process of ulna	Musculocutaneous and radial	Flexes elbow
Triceps brachii	Long head—infraglenoid tubercle on lateral border of scapula	Olecranon process of ulna	Radial	Extends elbow; extends shoulder and adducts arm
	Lateral head—lateral and posterior surface of humerus			
	Medial head—posterior humerus			

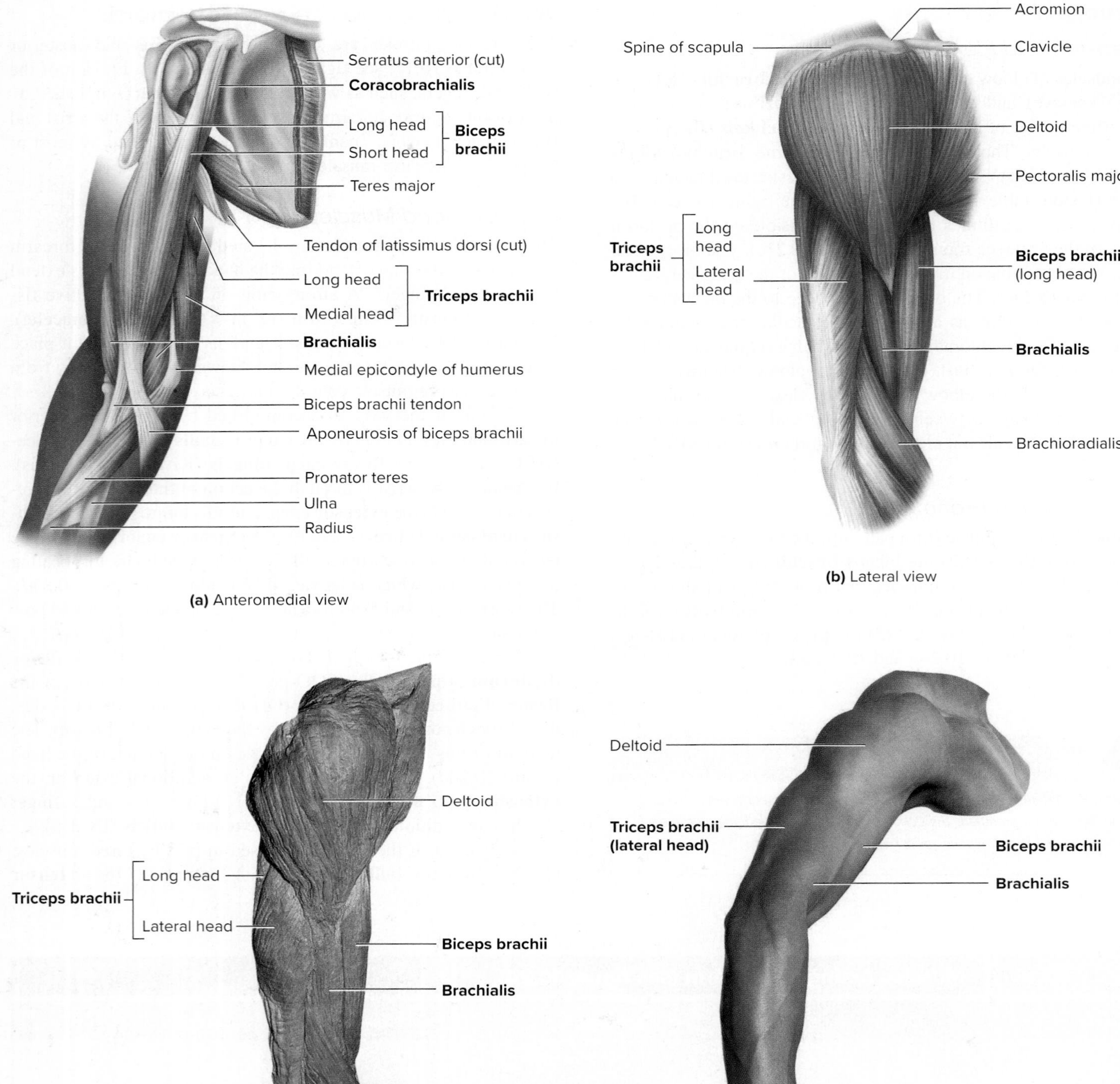

FIGURE 10.24 Lateral Right Arm Muscles

(*a*, *b*) The right shoulder and arm. (*c*) The right shoulder and arm muscles of a cadaver. (*d*) Surface anatomy of the right shoulder and arm. (Names of arm muscles are in bold.) (c) Rebecca Gray, photographer/Don Kincaid, dissections/McGraw Hill Education; (d) Jill Braaten/McGraw Hill Education APR

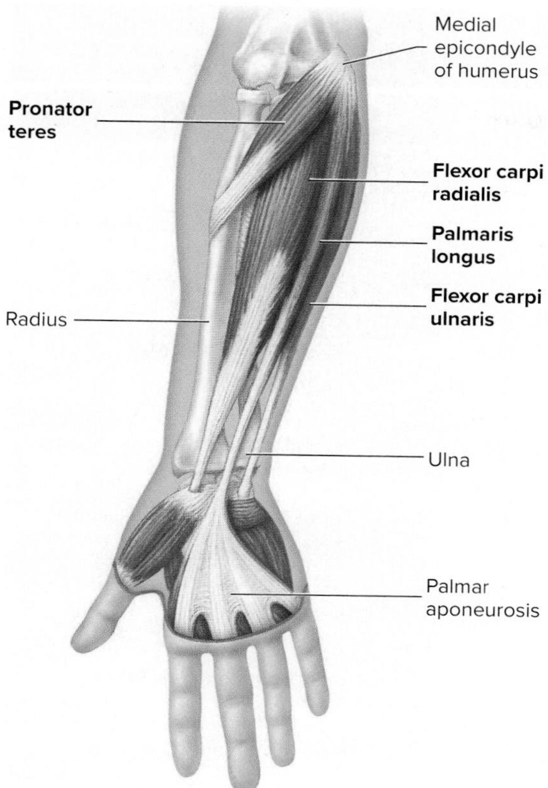

(a) Anterior view

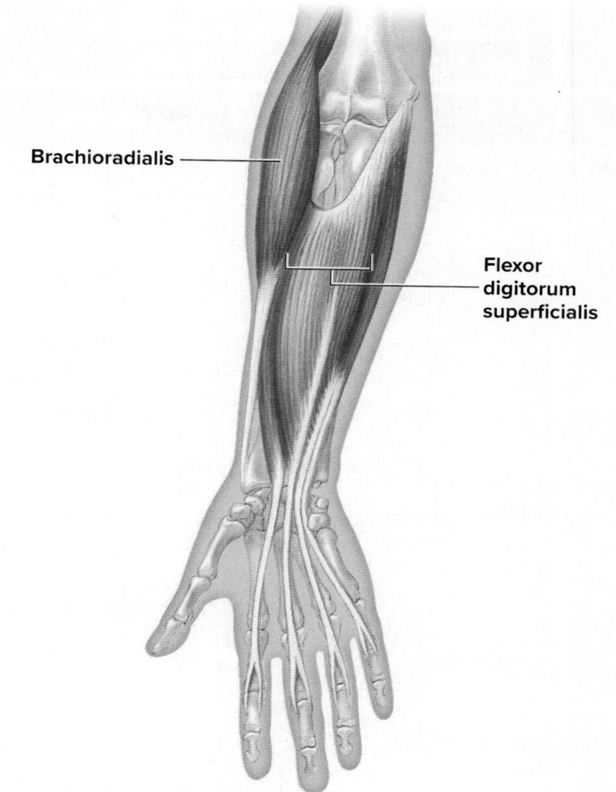

(b) Anterior view (deep)

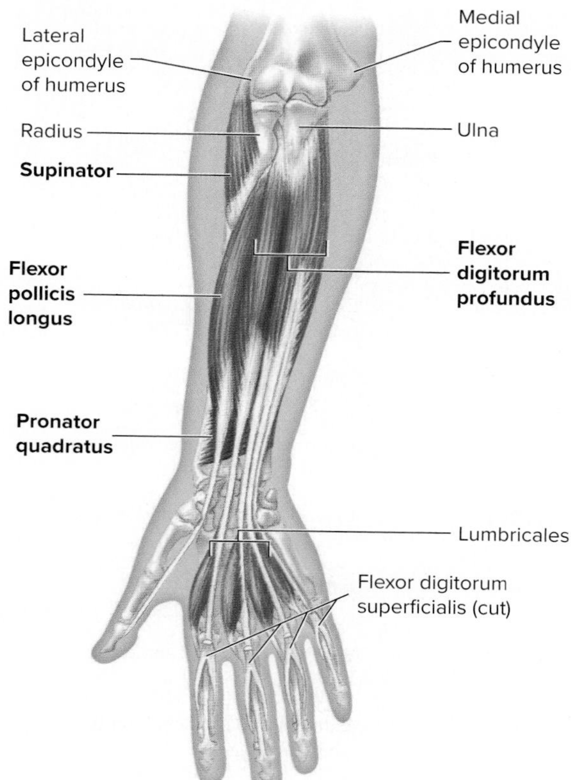

(c) Anterior view (deep to (b))

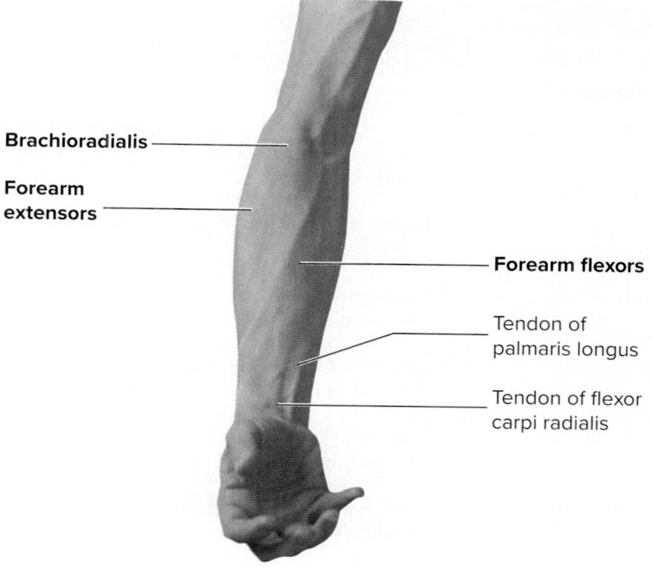

(d) Anterolateral view

FIGURE 10.25 Anterior Right Forearm Muscles
(*a*) Right forearm (superficial). The brachioradialis muscle is removed. (*b*) Right forearm (deeper than *a*). The pronator teres, flexor carpi radialis and ulnaris, and palmaris longus muscles are removed. (*c*) Right forearm (deeper than *a* or *b*). The brachioradialis, pronator teres, flexor carpi radialis and ulnaris, palmaris longus, and flexor digitorum superficialis muscles are removed. (*d*) Surface anatomy of anterior forearm muscles. (Muscle names are in bold.) (d) Jill Braaten/McGraw Hill Education

TABLE 10.17 Muscles of the Forearm Acting on the Wrist, Hand, and Fingers (see figures 10.25 and 10.26)

Muscle	Origin	Insertion	Nerve	Action
Anterior Forearm				
Brachioradialis	Lateral supracondylar ridge of humerus	Styloid process of radius	Radial	Flexes elbow
Flexor carpi radialis	Medial epicondyle of humerus	Second and third metacarpal bones	Median	Flexes and abducts wrist
Flexor carpi ulnaris	Medial epicondyle of humerus and ulna	Pisiform, hamate, and fifth metacarpal bones	Ulnar	Flexes and adducts wrist
Flexor digitorum profundus	Ulna	Distal phalanges of digits 2–5	Ulnar and median	Flexes fingers at metacarpophalangeal joints and interphalangeal joints and wrist
Flexor digitorum superficialis	Medial epicondyle of humerus, coronoid process, and radius	Middle phalanges of digits 2–5	Median	Flexes fingers at interphalangeal joints and wrist
Flexor pollicis longus	Radius	Distal phalanx of thumb	Median	Flexes thumb
Palmaris longus	Medial epicondyle of humerus	Palmar fascia	Median	Tenses palmar fascia; flexes wrist
Pronator quadratus	Distal ulna	Distal radius	Anterior interosseous	Pronates forearm (and hand)
Pronator teres	Medial epicondyle of humerus and coronoid process of ulna	Radius	Median	Pronates forearm (and hand)
Supinator	Lateral epicondyle of humerus and ulna	Radius	Radial	Supinates forearm (and hand)
Posterior Forearm				
Abductor pollicis longus	Posterior ulna and radius and interosseous membrane	Base of first metacarpal bone	Radial	Abducts and extends thumb; abducts wrist
Anconeus	Lateral epicondyle of humerus	Olecranon process and posterior ulna	Radial	Extends elbow
Extensor carpi radialis brevis	Lateral epicondyle of humerus	Base of third metacarpal bone	Radial	Extends and abducts wrist
Extensor carpi radialis longus	Lateral supracondylar ridge of humerus	Base of second metacarpal bone	Radial	Extends and abducts wrist
Extensor carpi ulnaris	Lateral epicondyle of humerus and ulna	Base of fifth metacarpal bone	Radial	Extends and adducts wrist
Extensor digiti minimi	Lateral epicondyle of humerus	Phalanges of digit 5	Radial	Extends little finger and wrist
Extensor digitorum	Lateral epicondyle of humerus	Extensor tendon expansion over phalanges of digits 2–5	Radial	Extends fingers and wrist
Extensor indicis	Ulna	Extensor tendon expansion over digit 2	Radial	Extends forefinger and wrist
Extensor pollicis brevis	Radius	Proximal phalanx of thumb	Radial	Extends and abducts thumb; abducts wrist
Extensor pollicis longus	Ulna	Distal phalanx of thumb	Radial	Extends thumb

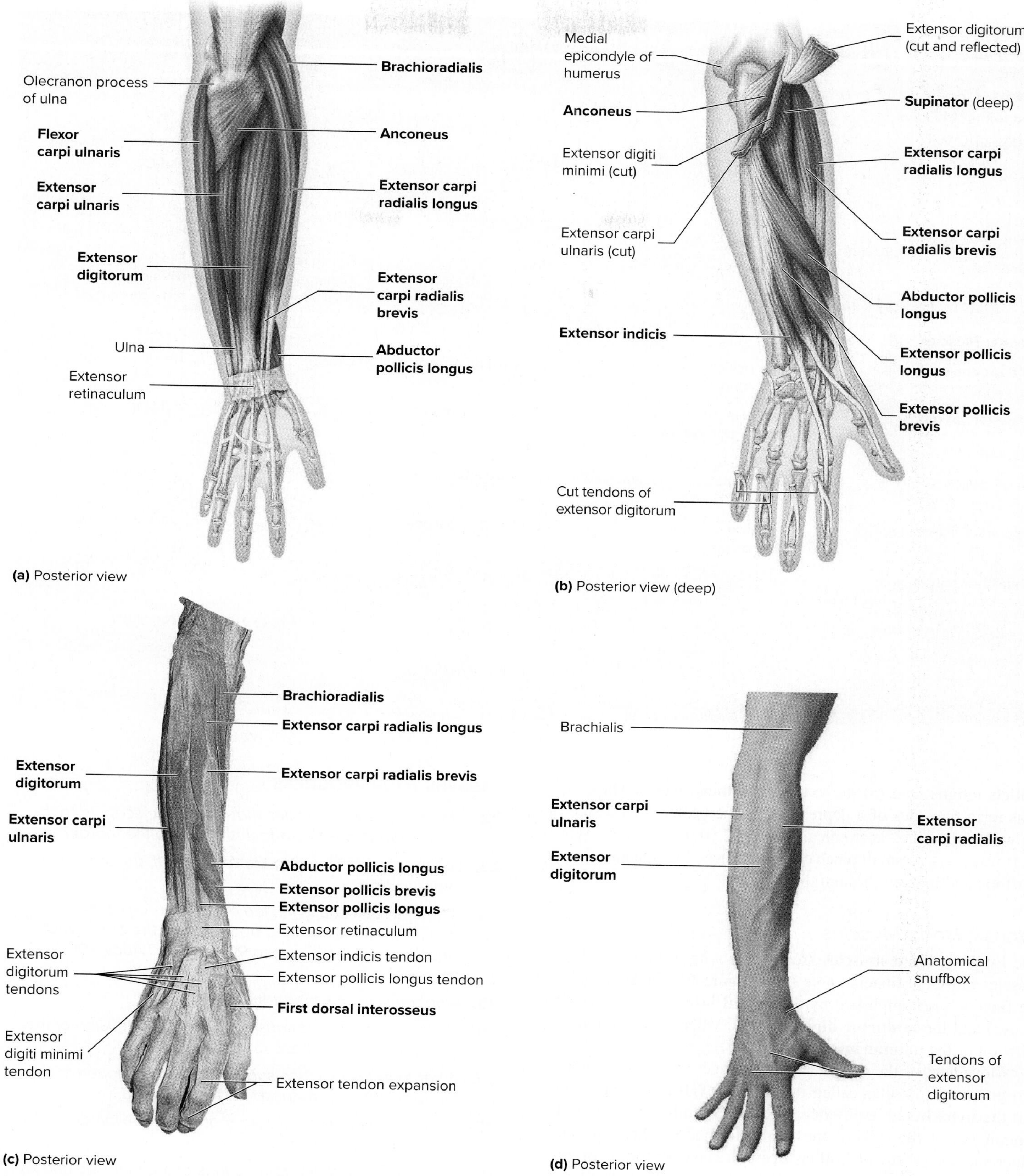

FIGURE 10.26 Posterior Right Forearm Muscles

(*a*) Right forearm (superficial). (*b*) Deep muscles of the right posterior forearm. The extensor digitorum, extensor digiti minimi, and extensor carpi ulnaris muscles are cut to reveal deeper muscles. (*c*) Photograph showing dissection of the posterior right forearm and hand. (*d*) Surface anatomy of posterior forearm. (Muscle names are in bold.) (c) Rebecca Gray/McGraw Hill Education; (d) Jill Braaten/McGraw Hill Education

TABLE 10.18 Intrinsic Hand Muscles (see figure 10.27)

Muscle	Origin	Insertion	Nerve	Action
Midpalmar Muscles				
Interossei				
Dorsal	Sides of metacarpal bones	Proximal phalanges of digits 2, 3, and 4	Ulnar	Abducts second, third, and fourth digits
Palmar	Second, fourth, and fifth metacarpal bones	Digits 2, 4, and 5	Ulnar	Adducts second, fourth, and fifth digits
Lumbricals	Tendons of flexor digitorum profundus	Digits 2–5	Two on radial side—median; two on ulnar side—ulnar	Flexes proximal and extends middle and distal phalanges
Thenar Muscles				
Abductor pollicis brevis	Flexor retinaculum, trapezium, and scaphoid	Proximal phalanx of thumb	Median	Abducts thumb
Adductor pollicis	Third metacarpal bone, second metacarpal bone, trapezoid, and capitate	Proximal phalanx of thumb	Ulnar	Adducts thumb
Flexor pollicis brevis	Flexor retinaculum and first metacarpal bone	Proximal phalanx of thumb	Median and ulnar	Flexes thumb
Opponens pollicis	Trapezium and flexor retinaculum	First metacarpal bone	Median	Opposes thumb
Hypothenar Muscles				
Abductor digiti minimi	Pisiform	Base of digit 5	Ulnar	Abducts and flexes little finger
Flexor digiti minimi brevis	Hamate	Base of proximal phalanx of digit 5	Ulnar	Flexes little finger
Opponens digiti minimi	Hamate and flexor retinaculum	Fifth metacarpal bone	Ulnar	Opposes little finger

pollicis longus, and (3) the **extensor pollicis brevis.** These tendons form the sides of a depression on the posterolateral side of the wrist called the "anatomical snuffbox" (figure 10.26*d*). When snuff was in use, a small pinch could be placed into the anatomical snuffbox and inhaled through the nose.

Intrinsic Hand Muscles

The **intrinsic hand muscles** are entirely within the hand. These muscles move the fingers (table 10.18; figure 10.27). Abduction of the fingers is accomplished by the **dorsal interossei** (IN-ter-OS-ee-eye) and the **abductor digiti minimi,** whereas adduction is a function of the **palmar interossei.**

Movement of the thumb and little finger is accomplished by two groups of muscles called the **thenar** (THEE-nar) **eminence** and the **hypothenar eminence.** The thenar eminence is a fleshy prominence at the base of the thumb formed by three muscles, which include (1) **flexor pollicis brevis,** (2) the **abductor pollicis brevis,** and (3) the **opponens pollicis** (figure 10.27*a*). The hypothenar eminence on the ulnar side of the hand is formed by (1) the **abductor digiti minimi,** (2) the **flexor digiti minimi brevis,** and (3) the **opponens digiti minimi** (figure 10.27*c*).

ASSESS YOUR PROGRESS

22. *Name the seven muscles that attach the scapula to the thorax. What muscles attach the arm to the thorax?*

23. *List the muscles forming the rotator cuff, and describe their function.*

24. *What muscles cause flexion and extension of the shoulder? Adduction and abduction of the arm? What muscle abducts the arm to 90 degrees? Above 90 degrees?*

25. *What muscles cause rotation of the arm?*

26. *List the muscles that cause flexion and extension of the elbow. Where are these muscles located?*

27. *What muscles produce supination and pronation of the forearm? Where are these muscles located?*

28. *Describe the muscle groups that cause flexion and extension of the wrist.*

29. *Contrast the location and actions of the extrinsic and intrinsic hand muscles. What is the retinaculum?*

30. *Describe the muscles that move the thumb. The tendons of what muscles form the anatomical snuffbox?*

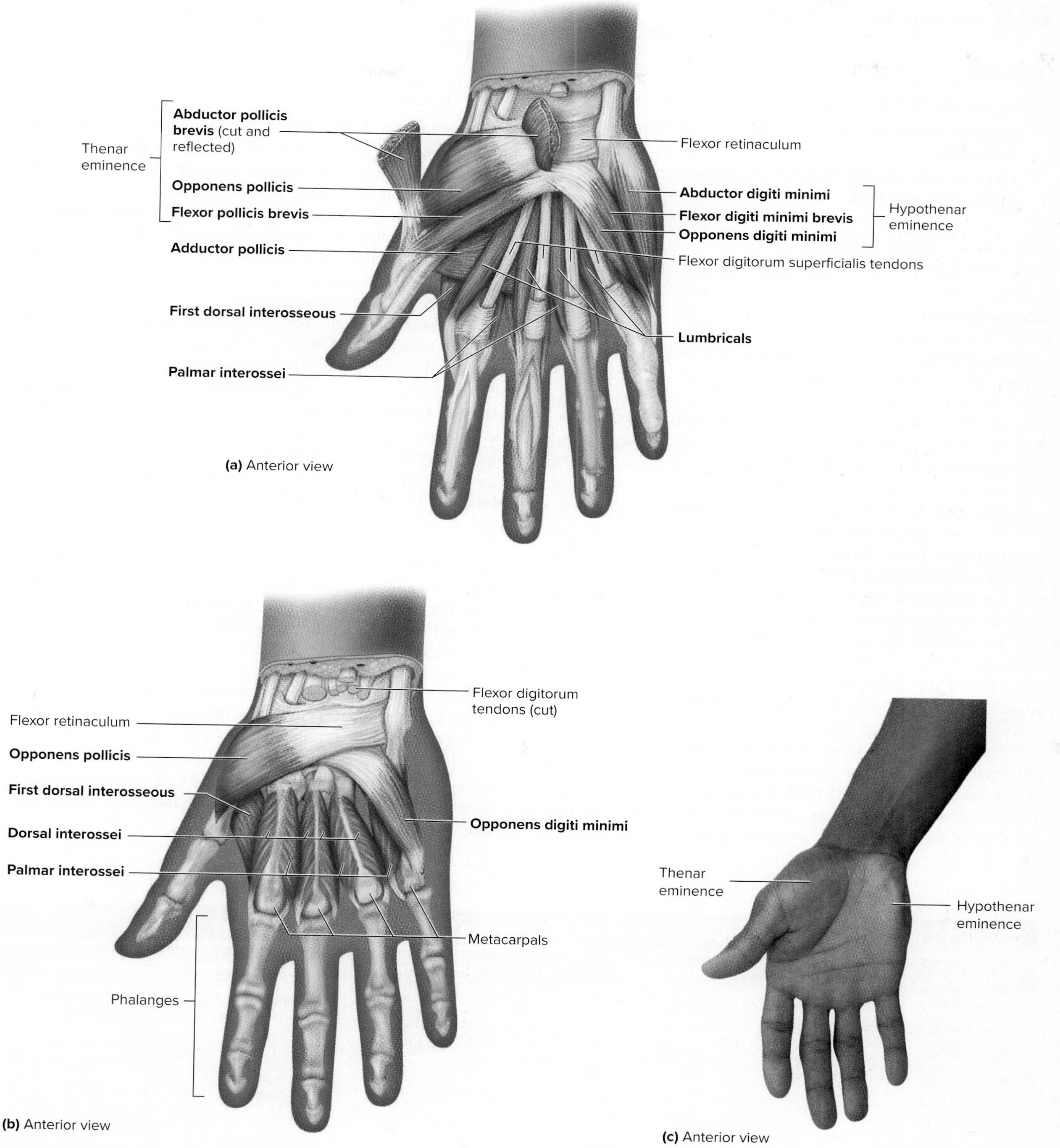

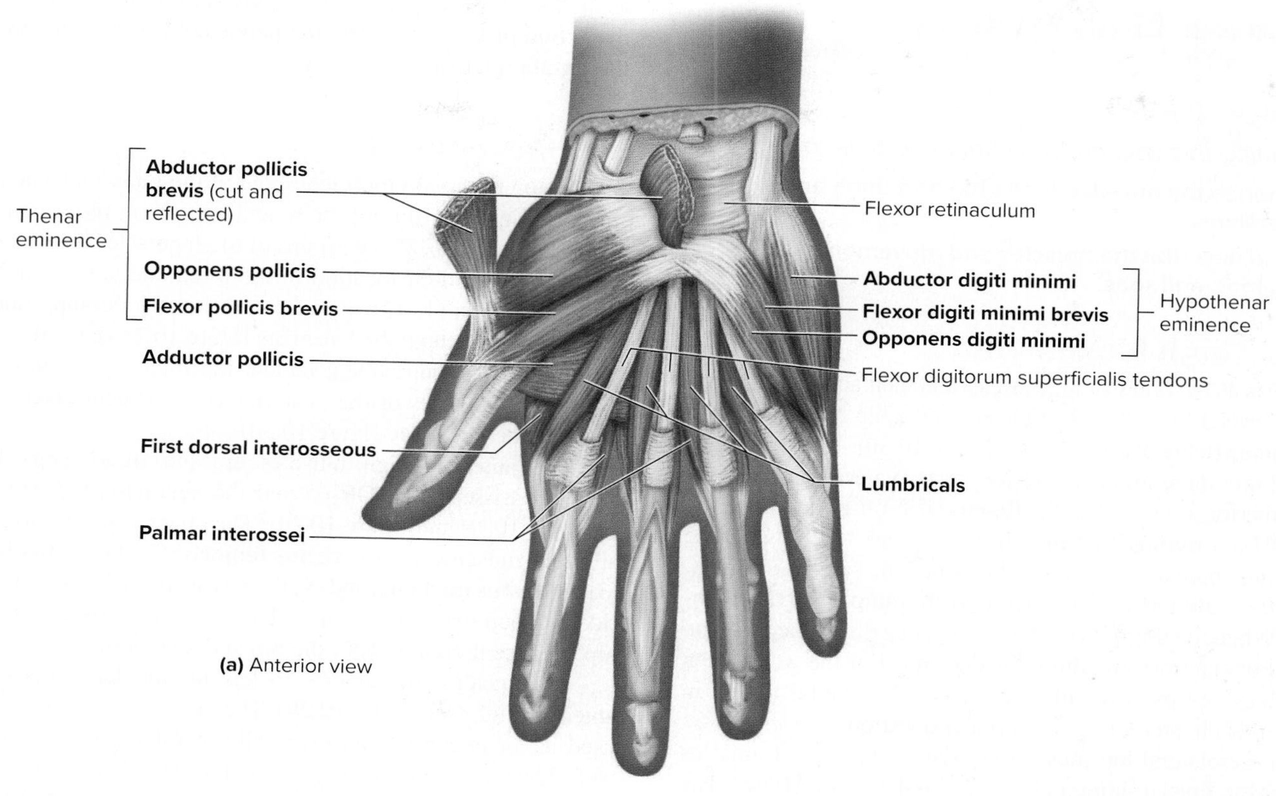

FIGURE 10.27 Right Hand Muscles

(*a*) Superficial muscles of the right hand. The abductor pollicis brevis is cut. (*b*) Deep muscles of the right hand. The flexor digitorum tendons are cut. (*c*) Surface anatomy of the palmar surface of the hand. (Muscle names are in bold.) (c) Jill Braaten/McGraw Hill Education

10.5 Lower Limb Muscles

LEARNING OUTCOMES

After reading this section, you should be able to

A. **Summarize the muscles of the hip and thigh and explain their actions.**

B. **List and describe the muscles and movements of the ankle, foot, and toes.**

Hip and Thigh Movements

Table 10.19 is an overview of the muscles and their actions in the hip and thigh. Several hip muscles originate on the hip bone and insert onto the femur (table 10.20; figures 10.28–10.30). These muscles are divided into three groups: anterior, posterolateral, and deep.

The anterior hip muscles, the **iliacus** (il-EYE-ah-kus) and the **psoas** (SOH-as) **major,** flex the hip (see figure 10.28). Because these muscles share an insertion and produce the same movement, they are often referred to collectively as the **iliopsoas** (IL-ee-oh-SOH-us). When the thigh is fixed, the iliopsoas flexes the trunk on the thigh. For example, the iliopsoas does most of the work when a person does sit-ups. This information will be helpful to you in answering this chapter's Learn to Predict question.

The posterolateral hip muscles consist of the gluteal muscles and the **tensor fasciae latae** (TEN-sor FA-she-ee LAH-tee). The **gluteus** (GLOO-tee-us) **maximus** contributes most of the mass that can be seen as the buttocks (see figure 10.28); the **gluteus medius,** a common site for injections, creates a smaller mass just superior and lateral to the gluteus maximus. The gluteus maximus functions at its maximum force in extension of the thigh when the hip is flexed at a 45-degree angle, so that the muscle is optimally stretched, which accounts for both the sprinter's stance and the bicycle racing posture.

The deep hip muscles, as well as the gluteus maximus, laterally rotate the thigh. The gluteus medius, gluteus minimus, and tensor fasciae latae medially rotate the hip (table 10.20; see figure 10.28). The gluteus medius and minimus muscles help tilt the pelvis and maintain the trunk in an upright posture during walking, as the foot of the opposite limb is raised from the ground. Without the action of these muscles, the pelvis tends to sag downward on the unsupported side.

Leg Movements

In addition to the hip muscles, some of the muscles located in the thigh originate on the hip bone and can cause movement of the thigh (table 10.21). Three groups of thigh muscles have been identified based on their location in the thigh and are organized into **compartments:** (1) The muscles of the anterior compartment flex the hip and/or extend the knee (see figure 10.28*a*); (2) the muscles of the medial compartment adduct the thigh (see figure 10.30); and (3) the muscles of the posterior compartment extend the hip and flex the knee (see figure 10.30).

The anterior thigh muscles are the **quadriceps femoris** (KWAH-dri-seps fe-MOR-is) and the **sartorius** (sar-TOR-ee-us; see table 10.19 and figure 10.29). The quadriceps femoris is actually four muscles: (1) the **rectus femoris,** (2) the **vastus lateralis,** (3) the **vastus medialis,** and (4) the **vastus intermedius.** The quadriceps group extends the knee. The rectus femoris also flexes the hip because it crosses both the hip and knee joints.

The quadriceps femoris makes up the large mass on the anterior thigh (see figure 10.29). The vastus lateralis is sometimes used as an injection site, especially in infants who do not have well-developed deltoid or gluteal muscles. The muscles of the quadriceps femoris have a common insertion, the patellar tendon, on and around the patella. The patellar ligament is an extension of the patellar tendon onto the tibial tuberosity. The patellar ligament is the point that is tapped with a rubber hammer when testing the knee-jerk reflex in a physical examination.

The sartorius is the longest muscle of the body, crossing from the lateral side of the hip to the medial side of the knee. As the muscle contracts, it flexes the hip and knee and laterally rotates the thigh. This is the action required for crossing the legs.

The medial thigh muscles (see figure 10.29) are involved primarily in adduction of the thigh. Some of these muscles also laterally rotate the thigh and/or flex or extend the hip. The gracilis also flexes the knee.

TABLE 10.19 Overview of Muscle Actions on the Hip and Thigh

Flexion	Extension	Abduction	Adduction	Medial Rotation	Lateral Rotation
Iliopsoas	Gluteus maximus	Gluteus maximus	Adductor magnus	Tensor fasciae latae	Gluteus maximus
Tensor fasciae latae	Semitendinosus	Gluteus medius	Adductor longus	Gluteus medius	Obturator internus
Rectus femoris	Semimembranosus	Gluteus minimus	Adductor brevis	Gluteus minimus	Obturator externus
Sartorius	Biceps femoris	Tensor fasciae latae	Pectineus		Superior gemellus
Adductor longus	Adductor magnus	Obturator internus	Gracilis		Inferior gemellus
Adductor brevis		Gemellus superior and inferior			Quadratus femoris
Pectineus		Piriformis			Piriformis
					Adductor magnus
					Adductor longus
					Adductor brevis

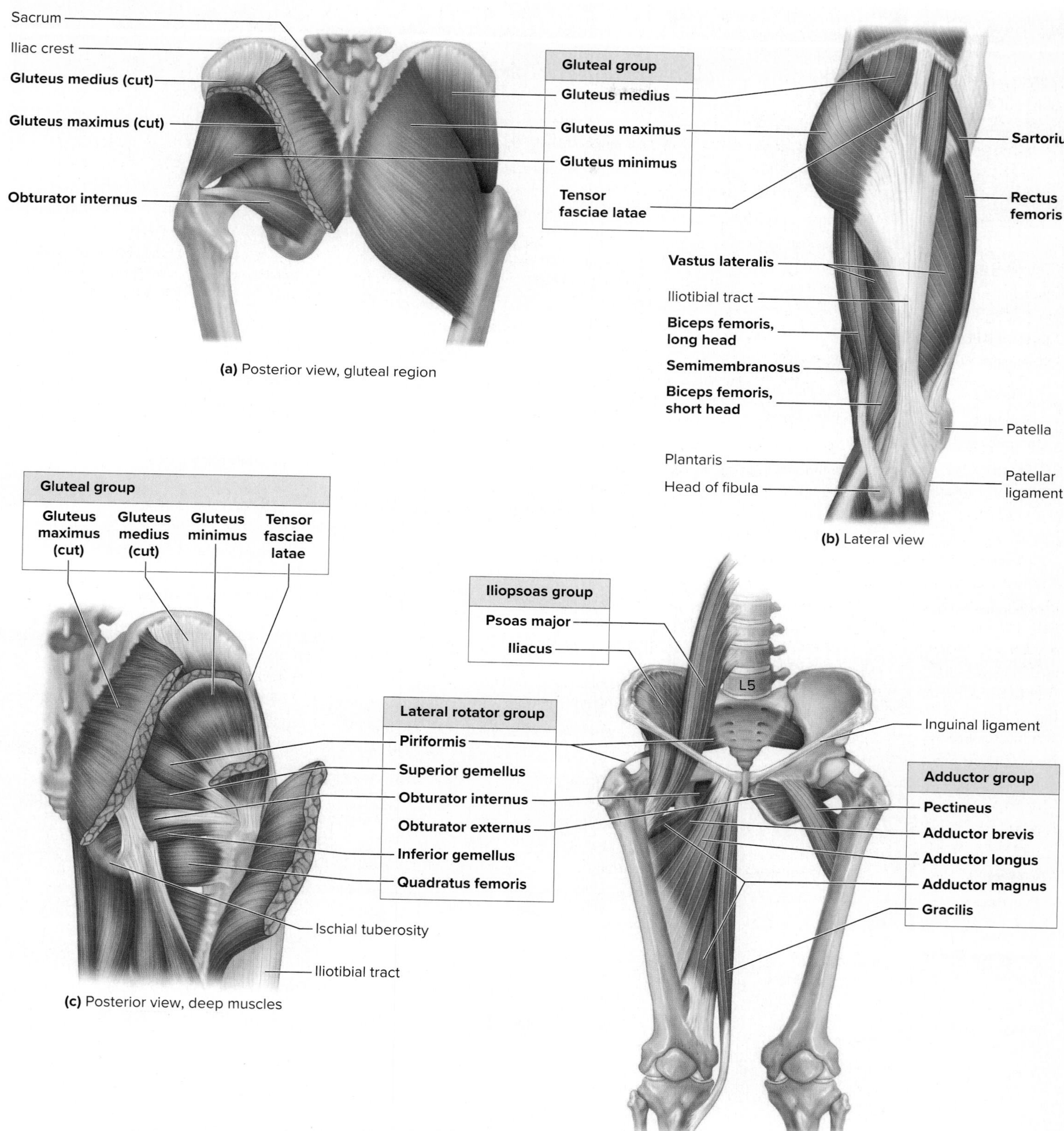

FIGURE 10.28 Right Anterior Hip and Thigh Muscles

(*a*) Posterior view of muscles in the gluteal group. (*b*) Lateral view of muscles of the hip and thigh. (*c*) Posterior view of deep gluteal muscles. (*d*) Anterior view of the iliopsoas and adductor groups. (Muscle names are in bold.) APR

TABLE 10.20 Muscles Acting on the Hip and Thigh (see figure 10.28)

Muscle	Origin	Insertion	Nerve	Action
Gluteal Group				
Gluteus maximus	Posterior surface of ilium, sacrum, and coccyx	Gluteal tuberosity of femur and iliotibial tract	Inferior gluteal	Extends hip; abducts and laterally rotates thigh
Gluteus medius	Posterior surface of ilium	Greater trochanter of femur	Superior gluteal	Abducts and medially rotates thigh; tilts pelvis toward supported side
Gluteus minimus	Posterior surface of ilium	Greater trochanter of femur	Superior gluteal	Abducts and medially rotates thigh; tilts pelvis toward supported side
Tensor fasciae latae	Anterior superior iliac spine	Through iliotibial tract to lateral condyle of tibia	Superior gluteal	Tenses lateral fascia and stabilizes femur on tibia when standing; flexes hip; abducts and medially rotates thigh; tilts pelvis
Lateral Rotator Group				
Gemellus				
Inferior	Ischial tuberosity	Obturator internus tendon	L5 and S1	Laterally rotates and abducts thigh
Superior	Ischial spine	Obturator internus tendon	L5 and S1	Laterally rotates and abducts thigh
Obturator				
Externus	Inferior margin of obturator foramen	Greater trochanter of femur	Obturator	Laterally rotates thigh
Internus	Interior margin of obturator foramen	Greater trochanter of femur	L5 and S1	Laterally rotates thigh
Piriformis	Sacrum and ilium	Greater trochanter of femur	S1 and S2	Laterally rotates and abducts thigh
Quadratus femoris	Ischial tuberosity	Intertrochanteric ridge of femur	L5 and S1	Laterally rotates thigh
Adductor Group				
Adductor brevis	Pubis	Pectineal line and linea aspera of femur	Obturator	Adducts and laterally rotates thigh; flexes hip
Adductor longus	Pubis	Linea aspera of femur	Obturator	Adducts and laterally rotates thigh; flexes hip
Adductor magnus	Adductor part: pubis and ischium Hamstring part: ischial tuberosity	Adductor part: linea aspera of femur Hamstring part: adductor tubercle of femur	Adductor part: obturator Hamstring part: tibial	Adductor part: adducts thigh and flexes hip Hamstring part: extends hip and adducts thigh
Gracilis	Pubis near symphysis	Tibia	Obturator	Adducts thigh; flexes knee
Pectineus	Pubic crest	Pectineal line of femur	Femoral and obturator	Adducts thigh; flexes hip
Iliopsoas Group				
Iliacus	Iliac fossa	Lesser trochanter of femur and capsule of hip joint	Lumbar plexus	Flexes hip
Psoas major	T12–L5	Lesser trochanter of femur	Lumbar plexus	Flexes hip

The posterior thigh muscles (see figure 10.29), collectively called the hamstring muscles, consist of the **biceps femoris,** the **semimembranosus** (SE-mee-MEM-brah-NOH-sus), and the **semitendinosus** (SE-mee-TEN-di-NOH-sus; table 10.21). Their tendons are easily seen or felt on the medial and lateral posterior aspect of a slightly bent knee (figure 10.31).

Ankle, Foot, and Toe Movements

The muscles of the leg that move the ankle and the foot are located in the leg and have tendons that extend into the foot similarly to the extrinsic hand muscles (table 10.22 and figure 10.31). These **extrinsic foot muscles** are divided into three groups, each located within a separate compartment of the

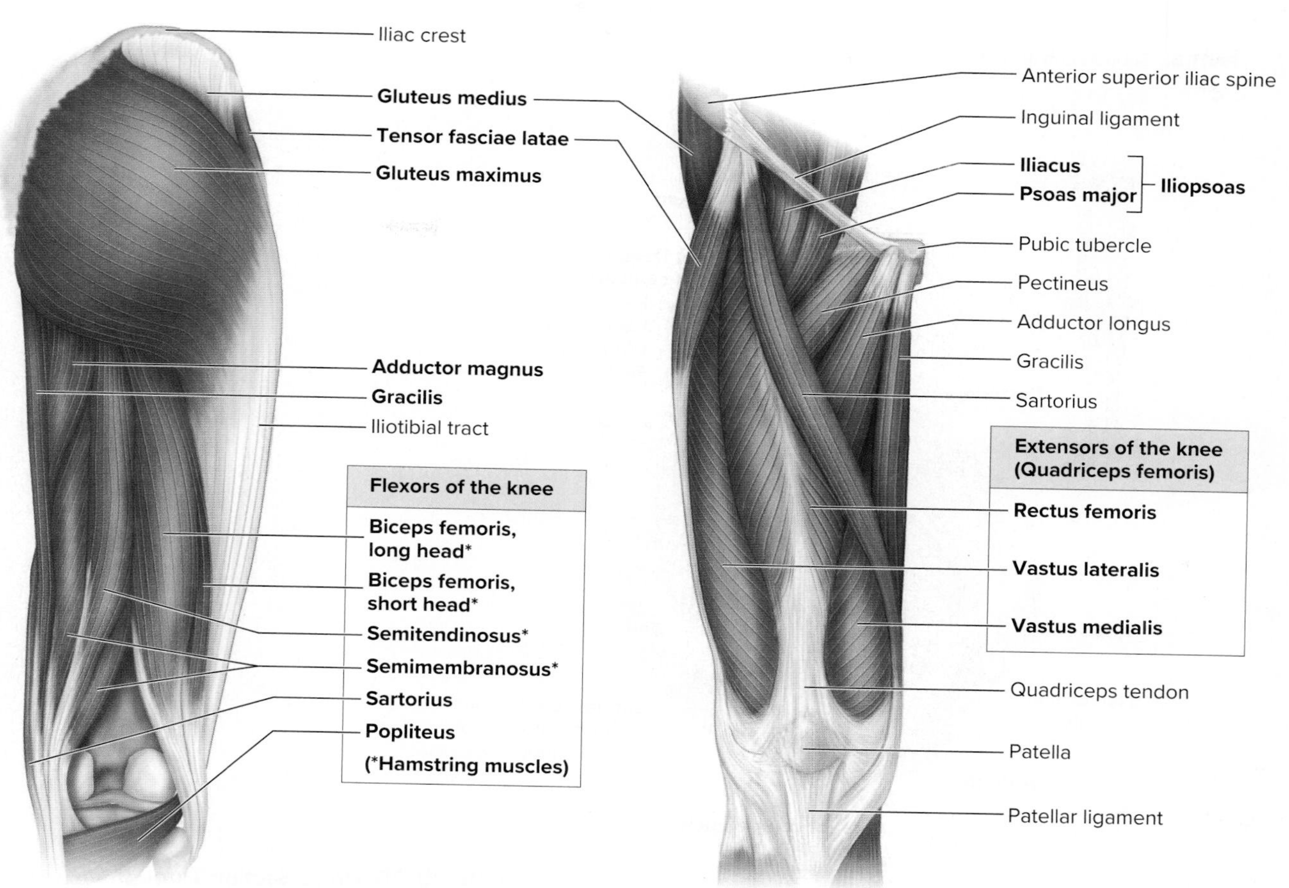

(a) Posterior view, hip and thigh

(b) Anterior view, quadriceps femoris and thigh muscles

FIGURE 10.29 Muscles That Move the Leg
(*a*) Posterior view of muscles of the thigh. (*b*) Anterior view of the muscles of the thigh. (Muscle names are in bold.) APR

TABLE **10.21** **Muscles of the Thigh (see figure 10.29)**

Muscle	Origin	Insertion	Nerve	Action
Extensors of the Knee				
Quadriceps femoris	Rectus femoris—anterior inferior iliac spine Vastus lateralis—greater trochanter and linea aspera of femur Vastus intermedius—body of femur Vastus medialis—linea aspera of femur	Patella and onto tibial tuberosity through patellar ligament	Femoral	Extends knee; rectus femoris also flexes hip
Flexors of the Knee				
Biceps femoris	Long head—ischial tuberosity Short head—femur	Head of fibula	Long head—tibial Short head—common fibular	Flexes knee; laterally rotates leg; extends hip
Popliteus	Lateral femoral condyle	Posterior tibia	Tibial	Flexes knee; medially rotates leg
Sartorius	Anterior superior iliac spine	Medial side of tibial tuberosity	Femoral	Flexes hip and knee; rotates thigh laterally and leg medially
Semimembranosus	Ischial tuberosity	Medial condyle of tibia and collateral ligament	Tibial	Flexes knee; medially rotates leg; tenses capsule of knee joint; extends hip
Semitendinosus	Ischial tuberosity	Tibia	Tibial	Flexes knee; medially rotates leg; extends hip

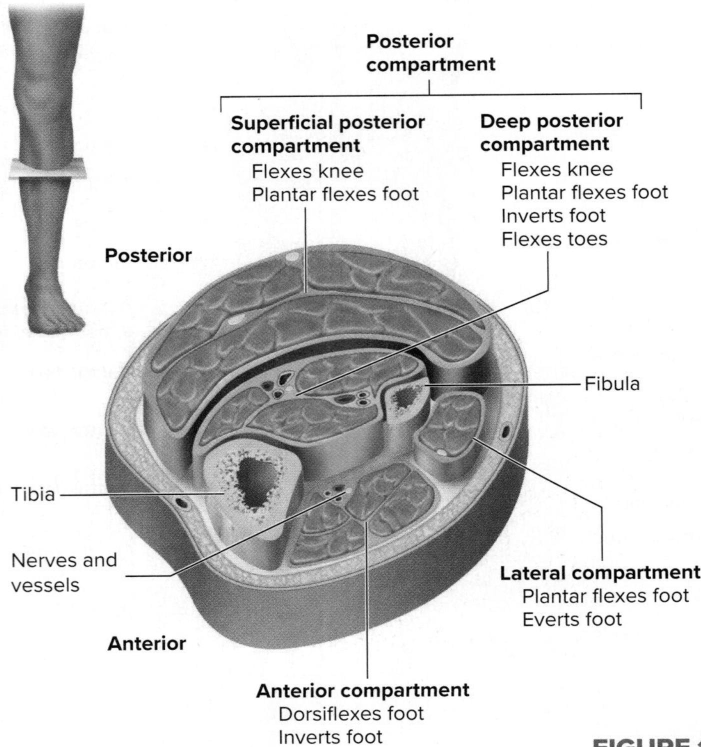

FIGURE 10.30 Cross Section Through the Left Leg
The anterior, posterior, and lateral compartments are labeled.

leg: anterior, posterior, and lateral (see figure 10.31). The anterior leg muscles (see figure 10.31) are extensor muscles. They cause dorsiflexion, eversion, and inversion of the foot as well as extension of the toes.

The lateral leg muscles (see figure 10.31) primarily evert the foot, but they also help plantar flex the foot. The **fibularis brevis** inserts onto the fifth metatarsal bone and everts and plantar flexes the foot. The **fibularis longus** crosses under the lateral four metatarsal bones to insert onto the first metatarsal bone and medial cuneiform. The tendons of the fibularis muscles can be seen on the lateral side of the ankle (see figure 10.31).

The superficial muscles of the posterior compartment of the leg, the **gastrocnemius** (GAS-trok-NEE-mee-us) and the **soleus,** form the bulge of the calf (posterior leg; see figure 10.31). They merge with the small **plantaris** muscle to form the common **calcaneal** (kal-KAY-nee-uhl; heel) **tendon,** or *Achilles tendon*. These muscles plantar flex the foot. The deep muscles of the posterior compartment plantar flex and invert the foot and flex the toes.

Intrinsic foot muscles, located within the foot itself (table 10.23; figure 10.32), flex, extend, abduct, and adduct the toes. They are arranged in a manner similar to that of the intrinsic muscles of the hand.

Clinical IMPACT 10.2

Shinsplints

Shinsplints is a general term involving any one of the following conditions associated with pain in the anterior portion of the leg:

1. Excessive stress on the tibialis anterior, resulting in pain along the origin of the muscle
2. Tibial periostitis, an inflammation of the tibial periosteum
3. Anterior compartment syndrome. During hard exercise, the anterior compartment muscles may swell with blood. The overlying fascia is very tough and does not expand; thus, the nerves and vessels are compressed, causing pain.
4. Stress fracture of the tibia 2–5 cm distal to the knee

Shinsplints can occur for several reasons: running with unsupportive shoes, running on a hard surface (such as concrete), or simply increasing your activity level too quickly. This injury can be treated by employing RICE and taking anti-inflammatory medicines. Runners might consider occasionally substituting a low-impact exercise, such as swimming or cycling.

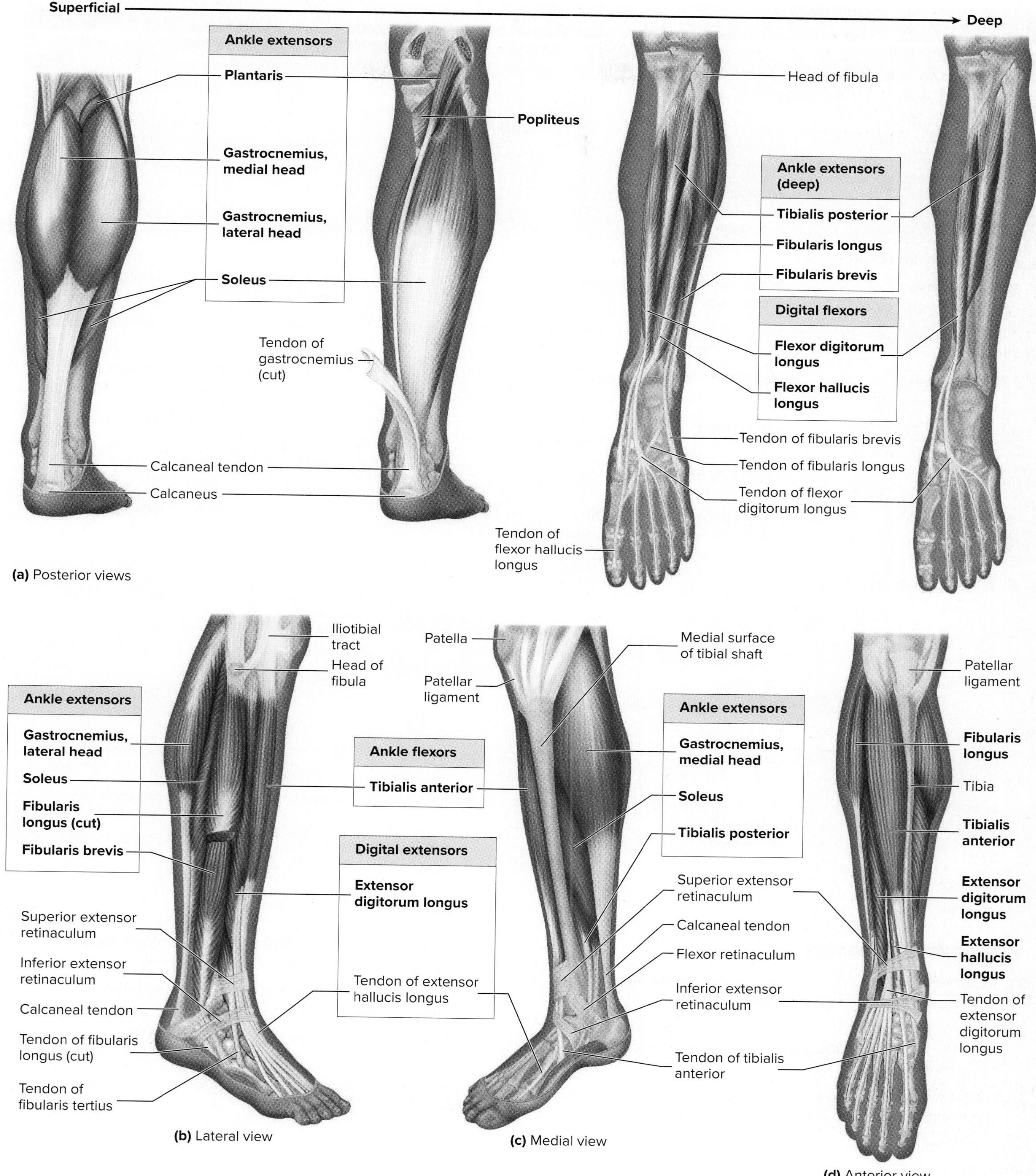

FIGURE 10.31 Muscles That Move the Leg
(*a*) Posterior view of the muscles that move the leg, ankle, and foot. (*b*) Lateral view. (*c*) Medial view. (*d*) Anterior view. (Muscle names are in bold.)

TABLE 10.22 Muscles of the Leg Acting on the Leg, Ankle, and Foot (see figure 10.31)

Muscle	Origin	Insertion	Nerve	Action
Muscles Acting on the Ankle and Leg				
Flexors (dorsiflexion)				
Fibularis tertius	Fibula and interosseous membrane	Fifth metatarsal bone	Deep fibular	Dorsiflexes and everts foot
Tibialis anterior	Proximal, lateral tibia and interosseous membrane	Medial cuneiform and first metatarsal bone	Deep fibular	Dorsiflexes and inverts foot
Extensors (plantar flexion)				
Fibularis brevis	Inferior two-thirds of lateral fibula	Fifth metatarsal bone	Superficial fibular	Everts and plantar flexes foot
Fibularis longus	Superior two-thirds of lateral fibula	First metatarsal bone and medial cuneiform	Superficial fibular	Everts and plantar flexes foot
Gastrocnemius	Medial and lateral condyles of femur	Through calcaneal (Achilles) tendon to calcaneus	Tibial	Plantar flexes foot; flexes knee
Plantaris	Femur	Through calcaneal tendon to calcaneus	Tibial	Plantar flexes foot; flexes knee
Soleus	Fibula and tibia	Through calcaneal tendon to calcaneus	Tibial	Plantar flexes foot
Tibialis posterior	Tibia, interosseous membrane, and fibula	Navicular, cuneiforms, cuboid, and second through fourth metatarsal bones	Tibial	Plantar flexes and inverts foot
Muscles Acting on the Foot				
Toe Flexors				
Flexor digitorum longus	Tibia	Four tendons to distal phalanges of four lateral toes	Tibial	Flexes four lateral toes; plantar flexes and inverts foot
Flexor hallucis longus	Fibula	Distal phalanx of great toe	Tibial	Flexes great toe; plantar flexes and inverts foot
Toe Extensors				
Extensor digitorum longus	Lateral condyle of tibia and fibula	Four tendons to phalanges of four lateral toes	Deep fibular	Extends four lateral toes; dorsiflexes and everts foot
Extensor hallucis longus	Middle fibula and interosseous membrane	Distal phalanx of great toe	Deep fibular	Extends great toe; dorsiflexes and inverts foot

ASSESS YOUR PROGRESS

31. *Name the anterior hip muscle that flexes the hip. What muscles act as synergists to this muscle?*

32. *How is it possible for thigh muscles to move both the thigh and the leg? Name the six muscles that can do this, and give their actions.*

33. *What movements are produced by the three muscle compartments of the leg? Name the muscles of each compartment, and describe the movements for which each muscle is responsible.*

34. *What movement do the fibularis muscles have in common? The tibialis muscles?*

35. *Name the leg muscles that flex the knee. Which of them can also plantar flex the foot?*

36. *List the general actions performed by the intrinsic foot muscles.*

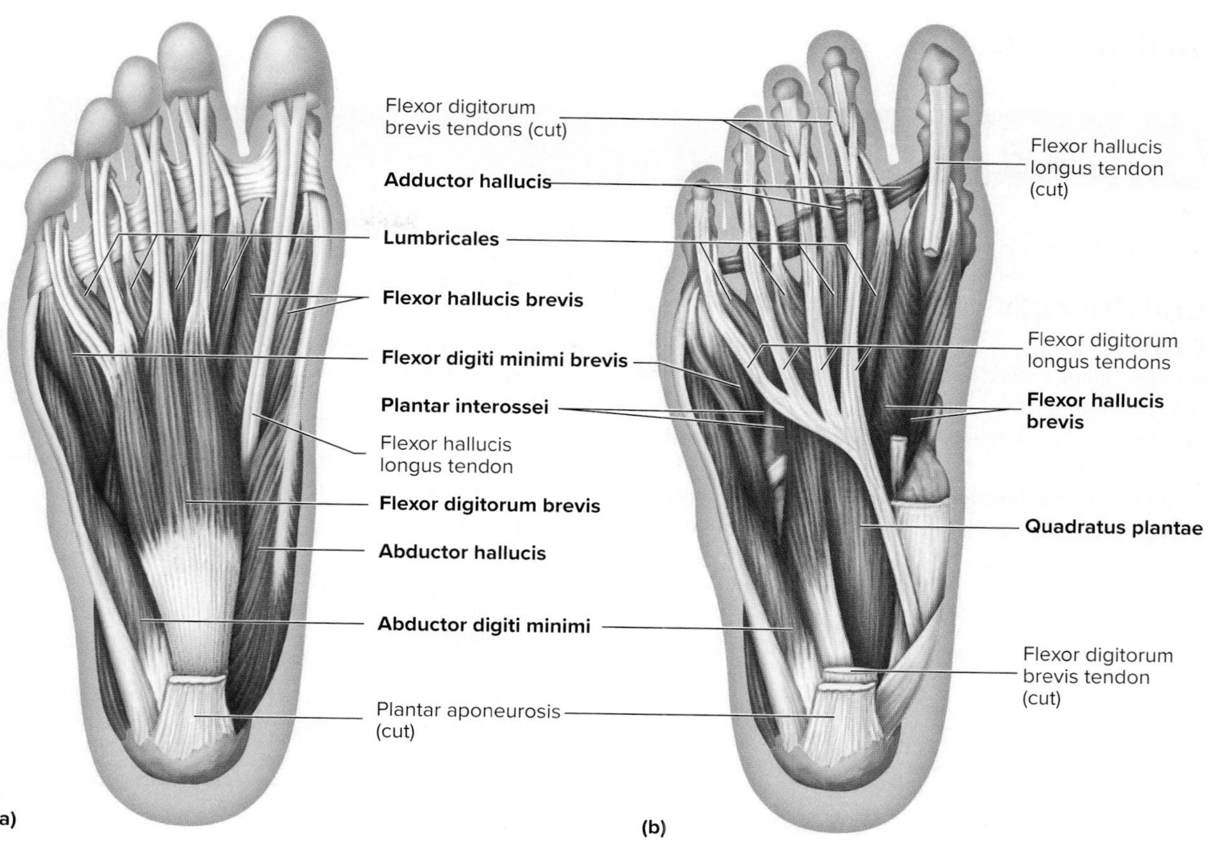

FIGURE 10.32 Right Foot Muscles

(*a*) Superficial muscles of the right foot. The plantar aponeurosis is cut. (*b*) Deep muscles of the right foot. The flexor digitorum brevis and flexor hallucis longus are cut. (Muscle names are in bold.)

TABLE 10.23 Intrinsic Muscles of the Foot (see figure 10.32)

Muscle	Origin	Insertion	Nerve	Action
Abductor digiti minimi	Calcaneus	Proximal phalanx of fifth toe	Lateral plantar	Abducts and flexes little toe
Abductor hallucis	Calcaneus	Base of proximal phalanx of great toe	Medial plantar	Abducts great toe
Adductor hallucis (not illustrated)	Lateral four metatarsal bones	Proximal phalanx of great toe	Lateral plantar	Adducts great toe
Extensor digitorum brevis (not illustrated)	Calcaneus	Four tendons fused with tendons of extensor digitorum longus	Deep fibular	Extends toes
Flexor digiti minimi brevis	Fifth metatarsal bone	Proximal phalanx of digit 5	Lateral plantar	Flexes little toe (proximal phalanx)
Flexor digitorum brevis	Calcaneus and plantar fascia	Four tendons to middle phalanges of four lateral toes	Medial plantar	Flexes lateral four toes
Flexor hallucis brevis	Cuboid; medial and lateral cuneiforms	Two tendons to proximal phalanx of great toe	Medial and lateral plantar	Flexes great toe
Dorsal interossei (not illustrated)	Metatarsal bones	Proximal phalanges of digits 2, 3, and 4	Lateral plantar	Abduct second, third, and fourth toes
Plantar interossei	Third, fourth, and fifth metatarsal bones	Proximal phalanges of digits 3, 4, and 5	Lateral plantar	Adduct third, fourth, and fifth toes
Lumbricales	Tendons of flexor digitorum longus	Extensor expansion of digits 2–5	Lateral and medial plantar	Flex proximal and extend middle and distal phalanges
Quadratus plantae	Calcaneus	Tendons of flexor digitorum longus	Lateral plantar	Assists flexor digitorum longus in flexing lateral four toes

Concept Check

Body movements result from the contraction of skeletal muscles.

10.1 General Principles of Skeletal Muscle Anatomy

A. The less movable end of a muscle attachment is the origin; the more movable end is the insertion.

B. An agonist causes a certain movement, and an antagonist acts in opposition to the agonist.

C. Synergists are muscles that function together to produce movement.

D. Prime movers are mainly responsible for a movement. Fixators stabilize the action of prime movers.

1. *Muscles that oppose one another are*

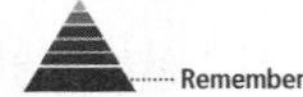

   a. synergists.
   b. levers.
   c. hateful.
   d. antagonists.
   e. fixators.

2. *The most movable attachment of a muscle is its*

   a. origin.
   b. insertion.
   c. fascia.
   d. fulcrum.
   e. belly.

Muscle Shapes

Muscle shape is determined primarily by the orientation of muscle fascicles.

Muscle Names

Muscles are named according to their location, size, shape, orientation of fascicles, origin and insertion, number of heads, or function.

3. *The muscle whose name means it is to the side of midline is the*
   a. gluteus maximus.
   b. vastus lateralis.
   c. teres major.
   d. latissimus dorsi.
   e. adductor magnus.

Muscle Movements

Contracting muscles generate a force that acts on bones (levers) across joints (fulcrums) to create movement. Three classes of levers have been identified.

4. *In a class III lever system, the*

   a. fulcrum is located between the pull and the weight.
   b. weight is located between the fulcrum and the pull.
   c. pull is located between the fulcrum and the weight.

Muscle Anatomy

The study of muscle anatomy is usually broken down into body regions: head and neck, trunk, upper limbs, and lower limbs.

10.2 Head and Neck Muscles

Neck Muscles

The origins of these muscles are mainly on the cervical vertebrae (except for the sternocleidomastoid); the insertions are on the occipital bone or mastoid process. They cause flexion, extension, rotation, and lateral flexion of the head and neck.

5. *A prominent lateral muscle of the neck that can cause flexion of the neck or rotate the head is the*
   a. digastric.
   b. mylohyoid.
   c. sternocleidomastoid.
   d. buccinator.
   e. platysma.

6. *A patient was involved in a rear-end auto collision, resulting in a whiplash injury to the head (hyperextension). What neck muscles might be injured in this type of accident? What is the easiest way to prevent such an injury in an automobile accident?*

Facial Expression

The origins of facial muscles are on skull bones or fascia; the insertions are into the skin, causing movement of the facial skin, lips, and eyelids.

7. *An aerial circus performer who supports her body only with her teeth while spinning around should have strong*
   a. temporalis muscles.
   b. masseter muscles.
   c. buccinator muscles.
   d. Both a and b are correct.
   e. All of these are correct.

8. *During surgery, a branch of a patient's facial nerve was accidentally cut on one side of the face. After the operation, the lower eyelid and the corner of the patient's mouth drooped on that side. What muscles were affected?*

Mastication

Three pairs of muscles close the jaw; gravity opens the jaw. Forced opening is caused by the lateral pterygoids and the hyoid muscles.

Tongue Movements

Intrinsic tongue muscles change the shape of the tongue; extrinsic tongue muscles move the tongue.

9. *The tongue's shape changes* primarily *because of the action of the*

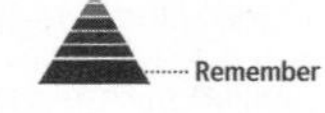

   a. extrinsic tongue muscles.
   b. intrinsic tongue muscles.

10. *When a person becomes unconscious, the tongue muscles relax and the tongue tends to retract, or fall back, and obstruct the airway. Which tongue muscle is responsible? How can this be prevented or reversed?*

Swallowing and the Larynx

A. Hyoid muscles can depress the jaw and assist in swallowing.

B. Muscles open and close the openings to the nasal cavity, auditory tubes, and larynx.

11. *The infrahyoid muscles*

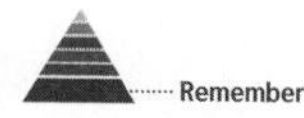

   a. *elevate the mandible.*
   b. *move the mandible from side to side.*
   c. *fix (prevent movement of) the hyoid.*
   d. *Both a and b are correct.*
   e. *All of these are correct.*

12. *The soft palate muscles*

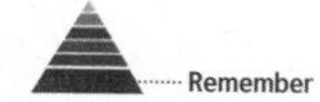

   a. *prevent food from entering the nasal cavity.*
   b. *close the auditory tube.*
   c. *force food into the esophagus.*
   d. *prevent food from entering the larynx.*
   e. *elevate the mandible.*

Movements of the Eyeball

Six muscles with their origins on the orbital bones insert on the eyeball and cause it to move within the orbit.

10.3 Trunk Muscles

Muscles Moving the Vertebral Column

A. These muscles extend, laterally flex, rotate, or flex the vertebral column.

B. A more superficial group of muscles runs from the pelvis to the skull, extending from the vertebrae to the ribs.

C. A deep group of muscles connects adjacent vertebrae.

13. *Which of these movements is* not *caused by contraction of the erector spinae muscles?* Remember
   a. *flexion of the vertebral column*
   b. *lateral flexion of the vertebral column*
   c. *extension of the vertebral column*
   d. *rotation of the vertebral column*

14. *For each of the following muscles—longus capitis, erector spinae, coracobrachialis:* Understand
   (1) *describe the movement the muscle produces, and*
   (2) *name the muscles that act as synergists and antagonists for them.*

Thoracic Muscles

A. Most respiratory movement is caused by the diaphragm.

B. Muscles attached to the ribs aid in respiration.

15. *Which of these muscles is* not *involved with the inspiration of air?* Remember
   a. *diaphragm*
   b. *external intercostals*
   c. *scalenes*
   d. *transversus thoracis*

Abdominal Wall

Abdominal wall muscles hold and protect abdominal organs and cause flexion, rotation, and lateral flexion of the vertebral column.

16. *Given these muscles:* Remember
   (1) *external abdominal oblique*
   (2) *internal abdominal oblique*
   (3) *transversus abdominis*

   Choose the arrangement that lists the muscles from most superficial to deepest.

   a. *1,2,3*
   b. *1,3,2*
   c. *2,1,3*
   d. *2,3,1*
   e. *3,1,2*

Pelvic Diaphragm and Perineum

These muscles support the abdominal organs inferiorly.

17. *Tendinous intersections*

   a. *attach the rectus abdominis muscles to the xiphoid process.*
   b. *divide the rectus abdominis muscles into segments.*
   c. *separate the abdominal wall from the thigh.*
   d. *are the sites where blood vessels exit the abdomen into the thigh.*
   e. *are the central point of attachment for all the abdominal muscles.*

10.4 Upper Limb Muscles

Scapular Movements

Six muscles attach the scapula to the trunk and enable the scapula to function as an anchor point for the muscles and bones of the arm.

18. *Which of these muscles can both elevate and depress the scapula?* Remember
   a. *rhomboideus major and minor*
   b. *levator scapulae*
   c. *serratus anterior*
   d. *trapezius*
   e. *pectoralis minor*

Arm Movements

Seven muscles attach the humerus to the scapula. Two additional muscles attach the humerus to the trunk. These muscles cause flexion and extension of the shoulder and abduction, adduction, rotation, and circumduction of the arm.

19. *Which of these muscles does* not *adduct the arm (humerus)?* Remember
   a. *latissimus dorsi*
   b. *deltoid*
   c. *teres major*
   d. *pectoralis major*
   e. *coracobrachialis*

20. *Which of these muscles would you expect to be especially well developed in a boxer known for his powerful jab (punching straight ahead)?*

   a. *biceps brachii*
   b. *brachialis*
   c. *trapezius*
   d. *triceps brachii*
   e. *supinator*

21. *Which of these muscles is an antagonist of the triceps brachii?*

   a. *biceps brachii*
   b. *anconeus*
   c. *latissimus dorsi*
   d. *brachioradialis*
   e. *supinator*

22. *The mechanical support of the head of the humerus in the glenoid fossa is weakest in the inferior direction. What muscles help prevent dislocation of the shoulder when a person carries a heavy weight, such as a suitcase?* Understand

Forearm Movements

A. Flexion and extension of the elbow are accomplished by three muscles in the arm and two in the forearm.

B. Supination and pronation are accomplished primarily by forearm muscles.

23. *The posterior group of forearm muscles is responsible for* Understand
    a. *flexion of the wrist.*
    b. *flexion of the fingers.*
    c. *extension of the fingers.*
    d. *Both a and b are correct.*
    e. *All of these are correct.*

24. *Consider only the effect of the brachioradialis muscle for these questions: If a weight is held in the hand and the forearm is flexed, what type of lever system is in action? If the weight is placed on the forearm? Which system can lift more weight, and how far?* Apply

25. *What muscles are required to turn the page of a book?* Apply

Wrist, Hand, and Finger Movements

A. Forearm muscles that originate on the medial epicondyle are responsible for flexion of the wrist and fingers. Muscles extending the wrist and fingers originate on the lateral epicondyle.

B. Extrinsic hand muscles are in the forearm. Intrinsic hand muscles are in the hand.

26. *Which of these muscles is an intrinsic hand muscle that moves the thumb?* Remember
    a. *flexor pollicis brevis*
    b. *flexor digiti minimi brevis*
    c. *flexor pollicis longus*
    d. *extensor pollicis longus*
    e. *All of these are correct.*

10.5 Lower Limb Muscles

Hip and Thigh Movements

A. Anterior pelvic muscles cause flexion of the hip.

B. Muscles of the buttocks are responsible for extension of the hip and abduction and rotation of the thigh.

27. *Given these muscles:*

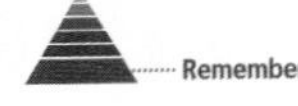

    (1) *iliopsoas*
    (2) *rectus femoris*
    (3) *sartorius*

    Which of the muscles flex the hip?

    a. *1*   c. *1,3*   e. *1,2,3*
    b. *1,2*   d. *2,3*

Leg Movements

A. Some muscles of the thigh also act on the leg. The anterior thigh muscles extend the leg, and the posterior thigh muscles flex the leg.

B. The thigh can be divided into three compartments.
- The anterior compartment muscles flex the hip and extend the knee.
- The medial compartment muscles adduct the thigh.
- The posterior compartment muscles extend the hip and flex the knee.

28. *Which of these muscles is found in the medial compartment of the thigh?* Remember
    a. *rectus femoris*
    b. *sartorius*
    c. *gracilis*
    d. *vastus medialis*
    e. *semitendinosus*

29. *Which of these is* not *a muscle that can flex the knee?*

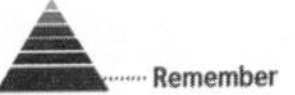

    a. *biceps femoris*
    b. *vastus medialis*
    c. *gastrocnemius*
    d. *gracilis*
    e. *sartorius*

30. *Savannah started a 200-meter dash and fell to the ground in pain. Examination of her right leg revealed the following symptoms: inability to plantar flex the foot against resistance, normal ability to evert the foot, abnormal dorsiflexion of the foot, and abnormal bulging of the calf muscles. Explain the nature of her injury.* Apply

Ankle, Foot, and Toe Movements

A. The leg is divided into three compartments.
- Muscles in the anterior compartment cause dorsiflexion, inversion, or eversion of the foot and extension of the toes.
- Muscles of the lateral compartment plantar flex and evert the foot.
- Muscles of the posterior compartment flex the leg, plantar flex and invert the foot, and flex the toes.

B. Intrinsic foot muscles flex or extend, and abduct or adduct, the toes.

31. *The* ________ *muscles evert the foot, whereas the* ________ *muscles invert the foot.* Remember
    a. *fibularis (longus and brevis), gastrocnemius and soleus*
    b. *fibularis (longus and brevis), tibialis anterior and extensor hallucis longus*
    c. *tibialis anterior and extensor hallucis longus, fibularis longus and brevis*
    d. *tibialis anterior and extensor hallucis longus, flexor digitorum longus and flexor hallucis longus*
    e. *flexor digitorum longus and flexor hallucis longus, gastrocnemius and soleus*

32. *Which of these muscles causes plantar flexion of the foot?*

    a. *tibialis anterior*
    b. *extensor digitorum longus*
    c. *fibularis tertius*
    d. *soleus*
    e. *sartorius*

Answers to this chapter's odd-numbered Concept Check questions appear in Appendix F.

11

CHAPTER

Functional Organization of Nervous Tissue

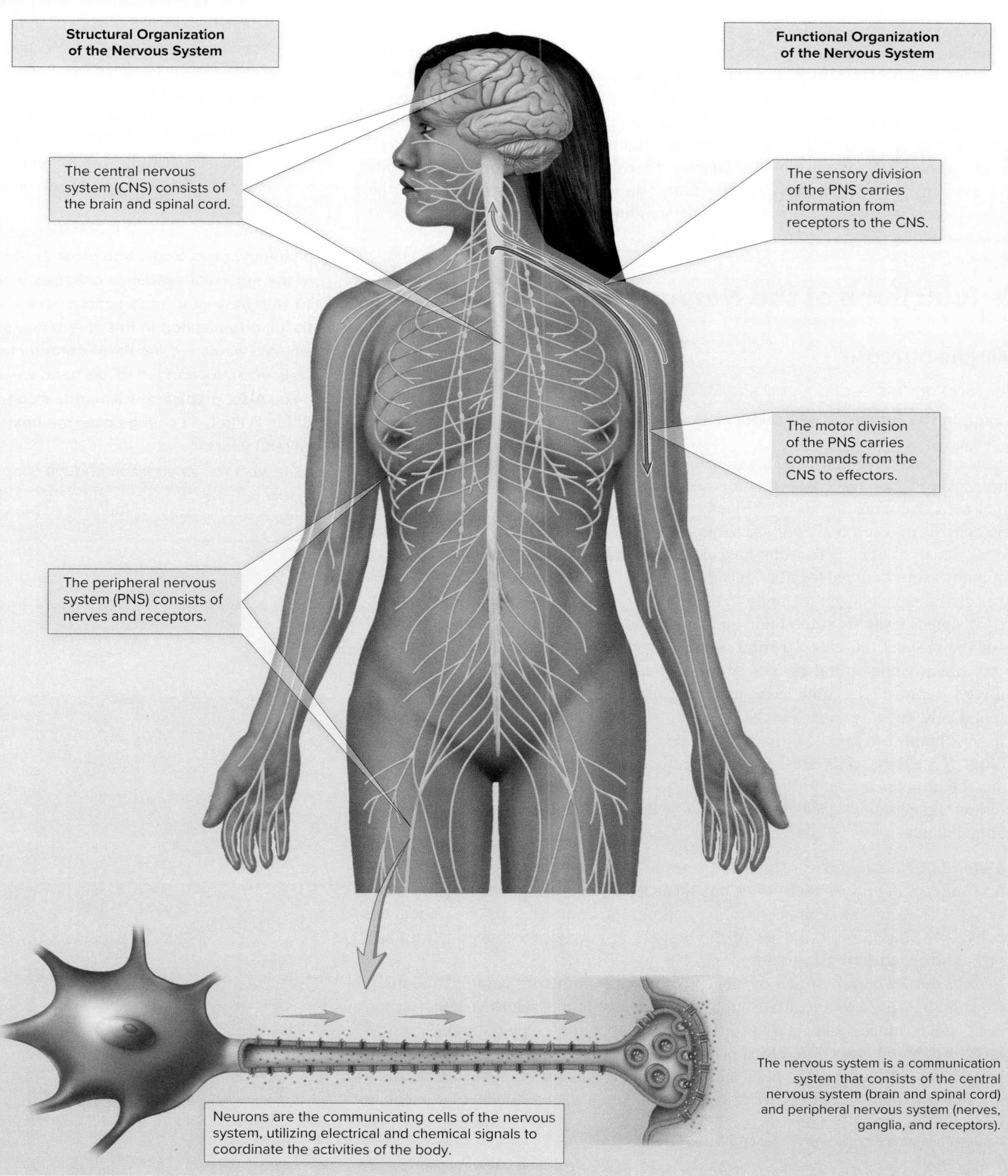

The nervous system is a communication system that consists of the central nervous system (brain and spinal cord) and peripheral nervous system (nerves, ganglia, and receptors).

From thinking and feeling to breathing, moving, and eating, virtually everything our body does is controlled by the nervous system. There are two major control systems in the body, the nervous system and the endocrine system. The nervous system is made up of the brain, spinal cord, nerves, and sensory receptors and uses electrical and chemical signals to control functions in the body. The endocrine system is made up of glands and specialized cells and uses chemical signals to control functions in the body (see chapters 17 and 18). We begin the study of the nervous system in this chapter by focusing on the physiology of nervous tissue. Chapters 12 and 13 discuss the anatomy of the spinal cord and spinal nerves and the brain and cranial nerves. Chapter 14 focuses on the integration of the nervous system components. Chapter 15 concentrates on the anatomy and physiology of the special senses. Finally, chapter 16 explores the autonomic nervous system anatomy and physiology. By the time you've finished learning about the nervous system, you will have a better understanding of your body's responses to different situations.

Learn to Predict

Once she turned 21, Amanda expected good times ahead. So why could she barely manage to climb the two flights of steps to her chemistry class? When she started experiencing weakness in her left hand, Amanda consulted a physician. After conducting numerous tests, Amanda's physician told her she had multiple sclerosis (MS), a condition in which the myelin sheaths of motor and sensory neurons in the brain and spinal cord are gradually destroyed.

By combining what you learned about the histology, physiology, and gross anatomy of the muscular system in chapters 9 and 10 with new information about nervous tissue organization in this chapter, explain why MS made it difficult for Amanda to walk up stairs and led to her hand weakness. Also, predict how Amanda's condition is likely to change over the next several years.

Answers to this question and the chapter's odd-numbered Predict questions can be found in Appendix E.

11.1 Functions of the Nervous System

LEARNING OUTCOME

After reading this section, you should be able to

A. **Explain the functions of the nervous system.**

The nervous system regulates and coordinates functions of the body required to maintain homeostasis. Nervous tissue is composed of two main cell types: (1) neurons and (2) glial cells. **Neurons** are the electrically excitable cells of the nervous system. A neuron consists of a cell body with several processes (see section 11.3). Neurons send electrical signals to other cells using long extensions called **axons.** A **nerve** is a collection of many axons bundled together outside the brain and the spinal cord. Some nerves carry electrical signals from the body to the brain and spinal cord. Other nerves carry electrical signals away from the brain and spinal cord out to body organs, such as the heart or the skeletal muscles. **Cranial nerves,** of which there are 12 pairs, originate from the brain, while **spinal nerves,** of which there are 31 pairs, originate from the spinal cord (figure 11.1). Some neurons form clusters of cell bodies outside the brain and spinal cord called ganglia (GANG-glee-ah; sing. GANG-lee-on; knot). A **plexus** (PLEK-sus; braid) is a bundle of nerves outside the brain and the spinal cord.

Glial (GLEE-al) **cells** are supportive cells that serve many functions for the neurons. Glial cells are fully discussed in section 11.3. Together, neurons and glial cells allow the nervous system to serve a multitude of functions for the body. These functions include:

1. *Maintaining homeostasis.* The trillions of cells in the human body do not function independently of each other but must work together to maintain homeostasis. For example, heart cells must contract at a rate that ensures adequate delivery of blood to all tissues of the body. The nervous system can stimulate or inhibit these activities to help maintain homeostasis.
2. *Receiving sensory input.* Sensory receptors monitor numerous external and internal stimuli. We are aware of sensations from some stimuli, such as vision, hearing, taste, smell, touch, pain, body position, and temperature. Other stimuli, such as blood pH, blood gases, and blood pressure, are processed at an unconscious level.
3. *Integrating information.* The brain and spinal cord are the major organs for processing sensory input and initiating responses. The input may produce an immediate response, be stored as memory, or be ignored.

Module 7
Nervous System

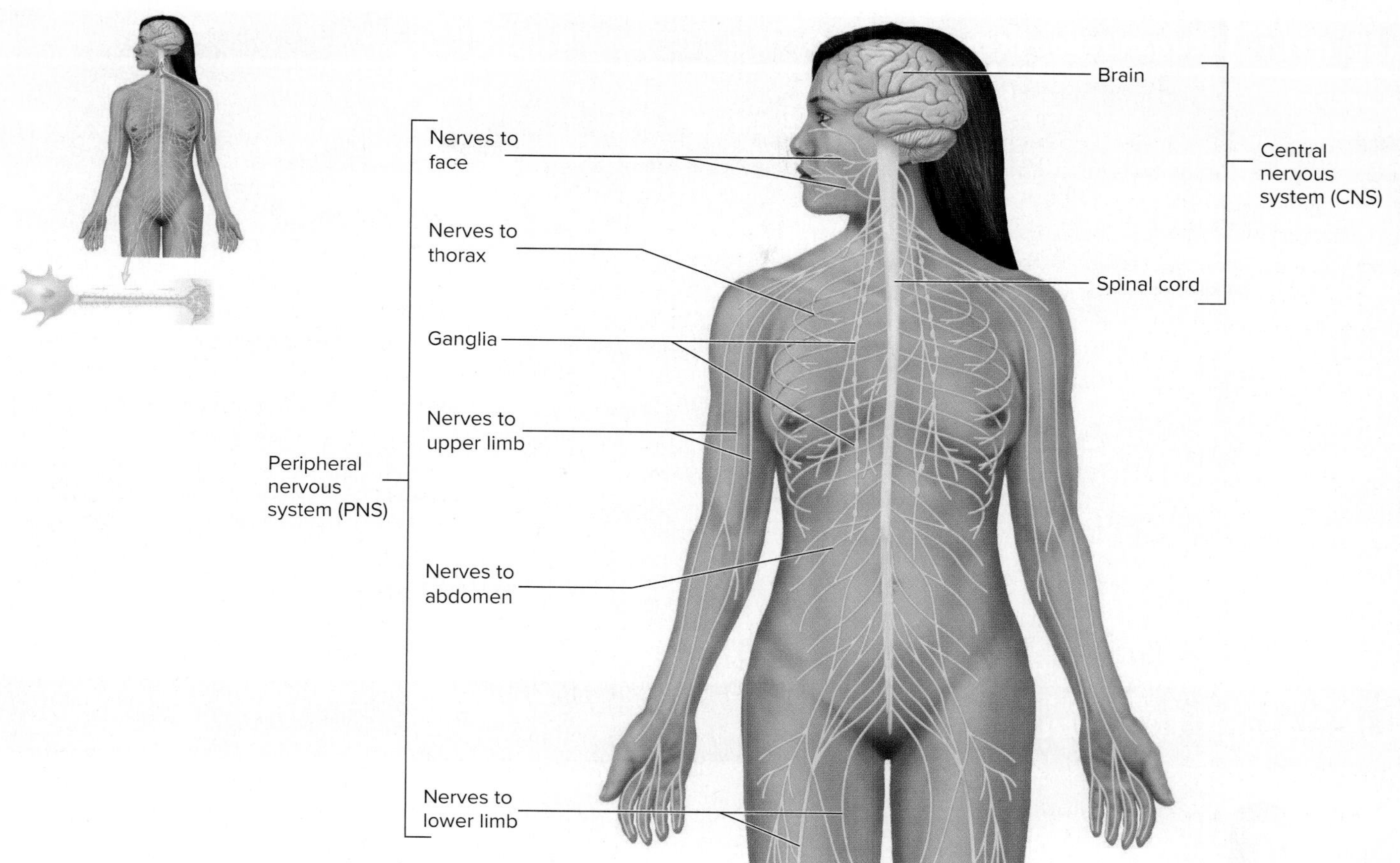

FIGURE 11.1 Nervous System
The central nervous system (CNS) consists of the brain and spinal cord. The peripheral nervous system (PNS) consists of cranial nerves, which arise from the brain, and spinal nerves, which arise from the spinal cord. The nerves, which are shown cut in the illustration, actually extend throughout the body.

4. *Controlling muscles and glands.* Skeletal muscles normally contract only when stimulated by the nervous system; thus, the nervous system controls the major movements of the body by controlling skeletal muscle. Some smooth muscle, such as that in the walls of blood vessels, contracts only when stimulated by the nervous system or by hormones (see chapter 18). Cardiac muscle and some smooth muscle, such as that in the wall of the stomach, contract autorhythmically—that is, no external stimulation is necessary for each contraction event. Although the nervous system does not initiate contraction in these muscles, it can cause the contractions to occur more rapidly or more slowly. Finally, the nervous system controls the secretions from many glands, including exocrine glands such as sweat glands, salivary glands, and glands of the digestive system as well as some endocrine glands.
5. *Establishing and maintaining mental activity.* The brain is the center of mental activities, including consciousness, thinking, memory, and emotions.

ASSESS YOUR PROGRESS

Answers to these questions are found in the section you have just completed. Re-read the section if you need help in answering these questions.

1. *List and give examples of the general functions of the nervous system.*

11.2 Divisions of the Nervous System

LEARNING OUTCOMES

After reading this section, you should be able to

A. **List the divisions of the nervous system and describe the characteristics of each.**
B. **Differentiate between the somatic and the autonomic nervous systems.**
C. **Contrast the general functions of the CNS and the PNS.**

The nervous system consists of two major divisions: (1) the central nervous system and (2) the peripheral nervous system (table 11.1; figure 11.2). These two systems communicate with each other and with the body to maintain homeostasis. The **central nervous system (CNS)** receives information from and sends information to the body. The **peripheral nervous system (PNS)** is responsible for detecting stimuli in and around the body and sending that information to the CNS and then communicating messages from the CNS to the body. The CNS can be thought of as the key decision maker, while the PNS is the messenger that provides input about the body to the CNS and then delivers the CNS decision on how the body is to respond to a particular set of stimuli.

TABLE 11.1 Organization of the Nervous System

Branch of Nervous System	Components	Division	Direction of Signal	Branch of PNS	Type of Control	Subdivisions	Effectors	Response at Effector
CNS	Brain and spinal cord	—	—	—	—	—	—	—
PNS	Receptors, nerves, ganglia, plexuses	Sensory	Afferent	—	—	—	—	—
		Motor	Efferent	Somatic	Voluntary	—	Skeletal muscle	Stimulates contraction
				Autonomic	Involuntary	Sympathetic	Cardiac and smooth muscle; glands	Readies body for physical activity
						Parasympathetic	Cardiac and smooth muscle; glands	Regulates resting functions

FUNDAMENTAL Figure

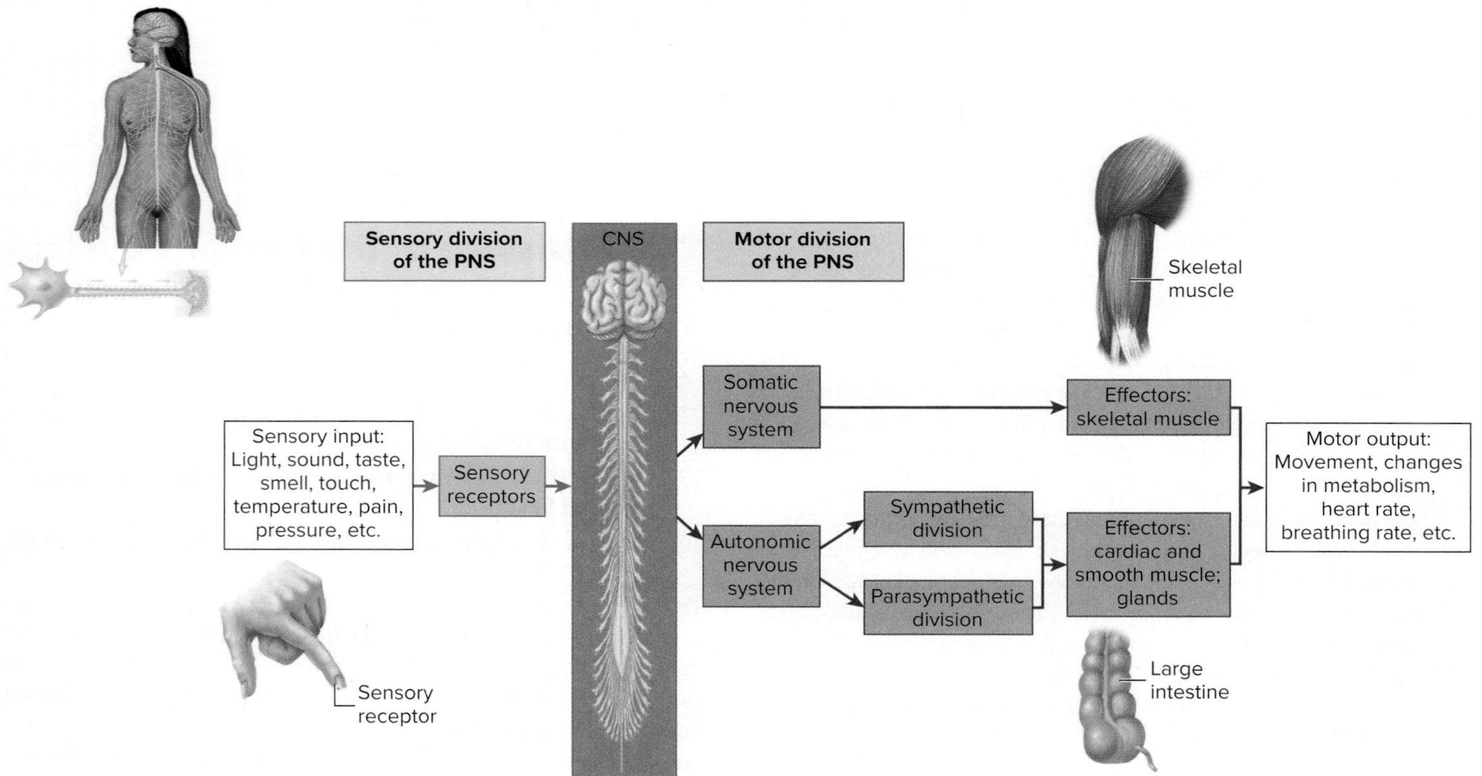

FIGURE 11.2 Information Flow in the Nervous System
The sensory division of the peripheral nervous system (PNS) detects stimuli and conducts action potentials to the central nervous system (CNS). The CNS interprets incoming action potentials and initiates action potentials that are conducted through the motor division to produce a response. The motor division is divided into the somatic nervous system and the autonomic nervous system. The enteric nervous system is an independent branch of the PNS and is not illustrated in this figure.

The CNS consists of the brain and the spinal cord. The brain is housed within the skull and the spinal cord is housed within the vertebral canal of the vertebral column (see chapter 7). The brain and spinal cord are continuous with each other, transitioning from brain to spinal cord at the foramen magnum of the skull.

The PNS consists of all the nervous tissue outside the CNS, which includes nerves, ganglia, and sensory receptors. The PNS has two primary divisions: (1) the sensory division and (2) the motor division.

The **sensory division** transmits electrical signals from specialized receptors in the body toward the CNS. For this reason, the sensory division is also called the *afferent division* (afferent = toward). **Sensory receptors** detect stimuli and then send input along nerves, which extend from the receptor to the brain or spinal cord. Sensory receptors can be neuron endings or specialized cells that detect external and internal environmental stimuli, such as temperature, pain, touch, pressure, and light, among others. Sensory receptors are distributed around the body within muscles, skin, joints, eyes, ears, and many other locations. These receptors constantly monitor body conditions and communicate that information to the CNS. The CNS processes the information and initiates a response by the body. For example, when turning on a bright light in a dark room, the CNS generates a message to constrict the pupil of the eye. It is the motor division of the PNS that actually communicates with the eye to cause constriction of the pupil.

The **motor division,** as described in the bright light example, transmits electrical signals from the CNS to effector organs, such as muscles and glands. Thus, the motor division is also called the *efferent division* (efferent = away). The motor division consists of two branches: (1) the somatic nervous system and (2) the autonomic nervous system.

The **somatic** (soh-MAT-ik; body) **nervous system** is the voluntary division of the motor division. It allows you to decide to move your skeletal muscles, such as when raising your hand to ask a question, or to stand and walk across the room. The CNS generates electrical signals that are sent to the skeletal muscles by nerves of the somatic nervous system (figure 11.2).

The **autonomic** (aw-toh-NOM-ik; self-governing) **nervous system** is the involuntary division of the motor division. It regulates activities without our conscious control such as contractions of cardiac muscle and smooth muscle and secretions by certain glands. For example, your heart rate increases when you hear an unexpected loud noise that startles you.

There are two major subdivisions of the ANS that regulate functions throughout the body. These are (1) the sympathetic division and (2) the parasympathetic division. The **sympathetic division** readies the body for physical activity and is called the fight-or-flight division. The **parasympathetic division** regulates resting functions, such as digesting food or slowing the heart rate, and is called the rest-and-digest division. A third division of the nervous system is the **enteric nervous system** (*entero,* intestine; **ENS**), which consists of neuronal networks within the wall of the digestive tract (see chapter 24).

In summary, the PNS includes the sensory division and the two motor divisions. These divisions of the PNS, along with the CNS, are highly integrated and work very efficiently to tightly regulate the internal environment of our body.

ASSESS YOUR PROGRESS

2. *Name the components of the CNS and the PNS.*
3. *What are the following: sensory receptor, nerve?*
4. *Based on the direction they transmit action potentials, what are the two subcategories of the PNS?*
5. *Based on the structures they supply, what are the two subcategories of the motor division?*
6. *What are the subcategories of the ANS?*
7. *Compare the general functions of the CNS and the PNS.*

11.3 Cells of the Nervous System

LEARNING OUTCOMES

After reading this section, you should be able to

A. **Describe the structure of neurons.**
B. **Describe the functions of the components of a neuron.**
C. **Classify neurons based on structure.**
D. **Classify neurons based on function.**
E. **Describe the location, structure, and functions of CNS glial cells.**
F. **Describe the location, structure, and functions of PNS glial cells.**
G. **Discuss the function of the myelin sheath.**
H. **Describe the formation of myelin sheaths in the CNS and PNS.**

The two cell types that make up the nervous system, neurons and glial cells, work together to monitor the body's environment and make changes when needed. There are an estimated 100 billion neurons in our body, yet glial cells account for over half of the brain's weight, and there can be 10 to 50 times more glial cells than neurons in various parts of the brain. In order to understand how the nervous system functions, a knowledge of neuron structure and glial cell types is important.

Neuron Structure

Neurons are the electrically excitable cells of the nervous system. There are three parts to most types of neuron (figure 11.3): (1) a neuron cell body, (2) dendrites, and (3) a single axon.

1. Neuron Cell Body
   The **neuron cell body,** or *soma* (SOH-mah; body), performs the typical functions of any cell, such as protein synthesis and packaging of proteins into vesicles. Each neuron cell body contains a single, relatively large, and centrally located nucleus with a prominent nucleolus. Neurons have extensive rough endoplasmic reticulum (ER), called **Nissl** (NIS-il) **bodies.** The abundance of Nissl bodies reflects the significant amount of protein synthesis neurons perform. The Golgi apparatuses are located near the nucleus, and mitochondria and other organelles are present. Large numbers of intermediate filaments (neurofilaments) and microtubules form bundles that organize the cytoplasm into different regions.

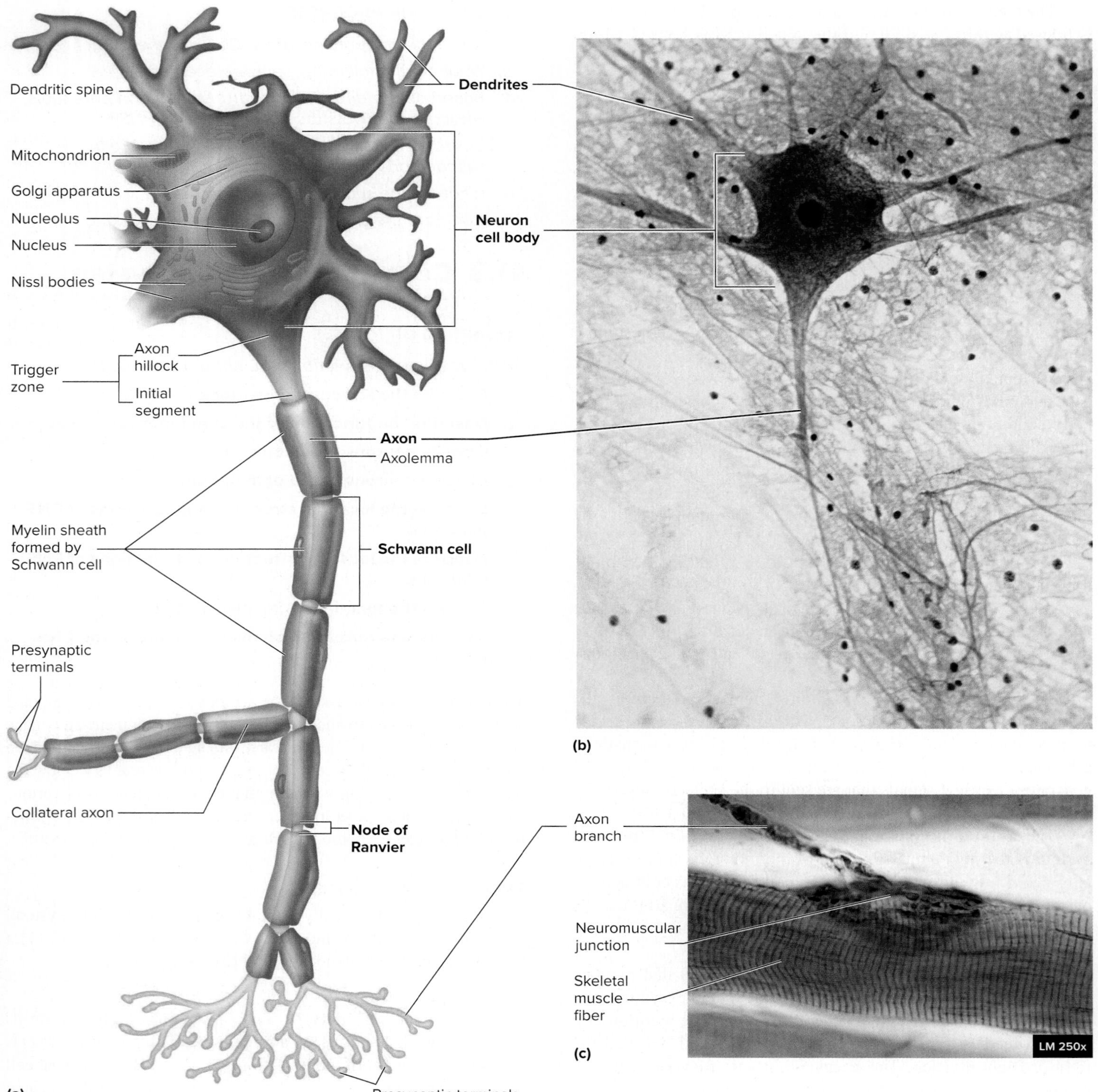

FIGURE 11.3 Neuron

(*a*) The structural features of a neuron are a cell body and two types of cell projections: dendrites and an axon. The neuron depicted here is a multipolar neuron. (*b*) Photomicrograph of a multipolar neuron. (*c*) Photomicrograph of a neuromuscular junction. (b) Ed Reschke/Getty Images; (c) Ed Reschke/Photolibrary/Getty Images APR

2. Dendrites
   Dendrites (DEN-drights; tree) are extensions of the cell body and receive information from other neurons or from sensory receptors. Dendrites are short, often highly branched cytoplasmic extensions that are tapered from their bases at the neuron cell body to their tips (figure 11.3). Many dendrite surfaces have small extensions, called **dendritic spines,** where axons of other neurons form connections with the dendrites. When stimulated, dendrites generate small electric currents, which are conducted toward the neuron cell body.

3. Axons
   In most neurons, a single axon arises from a cone-shaped area of the neuron cell body called the **axon hillock.** As the axon hillock narrows, it transitions into the **initial segment,** which is the actual beginning of the axon. The combination of the axon hillock and the initial segment is called the **trigger zone.** The trigger zone is where action potentials are generated. Many axons remain as a single structure, but others branch to form collateral axons, or side branches (figure 11.3). Each axon has a constant diameter, but axons can vary in length from a few millimeters to more than 1 meter. The cytoplasm of an axon is called the **axoplasm,** and its plasma membrane is called the **axolemma** (*lemma,* husk).

   The axon projects away from the cell body until it reaches the plasma membrane of the effector. The point of contact between the axon ending and its effector is called a **synapse** (SIN-aps). Usually, axons branch many times and form synapses with multiple effector cells. The region of the axon ending at the synapse is called the **presynaptic terminal.** Presynapatic terminals have many **synaptic vesicles,** which store the signal molecules produced by the neuron. These signal molecules control the effectors and are called **neurotransmitters.** We will discuss the specific role of neurotransmitters in section 11.6.

   Within the axoplasm, transport mechanisms move cytoskeletal proteins (see chapter 3), mitochondria, and synaptic vesicles down the axon toward the presynaptic terminals. Movement *away* from the cell body is called *anterograde*. In addition, damaged organelles, recycled plasma membrane, and substances taken in by endocytosis can be transported up the axon toward the neuron cell body. Movement *toward* the cell body is called *retrograde*.

   The movement of materials within the axon is necessary for its normal function, but, unfortunately, it also provides an entryway for infectious agents and harmful substances to the CNS. For example, rabies and herpes viruses can enter damaged axons in the skin and, in a retrograde fashion, be transported within the axons to the CNS.

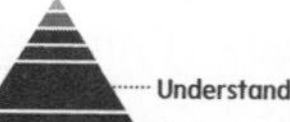

Predict 1

If an axon has been severed, so that it is no longer connected to its neuron cell body, what will be the effect on the distal and proximal portions of the axon? Explain your prediction.

Types of Neurons

Neurons can be classified based on either their function or their structure. There are three functional categories based on the direction of action potentials conduction: (1) **sensory neurons** (*afferent neurons*) conduct action potentials toward the CNS; (2) **motor neurons** (*efferent neurons*) conduct action potentials away from the CNS toward muscles or glands; and (3) **interneurons** conduct action potentials within the CNS from one neuron to another.

Based on the number of dendrites, there are four major structural categories: (1) multipolar, (2) bipolar, (3) pseudo-unipolar, and (4) anaxonic.

Multipolar neurons (*multi,* many) have many dendrites and a single axon. The dendrites vary in number and in their degree of branching (figure 11.4*a*). Motor neurons of the PNS and most of the neurons within the CNS are multipolar.

Bipolar neurons (*bi,* two) have two processes: one dendrite and one axon (figure 11.4*b*). The dendrite is often specialized to receive the stimulus, and the axon conducts action potentials. Bipolar neurons are located in some sensory organs, such as in the retina of the eye and in the nasal cavity.

Pseudo-unipolar neurons (*uni,* one) start out as bipolar neurons during development, but the two processes that extend from the cell body fuse into a single process. This single process divides into two branches a short distance from the cell body (figure 11.4*c*). The two branches function as a single axon. One branch, the peripheral process, extends to the periphery and has dendrites. These dendrites either act as a sensory receptor or communicate with a sensory receptor. The other branch, called the central process, extends to the CNS. In this way, stimuli that occur at a sensory receptor generate action potentials that are conducted along the peripheral process to the central process and ultimately to the CNS. Most sensory neurons are pseudo-unipolar.

Anaxonic neurons do not have axons and only have dendrites projecting from their cell body (figure 11.4*d*). Found within the brain and retina, these neurons communicate using only graded potentials and not action potentials (see section 11.5 for further discussion of these different potentials).

Glial Cells of the CNS

Glial cells are support cells for neurons. There are four types of CNS glial cells: (1) astrocytes, (2) ependymal cells, (3) microglia, and (4) oligodendrocytes. The major characteristics of glial cells are summarized in figure 11.5.

Astrocytes

Astrocytes (ASS-troh-sites; *aster,* star) are star-shaped glial cells with cytoplasmic processes extending from their cell bodies. These extensions widen and spread out to form foot processes, which cover the surfaces of blood vessels (figure 11.5*a*), neurons, and the pia mater. (The pia mater is a membrane covering the outside of the brain and spinal cord.) Astrocytes have an

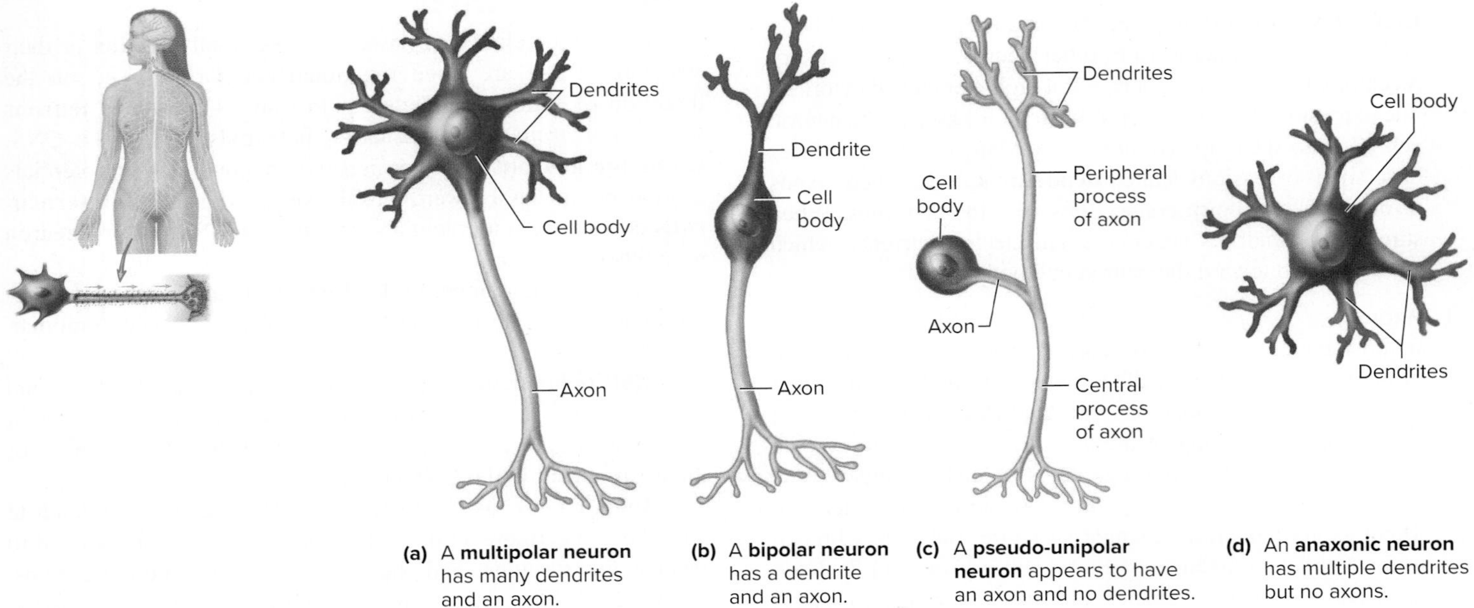

(a) A **multipolar neuron** has many dendrites and an axon.

(b) A **bipolar neuron** has a dendrite and an axon.

(c) A **pseudo-unipolar neuron** appears to have an axon and no dendrites.

(d) An **anaxonic neuron** has multiple dendrites but no axons.

FIGURE 11.4 Structural Classes of Neurons
Neurons are classified structurally by the number of cellular processes extending from their cell bodies. Dendrites and sensory receptors are specialized to receive stimuli, and axons are specialized to conduct action potentials.

extensive cytoskeleton of microfilaments (see chapter 3), which enables them to form a supporting framework for blood vessels and neurons.

Astrocytes help regulate the composition of extracellular brain fluid. They do this by releasing chemicals that promote the formation of tight junctions between the endothelial cells of capillaries. Recall from chapter 4 that tight junctions create an impermeable barrier between adjacent cells. The endothelial cells with their tight junctions form the **blood-brain barrier.** The blood-brain barrier determines which substances can pass from the blood into the nervous tissue of the brain and spinal cord. The blood-brain barrier protects neurons from toxic substances in the blood, allows the exchange of nutrients and waste products between neurons and the blood, and prevents fluctuations in blood composition from affecting brain functions.

Astrocytes aid both beneficial and detrimental responses to tissue damage in the CNS. Almost all injuries to CNS tissue induce **reactive astrocytosis,** in which astrocytes wall off the injury site and help limit the spread of inflammation to the surrounding healthy tissue. Reactive scar-forming astrocytes also limit the regeneration of the axons of injured neurons.

Astrocytes also release chemicals that promote the development of synapses and help regulate synaptic activity by synthesizing, absorbing, and recycling neurotransmitters.

Ependymal Cells

Ependymal (ep-EN-dih-mal) **cells** line the ventricles (cavities) of the brain and the central canal of the spinal cord (figure 11.5*b*). Specialized ependymal cells and blood vessels form structures called **choroid plexuses** (KO-royd PLEK-sus-ez), which are located within certain regions of the ventricles. The choroid plexuses secrete cerebrospinal fluid, which flows through the ventricles of the brain (see chapter 13). Some ependymal cells have patches of cilia that assist in the flow of cerebrospinal fluid. Ependymal cells also have long processes at their basal surfaces that extend deep into the brain and the spinal cord and seem, in some cases, to have astrocyte-like functions.

Microglia

Microglia (my-KROH-glee-ah) are CNS-specific immune cells derived from the same embryonic tissue as other immune cells within the blood. However, once these cells are established within the CNS, they are the sole source of new microglia. Microglia become mobile and phagocytic in response to inflammation. They phagocytize necrotic tissue, microorganisms, and other foreign substances that invade the CNS (figure 11.5*c*). Areas of the brain or spinal cord that have been damaged by infection, trauma, or stroke have more microglia than healthy areas. There the microglia perform phagocytosis of dead cells and pathogens. A pathologist can identify these damaged areas in the CNS during an autopsy because large numbers of microglia are found there.

Oligodendrocytes

Oligodendrocytes (OL-i-goh-DEN-droh-sites) form an insulating layer around axons. Oligodendrocytes have cytoplasmic

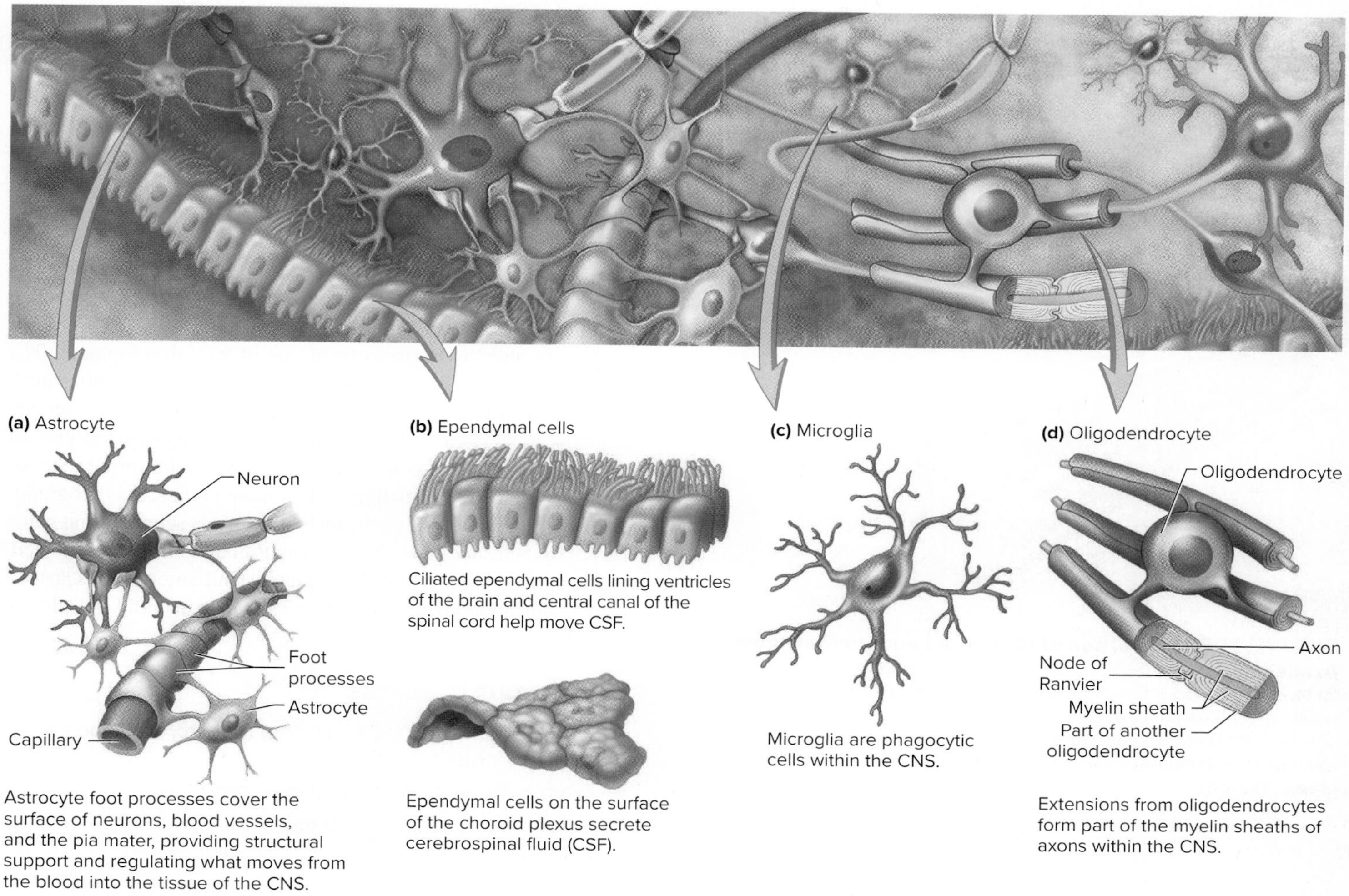
(a) Astrocyte
Neuron
Foot processes
Astrocyte
Capillary
Astrocyte foot processes cover the surface of neurons, blood vessels, and the pia mater, providing structural support and regulating what moves from the blood into the tissue of the CNS.
(b) Ependymal cells
Ciliated ependymal cells lining ventricles of the brain and central canal of the spinal cord help move CSF.
Ependymal cells on the surface of the choroid plexus secrete cerebrospinal fluid (CSF).
(c) Microglia
Microglia are phagocytic cells within the CNS.
(d) Oligodendrocyte
Oligodendrocyte
Axon
Node of Ranvier
Myelin sheath
Part of another oligodendrocyte
Extensions from oligodendrocytes form part of the myelin sheaths of axons within the CNS.

FIGURE 11.5 Glial Cells of the CNS
Glial cells of the CNS include (*a*) astrocytes, (*b*) ependymal cells, (*c*) microglia, and (*d*) oligodendrocytes.

extensions that wrap many times around axons forming the **myelin** (MY-eh-lin) **sheath.** One oligodendrocyte forms myelin sheaths for axons of multiple neurons (figure 11.5*d*).

Glial Cells of the PNS

There are two types of glial cells in the PNS: (1) Schwann cells and (2) satellite cells. **Schwann cells** form myelin sheaths. However, unlike oligodendrocytes, each Schwann cell forms a portion of the myelin sheath around only one axon (figure 11.6). The outermost layer of each Schwann cell is called the **neurilemma.** It contains the majority of the Schwann cell cytoplasm, nucleus, and organelles (see figure 11.3).

Satellite cells surround neuron cell bodies in sensory and autonomic ganglia (figure 11.6). Besides providing support and nutrition to the neuron cell bodies, satellite cells protect neurons from heavy-metal poisons, such as lead and mercury, by absorbing them and reducing their access to the neuron cell bodies.

Satellite cells
Neuron cell body
Schwann cells
Axon
Myelin sheath
Node of Ranvier

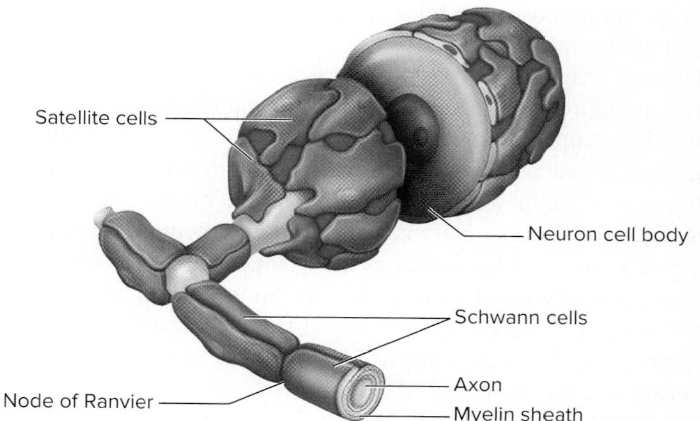

FIGURE 11.6 Glial Cells of the PNS
Glial cells of the PNS include Schwann cells, which form the myelin of axons of the PNS, and satellite cells, which are found around the cell body of neurons.

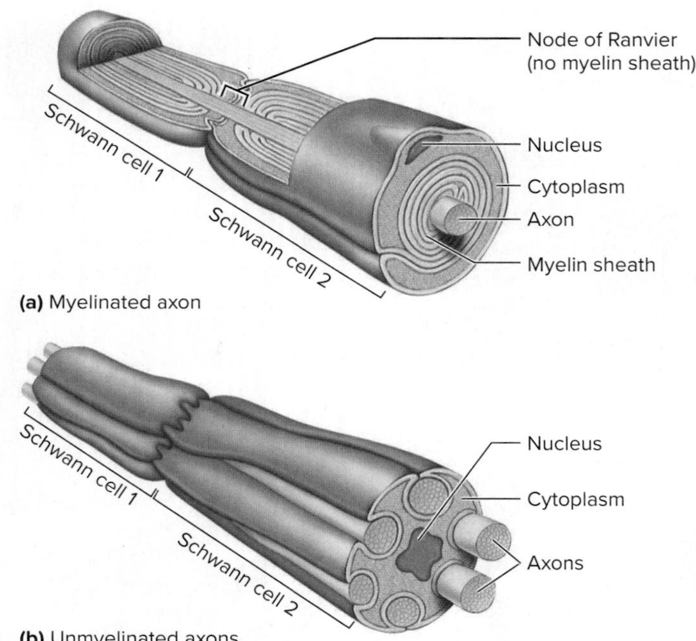

FIGURE 11.7 Comparison of Myelinated and Unmyelinated Axons

(*a*) Myelinated axon with two Schwann cells forming part of the myelin sheath around a single axon. Each Schwann cell surrounds part of one axon. (*b*) Unmyelinated axons with two Schwann cells surrounding several axons in parallel formation. Each Schwann cell surrounds part of several axons.

Myelinated and Unmyelinated Axons

In **myelinated axons,** Schwann cells in the PNS or oligodendrocyte extensions in the CNS repeatedly wrap around a segment of an axon to form a series of tightly wrapped membranes rich in phospholipids, with little cytoplasm sandwiched between the membrane layers (figure 11.7*a*). One way to picture the overlapping wrappings, especially for Schwann cells, is to imagine rolling up a hot dog (axon) inside a tortilla (Schwann cell). The tightly wrapped membranes of the Schwann cells constitute the myelin sheath and give myelinated axons a white appearance because of the high lipid concentration. The myelin sheath is not a continuous covering of the axon. Instead, it contains gaps every 0.3–1.5 mm. At these locations are slight constrictions where the myelin sheaths of adjacent glial cells dip toward the axon but do not cover it, leaving an area where the myelin sheath is much thinner and about 2–3 μm in length. These gaps in the myelin sheath are the **nodes of Ranvier** (RON-vee-ay) (figure 11.7*a* see figure 11.5*d* and 11.6). Although, at a node of Ranvier, the axon is not wrapped in myelin, Schwann cells or oligodendrocytes extend across the node and connect to each other. The myelin sheath protects and electrically insulates each axon. These characteristics help myelinated axons conduct electrical signals more rapidly than unmyelinated axons.

Unmyelinated axons are not devoid of myelin, as their name suggests. Instead, the axons rest in invaginations of the Schwann cells or oligodendrocytes (figure 11.7*b*). The glial cell's plasma membrane surrounds each axon but does not wrap around it many times. Thus, each axon is surrounded by a series of Schwann cells, and each Schwann cell can simultaneously surround more than one unmyelinated axon.

Myelin sheaths begin to form late in fetal development. The process continues rapidly until the end of the first year after birth and continues more slowly thereafter. The development of myelin sheaths is associated with the infant's continuing development of more rapid and better coordinated responses. The importance of myelinated axons is dramatically illustrated in diseases that gradually destroy the myelin sheath, such as multiple sclerosis and some cases of diabetes mellitus. Action potential transmission is slowed, resulting in impaired control of skeletal and smooth muscles. In severe cases, action potential transmission can become completely blocked.

ASSESS YOUR PROGRESS

8. *Describe and give the function of a neuron cell body, a dendrite, and an axon.*
9. *What is the function of the trigger zone?*
10. *What is the role of a neurotransmitter? Where is it stored?*
11. *Describe the three types of neurons based on function.*
12. *Explain the four types of neurons based on structure, and give an example of where each type is found.*
13. *What characteristic makes glial cells different from neurons?*
14. *Which glial cells are found in the CNS? In the PNS?*
15. *Which type of glial cell supports neurons and blood vessels and promotes formation of the blood-brain barrier? What is the blood-brain barrier, and what is its function?*
16. *Name the different kinds of glial cells that are responsible for the following functions: production of cerebrospinal fluid, phagocytosis, production of myelin sheaths in the CNS, production of myelin sheaths in the PNS, support of neuron cell bodies in the PNS.*
17. *What is a myelin sheath? How is it formed in the CNS? In the PNS?*
18. *How do myelinated axons differ from unmyelinated axons?*

Clinical IMPACT 11.1 Nervous Tissue Response to Injury

When a nerve is cut, either it eventually heals or it is permanently damaged. The final outcome depends on the severity of the injury and on its treatment.

Several degenerative changes result when a nerve is cut (figure 11.8). Within about 3–5 days, the axons in the part of the nerve distal to the cut break into irregular segments and degenerate. This occurs because the neuron cell body produces the substances essential to maintain the axon, and these substances have no way of reaching parts of the axon distal to the point of damage. Eventually, the distal part of the axon completely degenerates. As the axons degenerate, the myelin part of the Schwann cells around them also degenerates, and macrophages invade the area to phagocytize the myelin. The Schwann cells then enlarge, undergo mitosis, and finally form a column of cells along the regions once occupied by the axons. The columns of Schwann cells are essential for the growth of new axons. If the ends of the regenerating axons encounter a Schwann cell column, they grow more rapidly, and reinnervation of their target is likely. If the ends of the axons do not encounter the columns, they fail to reinnervate their target.

Treatment strategies that increase the probability of reinnervation involve bringing the ends of the severed nerve close together surgically. When a section of nerve is destroyed as a result of trauma, a surgeon can perform a nerve transplant to replace the damaged segment. The transplanted nerve eventually degenerates, but it does provide Schwann cell columns through which axons can grow.

The regeneration of damaged nerve tracts within the CNS is very limited, especially when compared with the regeneration of nerves in the PNS. In part, the difference may result from the oligodendrocytes, which exist only in the CNS. An oligodendrocyte has several processes, each of which forms part of a myelin sheath. The cell bodies of the oligodendrocytes are a short distance from the axons they ensheathe, and fewer oligodendrocytes than Schwann cells are present. Consequently, when the myelin degenerates following damage, no column of cells remains in the CNS to act as a guide for the growing axons.

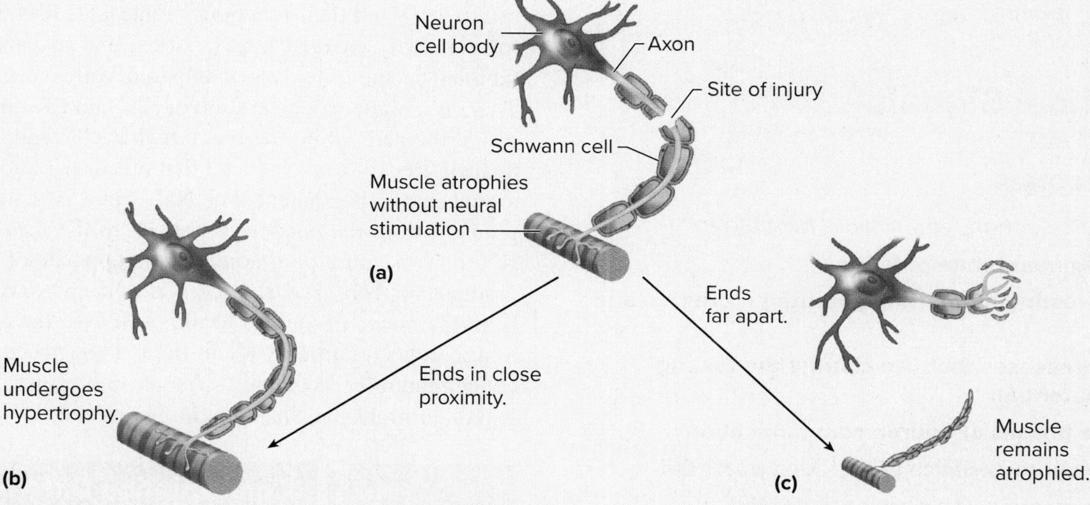

FIGURE 11.8 Responses to Injury in an Axon
(*a*) When a nerve is injured, there are two possible outcomes. Regardless, the muscle will initially atrophy (shrink in size). (*b*) When the two ends of an injured axon are aligned in close proximity, healing and regeneration of the axon are likely to occur. After reinnervation, the muscle can become functional and hypertrophy (increase in size). (*c*) When the two ends of an injured axon are not aligned in close proximity, regeneration is unlikely to occur. Without innervation from the nerve, muscle function is completely lost, and the muscle remains atrophied.

11.4 Organization of Nervous Tissue

LEARNING OUTCOMES

After reading this section, you should be able to

A. **Distinguish between gray matter and white matter.**
B. **Describe the components of gray matter in the CNS and PNS.**
C. **Describe the components of white matter in the CNS and PNS.**

In both the CNS and the PNS, nervous tissue is organized such that axons are grouped together, forming bundles, while neuron cell bodies and dendrites are also grouped together. These groupings give nervous tissue distinctive areas, called **gray matter** and **white matter.** Because gray matter consists of groups of neuron cell bodies and their dendrites, where there is very little myelin, these areas are darker in appearance. In the CNS, the **cortex** consists of gray matter on the surface of the brain. **Nuclei** are clusters of gray matter located deeper within the brain. In the PNS, gray matter consists of clusters of neuron cell bodies, or **ganglia.** Conversely, because white matter consists of bundles of parallel myelinated axons, they are whitish in color. White matter of the CNS forms **nerve tracts,** which propagate action potentials from one area of the CNS to another. In contrast, in the PNS, bundles of axons and their connective tissue sheaths are simply called **nerves.**

Predict 2

A 75-year-old man was found unconscious in his bathroom after falling and hitting his head. He survived for several hours but died later in the hospital. An autopsy was performed to determine the exact cause of death. Evidence indicated that the man had suffered two strokes, both due to blocked blood vessels. One had occurred a few weeks earlier; the other had occurred very recently and may have led to the fall. Autopsy findings also indicated that, when the man hit his head, some damage to his brain occurred as well. Based on what you know about inflammation and the cellular structure of the brain, describe what the pathologist found in each of the damaged areas of the brain.

ASSESS YOUR PROGRESS

19. *What makes up gray matter and white matter?*

20. *Describe and state the location of the following: nerve tracts, nerves, the brain cortex, nuclei, ganglia.*

11.5 Electrical Signals

LEARNING OUTCOMES

After reading this section, you should be able to

A. **Define resting membrane potential.**
B. **Explain how resting membrane potential is created and maintained.**
C. **Explain the processes that can change the resting membrane potential.**
D. **List the three phases of neuron communication.**
E. **Describe the characteristics of a graded potential.**
F. **Describe the creation of an action potential.**
G. **Explain how an action potential is propagated.**
H. **Discuss the all-or-none principle as it applies to action potentials.**
I. **Explain the characteristics and purpose of the refractory period.**
J. **Explain the factors that determine action potential frequency.**
K. **Explain the five levels of stimulation.**
L. **Describe the effect of myelination on the speed of action potential propagation.**
M. **Describe other factors that affect the speed of action potential conduction.**

The electrical signals produced by the nervous system are called **action potentials.** Our ability to perceive our environment, perform complex mental activities, and respond to stimuli depends on action potentials. For example, the brain interprets action potentials received from sensory cells as vision, hearing, or touch. Complex mental activities, such as conscious thought, memory, and emotions, result from action potentials. The contraction of muscles and the secretion of certain glands occur in response to action potentials generated within them.

A basic knowledge of the electrical properties of cells is necessary for understanding many of the normal functions and pathologies of the body. The **membrane potential** is a measure of the electrical properties of the plasma membrane and is due to two major characteristics:

1. Ionic concentration differences across the plasma membrane
2. Permeability characteristics of the plasma membrane

Ionic Concentration Differences Across the Plasma Membrane

As you learned in chapter 9, electrically excitable cells, such as muscle cells and neurons, operate through ion movements across the plasma membrane. As you will see, many of the principles you studied for skeletal muscle fibers also apply to neurons.

Cells have different concentrations of ions in the cytoplasm when compared with the extracellular fluid around the cell. It is this difference in ion concentrations that electrically excitable cells use to carry out their functions. Table 11.2 lists the concentrations for positively charged ions (cations) and negatively charged ions (anions) in the cytoplasm compared with the extracellular fluid. There is a higher concentration of Na^+ and Cl^- outside the cell than inside the cell, while there is a higher concentration of K^+ inside the cell. Recall from chapter 3 that this distribution of ions is called a concentration gradient. For Na^+, there is a steep concentration gradient from the *outside* of the cell to the *inside* of the cell. For K^+, the concentration gradient is the opposite of the concentration gradient for Na^+. For K^+, there is a steep concentration gradient from the *inside* of the cell to the *outside* of the cell. In addition to a high concentration of K^+ in the cytoplasm, there is also a high concentration of negatively charged molecules, such as proteins, and other molecules that contain phosphate.

TABLE 11.2 Concentration Differences Between Cytoplasmic and Extracellular Ions

Ions	Cytoplasm (mEq/L)	Extracellular Fluid (mEq/L)
Cations (Positive)		
Potassium (K^+)	148	5
Sodium (Na^+)	10	142
Calcium (Ca^{2+})	<1	5
Others	41	3
TOTAL	200	155
Anions (Negative)		
Proteins	56	16
Chloride (Cl^-)	4	103
Others	140	36
TOTAL	200	155

Permeability Characteristics of the Plasma Membrane

Differences in cytoplasmic and extracellular concentrations of ions result primarily from the sodium-potassium pump and the permeability characteristics of the plasma membrane. Neurons expend ATP to maintain an uneven distribution of ions across the plasma membrane. All along the neuron axon, the **sodium-potassium pumps** actively pump K^+ against its concentration gradient into the cell while, at the same time, they pump Na^+ against its concentration gradient out of the cell. By transporting K^+ into the cytoplasm, the sodium-potassium pumps maintain the high concentration of K^+ in the cytoplasm. Simultaneously, the sodium-potassium pumps maintain the higher concentration of extracellular Na^+ (see figure 3.15). Three Na^+ are transported out of the cell and two K^+ are transported into the cell for each ATP molecule used.

As noted in chapter 3, the plasma membrane is selectively permeable, thus allowing some, but not all, substances to pass through it. Negatively charged proteins are regularly synthesized inside the cell. Because proteins are large and relatively insoluble, they cannot easily diffuse across the plasma membrane and stay inside the cell. Because negatively charged Cl^- is repelled by the negatively charged proteins and other negatively charged ions inside the cell, Cl^- exits the cell, resulting in a higher concentration of Cl^- outside the cell than inside.

Ions must pass through the plasma membrane through ion channels. The two major types of ion channels are leak ion channels and gated ion channels (see figure 3.5).

Leak Ion Channels

Leak ion channels, or *nongated ion channels,* are always open and are responsible for the permeability of the plasma membrane to ions when the plasma membrane is unstimulated, or at rest. Each ion channel is specific for one type of ion, although the specificity is not absolute. The number of each type of leak ion channel in the plasma membrane determines the permeability characteristics of the resting plasma membrane to different types of ions. The plasma membrane is more permeable to K^+ and Cl^- and much less permeable to Na^+ because the membrane has many more K^+ and Cl^- leak ion channels than Na^+ leak ion channels.

Gated Ion Channels

Gated ion channels are closed until opened by specific signals. By opening and closing, these channels can change the permeability of the plasma membrane. There are three major types of gated ion channels:

1. *Ligand-gated ion channels.* **Ligand-gated ion channels** are stimulated to open by the binding of a specific molecule to the receptor site of the ion channel. The receptor site of the ion channel is located on its extracellular side, which allows it to receive signals from the environment. The membrane-spanning part forms a channel through the phospholipid bilayer. The specific molecule that binds to the receptor site can be referred to as a ligand. Ligands could be neurotransmitters or hormones, but there is one particular ligand for each ligand-gated ion channel. When the ligand binds to the receptor site, the ion channel opens or closes. For example, the neurotransmitter acetylcholine released from the presynaptic terminal of a neuron is the ligand that binds to a ligand-gated Na^+ channel in the membrane of a skeletal muscle fiber. As a result, the Na^+ channel opens, allowing Na^+ to enter the fiber (see figure 9.12). Ligand-gated ion channels exist for Na^+, K^+, Ca^{2+}, and Cl^-, and these channels are common in cells of nervous and muscle tissues, as well as in glands.
2. *Voltage-gated ion channels.* **Voltage-gated ion channels** open and close in response to a specific, small voltage change across the plasma membrane. In an unstimulated cell, the inside of the cell is negatively charged relative to the outside. This charge difference can be measured in units called **millivolts (mV;** 1 mV = 1/1000 V). For reference, a "double-A" battery generates 1.5 V of electricity. When a cell is stimulated, the permeability of the plasma membrane changes because gated ion channels open or close. The movement of ions into or out of the cell changes the charge difference across the plasma membrane, which, in turn, can cause voltage-gated ion channels to open or close. Voltage-gated channels specific for Na^+ and K^+ are most numerous in electrically excitable tissues, but voltage-gated Ca^{2+} channels are also important, especially in smooth muscle and cardiac muscle fibers (see chapters 9 and 20).
3. *Other gated ion channels.* Gated ion channels that respond to stimuli other than ligands or voltage changes are present in specialized electrically excitable tissues. For example, touch receptors of the skin respond to mechanical stimulation using **mechanically gated ion channels.** Temperature receptors respond to temperature changes in the skin.

ASSESS YOUR PROGRESS

21. *Describe the concentration differences for Na^+ and K^+ that exist across the plasma membrane.*
22. *Explain how the sodium-potassium pump works to move ions.*
23. *Describe leak ion channels and gated ion channels. How are they responsible for the permeability of a resting versus a stimulated plasma membrane?*
24. *Define* ligand, receptor, *and* receptor site.
25. *What kinds of stimuli cause gated ion channels to open or close?*

Establishing the Resting Membrane Potential

Cytoplasm is electrically neutral because the number of positively charged cations is equal to the number of negatively charged anions (table 11.2). Similarly, extracellular fluid is electrically neutral. However, there is a difference in *charge* across the plasma membrane because of the uneven distribution of positive and negative ions across it. For simplicity, we can say that the inside of the cell is negative compared with the outside of the cell (figure 11.9*b*). Because there are opposite charges, or poles, across the membrane, the plasma membrane is referred to as being **polarized.**

FUNDAMENTAL **Figure**

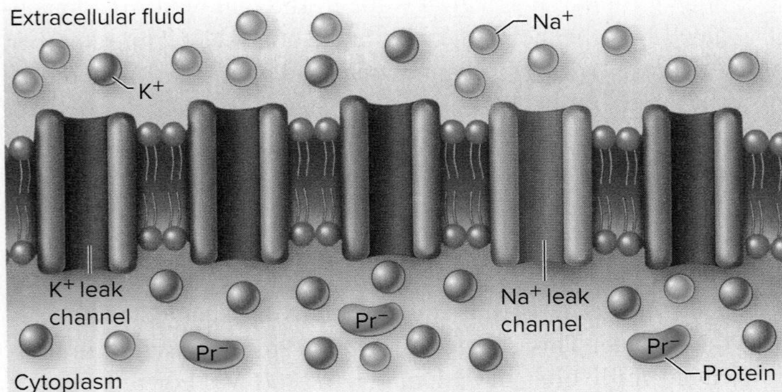

1 Distribution of ions and proteins across the plasma membrane

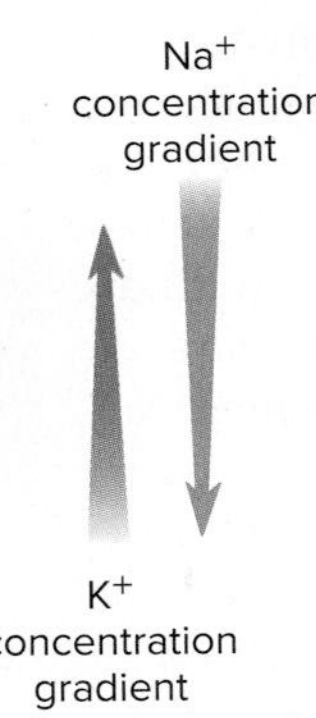

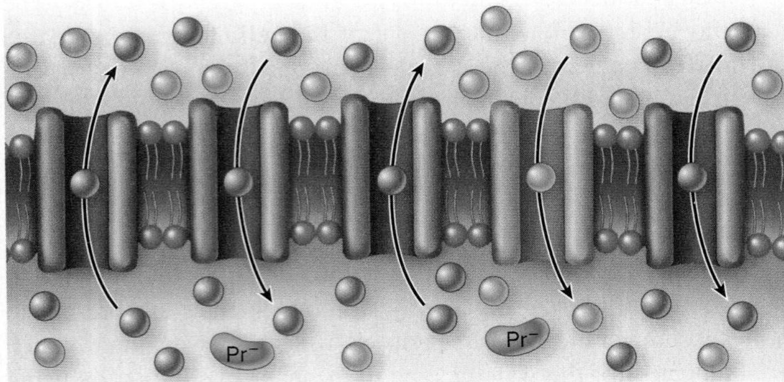

2 Movement of ions through leak channels

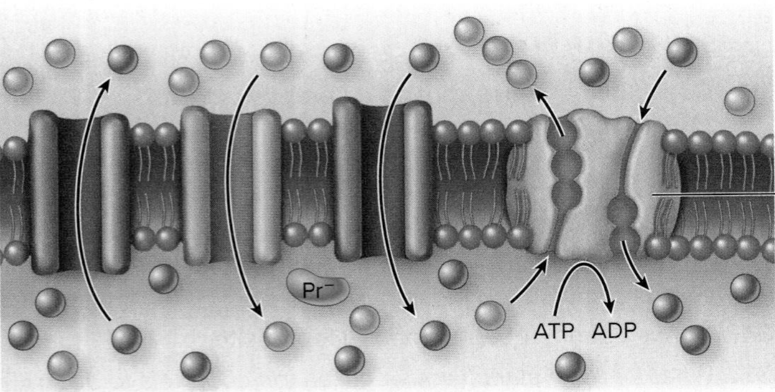

3 Sodium-potassium pump maintains resting levels of ions across the plasma membrane

(a)

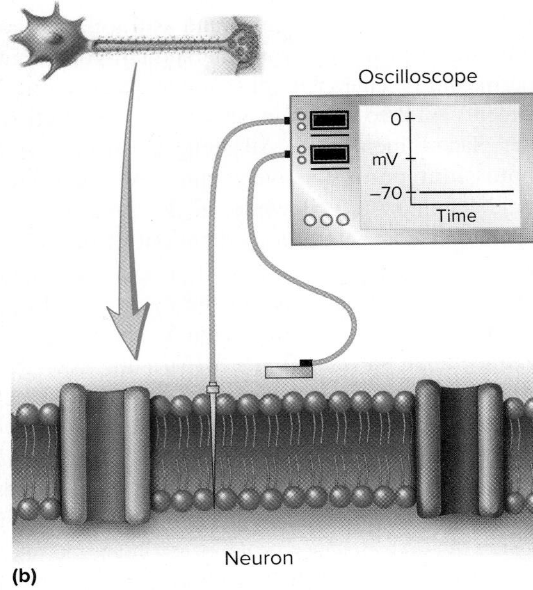

(b)

PROCESS **Figure 11.9**

Resting Membrane Potential

(*a*) In a resting cell, there is a higher concentration of K^+ inside the cell and a higher concentration of Na^+ outside the cell. In a resting cell, only the leak ion channels are open; the gated ion channels are closed. There are many more K^+ leak ion channels than Na^+ leak ion channels. As a result, K^+ diffuses out of the cell down its concentration gradient. The membrane is not permeable to the negatively charged proteins inside the cell. The tendency for the K^+ to diffuse to the outside of the cell down its concentration gradient is opposed by the tendency for the positively charged K^+ to be attracted back into the cell by the negatively charged proteins. A small amount of Na^+ diffuses into the cell (not shown). The sodium-potassium pump helps maintain the differential levels of Na^+ and K^+ by pumping three Na^+ out of the cell in exchange for two K^+ into the cell. The pump is driven by ATP hydrolysis. (*b*) The recording electrode is inside the cell; the reference electrode is outside. A potential difference of about −70 mV is recorded, with the inside of the plasma membrance negative with respect to the outside of the membrane. APR

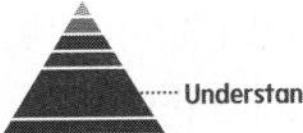

Though not shown in this figure, Cl^- concentrations are higher outside the cell. However, Cl^- movement across the membrane is limited. Given that the membrane is relatively permeable to Cl^-, explain what factor limits the movement of Cl^- across the membrane.

This electrical charge difference across the plasma membrane is called a **potential difference.** In an unstimulated, or resting, cell, the potential difference is called the **resting membrane potential.** It can be measured using an oscilloscope or a voltmeter connected to microelectrodes positioned inside and outside the plasma membrane (figure 11.9*b*). The resting membrane potential of neurons is approximately −70 mV, and that of skeletal muscle fibers is approximately −90 mV (see chapter 9). By convention, the potential difference is reported as a negative number because the inside of the plasma membrane is negative compared with the outside. The greater the charge difference across the plasma membrane, the greater the potential difference. A cell with a resting membrane potential of −90 mV has a greater charge difference between the inside of the plasma membrane and the outside of the plasma membrane than a cell with a resting membrane potential of −70 mV.

The resting membrane potential results from two characteristics of neurons:

1. The permeability characteristics of the resting plasma membrane
2. Differences in concentration of ions between the cytoplasm and the extracellular fluid

Figure 11.9 illustrates the establishment of the resting membrane potential of a neuron.

1. *Distribution of ions and proteins across the plasma membrane:* In a resting cell, there is a higher concentration of K^+ inside the plasma membrane and a higher concentration of Na^+ outside the plasma membrane. Negatively charged proteins are isolated to the cytoplasm because they cannot move easily across the plasma membrane.
2. *Movement of ions through leak channels:* The plasma membrane is more permeable to K^+ because of a higher proportion of K^+ leak ion channels compared with leak channels for other ions. Positively charged K^+ can therefore diffuse down its concentration gradient from inside to outside the cell. As K^+ diffuses out of the cell, the loss of positive charges makes the inside of the plasma membrane more negative. Because opposite charges attract, K^+ is attracted back toward the cell. The accumulation of K^+ outside the plasma membrane makes the outside of the plasma membrane positive relative to the inside. The resting membrane potential is an equilibrium. This equilibrium is established when the tendency for K^+ to diffuse out of the cell is equal to the tendency for K^+ to move into the cell. To reiterate, the concentration gradient for K^+ is toward the outside of the cell, but because of the negative charge inside the cell, K^+ tends to be pulled back toward the interior of the cell.
3. *Sodium-potassium pump maintains resting levels of ions across the plasma membrane:* The sodium-potassium pump maintains the uneven distribution of Na^+ and K^+ across the plasma membrane. The pump is also responsible for a small portion of the resting membrane potential, usually less than 15 mV, because it transports approximately three Na^+ out of the cell and two K^+ into the cell for each ATP molecule used (see figure 3.15). The outside of the plasma membrane becomes more positively charged than the inside because more positively charged ions are pumped out of the cell than are pumped into it.

Predict 3

Given that tissue A has significantly more K^+ leak ion channels than tissue B, which tissue has the larger resting membrane potential?

Other ions, such as Na^+, Cl^-, and Ca^{2+}, have a minor influence on the resting membrane potential, but the major influence is from K^+. The resting plasma membrane is not very permeable to Na^+. In fact, because the resting plasma membrane is 50–100 times less permeable to Na^+ than to K^+, very little Na^+ can diffuse into the resting cell. The resting plasma membrane is not very permeable to Ca^{2+}, either. The plasma membrane is relatively permeable to Cl^-, but these negatively charged ions are repelled by the negative charge inside the cell.

The resting membrane potential is proportional to the tendency for K^+ to diffuse out of the cell, not to the actual rate of flow for K^+. At equilibrium, very few of these ions pass through the plasma membrane because their movement out of the cell is opposed by the negative charge inside the cell. Still, some Na^+ and K^+ diffuse continuously across the plasma membrane, although at a low rate. The large concentration gradients for Na^+ and K^+ would eventually disappear without the continuous activity of the sodium-potassium pump.

The characteristics responsible for the resting membrane potential are summarized in table 11.3. Changes in the resting membrane potential are responsible for electrical communication by neurons.

TABLE 11.3	Characteristics Responsible for the Resting Membrane Potential
1.	The concentration of K^+ is higher inside the cell than outside, and the concentration of Na^+ is higher outside the cell than inside.
2.	Due to the K^+ leak channels, the plasma membrane is 50–100 times more permeable to K^+ than to other positively charged ions, such as Na^+.
3.	The plasma membrane is impermeable to large, cytoplasmic, negatively charged molecules, such as proteins. In other words, these anions are "trapped" inside the cell.
4.	Potassium ions tend to diffuse across the plasma membrane from the inside to the outside of the cell.
5.	Because negatively charged molecules cannot follow the positively charged K^+, a small negative charge develops inside the plasma membrane.
6.	The negative charge inside the cell attracts positively charged K^+. When the negative charge inside the cell is great enough to prevent additional K^+ from diffusing out of the cell through the plasma membrane, an equilibrium is established.
7.	The charge difference across the plasma membrane at equilibrium is reflected as a difference in potential, which is measured in millivolts (mV).
8.	The resting membrane potential is proportional to the potential for K^+ to diffuse out of the cell but not to the actual rate of flow for K^+.
9.	At equilibrium, very little movement of K^+ or other ions takes place across the plasma membrane.

Changing the Resting Membrane Potential

It cannot be overemphasized that the characteristics of electrically excitable cells and the generation of action potentials are each due to the fundamental principle of diffusion. Cytoplasmic and extracellular ions diffuse down their concentration gradients into or out of the cell. Because of the charge these ions possess, their movement results in an electrical current and the resting membrane potential is altered. There are two types of changes to the resting membrane potential: (1) depolarization and (2) hyperpolarization.

Depolarization

Depolarization (dee-POH-lar-ih-ZAY-shun) occurs when the inside of the cell becomes more positive (figure 11.10). Recall that

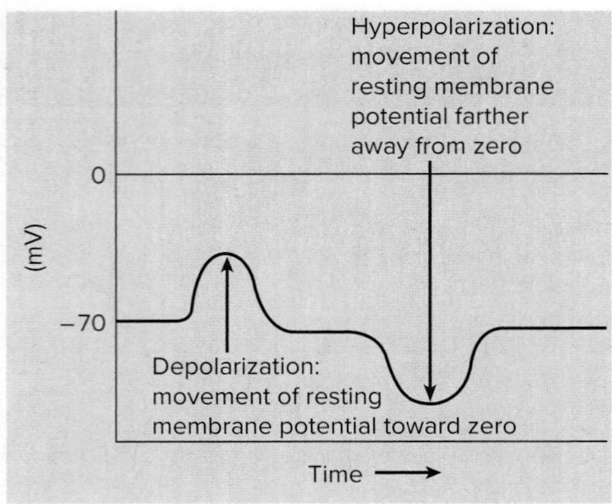

FIGURE 11.10 Depolarization and Hyperpolarization of the Resting Membrane Potential

In depolarization, the charge inside the plasma membrane becomes more positive. In hyperpolarization, the charge inside the plasma membrane becomes more negative.

membrane potential is measured by comparing the charge inside the cell to the charge outside the cell. As a result, the membrane potential becomes more positive. For example, if the membrane potential increases from −70 mV to −55 mV, then an action potential is generated. We also say that depolarization is movement of the membrane potential closer to zero. Because depolarization moves the membrane potential closer to the point of action potential generation, it is always *excitatory* to the cell. In other words, depolarization makes a neuron more likely to generate an action potential. Several factors can lead to depolarization of neurons, including (1) Na^+ entry, (2) Ca^{2+} entry, and (3) changes in extracellular K^+ concentration.

Sodium Ions

There are several ways neurons become depolarized, but Na^+ entry is the most common. Because there are few Na^+ leak channels, entry of Na^+ into the cell is typically a regulated process. If either ligand-gated Na^+ or voltage-gated Na^+ channels open, Na^+ diffuses into the cell down its concentration gradient. As Na^+ diffuses into the cell, the inside of the membrane becomes more positive, or is depolarized. This is the principal way most neurons respond to excitatory stimuli.

Calcium Ions

Calcium entry into an electrically excitable cell also causes depolarization. Calcium is in higher concentration in the extracellular fluid and when voltage-gated Ca^{2+} channels open, it diffuses into the cell depolarizing it. This is how some cardiac muscle cells generate action potentials.

However, Ca^{2+} also plays two other significant roles in action potentials: (1) regulation of voltage-gated Na^+ channels and (2) regulation of neurotransmitter secretion at the presynaptic terminal. Tight regulation of voltage-gated Na^+ channels is important for the synchronization of membrane permeability to Na^+. It seems that closed voltage-gated Na^+ channels are stabilized by Ca^{2+} and thus are sensitive to changes in the extracellular concentration of Ca^{2+}. Positively charged Ca^{2+} in the extracellular fluid is attracted to the negatively charged groups of proteins within the voltage-gated Na^+ channels. If the extracellular concentration of Ca^{2+} decreases, these ions diffuse away from the voltage-gated Na^+ channels, causing the channels to open. If the extracellular concentration of Ca^{2+} increases, it binds to voltage-gated Na^+ channels, causing them to close. Therefore, normal levels of Ca^{2+} in the extracellular fluid are crucial to keeping voltage-gated Na^+ channels closed until the neuron generates an action potential.

At the presynaptic terminal, voltage-gated Ca^{2+} channels are opened by an action potential, which allows Ca^{2+} to diffuse into the axon terminal. There, Ca^{2+} stimulates exocytosis of synaptic vesicles, which contain neurotransmitters to communicate with the neuron's target. The chemical synapse is discussed fully in section 11.6.

Sometimes, an individual may experience **hypocalcemia** (high-poh-kal-SEE-mee-ah), a lower-than-normal level of Ca^{2+} in the blood. Because normal levels of Ca^{2+} are required to keep voltage-gated Na^+ channels closed, hypocalcemia allows for their spontaneous opening. Thus, hypocalcemia symptoms include nervousness and uncontrolled skeletal muscle contraction. Hypocalcemia can result from a lack of dietary Ca^{2+} or vitamin D or insufficient PTH levels (see chapter 6).

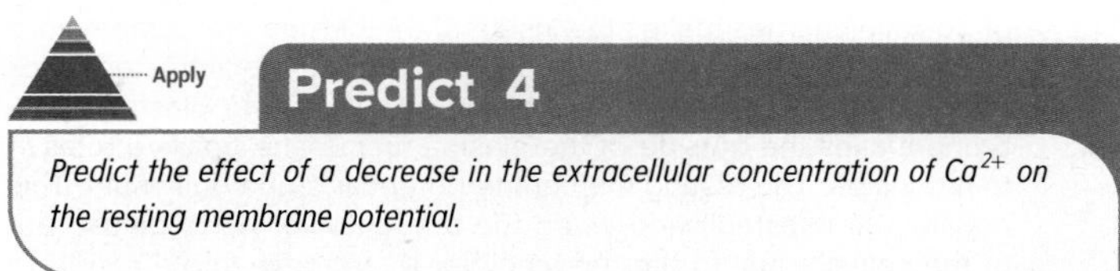

Predict the effect of a decrease in the extracellular concentration of Ca^{2+} on the resting membrane potential.

Potassium Ions

Normally, due to its concentration gradient, K^+ diffuses out of the cell. However, changes in the extracellular concentration of K^+ can affect the resting membrane potential. If K^+ concentration increases outside the neuron, cytoplasmic K^+ stays inside the cell because the concentration gradient is now less. When K^+ stays inside the cell, rather than diffusing out through K^+ leak channels as normal, the cell becomes depolarized.

Hyperpolarization

Hyperpolarization (HIGH-per-POH-lar-ih-ZAY-shun) occurs when the inside of the cell becomes even more negative compared to the outside (figure 11.10). As a result, the membrane potential becomes more negative. For example, if the membrane potential decreases from −70 mV to −90 mV, then the cell is less likely to generate an action potential. Hyperpolarization is movement of the membrane potential further from zero. Because the cell is less likely to generate an action potential, hyperpolarization is always *inhibitory* to the cell. There are two major ways to hyperpolarize neurons: (1) K^+ exit and (2) Cl^- entry.

Potassium Ions

The exit of K^+ ions is the primary way neurons are hyperpolarized after an action potential. When voltage-gated K^+ channels open, K^+ diffuses out of the cell, down its concentration gradient. Likewise, opening of ligand-gated K^+ channels would hyperpolarize a neuron. This is the mechanism employed by some

voltage-gated K^+ channels open so slowly, only a small number of them are open, compared with the number of voltage-gated Na^+ channels. Depolarization occurs because much more Na^+ diffuses into the cell than K^+ diffuses out of it.

Predict 5

Predict the effect of a reduced extracellular concentration of Na^+ on the action potential in an electrically excitable cell.

3. *Repolarization* The repolarization phase is characterized by the rapid return of the membrane potential to the resting membrane potential. The inside of the cell returns to its negative state. Repolarization occurs as the membrane potential approaches its maximum depolarization. There, the inactivation gates of the voltage-gated Na^+ channels are triggered to close by the specific membrane potential and Na^+ entry stops. The voltage-gated K^+ channels are now fully open and K^+ exits the cell. The increased diffusion of K^+ out of the cell causes repolarization.
4. *End of repolarization:* At the end of repolarization, the return toward resting membrane potential causes the activation gates in the voltage-gated Na^+ channels to close and the inactivation gates to open. Although this change does not affect the diffusion of Na^+, it does return the voltage-gated Na^+ channels to their resting state. In many cells, a period of hyperpolarization, called **afterpotential,** follows each action potential. The afterpotential occurs because the voltage-gated K^+ channels remain open for a slightly longer time than it takes to bring the membrane potential back to its original resting level. This allows extra K^+ to leave the cell, hyperpolarizing it.
5. *Resting membrane potential reestablished:* As the voltage-gated K^+ channels close, the original resting membrane potential is reestablished by the sodium-potassium pump.

During an action potential, a small amount of Na^+ diffuses into the cell and a small amount of K^+ diffuses out of the cell. The sodium-potassium pump restores normal resting ion concentrations by transporting these ions in the opposite direction of their movement during the action potential. That is, Na^+ is pumped out of the cell and K^+ is pumped into the cell. The sodium-potassium pump is too slow to have an effect on either the depolarization or the repolarization phase of individual action potentials. As long as the Na^+ and K^+ concentrations remain unchanged across the plasma membrane, all the action potentials produced by a cell are identical. They all take the same amount of time, and they all exhibit the same magnitude.

ASSESS YOUR PROGRESS

30. *What is a graded potential, and what four events can cause it? Define* decremental conduction *of graded potentials.*
31. *What does it mean to say a graded potential can summate and then spread in a decremental fashion?*
32. *How does an action potential differ from a graded potential? How do depolarizing and hyperpolarizing graded potentials affect the likelihood of generating an action potential?*
33. *Explain the "all" and the "none" parts of the all-or-none principle of action potentials.*
34. *What are the depolarization and repolarization phases of an action potential?*
35. *What happens when the activation gates in the voltage-gated Na^+ channels open and the inactivation gates close?*
36. *Describe the afterpotential and its cause.*

Refractory Period

Once an action potential is produced at a given point on the plasma membrane, that area becomes less sensitive to further stimulation. This time period is called the **refractory** (ree-FRAK-tohr-ee) **period.** The first part of the refractory period, during which complete insensitivity exists to another stimulus, is called the **absolute refractory period.** In many cells, it occurs from the beginning of the action potential until near the end of repolarization (figure 11.15). At the beginning of the action potential, depolarization occurs when the activation gates in the voltage-gated Na^+ channel open. At this time, the inactivation gates in the voltage-gated Na^+ channels are already open (see figure 11.14, *step 2*). Depolarization ends as the inactivation gates close (see figure 11.14, *step 3*). As long as the inactivation gates are closed, further depolarization cannot occur. Near the end of repolarization when the inactivation gates open and the activation gates close (see figure 11.14, *step 4*), it is possible, once again, to stimulate another action potential if the activation gates reopen.

The existence of the absolute refractory period guarantees that, once an action potential is begun, both the depolarization and the repolarization phases will be completed, or nearly completed, before another action potential can begin and that a strong

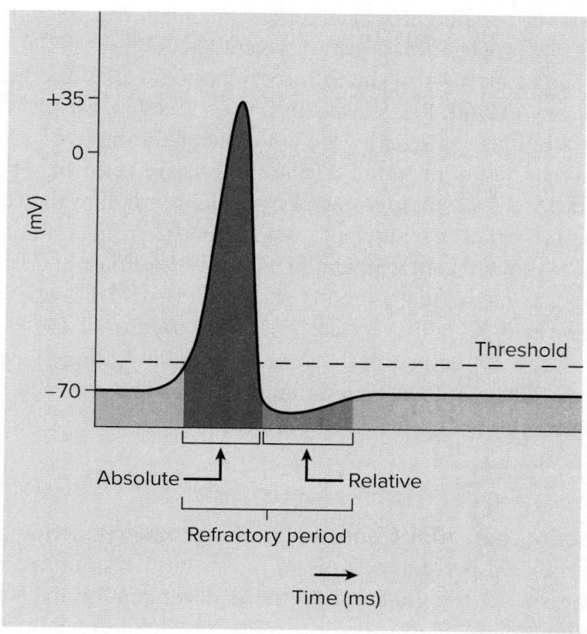

FIGURE 11.15 Refractory Period
The refractory period of an action potential is divided into the absolute refractory period and the relative refractory period. In some cells, the absolute refractory period ends during the repolarization phase of the action potential.

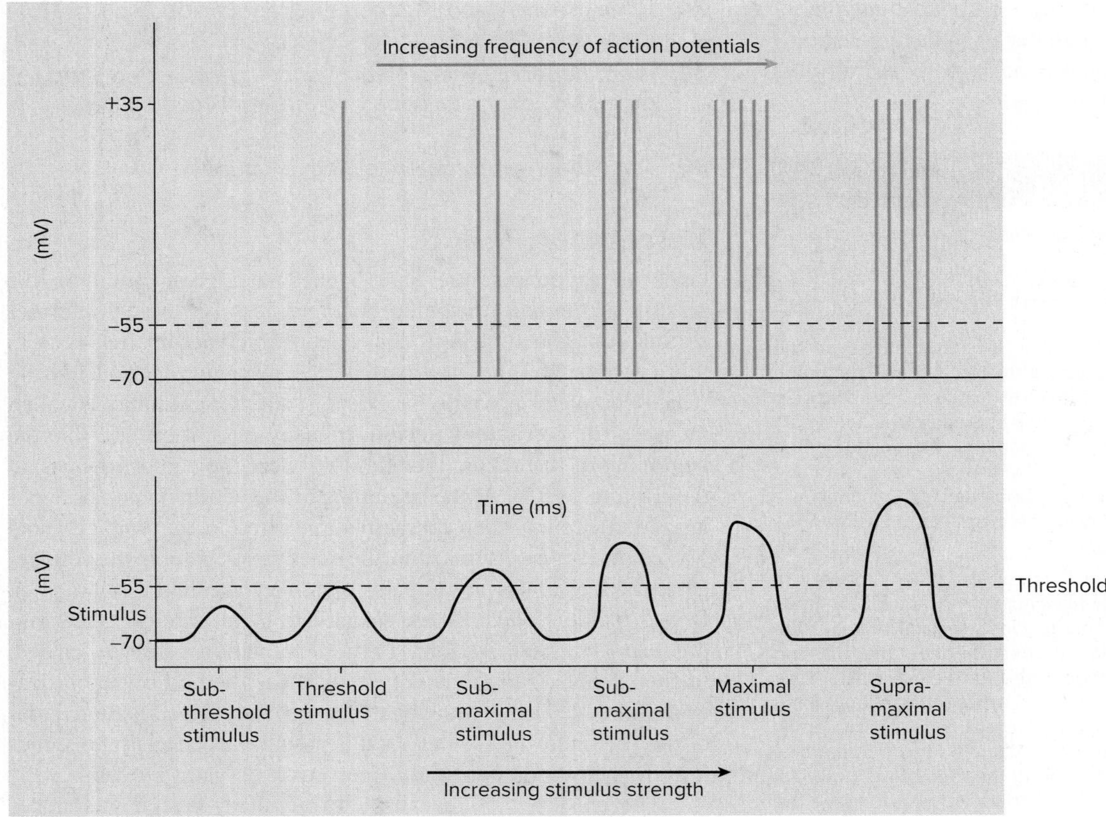

FIGURE 11.16 Stimulus Strength and Action Potential Frequency
From left to right, each stimulus in the figure is stronger than the previous one. As stimulus strength increases, the frequency of action potentials increases until a maximal rate is produced. Thereafter, increasing stimulus strength does not increase action potential frequency due to the refractory period.

stimulus cannot lead to prolonged depolarization of the plasma membrane. The absolute refractory period has important consequences for the rate at which action potentials can be generated and for the propagation of action potentials.

The second part of the refractory period, called the **relative refractory period,** follows the absolute refractory period. A very strong stimulus, or a stronger-than-threshold stimulus, can initiate another action potential during the relative refractory period. Thus, after the absolute refractory period, but before the relative refractory period is completed, a sufficiently strong stimulus can produce another action potential. During the relative refractory period, the membrane is more permeable to K^+ because many voltage-gated K^+ channels are open (see figure 11.14, *step 4*). The relative refractory period ends when the voltage-gated K^+ channels close and the membrane potential has returned to the resting level (see figure 11.14, *step 5*).

Action Potential Frequency

The **action potential frequency** is the number of action potentials produced per unit of time in response to a stimulus. Recall that the size of the graded potential is dependent on the strength of a stimulus. A small stimulus results in a small graded potential and, as stimulus strength increases, the size of the graded potentials increases (see figure 11.12). Thus, action potential frequency is directly proportional to stimulus strength and to the size of the graded potential. For example, a **subthreshold stimulus** is any stimulus not strong enough to produce a graded potential that reaches threshold. Therefore, no action potential is produced (figure 11.16). A **threshold stimulus** produces a graded potential that is just strong enough to reach threshold and cause the production of a single action potential. A **maximal stimulus** is just strong enough to produce a maximum frequency of action potentials. A **submaximal stimulus** includes all stimuli between threshold and the maximal stimulus strength. For submaximal stimuli, the action potential frequency increases in proportion to the strength of the stimulus because the size of the graded potential increases with stimulus strength. A **supramaximal stimulus** is any stimulus stronger than a maximal stimulus. Because an axon's ability to produce action potentials is limited, these stimuli cannot produce a greater frequency of action potentials than a maximal stimulus.

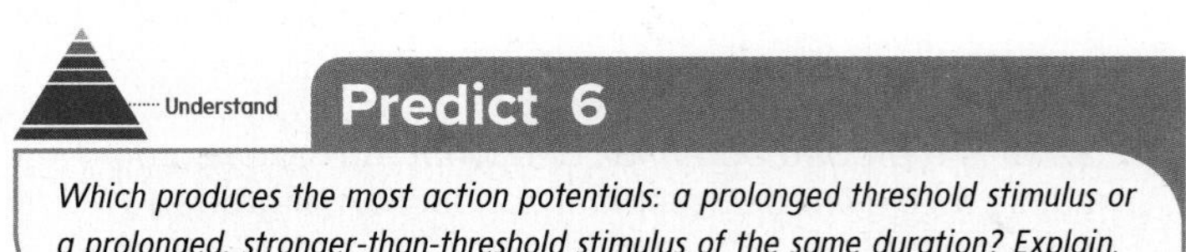

The duration of the absolute refractory period determines the maximum frequency of action potentials generated in an excitable cell. During the absolute refractory period, a second stimulus, no matter how strong, cannot stimulate an additional action potential. However, as soon as the absolute refractory period ends, it is possible for a second stimulus to cause the production of an action potential.

Predict 7

If the duration of the absolute refractory period of a neuron is 1 millisecond (ms), how many action potentials are generated by a maximal stimulus in 1 second?

A stronger stimulus will result in a greater frequency of action potentials, rather than larger magnitudes of each action potential. Communication regarding the strength of stimuli cannot depend on the magnitudes of action potentials because, according to the all-or-none principle, the magnitudes of action potentials produced by weak and strong stimuli are always the same. For example, a weak pain stimulus generates a low frequency of action potentials, whereas a stronger pain stimulus generates a higher frequency of action potentials. The ability to interpret a stimulus as mildly painful versus very painful depends, in part, on the frequency of action potentials generated by individual pain receptors.

The ability to stimulate muscle or gland cells also depends on action potential frequency. A low frequency of action potentials produces a weaker muscle contraction or less secretion than does a higher frequency. For example, a low frequency of action potentials in a muscle results in incomplete tetanus, and a high frequency results in complete tetanus (see chapter 9).

In addition to the frequency of action potentials, how long the action potentials are produced provides important information. For example, a pain stimulus of 1 second is interpreted differently than a pain stimulus applied for 30 seconds.

Propagation of Action Potentials

A single action potential occurs in one very small area of the plasma membrane and does not occur over the entire membrane at one time. Additionally, the same action potential does not travel down the entire length of an axon. Movement of action potentials down an axon is like a row of toppling dominoes. A single domino does not travel along the entire row. Rather, each domino must trigger the next domino to fall over, and so on. The row of dominoes represents the axon, and each falling domino represents an individual action potential. Thus, we see that action potentials can **propagate,** or spread, across the plasma membrane. An action potential produced at one point on the plasma membrane stimulates the production of an action potential at the adjacent point of the same plasma membrane.

In a neuron, action potentials are normally produced at the trigger zone and propagate in one direction along the axon (see figure 11.11, *step 2*). The location at which the next action potential is generated is different for unmyelinated and myelinated axons (see figure 11.6). There are two types of action potential propagation: (1) continuous conduction and (2) saltatory conduction.

Unmyelinated axons use **continuous conduction** in which each section of membrane along the length of the axon generates an action potential. Figure 11.17 illustrates the process of continuous conduction along an unmyelinated axon.

PROCESS **Figure**

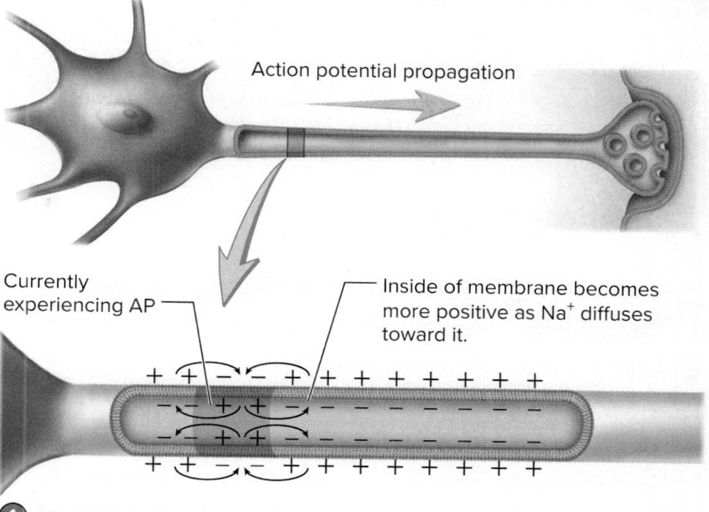

1. Generation of local currents

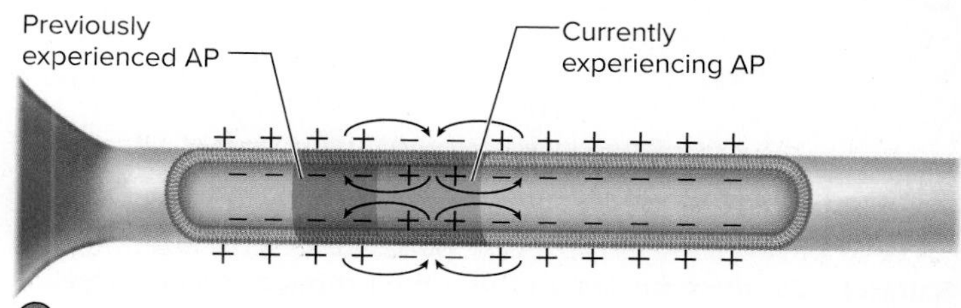

2. Action potential produced in adjacent region

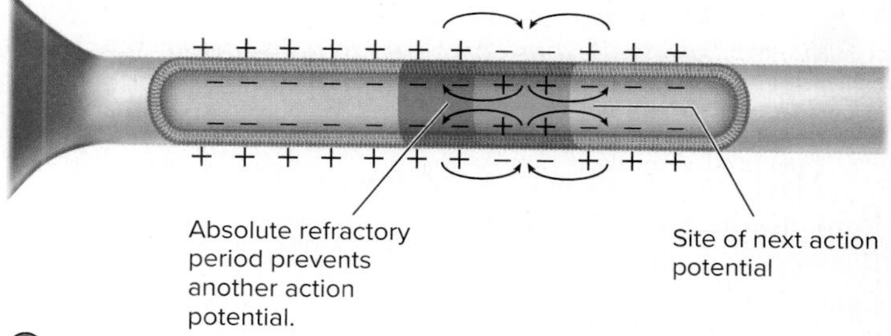

3. Absolute refractory period ensures propogation in one direction

PROCESS **Figure 11.17**

Action Potential Propagation in an Unmyelinated Axon
Entry of Na^+ depolarizes the adjacent section of membrane to threshold, which stimulates more voltage-gated Na^+ to open and more Na^+ diffuses into the cell.

Why does an action potential cause local currents in the adjacent part of the cell membrane?

1. When an action potential is produced, the inside of the membrane becomes more positive than the outside. On the outside of the membrane, Na^+ from the adjacent area is attracted to the negative charges at the site of the action potential. Once inside the cell, Na^+ diffuses away from its entry point. This diffusion of Na^+ is called a **local current.**
2. As a result of the local current, the part of the membrane immediately adjacent to the action potential depolarizes.
3. If an action potential is initiated at one end of an axon, it is propagated in one direction down the axon. The absolute refractory period ensures one-way propagation of an action potential because it prevents the local current from stimulating the production of an action potential in the reverse direction.

PROCESS Figure

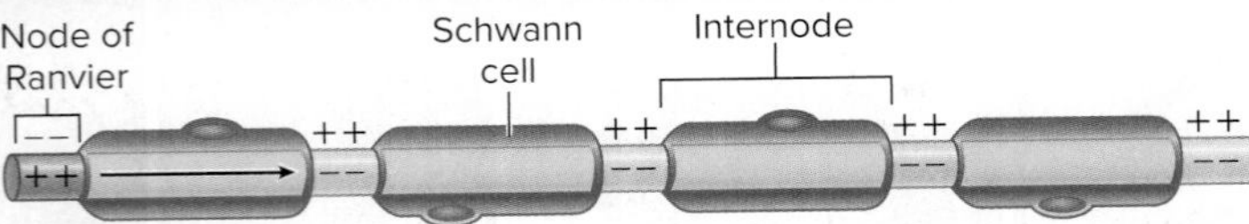

1 Generation of local current

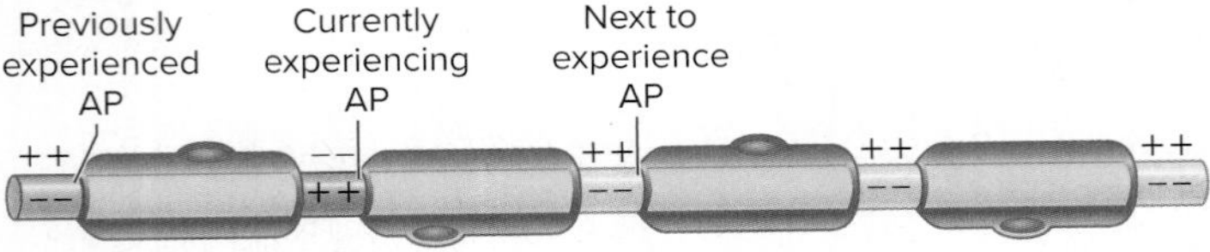

2 Action potential occurs at next node of Ranvier

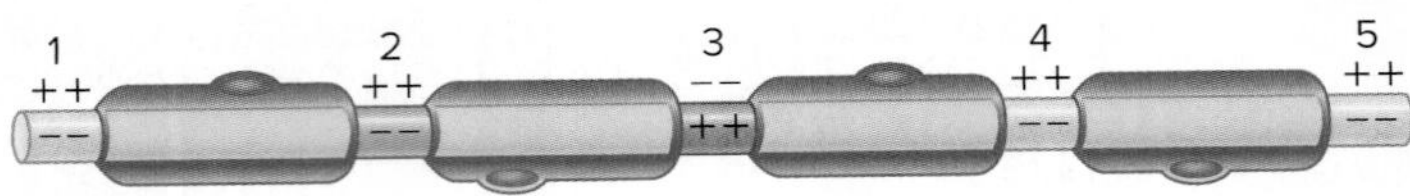

3 Action potential occurs at third node of Ranvier

Direction of action potential propagation

PROCESS Figure 11.18

Saltatory Conduction: Action Potential Propagation in a Myelinated Axon

Action potentials effectively "jump" from node to node. The gaps between the Schwann cells are exaggerated for clarity.

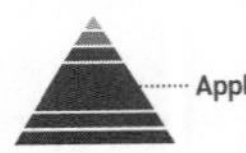

Myelinated axons can be described as "functionally shorter" axons compared to unmyelinated axons. Explain what is meant by "functionally shorter."

Myelinated axons employ **saltatory conduction** (*saltare*, to leap), in which an action potential is conducted from one node of Ranvier to another. Saltatory conduction is illustrated in figure 11.18.

1. An action potential at one node of Ranvier generates local currents that flow rapidly toward the next node of Ranvier. The lipids within the membranes of the myelin sheath act as a layer of insulation, forcing the local currents to flow from one node of Ranvier to the next.
2. Voltage-gated Na^+ channels are highly concentrated at the nodes of Ranvier. Therefore, the local current quickly flows to the next node and stimulates the voltage-gated Na^+ channels to open, resulting in the production of an action potential.
3. The action potential seems to jump from node to node.

The speed of action potential conduction along an axon depends on the myelination of the axon. Action potentials are conducted more rapidly in myelinated than unmyelinated axons because they are formed quickly at each successive node of Ranvier (figure 11.18, *step 3*), instead of being propagated more slowly through every part of the axon's membrane, as in unmyelinated axons (see figure 11.17). Action potential conduction in a myelinated axon is like a child skipping across the floor; in an unmyelinated axon, it is like a child walking heel to toe across the floor. The child (action potential) moves more rapidly by skipping. The generation of action potentials at nodes of Ranvier occurs so rapidly that as many as 30 successive nodes of Ranvier are simultaneously in some phase of an action potential.

The speed of action potential conduction is also affected by the thickness of the myelin sheath, which is determined by how many times oligodendrocytes or Schwann cells wrap around the axon. Heavily myelinated axons have a thicker myelin sheath and conduct action potentials more rapidly than lightly myelinated axons. Loss of the myelin sheath surrounding neurons in the CNS is characteristic of multiple sclerosis. The accompanying reduction in action potential speed accounts for a reduced ability to regulate skeletal muscle movements. (This information will be helpful in answering the Learn to Predict question at the beginning of the chapter.)

In addition to myelination, the diameter of an axon affects the speed of action potential conduction. Large-diameter axons conduct action potentials more rapidly than small-diameter axons because large-diameter axons have a greater surface area. Consequently, at a given site on an axon, more voltage-gated Na^+ channels open during depolarization, resulting in a greater local current flow, which more rapidly stimulates adjacent membrane areas.

Nerve fibers (axons) are classified according to their size and degree of myelination. It is not surprising that the structure of nerve fibers reflects their functions. There are three nerve fiber types: (1) type A, (2) type B, and (3) type C.

Type A fibers are large-diameter, myelinated axons that conduct action potentials at 15–120 m/s (34–268 mph). Motor neurons supplying skeletal muscles and most sensory neurons have type A fibers. Rapid response to the external environment is possible because of the rapid input of sensory information to the CNS and the rapid output of action potentials to skeletal muscles.

Type B fibers are medium-diameter, lightly myelinated axons that conduct action potentials at 3–15 m/s (7–34 mph), and type C fibers are small-diameter, unmyelinated axons that conduct action potentials at 2 m/s or less (4.5 mph). Types B and C fibers are primarily part of the ANS, which stimulates internal organs, such as the stomach, intestines, and heart. The responses necessary to maintain internal homeostasis, such as digestion, need not be as rapid as responses to the external environment.

ASSESS YOUR PROGRESS

37. *Describe the absolute and relative refractory periods. Relate them to the depolarization and repolarization phases of the action potential.*
38. *What is action potential frequency? What two factors determine action potential frequency?*
39. *Describe subthreshold, threshold, maximal, submaximal, and supramaximal stimuli. What determines the maximum frequency of action potential generation?*
40. *What is a local current? How do local currents cause the propagation of action potentials in unmyelinated axons?*
41. *What prevents an action potential from reversing its direction of propagation?*
42. *Describe saltatory conduction of an action potential.*

43. *Compare the speed of action potential conduction in (a) heavily myelinated, lightly myelinated, and unmyelinated axons and (b) large-diameter and small-diameter axons.*

44. *Compare the function of type A nerve fibers with those of types B and C nerve fibers.*

11.6 The Synapse

LEARNING OUTCOMES

After reading this section, you should be able to

A. **Describe the general structure and function of a synapse.**
B. **Distinguish between electrical and chemical synapses as to mode of operation and types of tissues where they are found.**
C. **Describe the release of a neurotransmitter in a chemical synapse.**
D. **Describe the removal of a neurotransmitter from the synapse.**
E. **Explain the effects of neurotransmitter binding to receptors in a chemical synapse.**
F. **Discuss the effects of neuromodulators in a chemical synapse.**
G. **Contrast excitatory and inhibitory postsynaptic potentials.**
H. **Explain the role of presynaptic inhibition.**
I. **Define *facilitation*.**
J. **Describe the process of spatial summation.**
K. **Describe the process of temporal summation.**

Just as the fire from one lit torch can light another torch, action potentials in one cell can stimulate action potentials in another cell, thereby allowing communication between the cells (see figure 11.11, *step 3*). For example, if your finger touches a hot pan, the heat is a stimulus that produces action potentials in sensory nerve fibers. The action potentials are propagated along the sensory fibers from the finger toward the CNS. For the CNS to get this information, the action potentials of the sensory neurons must produce action potentials in CNS neurons. After the CNS has received the information, it produces a response. One response is the contraction of the appropriate skeletal muscles that causes the finger to move away from the hot pan. CNS action potentials cause motor neurons to produce action potentials that are then transmitted by the motor neurons toward skeletal muscles. The action potentials of the motor neuron produce skeletal muscle action potentials, which are the stimuli that cause muscle fibers to contract (see chapter 9).

As stated in section 11.2, the synapse is the junction between two cells where they communicate with each other. The cell that transmits a signal toward the synapse is called the **presynaptic cell** (before the synapse), and the target cell receiving the signal is called the **postsynaptic cell** (after the synapse).

PROCESS **Figure**

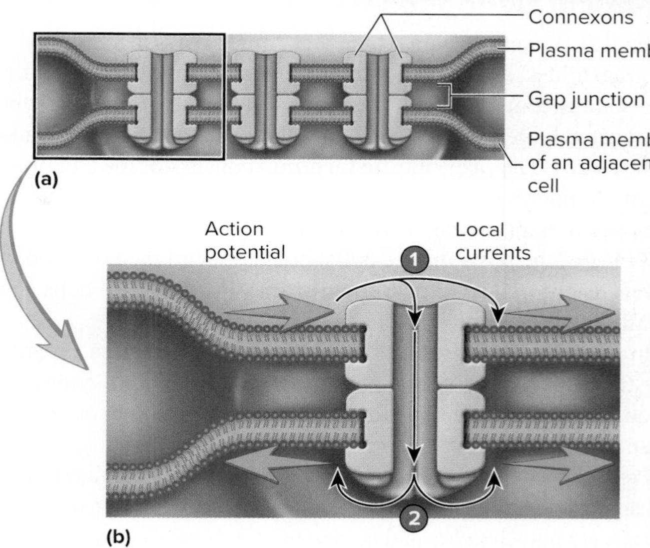

PROCESS **Figure 11.19**

Electrical Synapse
(*a*) Gap junctions allow ions to flow directly from and into the adjacent cell. (*b*) An action potential in one cell generates local currents as Na^+ flows through the gap junction (step 1). This stimulates an action potential in the adjacent cell (step 2).

In step 2, why does the action potential proceed in both directions away from the point of local current entry into the adjacent cell?

Electrical Synapses

Electrical synapses occur between cells connected by gap junctions. Recall from chapter 4 that a gap junction is a 2 nm gap between adjacent plasma membranes where cytoplasm is shared through tunnel-like protein structures called **connexons.** The connexons are groups of six tubular proteins, each called a connexin. By allowing cytoplasm to freely flow from one cell to the next, the adjacent cells function like one cell. The gap junctions allow Na^+ to flow directly from one cell to a neighboring cell.

Figure 11.19 illustrates the communication at an electrical synapse.

1. An action potential in one cell produces a local current as Na^+ from one cell flow to the adjacent part of the plasma membrane and through the gap junction.
2. The movement of Na^+ generates an action potential in the adjacent cell almost as if the two cells had the same membrane. As a result, action potentials are conducted rapidly between cells, allowing the cells' activity to be synchronized.

Electrical synapses are not common in the nervous system of vertebrates, but some do exist in other tissues, such as between adjacent cardiac muscle cells. Electrical synapses are also important in many types of smooth muscle. Coordinated contractions of these muscle cells occur when action potentials in one cell propagate to adjacent cells because of electrical synapses (see chapters 9 and 20).

Chemical Synapses

A chemical synapse occurs where a chemical messenger, called a neurotransmitter, is used to communicate a message to an effector. The essential components of a **chemical synapse** are the presynaptic terminal, the synaptic cleft, and the postsynaptic membrane (figure 11.20). The **presynaptic terminal** consists of the end of an axon of the presynaptic cell. The space separating the axon ending and the cell with which it synapses is the **synaptic cleft.** The membrane of the postsynaptic cell associated with the presynaptic terminal is the **postsynaptic membrane.** Postsynaptic cells are typically other neurons, muscle cells, or gland cells.

In chemical synapses, action potentials do not pass directly from the presynaptic terminal to the postsynaptic membrane. Instead, the action potentials in the presynaptic terminal cause the release of neurotransmitters from its terminal.

Presynaptic terminals are specialized to produce and release neurotransmitters. The major cytoplasmic organelles within presynaptic terminals are mitochondria and numerous membrane-bound **synaptic vesicles,** which contain neurotransmitters, such as acetylcholine. Figure 11.20 illustrates the communication at a chemical synapse.

1. Each action potential arriving at the presynaptic terminal initiates a series of specific events, which result in the release of neurotransmitters. In response to an action potential, voltage-gated Ca^{2+} channels open in the presynaptic cell's axon terminal.
2. Ca^{2+} diffuses into the presynaptic terminal. There, Ca^{2+} serves as a cytoplasmic signal to induce exocytosis of the synaptic vesicles. The precise molecular mechanism regulating synaptic transmission is still an area of intense research. However, most neurophysiologists agree that synaptic vesicle membranes have a Ca^{2+} sensor, such as **synaptotagmin.** Once Ca^{2+} binds to the vesicle, the vesicle interacts with membrane-trafficking proteins that guide the vesicle to the presynaptic terminal. The vesicle fuses with the membrane of the presynaptic terminal and releases its contents into the synaptic cleft.
3. Once neurotransmitters are released from the presynaptic terminal, they diffuse rapidly across the synaptic cleft, which is about 20 nm wide.
4. Neurotransmitter molecules bind reversibly to specific receptors, such as ligand-gated ion channels, in the postsynaptic membrane. Depending on the ion channel type, this binding produces a depolarizing or hyperpolarizing graded potential in the postsynaptic membrane. In this example, the binding of the neurotransmitter to ligand-gated Na^+ channels causes the gates to open, allowing Na^+ to diffuse into the postsynaptic cell. If the resulting depolarizing graded potential reaches threshold, an action potential is produced. On the other hand, the opening of K^+ or Cl^- channels results in a hyperpolarizing graded potential.

Predict 8

Is an action potential transmitted faster between cells connected by an electrical synapse or by a chemical synapse? Explain.

Neurotransmitter Removal

The interaction between a neurotransmitter and a receptor represents an equilibrium:

$$\text{Neurotransmitter} + \text{Receptor} \rightleftarrows \text{Neurotransmitter} - \text{Receptor complex}$$

When the neurotransmitter concentration in the synaptic cleft is high, many of the receptor molecules have neurotransmitter molecules bound to them; when the neurotransmitter concentration

FUNDAMENTAL **Figure**

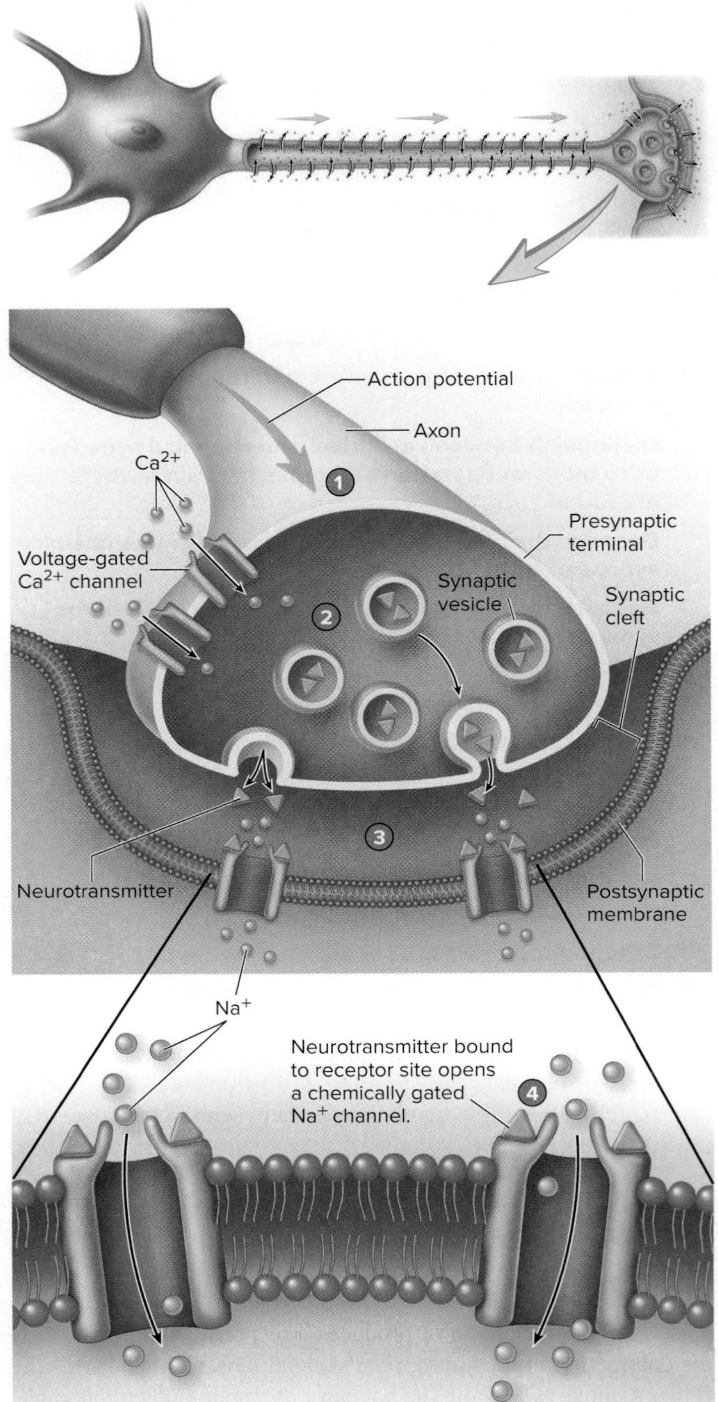

PROCESS **Figure 11.20**

A Chemical Synapse

A synapse consists of the end of a neuron (presynaptic terminal), a small space (synaptic cleft), and the postsynaptic membrane of another neuron or an effector cell, such as a muscle or gland cell. APR

Does the movement of Na^+ into the cell shown in step 4 immediately result in an action potential? Why or why not?

declines, the neurotransmitter molecules diffuse away from the receptor molecules.

Neurotransmitters have short-term effects on postsynaptic membranes because the neurotransmitter is rapidly destroyed or removed from the synaptic cleft. Figure 11.21*a* illustrates the breakdown of acetylcholine.

1. Acetylcholine molecules are released from their receptors.
2. The enzyme **acetylcholinesterase** (AS-eh-til-KOH-leen-ESS-ter-ase) breaks down the acetylcholine into acetic acid and choline.
3. Choline is then transported back into the presynaptic terminal and combines with acetyl-CoA to re-form acetylcholine.
4. Other acetylcholine molecules simply diffuse away from the synaptic cleft.

Another commonly discussed neurotransmitter is norepinephrine. Figure 11.21*b* illustrates norepinephrine removal from the synapse.

1. Norepinephrine is released into the synaptic cleft.
2. Most of the norepinephrine is transported back into the presynaptic terminal.
3. In the presynaptic terminal, the norepinephrine is repackaged into synaptic vesicles for later use.
4. The enzyme **monoamine oxidase** (mon-oh-AM-een OK-si-days; **MAO**) breaks down some of the norepinephrine.

Diffusion of neurotransmitter molecules away from the synapse and into the extracellular fluid also limits the length of time the neurotransmitter molecules remain bound to their receptors. When norepinephrine is secreted into the blood from the adrenal medulla, it functions as a hormone. In the circulation norepinephrine is taken up primarily by liver and kidney cells, where the enzymes monoamine oxidase and **catechol-O-methyltransferase** (KAT-eh-kol-oh-meth-il-TRANS-fer-aze) convert it into inactive metabolites.

Receptor Molecules in Synapses

Receptor molecules in synapses are highly specific for particular ligands. Most of these receptors are membrane-bound, ligand-activated receptors. Consequently, only neurotransmitter molecules or very closely related substances normally bind to their receptors. For example, acetylcholine binds to acetylcholine receptors but not to norepinephrine receptors, whereas norepinephrine binds to norepinephrine receptors but not to acetylcholine receptors. Any given cell does not have all possible receptors. Therefore, a neurotransmitter affects only the cells with receptors for that neurotransmitter.

A neurotransmitter can stimulate some cells but inhibit others. More than one type of receptor molecule exists for some neurotransmitters. Different cells respond differently to a neurotransmitter when these cells have different receptors. For example, norepinephrine can bind to one type of norepinephrine receptor to cause depolarization in one synapse and to another type of norepinephrine receptor to cause hyperpolarization in another synapse. Thus, norepinephrine is either stimulatory or inhibitory, depending on the type of norepinephrine receptor to which it binds and on the effect that receptor has on the permeability of the postsynaptic membrane.

Although neurotransmitter receptors are in greater concentrations on postsynaptic membranes, some receptors exist on

PROCESS **Figure**

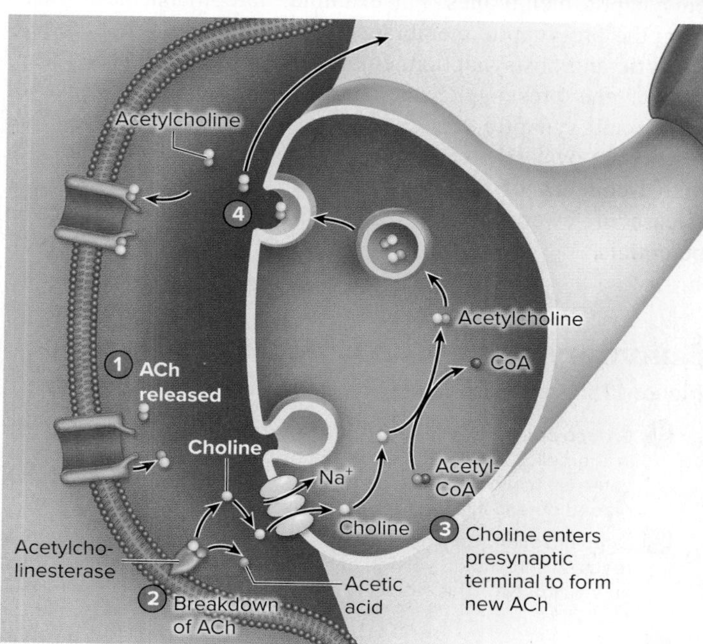

(a)

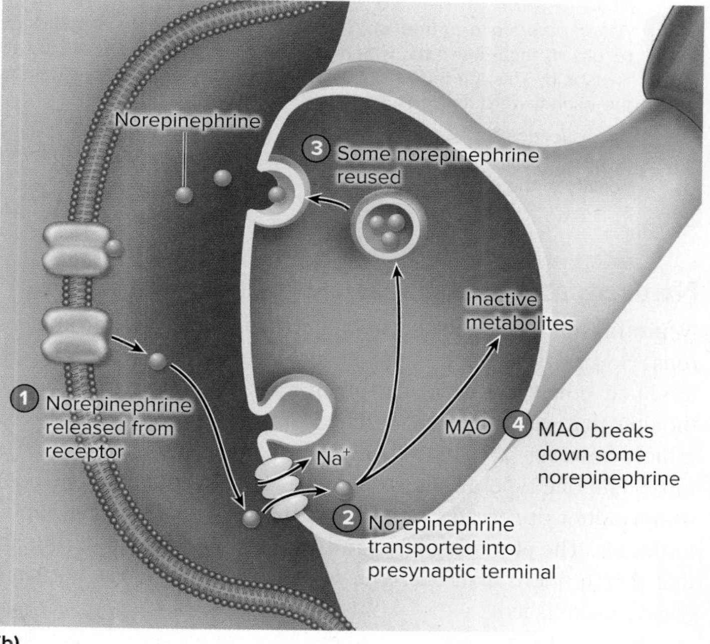

(b)

PROCESS **Figure 11.21**

Removal of Neurotransmitters from the Synaptic Cleft

(*a*) In some synapses, neurotransmitters are broken down by enzymes and recycled into the presynaptic terminal. (*b*) In other synapses, neurotransmitters are taken up whole into the presynaptic terminal.

Some forms of anxiety are thought to be associated with insufficient levels of norepinephrine. Explain how an MAO inhibitor could help with treatment of anxiety.

presynaptic membranes. For example, norepinephrine released from the presynaptic membrane binds to receptors on both presynaptic and postsynaptic membranes. Its binding to the receptors of the presynaptic membrane decreases the release of additional synaptic vesicles. Norepinephrine can therefore modify its own release by binding to presynaptic receptors. A high frequency of presynaptic action potentials results in the release of fewer synaptic vesicles in response to later action potentials.

Summary of Neuron Communication

Figure 11.22 summarizes the process of neuron communication.

1. *Graded potential:* Stimulation of a neuron initiates a graded potential in the cell body. This is often the result of the opening of ligand-gated Na^+ channels. If the degree of stimulation is great enough, the graded potential reaches threshold (see figures 11.12 and 11.15).
2. *Depolarization at axon hillock:* When the membrane potential reaches threshold, voltage-gated Na^+ channels open, allowing an influx of Na^+. This results in rapid depolarization (see figure 11.14, *step 2*).
3. *Repolarization:* Na^+ channels become inactivated and K^+ channels open, allowing K^+ to move out of the cell. This results in the repolarization of the plasma membrane (see figure 11.14, *step 3*).
4. *Action potential propagation:* The action potential at the axon hillock results in local currents, which bring the next area of the axon to threshold. This leads to the propagation of action potentials along the axon toward the presynaptic terminal (see figure 11.17).
5. *Synaptic communication:* An action potential at the presynaptic terminal results in the release of neurotransmitters that will alter the activity of the postsynaptic cell (see figure 11.20).

Neurotransmitters and Neuromodulators

Neurotransmitters are the chemical messengers secreted from neurons. Several substances have been identified as neurotransmitters, and others are suspected neurotransmitters. Scientists once thought that each neuron contained only one type of neurotransmitter; however, they now know that some neurons can secrete more than one type. If a neuron does produce more than one neurotransmitter, it secretes all of them from each of its presynaptic terminals. The physiological significance of presynaptic terminals that secrete more than one type of neurotransmitter has not been clearly established.

In order to be considered a neurotransmitter, a molecule must meet very specific criteria: (1) it must be synthesized by a neuron and stored within synaptic vesicles in presynaptic terminals, (2) an action potential must stimulate its exocytosis into the synaptic cleft, (3) it must bind to a specific receptor on the postsynaptic membrane, and (4) it must evoke a response in the postsynaptic cell.

At least 100 different neurotransmitters have been identified. Table 11.6 provides a summary of the most prevalent neurotransmitters. Neurotransmitters can be classified on the basis of (1) their chemical structure, (2) their effect on the postsynaptic membrane, and (3) their mechanism of action at their target. There are at least six chemical classes of neurotransmitters. They include the following:

1. **Acetylcholine** (AS-eh-til-KOH-leen; **ACh**) is the most well understood of the neurotransmitters. ACh is synthesized from the precursors acetic acid and choline.
2. Biogenic amines fall into two categories: (a) catecholamines and (b) indoleamines. The **chatecholamine** (KAT-ih-KOH-la-meen) neurotransmitters are derived from the amino acid tyrosine and include dopamine, norepinephrine, and epinephrine. The **indoleamine** (IN-doh-LAM-een) neurotransmitters are derived from the amino acids histidine and tryptophan and include histamine and serotonin, respectively.
3. Certain amino acids serve as neurotransmitters in addition to being the monomers for protein synthesis. The amino acids that function as neurotransmitters include gamma (γ)-aminobutyric acid (GABA), glycine, and glutamate.
4. Purines are nitrogen-containing compounds that are derived from nucleic acids. The most well understood of these are adenosine and ATP.
5. Neuropeptides are short chains of amino acids, ranging from 10 amino acids to 40 amino acids. These molecules include substance P and endorphins.
6. Some gases and lipids also serve as neurotransmitters. The gases nitric oxide (NO) and carbon monoxide (CO) serve as neurotransmitters and are sometimes referred to as **gasotransmitters.** The lipid-derived neurotransmitters include endocannabanoids, chemicals that bind to the same receptor as the active ingredient in marijuana.

Neurotransmitters can have one of two effects on the postsynaptic cell: (1) excitatory or (2) inhibitory. An excitatory effect is one where the neurotransmitter induces a depolarization making the cell more likely to generate an action potential. An inhibitory effect is where the neurotransmitter induces a hyperpolarization making the cell less likely to generate an action potential.

Neurotransmitters mediate their excitatory or inhibitory effects in a variety of ways. However, these mechanisms can be placed into two broad categories: (1) binding to ion channels, having an **ionotropic effect,** or (2) binding to G protein–linked receptors, having a **metabotropic effect** (see chapter 3 for a description of G proteins). Some neurotransmitter molecules can be both excitatory at one target cell and inhibitory at a different target cell. In addition, some neurotransmitters can be excitatory at one target by binding to an ion channel and excitatory at a different target by binding to a G protein–linked receptor. Thus, a critical concept to remember is that the function of a neurotransmitter is determined by its receptor in the target cell.

ASSESS YOUR PROGRESS

45. *What are the components of a synapse? What is the purpose of a synapse?*
46. *What is an electrical synapse? Describe its operation.*
47. *Describe the release of neurotransmitter in a chemical synapse.*
48. *Name three ways to stop the effect of a neurotransmitter on the postsynaptic membrane. Give an example of each.*
49. *Why does a given type of neurotransmitter affect only certain types of cells? How can a neurotransmitter stimulate one type of cell but inhibit another type?*

10. *Leak ion channels*

Remember

   a. open in response to small voltage changes.
   b. open when a chemical signal binds to its receptor.
   c. are responsible for the ion permeability of the resting plasma membrane.
   d. allow substances to move into the cell but not out.
   e. All of these are correct.

Establishing the Resting Membrane Potential

A. The resting membrane potential is a charge difference across the plasma membrane when the cell is in an unstimulated condition. The inside of the plasma membrane is negatively charged compared with the outside of the plasma membrane.

B. The resting membrane potential is due mainly to the tendency of positively charged K^+ to diffuse out of the cell, which is opposed by the negative charge that develops inside the plasma membrane.

Changing the Resting Membrane Potential

A. Depolarization, when the inside of the plasma membrane becomes more positive, can result from a decrease in the K^+ concentration gradient, a decrease in membrane permeability to K^+, an increase in membrane permeability to Na^+, an increase in membrane permeability to Ca^{2+}, or a decrease in extracellular Ca^{2+} concentration.

B. Hyperpolarization, when the inside of the plasma membrane becomes more negative, can result from an increase in the K^+ concentration gradient, an increase in membrane permeability to K^+, an increase in membrane permeability to Cl^-, a decrease in membrane permeability to Na^+, or an increase in extracellular Ca^{2+} concentration.

11. *The resting membrane potential results when the tendency for __________ to diffuse out of the cell is balanced by its attraction to opposite charges inside the cell.*

Remember

   a. Na^+
   b. K^+
   c. Cl^-
   d. negatively charged protein

12. *If the permeability of the plasma membrane to K^+ increases, the resting membrane potential difference ________________. This is called ________________.*

Understand

   a. increases, hyperpolarization
   b. increases, depolarization
   c. decreases, hyperpolarization
   d. decreases, depolarization

13. *Decreasing the extracellular concentration of K^+ affects the resting membrane potential by causing*

Understand

   a. hyperpolarization.
   b. depolarization.
   c. no change.

14. *Which of these terms is correctly matched with its definition or description?*

Remember

   a. depolarization: membrane potential becomes more negative
   b. hyperpolarization: membrane potential becomes more negative
   c. hypopolarization: membrane potential becomes more negative

15. *Which of these statements about ion movement through the plasma membrane is true?*

Understand

   a. Movement of Na^+ out of the cell requires energy (ATP).
   b. When Ca^{2+} binds to proteins in ion channels, the diffusion of Na^+ into the cell is inhibited.
   c. Specific ion channels regulate the diffusion of Na^+ through the plasma membrane.
   d. All of these are true.

16. *The major function of the sodium-potassium pump is to*

   a. pump Na^+ into and K^+ out of the cell.
   b. generate the resting membrane potential.
   c. maintain the concentration gradients of Na^+ and K^+ across the plasma membrane.
   d. oppose any tendency of the cell to undergo hyperpolarization.

Neuron Communication

A. Neuron communication can be described in three phases
   - Generation of action potential
   - Propagation of action potential
   - Communication with target cell at the synapse

Graded Potentials

A. A graded potential is a small change in the resting membrane potential that is confined to a small area of the plasma membrane.

B. An increase in membrane permeability to Na^+ can cause graded depolarization, and an increase in membrane permeability to K^+ or Cl^- can result in graded hyperpolarization.

C. The term *graded potential* is used because a stronger stimulus produces a greater potential change than a weaker stimulus.

D. Graded potentials can summate, or add together.

E. A graded potential decreases in magnitude as the distance from the stimulation increases.

17. *Graded potentials*

   a. spread over the plasma membrane in decremental fashion.
   b. are not propagated for long distances.
   c. are confined to a small region of the plasma membrane.
   d. can summate.
   e. All of these are correct.

Action Potentials

A. An action potential is a larger change in the resting membrane potential that spreads over the entire surface of the cell.

B. Threshold is the membrane potential at which a graded potential depolarizes the plasma membrane sufficiently to produce an action potential.

C. Action potentials occur in an all-or-none fashion. If action potentials occur, they are of the same magnitude, no matter how strong the stimulus.

D. Depolarization occurs as the inside of the membrane becomes more positive because Na^+ diffuses into the cell through voltage-gated ion channels.

E. Repolarization is a return of the membrane potential toward the resting state. It occurs because voltage-gated Na^+ channels close and Na^+ diffusion into the cell slows to resting levels and because voltage-gated K^+ channels continue to open and K^+ diffuses out of the cell.

F. The afterpotential is a brief period of hyperpolarization following repolarization.

18. *During the depolarization phase of an action potential, the permeability of the membrane*

Remember

   a. to K^+ is greatly increased.
   b. to Na^+ is greatly increased.
   c. to Ca^{2+} is greatly increased.
   d. is unchanged.

19. During repolarization of the plasma membrane, Remember

a. Na^+ diffuses into the cell.
b. Na^+ diffuses out of the cell.
c. K^+ diffuses into the cell.
d. K^+ diffuses out of the cell.

Refractory Period

A. The absolute refractory period is the time during an action potential when a second stimulus, no matter how strong, cannot initiate another action potential.

B. The relative refractory period follows the absolute refractory period and is the time during which a stronger-than-threshold stimulus can evoke another action potential.

20. The absolute refractory period

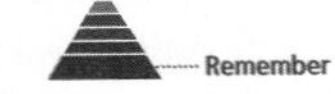

a. limits how many action potentials can be produced during a given period of time.
b. prevents an action potential from starting another action potential at the same point on the plasma membrane.
c. is the period of time when a strong stimulus can initiate a second action potential.
d. Both a and b are correct.
e. All of these are correct.

Action Potential Frequency

A. The strength of stimuli affects the frequency of action potentials.
- A subthreshold stimulus produces only a graded potential.
- A threshold stimulus causes a graded potential that reaches threshold and results in a single action potential.
- A submaximal stimulus is greater than a threshold stimulus and weaker than a maximal stimulus. The action potential frequency increases as the strength of the submaximal stimulus increases.
- A maximal or a supramaximal stimulus produces a maximum frequency of action potentials.

B. A low frequency of action potentials represents a weaker stimulus than a high frequency.

21. A subthreshold stimulus

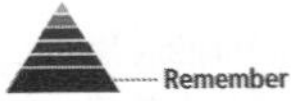

a. produces an afterpotential.
b. produces a graded potential.
c. causes an all-or-none response.
d. produces more action potentials than a submaximal stimulus.

22. A child eats a whole bottle of salt (NaCl) tablets. What effect does this have on action potentials? Apply

23. Some smooth muscle has the ability to contract spontaneously—that is, it contracts without any external stimulation. Propose an explanation for this ability based on what you know about membrane potentials. Assume that an action potential in a smooth muscle cell causes it to contract. Apply

24. Epilepsy is a chronic disorder characterized by seizures that result when neurons in the brain produce excessive action potentials. Channelopathies are genetic disorders caused by mutations in ion channel genes, which result in ion channels that do not function normally. What kind of Na^+ or Ca^{2+} channelopathies might contribute to epilepsy? Apply

Propagation of Action Potentials

A. An action potential generates local currents, which stimulate voltage-gated Na^+ channels in adjacent regions of the plasma membrane to open, producing a new action potential.

B. In an unmyelinated axon, action potentials are generated immediately adjacent to previous action potentials.

C. In a myelinated axon, action potentials are generated at successive nodes of Ranvier.

D. Reversal of the direction of action potential propagation is prevented by the absolute refractory period.

E. Action potentials propagate most rapidly in myelinated, large-diameter axons.

25. Assume that two nerve fibers have the same diameter, but one is myelinated and the other is unmyelinated. The conduction of an action potential is most energy-efficient along which type of fiber? (Hint: Think about the required ATP.) Apply

11.6 The Synapse

Electrical Synapses

A. Electrical synapses are gap junctions in which tubular proteins called connexons allow local currents to move between cells.

B. At an electrical synapse, an action potential in one cell generates a local current that causes an action potential in an adjacent cell.

Chemical Synapses

A. Anatomically, a chemical synapse has three components.
- The enlarged ends of the axon are the presynaptic terminals containing synaptic vesicles.
- The postsynaptic membranes contain receptors for the neurotransmitter.
- The synaptic cleft is a space separating the presynaptic and postsynaptic membranes.

B. An action potential arriving at the presynaptic terminal causes the release of a neurotransmitter, which diffuses across the synaptic cleft and binds to the receptors of the postsynaptic membrane.

C. The effect of the neurotransmitter on the postsynaptic membrane is stopped in several ways.
- The neurotransmitter is broken down by an enzyme.
- The neurotransmitter is taken up by the presynaptic terminal.
- The neurotransmitter diffuses out of the synaptic cleft.

26. Neurotransmitter substances are stored in vesicles located in specialized portions of the Remember

a. neuron cell body.
b. axon.
c. dendrite.
d. postsynaptic membrane.

27. In a chemical synapse,

a. action potentials in the presynaptic terminal cause voltage-gated Ca^{2+} channels to open.
b. neurotransmitters can cause ligand-gated Na^+ channels to open.
c. neurotransmitters can be broken down by enzymes.
d. neurotransmitters can be taken up by the presynaptic terminal.
e. All of these are correct.

28. Explain the consequences when an inhibitory neuromodulator is released from a presynaptic terminal and a stimulatory neurotransmitter is released from another presynaptic terminal, both of which synapse with the same neuron. Understand

29. *The speed of action potential propagation and synaptic transmission decreases with aging. List possible explanations.* Apply

30. *Students in a veterinary school are given the following hypothetical problem: A dog ingests organophosphate poison, and the students are responsible for saving the animal's life. Organophosphate poisons bind to and inhibit acetylcholinesterase. Several substances the students could inject include the following: acetylcholine, curare (which blocks acetylcholine receptors), and potassium chloride. If you were a student in the class, what would you advise to save the animal?* Apply

31. *Strychnine blocks receptor sites for inhibitory neurotransmitter substances in the CNS. Explain how strychnine can produce tetanus in skeletal muscles.* Apply

32. *Alcohol affects the central nervous system by enhancing the effect of GABA at its receptor. GABA binds to GABA receptors and opens ligand-gated Cl^- channels. However, chronic consumption of alcohol makes the GABA receptor less sensitive to both alcohol and GABA, which increases alcohol dependence as well as alcohol withdrawal symptoms, such as anxiety, tremors, and insomnia. Benzodiazepines enhance the binding of GABA molecules to their receptors and thus are sometimes used to treat people with alcohol withdrawal symptoms. For synapses involving GABA, predict the effect of alcohol on the postsynaptic membranes; compare the effect of chronic alcohol consumption on the postsynaptic membranes in these synapses; and predict the effect of benzodiazepine treatment on the degree of polarization of postsynaptic membranes in people who are experiencing alcohol withdrawal symptoms.* Apply

33. *The venom of many cobras contains a potent neurotoxin that binds to ligand-gated Na^+ channels, causing them to open. Unlike ACh, which binds to and then rapidly unbinds from ligand-gated Na^+ channels, the neurotoxin tends to remain bound to ligand-gated Na^+ channels. How does this neurotoxin affect the nervous system's ability to stimulate skeletal muscle contraction? How does it affect the ability of skeletal muscle fibers to respond to stimulation?* Apply

Summary of Neuron Communication

A. A graded potential that reaches threshold results in an action potential.
B. An action potential at the axon hillock of a neuron is propagated along the axon toward the presynaptic terminal.
C. The arrival of an action potential at the presynaptic terminal causes the release of neurotransmitters at the synapse that alter the activity of the post synaptic cell.

Neurotransmitters and Neuromodulators

A. Neurotransmitters are specific for their receptors. A neurotransmitter can be stimulatory in one synapse and inhibitory in another, depending on the type of receptor present.
B. Neuromodulators influence the likelihood that an action potential in a presynaptic terminal will result in an action potential in the membrane of a postsynaptic cell.
C. An excitatory postsynaptic potential (EPSP) is a depolarizing graded potential of the postsynaptic membrane. It can be caused by an increase in membrane permeability to Na^+.
D. An inhibitory postsynaptic potential (IPSP) is a hyperpolarizing graded potential of the postsynaptic membrane. It can be caused by an increase in membrane permeability to K^+ or Cl^-.
E. Presynaptic inhibition decreases neurotransmitter release. Presynaptic facilitation increases neurotransmitter release.

Spatial and Temporal Summation

A. Presynaptic action potentials through neurotransmitters produce graded potentials in postsynaptic neurons. The graded potential can summate to produce an action potential at the trigger zone.
B. Spatial summation occurs when two or more presynaptic terminals simultaneously stimulate a postsynaptic neuron.
C. Temporal summation occurs when two or more action potentials arrive in succession at a single presynaptic terminal.
D. Inhibitory and excitatory presynaptic neurons can converge on a postsynaptic neuron. The activity of the postsynaptic neuron is determined by the integration of the EPSPs and IPSPs produced in the postsynaptic neuron.

34. *An inhibitory presynaptic neuron can affect a postsynaptic neuron by*

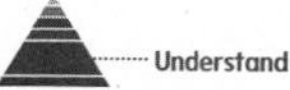

   a. *producing an IPSP in the postsynaptic neuron.*
   b. *hyperpolarizing the plasma membrane of the postsynaptic neuron.*
   c. *causing K^+ to diffuse out of the postsynaptic neuron.*
   d. *causing Cl^- to diffuse into the postsynaptic neuron.*
   e. *All of these are correct.*

35. *Summation* Understand
   a. *is caused by combining two or more graded potentials.*
   b. *occurs at the trigger zone of the postsynaptic neuron.*
   c. *results in an action potential if it reaches the threshold potential.*
   d. *can occur when two action potentials arrive in close succession at a single presynaptic terminal.*
   e. *All of these are correct.*

11.7 Neuronal Pathways and Circuits

A. Convergent pathways have many neurons synapsing with a few neurons.
B. Divergent pathways have a few neurons synapsing with many neurons.
C. Reverberating circuits have collateral branches of postsynaptic neurons synapsing with presynaptic neurons.
D. Parallel after-discharge circuits have neurons that stimulate several neurons arranged in parallel that stimulate a common output.

36. *In convergent pathways,*

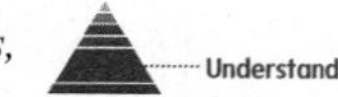

   a. *the response of the postsynaptic neuron depends on the summation of EPSPs and IPSPs.*
   b. *a smaller number of presynaptic neurons synapse with a larger number of postsynaptic neurons.*
   c. *information transmitted in one neuronal pathway can go into two or more pathways.*
   d. *All of these are correct.*

Answers to this chapter's odd-numbered Concept Check questions appear in Appendix F.

12 CHAPTER

Spinal Cord and Spinal Nerves

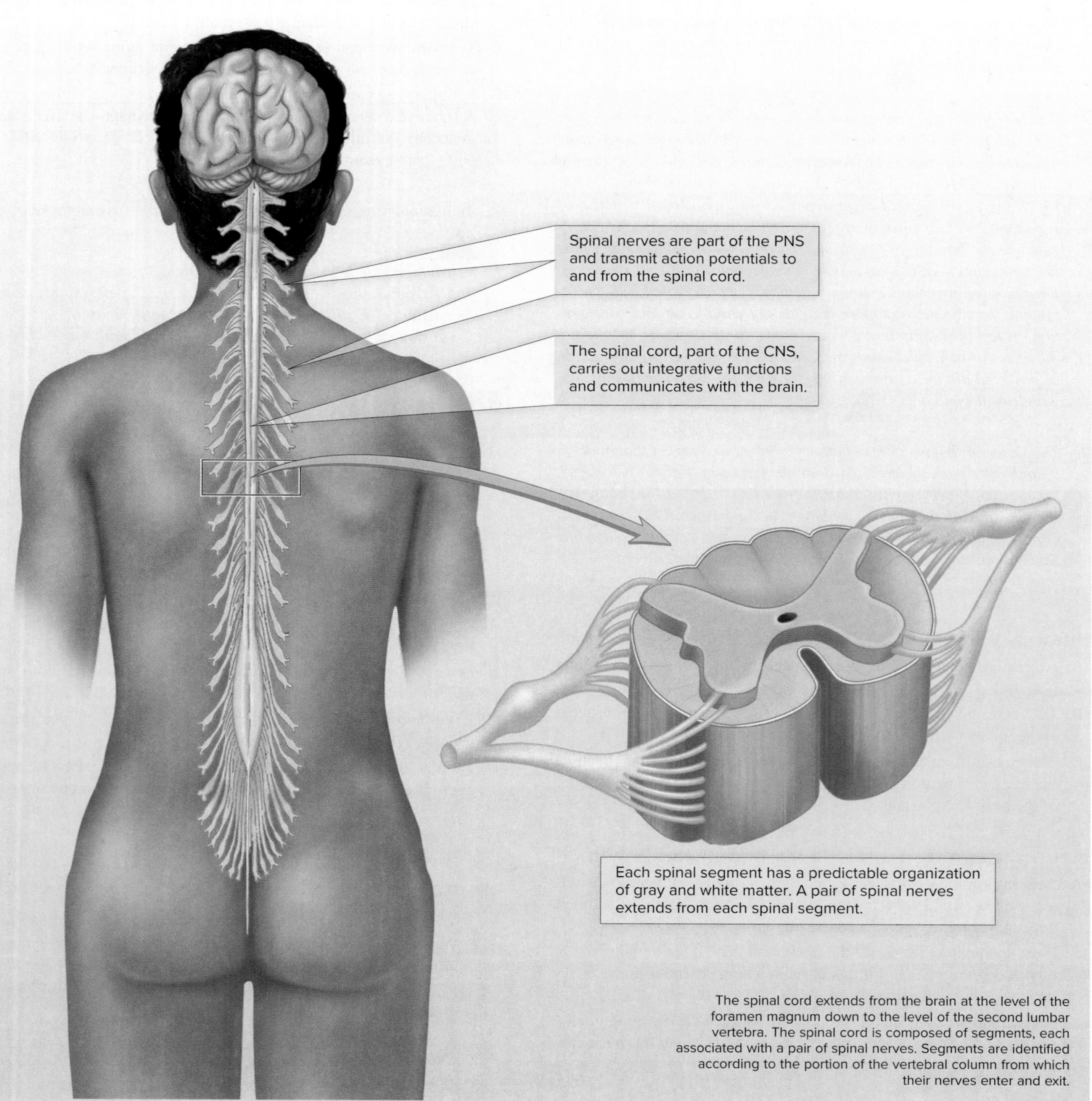

The spinal cord extends from the brain at the level of the foramen magnum down to the level of the second lumbar vertebra. The spinal cord is composed of segments, each associated with a pair of spinal nerves. Segments are identified according to the portion of the vertebral column from which their nerves enter and exit.

Each year, over 10,000 people, usually males in their late teens and twenties, suffer spinal cord injuries. As we learn more about the spinal cord, there is growing hope for improved therapies for these injuries and other disorders. Representative disorders of the spinal cord and spinal nerves are listed at the end of the chapter (table 12.1). The spinal cord and the associated spinal nerves play a central role in communication between the brain and the rest of the body.

Before focusing on the functions of the spinal cord and spinal nerves, it is important to understand their relationship to the nervous system as a whole. Recall from chapter 11 that the central nervous system (CNS) consists of the brain and spinal cord, whereas the peripheral nervous system (PNS) consists of the nerves and ganglia outside the CNS. The PNS includes 12 pairs of cranial nerves and 31 pairs of spinal nerves and their ganglia. The spinal cord is part of the CNS, and the spinal nerves are part of the PNS, so in this chapter we begin to see how the two systems work together. The PNS collects information from numerous sources, both inside and outside the body, and relays it through axons of sensory neurons to the CNS. The CNS receives this sensory information, integrates and evaluates the information, stores some information, and initiates reactions. Axons of motor neurons in the PNS relay information from the CNS to various parts of the body, primarily to muscles and glands, thereby regulating activity in those structures.

The spinal cord and spinal nerves are described in this chapter. The brain and cranial nerves are discussed in chapter 13.

Learn to Predict

How many times had Javier told his kids not to leave their toys lying around on the floor? While walking down a dark hallway in the middle of the night, Javier stepped on a tiny race car with his right foot. He immediately withdrew his foot from the painful stimulus but then stepped on a second car with his left foot. Fortunately, he was able to shift his weight back to his other foot, therefore preventing a fall.

After reading this chapter and using your knowledge of nervous system organization from chapter 11, explain the spinal reflexes that kept Javier on his feet.

Answers to this question and the chapter's odd-numbered Predict questions can be found in Appendix E.

12.1 Spinal Cord

LEARNING OUTCOMES

After reading this section, you should be able to

A. **Describe the general structure of the spinal cord.**
B. **Name the meninges (sing. meninx) and their related spaces surrounding the spinal cord.**
C. **Draw and label a cross section of the spinal cord with its dorsal and ventral nerve roots.**

The **spinal cord** is the major communication link between the brain and the PNS inferior to the head. It integrates incoming information and produces responses through reflex mechanisms.

General Structure

The spinal cord extends from the brain at the level of the foramen magnum down to the level of the second lumbar vertebra (figure 12.1). It is considerably shorter than the vertebral column because it does not grow as rapidly during development. The spinal cord is composed of cervical, thoracic, lumbar, and sacral segments, named according to the portion of the vertebral column from which their nerves enter and exit. The spinal cord gives rise to 31 pairs of **spinal nerves,** which exit the vertebral column through intervertebral and sacral foramina (see figure 7.14). Each spinal nerve is a bundle of axons, Schwann cells, and connective tissue sheaths. Because the spinal cord is shorter than the vertebral column, the nerves from the lower segments descend some distance in the vertebral canal before they exit.

The diameter of the spinal cord is about 1–1.5 cm on average. The diameter is larger at its superior end, and it gradually decreases toward its inferior end. Two enlargements occur where nerves supplying the upper and lower limbs enter and leave

Module 7
Nervous System

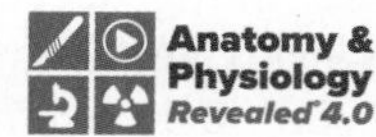

the spinal cord. The **cervical enlargement** in the inferior cervical region corresponds to the location where nerve fibers that supply the upper limbs enter and leave the spinal cord (figure 12.1). The **lumbosacral enlargement** in the inferior thoracic, lumbar, and superior sacral regions is the site where the nerve fibers supplying the lower limbs enter or leave the spinal cord.

Immediately inferior to the lumbosacral enlargement, the spinal cord tapers to form a conelike region called the **conus medullaris** (figure 12.1). Its tip is the inferior end of the spinal cord and extends to the level of the second lumbar vertebra. The nerves supplying the lower limbs and other inferior structures of the body arise from the lumbar and sacral regions. They exit the lumbosacral enlargement and conus medullaris, course inferiorly through the vertebral canal, and exit through the intervertebral and sacral foramina from the second lumbar to the fifth sacral vertebrae. The numerous roots (origins) of spinal nerves extending inferiorly from the lumbosacral enlargement and conus medullaris resemble a horse's tail and are therefore called the **cauda** (KAW-dah; tail) **equina** (ee-KWIE-nah; horse; figure 12.1).

Meninges of the Spinal Cord

The **meninges** (meh-NIN-jeez) are connective tissue membranes that surround the spinal cord and brain, separating them from the bones that surround them (figure 12.2). The meninges function to protect the spinal cord and brain from mechanical damage. Also, the meninges provide a passageway for blood vessels that service the spinal cord and brain. There are three layers that compose the meninges. From superficial to deepest, these layers are (1) dura mater, (2) arachnoid mater, and (3) pia mater. Surrounding each layer are three spaces: (1) epidural space between the bone and the dura mater, (2) subdural space between the dura mater and the arachnoid mater, and (3) subarachnoid space between the arachnoid mater and the pia mater.

The most superficial and thickest membrane is the **dura mater** (DYU-rah MAY-ter; tough mother). The dura mater forms a sac, often called the **thecal** (THEE-kal) **sac,** which surrounds the spinal cord. The thecal sac attaches to the rim of the foramen magnum and ends at the level of the second sacral vertebra. The spinal dura mater is continuous with the dura mater surrounding the brain and the connective tissue surrounding the spinal nerves. The dura mater around the spinal cord is separated from the periosteum of the vertebral canal by the **epidural space.** This is a true space between the walls of the vertebral canal and the dura mater of the spinal cord that contains spinal nerve roots, blood vessels, areolar connective tissue, and adipose tissue. In contrast, the epidural space around the brain is only a potential space. **Epidural anesthesia** of the spinal nerves is often administered to females during childbirth by injecting anesthetics into the epidural space of the spinal cord.

The middle meningeal membrane is a very thin, wispy **arachnoid** (ah-RAK-noyd; spiderlike—i.e., cobwebs) **mater.** The space between this membrane and the dura mater is the **subdural space;** it contains only a very small amount of serous fluid.

The third, deepest meningeal layer, the **pia** (PEE-ah; affectionate) **mater** is bound very tightly to the surface of the spinal cord. Between the arachnoid mater and the pia mater is the **subarachnoid space,** which contains weblike strands of the arachnoid mater, blood vessels, and **cerebrospinal** (SER-eh-broh-SPY-nal) **fluid (CSF)** (see description in chapter 13).

FUNDAMENTAL **Figure**

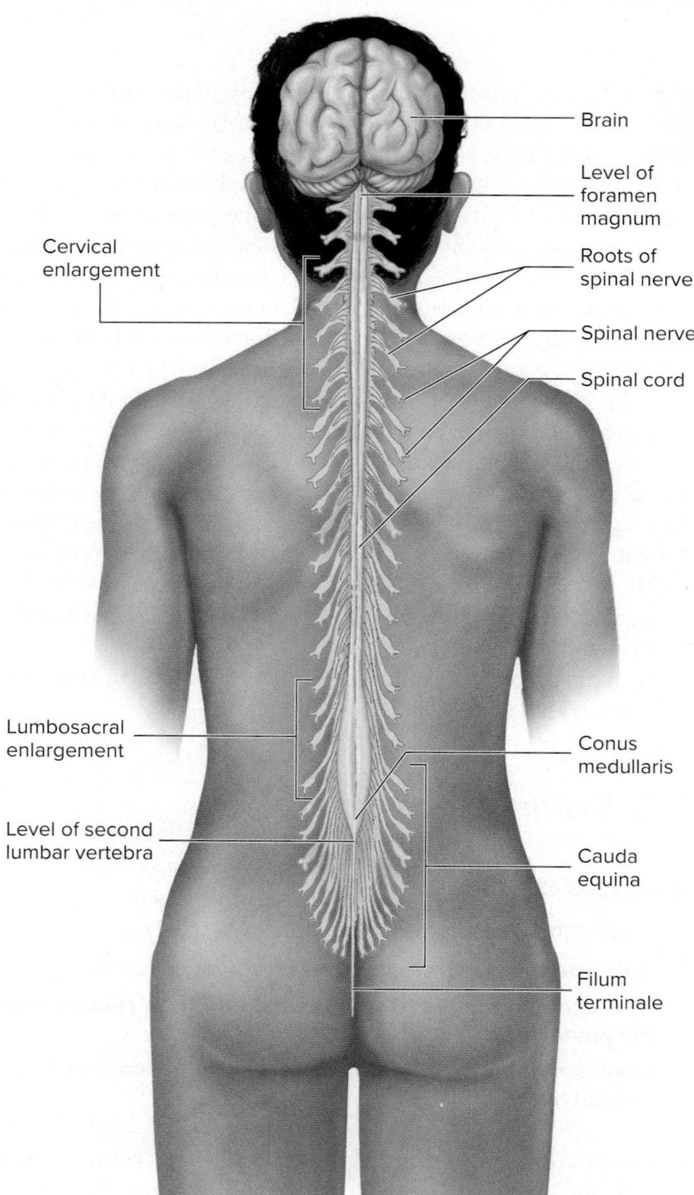

FIGURE 12.1 Spinal Cord and Spinal Nerve Roots
The spinal cord extends from the foramen magnum of the skull down to the second lumbar vertebra. The cord is slightly enlarged in the cervical and lumbrosacral regions where the roots of spinal nerves supplying the arms and legs enter and leave the spinal cord. APR

Holding the spinal cord in place within the thecal sac are the denticulate ligaments and the filum terminale. The paired **denticulate** (den-TIK-yoo-late) **ligaments** are connective tissue septa extending from the lateral sides of the spinal cord to the dura mater (figure 12.2*a*). The term *denticulate* refers to having

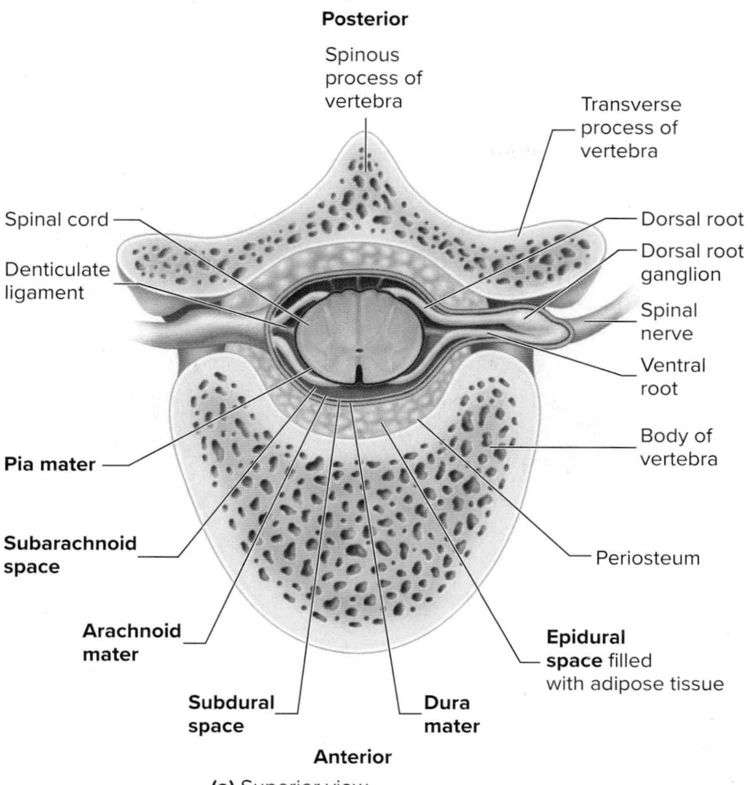

(a) Superior view

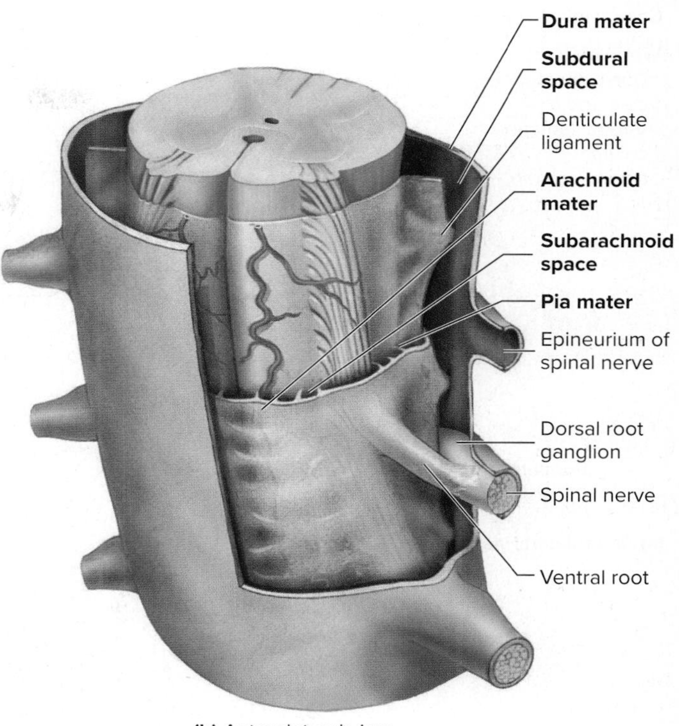

(b) Anterolateral view

FIGURE 12.2 Meningeal Membranes Surrounding the Spinal Cord
(*a*) Superior view showing the meninges in relation to the bone, spinal cord, and spinal nerves. The epidural space filled with adipose tissue can be seen in this view. (*b*) Anterolateral view of the spinal cord and spinal nerves showing the meningeal membranes from superficial to deepest: dura mater, arachnoid mater, and pia mater, with the associated subdural and subarachnoid spaces. APR

small teeth, and the denticulate ligaments attach to the dura mater by toothlike processes between the exits of the cervical and thoracic spinal nerves. The denticulate ligaments limit the lateral movement of the spinal cord. The **filum terminale** (FIH-lum TER-mi-NAL-ee) is a connective tissue strand that anchors the conus medullaris and the thecal sac to the first coccygeal vertebra, limiting their superior movement.

Cross Section of the Spinal Cord

A cross section reveals that the spinal cord consists of superficial, white matter and deep, gray matter (figure 12.3*a*,*b*). The white matter consists of myelinated axons, which form nerve tracts, and the gray matter consists of neuron cell bodies, dendrites, and axons. An **anterior median fissure** and a **posterior median sulcus** are deep clefts partially separating the two halves of the cord. The white matter in each half of the spinal cord is organized into three **columns,** or *funiculi* (fyoo-NIK-yoo-lye), called the **ventral** (anterior), **dorsal** (posterior), and **lateral columns.** Each column of the spinal cord is subdivided into **tracts,** or *fascicles,* also referred to as *pathways*. A collection of axons within the CNS is called a *tract,* whereas a collection of axons within the PNS is

Clinical IMPACT 12.1

Introduction of Needles into the Subarachnoid Space

Several clinical procedures involve inserting a needle into the subarachnoid space at either the L3/L4 or L4/L5 level. The needle does not puncture the spinal cord because the cord extends only approximately to the second lumbar vertebra of the vertebral column, but the subarachnoid space extends to level S2 of the vertebral column. The nerve roots of the cauda equina located in the subarachnoid space are not damaged because the needle quite easily pushes them aside. In **spinal anesthesia,** or spinal block, drugs that block action potential transmission are introduced into the subarachnoid space to prevent pain sensations in the lower half of the body. There are advantages and disadvantages to spinal versus epidural anesthesia. In spinal anesthesia, the drugs are delivered directly to the CSF, so the anesthesia is generally stronger and takes effect faster than epidural anesthesia. With epidural anesthesia, the needle does not penetrate the dura mater, so the drugs must first diffuse into the CSF. However, an advantage is that the drugs can be readministered via a catheter (flexible tube) to maintain longer anesthesia. In some instances, a combination of spinal and epidural anesthesia is used. In a **lumbar puncture,** or *spinal tap,* CSF is removed from the subarachnoid space in order to examine it for infectious agents (meningitis) or for the presence of blood (hemorrhage) or to measure the CSF pressure. Sometimes clinicians inject a radiopaque substance into this area and take a **myelogram** (radiograph of the spinal cord) to visualize spinal cord defects or damage.

FUNDAMENTAL **Figure**

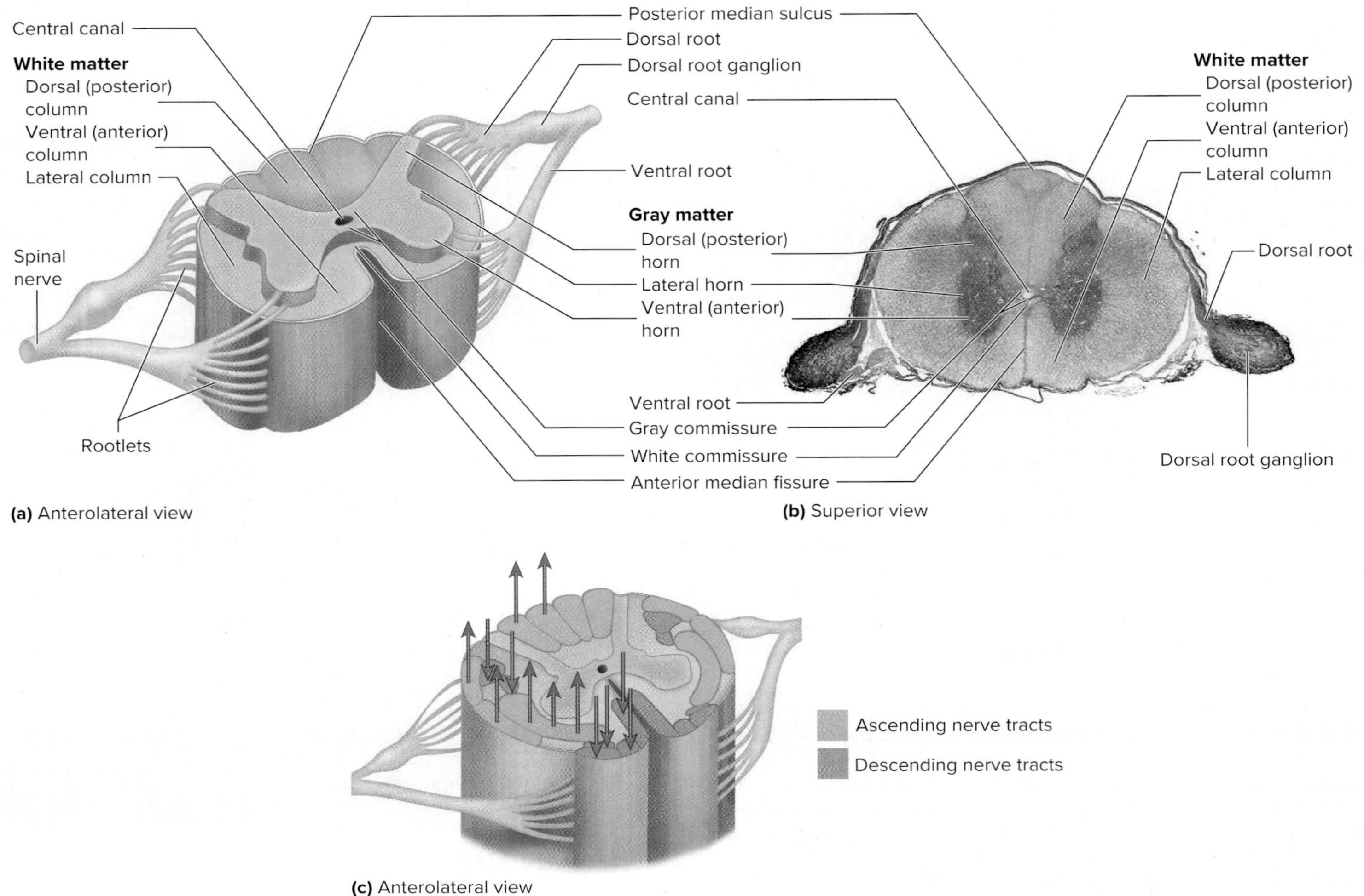

(a) Anterolateral view

(b) Superior view

(c) Anterolateral view

FIGURE 12.3 Cross Section of the Spinal Cord

(*a*) A segment of the spinal cord showing one dorsal and one ventral root on each side and the rootlets that form them. The dorsal, ventral, and lateral divisions of the white matter columns and the gray matter horns are indicated. (*b*) Photograph of a cross section through the midlumbar region. The *lighter areas* are white matter, where myelinated tracts are located. The *darker area* is gray matter, where neuron cell bodies are located. (*c*) Ascending and descending tracts in the spinal cord. Ascending nerve tracts are *green;* descending nerve tracts are *purple*. The arrows (shown only on one side) indicate the direction of action potential propagation in each pathway. (b) Ed Reschke/Photolibrary/Getty Images APR

called a *nerve*. Tracts have different myelination than nerves and lack the extensive connective tissue of nerves. Individual axons ascending to the brain or descending from the brain are usually grouped together within the tracts (figure 12.3*c*). Axons within a given tract carry basically the same type of information, although they may overlap to some extent. For example, one ascending tract carries action potentials related to pain and temperature sensations, whereas another carries action potentials related to light touch.

The central gray matter is organized into horns. Each half of the central gray matter of the spinal cord consists of a relatively thin **dorsal** (posterior) **horn** and a larger **ventral** (anterior) **horn.** Small **lateral horns** exist in the levels of the cord associated with the autonomic nervous system (see chapter 16). The two halves of the spinal cord are connected by structures called the **gray** and **white commissures** (figure 12.3*a*,*b*). The gray and white commissures contain axons that cross from one side of the spinal cord to the other. The **central canal,** located in the center of the gray commissure, helps circulate CSF produced by ependymal cells within the ventricles of the brain (see chapter 13).

Spinal nerves arise from numerous rootlets along the dorsal and ventral surfaces of the spinal cord (figure 12.3*a*). Six to eight of these rootlets combine to form a **ventral root** on the ventral side of the spinal cord, and another six to eight form a **dorsal root** on the dorsal side of the cord at each segment. The ventral and dorsal roots extend laterally from the spinal cord, passing through the subarachnoid space, piercing the arachnoid mater and dura mater, and joining one another to form a spinal nerve.

The dorsal roots contain axons of sensory neurons. Sensory neuron cell bodies are contained within the **dorsal root ganglion,**

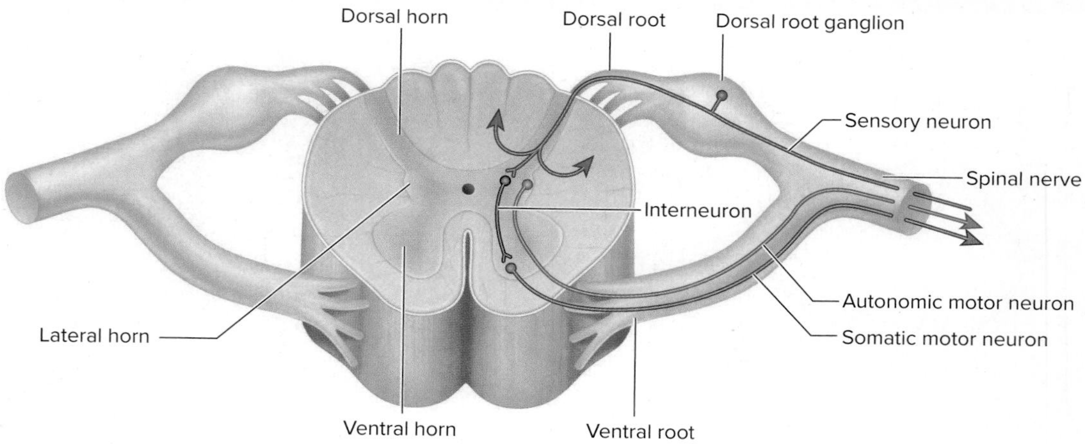

FIGURE 12.4 Relationship of Sensory and Motor Neurons to the Spinal Cord
Schematic representation of the spinal cord at the thoracic level. Sensory neurons enter the dorsal horn of the spinal cord from the dorsal root ganglion through the dorsal root, with collaterals (*green arrows*) extending up to the brain. Motor neurons exit the ventral horn of the spinal cord at the ventral root. The filled circles represent cell bodies and arrows represent axons.

or *spinal ganglion* (GANG-lee-on; a swelling or knot; figure 12.4). The axons of these pseudo-unipolar sensory neurons extend from various parts of the body and pass through spinal nerves to the dorsal root ganglia. The axons do not synapse in the dorsal root ganglion but pass through the dorsal root into the dorsal horn of the spinal cord gray matter. The axons either synapse with interneurons in the dorsal horn or pass into the white matter and ascend or descend in the spinal cord.

The ventral roots contain the axons of motor neurons. Motor neurons innervate muscles and glands. Unlike the sensory neurons, the cell bodies of the motor neurons are located in the spinal cord gray matter (figure 12.4). The cell bodies of multipolar somatic motor neurons are in the ventral horn, also called the motor horn. Autonomic motor neuron cell bodies are in the lateral horn. Axons of the motor neurons form the ventral roots and pass into the spinal nerves. Thus, dorsal roots contain sensory axons, ventral roots contain motor axons, and spinal nerves have both sensory and motor axons.

Understand

Predict 1

Explain why the dorsal root ganglia are larger in diameter than the dorsal roots, and describe the direction of action potential propagation in the spinal nerves, dorsal roots, and ventral roots.

ASSESS YOUR PROGRESS

Answers to these questions are found in the section you have just completed. Re-read the section if you need help in answering these questions.

1. *Where does the spinal cord begin and end? How many pairs of spinal nerves exit the spinal cord?*
2. *Name the meninges surrounding the spinal cord. What is found within each of these spaces: the epidural space, the subdural space, and the subarachnoid space?*
3. *What is the thecal sac? What two structures hold the thecal sac in the vertebral canal?*
4. *Describe the arrangement of gray and white matter in the spinal cord. What are the divisions of the gray matter and white matter? What are commissures?*
5. *Where are the cell bodies of somatic motor and autonomic motor neurons located in the gray matter?*
6. *What kinds of neurons are in the dorsal roots, in the ventral roots, and in the spinal nerves? What is found in the dorsal root ganglion?*

12.2 Reflexes

LEARNING OUTCOMES

After reading this section, you should be able to

A. **Describe the components of a reflex arc.**
B. **Explain the four ways reflexes can be classified.**
C. **Describe the features of a stretch reflex.**
D. **Explain the function of a Golgi tendon reflex.**
E. **Describe a withdrawal reflex.**
F. **Explain the purpose of a crossed extensor reflex.**

A **reflex** is an automatic response to a stimulus, which means it occurs without conscious thought. Reflexes are homeostatic. For example, a number of reflexes, called autonomic reflexes, are responsible for maintaining relatively constant blood pressure, blood CO_2 levels, and water intake. Other reflexes, called somatic reflexes, function to maintain posture, remove the body from painful stimuli that would cause tissue damage, or keep the body from suddenly falling or moving because of external forces.

FUNDAMENTAL **Figure**

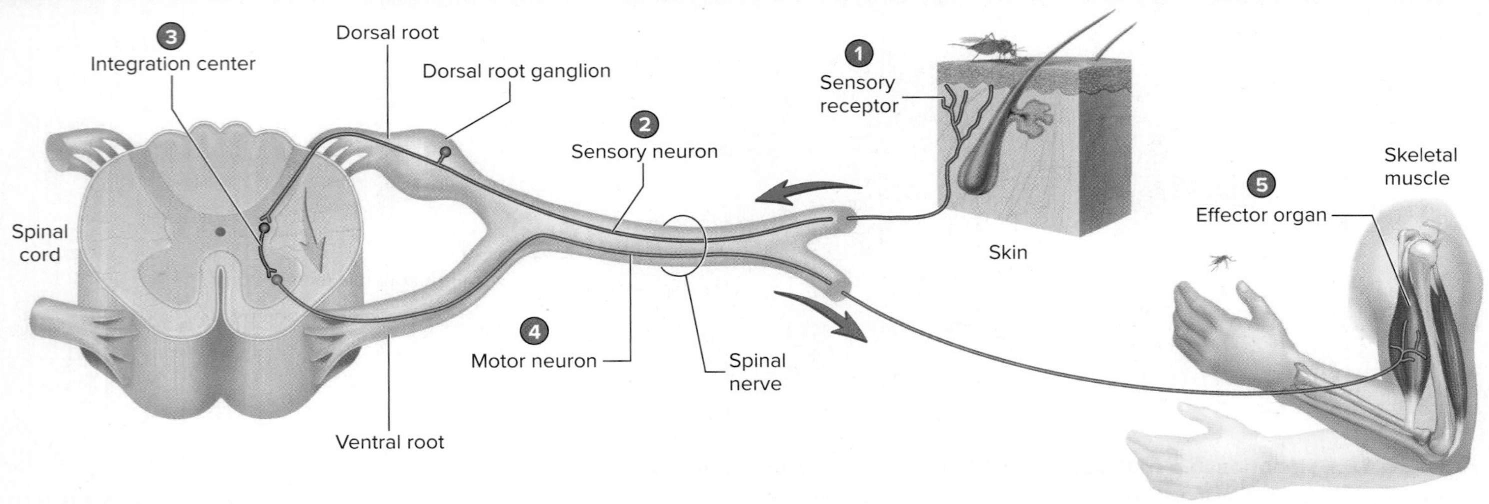

PROCESS **Figure 12.5**

Reflex Arc

The parts of a reflex arc are labeled in the order in which action potentials pass through them. A polysynaptic reflex arc containing an interneuron is shown. APR

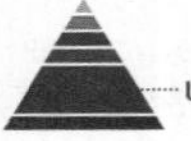

Reflexes can be classified as somatic or autonomic, depending on the effector. Is the reflex illustrated in this figure somatic or autonomic? How do you know?

The **reflex arc** is the neural pathway that controls a reflex. It is the basic *functional unit* of the nervous system that is capable of receiving a stimulus and producing a response. The reflex arc generally has five components: (1) a sensory receptor, (2) a sensory neuron, (3) an integration center, (4) a motor neuron, and (5) an effector organ. Figure 12.5 illustrates the process of a reflex arc.

1. A sensory receptor detects a stimulus, generating action potentials.
2. A sensory neuron conducts action potentials through a nerve and dorsal root to the spinal cord.
3. In the spinal cord, the action potential is carried to the integration center, which in this example involves an interneuron. Simple reflexes do not involve an interneuron.
4. The interneuron synapses with the motor neuron.
5. The motor neuron axon conducts action potentials through the ventral root and spinal nerve to an effector organ.

Reflexes of the body vary in many aspects. Reflexes can be classified based on (1) complexity, (2) development, (3) effector, and (4) location of integration center (figure 12.6).

When classifying a reflex based on complexity, we consider the number of synapses between the sensory neuron and the motor neuron. **Monosynaptic reflexes** involve simple neuronal pathways in which sensory neurons synapse directly with motor neurons without any interneurons. **Polysynaptic reflexes** involve more complex pathways that have multiple synapses with interneurons between the sensory and motor neurons When considering the classification of reflexes based on development, many reflexes are part of our normal development, such as turning our head toward a loud noise. These are called **innate reflexes.** Others develop as we repeat activities over and over again, such as typing on a keyboard. These are known as **learned reflexes.** We can classify reflexes by effector type. A reflex is considered a **somatic reflex** if the effector is skeletal muscle. A reflex is considered an **autonomic,** or *visceral*, **reflex** if the effector is smooth muscle, cardiac muscle, or a gland. Finally, we can classify reflexes by the location of their integration center. A reflex is called a **cranial reflex** if the integration center is in the brain, or a **spinal reflex** if the integration center is in the spinal cord. It is important to note that a single reflex can be classified in each of these four groupings.

The response of initiating a reflex is not always excitatory, nor is the response solely controlled by a reflex arc. Some reflexes involve excitatory neurons and result in a response, as when a muscle contracts (see chapter 11). Other reflexes involve inhibitory neurons and result in the inhibition of a response, as when a muscle relaxes. In addition, higher brain centers influence reflexes by either suppressing or exaggerating them. The subsequent discussion describes three major spinal cord reflexes: the stretch reflex, the Golgi tendon reflex, and the withdrawal reflex.

Stretch Reflex

The simplest reflex is the **stretch reflex** (figure 12.7). The stretch reflex is a reflex contraction of muscles in response to stretching

Classification of Reflexes

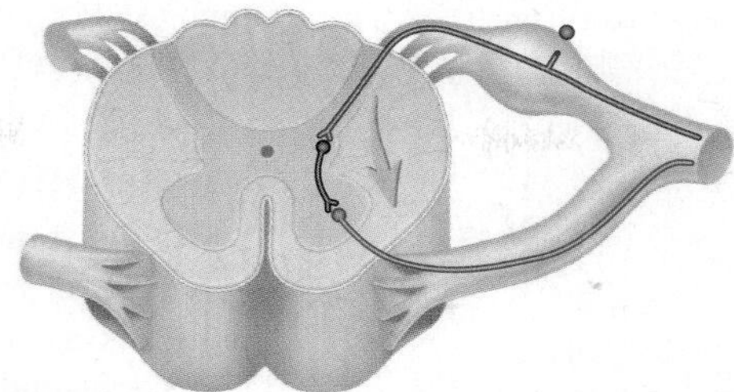

Complexity	Development	Effector	Integration Center
Monosynaptic: Sensory neuron synapses directly on motor neuron at the integration center **Polysynaptic:** Involves at least one interneuron between the sensory and motor neuron	**Innate:** Part of normal development **Learned:** Developed after repetition of activity	**Somatic:** Skeletal muscle **Autonomic:** Cardiac muscle, smooth muscle, or glands	**Spinal:** Integration occurs within the spinal cord **Cranial:** Integration occurs within the brain

FIGURE 12.6 Classification of Reflexes
Reflexes can be classified based on the complexity of the reflex arc, development of the reflex, the type of effector involved, and location of integration within the CNS.

of that same muscle. The sensory receptor of this reflex is the **muscle spindle,** which consists of 3–10 small, specialized skeletal muscle fibers that are contractile only at their ends. Sensory neurons innervate the noncontractile centers of the muscle spindle cells. The stretch reflex is a monosynaptic reflex because there is no interneuron between the sensory neuron and the lower motor neuron. The motor neuron involved is called an **alpha motor neuron** and it causes the muscle to contract. The classic example of a stretch reflex is the **knee-jerk reflex,** or *patellar reflex,* which happens when a clinician taps the patellar ligament.

Figure 12.7 illustrates the steps involved in the knee-jerk reflex.

1. When the patellar ligament is tapped, the tendons and muscles of the quadriceps femoris muscle group stretch. Muscle spindle receptors within the muscles stretch, which activates the stretch reflex.
2. Axons of these sensory neurons extend to the spinal cord.
3. In the spinal cord, the sensory neurons synapse directly with alpha motor neurons.
4. Alpha motor neurons then stimulate the muscle in which the muscle spindle is embedded.
5. The same muscle that was stretched now contracts in response to the action potentials stimulated by the alpha motor neuron.
6. Gamma motor neurons, described below, contract the muscle spindles to allow them to detect further stretch.

The rapid contraction of the stretched muscle opposes the stretch of the muscle. The postural muscles demonstrate the adaptive nature of this reflex. If a person is standing upright and then begins to tip slightly to one side, the postural muscles associated with the vertebral column on the other side are stretched. As a result, stretch reflexes are initiated in those muscles, which cause them to contract and reestablish normal posture.

Collateral axons from the sensory neurons of the muscle spindles also synapse with neurons whose axons contribute to ascending nerve tracts. This enables the brain to perceive that a muscle has been stretched (see figure 12.3*c*). Descending upper motor neurons from the brain synapse in the spinal cord with the neurons of the stretch reflex modifying their activity. The upper motor neurons modulate both the alpha motor neurons and gamma motor neurons (described below). This activity is important in maintaining posture and in coordinating muscle actions.

In addition to the alpha motor neurons, **gamma motor neurons** innervate the ends of the muscle spindles (figure 12.7, *step 6*). The term *gamma* refers to the small-diameter axons of these neurons compared to the large-diameter axons of alpha motor neurons. The gamma motor neurons originate in the spinal cord and control the sensitivity of the muscle spindle cells. As a skeletal muscle contracts, the tension on the centers of muscle spindles within the muscle decreases because the muscle spindles passively shorten as the muscle shortens. The decrease in tension in the centers of the muscle spindles causes them to be less sensitive to stretch. Sensitivity is maintained because, while alpha motor neurons are stimulating the muscle to contract, gamma motor neurons are stimulating the muscle spindles to also contract. The contraction of the muscle fibers at the ends of the muscle spindles pulls on the center part of the muscle spindles and maintains the proper tension. The activity of the muscle spindles helps control posture, muscle tension, and muscle length.

Clinicians use the knee-jerk reflex to determine whether the higher CNS centers that normally influence this reflex are functional. A greatly exaggerated stretch reflex indicates that the neurons within the brain that innervate the gamma motor neurons are overly active. On the other hand, if the neurons that innervate the

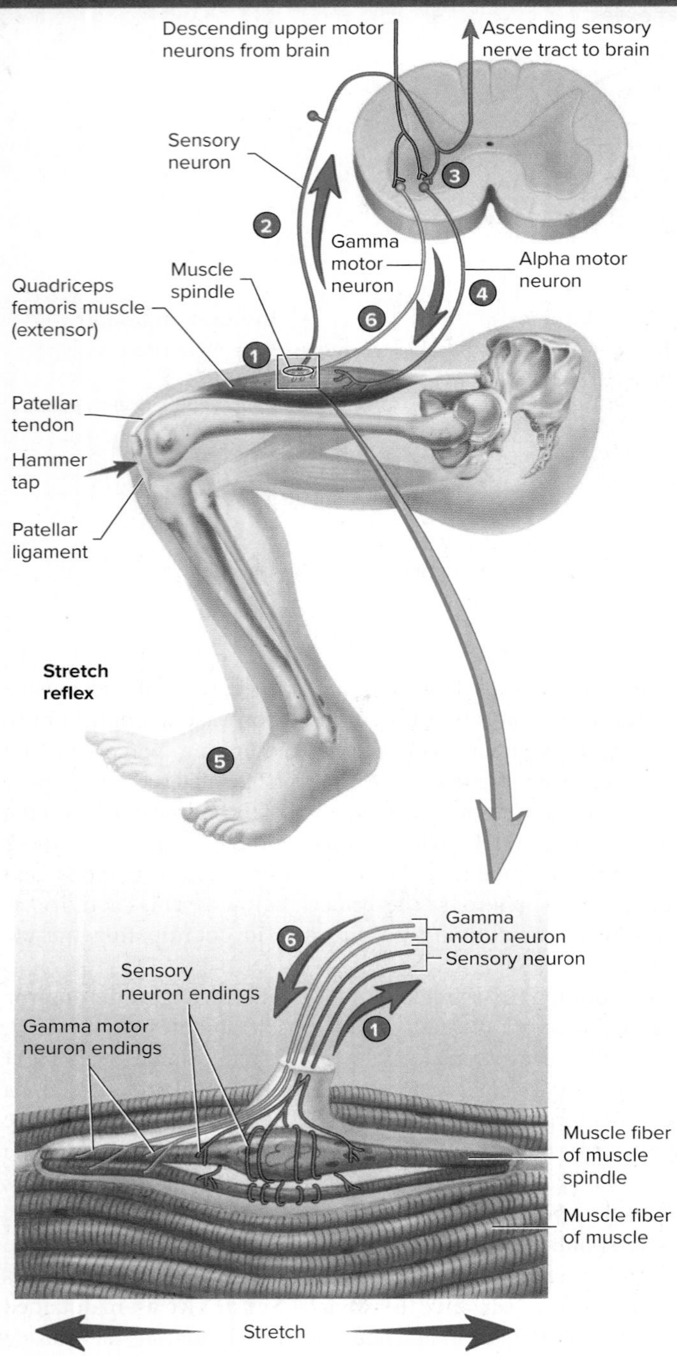

PROCESS **Figure 12.7**

Stretch Reflex

The knee-jerk reflex is an example of a stretch reflex whereby the stretching of a muscle stimulates the same muscle to contract. Stretch of the muscle spindle activates sensory neurons that send signals to the brain and directly to alpha motor neurons in the spinal cord. Muscle contraction is mediated by the alpha motor neurons. Descending upper motor neurons from the brain can also modulate the alpha motor neurons and the gamma motor neurons. Gamma motor neurons stimulate the muscle spindle, as indicated in the inset.

Stretch reflexes occur in many of the muscles of the body. Using table 10.16, determine which muscles would need to be stretched to cause the upper limb to reflexively bend.

gamma motor neurons are depressed, the stretch reflex may be suppressed or absent. Absence of the stretch reflex may also indicate that the reflex pathway is not intact.

Golgi Tendon Reflex

The **Golgi tendon reflex** prevents contracting muscles from applying excessive tension to tendons. The sensory receptors for this reflex are called **Golgi tendon organs.** These are encapsulated nerve endings that have at their ends numerous branches with small swellings adjacent to bundles of collagen fibers in tendons. Golgi tendon organs are located near the muscle-tendon junction.

Figure 12.8 illustrates the steps of the Golgi tendon reflex.

1. As a muscle contracts, the attached tendons stretch, resulting in increased tension in the tendon.
2. The increased tension stimulates action potentials in the sensory neurons from the Golgi tendon organs. The sensory neurons pass through the dorsal root to the spinal cord and enter the dorsal gray horn.
3. At the integration center in the dorsal horn, the sensory neurons branch and synapse with inhibitory interneurons.
4. The interneurons synapse with alpha motor neurons that innervate the muscle to which the Golgi tendon organ is attached.
5. Inhibition of the alpha motor neurons results in relaxation of the muscle and a reduction in tension in the tendon.

The key feature of the Golgi tendon reflex is that the sensory neurons stimulate the interneurons to release *inhibitory* neurotransmitters that inhibit the alpha motor neurons of the associated muscle and cause it to relax. The sudden relaxation of the muscle reduces the tension applied to the muscle and tendons. This reflex protects muscles and tendons from damage caused by excessive tension. For example, a weight lifter who suddenly drops a heavy weight after straining to lift it does so, in part, because of the effect of the Golgi tendon reflex.

The muscles and tendons of the legs sustain tremendous amounts of tension, particularly in athletes. Frequently, an athlete's Golgi tendon reflex is inadequate to protect muscles and tendons from excessive tension. For example, the large muscles and sudden movements of football players and sprinters can make them vulnerable to relatively frequent hamstring pulls and calcaneal (Achilles) tendon injuries.

Withdrawal Reflex

The function of the **withdrawal reflex,** or *flexor reflex,* is to remove a limb or another body part from a painful stimulus. Figure 12.9 illustrates the steps of the withdrawal reflex.

1. Sensory receptors that detect painful stimuli are activated (see chapter 14).
2. Sensory neurons conduct action potentials through the dorsal root to the spinal cord.
3. At the integration center within the spinal cord, the sensory neurons synapse with excitatory interneurons, which in turn synapse with alpha motor neurons.
4. The alpha motor neurons stimulate muscles, usually flexor muscles.
5. Contraction of the muscle removes the limb from the source of the painful stimulus.

PROCESS **Figure**

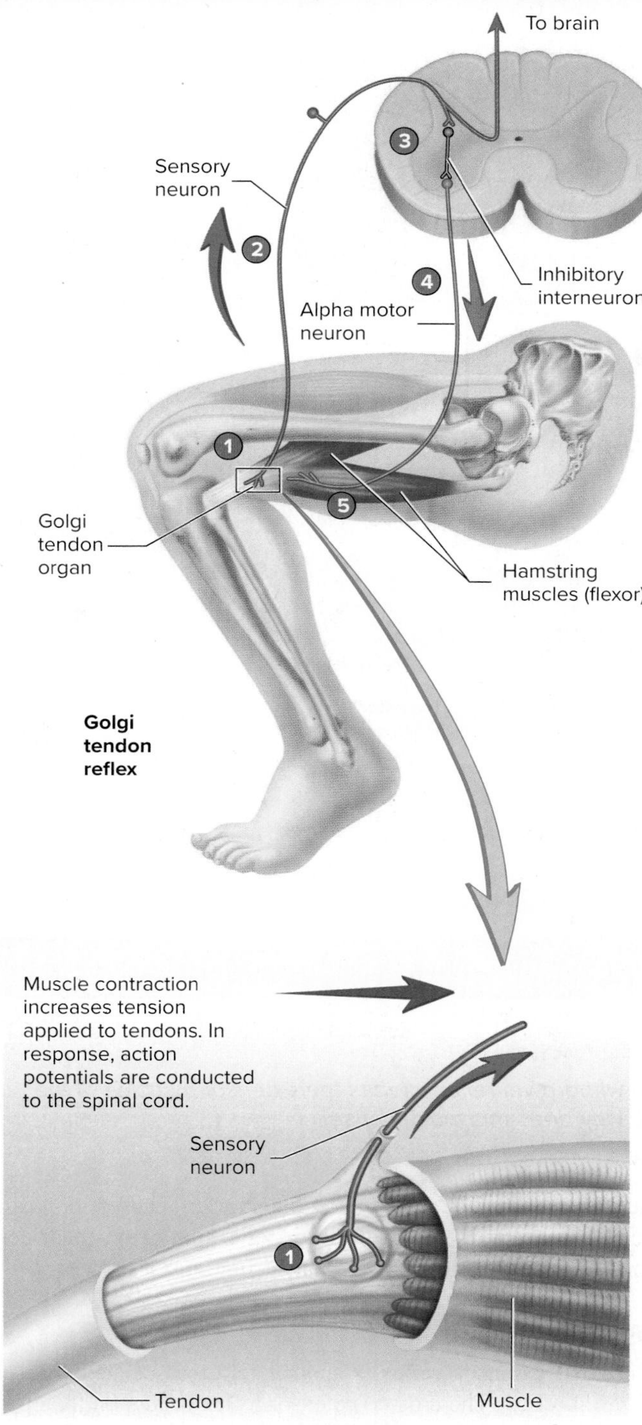

PROCESS Figure 12.8

Golgi Tendon Reflex

The Golgi tendon reflex is a protective reflex that prevents damage to tendons.

Predict what might happen to a person trying to lift a heavy weight following injury of sensory nerves from muscle tendons to the spinal cord.

PROCESS **Figure**

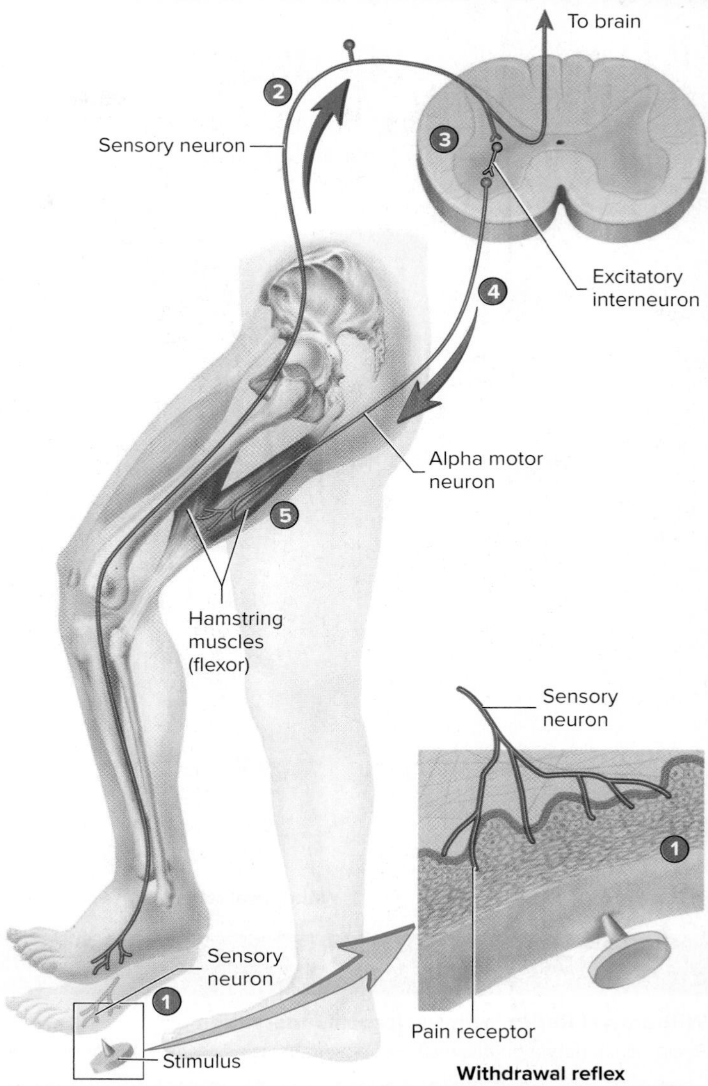

PROCESS Figure 12.9

Withdrawal Reflex

The withdrawal reflex moves a body part away from a painful stimulus.

Both the withdrawal reflex and the Golgi tendon reflex involve sensory signals that ultimately control the same type of motor neurons, and both are protective. Explain how one reflex can cause muscle contraction while the other causes muscle relaxation.

Collateral branches of the sensory neurons synapse with ascending fibers to the brain, providing conscious awareness of the painful stimuli.

Reciprocal Innervation

Reciprocal innervation is a phenomenon that allows opposing muscles to reinforce the efficiency of the withdrawal reflex. Reciprocal innervation allows the coordinated contraction of

PROCESS **Figure**

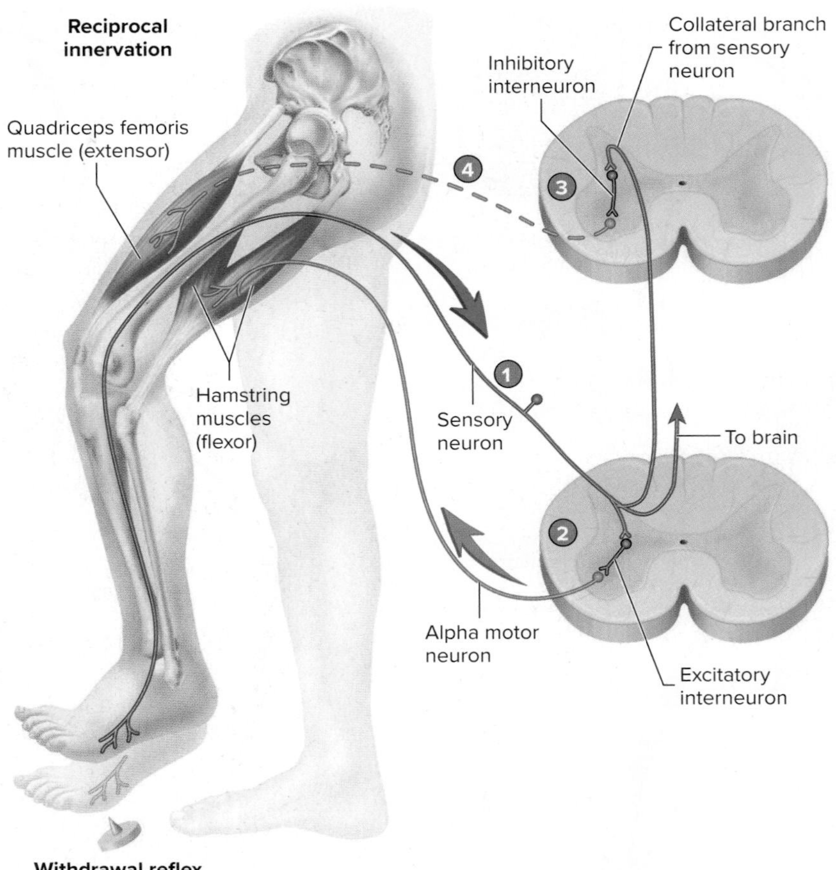

PROCESS **Figure 12.10**

Withdrawal Reflex with Reciprocal Innervation

Reciprocal innervation allows the opposing muscles of the same limb to reinforce the withdrawal reflex.

The motor neuron involved in reciprocal innervation of the withdrawal reflex inhibits the extensor muscles of the limb. Considering what you learned about stretch reflexes, why does this make sense?

flexor muscles and relaxation of the opposing extensor muscles. Figure 12.10 illustrates how reciprocal innervation of opposing muscle groups reinforces the withdrawal reflex.

1. During the withdrawal reflex, sensory neurons conduct action potentials from pain receptors to the spinal cord.
2. At the integration center, sensory neurons synapse with excitatory interneurons, which are part of the withdrawal reflex.
3. Collateral axons of sensory neurons that carry action potentials from pain receptors synapse with inhibitory interneurons in the dorsal horn of the spinal cord.
4. The inhibitory interneurons synapse with and inhibit alpha motor neurons of extensor (antagonist) muscles. When the withdrawal reflex is initiated, flexor muscles contract and reciprocal innervation causes the extensor muscles to relax. This reduces the resistance to movement that the extensor muscles would otherwise generate.

In addition to the withdrawal reflex, reciprocal innervation is also involved in the stretch reflex. When the stretch reflex causes a muscle to contract, reciprocal innervation causes opposing muscles to relax. In the patellar reflex, for example, the quadriceps femoris muscle contracts and the hamstring muscles relax.

Crossed Extensor Reflex

The **crossed extensor reflex** is another reflex associated with the withdrawal reflex. The crossed extensor reflex occurs on the opposite side of the body from the stimulus. When the withdrawal reflex occurs in one limb, the crossed extensor reflex causes the opposite response to occur in the other limb. Figure 12.11 illustrates how reciprocal innervation of opposing muscle groups reinforces the withdrawal reflex.

1. During the withdrawal reflex, sensory neurons conduct action potentials from pain receptors to the spinal cord.
2. At the integration center, sensory neurons synapse with excitatory interneurons, which are part of the withdrawal reflex.

PROCESS **Figure**

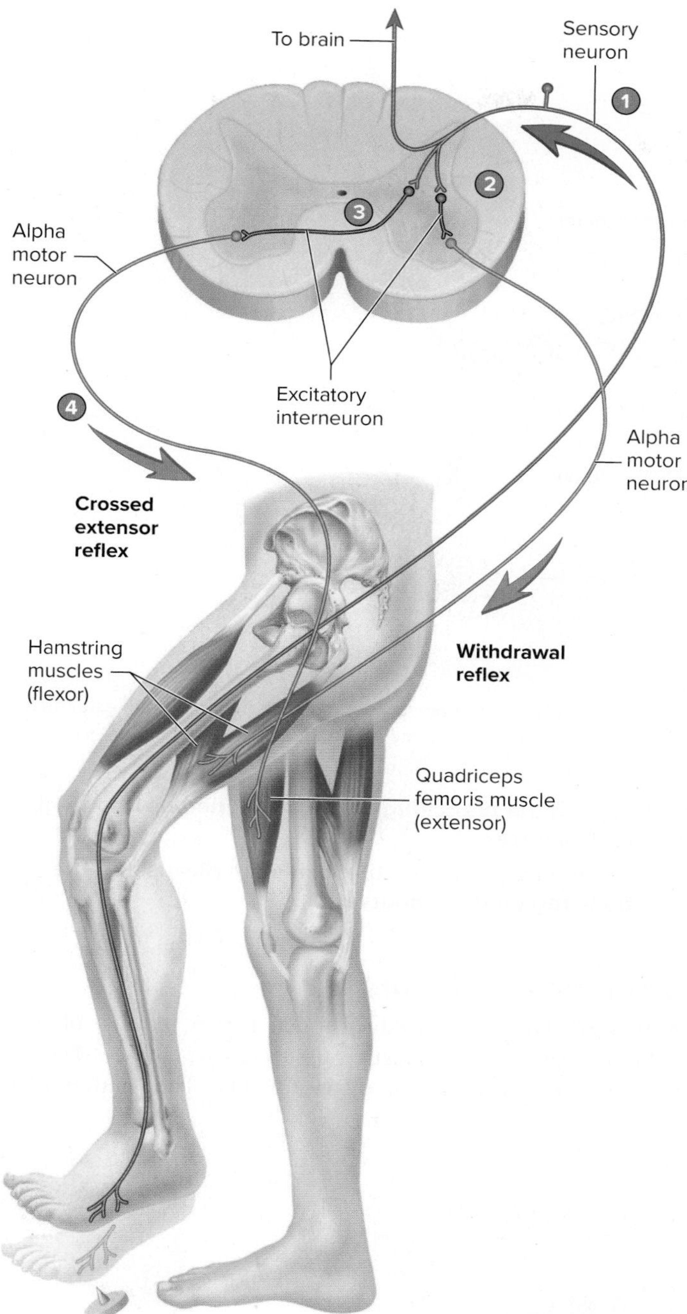

3 Collateral axons from the sensory neurons synapse with excitatory interneurons that extend through the white commissure to the opposite side of the spinal cord.

4 These interneurons synapse with alpha motor neurons that innervate extensor muscles in the opposite side of the body. When a withdrawal reflex is initiated in one lower limb, the crossed extensor reflex causes extension of the opposite lower limb.

PROCESS **Figure 12.11**

Withdrawal Reflex with Crossed Extensor Reflex

The crossed extensor reflex allows the muscles of the opposite limb to compensate for the withdrawal reflex in the affected limb.

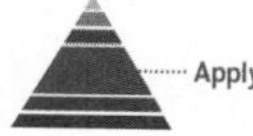

What would happen to a person if they stepped on a tack, but instead of having a withdrawal reflex with a crossed extensor reflex, they hypothetically had a withdrawal reflex with a non–crossed extensor reflex?

The crossed extensor reflex is adaptive in that it helps prevent falls by shifting the weight of the body from the affected to the unaffected limb. For example, when you step on a sharp object with your right foot, you withdraw your right lower limb from the stimulus (withdrawal reflex) while extending your left lower limb (crossed extensor reflex). Therefore, your body weight shifts from the right to the left lower limb. Initiating a withdrawal reflex in both legs at the same time would cause you to fall. (*Note:* This information will be useful when answering the Learn to Predict question at the beginning of the chapter.)

Interactions with Spinal Cord Reflexes

Reflexes do not operate as isolated entities. Rather, because of divergent and convergent pathways (see chapter 11), their activities are integrated with the functions of the nervous system as a whole. Diverging branches of the sensory neurons or interneurons in a reflex arc send action potentials along ascending nerve tracts to the brain (figure 12.12). A pain stimulus, for example, not only initiates a withdrawal reflex, causing you to remove the affected body part from the painful stimulus, but also enables you to perceive the pain as a result of action potentials sent to your brain.

Axons within descending tracts from the brain carry action potentials to motor neurons in the ventral horn of the spinal cord, converging with neurons of reflex arcs. The neurotransmitters released from the axons of these tracts either stimulate or inhibit the motor neurons in the ventral horn. Neurotransmitters change the sensitivity of the reflex by stimulating (EPSP) or inhibiting (IPSP) the motor neurons (see chapter 11).

ASSESS YOUR PROGRESS

7. *Explain the four ways reflexes can be classified.*
8. *Name the parts of a monosynaptic and of a polysynaptic reflex arc. What is a reflex? Explain how reflexes are homeostatic.*
9. *Describe the operation of a gamma motor neuron.*
10. *Contrast and give the functions of a stretch reflex and a Golgi tendon reflex. Describe the sensory receptors for each.*
11. *What is a withdrawal reflex? How do reciprocal innervation and the crossed extensor reflex assist the withdrawal reflex?*
12. *How do ascending and descending pathways relate to reflexes and other neuron functions?*

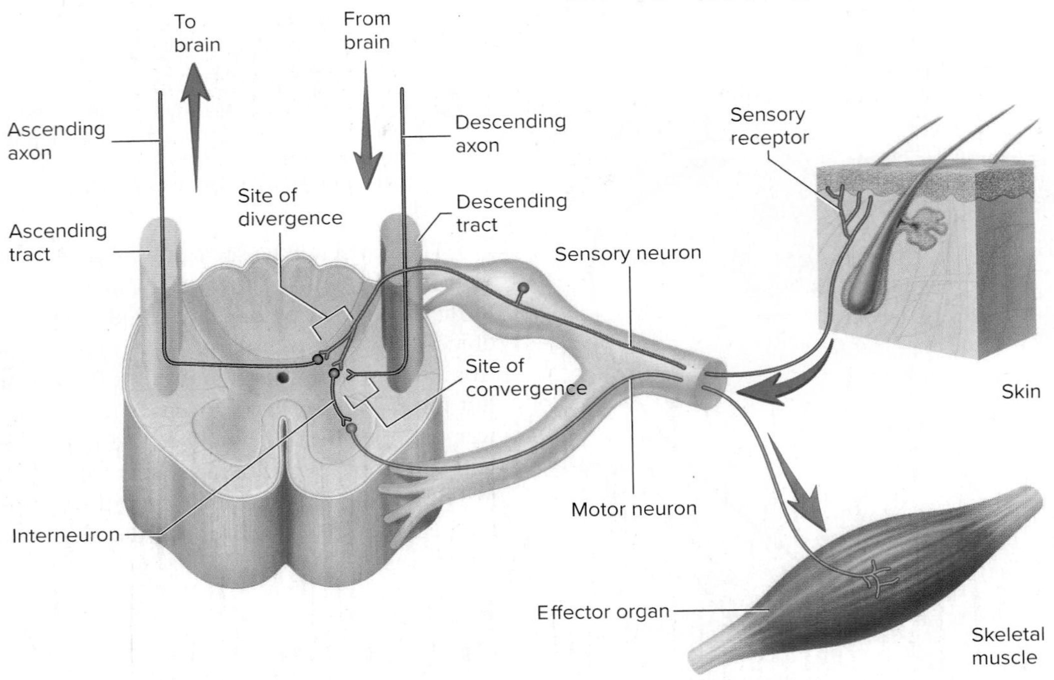

FIGURE 12.12 Spinal Reflex, with Ascending and Descending Axons
A diverging branch of a sensory neuron synapses with a neuron that extends to the brain in an ascending tract (*green*). An axon from the brain extends to the spinal cord in a descending tract (*purple*) and synapses with an interneuron, influencing its action on the motor neuron.

12.3 Spinal Nerves

LEARNING OUTCOMES

After reading this section, you should be able to

A. **Describe the connective tissue components of a nerve.**
B. **List the number and locations of the 31 pairs of spinal nerves.**
C. **Describe a dermatome and its clinical importance.**
D. **Explain the branching of the spinal nerves into rami and plexuses.**
E. **List the major nerves that exit each plexus and the body region they innervate.**

Structure of Nerves

Nerves of the PNS, including spinal nerves, consist of axons, Schwann cells, and connective tissue (figure 12.13). There are three layers of connective tissue: (1) The **endoneurium**

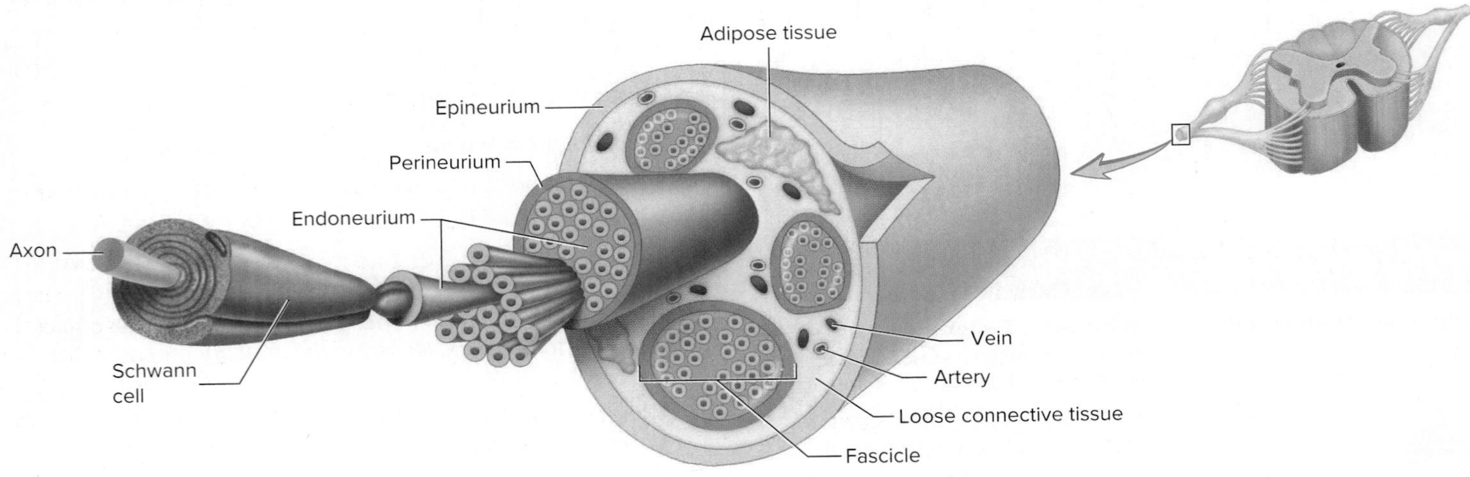

FIGURE 12.13 Structure of a Nerve
A nerve consists of axons surrounded by various layers of connective tissue: Epineurium surrounds the whole nerve, perineurium surrounds nerve fascicles, and endoneurium surrounds Schwann cells and axons. Loose connective tissue also surrounds the nerve fascicles.

(en-doh-NOO-ree-um) is a delicate connective tissue layer that surrounds each axon, or nerve fiber, and its Schwann cell sheath. (*Note:* Endoneurium is not the same as myelin. Remember that the Schwann cells form the myelin sheaths around PNS axons.) (2) The **perineurium** (per-i-NOO-ree-um) is a heavier connective tissue layer that surrounds groups of axons to form nerve **fascicles** (FAS-i-kuhls). (3) The **epineurium** (ep-i-NOO-ree-um) is a third layer of dense connective tissue that binds the nerve fascicles together to form a nerve. The connective tissue of the epineurium is continuous with the dura mater surrounding the CNS. The connective tissue layers of nerves make them tougher than the tracts in the CNS.

Organization of Spinal Nerves

All of the 31 pairs of spinal nerves, except the first pair and those in the sacrum, exit the vertebral column through intervertebral foramina located between adjacent vertebrae (see figure 7.14). The first pair of spinal nerves exit between the skull and the first cervical vertebra. The nerves of the sacrum exit from the single bone of the sacrum through the sacral foramina (see chapter 7). Eight spinal nerve pairs exit the vertebral column in the cervical region, 12 in the thoracic region, 5 in the lumbar region, 5 in the sacral region, and 1 in the coccygeal region (figure 12.14). For convenience, each of the spinal nerves is designated by a letter and a number. The letter indicates the region of the vertebral column from which the nerve emerges: **C,** cervical; **T,** thoracic; **L,** lumbar; and **S,** sacral. The single coccygeal nerve is often not designated, but when it is, the symbol **Co** is usually used. The number indicates the location in each region where the nerve emerges from the vertebral column, with the smallest number always representing the most superior origin. For example, the most superior nerve exiting the thoracic region of the vertebral column is designated T1. The cervical nerves are designated C1–C8, the thoracic nerves T1–T12, the lumbar nerves L1–L5, and the sacral nerves S1–S5.

The nerves arising from each region of the spinal cord and vertebral column supply specific regions of the body. A **dermatome** is the area of skin supplied with sensory innervation by a pair of spinal nerves. Each of the spinal nerves except C1 has a specific cutaneous sensory distribution. Figure 12.15 illustrates the dermatomal (der-mah-TOH-mal) map for the sensory cutaneous distribution of the spinal nerves.

Predict 2

Loss of sensation in a dermatomal pattern can provide valuable information about the location of nerve damage. Using the dermatomal map in figure 12.15, predict the possible site of nerve damage for a patient who suffered whiplash in an automobile accident and subsequently developed anesthesia (no sensation) in the left arm, forearm, and hand.

A **ramus** (RAY-mus; branch) is a major branch of a spinal nerve. Figure 12.16*a* depicts an idealized section through the trunk. Each spinal nerve has a dorsal and a ventral ramus. Additional rami (RAY-mye), called communicating rami, from the thoracic and upper lumbar spinal cord regions carry axons associated with the sympathetic division of the autonomic nervous system (see chapter 16).

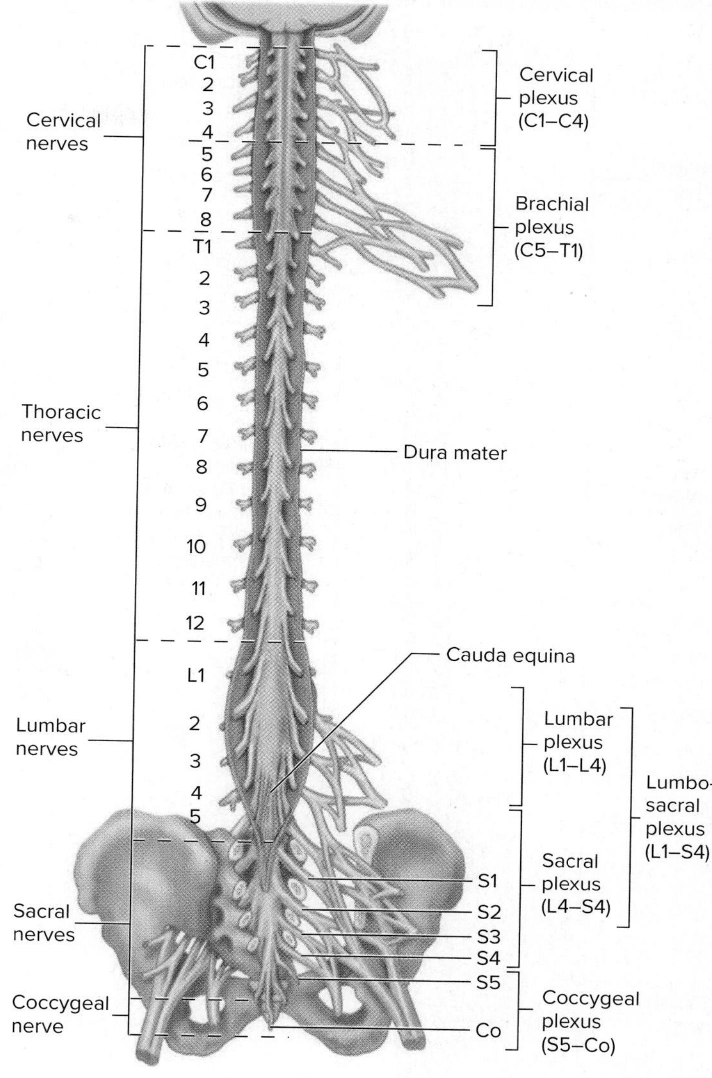

FIGURE 12.14 Spinal Nerves and Plexuses
The regional designations and the numbers of the spinal nerves are shown on the left. The plexuses formed by the spinal nerves are shown on the right. APR

The **dorsal rami** innervate most of the deep muscles of the dorsal trunk responsible for moving the vertebral column. They also innervate the connective tissue and skin near the midline of the back.

The **ventral rami** are distributed in two ways. In the thoracic region, the ventral rami form **intercostal** (between ribs) **nerves** (figure 12.16*a*), which extend along the inferior margin of each rib and innervate the intercostal muscles and the skin over the thorax. The ventral rami of the remaining spinal nerves form five major **plexuses** (PLEK-sus-ez; braids). A plexus is an intermingling of nerves, much like the intermingling of hair in a braid.

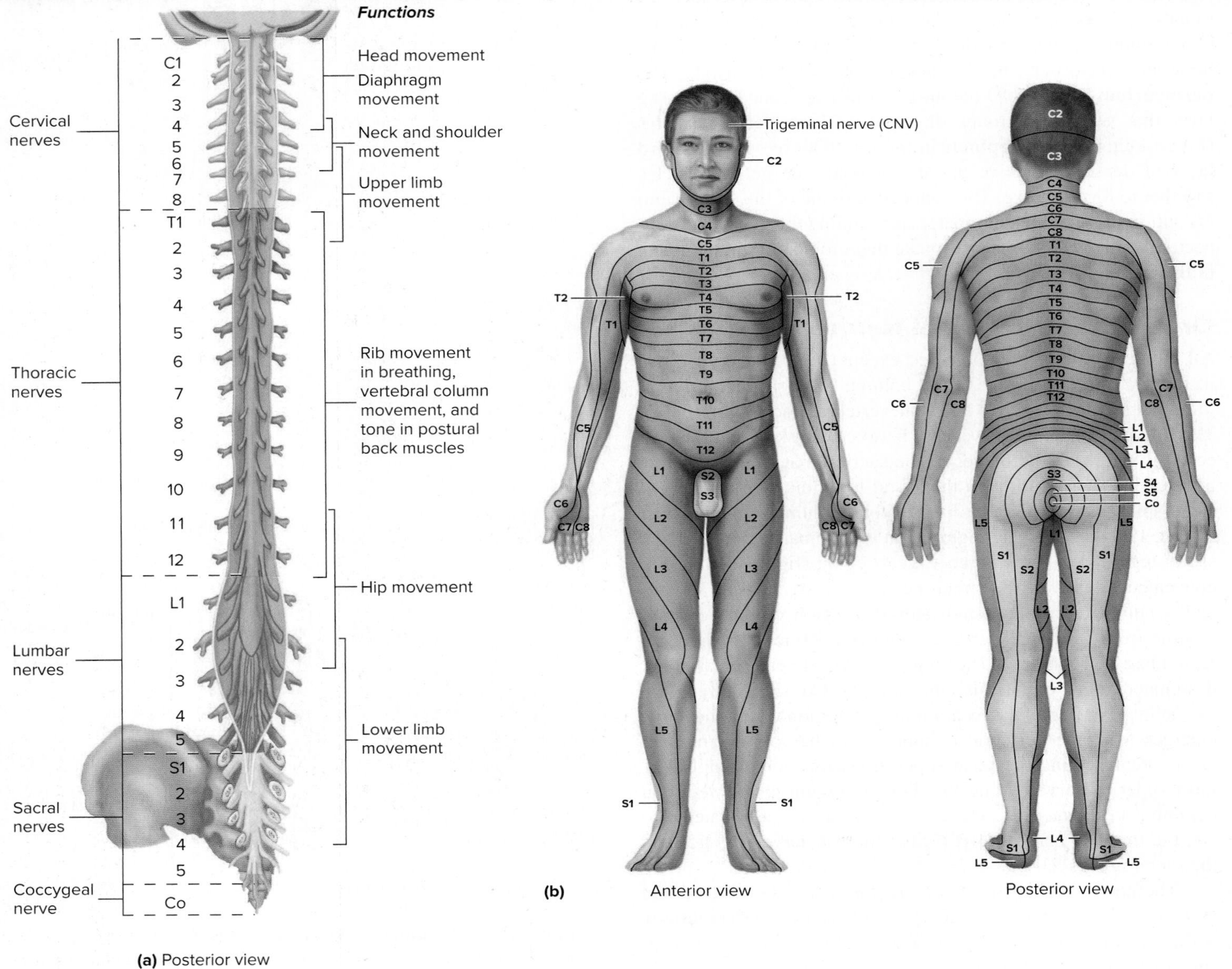

FIGURE 12.15 Spinal Cord and Dermatomal Map

(*a*) Nerves of the spinal cord and their functions. The regions are color-coded. (*b*) Letters and numbers indicate the spinal nerves innervating a given region of skin (dermatome). APR

The ventral rami of different spinal nerves, called the **roots,** join with each other to form a plexus. These roots should not be confused with the dorsal and ventral roots from the spinal cord, which are more medial. Nerves that arise from plexuses usually have axons from more than one spinal nerve and thus more than one level of the spinal cord. The ventral rami of spinal nerves C1–C4 form the cervical plexus, C5–T1 form the brachial plexus, L1–L4 form the lumbar plexus, L4–S4 form the sacral plexus, and S5 and the coccygeal nerve (Co) form the coccygeal plexus. An important functional aspect of these plexuses is that the intermingling of nerves from multiple spinal cord levels often minimizes the loss of control and feeling to a specific area of the body following spinal cord injury.

Several smaller somatic plexuses, such as the pudendal plexus in the pelvis, are derived from more distal branches of the spinal nerves. Some of the somatic plexuses are described later in this section. Autonomic plexuses (described in chapter 16) also exist in the thorax and abdomen. In the following discussion, we investigate the five major plexuses derived from the ventral rami of spinal nerves.

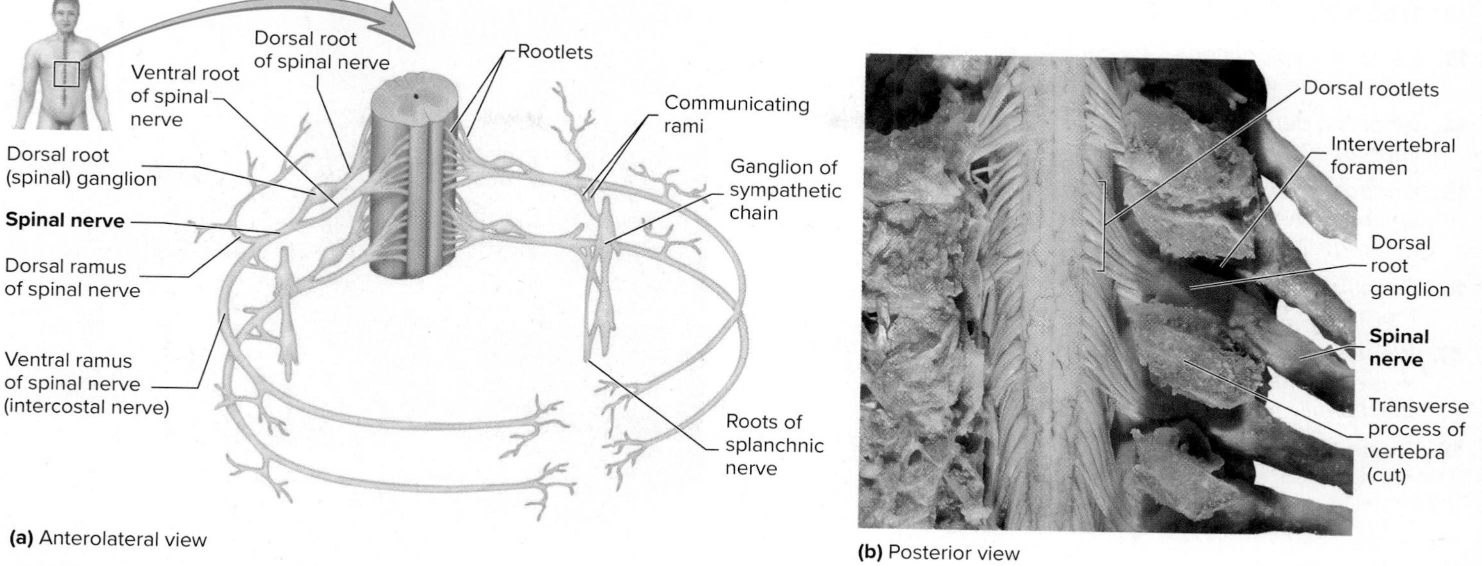

(a) Anterolateral view

(b) Posterior view

FIGURE 12.16 Spinal Nerves

(*a*) Typical thoracic spinal nerves have dorsal and ventral roots, as well as dorsal, ventral, and communicating rami. Communicating rami connect to the sympathetic chain (see chapter 16). (*b*) Photograph of four dorsal roots in place along the vertebral column. (b) Rebecca Gray/Don Kincaid/McGraw Hill Education APR

Clinical IMPACT 12.2 Spinal Cord Injury

Damage to the spinal cord can disrupt ascending tracts to the brain, resulting in the loss of sensation. Conversely, the disruption of descending tracts from the brain to motor neurons in the spinal cord can result in the loss of motor functions. About 10,000 new cases of **spinal cord injury** occur each year in the United States. Leading causes are automobile and motorcycle accidents, followed by gunshot wounds, falls, and swimming accidents. The primary mechanisms include concussion (an injury caused by a blow), contusion (an injury resulting in hemorrhage), and laceration (a tear or cut). Spinal cord injuries often involve excessive flexion, extension, rotation, or compression of the vertebral column. Most spinal cord injuries are acute contusions of the cord due to bone or disk displacement into the cord and involve a combination of excessive directional movements, such as simultaneous flexion and compression.

Spinal cord injury is classified according to the vertebral level at which the injury occurred, whether the entire cord or only a portion is damaged at that level, and the mechanism of injury. Most spinal cord injuries occur in the cervical region or at the thoracolumbar junction and are incomplete. Injuries in the cervical region above T1 are the most severe and can result in paralysis of all four limbs (quadriplegia or tetraplegia), with the abdominal and chest muscles also affected. Injuries at or below T1 can result in varying degrees of paralysis of the legs (paraplegia) and the abdomen, while retaining full function of the upper limbs.

For a long time, researchers thought the spinal cord was incapable of regeneration following severe damage. But they have now learned that most neurons of the adult spinal cord survive the injury and begin to regenerate, growing about 1 mm into the site of damage. Unfortunately, the neurons then regress to an inactive, atrophic state. A major block to adult spinal cord regeneration is the formation of a scar, consisting mainly of myelin and astrocytes, at the site of the injury. Implantation of stem cells can partially bridge the scar and stimulate some regeneration. Certain growth factors can also stimulate regeneration, and blocking inhibitory factors may be able to prevent the formation of the glial scar to allow axon regeneration. Advances in electrical stimulation and integrated computer technologies have shown promising results for many patients with spinal cord injuries. Current research continues to look for the right combination of cells, electrical stimulation, and devices to stimulate regeneration of the spinal cord following injury.

ASSESS YOUR PROGRESS

13. *List all the spinal nerves by name and number. Where do they exit the vertebral column?*
14. *What is a dermatome? Why are dermatomes clinically important?*
15. *Contrast the dorsal and ventral rami of the spinal nerves. What muscles do the dorsal rami innervate?*
16. *Describe the distribution of the ventral rami of the thoracic region.*
17. *What is a plexus? What happens to the axons of spinal nerves as they pass through a plexus? Why is this functionally important?*
18. *Name the five major spinal plexuses and the spinal nerves associated with each.*

Cervical Plexus

The **cervical plexus** is a relatively small plexus originating from spinal nerves C1–C4 (figure 12.17). Branches derived from this plexus innervate superficial neck structures, including several of the muscles attached to the hyoid bone. The cervical plexus innervates the skin of the neck and posterior portion of the head (see figure 12.15). An unusual part of the cervical plexus, the **ansa** (AN-sah; bucket handle) **cervicalis,** is a loop between C1 and C3. Nerves to the infrahyoid muscles branch from the ansa cervicalis (see chapter 10).

One of the most important derivatives of the cervical plexus is the **phrenic** (FREN-ik) **nerve,** which is important for breathing. The phrenic nerve originates from spinal nerves C3–C5 and is derived from both the cervical and brachial plexuses. The phrenic nerves descend along each side of the neck to enter the thorax and then descend along the sides of the mediastinum to reach the diaphragm, which they innervate. Contraction of the diaphragm is largely responsible for a person's ability to breathe; therefore, damage to the phrenic nerve during surgery or compression of the nerve by a tumor at the base of the lung severely limits breathing. The phrenic nerve also contains sensory fibers that communicate sensory information to the CNS from serous membranes within the thoracic cavity.

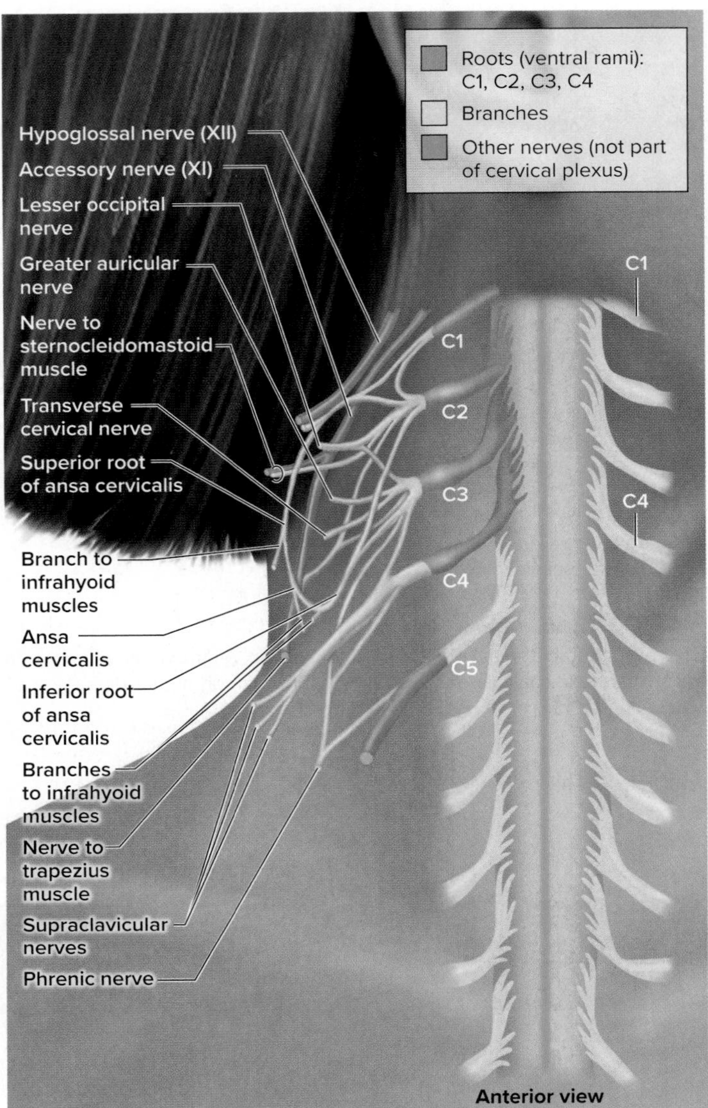

FIGURE 12.17 Cervical Plexus
The roots of the plexus are formed by the ventral rami of spinal nerves C1–C4. Branches of the cervical plexus innervate the muscles (infrahyoid) and skin of the neck. The phrenic nerve (C3–C5) innervates the diaphragm. APR

Predict 3

Explain how damage to or compression of the right phrenic nerve affects the diaphragm. How would breathing be affected if the spinal cord were completely severed at the level of C2 versus at the level of C6?

Brachial Plexus

The **brachial plexus** originates from spinal nerves C5–T1 (figure 12.18). The five ventral rami that constitute the brachial plexus join to form three **trunks,** which separate into six **divisions** and then join again to create three **cords** (posterior, lateral, and medial) from which five **branches,** or nerves of the upper limb, emerge.

The five major nerves emerging from the brachial plexus to supply the upper limb are the axillary, radial, musculocutaneous, ulnar, and median nerves. The axillary nerve innervates part of the shoulder; the radial nerve innervates the posterior arm, forearm, and hand; the musculocutaneous nerve innervates the anterior arm; and the ulnar and median nerves innervate the anterior forearm and hand. Smaller nerves from the brachial plexus innervate the shoulder and pectoral muscles. Because of this anatomical organization, the entire upper limb can be anesthesized by injecting an anesthetic near the brachial plexus between the neck and

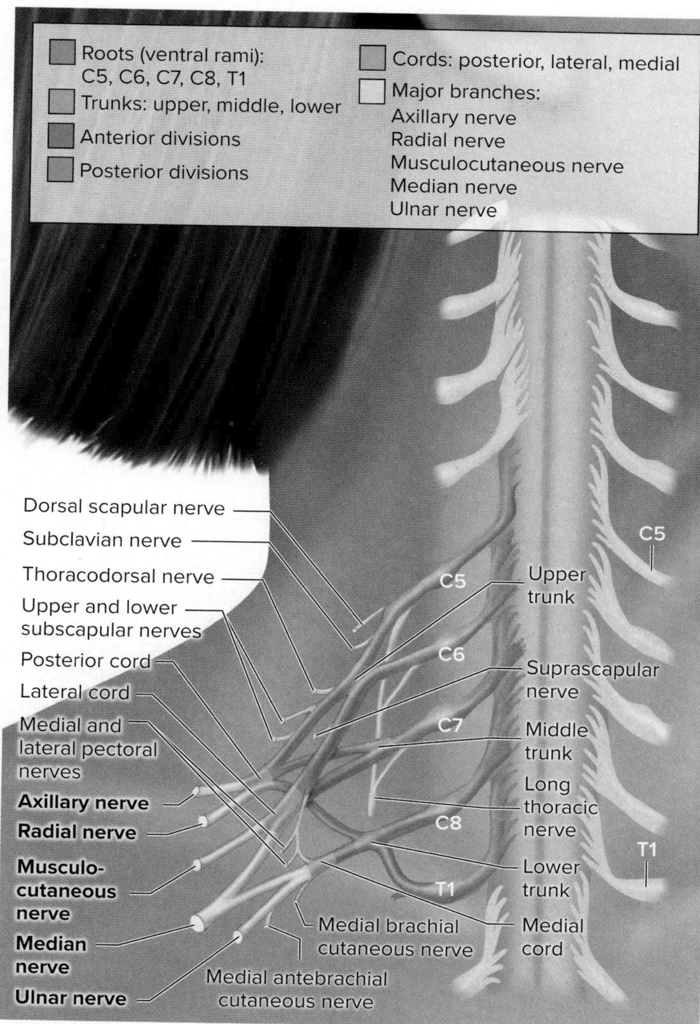

(a) Anterior view

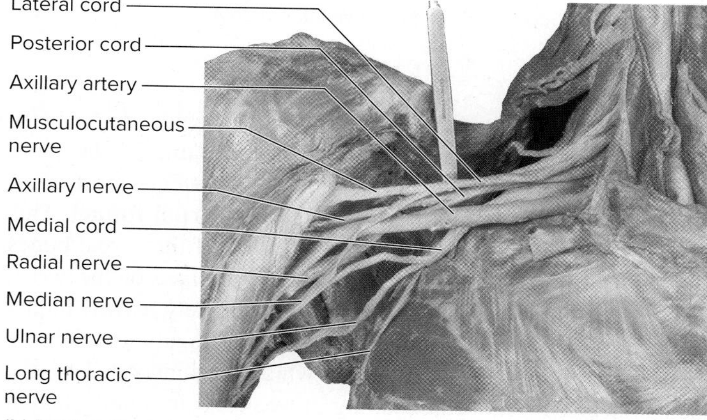

(b) Right axilla, anterior view

FIGURE 12.18 Brachial Plexus
The roots of the plexus are formed by the ventral rami of spinal nerves C5–T1 and join to form an upper, a middle, and a lower trunk. Each trunk divides into anterior and posterior divisions. The divisions join to form the posterior, lateral, and medial cords from which the major brachial plexus nerves arise. The major brachial plexus nerves include the axillary, radial, musculocutaneous, median, and ulnar nerves, which innervate the muscles and skin of the upper limb. (b) Christine Eckel/McGraw Hill APR

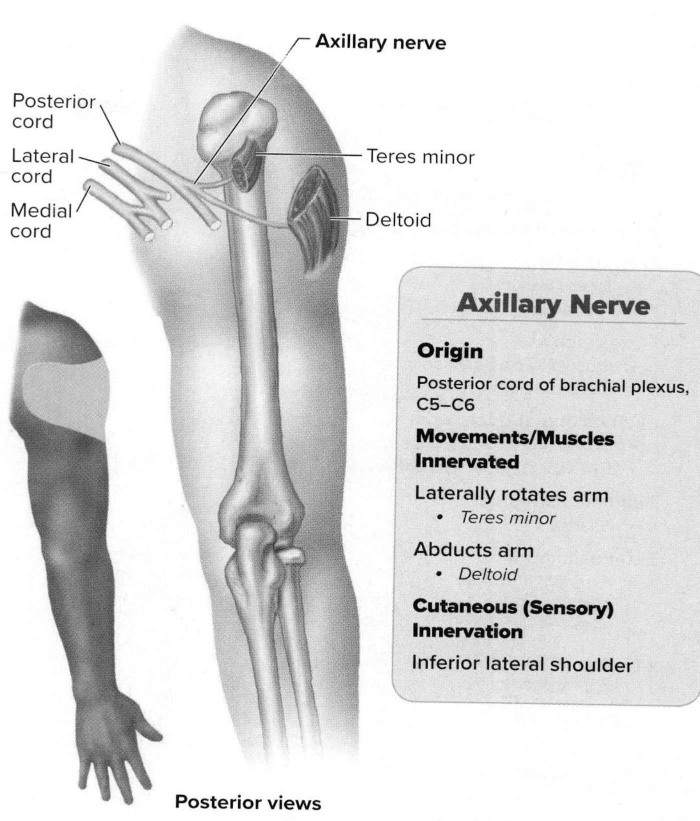

Axillary Nerve

Origin

Posterior cord of brachial plexus, C5–C6

Movements/Muscles Innervated

Laterally rotates arm
- *Teres minor*

Abducts arm
- *Deltoid*

Cutaneous (Sensory) Innervation

Inferior lateral shoulder

FIGURE 12.19 Axillary Nerve
The route of the axillary nerve and the muscles it innervates. The *inset* depicts the cutaneous (sensory) distribution of the nerve (*blue area*).

the shoulder posterior to the clavicle. This is called **brachial anesthesia.**

Axillary Nerve

The **axillary** (AK-sil-air-ee) **nerve** innervates the deltoid and teres minor muscles (figure 12.19). It also provides sensory innervation to the shoulder joint and to the skin over part of the shoulder.

Radial Nerve

The **radial nerve** innervates all of the extensor muscles of the upper limb (triceps brachii), the supinator muscle, and the brachioradialis. Its cutaneous sensory distribution is to the posterior portion of the upper limb, including the posterior surface of the hand. The nerve emerges from the posterior cord of the brachial plexus and descends within the deep aspect of the posterior arm (figure 12.20). About midway down the shaft of the humerus, it lies against the bone in the radial groove.

Musculocutaneous Nerve

The **musculocutaneous** (MUS-kyoo-loh-kyoo-TAY-nee-us) **nerve** provides motor innervation to the anterior muscles of the arm, as well as cutaneous sensory innervation to part of the forearm (figure 12.21).

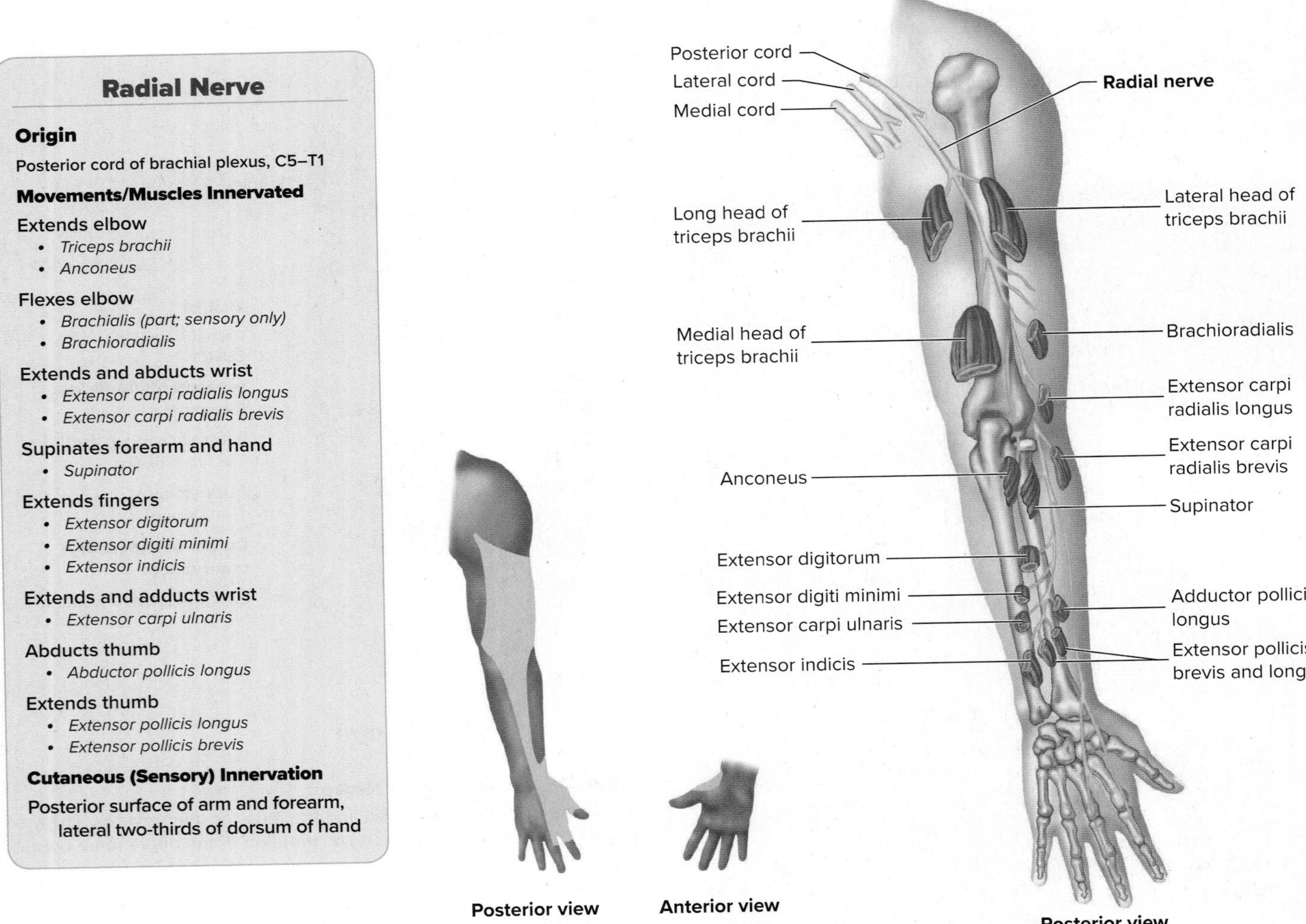

FIGURE 12.20 Radial Nerve
The route of the radial nerve and the muscles it innervates. The *insets* depict the cutaneous (sensory) distribution of the nerve (*blue areas*).

Ulnar Nerve

The **ulnar** (UL-nair) **nerve** innervates two forearm muscles plus most of the intrinsic hand muscles, except some associated with the thumb. Its sensory distribution is to the ulnar side of the hand (figure 12.22).

The ulnar nerve is the most easily damaged of all the spinal nerves, but such damage is almost always temporary. The ulnar nerve passes posterior to the medial epicondyle of the humerus and can be felt just below the skin at this region. If the elbow is banged against a hard object, temporary ulnar nerve damage may occur, causing painful tingling to radiate down the ulnar side of the forearm and hand. Because of this sensation, we often call this area of the elbow the *funny bone* or *crazy bone*.

Median Nerve

The **median nerve** innervates all but one of the flexor muscles of the forearm and most of the hand muscles at the base of the thumb, called the thenar area of the hand. The nerve's cutaneous sensory distribution is to the radial portion of the palm of the hand (figure 12.23). Damage to the median nerve occurs most commonly where it enters the wrist through the **carpal tunnel.** This tunnel is created by the concave organization of the carpal bones and the flexor retinaculum on the anterior surface of the wrist. Compression of the median nerve in this relatively narrow tunnel produces numbness, tingling, and pain in the fingers. In addition, the function of the thenar muscles, which are innervated by the median nerve, is reduced, resulting in weakness in thumb flexion and opposition. This condition is called **carpal tunnel syndrome.** In general, anything that compresses the median nerve in the carpal tunnel can cause the syndrome

Other Nerves of the Brachial Plexus

Several nerves, other than the five just described, arise from the brachial plexus (see figure 12.18). They supply most of the muscles acting on the scapula and arm and include the pectoral, long thoracic, thoracodorsal, subscapular, and suprascapular nerves. In addition, brachial plexus nerves innervate the skin of the medial arm and forearm.

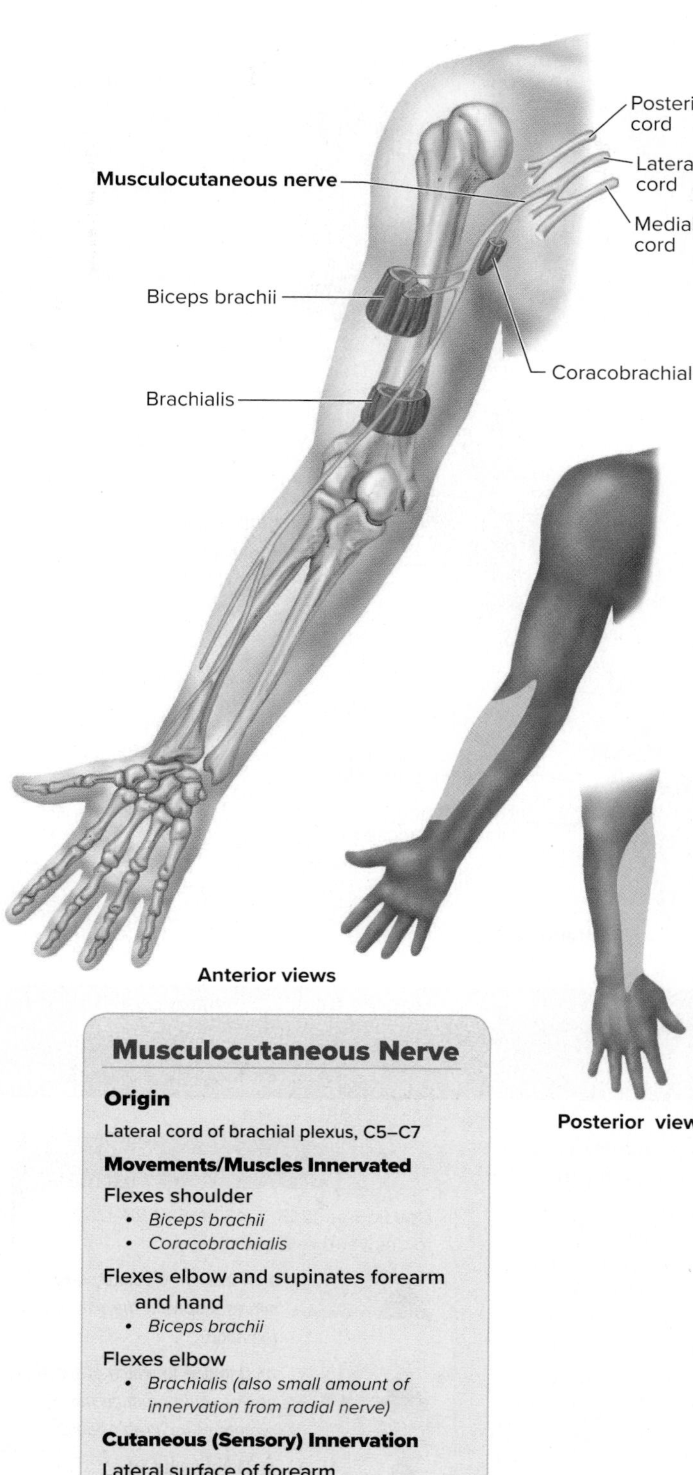

FIGURE 12.21 Musculocutaneous Nerve
The route of the musculocutaneous nerve and the muscles it innervates. The *insets* depict the cutaneous (sensory) distribution of the nerve (*blue areas*).

Lumbar and Sacral Plexuses

The **lumbar plexus** originates from the ventral rami of spinal nerves L1–L4, and the **sacral plexus** originates from L4 to S4. However, because of their close, overlapping relationship and similar distribution, the two plexuses are often considered together as a single **lumbosacral plexus** (L1–S4; figure 12.24). Four major nerves exit the lumbosacral plexus and enter the lower limb: (1) the obturator, (2) the femoral, (3) the tibial, and (4) the common fibular (peroneal). Other lumbosacral nerves supply the lower back, hip, and lower abdomen.

Obturator Nerve

The **obturator** (OB-tour-ate-or) **nerve** innervates the muscles of the medial thigh that adduct the thigh. Its cutaneous sensory distribution is to the medial side of the thigh (figure 12.25).

Femoral Nerve

The **femoral nerve** innervates the iliopsoas and sartorius muscles and the quadriceps femoris group. Its cutaneous sensory distribution is the anterior and lateral thigh and the medial leg and foot (figure 12.26).

Predict 4

While moving a large box in his garage, Carl hurt his back. Within hours, the pain in his back was radiating down the medial side of his left thigh and knee. It was especially difficult for Carl to flex his left hip and extend his left knee. He could not stand the pain, so he went to the emergency room. Radiographs and an MRI revealed a bulging intervertebral disk. Which spinal nerve was most likely affected, and why were Carl's motor movements affected? Also, explain the referred pain.

Tibial and Common Fibular Nerves

The **tibial** and **common fibular nerves,** or *peroneal* (per-oh-NEE-al) *nerves,* originate from spinal segments L4–S3 and are bound together within a connective tissue sheath for the length of the thigh (figures 12.27 and 12.28; see figure 12.24). These two nerves, combined within the same sheath, are referred to jointly as the **sciatic** (sigh-AT-ik) **nerve,** or *ischiadic* (is-kee-AD-ik) *nerve* (see figure 12.24). The sciatic nerve is the largest nerve in the body. It passes through the greater sciatic notch in the pelvis and descends in the posterior thigh to the popliteal fossa, where the two portions of the sciatic nerve separate.

The tibial nerve innervates most of the posterior thigh and leg muscle (see figure 12.27). It branches in the foot to form the **medial** and **lateral plantar** (PLAN-tar) **nerves,** which innervate the plantar muscles of the foot and the skin over the sole of the foot. Another branch, the **sural** (SOO-ral) **nerve,** supplies part of

Ulnar Nerve

Origin

Medial cord of brachial plexus, C8–T1

Movements/Muscles Innervated

Flexes and adducts wrist

- *Flexor carpi ulnaris*

Flexes fingers

- *Part of the flexor digitorum profundus controlling the distal phalanges of little and ring fingers*

Adducts thumb

- *Adductor pollicis*

Controls hypothenar muscles

- *Flexor digiti minimi brevis*
- *Abductor digiti minimi*
- *Opponens digiti minimi*

Flexes metacarpophalangeal joints and extends interphalangeal joints

- *Two medial (ulnar) lumbricales*

Abducts and adducts fingers

- *Interossei*

Cutaneous (Sensory) Innervation

Medial third of hand, little finger, and medial half of ring finger

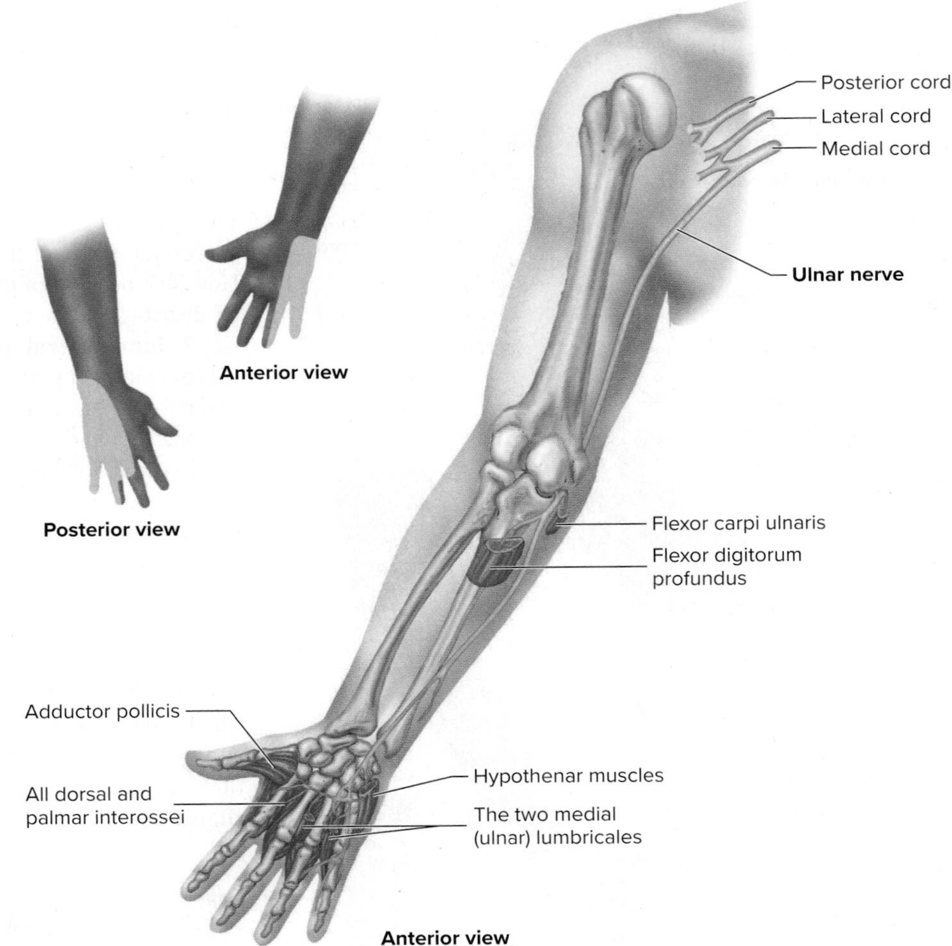

FIGURE 12.22 Ulnar Nerve
The route of the ulnar nerve and the muscles it innervates. The *insets* depict the cutaneous (sensory) distribution of the nerve (*blue areas*).

Case STUDY 12.1 Thoracic Outlet Syndrome

Sarah, age 26, noticed that over a period of time she experienced pain, tingling, and numbness in the ring finger and little finger of her right hand. She also felt pain in her elbow that radiated down the posteromedial portion of her forearm and hand, so she made an appointment with her physician. After careful examination of Sarah's upper limb, her physician ordered an x-ray of her neck. The x-ray disclosed a cervical rib on the right, which was attached to the C7 vertebra. Cervical ribs are extra ribs that occur in about 0.5% of the population, yet most people exhibit no symptoms. In Sarah's case, the extra rib was compressing the inferior roots of the brachial plexus (see figure 12.18), a condition called **thoracic outlet syndrome.** This syndrome is a group of related disorders that involve compression of the nerves and vessels in the "thoracic outlet" region of the lower neck and upper chest. The syndrome is generally caused by compression of the brachial plexus or the subclavian artery or vein. Compression can result from an anatomical abnormality, such as Sarah's extra rib, but to become symptomatic there is often an associated injury or overuse activity, such as repetitive overhead arm motions in sports and occupations, droopy shoulders, joint pressure from heavy backpacks or obesity, joint changes during pregnancy, and trauma, such as whiplash. Thoracic outlet syndrome can also result from these injuries and activities in the absence of a cervical rib. Treatment of thoracic outlet syndrome first involves physical therapy to improve shoulder alignment, range of motion, and strength. In more severe and persistent cases, surgery may be required to alleviate compression of the plexus or blood vessels.

Predict 5

Use figures 12.15, 12.18, and 12.20–12.22 to answer these questions:

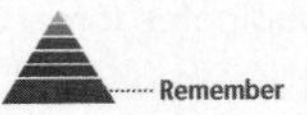

a. Name the brachial plexus nerves supplying the skin of the hand.

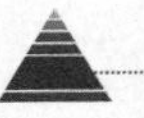

b. Damage to which of these nerves could produce the symptoms in Sarah's hand?

c. What made Sarah's physician suspect thoracic outlet syndrome rather than damage to an individual nerve?

d. Thoracic outlet syndrome can also affect muscles, producing muscle weakness and paralysis. Muscles supplied by what nerves could be affected by a cervical rib?

Median Nerve

Origin

Medial and lateral cords of brachial plexus, C5–T1

Movements/Muscles Innervated

Pronates forearm and hand
- *Pronator teres*
- *Pronator quadratus*

Flexes and abducts wrist
- *Flexor carpi radialis*

Flexes wrist
- *Palmaris longus*

Flexes fingers
- *Part of flexor digitorum profundus controlling the distal phalanx of the middle and index fingers*
- *Flexor digitorum superficialis*

Controls thumb muscle
- *Flexor pollicis longus*

Controls thenar muscles
- *Abductor pollicis brevis*
- *Opponens pollicis*
- *Flexor pollicis brevis*

Flexes metacarpophalangeal joints and extends interphalangeal joints
- *Two lateral (radial) lumbricales*

Cutaneous (Sensory) Innervation

Lateral two-thirds of palm of hand, thumb, index and middle fingers, and the lateral half of ring finger and dorsal tips of the same fingers

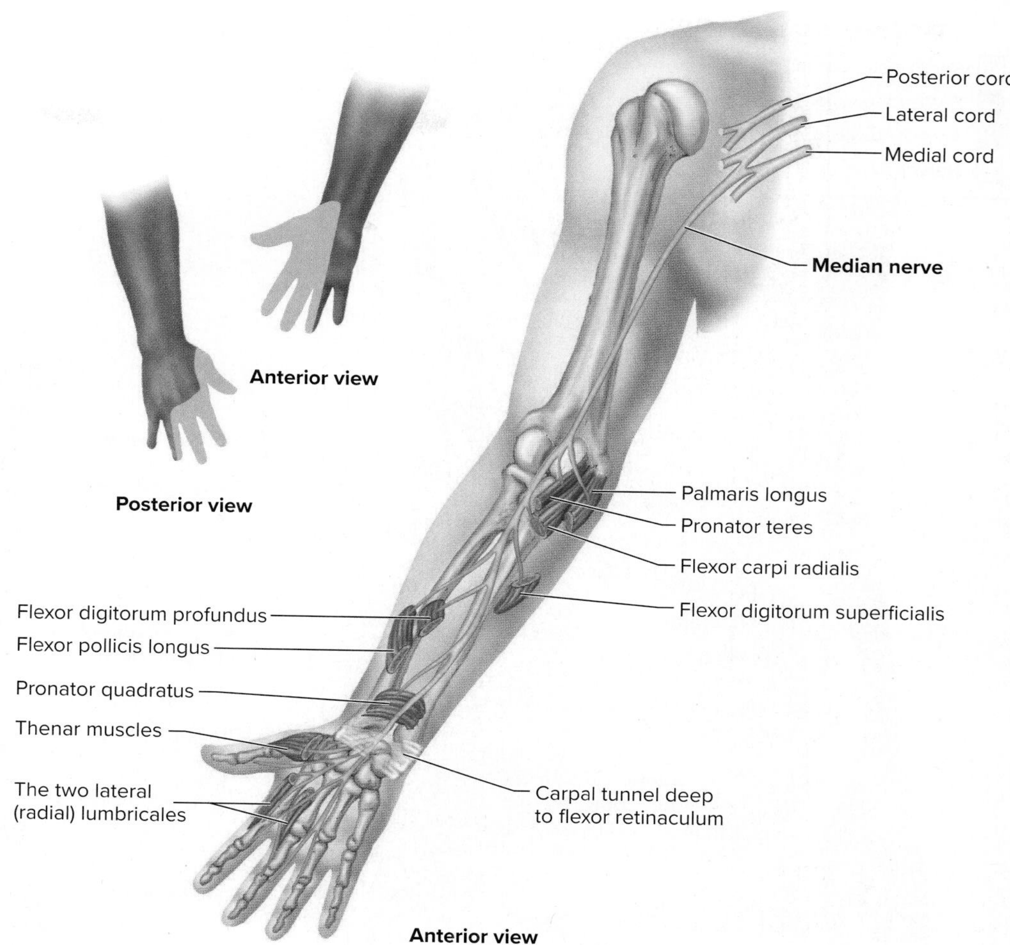

FIGURE 12.23 Median Nerve

The route of the median nerve and the muscles it innervates. The *insets* depict the cutaneous (sensory) distribution of the nerve (*blue areas*). 

Clinical IMPACT 12.3

Sciatic Nerve Damage

If a person sits on a hard surface for a considerable time, the sciatic nerve may be compressed against the ischial portion of the hip bone. When the person stands up, he or she feels a tingling sensation, described as "pins and needles," throughout the lower limb and often remarks that the limb has "gone to sleep." This condition is temporary, but the sciatic nerve can be seriously injured in a number of ways. A ruptured intervertebral disk or pressure from the uterus during pregnancy may compress the roots of the sciatic nerve. Other causes of sciatic nerve damage include hip injury, compression of the nerve by the piriformis muscle (piriformis syndrome), and an improperly administered injection in the hip region (see Clinical Impact 7.3).

the cutaneous innervation over the calf of the leg and the plantar surface of the foot.

The common fibular nerve divides into the **deep** and **superficial fibular (peroneal) nerves.** These branches innervate the anterior and lateral muscles of the leg and foot. The cutaneous distribution of the common fibular nerve and its branches is the lateral and anterior leg and the dorsum of the foot (figure 12.28).

Other Lumbosacral Plexus Nerves

In addition to the nerves just described, the lumbosacral plexus gives rise to **gluteal nerves,** which supply the hip muscles that act on the femur, and the **pudendal** (pu-DEN-dal) **nerve,** which supplies the muscles of the abdominal floor (see figure 12.24). The **iliohypogastric** (IL-ee-oh-high-poh-GAS-trik), **ilioinguinal** (IL-ee-oh-ING-gwi-nal), **genitofemoral** (JEN-i-toh-FEM-oh-ral), **cutaneous femoral,** and pudendal nerves innervate the skin of the

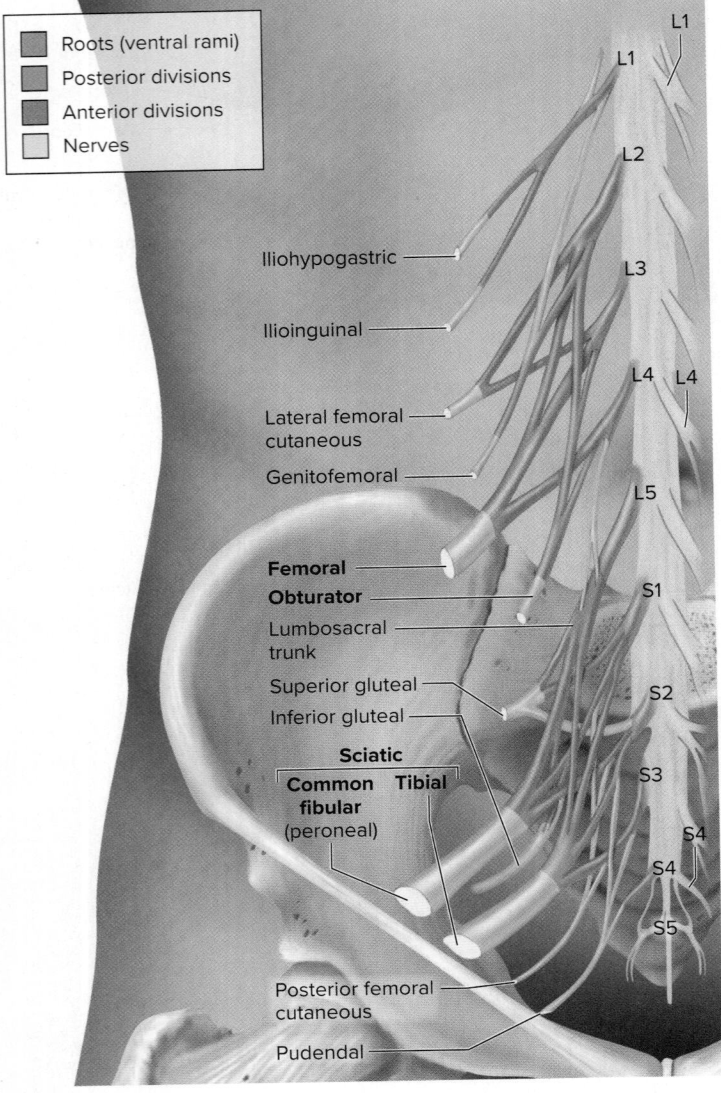

(a) Anterior view

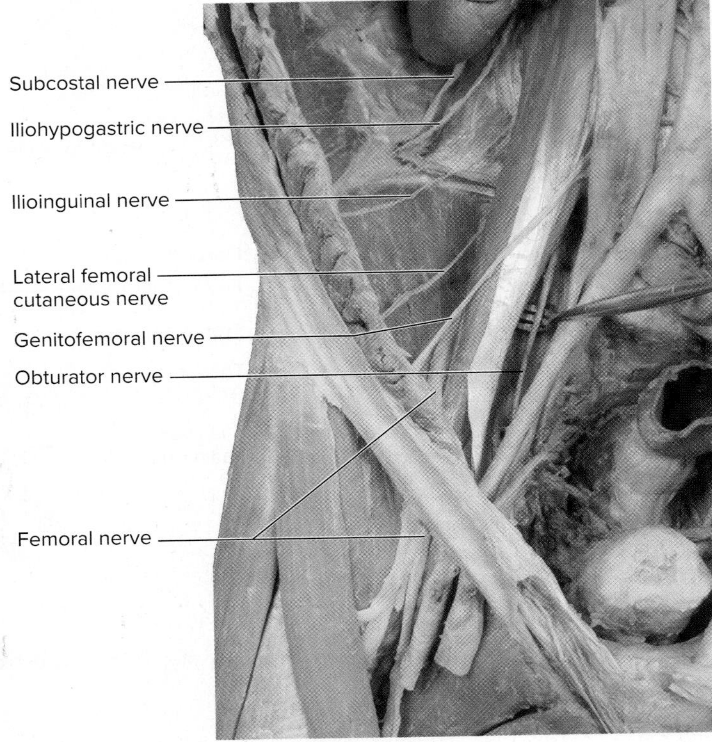

(b) Right pelvic region, anterior view

FIGURE 12.24 Lumbosacral Plexus
The roots of the plexus are formed by the ventral rami of the spinal nerves L1–S4 and form anterior and posterior divisions, which give rise to the lumbosacral nerves. The lumbosacral trunk joins the lumbar and sacral plexuses. (b) Christine Eckel/McGraw Hill APR

suprapubic area, the external genitalia, the superior medial thigh, and the posterior thigh. The pudendal nerve plays a vital role in sexual stimulation and response. Branches of the pudendal nerve are anesthetized during childbirth before a doctor performs an **episiotomy** (eh-peez-ee-OT-oh-mee), a cut in the perineum that enlarges the opening of the birth canal.

Coccygeal Plexus

The **coccygeal** (kok-SIJ-ee-al) **plexus** is a very small plexus formed from the ventral rami of spinal nerve S5 and the coccygeal nerve (Co). This small plexus supplies motor innervation to the muscles of the pelvic floor and sensory cutaneous innervation to the skin over the coccyx. The dorsal rami of the coccygeal nerves innervate some skin over the coccyx.

ASSESS YOUR PROGRESS

19. *Name the structures innervated by the cervical plexus. Describe the makeup of the phrenic nerve.*
20. *Name the five major nerves that emerge from the brachial plexus. List the muscles they innervate and the areas of skin they supply.*
21. *Name the four major nerves that arise from the lumbosacral plexus, and describe the muscles and skin areas they supply.*
22. *What is the name given to the tibial and common fibular nerves that are bound together?*
23. *Describe the structures innervated by the obturator and femoral nerves.*
24. *What structures are innervated by the coccygeal plexus?*

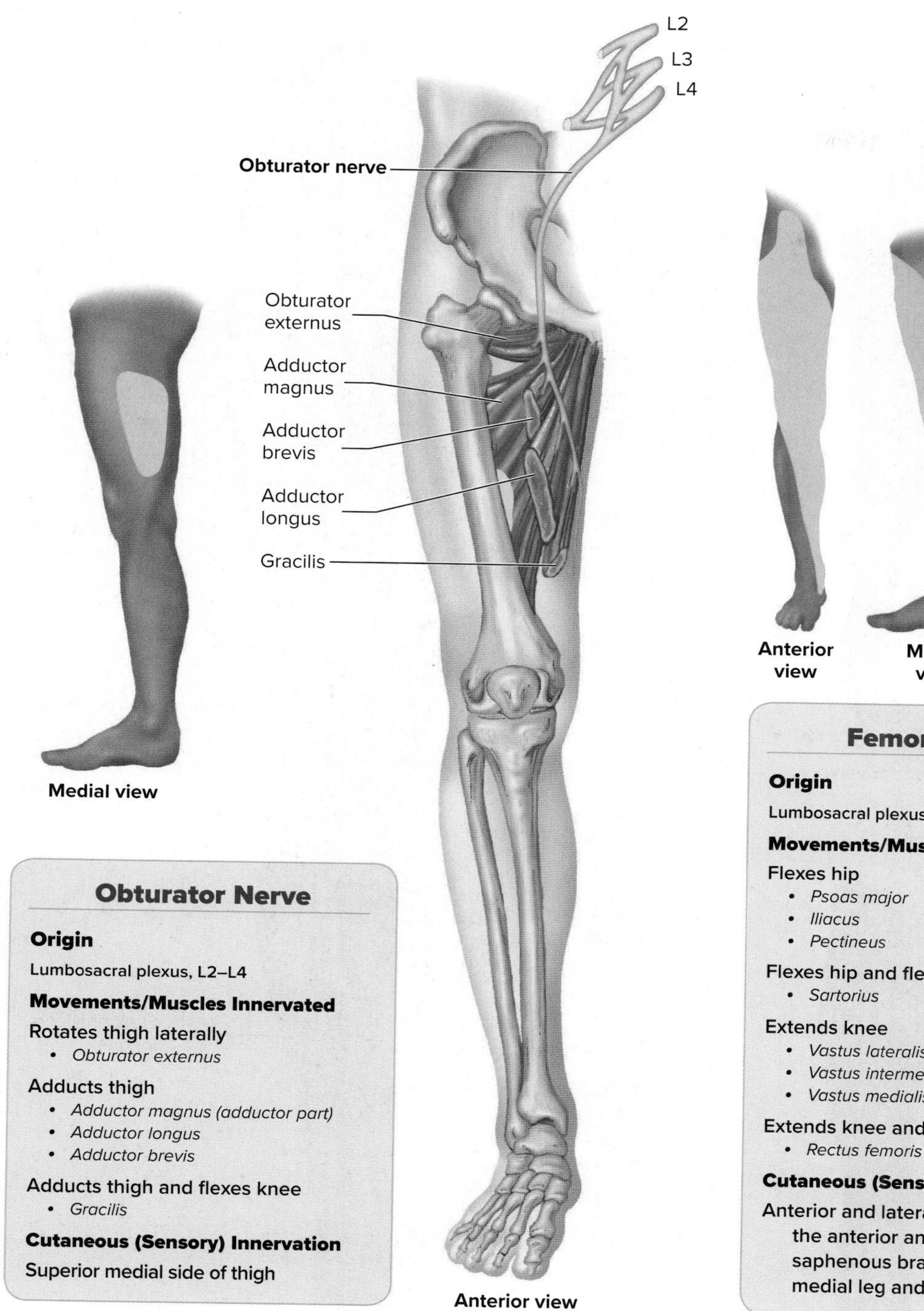

FIGURE 12.25 Obturator Nerve
The route of the obturator nerve and the muscles it innervates. The *inset* depicts the cutaneous (sensory) distribution of the nerve (*blue area*).

L2
L3
L4
Psoas major
Iliacus
Femoral nerve
Sartorius
Pectineus
Vastus lateralis
Rectus femoris
Vastus intermedius
Vastus medialis
Anterior view
Medial view
Anterior view

Femoral Nerve

Origin

Lumbosacral plexus, L2–L4

Movements/Muscles Innervated

Flexes hip
- *Psoas major*
- *Iliacus*
- *Pectineus*

Flexes hip and flexes knee
- *Sartorius*

Extends knee
- *Vastus lateralis*
- *Vastus intermedius*
- *Vastus medialis*

Extends knee and flexes hip
- *Rectus femoris*

Cutaneous (Sensory) Innervation

Anterior and lateral branches supply the anterior and lateral thigh; saphenous branch supplies the medial leg and foot

FIGURE 12.26 Femoral Nerve
The route of the femoral nerve and the muscles it innervates. The *insets* depict the cutaneous (sensory) distribution of the nerve (*blue areas*).

Tibial Nerve

Origin

Lumbosacral plexus, L4–S3

Movements/Muscles Innervated

Extends hip and flexes knee
- *Biceps femoris (long head)*
- *Semitendinosus*
- *Semimembranosus*

Extends hip and adducts thigh
- *Adductor magnus (hamstring part)*

Plantar flexes foot
- *Plantaris*
- *Gastrocnemius*
- *Soleus*
- *Tibialis posterior*

Flexes knee
- *Popliteus*

Flexes toes
- *Flexor digitorum longus*
- *Flexor hallucis longus*

Cutaneous (Sensory) Innervation

None

Medial and Lateral Plantar Nerves

Origin

Tibial nerve

Movements/Muscles Innervated

Flex and adduct toes
- *Plantar muscles of foot*

Cutaneous (Sensory) Innervation

Sole of foot

Sural Nerve (Not Shown)

Origin

Tibial nerve

Movements/Muscles Innervated

None

Cutaneous (Sensory) Innervation

Lateral and posterior one-third of leg and lateral side of foot

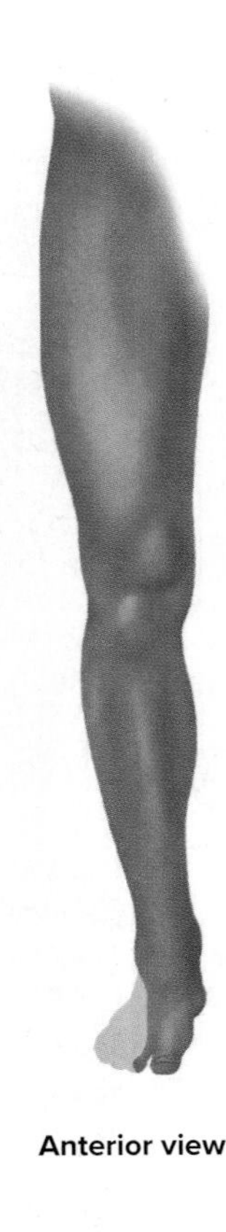

Anterior view

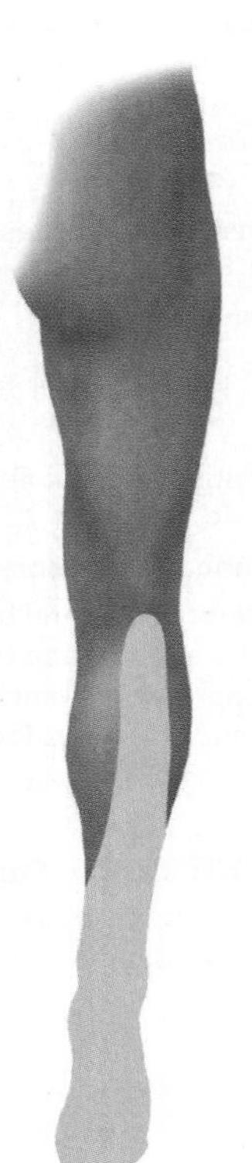

Posterior view

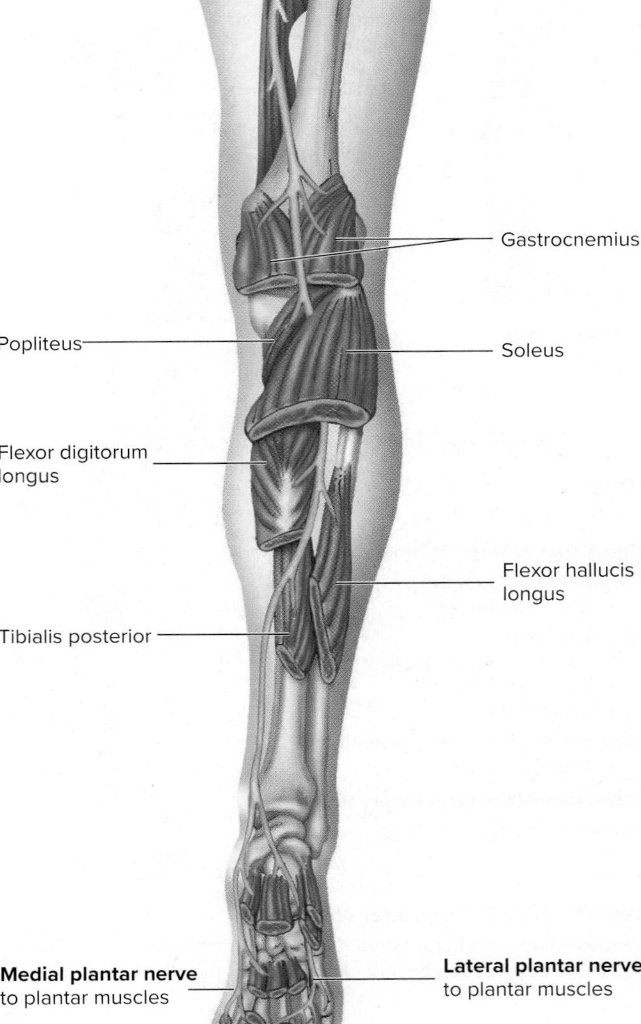

Posterior view

FIGURE 12.27 Tibial Nerve

The route of the tibial nerve and the muscles it innervates. The *insets* depict the cutaneous (sensory) distribution of the nerve (*blue areas*).

Common Fibular (Peroneal) Nerve

Origin

Lumbosacral plexus, L4–S2

Movements/Muscles Innervated

Extends hip and flexes knee

- *Biceps femoris (short head)*

Cutaneous (Sensory) Innervation

Lateral surface of knee

Deep Fibular (Peroneal) Nerve

Origin

Common fibular (peroneal) nerve

Movements/Muscles Innervated

Dorsiflexes foot

- *Tibialis anterior*
- *Fibularis tertius*

Extends toes

- *Extensor digitorum longus*
- *Extensor hallucis longus*
- *Extensor digitorum brevis*

Cutaneous (Sensory) Innervation

Great and second toes

Superficial Fibular (Peroneal) Nerve

Origin

Common fibular (peroneal) nerve

Movements/Muscles Innervated

Plantar flexes and everts foot

- *Fibularis longus*
- *Fibularis brevis*

Cutaneous (Sensory) Innervation

Dorsal anterior third of leg and dorsum of foot

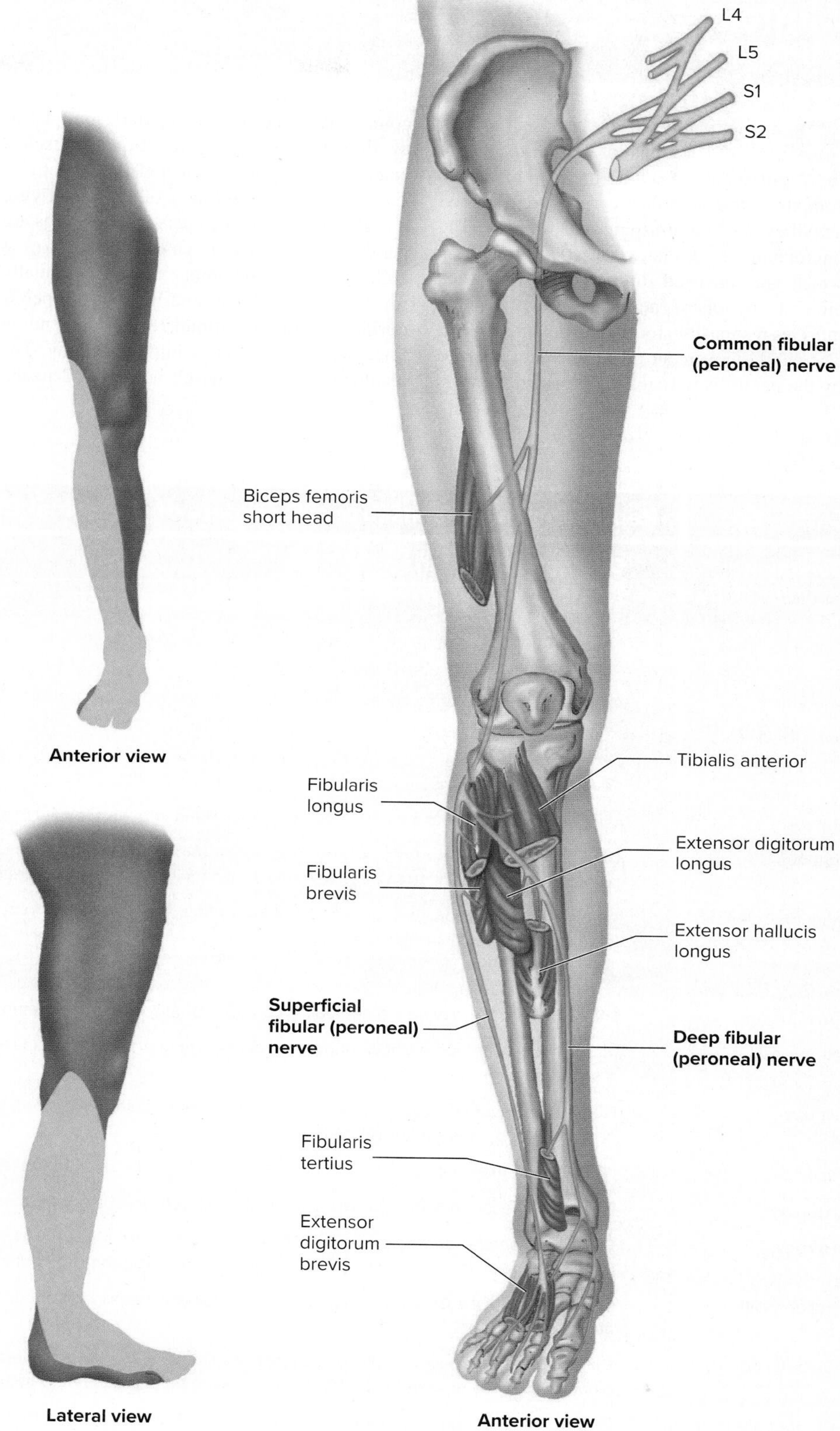

FIGURE 12.28 Fibular Nerve

The route of the common fibular (peroneal) nerve and the muscles it innervates. The *insets* depict the cutaneous (sensory) distribution of the nerve (*blue areas*).

Clinical IMPACT 12.4 Bionic Sensors

Patients paralyzed by strokes or spinal cord lesions are able to regain some functions with the help of microcomputers that stimulate certain programmed activities, such as grasping and walking. The microcomputer initiates electrical impulses, which are conveyed through fine wire leads either to peripheral nerves or directly to the muscles responsible for the desired movement. The subtle movement of muscles not affected by the paralysis initiates the program. Sensors connected to the microcomputer are attached to the skin overlying functional muscles, where they are able to detect electrical activity associated with movement of the underlying muscles. For example, a person whose legs are paralyzed may have a sensor attached to the abdomen. The abdominal muscles normally involved in stabilizing and moving the pelvis during walking are stimulated by descending tracts when CNS centers initiate walking. The resultant abdominal muscle activity is detected by the sensor, which activates the program that stimulates the appropriate sequence of muscles in the lower limbs, and the paralyzed person walks. Similarly, a quadriplegic using subtle movements of the shoulder, neck, or face, where specific sensors can be placed, can initiate certain upper limb and grasping actions. Recent advances are now even allowing sensory feedback, so that a person can "feel" pressure and heat from an object being held by a bionic hand.

TABLE 12.1 Representative Diseases and Disorders of the Spinal Cord and Spinal Nerves

Condition	Description
SPINAL CORD DISORDERS	
Spinal stenosis	Narrowing of spinal canal or area around nerve roots; leads to compression of nerves; usually cervical (neck) or lumbar (lower back); can cause pain, numbness, or weakness
Encephalitis	Inflammation of the brain caused by a virus and less often by bacteria or other agents; symptoms include fever, coma, and convulsions
Meningitis	Inflammation of meninges caused by viral or bacterial infection; symptoms include stiffness in the neck, headache, and fever; severe cases can cause paralysis, coma, or death
Rabies	Viral disease transmitted by an infected animal; brain infection results in abnormal excitability, aggression, paralysis, and death
Tetanus	Caused by bacterial neurotoxin; affects lower motor neurons in spinal cord and brainstem, leading to muscle contraction; prevents muscle relaxation; body becomes rigid, including "lockjaw"; death results from spasms in respiratory muscles
Multiple sclerosis	Autoimmune condition; may be initiated by viral infection; inflammation in brain and spinal cord with demyelination and sclerotic (hard) sheaths results in poor conduction of action potentials; symptoms include exaggerated reflexes, tremor, and speech defects
SPINAL NERVE DISORDERS	
Anesthesia	Loss of sensation; may be a pathological condition or may be induced temporarily to facilitate medical action
Neuritis	Inflammation of a nerve from a number of causes; in motor nerves, can result in loss of motor function; in sensory nerves, can result in anesthesia or neuralgia
Neuralgia	Nerve pain; involves severe spasms of throbbing or stabbing pain along the pathway of a nerve; can result from inflammation, nerve damage, or an unknown cause
Sciatica	Neuralgia of the sciatic nerve, with pain radiating down the back of the leg; most common cause is a herniated lumbar disk
Leprosy	Bacterial disease that kills skin and PNS cells; characterized by disfiguring nodules and tissue necrosis
Herpes	Family of diseases characterized by skin lesions due to herpes viruses in sensory ganglia; different viruses cause oral lesions (cold sores), sexually transmitted disease with lesions on genitalia, or chickenpox in children (shingles in adults)
Poliomyelitis	Viral infection of the CNS, but primarily damages somatic motor neurons, leaving muscles without innervation; leads to paralysis and atrophy
Diabetic neuropathy	Damage to nerves occurs in diabetic patients due to high blood sugar levels and decreased blood flow; occurs in over half of diabetics; symptoms develop slowly, often including pain or numbness in extremities but can be manifested in every organ system
Charcot-Marie-Tooth disease	One of the most common hereditary neurological disorders (named for three neurologists who described it); different forms caused by mutations that generally lead to damage of the myelin sheath; characterized primarily by muscle weakness, dysfunction, atrophy, and loss of sensation primarily in lower extremities
Neurofibromatosis	Genetic disorder; neurofibromas (benign tumors along peripheral nerve tract) occur in early childhood and result in skin growths
Myasthenia gravis	Autoimmune disorder affecting acetylcholine receptors; makes the neuromuscular junction less functional; muscle weakness and increased fatigue lead to paralysis

Concept Check

12.1 Spinal Cord

General Structure

A. The spinal cord gives rise to 31 pairs of spinal nerves. Nerves of the limbs enter and leave the spinal cord at the cervical and lumbosacral enlargements.

B. The spinal cord is shorter than the vertebral column. Nerves from the end of the spinal cord form the cauda equina.

Meninges of the Spinal Cord

Three meningeal layers surround the spinal cord: the dura mater, arachnoid mater, and pia mater.

Cross Section of the Spinal Cord

A. The spinal cord consists of peripheral white matter and central gray matter.

B. White matter is organized into columns, which are subdivided into nerve tracts, or fascicles, which carry action potentials to and from the brain.

C. Gray matter is divided into horns.

- The dorsal horns contain sensory axons that synapse with interneurons. The ventral horns contain the neuron cell bodies of somatic motor neurons, and the lateral horns contain the neuron cell bodies of autonomic motor neurons.
- The gray and white commissures connect each half of the spinal cord.

D. The dorsal root conveys sensory input into the spinal cord, and the ventral root conveys motor output away from the spinal cord.

1. The spinal cord extends from the Remember

a. medulla oblongata to the coccyx.
b. level of the third cervical vertebra to the coccyx.
c. level of the axis to the lowest lumbar vertebra.
d. level of the foramen magnum to the second lumbar vertebra.
e. axis to the sacral hiatus.

2. The structure that anchors the inferior end of the spinal cord to the coccyx is the Remember

a. conus medullaris.
b. cauda equina.
c. filum terminale.
d. lumbar enlargement.
e. posterior median sulcus.

3. Axons of sensory neurons synapse with the cell bodies of interneurons in the ________ of spinal cord gray matter. Remember

a. ventral horn
b. lateral horn
c. dorsal horn
d. gray commissure
e. lateral columns

12.2 Reflexes

A. A reflex arc is the functional unit of the nervous system.

- Sensory receptors respond to stimuli and produce action potentials in sensory neurons.
- Sensory neurons propagate action potentials to the CNS.
- Interneurons in the CNS synapse with sensory neurons and with motor neurons.
- Motor neurons carry action potentials from the CNS to effector organs.
- Effector organs, such as muscles or glands, respond to the action potentials.

B. Reflexes do not require conscious thought, and they produce a consistent and predictable result.

C. Reflexes are homeostatic.

D. Reflexes are integrated within the brain and spinal cord. Higher brain centers can suppress or exaggerate reflexes.

E. Reflexes can be classified by complexity, development, effector, and integration center.

Stretch Reflex

Muscle spindles detect the stretch of skeletal muscles and cause the muscle to shorten reflexively.

Golgi Tendon Reflex

Golgi tendon organs respond to increased tension within tendons and cause skeletal muscles to relax.

Withdrawal Reflex

A. Activation of pain receptors causes muscles to contract and move some part of the body away from a painful stimulus.

B. Reciprocal innervation causes muscles that would oppose withdrawal to relax.

C. In the crossed extensor reflex, flexion of one limb caused by the withdrawal reflex stimulates the opposite limb to extend.

Interactions with Spinal Cord Reflexes

Convergent and divergent pathways interact with reflexes.

4. Given these components of a reflex arc:

(1) effector organ
(2) interneuron
(3) motor neuron
(4) sensory neuron
(5) sensory receptor

Choose the correct order an action potential follows after a sensory receptor is stimulated.

a. 5,4,3,2,1
b. 5,4,2,3,1
c. 5,3,4,1,2
d. 5,2,4,3,1
e. 5,3,2,1,4

5. A reflex response accompanied by the conscious sensation of pain is possible because of Understand

a. convergent pathways.
b. divergent pathways.
c. a reflex arc that contains only one neuron.
d. sensory perception in the spinal cord.

6. Several of the events that occur between the time a physician strikes a patient's patellar tendon with a rubber hammer and the time the quadriceps femoris contracts (knee-jerk reflex) are listed below: Remember

(1) increased frequency of action potentials in sensory neurons
(2) stretch of the muscle spindles
(3) increased frequency of action potentials in the alpha motor neurons
(4) stretch of the quadriceps femoris
(5) contraction of the quadriceps femoris

Which of the following most closely describes the sequence of events as they normally occur?

a. 4,1,2,3,5 *b. 4,1,3,2,5* *c. 1,4,3,2,5* *d. 4,2,1,3,5* *e. 4,2,3,1,5*

7. *________ are responsible for regulating the sensitivity of the muscle spindle.* Remember
   a. Alpha motor neurons
   b. Sensory neurons
   c. Gamma motor neurons
   d. Golgi tendon organs
   e. Inhibitory interneurons

8. *Which of these events occurs when a person steps on a tack with the right foot?* Understand
   a. The right foot is pulled away from the tack because of the Golgi tendon reflex.
   b. The left leg is extended to support the body because of the stretch reflex.
   c. The flexor muscles of the right thigh contract, and the extensor muscles of the right thigh relax because of reciprocal innervation.
   d. Extensor muscles contract in both thighs because of the crossed extensor reflex.

12.3 Spinal Nerves

Structure of Nerves

In the PNS, individual axons are surrounded by the endoneurium. Groups of axons, called fascicles, are bound together by the perineurium. The fascicles form the nerve and are held together by the epineurium.

Organization of Spinal Nerves

A. Eight cervical, 12 thoracic, 5 lumbar, 5 sacral pairs, and 1 coccygeal pair make up the spinal nerves.
B. Spinal nerves have specific cutaneous distributions called dermatomes.
C. Spinal nerves branch to form rami.
   - The dorsal rami supply the muscles and skin near the midline of the back.
   - The ventral rami in the thoracic region form intercostal nerves, which supply the thorax and upper abdomen. The remaining ventral rami join to form plexuses. Communicating rami supply sympathetic nerves.

9. *Damage to the dorsal ramus of a spinal nerve results in*

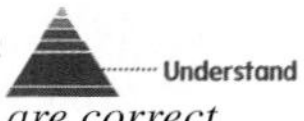

   a. loss of sensation.
   b. loss of motor function.
   c. Both a and b are correct.

10. *A collection of spinal nerves that join together after leaving the spinal cord is called a* Remember
   a. ganglion.
   b. nucleus.
   c. projection nerve.
   d. plexus.

11. *A dermatome*

   a. is the area of skin supplied by a pair of spinal nerves.
   b. exists for each spinal nerve except C1.
   c. can be used to locate the site of spinal cord or nerve root damage.
   d. All of these are correct.

12. *Describe how stimulation of a neuron that has its cell body in the cerebrum can inhibit a reflex that is integrated within the spinal cord.* Understand

Cervical Plexus

Spinal nerves C1–C4 form the cervical plexus, which supplies some muscles and the skin of the neck and shoulder. The phrenic nerves innervate the diaphragm.

13. *Which of these nerves arises from the cervical plexus?*

   a. median
   b. musculocutaneous
   c. phrenic
   d. obturator
   e. ulnar

14. *A cancer patient has his left lung removed. To reduce the space remaining where the lung is removed, the diaphragm on the left side is paralyzed to allow the abdominal viscera to push the diaphragm upward. What nerve is cut? Where is a good place to cut it, and when would the surgery be done?* Apply

Brachial Plexus

A. Spinal nerves C5–T1 form the brachial plexus, which supplies the upper limb.
B. The axillary nerve innervates the deltoid and teres minor muscles and the skin of the shoulder.
C. The radial nerve supplies the extensor muscles of the arm and forearm and the skin of the posterior surface of the arm, forearm, and hand.
D. The musculocutaneous nerve supplies the anterior arm muscles and the skin of the lateral surface of the forearm.
E. The ulnar nerve innervates most of the intrinsic hand muscles and the skin on the ulnar side of the hand.
F. The median nerve innervates the pronator and most of the flexor muscles of the forearm, most of the thenar muscles, and the skin of the radial side of the palm of the hand.
G. Other nerves supply most of the muscles that act on the arm, the scapula, and the skin of the medial arm and forearm.

15. *The skin on the posterior surface of the hand is supplied by the* Remember
   a. median nerve.
   b. musculocutaneous nerve.
   c. ulnar nerve.
   d. axillary nerve.
   e. radial nerve.

16. *During a difficult delivery, the baby's arm delivered first. The attending physician grasped the arm and forcefully pulled it. Later, a nurse observed that the baby could not abduct or adduct the medial four fingers, and flexion of the wrist was impaired. What nerve was damaged?* Apply

Lumbar and Sacral Plexuses

A. Spinal nerves L1–S4 form the lumbosacral plexus.
B. The obturator nerve supplies the muscles that adduct the thigh and the skin of the medial thigh.
C. The femoral nerve supplies the muscles that flex the thigh and extend the leg and the skin of the anterior and lateral thigh and the medial leg and foot.
D. The tibial nerve innervates the muscles that extend the thigh and flex the leg and the foot. It also supplies the plantar muscles and the skin of the posterior leg and the sole of the foot.
E. The common fibular nerve and its branches supply the short head of the biceps femoris, the muscles that dorsiflex and plantar flex the foot, and the skin of the lateral and anterior leg and the dorsum of the foot.

F. In the thigh, the tibial nerve and the common fibular nerve are combined as the sciatic nerve.

G. Other lumbosacral nerves supply the lower abdominal muscles, the hip muscles, and the skin of the suprapubic area, external genitalia, and upper medial thigh.

17. *The sciatic nerve is actually two nerves combined within the same sheath. The two nerves are the* Remember

    a. femoral and obturator.
    b. femoral and gluteal.
    c. common fibular (peroneal) and tibial.
    d. common fibular (peroneal) and obturator.
    e. tibial and gluteal.

18. *The muscles of the anterior compartment of the thigh are supplied by the* Remember

    a. obturator nerve.
    b. gluteal nerve.
    c. sciatic nerve.
    d. femoral nerve.
    e. ilioinguinal nerve.

19. *Two patients are admitted to the hospital. According to their charts, both have herniated disks that are placing pressure on the roots of the sciatic nerve. One patient has pain in the buttocks and the posterior aspect of the thigh. The other patient experiences pain in the posterior and lateral aspects of the leg and the lateral part of the ankle and foot. Explain how the same condition, a herniated disk, can produce such different symptoms.* Apply

20. *In an automobile accident, a woman suffers a crushing hip injury. For each of the following conditions, state what nerve is damaged.* Apply

    a. unable to adduct the thigh
    b. unable to extend the knee
    c. unable to flex the knee
    d. loss of sensation from the skin of the anterior thigh
    e. loss of sensation from the skin of the medial thigh

21. *A skier breaks his ankle. As part of his treatment, the ankle and leg are placed in a plaster cast. Unfortunately, the cast is too tight around the proximal portion of the leg and presses in against the neck of the fibula. Predict where the patient will experience tingling or numbness in the leg. Explain.* Apply

22. *Cecil's motorcycle collided with a tree. When the ambulance arrived, he complained of loss of sensation and voluntary movement in his lower limbs, as well as impaired mobility in his upper limbs, especially his hands. Examination revealed that the accident had permanently damaged his spinal cord. Cecil was able to breathe on his own and, with exercise, movement of his upper limbs eventually improved, although the mobility of his hands was still impaired, and he never regained the use of his lower limbs. At which level was Cecil's spinal cord injured? Explain how you were able to determine your answer.* Apply

Coccygeal Plexus

Spinal nerve S5 and the coccygeal nerve form the coccygeal plexus, which supplies the muscles of the pelvic floor and the skin over the coccyx.

Answers to this chapter's odd-numbered Concept Check questions appear in Appendix F.

Brain and Cranial Nerves

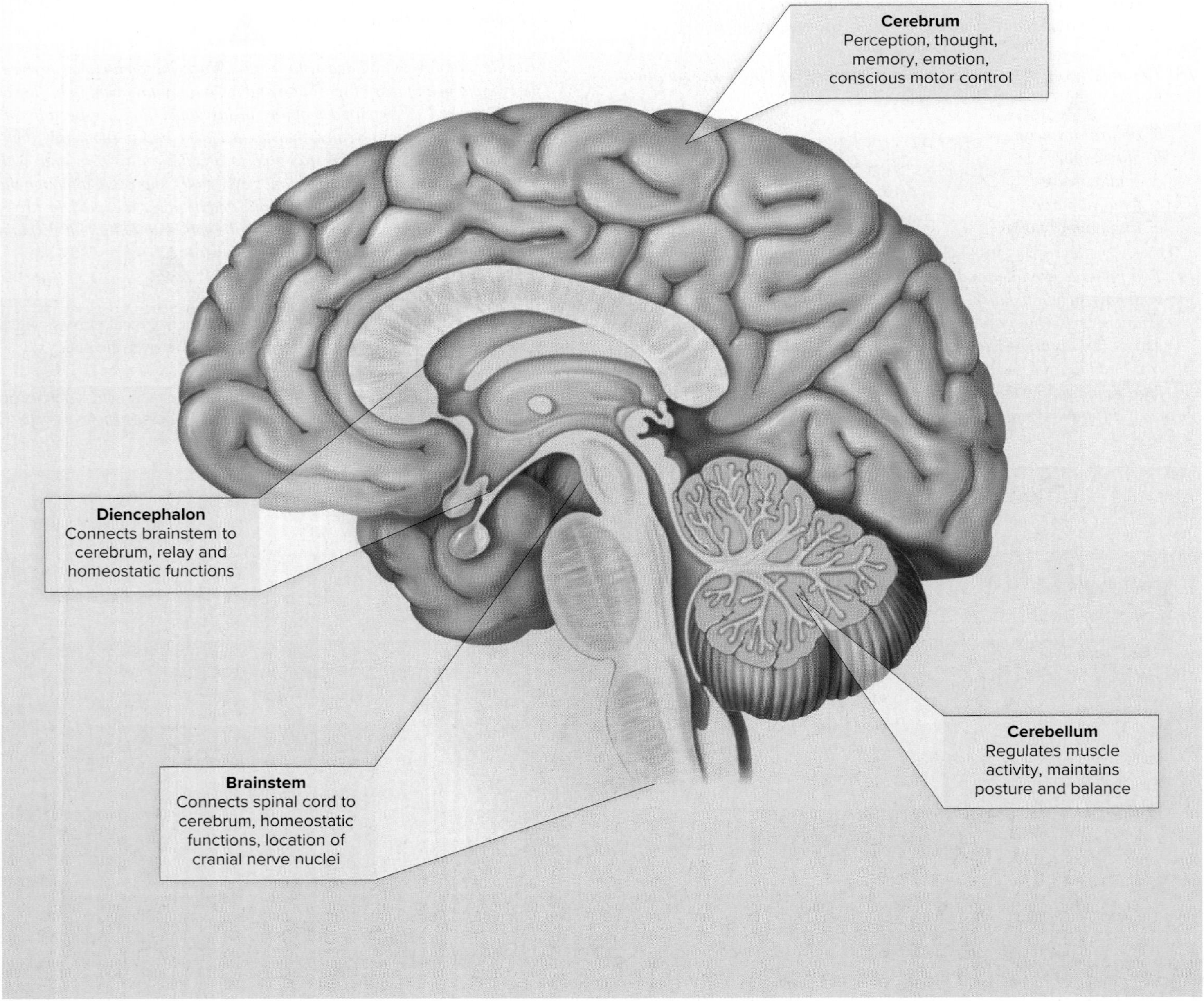

Cerebrum
Perception, thought, memory, emotion, conscious motor control

Diencephalon
Connects brainstem to cerebrum, relay and homeostatic functions

Cerebellum
Regulates muscle activity, maintains posture and balance

Brainstem
Connects spinal cord to cerebrum, homeostatic functions, location of cranial nerve nuclei

The brain, part of the CNS, is composed of four major divisions: brainstem, cerebellum, diencephalon, and cerebrum.

The complexity of the human brain is mind-boggling. It contains around 100 billion neurons and another trillion glial cells. Even more amazing is that each neuron has an average of 10,000 connections with other neurons. From that complexity arises the command and control of our bodies. A common myth is that we use only 10% of our brain and that if we could somehow tap into the remainder, imagine how smart we could be! However, there is absolutely no truth to the 10% myth for many reasons. For example, imaging studies clearly demonstrate that we use nearly every part of the brain. This chapter describes the structure of the brain, its functional units, and its associated cranial nerves. Representative disorders of the brain and cranial nerves are listed at the end of the chapter (see table 13.6). The integration of brain functions is discussed in chapter 14.

Learn to Predict

After mastering the mechanical bull at a local amusement park, Marvin decided he was ready to compete in an amateur rodeo. But during the very first event, a live bull threw Marvin to the dirt and kicked him in the side of the face. Clinicians in the emergency room diagnosed a broken jaw, and they noted that Marvin's tongue deviated to the right when they asked him to stick it out. A magnetic resonance imaging (MRI) scan was performed to detect the presence of brain or cranial nerve damage.

By recalling your knowledge of nervous system organization from chapter 11 and combining it with new information about the cranial nerves in this chapter, explain the results of Marvin's tongue protrusion test.

Answers to this question and the chapter's odd-numbered Predict questions can be found in Appendix E.

13.1 Development of the Brain

LEARNING OUTCOMES

After reading this section, you should be able to

A. **Describe the development of the neural tube.**
B. **Name the embryonic pouches and the adult brain structures that they become.**
C. **Explain the origin of the ventricles of the brain.**

The brain is the part of the central nervous system (CNS) that is contained within the cranial cavity (figure 13.1). The four divisions of the brain are the (1) brainstem, (2) cerebellum, (3) diencephalon, and (4) cerebrum (table 13.1). We begin our study of the brain by examining how the CNS develops in the fetus.

Figure 13.2 illustrates the formation of the neural tube, which gives rise to the CNS.

1. A flat plate of ectodermal tissue (see chapter 4) called the **neural plate** is located on the dorsal surface of the embryo. Just ventral to the neural plate is the **notochord,** a rod-shaped tissue that defines the axis of the embryo and eventually gives rise to the central region of the intervertebral disks.
2. The lateral sides of the neural plate become elevated as waves, forming **neural folds.**
3. The crest of each fold is called a **neural crest,** and the center of the neural plate becomes the neural groove. **Neural crest cells** migrate away from the neural crests to give rise to all the sensory, autonomic, and enteric neurons of the peripheral nervous system. They also give rise to all the pigmented cells of the body, the adrenal medulla, the facial bones, and the dentin of the teeth.
4. The neural folds move toward each other in the midline and fuse to create a **neural tube,** which gives rise to the CNS. The cephalic portion of the neural tube becomes the brain, and the caudal portion becomes the spinal cord.

A series of pouches develops in the anterior part of the neural tube, forming three brain regions in the early embryo (figure 13.3*a*): (1) a **forebrain,** or *prosencephalon* (pros-en-SEF-ah-lon); (2) a **midbrain,** or *mesencephalon* (mez-en-SEF-ah-lon); and (3) a **hindbrain,** or *rhombencephalon* (rom-ben-SEF-ah-lon). The forebrain divides into the **telencephalon** (tel-en-SEF-ah-lon), which becomes the cerebrum, and the **diencephalon** (die-en-SEF-a-lon). The midbrain remains a single structure as in the embryo. The hindbrain divides into the **metencephalon** (MET-en-SEF-ah-lon), which becomes the pons and cerebellum, and the **myelencephalon** (MY-el-en-SEF-ah-lon), which becomes the medulla oblongata (figure 13.3*b,c*). Table 13.2 summarizes the development of the CNS.

Module 7
Nervous System

FUNDAMENTAL **Figure**

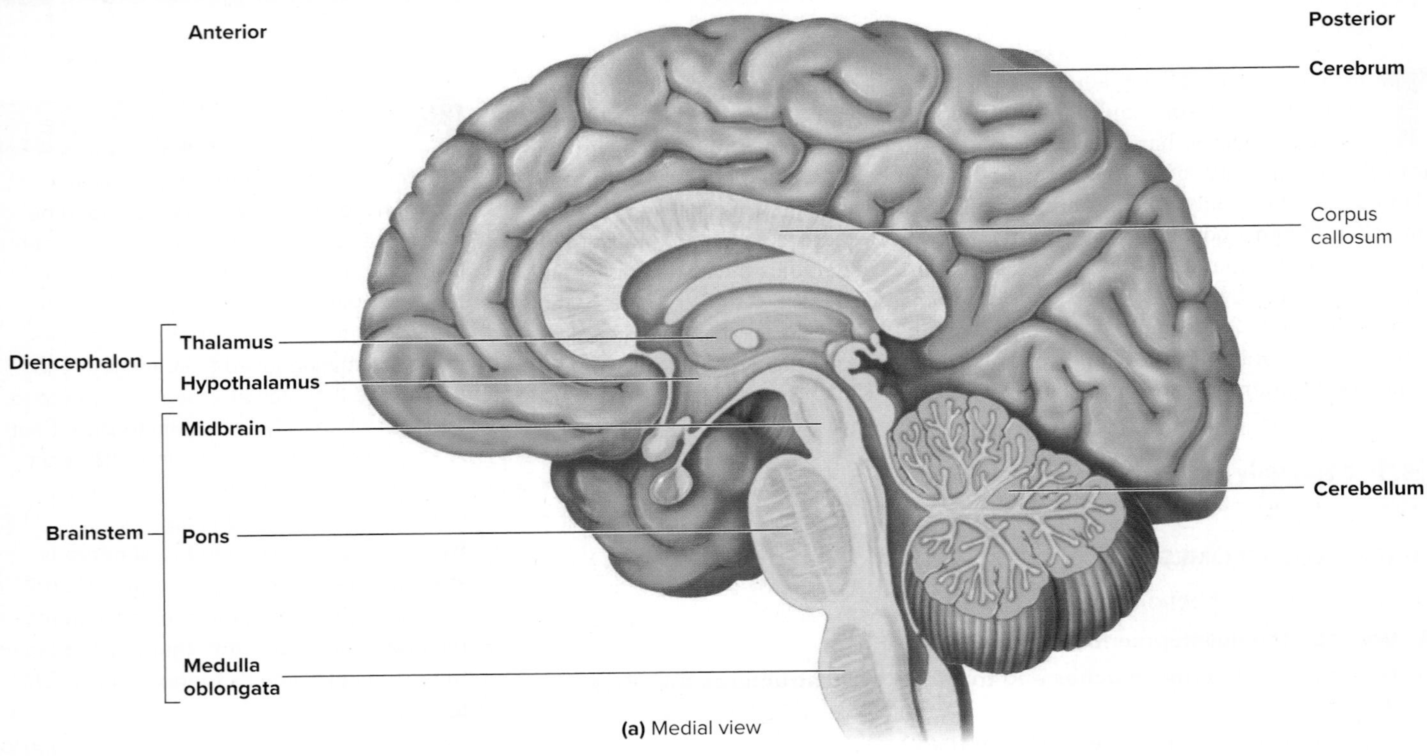

(a) Medial view

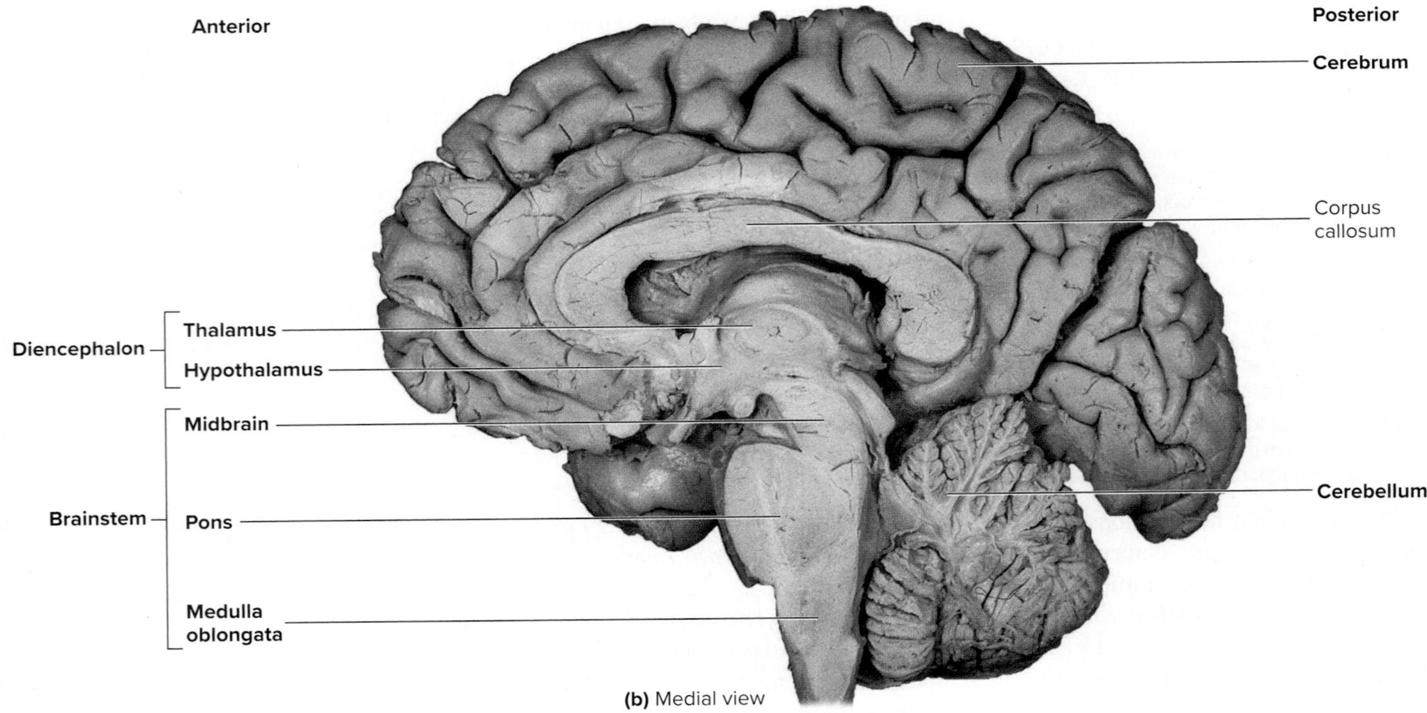

(b) Medial view

FIGURE 13.1 Regions of the Brain

(*a*) Medial view of a midsaggital section of the right half of the brain. (*b*) Photograph of medial view of a midsaggital section of the right half of the brain.

(b) Rebecca Gray/Dennis Strete/McGraw Hill APR

TABLE 13.1 Divisions of the Brain and Their Functions

Division	Functions
Brainstem 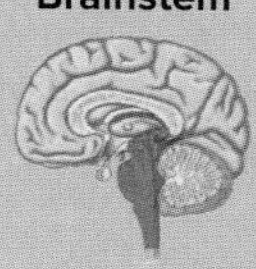	Connects the spinal cord to the cerebrum; consists of the medulla oblongata, pons, and midbrain, with the reticular formation scattered throughout the three regions; has many important functions, as listed under each subdivision; is the location of cranial nerve nuclei
Medulla oblongata 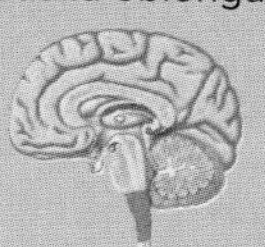	Pathway for ascending and descending nerve tracts; center for several important reflexes (e.g., heart rate, breathing, swallowing, vomiting)
Pons 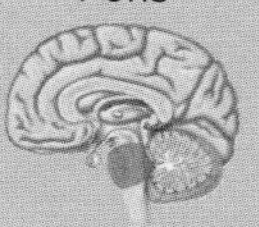	Contains ascending and descending nerve tracts; relays information between cerebrum and cerebellum; site of reflex centers
Midbrain 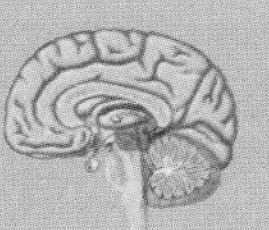	Contains ascending and descending nerve tracts; serves as visual reflex center; part of auditory pathway
Reticular formation	Scattered throughout brainstem; controls many brainstem activities, including motor control, pain perception, rhythmic contractions, and the sleep-wake cycle
Cerebellum 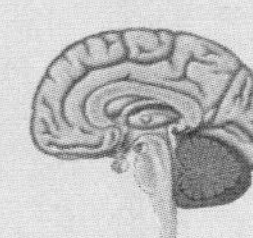	Controls muscle movement and tone; governs balance; regulates extent of intentional movement; involved in learning motor skills
Diencephalon 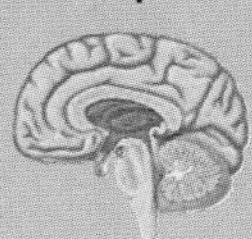	Connects the brainstem to the cerebrum; has many relay and homeostatic functions, as listed under each subdivision
Thalamus	Major sensory relay center; influences mood and movement
Subthalamus	Contains nerve tracts and nuclei
Epithalamus	Contains nuclei involved in motivation and reward behavior, and contains pineal gland
Hypothalamus	Major control center for maintaining homeostasis and regulating endocrine function
Cerebrum 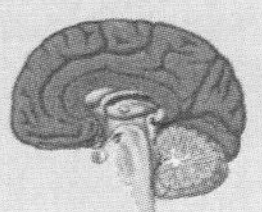	Controls perception, thought, memory, emotion, and conscious motor activity; can override most other systems
Cerebral cortex	Contains sensory, motor, and association areas
Hippocampus	Involved with learning and memory
Amygdala	Involved with social behavior and emotions
Basal nuclei	Controls muscle activity and posture; largely inhibits unintentional movement when at rest

PROCESS Figure

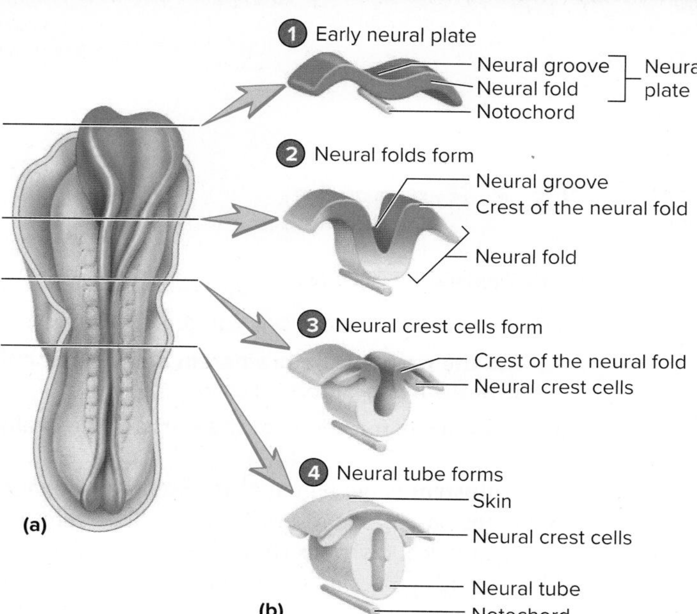

PROCESS Figure 13.2

Formation of the Neural Tube

(*a*) A 21-day-old human embryo (superior view), with cross sections through the embryo shown to the right. (*b*) The level of each transverse section is indicated by a line.

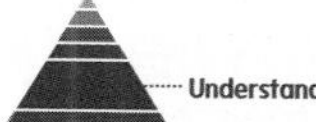

Many birth defects involve abnormalities of craniofacial structures, such as cleft lip and palate. Which portion of the developing CNS is responsible for many craniofacial defects?

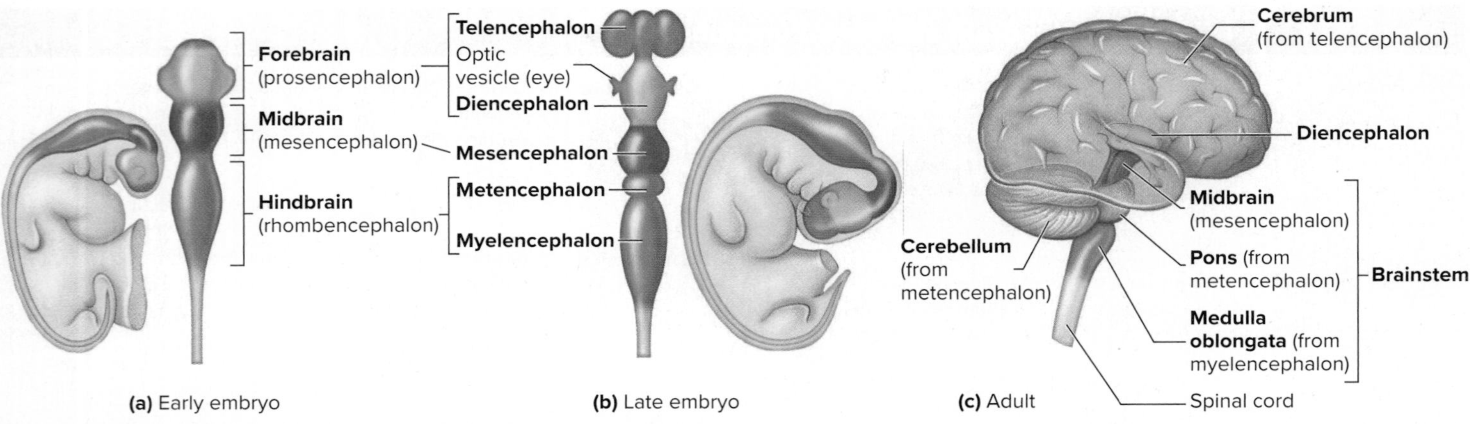

FIGURE 13.3 Development of the Brain Segments and Ventricles
(*a*) and (*b*) The CNS develops from three regions of the early embryonic brain called the forebrain (prosencephalon), midbrain (mesencephalon), and hindbrain (rhom-bencephalon). (*c*) The forebrain gives rise to the adult cerebrum and diencephalon; the midbrain gives rise to the adult midbrain; the hindbrain gives rise to the adult pons, cerebellum, and medulla oblongata.

TABLE 13.2 Development of the Central Nervous System (see figure 13.3)

Early Embryo	Late Embryo	Adult	Cavity	Function
Forebrain (prosencephalon)	**Telencephalon**	**Cerebrum**	Lateral ventricles	Higher brain functions
	Diencephalon	**Diencephalon** (thalamus, subthalamus, epithalamus, hypothalamus)	Third ventricle	Relay center, autonomic nerve control, endocrine control
Midbrain (mesencephalon)	**Midbrain** (mesencephalon)	**Midbrain** (mesencephalon)	Cerebral aqueduct	Nerve pathways, reflex centers
Hindbrain (rhombencephalon)	**Metencephalon**	**Pons** and **cerebellum**	Fourth ventricle	Nerve pathways, reflex centers, muscle coordina-tion, balance
	Myelencephalon	**Medulla oblongata**	Central canal	Nerve pathways, reflex centers

The pouch cavities become fluid-filled **ventricles** (VEN-tri-kulz). The ventricles are continuous with each other and with the **central canal** of the spinal cord. The neural tube develops flexures that cause the brain to be oriented almost 90 degrees to the spinal cord.

ASSESS YOUR PROGRESS

Answers to these questions are found in the section you have just completed. Re-read the section if you need help in answering these questions.

1. *Name the five pouches of the neural tube and the part of the adult brain that each division becomes.*
2. *What do the cavities of the neural tube become in the adult brain?*

13.2 Brainstem

LEARNING OUTCOMES

After reading this section, you should be able to

A. **List the parts of the brainstem and describe their structural characteristics.**
B. **Explain the functions of the parts of the brainstem.**

The **brainstem** is the region of the brain that connects the spinal cord to the base of the rest of the brain. The brainstem consists of three anatomical divisions (from inferior to superior): (1) medulla oblongata, (2) pons, and (3) midbrain (figure 13.4). In addition to these anatomical divisions, the reticular formation is a functional

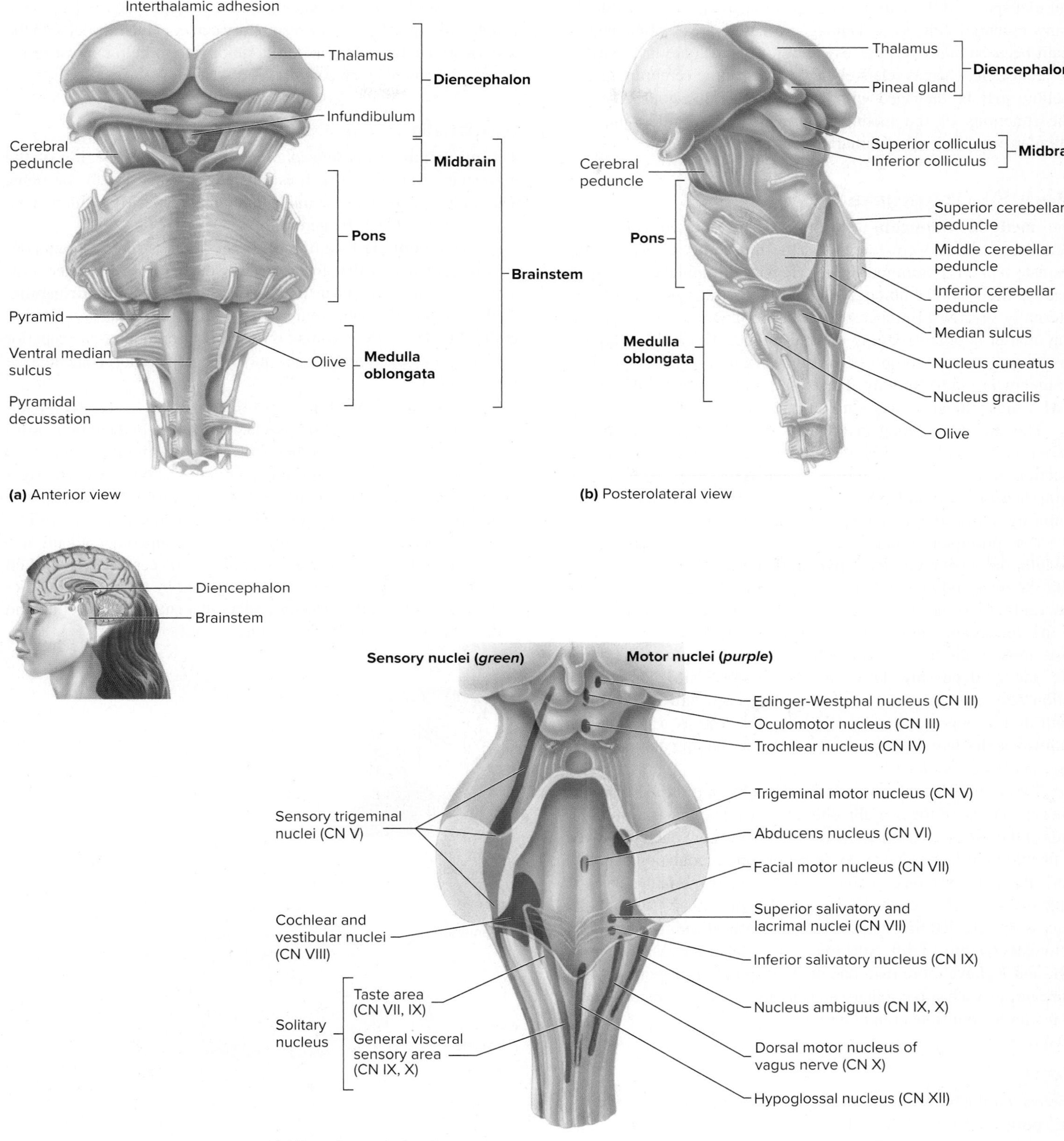

FIGURE 13.4 Diencephalon and Brainstem

(*a*) Anterior view. (*b*) Posterolateral view. The inset shows the location of the diencephalon (*red*) and the brainstem (*blue*). (*c*) Brainstem nuclei. The sensory nuclei are shown on the left (*green*). The motor nuclei are shown on the right (*purple*). Even though the nuclei are shown on only one side, each half of the brainstem has both sensory and motor nuclei. The cranial nerves will be discussed later in this chapter. (CN = cranial nerve) APR

unit that spans all three divisions. The brainstem is responsible for many essential functions. Damage to small areas often causes death because many reflexes essential for survival are integrated in the brainstem, whereas relatively large areas of the cerebrum or cerebellum may be damaged without life-threatening consequences. The functions of the medulla oblongata, pons, midbrain, and reticular formation are summarized in table 13.1.

Medulla Oblongata

The **medulla oblongata** (ob-lon-GAH-tah), often called the medulla, is about 3 cm long. It is the most inferior part of the brainstem and is continuous inferiorly with the spinal cord. Superficially, the medulla oblongata blends into the spinal cord, but internally several differences exist. In the medulla oblongata, the gray matter is organized into discrete **nuclei** (figure 13.4*b*), clusters of gray matter composed mostly of neuron cell bodies. This arrangement contrasts with that of the gray matter of the spinal cord, which extends as a continuous mass in the center of the cord.

The medulla oblongata contains sensory and motor tracts, cranial nerve nuclei, and related nuclei. Several medullary nuclei function as centers for vital reflexes, such as those involved in regulating heart rate, blood vessel diameter, respiration, swallowing, vomiting, hiccuping, coughing, and sneezing.

Two prominent enlargements on the anterior surface of the medulla oblongata are called **pyramids** because they are broader near the pons and taper toward the spinal cord (figure 13.4*a*). The pyramids are formed by the large descending motor tracts involved in the conscious control of skeletal muscles. Near their inferior ends, most of the fibers of the descending tracts cross to the opposite side, or **decussate** (DEE-ku-sate, dee-KUS-ate). This decussation accounts, in part, for the fact that each half of the brain controls the opposite half of the body. Its role as a conduction pathway is discussed in the description of ascending and descending tracts (see chapter 14).

Two rounded, oval structures, called **olives,** protrude from the anterior surface of the medulla oblongata just lateral to the superior ends of the pyramids (figure 13.4*a,b*). The olives are nuclei involved in functions such as balance, coordination, and modulation of sound from the inner ear (see chapter 15). Nuclei of cranial nerves V (trigeminal), VII (facial), IX (glossopharyngeal), X (vagus), XI (accessory), and XII (hypoglossal) are also located within the medulla oblongata (figure 13.4*c*). Note that some cranial nerves, such as V, VII, and X, have more than one nucleus in the brainstem and that some nuclei, such as the solitary nucleus and nucleus ambiguus, serve as nuclei for multiple cranial nerves.

Pons

The part of the brainstem just superior to the medulla oblongata is the **pons** (figure 13.4*a*). The pons contains ascending and descending tracts and several nuclei. The pontine nuclei, located in the anterior portion of the pons, relay information from the cerebrum to the cerebellum.

The posterior region of the pons contains nuclei for cranial nerves V (trigeminal), VI (abducens), VII (facial), and VIII (vestibulocochlear). Other important pontine areas are the pontine sleep center, which initiates rapid eye movement sleep (see chapter 14), and the pontine respiratory center, which works with the respiratory centers in the medulla oblongata to help control respiratory movements (see chapter 23).

Midbrain

The **midbrain,** or *mesencephalon,* is the smallest region of the brainstem (figure 13.4*b*). It is located just superior to the pons. The midbrain contains the nuclei of cranial nerves III (oculomotor), IV (trochlear), and V (trigeminal).

The **tectum** (TEK-tum; roof; figure 13.5) of the midbrain consists of four nuclei that form mounds on the dorsal surface, collectively called **corpora** (KOR-pohr-ah; bodies) **quadrigemina** (KWAH-dri-JEM-i-nah; four twins). Each mound is called a **colliculus** (koh-LIK-yoo-lus); the two superior mounds are superior colliculi, and the two inferior mounds are inferior colliculi (see figure 13.4*b*).

The **superior colliculi** receive sensory input from visual, auditory, and tactile sensory systems and are involved in the reflex movements of the head, eyes, and body toward these stimuli, such as loud noises, flashing lights, or startling pain. For example, when a bright object suddenly appears in our field of vision, we reflexively turn to focus on it. Similarly, when we hear a sudden, loud noise, we reflexively turn our head and eyes toward it. The superior colliculi also receive input from the inferior colliculi and the cerebrum. Based on your understanding of the reflexes integrated by the superior colliculi, explain why your instructor prefers that students not get up and walk out of the room during a lecture.

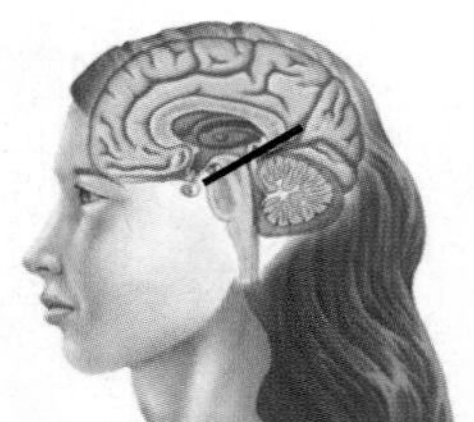

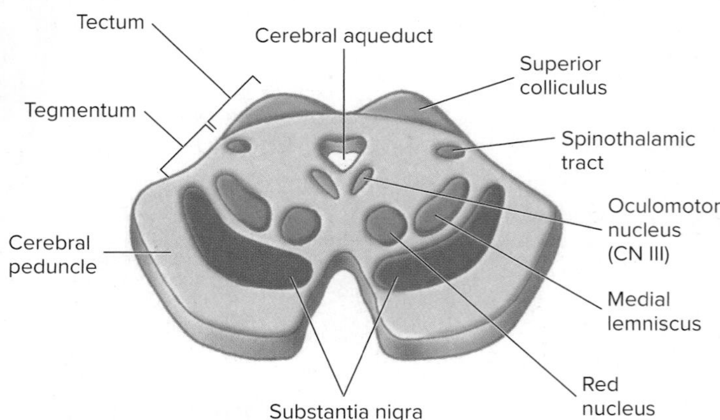

FIGURE 13.5 Midbrain
An anterosuperior view of an oblique section shows the superior colliculi and tegmentum structures. Inset shows the level of section.

The **inferior colliculi** are involved in hearing and are an integral part of the auditory pathways in the CNS. Neurons conducting action potentials from the structures of the inner ear (see chapter 15) to the brain synapse in the inferior colliculi. Collateral fibers from the inferior colliculi to the superior colliculi provide auditory input that stimulates visual reflexes.

The **tegmentum** (teg-MEN-tum) of the midbrain largely consists of ascending tracts, such as the spinothalamic tract and the medial lemniscus, that carry sensory information from the spinal cord to the brain. The tegmentum also contains the red nuclei, the cerebral peduncles, and the substantia nigra. The paired **red nuclei** (figure 13.5) are so named because in fresh brain specimens they are pinkish in color as a result of an abundant blood supply. The red nuclei aid in the unconscious regulation and coordination of motor activities. **Cerebral peduncles** (pe-DUNG-kulz; the foot of a column) constitute the portion of the midbrain ventral to the tegmentum. They consist primarily of descending tracts, which carry motor information from the cerebrum to the brainstem and spinal cord. The **substantia nigra** (sub-STAN-shee-ah NYE-grah; black substance) is a nuclear mass between the tegmentum and cerebral peduncles containing cytoplasmic melanin granules that give it a dark gray or black color (figure 13.5). The substantia nigra is interconnected with other basal nuclei of the cerebrum, described in section 13.5, and it is involved in maintaining muscle tone and coordinating movements. See Clinical Impact 14.3 to learn about the relationship between the substania nigra and Parkinson disease.

Reticular Formation

The **reticular formation** is a diffuse, but interconnected, system of loosely packed nuclei scattered throughout the brainstem. Reticular formation neurons play roles in arousal and awareness. The reticular formation receives axons from a large number of sources and especially from nerves that innervate the face. The reticular formation modulates and controls many functions mediated by the brainstem, only a few of which are listed here. Some reticular formation neurons send axons to the spinal cord in a motor tract that controls posture, whereas others send axons that reduce the transmission of pain signals from the spinal cord (see chapter 14). By modulating the activity of cranial nuclei within the brainstem, the reticular formation coordinates the rhythmic activities of swallowing, breathing, and the heart rate. Finally, the reticular formation controls the state of alertness and consciousness, including the sleep-wake cycle (see chapter 14).

Predict 1

Willy was driving his car too fast on his way to school, when the car left the road and hit a guard rail. Elizabeth saw the accident and called 911 on her cell phone. Willy's injuries resulted in extensive blood loss and, while waiting for Life Flight, his heart rate became rapid and his blood pressure fell to a very low level. Pallor (pale complexion) developed progressively, and his breathing was heavy. Which areas of Willy's brain were most important in integrating these responses?

ASSESS YOUR PROGRESS

3. *What are the major functions of the medulla oblongata? What cranial nerves have nuclei in the medulla oblongata?*
4. *What activities do the pontine nuclei help control? What cranial nerves have nuclei in the pons?*
5. *What are the parts of the midbrain and their functions?*
6. *What is the function of the reticular formation?*

13.3 Cerebellum

LEARNING OUTCOME

After reading this section, you should be able to

A. **List the major regions of the cerebellum and describe the functions of each.**

The **cerebellum** (ser-eh-BELL-um; little brain) is attached to the brainstem posterior to the pons (figure 13.6). The cerebellum has a gray cortex and nuclei, with white medulla in between. (*Medulla* in this case is a general term meaning "center of a structure.") The cerebellar cortex has ridges called **folia.** The white matter of the medulla resembles a branching tree and is called the **arbor vitae** (AR-bohr VIE-tee; tree of life). The **nuclei** of the cerebellum are located in the deep inferior center of the white matter. The functions of the cerebellum are summarized in table 13.1.

The cerebellum consists of three parts: (1) a small, inferior **flocculonodular** (FLOK-yoo-loh-NOD-yoo-lar) **lobe;** (2) a narrow, central **vermis** (worm-shaped); and (3) two large, **lateral hemispheres** (figure 13.6*b*,*c*). The flocculonodular lobe, the simplest part of the cerebellum, helps control balance and eye movements. The vermis and the medial portion of the lateral hemispheres are involved in controlling posture, locomotion, and fine motor coordination, thereby producing smooth, flowing movements. The major portions of the lateral hemispheres of the cerebellum function in concert with the frontal lobes of the cerebral cortex in planning, practicing, and learning complex movements. Each lateral hemisphere is divided by a **primary fissure** into an **anterior lobe** and a **posterior lobe.** The lobes are subdivided into **lobules,** which contain the folia.

Remarkably, the cerebellar cortex contains more neurons than the entire cerebral cortex. These neurons include (1) stellate, (2) basket, (3) granule, (4) Golgi, and (5) Purkinje cells. The cerebellar cortex also contains mossy fibers, which are afferent axons from elsewhere in the brain that branch extensively within the cerebellum. **Purkinje** (per-KIN-jee) cells are the largest cells in the CNS. Each Purkinje cell receives about 200,000 synapses from passing fibers. Purkinje cells are inhibitory neurons and are the only cerebellar cortex neurons that send axons to the cerebellar nuclei.

The cerebellum communicates with other regions of the CNS through three large tracts called cerebellar peduncles (see figure 13.4*b*). The superior, middle, and inferior cerebellar peduncles connect the cerebellum to the midbrain, pons, and medulla oblongata, respectively.

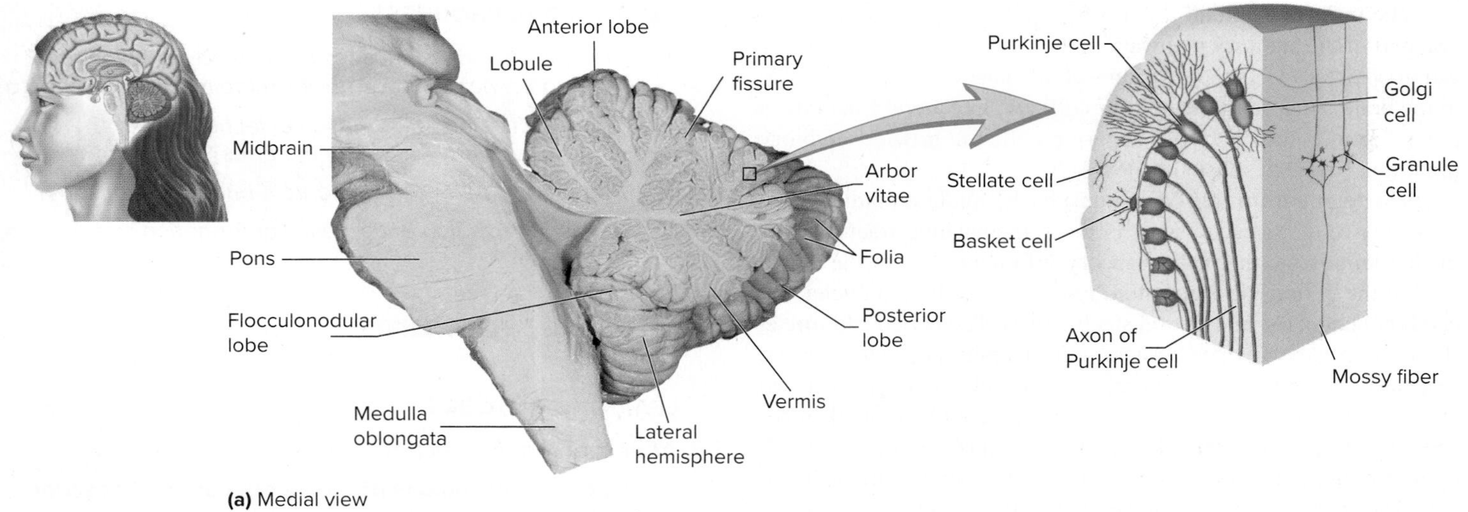

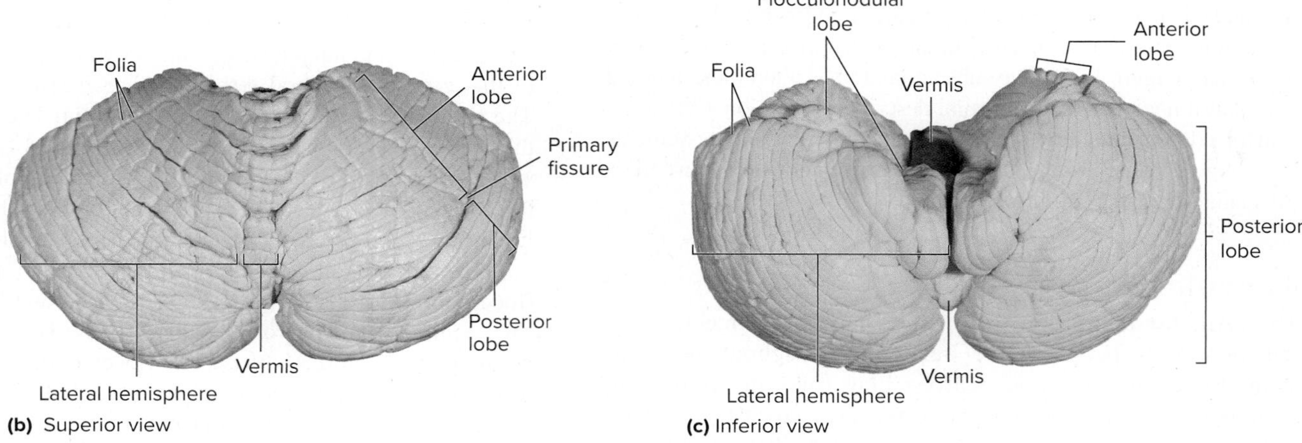

FIGURE 13.6 Cerebellum
(*a*) Right half of the cerebellum and brainstem as seen in a median section. Inset shows the histology of the cerebellum. (*b*) Superior view of the cerebellum. (*c*) Inferior view of the cerebellum. Rebecca Gray/McGraw Hill Education APR

ASSESS YOUR PROGRESS

7. *How are the gray matter and white matter arranged in the cerebellum? What is the arbor vitae?*
8. *What are the major regions of the cerebellum? What are the primary functions of each?*

13.4 Diencephalon

LEARNING OUTCOME

After reading this section, you should be able to

A. **List the parts of the diencephalon and state their functions.**

The **diencephalon** is the part of the brain between the brainstem and the cerebrum (figure 13.7; see figures 13.1 and 13.4). Its main components are the (1) thalamus, (2) subthalamus, (3) epithalamus, and (4) hypothalamus. The functions of each of these regions are summarized in table 13.1.

Thalamus

The **thalamus** (THAL-ah-mus; figure 13.7*a,b*) is by far the largest part of the diencephalon, constituting about four-fifths of its weight. It consists of a cluster of nuclei shaped somewhat like a yo-yo, with two large, lateral portions connected in the center by a small stalk called the **interthalamic adhesion,** or *intermediate mass*. The space surrounding the interthalamic adhesion and separating the two large portions of the thalamus is the third ventricle of the brain.

The thalamus is considered the **sensory relay center** of the brain. With only one exception, all sensory neurons project to the cerebrum first synapse in the thalamus. The exception is the olfactory neurons, which project directly to the cerebral cortex. Thalamic neurons send projections to the appropriate areas of the

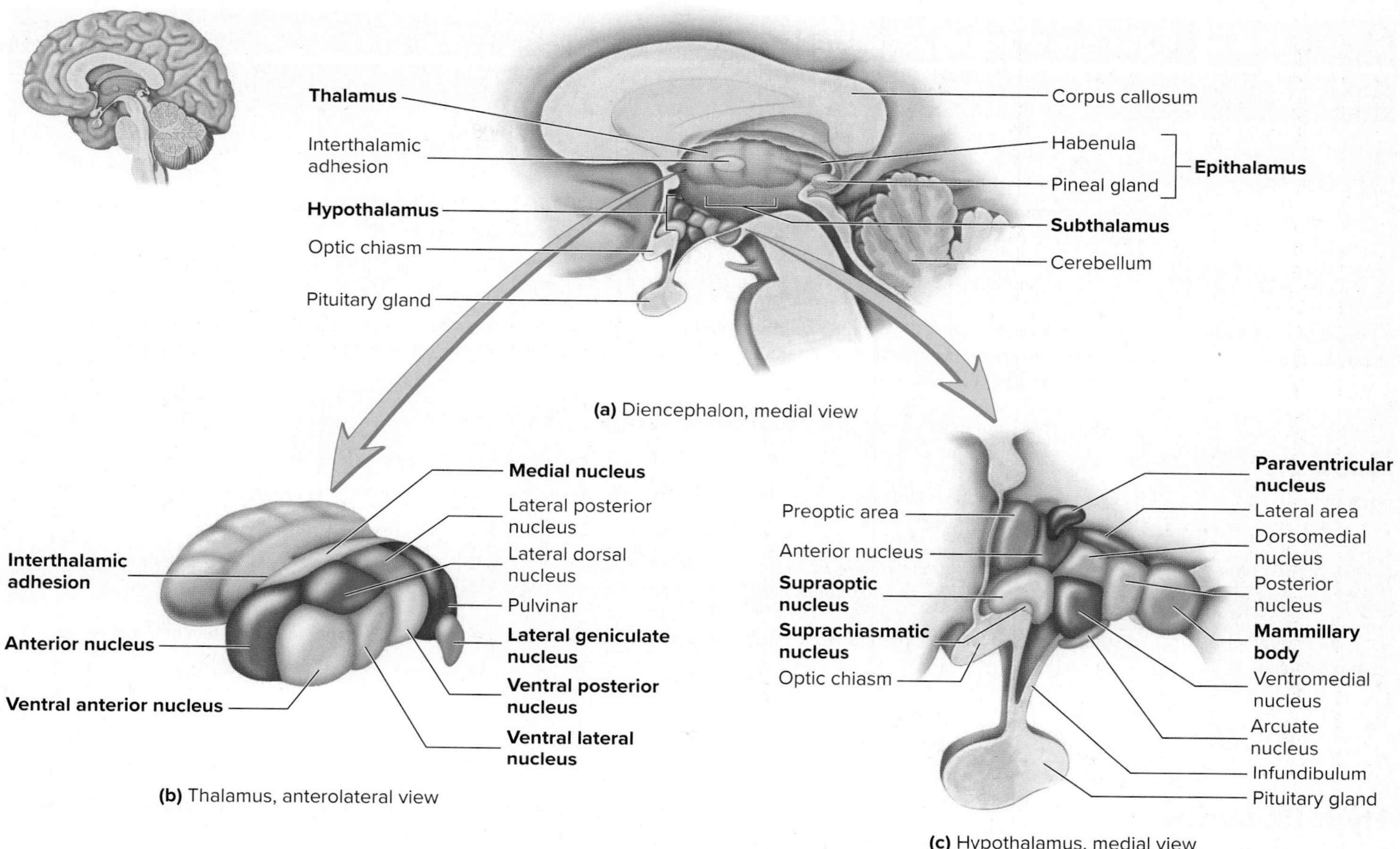

FIGURE 13.7 Diencephalon

(*a*) General overview of the right half of the diencephalon as seen in a median section. (*b*) Thalamus, showing the nuclei of the left half. (*c*) Hypothalamus, showing the nuclei and right half of the pituitary.

cerebral cortex where sensory input is localized (see chapter 14). Axons carrying auditory information synapse in the **medial geniculate** (je-NIK-yoo-late) **nucleus** of the thalamus. Axons carrying visual information synapse in the **lateral geniculate nucleus.** Most other sensory impulses synapse in the **ventral posterior nucleus.** Axons originating in the ventral posterior nucleus project to the dorsal tier of nuclei, which register pain (figure 13.7*b*). Other axons project to the cerebral cortex where sensory input is localized (see chapter 14). The **ventral anterior nucleus** and the **ventral lateral nucleus** are involved with motor functions, communicating among the basal nuclei, the cerebellum, and the motor cortex (areas described later in this chapter).

The thalamus also influences mood and actions associated with strong emotions, such as fear and rage. The **anterior** and **medial nuclei** are connected to the limbic system and to the prefrontal cortex (described later in this chapter and in chapter 14). These nuclei are involved in mood modification. The **lateral dorsal nuclei,** which are connected to other thalamic nuclei and to the cerebral cortex, are involved in regulating emotions. The **lateral posterior nuclei** and the **pulvinar** (pul-VYE-nar) also have connections to other thalamic nuclei and are involved in sensory integration.

Subthalamus

The **subthalamus** is a small area immediately inferior to the thalamus (figure 13.7*a*). It contains the **subthalamic nuclei** and several ascending and descending tracts. The subthalamic nuclei are functionally part of the subcortical basal nuclei (see section 13.5) that are involved in controlling motor functions.

Epithalamus

The **epithalamus** is a small area superior and posterior to the thalamus (figure 13.7*a*). It consists of the habenula and the pineal gland. The **habenula** (ha-BEN-yoo-lah) is involved in motivational control of behavior. It plays an integrative role with the limbic system, basal nuclei, and other brain regions in behaviors that involve rewards and subsequent addictions. The **pineal** (PIN-ee-al) **gland,** or *pineal body,* is shaped somewhat like a pinecone, from which the name *pineal* is derived. Pineal gland functions in humans are not fully understood, but they involve modulation of the sleep-wake cycle and other biorhythms (see chapter 18). Try doing a quick Internet search on treatments for "jet lag." How do your results relate to the pineal gland?

TABLE 13.3 Functions of the Hypothalamus

Function	Description
Autonomic	Helps control heart rate, urine release from the bladder, movement of food through the digestive tract, and blood vessel diameter
Endocrine	Helps regulate pituitary gland secretions and influences metabolism, ion concentration, sexual development, and sexual functions; serves as the site of antidiuretic hormone and oxytocin production (see chapter 18)
Muscle control	Controls the muscles involved in swallowing; stimulates shivering
Regulation of body temperature	Promotes heat loss when the hypothalamic temperature increases by stimulting sweat production (anterior nucleus); promotes heat production when the hypothalamic temperature decreases by stimulating shivering (posterior nucleus); aspirin reduces fever by affecting the preoptic area
Regulation of food and water intake	Hunger center promotes eating; satiety center inhibits eating; thirst center promotes water intake
Emotions	Large range of emotional influences over body functions; directly involved in stress-related and psychosomatic illnesses and in feelings of fear and rage
Regulation of the sleep-wake cycle	Coordinates responses to the sleep-wake cycle with the other areas of the brain (e.g., the reticular activating system); suprachiasmatic nucleus receives direct input from the eyes concerning light-dark cycles and is implicated in jet lag
Sexual development and behavior	Stimulates sexual development, sexual arousal, and sexual behavior; the preoptic area is larger in males than in females

Hypothalamus

The **hypothalamus** is the most inferior portion of the diencephalon (figure 13.7*a,c*). It contains a cluster of small nuclei and tracts. The most conspicuous nuclei, called the **mammillary bodies,** appear as bulges on the ventral surface of the diencephalon. They are involved in olfactory reflexes and emotional responses to odors. They may also be involved in memory.

The hypothalamus is a central controller of the endocrine system. A funnel-shaped stalk, the infundibulum (IN-fun-DIB-you-lum), extends from the floor of the hypothalamus and connects it to the pituitary gland. The **paraventricular nucleus** and **supraoptic nucleus** of the hypothalamus regulate the pituitary gland's secretion of hormones, which influence functions as diverse as metabolism, reproduction, responses to stressful stimuli, and urine production (table 13.3; see chapter 18).

The hypothalamus receives and coordinates the responses to sensory input from multiple systems. Sensory neurons that terminate in the hypothalamus provide input from (1) internal organs; (2) taste receptors of the tongue; (3) the limbic system, which is involved in many activities, including responses to smell; (4) specific cutaneous areas, such as the nipples and external genitalia; and (5) the eyes. Efferent fibers from the hypothalamus extend into the brainstem and the spinal cord, where they synapse with neurons of the autonomic nervous system (see chapter 16). In this way, the hypothalamus serves as the major coordinating center of the autonomic nervous system. These connections regulate functions such as heart rate and digestive activities (table 13.3).

In addition to regulating autonomic functions, other hypothalamic efferent fibers extend through the infundibulum to the posterior portion of the pituitary gland (see chapter 18). Some hypothalamic fibers extend to trigeminal and facial nerve nuclei to help control the muscles involved in swallowing; and some extend to motor neurons of the spinal cord to stimulate shivering. Hypothalamic nuclei can directly control body temperature by stimulating sweating or shivering.

Hypothalamic nuclei are also involved in controlling thirst, hunger, sex drive, and our biological clock (table 13.3). In particular, they are very important in a number of functions related to mood, motivation, and emotion. Sensations such as sexual pleasure, relaxation after a meal, rage, and fear are related to hypothalamic functions. This is one reason that strong emotional experiences may affect a person's desire or ability to eat, drink, or experience sexual pleasure, and vice versa.

Input from the eyes to the **suprachiasmatic nucleus** helps establish the rhythm of our light-dark cycle. Further interactions between the hypothalamus and the reticular activating system in the brainstem coordinate the sleep-wake cycle (see chapter 18).

ASSESS YOUR PROGRESS

9. *What are the four main components of the diencephalon?*
10. *Which part serves as the sensory relay center of the brain? As the link between the nervous system and the endocrine system?*
11. *What is the role of the subthalamus? Name the parts of the epithalamus, and give their functions.*
12. *List and explain the functions of the hypothalamus.*

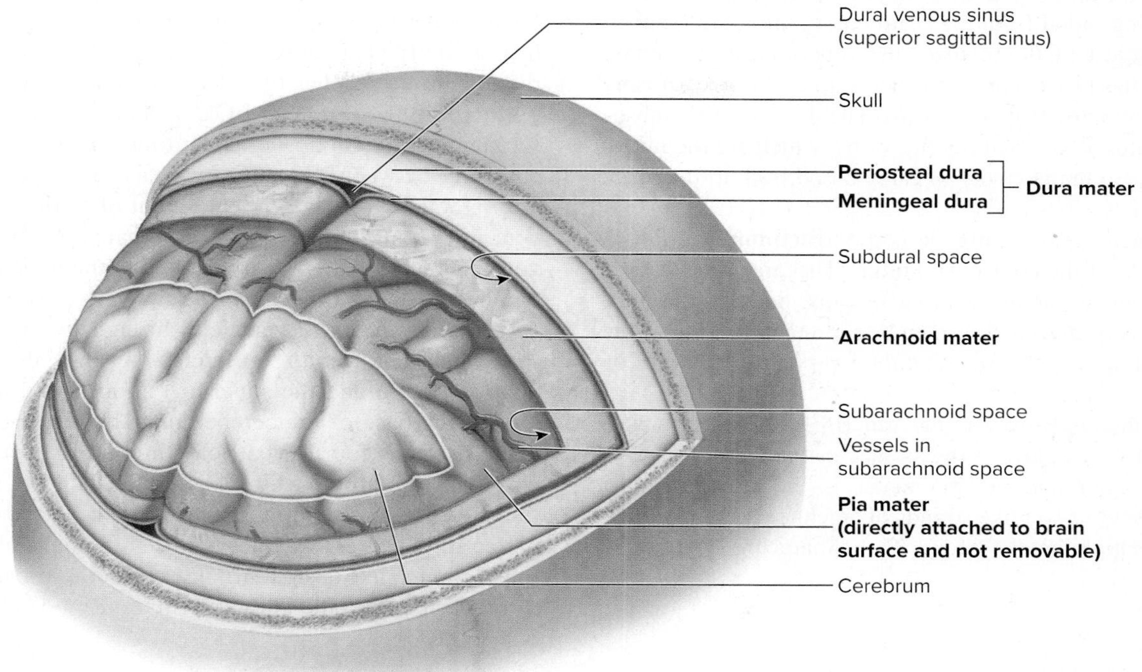

(a) Anterosuperior view

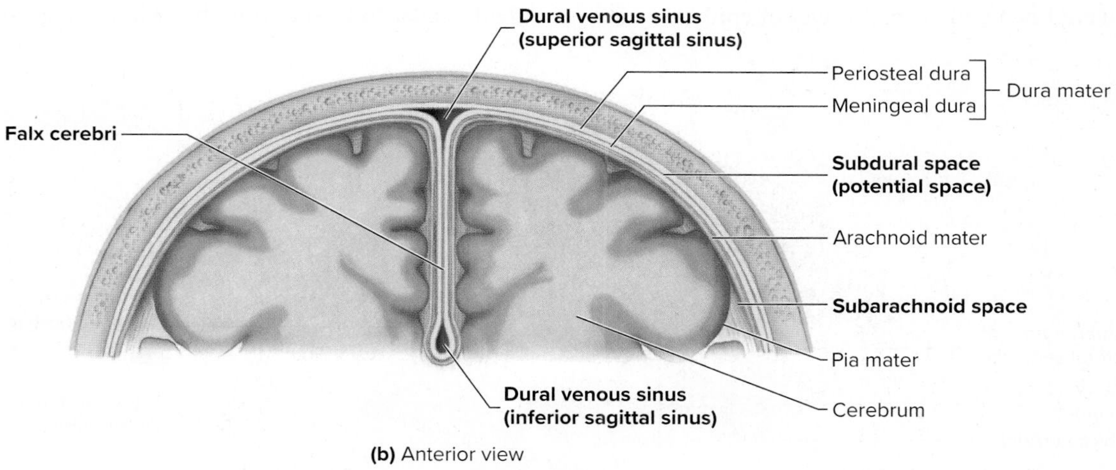

(b) Anterior view

FIGURE 13.12 Meninges
(*a*) Meningeal membranes surrounding the brain. (*b*) Frontal section of the head to show the meninges. 

around too freely. The largest of the dural folds is the **falx cerebri** (falks se-REE-bree; sickle-shaped). The falx cerebri lies in the longitudinal fissure that separates the left and right hemispheres. It is anchored anteriorly to the ethmoid bone. Two other important dural folds are the **tentorium** (ten-TOH-ree-um; tent) **cerebelli** (ser-eh-BEL-ee), which lies between the cerebrum and the cerebellum, and the **falx cerebelli,** which lies between the two cerebellar hemispheres.

Dural venous sinuses are drainage channels that form where the two layers of the dura mater are separated from each other. The dural venous sinuses are lined with endothelium and transport venous blood and cerebrospinal fluid (CSF; see

"Cerebrospinal Fluid" later in this section) away from the brain. All veins draining blood from the brain empty into dural venous sinuses. The largest of the sinuses, the superior sagittal sinus, forms between the falx cerebri and the periosteal dura and runs along the median plane (figure 13.12*b*). The dural sinuses subsequently drain into the internal jugular veins, which are the major veins that exit the cranial cavity to carry blood back to the heart (see chapter 21).

The next meningeal membrane is the **arachnoid** (ah-RAK-noyd; spiderlike, as in cobwebs) **mater.** The arachnoid mater is a very thin, wispy membrane that lies just beneath the dura mater. The space between this membrane and the dura mater is the **subdural space;** it contains only a very small amount of serous fluid.

The third meningeal layer, the **pia** (PEE-ah; affectionate) **mater** is bound very tightly to the surface of the brain. Between the arachnoid mater and the pia mater is the **subarachnoid space,** which contains weblike strands of arachnoid mater and the blood vessels supplying the brain. The subarachnoid space is filled with CSF.

Ventricles

The **ventricles** of the CNS are an interconnected series of cavities that bathe the brain with cerebrospinal fluid. They are derived from the hollow tube of the embryonic neural tube (see section 13.1) and are lined with a single layer of epithelial cells called **ependymal** (ep-EN-dih-mal) **cells** (see chapter 11). Each cerebral hemisphere contains a relatively large cavity, the **lateral ventricle** (figure 13.13). The lateral ventricles are separated from each other by a thin membrane called the **septum pellucidum** (SEP-tum pe-LOO-si-dum; translucent walls). The septum pellucidum lies in the midline just inferior to the corpus callosum between the anterior horns of the lateral ventricles. The lateral ventricles can be thought of as the first and second ventricles, but they are not designated as such. The **third ventricle** is a smaller cavity located at the midline between the two halves of the thalamus. The two lateral ventricles are connected with the third ventricle through two **interventricular foramina.** The **fourth ventricle** is in the inferior part of the pontine region and the superior region of the medulla oblongata at the base of the cerebellum. The third ventricle is connected to the fourth ventricle through a narrow canal, the **cerebral aqueduct,** which passes through the midbrain. The fourth ventricle is continuous with the central canal of the spinal cord, which extends nearly the full length of the cord. The fourth ventricle is also continuous with the subarachnoid space through apertures to allow circulation of cerebrospinal fluid out of the CNS.

Cerebrospinal Fluid

Cerebrospinal (seh-ree-broh-SPY-nal) **fluid (CSF)** is a clear fluid similar to blood serum but without most of the proteins. It

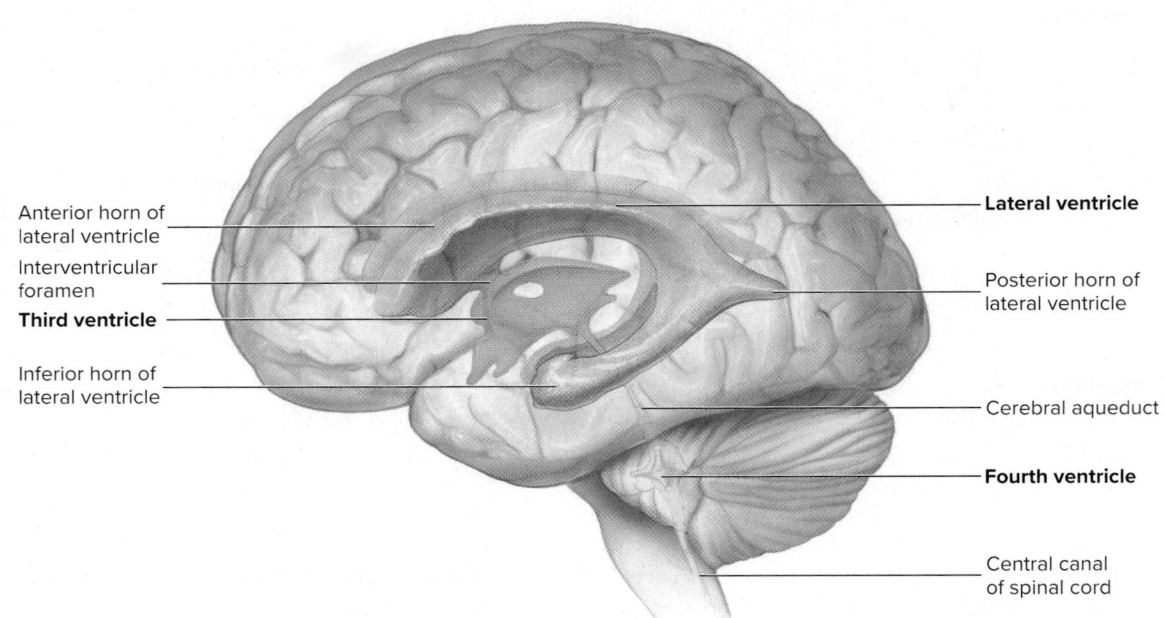

FIGURE 13.13 Ventricles of the Brain

The lateral, third, and fourth ventricles seen in a lateral view from the left.

bathes the brain and the spinal cord and provides a protective cushion around the CNS. CSF allows the brain to float within the cranial cavity, so that it does not rest directly on the surface of the skull or dura mater. In addition, it protects the brain against the shock of rapid head movements. It also provides some nutrients to CNS tissues.

The CSF is produced by a secretory structure called the **choroid** (KOR-oid; lacy) **plexus** (PLEK-sus). The choroid plexus consists of a layer of specialized ependymal cells surrounded by supportive loose connective tissue and associated blood vessels. The choroid plexuses are formed by invaginations of the vascular pia mater into the ventricles, thus producing a vascular connective tissue core covered by ependymal cells (figure 13.14 *inset, lower left*). There is a choroid plexus in each of the ventricles, although about 80–90% of the CSF is produced within the lateral ventricles.

CSF is formed by the transport of water and solutes from the blood through a variety of mechanisms. The majority of the fluid enters the ventricles by following a Na^+ concentration gradient. Ependymal cells of the choroid plexus actively transport Na^+ into the ventricles, and water passively follows. Large molecules are transported by pinocytosis. Glucose is transported by facilitated diffusion mediated by a specific glucose transporter (see chapter 3). Because glucose is the primary energy source for the brain, patients with mutations in this transporter (GLUT1) are severely affected with CNS disorders.

Endothelial cells of the blood vessels in the choroid plexuses, which are joined by tight junctions (see chapter 4), form the blood-brain barrier, or more correctly the blood–cerebrospinal fluid barrier (see section 13.7). Consequently, substances do not pass between the cells but must pass through the cells.

CSF fills all the open spaces of the CNS. This includes all the ventricles, the subarachnoid space of the brain and spinal cord, and the central canal of the spinal cord. The route taken by the CSF from its origin in the choroid plexuses to its return to the circulation is depicted in figure 13.14.

1. CSF is produced by the choroid plexuses of each of the four ventricles.
2. CSF passes from the lateral ventricles through the interventricular foramina into the third ventricle.
3. CSF flows from the third ventricle through the cerebral aqueduct into the fourth ventricle.
4. CSF can exit the interior of the brain only from the fourth ventricle. One **median aperture** (foramen of Magendie), which opens through the roof of the fourth ventricle, and two **lateral apertures** (foramina of Luschka), which open through the walls, allow the CSF to pass from the fourth ventricle to the subarachnoid space. Some CSF continues to flow inferiorly into the central canal of the spinal cord. However, parts of the central canal are closed off in adults, so the amount circulating there is very small.
5. Clusters of fingerlike protusions of arachnoid tissue called **arachnoid granulations** penetrate into the dural venous sinuses, especially the superior sagittal sinus. CSF passes into the blood-filled dural venous sinuses through these granulations.

From the dural venous sinuses, the blood drains into the internal jugular veins to enter the veins of the general circulation; in this way, the CSF reenters the bloodstream. The flow rate of CSF from its origin to the point at which it enters the bloodstream is about 0.4 mL/min, and the entire CSF volume of about 117 mL in the subarachnoid space and 23 mL in the ventricles is replenished about 4–5 times a day.

Clinical IMPACT 13.2

Hydrocephalus

The cerebral aqueduct may be blocked at the time of birth or may become blocked later in life because of a tumor growing in the brainstem. If the apertures of the fourth ventricle or the cerebral aqueduct are blocked, CSF can accumulate within the ventricles, resulting in a condition called **internal hydrocephalus** (*noncommunicating hydrocephalus*). The production of CSF continues, even when the passages that normally allow it to exit the brain are blocked. Consequently, fluid builds inside the brain, causing pressure, which compresses the nervous tissue and dilates the ventricles. Compression of the nervous tissue usually results in irreversible brain damage. If the skull bones are not completely ossified when the hydrocephalus occurs, the pressure may also severely enlarge the head.

Internal hydrocephalus can be treated successfully by placing a drainage tube (shunt) between the brain ventricles and the abdominal cavity to eliminate the high internal pressures. However, there is some risk of introducing infection into the brain through these shunts, and the shunts must be replaced as the person grows.

A subarachnoid hemorrhage may block the return of CSF to the circulation. If CSF accumulates in the subarachnoid space, the condition is called **external hydrocephalus** (*communicating hydrocephalus*). In this condition, pressure is applied to the brain externally, compressing neural tissues and causing brain damage. The condition usually resolves without treatment.

ASSESS YOUR PROGRESS

19. *Describe the three meninges that surround the brain. What are the falx cerebri, tentorium cerebelli, and falx cerebelli?*
20. *Describe the contents of the dural sinuses, subdural space, and subarachnoid space.*
21. *Name the four ventricles of the brain. Describe their locations and the connections between them. What are the septum pellucida?*
22. *Describe the production and circulation of CSF. Where does the CSF return to the blood?*

PROCESS Figure

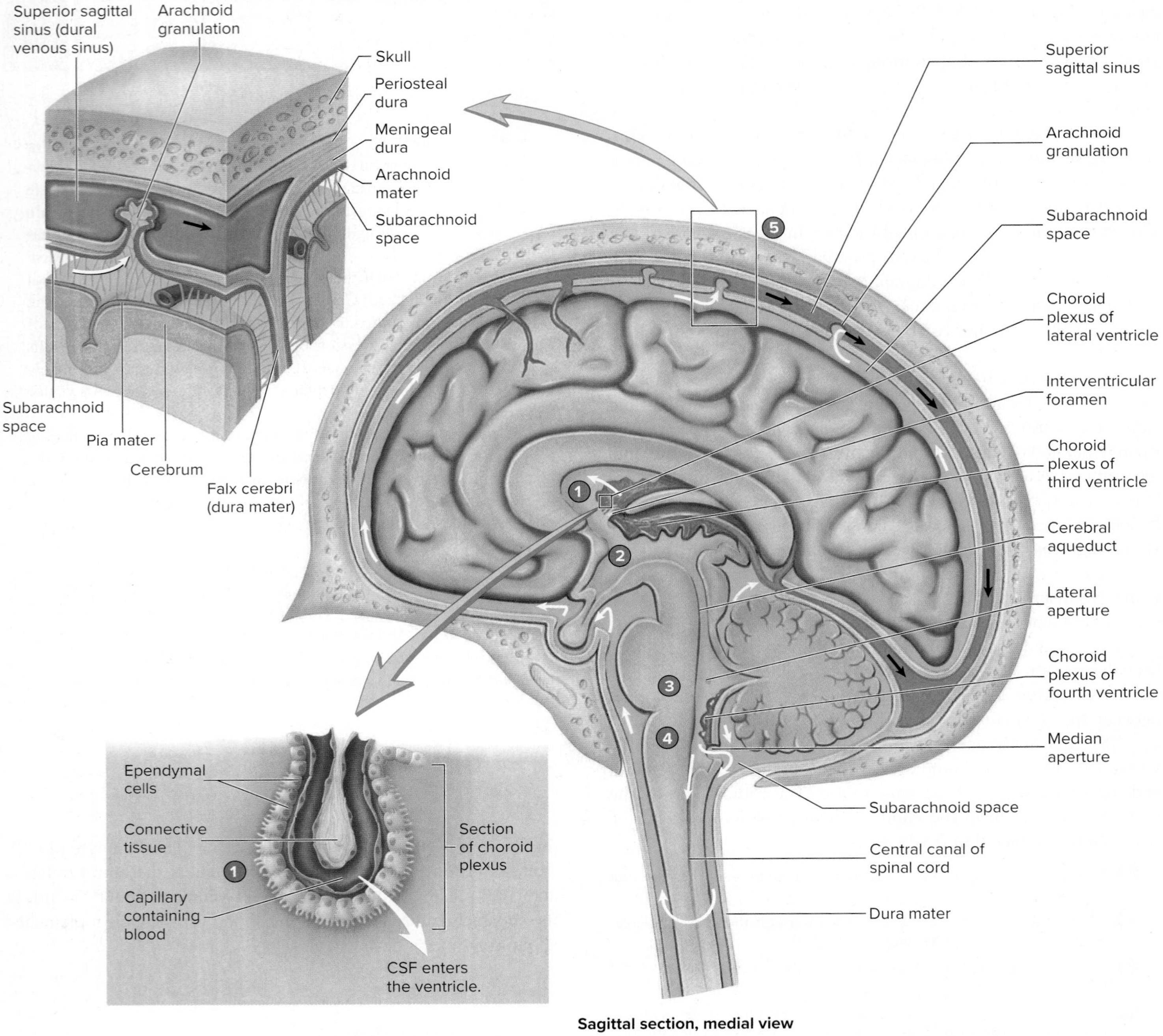

Superior sagittal sinus (dural venous sinus)
Arachnoid granulation
Skull
Periosteal dura
Meningeal dura
Arachnoid mater
Subarachnoid space
Subarachnoid space
Pia mater
Cerebrum
Falx cerebri (dura mater)

Superior sagittal sinus
Arachnoid granulation
Subarachnoid space
Choroid plexus of lateral ventricle
Interventricular foramen
Choroid plexus of third ventricle
Cerebral aqueduct
Lateral aperture
Choroid plexus of fourth ventricle
Median aperture
Subarachnoid space
Central canal of spinal cord
Dura mater

1 2 3 4 5

Ependymal cells
Connective tissue
Capillary containing blood
1
Section of choroid plexus
CSF enters the ventricle.

Sagittal section, medial view

PROCESS Figure 13.14

Choroid Plexuses and the Flow of CSF

CSF flows through the ventricles and subarachnoid space, as shown by the *white arrows*. Arrows going through the foramina in the wall and roof of the fourth ventricle represent the CSF entering the subarachnoid space. CSF passes back into the blood through the arachnoid granulations (*white and black arrows*), which penetrate the dural sinus. The *black arrows* show the direction of blood flow in the sinuses. *Yellow* indicates CSF; *blue* indicates venous blood.

Hydrocephalus occurs when CSF accumulates in the ventricles and passageways of the brain. Assuming that CSF production is normal, propose reasons for the accumulation of the fluid.

13.7 Blood Supply to the Brain

LEARNING OUTCOMES

After reading this section, you should be able to

A. **Describe how the brain is supplied with blood.**

B. **Explain the role of the blood-brain barrier.**

The brain requires a tremendous amount of blood to maintain its normal functions. The brain has a very high metabolic rate, and brain cells are not capable of storing high-energy molecules for any length of time. In addition, brain cells depend almost entirely on glucose as their energy source (see chapter 25). Thus, the brain requires a constant blood supply to meet the demands of brain cells for both glucose and O_2. Even though the brain accounts for only about 2% of total body weight, it receives approximately 15–20% of the blood pumped by the heart. Interruption of the brain's blood supply for only seconds can cause unconsciousness, and interruption for minutes can cause irreversible brain damage.

The brain's blood supply is illustrated in chapter 21 (see figures 21.10 and 21.11). Blood reaches the brain through the **internal carotid arteries,** which ascend to the head along the anterolateral part of the neck, and the **vertebral arteries,** which ascend along the posterior part of the neck, through the transverse foramina of the cervical vertebrae. The internal carotid arteries enter the cranial cavity through the carotid canals, and the vertebral arteries enter through the foramen magnum. The vertebral arteries join to form the **basilar artery,** which lies on the ventral surface of the pons. The basilar artery and the internal carotid arteries contribute to the **cerebral arterial circle** (circle of Willis). Branches from this circle and from the basilar artery supply blood to the brain.

The cerebral cortex on each side of the brain is supplied by three branches that arise from the cerebral arterial circle: the **anterior, middle,** and **posterior cerebral arteries.** The middle cerebral artery supplies most of the lateral surface of each cerebral hemisphere. The anterior cerebral artery supplies the medial portion of the parietal and frontal lobes. The posterior cerebral artery supplies the occipital lobe and the medial surface of the temporal lobe.

The arteries to the brain and their larger branches are located in the subarachnoid space. Small cortical arterial branches leave the subarachnoid space and enter the pia mater, where they branch extensively. Precapillary branches leave the pia mater and enter the tissue of the brain. Most of these branches are short and remain in the cortex. Fewer, longer branches extend into the medulla.

Hemorrhagic brain injury is characterized by bleeding outside the dura (extradural or epidural), between the dura and the brain (subdural), or within the brain (intracerebral). A hemorrhage, which is bleeding, results in a hematoma, an accumulation of blood. Extradural or epidural hematomas occur in about 1–2% of major head injuries. They usually affect the middle cranial fossa and involve a tear in the middle meningeal artery. Subdural hematomas are much more common, occurring in 10–20% of major head injuries. They most commonly involve tears in the cortical veins or dural venous sinuses in the superior portion of the cranial cavity. Intracerebral hematomas occur in about 2–3% of major head injuries and involve damage to small vessels within the brain itself. An injury may cause brain trauma and bleeding on either the same side as the impact (coup, KOO), or on the opposite side (contrecoup, KON-tra-koo), as a result of the brain moving within the skull.

The arteries within the brain tissue quickly divide into capillaries. These capillaries have a highly selective permeability barrier called the **blood-brain barrier.** The blood-brain barrier is formed by tight junctions between the capillary endothelial cells. The endothelial cells are surrounded by the foot processes of brain astrocytes (see table 11.2). The astrocytes promote the formation of tight junctions between the endothelial cells. The blood-brain barrier regulates the movement of materials from the blood into the brain. Materials that would enter many tissues by passing between the endothelial cells of capillaries cannot pass through the blood-brain barrier because of the tight junctions. Most materials that enter the brain pass through the endothelial cells. Water-soluble molecules, such as amino acids and glucose, require specific transporters to move across the plasma membranes by mediated transport (see chapter 3). However, gases, such as O_2, and lipid-soluble substances, such as nicotine and ethanol, can freely diffuse through the plasma membranes of the endothelial cells and enter the brain.

The permeability characteristics of the blood-brain barrier are an important consideration when developing drugs to affect the CNS. For example, Parkinson disease is caused by a lack of the neurotransmitter dopamine, which is normally produced by certain neurons of the brain. Lack of dopamine results in decreased muscle control and shaky movements. However, administering dopamine is

Case STUDY 13.1 | Subdural Hematoma

The body of a 20-year-old man was being examined by a hospital pathologist to determine the cause of death. He had been taken to the emergency room after being found not breathing at the base of a cliff popular with rock climbers. Bleeding over the occipital region of his scalp led the pathologist to hypothesize that he had slipped and fallen while climbing and had hit the back of his head on a rock. The pathologist noted a large subdural hematoma above the right frontal lobe of the man's brain. In addition, he saw that the brain had shifted due to the extensive bleeding, so that the medulla oblongata had been pushed inferiorly (herniated) through the foramen magnum into the vertebral canal. He determined that a subdural hematoma resulting from traumatic brain injury had caused the man's death.

Predict 2

a. Explain why the subdural hematoma was found in the frontal region of the brain, when the blow to the head occurred over the occipital region.

b. How did the herniation of the medulla oblongata into the vertebral canal affect brain function and contribute to the man's death?

FUNDAMENTAL **Figure**

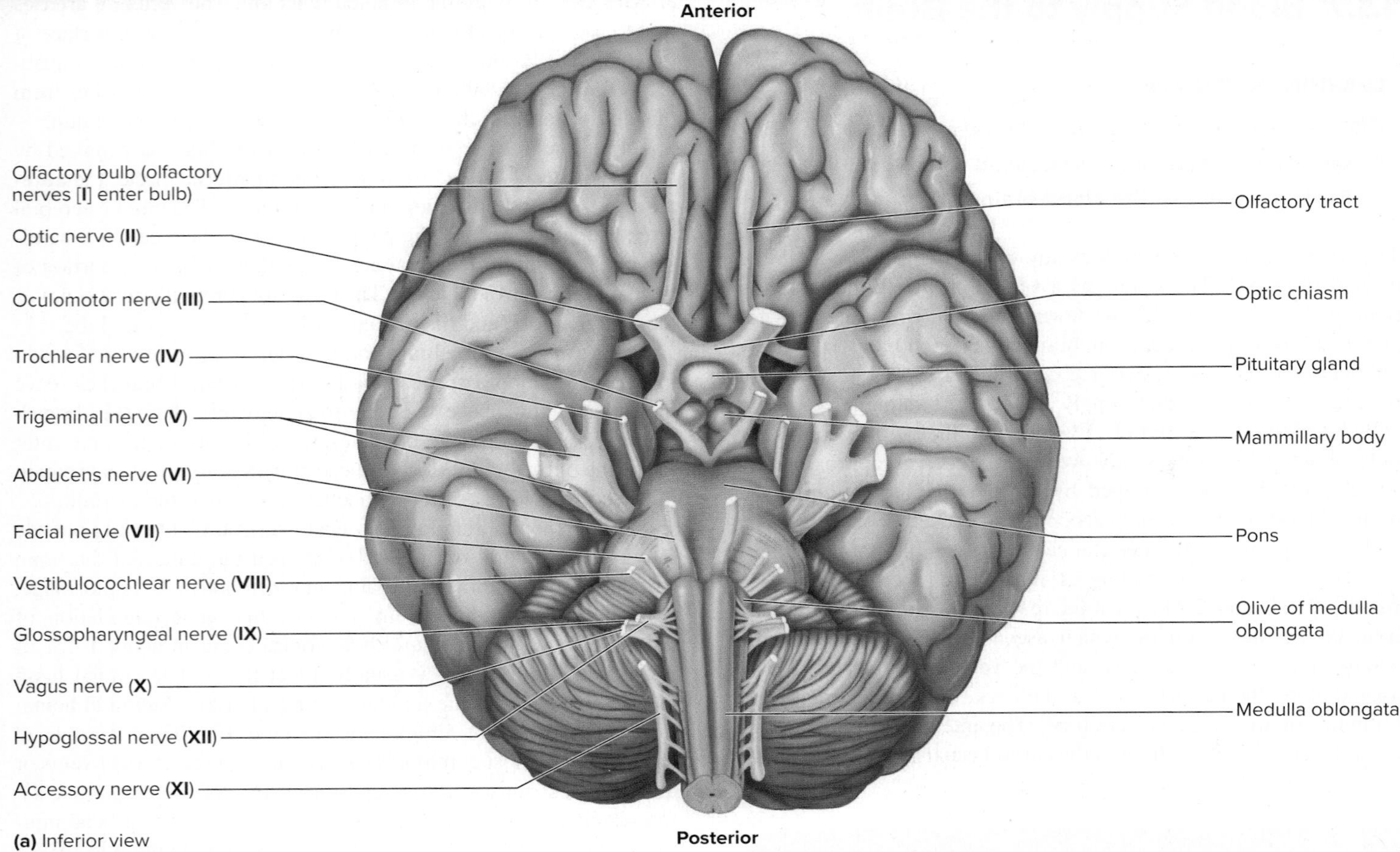

(a) Inferior view

FIGURE 13.15 Inferior Surface of the Brain, Showing the Origins of the Cranial Nerves APR

(*a*) The cranial nerves transmit and relay sensory, somatic motor, and parasympathetic information to and from the brain. Most cranial nerves connect directly to the brainstem, except the olfactory nerve (I) to the cerebrum, optic nerve (II) to the diencephalon, and accessory nerve (XI) to the spinal cord. (*b*) Photograph of an inferior view of the brain. (b) McGraw Hill Education

not helpful because dopamine cannot cross the blood-brain barrier. Instead, physicians prescribe levodopa (L-dopa), a precursor to dopamine, because it can cross the blood-brain barrier. CNS neurons then convert levodopa to dopamine, which helps reduce the symptoms of Parkinson disease (see chapter 14).

ASSESS YOUR PROGRESS

23. *Describe the blood supply to the brain. List the arteries supplying each part of the cerebral cortex.*

24. *Explain how the blood-brain barrier functions.*

13.8 Cranial Nerves

LEARNING OUTCOMES

After reading this section, you should be able to

A. **List the 12 cranial nerves and give the primary sensory, somatic motor, and/or parasympathetic functions of each.**

B. **Describe cranial reflexes.**

Cranial nerves transmit and relay information to and from the brain analogous to the spinal nerves, except they do so by direct connections to the brain instead of the spinal cord.

A given cranial nerve may have one or more of three functions: sensory, somatic motor, and parasympathetic (table 13.4).

1. **Sensory** functions include the special senses, such as vision, and the more general senses, such as touch and pain.
2. **Somatic motor** functions involve the control of skeletal muscles through motor neurons. The cranial nerves innervating skeletal muscles also contain proprioceptive sensory fibers, which convey action potentials to the CNS from those muscles and associated joints. **Proprioception** (proh-pree-oh-SEP-shun) is the awareness of the position of your various body parts. However, because proprioception is the only sensory function of several otherwise somatic motor cranial nerves, that function is usually ignored, and the nerves are designated by convention as somatic motor only.
3. **Parasympathetic** functions involve the regulation of glands, smooth muscles, and cardiac muscle. These functions are part of the autonomic nervous system and are discussed in

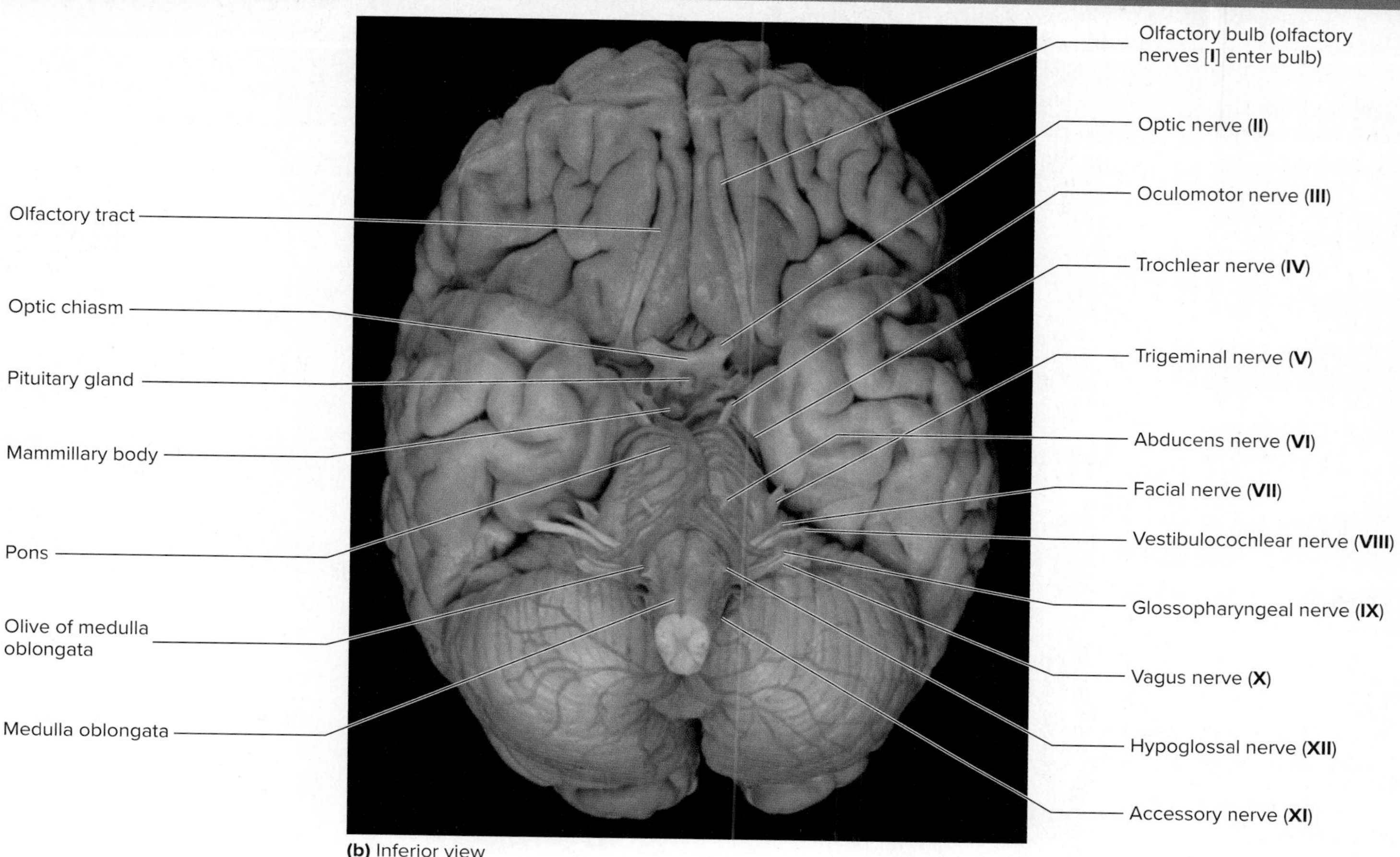

(b) Inferior view

FIGURE 13.15 (continued)

TABLE 13.4 Functional Organization of the Cranial Nerves

Nerve Function	Cranial Nerve	
Sensory	I	Olfactory
	II	Optic
	VIII	Vestibulocochlear
Somatic motor	IV	Trochlear
	VI	Abducens
	XI	Accessory
	XII	Hypoglossal
Somatic motor and sensory	V	Trigeminal
Somatic motor and parasympathetic	III	Oculomotor
Somatic motor, sensory, and parasympathetic	VII	Facial
	IX	Glossopharyngeal
	X	Vagus

chapter 16. Several of the cranial nerves have associated ganglia, and these ganglia are of two types: parasympathetic and sensory.

By convention, the 12 pairs of cranial nerves are indicated by Roman numerals (I–XII) from anterior to posterior (figure 13.15). The first 2 pairs of cranial nerves connect directly to the cerebrum (I) or the diencephalon (II). Nine pairs of cranial nerves connect to the brainstem. The remaining pair of cranial nerves (XI) is connected to the spinal cord and has no direct connection to brain structures.

Characteristics of the Cranial Nerves

It may be helpful to refer to table 13.5 while reading the following descriptions of the cranial nerves. The **olfactory (I)** and **optic (II) nerves** are exclusively sensory and are involved in the special senses of smell and vision, respectively. The functions of these nerves are discussed in chapter 15.

The **oculomotor nerve (III)** innervates four of the six muscles that move the eyeball (the superior, inferior, and medial rectus muscles and the inferior oblique muscle; see chapter 10) and the levator palpebrae superioris muscle, which raises the superior eyelid. In addition, parasympathetic nerve fibers in the oculomotor nerve

TABLE 13.5 Cranial Nerves and Their Functions

Cranial Nerve	Foramen or Fissure*	Function	Consequences of Lesions to Nerve
I: Olfactory	Cribriform plate	**Sensory:** sense of smell	Inability to smell
II: Optic	Optic foramen	**Sensory:** sense of vision	Blindness on the affected side
III: Oculomotor	Superior orbital fissure	**Motor†:** motor to eye muscles (superior, medial, and inferior rectus: inferior oblique) and upper eyelid (levator palpebrae superioris) Proprioceptive from those muscles **Parasympathetic:** parasympathetic to the sphincter of the pupil (causing constriction) and the ciliary muscle of the lens (causing accommodation)	Pupil dilation; eye deviates inferiorly and laterally due to muscle paralysis, resulting in double vision; eyelid droops (ptosis); blurred vision due to loss of accommodation

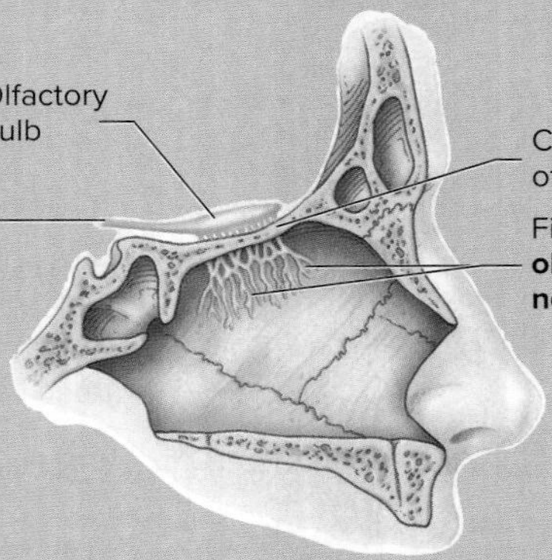

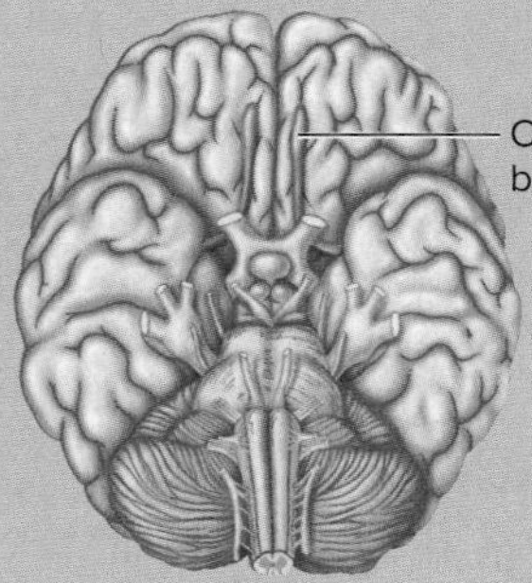

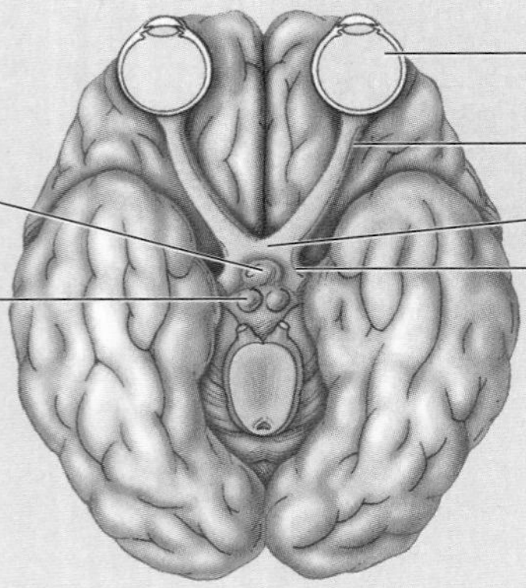

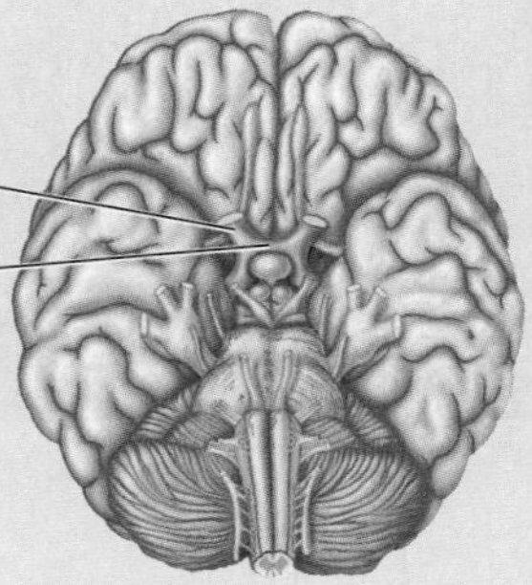

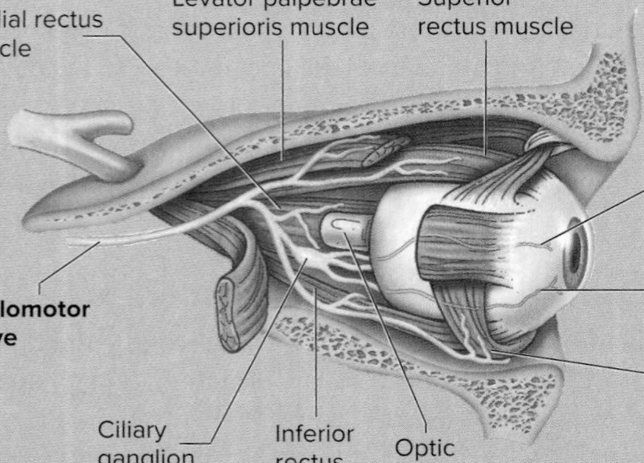

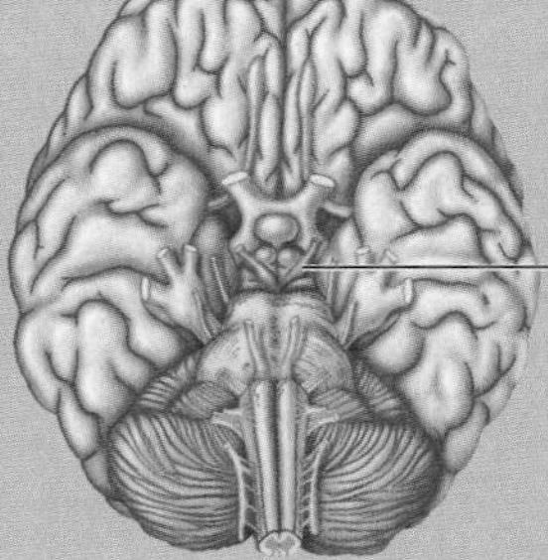

*Route of entry or exit from the skull.

†Proprioception is a sensory function, not a motor function; however, motor nerves to muscles also contain some proprioceptive afferent fibers from those muscles. Because proprioception is the only sensory information carried by some cranial nerves, these nerves are still considered "motor."

TABLE 13.5 Cranial Nerves and Their Functions—Continued

Cranial Nerve	Foramen or Fissure*	Function	Consequences of Lesions to Nerve
IV. Trochlear	Superior orbital fissure	**Motor†:** motor to one eye muscle (superior oblique) Proprioceptive from that muscle	Difficulty moving the eye inferiorly and laterally, which leads to double vision
V. Trigeminal Ophthalmic branch (V_1) Maxillary branch (V_2) Mandibular branch (V_3)	 Superior orbital fissure Foramen rotundum Foramen ovale	**V_1 sensory:** sensory from scalp, forehead, nose, upper eyelid, and cornea **V_2 sensory:** sensory from palate, upper jaw, upper teeth and gums, nasopharynx, nasal cavity, skin and mucous membrane of cheek, lower eyelid, and upper lip **V_3 sensory:** sensory from lower jaw, lower teeth and gums, anterior two-thirds of tongue, mucous membrane of cheek, lower lip, skin of cheek and chin, auricle, and temporal region **V_3 motor†:** motor to muscles of mastication (masseter, temporalis, medial and lateral pterygoids), soft palate (tensor veli palatini), throat (anterior belly of digastric, mylohyoid), and middle ear (tensor tympani) Proprioceptive from those muscles	Trigeminal neuralgia; intense pain along the course of a branch of the nerve; loss of tactile sensation in the face; weakness in biting or clenching jaw

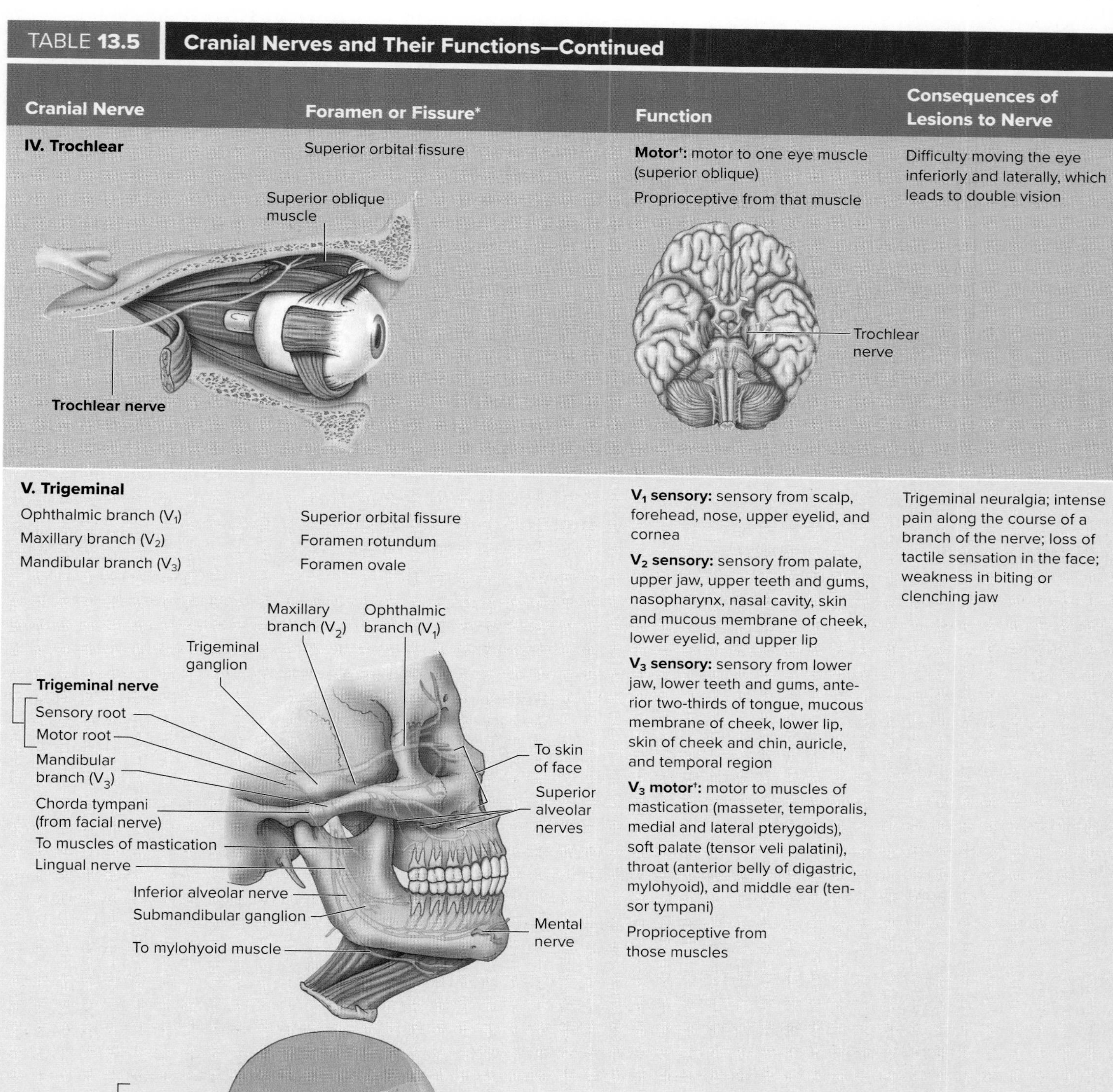

TABLE 13.5 Cranial Nerves and Their Functions—Continued

Cranial Nerve	Foramen or Fissure*	Function	Consequences of Lesions to Nerve
VI. Abducens	Superior orbital fissure	**Motor**[†]: motor to one eye muscle (lateral rectus) Proprioceptive from that muscle	Eye deviates medially (adducts) causing double vision
VII. Facial	Internal auditory canal Stylomastoid foramen	**Sensory:** sense of taste from anterior two-thirds of tongue, sensory from some of external ear and palate **Motor**[†]: motor to muscles of facial expression, throat (posterior belly of digastric, stylohyoid), and middle ear (stapedius) Proprioceptive from those muscles **Parasympathetic:** parasympathetic to submandibular and sublingual salivary glands, lacrimal gland, and glands of nasal cavity and palate	Facial palsy; loss of taste sensation on the anterior two-thirds of tongue; decreased salivation

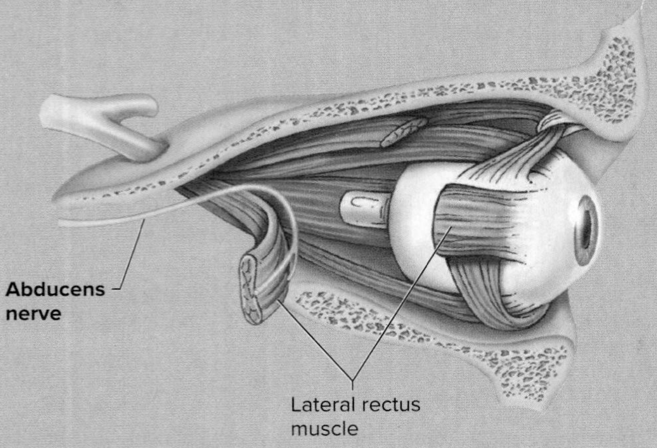

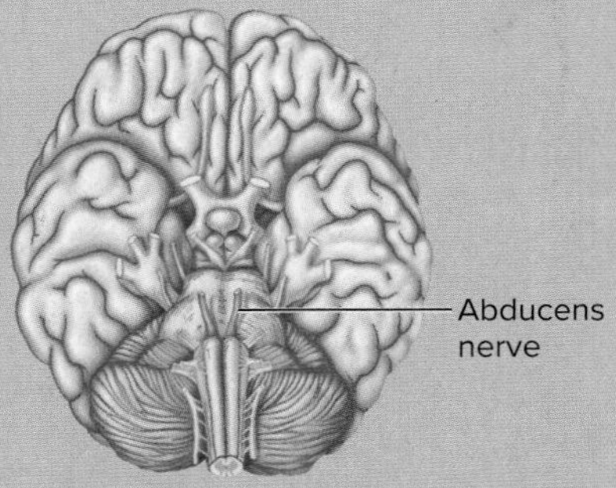

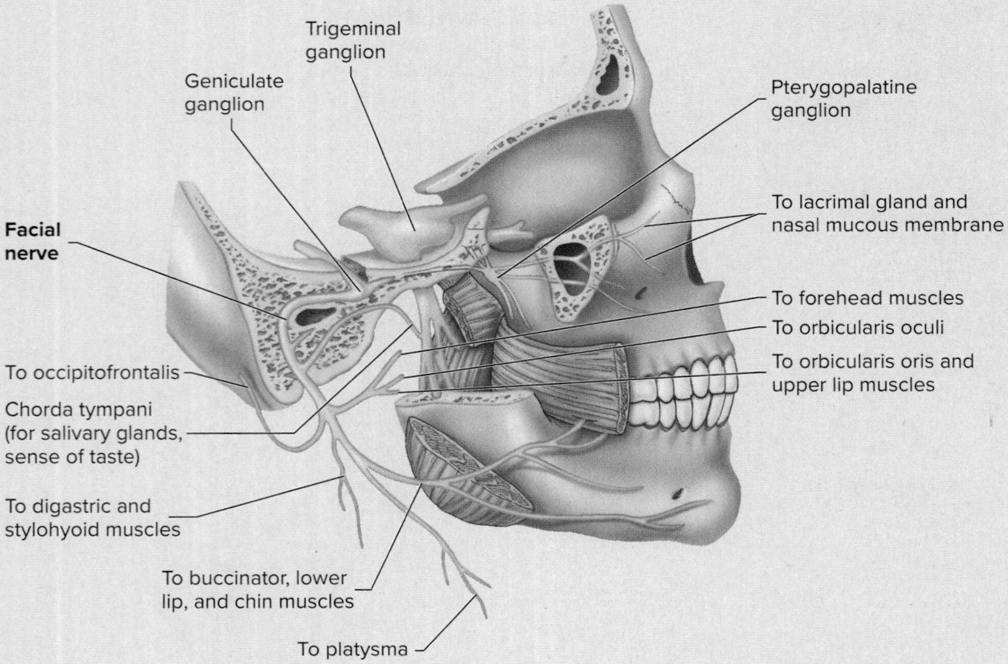

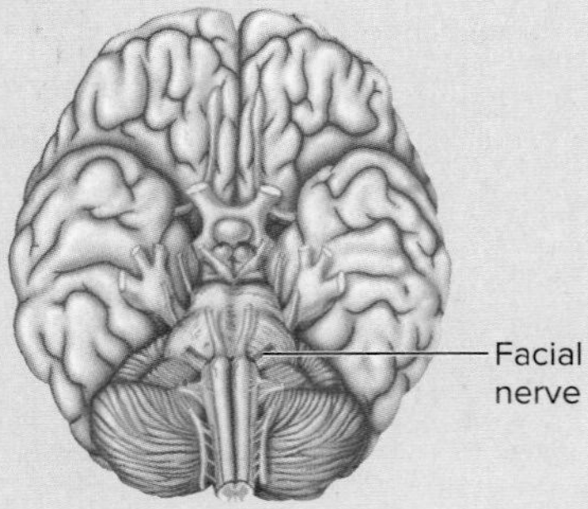

TABLE 13.5 Cranial Nerves and Their Functions—Continued

Cranial Nerve	Foramen or Fissure*	Function	Consequences of Lesions to Nerve
VIII. Vestibulocochlear	Internal auditory canal	**Sensory:** senses of hearing (cochlear nerve) and balance (vestibular nerve)	Loss of hearing (cochlear nerve); loss of balance and equilibrium; nausea, vertigo, vomiting (vestibular nerve)

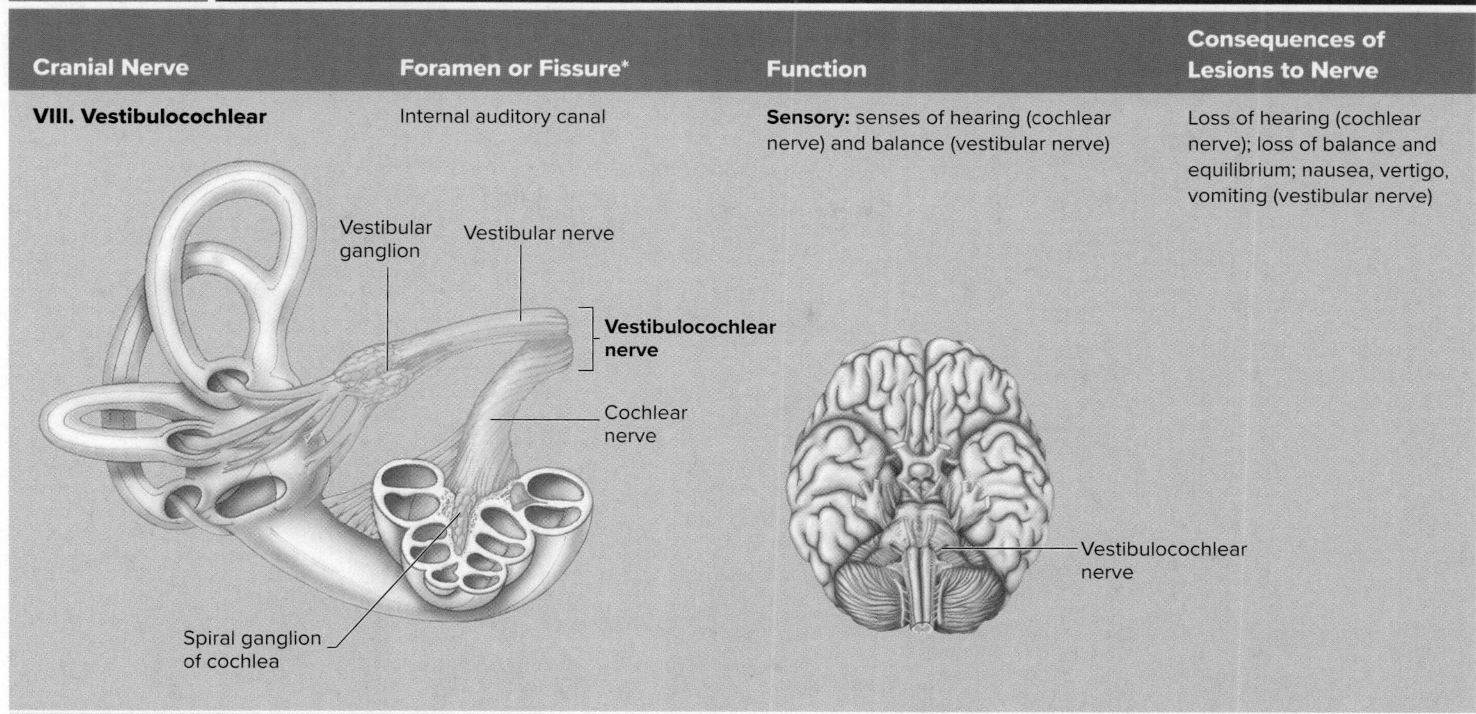

Cranial Nerve	Foramen or Fissure*	Function	Consequences of Lesions to Nerve
IX. Glossopharyngeal	Jugular foramen	**Sensory:** sense of taste from posterior one-third of tongue; sensory from pharynx, palatine tonsils, posterior one-third of tongue, middle ear, carotid sinus, and carotid body **Motor**[†]**:** motor to pharyngeal muscle (stylopharyngeus) Proprioceptive from pharyngeal muscle **Parasympathetic:** parasympathetic to parotid salivary gland and glands of the posterior one-third of tongue	Difficulty swallowing; loss of taste sensation in posterior one-third of tongue; decreased salivation

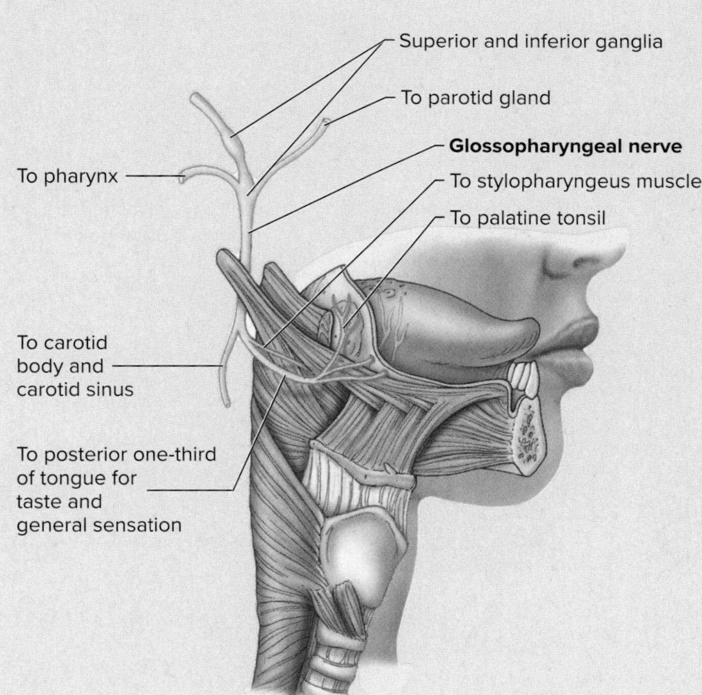

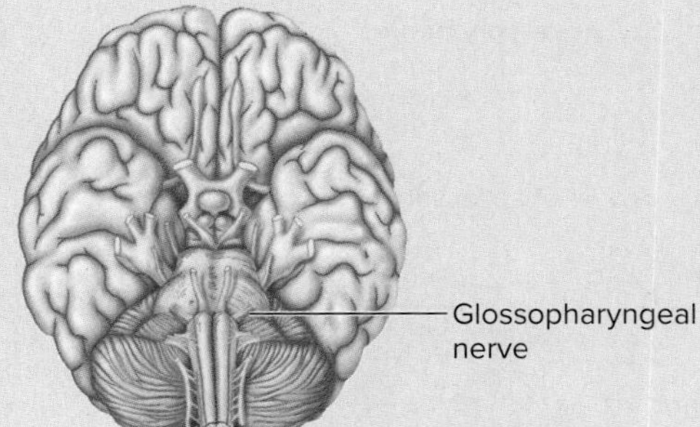

TABLE 13.5 Cranial Nerves and Their Functions—Continued

Cranial Nerve	Foramen or Fissure*	Function	Consequences of Lesions to Nerve
X. Vagus	Jugular foramen	**Sensory:** sensory from inferior pharynx, larynx, thoracic and abdominal organs; sense of taste from posterior tongue **Motor†:** motor to soft palate, pharynx, intrinsic laryngeal muscles (voice production), and an extrinsic tongue muscle (palatoglossus) Proprioceptive from those muscles **Parasympathetic:** parasympathetic to thoracic and abdominal viscera	Difficulty swallowing and/or hoarseness; uvula deviates away from side of the dysfunction

Cranial Nerve	Foramen or Fissure*	Function	Consequences of Lesions to Nerve
XI. Accessory	Foramen magnum Jugular foramen	**Motor†:** motor to sternocleidomastoid and trapezius	Difficulty elevating the scapula or rotating the neck

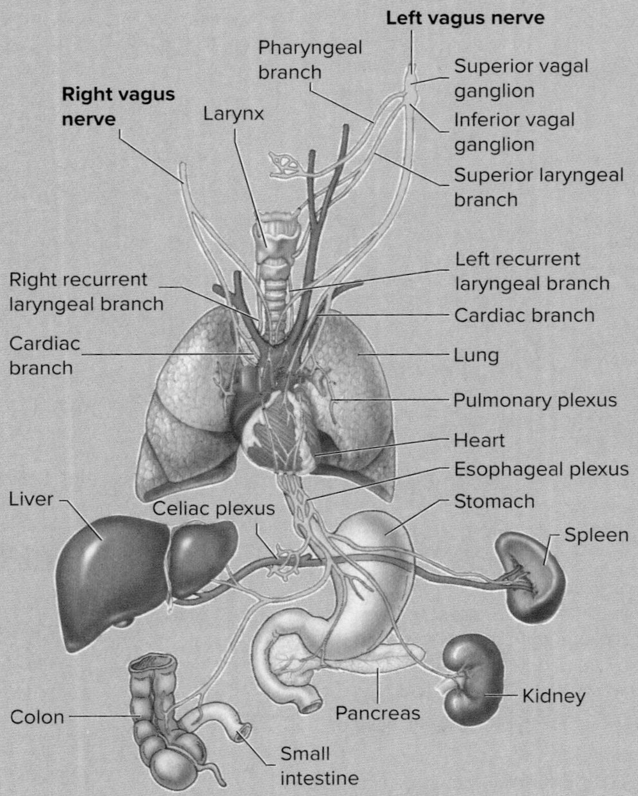

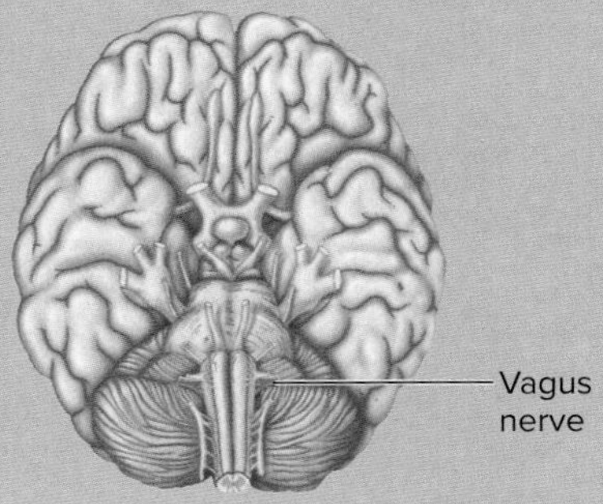

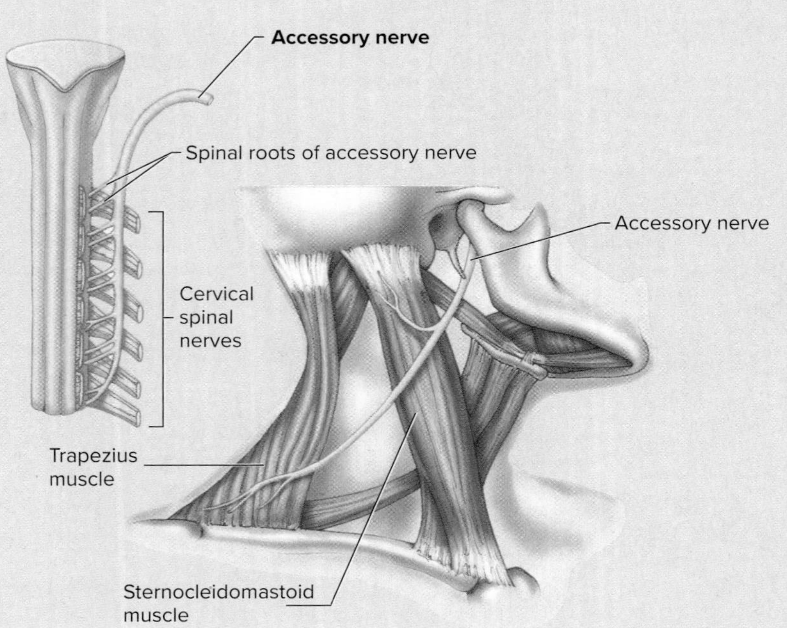

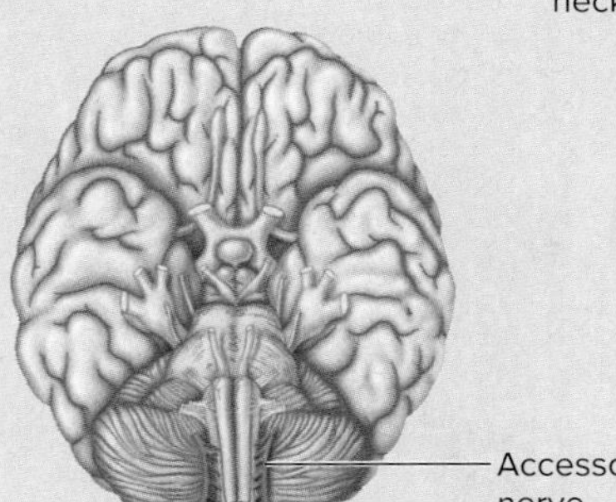

TABLE 13.5 Cranial Nerves and Their Functions—Continued

Cranial Nerve	Foramen or Fissure*	Function	Consequences of Lesions to Nerve
XII. Hypoglossal	Hypoglossal canal	**Motor†:** motor to intrinsic and extrinsic tongue muscles (styloglossus, hypoglossus, genioglossus) and throat muscles (thyrohyoid and geniohyoid) Proprioceptive from those muscles	When protruded, the tongue deviates toward the side of the damaged nerve

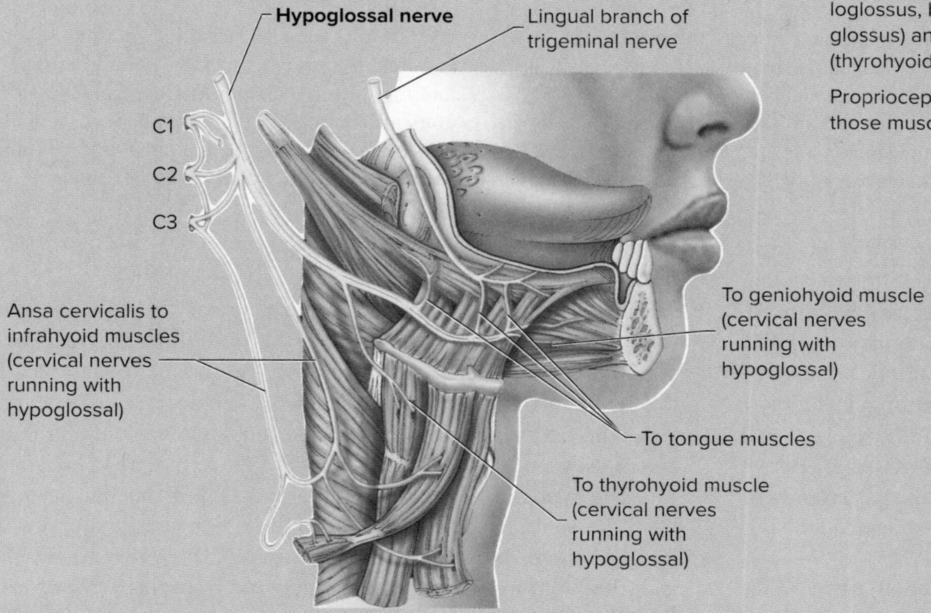

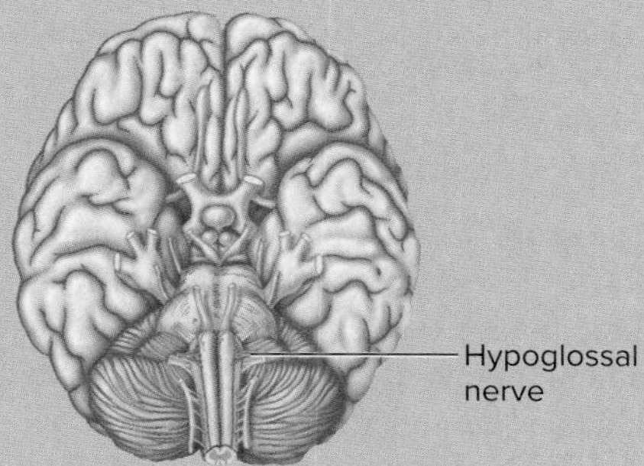

innervate smooth muscles in the eye and regulate the size of the pupil and the shape of the lens of the eye.

The **trochlear** (TROK-lee-ar) **nerve (IV)** is a somatic motor nerve that innervates one of the six eye muscles responsible for moving the eyeball (superior oblique).

The **trigeminal** (try-JEM-i-nal) **nerve (V)** has somatic motor, proprioceptive, and cutaneous sensory functions. It supplies motor innervation to the muscles of mastication, one middle ear muscle, one palatine muscle, and two throat muscles. In addition to the proprioception associated with its somatic motor functions, the trigeminal nerve also carries proprioceptive information from the temporomandibular joint, tongue, and cheek, which allows you to chew food without biting your tongue or cheek. Damage to the trigeminal nerve may impede chewing.

The trigeminal nerve has the greatest general sensory function of all the cranial nerves and is the only cranial nerve involved in **sensory cutaneous innervation** of the head. It also provides sensory innervation of blood vessels in the meninges that are associated with the pain of migraine headaches (see chapter 14). Although the mechanisms are not fully understood, the trigeminal nerve is responsible for the pain of a headache. All other cutaneous innervation comes from spinal nerves (see figure 12.14). *Trigeminal* means "three twins," and the sensory distribution of the trigeminal nerve in the face is divided into three regions, each supplied by a branch of the nerve. The three branches—ophthalmic (V_1), maxillary (V_2), and mandibular (V_3)—arise directly from the trigeminal ganglion, which serves the same function as the dorsal root ganglia of the spinal nerves. Only the mandibular branch contains motor axons, which bypass the trigeminal ganglion, much as the ventral root of a spinal nerve bypasses a dorsal root ganglion.

In addition to these cutaneous functions, the maxillary and mandibular branches are important in dentistry (see Clinical Impact 13.3). The maxillary nerve supplies sensory innervation to the maxillary teeth, palate, and gingiva (JIN-jih-vah; gum). The mandibular branch supplies sensory innervation to the mandibular teeth, tongue, and gingiva. The various nerves innervating the teeth are referred to as **alveolar** (al-VEE-oh-lar; socket) **nerves.** The **superior alveolar nerves** to the maxillary teeth are derived from the maxillary branch of the trigeminal nerve, and the **inferior alveolar nerves** to the mandibular teeth are derived from the mandibular branch of the trigeminal nerve.

The **abducens** (ab-DOO-senz) **nerve (VI),** like the trochlear nerve, is a somatic motor nerve that innervates one of the six muscles responsible for moving the eyeball (lateral rectus).

Predict 3

A drooping upper eyelid on one side of the face is a sign of possible oculomotor nerve damage. Describe how a patient could be tested for this type of damage by examining other oculomotor nerve functions. Describe the eye movements that distinguish among oculomotor, trochlear, and abducens nerve damage.

The **facial nerve (VII)** is somatic motor, sensory, and parasympathetic in function. It controls all the muscles of facial

Clinical IMPACT 13.3 Dental Anesthesia

Dentists inject anesthetic to block sensory transmission by the alveolar nerves. The superior alveolar nerves are not usually anesthetized directly because they are difficult to approach with a needle. For this reason, the maxillary teeth are usually anesthetized locally by inserting the needle beneath the oral mucosa surrounding the teeth. The inferior alveolar nerve is probably anesthetized more often than any other nerve in the body. To anesthetize this nerve, the dentist inserts the needle somewhat posterior to the patient's last molar and extends the needle near where the mandibular branch of the trigeminal nerve enters the mandibular foramen.

During an inferior alveolar block, several nondental nerves are usually anesthetized. The mental nerve, which supplies cutaneous innervation to the anterior lip and chin, is a distal branch of the inferior alveolar nerve. When the inferior alveolar nerve is blocked, the mental nerve is blocked also, resulting in a numb lip and chin. Nerves lying near the point where the inferior alveolar nerve enters the mandible are often also anesthetized during inferior alveolar anesthesia. For example, the lingual nerve can be anesthetized to produce a numb tongue.

expression, a small muscle in the middle ear, and two hyoid muscles. It is sensory for the sense of taste in the anterior two-thirds of the tongue (see chapter 15). The facial nerve supplies parasympathetic innervation to the submandibular and sublingual salivary glands of the mouth and to the lacrimal glands of the eye.

The **vestibulocochlear** (ves-TIB-yoo-loh-KOK-lee-ar) **nerve (VIII),** like the olfactory and optic nerves, is exclusively sensory and transmits action potentials from the inner ear responsible for the special senses of hearing and balance (see chapter 15).

The **glossopharyngeal** (GLOS-oh-fah-RIN-jee-al) **nerve (IX),** like the facial nerve, is somatic motor, sensory, and parasympathetic in function and has both sensory and parasympathetic ganglia. The glossopharyngeal nerve is somatic motor to one muscle of the pharynx and supplies parasympathetic innervation to the parotid salivary glands. The glossopharyngeal nerve is sensory for the sense of taste in the posterior one-third of the tongue. It also supplies tactile sensory innervation from the posterior tongue, middle ear, and pharynx, and it transmits sensory stimulation from receptors in the carotid arteries, which monitor blood pressure and blood carbon dioxide, oxygen, and pH levels (see chapter 21).

The **vagus** (VAY-gus) **nerve (X),** like the facial and glossopharyngeal nerves, is somatic motor, sensory, and parasympathetic in function and has both sensory and parasympathetic ganglia. Most muscles of the soft palate, pharynx, and larynx are innervated by the vagus nerve. Damage to the laryngeal branches of the vagus nerve can interfere with normal speech. The vagus nerve is sensory for taste from the root of the tongue (see chapter 15). It is sensory for the inferior pharynx and the larynx and transmits sensory input from receptors in the aortic arch, which monitor blood pressure and the levels of carbon dioxide, oxygen, and pH in the blood (see chapter 21). In addition, the vagus nerve conveys sensory information from the thoracic and abdominal organs. The parasympathetic part of the vagus nerve is very important in regulating the functions of the thoracic and abdominal organs. It carries parasympathetic fibers to the heart and lungs in the thorax and to the digestive organs and kidneys in the abdomen.

The **accessory nerve (XI)** is a somatic motor nerve that has both cranial and spinal roots. The cranial root joins the vagus nerve (hence the name *accessory*) and participates in its function. However, the presence of the cranial root in the human brainstem is variable. The major component of the accessory nerve is the spinal root, which originates from the superior part of the cervical spinal cord, enters the cranial cavity through the foramen magnum, and then exits through the jugular foramen. The accessory nerve provides the major innervation to the sternocleidomastoid and trapezius muscles of the neck and shoulder.

The **hypoglossal nerve (XII)** is a somatic motor nerve that arises from the ventral surface of the medulla oblongata. It supplies the intrinsic tongue muscles, three of the four extrinsic tongue muscles, and the thyrohyoid and the geniohyoid muscles. (*Note:* This information may be helpful in answering the Learn to Predict question at the beginning of the chapter.)

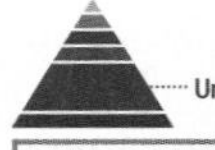

Predict 4

Injury to the accessory nerve may result in sternocleidomastoid muscle dysfunction, a condition called torticollis (sometimes called wry neck), in which the head is drawn to one side. If the head is turned to the left, does this position indicate injury to the left or the right spinal component of the accessory nerve?

Reflexes Involving Cranial Nerves

Reflexes integrated within the spinal cord were discussed in chapter 12. Many of the body's functions, especially those involved in maintaining homeostasis, involve reflexes that are integrated within the brain. Some of these reflexes, such as those involved in controlling heart rate (see chapter 20), blood pressure (see chapter 21), and respiration (see chapter 23), are integrated in the brainstem and many involve cranial nerve X (vagus nerve).

Many of the brainstem reflexes are associated with cranial nerve function. In general, these reflexes involve sensory input from the cranial nerves or spinal cord and the motor output of the cranial nerves.

Turning the eyes toward a flash of light, a sudden noise, or a touch on the skin is an example of a brainstem reflex. Moving the eyes to track a moving object is another complex brainstem reflex. Some of the sensory neurons from cranial nerve VIII form a reflex arc with neurons of cranial nerves V and VII, which send axons to muscles of the middle ear and dampen the effects of very loud,

TABLE 13.6 Representative Diseases and Disorders of the CNS and Cranial Nerves

Condition	Description
CNS DISORDERS*	
Cerebral aneurysm	Excessive dilation or ballooning of an artery; hemorrhaging (leaking) of the aneurysm leads to a hematoma within the brain or in the extradural, subdural, or subarachnoid spaces around the brain
Stroke	Loss of blood flow to the brain; caused by bleeding in the brain or meninges or a clot or spasm blocking cerebral blood vessels, which results in a local area of cell death; symptoms include general intellectual deficiency, memory loss, short attention span, moodiness, disorientation, and irritability
Concussion	A blow to the head that produces momentary loss of consciousness; can lead to *postconcussion syndrome,* which can include headaches, fatigue, difficulties with mental tasks, depression, and personality changes
Cerebral compression	Increased intracranial pressure; can be caused by hematomas, hydrocephalus, tumors, edema from a severe head blow, or spinal cord injury
CRANIAL NERVE DISORDERS	
Trigeminal neuralgia	Sharp pain in the face involving the trigeminal nerve; cause is unknown; can be triggered by touch near the mouth area
Migraine	Severe headache with associated sensory symptoms; cause unknown but involves the trigeminal nerve; can be triggered by environmental factors; tends to be hereditary
Facial palsy	Unilateral paralysis of the facial muscles involving the facial nerve; side of the face droops; can result from a stroke, infections, acute nerve damage, or a brain tumor; most common type is called *Bell's palsy,* in which cause is unknown, but it is believed to be due to viral infection of the facial nerve
Herpes simplex I	Viral infection characterized by lesions (*cold sores*) on the lips or nasal region; virus can remain dormant in trigeminal ganglion; reactivated often at times of stress or reduced immune resistance

*For more CNS disorders, see Representative Diseases and Disorders tables in chapters 12 and 14.

sustained noises on delicate inner ear structures (see chapter 15). Reflexes that occur during chewing allow the jaws to react to foods of various hardness and protect the teeth from breaking on very hard foods. Both the sensory and motor components of the reflex arc are carried by cranial nerve V. Reflexes involving input through cranial nerve V and output through cranial nerve XII move the tongue to position food between the teeth for chewing and then move the tongue out of the way, so that it is not bitten.

ASSESS YOUR PROGRESS

25. *What are the three major functions of the cranial nerves?*

26. *Which cranial nerves are sensory only? With what sense is each of these associated?*

27. *Name the cranial nerves that are somatic motor and proprioceptive only. What muscles or groups of muscles does each nerve supply? What is proprioception?*

28. *What cranial nerve provides the sensory cutaneous innervation of the face? How is this nerve important in dentistry? Name the muscles that would not function if this nerve were damaged.*

29. *Which four cranial nerves have a parasympathetic function? Describe the functions of each of these nerves.*

30. *Which cranial nerve leaves the head and neck region?*

31. *Give an example of reflex integration by cranial nerves.*

Concept Check

13.1 Development of the Brain

The brain and spinal cord develop from the neural tube. The ventricles and central canal develop from the lumen of the neural tube.

1. *Which of these parts of the embryonic brain is correctly matched with the structure it becomes in the adult brain?* Remember
   a. *mesencephalon—midbrain*
   b. *metencephalon—medulla oblongata*
   c. *myelencephalon—cerebrum*
   d. *telencephalon—pons and cerebellum*
2. *What happens to the developing brain if the CSF is not properly drained, resulting in early hydrocephalus?* Apply

13.2 Brainstem

Medulla Oblongata

A. The medulla oblongata is continuous with the spinal cord and contains ascending and descending tracts.

B. The pyramids are tracts controlling voluntary muscle movement.

C. The olives are nuclei that function in equilibrium, coordination, and modulation of sound from the inner ear.

D. Medullary nuclei regulate the heart, blood vessels, respiration, swallowing, vomiting, coughing, sneezing, and hiccuping. The nuclei of cranial nerves V, VII, and IX–XII are in the medulla oblongata.

Pons

A. The pons is superior to the medulla oblongata.
B. Ascending and descending tracts pass through the pons.
C. Pontine nuclei regulate sleep and respiration. The nuclei of cranial nerves V–VIII are in the pons.

Midbrain

A. The midbrain is superior to the pons.
B. The midbrain contains the nuclei for cranial nerves III, IV, and V.
C. The tectum consists of four colliculi. The two inferior colliculi are involved in hearing, and the two superior colliculi in visual reflexes.
D. The tegmentum contains ascending tracts and the red nuclei, which are involved in motor activity.
E. The cerebral peduncles are the major descending motor pathway.
F. The substantia nigra connects to other basal nuclei and is involved with muscle tone and movement.

Reticular Formation

The reticular formation consists of nuclei scattered throughout the brainstem. The reticular system functions in many brainstem activities, including motor control, pain perception, rhythmic contractions, and the sleep-wake cycle.

3. *To separate the brainstem from the rest of the brain, a cut would have to be made between the* Understand
   a. medulla oblongata and pons.
   b. pons and midbrain.
   c. midbrain and diencephalon.
   d. thalamus and cerebrum.
   e. medulla oblongata and spinal cord.

4. *Important centers for heart rate, blood pressure, respiration, swallowing, coughing, and vomiting are located in the* Remember
   a. cerebrum.
   b. medulla oblongata.
   c. midbrain.
   d. pons.
   e. cerebellum.

5. *In which part of the brain does decussation of descending tracts involved in the conscious control of skeletal muscles occur?* Remember
   a. cerebrum
   b. diencephalon
   c. midbrain
   d. pons
   e. medulla oblongata

6. *The cerebral peduncles are a major descending motor pathway in the* Remember
   a. cerebrum.
   b. cerebellum.
   c. pons.
   d. midbrain.
   e. medulla oblongata.

7. *The superior colliculi are involved in ________, whereas the inferior colliculi are involved in ________.* Remember
   a. hearing, visual reflexes
   b. visual reflexes, hearing
   c. balance, motor pathways
   d. motor pathways, balance
   e. respiration, sleep

13.3 Cerebellum

A. The cerebellar cortex contains more neurons than the cerebral cortex does. The Purkinje cells are the largest cells in the CNS.
B. The cerebellum has three parts, which control balance, gross motor coordination, and fine motor coordination.
C. The cerebellum corrects discrepancies between intended movements and actual movements.
D. The cerebellum can "learn" highly specific, complex motor activities.

8. *The cerebellum communicates with other regions of the CNS through the*

   a. flocculonodular lobe.
   b. cerebellar peduncles.
   c. vermis.
   d. lateral hemispheres.
   e. folia.

9. *The major relay station for sensory input that projects to the cerebral cortex is the* Remember
   a. hypothalamus.
   b. thalamus.
   c. pons.
   d. cerebellum.
   e. midbrain.

13.4 Diencephalon

The diencephalon is located between the brainstem and the cerebrum.

Thalamus

A. The thalamus consists of two lobes connected by the interthalamic adhesion. The thalamus functions as an integration center.
B. Most sensory input synapses in the thalamus. Pain is registered in the thalamus.
C. The thalamus also has some motor functions.

Subthalamus

The subthalamus is inferior to the thalamus and is involved in motor function.

Epithalamus

The epithalamus is superior and posterior to the thalamus and contains the habenula, which is involved in motivation and reward behavior. The pineal gland may play a role in the onset of puberty.

Hypothalamus

A. The hypothalamus, the most inferior portion of the diencephalon, contains several nuclei and tracts.
B. The mammillary bodies are reflex centers for olfaction.

C. The hypothalamus regulates many endocrine functions (e.g., metabolism, reproduction, response to stress, and urine production). The pituitary gland attaches to the hypothalamus.

D. The hypothalamus regulates body temperature, hunger, thirst, satiety, swallowing, and emotions.

10. *The part of the diencephalon directly connected to the pituitary gland is the* Remember

 a. *hypothalamus.*
 b. *epithalamus.*
 c. *subthalamus.*
 d. *thalamus.*

11. *Which of the following is a function of the hypothalamus?*

 a. *regulates autonomic nervous system functions*
 b. *regulates the release of hormones from the posterior pituitary*
 c. *regulates body temperature*
 d. *regulates food intake (hunger) and water intake (thirst)*
 e. *All of these are correct.*

13.5 Cerebrum

A. The cortex of the cerebrum is folded into ridges called gyri and grooves called sulci, or fissures.

B. The longitudinal fissure divides the cerebrum into left and right hemispheres. Each hemisphere has five lobes.

- The frontal lobes are involved in smell, voluntary motor function, motivation, aggression, and mood.
- The parietal lobes contain the major sensory areas receiving general sensory input, taste, and balance.
- The occipital lobes contain the visual centers.
- The temporal lobes receive olfactory and auditory input and are involved in memory, abstract thought, and judgment.
- The insula lobes receive taste input.

C. Tracts connect areas of the cortex within the same hemisphere (association fibers), between hemispheres (commissural fibers), and with other parts of the brain and the spinal cord (projection fibers).

Basal Nuclei

A. Basal nuclei include the corpus striatum, subthalamic nuclei, and substantia nigra.

B. The basal nuclei are important in controlling motor functions.

Limbic System

A. The limbic system includes parts of the cerebral cortex, the hippocampus, the amygdala, the thalamus, the hypothalamus, and the olfactory cortex.

B. The limbic system controls visceral functions through the autonomic nervous system and the endocrine system and is involved in emotions and memory.

12. *The grooves on the surface of the cerebrum are called the* Remember

 a. *nuclei.*
 b. *commissures.*
 c. *tracts.*
 d. *sulci.*
 e. *gyri.*

13. *Which of these areas is located in the postcentral gyrus of the cerebral cortex?* Remember

 a. *olfactory cortex*
 b. *visual cortex*
 c. *primary motor cortex*
 d. *primary somatic sensory cortex*
 e. *primary auditory cortex*

14. *Which of these cerebral lobes is important in voluntary motor function, motivation, aggression, sense of smell, and mood?* Remember

 a. *frontal*
 b. *insula*
 c. *occipital*
 d. *parietal*
 e. *temporal*

15. *Fibers that connect areas of the cerebral cortex within the same hemisphere are* Remember

 a. *projection fibers.*
 b. *commissural fibers.*
 c. *association fibers.*
 d. *All of these are correct.*

16. *The basal nuclei are located in the*

 a. *inferior cerebrum.*
 b. *diencephalon.*
 c. *midbrain.*
 d. *All of these are correct.*

17. *A patient presented to her physician with a loss of muscle tone and coordination. She was unable to perform coordinated tasks, such as touching the tip of her finger to her nose. Which part of her brain did the physician conclude was damaged?* Apply

13.6 Meninges, Ventricles, and Cerebrospinal Fluid

Meninges

A. The brain and spinal cord are covered by the dura, arachnoid, and pia mater.

B. The dura mater attaches to the skull and has two layers that can separate to form dural sinuses.

C. Beneath the arachnoid mater, the subarachnoid space contains CSF, which helps cushion the brain.

D. The pia mater attaches directly to the brain.

Ventricles

A. The lateral ventricles in the cerebrum are connected to the third ventricle in the diencephalon by the interventricular foramen.

B. The third ventricle is connected to the fourth ventricle in the pons by the cerebral aqueduct. The central canal of the spinal cord is connected to the fourth ventricle.

Cerebrospinal Fluid

A. CSF is produced from the blood in the choroid plexus of each ventricle. CSF moves from the lateral to the third and then to the fourth ventricle.

B. From the fourth ventricle, CSF enters the subarachnoid space through three apertures.

C. CSF leaves the subarachnoid space through arachnoid granulations and returns to the blood in the dural venous sinuses.

18. *The most superficial of the meninges is a thick, tough membrane called the* Remember
    a. *pia mater.*
    b. *dura mater.*
    c. *arachnoid mater.*
    d. *epidural mater.*

19. *The ventricles of the brain are interconnected. Which of these ventricles are* not *correctly matched with the structures that connect them?* Remember
    a. *lateral ventricle to the third ventricle—interventricular foramina*
    b. *left lateral ventricle to right lateral ventricle—central canal*
    c. *third ventricle to fourth ventricle—cerebral aqueduct*
    d. *fourth ventricle to subarachnoid space—median and lateral apertures*

20. *Cerebrospinal fluid is produced by the ________, circulates through the ventricles, and enters the subarachnoid space. The cerebrospinal fluid leaves the subarachnoid space through the ________.* Remember
    a. *choroid plexuses, arachnoid granulations*
    b. *arachnoid granulations, choroid plexuses*
    c. *dural venous sinuses, dura mater*
    d. *dura mater, dural venous sinuses*

21. *A patient exhibits enlargement of the lateral and third ventricles, but no enlargement of the fourth ventricle. What do you conclude?*

22. *During a lumbar puncture (spinal tap), blood is discovered in the patient's CSF. What does this finding suggest?* Apply

13.7 Blood Supply to the Brain

A. The brain receives blood from the internal carotid and vertebral arteries. The latter form the basilar artery. The basilar and internal carotid arteries contribute to the cerebral arterial circle. Branches from the circle and basilar artery supply the brain.

B. The blood-brain barrier is formed from the endothelial cells of the capillaries in the brain and the astrocytes in the brain tissue.

23. *Water-soluble molecules of the blood plasma move across the blood-brain barrier by* Remember
    a. *diffusion.*
    b. *endocytosis.*
    c. *exocytosis.*
    d. *symport.*
    e. *filtration.*

13.8 Cranial Nerves

Cranial nerves perform sensory, somatic motor, and parasympathetic functions.

Characteristics of the Cranial Nerves

A. The olfactory (I) and optic (II) nerves are involved in the senses of smell and vision, respectively.

B. The oculomotor nerve (III) innervates four of six extrinsic eye muscles and the upper eyelid. The oculomotor nerve also provides parasympathetic supply to the iris and lens of the eye.

C. The trochlear nerve (IV) controls one of the extrinsic eye muscles.

D. The trigeminal nerve (V) supplies the muscles of mastication, as well as a middle ear muscle, a palatine muscle, and two throat muscles. The trigeminal nerve has the greatest cutaneous sensory distribution of any cranial nerve. Two of the three trigeminal nerve branches innervate the teeth.

E. The abducens nerve (VI) controls one of the extrinsic eye muscles.

F. The facial nerve (VII) supplies the muscles of facial expression, an inner ear muscle, and two throat muscles. It is involved in the sense of taste. It is parasympathetic to two sets of salivary glands and to the lacrimal glands.

G. The vestibulocochlear nerve (VIII) is involved in the senses of hearing and balance.

H. The glossopharyngeal nerve (IX) is involved in taste and supplies tactile sensory innervation from the posterior tongue, middle ear, and pharynx. It is also sensory for receptors that monitor blood pressure and gas levels in the blood. The glossopharyngeal nerve is parasympathetic to the parotid salivary glands.

I. The vagus nerve (X) innervates the muscles of the pharynx, palate, and larynx. It is also involved in the sense of taste. The vagus nerve is sensory for the pharynx and larynx and for receptors that monitor blood pressure and gas levels in the blood. The vagus nerve is also sensory for thoracic and abdominal organs. The vagus nerve provides parasympathetic innervation to the thoracic and abdominal organs.

J. The accessory nerve (XI) has only a spinal component. It supplies the sternocleidomastoid and trapezius muscles.

K. The hypoglossal nerve (XII) supplies the intrinsic tongue muscles, three of four extrinsic tongue muscles, and two throat muscles.

Reflexes Involving Cranial Nerves

Many reflexes involved in homeostasis involve the cranial nerves and occur in the brainstem.

24. *The cranial nerve involved in chewing food is the*

    a. *trochlear (IV).*
    b. *trigeminal (V).*
    c. *abducens (VI).*
    d. *facial (VII).*
    e. *vestibulocochlear (VIII).*

25. *The cranial nerve responsible for focusing the eye (innervating the ciliary muscle of the eye) is the* Remember
    a. *optic (II).*
    b. *oculomotor (III).*
    c. *trochlear (IV).*
    d. *abducens (VI).*
    e. *facial (VII).*

26. *The cranial nerve involved in moving the tongue is the*

    a. *trigeminal (V).*
    b. *facial (VII).*
    c. *glossopharyngeal (IX).*
    d. *accessory (XI).*
    e. *hypoglossal (XII).*

27. *The cranial nerve involved in feeling a toothache is the*

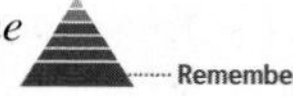

    a. *trochlear (IV).*
    b. *trigeminal (V).*

c. abducens (VI).
d. facial (VII).
e. vestibulocochlear (VIII).

28. *From this list of cranial nerves:*

(1) olfactory (I)
(2) optic (II)
(3) oculomotor (III)
(4) abducens (VI)
(5) vestibulocochlear (VIII)

Select the nerves that are sensory only.

a. 1,2,3 b. 2,3,4 c. 1,2,5 d. 2,3,5 e. 3,4,5

29. *From this list of cranial nerves:*

(1) trigeminal (V)
(2) facial (VII)
(3) glossopharyngeal (IX)
(4) vagus (X)
(5) hypoglossal (XII)

Select the nerves involved in the sense of taste.
a. 1,2,3 b. 1,4,5 c. 2,3,4 d. 2,3,5 e. 3,4,5

30. *From this list of cranial nerves:*

(1) oculomotor (III)
(2) trigeminal (V)
(3) facial (VII)
(4) vestibulocochlear (VIII)
(5) glossopharyngeal (IX)
(6) vagus (X)

Select the nerves that are part of the parasympathetic division of the ANS.
a. 1,2,4,5 b. 1,3,5,6 c. 1,4,5,6 d. 2,3,4,5 e. 2,3,5,6

31. *Describe a clinical test to evaluate each of the 12 cranial nerves.* Apply

32. *A baseball player was accidentally struck on the bridge of his nose with a baseball, resulting in fractures of several facial bones. Soon after sustaining the injury, he noticed that he had lost his sense of smell. Explain how this probably happened.* Apply

33. *Following a car accident in which he hit the left side of his head on the car door, Stanley developed diplopia (double vision) and was unable to move his left eye laterally (abduct the left eye). Explain how this injury caused Stanley's symptoms.* Apply

34. *Over the past month, Andy has noticed that touching his upper lip, even during eating or drinking, produces intense pain in the area extending from the upper lip to just below his right eye. His ability to chew and swallow is not affected. Andy's dentist told him it was not a dental problem and he should see his physician. The physician explained that the condition might be temporary and that the cause is unknown. Explain what cranial nerve is responsible for these symptoms.* Apply

35. *Afton, a teacher for the past 25 years, spent Saturday and Sunday skiing in very cold weather. The following Friday, she got up to get ready for school and was shocked to find that the right side of her face was drooping. She went to the emergency room, where tests could find no evidence of a stroke or a tumor. A physician diagnosed the condition and told Afton that it might be temporary. After about a week, her condition improved. What disorder did the physician diagnose, and what probably brought it on?* Apply

Answers to this chapter's odd-numbered Concept Check questions appear in Appendix F.

14

CHAPTER

Integration of Nervous System Functions

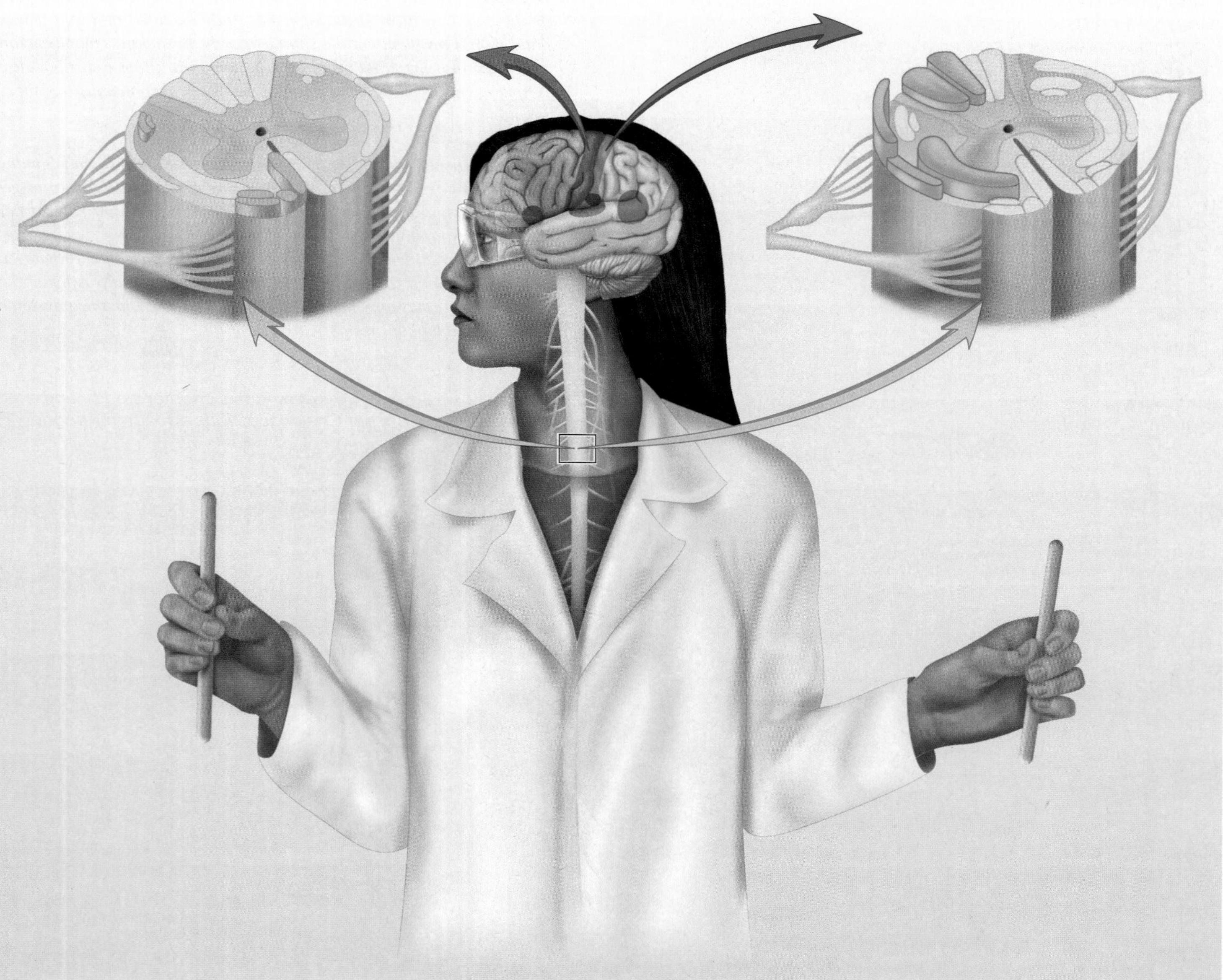

Integration of the nervous system involves the communication of sensory information from areas of the body to the CNS through specific sensory pathways and the control of effectors by the CNS through specific motor pathways.

It is thought that there are more connections in the human brain than there are stars in the Milky Way. These connections allow you to read and understand this paragraph while disregarding the weight of the book in your hands, if you are holding it, or the weight of your forearms on the desk. You are also probably not aware of the small noises around you or the clothes touching your body, until your attention is drawn to them. You certainly are not aware of changes in your blood pressure or your body fluid pH and blood glucose levels, yet your nervous system is actively processing all this sensory input and controlling the responses to that input. On top of this, the human brain is capable of a host of complex higher order functions, such as recording history, reasoning, and planning. The integration of brain and body underlying all of these remarkable abilities makes understanding human brain function one of the most challenging and exciting frontiers of anatomy and physiology.

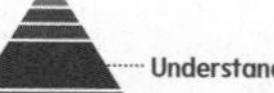

Learn to Predict

When told to put on blindfolds, the students in the anatomy and physiology lab became somewhat nervous—but it turned out to be a simple demonstration of how receptors in the skin detect hot and cold. Each blindfolded student was told to touch a hot object (55°C) with one hand and a cold object (5°C) with the other hand. After a few seconds, the instructor asked the students to identify which hand was touching each object. Were they able to answer correctly? After reading the chapter and recalling how spinal nerves and cranial nerves convey information to the brain, as described in chapters 12 and 13, you will be ready to answer the question.

Determine whether the students could tell which hand was touching which object; then, keeping in mind the complexity of the brain, identify the parts of the CNS involved in making this distinction.

Answers to this question and the chapter's odd-numbered Predict questions can be found in Appendix E.

14.1 Sensation

LEARNING OUTCOMES

After reading this section, you should be able to

A. **List the types of somatic and visceral sensory receptors, tell where they are located, and describe how they function in sensation.**
B. **Describe the roles of receptor potentials and adaptation.**
C. **Differentiate between primary and secondary receptors.**
D. **Differentiate between tonic and phasic receptors.**
E. **List the major ascending sensory tracts and state a function for each.**
F. **Describe the sensory and association areas of the cerebral cortex and discuss their interactions.**

Sensation is the process initiated by stimuli acting on sensory receptors. **Perception** is the conscious awareness of those sensations. The brain constantly receives sensations as action potentials from a wide variety of sensory receptors that receive stimuli from both inside and outside the body. Sensory receptors respond to stimuli by generating action potentials that are propagated along nerves to the spinal cord and brain. Perception results when the brain interprets the sensation-generated action potentials in the cerebral cortex. Some other parts of the brain are involved in modulating sensations before they are perceived. For example, the thalamus and amygdala receive and integrate pain signals.

The **senses** are the means by which the brain receives information about the environment and the body. Historically, five senses were recognized: smell, taste, vision, hearing, and touch. Today, the senses are divided into two basic groups: general and special.

The **general senses** have receptors distributed over a large part of the body. They are divided into two groups: (1) somatic senses and (2) visceral senses (table 14.1; figure 14.1). The **somatic senses** provide sensory information about the body and the environment. Somatic senses include (1) touch, (2) pressure, (3) temperature, (4) pain, and (5) proprioception. **Proprioception** (proh-pree-oh-SEP-shun) is the sense of your body's position and movement. An example of proprioception is the ability of a person to touch their nose when their eyes are closed. This is often used as a field sobriety test. The **visceral senses** provide information about various internal organs and consist primarily of (1) pain and (2) pressure.

The **special senses** are localized to specific organs that have specialized receptors (see table 14.1). The special senses—smell, taste, vision, hearing, and balance—are considered in detail in chapter 15.

Module 7
Nervous System

TABLE 14.1 Classification of the Senses

Types of Sense	Receptor Type	Initiation of Response	Specific Examples
GENERAL SENSES			
Somatic			
Touch	Mechanoreceptors	Compression of receptors	
Stroking			Meissner corpuscle Hair follicle receptor
Texture			Merkel disk
Vibration			Pacinian corpuscle
Skin stretch			Ruffini end organ
Itch, tickle			Free nerve endings
Pressure	Mechanoreceptors	Compression of receptors	Merkel disk
Proprioception	Mechanoreceptors	Compression of receptors	Free nerve endings Pacinian corpuscle Muscle spindle Golgi tendon organ
Temperature	Thermoreceptors	Temperature around nerve endings	Free nerve endings Cold receptors Warm receptors
Pain	Nociceptors	Irritation of nerve endings (e.g., mechanical, chemical, or thermal)	Free nerve endings
Visceral			
Pain	Nociceptors	Irritation of nerve endings	Free nerve endings
Pressure	Mechanoreceptors	Compression of receptors	Pacinian corpuscle
SPECIAL SENSES			
Smell	Chemoreceptors	Binding of molecules to membrane receptors	Olfactory receptor
Taste	Chemoreceptors	Binding of molecules to membrane receptors	Taste receptor
Vision	Photoreceptors	Chemical change in receptors initiated by light	Rods and cones
Hearing	Mechanoreceptors	Bending of microvilli on receptor cells	Hair cells
Balance	Mechanoreceptors	Bending of microvilli on receptor cells	Hair cells

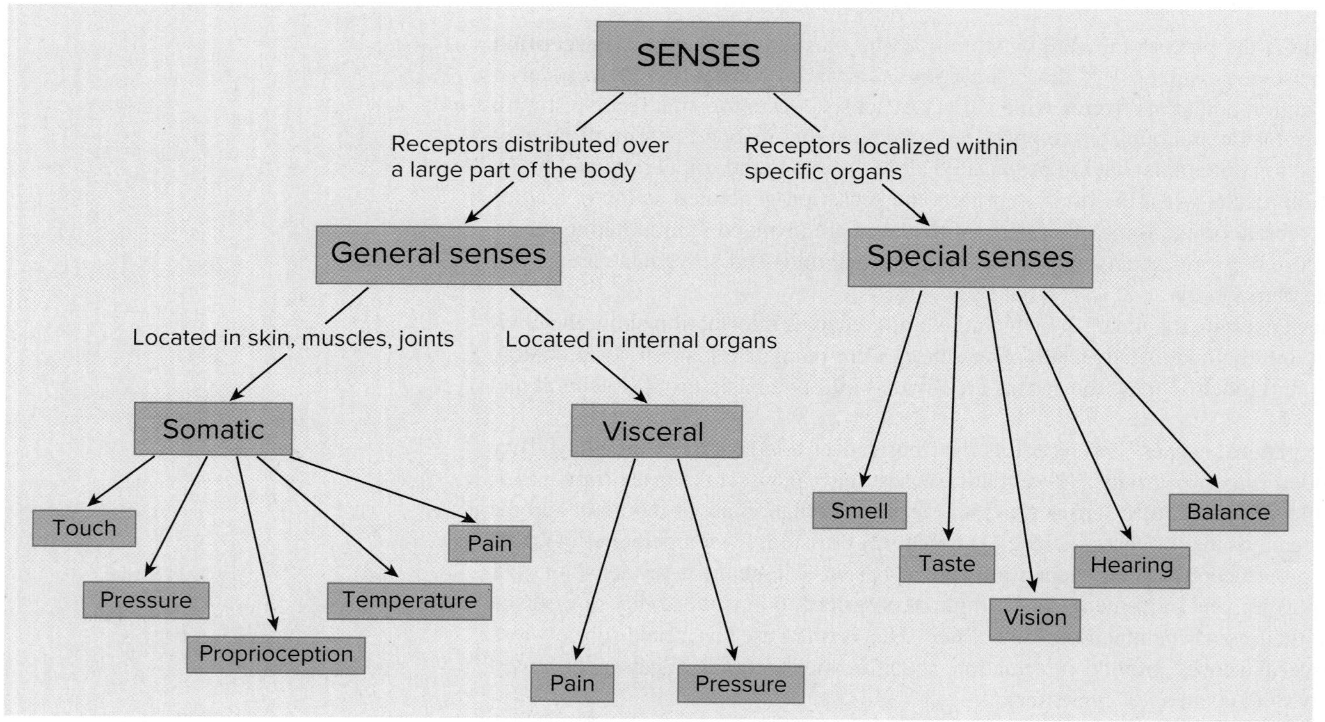

FIGURE 14.1 Classification of the Senses
The senses are classified based on the location of the sensory receptors, as well as the types of stimuli involved.

Not all of the sensory information detected by sensory receptors results in perception. Some action potentials reach areas of the brain where they are not consciously perceived. Two examples are proprioception and detection of change in homeostatic variables. For proprioception, although we can be consciously aware of body position and movements, much of this sensory information is propagated to the cerebellum, where it is processed at an unconscious level. For homeostasis, sensory information from receptors that monitor body variables, such as blood pressure, are processed unconsciously in the medulla oblongata. Because blood pressure must be regulated constantly to maintain homeostasis, if we had to regulate blood pressure consciously, we would not be able to think of much else. Homeostasis, therefore, is controlled largely without our conscious involvement.

Even the cerebral cortex screens much of what it receives and does not perceive many of the action potentials that reach it. In addition, humans exhibit selective awareness. We are more aware of sensations on which we focus our attention than on other sensations. If we were aware of all the sensory information that arrived at the cerebral cortex, we would probably not be able to function.

Sensory Receptors

Types of Sensory Receptors

Sensory receptors are commonly classified by three criteria: (1) type of stimulus they detect (table 14.1), (2) location in the body, and (3) receptor structure (table 14.2).

There are five types of sensory receptors based on the type of stimulus they detect (see table 14.1).

1. **Mechanoreceptors** respond to mechanical force such as compression, bending, or stretching of cells. The senses of touch, pressure, proprioception, hearing, and balance all depend on a variety of mechanoreceptors.
2. **Chemoreceptors** respond to chemicals. Smell and taste depend on chemoreceptors.
3. **Thermoreceptors** respond to changes in temperature at the site of the receptor and are necessary for the sense of temperature.
4. **Photoreceptors** respond to light striking the receptor cells and are necessary for vision.
5. **Nociceptors** (noh-sih-SEP-ters; L., *noceo,* hurt), or *pain receptors,* respond to extreme mechanical, chemical, and thermal stimuli. Most sensory receptors typically respond to one type of stimulus, but some nociceptors respond to more than one.

There are three types of sensory receptors based on their location.

1. **Cutaneous receptors** are associated with the skin. Cutaneous receptors provide information about the external environment.
2. **Visceroreceptors** are associated with the viscera or organs. Visceroreceptors provide information about the internal environment.
3. **Proprioceptors** are associated with joints, tendons, and other connective tissue. Proprioceptors provide information about body position, movement, and the extent of stretch or the force of muscular contractions.

Table 14.2 summarizes eight types of general sensory receptors based on structure. Each of these receptor types responds to specific types of stimuli. Structurally, the simplest and most common sensory receptors are the **free nerve endings** (figure 14.2*a*), which are relatively unspecialized neuronal branches similar to dendrites. Free nerve endings are distributed throughout most parts of the body and are especially abundant

TABLE 14.2 Structural Classification of General Sensory Receptors

Type of Receptor	Structure	Function
Free nerve ending	Branching, no capsule	Pain, itch, tickle, temperature, joint movement, and proprioception
Merkel disk	Consists of flattened expansions at the end of axons; each expansion is associated with a Merkel cell	Light touch and superficial pressure
Hair follicle receptor	Wrapped around hair follicles or extending along the hair axis; each axon supplies several hairs, and each hair receives branches from several neurons, resulting in considerable overlap	Light touch; responds to very slight bending of the hair
Pacinian corpuscle	Onion-shaped capsule composed of several cell layers with a single central nerve process	Deep cutaneous pressure, vibration, and proprioception
Meissner corpuscle	Several branches of a single axon associated with specialized Schwann cells and surrounded by a connective tissue capsule	Two-point discrimination
Ruffini end organ	Branching axon with numerous small, terminal knobs surrounded by a connective tissue capsule	Continuous touch or pressure; responds to depression or stretch of the skin
Muscle spindle	Three to 10 striated muscle fibers enclosed by a loose connective tissue capsule, striated only at the ends, with sensory nerve endings in the center	Proprioception associated with detection of muscle stretch; important for control of muscle tone
Golgi tendon organ	Surrounds a bundle of tendon fasciculi and is enclosed by a delicate connective tissue capsule; nerve terminations are branched, with small swellings applied to individual tendon fasciculi	Proprioception associated with the stretch of a tendon; important for control of muscle contraction

FUNDAMENTAL **Figure**

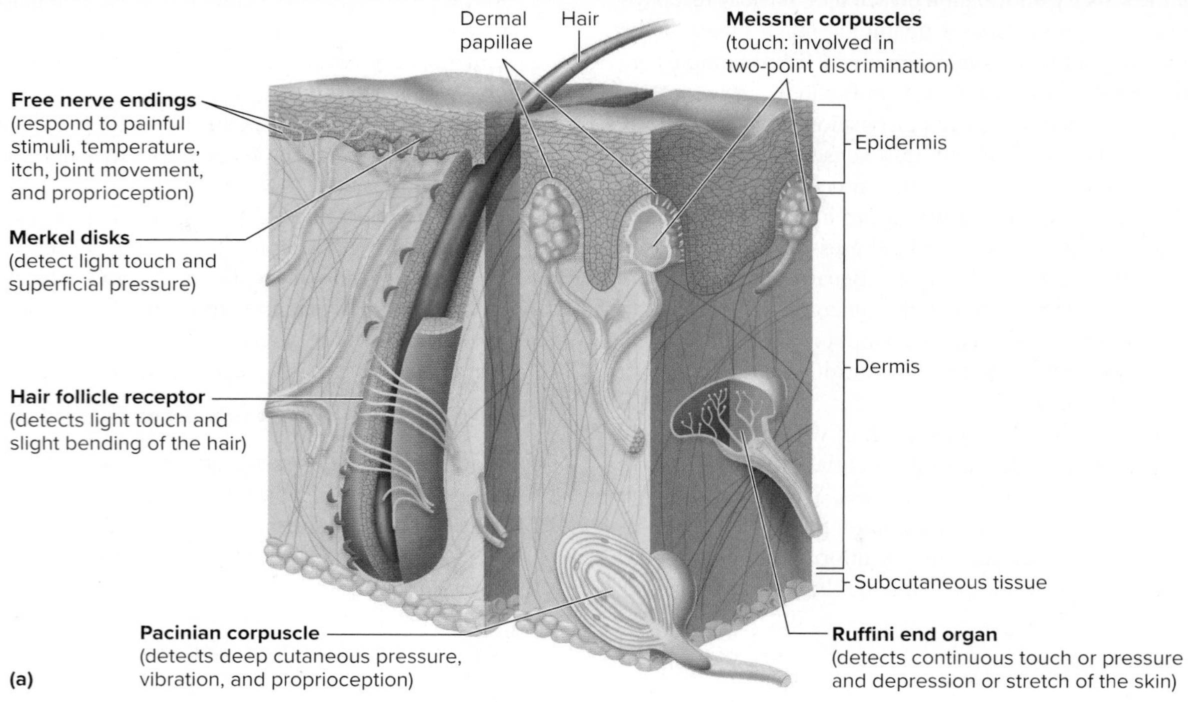

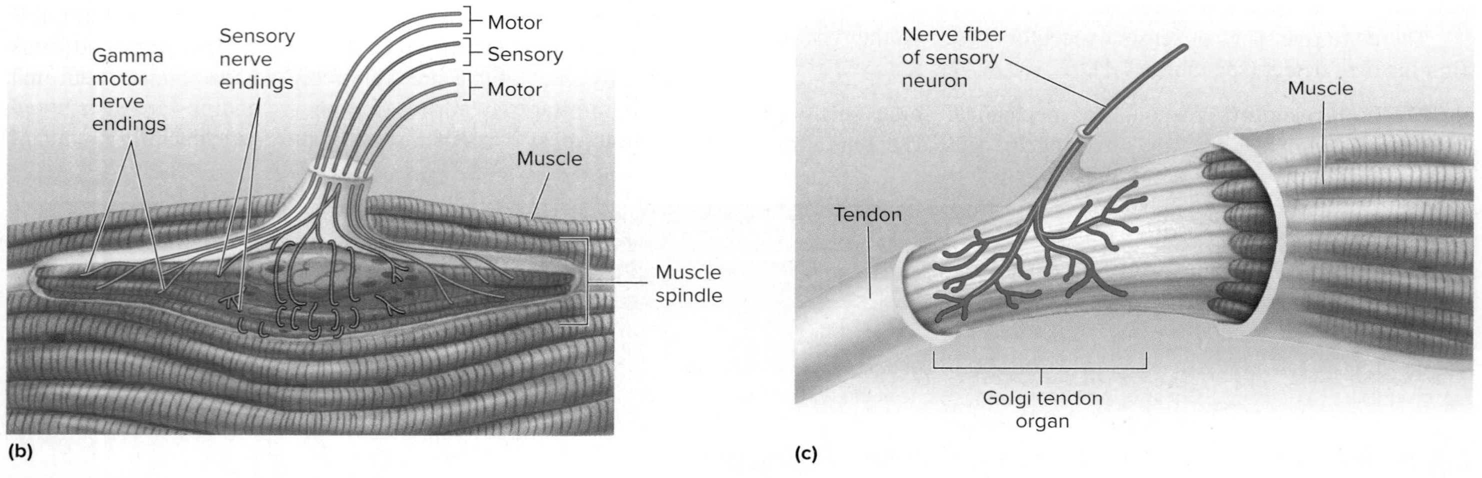

FIGURE 14.2 General Sensory Receptors

(*a*) The sensory receptors of the skin vary in structure and sensitivity, allowing us to interact with our environment while still maintaining homeostasis.
(*b*) Muscle spindles are specialized muscle fibers in skeletal muscles. They send information about the length of the muscle via sensory neurons.
(*c*) Golgi tendon organs are proprioceptive receptors in the tendon near the muscle. When activated by stretch, they send signals via sensory neurons.

in epithelial and connective tissues. These receptors are responsible for a number of sensations, including pain, temperature, itch, and movement.

The free nerve endings responsible for temperature detection respond to three types of sensations: (1) increase in skin temperature, (2) decrease in skin temperature, and (3) pain. **Cold receptors** increase their rate of action potential production as the skin is cooled. Cold receptors are also activated by menthol, which gives mint its cool taste. **Warm receptors** increase their rate of action potential production as skin temperature increases. Both cold and warm receptors respond most strongly to changes in temperature. Cold receptors are 10 to 15 times more numerous than warm receptors in any given area of skin. The third type of free nerve ending that responds to temperature is a pain receptor that is stimulated by extreme cold or heat. At very cold temperatures (0°–12°C), only pain receptors are stimulated. As the temperature increases above 15°C, the pain sensation ends. Between 12°C and 35°C, cold fibers are stimulated and, between 25°C and 47°C, nerve fibers from warm receptors are

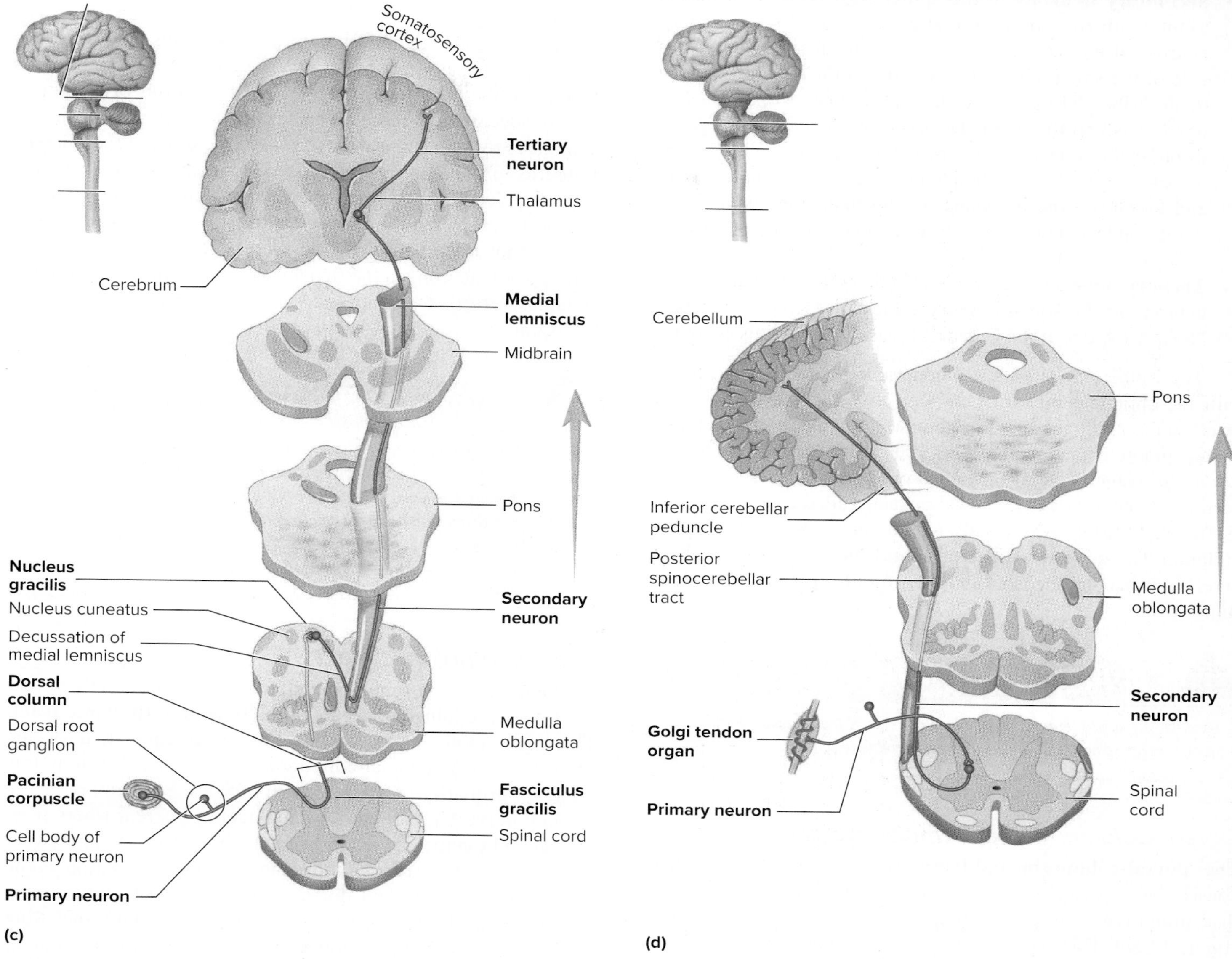

FIGURE 14.5 (continued)

Anterolateral System

The **anterolateral system** is one of the two major systems that convey cutaneous sensory information to the brain (figure 14.5*a*). The anterolateral system includes three tracts: (1) spinothalamic, (2) spinoreticular, and (3) spinomesencephalic. The **spinothalamic tract** allows conscious perception of pain and temperature information, as well as light touch and pressure, tickle, and itch sensations (figure 14.5*b*). The **spinoreticular tract** and the **spinomesencephalic tract** carry pain and touch sensations to other parts of the brain, where the information is not consciously perceived (see table 14.3). There is, however, considerable overlap among these three tracts within the anterolateral system.

The spinothalamic tract transmits sensory signals from peripheral receptors to the cerebral cortex through three neurons in sequence—the primary, secondary, and tertiary neurons (figure 14.5*b*).

- **Primary neurons** conduct action potentials that originate at the sensory receptor to the CNS. The axons of these neurons form the dorsal root of a spinal segment and their cell bodies are located in the dorsal root ganglia (see chapter 12). The primary neurons relay sensory input from the periphery to the dorsal horn of the spinal cord, where they synapse with interneurons. The interneurons, which are not specifically named in the three-neuron sequence, synapse with secondary neurons.

- **Secondary neurons** in the spinal cord relay information to the brain. Within the spinal cord, axons from secondary neurons decussate (cross) to the *contralateral* (opposite) side of the spinal cord. **Decussation** is the term often used to describe the crossover of nerve fibers from one side of the CNS to the other. Decussation of the axons occurs through the anterior portion of the gray and white commissures. The axons then enter the spinothalamic tract and ascend to the thalamus. In the thalamus, axons from the secondary neurons synapse with cell bodies of tertiary neurons.
- **Tertiary neurons** in the thalamus relay information to neurons in the somatosensory cortex of the cerebrum (see "Sensory Areas of the Cerebral Cortex" later in this chapter).

The spinoreticular and spinomesencephalic tracts ascend with the spinothalamic tract through the spinal cord but then divert to the midbrain and other brainstem nuclei. Some neurons in the spinoreticular tracts do not cross over but ascend on the *ipsilateral* (same) side of the spinal cord on which they enter. A portion of the spinomesencephalic tract, called the **spinotectal** (SPY-noh-TEK-tal) **tract,** ends in the superior colliculi of the midbrain. The spinotectal tract transmits action potentials involved in reflexes that turn the head and eyes toward a point of cutaneous stimulation.

Predict 1

Describe the clinical effect of a lesion on one side of the spinal cord that interrupts the spinothalamic tract of the anterolateral system.

Dorsal-Column/Medial-Lemniscal System

The **dorsal-column/medial-lemniscal** (lem-NIS-kal) **system** consists of two pathways that carry the sensations of two-point discrimination, proprioception, pressure, and vibration (figure 14.5*c*). This system is named for the dorsal column of the spinal cord and the medial lemniscus, which is the continuation of the dorsal column in the brainstem. The term *lemniscus* means "ribbon" and refers to the thin, ribbonlike appearance of the pathway as it passes through the brainstem.

Primary neurons of the dorsal-column/medial-lemniscal system are located in the dorsal root ganglia. They are the largest cell bodies in the dorsal root ganglia, especially those for two-point discrimination. Many axons of the primary neurons of the dorsal-column/medial-lemniscal system enter the spinal cord, ascend its entire length without crossing to its opposite side, and synapse with secondary neurons located in the medulla oblongata. Others synapse in the thoracic portion of the spinal cord.

In the spinal cord, the dorsal-column/medial-lemniscal system is divided into two tracts (see figure 14.5*a*) based on the source of the stimulus. The **fasciculus gracilis** (GRAS-i-lis; thin) conveys sensations from the lower part of the body, *below* the midthoracic level. The **fasciculus cuneatus** (KYOO-nee-AH-tus; wedge-shaped) conveys sensations from the upper part of the body, *above* the midthorax. The fasciculus gracilis terminates by synapsing with secondary neurons in the **nucleus gracilis** of the medulla oblongata or with neurons of the posterior spinocerebellar tracts. The fasciculus cuneatus primarily terminates by synapsing with secondary neurons in the **nucleus cuneatus** of the medulla oblongata. Secondary neurons exit the nucleus gracilis and the nucleus cuneatus, cross to the opposite side of the medulla through the decussations of the medial lemniscus, and ascend through the medial lemniscus to synapse with tertiary neurons in the thalamus. Tertiary neurons from the thalamus project to the primary somatosensory cortex of the cerebrum.

Predict 2

Bill and Mary were involved in an accident, and each experienced loss of proprioception, fine touch, and vibration on the left side of the body below the waist. Physicians determined by magnetic resonance imaging (MRI) that Bill had damage to his spinal cord and that Mary had damage to her brainstem. Explain which side of the spinal cord was damaged in Bill and which side of the brainstem was damaged in Mary.

Trigeminothalamic Tract

As the fibers of the spinothalamic tracts pass through the brainstem, they are joined by fibers of the **trigeminothalamic tract.** The trigeminothalamic tract is the facial equivalent of the spinothalamic and dorsal-column/medial-lemniscal system. It is made up primarily of afferent fibers from the trigeminal nerve (cranial nerve V), along with a few tactile afferent fibers from the ear and tongue carried by cranial nerves VII, IX, and sometimes X. This tract carries the same sensory information as the spinothalamic tracts and dorsal-column/medial-lemniscal system but from the face, nasal cavity, and oral cavity, including the teeth. As with the spinothalamic tracts and dorsal-column/medial-lemniscal system, primary neurons of the trigeminothalamic tract from one side of the face synapse with secondary neurons that decussate to the opposite side of the brainstem. These secondary neurons synapse with tertiary neurons in the thalamus, which project to the primary somatosensory cortex of the cerebrum.

Spinocerebellar Tracts

The **spinocerebellar tracts** carry proprioceptive information to the cerebellum, where information concerning actual movements can be monitored and compared with cerebral information representing intended movements. Two spinocerebellar tracts extend through the spinal cord: the posterior and anterior spinocerebellar tracts (see figure 14.5*a*).

The **posterior spinocerebellar tract** (figure 14.5*d*) carries information from the upper part of the body in the thoracic and upper lumbar regions. It contains uncrossed nerve fibers that enter the cerebellum through the inferior cerebellar peduncles. The **anterior spinocerebellar tract** carries information from the lower trunk and lower limbs. It contains both crossed and uncrossed nerve fibers that enter the cerebellum through the superior cerebellar peduncle. The crossed fibers recross in the cerebellum. Both spinocerebellar tracts transmit proprioceptive information to the cerebellum from the same side of the body as the cerebellar hemisphere to which they project. Why the anterior spinocerebellar tract decussates twice to accomplish this feat is unknown. Much of the proprioceptive information carried from the lower limbs by the fasciculus gracilis of the dorsal-column/medial-lemniscal system is transferred by synapses in the inferior thorax to the spinocerebellar system and enters the cerebellum as unconscious proprioceptive information. The spinocerebellar tracts convey very little information from the upper limbs to the cerebellum. Proprioception from the upper limbs is projected to the thalamus. This input enters the cerebellum through the inferior peduncle from the nucleus cuneatus of the dorsal-column/medial-lemniscal system. Therefore, the dorsal-column/medial-lemniscal system is involved not only in conscious awareness of proprioception but also in unconscious neuromuscular functions.

Predict 3

Most of the neurons from the fasciculus gracilis synapse in the inferior thorax and enter the spinocerebellar system, whereas most of the neurons from the fasciculus cuneatus synapse in the nucleus cuneatus and then continue to the thalamus and cerebrum. Therefore, it can be deduced that most of the proprioception from the lower limbs is unconscious and most of the proprioception from the upper limbs is conscious. Explain why this difference in the two sets of limbs is of value.

Descending Pathways Modifying Sensation

The cerebral cortex, as well as other brain regions, may reduce conscious perception of sensation, including pain, through descending pathways. Descending pathways "descend" from the brain to the spinal cord. Neurons in these pathways send collateral branches to the thalamus, reticular formation, trigeminal nuclei, and spinal cord. Neuromodulators, such as endorphins and enkephalin, released from axons originating in these CNS regions, decrease the frequency of action potentials in sensory tracts (see the discussion of presynaptic inhibition in chapter 11).

Pain Pathways

Pain is a sensation characterized by a group of unpleasant and complex perceptual and emotional experiences that trigger autonomic, psychological, and somatic motor responses. Pain sensation has two components: (1) rapidly conducted action potentials carried by large-diameter, myelinated axons, resulting in sharp, well-localized, pricking or cutting pain, followed by (2) more slowly propagated action potentials, carried by smaller, less heavily myelinated axons, resulting in diffuse burning or aching pain. The variations in pain sensation that we experience result from (1) the mechanisms by which pain receptors are stimulated, (2) differences in the integration of action potentials from the pain receptors, and (3) complex interactions in the cerebral cortex, cingulate gyrus, and thalamus, where the emotional component of pain is registered. Neurons in the cerebral cortex respond to pain stimuli selectively based on prior experience and context.

The sensation of pain involves sensory pathways that are activated by both pain receptors and nearby mechanoreceptors. Tactile mechanoreceptors in the dorsal-column/medial-lemniscal system are often activated by the same stimuli that affect pain receptors. Action potentials from tactile receptors provide information that allows the pain sensation to be localized. Superficial pain is highly localized, in part, because of the simultaneous stimulation of pain receptors and mechanoreceptors in the skin. Deep, or visceral, pain is not highly localized because of fewer mechanoreceptors in the deeper structures, and it is normally perceived as a diffuse pain.

Dorsal-column/medial-lemniscal system neurons are involved in what is called the **gate-control theory** of pain control. Primary neurons of this system send out collateral branches that synapse with interneurons in the dorsal horn of the spinal cord. These

Clinical IMPACT 14.1

Headaches

Headaches have a variety of causes and are generally poorly understood. **Tension headaches** are caused by muscle tension. They consist of a dull, steady pain in the forehead, temples, and neck or throughout the head. Tension headaches are associated with stress, fatigue, and poor posture.

Migraine headaches (*migraine,* half a skull) usually occur on only one side of the head and appear to involve a combination of neurological dysfunction and abnormal dilation and constriction of blood vessels. For some people, a migraine can start with an aura, which is a sensation that often involves distorted vision, shooting lines, and blind spots. Migraines consist of severe throbbing, pulsating pain, along with sensitivity to sensory input, especially light and sound. They are also accompanied by nausea or vomiting. About 12% of the population suffers from migraines, with about 70% having a family history of the disorder. Women are affected three times more often than men. Common triggers include stress, certain foods and alcohol, altered sleep patterns, strong sensory stimuli (lights, sounds, smells), weather changes, and, for women, the menstrual cycle. Fortunately, the severity and frequency of attacks usually decrease with age.

interneurons have an inhibitory effect on secondary neurons of the spinothalamic tract. Thus, pain action potentials traveling through the spinothalamic tract can be suppressed by action potentials that originate in neurons of the dorsal-column/medial-lemniscal system. The arrangement may act as a "gate" for pain action potentials transmitted in the spinothalamic tract. Increased activity in the dorsal-column/medial-lemniscal system tends to close the gate, thereby reducing pain action potentials transmitted in the spinothalamic tract. Descending pathways from the cerebral cortex or other brain regions can also regulate the gate. The gate-control theory may explain the physiological basis for reducing the intensity of chronic pain by rubbing the area around an injury, transcutaneous electrical stimulation, acupuncture, massage, and exercise. Exercise decreases the sensation of pain and is important in managing chronic pain not associated with illness. Acupuncture may lessen pain through the action of a gating mechanism that inhibits pain transmission upward in the spinal cord.

Analgesics are pain-relieving medications that act in much the same way as gate control. Some analgesics act in the periphery to reduce inflammation and the activation of peripheral nerves; others block the transmission of pain sensations in the spinal cord from primary neurons to neurons of the ascending pathways. Other analgesics function at the level of the cerebral cortex to modulate pain.

Referred pain is a painful sensation in a region of the body that is not the source of the pain stimulus. Most commonly, patients sense referred pain in the skin or other superficial structures when internal organs are damaged or inflamed. This sensation usually occurs because both the area of skin to which the pain is referred and the visceral area that is damaged are innervated by neurons that project to the same area of the cerebral cortex. The brain cannot distinguish between the two sources of painful stimuli, and the painful sensation is referred to the most superficial structures innervated by the converging neurons. This referral may occur because the number of receptors is much greater in superficial structures than in deep structures and the brain is more "accustomed" to dealing with superficial stimuli. Referred pain is clinically useful in diagnosing the actual cause of a painful stimulus. Heart attack victims often feel cutaneous pain radiating from the left shoulder down the arm. Other examples of referred pain are shown in figure 14.6.

Chronic pain is long lasting. Some chronic pain has a known cause, such as tissue damage in the case of arthritis. Other chronic pain has no clear cause and can be very debilitating, such as migraine or back pain. Hence, while acute pain is important in warning us of potentially injurious conditions, chronic pain loses its value of providing information about the condition of the body. People suffering from chronic pain often feel helpless and hopeless, and they may become dependent on drugs. Over 2 million people in the United States at any given time experience chronic pain sufficient to impair activity.

Apply

Predict 4

A man has constipation that is causing distension and painful cramping in his colon. What kind of pain does he experience (local or diffuse), and where does he perceive it? Explain.

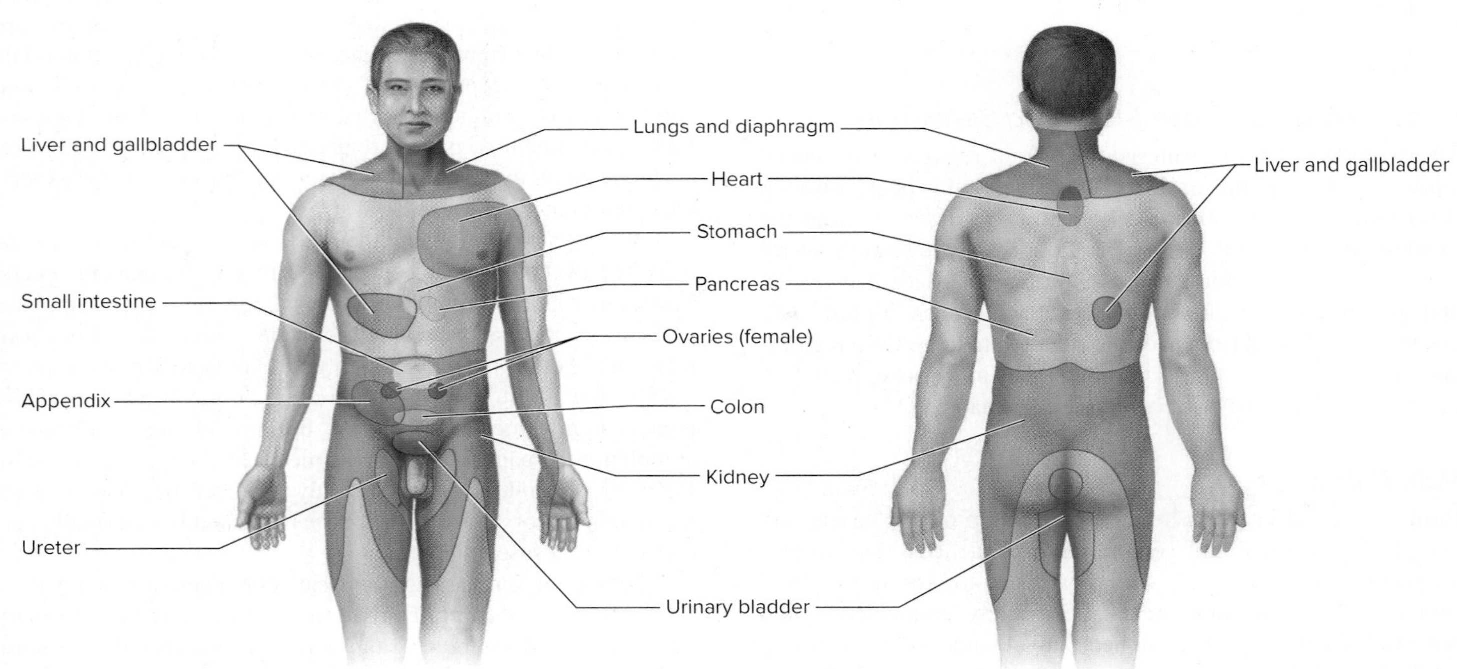

FIGURE 14.6 Areas of Referred Pain on the Body Surface
Pain from the indicated internal organs is referred to the surface areas shown.

ASSESS YOUR PROGRESS

5. *What are the functions of the anterolateral and dorsal-column/medial-lemniscal systems? Describe where the neurons of these systems cross over and synapse.*
6. *How is the trigeminothalamic tract different from the spinothalamic tract?*
7. *What kind of information is carried by the spinocerebellar tracts? Where do the anterior and posterior spinocerebellar tracts originate? Do these tracts terminate on the same or opposite side of the body from where they originate?*
8. *How do descending pathways modulate sensation?*
9. *How are pain sensations localized? What is referred pain?*

Sensory Areas of the Cerebral Cortex

Sensory pathways project to specific regions of the cerebral cortex called **primary sensory areas** (figure 14.7). The terms *area* and *cortex* are often used interchangeably to refer to the same functional region of the cerebral cortex. These areas are where sensations are perceived. The primary sensory areas of the cerebral cortex must be intact in order for conscious perception, localization, and identification of a stimulus.

Clinical IMPACT 14.2

Phantom Pain

Phantom pain occurs in people who have had appendages amputated or a structure, such as a tooth, removed. Many of these people perceive pain (which may be intense) or other sensations in the amputated structure as if it were still in place. If a neuron pathway that transmits action potentials is stimulated at any point along that pathway, action potentials are initiated and propagated toward the CNS. Integration results in the perception of pain that is projected to the site of the sensory receptors, even if those sensory receptors are no longer present. A similar phenomenon can be easily demonstrated by bumping the ulnar nerve where it crosses the elbow (the funny bone). Even though the neurons are stimulated at the elbow, we often feel a sensation of pain in the fourth and fifth digits.

A factor that may be important in phantom pain is the lack of touch, pressure, and proprioceptive impulses from the amputated limb. Those action potentials suppress the transmission of pain action potentials in the pain pathways, as explained by the gate-control theory of pain. When a limb is amputated, the inhibitory effect of sensory information is removed. As a consequence, the intensity of phantom pain may increase. Another factor in phantom pain may be that the cerebral cortex retains an image of the amputated body part.

FUNDAMENTAL **Figure**

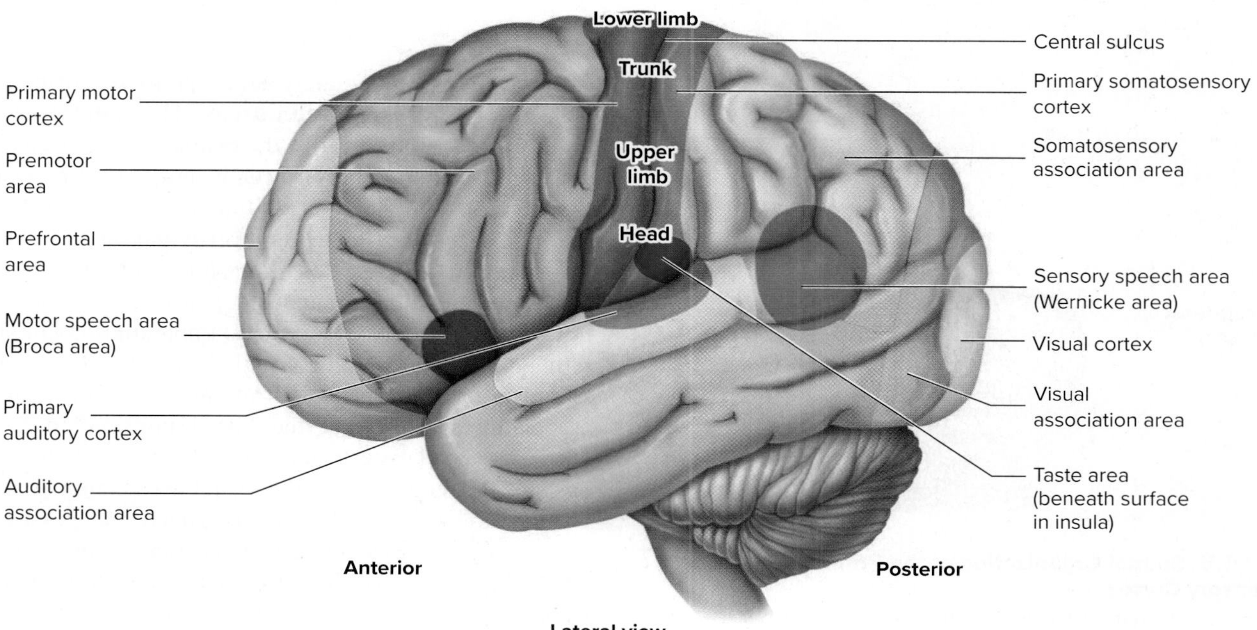

FIGURE 14.7 Functional Regions of the Lateral Side of the Left Cerebral Cortex
Sensory and motor areas are indicated by different colors. Notice the body areas are associated with specific regions of the primary motor cortex and primary somatosensory cortex. APR

The **primary somatosensory cortex,** or *general sensory area,* receives general sensory input, such as pain, pressure, and temperature, from the thalamus. The primary somatosensory cortex occupies most of the postcentral gyrus in the parietal lobes of the cerebrum (see chapter 13).

The primary somatosensory cortex is organized spatially relative to the general plan of the body (figure 14.8). For example, sensory impulses conducting input from the feet project to the most superior portion of the primary somatosensory cortex, and sensory impulses from the face project to the most inferior portion. The pattern of the primary somatosensory cortex in each hemisphere is arranged in the form of an upside-down half **homunculus** (hoh-MUNGK-yoo-lus; little human) representing the opposite side of the body, with the feet located superiorly and the head inferiorly. The size of various regions of the primary somatosensory cortex is related to the number of sensory receptors in that area of the body. For example, the density of sensory receptors is much greater in the face than in the legs; therefore, a greater area of the primary somatosensory cortex contains sensory neurons associated with the face, and the homunculus has a disproportionately large face. In addition to allowing perception of somatic stimuli, the primary somatosensory cortex also localizes the site of sensation on the surface of the body. This phenomenon, called **projection,** allows the brain to refer a stimulus to the appropriate location on the surface of the body. An example is when you feel the touch of a mosquito landing on your arm and you know exactly where to slap.

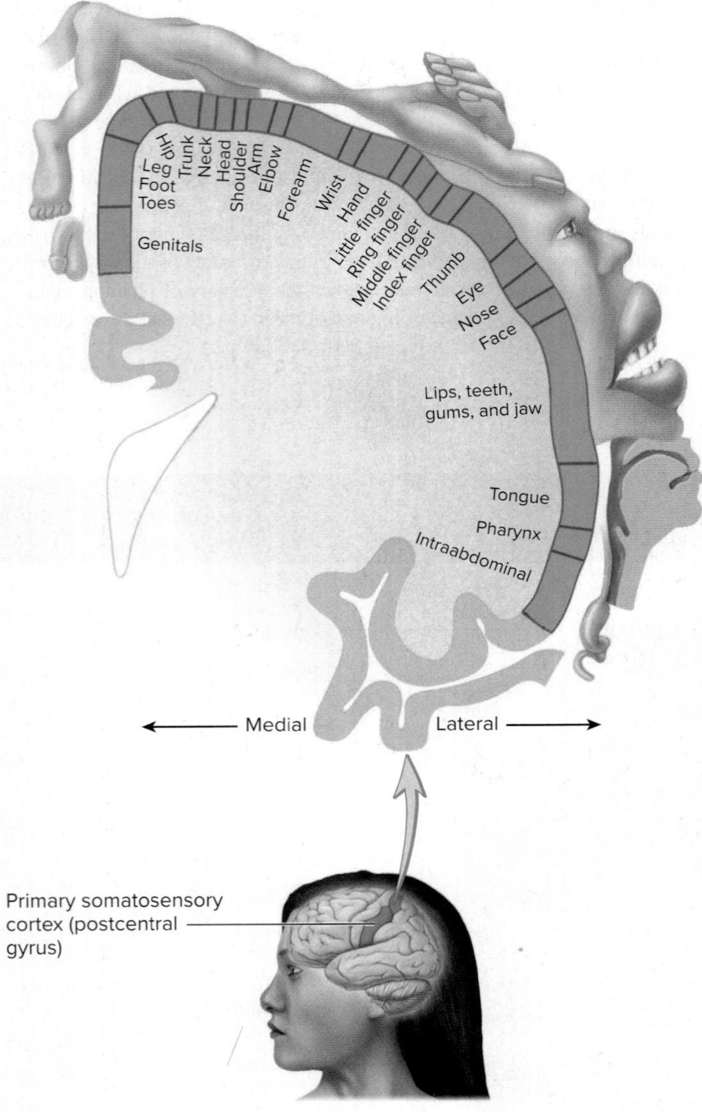

FIGURE 14.8 Spatial Organization of the Primary Somatosensory Cortex

Cerebral cortex seen in frontal section on the left side of the brain. The figure of the body (homunculus) depicts the nerve distributions; the size of each body region shown indicates relative innervation. The cortex occurs on both sides of the brain but appears on only one side in this illustration. The inset shows the somatosensory region of the left hemisphere (*green*). APR

There are other primary sensory areas of the cerebral cortex (see figure 14.7). The **taste area,** where taste sensations are consciously perceived in the cortex, is located in the insula, deep to the inferior end of the postcentral gyrus. The **olfactory cortex** (not shown in figure 14.7) is on the inferior surface of the temporal lobe and is where both conscious and unconscious responses to odor are perceived and processed (see chapter 15). The **primary auditory cortex,** where auditory stimuli are processed by the brain, is located in the superior part of the temporal lobe. The **visual cortex,** where portions of visual images are processed, is located in the occipital lobe. In the visual cortex, color, shape, and movement are processed separately rather than as a complete "color motion picture." These sensory areas are discussed more fully in chapter 15.

Sensory Processing

Cortical areas immediately adjacent to the primary sensory areas are called **association areas.** The **somatosensory association area** is posterior to the primary somatosensory cortex, and the **visual association area** is anterior to the visual cortex (see figure 14.7). These areas function in the process of recognition. The association areas receive and integrate information from the primary somatosensory area and other brain regions. This allows evaluation and recognition of the sensory input. For example, when sensory action potentials originating in the retina of the eye reach the visual cortex, the image is perceived. Action potentials then pass from the visual cortex to the visual association area, where the visual information is compared with past visual experience ("Have I seen this before?"). On the basis of this comparison, the visual association area "decides" whether the visual input is recognized and passes judgment concerning the significance of the input. For example, when surveying a crowd, we generally pay more attention to a person we know than someone we have never seen.

The visual association area, like other association areas of the cortex, has reciprocal connections with other parts of the cortex that influence decisions. For example, the visual association area has input from the frontal lobe, where emotional value is placed on the visual input. Because of these numerous connections, visual information is judged several times as it passes beyond the visual association area. This may be one of the reasons that two individuals' perceptions of the same painting can be vastly different.

ASSESS YOUR PROGRESS

10. *Where are the locations of the primary sensory areas of the cerebral cortex, and what are the functions of each area?*
11. *Describe the spatial organization of the general body plan in the primary somatosensory cortex. Why are some areas of the body represented as larger than other areas?*
12. *What is the role of an association area? Where are they located in reference to the primary sensory cortices?*

14.2 Control of Skeletal Muscles

LEARNING OUTCOMES

After reading this section, you should be able to

A. **Describe the primary motor area of the cerebral cortex.**
B. **Discuss how the primary motor area interacts with other parts of the frontal lobe of the cerebrum.**
C. **Distinguish between upper and lower motor neurons.**
D. **Distinguish between direct and indirect tracts.**
E. **Explain how the basal nuclei and the cerebellum regulate motor function.**

The motor system of the brain and spinal cord is responsible for maintaining the body's posture and balance; for moving the trunk, head, limbs, and eyes; and for communicating through facial expressions and speech. Reflexes mediated through the spinal cord (see chapter 12) and the brainstem (see chapter 13) are responsible for some body movements. These are called **involuntary movements** because they occur without conscious thought. **Voluntary movements,** on the other hand, are consciously activated to achieve a specific goal, such as walking or typing. Although consciously activated, most voluntary movements occur automatically once learned. Thus, a toddler who is just learning to walk must concentrate on every step. However, once the toddler has mastered walking, he or she does not have to think about the moment-to-moment control of every muscle because neural circuits in the reticular formation and spinal cord automatically control the limbs. After learning a complex task, such as texting or typing, people can perform it relatively automatically.

Voluntary movements depend on upper and lower motor neurons. **Upper motor neurons** connect the cerebral cortex to lower motor neurons directly or through interneurons. The cell bodies of upper motor neurons are in the cerebral cortex. **Lower motor neurons** connect upper motor neurons to skeletal muscles. They have axons that leave the central nervous system and extend through nerves to innervate skeletal muscles. The cell bodies of lower motor neurons are located in the ventral horns of the spinal cord gray matter and in the cranial nerve nuclei of the brainstem.

Voluntary movements require the following steps:

1. Cerebral cortex communicates with the basal nuclei and cerebellum to plan, coordinate, and execute movements.
2. Upper motor neurons in the premotor areas of the cerebral cortex are stimulated and send action potentials down the descending tracts to the lower motor neurons.
3. Lower motor neurons are stimulated, and they then stimulate skeletal muscles to contract.

Motor Areas of the Cerebral Cortex

Body movements are controlled by several motor areas of the brain. Motor pathways from the **primary motor cortex,** or *primary motor area* (see figure 14.7), control many voluntary movements, especially the fine motor movements of the hands. The primary motor cortex occupies the precentral gyrus in the frontal lobes (see chapter 13). Upper motor neurons are located in three areas of the cortex. (1) The primary motor cortex contains about 30% of the upper motor neurons. (2) The premotor area contains another 30%. (3) The primary somatosensory cortex contains the rest.

The cortical functions of the primary motor cortex are spatially arranged according to the general body plan—similar to the spatial arrangement of the primary somatosensory cortex (figure 14.9). Thus, the neuron cell bodies controlling motor functions of the feet are in the most superior and medial portions of the precentral gyrus, whereas those for the face are in the inferior region. As with the primary somatosensory cortex, the size of various regions in the primary motor cortex is related to the number of motor units in that area of the body. Hence, some body parts in the primay motor cortex are represented as relatively large areas, such as the thumb and tongue. These muscle groups have many motor units. Muscles performing precise movements, such as those controlling the hands and face, have many motor units, each of which has a small number of muscle fibers. Multiple-motor-unit summation (see chapter 9) can precisely control the force of contraction of these muscles because only a few muscle fibers at a time are recruited. On the other hand, muscle groups with few motor units are represented by relatively small areas of the primary motor cortex, even if the muscles innervated are quite large. For example, the muscles controlling movements of the thigh and leg have proportionately fewer motor units than the muscles of the hand, but they have many more and much larger muscle fibers per motor unit. Thigh and leg muscles are less precisely controlled because the activation of a motor unit stimulates the contraction of many large muscle fibers.

The **premotor area** of the cerebral cortex is located anterior to the primary motor cortex (see figure 14.7). It is the staging area where motor functions are organized before they are initiated in the primary motor cortex. For example, if a person

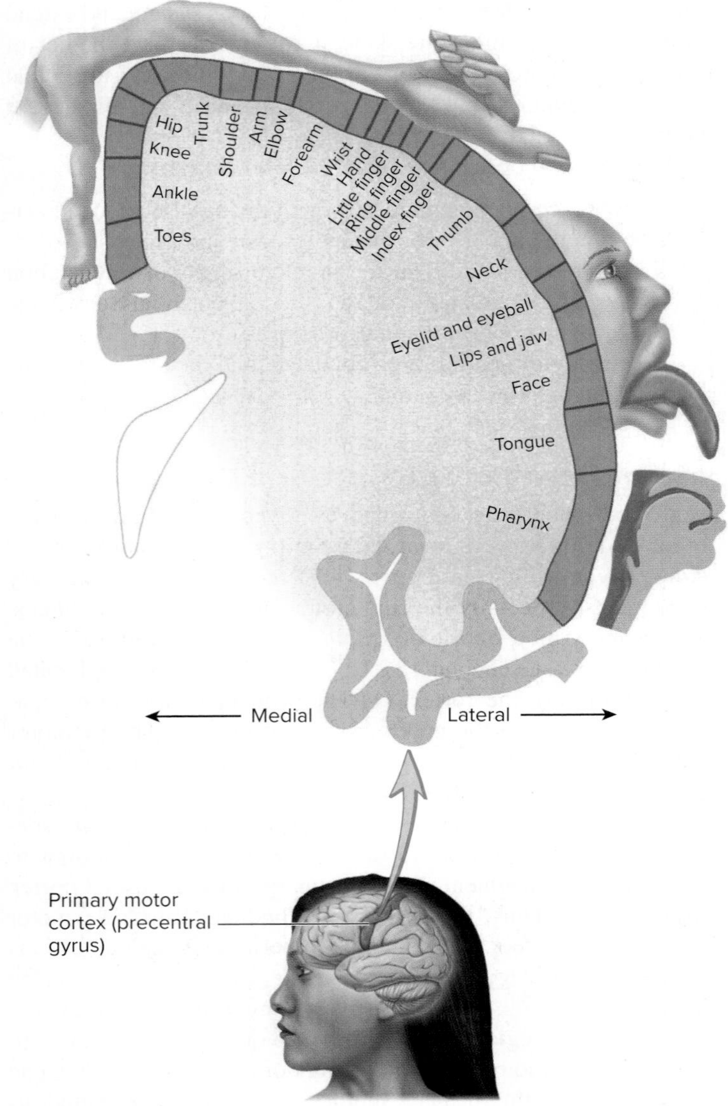

FIGURE 14.9 Spatial Organization of the Primary Motor Cortex
Cerebral cortex seen in frontal section on the left side of the brain. The figure of the body (homunculus) depicts the nerve distributions; the size of each body region shown indicates relative innervation. The cortex occurs on both sides of the brain but appears on only one side in this illustration. The inset shows the motor region of the left hemisphere (*purple*).

decides to take a step, the neurons of the premotor area are stimulated first. The determination is made in the premotor area as to which muscles must contract, in what order, and to what degree. Action potentials are then passed to the upper motor neurons in the primary motor cortex, which actually initiate the planned movements.

The **prefrontal area** controls the motivation and foresight to plan and initiate movements. It is the next most anterior portion of the brain. This association area is well developed only in primates and especially in humans. Along with motivation, the prefrontal area is involved in the regulation of emotional behavior and mood. The large size of this area of the brain in humans may account for our emotional complexity and our relatively well-developed capacity to think ahead and feel motivated.

Clinical IMPACT 14.3

Amyotrophic Lateral Sclerosis

Amyotrophic (ah-my-oh-TROH-fik) **lateral sclerosis (ALS),** also called Lou Gehrig disease, usually affects people between the ages of 40 and 70. About 5–10% of ALS cases are inherited. The condition begins with weakness and clumsiness and progresses within 2–5 years to loss of muscle control as both upper and lower motor neurons are selectively destroyed. ALS patients progressively lose their ability to stand, walk, use their hands, swallow, chew, and eventually breathe. In contrast to the loss of motor functions, cognitive abilities are relatively unaffected. Most people die from respiratory failure within 3–5 years, but there can be very different rates of progression. For example, the physicist Stephen Hawking survived for more than 50 years, but that is very unusual. The causes of noninherited ALS remain unknown. About 20% of the inherited forms result from a mutation in DNA coding for the enzyme **superoxide dismutase (SOD).** SOD is involved in eliminating the free radical superoxide from the body.

Free radicals are molecules that readily accept electrons, which makes them highly reactive. They can strip electrons from proteins, lipids, or nucleic acids, thereby destroying their functions and resulting in cell dysfunction or death. Free-radical damage has been implicated in ALS, arteriosclerosis, arthritis, cancer, and aging. Superoxide, one of the most important and toxic free radicals, forms as oxygen reacts with other free radicals. Although oxygen is critical for aerobic respiration, it is also dangerous to tissues. SOD catalyzes the conversion of superoxide to hydrogen peroxide, which is then converted by catalase to oxygen and water. Apparently, if SOD is defective, superoxide is not degraded and can destroy cells. Motor neurons appear to be particularly sensitive to superoxide attack.

ASSESS YOUR PROGRESS

13. *Compare upper motor neurons with lower motor neurons.*
14. *Where are the primary motor, premotor, and prefrontal areas of the cerebral cortex located? Explain the sequential nature of their functions.*
15. *Why are some areas of the body represented as larger than other areas on the spatial map of the primary motor cortex?*

Motor Pathways

Motor pathways, or tracts, are *descending* pathways from regions of the cerebrum or cerebellum to the brainstem or spinal cord. The pathways carry action potentials along axons of upper motor neurons. The names of motor pathways are based on their origin and termination. Much like the names of sensory pathways, the prefix indicates a pathway's origin, and the suffix indicates its destination. For example, the corticospinal tract is a motor pathway that originates in the cerebral cortex and terminates in the spinal cord (figure 14.10).

The descending motor fibers are divided into two groups: (1) direct pathways and (2) indirect pathways (table 14.4; figure 14.10). The **direct pathways,** also called the *pyramidal* (pi-RAM-i-dal) *system,* are involved in maintaining muscle tone and controlling the speed and precision of skilled movements. These are primarily fine movements involved in dexterity. Most of the **indirect pathways,** sometimes called the *extrapyramidal system,* are involved in less precise control of motor functions, especially those associated with overall body coordination and cerebellar function, such as posture. Many of the indirect pathways are phylogenetically older and control more "primitive" movements of the trunk and proximal portions of the limbs. The direct pathways, which exist only in mammals, may be thought of as overlying the indirect pathways and are more involved in finely controlled movements of the face and distal portions of the limbs. Some indirect pathways, such as those from the basal nuclei and cerebellum, help in fine control of the direct pathways.

Direct Pathways

Direct pathways (figure 14.10*b*) are so named because upper motor neurons in the cerebral cortex, whose axons form these pathways, synapse directly with lower motor neurons in the brainstem or spinal cord. They are also called the pyramidal system because the fibers of these pathways form the medullary **pyramids.** The direct pathways include groups of nerve fibers arrayed into two tracts: (1) the corticospinal tract and (2) the corticobulbar tract. The **corticospinal tract** is involved in direct cortical control of movements below the head (figure 14.10*b*). The **corticobulbar tract** is involved in direct cortical control of movements in the head and neck.

The corticospinal tract consists of axons of upper motor neurons located in the primary motor and premotor areas of the frontal lobes and the somatosensory parts of the parietal lobes. The axons descend through the **internal capsules** and the cerebral peduncles of the midbrain to the pyramids of the medulla oblongata. At the inferior end of the medulla, most (75–85%) of the corticospinal fibers cross to the opposite side of the CNS through the **pyramidal decussation.** This is visible on the anterior surface of the inferior medulla. The crossed fibers descend in the **lateral corticospinal tract** of the spinal cord. The remaining fibers (15–25%) descend uncrossed in the **anterior corticospinal tract** and decussate near the level where they synapse with lower motor neurons. The anterior corticospinal tracts supply the neck and upper limbs, and the lateral corticospinal tracts supply all levels of the body (see table 14.4).

Most of the corticospinal fibers synapse with interneurons in the lateral portions of the spinal cord central gray matter. The interneurons, in turn, synapse with the lower motor neurons of the ventral horn that innervate primarily distal limb muscles.

Clinical IMPACT 14.4

Parkinson Disease

Parkinson disease is characterized by muscular rigidity; loss of facial expression; tremor; a slow, shuffling gait; and general lack of movement. The disease usually occurs after age 55. A resting tremor, called "pill-rolling," is characteristic of Parkinson disease; it consists of circular movement of the opposed thumb and index fingertips. The increased muscular rigidity in Parkinson disease results from defective inhibition of some of the basal nuclei by the substantia nigra, one of the basal nuclei in the midbrain. Parkinson disease is caused by the death of dopamine-containing neurons in the substantia nigra. However, the cause of the neuronal death is not known. Dopamine is an inhibitory neurotransmitter that is required to modulate motor activity.

Parkinson disease can be treated with levodopa (lee-voh-DOH-pah; L-dopa), a precursor to dopamine, or more effectively with Sinemet®, a combination of L-dopa and carbidopa (kar-bi-DOH-pah). Carbidopa is a decarboxylase inhibitor that prevents L-dopa from breaking down before it can reach the brain. Because of the long-term side effects associated with levodopa, including dyskinesias, other dopamine agonists, such as ropinirole and pramipexole, are also prescribed. Researchers have discovered a protein, called **glial cell line-derived neurotrophic factor (GDNF),** that selectively promotes the survival of dopamine-secreting neurons. Alternatively, chronic stimulation of the globus pallidus (part of the lentiform nucleus) with an electrical pulse generator has shown some success. Treatment of the disorder by transplanting fetal tissues or stem cells from adult tissues that are capable of producing dopamine is also under investigation.

Damage to the corticospinal tracts results in reduced muscle tone, clumsiness, and weakness but not in complete paralysis, even if the damage is bilateral. Experiments have demonstrated that bilateral sectioning of the medullary pyramids results in (1) loss of contact-related activities, such as tactile placing of the foot and grasping; (2) defective fine movements; and (3) hypotonia (reduced tone). These and other experimental data support the conclusion that the corticospinal system is superimposed over the older, indirect pathways and that it has many parallel functions. The main function of the direct pathways is to add speed and agility to conscious movements, especially of the hands, and to provide a high degree of fine motor control, as in movements of individual fingers. Spinal cord lesions that affect both the direct and the indirect pathways result in complete paralysis.

The corticobulbar tracts are analogous to the corticospinal tracts. The corticobulbar tracts extend to the brainstem (*bulbar,* brainstem) and innervate the head, whereas the corticospinal tracts extend to the spinal cord and innervate the rest of the body. Cells that contribute to the corticobulbar tracts are in regions of the cortex similar to those of the corticospinal tracts. Corticobulbar

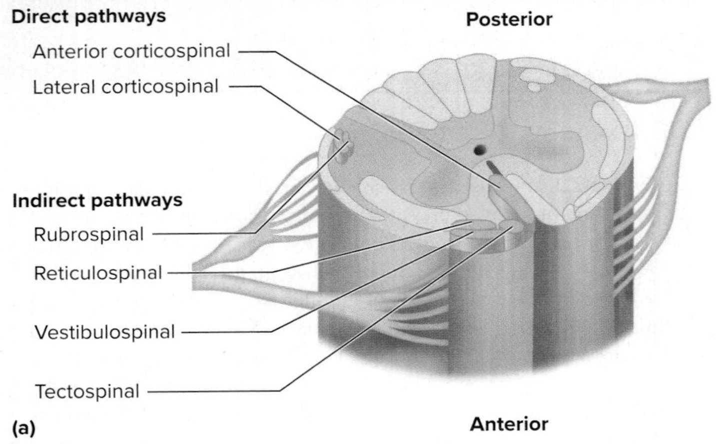

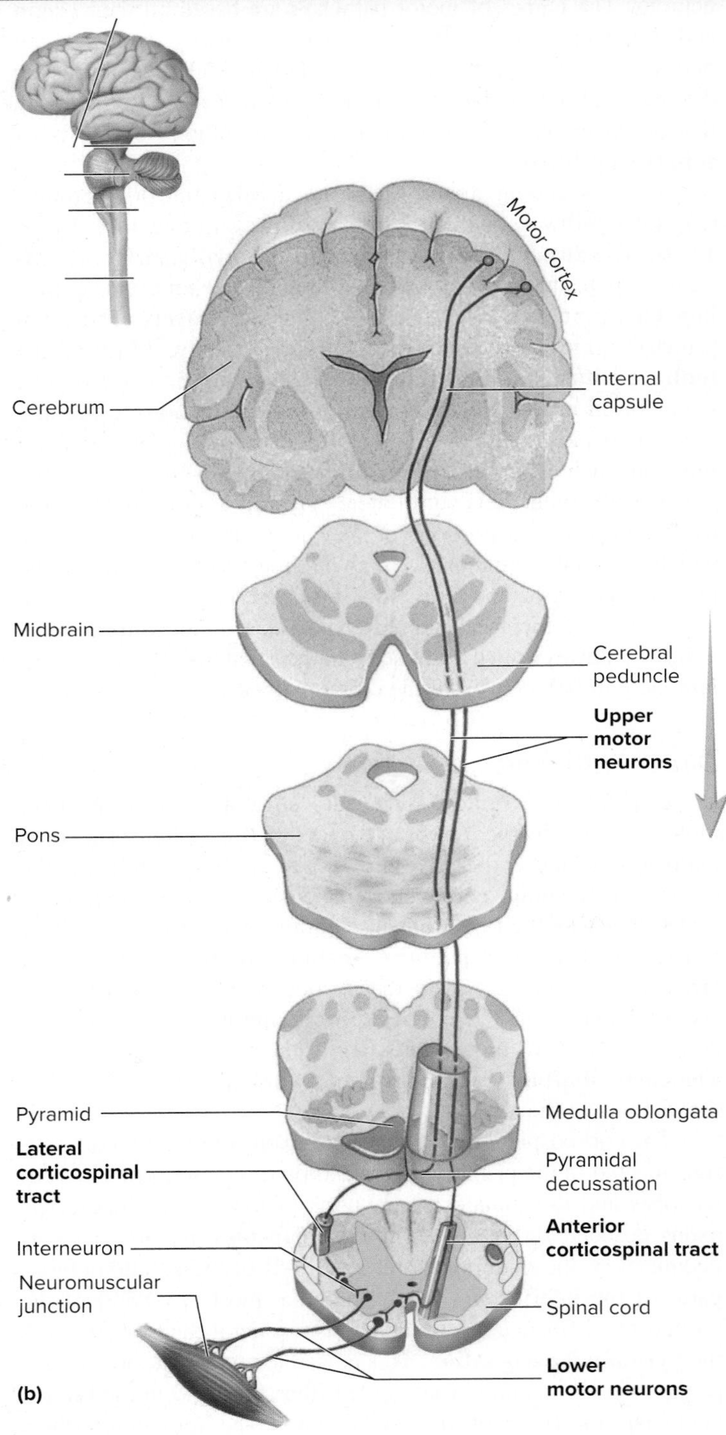

FIGURE 14.10 Somatic Motor Pathways

(*a*) Somatic motor pathways (*highlighted in purple*) in the spinal cord. Pathways are labeled on the left side of the figure only, although they exist on both sides. Parts *b* and *c* illustrate the direct and indirect motor pathways. Lines on the inset indicate levels of section. The *arrow* on the right indicates direction of action potentials. (*b*) Direct pathways: Lateral and anterior corticospinal tracts are responsible for movement below the head. (*c*) Indirect pathways: Examples of indirect pathways are rubrospinal and reticulospinal tracts. APR

tracts follow the same basic route as the corticospinal system down to the level of the brainstem. At that point, most corticobulbar fibers terminate in the **cranial nerve nuclei,** where they synapse with interneurons and lower motor neurons. These nuclei give rise to the nerves that control tongue movements, mastication, facial expression, some eye movements, and palatine, pharyngeal, and laryngeal movements.

Indirect Pathways

The indirect pathways (figure 14.10*c*) are so named because axons from motor neurons of the cerebrum and cerebellum do not directly synapse with lower motor neurons. Instead, they first synapse in an intermediate nucleus in the brainstem. The indirect pathways begin with the neurons in those brainstem nuclei. They do not pass through the pyramids or through the corticobulbar tracts and, therefore, are sometimes called extrapyramidal. There are four major indirect pathways: (1) the rubrospinal tract, (2) the vestibulospinal tract, (3) the reticulospinal tract, and (4) the tectospinal tract. Many interconnections and feedback loops are present in this system.

Neurons of the **rubrospinal tract** begin in the red nucleus (*rubro* means "red"), which is located at the boundary between the diencephalon and the midbrain. The tract decussates in the midbrain and descends in the lateral column of the spinal cord. The red nucleus receives input from both the motor cortex and the cerebellum. Lesions in the red nucleus result in *intention tremors* (action tremors) similar to those seen in cerebellar lesions (table 14.5). The function of the red nucleus, therefore, is closely related to cerebellar function. The rubrospinal tract is the one indirect tract that is very closely related to the direct, corticospinal tract. It terminates in the lateral portion of the spinal cord

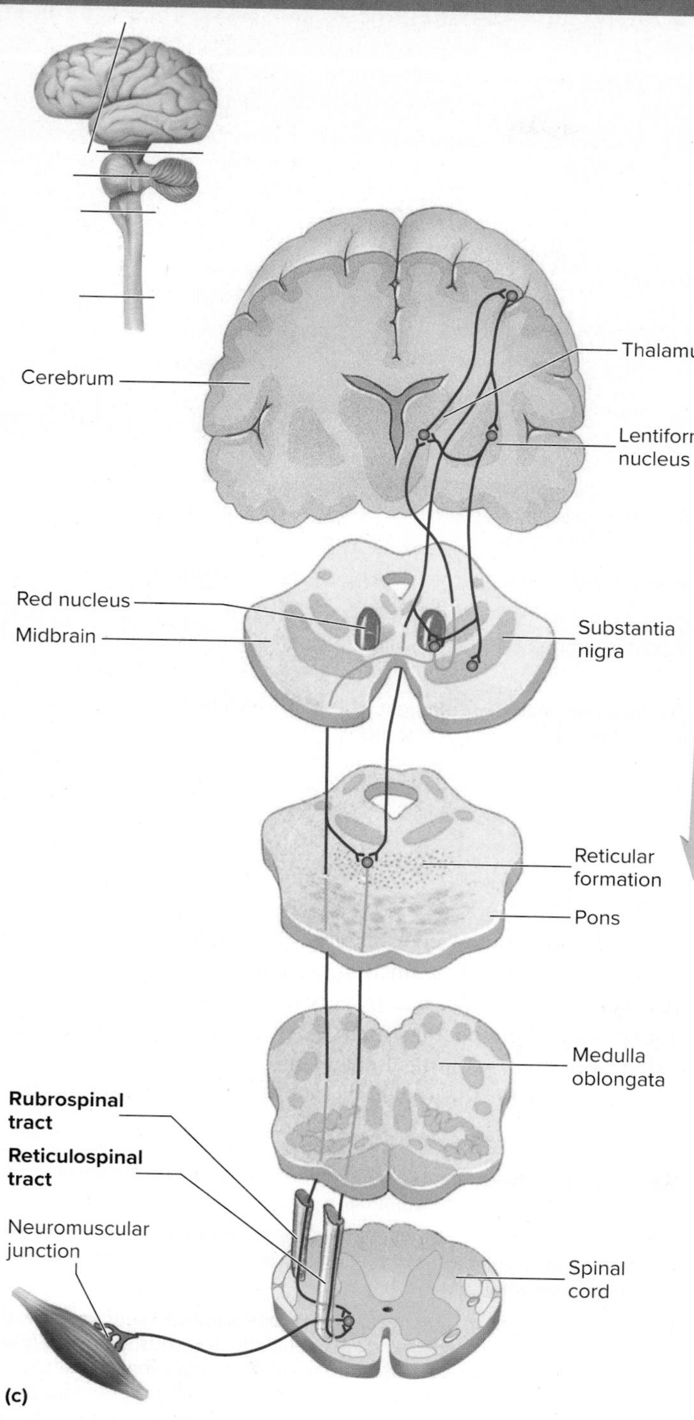

FIGURE 14.10 (continued)

central gray matter with the corticospinal tract. It plays a major role in regulating fine motor control of muscles in the distal part of the upper limbs. Damage to the rubrospinal tract impairs forearm and hand movements but does not greatly affect general body movements.

The **vestibulospinal tracts** (figure 14.10*a*) originate in the vestibular nuclei of the medulla oblongata and descend in the anterior column of the spinal cord. They then synapse with interneurons and lower motor neurons in the ventromedial portion of the spinal cord central gray matter. Their fibers preferentially influence neurons innervating extensor muscles in the trunk and the proximal portion of the lower limbs and are involved primarily in the maintenance of upright posture. The vestibular nuclei receive major input from the vestibular nerve, which is involved in maintaining balance (see chapter 15), and the cerebellum.

The **reticulospinal tract** (figure 14.10*a*) originates in the reticular formation of the pons and medulla oblongata and descends in the anterior portion of the lateral column of the spinal cord. It then synapses with interneurons and lower motor neurons in the ventromedial portion of the spinal cord central gray matter. The reticulospinal tract maintains posture by controlling the trunk and proximal upper and lower limb muscles during certain movements. For example, when a person who is standing lifts one foot off the ground, the weight of the body shifts to the other limb. During this type of movement, the reticulospinal tract apparently enhances the functions of the alpha motor neurons in the crossed extensor reflex, so that balance is maintained.

The **tectospinal tract** originates in the superior colliculus, which has been called the *tectum,* or roof, of the mesencephalon. This tract controls reflex movement of the head to bright lights, noises, and rapid movements.

Another major portion of the indirect pathways involves the basal nuclei (see chapter 13). The basal nuclei have a number of connections within the brain, and they interact with indirect pathways, such as the rubrospinal tract, by which they modulate motor functions.

ASSESS YOUR PROGRESS

16. *What are the structural and functional differences between direct and indirect pathways?*
17. *What two tracts form the direct pathways? What area of the body is supplied by each tract?*
18. *Describe the location of the neurons in each tract, as well as where they synapse.*
19. *Name the structures and tracts that form the indirect pathways. What functions do they control?*

Modifying and Refining Motor Activities

Basal Nuclei

The **basal nuclei** (see figure 13.10) are important in planning, organizing, and coordinating motor movements and posture. Complex neural circuits connect the basal nuclei with each other, with the thalamus, and with the cerebral cortex. These connections form several feedback loops, some of them stimulatory and others inhibitory.

The basal nuclei stimulatory circuits facilitate muscle activity, especially at the beginning of a voluntary movement, such as rising from a sitting position or beginning to walk. The inhibitory circuits facilitate the actions of the stimulatory

TABLE 14.4 Descending Spinal Pathways

Pathway	Functions Controlled	Examples of Movements Controlled	Origin	Crossover
Direct	Conscious, skilled movements			
Corticospinal tract	Movements below the head, especially of the hands			
Lateral	Movements of the neck, trunk, upper and lower limbs, especially the fingers	Typing and push-ups	Cerebral cortex	Inferior end of the medulla oblongata
Anterior	Movements of the neck and trunk	Moving with a Hula-Hoop	Cerebral cortex	Level of the lower motor neuron
Corticobulbar tract	Movements of the head and face	Facial expression and chewing	Cerebral cortex	Varies for the different cranial nerves
Indirect	Unconscious movements			
Rubrospinal	Movement coordination	Positioning of digits and the palm of the hand when reaching out to grasp	Red nucleus	Midbrain
Vestibulospinal	Maintenance of upright posture and balance	Extension of the upper limbs when falling	Vestibular nucleus	Uncrossed
Reticulospinal	Posture adjustment and walking	Maintenance of posture when standing on one foot	Reticular formation	Some uncrossed; some cross at termination
Tectospinal	Movements of the head and neck in response to visual and auditory reflexes	Movement of the head and neck away from a sudden flash of light	Superior colliculus	Midbrain

circuits by inhibiting muscle activity in antagonist muscles. Inhibitory circuits also decrease muscle tone when the body, limbs, and head are at rest (eliminating random and "unwanted" movements of the trunk and limbs). Disorders of the basal nuclei result in increased muscle tone and exaggerated, uncontrolled movements when at rest. Some people have difficulty rising from a sitting position and initiating walking. A specific feature of some basal nuclei disorders is a *resting tremor,* slight shaking of the hands when the muscle is relaxed and not performing a task. Parkinson disease and cerebral palsy are basal nuclei disorders.

Cerebellum

The **cerebellum** (see figure 13.6) consists of three functional parts: (1) the vestibulocerebellum, (2) the spinocerebellum, and (3) the cerebrocerebellum.

The **vestibulocerebellum,** or flocculonodular lobe, receives direct input from the vestibular structures, especially the semicircular canals (see chapter 15), and sends axons to the vestibular nuclei of the brainstem. It helps maintain muscle tone in postural muscles. It also helps coordinate eye movement and control balance, especially during movements.

The **spinocerebellum** consists of the **vermis** and the medial portion of the **lateral hemisphere.** The spinocerebellum helps accomplish fine motor coordination of simple movements by means of its comparator function. A **comparator** is a sensing device that compares the data from two sources—in this case, the motor cortex and peripheral structures. In this way, the comparator function coordinates simple movements, such as touching your nose. Figure 14.11 illustrates the comparator function of the cerebellum.

1. Action potentials from the motor cortex descend into the spinal cord to initiate voluntary movements.
2. At the same time, action potentials are carried from the motor cortex to the cerebellum to give the cerebellar neurons information representing the intended movement.
3. In addition, action potentials from proprioceptive neurons ascend through the spinocerebellar tracts and simultaneously arrive at the cerebellum. Proprioceptive neurons innervate the joints and tendons of the structure being moved, such as the elbow or knee, and provide information about the position of the body or body parts. These action potentials give the cerebellar neurons information from the periphery about the actual movements.
4. The cerebellum compares the action potentials from the motor cortex with those from the moving structures. That is, it compares the intended movement with the actual movement.
5. If a difference is detected, the cerebellum sends action potentials to the motor cortex, via the thalamus, and to the spinal cord to correct the discrepancy.
6. The result is smooth, coordinated movements.

Termination	Side of Body Where Fibers Terminate
Ventral horn of the spinal cord	Contralateral
Ventral horn of the spinal cord	Contralateral
Cranial nerve nuclei in the brainstem (lower motor neuron)	Contralateral
Ventral horn of the spinal cord	Contralateral
Ventral horn of the spinal cord	Ipsilateral
Ventral horn of the spinal cord	Ipsilateral or contralateral
Cranial nerve nucleus in the medulla oblongata and ventral horn of the upper levels of the spinal cord (lower motor neurons that turn the head and neck)	Contralateral

The **cerebrocerebellum** consists of the lateral two-thirds of the lateral hemispheres. It communicates with the motor, premotor, and prefrontal portions of the cerebral cortex in planning and practicing rapid, complex motor actions that require coordination and training. These connections from the cerebrum to the cerebellum constitute a large portion of the axons in the cerebral peduncles. Because of the cerebrocerebellum, with training, a person can perform highly skilled and rapid movements more quickly than would be possible with only the comparator function of the cerebellum. In these cases, the cerebellum participates with the cerebrum in learning highly specialized movements, such as playing the piano or swinging a baseball bat. The cerebrocerebellum is also involved in cognitive functions, such as rhythm, conceptualization of time intervals, some word associations, and solutions to pegboard puzzles—tasks once thought to occur only in the cerebrum.

Cerebellar dysfunction results in (1) decreased muscle tone, (2) balance impairment, (3) a tendency to overshoot when reaching for or touching an object, and (4) an intention tremor, which is shaking in the hands that occurs only while attempting to perform a task. Although the cerebellum and basal nuclei both control motor functions, they have opposite effects, and they exhibit opposite symptoms when injured. Cerebellar dysfunction results in decreased muscle tone and an intention tremor, whereas basal nuclei dysfunction often results in increased muscle tone and a resting tremor.

PROCESS Figure

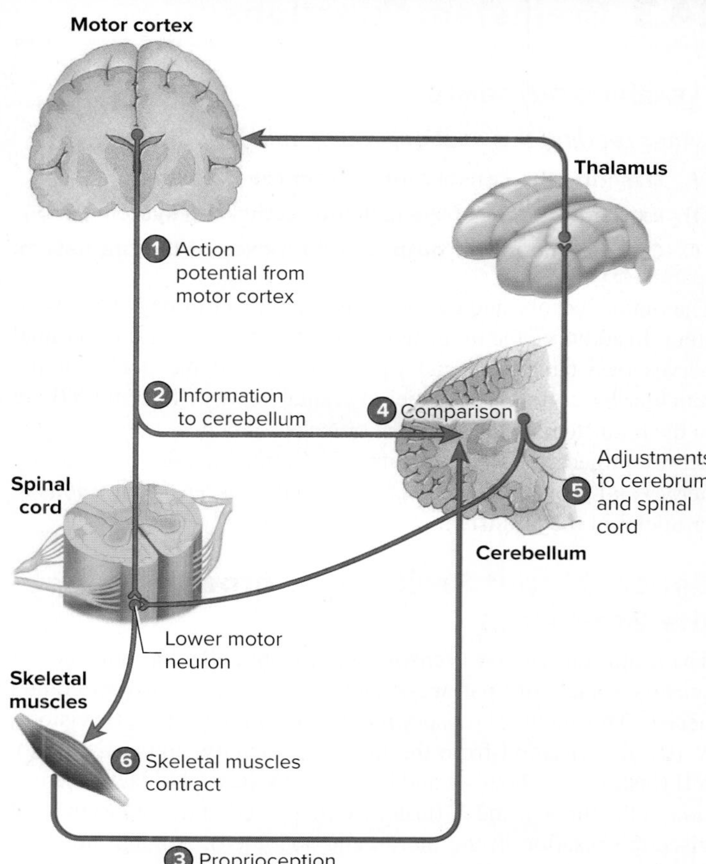

PROCESS Figure 14.11

Cerebellar Comparator Function

The cerebellar comparator ensures smooth and coordinated skeletal muscle movement by comparing intended movements with sensory information from actively moving body parts.

A kicker on the local football team has experienced head trauma. When attempting to kick the ball, his movements were jerky and exaggerated. The team's athletic trainer was convinced that the kicker had damage to his cerebellum and insisted that he be transported to the hospital. Does the athletic trainer's conclusion make sense? Why or why not?

ASSESS YOUR PROGRESS

20. *What are the functions of the basal nuclei?*

21. *What are the general symptoms of basal nuclei disorders?*

22. *What are the three functional parts of the cerebellum, and what are the functions of each?*

23. *Explain the comparator activities of the spinocerebellum.*

24. *What are the general symptoms of cerebellar dysfunction?*

14.3 Brainstem Functions

LEARNING OUTCOMES

After reading this section, you should be able to

A. **Describe the sensory input from the brainstem.**

B. **Explain the role of the reticular activating system (RAS).**

C. **Discuss the motor output and reflexes of the brainstem.**

The major sensory and motor pathways project through the brainstem. In addition, the brainstem contains the nuclei of most cranial nerves (see table 13.4 and figure 13.4*c*) and the nuclei of the reticular formation. The nuclei of cranial nerves III–X and XII are in the brainstem. Only collateral branches of cranial nerve II (optic nerve) project to brainstem nuclei. Cranial nerves I (olfactory nerve) and XI (spinal accessory nerve) do not have projections to or nuclei in the brainstem.

Sensory Input Projecting Through the Brainstem

The brainstem receives sensory input from collateral branches of sensory spinal cord pathways and from the axons of most cranial nerves. This includes sensory input from cranial nerves II (vision), V (tactile sensation from the face, nasal cavity, and oral cavity), VII (taste), VIII (hearing and balance), IX (taste and tactile sensation in the throat), and X (taste, tactile sensation in the larynx, and visceral sensation in the thorax and abdomen). Among these, all except cranial nerve II have sensory nuclei in the brainstem. Many of these nuclei are involved in the special senses (see chapter 15).

As noted earlier, fibers of the spinothalamic tracts passing through the brainstem are joined by fibers of the trigeminothalamic tract. This tract carries tactile sensations, such as pain and temperature, two-point discrimination, and light touch, from the face, the nasal cavity, and the oral cavity, including the teeth.

RAS Functions of the Brainstem

The **reticular formation** is a group of nuclei scattered throughout the brainstem that is involved in regulating cyclical motor functions.

An important part of the reticular formation is the **reticular activating system (RAS).** The RAS regulates the sleep-wake cycle. Collateral branches of trigeminothalamic tract neurons project to the RAS, where they stimulate wakefulness and consciousness. Also projecting to the RAS are collateral branches of cranial nerves II (optic), V (trigeminal), and VIII (vestibulocochlear); ascending tactile sensory pathways; and descending neurons from the cerebrum. Visual and acoustic stimuli, as well as mental activities, stimulate the RAS to help maintain alertness and attention. A stimulus such as a sudden flash of bright light, a ringing alarm clock, the smell of coffee, or a feather touching the face can arouse consciousness (figure 14.12). The removal of auditory, visual, and other stimuli may lead to drowsiness or sleep. For example, consider what happens to students during a monotonous lecture in a dark lecture hall. The RAS controls the brain's level of arousal or consciousness. Damage to RAS cells of the reticular formation can result in a lack of consciousness or coma.

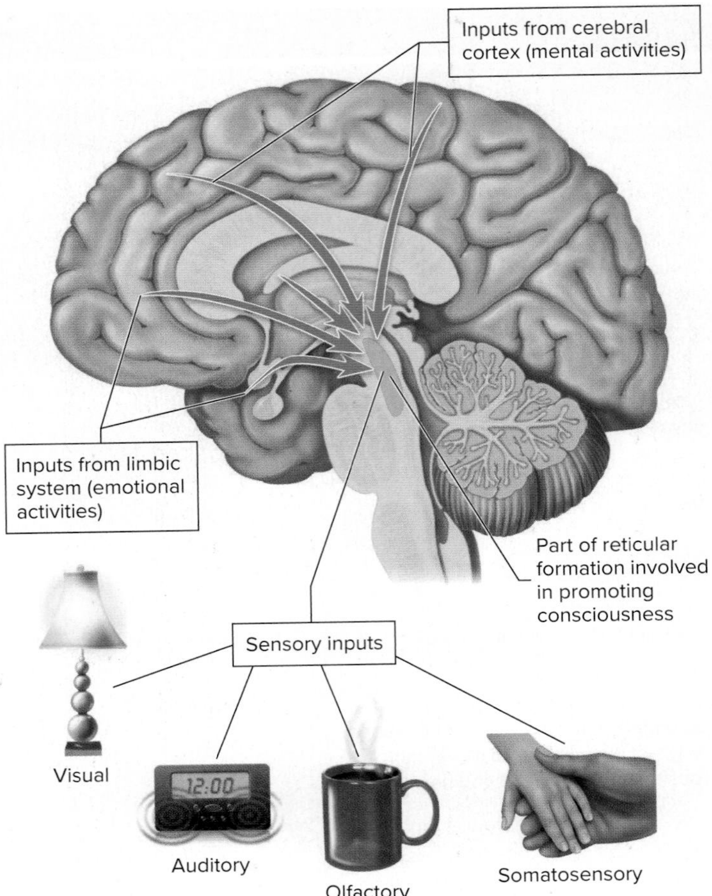

FIGURE 14.12 Reticular Activating System
The reticular activating system can be stimulated by inputs from the cerebral cortex (mental activities) and from the limbic system (emotional activities), as well as by a variety of sensory inputs from other stimuli, such as visual (sudden flashes of light), auditory (a ringing alarm clock), olfactory (the smell of coffee), and somatosensory (touching the face) stimuli. (Bottom right) Howard Shooter/Getty Images APR

Certain drugs can either depress or stimulate the RAS. General anesthetics and many tranquilizers depress it. On the other hand, ammonia (smelling salts) and other irritants stimulate trigeminal nerve endings in the nose. As a result, action potentials travel to the reticular formation and the cerebral cortex to arouse an unconscious patient.

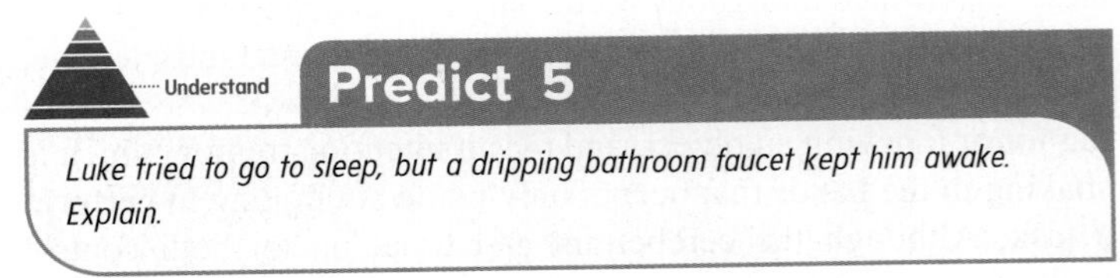

Predict 5

Luke tried to go to sleep, but a dripping bathroom faucet kept him awake. Explain.

Motor Output and Reflexes Projecting Through the Brainstem

The brainstem is an important conduit and integration site for motor pathways and reflexes. Both direct and indirect motor pathways pass through the brainstem. As discussed earlier, the

Case STUDY 14.1 Multiple Sclerosis

Betty, a 32-year-old woman, woke up one morning with weakness in her lower limbs. By that afternoon, she had become completely exhausted, with a familiar ache in her left eye and tingling sensations in her fingers. At the end of the day, she could barely stand up, and her left eye was blurry and increasingly painful. Betty's family physician made an appointment for her with a neurologist. The neurologist suspected **multiple sclerosis (MS),** an autoimmune disease that results in the demyelination of CNS neurons, which become sclerotic, or hard. He ordered an MRI scan and a **visual evoked potential (VEP) test,** which is a recording of action potentials in the optic nerve "evoked" in response to visual stimuli. During the VEP test, electrodes were placed on Betty's scalp, and she was asked to respond to visual stimuli, first with her normal eye covered by an eye patch and then with her normal eye uncovered.

The MRI scan showed lesions in the optic nerve and white matter of the brain, and the VEP test showed optic nerve dysfunction. These results confirmed a diagnosis of multiple sclerosis accompanied by **optic neuritis,** or inflammation of the optic nerve. Betty's neurologist explained that, in multiple sclerosis, damage has occurred to sensory neurons that conduct sensory information to the brain, as well as to motor neurons that conduct motor stimulation from the brain to the muscles. Betty asked if she could be cured. The neurologist replied that she would experience periods of remission, which might be interrupted by symptomatic periods. He also warned that, with each successive episode, neurons might become progressively more damaged.

Predict 6

a. *What effect does demyelination have on action potential propagation along axons? How does this explain blurred vision?*

b. *How would you explain the weakness and tingling that Betty experienced?*

direct motor pathways originate in the cerebral cortex and pass directly through the brainstem (corticospinal tracts) or synapse in cranial nerve motor nuclei to initiate movements within the head, such as eye movements (corticobulbar tract). The indirect pathways synapse with brainstem nuclei, which in turn send descending fibers into the spinal cord. Descending fibers from the reticular formation constitute one of the body's most important motor pathways. Fibers from the reticular formation are critical in controlling many functions, such as respiratory movements and cardiac rhythms. The brainstem contains the motor nuclei of cranial nerves III–VII, IX, X, and XII. Functionally, the motor output projecting through the brainstem can be classified into two categories: (1) somatic motor and (2) parasympathetic.

Somatic Motor Output and Reflexes

The superior colliculi are midbrain structures involved in visual reflexes in response to auditory, visual, and tactile stimuli (see chapter 13). The superior colliculi control three cranial nerves involved in voluntary and reflex eye movements: (1) oculomotor (III), (2) trochlear (IV), and (3) abducens (VI) are involved in voluntary and reflex eye movements. An example of voluntary eye movement that involves the superior colliculi is visual tracking of moving objects, which involves action potentials from the cerebrum to the superior colliculi. Visual tracking with both eyes to the right involves the lateral rectus muscle and abducens nerve of the right eye and the medial rectus muscle and oculomotor nerve of the left eye. Coordination of these two nerves and muscles requires nuclei of the reticular formation.

The eye muscles, along with the muscles of the neck (mainly the trapezius and sternocleidomastoid, innervated by the glossopharyngeal nerve (IX)), can also be involved in reflexes initiated in the superior colliculi in response to visual and auditory stimuli. Collateral branches from the optic tract (II) synapse in the superior colliculi. Axons from the superior colliculi project to oculomotor, trochlear, and abducens nuclei and to the upper cervical part of the spinal cord (motor neurons of the accessory nerve (XI)), where they stimulate the motor neurons involved in turning the eyes and head toward a visual stimulus. Similarly, the superior colliculi also receive input from auditory pathways, which can initiate a reflex that turns the eyes and head toward a sudden noise. Reflex movement of the head and neck in response to tactile stimuli from the body involve the spinomesencephalic pathway of the spinal cord (see table 14.3), which also projects to the superior colliculi.

Chewing, or mastication, is a reflexive activity. Even though the initiation of chewing can be under conscious control, the presence of food in the mouth initiates a reflex between the sensory nuclei and the motor nucleus of the trigeminal nerve (V), thereby starting the chewing cycle. Motor fibers from cranial nerve V innervate the muscles of mastication and control chewing; however, once the chewing cycle is initiated, the reticular formation regulates the cycle. Other reflexes in the trigeminal nerve system detect how hard or soft an item is in the mouth and adjust the bite accordingly. Reflexes between the trigeminal sensory nuclei and the motor nucleus of the hypoglossal nerve (XII) control the tongue to help place the food between the teeth for chewing, while keeping the tongue out of harm's way.

The facial nerve (VII), which innervates the muscles of facial expression, is controlled by the cerebrum and is very important in communication.

The glossopharyngeal (IX) and vagus (X) nerves send somatic motor fibers to muscles of the pharynx and larynx associated with swallowing and speech. Swallowing, once initiated under conscious control, continues as a reflex. The pharyngeal muscles of swallowing are largely innervated by the vagus nerve and, to a smaller extent, by the glossopharyngeal nerve.

Unlike swallowing, which is largely a reflex, speech is highly controlled by the cerebrum. The vagus nerve innervates the muscles of the larynx responsible for voice production and controls the pharyngeal and most palatine muscles responsible for moving the soft palate during speech. The complex movements of the tongue during speech are controlled by the hypoglossal nerve (XII), which innervates nearly all the muscles of the tongue.

Parasympathetic Output and Reflexes

The constriction of the pupil involves parasympathetic stimulation through the oculomotor (III) nerve. The visual reflexes resulting in pupil constriction are coordinated through nuclei in the reticular formation. These reflexes are also coordinated by a nuclear region in the diencephalon called the pretectal area (so named because it is in front of the tectum, the roof of the midbrain).

Sensory input from the trigeminal (V) nerve can initiate several reflexes. Tactile sensory input from the nasal cavity via the trigeminal nerve can trigger a sneeze reflex. Tactile sensory input from the oral cavity via the trigeminal nerve informs the cerebrum that food or some other object is in the mouth. The presence of an object in the mouth—even a nonfood item, such as a marble—stimulates a reflex between the trigeminal sensory nuclei and the motor nuclei of the facial (VII) and glossopharyngeal (IX) nerves, which innervate the salivary glands to stimulate salivation.

Sensory input from the glossopharyngeal nerve (IX) conveys tactile information from the back of the tongue, the soft palate, and the pharynx (throat) to the brainstem. Mechanical stimulation of these areas can initiate a gag reflex, whereas other stimulation of the pharynx can initiate a cough reflex. Sensory input from the vagus nerve conveys tactile information from the larynx (voicebox) and the thoracic and abdominal viscera. Tactile input from the larynx can also initiate a cough reflex. In addition, the vagus nerve is involved in many complex reflexes associated with vital functions, such as heart rate, respiration, and digestion. Many of these involve the reticular formation and are discussed in later chapters.

Vital Functions Controlled in the Brainstem

Many vital functions, such as heart rate, blood pressure, and respiration, are regulated by nuclei in the brainstem. When a person is involved in a serious accident or is extremely ill, these vital functions may be affected. Therefore, many emergency medical procedures are designed to evaluate brainstem function.

Predict 7

Some types of epilepsy are treated by placing an electronic device inside the neck to stimulate the vagus nerve. Minor injury to the vagus nerve during implantation of the device can lead to hoarseness. Why is this so? Can you predict two other consequences of minor injury to the vagus nerve?

ASSESS YOUR PROGRESS

25. *Which cranial nerves provide sensory input to brainstem nuclei?*
26. *What is the reticular formation? What are the roles of the reticular activating system?*
27. *Discuss the somatic motor output and reflexes from the brainstem.*
28. *Describe the parasympathetic reflexes that involve the brainstem.*
29. *What are some vital functions that are regulated by the brainstem?*

14.4 Higher Brain Functions

LEARNING OUTCOMES

After reading this section, you should be able to

A. **Compare and contrast the two cortical areas required for speech.**
B. **Describe the pathway that connects the cerebral hemispheres.**
C. **Describe the types of brain wave patterns and how they relate to sleep.**
D. **Compare and contrast the features of working, short-term, and both types of long-term memory.**
E. **Describe the functions of the limbic system, including the impact of olfactory stimuli.**

The human brain is capable of many functions besides awareness of sensory input and control of skeletal muscles. Speech, mathematical and artistic abilities, sleep, memory, emotions, and judgment are functions of the brain.

Speech

In most people, the speech areas are in the left cerebral cortex. Two major cortical areas are involved in speech: (1) the **Wernicke area** (sensory speech area) in a portion of the parietal lobe and (2) the **Broca area** (motor speech area) in the inferior part of the frontal lobe (see figure 14.7). The Wernicke area is necessary for understanding and formulating coherent speech. The Broca area initiates the complex series of movements necessary for speech. The Wernicke and Broca areas are connected by a bundle of neurons known as the **arcuate fasciculus** (figure 14.13*a*).

Figure 14.13*b* illustrates the sequence of events that occurs for someone to speak a word that he or she sees, as when reading aloud.

1. *Visual cortex.* Action potentials from the eyes reach the visual cortex, where the word is seen. The word is then recognized in the visual association area.
2. *Wernicke area.* The signal representing the word is understood in parts of the Wernicke area.
3. *Broca area.* Action potentials representing the word are conducted through association fibers that connect the Wernicke and Broca areas. In the Broca area, the word is formulated as it will be spoken.
4. *Primary motor cortex.* Action potentials are then propagated to the premotor area, where the movements are programmed, and finally to the primary motor cortex, where the proper movements are triggered.

The sequence of events required to repeat a word that has been heard is similar.

1. *Primary auditory cortex.* The information passes from the ears to the primary auditory cortex and then to the auditory association area, where the word is recognized.

PROCESS **Figure**

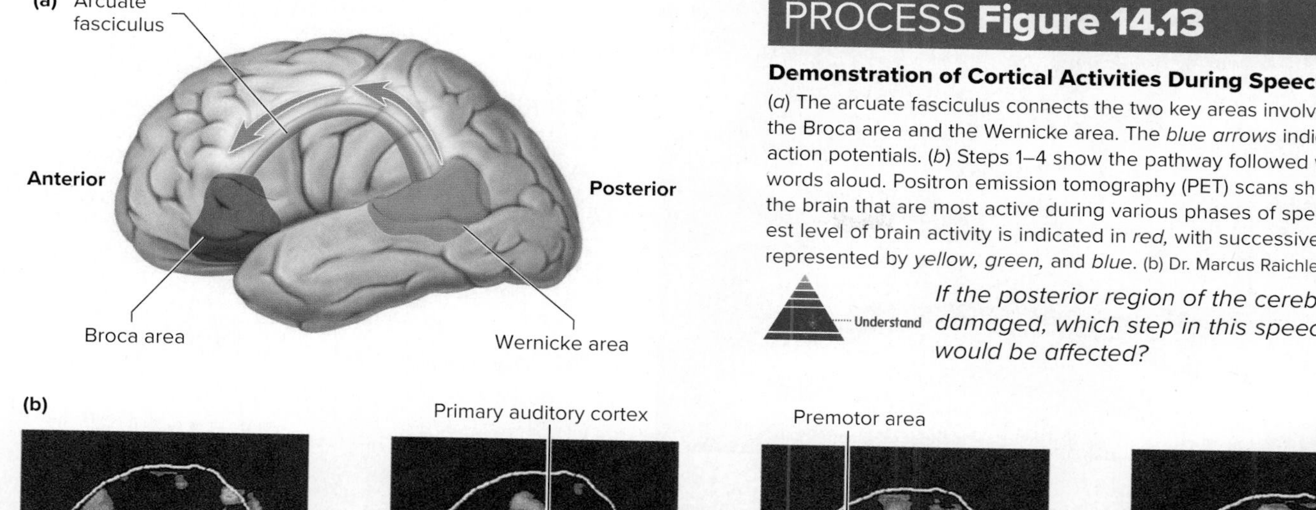

PROCESS **Figure 14.13**

Demonstration of Cortical Activities During Speech

(*a*) The arcuate fasciculus connects the two key areas involved in speech: the Broca area and the Wernicke area. The *blue arrows* indicate direction of action potentials. (*b*) Steps 1–4 show the pathway followed when reading words aloud. Positron emission tomography (PET) scans show the areas of the brain that are most active during various phases of speech. The highest level of brain activity is indicated in *red*, with successively lower levels represented by *yellow, green,* and *blue*. (b) Dr. Marcus Raichle, MD

Understand *If the posterior region of the cerebrum were damaged, which step in this speech process would be affected?*

2. *Wernicke area.* The signal representing the word continues to the Wernicke area, where it is understood.
3. *Broca area.* From the Wernicke area, the signal follows the same route as for speaking words that are seen, going to the Broca area.
4. *Primary motor cortex.* The signal for the word finally goes to the premotor area and primary motor cortex.

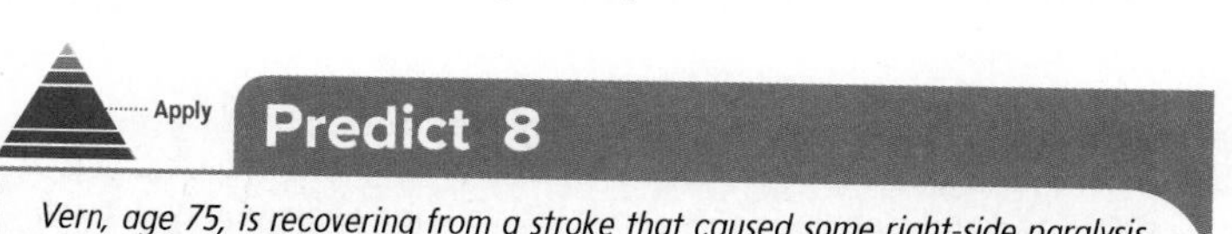

Apply **Predict 8**

Vern, age 75, is recovering from a stroke that caused some right-side paralysis. He understands verbal commands and instructions, but his speech is hesitant and distorted. In addition, Vern's facial expressions, especially on the right side, are limited, and he has some difficulty chewing and swallowing. Explain these manifestations.

Communication Between the Right and Left Hemispheres

The cortex of the right cerebral hemisphere controls muscular activity in and receives sensory input from the left half of the body. The left cerebral hemisphere controls muscles in and receives sensory input from the right half of the body. Sensory information received by the cortex of one hemisphere is shared with the other through connections between the two hemispheres called **commissures.** The largest of these commissures is the **corpus callosum,** which is a broad band of tracts at the base of the longitudinal fissure (see figure 13.1).

Language and perhaps other functions, such as artistic activities, are not shared equally between the left and right cerebral hemispheres. The left hemisphere is more involved in analytical skills, such as mathematics and speech. The right hemisphere is involved in activities such as spatial perception, the recognition of faces, and musical ability.

Brain Waves and Sleep

Different levels of consciousness can be revealed by different patterns of electrical activity in the brain. Electrodes placed on a person's scalp and attached to a recording device can record the brain's electrical activity, producing an **electroencephalogram** (eh-LEK-troh-en-SEF-ah-loh-gram; **EEG;** figure 14.14). These electrodes are not sensitive enough to detect individual action potentials, but they can detect the simultaneous action potentials in large numbers of neurons. As a result, the EEG displays wavelike patterns of electrical activity known as **brain waves.** Brain waves are produced continuously, but their intensity and frequency differ from time to time based on the state of brain activity. Most of the time, EEG patterns from a given individual are irregular, with no particular pattern, because, although the normal brain is active, most of its electrical activity is not synchronous. At other times, however, specific patterns can be detected.

The different levels of consciousness in an awake and a sleeping person are marked by different types of brain wave patterns. These regular patterns are classified as (1) alpha, (2) beta, (3) theta, or (4) delta waves (figure 14.14*b*). **Alpha waves** are observed in a

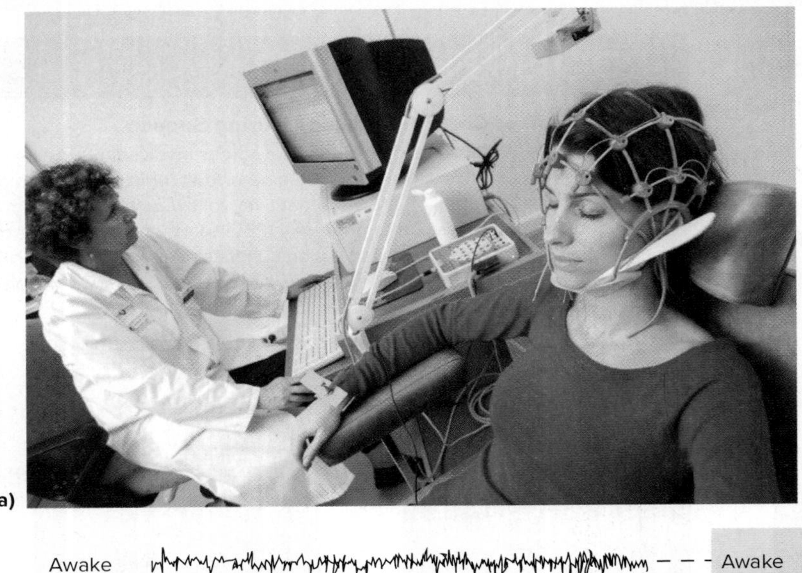

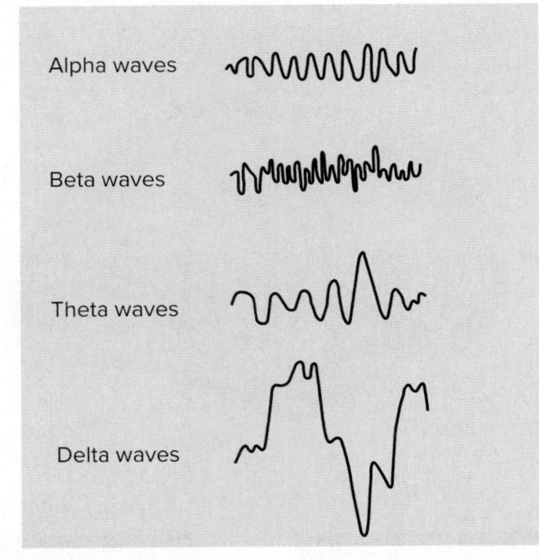

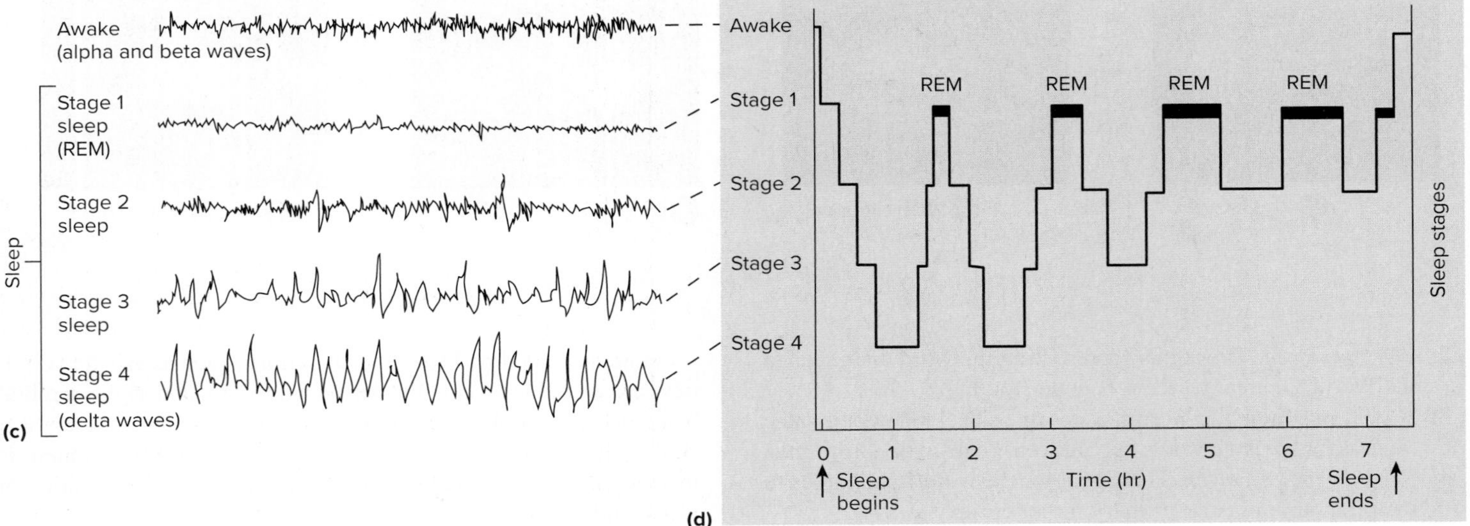

FIGURE 14.14 Electroencephalograms (EEGs) Showing Brain Waves

(*a*) A patient with electrodes attached to her head. (*b*) Four EEG tracings: alpha waves, often seen in a relaxed individual with eyes closed; beta waves, typical of an alert individual; theta waves, seen in the first stage of sleep; and delta waves, characteristic of deep sleep. (*c*) EEG tracings when a person is awake and during four stages of sleep. (*d*) A typical night's sleep pattern in a young adult. The time spent in REM sleep is labeled and shown by dark bars.

(a) Phanie/Science Source

normal person who is awake but in a quiet, resting state with the eyes closed. **Beta waves** have a higher frequency than alpha waves and occur during intense mental activity. **Theta waves** usually occur in children, but they can also occur in adults who are experiencing frustration or who have certain brain disorders. **Delta waves** occur in infants, in patients with severe brain disorders, and in people who are in deep sleep.

Brain wave patterns vary during the four stages of sleep (figure 14.14*c,d*). During the beginning of sleep, a rapid transition takes place from a beta rhythm to an alpha rhythm. Dreaming occurs during this period when eye movement can be observed in a sleeping person. This state is called **rapid eye movement (REM)** sleep. As sleep deepens, progressively more delta waves occur and REM is not observed. A sleeping person arouses several times during a period of sleep in a cyclic pattern so that REM and dreams occur throughout the night.

Distinct types of EEG patterns can be detected in patients with specific brain disorders, such as epileptic seizures. Similar to EEG patterns, neurologists can also measure **evoked potentials,** which are electrical responses caused by light, sound, or somatosensory stimuli. EEGs and evoked potentials are useful tools to diagnose neurological disorders and determine the appropriate treatment.

ASSESS YOUR PROGRESS

30. *Trace the sequence of events that must occur for a person to repeat a word that he or she hears.*

31. *Name the largest pathway that connects the right and left cerebral hemispheres.*

Clinical IMPACT 14.5

Aphasia

Damage to the language areas of the cerebral cortex may result in **aphasia** (ah-FAY-zee-ah), absent or defective speech or language comprehension. The most common cause is a stroke. It is estimated that 25–40% of stroke survivors exhibit aphasia.

There are several types of aphasia, depending on the site of the lesion. **Receptive aphasia** (Wernicke aphasia) is caused by a lesion in the Wernicke area. This condition is characterized by defective auditory and visual comprehension of language, defective naming of objects, and repetition of spoken sentences. Both **jargon aphasia,** in which a person may speak fluently but unintelligibly, and **conduction aphasia,** characterized by poor repetition but relatively good comprehension, can result from a lesion in the tracts between the Wernicke and Broca areas. **Anomic** (ah-NOH-mik) **aphasia,** caused by the isolation of the Wernicke area from the parietal or temporal association areas, is characterized by fluent but circular speech resulting from poor word-finding ability. **Expressive aphasia** (Broca aphasia), caused by a lesion in the Broca area, is characterized by hesitant and distorted speech.

32. *What functions are localized in each cerebral hemisphere?*
33. *What does an EEG measure?*
34. *What conditions produce alpha, beta, theta, and delta waves, respectively?*
35. *Explain how brain waves change during sleep. What is REM sleep?*

Memory

Memory can be viewed as the capacity to store knowledge for later retrieval. The storage of memory can be divided into three stages: (1) working, (2) short-term, and (3) long-term (figure 14.15).

Working memory → (Long-term potentiation) → Short-term memory → (Consolidation) → Long-term memory (Declarative | Procedural)

Working memory: Most is lost immediately.
Short-term memory: Most is lost within a short time.
Declarative: Much is lost through time.
Procedural: A small amount is lost through time.

FIGURE 14.15 Memory Processing
Memory is processed in the brain over time through working, short-term, and long-term stages.

Long-term memories can also be subdivided based on the type of the memory: those dealing with facts (*declarative*) and those dealing with skills (*procedural*). Both types involve networks of neurons that work together to form a memory.

Working Memory

Working memory is a task-associated memory. It occurs when the brain briefly stores information required for the immediate performance of a task. It is transient, lasting only a few seconds to minutes, but highly detailed. It occurs mostly in the frontal cortex. The number of information bits (about seven) that can be stored at any one time is the primary limiting factor for working memory. However, the amount varies from person to person. More bits can be stored when they are grouped into segments separated by spaces—as is done with phone numbers. When new information is presented, or when the person is distracted, information previously stored in working memory is eliminated; therefore, if a person is given a second telephone number or if the person's attention is drawn to something else, the first number is usually forgotten.

Short-Term Memory

Short-term memory lasts longer than working memory and can be stored from minutes to days. Short-term memories are stored by a mechanism involving increased synaptic transmission. Short-term memory is susceptible to brain trauma, such as physical injury or decreased O_2, and to certain drugs that affect neural function, such as general anesthetics. The formation of short-term memory involves the enhancement of synaptic activity by long-term potentiation. **Long-term potentiation** is the facilitation or *potentiation* of the future transmission of action potentials. In long-term potentiation, there is either (a) an increase in the number of vesicles containing the neurotransmitter glutamate released on the presynaptic side or (b) an increase in the number and activity of glutamate receptors on the postsynaptic side. In both cases, glutamate-mediated synaptic transmission is increased in the postsynaptic neuron. The mechanism of long-term potentiation is illustrated in figure 14.16.

1. The presynaptic cell increases the amount of glutamate release.
2. Glutamate binds to its receptors on the postsynaptic membrane and causes ligand-gated Ca^{2+} channels to open. Ca^{2+} enters the postsynaptic cell.
3. Calcium activates **calmodulin-dependent protein kinase II,** which phosphorylates glutamate receptors to increase their activity.
4. Calmodulin-dependent protein kinase II also sends signals to move additional glutamate receptors from internal vesicles to the postsynaptic membrane.

Thus, long-term potentiation increases transmission at selected synapses to allow short-term memory. This is best understood from studies of the hippocampus, described later in this section.

PROCESS **Figure**

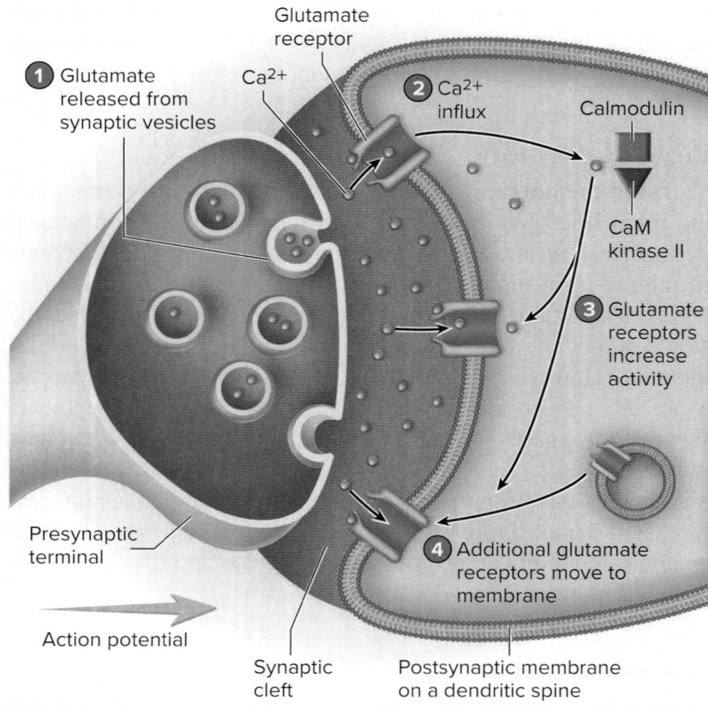

PROCESS **Figure 14.16**

Cellular Mechanisms of Long-Term Potentiation

Both presynaptic and postsynaptic mechanisms are shown, although usually only one occurs at a single synapse. APR

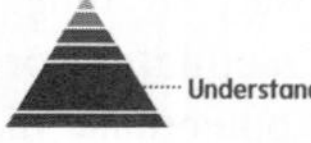

Predict whether inhibition of glutamate signaling activity, for example, by using a drug that blocks glutamate receptors, would inhibit presynaptic, postsynaptic, or both mechanisms.

Long-Term Memory

Long-term memory requires the prior formation of short-term memory. It is a more stable storage state that lasts from days to years or a lifetime. Long-term memories are stabilized by the formation of additional synaptic connections following new protein synthesis. Unlike short-term memories, long-term memories are more resistant to disruption by brain trauma.

The process of transferring short-term memory to long-term memory is called **consolidation.** Consolidation is a gradual process involving the formation of new and stronger synaptic connections that can occur over a period of years and probably involves multiple steps. Repeating the information and associating it with existing memories or a strong emotion increases the consolidation of short-term to long-term memory.

The process of consolidation involves the synthesis of new proteins that increase the number and size of synaptic contacts, along with the increased synaptic transmission of long-term potentiation. Genes that encode proteins involved in synapse formation are turned on by cAMP and calcium signaling pathways. A **cAMP-responsive transcription factor** called CREB is particularly important for activating gene transcription. The newly synthesized proteins include cytoskeletal proteins that create small protrusions from dendrites called **dendritic spines.** New synapses are then formed on the dendritic spines. Thus, long-term memory is longer-lasting due to an increased number of strengthened synapses.

Declarative and Procedural Memories

Another way to classify memory is in terms of the type of information stored: declarative or procedural. Both types of memory appear to use similar neural mechanisms at the cellular level, but in response to different types of information and in different parts of the brain.

Declarative memory, also called *explicit memory,* involves the retention of facts you can easily state or *declare*. For example, names, dates, and places involve declarative memory. The formation of declarative short-term memory involves the parts of the temporal lobe called the **hippocampus** (hip-poh-KAM-pus; shaped like a seahorse) and the **amygdala** (ah-MIG-dah-lah; almond-shaped; see figure 13.11). The hippocampus is required for the factual content, such as a person's name, whereas the amygdala contributes emotional overtones to the memory, such as feelings of like or dislike associated with that person. Emotion and mood apparently serve as gates in the brain, influencing what is stored in declarative memory. The amygdala is also a key to the development of fear, along with the prefrontal cortex and the hypothalamus. Much of what is stored as declarative memory is not consolidated or is gradually lost through time, although memories with emotional overtones persist longer.

Procedural memory, also called *implicit* or *reflexive memory,* involves the development of skills or *procedures*. For example, riding a bicycle and playing the piano involve procedural memory. Procedural memory is stored primarily in the cerebellum (see figure 13.6) and the **premotor area** of the cortex (see figure 14.7). Procedural memory is also involved in conditioned reflexes. A famous example is Pavlov's experiments—each time he fed a group of dogs, a bell was rung; soon the dogs salivated when the bell rang, even if no food was present. Only a small amount of procedural memory is lost through time.

Storage and Retrieval of Memories

Memory appears to be distributed in large networks in the brain rather than confined to a particular storage area. A network of neurons and their pattern of activity, called a **memory engram,** or *memory trace,* is probably involved in the long-term retention of information, a thought, or an idea. In other words, memories are not a single set of neurons but, rather, a collection of the activity between groups of interconnected neurons. For example, there is no "Grandma" neuron, whereby Grandma is completely forgotten if that neuron is damaged. In this model, the pattern of strengthened synapses distributed throughout the memory engram

22. *A person with a spinal cord injury is suffering from paresis (partial paralysis) in the right lower limb. Which of these pathways is probably involved?* Understand

    a. *left lateral corticospinal tract*
    b. *right lateral corticospinal tract*
    c. *left dorsal-column/medial-lemniscal system*
    d. *right dorsal-column/medial-lemniscal system*

23. *Which of these pathways is* not *an indirect (extrapyramidal) pathway?* Remember

    a. *reticulospinal tract*
    b. *corticobulbar tract*
    c. *rubrospinal tract*
    d. *vestibulospinal tract*

24. *The indirect (extrapyramidal) system is concerned with* Remember

    a. *posture.*
    b. *trunk movements.*
    c. *proximal limb movements.*
    d. *All of these are correct.*

25. *A person who was injured in a car accident exhibits the following symptoms: extreme paresis on the right side, including the arm and leg; reduction of pain sensation on the left side; and normal tactile sensation on both sides. Which tracts are damaged? Where in the spinal cord did the patient suffer tract damage?* Apply

26. *A patient with a cerebral lesion exhibits loss of fine motor control of the left hand, arm, forearm, and shoulder. All other motor and sensory functions appear to be intact. Describe the location of the lesion as precisely as possible.* Apply

Modifying and Refining Motor Activities

A. Basal nuclei are important in planning, organizing, and coordinating motor movements and posture.

B. The cerebellum has three parts.
- The vestibulocerebellum controls balance and eye movement.
- The spinocerebellum has a comparator function that corrects discrepancies between intended movements and actual movements.
- The cerebrocerebellum can "learn" highly specific complex motor activities.

27. *The major effect of the basal nuclei is*

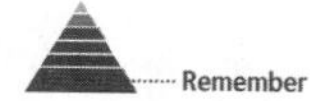

    a. *to act as a comparator for motor coordination.*
    b. *to decrease muscle tone and inhibit unwanted muscular activity.*
    c. *to affect emotions and emotional responses to odors.*
    d. *to modulate pain sensations.*

28. *Which part of the cerebellum is correctly matched with its function?* Remember

    a. *vestibulocerebellum—planning and learning rapid, complex movements*
    b. *spinocerebellum—comparator function*
    c. *cerebrocerebellum—balance*
    d. *None of these are correct.*

29. *Given the following events:*

    (1) *Action potentials from the cerebellum go to the motor cortex and spinal cord.*
    (2) *Action potentials from the motor cortex go to lower motor neurons and the cerebellum.*
    (3) *Action potentials from proprioceptors go to the cerebellum.*

    Arrange the events in the order they occur in the cerebellar comparator function.

    a. *1,2,3*
    b. *1,3,2*
    c. *2,1,3*
    d. *2,3,1*
    e. *3,2,1*

30. *A patient suffers brain damage in an automobile accident. Physicians suspect that the cerebellum is the part of the brain affected. On the basis of what you know about cerebellar function, how can they confirm that the cerebellum is involved?* Apply

14.3 Brainstem Functions

The brainstem contains nuclei for cranial nerves III–X and XII and nuclei of the reticular formation.

Sensory Input Projecting Through the Brainstem

The brainstem receives sensory input from ascending spinal cord pathways and from the axons of cranial nerves.

RAS Functions of the Brainstem

Collateral branches of cranial nerves II, V, and VIII project to the reticular activating system (RAS) of the brainstem, where they stimulate wakefulness and consciousness.

Motor Output and Reflexes Projecting Through the Brainstem

A. Descending spinal pathways either pass directly through the brainstem or synapse with brainstem nuclei.

B. The brainstem controls several somatic motor and parasympathetic reflexes.

Vital Functions Controlled in the Brainstem

The brainstem controls many vital functions, including heart rate, blood pressure, and respiration.

31. *Perry is a 93-year-old man who uses his computer to communicate with family and friends and to write poems and essays. One day last week, his daughter noticed that Perry was unable to use the computer keyboard normally with his right hand, and this ability deteriorated further over the next few hours. Perry was also experiencing muscle weakness on the right side, and soon he could not support himself with his right lower limb without using a cane; later in the day, he could hardly move his right lower limb at all. Concerned about a stroke, Perry's daughter took him to the emergency room, where radiographs and an MRI revealed a subdural hematoma. Explain how a subdural hematoma could be responsible for Perry's condition.* Apply

32. *The brainstem*

    a. *consists of ascending and descending pathways.*
    b. *contains cranial nerve nuclei III–X and XII.*
    c. *has nuclei and connections that form the reticular activating system.*
    d. *has many important reflexes, some of which are necessary for survival.*
    e. *has all of these features.*

14.4 Higher Brain Functions

Speech

A. The speech area is in the left cerebral cortex in most people.
B. The Wernicke area comprehends and formulates speech.
C. The Broca area receives input from the Wernicke area and sends impulses to the premotor and motor areas, which cause the muscle movements required for speech.

Communication Between the Right and Left Hemispheres

A. Each cerebral hemisphere controls and receives input from the opposite side of the body.
B. The right and left hemispheres are connected by commissures. The largest commissure is the corpus callosum, which allows the sharing of information between hemispheres.
C. In most people, the left hemisphere is dominant, controlling speech and analytical skills. The right hemisphere controls spatial and musical abilities.

Brain Waves and Sleep

A. Electroencephalograms (EEGs) record the electrical activity of the brain as alpha, beta, theta, and delta waves.
B. Some brain disorders can be detected with EEGs.
C. Sleep patterns are characterized by specific EEGs.

Memory

A. Three stages of memory exist: working, short-term, and long-term.
B. Short-term memory requires long-term potentiation.
C. Long-term memory is converted from short-term by consolidation.
D. The two types of memory are declarative and procedural.

Limbic System

A. The limbic system includes cortical and subcortical regions and nuclei, including the olfactory cortex and the hippocampus.
B. The limbic system is involved with emotions, motivation, mood, visceral functions, and memory. Olfactory stimulation is a major influence.

33. *Given these areas of the cerebral cortex:*

(1) Broca area
(2) premotor area
(3) primary motor cortex
(4) Wernicke area

If a person hears and understands a word and then says the word out loud, in what order are the areas used?

a. 1,4,2,3
b. 1,4,3,2
c. 3,1,4,2
d. 4,1,2,3
e. 4,1,3,2

34. *The main connection between the right and left hemispheres of the cerebrum is the* Remember

a. intermediate mass.
b. corpus callosum.
c. vermis.
d. unmyelinated nuclei.
e. thalamus.

35. *Which of these activities is associated with the left cerebral hemisphere in most people?* Remember

a. sensory input from the left side of the body
b. mathematics and speech
c. spatial perception
d. recognition of faces
e. musical ability

36. *The limbic system is involved in the control of*

a. sleep and wakefulness.
b. posture.
c. higher intellectual processes.
d. emotion, mood, and sensations of pain or pleasure.
e. hearing.

37. *Long-term memory involves*

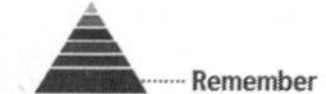

a. a change in the cytoskeleton of neurons.
b. an increased number of dendritic spines.
c. cAMP signaling pathways that increase gene transcription.
d. specific protein synthesis.
e. All of these are correct.

38. *Concerning long-term memory*

a. declarative (explicit) memory involves the development of skills, such as riding a bicycle.
b. procedural (implicit, or reflexive) memory involves the retention of facts, such as names, dates, or places.
c. much of declarative (explicit) memory is lost through time.
d. declarative (explicit) memory is stored primarily in the cerebellum and premotor area of the cerebrum.
e. All of these are correct.

39. *Woody was accidentally struck in the head with a baseball bat. He fell to the ground, unconscious. Later, when he regained consciousness, he could not remember any of the events that happened 10 minutes before the accident. Explain. What complications might develop at a later time?* Apply

Answers to this chapter's odd-numbered Concept Check questions appear in Appendix F.

15

CHAPTER

The Special Senses

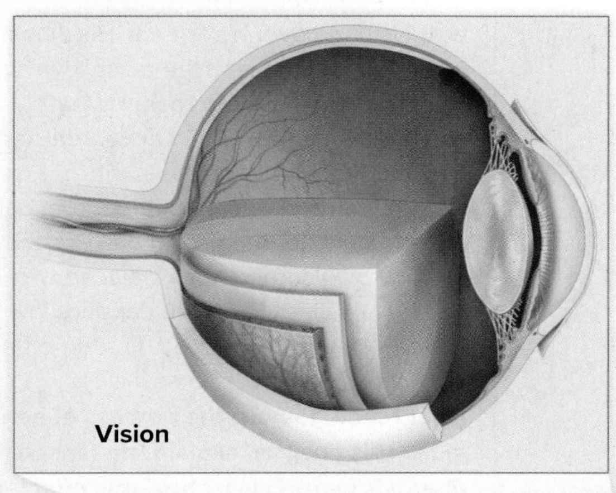

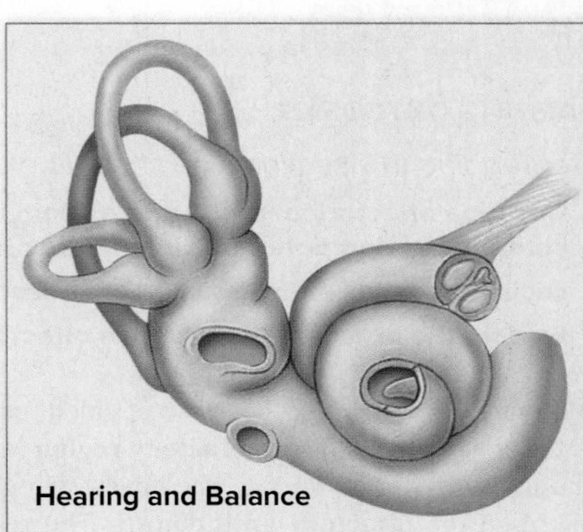

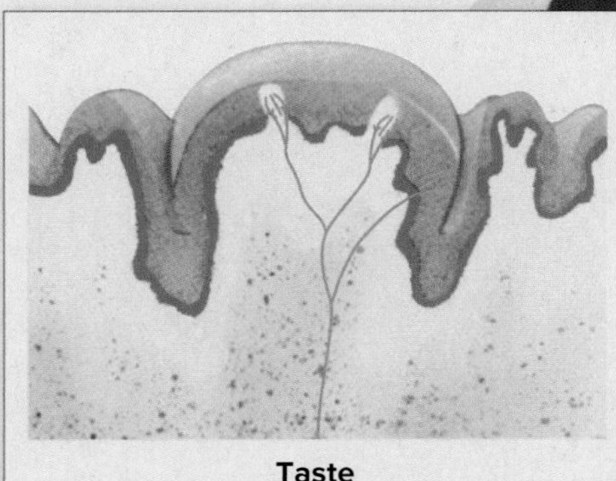

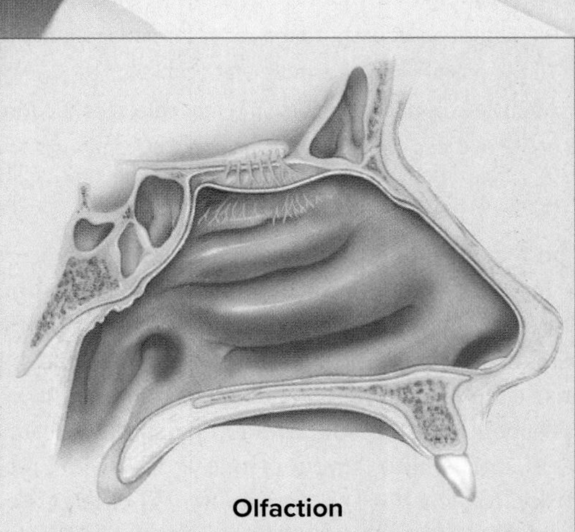

The special senses include olfaction, taste, vision, hearing, and balance.
m-imagephotography/iStock/Getty Images

Historically, physiologists thought humans had just five senses: smell, taste, vision, hearing, and touch. Today, they recognize many more. The original sense of "touch" has been categorized into multiple types of *general senses,* including pressure, touch, pain, and others. The general senses are described in chapter 14. Smell, taste, vision, hearing, and balance are now classified as *special senses*. This chapter describes the five special senses and the organs associated with each.

Learn to Predict

Freddy, a 67-year-old father and grandfather, was sitting on his couch with his hand over his left ear. His whole family was visiting and the noise level was pretty high in the living room. "What's wrong?" asked his wife. "I never realized how loud our family is," he laughed. For most of his life, Freddy suffered from complete hearing loss in his left ear. Recently, he underwent a surgery that replaced two auditory ossicles in his left ear and now his hearing has been restored. Freddy is hearing his family in a whole new way.

After reading about the process of hearing in this chapter, explain the reason for Freddy's hearing loss, how this affected his ability to locate the direction of noises, and how his hearing was restored.

Answers to this question and the chapter's odd-numbered Predict questions can be found in Appendix E.

15.1 Olfaction

LEARNING OUTCOMES

After reading this section, you should be able to

A. **Describe olfactory neurons and explain how airborne molecules can stimulate action potentials in olfactory nerves.**
B. **Locate the areas of the brain where olfaction is processed.**
C. **Explain the processes involved in olfactory adaptation.**

Olfaction (ol-FAK-shun), the sense of smell, occurs in response to odors that stimulate sensory receptors in the **olfactory region** located in the extreme superior area of the nasal cavity (figure 15.1*a*). The olfactory region is lined with a specialized epithelium called the **olfactory epithelium.** (The rest of the nasal cavity is involved in respiration, and its major anatomical features are described in chapter 23.)

Olfactory Epithelium

The olfactory epithelium contains the cell bodies and dendrites of approximately 10 million **olfactory neurons,** which are olfactory receptor cells (figure 15.1*b*). The dendrites of olfactory neurons extend to the epithelial surface of the nasal cavity, and their ends are modified into bulbous enlargements called **olfactory vesicles** (figure 15.1*b*). These vesicles possess cilia called **olfactory hairs,** which lie in a thin mucous film on the epithelial surface.

Airborne molecules enter the nasal cavity and are dissolved in the fluid covering the olfactory epithelium. Some of these molecules, referred to as **odorants** (OH-dor-ants), bind to odorant receptor molecules of the olfactory hair membranes; thus, the olfactory neurons are considered chemoreceptors. Figure 15.2 illustrates the binding of an odorant to a G protein–coupled receptor on the membrane of an olfactory hair.

1. Each odorant receptor molecule is associated with a G protein (see chapter 3).
2. Binding of an odorant to the receptor molecule activates the G protein.
3. The G protein activates adenylate cyclase.
4. Adenylate cyclase is an enzyme that catalyzes the formation of cyclic AMP (cAMP) from ATP.
5. cAMP in these cells causes Na^+ and Ca^{2+} channels to open. The influx of ions into the olfactory hairs results in depolarization and the production of action potentials in the olfactory neurons.

The receptor molecules on olfactory neurons vary considerably in structure, which allows for the production of approximately 1000 different odorant receptor molecules. These receptor molecules can react to odorants of different sizes, shapes, and functional groups. These capabilities, together with multiple intracellular pathways involving G proteins, adenylate cyclase, and ion channels, allow for a wide variety of detectable smells—about 4000 for the average person. Some researchers have grouped this wide range of smells into seven primary classes: (1) camphoraceous (e.g., mothballs), (2) musky, (3) floral, (4) pepperminty, (5) ethereal (e.g., fresh pears), (6) pungent, and (7) putrid. However, other studies point to the possibility of as many as 50 primary odors.

Module 7
Nervous System

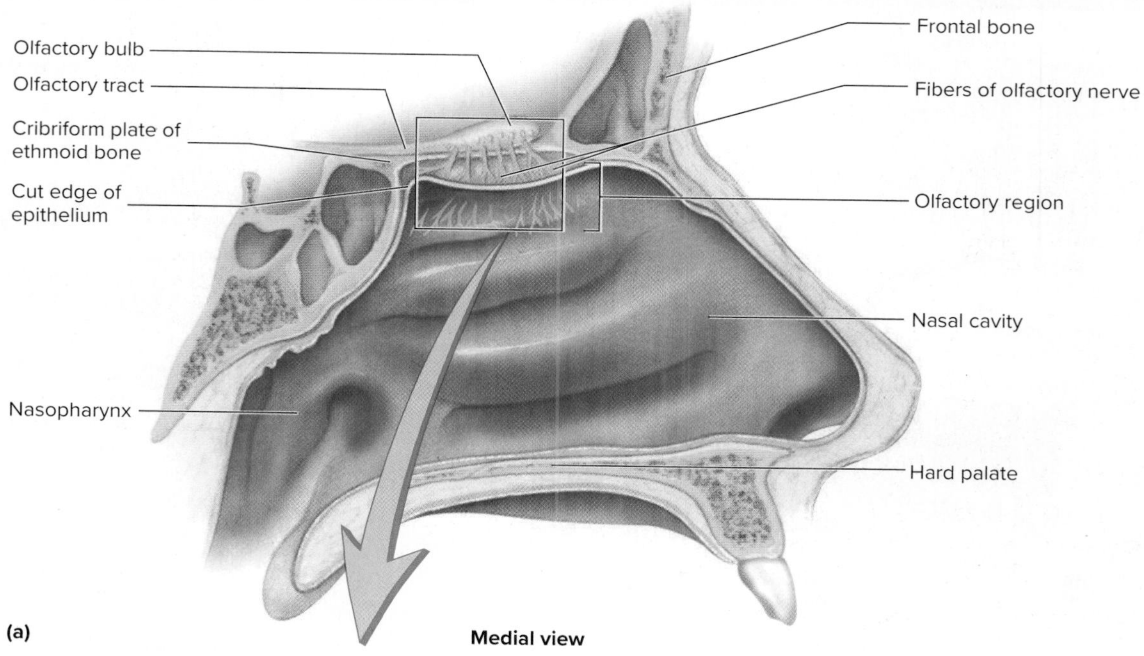

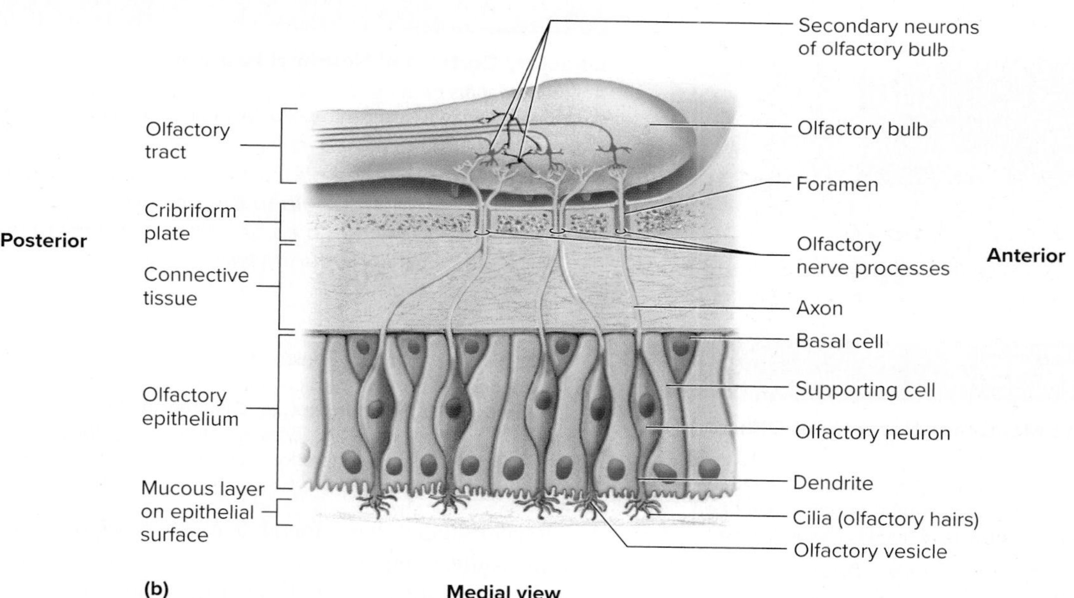

FIGURE 15.1 Olfactory Region, Epithelium, and Bulb
(*a*) The lateral wall of the nasal cavity (cut in sagittal section), showing the olfactory region and olfactory bulb. (*b*) Close-up of the olfactory epithelium, showing the olfactory nerve processes passing through the cribriform plate and the fine structure of the olfactory bulb. APR

In most people, the threshold for detecting odors is extremely low, so very few odorant molecules are required to trigger a response. Apparently, there is rather low specificity in the olfactory epithelium, so that a given receptor molecule may react to more than one type of odorant. However, if odorant receptor molecules become saturated with odorants, they no longer respond to odorant molecules. This adaptation makes a person less sensitive to an odorant after being exposed to it for a short time. For example, when you first enter a movie theater, the distinctive odor of popcorn is very noticeable, but it becomes almost unnoticeable after you have been in the theater for a short time.

The primary olfactory neurons in the olfactory epithelium have the most exposed nerve endings of any neurons of the human body, and they are constantly being replaced. The entire olfactory epithelium, including the olfactory neurons, degenerates and is lost from the surface of the olfactory epithelium about every 2 months. Lost

PROCESS **Figure**

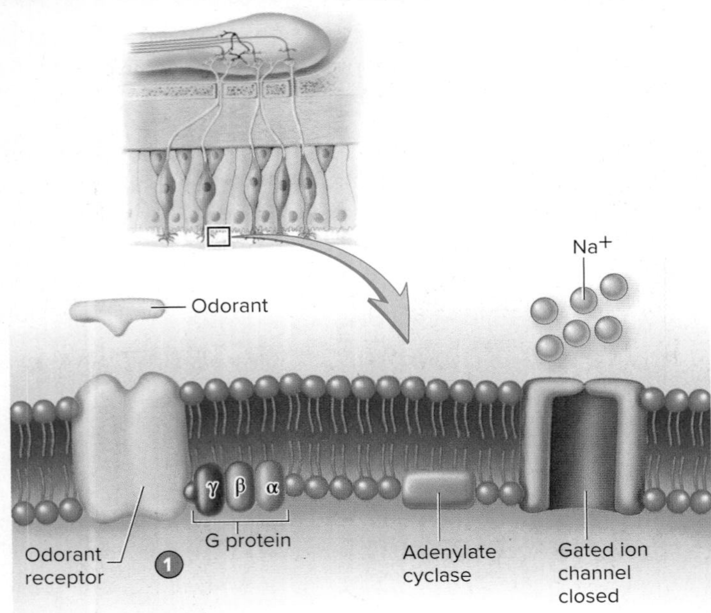

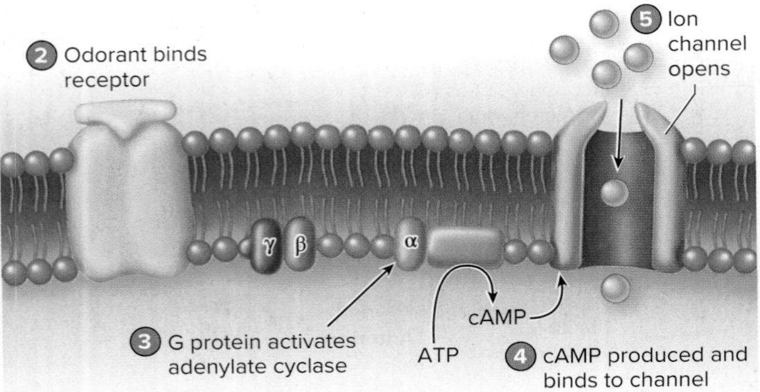

PROCESS **Figure 15.2**

Action of Odorant Binding to Membrane Receptor of Olfactory Hair

Odorant binding results in the activation of a G protein and subsequent formation of cAMP. cAMP interacts with ion channels. Ion channels open, allowing ions to enter the olfactory neuron, resulting in depolarization.

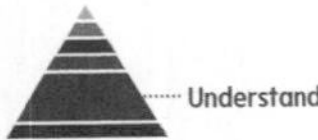

Compare the opening of ion channels in this scenario with the opening of ion channels at a cholinergic synapse, such as at a neuromuscular junction described in chapters 9 and 11.

olfactory cells are replaced by a proliferation of **basal cells** in the olfactory epithelium. Recall from chapter 4 that most neurons are permanent cells that have a very limited ability to replicate. So this replacement of olfactory neurons is unique among neurons.

Neuronal Pathways for Olfaction

Figure 15.3 illustrates the neuronal pathway of olfaction.

1. Axons from the olfactory neurons, which form the olfactory nerves (cranial nerve I), project through numerous small foramina in the bony cribiform plate (see chapter 7) to the **olfactory bulb** (see figure 15.1*b*).

PROCESS **Figure**

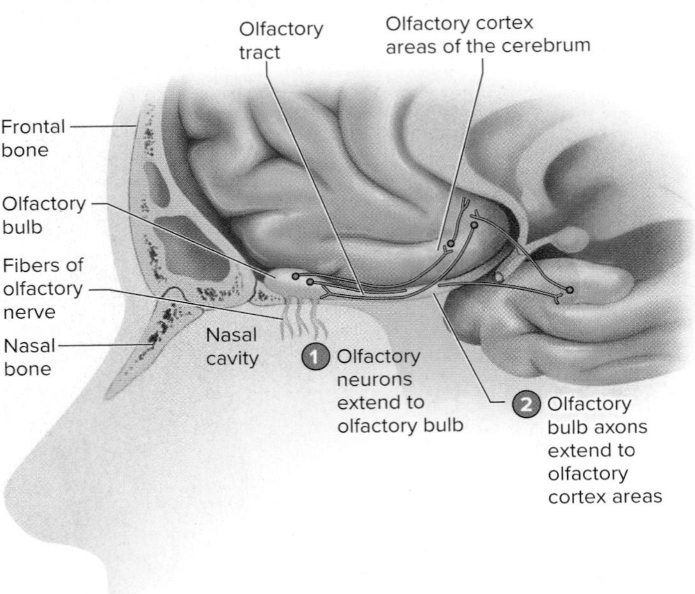

PROCESS **Figure 15.3**

Olfactory Cortex and Neuronal Pathways

Action potentials generated in olfactory neurons are conducted along the olfactory pathway to the central olfactory cortex areas in the temporal and frontal lobes of the cerebrum.

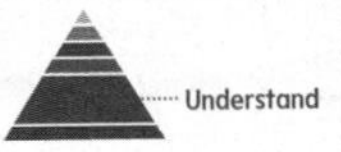

Does the olfactory neuronal pathway from the olfactory bulb to the olfactory cortex areas represent a converging or diverging pathway? Explain your answer.

2. Within the olfactory bulbs, the olfactory neurons synapse with secondary neurons, which relay olfactory information to the brain through the **olfactory tracts.** Olfactory bulb neurons also receive input from nerve cell processes entering the olfactory bulb from the brain, enhancing adaptation that occurs along this first part of the olfactory pathway.

Recent studies have found that the processing of olfactory stimuli is quite complex, involving multiple areas of the cerebrum. This dispersed organization differs from other sensory projections, which generally lead to specific regions of the brain. The consequence of the complex organization is that olfactory stimuli cause not only perception of specific odors but also emotional and autonomic responses. The majority of neurons in the olfactory tracts project to **central olfactory cortex areas** in the temporal and frontal lobes of the cerebrum (figure 15.3), where olfactory stimuli are processed to allow us to perceive odors. These central areas include the **piriform cortex** located at the junction between the temporal and frontal lobes, the **amygdala** of the temporal lobe, and the **orbitofrontal cortex.** In addition, olfactory tract neurons project to secondary olfactory areas, which appear to be involved with emotional and autonomic responses to olfactory stimuli. **Secondary olfactory areas** include the hypothalamus, hippocampus, and structures of the limbic system (see chapters 13 and 14).

ASSESS YOUR PROGRESS

Answers to these questions are found in the section you have just completed. Re-read the section if you need help in answering these questions.

1. *Where are olfactory neurons located? Explain their structure.*
2. *Describe the initiation of an action potential in an olfactory neuron. Name all of the structures and cells that the action potential encounters on its way to the olfactory cortex.*
3. *What is unique about olfactory neurons with respect to replacement?*
4. *Where are the central olfactory cortex areas located?*

15.2 Taste

LEARNING OUTCOMES

After reading this section, you should be able to

A. **List the types of papillae.**
B. **Outline the structure and function of a taste bud.**
C. **List the five major tastants.**
D. **Relate the relationship of taste to smell.**
E. **Describe the formation of an action potential in a taste cell.**
F. **Trace the pathway of the action potential to the taste area of the cerebral cortex.**

The sensory structures that detect **taste,** or *gustatory,* stimuli are the **taste buds.** You may think that those bumps on your tongue are your taste buds. That is a common misconception, but those bumps are actually **papillae** (pah-PILL-ee). Taste buds, on the other hand, are much smaller. Most taste buds are located along the edges of those papillae. However, taste buds are also located on other areas of the tongue, the palate, and even the lips and throat, especially in children. The four major types of papillae are named according to their shape (figure 15.4): (1) **filiform** (FIL-i-form; filament-shaped), (2) **vallate** (VAL-ate; surrounded by a wall), (3) **foliate** (FOH-lee-ate; leaf-shaped), and (4) **fungiform** (FUN-ji-form; mushroom-shaped). Taste buds (figure 15.4*f*) are associated with vallate, foliate, and fungiform papillae. Filiform papillae are the most numerous papillae on the surface of the tongue but have no taste buds. Rather, filiform papillae provide a rough surface on the tongue, allowing it to manipulate food more easily.

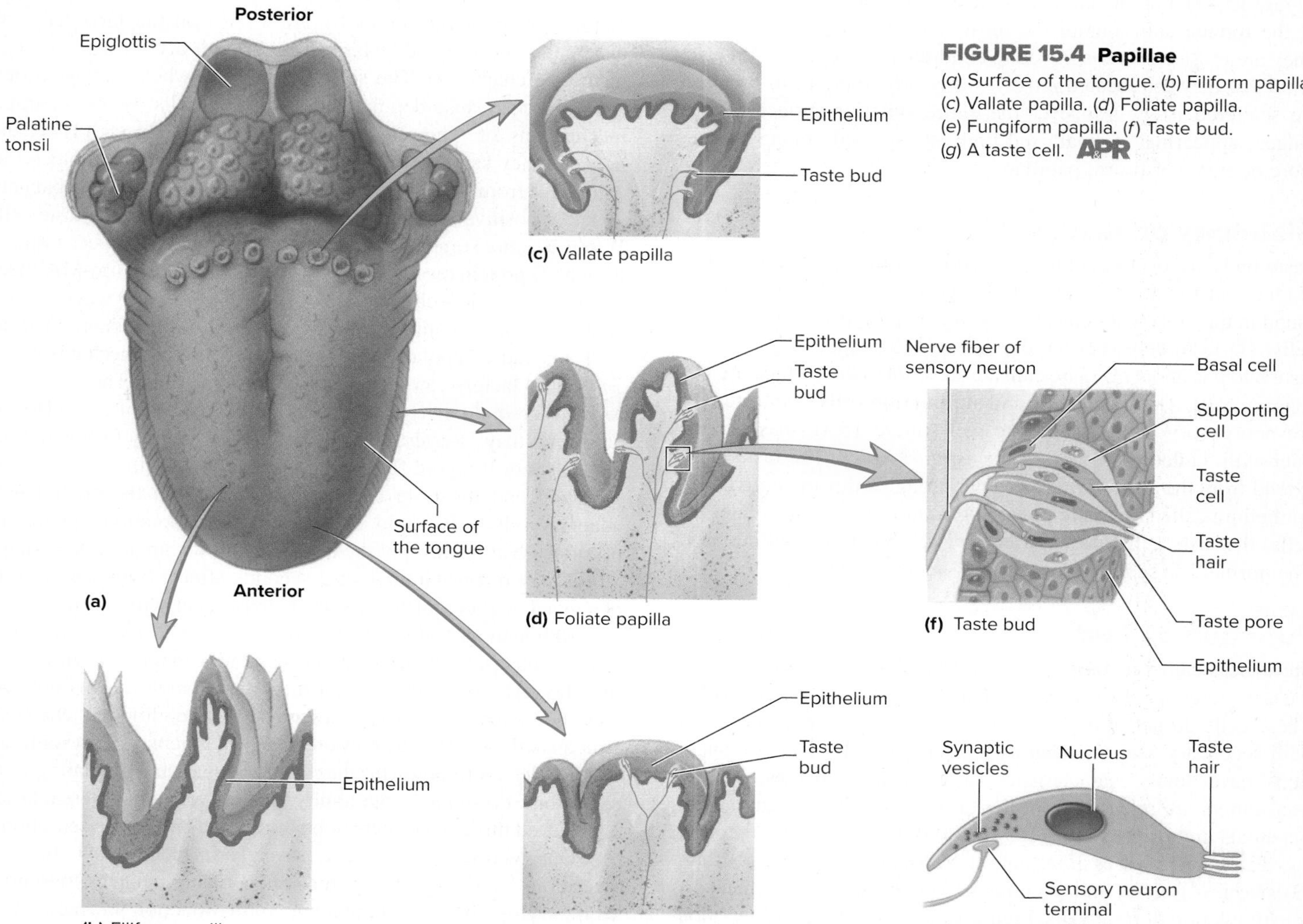

FIGURE 15.4 Papillae
(*a*) Surface of the tongue. (*b*) Filiform papilla. (*c*) Vallate papilla. (*d*) Foliate papilla. (*e*) Fungiform papilla. (*f*) Taste bud. (*g*) A taste cell. APR

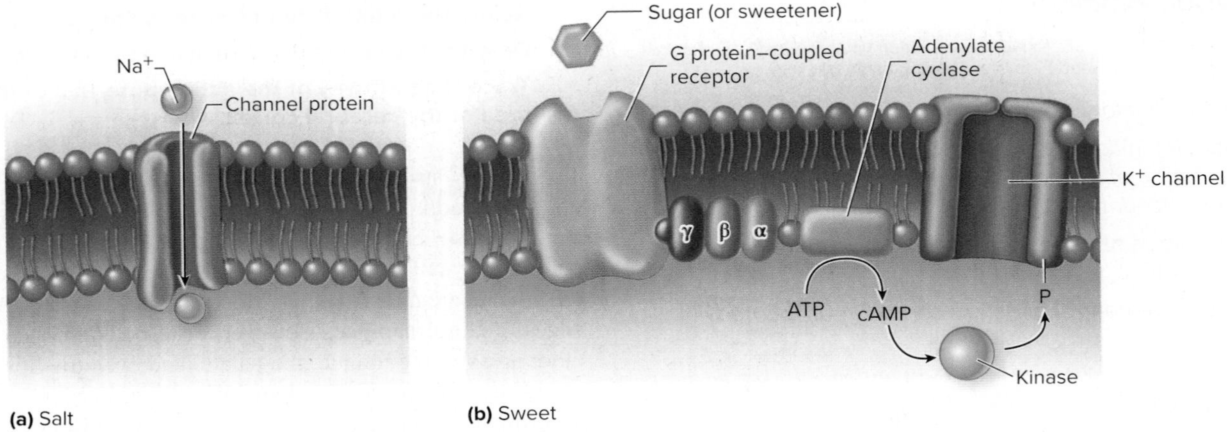

FIGURE 15.5 Stimulation of Taste Receptors
(*a*) The taste of salt results when Na^+ enters taste cells through Na^+ ion channels, leading to depolarization of the taste cell. (*b*) Receptors associated with sweet tastes involve sugar molecules binding to G protein–coupled receptors on the taste cells. This binding activates G proteins and leads to depolarization of the taste cell.

Vallate papillae are the largest but least numerous of the papillae. Eight to 12 of these papillae form a V-shaped row along the border between the anterior and posterior parts of the tongue (figure 15.4*a*). Foliate papillae are distributed in folds on the sides of the tongue and contain the most sensitive of the taste buds. They are most numerous in young children and decrease with age. In adults, they are located mostly posteriorly. Fungiform papillae are scattered irregularly over the entire superior surface of the tongue, appearing as small, red dots interspersed among the far more numerous filiform papillae.

Histology of Taste Buds

Taste buds are oval structures embedded in the epithelium of the tongue and mouth (figure 15.4*f*). Each of the 10,000 taste buds found in the oral cavity consists of three major types of specialized cells: (1) taste cells, (2) basal cells, and (3) supporting cells. A taste bud has about 50 **taste cells,** or *gustatory cells,* which are the sensory cells. The **basal cells** and **supporting cells** of a taste bud are nonsensory cells. Each taste cell (figure 15.4*g*) has several microvilli, called **taste hairs,** or *gustatory hairs.* The taste hairs extend from the apex of the taste cell through a tiny opening in the epithelium called the **taste pore,** or *gustatory pore.* Like olfactory cells, the taste cells are exposed and are replaced continuously. The normal life span of a taste cell is about 10 days.

Function of Taste

Substances called **tastants** (TAYS-tants), dissolved in saliva, enter the taste pores and, by various mechanisms, stimulate the taste cells. These cells do not have classic axons but have short connections with secondary sensory neurons (see chapter 14). Those connections have some characteristics of chemical synapses. Neurotransmitters are released from the taste cells and stimulate action potentials in the axons of sensory neurons associated with them.

Five major classes of tastants are recognized: (1) salt, (2) sour, (3) sweet, (4) bitter, and (5) umami. The are several mechanisms for stimulation of taste cells. Figure 15.5 illustrates the stimulation of receptors associated with salt and sweet tastants. The taste of **salt** results when Na^+ diffuses through Na^+ channels (figure 15.5*a*) of the taste hairs or other cell surfaces of taste cells, resulting in depolarization of the cells. **Sweet** tastants bind to G protein–coupled receptor molecules (figure 15.5*b*) on the taste hairs of taste cells and cause depolarization through a G protein mechanism (see chapter 3). The **sour** taste results when hydrogen ions (H^+) of acids cause depolarization of taste cells by one of three mechanisms: (1) They can enter the cell directly through H^+ channels, (2) they can bind to ligand-gated K^+ channels and block the exit of K^+ from the cell, or (3) they can open ligand-gated channels for other positive ions and allow them to diffuse into the taste cell. **Bitter** tastants stimulate action potential similar to sweet tastants through G protein mechanisms. A taste called **umami** (oo-MA-mee; Japanese term loosely translated as savory) results when amino acids, such as glutamate, bind to receptors on taste hairs of taste cells and cause depolarization through a G protein mechanism.

Other factors can influence the sense of taste. The texture of food in the oral cavity also affects the perception of taste. Hot or cold food may interfere with the taste buds' ability to function in tasting food. If a cold fluid is held in the mouth, the body warms the fluid and the taste becomes enhanced. On the other hand, adaptation is very rapid for taste. This adaptation apparently occurs both at the level of the taste bud and within the CNS. Adaptation may begin within 1 or 2 seconds after a taste sensation is perceived, and complete adaptation may occur within 5 minutes.

Although all taste buds are able to detect all five of the basic tastes, each taste cell is usually most sensitive to one. As with olfaction, however, the specificity of the receptor molecules is not perfect. For example, artificial sweeteners have different chemical structures than the sugars they are designed to replace, and some are many times more powerful than natural sugars in stimulating taste sensations. Presumably, our ability to perceive many different tastes is achieved through combinations of the five basic taste sensations.

Our perception of taste is strongly influenced by olfactory sensations. To demonstrate this phenomenon, pinch your nose while trying to taste something. With olfaction blocked, it is difficult to distinguish between the tastes of a piece of apple and a piece of potato. This is one reason that a person with a cold has a reduced sensation of taste.

Thresholds vary for the five primary tastes. Sensitivity for bitter substances is the highest; sensitivities for sweet and salty tastes are the lowest. Sugars, some other carbohydrates, and certain proteins produce sweet tastes; many proteins and amino acids produce umami tastes; acids produce sour tastes; metal ions tend to produce salty tastes; and alkaloids (bases) produce bitter tastes. Many alkaloids are poisonous; thus, the high sensitivity for bitter tastes may be protective. On the other hand, humans tend to crave sweet, salty, and umami tastes, perhaps in response to the body's need for sugars, other carbohydrates, proteins, and minerals.

Neuronal Pathways for Taste

Taste sensations are carried by three cranial nerves:

1. *Facial nerve (VII):* A branch of the facial nerve, the **chorda tympani** (KOR-dah TIM-pah-nee; so named because it crosses over the surface of the tympanic membrane of the middle ear), transmits taste sensations from the anterior two-thirds of the tongue, except from the vallate papillae.
2. *Glossopharyngeal nerve (IX):* The glossopharyngeal nerve carries taste sensations from the posterior one-third of the tongue, the vallate papillae, and the superior pharynx.
3. *Vagus nerve (X):* The vagus nerve carries a few fibers for taste sensation from the root of the tongue and the epiglottis.

Figure 15.6 illustrates the neuronal pathway of taste.

1. Axons of cranial nerves extend from the taste buds to the tractus solitarius of the medulla oblongata.
2. Fibers from this nucleus extend to the thalamus, decussating at the level of the midbrain (not shown in figure).
3. Neurons from the thalamus project bilaterally to the taste areas of both hemispheres of the cerebrum. The taste areas are located in the insula, deep within the lateral fissure between the temporal and parietal lobes.

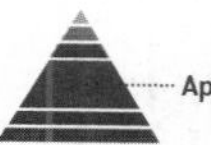

Predict 1

Ernie has difficulty swallowing, loss of taste sensation in the posterior one-third of the right half of his tongue, and decreased salivation, especially on the right side. Describe the sensory portion of the affected neuropathway in Ernie.

ASSESS YOUR PROGRESS

5. *Name and describe the four kinds of papillae on the tongue. Which ones are associated with taste buds?*
6. *Describe the structure of a taste bud.*
7. *What are the five primary tastes? Describe how each type of tastant causes depolarization of a taste cell.*
8. *Starting with the taste hair, name the structures and cells that an action potential would encounter on the way to the taste area of the cerebral cortex.*
9. *How is the sense of taste related to the sense of smell?*

PROCESS **Figure**

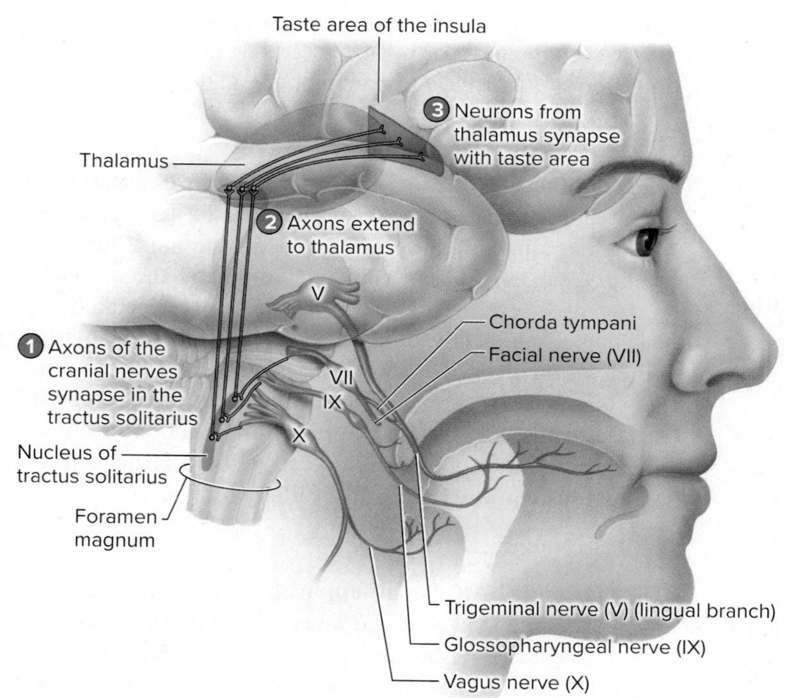

PROCESS **Figure 15.6**

Pathways for the Sense of Taste

The facial nerve (anterior two-thirds of the tongue), glossopharyngeal nerve (posterior one-third of the tongue), and vagus nerve (root of the tongue and epiglottis) all carry taste sensations. The trigeminal nerve carries tactile sensations from the anterior two-thirds of the tongue. The chorda tympani from the facial nerve (carrying taste input) joins the trigeminal nerve.

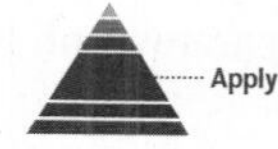

Which would affect the sense of taste more, damage to the glossopharyngeal nerve or damage to the tractus solitarius of the medulla oblongata? Explain your answer.

15.3 Visual System

LEARNING OUTCOMES

After reading this section, you should be able to

A. **List the accessory structures of the eye and explain their functions.**

B. **Describe the chambers of the eye and the fluids they contain.**

C. **Name the tunics of the eye, list the parts of each tunic, and describe the function of each part.**

D. **Explain the differences between rods and cones.**

E. **Describe the structure of the retina.**

F. **Explain how light stimulates action potentials in the optic nerves.**

G. **Relate how images are focused on the retina.**

H. **Define *visual acuity, myopia,* and *hyperopia.***

I. **Describe the pathway an action potential will travel from the rods and cones to the visual cortex.**

J. **Relate the arrangement of the visual field to binocular vision and depth perception.**

The visual system includes the eyes, the accessory structures, and the optic nerves (II), tracts, and pathways. The **eye** includes the eyeball (the globe of the eye) and the lens. The eyes respond to light and initiate afferent action potentials, which are transmitted from the eyes to the brain by the optic nerves and tracts. We obtain much of our information about the world through the visual system. For example, education is largely based on visual input, and much of the information is conveyed through reading material, such as this textbook. Visual input includes information about light and dark, movement, and color. Visual stimuli can come from far greater distances than can stimuli for any other sense. The eye can detect light originating from stars billions of miles away.

Accessory Structures

Accessory structures of the visual system are important for the maintenance and protection of the eyes. These structures function to protect, lubricate, move, and in other ways aid the function of the eye. The accessory structures include the (1) eyebrows, (2) eyelids, (3) eyelashes, (4) conjunctiva, (5) lacrimal apparatus, and (6) extrinsic eye muscles (figure 15.7*a*).

Eyebrows

The **eyebrows** are a collection of hairs superior to the orbits. A major function of the eyebrows is to prevent perspiration from running down the forehead and into the eyes and irritating them. Eyebrows also help shade the eyes from direct sunlight.

Eyelids

The **eyelids,** or *palpebrae* (pal-PEE-bree), with their associated eyelashes, protect the eyes from foreign objects. The space between the two eyelids is called the **palpebral fissure,** and the angles where the eyelids join at the medial and lateral margins of the eye are called **canthi** (KAN-thigh; corners of the eye; figure 15.7*a*). The medial canthus contains a small, reddish-pink mound called the **caruncle** (KAR-ung-kul; mound of tissue), which houses some modified sebaceous and sweat glands.

The eyelids consist of five layers of tissue (figure 15.7*b*). From the outer to the inner surface, they are

1. a thin layer of skin on the external surface;
2. a thin layer of areolar connective tissue;
3. a layer of skeletal muscle consisting of the orbicularis oculi and levator palpebrae superioris muscles;
4. a crescent-shaped layer of dense connective tissue called the **tarsal** (TAR-sahl) **plate,** which helps maintain the shape of the eyelid; and
5. the palpebral conjunctiva (described in the next section), which lines the inner surface of the eyelid and the anterior surface of the eyeball.

If an object suddenly approaches the eye, the eyelids protect the eye by rapidly closing and then opening (blink reflex). Blinking, which normally occurs about 25 times per minute, also helps keep the eye lubricated by spreading tears over the surface. Two pairs of skeletal muscles are responsible for the movements of the eyelids. The orbicularis oculi muscle closes the lids, and the levator palpebrae superioris elevates the upper lid (see figures 10.8 and 15.7). The eyelids also help regulate the amount of light entering the eye.

Eyelashes (see figure 15.7) are attached as a double or triple row of hairs to the free edges of the eyelids. **Ciliary glands** are modified sweat glands that open into the follicles of the eyelashes to keep them lubricated. A **sty** forms when one of these glands becomes inflamed. **Meibomian** (my-BOH-mee-an) **glands,** or *tarsal glands,* are sebaceous glands near the inner margins of the eyelids; they produce **sebum** (SEE-bum), which lubricates the lids and restrains tears from flowing over the margin of the eyelids. A **chalazion** (ka-LAY-zee-on), or *meibomian cyst,* is an infection or a blockage of a meibomian gland.

Conjunctiva

The **conjunctiva** (kon-junk-TIE-vah) is a thin, transparent mucous membrane associated with the eyelids and the exposed areas of the eye. The **palpebral conjunctiva** covers the inner surface of the eyelids, and the **bulbar conjunctiva** covers the anterior white surface of the eye (figure 15.7*b*). The points at which the palpebral and bulbar conjunctivae meet are the superior and inferior **conjunctival fornices** (sing. fornix). The secretions of the conjuctiva help lubricate the surface of the eye. **Conjunctivitis** is an inflammation of the conjunctiva caused by an infection or other irritation. One type of conjunctivitis caused by a bacterium is **acute contagious conjunctivitis,** also called *pinkeye.*

Lacrimal Apparatus

The **lacrimal** (LAK-ri-mal) **apparatus** (figure 15.8) consists of a lacrimal gland situated in the superolateral corner of the orbit and a nasolacrimal duct beginning in the inferomedial corner of the orbit. The **lacrimal gland** is innervated by parasympathetic fibers

FIGURE 15.7 Structures of the Eye

(*a*) Photo of the accessory structures of the left eye. (*b*) Sagittal section through the eye, showing internal and external structures of the eyeball, as well as accessory structures. ©Eric A. Wise APR

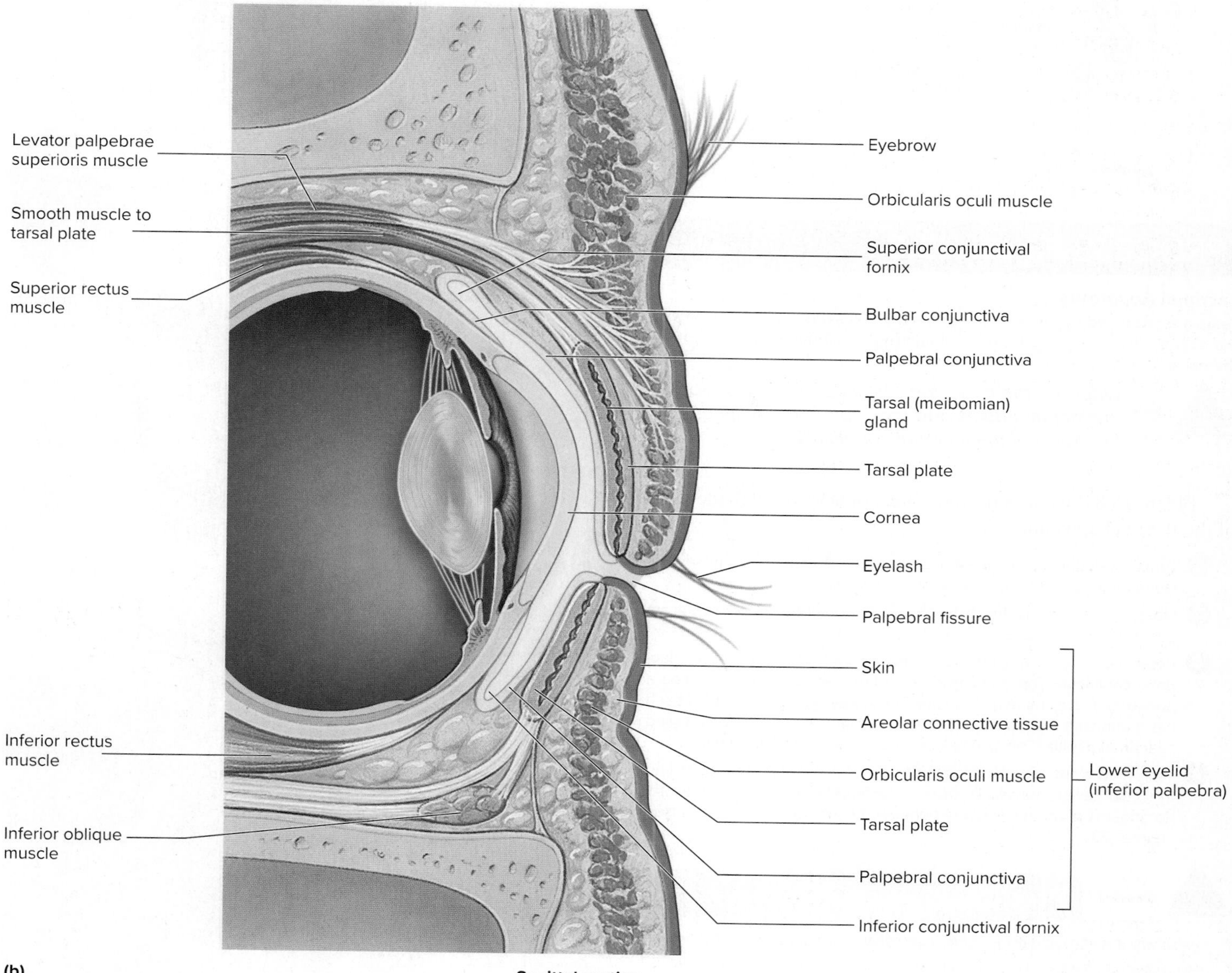

from the facial nerve (VII). The gland produces tears, which leave the gland through several **lacrimal ducts** and pass over the anterior surface of the eyeball. The gland produces tears constantly at the rate of about 1 mL/day to moisten the surface of the eye, lubricate the eyelids, and wash away foreign objects. As you might guess, tears are mostly water. However, tears also contain other substances such as salts, mucus, and lysozyme, an enzyme that kills certain bacteria.

PROCESS **Figure**

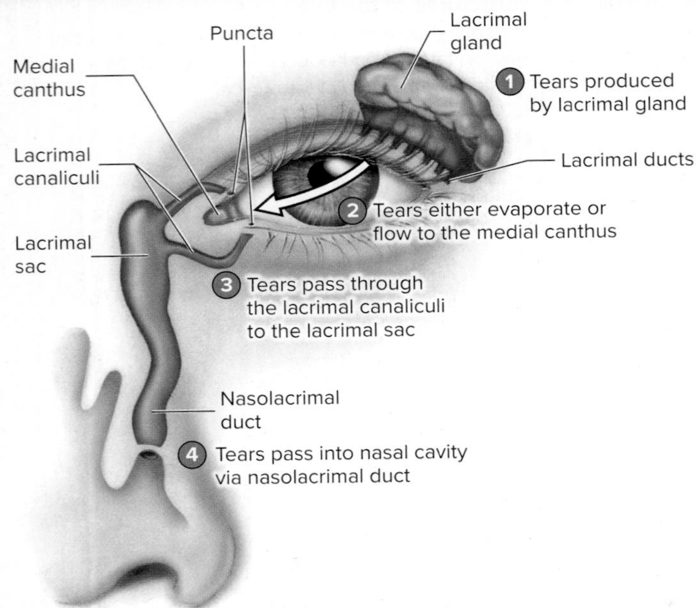

PROCESS **Figure 15.8**

Lacrimal Apparatus

Tears are produced by the lacrimal glands and released onto the surface of the eyeball. Eventually, excess tears drain from the surface of the eye into the nasal cavity.

What are the expected results of a blockage of the lacrimal ducts and the expected results of a blockage of the lacrimal canaliculi?

Figure 15.8 illustrates the movement of tears through the parts of the lacrimal apparatus.

1. Tears produced by the lacrimal glands are released through several lacrimal ducts onto the surface of the eyeball.
2. Most of the fluid produced by the lacrimal glands evaporates from the surface of the eye.
3. Excess tears are collected in the medial corner of the eye by the **lacrimal canaliculi.** The opening of each lacrimal canaliculus is called a **punctum** (PUNGK-tum; pl. puncta). The upper and lower eyelids each has a punctum located near the medial canthus on a small lump called a **lacrimal papilla.** The lacrimal canaliculi open into a **lacrimal sac.**
4. Tears flow from the lacrimal sac through the **nasolacrimal duct** into the nasal cavity. Specifically, the nasolacrimal duct opens into the inferior meatus of the nasal cavity beneath the inferior nasal concha (see chapter 23).

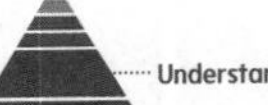

Predict 2

Explain why it is often possible to "taste" medications, such as eyedrops, that have been placed into the eyes. Why does a person's nose "run" when he or she cries?

Extrinsic Eye Muscles

As you are reading the words on this page, your eyes are moving from side to side as you scan the lines of text. Our ability to move the eye within the orbit depends on the **extrinsic muscles.** There are six **extrinsic muscles** attached to each eye (figure 15.9; see chapter 10).

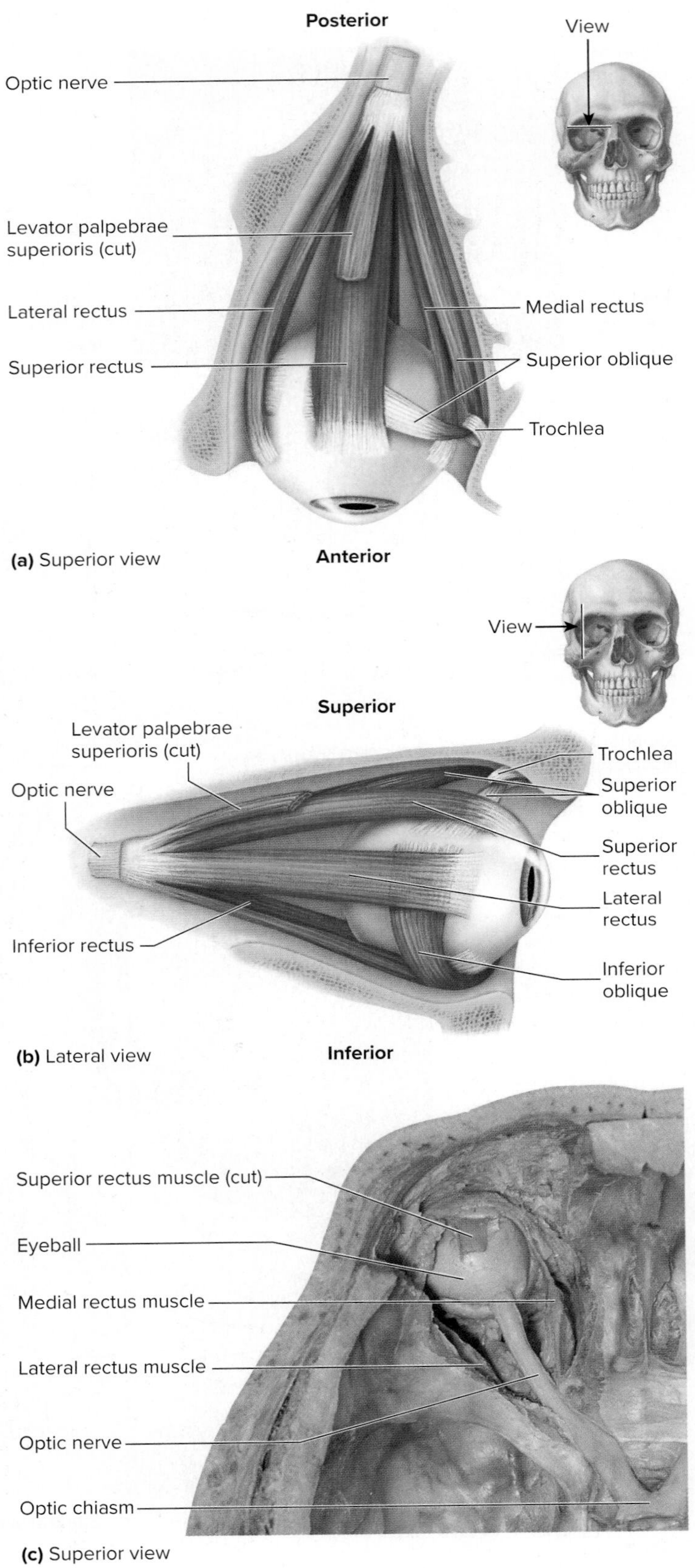

FIGURE 15.9 Extrinsic Muscles of the Eye

Six extrinsic muscles of the eye cause the eyeball to move within the orbit. (*a*) Superior view of the eyeball and extrinsic muscles. (*b*) Lateral view of the eyeball and extrinsic muscles. *(c)* Photograph of superior view of the eyeball, optic nerve, and extrinsic eye muscles. (c) Rebecca Gray/McGraw Hill

FUNDAMENTAL **Figure**

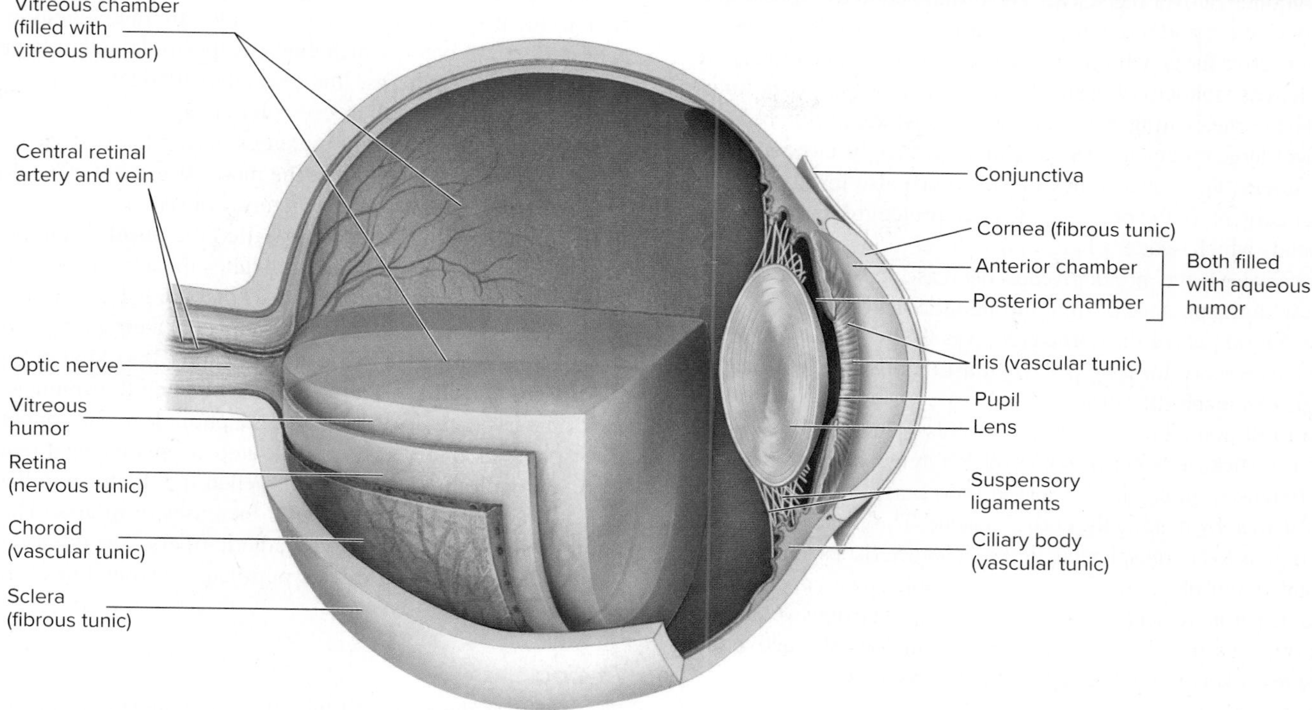

FIGURE 15.10 Tunics and Structures of the Eyeball, Sagittal Section
The eyeball wall consists of three tunics. The outer fibrous tunic includes the sclera and the cornea. The middle vascular tunic includes the choroid, ciliary body, and iris. The inner nervous tunic is also called the retina.

Four of these muscles run more or less straight anteroposteriorly: the superior, inferior, medial, and lateral **rectus muscles.** Two other muscles, the superior and inferior **oblique muscles,** are positioned at an angle to the globe of the eye.

The specific actions of the eye muscles are listed in table 10.8. The movements of the eye can be described graphically by a figure resembling the letter *H*. The clinical test for normal eye movement is therefore called the **H test.** A person's inability to move the eye toward one part of the *H* may indicate dysfunction of either an extrinsic eye muscle or the cranial nerve to the muscle.

The superior oblique muscle is innervated by the trochlear nerve (IV). The nerve is so named because the superior oblique muscle goes around a little pulley, or trochlea, in the superomedial corner of the orbit. The lateral rectus muscle is innervated by the abducens nerve (VI), so named because the lateral rectus muscle abducts the eye. The other four extrinsic eye muscles are innervated by the oculomotor nerve (III).

ASSESS YOUR PROGRESS

10. *Describe the structures and state the functions of the eyebrows, eyelids, and eyelashes.*

11. *How do the conjunctiva, lacrimal apparatus, and extrinsic eye muscles aid in the function of the eye?*

Anatomy of the Eye

The eyeball is a hollow, fluid-filled sphere. The wall of the eyeball is composed of three layers, or **tunics** (figure 15.10).

1. The outer layer is the **fibrous tunic** and it consists of the sclera and cornea.
2. The middle layer is the **vascular tunic** and it consists of the choroid, ciliary body, and iris.
3. The inner layer is the **nervous tunic** and it consists of the retina.

Fibrous Tunic

As stated previously, the fibrous tunic consists of two parts: (1) the sclera and (2) the cornea. The **sclera** (SKLAIR-ah) is the white, outer layer of the posterior five-sixths of the eyeball. It is a firm, opaque tissue layer that consists of dense collagenous connective tissue with elastic fibers. The sclera helps maintain the shape of the eyeball, protects its internal structures, and provides an attachment point for the muscles that move it. Usually, a small portion of the sclera can be seen as the "white of the eye" when the eye and its surrounding structures are intact (see figure 15.7*a*). The bulbar conjunctiva is loosely attached to the sclera.

The sclera is continuous anteriorly with the cornea. The **cornea** (KOR-nee-ah) is an avascular, transparent structure that permits light to enter the eye. As light passes through the cornea, the light bends, or refracts. Refraction of light is an important part of focusing, so the cornea is also a part of the eye's focusing system. The cornea consists of a connective tissue matrix with epithelial tissue on either side. The connective tissue matrix contains collagen, elastic fibers, and proteoglycans. The epithelial layers include a layer of stratified squamous epithelium covering the outer surface of the cornea and a layer of simple squamous epithelium on the inner surface of the cornea. The outer epithelium is continuous with the bulbar conjunctiva over the sclera. The difference in the appearance of the white sclera and the transparent cornea is due to the variation in the connective tissue within each region. Large collagen fibers are white, whereas smaller collagen fibers and proteoglycans are transparent. The cornea is transparent, rather than white, in part because it has fewer large collagen fibers and more proteoglycans compared with the sclera. The transparency of the cornea also results from its low water content. In the presence of water, proteoglycans trap water and expand, which scatters light and reduces transparency. In the absence of water, the proteoglycans decrease in size and do not interfere with the passage of light through the matrix.

The central part of the cornea receives O_2 from the outside air. Contact lenses worn for long periods must therefore be permeable, so that air can reach the cornea.

The most common eye injuries are cuts or tears of the cornea caused by a stick, a stone, or some other foreign object hitting the cornea. Extensive injury to the cornea may cause connective tissue deposition, thereby making the cornea opaque. The cornea was one of the first organs to be transplanted. Several characteristics make it relatively easy to transplant: (1) It is easily accessible and relatively easily removed. (2) It is avascular, so it does not require extensive circulation, as other tissues do. (3) It is less immunologically active and therefore less likely to be rejected than other tissues are.

Vascular Tunic

The middle tunic of the eyeball is called the vascular tunic because it contains most of the blood vessels of the eyeball (figure 15.10). The arteries of the vascular tunic are derived from a number of arteries called **short ciliary arteries,** which pierce the sclera in a circle around the optic nerve. These arteries are branches of the **ophthalmic** (of-THAL-mik) **artery,** which is a branch of the internal carotid artery. The vascular tunic contains a large number of melanin-containing pigment cells and appears black in color. The vascular tunic consists of three parts: (1) the choroid, (2) the ciliary body, and (3) the iris. The portion of the vascular tunic associated with the sclera of the eye is the **choroid** (KOR-oid). The term *choroid* means "membrane" and suggests that this layer is relatively thin (0.1–0.2 mm thick). The ciliary body and the iris make up the anterior region of the vascular tunic.

The **ciliary** (SILL-ee-air-ee) **body** is continuous with the choroid, and the **iris** is attached at its lateral margins to the ciliary body (figure 15.11*a,b*). The ciliary body consists of an outer **ciliary ring** and an inner group of **ciliary processes,** which are attached to the lens by **suspensory ligaments.** The ciliary body contains smooth muscles called the **ciliary muscles,** which are arranged with the outer muscle fibers oriented radially and the central fibers oriented circularly. The ciliary muscles function as a sphincter, and contraction of these muscles can change the shape of the lens. (This function is described in more detail later in this section.) The ciliary processes are a complex of capillaries and cuboidal epithelium that produces aqueous humor.

The iris is the "colored part" of the eye, and its color differs from person to person. A large amount of melanin in the iris causes it to appear brown or even black. Less melanin results in light brown, green, or gray irises. Even less melanin causes the eyes to appear blue. If there is no pigment in the iris, as occurs in albinism, the iris appears pink because blood vessels in the eye reflect light back to the iris. The genetics of eye color are quite complex. Many genes affect eye color, which explains the complexity of eye colors and inheritance patterns. Interestingly, although many newborn babies have blue eyes, their eye color changes over the first year of life. As melanin production increases during the first year, it accumulates in the iris, resulting in the more permanent eye color.

The iris is a contractile structure, consisting mainly of smooth muscle, surrounding an opening called the **pupil.** Light enters the eye through the pupil. The iris regulates the amount of light entering the eye by controlling the size of the pupil. The smooth muscle of the iris is organized into two groups: (1) a circular group called the **sphincter pupillae** (pyoo-PIL-ee) and (2) a radial group called the **dilator pupillae** (figure 15.11*c,d*). When the sphincter pupillae of the iris contract, the size of the pupil decreases or constricts. The sphincter pupillae are innervated by parasympathetic fibers from the oculomotor nerve (III). When the dilator pupillae of the iris contract, the size of the pupil increases or dilates. The dilator pupillae are innervated by sympathetic fibers. The ciliary muscles, sphincter pupillae, and dilator pupillae are sometimes referred to as the *intrinsic eye muscles.*

Retina

The **retina** is the nervous tunic of the eyeball (see figure 15.10). It consists of the outer **pigmented layer,** which is composed of pigmented simple cuboidal epithelium, and the inner **neural layer,** which responds to light. The neural layer contains numerous photoreceptor cells: 120 million **rods** and 6 or 7 million **cones,** as well as numerous relay neurons. The retina covers the inner surface of the eyeball posterior to the ciliary body. A more detailed description of the histology and function of the retina is presented later in this section.

When the posterior region of the retina is examined with an **ophthalmoscope** (of-THAL-moh-scope), two important features can be observed: the macula and the optic disc (figure 15.12*a*). The **macula** (MAK-you-lah) is a small, yellow spot, approximately 4 mm in diameter, near the center of the posterior retina. In the center of the macula is a small pit, the **fovea** (FOH-vee-ah) **centralis.** The fovea centralis is the region of the retina where light is most focused when the eye is looking directly at an object. The fovea centralis contains only cone cells, and the cells are more tightly packed there than anywhere else in the retina. Because of the high number of photoreceptors in this area, the fovea centralis is the portion of the retina with the greatest visual acuity (the ability to see fine images). This is why objects are best seen when viewed directly in front of the eye.

The **optic disc** is a white spot just medial to the macula through which the central retinal artery enters and the central retinal vein exits the eyeball. Branches from these vessels spread over the surface of the retina. This is also the spot where nerve processes from the neural layer of the retina meet, pass through the two outer tunics, and exit the eye as the optic nerve. The optic disc contains no photoreceptor cells and does not respond to light. Because of its lack of photoreceptors, the optic disc is called the **blind spot** of the eye (figure 15.12*b*).

Eye doctors use ophthalmoscopes to examine the retina during a routine eye exam. Often the pupils are dilated to increase the

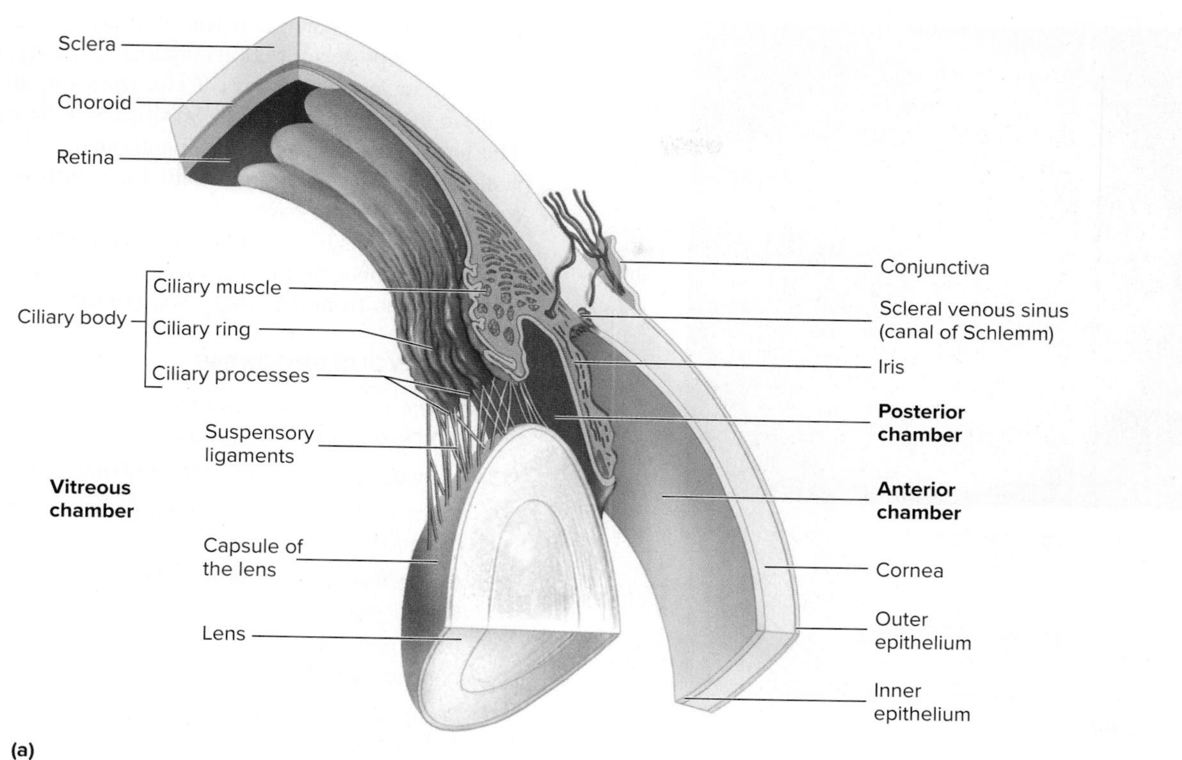

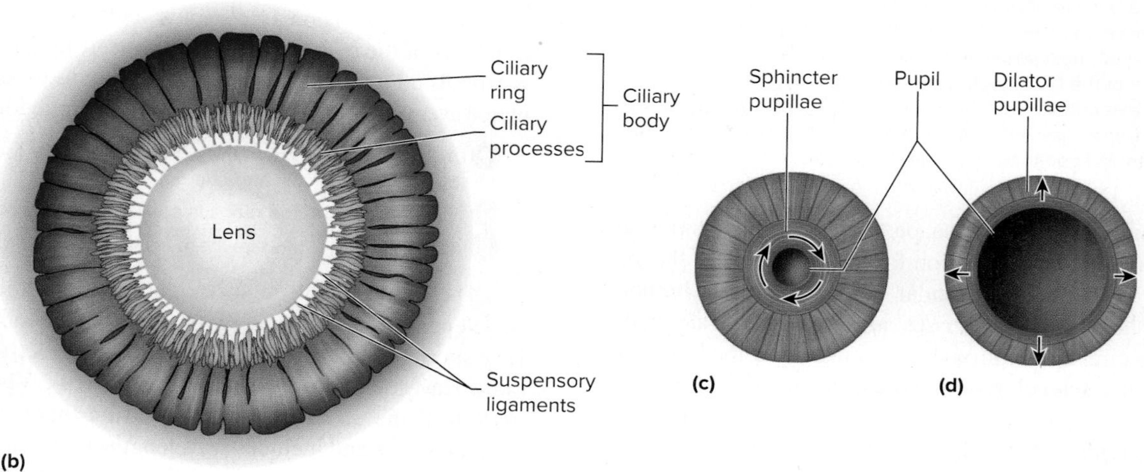

FIGURE 15.11 Lens, Cornea, Iris, and Ciliary Body
(*a*) Section illustrating regions of the wall of the eyeball and lens. (*b*) The lens and ciliary body. (*c*) The sphincter pupillae muscles of the iris constrict the pupil. (*d*) The dilator pupillae muscles of the iris dilate the pupil.

"window" in which to see the eye's interior. Examination of the retina can reveal some general body disorders. **Hypertension,** or high blood pressure, results in "nicking" (compression) of the retinal veins where the abnormally pressurized arteries cross them. **Increased cerebrospinal fluid (CSF) pressure** associated with hydrocephalus may cause the optic disc to swell, a condition referred to as **papilledema** (pah-pil-e-DEE-mah). Furthermore, **cataracts** (opacity of the lens; see table 15.2) are usually discovered or confirmed by ophthalmoscopic examination.

Chambers of the Eye

The interior of the eye is divided into three chambers: (1) the **anterior chamber,** (2) the **posterior chamber,** and (3) the **vitreous chamber** (*postremal chamber;* see figure 15.10). The anterior chamber is the area between the cornea and the iris. The smaller posterior chamber lies between the iris and the lens (see figure 15.11*a*). The anterior and posterior chambers are filled with **aqueous humor,** which helps maintain intraocular pressure. The pressure within the eyeball keeps it inflated and is largely responsible

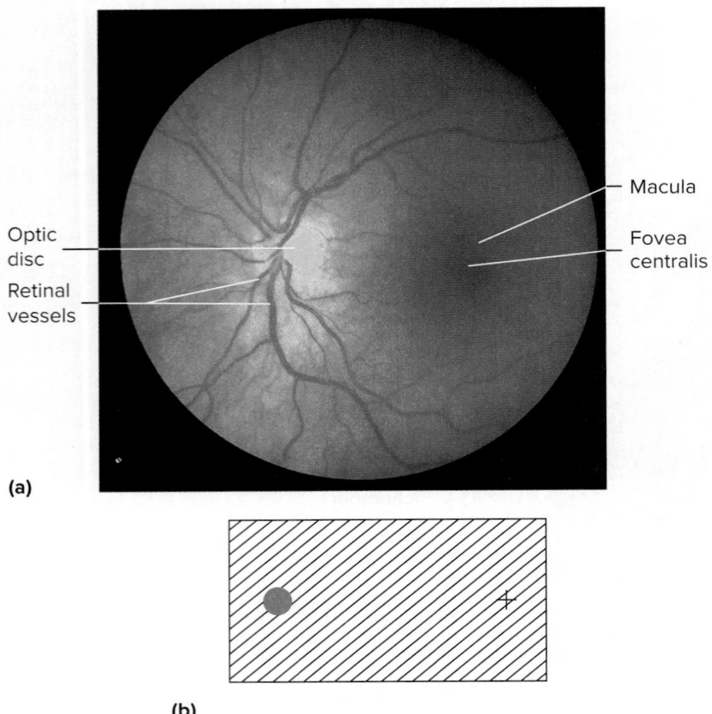

FIGURE 15.12 Ophthalmoscopic View of the Left Retina
(*a*) The posterior wall of the retina as seen when looking through the pupil. The optic disc is the white area where the blood vessels and optic nerve associate with the retina. The macula with the fovea centralis (the part of the retina with the greatest visual acuity) is the darker spot at the center. (*b*) Demonstration of the blind spot. Close your right eye. Hold the figure in front of your left eye and stare at the +. Move the figure toward your eye. At a certain point, when the image of the spot is over the optic disc, the red spot seems to disappear. (a) Steve Allen/Brand X Pictures/Getty Images

for maintaining the eyeball's shape. The aqueous humor also refracts light and provides nutrition for the structures of the anterior chamber, such as the avascular cornea. Aqueous humor is produced by the ciliary processes as a blood filtrate and is returned to the circulation through a venous ring at the base of the cornea called the **scleral venous sinus** (canal of Schlemm; see figure 15.11*a*). The production and removal of aqueous humor result in the "circulation" of aqueous humor and maintenance of a constant intraocular pressure. If circulation of the aqueous humor is inhibited, a defect called **glaucoma** (glaw-KOH-mah), characterized by an abnormal increase in intraocular pressure, can result.

The vitreous chamber of the eye is much larger than the anterior and posterior chambers. It is almost completely surrounded by the retina and is filled with a transparent, jellylike substance called **vitreous humor.** Vitreous humor is not produced as rapidly as the aqueous humor is, and its turnover is extremely slow. Like the aqueous humor, the vitreous humor helps maintain intraocular pressure and therefore the shape of the eyeball, and it holds the lens and retina in place. It also functions in the refraction of light in the eye.

Lens

The **lens** is an unusual biological structure. It is transparent and biconvex, with the greatest convexity on its posterior side. The lens's anterior surface consists of a layer of cuboidal epithelial cells, and its posterior region contains very long, columnar epithelial cells called **lens fibers.** Cells from the anterior epithelium proliferate and give rise to the lens fibers at the equator of the lens. The lens fibers lose their nuclei and other cellular organelles and accumulate a set of proteins called **crystallins.** A highly elastic, transparent **capsule** covers the lens.

The lens is suspended between the posterior chamber and the vitreous chamber by the suspensory ligaments of the lens, which are connected from the ciliary body to the lens capsule.

ASSESS YOUR PROGRESS

12. *Name the three tunics of the eye, describe the parts of the tunics, and explain their functions.*
13. *How does the pupil constrict? How does it dilate?*
14. *What is the blind spot? What are the fovea centralis and macula?*
15. *Name the three chambers of the eye and the substances that fill each chamber.*
16. *What is the function of the ciliary process and the scleral venous sinus?*
17. *Describe the structure of the lens, and explain how it is held in place.*

Functions of the Eye

The process of vision is complex and fascinating. Through the functions of the eye, we are able to convert light energy into action potentials conveyed to our brains, allowing us to see our world. The major events of the vision process are illustrated in figure 15.13.

1. As light passes through the pupil of the iris, it is focused on the retina by the cornea, lens, and humors.
2. The light striking the retina is converted into action potentials.
3. The optic nerve conveys these action potentials to the brain.

The electromagnetic spectrum comprises the entire range of wavelengths, or frequencies, of electromagnetic radiation, from very short gamma waves at one end of the spectrum to the longest radio waves at the other end (figure 15.14). **Visible light** is the portion of the electromagnetic spectrum that can be detected by the human eye and includes wavelengths between 380 and 750 nm. This range is sometimes called the **visible spectrum.** Within the visible spectrum, each color has a different wavelength.

An important characteristic of light rays is that they can bend. As light passes from air to a denser substance, such as glass or water, its speed slows. If the surface of that substance is at an angle other than 90 degrees to the direction the light rays are traveling, the rays bend because the speed of light varies as it encounters the new medium. This bending of light is called **refraction.**

If the surface of a lens is concave, with the lens thinnest in the center, the light rays diverge as a result of refraction. If the surface is convex, with the lens thickest in the center, the light rays tend to converge. As light rays converge, they finally reach a point at which they cross. This point is called the **focal point (FP),** and causing light to converge is called **focusing.** No image forms exactly at the focal point, but an inverted, focused image can form

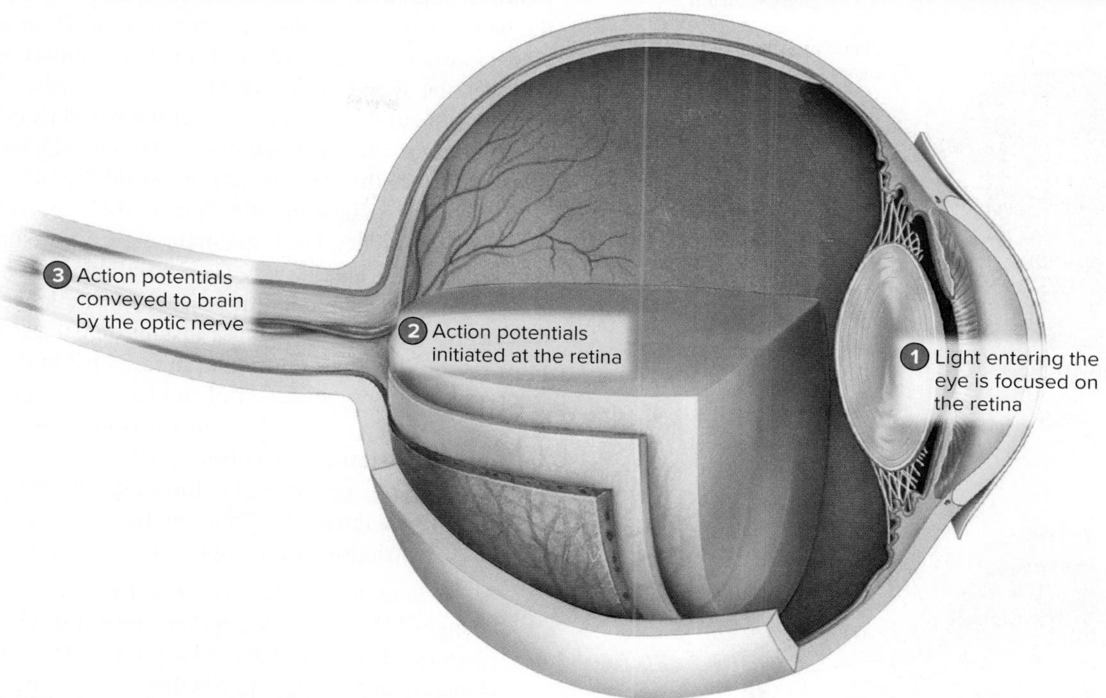

PROCESS Figure 15.13

The Process of Vision

The process of vision involves the stimulation of photoreceptors as light is focused on the retina.

Considering the steps outlined in the figure, which steps would involve the movement of ions across plasma membranes. Explain your answer.

on a surface some distance past the focal point. How far past the focal point the focused image forms depends on a number of factors. A biconvex lens causes light to focus closer to the lens than does a lens with a single convex surface. Furthermore, the more nearly spherical the lens, the closer to the lens the light is focused; the more flattened the biconcave lens, the more distant is the point where the light is focused.

If light rays strike an object that is not transparent, they bounce off the surface. This phenomenon is called **reflection.** If the surface is very smooth, such as the surface of a mirror, the light rays bounce off in a specific direction. If the surface is rough, the light rays are reflected in several directions and produce a more diffuse reflection.

The focusing system of the eye projects a clear image on the retina. Light rays converge as they pass from the air through the convex cornea. Additional convergence occurs as light encounters the aqueous humor, lens, and

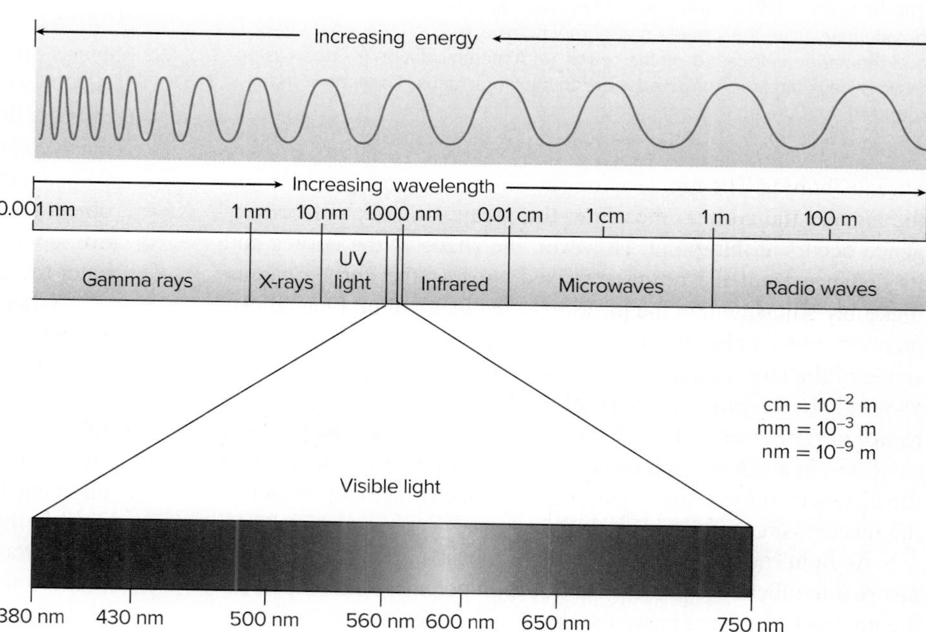

FIGURE 15.14 Electromagnetic Spectrum

The visible light spectrum is enlarged to show the wavelengths of the various colors.

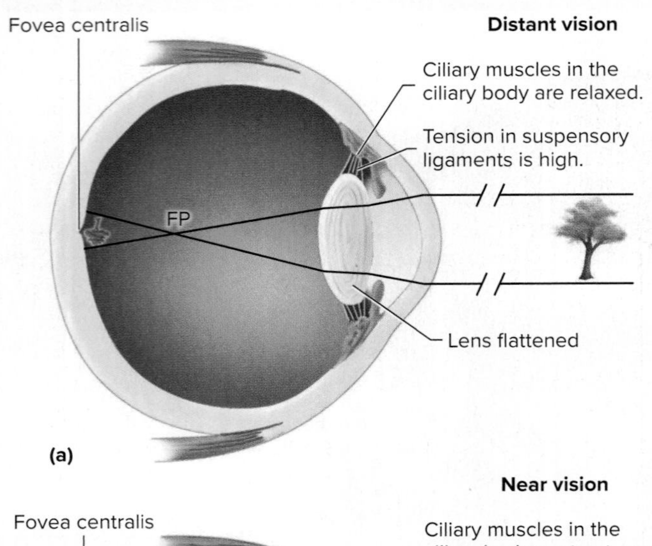

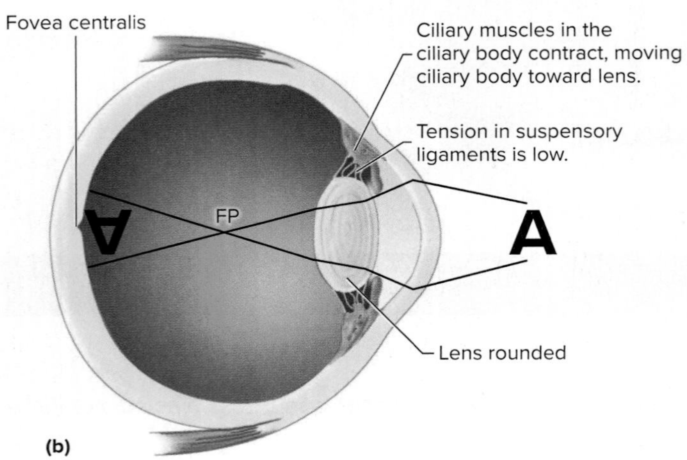

FIGURE 15.15 Focus and Accommodation

The focal point (FP) is where light rays cross. (*a*) Distant vision. Mainly parallel rays from the viewed object reach the eye. The lens is flattened, and the image is focused on the retina. (*b*) Accommodation for near vision. Oblique rays must be refracted more to allow for focus. The lens is more rounded, and the image is focused on the retina.

vitreous humor. The greatest contrast in media density is between the air and the cornea; therefore, the greatest amount of convergence occurs at that point. However, the shape of the cornea and its distance from the retina are fixed, so that the cornea cannot make any adjustment in the location of the focal point. Fine adjustment in focal point location is accomplished by changing the shape of the lens. In general, focusing can be accomplished in two ways: (1) by keeping the shape of the lens constant and moving it nearer or farther from the point at which the image will be focused, as occurs in a camera, microscope, or telescope, or (2) by keeping the distance constant and changing the shape of the lens, which is the mechanism used in the eye.

As light rays enter the eye and are focused, the image formed just past the focal point is inverted. Action potentials that represent the inverted image are passed to the visual cortex of the cerebrum, where the brain interprets them as being right side up.

Because the visual image is inverted when it reaches the retina, the image of the world focused on the retina is upside down. However, the brain processes information from the retina so that the world is perceived the way "it really is." If, as an experiment, a person wears glasses that invert the image entering the eye, he or she sees the world upside down for a few days, after which the brain adjusts to the new input to set the world right side up again. If the glasses are then removed, another adjustment period is required before the brain makes the world "right" again.

When the ciliary muscles are relaxed, the suspensory ligaments of the ciliary body maintain elastic pressure on the lens, thereby keeping it relatively flat and allowing for distant vision (figure 15.15*a*). The condition in which the lens is flattened so that nearly parallel rays from a distant object are focused on the retina is referred to as **emmetropia** (em-eh-TROH-pee-ah) and is the normal resting condition of the lens. The point at which the lens does not have to thicken for focusing to occur is called the **far point of vision** and is normally 20 feet or more from the eye.

When an object is brought closer than 20 feet to the eye, three events bring the image into focus on the retina: accommodation by the lens, constriction of the pupil, and convergence of the eyes.

1. *Accommodation.* The lens is a flexible structure that can change shape depending on the amount of tension in the suspensory ligaments of the ciliary body. The shape of the lens changes, depending on whether the eye is focusing on an object that is near or farther away. The process of changing the shape of the lens is referred to as **accommodation.** When the eye focuses on a nearby object, the ciliary muscles contract as a result of parasympathetic stimulation from the oculomotor nerve (III). This sphincterlike contraction pulls the choroid more anteriorly, toward the lens, reducing the tension on the suspensory ligaments. The decrease in tension allows the lens to assume a more spherical shape because of its own elastic nature (figure 15.15*b*). The more spherical lens then has a more convex surface, causing greater refraction of light.

   As light strikes a solid object, the rays are reflected in every direction from the object's surface. However, only a small portion of the light rays reflected from a solid object pass through the pupil and enter the eye. An object far away from the eye appears small compared with a nearby object because only nearly parallel light rays enter the eye from a distant object (figure 15.15*a*). When viewing an object closer to the eye, converging rays and parallel rays leaving the object can enter the eye (figure 15.15*b*), and the object appears larger.

   When rays from a distant object reach the lens, they do not have to be refracted to any great extent to be focused on the retina, and the lens can remain fairly flat. When an object is closer to the eye, the more obliquely directed rays must be refracted to a greater extent to be focused on the retina. Accommodation occurs as the lens becomes more spherical, allowing for the refraction of light needed to focus the light rays on the retina (see figure 15.15*b*).

   If you move this book closer and closer to your eyes, eventually you will not be able to see the words clearly. As an object is brought closer and closer to the eye, accommodation becomes more and more difficult because the lens cannot become any more convex. At some point, the eye can no longer focus the object, and it is seen as a blur. The point at which this blurring occurs is called the **near point of vision.** It is usually 2–3 inches from the eye for a child, 4–6 inches for a young adult, 20 inches for a 45-year-old adult, and 60 inches for an 80-year-old adult. The increase in the near point of vision that develops with age is called **presbyopia.** It occurs because the lens becomes less flexible with increasing age, and it is the reason some older people jokingly say they could see an item they are holding with no problem if only they had longer arms.

2. *Pupil constriction.* Similarly to the previous description, as you move this book closer and closer to your eye, the words will remain in focus until you reach the near point of vision. That means that there is a range of distances from which you can still see objects clearly. **Depth of focus** is the greatest distance through which an object (for example, a book that you are reading) can be moved and still remain in focus on the retina. The main factor affecting depth of focus is the size of the pupil. If the pupil diameter is small, the depth of focus is greater than if the pupil diameter is large. Therefore, with a smaller pupil opening, an object may be moved slightly nearer or farther from the eye without disturbing its focus. This is particularly important when viewing an object at close range because the interest in detail is much greater, and thus the acceptable margin for error is smaller. When the pupil is constricted, the light entering the eye tends to pass more nearly through the center of the lens and is more accurately focused than light passing through the edges of the lens. Recall that the pupil diameter also regulates the amount of light entering the eye. The dimmer the light, the greater the pupil diameter must be. Therefore, as the pupil constricts during close vision, more light is required on the object being observed to see it clearly.
3. *Convergence.* Because the light rays entering the eyes from a distant object are nearly parallel, both pupils can pick up the light rays when the eyes are directed more or less straight ahead. As an object moves closer, however, the eyes must be rotated medially, so that the object is kept focused on corresponding areas of each retina. Otherwise, the object appears blurry. This medial rotation of the eyes, called **convergence,** is accomplished by a reflex that stimulates the medial rectus muscle of each eye to contract. To observe convergence, have someone stand facing you. Ask the person to reach out one hand and extend an index finger as far in front of his or her face as possible. Then have the person keep the gaze fixed on the finger while slowly bringing the finger in toward his or her nose until finally touching it. Notice the movement of the person's pupils. What happens?

Apply

Predict 3

During a recent Alaskan cruise, Max and his grandfather were staring at a glacier some distance from their tour boat. Suddenly, Max's mother interrupted them to show them a piece of ice one of the deck hands had scooped from the water in the bay. Max was able to focus on the piece of ice and see its clear blue features, but his grandfather had to reach for his glasses. What changes occurred in their eyes between the time they were staring at the glacier and the time they were looking at the piece of ice? Explain why Max's grandfather reached for his glasses.

Visual Acuity

Visual acuity is the eye's ability to focus an image on the retina so that a clear image is perceived. Many factors affect visual acuity, including the shape of the eyeball and the flexibility of the lens. When a person's visual acuity is tested, a chart with rows of letters of decreasing size is placed 20 feet from the eye, and the person is asked to read the row of the smallest letters they can see clearly. The rows of letters are standardized for normal vision at 20 feet. If the person can clearly see the row of letters identified as 20 feet, their vision is considered 20/20, meaning the person can see at 20 feet what a person with normal vision can see at 20 feet. On the other hand, if the person can clearly see the row of letters identified as 40 feet, their vision is 20/40, meaning the person can see at 20 feet what a person with normal vision can see at 40 feet. In this case, a defect in visual acuity is diagnosed, and corrective lenses are usually prescribed. Some common visual acuity defects are myopia, hyperopia, presbyopia, and astigmatism.

People who have **myopia** (my-OH-pee-ah), or nearsightedness, can see close objects clearly, but distant objects appear blurry. Myopia is a defect of the eye in which the focusing system, the cornea and lens, is optically too powerful, or the eyeball is too long (axial myopia). As a result, the focal point is too near the lens, and the image is focused in front of the retina (figure 15.16*a*).

Myopia is corrected by a concave lens that counters the refractive power of the eye. Concave lenses cause the light rays coming to the eye to diverge and are therefore called "minus" lenses (figure 15.16*b*).

Other techniques for correcting mild myopia include **radial keratotomy** (KER-ah-TOT-oh-mee) and **LASIK.** In radial keratotomy, a series of four to eight radiating cuts are made in the cornea. The cuts are intended to weaken the dome of the cornea slightly so that it becomes more flattened and eliminates the myopia. One problem with the technique is that it is difficult to predict how much flattening will occur, so some visual acuity problems may persist. Another problem is that some patients are bothered by glare following radial keratotomy because the slits apparently do not heal evenly. LASIK, or *laser corneal sculpturing,* is a laser surgery procedure in which a thin portion of the cornea is etched away to make the cornea less convex. The advantage of this procedure is that the results can be predicted more accurately than can those of radial keratotomy.

People who have **hyperopia** (high-per-OH-pee-ah), or farsightedness, can see distant objects clearly, but close objects appear blurry. In hyperopia, the cornea and lens system is optically too weak or the eyeball is too short. The image is focused behind the retina (figure 15.16*c*). Hyperopia can be corrected by convex lenses that cause light rays to converge as they approach the eye (figure 15.16*d*). Such lenses are called "plus" lenses.

Presbyopia (prez-bee-OH-pee-ah) is the normal, presently unavoidable degeneration of the accommodation power of the eye associated with aging. It occurs because the lens becomes sclerotic and less flexible. The eye is presbyopic when the near point of vision has increased beyond 9 inches. The average age for the onset of presbyopia is the mid-40s. Avid readers and people who engage in fine, close work may develop the symptoms earlier. Presbyopia can be corrected by wearing "reading glasses" for close work and removing them to see at a distance. Because constantly

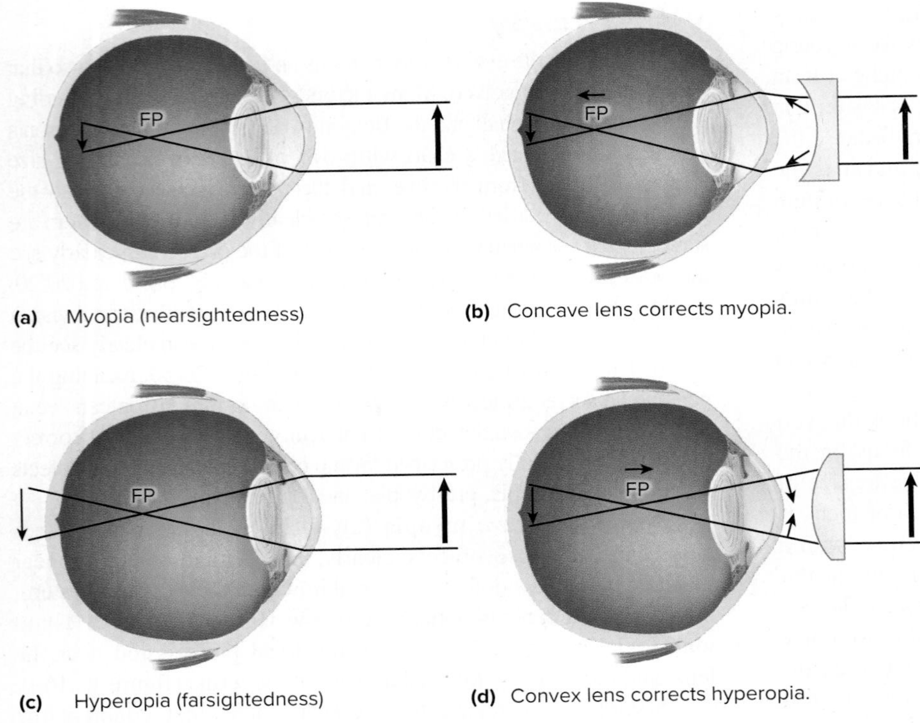

(a) Myopia (nearsightedness)

(b) Concave lens corrects myopia.

(c) Hyperopia (farsightedness)

(d) Convex lens corrects hyperopia.

FIGURE 15.16 Visual Disorders and Their Correction
(*a*) An individual with myopia, or nearsightedness, cannot see distant objects clearly. (*b*) A concave lens corrects myopia. (*c*) An individual with hyperopia, or farsightedness, cannot see close objects clearly. (*d*) A convex lens corrects hyperopia.

removing and replacing glasses is annoying and because reading glasses hamper vision of only a few feet away, many people wear **bifocals,** which have different lenses in the top and the bottom, or **progressive lenses,** which have a graded lens.

Astigmatism (ah-STIG-mah-tiz-em) is a type of refractive error that affects the quality of focus. If the cornea or lens is not uniformly curved, the light rays do not focus at a single point, but fall as a blurred circle. Regular astigmatism can be corrected by glasses formed with the opposite curvature gradation. In irregular astigmatism, the abnormal form of the cornea fits no specific pattern and is very difficult to correct with glasses.

ASSESS YOUR PROGRESS

18. *What causes light to refract? What is a focal point? What is emmetropia?*
19. *What three processes occur to focus an object on the retina that is closer than 20 feet? Explain what occurs in each process.*
20. *How are far point of vision and near point of vision determined?*
21. *Describe the image of an object as it is focused on the retina.*
22. *Distinguish among myopia, hyperopia, and presbyopia. Define* astigmatism.

Structure and Function of the Retina

Leonardo da Vinci, speaking of the eye, said, "Who would believe that so small a space could contain the images of all the universe?" The retina of each eyeball, which gives us the potential to see the whole world, is about the size and thickness of a postage stamp.

As stated earlier in this section, the retina consists of a neural layer and a pigmented layer (figure 15.17). The neural layer, in turn, has several sublayers: three neuron layers (composed of photoreceptor cells, bipolar cells, and ganglionic cells, respectively) and two plexiform (networklike) layers, where the neurons of adjacent layers synapse with each other. The outer plexiform layer is between the photoreceptor and bipolar cell layers. The inner plexiform layer is between the bipolar and ganglionic cell layers (figure 15.17*a*).

The pigmented layer, or pigmented epithelium, of the retina consists of a single layer of cells filled with the pigment melanin. Together with the pigment in the choroid, the pigmented layer isolates individual photoreceptors and reduces light scattering by providing a black matrix that absorbs light and enhances visual acuity. However, this pigmentation is not strictly necessary for vision. People with albinism (lack of pigment) can see, although their visual acuity is reduced because of some light scattering.

Clinical IMPACT 15.1

Eye Pigment

The eyeball is a closed chamber that allows light to enter only through the pupil. The light is absorbed by the pigmented inner lining of the eyeball; thus, looking into it is like looking into a dark room. The pupil appears black because of the pigment in the choroid and the pigmented portion of the retina. However, if a bright light is directed into the pupil, the reflected light is red because of the blood vessels on the surface of the retina. This is why the pupils of a person looking directly at a flash camera often appear red in a photograph.

People with albinism lack the pigment melanin, and the pupil always appears red because the eyeball's inner lining lacks melanin to absorb light and prevent it from being reflected from the back of the eyeball. The diffusely lighted blood vessels in the interior of the eyeball contribute to the red color of the pupil.

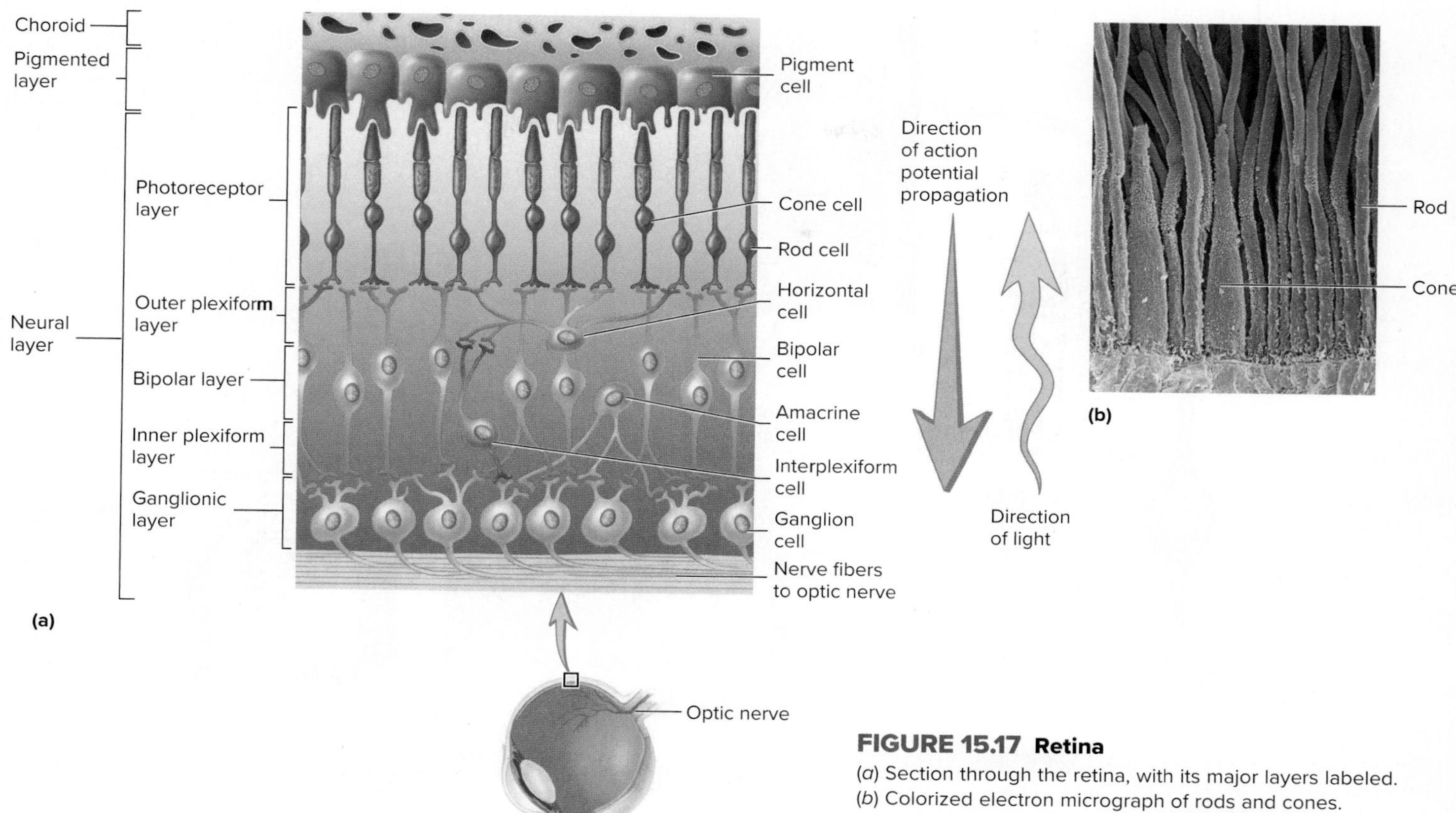

FIGURE 15.17 Retina

(*a*) Section through the retina, with its major layers labeled.
(*b*) Colorized electron micrograph of rods and cones.
(b) Steve Gschmeissner/Science Source APR

The portion of the neural layer nearest the pigmented layer consists of photoreceptor cells called rods and cones (figure 15.17*b*). The rods and cones are sensitive to stimulation from visible light. The light-sensitive portion of each photoreceptor cell is adjacent to the pigmented layer.

Rods

Rods are bipolar photoreceptor cells that are involved in noncolor vision; they are responsible for vision under conditions of reduced light (table 15.1). The modified, dendritic, light-sensitive part of a rod cell is cylindrical, with no taper from base to apex (figure 15.18*a*). This rod-shaped photoreceptive part contains about 700 double-layered membranous discs. The discs contain **rhodopsin** (roh-DOP-sin), a purple pigment that consists of the protein **opsin** covalently bound to a yellow photosensitive pigment called **retinal** (derived from vitamin A). Retinal alternates between two conformations (shapes): (1) 11-*cis*-retinal and (2) all-*trans*-retinal, depending on exposure to light. Opsin is a protein much like a channel protein, consisting of seven transmembrane helical regions. An extracellular plug closes the external opening of the opsin "channel." G proteins and cyclic GMP (cGMP) phosphodiesterase enzymes are also associated with the disc membranes. In addition to the rhodopsin molecule and G protein, sodium ion

TABLE 15.1 Rods and Cones

Photoreceptive End	Photoreceptive Molecule	Function	Location
Rod			
Cylindrical	Rhodopsin	Noncolor vision; vision under conditions of low light	Over most of retina; none in fovea centralis
Cone			
Conical	Iodopsin	Color vision; visual acuity	Numerous in fovea centralis and macula; sparse over rest of retina

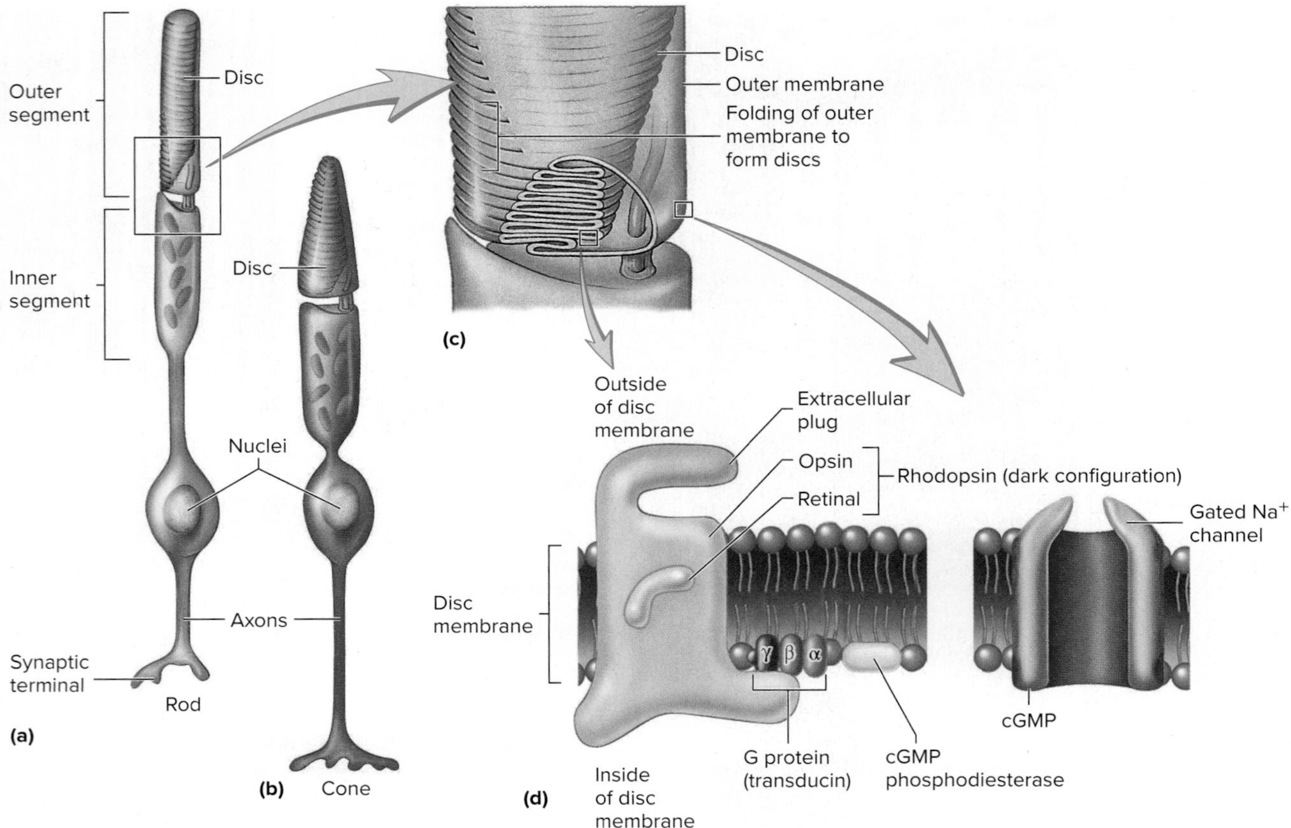

FIGURE 15.18 Sensory Receptor Cells of the Retina

(*a*) Rod cell. (*b*) Cone cell. (*c*) Enlargement of the discs in the outer segment of a rod cell. (*d*) Enlargement of one of the discs, showing the relation of rhodopsin, a G protein, and a gated Na^+ channel in the membrane.

channels are located in the outer membrane of the rod cell outer segment (figure 15.18*d*). The response of photoreceptors to light depends on the arrangement of these membrane proteins.

Figure 15.19 depicts the changes that rhodopsin undergoes in response to light.

1. In the resting (dark) state, 11-*cis*-retinal is tightly bound to the internal surface of opsin. The extracellular plug helps keep retinal from dissociating from the opsin subunit through its "channel." Cyclic GMP is attached to the Na^+ channel, keeping it open.
2. As rod cells absorb light, retinal changes shape from 11-*cis*-retinal to all-*trans*-retinal. This change causes opsin to also change shape (dark to light state). The changes in opsin activate a G protein called **transducin** (trans-DOO-sin), which activates a cyclic GMP phosphodiesterase.
3. The cGMP phosphodiesterase catalyzes the conversion of cGMP to GMP. This reaction causes cGMP to diffuse away from Na^+ channels, resulting in closure of the Na^+ channels and hyperpolarization of the cell.
4. In the all-*trans* conformation, retinal detaches from the opsin molecule. Transducin reassociates with opsin, leading to the deactivation of cGMP phosphodiesterase.
5. In the absence of cGMP phosphodiesterase activity, cGMP concentration increases. cGMP binds to the Na^+ channels, causing them to open again.
6. In a process requiring ATP, all-*trans*-retinal is converted to 11-*cis*-retinal.
7. In the 11-*cis* conformation, retinal can attach to opsin, returning it to its original (dark) conformation.

The hyperpolarization of the photoreceptor cells is somewhat remarkable because most neurons respond to stimuli by depolarizing. Figure 15.20 compares the activity of a rod cell in (a) dark and (b) light conditions.

1. When photoreceptor cells are not exposed to light and are in a resting, nonactivated state, gated Na^+ channels in their membranes are open, and Na^+ flows into the cell.
2. This influx of Na^+, referred to as the dark current, causes the photoreceptor cells to release the neurotransmitter glutamate from their presynaptic terminals.
3. Glutamate binds to receptors on the postsynaptic membranes of the bipolar cells of the retina, causing them to hyperpolarize. Thus, glutamate causes an inhibitory postsynaptic potential (IPSP) in the bipolar cells. The influx of Na^+ is offset by the efflux of K^+ through nongated K^+ channels. Equilibrium of Na^+ and K^+ in the cell is maintained by a sodium-potassium pump.
4. When photoreceptor cells are exposed to light, the Na^+ channels close, through the process illustrated in figure 15.19.
5. As less Na^+ enters the cell, the amount of glutamate released from the presynaptic terminals decreases.
6. The hyperpolarization in the bipolar cells decreases, and they depolarize sufficiently to release neurotransmitters.
7. The neurotransmitters released by the bipolar cell stimulate ganglionic cells to generate action potentials.

As we move from bright areas to darker areas, our eyes adjust to the changes in light. The adjustment of the eyes to changes in

PROCESS **Figure**

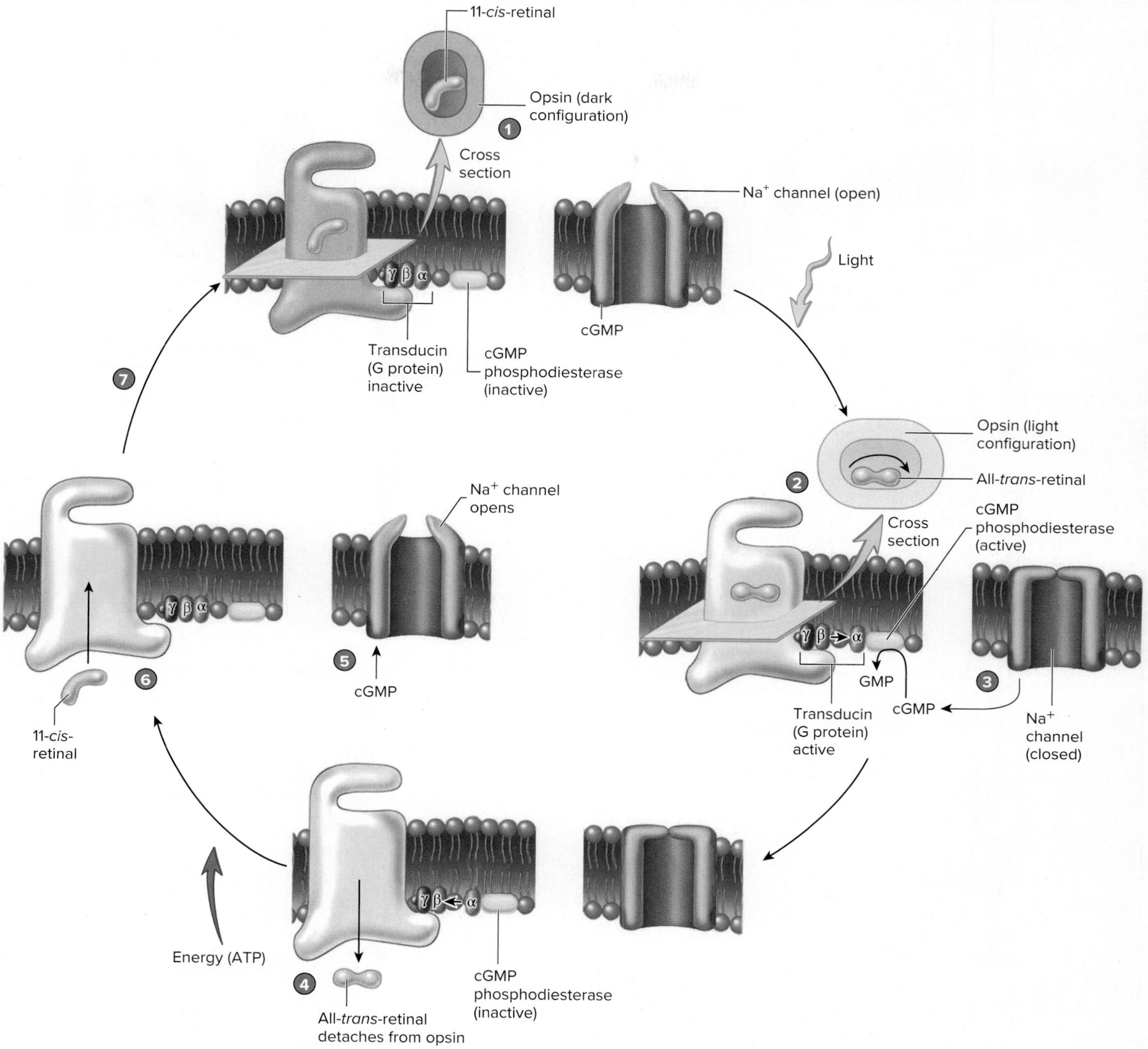

11-*cis*-retinal

Opsin (dark configuration)

1

Cross section

Na$^+$ channel (open)

Light

cGMP

Transducin (G protein) inactive

cGMP phosphodiesterase (inactive)

7

Opsin (light configuration)

All-*trans*-retinal

2

Cross section

cGMP phosphodiesterase (active)

Na$^+$ channel opens

5

cGMP

6

11-*cis*-retinal

GMP

cGMP

3

Transducin (G protein) active

Na$^+$ channel (closed)

Energy (ATP)

4

All-*trans*-retinal detaches from opsin

cGMP phosphodiesterase (inactive)

PROCESS **Figure 15.19**

Rhodopsin Cycle

When exposed to light, rhodopsin is activated as retinal changes conformation and exits the opsin. ATP is needed to recombine the opsin and retinal.

A common symptom of mitochondrial diseases is blindness. Develop a likely explanation for this relationship based on your knowledge of mitochondria and the rhodopsin cycle.

FUNDAMENTAL **Figure**

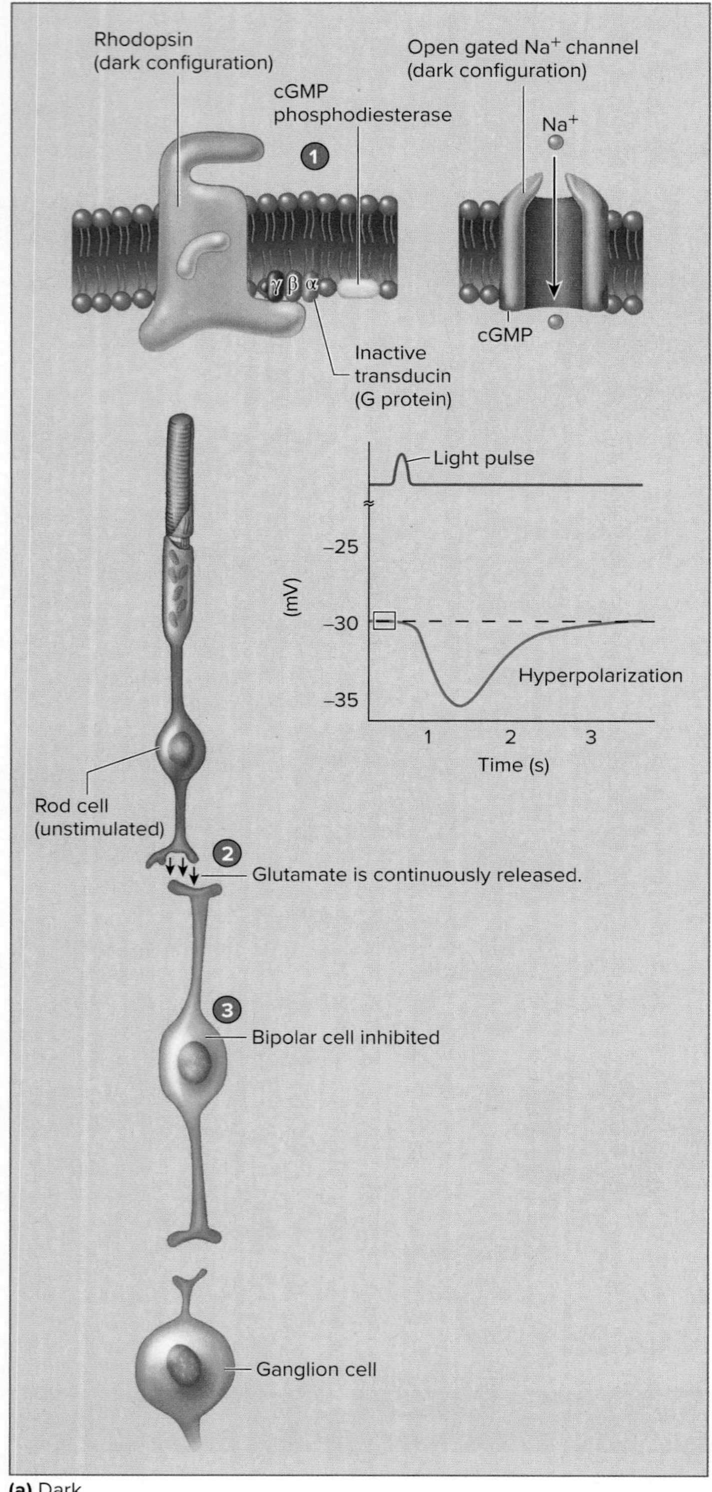

(a) Dark

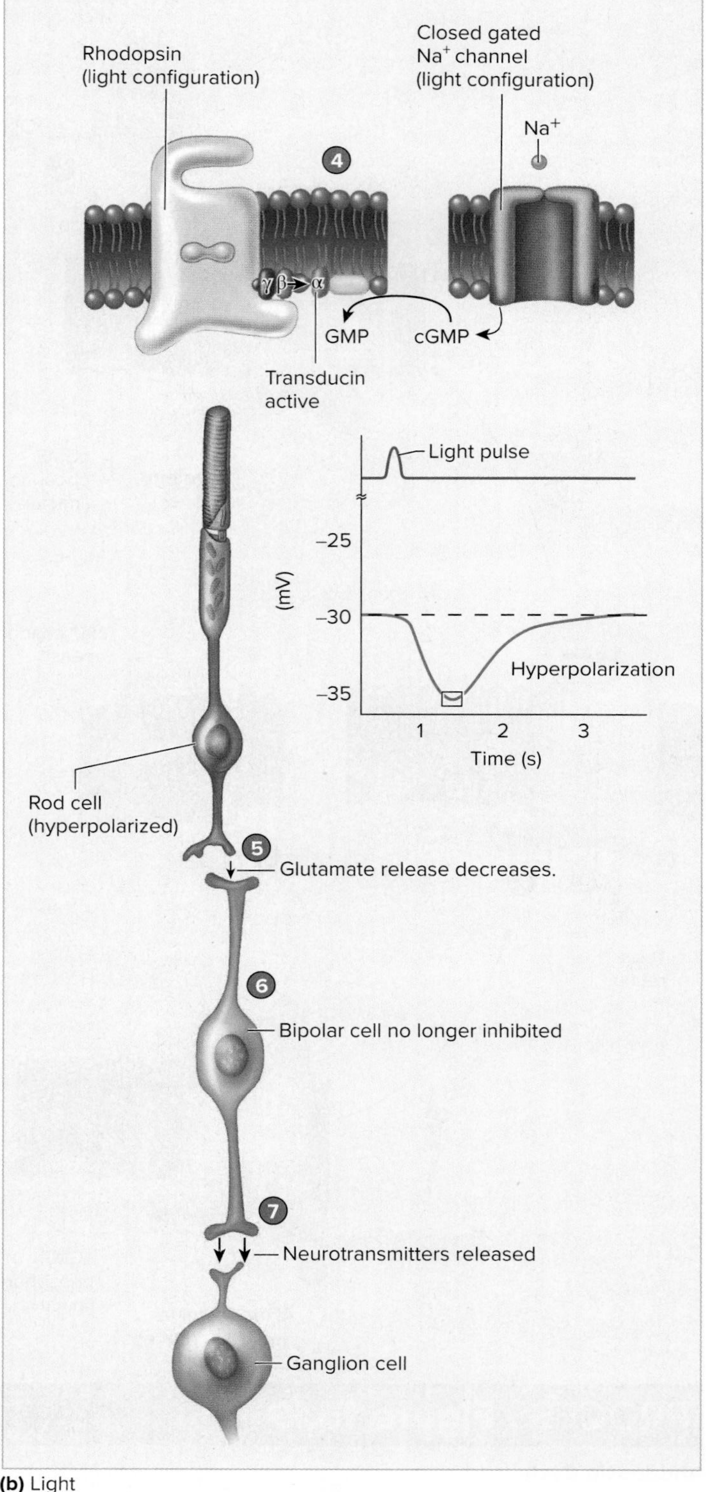

(b) Light

PROCESS **Figure 15.20**

Rod Cell Hyperpolarization

(*a*) In the dark, the rod cell is unstimulated. (*b*) In light, the rod cell becomes hyperpolarized.

Imagine you are sitting in a poorly lit lecture hall. The students sitting close to the front of class are under the only lights on in the room. You are sitting in the very back row, as far from the lights as possible. How would the amount of glutamate released from the rods of your eyes differ from the students sitting at the front of the room?

light is called **light adaptation** and **dark adaptation.** This adaptation is accomplished by three mechanisms:

- *Changes in amount of available rhodopsin:* In bright light, excess rhodopsin is broken down so that not as much is available to initiate action potentials, and the eyes become adapted to bright light. Conversely, in a dark room more rhodopsin is produced, making the retina more light-sensitive.
- *Pupil reflexes:* In dim light, the pupil enlarges to allow more light into the eye; in bright light, the pupil constricts to allow less light into the eye.
- *Changes in level of photoreceptor function:* During light conditions, rod function decreases and cone function increases, whereas the opposite happens during dark conditions. This occurs because rod cells are more sensitive to light than cone cells and because the rhodopsin in rods is depleted more rapidly than the visual pigment in cones.

Cones

Cones are bipolar photoreceptor cells with a conical, light-sensitive part that tapers slightly from base to apex (see figure 15.18*b*). The outer segments of the cone cells, like those of the rods, consist of double-layered discs. The discs are slightly more numerous and more closely stacked in the cones than in the rods.

Color vision and visual acuity are the functions of cone cells (see table 15.1). Color is a function of the wavelength of light, and each color results from a certain wavelength within the visible spectrum. Even though rods are very sensitive to light, they cannot detect color, and sensory input that ultimately reaches the brain from these cells is interpreted by the brain as shades of gray. Cones require relatively bright light to function. As a result, as the light decreases, so does the color of objects that can be seen until, under conditions of very low illumination, the objects appear gray. This occurs because, as the light decreases, fewer cone cells respond to the dim light.

Cone cells contain a visual pigment, **iodopsin** (eye-oh-DOP-sin), which consists of retinal combined with a photopigment opsin protein. Three major types of color-sensitive opsin exist—blue, red, and green; each closely resembles the opsin proteins of rod cells but with somewhat different amino acid sequences. These color photopigments function in much the same manner as rhodopsin (see figure 15.19); however, whereas rhodopsin responds to the entire spectrum of visible light, each iodopsin is sensitive to a much narrower spectrum.

As can be seen in figure 15.21, considerable overlap occurs in the wavelength of light to which the blue, green, and red pigments are sensitive; however, each pigment absorbs light of a certain range of wavelengths. As light of a given wavelength, representing a certain color, strikes the retina, all cone cells containing photopigments capable of responding to that wavelength generate action potentials within the retina. Because of the overlap among the three types of cones, especially between the green and red pigments, different proportions of cone cells respond to each wavelength, thus allowing color perception over a wide range. Color is interpreted in the visual cortex of the occipital lobe as combinations of sensory input originating from cone cells. For example, when orange light strikes the retina, 99% of the red-sensitive cones respond, 42% of the green-sensitive cones respond, and no blue cones respond. When yellow light strikes the retina, the response shifts, so that a greater number of green-sensitive cones respond. The variety of combinations created allows humans to distinguish among several million gradations of light and shades of color.

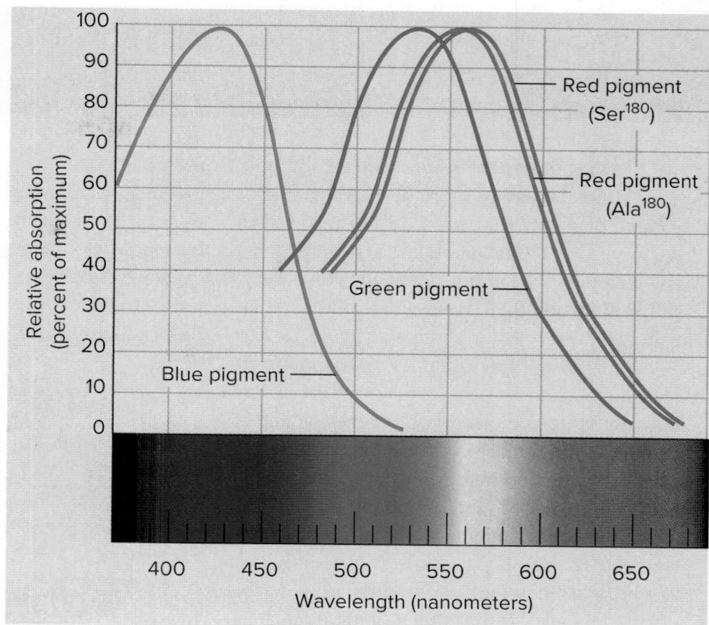

FIGURE 15.21 Wavelengths to Which Blue, Green, and Red Pigments Are Sensitive

The red pigment exists in two chemical forms. One, found in 60% of the population, has the amino acid serine at position 180; the other, found in 40% of the population, has an alanine at position 180. Each red pigment has a slightly different wavelength sensitivity.

Not everyone sees the same red. Two forms of the red photopigment are common in humans. Approximately 60% of people have the amino acid serine in position 180 of the red opsin protein, whereas 40% have alanine in that position. That subtle difference in the protein results in slightly different absorption characteristics (figure 15.21). Even though we were each taught to recognize red when we see a certain color, apparently we do not all see that color in quite the same way.

Distribution of Rods and Cones in the Retina

Rods and cones are not evenly distributed across the retina. Cones are more numerous in the fovea centralis and macula, areas of the retina associated with visual acuity. The fovea centralis has about 35,000 cones and no rods. The rest of the macula has more cones than rods. However, the 120 million rods are 10–20 times more plentiful than cones over most of the remaining retina. Rods are more highly concentrated in regions of the retina away from the macula and are more important in low-light conditions.

Predict 4

Explain why at night a person may notice a movement "out of the corner of the eye" but, when the person tries to focus on the area of movement, nothing seems to be there.

Clinical GENETICS 15.1 Color Blindness

Color blindness results from the dysfunction of one or more of the three photopigments (red, green, blue) involved in color vision. If one pigment is dysfunctional and the other two are functional, the condition is called **dichromatism.** An example of dichromatism is red-green color blindness (figure 15.22).

Red-green color blindness is common in males, but not females. About 7% of males have some degree of color blindness, which is over eight times more common than in females. The basis for this male prevalence is that the genes for the red and green photopigments are arranged in tandem on the X chromosome (see chapter 29). Because males have only one X chromosome, they are more likely to be affected by an X-linked mutation than females, who have a higher probability of having a good gene on one of their two X chromosomes.

The vast majority, over 95%, of color blindness involves red-green color vision, not blue vision. The reason can be traced to the tandem arrangement of the red and green photopigment genes. Not only are the two genes next to each other, but they are also nearly identical; differences in only 3 of the 360 amino acids determine the red versus green wavelength absorption characteristics. Because the red and green genes are so similar and adjacent to each other, it is relatively easy for mistakes to occur during development as DNA is replicated and exchanged between chromosomes (see chapter 29). Hence, an X chromosome may lack one or both genes, or it may have a hybrid gene containing exons from both red and green genes, which may or may not alter their degree of functionality. The blue photopigment gene is rarely associated with color blindess because it is not adjacent to another photopigment gene. It is also not X-linked, so it is equally rare in males and females.

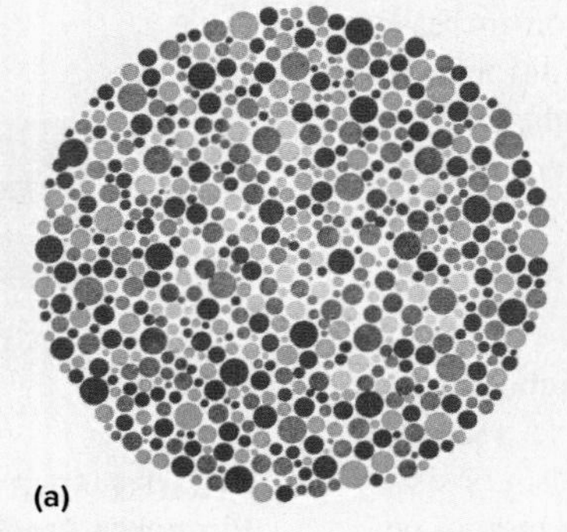

(a)

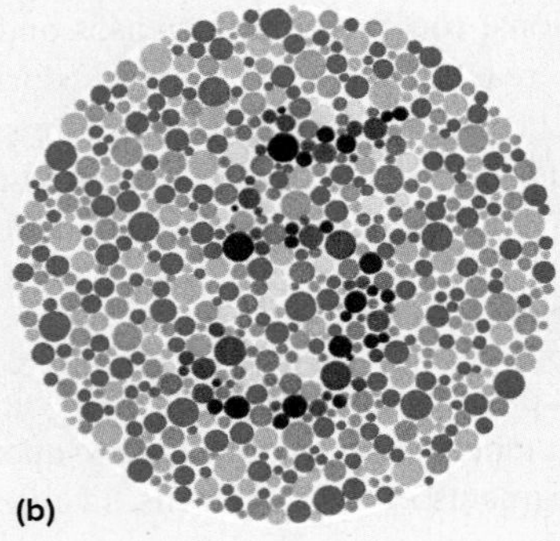

(b)

FIGURE 15.22 Color Blindness Charts
(*a*) A person with normal color vision can see the number 74, whereas a person with red-green color blindness sees the number 21. (*b*) A person with normal color vision can see the number 5, whereas a person with red-green color blindness sees the number 2. (a) Steve Allen/Brand X Pictures/Getty Images; (b) Prisma Bildagentur AG/Alamy Stock Photo

Inner Cell Layers of the Retina

The middle and inner cell layers of the neural layer of the retina consist of two major neuron types: (1) bipolar cells and (2) ganglion cells (see figure 15.17*a*). The rod and cone photoreceptor cells synapse with **bipolar cells,** which in turn synapse with **ganglion cells.** Except in the area of the fovea centralis, axons from the ganglion cells pass over the inner surface of the retina, converge at the **optic disc,** and exit the eye as the **optic nerve (II).** The fovea centralis is devoid of ganglion cell processes, resulting in a small depression in this area—thus the name *fovea,* meaning "small pit." Due to the absence of ganglion cell processes as well as the concentration of cone cells mentioned previously, visual acuity is further enhanced in the fovea centralis because light rays do not have to pass through as many tissue layers before reaching the photoreceptor cells.

Rod and cone cells differ in the way they interact with bipolar and ganglion cells. These differences, in addition to those discussed earlier, account for the differences in light sensitivity and visual acuity of the two types of photoreceptors. Rods exhibit higher levels of convergence in their relationship to bipolar cells compared with cones. One bipolar cell receives input from numerous rods, and one ganglion cell receives input from several bipolar cells, so that spatial summation occurs and the signal is enhanced. This system has an enhanced light sensitivity and allows awareness of stimuli from very dim light sources. However, the high degree of convergence also decreases visual acuity associated with these cells. Cones, on the other hand, exhibit little or no convergence on bipolar cells, so that one cone cell may synapse with only one bipolar cell. This system reduces light sensitivity but enhances visual acuity.

The area from which a ganglion cell receives input is called the **receptive field.** The receptive field is roughly circular, with a smaller portion in the center, called the receptive field center, and a larger surrounding area. Two types of receptive fields exist: (1) on-center ganglion cells and (2) off-center ganglion cells. On-center ganglion cells generate more action potentials when light is directed onto the receptive field center. Off-center ganglion cells generate more action potentials when light is turned off in the receptive field center or when light shines on the surrounding area. Receptive fields of off-center ganglion cells respond primarily to contrasts in light (edges) rather than to the absolute intensity of light.

Within the inner layers of the retina, interneurons modify the signals from the photoreceptor cells before the signal ever leaves the retina (see figure 15.17). **Horizontal cells** form the outer plexiform layer and synapse with photoreceptor cells and bipolar cells. **Amacrine** (AM-ah-krin) **cells** form the inner plexiform layer and synapse with bipolar and ganglion cells. **Interplexiform cells** form the bipolar layer and synapse with amacrine, bipolar, and horizontal cells to form a feedback loop. The interneurons are either excitatory or inhibitory on the cells with which they synapse. These interneurons enhance borders and contours, thereby increasing the intensity at boundaries, such as the edge of a dark object against a light background.

ASSESS YOUR PROGRESS

23. *What function do the pigmented layer of the retina and the pigment of the choroid perform?*

24. *Describe the changes that occur in a rod cell after light strikes rhodopsin. How does rhodopsin re-form? Why is the response of a rod cell to a stimulus unusual?*

25. *How do dark and light adaptation occur?*

26. *What are the three types of cone cells? How do they produce the color we see?*

27. *Describe the arrangement of rods and cones in the fovea centralis, the macula, and the peripheral parts of the retina.*

28. *Starting with a rod or cone cell, name the cells or structures that an action potential encounters while traveling to the optic nerve.*

Neuronal Pathways for Vision

Figure 15.23 shows the neuronal pathways that transmit action potentials generated by light from the time light enters the eye until it reaches the area of the cerebrum where vision is perceived.

1. Each eye has an area from which it collects light, referred to as the visual field. Each field is divided into the temporal part and the nasal part.
2. After passing through the cornea and lens, light from each half of the visual field projects to the opposite side of the retina, stimulating photoreceptors. Action potentials are conducted along the optic nerve.
3. The optic nerve leaves the eye and exits the orbit through the optic foramen to enter the cranial cavity. Just inside the cranial cavity and just anterior to the pituitary gland, the optic nerves are connected to each other at the **optic chiasm** (KAI-azm). At this point, axons from some ganglion cells cross over and project to the opposite side of the brain.
4. Specifically, ganglion cell axons from the nasal retina (the medial portion of the retina) cross through the optic chiasm and project to the opposite side of the brain. Ganglion cell axons from the temporal retina (the lateral portion of the retina) pass through the optic nerves and project to the brain on the same side of the body without crossing. This results in both hemispheres receiving visual input from both eyes.
5. Beyond the optic chiasm, the route of the ganglionic axons is called the **optic tract.** Most of the optic tract axons terminate in the lateral geniculate nucleus of the thalamus. However, some axons do not terminate in the thalamus but separate from the optic tract to terminate in the **superior colliculi,** the center for visual reflexes.
6. Neurons of the lateral geniculate nucleus of the thalamus form the fibers of the **optic radiations,** which project to the **visual cortex** in the **occipital lobe.**

Neurons of the visual cortex integrate the messages coming from the retina into a single message, translate that message into a mental image, and then transfer the image to other parts of the brain, where it is evaluated and either acted on or ignored.

PROCESS **Figure**

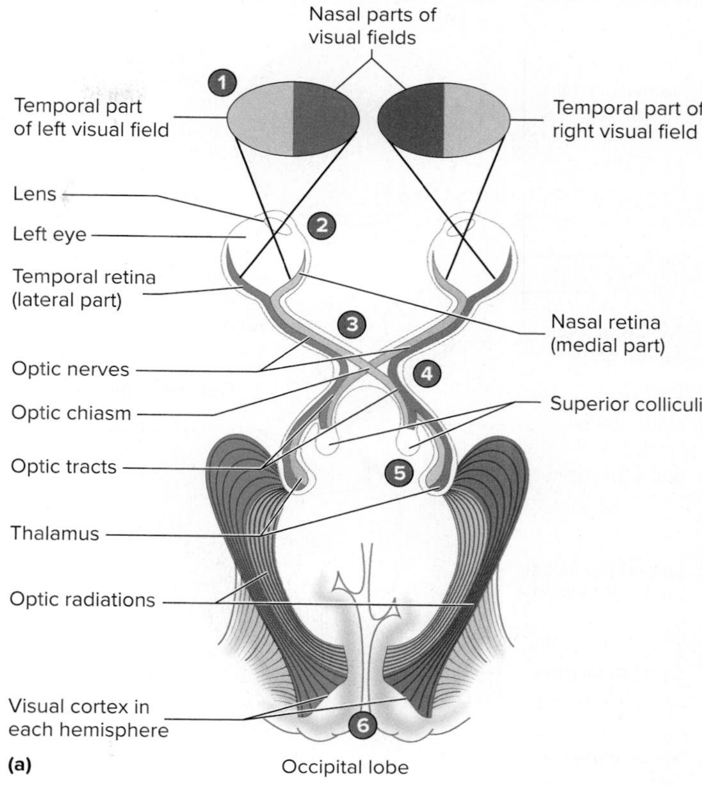

(a)

Anterior

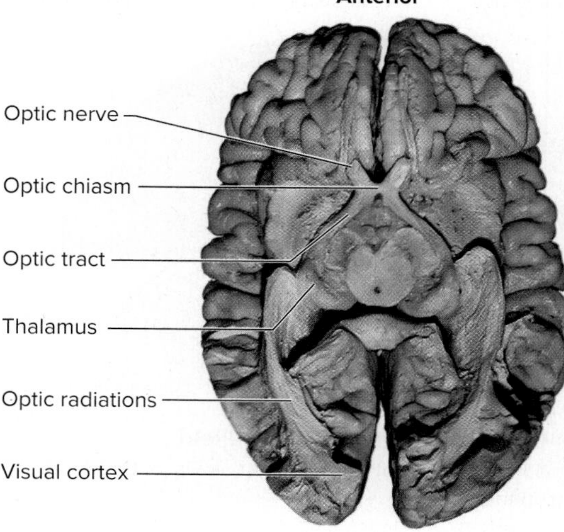

(b) Posterior

PROCESS **Figure 15.23**

Visual Pathways

(*a*) Neuronal pathways for both eyes (superior view). (*b*) Inferior view of the brain, showing the visual nerves, tracts, and pathways. (b) Rebecca Gray/Wise Anatomy/McGraw Hill APR

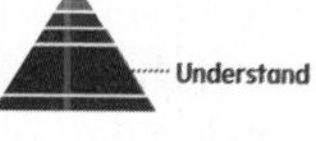

What is the importance of visual stimuli being conducted to the superior colliculi of the midbrain?

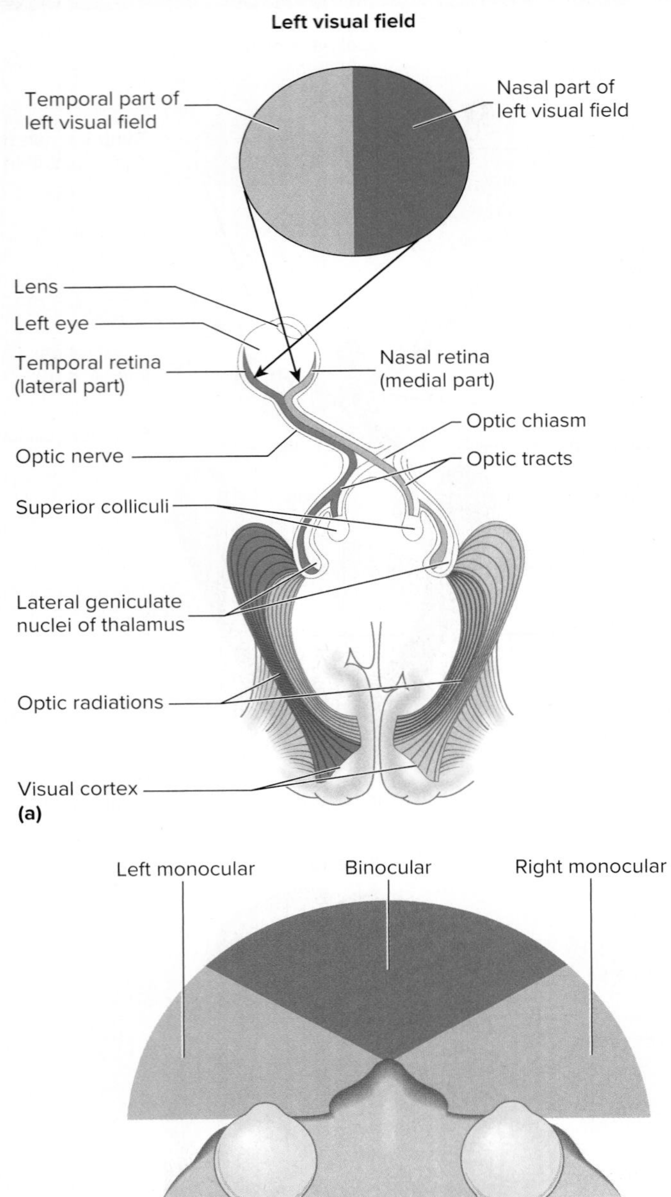

FIGURE 15.24 Organization of the Visual Field
(*a*) Visual field and pathway of the left eye (superior view). (*b*) Overlap of the fields of vision (superior view).

The projections of ganglion cells from the retina of each eye can be related to the **visual field** for each eye (figure 15.24*a*). You can observe the visual field by closing one eye. Everything that you can see with the one open eye is the visual field of that eye. The visual field of each eye can be divided into temporal (lateral) and nasal (medial) parts. The temporal part of the visual field projects onto the nasal retina, whereas the nasal part projects to the temporal retina. The projections and nerve pathways are arranged such that images entering the eye from the right part of each visual field project to the left side of the brain. Conversely, the left part of each visual field projects to the right side of the brain.

Apply

Predict 5

In figure 15.25, the lines at A and B depict two lesions on the visual pathways. The effect of a lesion at A in the optic radiations on the visual fields is depicted (with the right and left fields separated) in the ovals at the bottom of the figure. The black areas indicate what parts of the visual fields are defective. Describe the effect that the lesion at B has on the visual fields (see figure 15.24 for help).

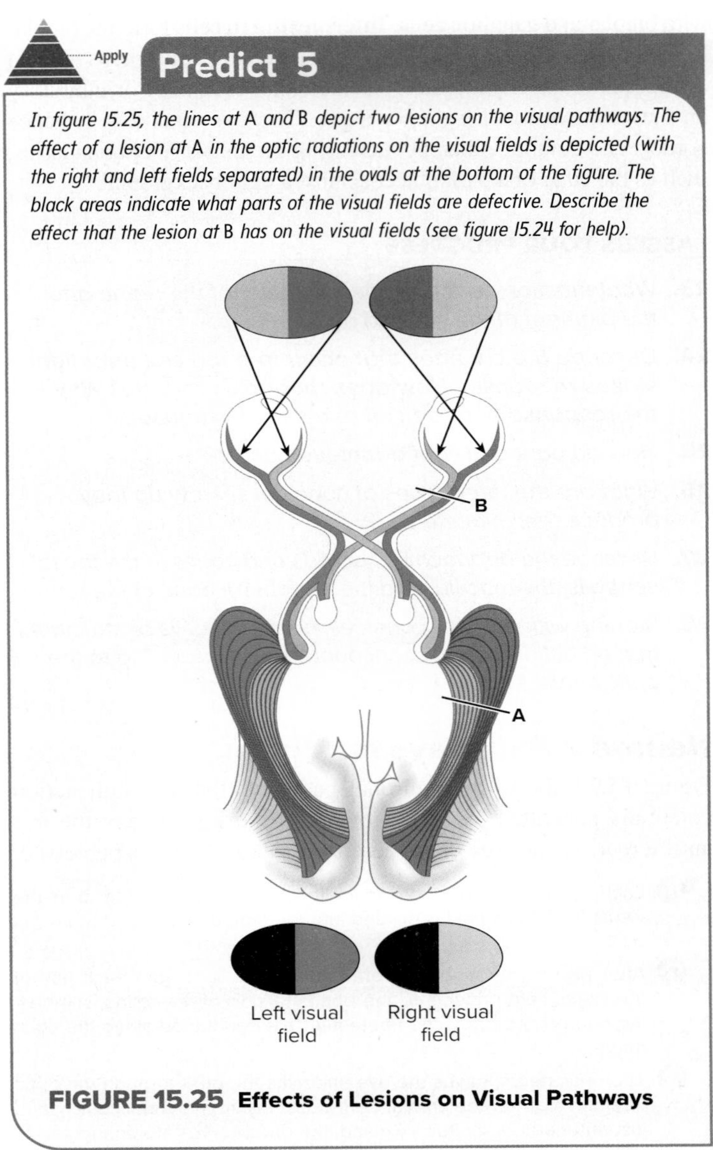

FIGURE 15.25 Effects of Lesions on Visual Pathways

Because the optic chiasm lies just anterior to the pituitary gland, a pituitary tumor can put pressure on the optic chiasm and cause visual defects. Because the nerve fibers crossing in the optic chiasm are carrying information from the temporal halves of the visual fields, a person with optic chiasm damage cannot see objects in the temporal halves of the visual fields. This condition, called **tunnel vision,** is often an early sign of a pituitary tumor.

The visual fields of the eyes partially overlap (figure 15.24*b*). The region of overlap—the area seen with both eyes at the same time—is the area of **binocular vision.** Because humans see the same object with both eyes, the image of the object reaches the retina of one eye at a slightly different angle from that of the other. With experience, the brain can interpret these differences in angle, so that distance can be judged quite accurately. Thus, binocular vision gives us **depth perception,** which is the ability to distinguish between near and far objects and to judge their distance.

FUNDAMENTAL **Figure**

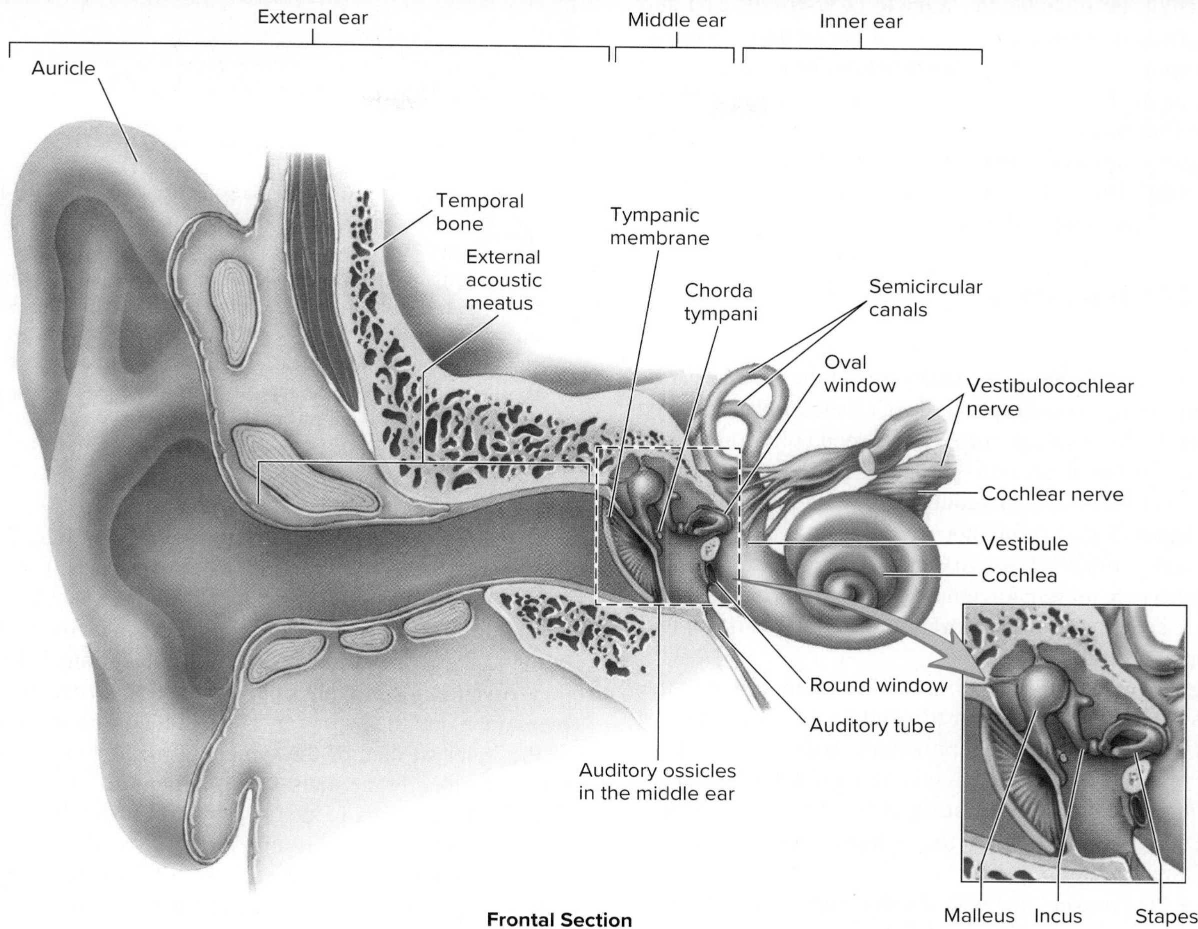

FIGURE 15.26 External, Middle, and Inner Ears
Frontal view of the regions of the ear. The smaller image illustrates the auditory ossicles of the middle ear: malleus, incus, and stapes. APR

ASSESS YOUR PROGRESS

29. *What is a visual field?*
30. *Starting with the optic nerve, trace the action potential going from the right temporal visual field to the visual cortex.*
31. *Explain how binocular vision allows for depth perception.*

15.4 Hearing and Balance

LEARNING OUTCOMES

After reading this section, you should be able to

A. **Describe the structures of the external ear and state the function of each.**
B. **Describe the structures of the middle ear and state the function of each.**
C. **Explain the tunnels and chambers of the inner ear.**
D. **State the fluids contained in the tunnels and chambers of the inner ear.**
E. **Describe the anatomy of the cochlea and, in particular, the cochlear duct.**
F. **Discuss the characteristics of sound.**
G. **Explain the process by which an action potential is generated by the hair cells of the spiral organ.**
H. **Trace a sound wave through the external, middle, and inner ears to the spiral organ.**
I. **Describe the pathway of an action potential from the hair cells of the spiral organ to the auditory cortex.**
J. **Explain how the structures of the vestibule function in static equilibrium.**
K. **Explain how the structures of the semicircular canals function in dynamic equilibrium.**
L. **Describe the pathway of an action potential from the balance organs to the various parts of the central nervous system and eyes.**

The organs of hearing and balance are divided into three parts: (1) the external ear, (2) the middle ear, and (3) the inner ear (figure 15.26). The external and middle ears are involved in hearing only, whereas the inner ear functions in both hearing and balance.

The **external ear** includes the **auricle** (AW-ri-kul; ear) and the **external acoustic meatus.** The external ear terminates medially at the **tympanic** (tim-PAN-ik) **membrane,** or *eardrum.* The **middle ear** is an air-filled space within the petrous portion of the temporal bone that contains the **auditory ossicles.** The **inner ear** houses the sensory organs for both hearing and balance. It consists of interconnecting, fluid-filled tunnels and chambers within the petrous portion of the temporal bone.

Auditory Structures and Their Functions

External Ear

The auricle, or *pinna* (PIN-ah), is the fleshy part of the external ear on the outside of the head; it consists primarily of elastic cartilage covered with skin (figure 15.26). Its shape helps collect sound waves and direct them toward the external acoustic meatus. The external acoustic meatus is lined with hairs and **ceruminous** (se-ROO-mi-nus) **glands.** Recall from chapter 5 that ceruminous glands are skin glands that produce **cerumen,** a modified sebum commonly called earwax. The hairs and cerumen help prevent foreign objects from reaching the delicate tympanic membrane. However, overproduction of cerumen may block the external acoustic meatus.

The tympanic membrane is a thin, semitransparent membrane that separates the external ear from the middle ear. It consists of three layers: (1) a simple cuboidal epithelium on the inner surface, (2) a middle layer of connective tissue, and (3) a thin stratified squamous epithelium on the outer surface. Sound waves reaching the tympanic membrane through the external acoustic meatus cause it to vibrate.

Rupture of the tympanic membrane can be caused by a foreign object thrust into the ear, an infection of the middle ear, or sufficient differential pressure between the middle ear and the outside air, as occurs when changing altitude in an airplane or diving into deep water. Rupture of the tympanic membrane may result in hearing impairment.

Middle Ear

Medial to the tympanic membrane is the air-filled cavity of the middle ear (see figure 15.26). Two covered openings, the round window and the oval window, on the medial side of the middle ear separate it from the inner ear. Two additional openings provide air passages from the middle ear. One passage opens into the **mastoid air cells** in the mastoid process of the temporal bone. The other passageway, the **auditory tube,** or *pharyngotympanic tube* (also called the eustachian [you-STAY-shun] tube), opens into the pharynx and equalizes air pressure between the outside air and the middle ear cavity. Unequal pressure between the middle ear and the outside environment can distort the tympanic membrane, dampen its vibrations, and make hearing difficult. Distortion of the tympanic membrane, which occurs under these conditions, also stimulates pain fibers associated with it. Because of this distortion, when a person changes altitude, sounds seem muffled and the eardrum may become painful. Swallowing, yawning, chewing, and holding the nose and mouth shut while gently forcing air out of the lungs can relieve distortion of the tympanic membrane. These actions open the auditory tube, which allows air to pass through the auditory tube and equalizes air pressure on each side of the eardrum.

Clinical IMPACT 15.2

Function of the Chorda Tympani

A structure you might be somewhat surprised to find in the middle ear is the **chorda tympani,** a branch of the facial nerve carrying taste impulses from the anterior two-thirds of the tongue. It crosses over the inner surface of the tympanic membrane (see figure 15.26). The chorda tympani has nothing to do with hearing but is just passing through. However, this nerve can be damaged during ear surgery or by a middle ear infection, resulting in loss of taste sensation from the anterior two-thirds of the tongue on the side innervated by that nerve.

The middle ear contains three auditory ossicles (figure 15.27; see figure 15.26): (1) the **malleus** (MAL-ee-us; hammer), (2) the **incus** (IN-cuss; anvil), and (3) the **stapes** (STAY-pees; stirrup). The auditory ossicles transmit vibrations from the tympanic membrane to the **oval window.** Like a flexible, bony bridge, the auditory ossicles form a physical connection between the tympanic membrane and the inner ear. The handle of the malleus is attached to the inner surface of the tympanic membrane. Vibration of the tympanic membrane causes the malleus to vibrate as well. The head of the malleus is attached by a very small synovial joint to the incus, which in turn is attached by a small synovial joint to the stapes. The foot plate of the stapes fits into the oval window and is held in place by a flexible **annular ligament.** Thus, movement of the tympanic membrane is conveyed through the malleus, incus, and stapes to the oval window.

Two small skeletal muscles originate from bone around the middle ear and insert onto auditory ossicles (figure 15.27). The **tensor tympani** (TEN-sohr TIM-pan-ee) muscle is attached to the malleus and is innervated by the trigeminal nerve (V). The **stapedius** (stay-PEE-dee-us) muscle is attached to the stapes and is innervated by the facial nerve (VII).

The tensor tympani and stapedius muscles, attached to auditory ossicles, reflexively dampen excessively loud sounds. This so-called **sound attenuation reflex** protects the delicate ear structures from damage by loud noises. The sound attenuation reflex responds most effectively to low-frequency sounds and can reduce by a factor of 100 the energy reaching the oval window. The facial nerve and stapedius are primarily involved in the sound attenuation reflex. The trigeminal nerve and tensor tympani are stimulated only by extremely loud noise. The reflex is too slow to prevent damage from a sudden noise, such as a gunshot, and it cannot function effectively for longer than about 10 minutes in response to prolonged noise.

Inner Ear

The tunnels and chambers inside the temporal bone are called the **bony labyrinth** (LAB-ih-rinth; maze; figure 15.28). Because the bony labyrinth consists of tunnels within the bone, it cannot easily be removed and examined separately. When viewing the inner ear shown separately from the remainder of the temporal bone, the bony

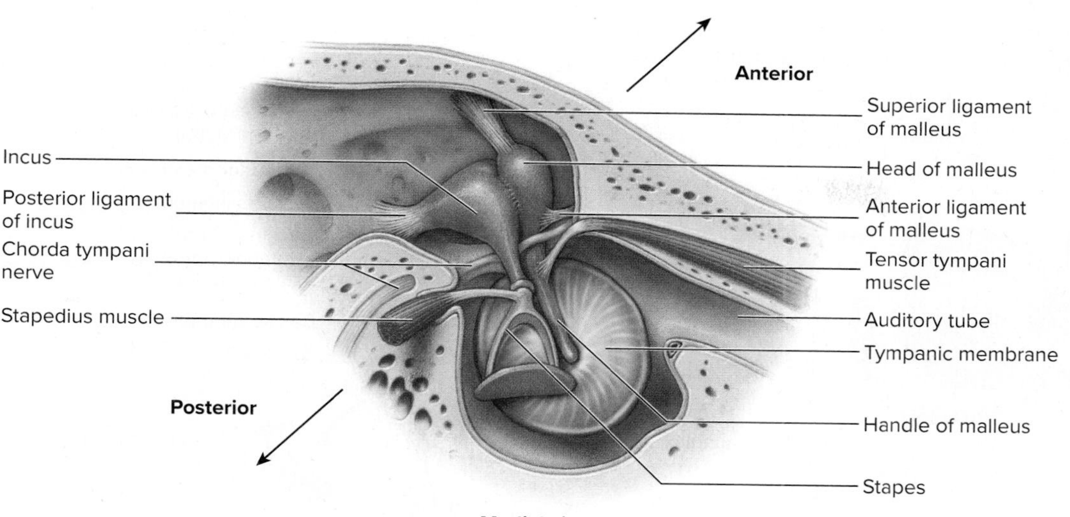

FIGURE 15.27 Auditory Ossicles and Muscles of the Middle Ear
Medial view of the middle ear (as though viewed from the inner ear), showing the three auditory ossicles with their ligaments and the two muscles of the middle ear: the tensor tympani and the stapedius.

labyrinth is composed primarily of endosteum (figure 15.28*c*). Recall from chapter 6 that endosteum is a single layer of connective tissue that lines internal surfaces within bone. Inside the bony labyrinth is a similarly shaped but smaller set of membranous tunnels and chambers called the **membranous labyrinth** (see figure 15.28*b*). The inner surface of the endosteum and the outer surface of the membranous labyrinth are covered with a very thin layer of cells called the **perilymphatic cells** (figure 15.28*c*). The membranous labyrinth is filled with a clear fluid called **endolymph,** and the space between the membranous labyrinth and bony labyrinth is filled with a fluid called **perilymph.** Perilymph has a low concentration of K^+ and a high concentration of Na^+, similar to cerebrospinal fluid. Endolymph has a different composition than perilymph in that endolymph has a high concentration of K^+ and a low concentration of Na^+.

The bony labyrinth is divided into three regions: (1) the vestibule, (2) the semicircular canals, and (3) the cochlea. The **vestibule** (VES-tih-byul) and **semicircular canals** are primarily involved in balance, and the **cochlea** (KOK-lee-ah) functions in hearing.

The arrangement of the membranous labyrinth within the bony labyrinth of the cochlea results in three distinct regions of the cochlea: (1) the scala vestibuli, (2) the scala tympani, and (3) the cochlear duct (figure 15.29*b*). The **scala vestibuli** (SKA-lah ves-TIB-you-lie) extends from the oval window to the **helicotrema** (HEL-ih-koh-TREE-mah) at the apex of the cochlea. The **scala tympani** (tim-PA-nee) extends from the helicotrema, back from the apex, parallel to the scala vestibuli, to the membrane of the **round window.** The scala vestibuli and the scala

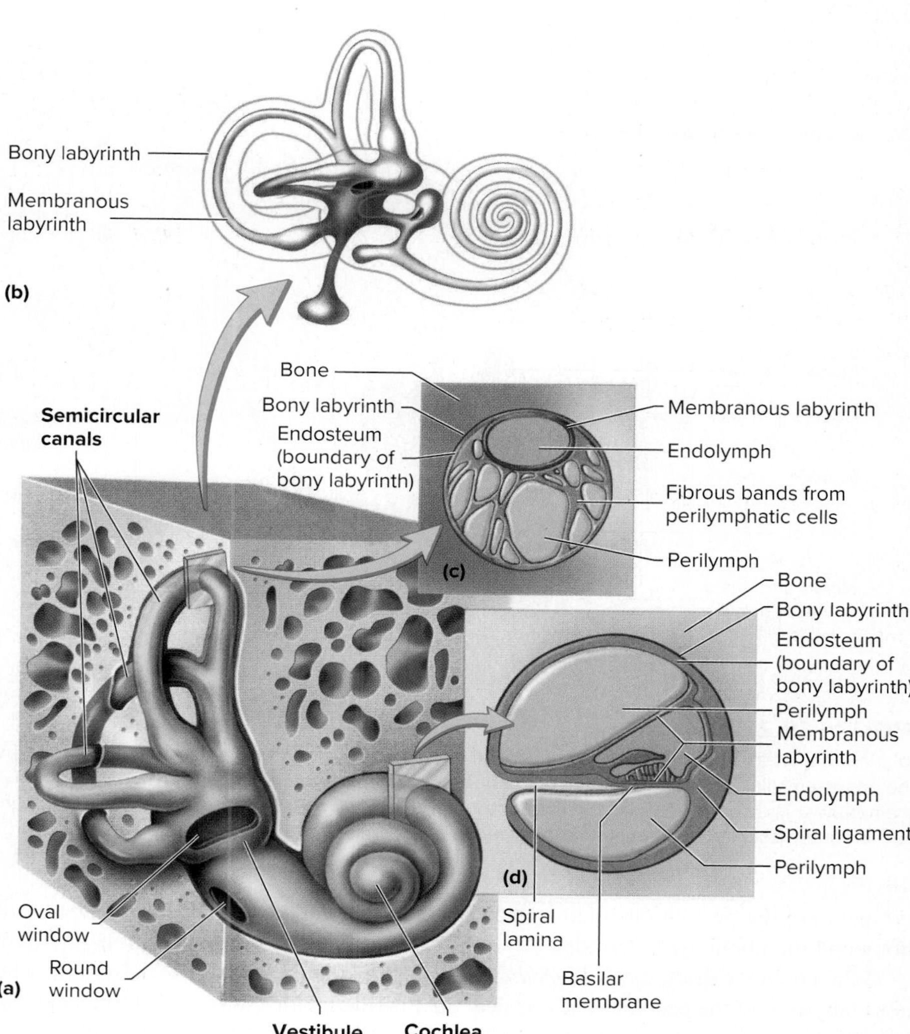

FIGURE 15.28 Inner Ear: Bony and Membranous Labyrinths
(*a*) The structures of the inner ear are embedded in the temporal bone. (*b*) The membranous labyrinth seen within the outline of the bony labyrinth. (c) A cross section through a semicircular canal and (*d*) a cross section through the cochlea show the relationship between the bony and membranous labyrinths.

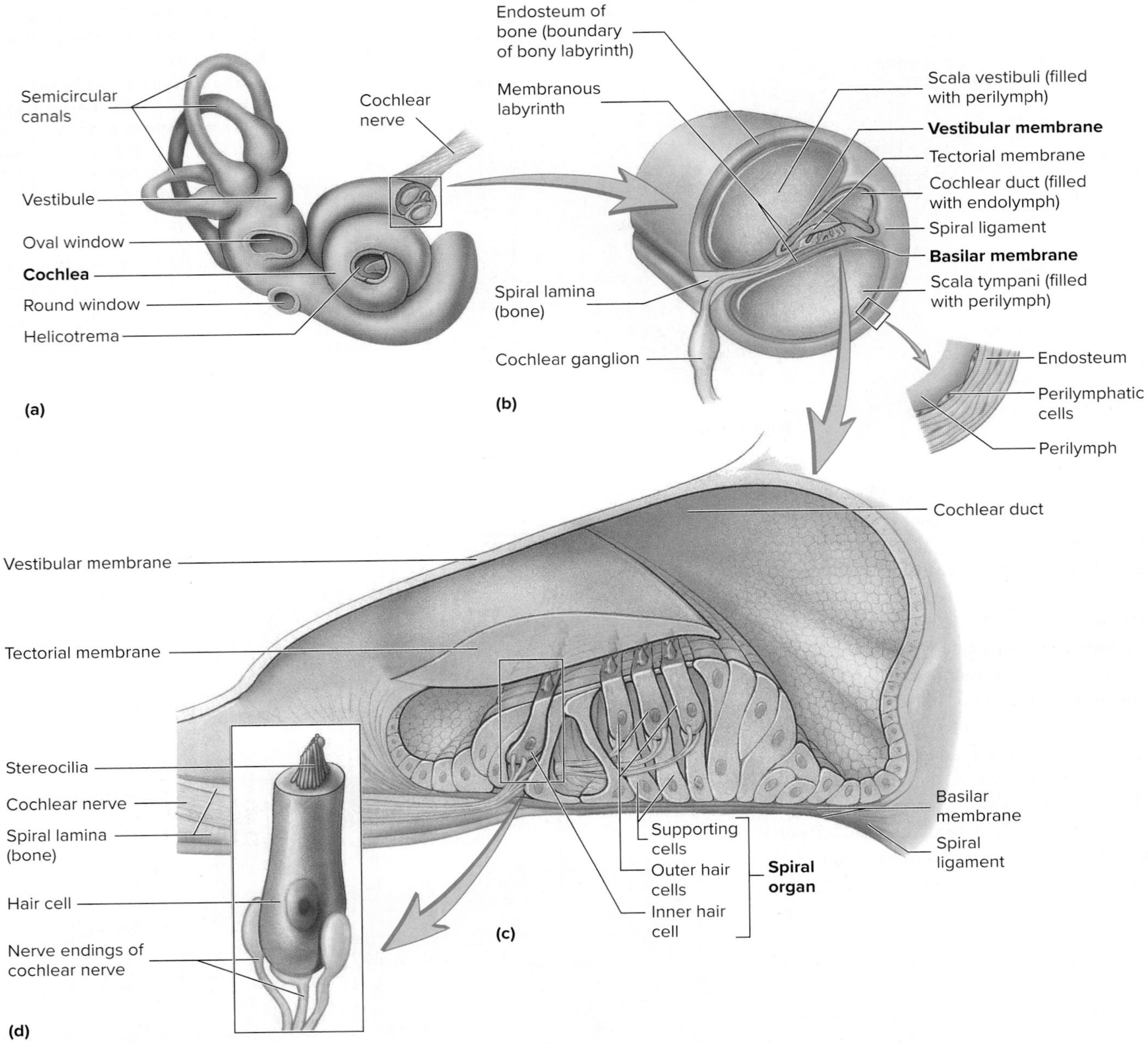

FIGURE 15.29 Cochlea
(*a*) Inner ear structures. The outer surface is the endosteum lining the inner surface of the bony labyrinth. (*b*) Cross section of the cochlea. The outer layer is the endosteum lining the inner surface of the bony labyrinth. The membranous labyrinth is very small in the cochlea and consists of the vestibular and basilar membranes. The space between the membranous and bony labyrinths consists of two parallel tunnels: the scala vestibuli and the scala tympani. (*c*) Enlarged section of the cochlear duct (membranous labyrinth). (*d*) Individual sensory hair cell, greatly enlarged. APR

tympani are the perilymph-filled spaces between the walls of the bony and membranous labyrinths.

The **cochlear duct,** or *scala media,* is formed by the membranous labyrinth of the cochlea. The cochlear duct is filled with endolymph. As you can see in figure 15.29*b,* the scala vestibuli is situated above the cochlear duct and the scala tympani is situated below the cochlear duct. The wall of the membranous labyrinth that borders the scala vestibuli is called the **vestibular membrane** (*Reissner membrane*); the wall of the membranous labyrinth bordering the scala tympani is the **basilar membrane** (figure 15.29*b,c*).

The vestibular membrane consists of a double layer of squamous epithelium and is the simplest region of the membranous labyrinth. The vestibular membrane is so thin that it has little or no mechanical effect on the transmission of sound waves through the inner ear; therefore, the perilymph and endolymph on the two sides of the vestibular membrane can be thought of mechanically as one fluid, even though they are chemically different. The basilar membrane is somewhat more complex and is of much greater physiological interest in relation to the mechanics of hearing. It has an acellular portion, consisting of collagen fibers, ground substance, and sparsely dispersed elastic fibers, and a cellular portion, composed of a thin layer of vascular connective tissue overlaid with simple squamous epithelium.

The basilar membrane is attached at one side to the bony **spiral lamina,** which projects from the sides of the **modiolus** (moh-DIE-oh-lus), the bony core of the cochlea, like the threads of a screw. At the other side, the basilar membrane is attached to the lateral wall of the bony labyrinth by the **spiral ligament,** a local thickening of the endosteum. The distance between the spiral lamina and the spiral ligament (i.e., the width of the basilar membrane) increases from 0.04 mm near the oval window to 0.5 mm near the helicotrema. The collagen fibers of the basilar membrane are oriented across the membrane between the spiral lamina and the spiral ligament, somewhat like the strings of a piano. The collagen fibers near the oval window are both shorter and thicker than those near the helicotrema. The diameter of the collagen fibers in the membrane decreases as the basilar membrane widens. As a result, the basilar membrane near the oval window is short and stiff, and it responds to high-frequency vibrations, whereas the region near the helicotrema is wide and limber and responds to low-frequency vibrations.

Within the cochlear duct is the **spiral organ,** or *organ of Corti,* where the sensory cells for hearing are found (figure 15.29*c*). The spiral organ contains supporting epithelial cells and specialized sensory cells called **hair cells** (figure 15.29*d*). These hair cells have hairlike projections at their apical ends. In children, these projections consist of one cilium (kinocilium) and about 80 very long microvilli, often referred to as **stereocilia.** In adults the cilium is absent from most hair cells; only the microvilli remain. The hair cells are arranged in the spiral organ in four long rows extending the length of the cochlear duct. Each row contains 3500–4000 hair cells. The inner row consists of **inner hair cells,** which are the hair cells primarily responsible for hearing. The outer three rows contain **outer hair cells,** which are involved in regulating the tension of the basilar membrane. The outer hair cells are separated from the inner hair cells by a gap in the basilar membrane (figure 15.29*c*). The stereocilia of one inner hair cell form a conical group called a **hair bundle** (figure 15.30*a*). The length of each stereocilium within a hair bundle increases gradually from one side of the hair cell to the other. The stereocilia of an outer hair cell are arranged in a curved line (figure 15.30*b*). The tips of the longest stereocilia of the outer hair cells are embedded within an acellular, gelatinous shelf called the **tectorial** (tek-TOR-ee-al) **membrane,** which is positioned over the spiral organ and attached to the spiral lamina.

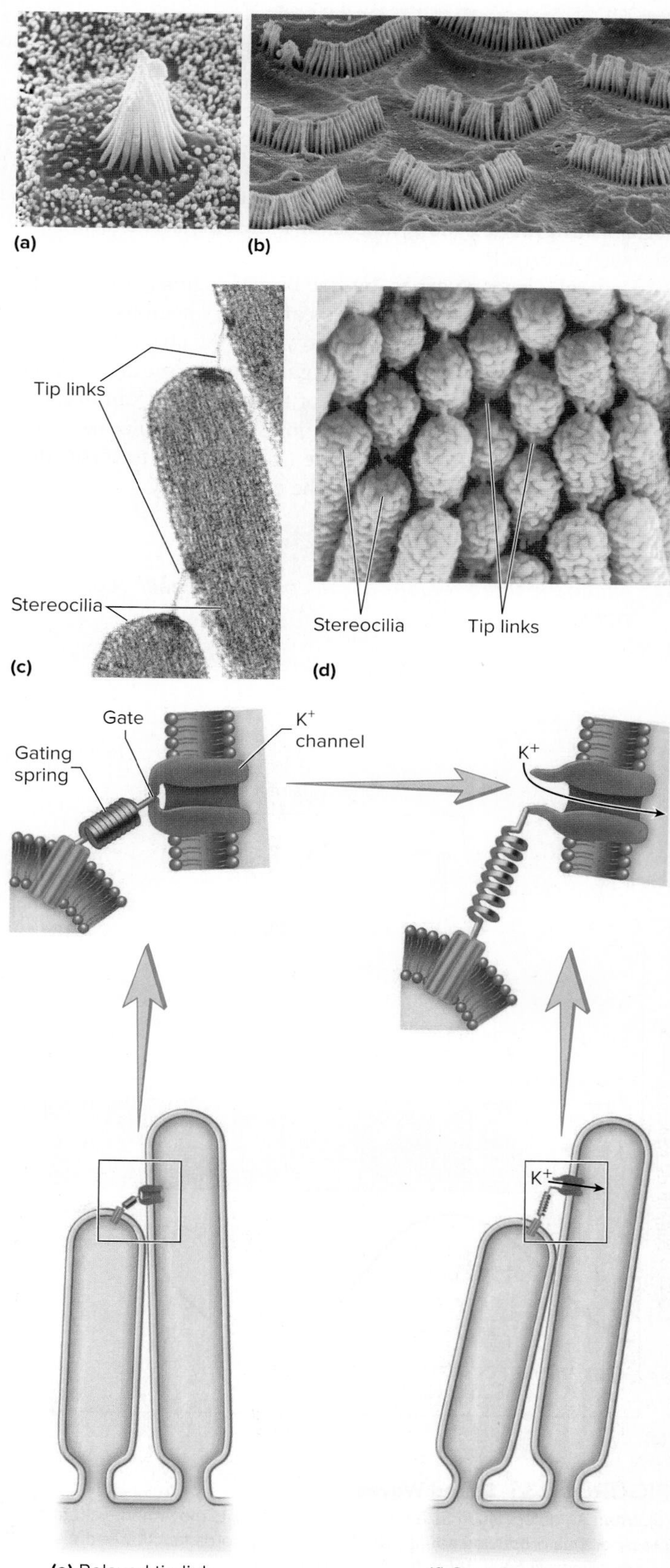

FIGURE 15.30 Cochlear Hair Cell Stereocilia

(*a*) Hair bundle of one inner hair cell. (*b*) Stereocilia of outer hair cells. (*c*) Transmission electron micrograph of three stereocilia and two tip links. (*d*) Scanning electron micrograph of the tops of stereocilia, showing tip links. (*e*) In an unstimulated cell, the tip link is relaxed and the K^+ channel gate is closed. (*f*) As the stereocilia are bent toward the taller stereocilium, the tip link stretches and the gate of the K^+ channel opens, allowing K^+ to enter the cell. (a) A. J. Hudspeth; (b) Steve Gschmeissner/Science Source (c) A. J. Hudspeth; (d) David Corey

A **tip link** connects the tip of each stereocilium in a hair bundle to the side of the next longer stereocilium (figure 15.30*c,e*). Each tip link is a *gating spring,* a pair of microtubule strands that attach to the gate of a gated K^+ channel. The gated K^+ channels of hair cells open mechanically. As the stereocilia bend, the tip link pulls the K^+ gate open (figure 15.30*f*). The response time for such a mechanism is very brief and much faster than for a gating mechanism involving the synthesis of intracellular chemical signals, such as cAMP.

Hair cells have no axons, but the basilar regions of each hair cell are covered by synaptic terminals of sensory neurons. The cell bodies of afferent neurons are located within the cochlear modiolus and are grouped into a **cochlear ganglion,** or *spiral ganglion* (see figure 15.29*b*). Afferent fibers of these neurons join to form the **cochlear nerve.** This nerve then joins the vestibular nerve to become the **vestibulocochlear nerve (VIII),** which traverses the internal acoustic meatus and enters the cranial cavity.

ASSESS YOUR PROGRESS

32. *Name the three regions of the ear, and list each region's parts.*
33. *Describe the relationship among the tympanic membrane, the auditory ossicles, and the oval window.*
34. *What are the functions of the external acoustic meatus and the auditory tube?*
35. *Explain how the membranous labyrinth of the cochlea is divided into three compartments. What is found in each compartment?*
36. *Describe the structure of the spiral organ.*
37. *Explain the differences between inner and outer hair cells.*
38. *Relate how tip links function.*
39. *How is the cochlear nerve formed?*

Auditory Function

Vibration of matter, such as air, water, or a solid material, creates sound. No sound occurs in a vacuum. When a person speaks, the vocal cords vibrate, causing the air passing out of the lungs to vibrate. The vibrations consist of bands of compressed air followed by bands of less compressed air (figure 15.31*a*). These vibrations are propagated through the air as sound waves,

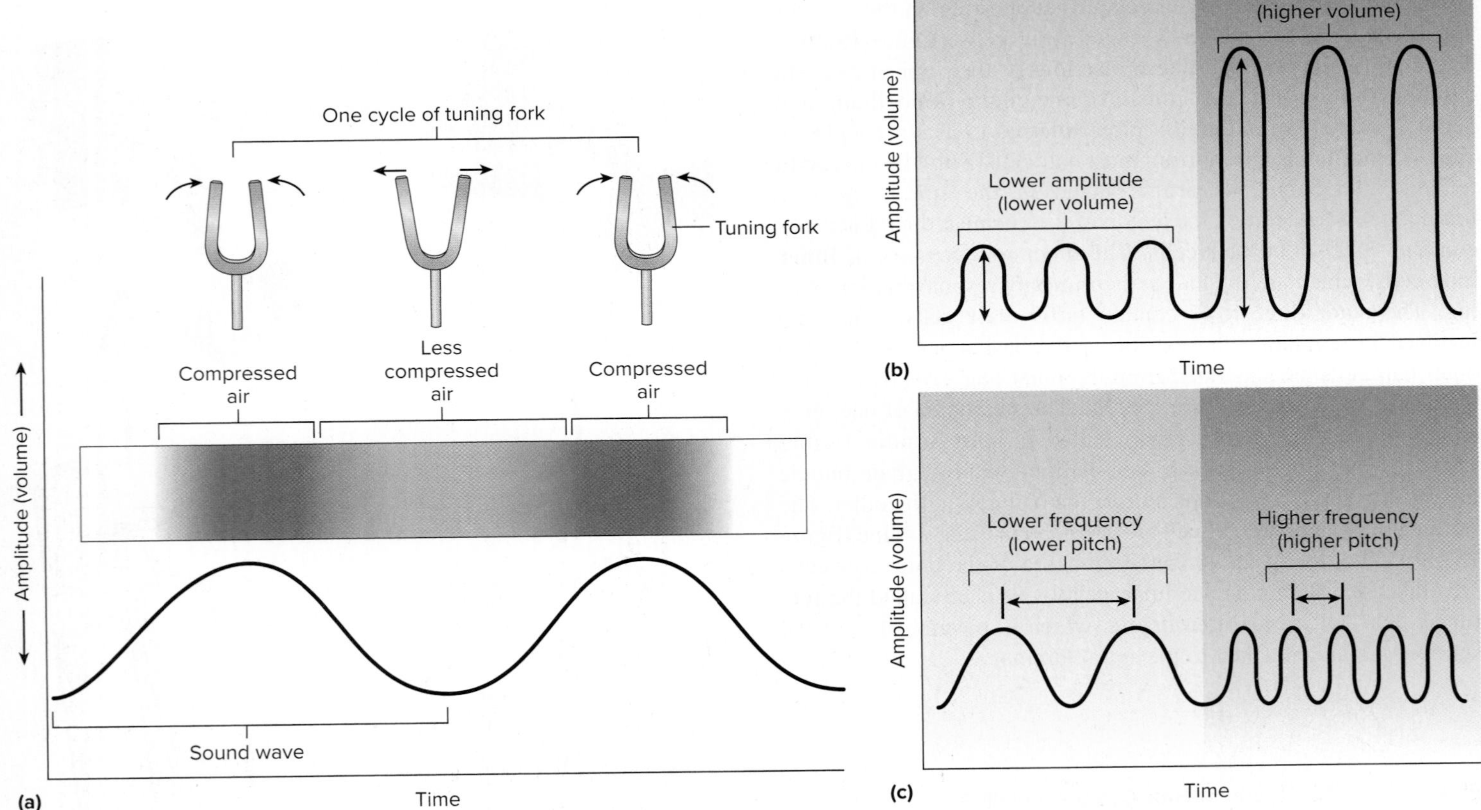

FIGURE 15.31 Sound Waves
(*a*) When an object, such as a tuning fork, vibrates, its movements alternate between compressing the air and decompressing the air, or making the air less compressed, thus producing sound. The human vocal cords function in the same way. Each sound wave consists of a region of compressed air between two regions of less compressed air (*blue bars*). The sigmoid (S-shaped) waves correspond to the regions of more compressed air (peaks) and less compressed air (troughs). The *green shadowed area* represents the width of one cycle (distance between peaks). (*b*) Low- and high-volume sound waves. Compare the relative lengths of the arrows indicating the wave height (amplitude). (*c*) Lower- and higher-pitch sound. Compare the relative number of peaks (frequency) within a given time interval (between arrows).

FUNDAMENTAL **Figure**

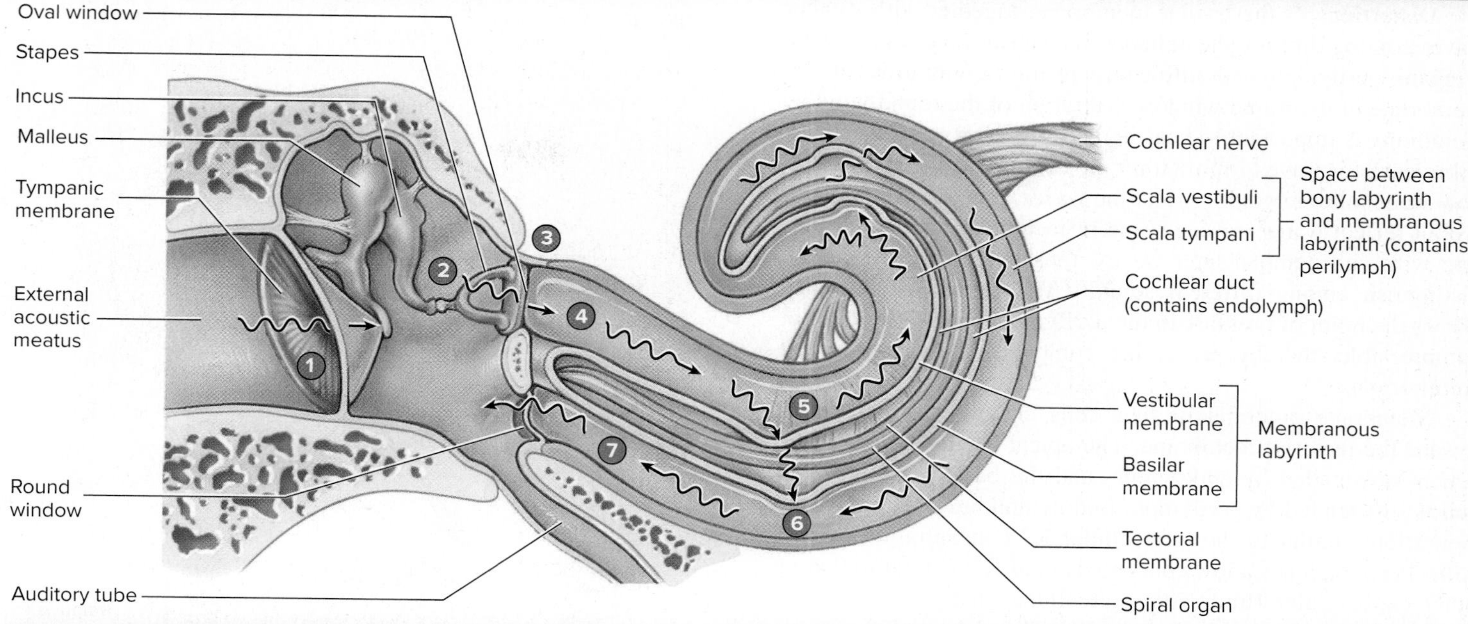

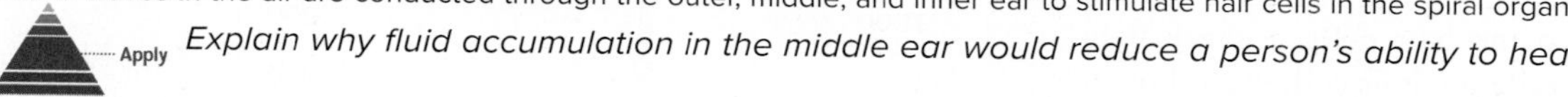

PROCESS **Figure 15.32**

Effect of Sound Waves on Cochlear Structures APR

Sound waves in the air are conducted through the outer, middle, and inner ear to stimulate hair cells in the spiral organ.

Apply *Explain why fluid accumulation in the middle ear would reduce a person's ability to hear.*

1. The auricle collects sound waves, which are then conducted through the external acoustic meatus toward the tympanic membrane. Sound waves travel relatively slowly in air (332 m/s), and a significant time interval may elapse between the time a sound wave reaches one ear and the time it reaches the other. The brain can interpret this interval to determine the direction from which a sound is coming.
2. Sound waves strike the tympanic membrane and cause it to vibrate. This vibration in turn causes the three auditory ossicles of the middle ear to vibrate; by this mechanical linkage, vibration is transferred to the oval window. More force is required to cause vibration in a liquid, such as the perilymph of the inner ear, than in air; thus, the vibrations reaching the perilymph must be amplified as they cross the middle ear.
3. The foot plate of the stapes and its annular ligament, which occupy the oval window, are much smaller than the tympanic membrane. The area of the tympanic membrane is roughly 20 times that of the oval window. Because of this size difference, the mechanical force of vibration is amplified about 20-fold as it passes from the tympanic membrane through the ossicles and to the oval window.
4. As the stapes vibrates against the oval window, it produces waves in the perilymph of the scala vestibuli.
5. Vibrations of the perilymph are transmitted through the thin vestibular membrane and cause simultaneous vibrations of the endolymph. The mechanical effect is as though the perilymph and endolymph were a single fluid.
6. Vibration of the endolymph causes distortion of the basilar membrane. The distortion is most important to hearing. As this membrane distorts, the hair cells resting on the basilar membrane move relative to the tectorial membrane, which remains stationary. The inner hair cell microvilli bend as they move against the tectorial membrane.
7. Waves in the perilymph of the scala vestibuli are transmitted also through the helicotrema and into the scala tympani. However, because the helicotrema is very small, this transmitted vibration is probably of little consequence.

somewhat as ripples are propagated over the surface of water. Two major features of sound—volume and pitch—are directly related to the characteristics of sound waves. **Volume,** or loudness, is a function of sound wave *amplitude,* or height, measured in decibels (db; figure 15.31*b*). The greater the amplitude, the louder the sound. **Pitch** is a function of the sound wave *frequency* (i.e., the number of waves or cycles per second) measured in hertz (Hz; figure 15.31*c*). The higher the frequency, the higher the pitch. The normal range of human hearing is 20–20,000 Hz and 0 or more db. Sounds louder than 125 db are painful to the ear. Normal human speech ranges in volume between 250 and 8000 Hz. This is the range that is used when testing for hearing impairment because it is the most important for communication.

Timbre (TAM-br, TIM-br) is the resonance quality or overtones of a sound. A "pure" sound wave would be represented by a smooth, sigmoid curve, but such a wave is extremely rare in nature. The sounds made by musical instruments and the human voice are not smooth, sigmoid curves but rough, jagged curves formed by numerous, superimposed curves of various amplitudes and frequencies. The roughness of the curve accounts for the timbre. Timbre is the difference in quality between, for example, an oboe and a French horn playing a note at the same pitch and volume.

The process of hearing involves mechanical movement of specific structures of the external, middle, and inner ear, which leads to the electrical signals typical of the nervous system. The steps involved in the mechanical part of hearing are illustrated in figure 15.32.

Distortions of the basilar membrane, together with weaker waves coming through the helicotrema, cause waves in the scala tympani perilymph and ultimately result in vibration of the membrane of the round window. Vibration of the round window membrane is important to hearing because it acts as a mechanical release for waves from within the cochlea. If the round window were solid, it would reflect the waves, much as the walls of a pool reflect water waves. These reflected waves would interfere with and dampen later waves, thus making it difficult to distinguish among different sounds. The round window also allows the relief of pressure in the perilymph because fluid is not compressible, thereby preventing compression damage to the spiral organ.

Membrane potential of hair cells changes as they move toward the tectorial membrane. The apical portion of each hair cell is surrounded by endolymph, and the basal portion of the cell is surrounded by perilymph. Endolymph has a high K^+ concentration, similar to the intracellular K^+ concentration of hair cells. Perilymph has a low concentration of K^+, similar to that of other extracellular fluid. The intracellular charge of hair cells compared with perilymph is −60 mV. The charge of the endolymph is +80 mV compared with the perilymph. This charge difference is called the **endocochlear potential.** Consequently, the intracellular charge of hair cells compared with endolymph is −140 mV, which is a large charge difference. Therefore, when K^+ channels open, K^+ flows into the hair cells because it is attracted to the negative charge inside the hair cell, even though the intracellular concentration of K^+ is about the same as in the endolymph. The movement of K^+ into the cells causes depolarization of the hair cells. This is a rare instance in which an increase in K^+ permeability of the plasma membrane of a cell results in depolarization.

In the unstimulated hair cell, approximately 15% of the gated K^+ channels are open, and the resting membrane potential of the cell is approximately −60 mV. If the hair bundle is bent toward the shortest stereocilium (negative stimulus), the tip link attached to the K^+ channel gates slackens, allowing the open K^+ channels to close, and the cell hyperpolarizes. If the hair bundle is bent toward the longest stereocilium (positive stimulus), the tip link pulls additional K^+ channel gates open, and K^+ rushes into the cell. The influx of K^+ into the hair cell causes a slight depolarization of the cell. This depolarization causes voltage-gated Ca^{2+} channels to open. Calcium ions rush into the cell, causing a further depolarization. The cell depolarizes by a total of about 10 mV. Depolarization of hair cells results in the increased release of neurotransmitters, which increases the action potential frequency in the sensory neurons at the basilar region of the hair cell. In contrast, hyperpolarization decreases neurotransmitter release and decreases action potential frequency in these sensory neurons. Depolarization of the hair cells also opens voltage-gated K^+ channels in their basal portion. Potassium ions tend to leave the hair cell, causing the cell to repolarize.

The neurotransmitter released by the inner hair cells is apparently glutamate, but other neurotransmitters may also be involved. The release of neurotransmitters from the inner hair cells induces action potentials in the sensory neurons, also called

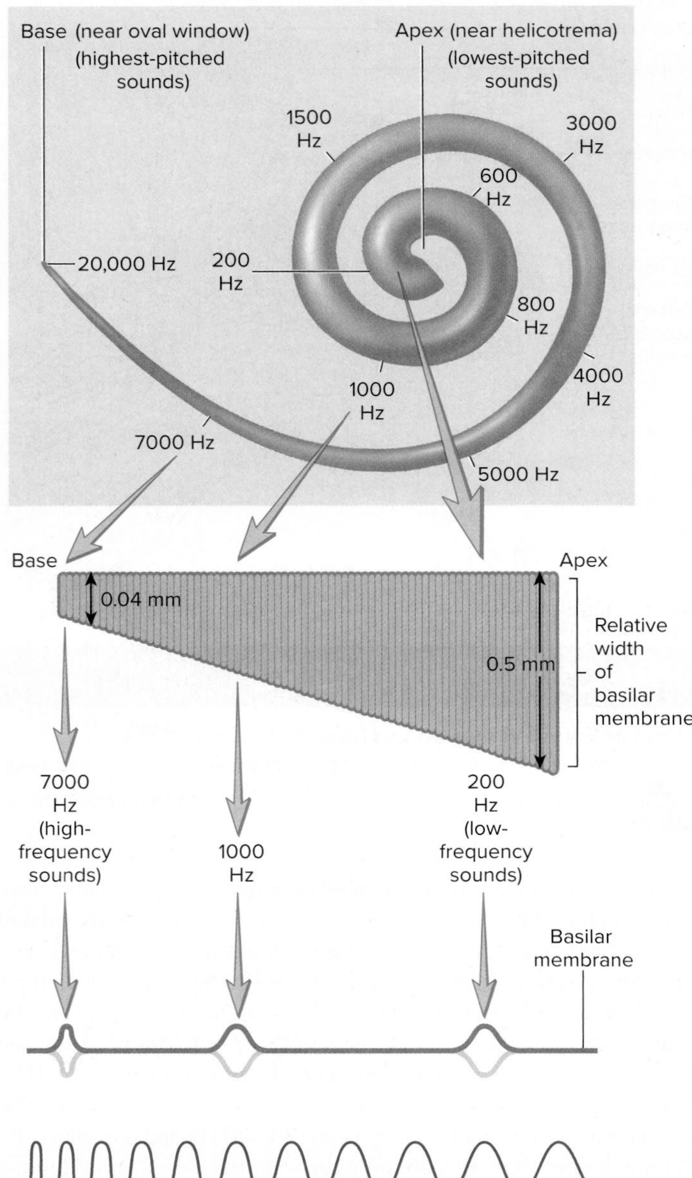

FIGURE 15.33 Effect of Sound Waves on Points Along the Basilar Membrane

Points of maximum vibration along the basilar membrane result from stimulation by sounds of various frequencies (in hertz).

cochlear neurons, that synapse on the hair cells. The cell bodies of those neurons are located in the cochlear ganglion.

The part of the basilar membrane that distorts as a result of endolymph vibration depends on the pitch of the sound that created the vibration and, as a result, on the vibration frequency within the endolymph. The location of the optimal amount of basilar membrane vibration produced by a given pitch is determined by two factors: (1) the width of the basilar membrane and (2) the length and diameter of the collagen fibers stretching across the membrane at each level along the cochlear duct (figure 15.33). Higher-pitched tones cause optimal vibration near the base of the

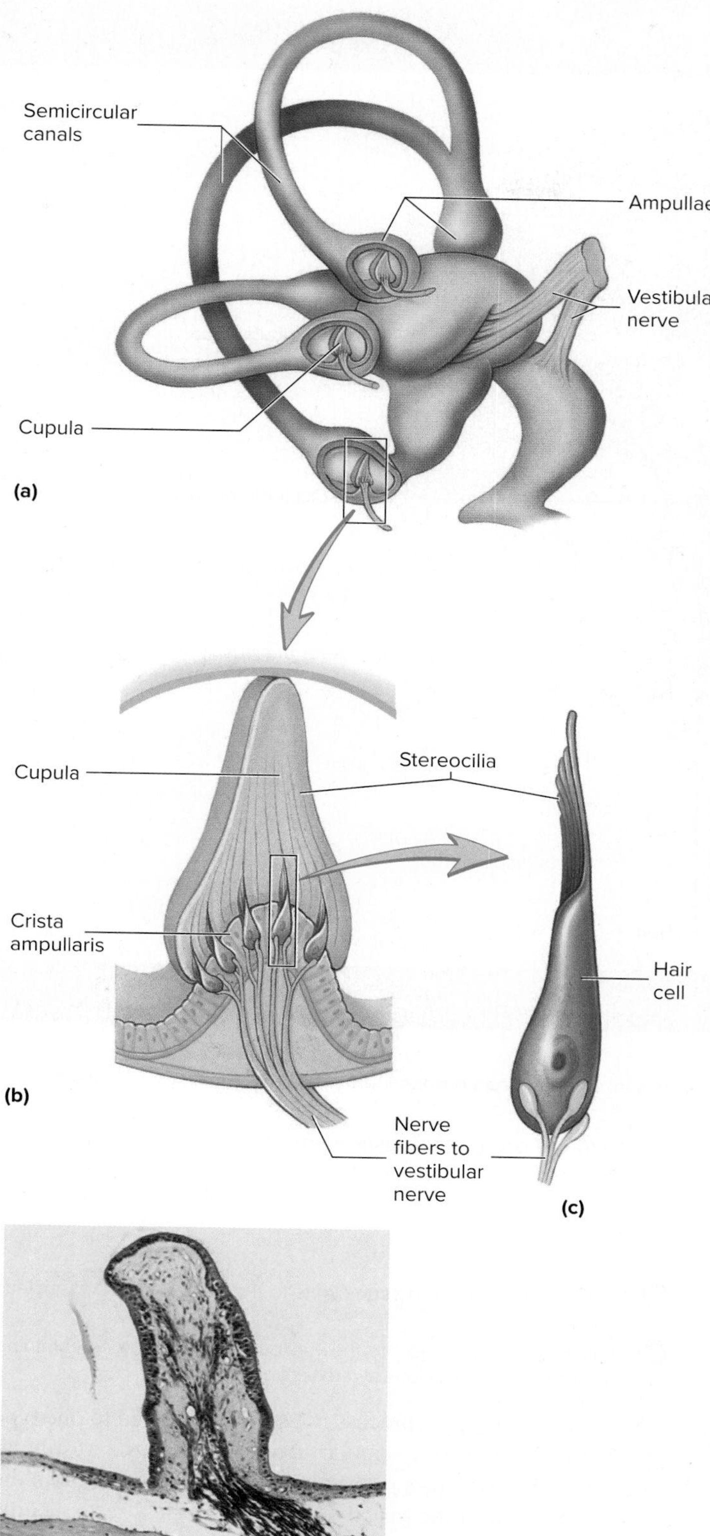

FIGURE 15.37 Semicircular Canals

(*a*) Semicircular canals, showing the location of the crista ampullaris in the ampullae. (*b*) Enlargement of the crista ampullaris, showing the cupula and hair cells. (*c*) Enlargement of a hair cell. (*d*) SEM of a crista ampullaris with hair cells. (d) Biophoto Associates/Science Source APR

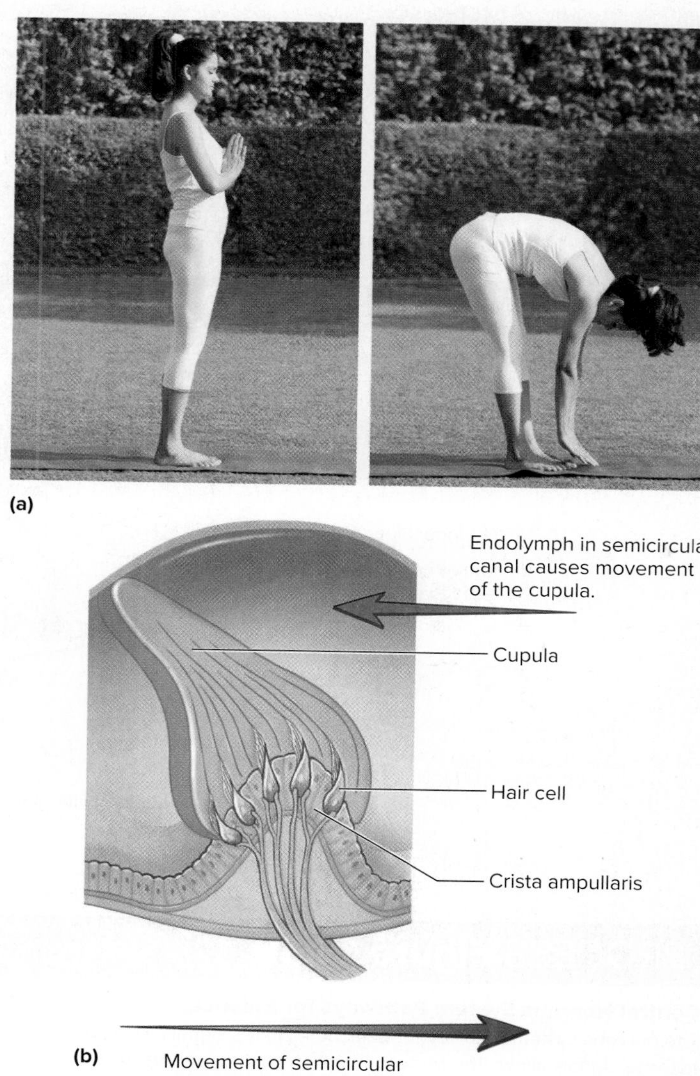

FIGURE 15.38 Function of the Semicircular Canals

The crista ampullaris responds to fluid movements within the semicircular canals. (*a*) When a person is still, the cupula is stationary, as when a person is standing (see figure 15.37*b*). (*b*) As a person moves (for example, when the person bends to touch their toes), the semicircular canals begin to move with the body (*blue arrow*), but the endolymph tends to remain stationary relative to the movement (*red arrow* pointing in opposite direction of body and semicircular canal movement), and the cupula is displaced by the endolymph in a direction opposite the direction of movement.
(a) uniquely india/Getty Images

the cupula in a direction opposite the direction the head is moving, resulting in relative movement between the cupula and the endolymph (figure 15.38). As movement continues, the fluid of the semicircular canals begins to move and catches up with the cupula, and stimulation stops. As the head stops moving, the endolymph continues to move because of its momentum, displacing the cupula in the same direction as the head was moving. Because displacement of the cupula is most intense when the rate of head

PROCESS **Figure**

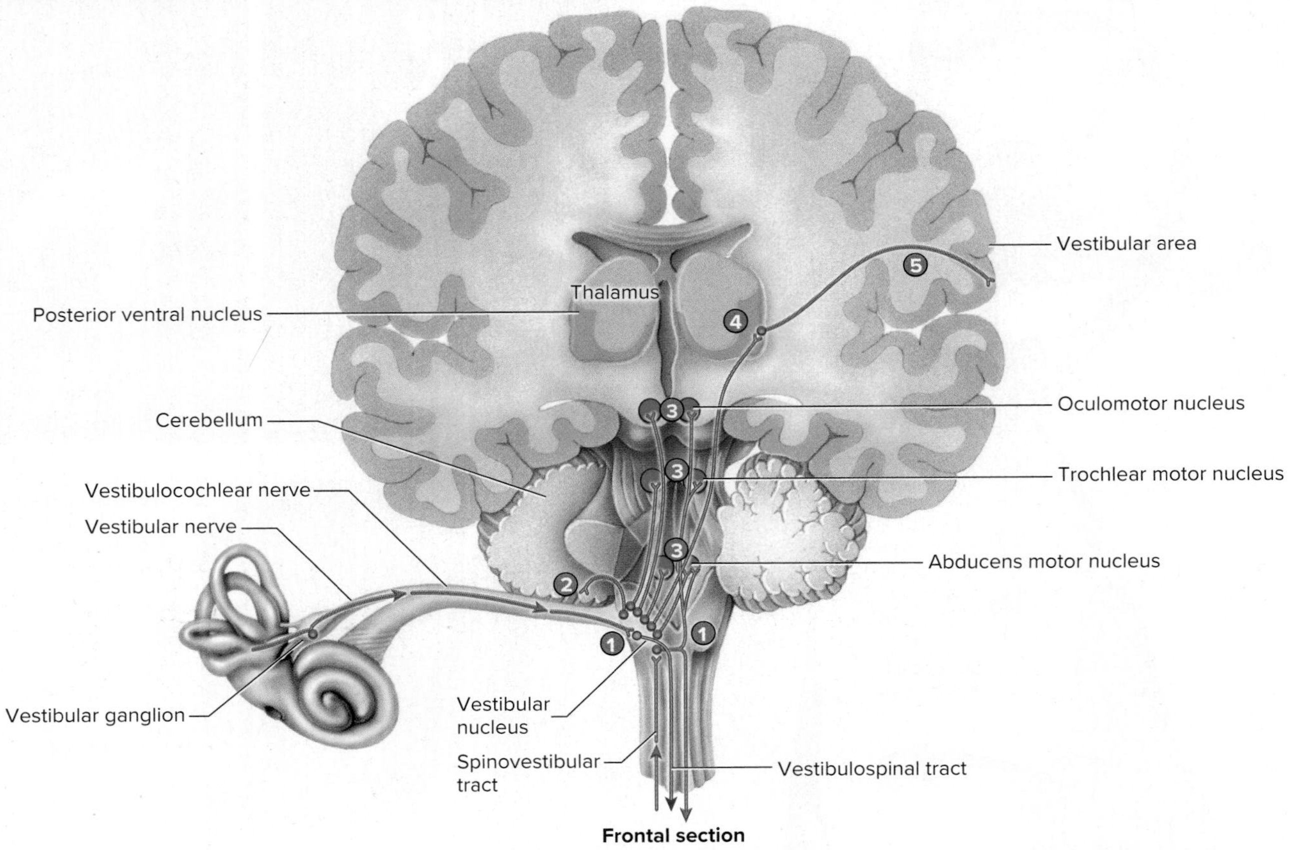

PROCESS **Figure 15.39**

Central Nervous System Pathways for Balance

The nervous system pathway for balance includes signals from the inner ear, as well as sensory input from proprioceptors and the visual system. Integration of these signals allows the body to maintain posture and balance.

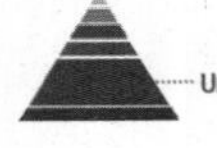

Which area of the brain receives signals about balance to which we are consciously aware?

movement changes, this system detects changes in the rate of movement rather than movement alone. As with the static labyrinth, the information the brain obtains from the dynamic labyrinth is largely subconscious.

Neuronal Pathways for Balance

Figure 15.39 illustrates the neuronal pathways for balance.

1. Neurons synapsing on the hair cells of the maculae and cristae ampullares converge into the **vestibular ganglion,** where their cell bodies are located. Sensory fibers from these neurons join sensory fibers from the cochlear ganglion to form the vestibulocochlear nerve (VIII) and terminate in the **vestibular nucleus** within the medulla oblongata.
2. Axons run from this nucleus to numerous areas of the CNS, such as the spinal cord, the cerebellum, and the cerebral cortex.
3. Additionally, axons from the vestibular nuclei synapse within motor nuclei of the oculomotor, trochlear, and abducens cranial nerves, which control reflexive movements of the extrinsic eye muscles.
4. Vestibular neurons also send axons to the posterior ventral nucleus of the thalamus.
5. Thalamic neurons project to the vestibular areas of the cerebral cortex, allowing for conscious awareness of balance.

Balance is a complex process not simply confined to one type of input. In addition to vestibular sensory input, the vestibular nucleus receives input from proprioceptive neurons throughout the body, as well as from the visual system. In sobriety tests, people are asked to close their eyes while their balance is evaluated because alcohol affects the proprioceptive and vestibular components of balance (cerebellar function) to a greater extent than it does the visual portion.

Reflex pathways exist between the dynamic part of the vestibular system and the nuclei controlling the extrinsic eye muscles (oculomotor, trochlear, and abducens). A reflex pathway allows a person to maintain visual fixation on an object while the head is in motion. To demonstrate this function, try spinning a person

Case STUDY 15.1 Motion Sickness

Earl booked his first trip on a charter fishing boat. Crossing the bar was invigorating, and Earl was surprised that all those warnings about seasickness did not seem to apply to him. At last, the boat arrived at the fishing site, the engine was cut, and the sea anchor was set. As the boat drifted, it began to roll and pitch. For the first time, Earl noticed the unpleasant mixture of smelly bait and diesel fumes. Earl felt a little light-headed and a bit drowsy; then he began to feel nauseated, and his face became pale. "I'm seasick," he realized. Trying to fish seemed to worsen his condition. Eventually, his nausea intensified and he leaned over the boat rail and vomited into the ocean. "Improves the fishing," the ship owner shouted to him cheerily. After that, Earl felt distinctly better, and his condition continued to improve. He found that looking at the horizon rather than at the water helped. He enjoyed the rest of the trip and even caught a couple of fish.

Seasickness is a form of **motion sickness,** which consists of nausea, weakness, and other dysfunctions resulting from stimulation of the semicircular canals during motion, as may occur while riding in a boat, an automobile, an airplane, a swing, or an amusement park ride. Motion sickness can progress to vomiting and incapacitation. It occurs because the brain simultaneously perceives differing sensory input from the semicircular canals, eyes, and proprioceptors in the lower limbs. Motion sickness can be decreased by closing the eyes or looking at a distant object, such as the horizon.

Various drugs are used to treat motion sickness. Antiemetics, such as anticholinergic or antihistamine medications, can counter the nausea and vomiting. Scopolamine is an anticholinergic drug that blocks acetylcholine-mediated transmission in the parasympathetic nervous system. Scopolamine can be administered transdermally in the form of a patch placed on the skin behind the ear (Transdermal-Scop). A patch lasts about 3 days. It depresses parasympathetic activity within areas of the CNS, such as the hypothalamus, in response to vestibular stimulation. Unfortunately, scopolamine also depresses other CNS functions, which may cause side effects such as restlessness, agitation, psychosis, mania, and Parkinson-like tremors. Cyclizine (Marezine), dimenhydrinate (Dramamine), and diphenhydramine (Benadryl) are antihistamines that affect the neural pathways from the vestibule.

Predict 8

Explain why closing your eyes can help decrease motion sickness. Why might looking at the horizon help?

Clinical IMPACT 15.4 Hearing Impairment and Functional Replacement of the Ear

The term **hearing-impaired** refers to any type or degree of hearing loss. Two types of hearing impairment have been identified: conductive and sensorineural. In **conductive hearing loss,** the spiral organ and neuronal pathways for hearing function normally, but there is a mechanical deficiency in the transmission of sound waves from the external ear to the spiral organ. Conductive hearing loss often can be treated—for example, by removing earwax blocking the external acoustic meatus or by replacing or repairing the auditory ossicles. If the degree of conductive hearing loss does not justify surgical treatment, or if treatment does not resolve the hearing loss, a hearing aid may be worn to help transmit the amplified (louder) sound waves through the conductive blockage and provide normal stimulation to the spiral organ.

Sensorineural hearing loss involves the spiral organ or neuronal pathways. Sound waves are transmitted normally to the spiral organ, but the nervous system's ability to respond to the sound waves is impaired. People with sensorineural hearing loss commonly use hearing aids, which produce amplified sound waves that stimulate the spiral organ more than normal, helping overcome the perception of reduced sound volume. Sound clarity also improves with sound amplification but may never be perceived as normal. (*Note:* This information will be helpful when answering the Learn to Predict question at the beginning of the chapter.)

The term **deaf** refers to sensorineural hearing loss so profound that the sense of hearing is nonfunctional, with or without amplification, for ordinary purposes of life. Stimulation of the spiral organ or hearing nerve pathways can help deaf people hear.

Research is being conducted on ways to replace the hearing pathways with electrical circuits. One approach involves directly stimulating the cochlear nerve using electrical impulses. Types of sensorineural deafness in which the hair cells of the spiral organ are impaired can now be partially corrected by implanting a prosthesis consisting of a microphone for picking up the initial sound waves, a microelectronic processor for converting the sound into electrical signals, a transmission system for relaying the signals to the inner ear, and a long, slender electrode threaded into the cochlea. This electrode delivers electrical signals directly to the endings of the cochlear nerve. High-frequency sounds are picked up by the microphone and transmitted through specific circuits to terminate near the oval window, whereas low-frequency sounds are transmitted farther up the cochlea to cochlear nerve endings near the helicotrema.

For patients with vestibulocochlear nerve damage, research is under way to develop a technique for implanting electrodes directly into the cochlear nucleus of the brainstem. These implanted electrodes would be of various lengths, so that they could stimulate parts of the cochlear nucleus, at various depths from the surface, that respond to sounds of different frequencies.

TABLE 15.2 Representative Diseases and Disorders of the Special Senses

VISION	
Condition	**Description**
Infections	
Conjunctivitis	Inflammation of conjunctiva, usually from bacterial infection; one form, pinkeye, occurs primarily in children
Stye	Infection of eyelash hair follicle
Defects of Focus, Alignment, or Color Vision	
Myopia	Nearsightedness—ability to see close but not distant objects; caused when refractive power of cornea and lens is too great relative to length of eye
Hyperopia	Farsightedness—ability to see distant but not close objects; caused when cornea is too flat or lens has too little refractive power relative to length of eye
Presbyopia	Decrease in near vision, a normal part of aging
Astigmatism	Cornea or lens is not uniformly curved, so image is not sharply focused
Diplopia	Double vision
Color blindness	Complete or partial absence of perception of one or more colors (see figure 15.22); most forms are more frequent in males
Blindness	
Cataract	Clouding of lens as a result of advancing age, infection, or trauma; most common cause of blindness in the world
Macular degeneration	Loss of sharp central vision, peripheral vision maintained; leading cause of legal blindness in older Americans; most causes not known
Glaucoma (glaw-KOH-mah)	Excessive pressure buildup in aqueous humor; may destroy retina or optic nerve, resulting in blindness
Diabetic retinopathy	Involves optic nerve degeneration, cataracts, retinal detachment; often caused by blood vessel degeneration and hemorrhage
HEARING AND BALANCE	
Conductive hearing loss	Mechanical deficiency in transmission of sound waves from external ear to spiral organ
Sensorineural hearing loss	Deficiencies of spiral organ or nerve pathways
Tinnitus (ti-NYE-tus)	Phantom sound sensations, such as ringing in ears; a common problem
Otitis media	Low-grade fever, lethargy, irritability, and pulling at ear; in extreme cases, can damage or rupture tympanic membrane; common in young children
Ménière disease	Vertigo, hearing loss, tinnitus, and a feeling of fullness in the affected ear; most common disease involving dizziness from inner ear; cause unknown but may involve a fluid abnormality in ears

around about 10 times in 20 seconds, then stopping him or her and observing eye movements. The reaction is most pronounced if the individual's head is tilted forward about 30 degrees while spinning, thus bringing the lateral semicircular canals into the horizontal plane. A slight oscillatory movement of the eyes occurs. The eyes track in the direction of motion and return with a rapid recovery movement before repeating the tracking motion. This oscillation of the eyes is called **nystagmus** (nis-TAG-mus). If then asked to walk in a straight line, the person deviates in the direction of rotation; if asked to point to an object, his or her finger deviates in the direction of rotation.

ASSESS YOUR PROGRESS

45. *What is static equilibrium? What structures are involved with static equilibrium?*

46. *Describe how the utricular macula and saccular macula function in static equilibrium.*

47. *What is dynamic equilibrium? What structures are involved with dynamic equilibrium?*

48. *Describe the crista ampullaris and its mode of operation.*

49. *Describe the neuronal pathways for balance.*

EFFECTS OF AGING ON THE SPECIAL SENSES

People experience only a slight loss in the ability to detect odors as they age. However, their ability to identify specific odors correctly decreases, especially in men over age 70.

In general, the sense of taste decreases as people age because the number of sensory receptors decreases and the brain's ability to interpret taste sensations declines. Responses to taste also change in some older people who are fighting cancer. One side effect of radiation treatment and chemotherapy is gastrointestinal discomfort, which causes patients to lose their appetite because of conditioned taste aversions.

Age-related visual changes are quite common and may become apparent as early as when a person is in their 40s. The lenses of the eyes lose flexibility as a person ages because the connective tissue of the lenses becomes more rigid. Consequently, the lenses' ability to change shape is at first reduced and eventually completely lost. Recall that this condition, called presbyopia, is the most common age-related change in the eyes. In addition, the number of cones decreases, especially in the fovea centralis. These changes cause a gradual decline in visual acuity and color perception. The most common visual problem in older people requiring medical treatment, such as surgery, is the development of cataracts. Macular degeneration, which affects visual acuity in the center of the visual field, is the leading cause of vision loss in people over the age of 60. Other age-related defects affecting vision include glaucoma and diabetic retinopathy (table 15.2).

As people age, the number of hair cells in the cochlea decreases, leading to age-related hearing loss, called **presbyacusis** (PREZ-bee-ah-KOO-sis). This decline does not occur equally in both ears, however. As a result, because direction is determined by comparing sounds coming into each ear, older people may experience a decreased ability to localize the origin of certain sounds. In some people, this leads to a general sense of disorientation. In addition, CNS defects in the auditory pathways can result in difficulty understanding sounds with echoes or background noise. Such a deficit makes it difficult for older people to understand rapid or broken speech.

With age, the number of hair cells in the saccule, utricle, and ampullae decreases. The number of otoliths also declines. As a result, older people experience decreased sensitivity to gravity, acceleration, and rotation, leading to dizziness (instability) and vertigo (a feeling of spinning). Many older people feel they cannot maintain posture and are prone to fall.

Concept Check

15.1 Olfaction

Olfaction is the sense of smell.

Olfactory Epithelium

A. Olfactory neurons in the olfactory epithelium are bipolar neurons. Their distal ends are enlarged as olfactory vesicles, which have long cilia.
B. The cilia have receptors that respond to dissolved substances. There are approximately 1000 different odorant receptors.
C. The receptors activate a G protein complex, which opens ion channels.
D. At least 7 (but perhaps as many as 50) primary odors exist. The olfactory neurons have a very low threshold and adapt rapidly.

Neuronal Pathways for Olfaction

A. Axons from the olfactory neurons extend as olfactory nerves to the olfactory bulb, where they synapse with secondary neurons of the olfactory bulb. Axons from these cells form the olfactory tracts. The olfactory bulb neurons can modulate output to the olfactory tracts.
B. The olfactory tracts terminate in the olfactory cortex of the temporal lobe, which is involved in the conscious perception of smell. Other areas of the brain, including parts of the limbic system and hypothalamus, are involved with visceral and emotional responses to smell.

1. *Which of these statements is not true with respect to olfaction?*

   a. *Olfactory sensation is relayed directly to the cerebral cortex without passing through the thalamus.*
   b. *Olfactory neurons are replaced about every 2 months.*
   c. *The olfactory cortex is involved in the conscious perception of smell.*
   d. *The secondary olfactory areas are responsible for visceral and emotional reactions to odors.*
   e. *The olfactory cortex is in the occipital lobe of the cerebrum.*

15.2 Taste

Taste buds are usually associated with vallate, foliate, and fungiform papillae. Filiform papillae do not have taste buds.

Histology of Taste Buds

A. Taste buds consist of basal cells, supporting cells, and taste cells.
B. The taste cells have taste hairs that extend into taste pores.

Function of Taste

A. Receptors on the taste hairs detect dissolved substances.
B. Five basic types of taste exist: salt, sour, sweet, bitter, and umami.

Neuronal Pathways for Taste

A. The facial nerve carries taste sensations from the anterior two-thirds of the tongue, the glossopharyngeal nerve from the posterior one-third of the tongue, and the vagus nerve from the root of the tongue and the epiglottis.
B. The neural pathways for taste extend from the medulla oblongata to the thalamus and to the cerebral cortex.

2. *Taste cells*

   a. *are found only on the tongue.*
   b. *extend through tiny openings called taste buds.*
   c. *have no axons but release neurotransmitters when stimulated.*
   d. *have axons that extend directly to the taste area of the cerebral cortex.*

3. *Which of these is* not *one of the basic tastes?*

   a. *spicy*
   b. *salt*
   c. *bitter*
   d. *umami*
   e. *sour*

4. *Which of these types of papillae have no taste buds associated with them?* Remember

   a. *vallate*
   b. *filiform*
   c. *foliate*
   d. *fungiform*

15.3 Visual System

Accessory Structures

A. The eyebrows prevent perspiration from entering the eyes and help shade the eyes.

B. The eyelids consist of five tissue layers. They protect the eyes from foreign objects and help lubricate the eyes by spreading tears over their surface.

C. The conjunctiva covers the inner eyelid and the anterior part of the eye.

D. Lacrimal glands produce tears, which flow across the surface of the eye. Excess tears enter the lacrimal canaliculi and reach the nasal cavity through the nasolacrimal canal. Tears lubricate and protect the eye.

E. The extrinsic eye muscles move the eyeball.

Anatomy of the Eye

A. The fibrous tunic is the outer layer of the eyeball. It consists of the sclera and the cornea.
   - The sclera is the posterior four-fifths of the eyeball. It is white connective tissue that maintains the shape of the eyeball and provides a site for muscle attachment.
   - The cornea is the anterior one-fifth of the eye. It is transparent and refracts light that enters the eye.

B. The vascular tunic is the middle layer of the eyeball.
   - The iris is smooth muscle regulated by the autonomic nervous system. It controls the amount of light entering the pupil.
   - The ciliary muscles control the shape of the lens. They are smooth muscles regulated by the autonomic nervous system. The ciliary process produces aqueous humor.

C. The retina is the nervous tunic of the eyeball and contains neurons sensitive to light.
   - The fovea centralis is the area of greatest visual acuity.
   - The optic disc is the location through which nerves exit and blood vessels enter the eye. It has no photosensory cells and is therefore the blind spot of the eye.

D. The eyeball has three chambers: anterior, posterior, and vitreous.
   - The anterior and posterior chambers are filled with aqueous humor, which circulates and leaves by way of the scleral venous sinus.
   - The vitreous chamber is filled with vitreous humor.

E. The lens is held in place by the suspensory ligaments, which are attached to the ciliary muscles.

5. *The fibrous tunic of the eye includes the*

   a. *conjunctiva.*
   b. *sclera.*
   c. *choroid.*
   d. *iris.*
   e. *retina.*

6. *The ciliary body*

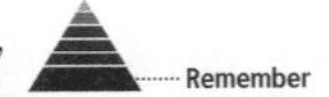

   a. *contains smooth muscles that attach to the lens by suspensory ligaments.*
   b. *produces the vitreous humor.*
   c. *is part of the iris of the eye.*
   d. *is part of the sclera.*
   e. *All of these are correct.*

7. *The lens normally focuses light onto the*

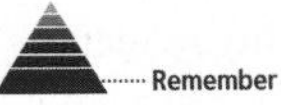

   a. *optic disc.*
   b. *iris.*
   c. *macula.*
   d. *cornea.*
   e. *ciliary body.*

8. *Given these structures:*

   (1) lens
   (2) aqueous humor
   (3) vitreous humor
   (4) cornea

   Which of the following arrangements lists the structures in the order that light entering the eye encounters them?

   a. *1,2,3,4*
   b. *1,4,2,3*
   c. *4,1,2,3*
   d. *4,2,1,3*
   e. *4,3,2,1*

9. *Contraction of the smooth muscle in the ciliary body causes the* Remember

   a. *lens to flatten.*
   b. *pupil to constrict.*
   c. *lens to become more spherical.*
   d. *pupil to dilate.*

Functions of the Eye

A. Light is the portion of the electromagnetic spectrum that humans can see.

B. When light travels from one medium to another, it can bend, or refract. Light striking a concave surface refracts outward (divergence). Light striking a convex surface refracts inward (convergence).

C. Converging light rays meet at the focal point and are said to be focused.

D. The cornea, aqueous humor, lens, and vitreous humor all refract light. The cornea is responsible for most of the convergence, whereas the lens can adjust the focal point by changing shape.
   - Relaxation of the ciliary muscles causes the lens to flatten into its normal resting condition, called emmetropia.
   - Contraction of the ciliary muscles causes the lens to become more spherical. This change in lens shape enables the eye to focus on objects that are nearby, a process called accommodation.

E. The far point of vision is the distance at which the eye no longer has to change shape to focus on an object. The near point of vision is the closest an object can come to the eye and still be focused.

F. The pupil becomes smaller during accommodation, increasing the depth of focus.

Visual Acuity

A. Visual acuity is the eye's ability to focus an image on the retina so that a clear image is perceived.

B. Visual acuity dysfunctions include myopia (nearsightedness), hyperopia (farsightedness), and astigmatism.

Structure and Function of the Retina

A. The pigmented layer of the retina provides a black backdrop for increasing visual acuity.

B. Rods are responsible for vision in low illumination (night vision).
   - A pigment called rhodopsin is split by light into retinal and opsin, producing hyperpolarization in the rod.
   - Light adaptation is caused by the reduction of rhodopsin; dark adaptation is caused by the production of rhodopsin.

C. Cones are responsible for color vision and visual acuity.
   - Cones are of three types, each with a different type of iodopsin photopigment. The photopigments are most sensitive to blue, red, and green wavelengths.
   - Perception of many colors results from mixing the ratio of the different types of cones that are active at a given moment.

D. Most visual images are focused on the fovea centralis, which has a very high concentration of cones. Moving away from the fovea centralis, fewer cones are present; the periphery of the retina contains mostly rods.

E. The rods and the cones synapse with bipolar cells, which in turn synapse with ganglion cells, which form the optic nerves.

F. Bipolar and ganglion cells in the retina can modify information sent to the brain.

G. Ganglion cells have receptive fields with on-centers or off-centers. This arrangement enhances contrast.

Neuronal Pathways for Vision

A. Ganglion cell axons extend to the lateral geniculate ganglion of the thalamus, where they synapse. From there, neurons form the optic radiations that project to the visual cortex.

B. Neurons from the nasal visual field (temporal retina) of one eye and the temporal visual field (nasal retina) of the opposite eye project to the same cerebral hemisphere. Axons from the nasal retina cross in the optic chiasm, and axons from the temporal retina remain uncrossed.

C. Depth perception is the ability to judge relative distances of an object from the eyes and is a property of binocular vision. Binocular vision results because a slightly different image is seen by each eye.

10. *Given these events:*

   (1) Bipolar cells depolarize.
   (2) Glutamate release from presynaptic terminals of photoreceptor cells decreases.
   (3) Light strikes photoreceptor cells.
   (4) Photoreceptor cells are depolarized.
   (5) Photoreceptor cells are hyperpolarized.

   Choose the arrangement that lists the correct order of events, starting with the photoreceptor cells in the resting, nonactivated state.

   a. 1,2,3,4,5
   b. 2,4,3,5,1
   c. 3,4,2,5,1
   d. 4,3,5,2,1
   e. 5,3,4,1,2

11. *Given these neurons in the retina:*

   (1) bipolar cells
   (2) ganglionic cells
   (3) photoreceptor cells

   Choose the arrangement that lists the correct order of the cells encountered by light as it enters the eye and travels toward the pigmented layer of the retina.

   a. 1,2,3 *b. 1,3,2* *c. 2,1,3* *d. 2,3,1* *e. 3,1,2*

12. *Which of these photoreceptor cells is* not *correctly matched with its function?* Remember

   a. rods—vision in low light
   b. cones—color vision
   c. rods—visual acuity

13. *Concerning dark adaptation,* Understand

   a. the amount of rhodopsin increases.
   b. the pupils constrict.
   c. it occurs more rapidly than light adaptation.
   d. All of these are correct.

14. *In the retina are cones that are most sensitive to a particular color. Given this list of colors:* Remember

   (1) red
   (2) yellow
   (3) green
   (4) blue

   Indicate which colors correspond to specific types of cones.

   a. 2,3 *b. 3,4* *c. 1,2,3* *d. 1,3,4* *e. 1,2,3,4*

15. *Given these areas of the retina:*

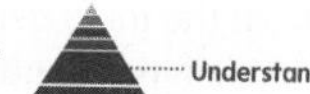

   (1) macula
   (2) fovea centralis
   (3) optic disc
   (4) periphery of the retina

   Choose the arrangement that lists the areas according to the density of cones, starting with the area that has the highest density of cones.

   a. 1,2,3,4 *b. 1,3,2,4* *c. 2,1,4,3* *d. 2,4,1,3* *e. 3,4,1,2*

16. *Axons in the optic nerve from the right eye*

   a. all go to the right occipital lobe.
   b. all go to the left occipital lobe.
   c. all go to the thalamus.
   d. go mostly to the thalamus, but some go to the superior colliculus.
   e. go partly to the right occipital lobe and partly to the left occipital lobe.

17. *A person with an abnormally powerful focusing system is ________ and uses a ________ to correct his or her vision.* Remember

   a. nearsighted, concave lens
   b. nearsighted, convex lens
   c. farsighted, concave lens
   d. farsighted, convex lens

18. *An older man with normal vision develops cataracts. He is surgically treated by removing the lenses of his eyes. What kind of glasses should he wear to compensate for the removal of his lenses?* Apply

19. *Perhaps you have heard that eating carrots is good for the eyes. What is the basis for this claim?* Understand

20. *A man stares at a black clock on a white wall for several minutes. Then he shifts his view and looks at only the blank white wall. Although he is no longer looking at the clock, he sees a light clock against a dark background. Explain what is happening.* Apply

21. *Describe the results of a lesion of the optic chiasm.* Apply

22. *Explain how several hours of reading can cause eyestrain, or eye fatigue. Describe what structures are involved.* Apply

15.4 Hearing and Balance

The external and middle ears are involved in hearing only, whereas the inner ear functions in both hearing and balance.

Auditory Structures and Their Functions

A. The external ear consists of the auricle and the external acoustic meatus.

B. The middle ear connects the external and inner ears.
- The tympanic membrane is stretched across the external acoustic meatus.
- The malleus, incus, and stapes connect the tympanic membrane to the oval window of the inner ear.
- The auditory tube connects the middle ear to the pharynx and equalizes pressure.
- The middle ear is connected to the mastoid air cells.

C. The bony labyrinth of the inner ear is a canal system within the temporal bone that contains perilymph and the membranous labyrinth.
- Endolymph is inside the membranous labyrinth.
- The bony labyrinth has three parts: the semicircular canals, the vestibule (containing the utricle and the saccule), and the cochlea.

D. The cochlea is a spiral-shaped canal within the temporal bone.
- The cochlea is divided into three compartments by the vestibular and basilar membranes. The scala vestibuli and scala tympani contain perilymph. The cochlear duct contains endolymph and the spiral organ.
- The spiral organ consists of inner and outer hair cells that attach to the tectorial membrane.

23. *Which of these structures is found within or is a part of the external ear?* Remember

    a. *oval window*
    b. *auditory tube*
    c. *ossicles*
    d. *external acoustic meatus*
    e. *cochlear duct*

24. *Given these ear bones:*

    (1) *incus*
    (2) *malleus*
    (3) *stapes*

    Choose the arrangement that lists the ear bones in order from the tympanic membrane to the inner ear.

    a. *1,2,3*
    b. *1,3,2*
    c. *2,1,3*
    d. *2,3,1*
    e. *3,2,1*

25. *Given these structures:*

    (1) *perilymph*
    (2) *endolymph*
    (3) *vestibular membrane*
    (4) *basilar membrane*

    Which of the following arrangements lists the structures in the order sound waves coming from the outside encounter them in producing sound?

    a. *1,3,2,4*
    b. *1,4,2,3*
    c. *2,3,1,4*
    d. *2,4,1,3*
    e. *3,4,2,1*

26. *The spiral organ is within the*

    a. *cochlear duct.*
    b. *scala vestibuli.*
    c. *scala tympani.*
    d. *vestibule.*
    e. *semicircular canals.*

Auditory Function

A. Sound waves are funneled by the auricle down the external acoustic meatus, causing the tympanic membrane to vibrate.

B. The tympanic membrane vibrations are passed along the auditory ossicles to the oval window of the inner ear.

C. Movement of the stapes in the oval window causes the perilymph, vestibular membrane, and endolymph to vibrate, producing movement of the basilar membrane.

D. Movement of the basilar membrane causes bending of the stereocilia of inner hair cells in the spiral organ.

E. Bending of the stereocilia pulls on tip links, which open K^+ channels.

F. Potassium ions entering the hair cell depolarize the cell, which opens Ca^{2+} channels. Calcium ions entering the cell cause further depolarization.

G. Depolarization causes the release of glutamate, generating action potentials in the vestibulocochlear nerve.

H. Some vestibulocochlear nerve axons synapse in the superior olivary nucleus. Efferent neurons from this nucleus project back to the cochlea, where they regulate the perception of pitch.

I. The round window protects the inner ear from pressure buildup and dissipates sound waves.

Neuronal Pathways for Hearing

A. Axons from the vestibulocochlear nerve synapse in the medulla oblongata. Neurons from the medulla oblongata project axons to the inferior colliculi, where they synapse. Neurons from this point project to the thalamus and synapse. Thalamic neurons extend to the auditory cortex.

B. Efferent neurons project to the cranial nerve nuclei responsible for controlling the muscles that dampen sound in the middle ear.

27. *An increase in the loudness of sound occurs as a result of an increase in the ____________ of the sound wave.* Remember

    a. *frequency*
    b. *amplitude*
    c. *resonance*
    d. *Both a and b are correct.*

28. *Interpretation of different sounds is possible because of the ability of the _____________ to vibrate at different frequencies and stimulate the _____________.* Understand
    a. *vestibular membrane, vestibular nerve*
    b. *vestibular membrane, spiral organ*
    c. *basilar membrane, vestibular nerve*
    d. *basilar membrane, spiral organ*

29. *Persistent exposure to loud noise can cause loss of hearing, especially for high-frequency sounds. What part of the ear is probably damaged? Be as specific as possible.* Apply

30. *Professional divers are subject to increased pressure as they descend to the bottom of the ocean. Sometimes this pressure can lead to damage to the ear and loss of hearing. Describe the normal mechanisms that adjust for changes in pressure, suggest some conditions that might interfere with pressure adjustment, and explain how the increased pressure might cause loss of hearing.* Apply

31. *If a vibrating tuning fork is placed against the mastoid process of the temporal bone, the vibrations are perceived as sound, even if the external acoustic meatus is plugged. Explain how this happens.* Apply

Balance

A. The static labyrinth is involved in evaluating the position of the head relative to gravity and detecting linear acceleration and deceleration.
- The utricle and saccule in the inner ear contain maculae. The maculae consist of hair cells with the hairs embedded in a membrane that contains otoliths.
- The ololithic membrane moves in response to gravity.

B. Dynamic balance evaluates movements of the head.
- Three semicircular canals at right angles to one another are present in the inner ear. The ampulla of each semicircular canal contains the crista ampullaris, which has hair cells with hairs embedded in a gelatinous mass, the cupula.
- When the head moves, endolymph within the semicircular canal moves the cupula.

Neuronal Pathways for Balance

A. Axons from the maculae and the cristae ampullares extend to the vestibular nucleus of the medulla oblongata. Fibers from the medulla run to the spinal cord, cerebellum, cortex, and nuclei that control the extrinsic eye muscles.

B. Balance also depends on proprioception and visual input.

32. *Which structure is a specialized receptor within the utricle?* Remember
    a. *macula*
    b. *crista ampullaris*
    c. *spiral organ*
    d. *cupula*

33. *Damage to the semicircular canals affects the ability to detect* Understand
    a. *sound.*
    b. *the position of the head relative to the ground.*
    c. *the movement of the head in all directions.*
    d. *All of these are correct.*

Answers to this chapter's odd-numbered Concept Check questions appear in Appendix F.

16 CHAPTER Autonomic Nervous System

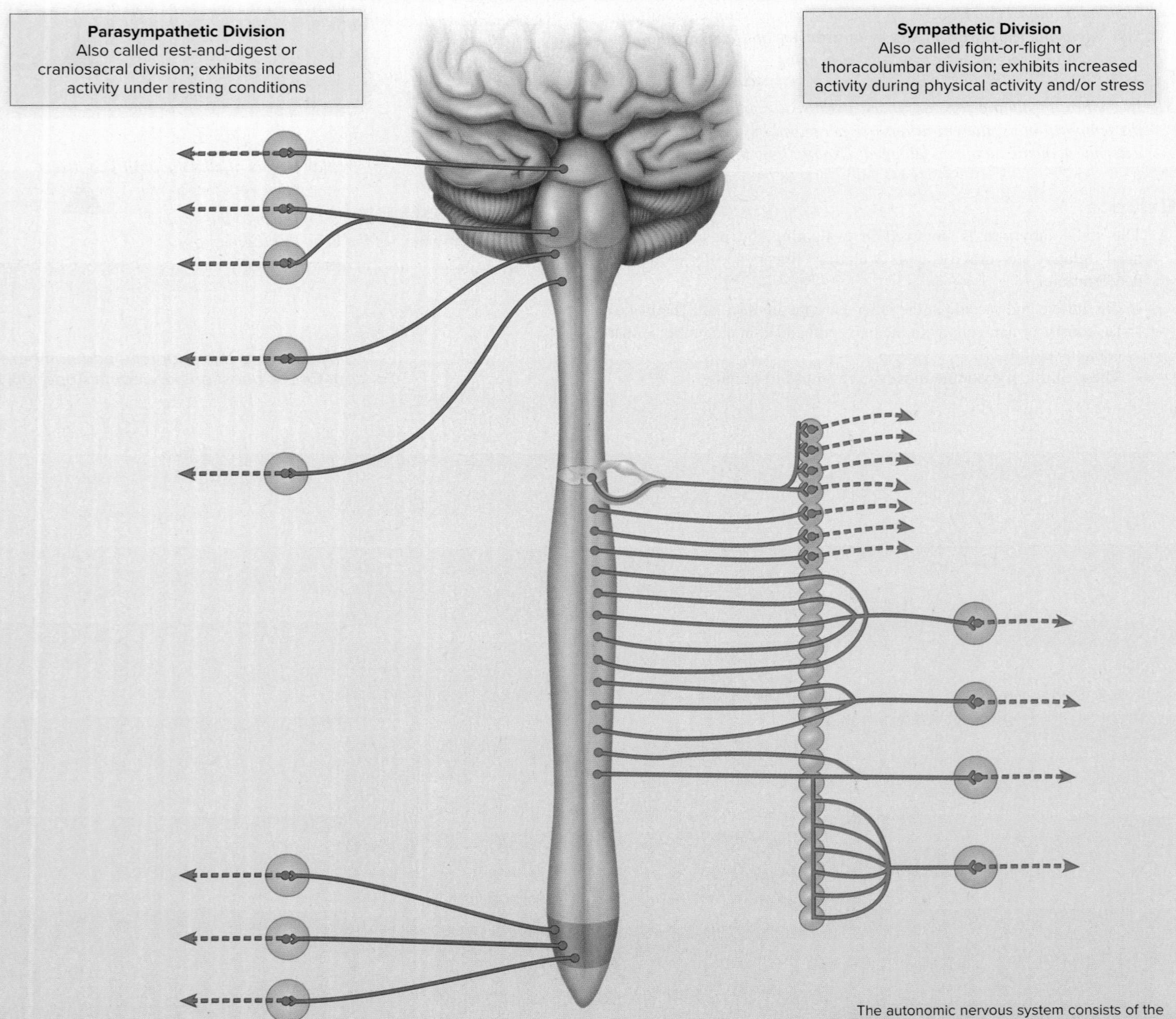

The autonomic nervous system consists of the parasympathetic division and sympathetic division.

During a picnic on a sunny spring day, it is easy to concentrate on the delicious food and the pleasant surroundings. Maintaining homeostasis requires no conscious thought. The autonomic nervous system (ANS) helps keep body temperature at a constant level by controlling the activity of sweat glands and the amount of blood flowing through the skin. The ANS also helps regulate the complex activities necessary for digesting food. Absorbed nutrients travel to the tissues through the bloodstream because the ANS controls the heart rate, which helps maintain the necessary blood pressure. Without the ANS, all of the activities necessary to maintain homeostasis would be overwhelming.

This chapter examines the autonomic nervous system. A functional knowledge of the ANS enables you to predict general responses to a variety of stimuli, explain responses to changes in environmental conditions, comprehend symptoms that result from abnormal autonomic functions, and understand how drugs affect the ANS.

Learn to Predict

On the first pretty day of spring, Officer Smith was sitting in her patrol car, observing traffic near the town's busy park, when a sports car suddenly sped past. Realizing that families with young children may be crossing the same street on their way to the park, Officer Smith quickly pursued the speeding car.

By recalling information about the integration of nervous system functions from previous chapters and reading chapter 16, describe in general the neural pathways involved in Officer Smith's quick reactions—the movement of her skeletal muscles, her increased heart rate, and the decreased movements and secretions in her digestive system.

Answers to this question and the chapter's odd-numbered Predict questions can be found in Appendix E.

16.1 Overview of the Autonomic Nervous System

LEARNING OUTCOMES

After reading this section, you should be able to

A. **Explain the basic function of the autonomic nervous system (ANS).**
B. **List the divisions of the autonomic nervous system and describe the conditions under which each is more influential.**

The autonomic nervous system (ANS) maintains homeostasis of the body by regulating many involuntary activities, including heart rate, breathing rate, body temperature, digestive processes, and urinary functions. Imagine the many changes that your body experiences during the day, from waking and preparing for the day to exercising and completing other daily tasks. All of these changes in activity involve differences in energy demands by your tissues. When you are very active, your contracting skeletal muscles require more energy reserves. When you are resting, the energy demands of your skeletal muscles decrease, but the energy demands of other tissues, such as the smooth muscle of your digestive tract, increase. It is the function of the ANS to alter the activity of smooth muscle, cardiac muscle, and glands to match the needs of the different tissues of the body during varying levels of activity.

Recall from chapter 11 that the motor division of the nervous system controls the effectors (muscles and glands) of the body. The motor division consists of two parts: (1) the somatic nervous system and (2) the ANS. The somatic nervous system regulates the activities of skeletal muscle (see chapter 14) and the ANS regulates the activity of all the other effectors (smooth muscle, cardiac muscle, and glands). The ANS is further subdivided into the sympathetic division, the parasympathetic division, and the enteric nervous system. The enteric nervous system consists of nervous tissue of the digestive tract. The sympathetic and parasympathetic divisions regulate the activity of effectors throughout the body, but each division influences the tissues under different conditions. The sympathetic division is often referred to as the fight-or-flight division because it has more influence on effectors under conditions of increased physical activity or stress. The parasympathetic division has more influence under conditions of rest and is often referred to as the rest-and-digest division.

Module 7
Nervous System

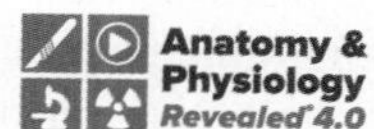

ASSESS YOUR PROGRESS

Answers to these questions are found in the section you have just completed. Re-read the section if you need help in answering these questions.

1. *Describe the function of the ANS.*
2. *List the divisions of the ANS. Under what conditions would each division be more influential?*

16.2 Contrasting the Somatic and Autonomic Nervous Systems

LEARNING OUTCOMES

After reading this section, you should be able to

A. **Describe the structural and functional differences between the somatic nervous system and the ANS.**
B. **Describe the relationship between preganglionic and postganglionic neurons.**
C. **Contrast somatic and autonomic motor neurons with sensory neurons.**

The peripheral nervous system (PNS) is composed of sensory and motor neurons (see figure 11.1). As described in chapter 11, **sensory neurons** carry action potentials from the many sensory receptors of the body to the central nervous system (CNS), and **motor neurons** carry action potentials from the CNS to the effectors of the body (muscles and glands). Motor neurons that innervate skeletal muscle are called somatic motor neurons, and they are part of the somatic nervous system. Motor neurons that innervate smooth muscle, cardiac muscle, and glands are called autonomic motor neurons, and they are part of the autonomic nervous system (ANS). In this section, we compare the somatic nervous system and the ANS. The rest of the chapter focuses on the structure and function of the autonomic nervous system.

A **nerve** is a bundle of axons, or nerve fibers, that connects the CNS to sensory receptors, muscles, and glands. A nerve may contain the axons of autonomic neurons, somatic motor neurons, and/or sensory neurons, but the proportions of the specific types of axons vary from nerve to nerve. For example, nerves innervating smooth muscle, cardiac muscle, and glands, such as the vagus nerves, consist primarily of axons of sensory neurons and autonomic motor neurons. Nerves innervating skeletal muscles, such as the sciatic nerves, consist primarily of axons of sensory neurons and somatic motor neurons. Some cranial nerves, such as the olfactory, optic, and vestibulocochlear nerves, are composed entirely of sensory neuron axons.

In the somatic nervous system, the cell bodies of somatic motor neurons are in the CNS. The axons of these somatic motor neurons extend from their location in the CNS to skeletal muscle (figure 16.1*a*). For the ANS, the organization is quite different. In contrast to a single neuron, the ANS has two neurons in a series extending between the CNS and the innervated organs (figure 16.1*b*). The first neuron of the series is called the **preganglionic neuron.** Its cell body is located in the CNS within either the brainstem or the lateral horn of the spinal cord gray matter, and its axon extends to an autonomic ganglion located outside the CNS. The **autonomic ganglion** contains the cell body of the second neuron of the series, called the **postganglionic neuron.** Preganglionic neurons synapse with postganglionic neurons in the autonomic ganglia. The axons of postganglionic neurons extend from autonomic ganglia to effector organs and synapse with their target tissues.

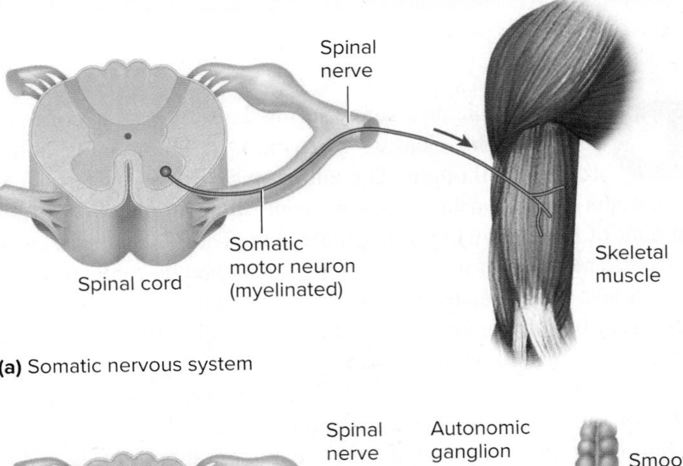

(a) Somatic nervous system

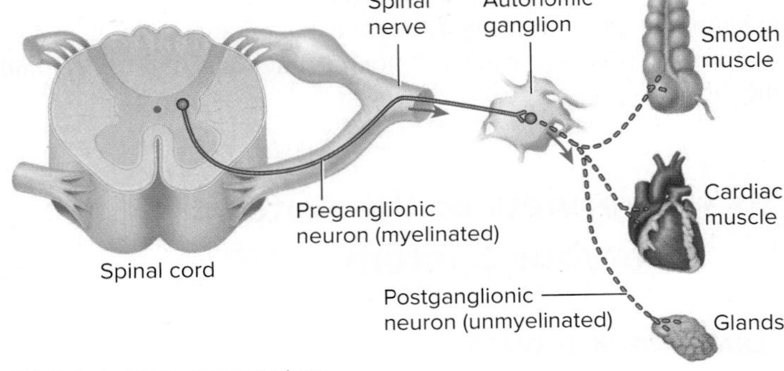

(b) Autonomic nervous system

FIGURE 16.1 Organization of Somatic and Autonomic Nervous System Neurons

(*a*) The cell body of the somatic motor neuron is in the CNS, and its axon extends to and synapses with a skeletal muscle. (*b*) The cell body of the preganglionic neuron is in the CNS, and its axon extends to an autonomic ganglion and synapses with a postganglionic neuron. The postganglionic neuron extends to and synapses with its effector.

In addition to the organization of the neural pathways, the somatic nervous system and ANS vary in other structural and functional ways:

- The axons of all somatic motor neurons are myelinated. In the ANS, the axons of preganglionic neurons are myelinated, but the axons of postganglionic neurons are unmyelinated.
- Many movements controlled by the somatic nervous system are voluntary, whereas ANS functions are involuntarily controlled.
- The effect of somatic motor neurons on skeletal muscle is always excitatory, but the effect of autonomic motor neurons on target tissues can be either excitatory or inhibitory. For example, after a meal the ANS can stimulate stomach activities, but during exercise the ANS can inhibit those activities.
- The major neurotransmitter in the somatic nervous system is acetylcholine (ACh), while ACh, epinephrine (E), and

TABLE 16.1 Comparison of the Somatic and Autonomic Nervous Systems

	Somatic Nervous System	Autonomic Nervous System
Effector	Skeletal muscle	Smooth muscle, cardiac muscle, and glands
Regulation	Controls all conscious and unconscious movements of skeletal muscle	Unconscious regulation, although influenced by conscious mental functions
Response to Stimulation	Skeletal muscle contracts.	Target tissues are stimulated or inhibited.
Neuron Arrangement	One neuron extends from the central nervous system (CNS) to skeletal muscle.	There are two neurons in series; the preganglionic neuron extends from the CNS to an autonomic ganglion, and the postganglionic neuron extends from the autonomic ganglion to the target tissue.
Neuron Cell Body Location	Neuron cell bodies are in motor nuclei of the cranial nerves and in the ventral horn of the spinal cord.	Preganglionic neuron cell bodies are in autonomic nuclei of the cranial nerves and in the lateral horn of the spinal cord; postganglionic neuron cell bodies are in autonomic ganglia.
Number of Synapses	One synapse between the somatic motor neuron and the skeletal muscle	Two synapses; first is in the autonomic ganglia, and second is at the target tissue
Myelination of Axons	Myelinated	Preganglionic axons are myelinated; postganglionic axons are unmyelinated.
Neurotransmitter	Acetylcholine	Preganglionic neurons release acetylcholine; postganglionic neurons release acetylcholine, norepinephrine, or epinephrine.
Receptor Molecules	Receptor molecules for acetylcholine are nicotinic.	In autonomic ganglia, receptor molecules for acetylcholine are nicotinic; in target tissues, receptor molecules for acetylcholine are muscarinic. In target tissues, receptor molecules for norepinephrine are either α- or β-adrenergic.

norepinephrine (NE) are used in the ANS. The neurotransmitters and their receptors are further discussed in section 16.4.

Table 16.1 summarizes the differences between the somatic nervous system and the ANS.

Sensory neurons are not classified as somatic or autonomic. These neurons propagate action potentials from sensory receptors to the CNS and can provide information for reflexes mediated through the somatic nervous system or the ANS. For example, stimulation of pain receptors can initiate somatic reflexes, such as the withdrawal reflex, and autonomic reflexes, such as an increase in heart rate. Although some sensory neurons primarily affect somatic functions and others primarily influence autonomic functions, functional overlap makes attempts to classify sensory neurons as either somatic or autonomic meaningless.

ASSESS YOUR PROGRESS

3. *Contrast the somatic nervous system with the ANS for each of the following:*
   a. *number of neurons between the CNS and the effector organ*
   b. *location of neuron cell bodies*
   c. *structures each innervates*
   d. *inhibitory or excitatory effects*
   e. *conscious or unconscious control*
   f. *neurotransmitter(s) used*
4. *Differentiate between preganglionic neurons and postganglionic neurons.*
5. *Why are sensory neurons not classified as somatic or autonomic?*

16.3 Anatomy of the Autonomic Nervous System

LEARNING OUTCOMES

After reading this section, you should be able to

A. **List the divisions of the ANS.**
B. **Describe the arrangement of sympathetic neurons and ganglia.**
C. **Describe the arrangement of parasympathetic neurons and ganglia.**
D. **Explain what an autonomic nerve plexus is and list the major autonomic nerve plexuses in the body.**
E. **Discuss the organization of the ENS.**

As described earlier, the ANS is subdivided into the **sympathetic division,** the **parasympathetic division,** and the **enteric** (en-TER-ik; bowels) **nervous system (ENS).** The sympathetic and parasympathetic divisions differ anatomically in (1) the location of their preganglionic neuron cell bodies within the CNS and (2) the location of their autonomic ganglia in the peripheral nervous system. The ENS is a complex network of neuron cell bodies and axons within the wall of the digestive tract. The ENS is considered part of the ANS because sympathetic and parasympathetic neurons are an important part of it. The anatomy of the sympathetic and parasympathetic divisions of the ANS will be described first, followed by a description of the ENS.

Sympathetic Division

The sympathetic division of the ANS is sometimes called the *fight-or-flight division* because of its physiological influence or the *thoracolumbar division* because of its anatomical organization. The sympathetic preganglionic neurons are associated with the thoracic and lumbar regions of the spinal cord, thus the name thoracolumbar. Specifically, the cell bodies of sympathetic preganglionic neurons are in the lateral horns of the spinal cord gray matter between the first thoracic (T1) segment and the second lumbar (L2) segment (figure 16.2). The axons of the preganglionic neurons exit through the ventral roots of spinal nerves T1–L2. These axons course through the spinal nerves for a short distance before they exit the nerves and project to sympathetic ganglia.

FUNDAMENTAL **Figure**

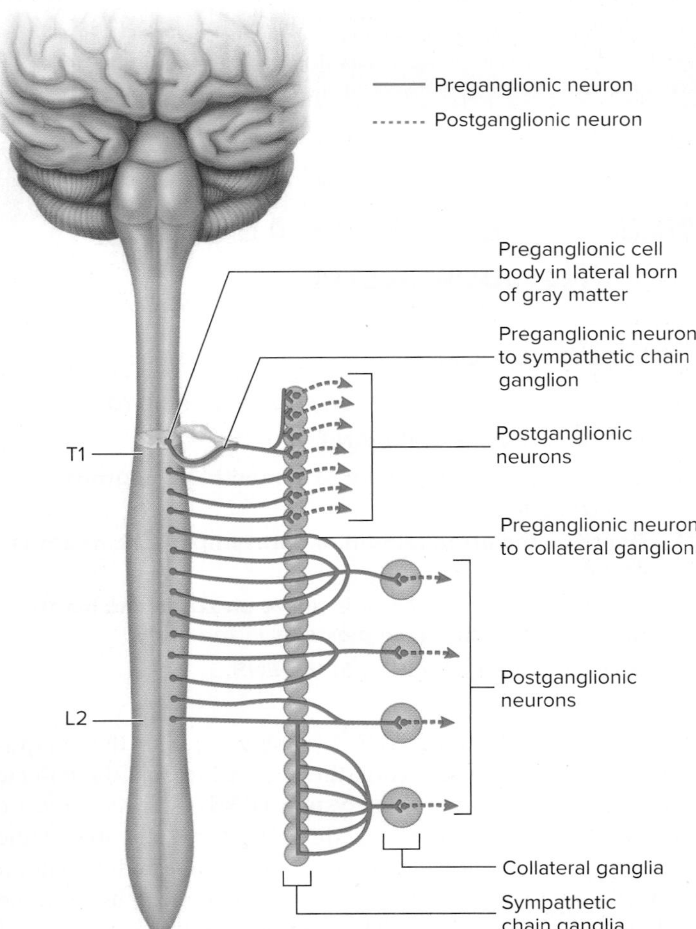

FIGURE 16.2 Sympathetic Division

The location of sympathetic preganglionic (*solid blue*) and postganglionic (*dashed blue*) neurons. The preganglionic cell bodies are in the lateral gray matter of the thoracic and lumbar parts of the spinal cord. The cell bodies of the postganglionic neurons are within the sympathetic chain ganglia or within collateral ganglia. APR

There are two types of sympathetic ganglia: (1) sympathetic chain ganglia and (2) collateral ganglia. **Sympathetic chain ganglia** are located along the left and right sides of the vertebral column. These ganglia are connected to each other, forming a chain; thus the name sympathetic chain. The sympathetic chain ganglia are also called *paravertebral ganglia* because of their location alongside the vertebral column. Although the sympathetic division originates in the thoracic and lumbar vertebral regions, the sympathetic chain ganglia extend into the cervical and sacral regions. As a result of ganglia fusion during fetal development, there are typically 3 pairs of cervical ganglia, 11 pairs of thoracic ganglia, 4 pairs of lumbar ganglia, and 4 pairs of sacral ganglia.

Collateral (meaning "accessory") **ganglia** are unpaired ganglia located in the abdominopelvic cavity. They are also called *prevertebral ganglia* because they are anterior to the vertebral column.

The axons of autonomic preganglionic neurons are small in diameter and myelinated. The sympathetic preganglionic axons pass through a short connection between a spinal nerve and a sympathetic chain ganglion called a **white ramus communicans** (RAY-mis koh-MYOO-ni-kans; pl. rami communicantes, RAY-my koh-myoo-ni-KAN-teez), so called because of the whitish color of the myelinated axons (figure 16.3).

Sympathetic preganglionic neurons either synapse with postganglionic neurons in the symphathetic chain ganglion or pass through to synapse in another area. The following are the four potential pathways of axons that exit the sympathetic chain ganglia. As you read each description, it may be helpful to develop a simple diagram of the pathway. Compare your diagram to a classmate's diagram and figure 16.3.

1. *Spinal nerves* (figure 16.3*a*). Preganglionic axons synapse with postganglionic neurons in sympathetic chain ganglia. They can synapse at the same level that the preganglionic axons enter the sympathetic chain, or they can pass superiorly or inferiorly through one or more ganglia and synapse with postganglionic neurons in a sympathetic chain ganglion at a different level. Axons of the postganglionic neurons pass through a **gray ramus communicans** and reenter a spinal nerve. Postganglionic axons are unmyelinated, thereby giving the gray ramus communicans its grayish color. All spinal nerves receive postganglionic axons from a gray ramus communicans. The postganglionic axons then project through the spinal nerve to the skin and blood vessels of skeletal muscles.
2. *Sympathetic nerves* (figure 16.3*b*). Preganglionic axons enter the sympathetic chain and synapse in a sympathetic chain ganglion at the same or a different level with postganglionic neurons. The postganglionic axons leaving the sympathetic chain ganglion form **sympathetic nerves,** which supply organs in the thoracic cavity, such as the heart.
3. *Splanchnic* (SPLANGK-nik) *nerves* (figure 16.3*c*). Some preganglionic axons enter sympathetic chain ganglia and, without synapsing, exit at the same or a different level to form **splanchnic nerves.** Those preganglionic axons extend to collateral ganglia, where they synapse with postganglionic neurons. Axons of the postganglionic neurons leave the collateral ganglia through small nerves that extend to

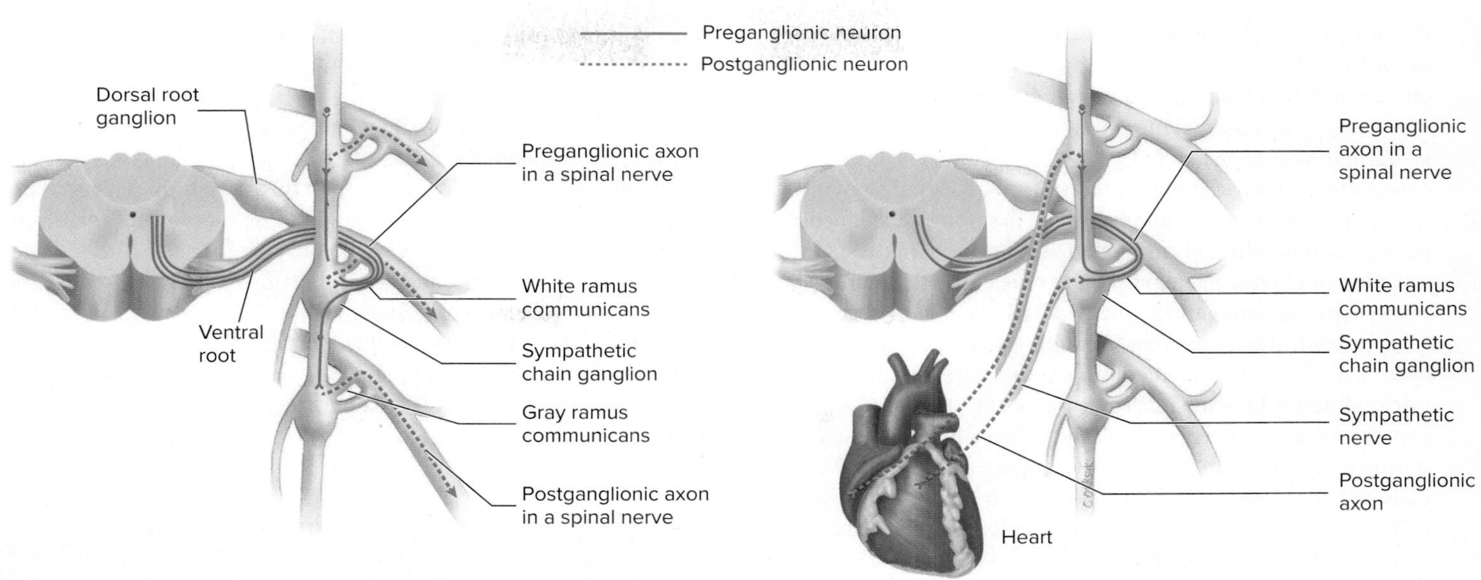

(a) Spinal nerve: Preganglionic axons from a spinal nerve pass through a white ramus communicans into a sympathetic chain ganglion. Some axons synapse with a postganglionic neuron at the level of entry; others ascend or descend to other levels before forming a synapse. Each postganglionic axon exits the sympathetic chain through a gray ramus communicans and enters a spinal nerve.

(b) Sympathetic nerve: Part (*b*) is like part (*a*), except that each postganglionic neuron exits a sympathetic chain ganglion through a sympathetic nerve.

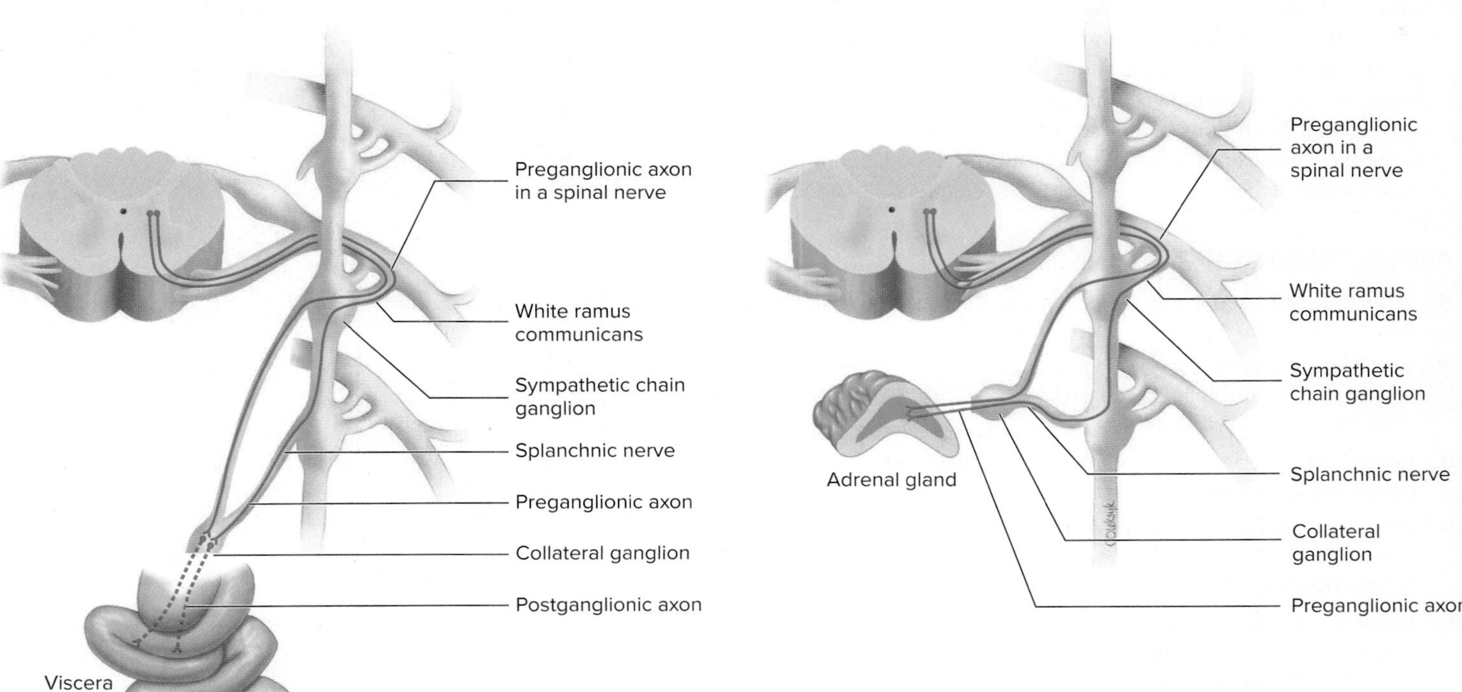

(c) Collateral ganglia via splanchnic nerve: Preganglionic neurons do not synapse in the sympathetic chain ganglia, but exit in splanchnic nerves and extend to a collateral ganglion, where they synapse with postganglionic neurons.

(d) Adrenal medulla via splanchnic nerve: Part (*d*) is like part (*c*), except that the preganglionic axons extend to the adrenal medulla, where they synapse with specialized adrenal medullary cells.

FIGURE 16.3 Routes Taken by Sympathetic Axons

(*a*) Sympathetic postganglionic axons pass through spinal nerves to the skin and blood vessels of skeletal muscles. (*b*) Sympathtetic postganglionic axons pass through sympathetic nerves to organs in the thoracic cavity. (*c*) Splanchnic nerves contain sympathetic preganglionic axons that extend to collateral ganglia. (*d*) Sympathetic preganglionic axons pass project to the adrenal medulla through a splanchnic nerve. Preganglionic axons are illustrated as *solid blue lines* and postganglionic axons as *dashed blue lines.* APR

effectors in the abdominopelvic cavity. Note that splanchnic nerves are different from the sympathetic nerves discussed earlier in that splanchnic nerves are composed of *preganglionic axons,* whereas sympathetic nerves are composed of *postganglionic axons*.

4. *Innervation to the adrenal gland* (figure 16.3*d*). The sympathetic innervation to the adrenal gland is through a splanchnic nerve, but it is different from other ANS nerves. In the case of the adrenal glands, the axons of the preganglionic neurons do not synapse in sympathetic chain ganglia or in collateral ganglia. Instead, the axons pass through those ganglia and synapse with cells in the medulla of the adrenal gland. The **adrenal medulla** is the inner portion of the adrenal gland and consists of specialized cells derived from neural crest cells during embryonic development (see figure 13.2). Neural crest cells are the same cells that give rise to the postganglionic cells of the ANS. Adrenal medullary cells are round, have no axons or dendrites, and are divided into two groups, depending on what substance they secrete. About 80% of the cells secrete **epinephrine** (ep-ih-NEF-rin), also called *adrenaline* (ah-DREN-ah-lin), and about 20% secrete **norepinephrine** (NOR-ep-ih-NEF-rin), also called *noradrenaline* (nor-ah-DREN-ah-lin). Stimulation of these cells by preganglionic axons causes the release of epinephrine and norepinephrine into the blood. These substances circulate in the blood and affect all tissues having receptors to which they can bind. The general response to epinephrine and norepinephrine released from the adrenal medulla is to prepare the individual for physical activity. Secretions of the adrenal medulla are considered hormones because they are released into the bloodstream and travel some distance to the effectors (see chapters 17 and 18).

ASSESS YOUR PROGRESS

6. *Where are the cell bodies of sympathetic preganglionic neurons located?*
7. *What types of axons (preganglionic or postganglionic, myelinated or unmyelinated) are found in the white and gray rami communicantes?*
8. *Where do preganglionic axons synapse with the postganglionic neurons in spinal and sympathetic nerves?*
9. *Where do preganglionic axons that form splanchnic nerves (except those to the adrenal gland) synapse with postganglionic neurons?*
10. *What is unusual about the splanchnic nerve innervation to the adrenal gland? What do the specialized cells of the adrenal medulla secrete, and what is the effect of these substances?*
11. *Describe the lengths of the preganglionic and postganglionic neurons of the sympathetic division.*

Parasympathetic Division

The parasympathetic division is called the *rest-and-digest* division because of its physiological influence and the *craniosacral* (KRAY-nee-oh-SAY-kral) *division* because of its anatomical organization. Cell bodies of parasympathetic preganglionic neurons are located either within cranial nerve nuclei in the brainstem or within the lateral horns of the gray matter in the sacral region of the spinal cord from S2 to S4 (figure 16.4).

Axons of the parasympathetic preganglionic neurons from the brain are in cranial nerves III, VII, IX, and X. The axons associated with the sacral region are in **pelvic splanchnic nerves.** The preganglionic axons course through these nerves to **terminal ganglia,** where they synapse with postganglionic neurons. The axons of the postganglionic neurons extend relatively short distances from the terminal ganglia to the effectors. The terminal ganglia are either near or embedded within the walls of the organs innervated by the parasympathetic neurons. Many of the parasympathetic ganglia are small, but some, such as those in the wall of the digestive tract, are large.

FUNDAMENTAL **Figure**

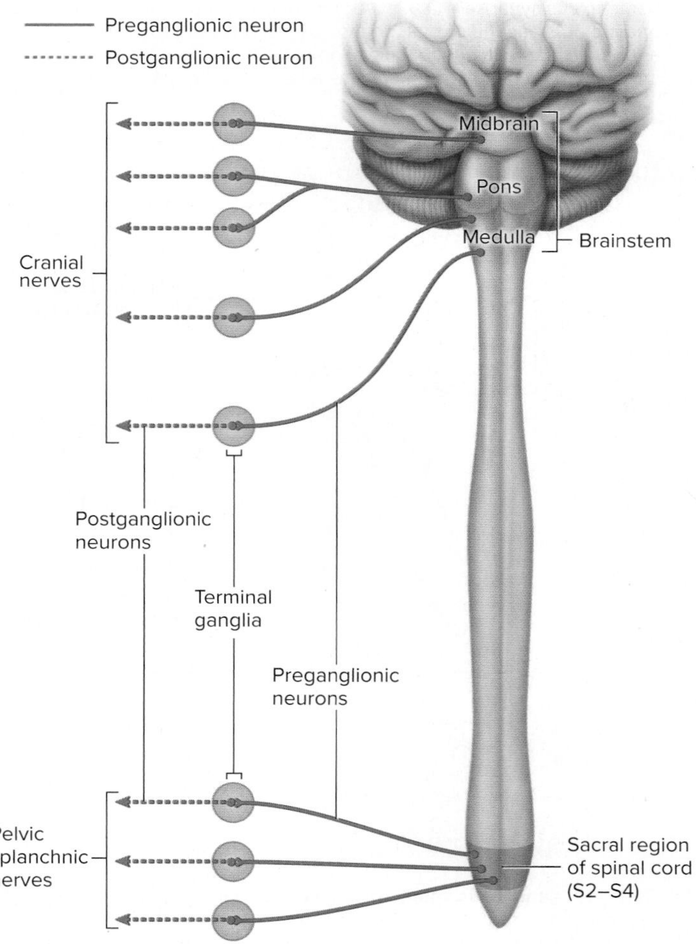

FIGURE 16.4 Parasympathetic Division

The location of parasympathetic preganglionic (*solid red*) and postganglionic (*dashed red*) neurons. The preganglionic neuron cell bodies are in the brainstem and the lateral gray horns of the sacral part of the spinal cord, and the postganglionic neuron cell bodies are within terminal ganglia. APR

TABLE 16.2 Comparison of the Sympathetic and Parasympathetic Divisions

	Sympathetic Division	Parasympathetic Division
Location of Preganglionic Cell Body	Lateral horns of thoracic and lumbar regions of the spinal cord gray matter (T1–L2)	Brainstem and lateral horns of the sacral region of the spinal cord gray matter (S2–S4)
Outflow from the CNS	Spinal nerves (postganglionic axons) Sympathetic nerves (postganglionic axons) Splanchnic nerves (preganglionic axons)	Cranial nerves (preganglionic axons) Pelvic splanchnic nerves (preganglionic axons)
Ganglia	Sympathetic chain ganglia along spinal cord for spinal and sympathetic nerves; collateral ganglia for splanchnic nerves	Terminal ganglia near or on effector organ
Number of Postganglionic Neurons for Each Preganglionic Neuron	Many (much divergence)	Few (less divergence)
Relative Length of Neurons	Short preganglionic Long postganglionic	Long preganglionic Short postganglionic

Table 16.2 summarizes the structural differences between the sympathetic and parasympathetic divisions.

ASSESS YOUR PROGRESS

12. *Where are the cell bodies of parasympathetic preganglionic neurons located?*
13. *In what structures do parasympathetic preganglionic neurons synapse with postganglionic neurons? Where are these structures located?*
14. *What nerves are formed by the axons of parasympathetic preganglionic neurons?*
15. *Describe the lengths of the preganglionic and postganglionic neurons of the parasympathetic division.*

Autonomic Nerve Plexuses and Distribution of Autonomic Nerve Fibers

In the previous sections, the major pathways for preganglionic and postganglionic neurons of the sympathetic and parasympathetic divisions were described. This section will detail the distribution of the autonomic pathways to the target organs (figures 16.5 and 16.6). In some cases, the postganglionic axons extend directly through nerves to the target organ. In other cases, the postganglionic axons become part of autonomic nerve plexuses. **Autonomic nerve plexuses** are complex, interconnected neural networks formed by neurons of the sympathetic and parasympathetic divisions. Axons of sensory neurons also contribute to these autonomic nerve plexuses. The autonomic nerve plexuses are typically named according to the organs they supply or the blood vessels along which they are found. For example, the cardiac plexus supplies the heart, and the thoracic aortic plexus is found along the thoracic aorta. Plexuses following the route of blood vessels are a major means by which autonomic axons are distributed throughout the body. Because they contain both sympathetic and parasympathetic neurons, autonomic nerve plexuses are associated with both the sympathetic and parasympathetic divisions.

Sympathetic Division Distribution

As described earlier, sympathetic outflow is through spinal nerves, sympathetic nerves, and splanchnic nerves (see figure 16.3). Branches of these nerves either extend directly to effectors or join autonomic nerve plexuses to be distributed to effectors. From all levels of the sympathetic chain, some postganglionic axons project through gray rami communicantes to spinal nerves. The axons extend to a specific region innervated by each pair of spinal nerves, regulating the activity of sweat glands in the skin, the smooth muscle in the blood vessels of the skin, and the smooth muscle of the arrector pili. See figure 12.15 for the distribution of spinal nerves to the skin. The major means by which sympathetic postganglionic axons reach effectors via autonomic plexuses are illustrated in figure 16.5 and include the following:

1. *Head and neck nerve plexuses.* Most of the sympathetic nerve supply to the head and neck is derived from the superior cervical ganglion. Postganglionic axons of sympathetic nerves form plexuses that extend superiorly to the head and inferiorly to the neck. The plexuses associated with the head and neck give off branches to regulate the activity of structures of the skin such as sweat glands, the smooth muscle in the blood vessels of the skin, and the smooth muscle of the arrector pili associated with hair follicles. Axons from the plexuses also join branches of the trigeminal nerves (cranial nerve V) to regulate the activity of the skin of the face, the salivary glands, as well as the ciliary muscles and the iris of the eye.
2. *Thoracic nerve plexuses.* The sympathetic innervation for organs of the thorax is mainly derived from the cervical and upper five thoracic sympathetic chain ganglia. Postganglionic axons in sympathetic nerves contribute to the **cardiac plexus,** regulating the heart; the **pulmonary plexus,** regulating the lungs; and other thoracic plexuses.
3. *Abdominopelvic nerve plexuses.* Sympathetic chain ganglia from T5 and below mainly innervate the abdominopelvic organs. The preganglionic axons of splanchnic nerves synapse with postganglionic neurons in the collateral ganglia of

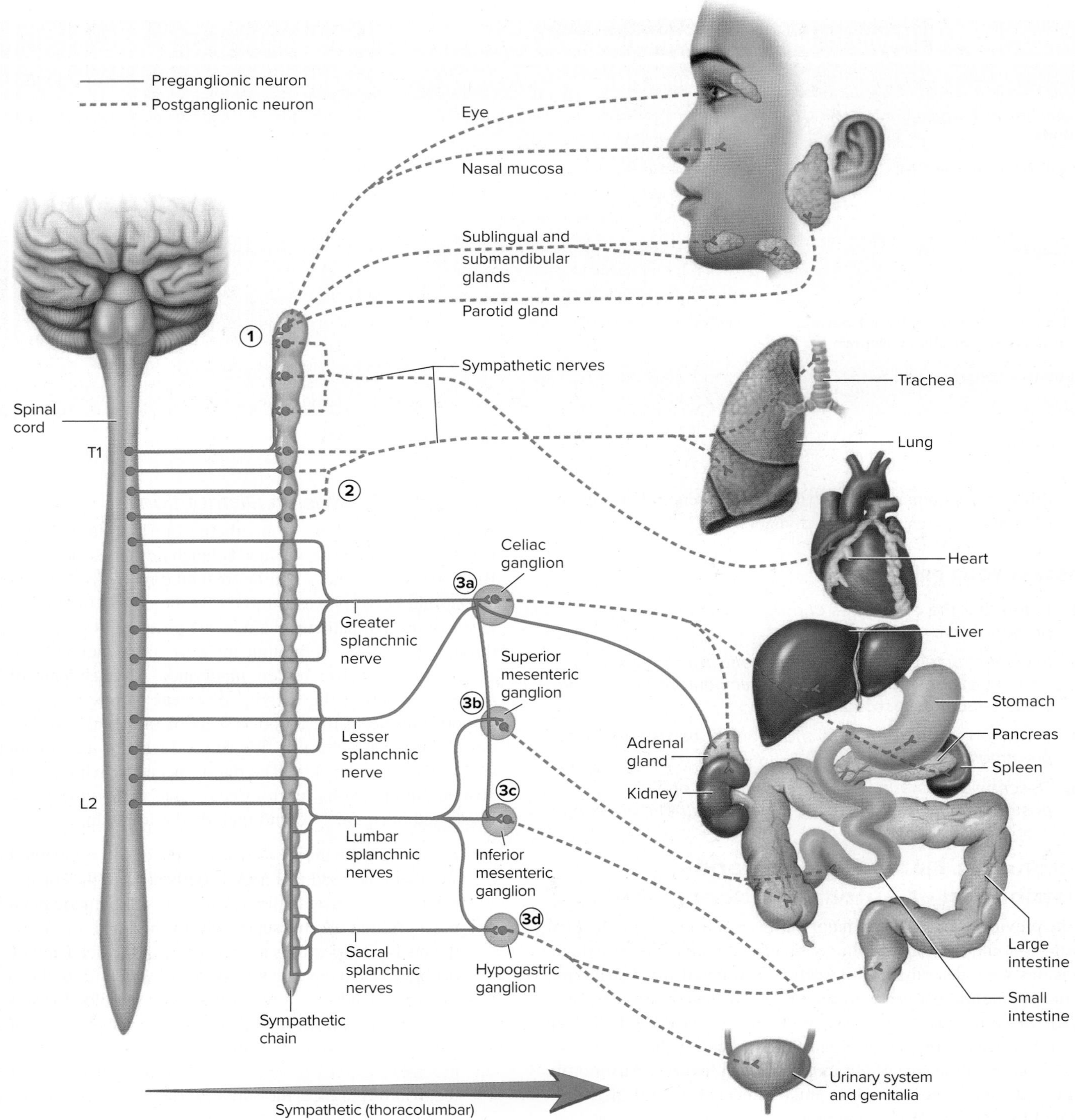

FIGURE 16.5 Sympathetic Outflow via Autonomic Plexuses

Sympathetic outflow via autonomic plexuses involves plexuses of the head and neck, thoracic cavity, and abdominopelvic cavity.

abdominopelvic nerve plexuses. Postganglionic axons from the collateral ganglia innervate smooth muscle and glands in the abdominopelvic organs. The following are the abdominopelvic nerve plexuses.

a. The **celiac** (SEE-lee-ak) **plexus** has two large celiac ganglia and other, smaller ganglia. The celiac plexus innervates the diaphragm, stomach, spleen, liver, gallbladder, adrenal glands, kidneys, testes, and ovaries.

b. The **superior mesenteric** (mez-en-TER-ik) **plexus** includes the superior mesenteric ganglion and innervates the pancreas, small intestine, ascending colon, and transverse colon.

c. The **inferior mesenteric plexus** includes the inferior mesenteric ganglion and innervates the transverse colon to the rectum.
d. The **hypogastric plexuses** innervate the descending colon to the rectum, urinary bladder, and reproductive organs in the pelvis.

Parasympathetic Division Distribution

As described earlier, parasympathetic preganglionic fibers extend from the CNS through cranial and pelvic splanchnic nerves. Branches of these nerves either directly innervate organs or join nerve plexuses to be distributed to organs. The major means by which parasympathetic postganglionic axons reach effectors are illustrated in figure 16.6 and include the following:

1. *Cranial nerves innervating the head and neck.* Three pairs of cranial nerves have parasympathetic preganglionic axons that extend to terminal ganglia in the head. Postganglionic neurons from the terminal ganglia innervate and thereby regulate nearby structures. The following are the parasympathetic cranial nerves, their terminal ganglia, and the structures innervated (see table 13.5):
   a. The **oculomotor nerve (III),** through the **ciliary** (SILL-ee-air-ee) **ganglion,** innervates the ciliary muscles and the iris of the eye.
   b. The **facial nerve (VII),** through the **pterygopalatine** (TER-i-goh-PAL-ah-tyne) **ganglion,** innervates the lacrimal gland and the mucosal glands of the nasal cavity and palate. The facial nerve, through the **submandibular ganglion,** also innervates the submandibular and sublingual salivary glands.
   c. The **glossopharyngeal nerve (IX),** through the **otic** (OH-tik) **ganglion,** innervates the parotid salivary gland.
2. *The vagus nerve and thoracic nerve plexuses.* Although the **vagus nerve (X)** has somatic motor and sensory functions in the head and neck, its parasympathetic distribution is to the thorax and abdomen. Preganglionic axons extend through the vagus nerves to the thorax. Within the thorax, the axons pass through branches of the vagus nerves to contribute to the cardiac plexus, which innervates the heart, and the pulmonary plexus, which innervates the lungs. The vagus nerves continue down the esophagus and give off branches to form the **esophageal plexus.**
3. *The vagus nerve and abdominal nerve plexuses.* After the esophageal plexus passes through the diaphragm, some of the vagal preganglionic axons innervate terminal ganglia in the wall of the stomach, whereas others contribute to the celiac and superior mesenteric plexuses. Through these plexuses, the preganglionic axons synapse in terminal ganglia in the walls of the gallbladder, biliary ducts, pancreas, small intestine, ascending colon, and transverse colon.
4. *Pelvic splanchnic nerves and pelvic nerve plexuses.* The parasympathetic preganglionic axons whose cell bodies are in the S2–S4 region of the spinal cord pass to the ventral rami of spinal nerves and enter the pelvic splanchnic nerves. The pelvic splanchnic nerves innervate terminal ganglia in the transverse colon to the rectum, and they contribute to the hypogastric plexus. The hypogastric plexus and its derivatives innervate the lower colon, rectum, urinary bladder, and the reproductive system organs in the pelvis.

Sensory Neurons in Autonomic Nerve Plexuses

The axons of sensory neurons run alongside ANS axons within ANS nerves and plexuses. These sensory neurons are not strictly part of the ANS, but they play important roles in monitoring the activity of structures regulated by the ANS. Some sensory neurons are part of reflex arcs regulating organ activities. Sensory neurons also transmit pain and pressure sensations from organs to the CNS. The cell bodies of these sensory neurons are found in the dorsal root ganglia of spinal nerves and in the cranial nerve sensory ganglia, which are swellings on the cranial nerves close to their attachment to the brain.

ASSESS YOUR PROGRESS

16. *From what are sympathetic autonomic nerve plexuses formed? How are they normally named?*

17. *Describe the four major ways by which sympathetic axons pass from sympathetic chain ganglia to effectors. Name four abdominopelvic autonomic nerve plexuses.*

18. *List the four major means by which parasympathetic axons reach effectors. List the cranial nerves and ganglia that supply the head and neck.*

19. *What are the roles of sensory neurons in the ANS?*

Enteric Nervous System

The enteric nervous system consists of nerve plexuses within the wall of the digestive tract (see chapter 24). The plexuses have contributions from three sources: (1) sensory neurons that connect the digestive tract to the CNS, (2) ANS motor neurons that connect the CNS to the digestive tract, and (3) enteric neurons, which are confined to the enteric plexuses. The CNS is capable of monitoring the digestive tract and controlling its smooth muscle and glands through autonomic reflexes (see section 16.5). For example, sensory neurons detect stretch of the digestive tract, and action potentials are transmitted to the CNS. In response, the CNS sends action potentials to glands in the digestive tract, causing them to secrete.

There are three major types of enteric neurons:

1. *Enteric sensory neurons* detect changes in the chemical composition of the contents of the digestive tract or detect stretch of the digestive tract wall.
2. *Enteric motor neurons* stimulate or inhibit smooth muscle contraction and gland secretion.
3. *Enteric interneurons* connect enteric sensory and motor neurons to each other.

A unique feature of enteric neurons is that they are capable of monitoring and controlling the digestive tract independently of the CNS through local reflexes (see section 16.5). For

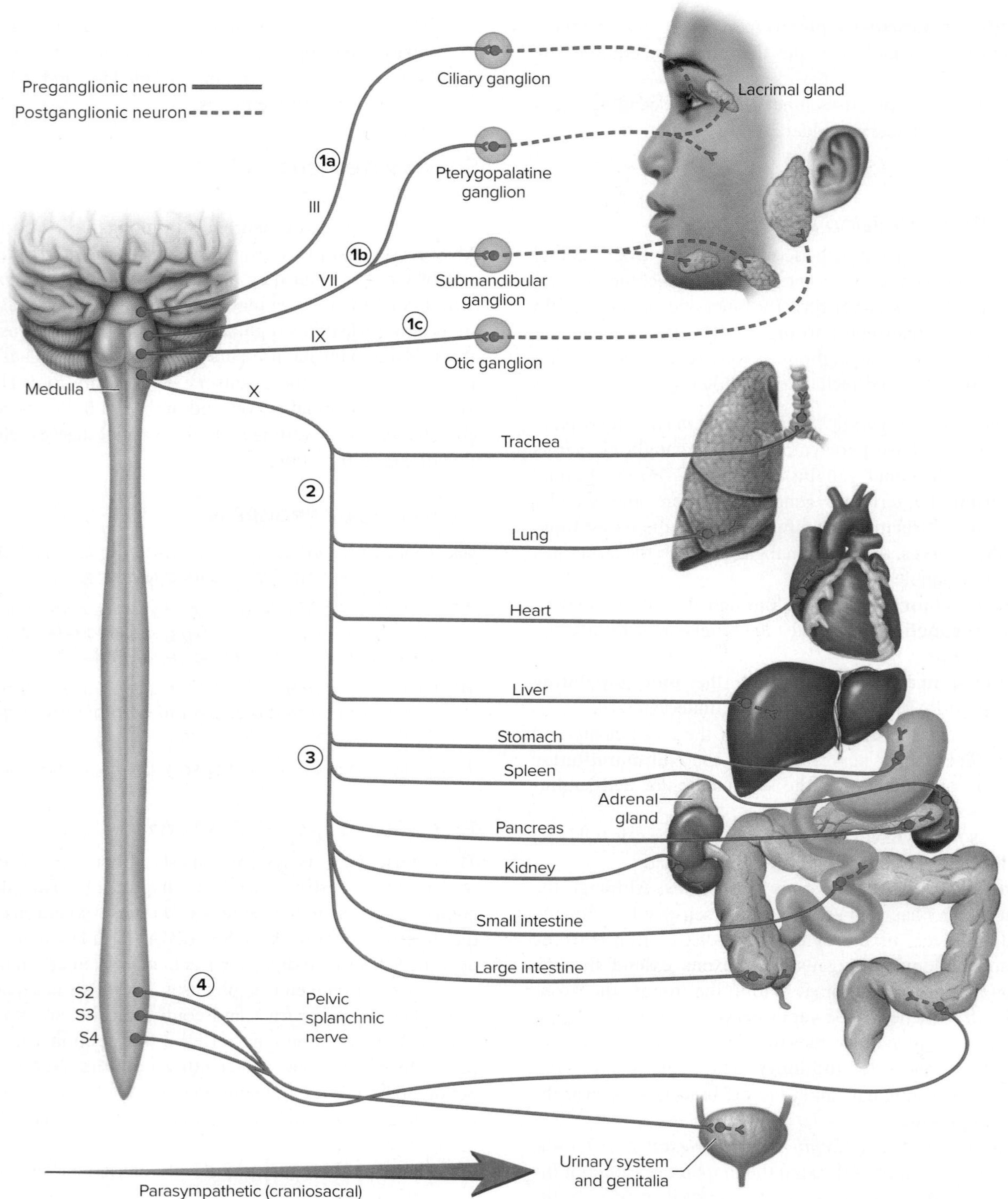

FIGURE 16.6 Parasympathetic Division Distribution of Autonomic Postganglionic Neurons
Parasympathetic outflow includes cranial nerves and pelvic splanchnic nerves. APR

example, stretch of the digestive tract is detected by enteric sensory neurons, which stimulate enteric interneurons. The enteric interneurons stimulate enteric motor neurons, which stimulate glands to secrete. Although the enteric nervous system is capable of controlling the activities of the digestive tract completely independently of the CNS, the two systems normally work together.

ASSESS YOUR PROGRESS

20. *What is the enteric nervous system (ENS), and where is it located?*

21. *What three sources contribute to ENS plexuses?*

22. *Name three major types of enteric neurons. How do enteric neurons monitor and control the digestive tract?*

17

CHAPTER

Functional Organization of the Endocrine System

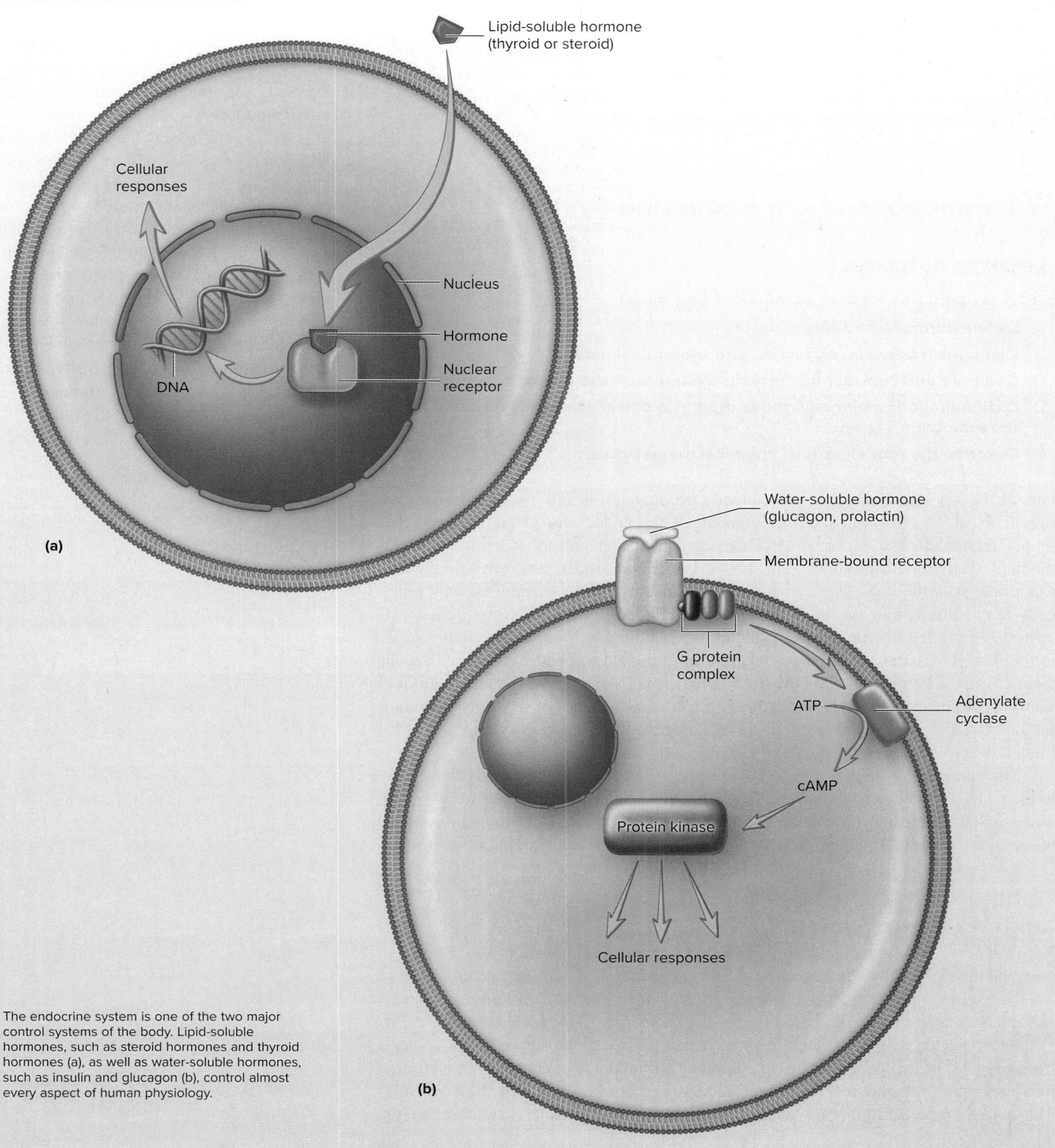

The endocrine system is one of the two major control systems of the body. Lipid-soluble hormones, such as steroid hormones and thyroid hormones (a), as well as water-soluble hormones, such as insulin and glucagon (b), control almost every aspect of human physiology.

If you search for the phrase "The Alton Giant" on the Internet, the image of Robert Wadlow will appear (see figure 18.8). Robert Wadlow was 8'11" when he died in 1940. His extraordinary growth was due to an overstimulation of human growth hormone (hGH; see chapter 6). Robert Wadlow's condition illustrates the powerful nature of chemical messengers in the human body and their critical role in homeostasis. Homeostasis is disrupted when hormone levels in the body are not tightly regulated. Growth hormone is one of hundreds of hormones that circulate in the body. These chemical messengers have differences, but they all share the fundamental property of transmitting signals to target cells to regulate almost every aspect of homeostasis. This chapter focuses on the general principles of hormones; chapter 18 discusses specific hormones and their functions.

Learn to Predict

Liu Dan was one of the top wrestlers on his high school team, but he knew that his small size would make it difficult to compete at the college level. He had tried lifting weights, but that did not seem to be working. So Liu decided to try something he had never thought he would do—he began taking anabolic steroids. At first he was excited because his muscles were larger and he felt stronger. After a few more weeks, though, he started noticing some troublesome changes: His pectoral muscles were getting larger, but they looked more feminine than masculine; his testes had shrunk; and he'd had some frightening episodes that could only be described as temper tantrums. **After reading this chapter, explain why anabolic steroids were able to alter muscle tissue growth and cause unintended changes in other tissues of the body.**

Answers to this question and the chapter's odd-numbered Predict questions can be found in Appendix E.

17.1 Functions of the Endocrine System

LEARNING OUTCOMES

After reading this section, you should be able to

A. **Define *hormone* and *target tissue*.**
B. **Distinguish between endocrine and exocrine glands.**
C. **Compare and contrast the nervous system with the endocrine system.**
D. **Define the four major categories of physiological processes regulated by the endocrine system.**
E. **Describe the four classes of chemical messengers.**

One of the key concepts we have frequently encountered is cell-to-cell communication. This is the fundamental characteristic of the endocrine system; through the highly regulated release of chemical messengers, the endocrine system is able to modulate activities in the body. The **endocrine** (EN-doh-krin; *endo,* within; *krino,* to secrete) **system** is composed of endocrine glands as well as specialized endocrine cells found throughout the body (figure 17.1). Endocrine glands secrete chemical messengers, called **hormones** (HOR-mohnz). Hormones are transported in the blood to their **target tissues,** or *effectors,* where they stimulate a specific response. Recall from chapter 4 that glands are classified as exocrine or endocrine. **Exocrine glands** secrete materials that are carried by ducts to epithelial surfaces of the body. Through the highly regulated release of chemical messengers, the endocrine system is able to modulate activities in the body.

The endocrine system is one of the major control systems in the body that regulates many physiological processes. However, the endocrine does not always work independently but often works closely with the body's other major regulatory system, the nervous system. Together, these two systems achieve and maintain homeostasis.

Comparison of the Nervous and Endocrine Systems

Both the nervous system and the endocrine system are communication systems. However, the mechanism by which each system communicates with its target cells differs. The nervous system transmits messages directly to its target cells through action potentials and the release of neurotransmitters at synapses. This is like sending a text to another person or to a group chat—the message is delivered directly to the electronic devices of that person or group. On the other hand, the endocrine system transmits messages to its target cells through secretion of hormones into the bloodstream. This is like a post in Instagram—posts are usually meant to be general announcements

Module 8
Endocrine System

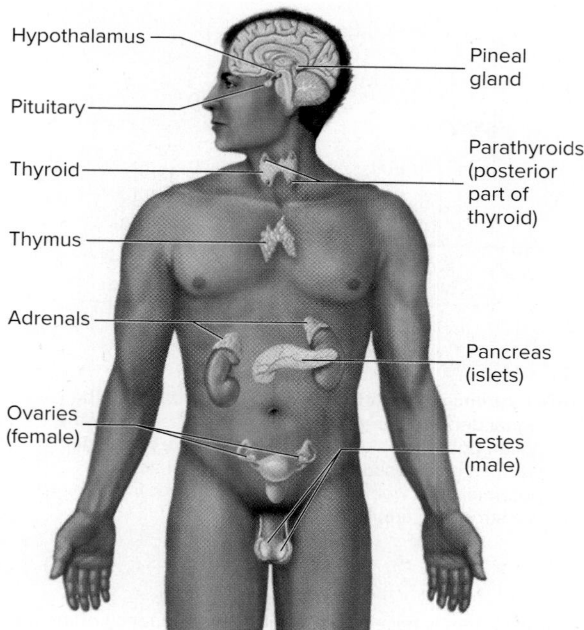

FIGURE 17.1 Major Endocrine Glands and Tissues
Glands that secrete chemical messengers that are transported to their targets by the blood are endocrine glands. APR

that are visible by any of your followers. The similarities between the nervous and endocrine systems include:

1. *Shared brain structures.* The hypothalamus regulates nervous system functions such as detecting changes in body temperature and serving as a regulator of autonomic function. It regulates endocrine function at the level of the pituitary gland. The hypothalamus synthesizes and secretes several hormones that can either stimulate or inhibit the release of other hormones from the pituitary gland. Hormones that are secreted by neurons are called **neuropeptides,** or *neurohormones.*
2. *Shared chemical messengers.* Certain molecules are used by both the nervous and endocrine systems. For example, norepinephrine functions as a neurotransmitter when secreted by a neuron and a hormone when secreted into the blood by the adrenal medulla.
3. *Shared regulatory processes.* The nervous system and the endocrine system work together almost simultaneously to regulate critical body processes. For example, in times of crisis, norepinephrine is secreted in a second or less by sympathetic nervous system neurons. This is followed within several seconds by hormonal norepinephrine as well as epinephrine secretion by the adrenal medulla (see chapter 16).
4. *Shared signaling pathways.* Both neurotransmitters and hormones can stimulate their target cells through specific G protein–coupled receptors (see chapter 3).

Despite the many similarities between these two systems, there are several important differences:

1. *Mode of transport.* The nervous system secretes neurotransmitters, which are released directly onto their target cells, whereas the endocrine system secretes hormones, which are transported in the bloodstream.
2. *Speed of response.* In general, the nervous system responds faster than the endocrine system. However, it is not accurate to say the endocrine system responds slowly; rather, it responds *more slowly* than the nervous system. Neurotransmitters, such as acetylcholine, are delivered to their target cells in milliseconds, whereas some hormones are delivered to their target cells in seconds.
3. *Duration of response.* The nervous system typically activates its targets quickly and only for as long as action potentials are sent to the target. The target cells' response is usually terminated shortly after action potentials cease, although there are exceptions to this within the nervous system. In contrast, the endocrine system tends to have longer-lasting effects. Hormones remain in the bloodstream for minutes, days, or even weeks and activate their target tissues as long as they are present in the circulation. The target tissue products may remain active for a substantial length of time after receiving a hormonal stimulus.
4. *Modulation of signal intensity.* The hormones secreted by most endocrine glands can be described as **amplitude-modulated signals.** The term *amplitude* refers to the total amount of a signal that is produced. This type of signal consists of fluctuations in the *concentration* of hormones in the bloodstream (figure 17.2), over a period of time. This time period can range from minutes to hours. On the other hand, the all-or-none action potentials carried along axons can be described as **frequency-modulated signals.** The term *frequency* refers to how often a signal is sent in a certain period of time (figure 17.2). These types of signals vary in the number of signals within that time period. A low frequency of action potentials is a weak stimulus, whereas a high frequency of action potentials is a strong stimulus.

Thus, both the nervous system and the endocrine system work to maintain homeostasis using chemical messengers; however, they differ from each other in the way their chemical messengers work.

Overview of Endocrine-Regulated Processes

There are at least four major categories of processes that the endocrine system helps coordinate. They include:

1. *Growth and development:* Hormones stimulate bone cells to secrete new matrix, neurons to form and strengthen synapses, enlargement of skeletal muscle fibers, among numerous other functions.
2. *Metabolism:* Hormones stimulate cells to take up or release glucose, produce enzymes essential for breakdown and absorption of food, as well as modifications in heart rate, blood pressure, and breathing rate to adapt to variations in metabolic demand.
3. *Blood composition:* Many hormones regulate actions of the kidney to conserve or excrete ions and water, as well as regulating pH of the plasma (the extracellular fluid of the blood),

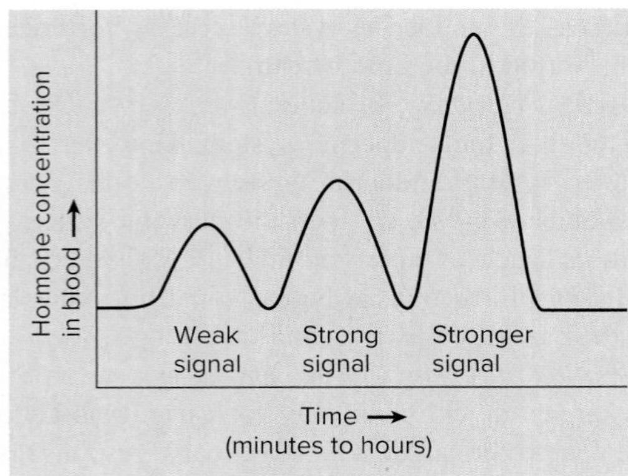

(a) Amplitude-modulated signals. The concentration of the hormone determines the strength of the signal and the magnitude of the response. For most hormones, a small concentration of a hormone is a weak signal and produces a small response, whereas a larger concentration is a stronger signal and results in a greater response.

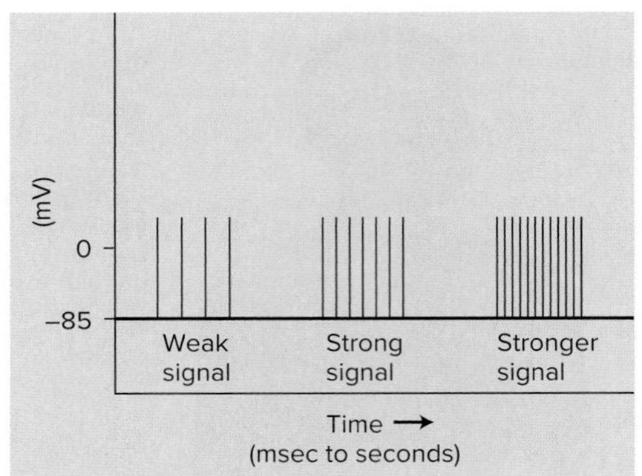

(b) Frequency-modulated signals. The strength of the signal depends on the frequency, not the size, of the action potentials. All action potentials are the same size in a given tissue. A low frequency of action potentials is a weak stimulus, and a higher frequency is a stronger stimulus.

FIGURE 17.2 Signaling in Endocrine and Nervous Systems
(*a*) The endocrine system is based on changing the concentration of hormones. (*b*) The nervous system is based on changing the frequency of the messages.

the number and types of blood cells, and the amount of certain proteins found in the plasma of blood (see chapter 19).

4. *Reproduction:* Hormones are the key regulators of reproduction. They allow males and females to produce gametes (eggs and sperm). In addition, hormones enable the female body to nourish offspring.

In chapter 18, we expand on these processes by examining specific endocrine glands, their secretory products, and the specific functions these secretions regulate.

Classes of Chemical Messengers

Hormones are not the only type of chemical messenger secreted and employed by the body. Throughout the body, there are four classes of chemical messengers. The class determination is based on the source of the chemical messenger and its mode of transport in the body (table 17.1). Chemical messengers are produced by a specific collection of cells or by a gland. A **gland** is an organ consisting of epithelial cells that specialize in **secretion,** the controlled release of chemicals from a cell (see chapter 4). In this section, we describe chemical messengers in terms of how they function. But it is important to note that some chemical messengers fall into more than one functional category. For example, the chemicals called prostaglandins are listed in multiple categories because they have several functions and cannot be restricted to just one class. Therefore, the study of the endocrine system includes several of the following categories:

1. *Autocrine chemical messengers.* An **autocrine** (*auto-,* self) chemical messenger stimulates the cell that originally secreted it. Good examples of autocrine chemical messengers are those secreted by white blood cells during an infection. Several types of white blood cells can stimulate their own replication so that the total number of white blood cells increases rapidly (see chapter 22).
2. *Paracrine chemical messengers.* **Paracrine** (*para,* next to) chemical messengers act locally on neighboring cells. These chemical messengers are secreted by one cell type into the extracellular fluid and affect surrounding cells. An example of a paracrine chemical messenger is histamine, released by certain white blood cells during allergic reactions. Histamine stimulates vasodilation in nearby blood vessels.
3. *Neurotransmitters.* **Neurotransmitters** are chemical messengers secreted by neurons that activate an adjacent cell, whether it is another neuron, a muscle cell, or a glandular cell. Neurotransmitters are secreted into a synaptic cleft, rather than into the bloodstream (see chapter 11). Therefore, in the strictest sense neurotransmitters are paracrine agents, but for our purposes it is most appropriate to consider them as a separate category.
4. *Endocrine chemical messengers.* **Endocrine** chemical messengers, hormones, are secreted into the bloodstream by certain glands and cells, which together make up the endocrine system. The hormones travel through the general circulation to their target cells.

ASSESS YOUR PROGRESS

Answers to these questions are found in the section you have just completed. Re-read the section if you need help in answering these questions.

1. *How does an endocrine gland differ from an exocrine gland?*
2. *Describe the similarities between the nervous system and the endocrine system.*
3. *In what ways does the nervous system differ from the endocrine system?*
4. *Name and describe the four classes of chemical messengers.*

TABLE 17.1 Classes of Chemical Messengers

Chemical Messenger	Description	Example	
Autocrine	Secreted by cells in a local area; influences the activity of the same cell from which it was secreted	Eicosanoids (prostaglandins, thromboxanes, prostacyclins, leukotrienes)	
Paracrine	Produced by a wide variety of tissues and secreted into extracellular fluid; has a localized effect on nearby tissues	Somatostatin, histamine, eicosanoids	
Neurotransmitter	Produced by neurons; secreted into a synaptic cleft by presynaptic nerve terminals; travels short distances; influences postsynaptic cells	Acetylcholine, epinephrine	
Endocrine	Secreted into the blood by specialized cells; travels some distance to target tissues; results in coordinated regulation of cell function; called hormones	Thyroid hormones, growth hormone, insulin, epinephrine, estrogen, progesterone, testosterone	

17.2 Hormones

LEARNING OUTCOMES

After reading this section, you should be able to

A. **List and describe the three stimulatory influences on hormone secretion and give examples of each.**

B. **Describe the three main patterns of hormone secretion.**

C. **List and describe the two classes of hormones.**

The word *hormone* is derived from the Greek word *hormon,* which means "set into motion." Hormones are incredibly powerful and important molecules. As you've learned so far, hormones are chemical messengers that are secreted into the blood by specialized cells, and then travel to distant target tissues and bind to a specific **receptor** (figure 17.3). Hormone actions result in a coordinated response of target cell function. In this chapter, we will discuss (1) the control of hormone secretion, particularly focusing on the types of stimuli that initiate hormone secretion; (2) the patterns of hormone secretion; (3) the different classes of hormones; (4) transport of the hormones to their target tissues; (5) the metabolism of hormones once in the circulation; and (6) the ways hormones can affect the target tissue response. The information in this section will be helpful in answering this chapter's Learn to Predict question.

Control of Hormone Secretion

Three types of stimuli regulate hormone release: (1) humoral, (2) neural, and (3) hormonal. No matter what stimulus causes the release of the hormone, however, the blood level of most hormones fluctuates within a homeostatic range through negative-feedback mechanisms (see chapter 1). In a few instances, positive-feedback systems also regulate blood hormone levels.

Humoral Stimuli

The term *humoral* refers to the fluids of the body. Metabolites and other molecules in the bloodstream can directly stimulate the release of some hormones. Given that the term *humoral* refers to body fluids, including blood, these metabolites and molecules in the blood are referred to as humoral stimuli. The cells that secrete

FUNDAMENTAL **Figure**

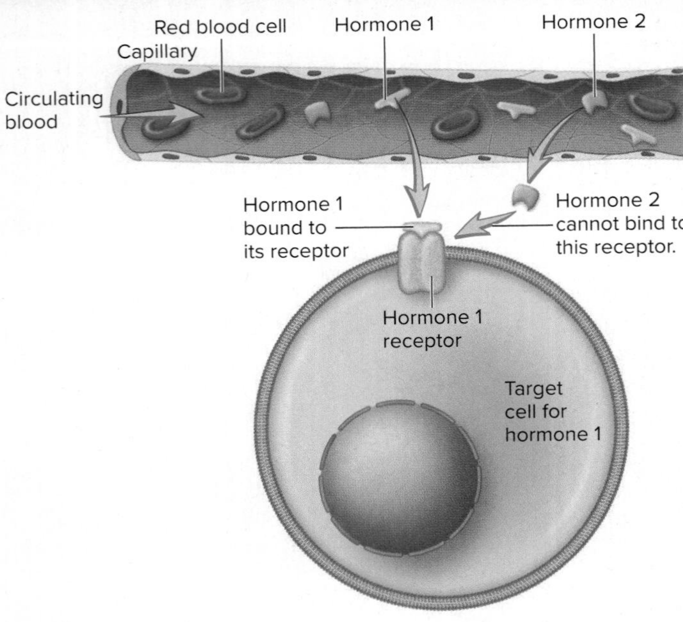

FIGURE 17.3 Target Tissue Specificity and Response
Hormones bind (physically attach) to receptor proteins. The shape and chemical nature of each receptor site allow only certain hormones to bind. This relationship is called specificity. In order for a target cell to respond to its hormone, the hormone must bind to its receptor.

these hormones have receptors for certain substances in the blood. For example, glucose, Ca^{2+}, and Na^{+} can stimulate hormone secretion. When the blood level of the particular substance changes, the hormone is released in response to the molecule's concentration (figure 17.4*a*). An example of a humoral regulated hormone is the Ca^{2+}-regulation hormone, parathyroid hormone (PTH). PTH secretion is stimulated when blood Ca^{2+} levels are too low and inhibited when blood Ca^{2+} levels increase (see chapter 6).

Neural Stimuli

The second type of hormone regulation involves **neural stimuli** that affect endocrine glands. Following an action potential, a neuron releases a neurotransmitter into a synapse with a hormone-producing cell. In this case, the neurotransmitter stimulates the cells to secrete their hormone. Figure 17.4*b* illustrates the neural control of hormone secretion from cells of an endocrine gland. For example, in response to stimuli, such as stress or exercise, neurons of the sympathetic division of the autonomic nervous system (see chapter 16) stimulate the adrenal gland to secrete epinephrine and norepinephrine into the bloodstream. Responses include an elevated heart rate and increased blood flow through the exercising muscles. When the stimulus is no longer present, the neural stimulation declines, and the secretion of epinephrine and norepinephrine decreases. However, some neurons secrete their chemical messengers directly into the blood when they are

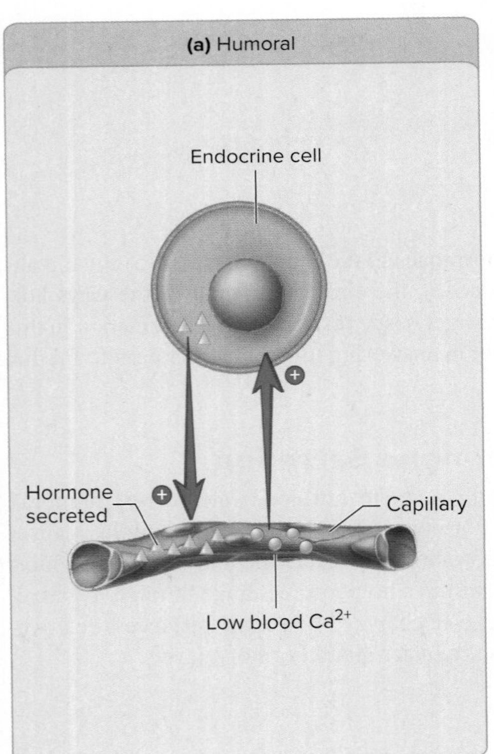

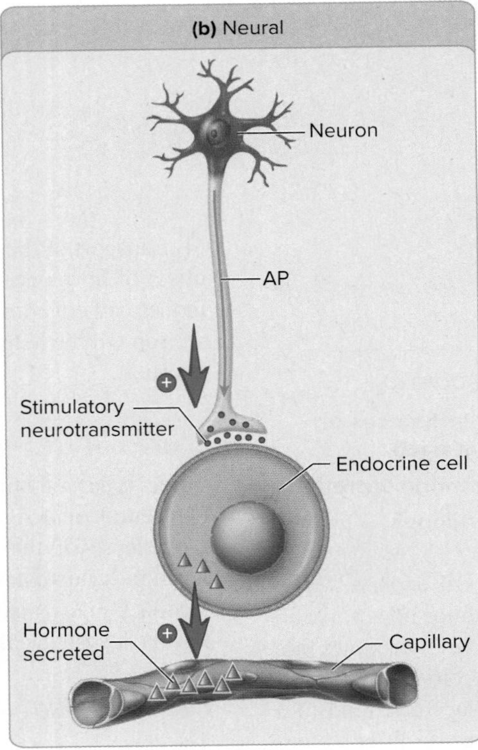

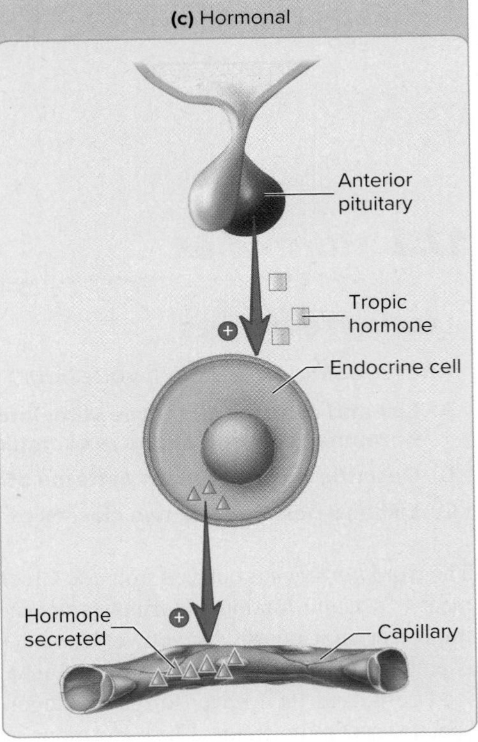

FIGURE 17.4 Regulation of Hormone Secretion
There are three principal mechanisms that regulate hormone secretion. (*a*) Humoral stimuli: Some hormones are released when the blood levels of a certain chemical change. (*b*) Neural Stimuli: Some hormones are released in response to a neurotransmitter. (*c*) Hormonal stimuli: Certain hormones are secreted in response to another hormone.

stimulated, which makes these chemical messengers hormones. Hormones released by a neuron are neuropeptides. Some neuropeptides stimulate hormone secretion from other endocrine cells and are called *releasing hormones,* a term usually reserved for hormones from the hypothalamus. Thus, when a neuron releases a neurotransmitter at a synapse to stimulate a hormone's secretion, it is considered a neural stimulus. But when a neuron releases a neuropeptide hormone into the blood, which stimulates another hormone's secretion, it is considered a hormonal stimulus.

Neurons inhibit targets just as often as they stimulate targets. If the neurotransmitter is inhibitory, it stops the target endocrine gland from secreting its hormone.

Hormonal Stimuli

The third type of regulation uses **hormonal stimuli.** It occurs when hormones stimulate the secretion of other hormones (figure 17.4*c*). The most common examples are hormones from the anterior pituitary gland, called **tropic** (TROH-pik) **hormones.** Many tropic hormones are part of a complex process in which a releasing hormone from the hypothalamus stimulates the release of a tropic hormone from the pituitary gland. The pituitary tropic hormone then travels to a separate endocrine gland and stimulates the release of a hormone from the target endocrine gland. For example, hormones from the hypothalamus and anterior pituitary regulate the secretion of thyroid hormones from the thyroid gland.

Some hormones prevent the secretion of other hormones. For example, hormones called **inhibiting hormones,** from the hypothalamus, prevent the secretion of tropic hormones from the anterior pituitary gland. Another example is when thyroid hormones control their own blood levels through negative feedback at the level of the anterior pituitary. The negative feedback results in the inhibition of the anterior pituitary tropic hormone normally responsible for thyroid hormone secretion. Without the original stimulus, less thyroid hormone is released.

Patterns of Hormone Secretion

Blood levels of hormones are determined, in part, by their overall pattern of secretion. There are three main patterns of hormone secretion; however, individual hormones can be secreted in more than one pattern. These three main patterns are (1) chronic, (2) acute, and (3) episodic (figure 17.5):

1. **Chronic hormone secretion** results in relatively constant blood levels of hormone over long periods of time. For example, thyroid hormones circulate in the blood within a small range of concentrations.
2. **Acute hormone secretion** occurs when the hormone's concentration changes suddenly and irregularly, and its circulating levels differ with each stimulus. For example, epinephrine is released in large amounts in response to stress or physical exercise.
3. **Episodic hormone secretion** occurs when hormones are secreted at fairly predictable intervals and concentrations. Reproductive hormones are an example of hormones secreted with this pattern. Some reproductive hormones fluctuate over a month in cyclic fashion during the human reproductive years.

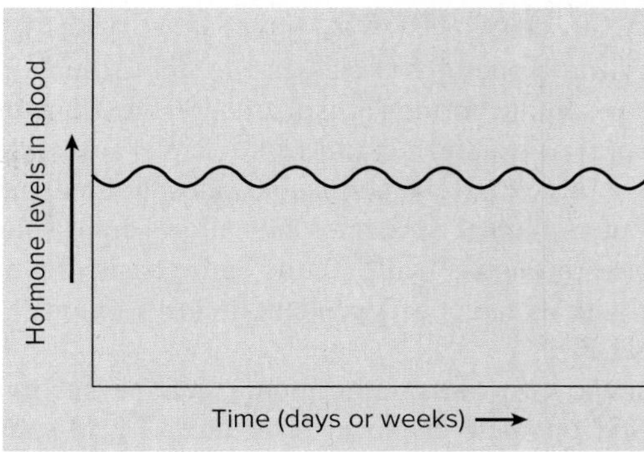

(a) Chronic hormone secretion. A relatively stable concentration of hormone is maintained in the circulating blood over a fairly long period, up to several weeks. This pattern is exemplified by the thyroid hormones.

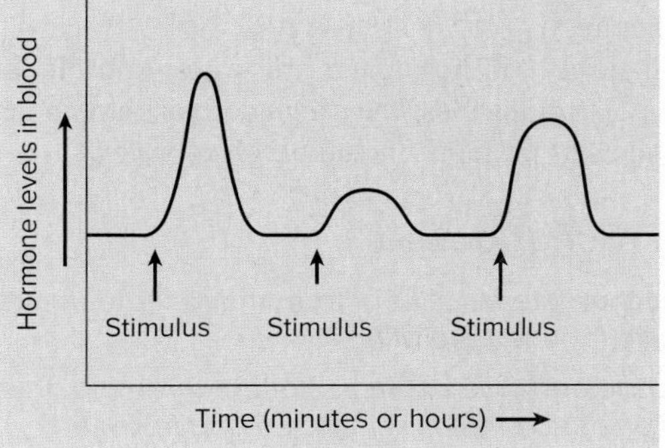

(b) Acute hormone secretion. A hormone rapidly increases in the blood for a short time in response to a specific stimulus—for example, insulin (the blood sugar–regulating hormone) secretion following a meal. Note that the size of the stimulus arrow represents the stimulus strength. A smaller stimulus does not activate as much hormone secretion as a larger stimulus.

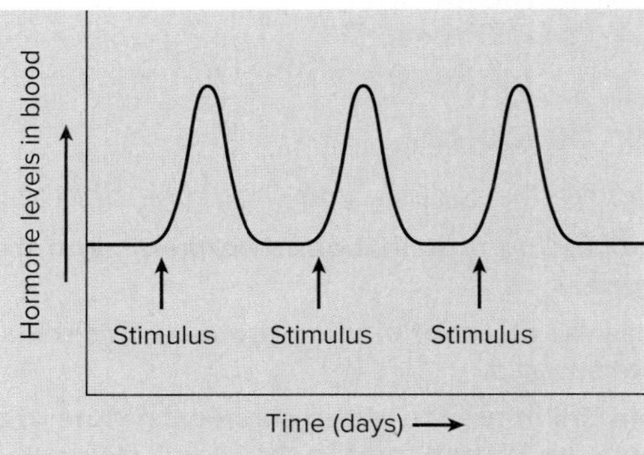

(c) Episodic hormone secretion. A hormone is stimulated so that it increases and decreases in the blood at a relatively consistent time and to roughly the same amount. Examples are the reproductive hormones regulating menstruation.

FIGURE 17.5 Patterns of Hormone Secretion
The overall pattern of hormone secretion is a result of the secretion, transport, and removal of the hormones, which is further dependent on the chemical nature of the hormones. (*a*) Chronic hormone secretion occurs over a relatively long period. (*b*) Acute hormone secretion occurs over a relatively short period. (*c*) Episodic hormone secretion occurs in relatively predictable bursts.

Classes of Hormones

Hormones fit into one of two classes: (1) lipid-soluble hormones and (2) water-soluble hormones, a distinction based on their chemical behavior. For example, recall from chapter 3 that the plasma membrane is a selectively permeable phospholipid bilayer that excludes water-soluble molecules but allows lipid-soluble molecules to pass through. Therefore, the entire basis of a hormone's interaction with its target is dependent on the hormone's chemical nature (table 17.2).

Within the two classes, hormones can be subdivided into groups based on their chemical structures. **Lipid-soluble hormones** are nonpolar and include steroid hormones, thyroid hormones, and fatty acid derivative hormones, such as certain eicosanoids. Steroid hormones are derived from cholesterol, and thyroid hormones are derived from the amino acid tyrosine. Being lipid-soluble, thyroid hormones are more like steroids in their chemical nature.

The majority of hormones are **water-soluble hormones,** which are polar molecules; they include most amino acid derivatives, peptides, or proteins, including glycoproteins.

ASSESS YOUR PROGRESS

5. *What characteristics of a hormone receptor make it specific for one type of hormone?*
6. *Describe and give examples of the three major ways hormone secretion is stimulated and inhibited.*
7. *Describe chronic, acute, and episodic patterns of hormone secretion.*
8. *What are the two classes of hormones? Give examples of both types.*

17.3 Transport and Metabolism of Hormones

LEARNING OUTCOMES

After reading this section, you should be able to

A. **Define *binding protein, bound hormone,* and *free hormone*.**
B. **Discuss the effect of binding proteins on circulating hormone levels.**
C. **Explain the influence of the chemical nature of a hormone on its transport in the blood, its removal from circulation, and its life span.**
D. **Describe the major mechanisms that maintain blood hormone levels.**

Hormones are transported by the blood to many locations and therefore have the potential to activate any cell in the body, including those far away from where they were produced. However, the blood contains many hydrolytic enzymes, which break down substances. In addition, blood is an aqueous solution. These factors can present a challenge when transporting hormones to their targets.

Binding Proteins

Due to the presence of hydrolytic enzymes in the blood, many hormones would be quickly broken down after entering the bloodstream. These hormones require binding proteins, which act as chaperones, protecting the hormone so that they arrive intact and functional at their target. Once hormones attach to a binding protein, they are then called **bound hormones.** For small hormones, the binding protein protects them from degradation by hydrolytic enzymes and from being filtered from the blood in the kidney. For lipid-soluble hormones that are insoluble in plasma, being bound to a binding protein causes them to become more water-soluble. Hormones bind to specific binding proteins. For example, thyroid hormones bind to the binding protein transthyretin; testosterone binds to a different type of binding protein, called testosterone-binding globulin; and progesterone binds to yet another type of binding protein, called progesterone-binding globulin.

The binding of hormones to binding proteins is reversible. Hormones dissociate (detach) from their binding proteins at their target tissues. Once the hormones detach from the binding protein, they are then called **free hormones.** It is important to note that some hormones always exist as free hormones because they do not have specific binding proteins to which they attach. Thus, some hormones are "always free," whereas other hormones are "sometimes free." The binding protein's affinity for its hormone determines the concentration of free hormones.

The reversible binding of hormones to their binding proteins is important because only free hormones are able to diffuse through capillary walls and bind to target tissues. When bound to a binding protein, a hormone is too large to pass through a capillary wall. The bound hormone thus serves as a reservoir for the hormone. If blood levels of the hormone begin to decline, some of the bound hormone is released from the binding proteins. Because of this reservoir function of the bound hormones, the circulating concentration of free hormones remains more stable than that of hormones that do not use binding proteins (figure 17.6). Consequently, hormones that attach to binding proteins tend to circulate longer than hormones that do not require binding proteins.

Because water-soluble hormones can dissolve in the plasma of the blood, many circulate as free hormones, meaning that most of them dissolve directly into the plasma and are delivered to their target tissue without binding to a binding protein. Because many water-soluble hormones are quite large, they do not readily diffuse through the walls of all capillaries. Instead, they tend to diffuse from the blood into tissue spaces more slowly. Thus, capillaries of organs that are regulated by protein hormones tend to be very porous, or *fenestrated* (see chapter 21).

Regulation of Hormone Levels in the Blood

Two major mechanisms maintain hormone levels in the blood within a particular range of concentrations: (1) negative feedback and (2) positive feedback (see chapter 1).

1. *Negative feedback.* Most hormones are regulated by a negative-feedback mechanism, whereby the hormone's secretion is

TABLE 17.2 Chemical Nature of Hormones

Chemical Nature	Examples	Structures
Lipid-Soluble Hormones	Steroids (all cholesterol-based) Testosterone, aldosterone	Aldosterone 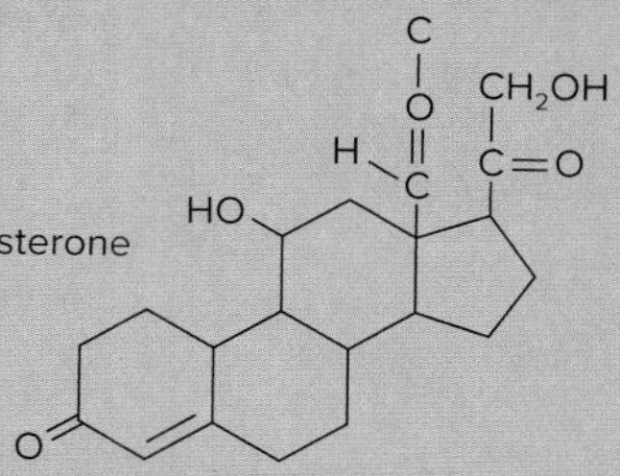 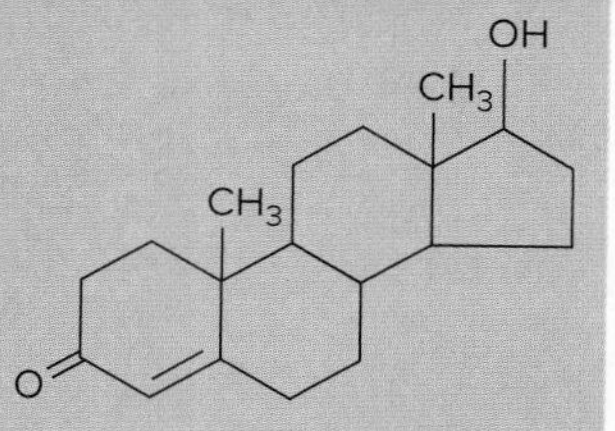 Testosterone
	Amino acid derivative (only one example of lipid-soluble) Thyroid hormone (thyroxine)	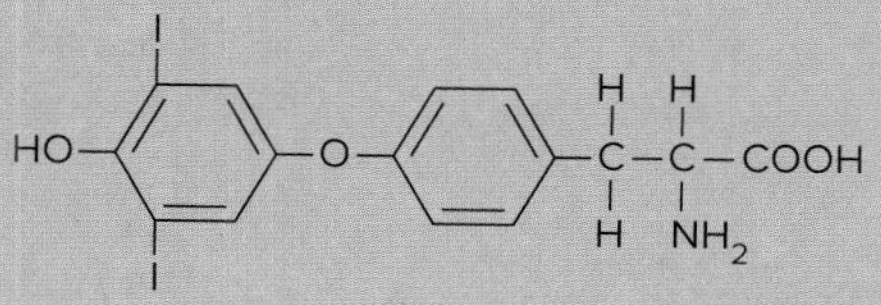 Tetraiodothyronine or thyroxine (T_4)
	Fatty acid derivatives Prostaglandins	Fatty acid derivative (formed from a fatty acid) 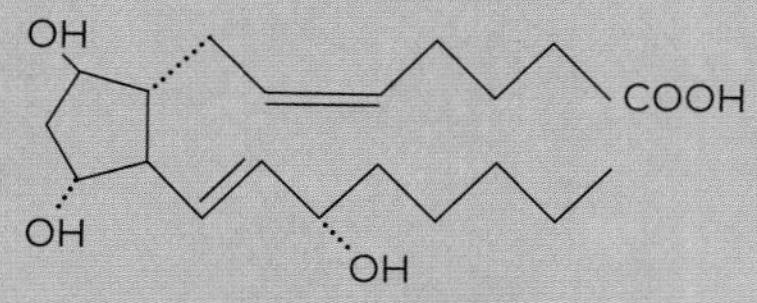 Prostaglandin $F_{2\alpha}$ ($PGF_{2\alpha}$)
Water-Soluble Hormones	Proteins Thyroid-stimulating hormone, growth hormone	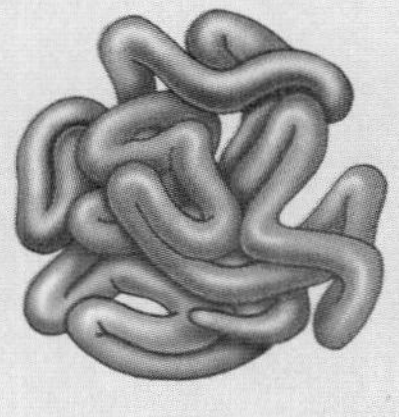 Thyroid-stimulating hormone (a glycoprotein) 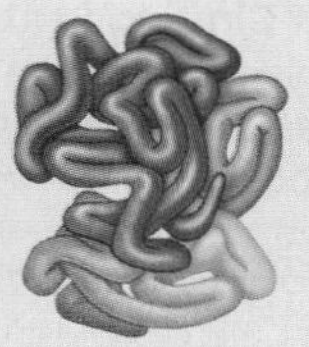 Growth hormone
	Peptides Insulin, thyrotropin-releasing hormone 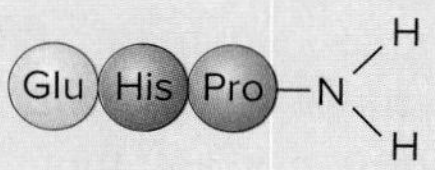Thyrotropin-releasing hormone	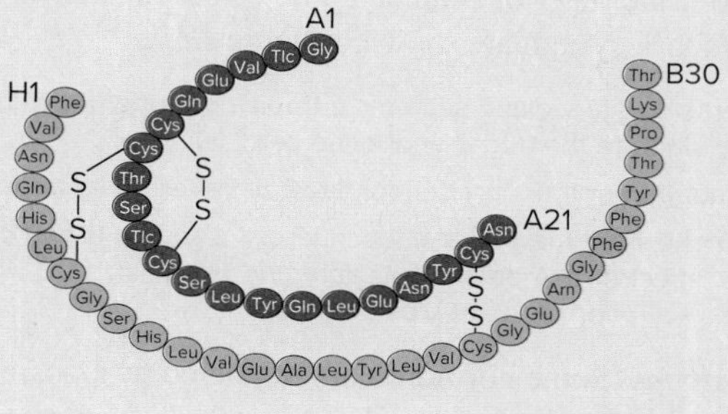 Insulin
	Amino acid derivatives Epinephrine	Epinephrine 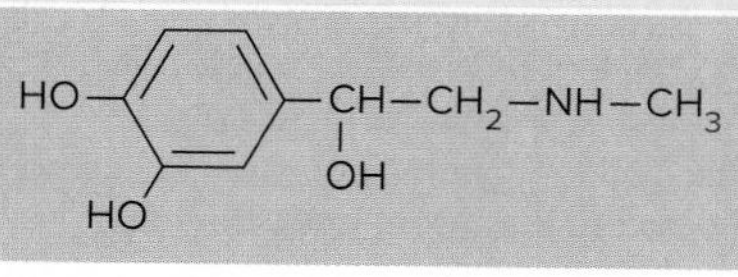

FUNDAMENTAL **Figure**

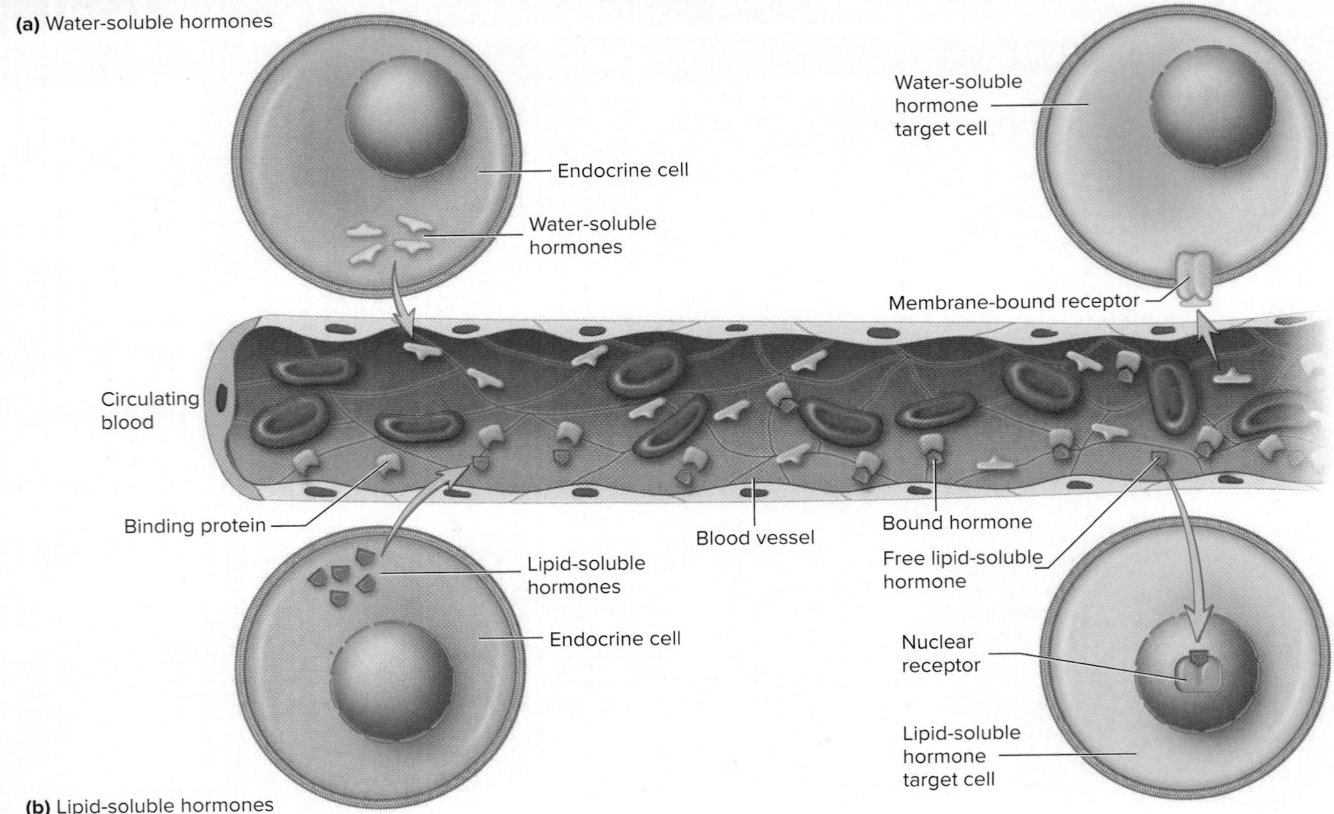

FIGURE 17.6 Effect of Binding Proteins
(*a*) Free hormones (those that circulate freely in the blood) immediately activate target cells once they are delivered from the blood. Thus, the blood levels of these hormones tend to fluctuate to a greater degree than the levels of hormones that attach to binding proteins; water-soluble hormones bind their receptors, which are membrane bound. (*b*) Hormones that are transported in the blood attached to binding proteins circulate in the blood as bound or free hormones. As the concentration of free hormones decreases, bound hormones are released from the binding proteins. This provides a chronic, stable supply of hormone and, thus, more consistent control of target cells. This is especially important for hormones that regulate basal metabolism. Lipid-soluble hormones bind their receptors in either the cytoplasm or the nucleus.

inhibited by the hormone itself. Thus, it is a self-limiting system. For example, thyroid hormones inhibit the secretion of their releasing hormone from the hypothalamus and their tropic hormone from the anterior pituitary. The steps for a hormone negative-feedback system are shown in figure 17.7*a*.

1. The anterior pituitary gland secretes a tropic hormone, which travels in the blood to the target endocrine cell.
2. The hormone from the target endocrine cell travels to its target.
3. The hormone from the target endocrine cell also has a negative-feedback effect on the anterior pituitary and hypothalamus, which decreases secretion of the tropic hormone.

2. *Positive feedback.* Some hormones are regulated by a positive-feedback mechanism, whereby the hormone's secretion is stimulated by the hormone itself. Thus, it is a self-perpetuating system. The steps in a hormone positive-feedback system are shown in figure 17.7*b*.

1. The anterior pituitary gland secretes a tropic hormone, which travels in the blood to the target endocrine cell.
2. The hormone from the target endocrine cell travels to its target.
3. The hormone from the target endocrine cell also has a positive-feedback effect on the anterior pituitary, which increases the secretion of the tropic hormone.

Half-Life of Hormones

Hormone concentrations are stable in the bloodstream; however, some hormones are more stable than others. The life span of a given hormone varies with its chemical nature. Larger, more complex hormones are more stable, whereas smaller, simpler hormones are less stable. A hormone's life span can be expressed as its **half-life,** which is the amount of time it takes for 50% of the circulating hormone to be removed from the circulation and excreted. Some hormones have a short half-life, whereas others have a much longer half-life. For example, thyrotropin-releasing hormone (TRH) is a three-amino-acid hormone with a short half-life. Because of TRH's simple composition, it is quickly degraded in the circulation and can activate only the target cells it can reach before it is destroyed. On the other hand, cortisol is a steroid hormone with a longer half-life, 90 minutes. Due to its lipid-soluble

PROCESS **Figure**

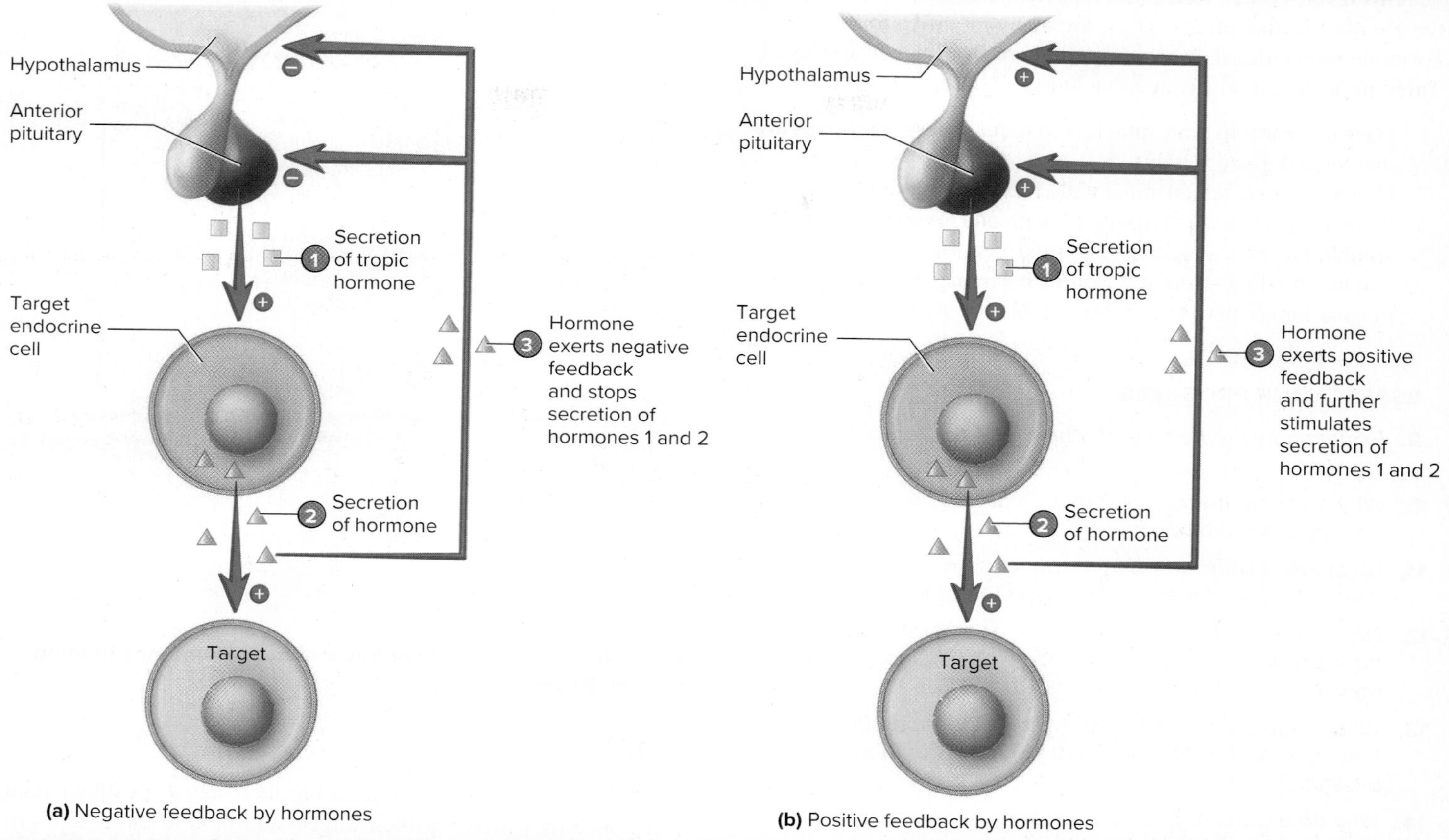

Hypothalamus

Anterior pituitary

1 Secretion of tropic hormone

Target endocrine cell

3 Hormone exerts negative feedback and stops secretion of hormones 1 and 2

2 Secretion of hormone

Target

(a) Negative feedback by hormones

Hypothalamus

Anterior pituitary

1 Secretion of tropic hormone

Target endocrine cell

3 Hormone exerts positive feedback and further stimulates secretion of hormones 1 and 2

2 Secretion of hormone

Target

(b) Positive feedback by hormones

PROCESS **Figure 17.7**

Negative and Positive Feedback

(*a*) Hormones whose blood levels are regulated by negative feedback are inhibited when they move outside a particular range. (*b*) Hormones whose levels are regulated by positive feedback are further stimulated by the original hormone in the pathway.

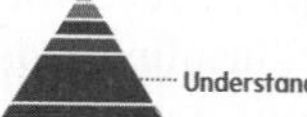

What is it that provides the negative-feedback signal for a hormone that is regulated by a humoral stimulus? Explain.

nature, it is not easily degraded and can continue to activate target cells for more than an hour.

Elimination of Hormones from the Bloodstream

All hormones, whether lipid-soluble or water-soluble, are destroyed either in the circulation or by enzymes at their target cells. The destruction and elimination of hormones limit the length of time they are active, and body processes change quickly when hormones are secreted and remain functional for only short periods.

Without binding proteins, lipid-soluble hormones would quickly diffuse out of capillaries and be degraded by enzymes of the liver and lungs or be filtered from the blood by the kidneys and would be unable to effectively regulate their targets. Circulating hydrolytic enzymes can also metabolize free lipid-soluble hormones. The breakdown products are then excreted in the urine or the bile. In order to terminate a lipid-soluble hormone response, these hormones are removed from the circulation through a process called **conjugation** (kon-ju-GAY-shun). Conjugation occurs when specific enzymes in the liver attach water-soluble molecules to the hormones. These water-soluble conjugation molecules are usually sulfate or glucuronic acid. Once the lipid-soluble hormones are conjugated, they cannot reenter the blood where they could overstimulate their targets. Instead, the kidneys and liver excrete them into the urine and bile.

The water-soluble hormones have relatively short half-lives because they are rapidly broken down by hydrolytic enzymes, called proteases, within the bloodstream. The kidneys then remove the hormone breakdown products from the blood. Target cells also destroy water-soluble hormones when the hormones are internalized via endocytosis. Once the hormones are inside the target cell, lysosomal enzymes degrade them. Often, the target cell recycles the amino acids of peptide and protein hormones and uses them to synthesize new proteins. Thus, hormones with short half-lives normally have concentrations that change rapidly within the blood and tend to regulate activities that have a rapid onset and short duration.

However, some water-soluble hormones are more stable in the circulation than others. There are many modifications made to hormone molecules that help protect them from being destroyed. Three important modifications include:

1. Having a carbohydrate attached to them. These hormones are then called glycoproteins.
2. Having a modified terminal end. These modifications protect them from protease activity to a greater extent than water-soluble hormones lacking such modifications.
3. Having binding proteins. Bound hormones circulate in the plasma longer than free water-soluble hormones do.

ASSESS YOUR PROGRESS

9. *Explain how the half-life of a hormone relates to its stability.*
10. *Why do some hormones require a binding protein during transport in the blood?*
11. *What effect does a bound hormone have on the concentration of a free hormone in the blood?*
12. *Describe how the chemical nature of a hormone affects its transport in the blood, its removal from circulation, and its half-life.*
13. *What happens to the half-life when a hormone binds to a binding protein? What kinds of hormones bind to binding proteins?*
14. *Why do organs regulated by protein hormones have fenestrated capillaries?*

17.4 Hormone Receptors and Mechanisms of Action

LEARNING OUTCOMES

After reading this section, you should be able to

A. **Describe the general properties of a receptor.**
B. **Explain the mechanisms of action for the two types of receptor classes.**
C. **Define *amplification* and explain how, despite small hormone concentrations, water-soluble hormones can cause rapid responses.**
D. **Describe how a target cell may decrease or increase its sensitivity to a hormone.**
E. **Define the three types of interactions between hormones at target tissues.**

Hormones must be able to interact with their target tissue in a specific manner in order to activate a coordinated set of events (figure 17.8). For example, the formation of reproductive organs in the fetus is activated by reproductive steroid hormones. This interaction occurs at a receptor on the target cells. Without a receptor for the male reproductive steroid testosterone, a newborn will have the outward appearance of a female despite being genetically male. Hormones must be able to regulate specific cellular pathways once they arrive at their targets and bind to target cell proteins called **receptors.** A hormone can stimulate only the cells that have the receptor for that hormone. The specific portion of each receptor molecule where a hormone binds is called a **binding site,** and the shape and chemical characteristics of each receptor site allow only a specific type of hormone to bind to it. The tendency for each type of hormone to bind to one type of receptor, and not to others, is called **specificity.** For example, insulin binds to insulin receptors, but not to receptors for thyroid hormones. However, some hormones, such as epinephrine, bind to a "family" of receptors that are structurally similar. This explains how it is possible for epinephrine to stimulate smooth muscle contraction in one target, such as certain blood vessels, while simultaneously promoting smooth muscle relaxation in a separate target, such as in the respiratory passages. Hormones have different effects at their target tissues depending on the specific receptor that is present in a particular target. Because hormone receptors have a high affinity for the hormones that bind to them, they are very sensitive to low levels of the hormone. Thus, only a small concentration of a given hormone is needed to activate a significant number of its receptors.

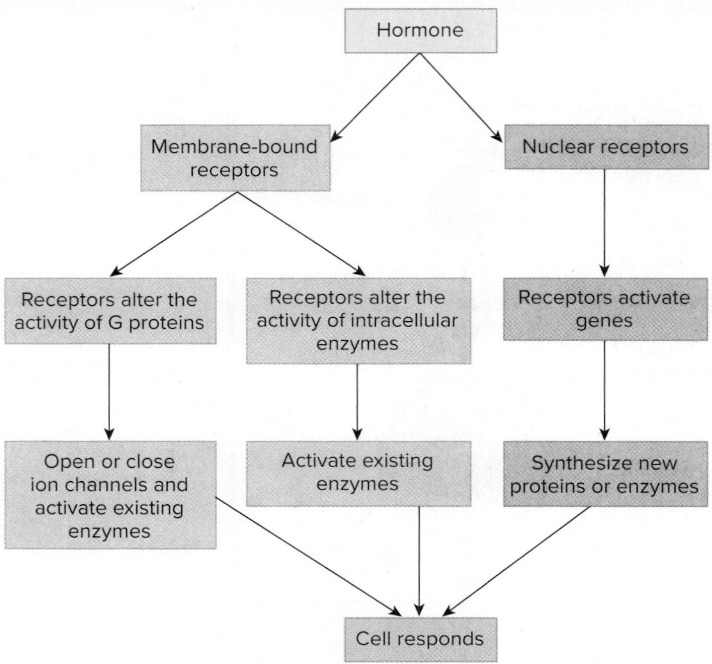

FIGURE 17.8 Overview of Responses to Hormones Binding to Their Receptors

Agonists and Antagonists

Drugs with structures similar to those of specific hormones will compete with those hormones for the same receptor (see chapter 3). A drug that binds to a hormone receptor and activates it is called an **agonist.** A drug that binds to a hormone receptor and inhibits its action is called an **antagonist.** For example, certain drugs

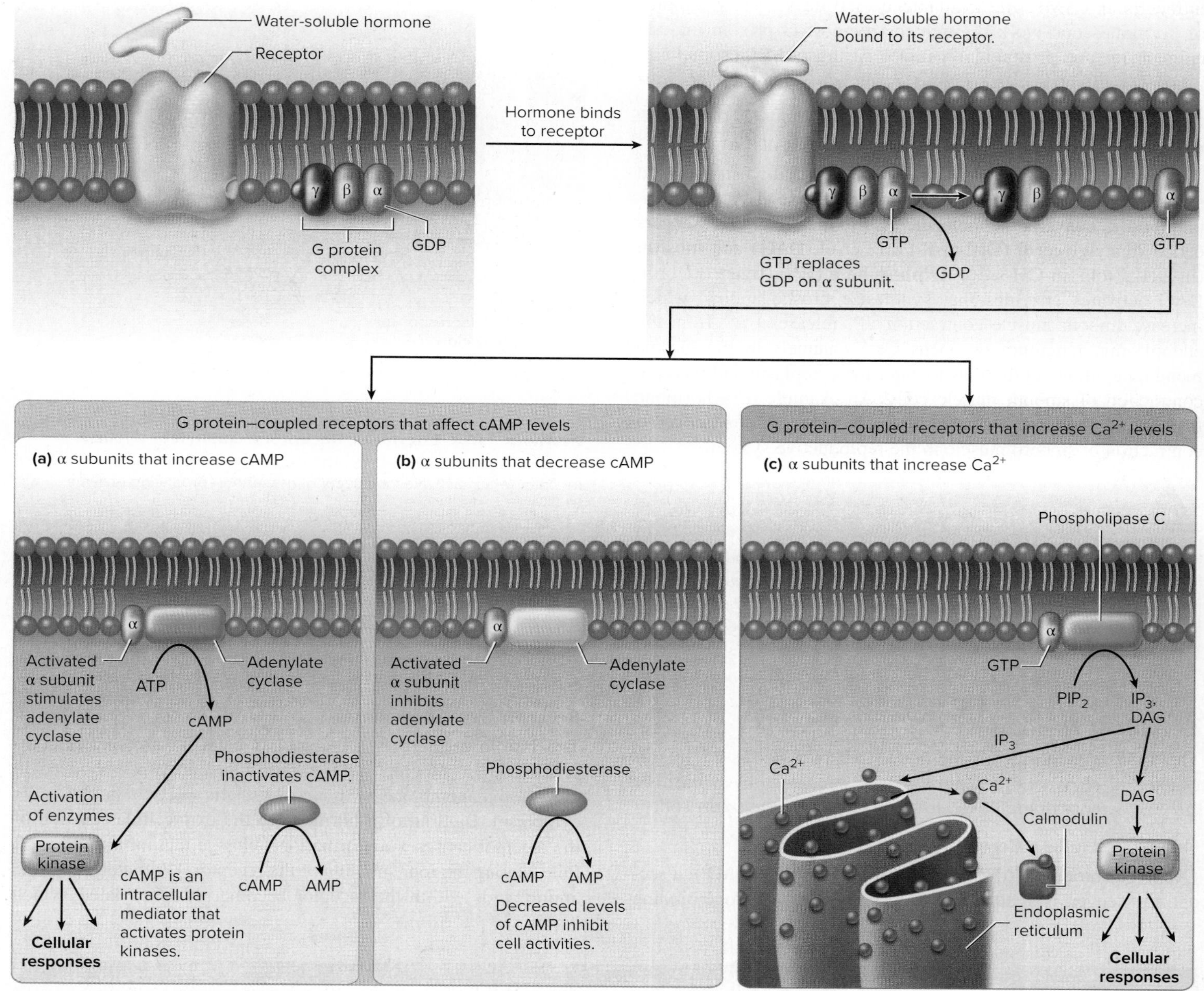

FIGURE 17.11 G Protein–Coupled Receptors

Water-soluble hormones must interact with the external portion of their receptor because they are unable to cross the plasma membrane. The cellular response is carried out through activation of a G protein and the second messenger, cAMP. Binding of the ligand to its receptor activates the G protein. The G protein activates the enzyme adenylate cyclase to produce the second messenger, cAMP. Epinephrine receptors in some smooth muscle cells are associated with G proteins. APR

enzyme in the cytoplasm, called **phosphodiesterase** (FOS-foh-die-ES-ter-ase), breaks down cAMP to AMP. Once cAMP levels drop, the enzymes in the cell are no longer stimulated. Cyclic AMP can elicit many different responses in the body because each cell type possesses a unique set of enzymes. For example, the hormone glucagon increases blood glucose levels when it binds to receptors on the surface of liver cells. Binding to the receptor activates G proteins and causes an increase in cAMP synthesis. Cyclic AMP then stimulates the activity of enzymes that break down glycogen into glucose for release from liver cells. Other hormones that utilize this pathway include epinephrine, antidiuretic hormone, luteinizing hormone, and follicle-stimulating hormone.

α Subunits That Decrease Intracellular Levels of cAMP

This family of G proteins has an α subunit that when activated inhibits adenylate cyclase, which results in a decrease in cAMP levels (figure 17.11*b*). By preventing synthesis of new cAMP and allowing phosphodiesterase to break down existing intracellular cAMP, the available cAMP decreases. Examples of hormones that work through this type of G protein include epinephrine and prostaglandins. Decreasing cAMP results in an inhibitory effect because important enzymes may not be activated in the absence of cAMP.

α Subunits That Increase Intracellular Levels of Ca^{2+}

The third family of G proteins has α subunits that when activated stimulate activation of the enzyme phospholipase C. Active phospholipase C converts the molecule PIP_2 to the second messengers called **diacylglycerol** (DIE-as-il-GLIS-er-ol; **DAG**) and **inositol** (in-OH-si-tohl, in-OH-si-tol) **triphosphate (IP_3)** (figure 17.11*c*). DAG activates enzymes that synthesize prostaglandins, which increase smooth muscle contraction. IP_3 releases Ca^{2+} from the endoplasmic reticulum or opens Ca^{2+} channels in the plasma membrane, allowing the ions to enter the cytoplasm and increase contraction of smooth muscle cells. An example of a hormone that operates through phospholipase C is oxytocin in stimulating contraction of smooth muscle in the reproductive system.

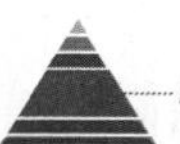

Predict 2

As long as the smooth muscle cells in the airways of the lungs are relaxed, breathing is easy. However, during asthma attacks, these smooth muscle cells contract, and breathing becomes very difficult. Some of the drugs used to treat asthma increase cAMP in smooth muscle cells. Explain some of the different ways in which these drugs work.

Enzymatic Receptors

The final type of membrane-bound receptor discussed in this chapter is enzymatic receptors. These receptors have intrinsic enzyme activity or are linked to enzymes within the target cell.

Guanylate Cyclase Receptors

Cyclic guanine (GWAHN-een) **monophosphate (cGMP),** a second messenger, is synthesized in response to a hormone binding to a membrane-bound receptor (figure 17.12). The hormone binds to its receptor, activating an enzyme called **guanylate cyclase** (GWAHN-i-late SIGH-klase) embedded in the plasma membrane. Guanylate cyclase converts guanine triphosphate (GTP) to cGMP. Cyclic GMP then activates specific enzymes in the target cell. These enzymes produce the cell's response to the hormone.

Water-soluble hormone
Guanylate cyclase (activated)
GTP
cGMP
Phosphodiesterase
Cellular responses: Activation of enzymes
cGMP GMP

FIGURE 17.12 Enzymatic Receptors: Guanylate Cyclase
Some second messengers are produced when the hormone binds to its receptor, which activates the second messenger–producing enzyme.

Receptor Tyrosine Kinases

The insulin receptor is a receptor tyrosine kinase that is composed of four subunits: two extracellular and two embedded in the plasma membrane with its enzymatic portion in the cell's cytoplasm. Binding of a hormone to the extracellular portion of the receptor causes a conformational change that initiates interactions among the four subunits of the receptor. Ultimately, tyrosine amino acids within the receptor become phosphorylated, which

Case STUDY 17.1 Elevated Blood Glucose: Insufficient Receptor Response or Insufficient Hormone Secretion

Sarah is a new mom. She gave birth to a beautiful baby boy after a challenging pregnancy. Sarah had been diagnosed with gestational diabetes, a temporary type of **diabetes mellitus** that occurs only during pregnancy. In diabetes mellitus including gestational diabetes, the hormone insulin does not properly regulate blood glucose levels. Despite trying to control her diet and exercising before the baby was born, she'd still gained 70 pounds during her pregnancy and her baby had weighed almost 10 pounds at birth. Since then, Sarah has not been sleeping, nor has she started the exercise program her doctor had recommended for her. Lately, she's also noticed a dark ring on the skin around her neck. She made another appointment with her doctor because her mother had experienced some of these same symptoms prior to being diagnosed with diabetes mellitus. Sarah's doctor ordered a fasting plasma glucose test, which showed that Sarah's glucose levels were 122 mg/dL. The American Diabetes Association classifies this glucose level as being prediabetic. This means that Sarah is at a higher risk for developing diabetes mellitus if she continues with her current lifestyle.

Predict 3

a. What is a likely mechanism for Sarah's elevated glucose levels?

b. What is the most important measure Sarah could take to reverse her condition?

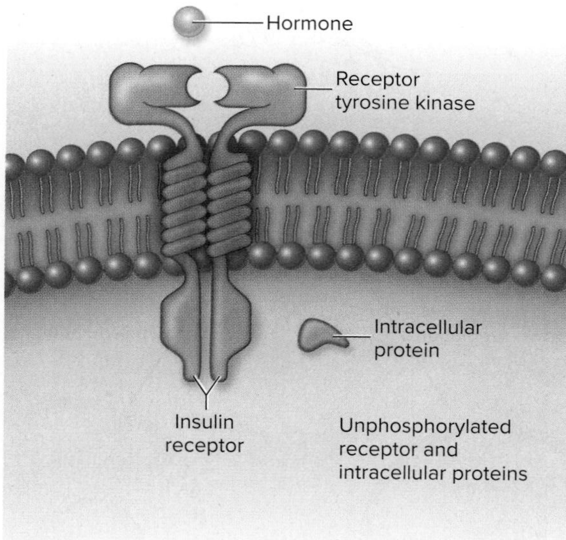

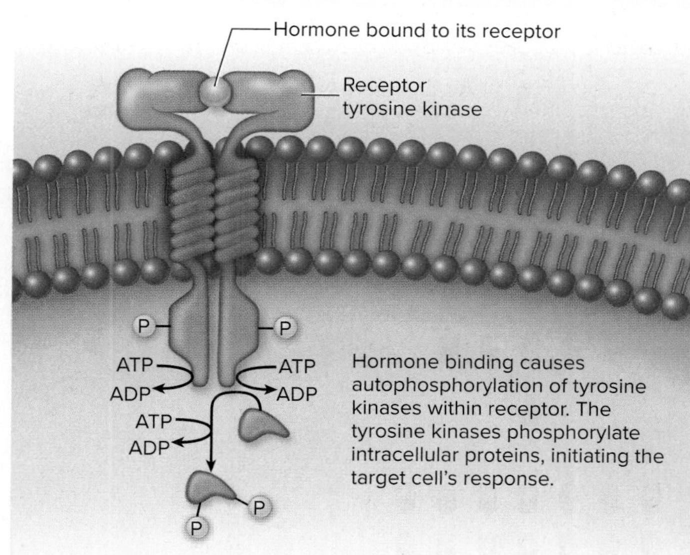

FIGURE 17.13 Enzymatic Receptors: Receptor Tyrosine Kinases
Some receptors serve as enzymes that phosphorylate intracellular molecules to activate them.

activates the receptor. The receptor then phosphorylates cytoplasmic proteins in the target cell that elicit the hormone's effects (figure 17.13). For example, insulin binds to its receptor, which phosphorylates regulatory intracellular proteins. These intracellular proteins trigger the insertion of the glucose transporter protein into the plasma membrane of insulin target cells, allowing glucose to enter the cell. Sometimes, individuals develop a reduced ability to respond properly to insulin, called **insulin resistance.** In insulin resistance, certain target cells for insulin, such as skeletal muscle fibers and liver cells, do not take up as much glucose as normal and blood glucose levels become elevated. The mechanism for insulin resistance is not well defined, but it is likely that the insulin receptor has reduced phosphorylation activity, which results in fewer glucose transporters being inserted into the plasma membrane of insulin target cells. With fewer glucose transporters, glucose would not be taken up as readily and blood glucose levels would increase.

Signal Amplification

The rate and magnitude at which a hormone's response is elicited are determined by its mechanism of action at the receptor. Nuclear receptors work by activating protein synthesis, which for some hormones can take several hours. However, hormones that stimulate the synthesis of second messengers can produce an almost instantaneous response because the second messenger influences existing enzymes. In other words, the response proteins are already present. Additionally, each receptor produces thousands of second messengers, leading to a cascade effect and ultimately **amplification** of the hormonal signal. With amplification, a single hormone activates many second messengers, each of which activates enzymes that produce an enormous amount of final product (figure 17.14). The efficiency of this second-messenger amplification is virtually unparalleled in the body and can be thought of as an "army of molecules" launching an offensive. In a war, the general gives the signal to attack, and thousands of soldiers carry out the order. The general alone could not neutralize thousands of enemies. Likewise, one hormone could not single-handedly produce millions of final products within a few seconds. However, with amplification, one hormone has an army of molecules working simultaneously to produce the final products.

Both nuclear receptor and membrane-bound receptor hormone systems are effective, but each is more suited to one type of response than another. For example, the reason epinephrine, which binds to membrane-bound receptors, is effective in a fight-or-flight situation is that it can turn on the target cell responses within a few seconds. If running away from an immediate threat depended on producing new proteins, which usually involves nuclear receptors, a process that can take several hours, many of us would have already perished. On the other hand, pregnancy maintenance is mediated by steroids, which also bind to nuclear receptors, long-acting hormones, which is reflected by the fact that pregnancy is a long-term process. Thus, it is important for our bodies to have hormones that can function over differing time scales.

Predict 4

Of membrane-bound receptors and nuclear receptors, which is better adapted for mediating a response that lasts a considerable length of time, and which is better for mediating a response with a rapid onset and short duration? Explain why.

Target Tissue Sensitivity

Target tissues' sensitivity to hormone levels can change for various reasons. Changing the receptor number at a target ensures an optimal target tissue response to a hormone.

FUNDAMENTAL **Figure**

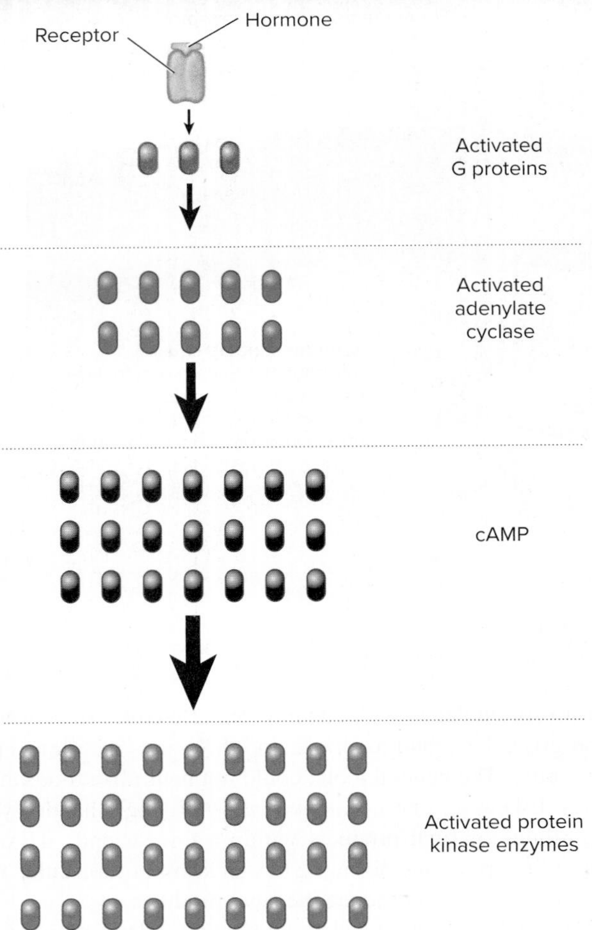

FIGURE 17.14 Amplification

The combination of a hormone with a membrane-bound receptor initiates a cascade effect that activates several G proteins. The G proteins, in turn, activate many inactive adenylate cyclase enzymes, which cause the synthesis of a large number of cAMP molecules. The large number of cAMP molecules, in turn, activate many inactive protein kinase enzymes, which produce a rapid and amplified response.

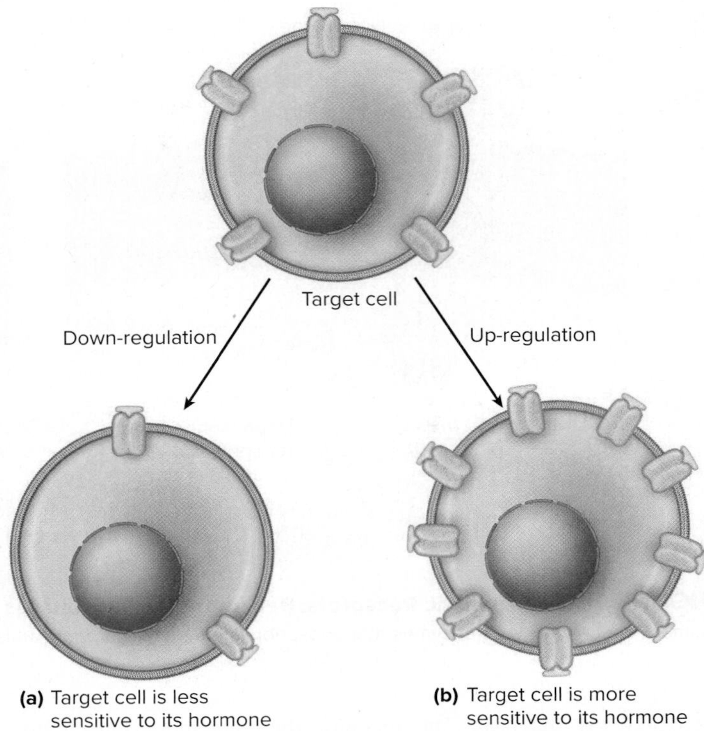

FIGURE 17.15 Down-Regulation and Up-Regulation of Target Cell Receptors

(*a*) Down-regulation occurs when the number of hormone receptors in a target cell decreases. Often, the target cells internalize the receptors and destroy them. (*b*) Up-regulation occurs when the number of receptors for a hormone in a target cell increases. Often, the hormone stimulates the synthesis of receptors in the target cells.

Down-Regulation of Receptors

The response of some target tissues rapidly decreases over time through desensitization. This happens because the cells' nutrient and energy supplies become depleted, causing the cells to lose the ability to respond to the hormone. Desensitization occurs when the number of receptors rapidly decreases after exposure to certain hormones, a phenomenon called down-regulation (figure 17.15*a*). Because most receptor molecules are degraded over time, a decrease in their synthesis rate reduces the total number of receptor molecules in a cell. Often, the target cells internalize the receptors and destroy them. For example, experimental exposure of anterior pituitary cells to the reproductive hormone gonadotropin-releasing hormone (GnRH) causes the number of receptor molecules for GnRH in the pituitary gland cells to decrease dramatically several hours after exposure to the hormone. This down-regulation causes the pituitary gland to become less sensitive to additional GnRH.

Up-Regulation of Receptors

On the other hand, a target tissue can also periodically increase sensitivity through up-regulation. **Up-regulation** results in an increase in the rate of receptor synthesis in the target cells, which increases the total number of receptor molecules in a cell (figure 17.15*b*). An example of up-regulation is a process that occurs to stimulate ovulation of the oocyte. During each menstrual cycle, there are an increased number of receptors for luteinizing hormone (LH) in ovary cells. This is important because a surge in LH will cause release of the oocyte.

Hormone Interactions

The response of a target tissue is rarely the result of a single hormone functioning independently. Instead, physiological processes are regulated by a network of chemical messengers. For processes involving predominantly hormones, we see three types of interactions among hormones (figure 17.16). These are:

1. *Permissive interactions.* Some hormones assist other hormones. Without the permissive effects of these types of hormones, the other hormone elicits a weaker response by the target tissue. For example, thyroid hormones promote

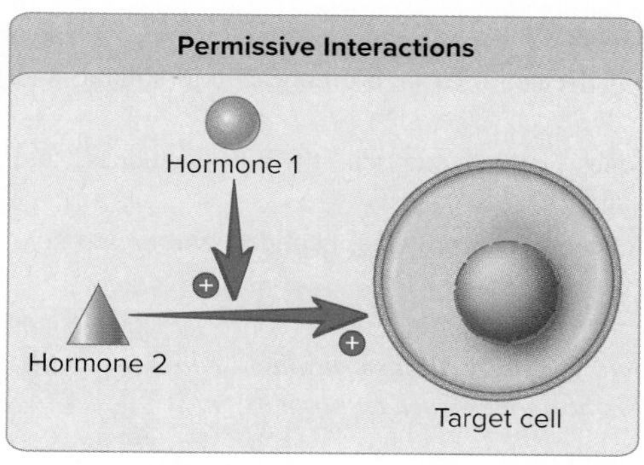

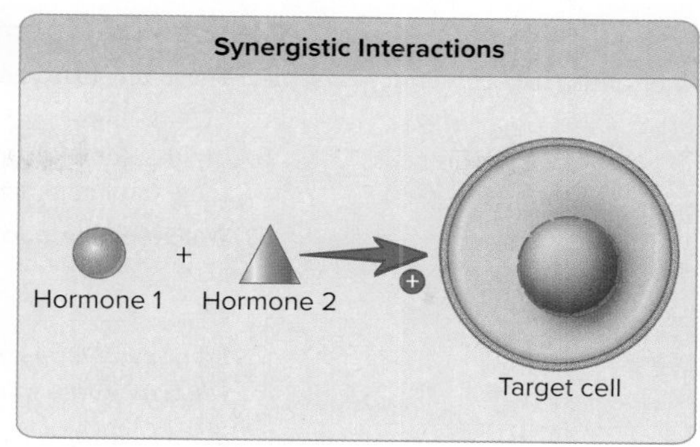

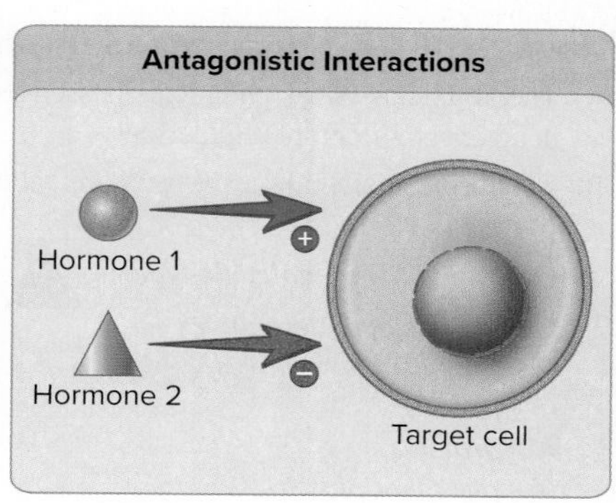

FIGURE 17.16 Hormone Interactions
Hormones can interact with other hormones through permissive actions where one hormone increases the actions of a second hormone. Synergistic hormones elicit a greater response by the target when they work together. Antagonistic hormones have opposite effects from each other.

synthesis of receptors for epinephrine in the heart. This is one reason why hyperthyroid individuals should only be administered epinephrine as an additive with a local anesthetic after careful consultation with the patient's physician.

2. *Synergistic interactions.* When two or more synergistic hormones exert their effects on a target tissue, the overall response is even larger than with either hormone alone. For example, in the reproductive system, reproductive steroid hormones synergize with hypothalamic hormones to promote the synthesis of gonad-regulating tropic hormones.
3. *Antagonistic interactions.* Certain hormones work in opposition to each other to very tightly regulate a specific parameter. For example, PTH and calcitonin are each sensitive to blood Ca^{2+} levels. However, PTH acts to increase blood Ca^{2+}, while calcitonin acts to decrease blood Ca^{2+} levels. Insulin and glucagon are probably the most well-known antagonistic hormones with insulin working to decrease blood glucose levels and glucagon working to increase blood glucose levels.

ASSESS YOUR PROGRESS

20. *What two ways can a membrane-bound receptor use to activate cellular response?*
21. *Explain how the hormone-receptor complex can alter the G proteins on the inner surface of the plasma membrane. Which subunit of the G protein alters the activity of molecules inside the plasma membrane or inside the cell?*
22. *List four intracellular mediators affected by G proteins.*
23. *Describe how G proteins can alter the permeability of the plasma membrane and how they can alter the synthesis of an intracellular mediator, such as cAMP. Give examples.*
24. *Describe how a hormone can bind to a membrane-bound receptor, directly change enzyme activity inside the cell, and increase phosphorylation of intracellular proteins. Give examples.*
25. *What limits the activity of intracellular mediators, such as cGMP, and phosphorylated proteins?*
26. *Explain the cascade effect for the second-messenger model of hormone action. Does the second-messenger amplification produce a slow or rapid response?*
27. *What is down-regulation, and what may cause it to occur? Give an example of down-regulation in the body.*
28. *What is up-regulation, and what may cause it to occur? Give an example of up-regulation in the body.*
29. *What are the three types of hormone interactions?*

Concept Check

17.1 Functions of the Endocrine System

A. The endocrine system includes glands and specialized endocrine cells that secrete hormones into the bloodstream.

B. A hormone is a chemical messenger that is secreted into the blood, travels to a distant target tissue, and binds to specific receptors to produce a coordinated set of events in that target tissue.

Comparison of the Nervous and Endocrine Systems

A. The endocrine system and the nervous system are closely related. They share anatomical structures in the brain, chemical messenger molecules, and they cooperate to regulate important processes.

B. The endocrine system and the nervous system have important differences such as mode of transport and speed of target tissue response.

1. *When comparing the endocrine system and the nervous system, the endocrine system generally* Remember

a. is faster-acting than the nervous system.
b. produces effects that are of shorter duration.
c. uses blood-borne chemical messengers.
d. produces more localized effects.
e. relies less on chemical messengers.

Classes of Chemical Messengers

A. The four classes of chemical messengers are autocrine, paracrine, neurotransmitter, and endocrine.

B. Endocrine chemical messengers are called hormones.

2. *Given this list of molecule types:* 

   (1) nucleic acid derivatives
   (2) fatty acid derivatives
   (3) peptides
   (4) proteins
   (5) phospholipids

   Which could be hormone molecules?

   a. 1,2,3
   b. 2,3,4
   c. 1,2,3,4
   d. 2,3,4,5
   e. 1,2,3,4,5

17.2 Hormones

Control of Hormone Secretion

Three types of stimuli result in hormone secretion: humoral, neural, and hormonal.

- Humoral stimulation is exhibited by hormones that are sensitive to circulating blood levels of certain molecules, such as glucose or calcium.
- Neural stimuli cause hormone secretion in direct response to action potentials in neurons, as occurs during stress or exercise.
- Hormonal stimulation of other hormone secretion is common in the endocrine system.
- Although the stimulus of hormone secretion is important, inhibition is equally important.

3. *Which of these can regulate the secretion of a hormone from an endocrine tissue?* Remember

   a. other hormones
   b. negative-feedback mechanisms
   c. humoral substances in the blood
   d. the nervous system
   e. All of these are correct.

4. *What cell membrane component must an endocrine cell have in order to respond to a neurotransmitter?* Understand

Patterns of Hormone Secretion

The three main patterns of hormone secretions are chronic, acute, and episodic.

5. *Hormones are released into the blood* 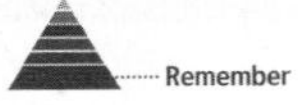

   a. at relatively constant levels.
   b. in large amounts in response to a stimulus.
   c. in an episodic fashion.
   d. All of these are correct.

6. *Consider a hormone that is secreted in large amounts at a given interval, modified chemically by the liver, and excreted by the kidneys at a rapid rate, thus making the half-life of the hormone in the circulatory system very short. The hormone therefore rapidly increases in the blood and then decreases rapidly. Suppose that a patient has both liver and kidney disease. Predict the consequences on the blood levels of that hormone.* Apply

Classes of Hormones

A. There are two chemical categories of hormones: lipid-soluble and water-soluble.

B. Lipid-soluble hormones include steroids, thyroid hormones, and some fatty acid derivatives.

C. Water-soluble hormones include proteins, peptides, and amino acid derivatives.

7. *Lipid-soluble hormones readily diffuse through capillary walls, whereas water-soluble hormones, such as proteins, must* Remember

   a. pass through capillary cells.
   b. pass through pores in the capillary endothelium.
   c. be moved out of the capillary by active transport.
   d. remain in the blood.
   e. be broken down to amino acids before leaving the blood.

17.3 Transport and Metabolism of Hormones

Binding Proteins

A. Most lipid-soluble hormones are transported bound to binding proteins.

B. Most water-soluble hormones circulate freely in the blood.

Regulation of Hormone Levels in the Blood

A. Two processes regulate the overall blood levels of hormones: negative feedback and positive feedback.
   - Negative feedback prevents further hormone secretion once a set point is achieved.
   - Positive feedback is a self-promoting system whereby the stimulation of hormone secretion increases over time.

B. Lipid-soluble hormones have a half-life that can extend from minutes to weeks. Water-soluble hormones have a shorter half-life due to the actions of proteases in the plasma.

C. Lipid-soluble hormones are removed from the circulation by conjugation to sulfate or glucuronic acid, which then allows them to be excreted in the bile. Proteases degrade protein and peptide hormones in the circulation; the breakdown products are then excreted in the urine. However, some water-soluble hormones have chemical modifications, such as the addition of a carbohydrate group, which prolongs their half-life.

8. *Consider a hormone that increases the concentration of a substance in the circulatory system. If a tumor begins to produce that substance in large amounts in an uncontrolled fashion, predict the effect on the hormone's secretion rate.* Understand

9. *Predict the effect on LH and FSH secretion if a small tumor in the hypothalamus continuously secretes large concentrations of GnRH. Given that LH and FSH regulate the function of the male and female reproductive systems, state whether the condition will increase or decrease the activity of these systems.* Apply

10. *Concerning the half-life of hormones,* 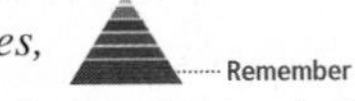

    a. lipid-soluble hormones generally have a longer half-life.
    b. hormones with a shorter half-life regulate activities with a slow onset and long duration.

c. *hormones with a shorter half-life are maintained at more constant levels in the blood.*
d. *lipid-soluble hormones are degraded rapidly by enzymes in the circulatory system.*
e. *water-soluble hormones usually bind to plasma proteins.*

11. *Thyroid hormones are important in regulating the body's basal metabolic rate. Thyroid hormones are lipid-soluble and have a long half-life. What are the advantages and disadvantages of a long half-life for thyroid hormones, compared with a short half-life?* Understand

12. *When an individual is confronted with a potentially harmful situation, the adrenal glands release epinephrine (adrenaline). Epinephrine prepares the body for action by increasing the heart rate and blood glucose levels. Explain the advantages or disadvantages associated with a shorter half-life for epinephrine, such as when it is released as a neurotransmitter, and those associated with a longer half-life, such as when it is secreted as a hormone.* Understand

13. *Which of these is* not *a means by which hormones are eliminated from the circulatory system?* Remember
    a. *excreted into urine or bile*
    b. *bound to binding proteins*
    c. *enzymatically degraded in the blood (metabolism)*
    d. *actively transported into cells*
    e. *conjugated with sulfate or glucuronic acid*

17.4 Hormone Receptors and Mechanisms of Action

Agonists and Antagonists

A. Agonists mimic the actions of a natural hormone.
B. Antagonists block the actions of a natural hormone.

Classes of Receptors

The two groups of hormones have their own class of receptors.

A. Lipid-soluble hormones bind to nuclear receptors located inside the nucleus of the target cell.
B. Water-soluble hormones bind to membrane-bound receptors, which are integral membrane proteins.

14. *Given these observations:*

    (1) *A hormone affects only a specific tissue (not all tissues).*
    (2) *A tissue can respond to more than one hormone.*
    (3) *Some tissues respond rapidly to a hormone, whereas others take many hours to respond.*

    Which of these observations can be explained by the characteristics of hormone receptors?

    a. *1* c. *2,3* e. *1,2,3*
    b. *1,2* d. *1,3*

15. *Predict some consequences of trying to use a skin patch to administer insulin, a protein hormone, to a person who has diabetes mellitus.*

Action of Nuclear Receptors

A. Nuclear receptors have portions that allow them to bind to the DNA in the nucleus once the hormone is bound.
B. The hormone-receptor complex activates genes, which in turn activate the DNA to produce mRNA.
C. The mRNA increases the synthesis of certain proteins that produce the target cell's response.

16. *When a hormone binds to a nuclear receptor*

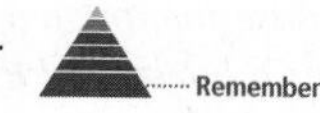

    a. *DNA produces mRNA.*
    b. *G proteins are activated.*
    c. *the hormone-receptor complex causes ion channels to open or close.*
    d. *the cell's response is faster than when a hormone binds to a membrane-bound receptor.*
    e. *the hormone is usually a large, water-soluble molecule.*

17. *Given these events:*

    (1) *activation of cAMP*
    (2) *activation of genes*
    (3) *alteration of enzyme activity*

    Which of these events can occur when a hormone binds to a nuclear hormone receptor?

    a. *1* c. *2,3*
    b. *1,2* d. *1,2,3*

Action of Membrane-Bound Receptors and Signal Amplification

A. Membrane-bound receptors activate a cascade of events once the hormone binds.
B. Some membrane-bound receptors are associated with membrane proteins called G proteins.
    - The α subunit of the G protein binds to ion channels and causes them to open or change the rate of synthesis second messengers, such as cAMP, cGMP, IP_3, and DAG.
C. Some membrane-bound receptors have intrinsic enzymatic activity.
D. Second-messenger systems act rapidly because they act on already existing enzymes to amplify the signal.

18. *Activated G proteins can*

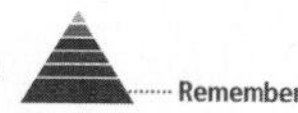

    a. *cause ion channels to open or close.*
    b. *activate adenylate cyclase.*
    c. *inhibit the synthesis of cAMP.*
    d. *alter the activity of IP_3.*
    e. *All of these are correct.*

19. *Given these events:*

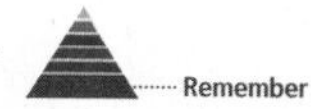

    (1) *GTP is converted to GDP.*
    (2) *The subunit separates from the β and γ units.*
    (3) *GDP is released from the α subunit.*

    List the order in which the events occur after a hormone binds to a membrane-bound receptor.

    a. *1,2,3*
    b. *1,3,2*
    c. *2,3,1*
    d. *3,2,1*
    e. *3,1,2*

20. *Given these events:* 

    (1) cAMP is synthesized.
    (2) The α subunit of G protein is activated.
    (3) Phosphodiesterase breaks down cAMP.

    Choose the arrangement that lists the events in the order they occur after a hormone binds to a receptor.

    a. 1,2,3 *c. 2,1,3* *e. 3,2,1*
    b. 1,3,2 *d. 2,3,1*

21. *Which of these can limit a cell's response to a hormone?* 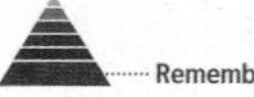

    a. phosphodiesterase
    b. converting GTP to GDP
    c. decreasing the number of receptors
    d. blocking binding sites
    e. All of these are correct.

22. *How could you determine whether a hormone-mediated response has resulted from the intracellular mediator mechanism or the nuclear receptor mechanism?* Apply

23. *If a hormone affects a target tissue through a membrane-bound receptor that has a G protein associated with it, predict the consequences if a genetic disease causes the α subunit of the G protein to have a structure that prevents it from binding to GTP.* Apply

24. *For a hormone that binds to a membrane-bound receptor and has cAMP as the intracellular mediator, predict and explain the consequences if a patient takes a drug that strongly inhibits phosphodiesterase.* Understand

Target Tissue Sensitivity

A. A target cell may decrease its sensitivity to a hormone through desensitization, which can occur through a decrease in receptor number, a process called down-regulation.

B. A target cell may increase its sensitivity to a hormone through sensitization, which can occur through an increase in receptor number, a process called up-regulation.

25. *Down-regulation* 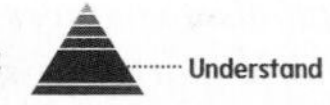

    a. produces a decrease in the number of receptors in the target cells.
    b. produces an increase in target cells' sensitivity to a hormone.
    c. is found in target cells that respond to hormones that are maintained at constant levels.
    d. occurs partly because of an increase in receptor synthesis by the target cell.
    e. All of these are correct.

Hormone Interactions

Hormones can act permissively, synergistically, or antagonistically with each other.

Answers to this chapter's odd-numbered Concept Check questions appear in Appendix F.

18

CHAPTER

Endocrine Glands

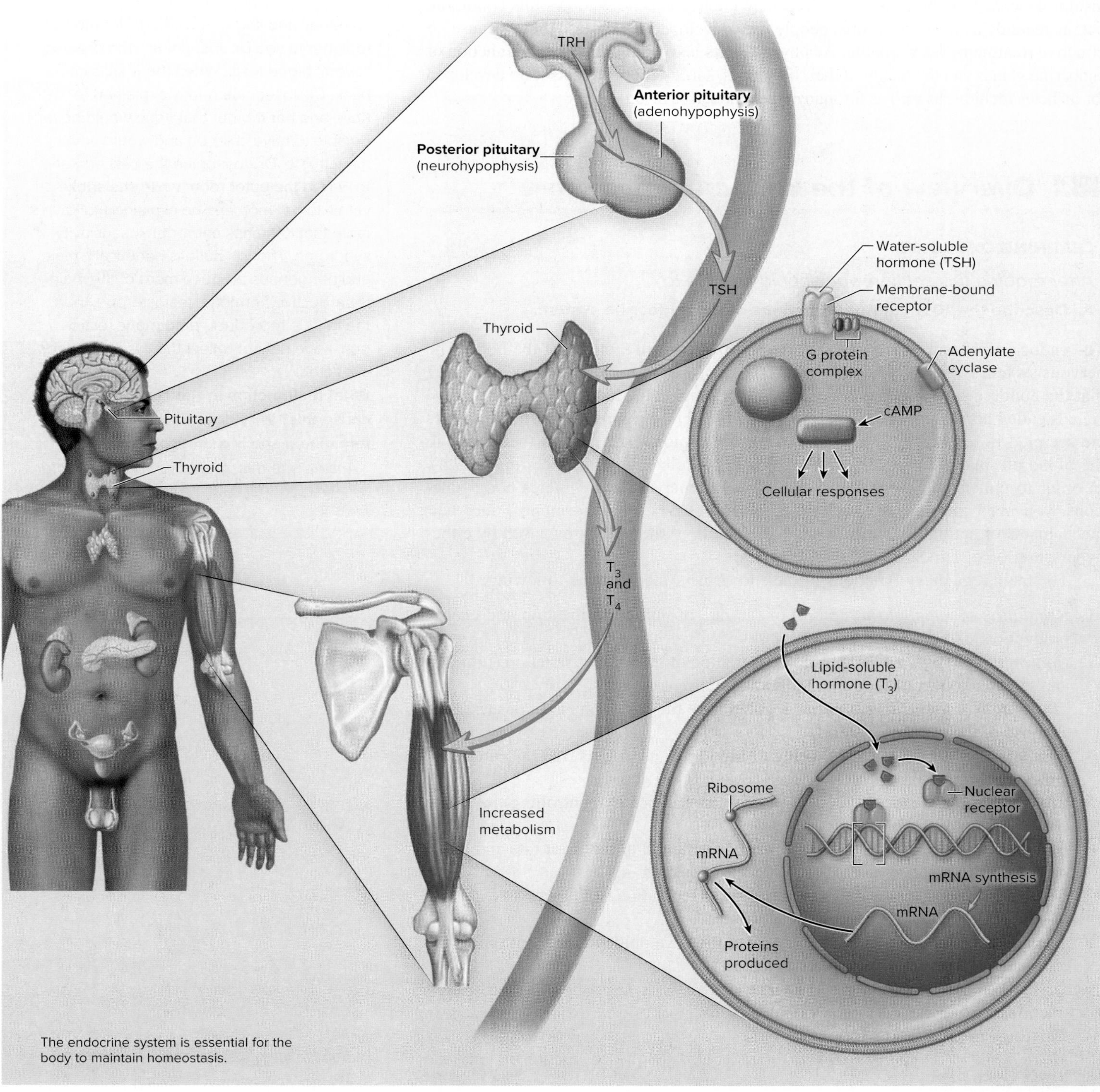

The endocrine system is essential for the body to maintain homeostasis.

This chapter examines each of the organs of the endocrine system, describes the hormones they secrete, and explains how hormone secretion is regulated so that homeostasis is maintained. The endocrine system works with the nervous system to regulate and coordinate the activities of nearly all the other body structures. When either system fails to function properly, conditions can rapidly deviate from homeostasis, and disease may result. One of the most common endocrine system disorders is insulin-dependent diabetes mellitus. You may know someone who has this condition, but, as recently as the early 1900s, people who developed the disease died because no effective treatment was available. As physiologists learned more about the function of endocrine glands and the nature of their hormones, successful treatments were developed for diabetes mellitus, as well as for many other endocrine disorders.

Learn to Predict

Katie was getting nervous. At 16, she was the only one in her group of friends who had not started menstruating. Katie had always dreamed of having three beautiful children someday and she was worried. Her mother took her to see Dr. Josephine, who ordered several blood tests. When the results came back, Dr. Josephine gently explained to Katie and her mother that Katie would never be able to have children and would never menstruate. Dr. Josephine then asked Katie to wait in the outer room while she spoke privately to her mother. She explained to Katie's mom that Katie has androgen insensitivity syndrome. Though Katie is genetically male and her gonads produce more of the male reproductive hormone, testosterone, than the female reproductive hormone, estrogen, Katie did not reflect the tissue changes expected.

What malfunction in Katie's body would cause this? Why does Katie's body look feminine if she is genetically male?

Answers to this question and the chapter's odd-numbered Predict questions can be found in Appendix E.

18.1 Overview of the Endocrine System

LEARNING OUTCOME

After reading this section, you should be able to

A. **Describe the 10 regulatory functions of the endocrine system.**

The endocrine system is one of the two important control systems of the body. The nervous system is the body's other important control system. Recall from chapter 17 that the endocrine system is composed of glands and cells that secrete the chemical signals called hormones into the plasma of the blood (see figure 17.1). The hormones are secreted in response to humoral, neural, or hormonal stimuli and then travel in the blood plasma to target cells, where they regulate homeostasis (see figure 17.4). In order to understand completely how the endocrine system regulates body functions, you need to know the various endocrine glands, their hormones, and their mechanisms of action. In addition, many disorders of the body are caused by either hypersecretion or hyposecretion of hormones.

The main regulatory functions of the endocrine system are the following:

1. *Regulation of metabolism:* control of the rate of nutrient utilization and energy production.
2. *Control of food intake and digestion:* regulation of the level of satiation (fullness) and the breakdown of food into individual nutrients.
3. *Modulation of tissue development:* regulation of the development of tissues, such as those of the nervous system.
4. *Regulation of ion levels:* monitoring of blood pH, as well as Na^+, K^+, and Ca^{2+} concentrations in the blood.
5. *Control of water balance:* regulation of water balance by controlling the solute concentration of the blood.
6. *Changes in heart rate and blood pressure:* regulation of the heart rate and blood pressure and preparation of the body for physical activity.
7. *Control of blood glucose and other nutrients:* regulation of the levels of glucose and other nutrients in the blood.
8. *Control of reproductive functions:* control of the development and functions of the reproductive systems in males and females.
9. *Stimulation of uterine contractions and milk release:* regulation of uterine contractions during delivery and stimulation of milk release from the breasts in lactating females.
10. *Modulation of immune system function:* control of the production of immune cells.

Module 8
Endocrine System

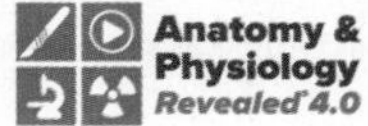

ASSESS YOUR PROGRESS

Answers to these questions are found in the section you have just completed. Re-read the section if you need help in answering these questions.

1. *List 10 regulatory functions of the endocrine system.*

18.2 Pituitary Gland and Hypothalamus

LEARNING OUTCOMES

After reading this section, you should be able to

A. **Describe the location and structure of the pituitary gland.**
B. **Explain the physical, neural, and vascular connections between the hypothalamus and the pituitary gland.**
C. **Describe how the hypothalamus regulates hormone secretion from the pituitary gland.**
D. **List the hormones produced by the hypothalamus and state their structural type, target tissues, and actions.**
E. **List the hormones produced by the anterior pituitary gland and state their structural type, target tissues, and actions.**
F. **Explain the nature of a tropic hormone.**
G. **Describe the conditions that result from over- and undersecretion of pituitary hormones.**

As you learned in chapter 17, the endocrine system works closely with the nervous system to regulate and maintain homeostasis. Two important structures for integrating the nervous system and the endocrine system are the **pituitary** (pih-TOO-ih-tair-ee) **gland,** or *hypophysis* (high-POF-ih-sis; an undergrowth), and the **hypothalamus** (high-poh-THAL-ah-muss; figure 18.1). The pituitary gland secretes nine major hormones that regulate numerous body functions and the secretory activity of several other endocrine glands. The hypothalamus regulates the secretory activity of the pituitary gland in response to other hormones, sensory information, and emotions.

Structure of the Pituitary Gland

The pituitary gland is connected to the base of the brain, just inferior to the hypothalamus. A stalk of tissue called the **infundibulum** (IN-fun-DIB-you-lum) connects the pituitary gland to the hypothalamus. The pituitary gland rests in the sella turcica of the sphenoid bone and is 1 cm in diameter and weighs 0.5–1.0 g, which is roughly the size of a pea (figure 18.1*a*).

The pituitary gland is divided into two lobes: (1) the **posterior pituitary gland,** or *neurohypophysis* (NOOR-oh-high-POF-i-sis), and (2) the **anterior pituitary gland,** or *adenohypophysis* (AD-eh-noh-high-POF-i-sis; *adeno,* gland).

Posterior Pituitary

The posterior pituitary is called the neurohypophysis because it is continuous with the hypothalamus in the brain (*neuro* refers to the nervous system). During embryonic development, the posterior pituitary forms from an outgrowth of the hypothalamus region of the brain (see chapter 29). The outgrowth of the brain forms the infundibulum, and the distal end of the infundibulum enlarges to form the posterior pituitary (figure 18.2*a*). Because the posterior pituitary is a part of the nervous system, its hormones are called **neuropeptides** or **neurohormones** (noor-oh-HOHR-monz).

Anterior Pituitary

The anterior pituitary is called the adenohypophysis (*adeno* refers to gland) because it is derived from glandular epithelium. It develops as an outpocketing of the roof of the embryonic oral cavity called the pituitary diverticulum, or Rathke pouch. The pituitary diverticulum continues growing toward the posterior pituitary. As it nears the posterior pituitary, the pituitary diverticulum loses its connection with the oral cavity and becomes the anterior pituitary. The anterior pituitary includes a thin band of tissue called the pars intermedia at its border with the posterior pituitary. The pars intermedia is not functional in adult humans (figure 18.2). Because the anterior pituitary is derived from epithelial tissue of the embryonic oral cavity, not from neural tissue, the hormones secreted from the anterior pituitary are traditional hormones, not neuropeptides.

Relationship of the Pituitary Gland to the Brain: The Hypothalamus

The pituitary is regulated by a small region of the brain just superior to the pituitary called the hypothalamus. The anterior and posterior pituitary are regulated by the hypothalamus in different ways. The hypothalamus regulates the anterior pituitary through a specialized set of blood vessels, called a portal system. A portal system consists of two capillary networks directly connected by portal system vessels. The portal system that connects the hypothalmus to the anterior pitituary is called the **hypothalamohypophysial portal system.** It is one of the major portal systems in the body. The others include the hepatic portal system and the renal nephron systems (see chapters 21 and 26). In contrast, the hypothalamus regulates the posterior pituitary through a specialized neural pathway called the hypothalamohypophysial tract.

Hypothalamic Control of the Posterior Pituitary

Secretion of hormones by the posterior pituitary is very different from that of the anterior pituitary. There is no portal system to carry hypothalamic neuropeptides to the posterior pituitary. The posterior pituitary is simply a storage location for two neuropeptides produced by neurosecretory neurons in the hypothalamus. The axons of these neurons extend from the hypothalamus through the infundibulum into the posterior pituitary and form a tract called the **hypothalamohypophysial tract** (figure 18.3).

Figure 18.3 outlines the relationship between the hypothalamus and the posterior pituitary.

1. Stimulation of neurons within the hypothalamus controls the secretion of the posterior pituitary hormones.
2. Action potentials are conducted by axons of the hypothalamic neurons through the hypothalamohypophysial tract to the posterior pituitary. The axon endings of neurons store hormones in the posterior pituitary.

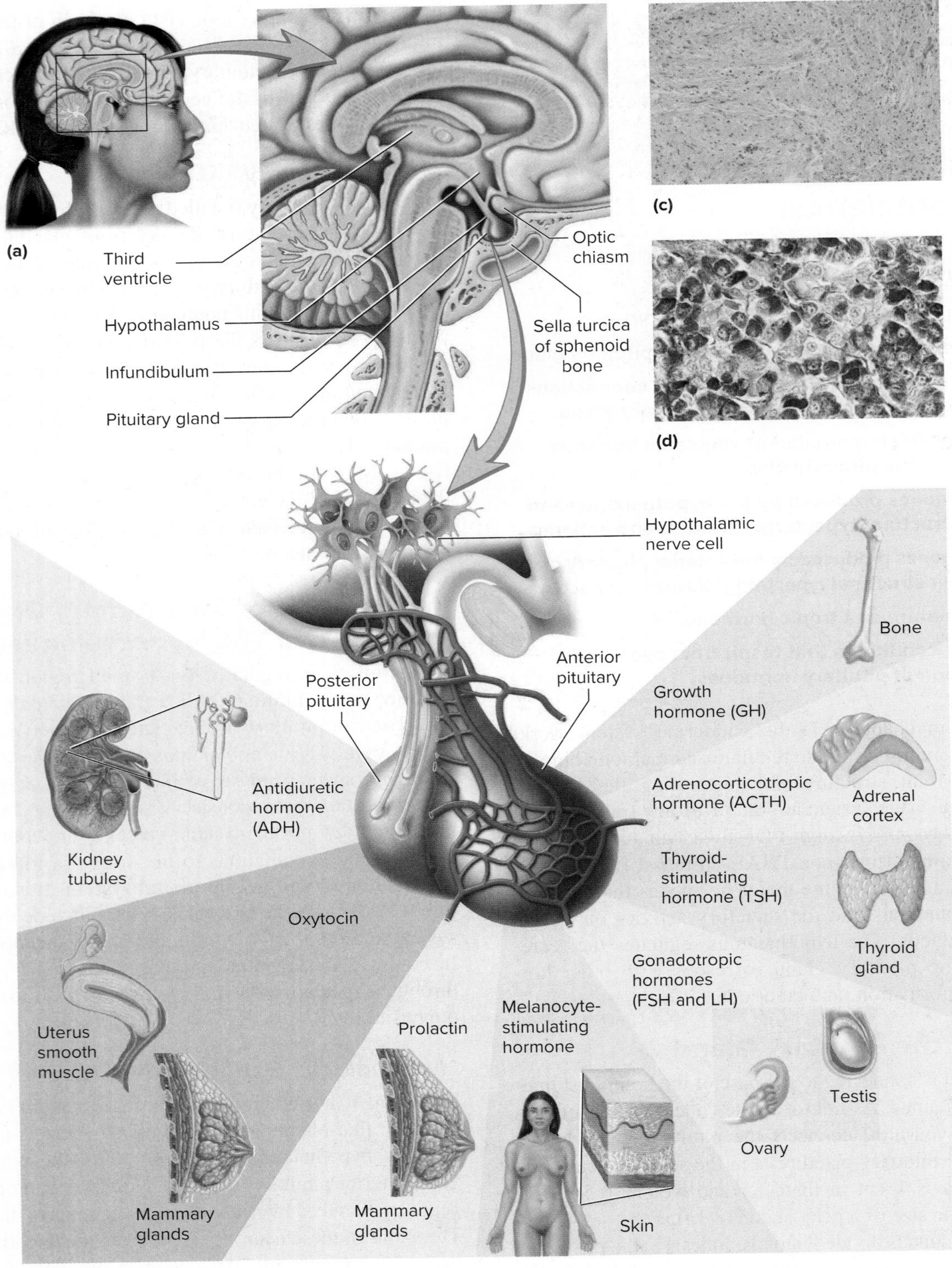

FIGURE 18.1 Subdivisions of the Pituitary Gland
(*a*) A midsagittal section of the head through the pituitary gland, showing the location of the hypothalamus of the brain and the pituitary gland. The pituitary gland is in a depression called the sella turcica in the floor of the skull. It is connected to the hypothalamus by the infundibulum. (*b*) The pituitary gland is divided into the anterior pituitary gland and the posterior pituitary gland. The posterior pituitary consists of the enlarged distal end of the infundibulum, which connects the posterior pituitary to the hypothalamus. (*c*,*d*) Histology of the pituitary gland: (*c*) The posterior pituitary consists of axon terminals, whereas (*d*) the anterior pituitary consists of groups of secretory cells. (c) APR Micrographs/Lutz Slomianka; (d) Victor P. Eroschenko APR

As the osmolality of the blood decreases, the action potential frequency in the osmoreceptors and the neurosecretory neurons decreases. Thus, less ADH is secreted from the posterior pituitary gland, and the reduction in ADH secretion causes more water to be eliminated in the form of urine.

Urine volume goes up within minutes to a few hours in response to the consumption of a large volume of water. In contrast, there is less urine, but it becomes highly concentrated within hours if little water is consumed. ADH regulates these changes in urine formation by controlling the permeability of kidney tubules to water. Its effect is to maintain the osmolality and the volume of the extracellular fluid within a normal range of values.

Because ADH regulates blood volume, its secretion is also controlled by blood pressure changes. Sensory receptors that detect changes in blood pressure send action potentials through sensory nerve fibers of the vagus nerve, which eventually communicate these changes to the ADH neurosecretory neurons. A drop in blood pressure, which normally accompanies a decrease in blood volume, stimulates ADH secretion, which causes the kidneys to retain water. Because the water in urine is derived from blood as it passes through the kidneys, ADH slows any further reduction in blood volume.

A rise in blood pressure reduces the action potential frequency in the ADH neurosecretory neurons. This leads to the secretion of less ADH from the posterior pituitary. As a result, the volume of urine produced by the kidneys goes up (figure 18.5). Even small changes in blood osmolality influence ADH secretion. Larger changes in blood pressure are required to influence ADH secretion. The effect of ADH on the kidney and its role in regulating extracellular osmolality and volume are described in greater detail in chapters 26 and 27.

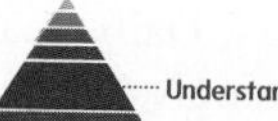

Predict 2

After his school's football team won the division championship, Luke went to a local bar with some friends and drank too much beer. Fortunately, one of his friends served as a designated driver. The next morning, Luke wondered why he was thirsty and felt somewhat dehydrated. His roommate, an anatomy and physiology student, pointed out that alcohol inhibits ADH secretion from the posterior pituitary. The roommate then explained why Luke was thirsty and dehydrated. What was the explanation?

Oxytocin

Oxytocin (OK-see-TOH-sin) is an important reproductive hormone, synthesized by the hypothalamic neurosecretory neuron cell bodies in the paraventricular nuclei. Oxytocin is transported to the posterior pituitary for storage.

Oxytocin stimulates labor in pregnant mammals. It does this by stimulating smooth muscle contraction in the uterus. It also causes contraction of uterine smooth muscle in nonpregnant females, primarily during menstruation and sexual intercourse. The uterine contractions help rid the uterus of its lining along with small amounts of blood during menstruation. Oxytocin can also facilitate the movement of sperm cells through the uterus after sexual intercourse. Oxytocin is responsible for milk letdown in breastfeeding females and other lactating mammals. It promotes

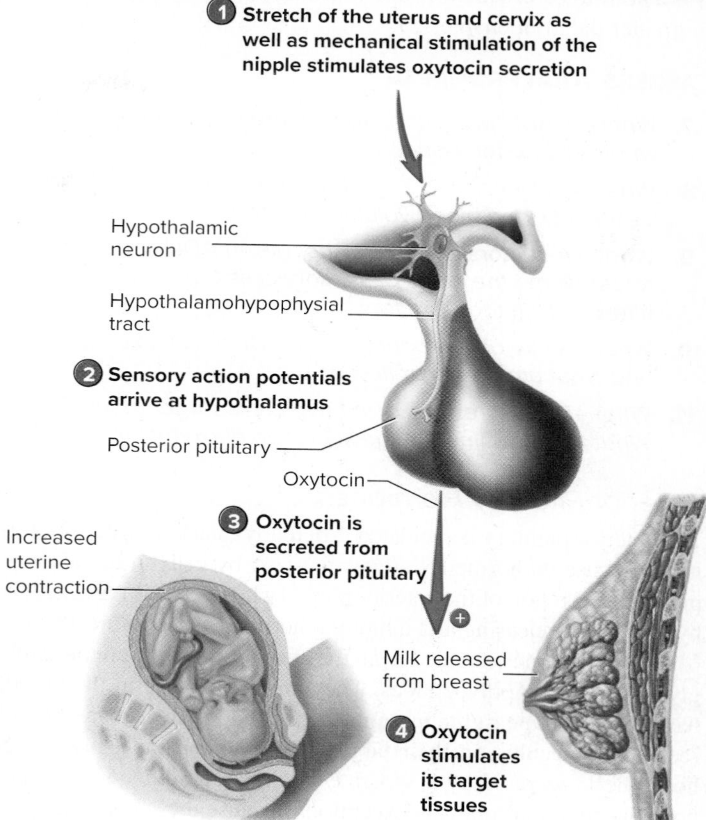

PROCESS Figure 18.6

Control of Oxytocin Secretion

Oxytocin secretion is stimulated by neural input from the nipples and the uterus.

What outcome might you expect if a pregnant female were to be given an oxytocin agonist?

the contraction of smooth-muscle-like cells surrounding the milk ducts in the mammary glands. In addition, oxytocin is associated with maternal nurturing and bonding (see chapter 29). Although little is known about the specific effects of oxytocin in males, evidence suggests that it promotes sperm movement during ejaculation as well as being associated with pair bonding.

Stretch of the uterus, mechanical stimulation of the cervix, and stimulation of the nipples of the breast when a baby nurses activate nervous reflexes that stimulate oxytocin release. Figure 18.6 outlines the mechanism controlling oxytocin secretion:

1. Stretch of the uterus and the uterine cervix or stimulation of the breasts' nipples increases action potentials in axons of oxytocin-secreting neurons.
2. Action potentials are conducted by sensory neurons from the uterus and breast to the spinal cord and up ascending tracts to the hypothalamus.
3. Action potentials are conducted by axons of oxytocin-secreting neurons in the hypothalamohypophysial tract to the posterior pituitary, where they increase oxytocin secretion.
4. Oxytocin enters the circulation, increasing contractions of the uterus and milk letdown from the lactating breast.

The role of oxytocin in the reproductive system is described in greater detail in chapter 29.

ASSESS YOUR PROGRESS

7. *Where is ADH produced, from where is it secreted, and what is its target tissue?*
8. *When ADH levels increase, how are urine volume, blood osmolarity, and blood volume affected?*
9. *What two factors will cause changes in ADH secretion rates? Name the types of sensory cells that respond to alterations in those factors.*
10. *Where is oxytocin produced, from where is it secreted, and what are its target tissues?*
11. *What effects does oxytocin have on its target tissues? What factors stimulate the secretion of oxytocin?*

Anterior Pituitary Hormones

The anterior pituitary is regulated differently than the posterior pituitary because its hormones are synthesized by cells in the anterior pituitary. Secretion of the anterior pituitary hormones is regulated by hypothalamic releasing and inhibiting hormones (see figure 18.3).

The hormones secreted from the anterior pituitary are proteins, glycoproteins, or polypeptides. They are transported in the blood, have a half-life measured in minutes, and bind to membrane-bound receptor molecules on their target cells. For the most part, each hormone is secreted by a separate cell type. Adrenocorticotropic hormone and lipotropin are exceptions because these hormones are derived from the same precursor protein.

Many hormones from the anterior pituitary gland are **tropic** (TROH-pik) **hormones,** which stimulate the secretion of other hormones from the target tissues. Tropic hormones also control the growth of target tissues. The anterior pituitary hormones include (1) growth hormone and prolactin, (2) adrenocorticotropic hormone and related substances, and (3) luteinizing hormone, follicle-stimulating hormone, and thyroid-stimulating hormone.

Growth Hormone

Growth hormone (GH), or *somatotropin,* is a protein hormone that stimulates growth in most tissues and plays an important role in determining how tall a person becomes. It also regulates metabolism. GH plays an important role in regulating blood nutrient levels after a meal and during periods of fasting. GH increases the movement of amino acids into cells, favors their incorporation into proteins, and slows protein breakdown. GH increases lipolysis (lipid breakdown) and the release of fatty acids from adipocytes into the blood. Fatty acids then can be used as energy sources to drive chemical reactions, including anabolic reactions, by other cells. GH also increases glucose synthesis by the liver, which releases glucose into the blood. The increased use of lipids as an energy source accompanies a decrease in glucose usage. Overall, GH activates the use of lipids to promote growth and protein synthesis.

GH binds directly to membrane-bound receptors on target cells (see chapter 17), such as adipocytes, to produce responses. These responses are called the direct effects of GH and include the increased breakdown of lipids and the decreased use of glucose as an energy source.

GH also has indirect effects on some tissues. It increases the production of a number of polypeptides, primarily by the liver but also by skeletal muscle and other tissues. These polypeptides are called **insulin-like growth factors (IGFs).** They are so named because of their structural resemblance to insulin and because the receptor molecules function through a mechanism similar to that of the insulin receptors. IGFs have paracrine effects and circulate in the blood until they bind to receptors on target tissues. IGFs stimulate growth in cartilage and bone and increase the synthesis of protein in skeletal muscles. Like IGFs, growth hormone and growth factors bind to membrane-bound receptors that phosphorylate intracellular proteins (see chapter 17).

Two neuropeptides released from the hypothalamus regulate the secretion of GH. One hormone, growth hormone–releasing hormone (GHRH), stimulates the secretion of GH, and the other, growth hormone–inhibiting hormone (GHIH; somatostatin), inhibits the secretion of GH. Stimuli that influence GH secretion act on the hypothalamus to increase or decrease the secretion of the releasing and inhibiting hormones. The steps in GH secretion can be seen in figure 18.7:

1. Stress and decreased blood glucose levels increase the release of growth hormone–releasing hormone (GHRH), and decrease the release of growth hormone–inhibiting hormone (GHIH), from the hypothalamus.
2. GHRH and GHIH travel through the hypothalamohypophysial portal system to the anterior pituitary.
3. Increased GHRH and reduced GHIH act on the anterior pituitary and result in increased GH secretion.
4. GH acts on target tissues.
5. Increasing GH and IGFs have a negative-feedback effect on the hypothalamus, resulting in decreased GHRH and increased GHIH release.

In most people, a rhythm of GH secretion occurs. Daily peak levels of GH are correlated with deep sleep. Surprisingly, rapidly growing children do not have chronically elevated blood GH levels. However, their levels tend to be higher than those of adults. In addition to GH, factors such as genetics, nutrition, and sex hormones influence growth.

Several pathological conditions are associated with abnormal GH secretion. In general, hypersecretion or hyposecretion of GH is caused by tumors in the hypothalamus or pituitary, the synthesis of structurally abnormal GH, the liver's inability to produce IGFs, or the lack of functional receptors in target tissues. The consequences of hypersecretion and hyposecretion of GH are described in Clinical Impact 18.1.

Predict 3

Zach has a son who wants to be a basketball player almost as much as Zach wants him to be one. Zach knows a little bit about growth hormone and asks his son's doctor if she would prescribe some for his son so that he can grow tall. What do you think the doctor tells Zach?

Prolactin

Prolactin (proh-LAK-tin; PRL), a protein hormone, plays an important role in milk production by the mammary glands of

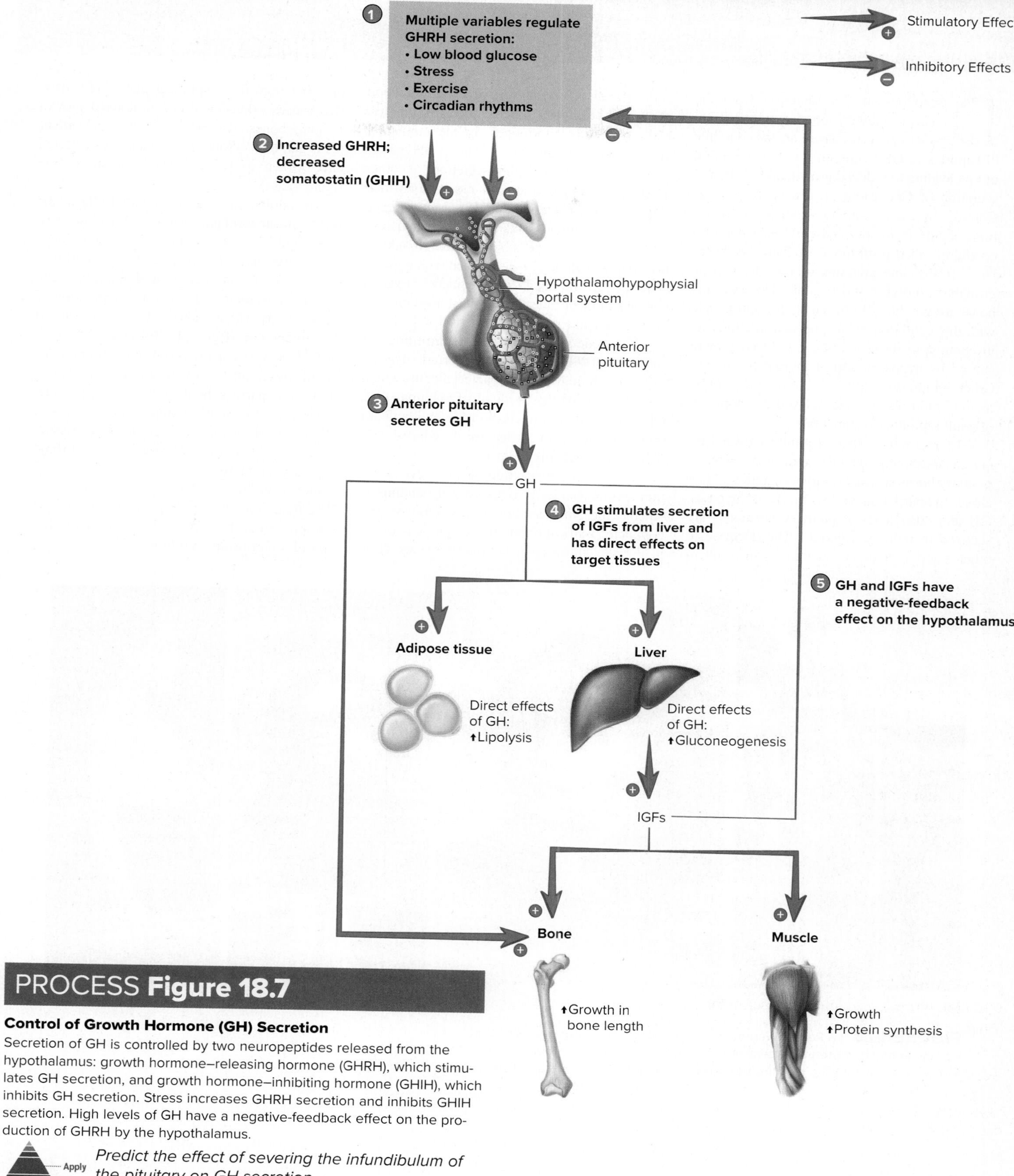

PROCESS **Figure 18.7**

Control of Growth Hormone (GH) Secretion

Secretion of GH is controlled by two neuropeptides released from the hypothalamus: growth hormone–releasing hormone (GHRH), which stimulates GH secretion, and growth hormone–inhibiting hormone (GHIH), which inhibits GH secretion. Stress increases GHRH secretion and inhibits GHIH secretion. High levels of GH have a negative-feedback effect on the production of GHRH by the hypothalamus.

Apply *Predict the effect of severing the infundibulum of the pituitary on GH secretion.*

Clinical IMPACT 18.1

Growth Hormone and Growth Disorders

Disruptions in GH secretion from the anterior pituitary interfere with normal growth patterns. There are two possible disruptions in GH secretion: (1) hyposecretion of GH leading to reduced growth and (2) hypersecretion of GH leading to excessive growth. Chronic hyposecretion, or insufficient secretion, of GH in infants and children leads to a condition called **pituitary dwarfism** (DWORF-izm). Insufficient amounts of GH delay bone growth, resulting in short stature. However, the bones usually have a normal shape, and people with this condition exhibit normal intelligence, in contrast to those who have reduced growth caused by hyposecretion of thyroid hormones. Other symptoms resulting from the lack of GH include mild obesity and delayed development of adult reproductive functions.

There are two types of pituitary dwarfism: (1) hyposecretion of GH and other anterior pituitary hormones and (2) hyposecretion of GH alone. In approximately two-thirds of the cases, GH and other anterior pituitary hormones are secreted in reduced amounts. The decrease in other anterior pituitary hormones can result in additional disorders caused by reduced secretion of thyroid hormones, adrenal cortex hormones, and reproductive hormones. In the remaining approximately one-third of cases, GH secretion is reduced, and the secretion of other anterior pituitary hormones is closer to normal. Therefore, these individuals do not experience additional hormone-related disorders, and normal reproduction is possible for them. In adults, no obvious pathology is associated with hyposecretion of GH, although some evidence suggests that lack of GH can lead to reduced bone mineral content in adults.

The gene responsible for determining the structure of GH has been transferred successfully from human cells to bacterial cells, which can produce GH that is identical to human GH. GH produced in this fashion is available to treat patients who suffer from reduced GH secretion, especially children.

Chronic hypersecretion, or excessive secretion, of GH also leads to disorder, depending on whether the hypersecretion occurs before or after complete ossification of the epiphyseal plates in the skeletal system. Chronic hypersecretion of GH before the epiphyseal plates have ossified causes exaggerated and prolonged growth in long bones, a condition called **gigantism** (JYE-gan-tizm). Some individuals thus affected have grown to be 8 feet tall or more (see figure 18.8*a*).

In adults, chronically elevated GH levels result in **acromegaly** (ak-roh-MEG-ah-lee). No height increase occurs because the epiphyseal plates have ossified. But the condition does result in an increased diameter of the fingers, toes, hands, and feet; the deposition of heavy bony ridges above the eyes; and a prominent jaw (figure 18.8*b*). The influence of GH on soft tissues results in a bulbous or broad nose, an enlarged tongue, thickened skin, and sparse subcutaneous adipose tissue. Nerves are frequently compressed as a result of the proliferation of connective tissue. Because GH spares glucose usage, chronic hyperglycemia results, frequently leading to diabetes mellitus and severe atherosclerosis. Treatment for chronic hypersecretion of GH often involves the surgical removal or irradiation of a GH-producing tumor.

(a)

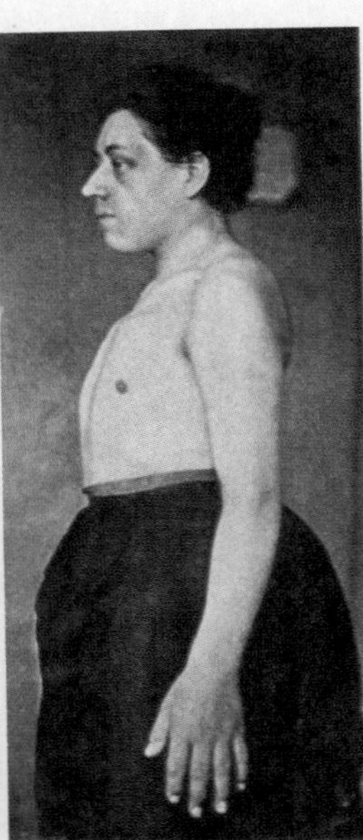

(b)

FIGURE 18.8 (*a*) Robert Wadlow, standing next to his father, was affected by GH hypersecretion (see chapter 17 introduction). (*b*) The woman in these photographs was affected by acromegaly. Here you can see the progression of her condition over time from left to right.

(a) Toronto Star Archives/Getty Images; (b) Atlas of Clinical Medicine/The U.S. National Library of Medicine

lactating females. It binds to a membrane-bound receptor, which is linked to a kinase that phosphorylates intracellular proteins. The phosphorylated proteins produce the response in the cell. PRL also can enhance progesterone secretion by the ovaries after ovulation. No role for this hormone has been clearly established in males. Several hypothalamic neuropeptides can be involved in the complex regulation of PRL secretion, but the principal control is exerted by prolactin-inhibiting hormone (PIH), which is more commonly called dopamine. Dopamine tonically inhibits PRL secretion. To release PRL, dopamine levels decrease and PRL is secreted. PRL functions fall into several categories, including regulation of the ion composition of blood, growth and development, behavior, metabolism, and immune function. The regulation of gonadotropin and PRL secretion and their specific reproductive effects are explained more fully in chapter 28.

Thyroid-Stimulating Hormone

Thyroid-stimulating hormone (TSH), also called *thyrotropin* (thigh-roh-TROH-pin), a glycoprotein hormone, stimulates the synthesis and secretion of thyroid hormones from the thyroid gland. TSH is a glycoprotein dimer consisting of two subunits, α and β, that bind to membrane-bound receptors of the thyroid gland. The α subunit is common among the glycoprotein hormones, TSH, luteinizing hormone, and follicle-stimulating hormone. It is the β subunit that dictates the specificity of each of the glycoprotein hormones. TSH receptors respond through a G protein mechanism that increases intracellular cAMP levels. cAMP then initiates a series of actions in the target tissue (see chapter 17).

TSH secretion is controlled by two mechanisms: (1) TRH from the hypothalamus and (2) negative feedback by thyroid hormones. The hypothalamic-releasing hormone TRH stimulates TSH secretion. Once thyroid hormone levels return to their set point, they inhibit both TRH and TSH levels. Although TSH is secreted in an episodic fashion and its blood levels are highest at night, thyroid hormone levels are maintained within a narrow range of values. This tight regulation of hormone levels is possible because thyroid hormone levels are regulated by negative feedback (see section 18.3).

Adrenocorticotropic Hormone and Related Substances

Adrenocorticotropic (ah-DREE-noh-KOR-tih-koh-TROH-pik) **hormone (ACTH),** a peptide hormone from the anterior pituitary, stimulates secretion of the hormone cortisol from the adrenal cortex (see section 18.5). ACTH is one of four smaller molecules derived from a large precursor protein called **proopiomelanocortin** (proh-OH-pee-oh-MEL-ah-noh-KOHR-tin; **POMC**). POMC is synthesized in the anterior pituitary and is subsequently broken down into multiple, smaller peptides. Many of these peptides are also hormones, including ACTH, lipotropins, β endorphins, and melanocyte-stimulating hormone.

Environmental stress is a key stimulus for ACTH secretion. Once ACTH arrives at its target tissues, it activates a G protein–mediated cAMP mechanism. The primary action of ACTH is release of the principal hormone that regulates chronic stress. This hormone is cortisol from the adrenal cortex. In pathological conditions such as chronic adrenocortical insufficiency (Addison disease), the adrenal cortex degenerates, usually due to an autoimmune condition (see chapter 22). Blood levels of ACTH and related hormones are chronically elevated, and the skin becomes markedly darker. This is because ACTH and melanocyte-stimulating hormone bind to melanocytes in the skin and increase skin pigmentation (see chapter 5). Regulation of ACTH secretion and the effects of the hypersecretion and hyposecretion of ACTH are described in section 18.5.

The **lipotropins** (li-poh-TROH-pinz) secreted from the anterior pituitary bind to membrane-bound receptor molecules on adipocytes. They cause lipid breakdown and the release of fatty acids into the blood.

The **β endorphins** (EN-dohr-finz) have the same effects as opiate drugs, such as morphine, and they can play a role in analgesia (pain relief) in response to stress and exercise. Other functions have been proposed for the β endorphins, including the regulation of body temperature, food intake, and water balance. Both ACTH and β-endorphin secretions increase in response to stress and exercise.

Melanocyte-stimulating hormone (MSH) binds to membrane-bound receptors on skin melanocytes and stimulates increased melanin deposition in the skin. The regulation of MSH secretion and its function in humans are not well understood, although studies have shown that MSH is also important in regulating appetite and sexual behavior.

Luteinizing Hormone and Follicle-Stimulating Hormone

Gonadotropins (GOH-nad-oh-TROH-pins) are glycoprotein hormones capable of promoting the growth and function of the **gonads,** the ovaries and testes. The two major gonadotropins secreted from the anterior pituitary are (1) **luteinizing** (LOO-tee-i-nyze-ing) **hormone (LH)** and (2) **follicle-stimulating hormone (FSH).** LH and FSH play important roles in regulating reproduction.

LH and FSH secreted into the blood bind to membrane-bound receptors, increase the intracellular synthesis of cAMP through G protein mechanisms, and stimulate the production of **gametes** (GAM-eets)—sperm cells in the testes and oocytes in the ovaries. LH and FSH also control the production of reproductive hormones—estrogens and progesterone in the ovaries and testosterone in the testes.

LH and FSH are released from anterior pituitary cells under the influence of the hypothalamic-releasing hormone gonadotropin-releasing hormone (GnRH). Gonadal steroid hormones are also critical regulators of the gonadotropins and exhibit a complex cycle of hormone interactions, which are further described in chapter 28.

ASSESS YOUR PROGRESS

12. *Structurally, what kinds of hormones are released from the anterior pituitary gland? Do these hormones bind to plasma proteins? How long is their half-life, and how do they activate their target tissues?*
13. *What effects do stress, blood amino acid levels, and blood glucose levels have on GH secretion?*
14. *Describe the effects of GH on its target tissues.*

15. *What stimulates the release of IGFs? Where are they produced, and what are their effects?*
16. *What pathological conditions are the result of hypersecretion of GH? Describe their symptoms.*
17. *What pathological conditions are the result of hyposecretion of GH? Describe their symptoms.*
18. *For each of the following hormones secreted by the anterior pituitary gland, name the target tissue and the hormone's effect on its target tissue: GH, prolactin, ACTH, LH, and FSH.*
19. *How are ACTH, lipotropins, β endorphins, and MSH related? What are the functions of these hormones?*
20. *What is a gonadotropin? Name two gonadotropins produced by the anterior pituitary gland, and explain their functions.*

18.3 Thyroid Gland

LEARNING OUTCOMES

After reading this section, you should be able to

A. **Describe the structure of the thyroid gland.**
B. **Explain the process for the synthesis of T_3 and T_4.**
C. **Explain the process for the secretion of T_3 and T_4.**
D. **Explain the process for the transport of T_3 and T_4.**
E. **Describe the mechanism of action and the effects of T_3 and T_4 in the body.**
F. **Relate how thyroid hormone secretion is regulated.**
G. **Describe the effects of hyposecretion and hypersecretion of thyroid hormones and the pathological conditions that cause the abnormalities.**
H. **Describe the role of calcitonin in the maintenance of blood calcium levels and in bone health.**

The **thyroid gland** synthesizes and secretes three hormones: (1) triiodothyronine, (2) tetraiodothyronine, and (3) calcitonin. It is composed of two lobes connected by a narrow band of thyroid tissue called the **isthmus.** The lobes are lateral to the upper portion of the trachea just inferior to the larynx, and the isthmus extends across the anterior aspect of the trachea (figure 18.9*a*). The thyroid gland is one of the largest endocrine glands, with a weight of approximately 20 g. Because it is highly vascular, it is a darker red than surrounding tissues.

The thyroid gland contains numerous **follicles,** which are small spheres whose walls are composed of a single layer of cuboidal epithelial cells (figure 18.9*b,c*). The center of each thyroid follicle is filled with a gelatinous material called colloid. Colloid is composed of a high concentration of a protein called **thyroglobulin** (thigh-roh-GLOB-you-lin). Thyroglobulin is synthesized and secreted by cells of the thyroid follicle. Thyroglobulin is the precursor to thyroid hormones. It is a large collection of individual thyroid hormone molecules. Thus, thyroglobulin stores a huge amount of thyroid hormones. Storage of such a large amount of hormone is unique to the thyroid gland.

Between the follicles, a delicate network of loose connective tissue contains numerous capillaries. Scattered between the follicles and the cells that make up the walls of the follicle are **parafollicular** (pair-ah-fo-LIK-yoo-lar) **cells.** The parafollicular cells secrete **calcitonin** (KAL-si-TOH-nin), which plays a role in reducing the concentration of calcium in the body fluids when calcium levels become elevated.

Thyroid Hormones

The thyroid gland secretes a total of three hormones, including calcitonin. Although calcitonin is secreted by the parafollicular cells of the thyroid gland, it constitutes only about 10% of the secretions from the thyroid gland. Because the remaining two hormones are secreted from the thyroid follicles, they are considered to be the thyroid hormones. The thyroid hormones include **triiodothyronine** (try-EYE-oh-doh-THIGH-roh-neen), commonly called **T_3,** and **tetraiodothyronine** (TET-rah-eye-oh-doh-THIGH-roh-neen). A more common name for tetraiodothyronine is **thyroxine** (THIGH-ROK-seen), or even more commonly **T_4.** T_4 is the precursor for T_3 and accounts for 80% of the secretions from the thyroid gland. T_3 accounts for the remaining 10% of thyroid gland secretions (table 18.3).

T_3 and T_4 Synthesis

Thyroid-stimulating hormone (TSH) from the anterior pituitary stimulates thyroid hormone synthesis and secretion. TSH causes an increase in the synthesis of T_3 and T_4, which are then stored inside the thyroid follicles as part of a large protein called thyroglobulin. TSH also causes T_3 and T_4 to be released from thyroglobulin and enter the plasma of the blood. Because iodine is an integral component of the T_3 and T_4 molecules, humans must consume an adequate amount of iodine in the diet to support thyroid hormone synthesis. In the United States, most of this dietary iodine is derived from iodized salt. The following events in the thyroid follicles result in T_3 and T_4 synthesis and secretion (figure 18.10):

1. Iodide ions (I^-) are taken up by thyroid follicle cells via secondary active transport by a **sodium-iodide symporter (NIS).** The active transport of the I^- is against a concentration gradient of approximately 30-fold in healthy individuals. The driving force of NIS is a Na^+ gradient generated by Na^+–K^+ ATPase.
2. Thyroglobulins, which contain numerous tyrosine molecules, are synthesized within the cells of the follicles.
3. The I^- diffuse into the lumen of the follicle through an I^- transporter. Nearly simultaneously, the I^- are oxidized to form iodine (I), and either one or two iodine atoms are bound to some of the tyrosine molecules of thyroglobulin by the enzyme thyroid peroxidase within the colloid.
4. The thyroglobulin contains iodinated tyrosine amino acids. If there is one iodine atom attached to the tyrosine amino acid, it is called a **monoiodotyrosine (MIT).** If there are two iodine atoms attached to the tyrosine, it is called a **diiodotyrosine (DIT).**
5. Thyroid hormones are synthesized within the colloid in the lumen of the follicle. If two diiodotyrosine molecules of thyroglobulin combine, **tetraiodothyronine (T_4)** is formed. If one monoiodotyrosine and one diiodotyrosine molecule combine, **triiodothyronine (T_3)** is formed. Large amounts of T_3 and T_4 are stored within the thyroid follicles as part of thyroglobulin. A reserve sufficient to supply thyroid hormones for approximately 2–3 months is stored in this form.

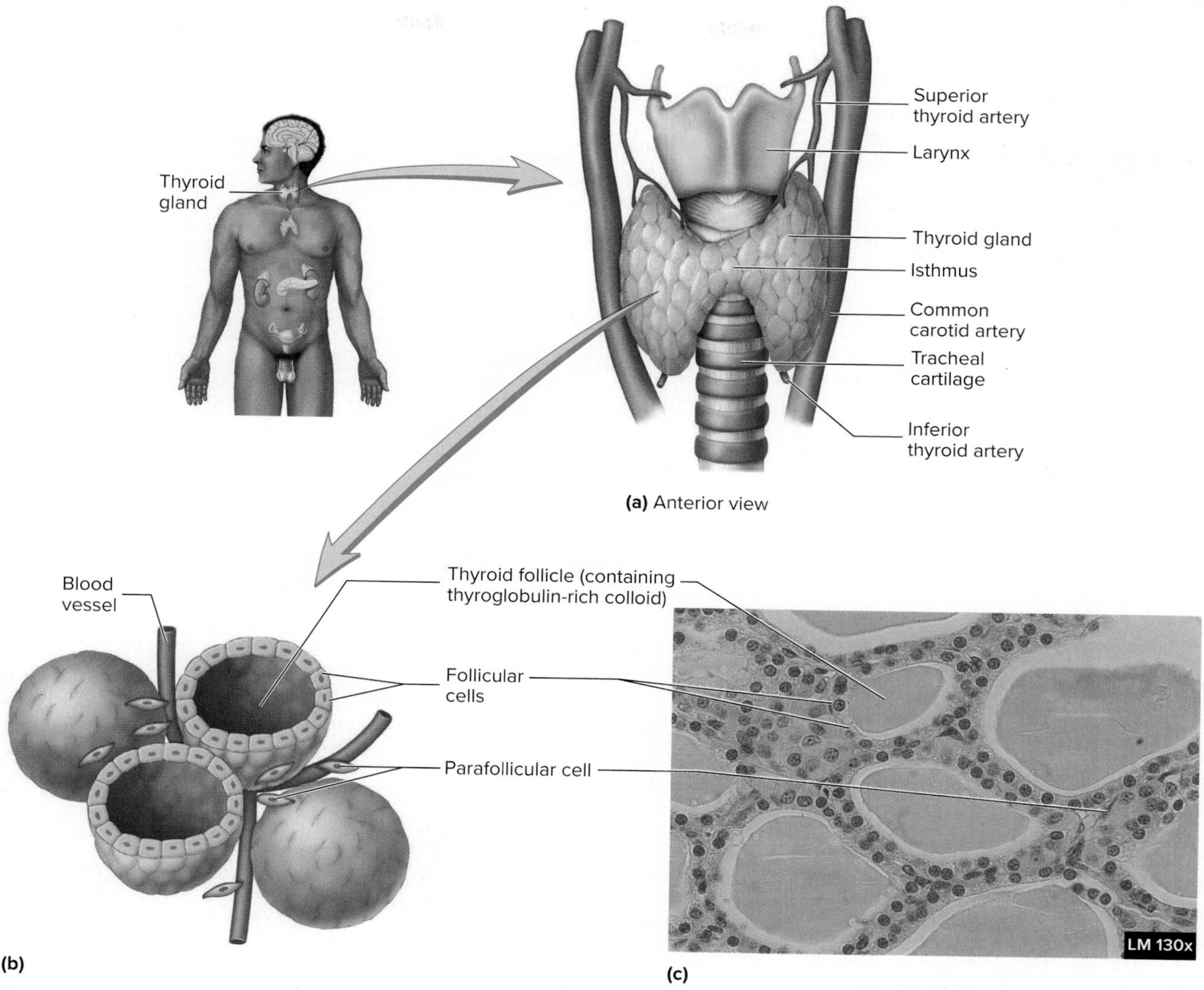

FIGURE 18.9 Anatomy and Histology of the Thyroid Gland
(*a*) Anterior view of the thyroid gland. (*b*) Histology of the thyroid gland. The gland is made up of many spheric thyroid follicles containing thyroglobulin-rich colloid. Parafollicular cells are in the tissue between the thyroid follicles. (*c*) Low-power photomicrograph of thyroid follicles. (c) Victor Eroschenko/McGraw Hill APR

TABLE 18.3 Hormones of the Thyroid and Parathyroid Glands

Hormone	Structure	Target Tissue	Response
Thyroid Gland			
Thyroid hormones (T_3 and T_4) Secreted by thyroid follicles	Amino acid derivative	Most cells of the body	Increased metabolic rate; increased protein synthesis; essential for normal growth and maturation
Calcitonin Secreted by parafollicular cells	Peptide	Bone	Decreased rate of breakdown of bone by osteoclasts; prevention of a large increase in blood Ca^{2+} levels
Parathyroid Gland			
Parathyroid hormone (PTH)	Peptide	Bone, kidneys, small intestine	Increased rate of breakdown of bone by osteoclasts; increased reabsorption of Ca^{2+} in kidneys; increased absorption of Ca^{2+} from the small intestine; increased vitamin D_3 synthesis; increased blood Ca^{2+} levels

PROCESS **Figure**

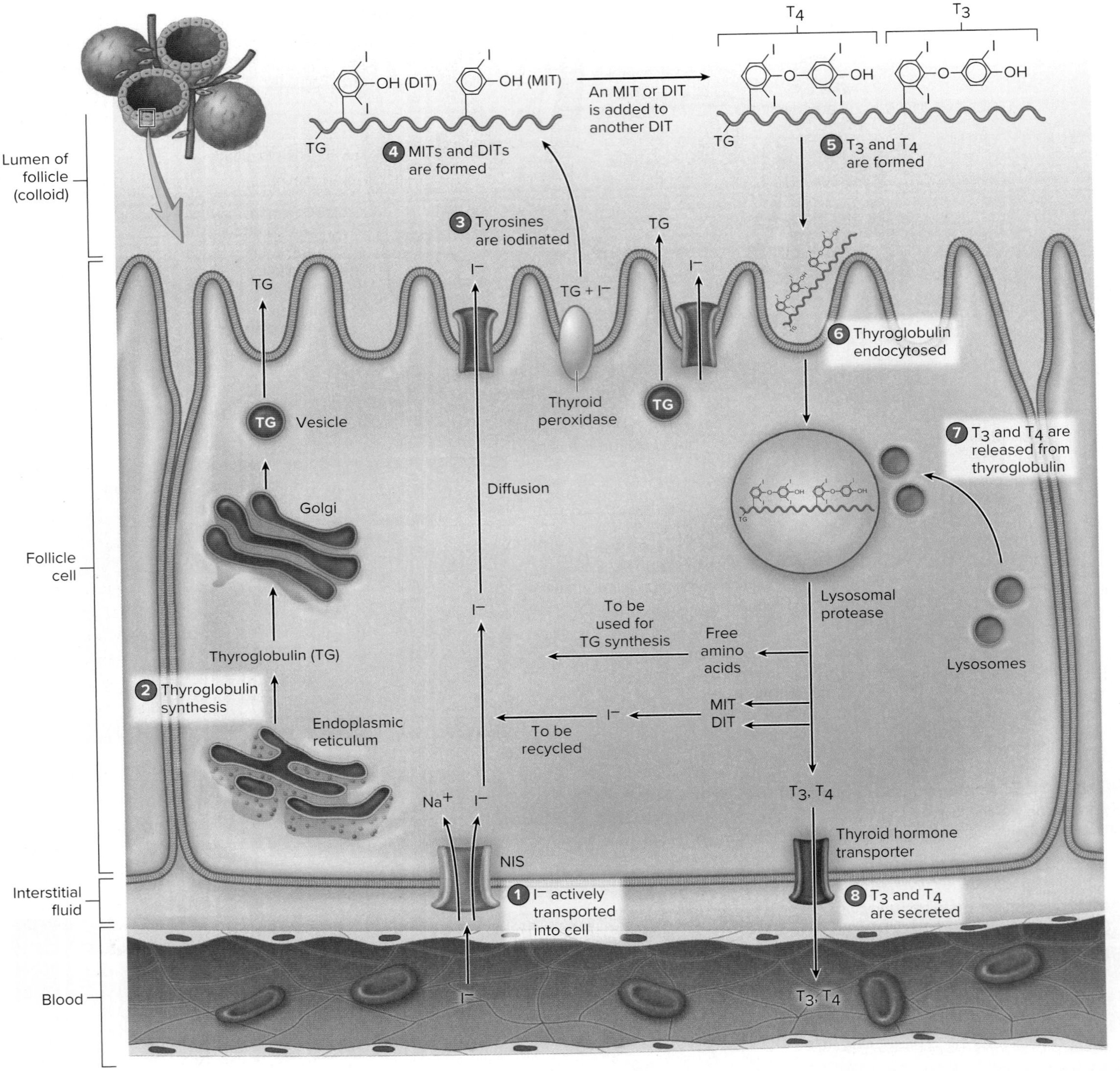

Lumen of follicle (colloid)

Follicle cell

Interstitial fluid

Blood

T_4 T_3

-OH (DIT) -OH (MIT) TG

An MIT or DIT is added to another DIT

I -O- -OH I -O- -OH TG

4 MITs and DITs are formed

5 T_3 and T_4 are formed

3 Tyrosines are iodinated

TG

I^-

I^-

TG

TG + I^-

6 Thyroglobulin endocytosed

Thyroid peroxidase

TG

TG Vesicle

7 T_3 and T_4 are released from thyroglobulin

Diffusion

Golgi

Lysosomal protease

I^-

To be used for TG synthesis

Free amino acids

Lysosomes

Thyroglobulin (TG)

2 Thyroglobulin synthesis

MIT DIT

I^-

To be recycled

Endoplasmic reticulum

Na^+ I^-

T_3, T_4

Thyroid hormone transporter

NIS

1 I^- actively transported into cell

8 T_3 and T_4 are secreted

I^-

T_3, T_4

PROCESS **Figure 18.10**

Biosynthesis of Thyroid Hormones

Thyroid hormones are synthesized in follicle cells of the thyroid gland. The hormones are stored as a component of a larger protein within a material called colloid, located in the center of each follicle.

If a person were injected with radioactive iodine, where would the highest concentration of radioactivity be located within the thyroid gland?

6 Thyroglobulin is taken into the thyroid follicle cells by endocytosis.

7 Lysosomes fuse with the endocytotic vesicles. Proteolytic enzymes break down thyroglobulin to release T_3 and T_4. The remaining amino acids and I^- of thyroglobulin are recycled to synthesize more thyroglobulin.

8 When being secreted from the thyroid gland, T_3 and T_4 are carried by specific transporters of the follicular cells into the interstitial spaces and then move into the capillaries of the thyroid gland.

Transport in the Blood

T_3 and T_4 are transported in combination with plasma proteins in the blood. Approximately 75% of the circulating T_3 and T_4 are bound to **thyroxine-binding globulin (TBG),** which is synthesized by the liver, and 20–30% are bound to other plasma proteins, including albumin. T_3 and T_4, bound to these plasma proteins, form a large reservoir of circulating thyroid hormones, and the half-life of these hormones is greatly increased because of this binding. After thyroid gland removal in experimental animals, it takes approximately 1 week for T_3 and T_4 levels in the blood to decrease by 50%. As free T_3 and T_4 levels decrease in the interstitial spaces, additional T_3 and T_4 dissociate from the plasma proteins to maintain the levels in the tissue spaces. When sudden secretion of T_3 and T_4 occurs, the excess binds to the plasma proteins. As a consequence, the concentration of thyroid hormones in the tissue spaces fluctuates very little.

Approximately 40% of the T_4 is converted to T_3 in the body tissues. This conversion is important for the action of thyroid hormones on their target tissues. T_3 is the major hormone that interacts with thyroid hormone target cells. T_3 is several times more potent than T_4 due to its higher affinity for the thyroid hormone receptor.

Much of the circulating T_4 is eliminated from the body by being converted to tetraiodothyroacetic acid, or by being modified, and then excreted in the urine or bile. In addition, a large amount is converted to an inactive form of T_3, rapidly metabolized, and excreted.

Mechanism of Action of T_3 and T_4

Because T_3 and T_4 are lipid-soluble hormones, they can bind to nuclear receptors in their target tissues (see section 17.4). Thyroid hormones are transported through the plasma membrane by **thyroid hormone transporters** into the cytoplasm of target cells, migrate to the nucleus, and bind to their receptors. When thyroid hormones are bound to their receptors, they interact with DNA in the nucleus to influence genes and generally stimulate protein synthesis. In addition, some effects of thyroid hormones are mediated through membrane-bound receptors. The newly synthesized proteins within the target cells mediate the cells' response to thyroid hormones.

Effects of T_3 and T_4

T_3 and T_4 affect nearly every tissue in the body, but not all tissues respond identically. There are two broad classes of thyroid hormone function: (1) increases in the basal metabolic rate and (2) regulation of cell growth and differentiation.

The normal rate of metabolism for an individual depends on an adequate supply of thyroid hormone, which increases the rate at which glucose, lipids, and protein are metabolized. The metabolic rate can increase 60–100% when blood T_3 and T_4 are elevated, whereas low levels of T_3 and T_4 lead to the opposite effect. Because the increased rate of metabolism produces heat, normal body temperature is partly due to adequate thyroid hormones. Thyroid hormones increase the activity of Na^+–K^+ pumps, which give off heat as a "by-product." T_3 and T_4 also alter the number and activity of mitochondria, resulting in greater ATP synthesis and thus heat production.

In addition to metabolism, T_3 and T_4 regulate the normal growth and maturation of organs. For example, the growth of bone, hair, teeth, connective tissue, and nervous tissue requires thyroid hormone. The actions of T_3 and T_4 through membrane-bound receptors have been linked to regulation of structural proteins of the plasma membrane, which indirectly initiates cell division as well as increased glucose uptake. One reason tissues require thyroid hormones for normal growth is that T_3 and T_4 play a permissive role for GH, which means that GH does not have its normal effect on target tissues if T_3 and T_4 are not present (see figure 17.16).

Failure to maintain homeostatic amounts of thyroid hormone dramatically affects the body's functions. Hypersecretion of T_3 and T_4 increases the rate of metabolism. High body temperature, weight loss, increased appetite, rapid heart rate, and an enlarged thyroid gland are major symptoms.

Hyposecretion of T_3 and T_4 decreases the rate of metabolism. Low body temperature, weight gain, reduced appetite, reduced heart rate, reduced blood pressure, weak skeletal muscles, and apathy are major symptoms. Hyposecretion of T_3 and T_4 that occurs during development causes a decreased metabolic rate, abnormal nervous system development, abnormal growth, and abnormal maturation of tissues. The consequence is neonatal hypothyroidism characterized by developmental delay, short stature, and specific physical deformities.

The specific effects of the hyposecretion and hypersecretion of thyroid hormones are outlined in table 18.4.

Regulation of Thyroid Hormone Secretion

Thyrotropin-releasing hormone (TRH) from the hypothalamus and TSH from the anterior pituitary function together to increase T_3 and T_4 secretion from the thyroid gland. Stress and exposure to cold cause increased TRH secretion, and prolonged fasting decreases TRH secretion. Figure 18.11 details the mechanism of thyroid hormone secretion.

1 Stress and hypothermia cause TRH to be released from neurons within the hypothalamus. It passes through the hypothalamohypophysial portal system to the anterior pituitary.

2 TRH causes cells of the anterior pituitary to secrete TSH, which passes through the general circulation to the thyroid gland.

3 TSH causes increased synthesis and release of T_3 and T_4 into the general circulation.

4 T_3 and T_4 act on target tissues to produce a response.

5 T_3 and T_4 also have an inhibitory effect on the secretion of TRH from the hypothalamus and TSH from the anterior pituitary.

TSH also causes hypertrophy (increased cell size) and hyperplasia (increased cell number) of the thyroid gland. Decreased blood

TABLE 18.4 Effects of Hyposecretion and Hypersecretion of Thyroid Hormones

Hypothyroidism	Hyperthyroidism
Decreased metabolic rate, low body temperature, cold intolerance	Increased metabolic rate, high body temperature, heat intolerance
Weight gain, reduced appetite	Weight loss, increased appetite
Reduced activity of sweat and sebaceous glands; dry, cold skin	Copious sweating; warm, flushed skin
Reduced heart rate, reduced blood pressure, dilated and enlarged heart	Rapid heart rate, elevated blood pressure, abnormal electrocardiogram
Weak, untoned skeletal muscles; sluggish movements	Weak skeletal muscles that exhibit tremors, quick movements with exaggerated reflexes
Constipation	Bouts of diarrhea
Myxedema (swelling of the face and body) as a result of subcutaneous mucoprotein deposits	Exophthalmos (protruding eyes) as a result of connective tissue proliferation and other deposits behind the eye
Apathy, somnolence	Hyperactivity, insomnia, restlessness, irritability, short attention span
Coarse hair; rough, dry skin	Soft, smooth hair and skin
Decreased iodide uptake	Increased iodide uptake
Possible goiter (enlargement of the thyroid gland) due to loss of negative feedback	Almost always a goiter

levels of TSH lead to decreased T_3 and T_4 secretion and to thyroid gland atrophy. If the thyroid gland is removed or if T_3 and T_4 secretion declines, TSH levels in the blood increase dramatically. Conditions in which TSH is elevated can often be charaterized by the abnormal thyroid gland overgrowth called goiter (table 18.5).

A dietary iodine deficiency can result in hypothyroidism, which is a reduction in secretion of thyroid hormones. Hypothyroidism can also result from taking certain drugs or being exposed to chemicals that inhibit T_3 and T_4 synthesis. It can also be caused by inadequate secretion of TSH, by an autoimmune disease that depresses thyroid hormone function, or by surgical removal of the thyroid gland. Hypersecretion of T_3 and T_4 can result from the synthesis of an immunoglobulin that stimulates TSH receptors and acts like TSH, from TSH-secreting tumors of the pituitary gland, and from thyroid tumors (see Systems Pathology).

Predict 4

Becky has lost 30 pounds over the past several months, even though her appetite has been good and she has been eating more than usual. She complains to her physician that she is nervous and restless, has a short attention span, becomes fatigued easily but cannot sleep well, moves compulsively, and sweats excessively. Her physician notes that she also exhibits tachycardia. Suspecting hyperthyroidism, he orders a blood test, which indicates elevated levels of T_3 and T_4 and low levels of TSH. Becky also has a TSH-like immunoglobulin in her plasma. Explain these results.

Calcitonin

Parafollicular cells, or C cells, secrete the hormone calcitonin in response to increased calcium levels in the blood. These cells are dispersed between the thyroid follicles throughout the thyroid gland.

The primary target tissue for calcitonin is bone (see chapter 6). Calcitonin binds to membrane-bound receptors, decreases osteoclast activity, and lengthens the life span of osteoblasts. The resulting bone deposition leads to decreases in blood calcium and phosphate levels.

Calcitonin has three important functions: (1) protection of young children and infants against hypercalcemia after a meal, (2) stimulation of Ca^{2+} and PO_4^- (phosphate) secretion in the kidney (removes them from the body), and (3) inhibition of the actions of parathyroid hormone (PTH) that dissolve bone to release Ca^{2+} and PO_4^-. The rate of calcitonin secretion increases in response to elevated blood Ca^{2+} levels. Blood levels of calcitonin decrease with age to a greater extent in females than in males.

Interestingly, complete thyroidectomy does not result in high blood Ca^{2+} levels, possibly because the regulation of blood Ca^{2+} levels by vitamin D_3 and other hormones, such as parathyroid hormone (if the parathyroid glands are retained in the body), compensates for the loss of calcitonin in individuals who have undergone a thyroidectomy. No pathological condition is directly associated with a lack of calcitonin secretion. Some evidence suggests that calcitonin may play a role in regulating food intake by decreasing appetite. Clinically, calcitonin nasal sprays have been effective in the management of postmenopausal osteoporosis.

ASSESS YOUR PROGRESS

21. *Where is the thyroid gland located? Describe the follicles and the parafollicular cells within the thyroid. What hormones do they produce?*

22. *Starting with the uptake of iodide by the follicles, describe the production and secretion of thyroid hormones (T_3 and T_4).*

23. *How are the thyroid hormones transported in the blood? What effect does this transport have on their half-life?*

24. *What are the target tissues of thyroid hormones? By what mechanism do thyroid hormones alter the activities of their target tissues? What effects are produced?*

PROCESS **Figure**

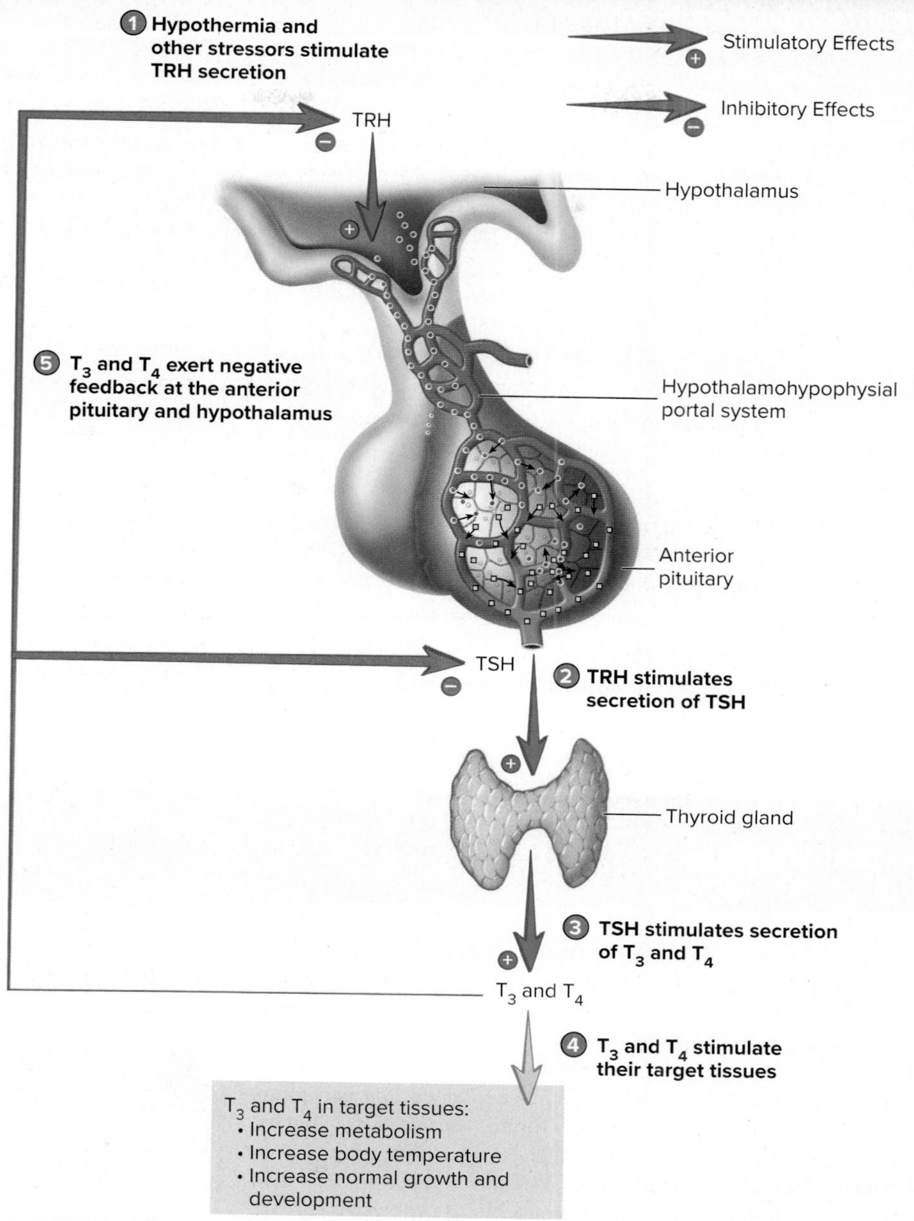

PROCESS **Figure 18.11**

Regulation of Thyroid Hormone (T_3 and T_4) Secretion

Thyroid hormones are regulated by the hypothalamus and pituitary.

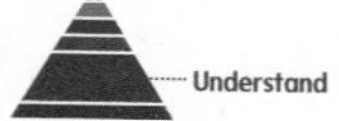

What is the general description for the role of TSH in stimulating T_3 and T_4 secretion?

25. *Starting in the hypothalamus, explain how chronic exposure to cold, food deprivation, or stress can affect thyroid hormone production.*

26. *Diagram two negative-feedback mechanisms involving hormones that regulate the production of thyroid hormones.*

27. *What is a goiter? What can cause one to develop?*

28. *What conditions cause hypothyroidism? Describe the effects of hyposecretion of thyroid hormones.*

29. *What conditions cause hyperthyroidism? Describe the effects of hypersecretion of thyroid hormones.*

30. *What effect does calcitonin have on osteoclasts, osteoblasts, and blood calcium levels? What stimulus can cause an increase in calcitonin secretion?*

TABLE 18.5 Abnormal Thyroid Conditions

Cause	Description
Hypothyroidism	
Iodine deficiency	Causes inadequate T_3 and T_4 synthesis, which results in elevated thyroid-stimulating hormone (TSH) secretion; thyroid gland enlarges (goiter) as a result of TSH stimulation; T_3 and T_4 frequently remain in the low to normal range
Goitrogenic (goiter-causing) substances	Inhibit T_3 and T_4 synthesis; found in certain drugs and in small amounts in certain plants, such as cabbage
Neonatal hypothyroidism	Caused by maternal iodine deficiency or congenital errors in thyroid hormone synthesis; results in developmental delay and a short, malformed appearance
Pituitary insufficiency	Results from lack of TSH secretion; often associated with inadequate secretion of other anterior pituitary hormones
Hashimoto disease	Autoimmune disease in which thyroid hormone secretion can be normal or depressed
Lack of thyroid gland	Partial or complete surgical removal or drug-induced destruction of the thyroid gland as a treatment for Graves disease (hyperthyroidism)
Hyperthyroidism	
Graves disease	Characterized by goiter and exophthalmos; apparently an autoimmune disease; most patients have a TSH-like immunoglobulin, called thyroid-stimulating immunoglobulin (TSI), in their plasma
Tumors—benign adenoma or cancer	Result in either normal secretion or hypersecretion of thyroid hormones (rarely hyposecretion)
Thyroiditis—a viral infection	Produces painful swelling of the thyroid gland with normal or slightly increased T_3 and T_4 production
Elevated TSH levels	Result from a pituitary tumor
Thyroid storm	Sudden release of large amounts of T_3 and T_4; caused by surgery, stress, infections, or other unknown factors

Case STUDY 18.1 Hypothyroidism

Josie owns a business and works hard to manage her employees and make time for her family. Over several months, she frequently felt weak, was often unable to concentrate, and felt cold when others did not. In addition, she began to gain weight, even though she had a small appetite. Finally, after noticing a large lump in her neck inferior and lateral to her larynx, Josie decided to see her physician. A blood sample was taken, and the results indicated low levels of thyroid hormones (hypothyroidism), high levels of TSH, and low levels of iodine.

The doctor concluded that Josie had developed a goiter, or an enlarged thyroid gland. Historically, iodine-deficiency goiters were common in people inhabiting areas where the soil was depleted of iodine, called "goiter belts." Consequently, plants grown in these areas had little iodine in them and caused iodine-deficient diets. In the United States, iodized salt has nearly eliminated iodine-deficiency goiters. However, iodine-deficiency diseases are still common throughout the world. The World Health Organization has called them the most common preventable cause of mental defects, and hypothyroidism may be the most common endemic disease on the planet.

Josie's doctor explained that her goiter had probably formed because her dietary intake of iodine was too low over a prolonged time. Without iodine, Josie's thyroid gland was unable to synthesize thyroid hormones. Thus, in response to low thyroid hormone levels, the anterior pituitary gland continued to secrete the tropic hormone TSH, which caused the thyroid gland to keep getting bigger and bigger. In addition, the hypothalamus continued to stimulate the anterior pituitary in the absence of thyroid hormones.

Josie was treated with radioactive iodine (^{131}I) atoms, which were actively transported into her thyroid cells, where the radiation helped shrink her thyroid gland back to normal size. Subsequently, Josie had to take dietary iodine supplements and thyroid hormone supplements until her thyroid gland was able to produce thyroid hormones on its own again.

Predict 5

a. Name and explain the mechanism controlling TSH in Josie's blood. Why were TSH levels high and the levels of thyroid hormones low prior to treatment?

b. Explain why the doctor could tell that Josie's condition was not the result of a tumor in the thyroid gland.

c. What role did a lack of iodine play in Josie's condition?

d. After treatment with iodine, predict how Josie's blood levels of thyroid hormones, as well as TSH, changed.

e. Explain why Josie had to take thyroid hormone supplements. Will Josie have to do this for the rest of her life?

18.4 Parathyroid Glands

LEARNING OUTCOMES

After reading this section, you should be able to

A. **Describe the location and structure of the parathyroid glands.**
B. **Explain the mechanism of parathyroid hormone action and its effects.**
C. **Describe the causes and symptoms of hypoparathyroidism and hyperparathyroidism.**

The **parathyroid** (pair-ah-THIGH-royd) **glands** are usually embedded in the posterior part of each lobe of the thyroid gland and are made up of two cell types: chief cells and oxyphils. The chief cells secrete parathyroid hormone, but, despite their relative abundance, the function of the oxyphils is not fully understood. Usually, four parathyroid glands are present, with their cells organized in densely packed masses, or cords, rather than in follicles (figure 18.12). In some cases, one or more of the parathyroid glands do not become embedded in the thyroid gland and remain in the nearby connective tissue.

Parathyroid hormone (PTH) is important in regulating calcium levels in body fluids (see table 18.3 and section 6.9). The major target tissues for PTH are (1) bone, (2) the kidneys, and (3) the small intestine. However, PTH targets the small intestine indirectly by stimulating vitamin D activation. The steroid hormone vitamin D_3 acts directly on cells of the small intestine. PTH binds to membrane-bound receptors and activates a G protein mechanism that increases intracellular cAMP levels in target tissues. Without functional parathyroid glands, the ability to adequately regulate blood calcium levels is lost.

PTH stimulates osteoclast activity in bone and can cause the number of osteoclasts to increase. The increased osteoclast activity results in bone reabsorption and the release of calcium and phosphate, causing an increase in blood calcium levels. Osteoclasts have no PTH receptors, but osteoblasts and red bone marrow stem cells do. PTH binds to receptors on osteoblasts, which then promote an increase in osteoclast activity (see chapter 6).

PTH causes calcium reabsorption within the kidneys, so that less calcium leaves the body in urine. It also increases the enzymatic formation of active vitamin D_3 in the kidneys. Calcium is actively absorbed by the epithelial cells of the small intestine, and the synthesis of transport proteins in the intestinal cells requires active vitamin D_3. PTH increases the rate of active vitamin D_3 synthesis, which in turn increases the rate of calcium and phosphate absorption in the intestine, thereby elevating blood levels of calcium.

Although PTH increases the release of phosphate ions (PO_4^{3-}) from bone and indirectly stimulates PO_4^{3-} absorption in the small intestine, it increases PO_4^{3-} excretion in the kidney. The overall effect of PTH is to decrease blood phosphate levels. A simultaneous increase in both Ca^{2+} and PO_4^{3-} is undesirable because calcium phosphate can precipitate in the body's soft tissues, causing irritation and inflammation.

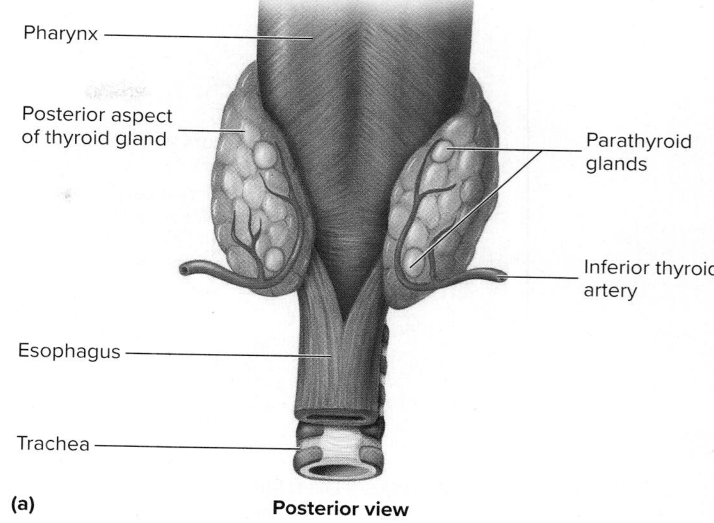

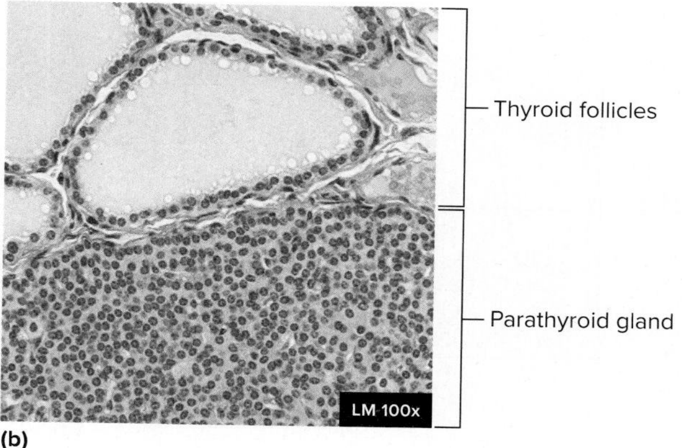

FIGURE 18.12 Anatomy and Histology of the Parathyroid Glands

(*a*) The parathyroid glands are embedded in the posterior part of the thyroid gland. (*b*) The parathyroid glands are composed of densely packed cords of cells. (b) Victor P. Eroschenko APR

The regulation of PTH secretion and the role of PTH and calcitonin in regulating blood Ca^{2+} levels are outlined in figure 18.13. The primary stimulus for the secretion of PTH is a decrease in blood Ca^{2+} levels, whereas elevated blood Ca^{2+} levels inhibit PTH secretion. This regulation keeps blood Ca^{2+} levels fluctuating within a normal range of values. Both hypersecretion and hyposecretion of PTH cause serious symptoms (table 18.6). The regulation of blood Ca^{2+} levels is discussed more thoroughly in chapter 27.

Inactive parathyroid glands result in **hypocalcemia,** abnormally low levels of calcium in the blood. Reduced extracellular calcium levels cause voltage-gated Na^+ channels in plasma membranes to open, which increases the permeability of plasma

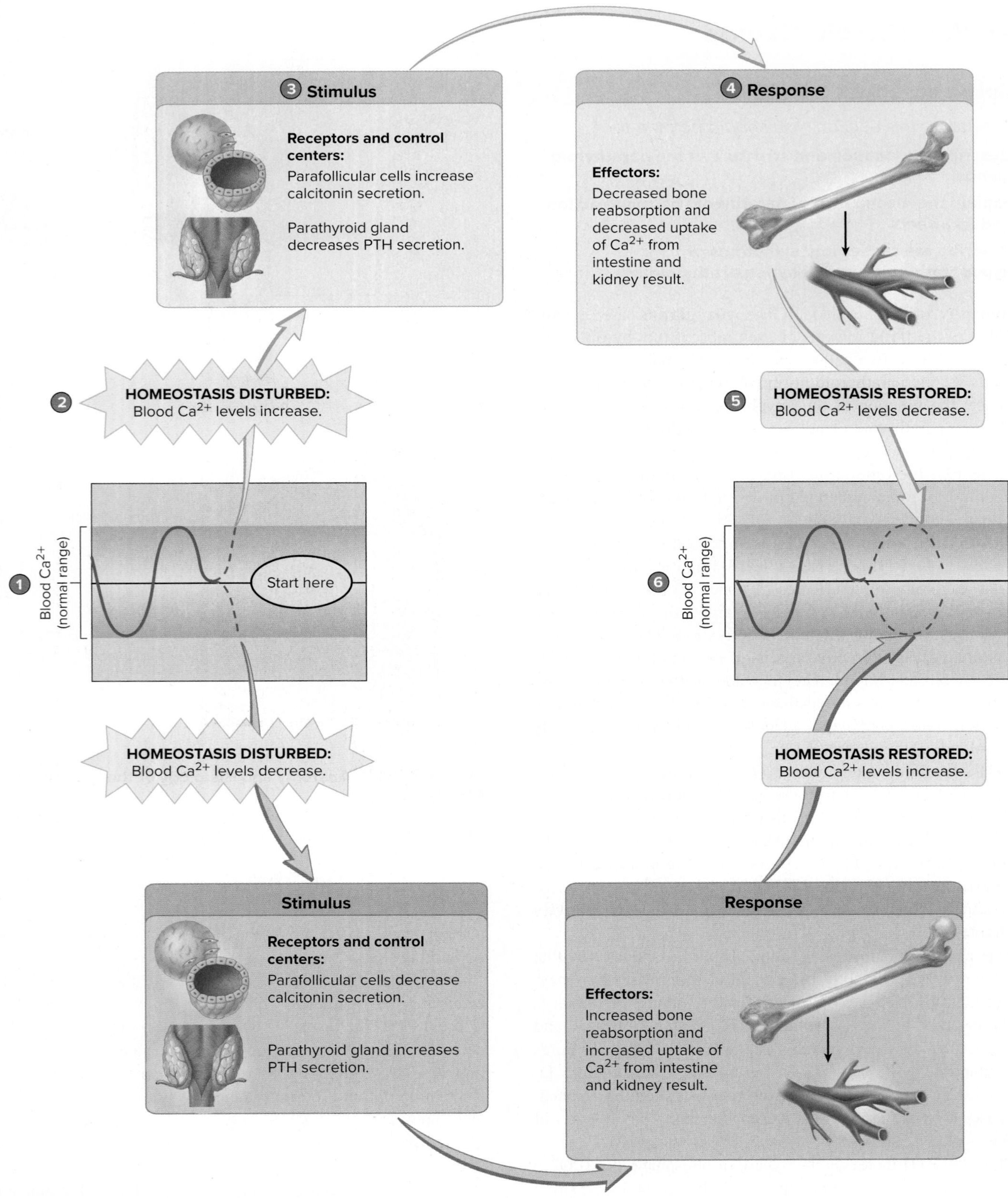

HOMEOSTASIS FIGURE 18.13 Regulation of Blood Levels of` Calcium Ions

(1) Blood Ca^{2+} is within its normal range. (2) Blood Ca^{2+} level increases outside the normal range. (3) The parafollicular cells and the parathyroid gland cells detect elevated blood Ca^{2+}. The parafollicular cells secrete calcitonin; the parathyroid gland cells decrease PTH secretion. (4) There is less bone reabsorption and less uptake of Ca^{2+} from both the kidney and the intestine. (5) Blood Ca^{2+} level drops back to its normal range. (6) Homeostasis is restored. Observe the response to a drop in blood Ca^{2+} by following the *lower pink arrows*.

TABLE 18.6 Causes and Symptoms of Hyposecretion and Hypersecretion of Parathyroid Hormone

	Cause	Symptoms
Hypoparathyroidism	Accidental removal during thyroidectomy	Hypocalcemia Increased neuromuscular excitability; possible tetany, laryngospasm, and death from asphyxiation Flaccid heart muscle; possible cardiac arrhythmia Diarrhea
Hyperparathyroidism	Primary hyperparathyroidism: a result of abnormal parathyroid function—adenomas of the parathyroid gland (90%), idiopathic (unknown cause) hyperplasia of parathyroid cells (9%), or carcinomas (1%) Secondary hyperparathyroidism: caused by conditions that reduce blood Ca^{2+} levels, such as inadequate Ca^{2+} in the diet, inadequate levels of vitamin D_3, pregnancy, or lactation	Hypercalcemia or normal blood Ca^{2+} levels; calcium carbonate salts may be deposited throughout the body, especially in the renal tubules (kidney stones), lungs, blood vessels, and gastric mucosa Bones weakened as a result of Ca^{2+} reabsorption; some cases are first diagnosed when a radiograph is taken of a broken bone Neuromuscular system less excitable; possible muscular weakness Increased force of contraction of cardiac muscle; at very high blood Ca^{2+} levels, possible cardiac arrest during contraction, constipation

membranes to Na^+. As a consequence, Na^+ diffuses into cells and causes depolarization (see chapter 11). Symptoms of hypocalcemia are nervousness, muscle spasms, cardiac arrhythmia, and convulsions. Extreme cases may lead to tetany of skeletal muscles, including the respiratory muscles, which can cause death.

Predict 6

A patient with a malignant tumor had his thyroid gland removed. What effect does this removal have on blood levels of Ca^{2+}? If the parathyroid glands are inadvertently removed along with the thyroid gland, death can result because the muscles of respiration undergo sustained contractions. Explain.

ASSESS YOUR PROGRESS

31. *Where are the parathyroid glands located, and what hormone do they produce?*
32. *What are the major target tissues for parathyroid hormone?*
33. *What effect does PTH have on osteoclasts, osteoblasts, the kidneys, the small intestine, and bone?*
34. *How are blood calcium and phosphate levels regulated by PTH?*
35. *What can cause hypoparathyroidism? Describe the symptoms.*
36. *What can cause hyperparathyroidism? Describe the symptoms.*

18.5 Adrenal Glands

LEARNING OUTCOMES

After reading this section, you should be able to

A. **Relate the location of the adrenal glands and explain the embryological origins of the two parts of the glands.**
B. **Describe the mechanisms and actions of the hormones secreted by the adrenal medulla.**
C. **Name the layers of the adrenal cortex, the type of product secreted by each layer, and the predominant hormone of each layer.**
D. **Describe the individual target tissues and their responses to the hormones of the adrenal cortex.**
E. **Explain the role of ACTH in the regulation of the adrenal cortex hormones.**
F. **Discuss the causes and symptoms of hyposecretion and hypersecretion of adrenal cortex hormones.**

The **adrenal** (ah-DREE-nal) **glands** produce a diverse set of hormones. The adrenal glands, also called the *suprarenal* (SOO-prah-REE-nal) *glands,* are near the superior poles of the kidneys. Like the kidneys, the adrenal glands lie behind the peritoneum, and they are surrounded by abundant adipose tissue. The adrenal glands are enclosed by a connective tissue capsule and have a well-developed blood supply (figure 18.14*a*).

The adrenal glands are composed of an inner **medulla** and an outer **cortex,** which are derived from two separate embryonic tissues. The adrenal medulla arises from neural crest cells, which also give rise to postganglionic neurons of the sympathetic division of the autonomic nervous system (see chapters 16 and 29). Unlike most glands of the body, which develop from invaginations of epithelial tissue, the adrenal cortex is derived from mesoderm.

Trabeculae of the connective tissue capsule penetrate the adrenal gland in several locations, and numerous small blood vessels course within the trabeculae to supply the gland. The adrenal medulla consists of closely packed polyhedral cells centrally located in the gland (figure 18.14*b*). The adrenal cortex is composed of smaller cells and forms three indistinct layers: (1) the **zona glomerulosa** (gloh-MARE-yoo-lohs-ah), (2) the **zona fasciculata** (fa-SIK-yoo-lah-tah), and (3) the **zona reticularis** (re-TIK-yoo-LAR-is). These three layers are functionally and structurally specialized. The zona glomerulosa, located immediately beneath the capsule, is composed of small clusters of cells, and secretes aldosterone. Beneath the zona glomerulosa is the thickest part of the

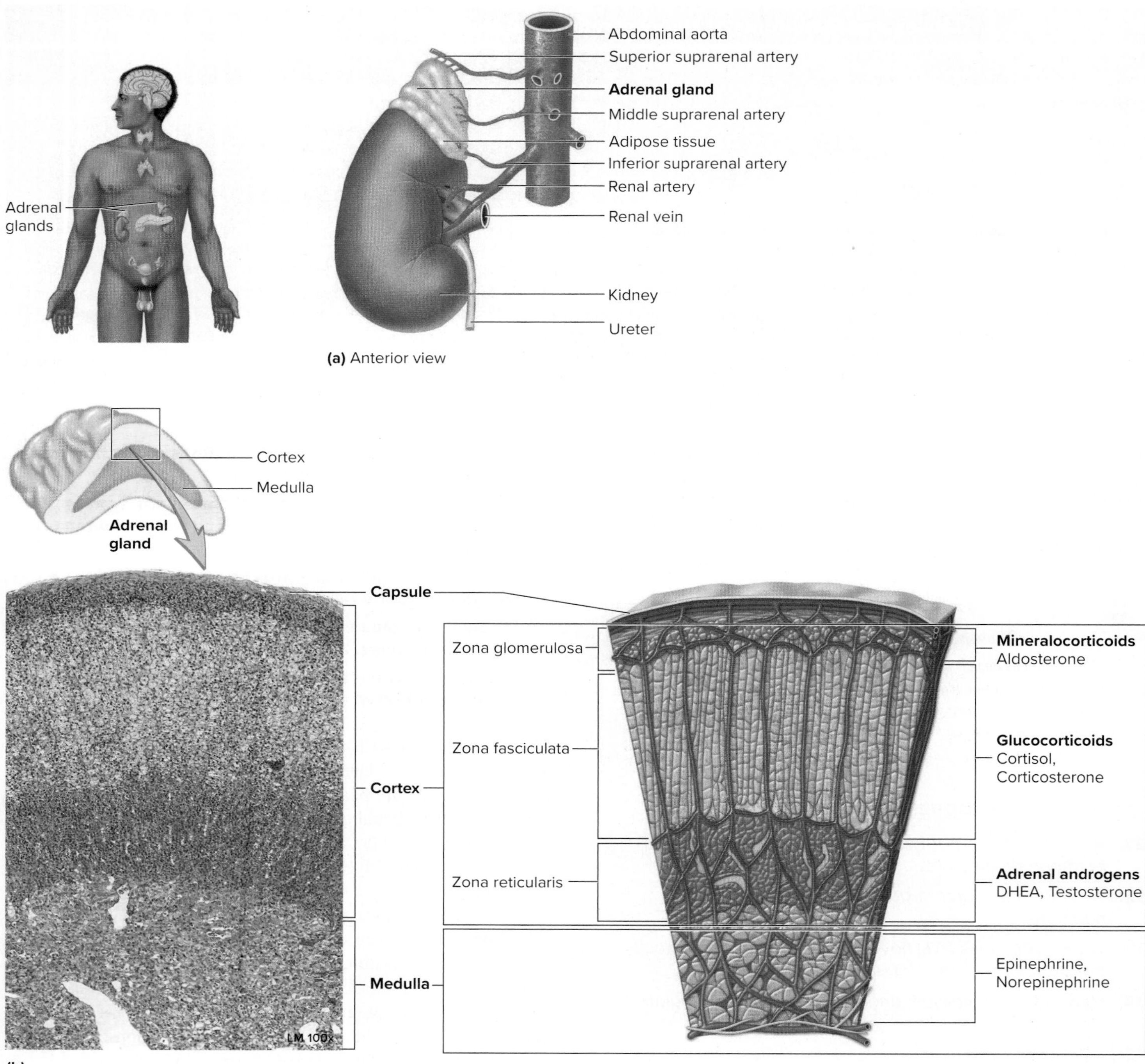

FIGURE 18.14 Anatomy and Histology of Adrenal Glands
(*a*) An adrenal gland is at the superior pole of each kidney. (*b*) The adrenal glands have an outer cortex and an inner medulla. The cortex is surrounded by a connective tissue capsule and consists of three layers: the zona glomerulosa, the zona fasciculata, and the zona reticularis. (b) Dr. Thomas Caceci APR

adrenal cortex, the zona fasciculata, which secretes cortisol. In this layer, the cells form long columns, or fascicles, that extend from the surface toward the medulla of the gland. The deepest layer of the adrenal cortex, the zona reticularis, secretes androgens and is a thin layer of irregularly arranged cords of cells.

Hormones of the Adrenal Medulla

The adrenal medulla is a modified sympathetic nervous system ganglion. It secretes two major hormones: **epinephrine** (ep-ih-NEF-rin; *adrenaline;* ah-DREN-ah-lin), which accounts for 80% of adrenal medulla hormones, and **norepinephrine** (NOR-ep-ih-NEF-rin;

TABLE **18.7** **Hormones of the Adrenal Gland**

Hormone	Structure	Target Tissue	Response
Adrenal Medulla			
Epinephrine primarily; norepinephrine	Amino acid derivatives	Heart, blood vessels, liver, adipose cells	Increased cardiac output; increased blood flow to skeletal muscles and to the heart (see chapter 20); vasoconstriction of blood vessels, especially in the viscera and skin; increased release of glucose and fatty acids into the blood; in general, preparation for physical activity
Adrenal Cortex			
Mineralocorticoids (aldosterone)	Steroids	Kidney	Increased Na^+ reabsorption and K^+ and H^+ excretion; enhanced water reabsorption
Glucocorticoids (cortisol)	Steroids	Most tissues	Increased protein and lipid breakdown; increased glucose production; inhibition of immune response and decreased inflammation
Androgens	Steroids	Many tissues	Of minor importance in males; in females, development of some secondary sex characteristics, such as axillary and pubic hair

noradrenaline; nor-ah-DREN-ah-lin), which accounts for 20% (table 18.7). Epinephrine and norepinephrine are closely related. In fact, norepinephrine is a precursor to the formation of epinephrine.

Epinephrine and norepinephrine combine with adrenergic receptors, which are membrane-bound receptors in target cells. They are classified as either α-adrenergic or β-adrenergic receptors, and each of these categories has subcategories that affect target tissues differently. All of the adrenergic receptors function through G protein mechanisms. In general, the α-adrenergic receptors cause Ca^{2+} channels to open, cause the release of Ca^{2+} from the endoplasmic reticulum by activating phospholipase enzymes, open K^+ channels, decrease cAMP synthesis, or stimulate the synthesis of eicosanoid molecules, such as prostaglandins. The β-adrenergic receptors all increase cAMP synthesis. A complete description of epinephrine and norepinephrine is not included in this chapter; rather, the effects of these hormones are described in the context of the body systems (see chapters 16, 20, 21, 24, and 26).

Secretion of adrenal medullary hormones prepares the individual for physical activity and is a major component of the fight-or-flight response (see chapter 16). This response results in reduced activity in organs not essential for physical activity, as well as increased blood flow and metabolic activity in organs that participate in physical activity. Epinephrine and norepinephrine increase the heart's rate and force of contraction and cause blood vessels to constrict in the skin, kidneys, gastrointestinal tract, and other viscera. Also, epinephrine causes dilation of blood vessels in skeletal muscles and cardiac muscle. In addition, epinephrine mobilizes nutrients that can be used to sustain physical exercise. The specific actions of epinephrine that mobilize nutrients include the following:

1. Epinephrine increases blood glucose levels. It binds to membrane-bound receptors in liver cells. Cyclic AMP, in turn, activates enzymes that catalyze the breakdown of glycogen to glucose and the release of glucose from the liver cells into the blood.
2. Epinephrine also increases the breakdown of glycogen in muscle cells, but muscle cells do not release glucose into the blood because glucose is utilized in muscle cells.
3. Epinephrine increases lipid breakdown in adipose tissue, releasing fatty acids into the blood. The fatty acids can be taken up and metabolized by tissues such as skeletal and cardiac muscle.

The effects of epinephrine and norepinephrine are short-lived because they are rapidly metabolized, excreted, or taken up by tissues. Their half-life in the blood is measured in minutes.

The adrenal medulla is a specialized part of the autonomic nervous system. Thus, the release of adrenal medullary hormones primarily occurs in response to stimulation by sympathetic neurons. Figure 18.15 outlines the steps in secretion of epinephrine and norepinephrine from the adrenal medulla.

1. Stress, physical activity, and low blood glucose levels act as stimuli to the hypothalamus, resulting in increased sympathetic nervous system activity.
2. An increased frequency of action potentials conducted through the sympathetic division of the autonomic nervous system stimulates the adrenal medulla to secrete epinephrine and some norepinephrine into the blood.
3. Epinephrine and norepinephrine act on their target tissues to produce responses.

ASSESS YOUR PROGRESS

37. *Where are the adrenal glands located? Describe the embryonic origins of the adrenal medulla and the adrenal cortex.*

38. *Name two hormones secreted by the adrenal medulla, and list the effects of these hormones.*

39. *List several conditions that can stimulate the production of adrenal medullary hormones. What role does the nervous system play in the release of these hormones? How does this role relate to the embryonic origin of the adrenal medulla?*

Hormones of the Adrenal Cortex

The adrenal cortex is organized into three distinct layers, each of which produces a different type of steroid hormone. The three

PROCESS **Figure**

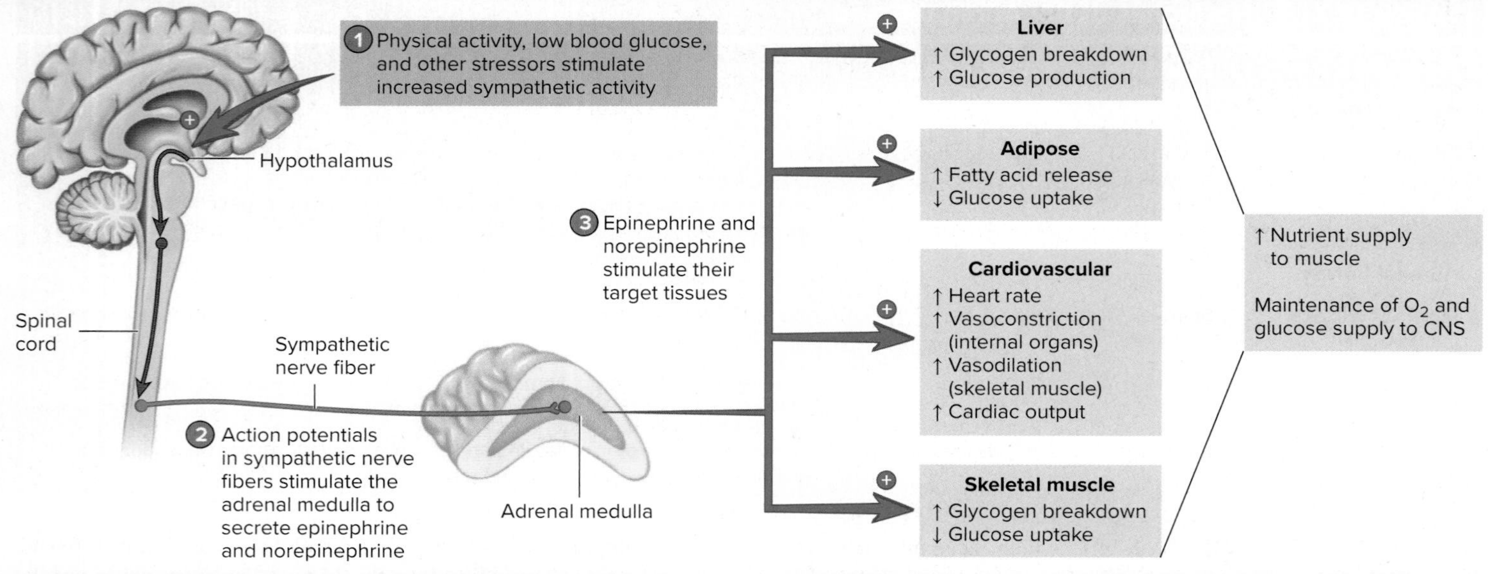

PROCESS **Figure 18.15**

Regulation of Adrenal Medulla Secretions

Stress, physical exercise, and low blood glucose levels cause increased activity of the sympathetic nervous system, which increases epinephrine and norepinephrine secretion from the adrenal medulla.

How does norepinephrine from the adrenal medulla differ from norepinephrine released by neurons of the sympathetic nervous system?

types of steroid hormone are (1) **mineralocorticoids** (MIN-er-al-oh-KOR-tih-koydz), secreted by the *zona glomerulosa;* (2) **glucocorticoids** (glue-koh-KOR-tih-koydz), secreted by the *zona fasciculata;* and (3) **adrenal androgens** (AN-droh-jenz, secreted by the *zona reticularis;* see table 18.7). All adrenal cortex hormones have a similar structure in that they are steroids, which are highly specialized lipids derived from cholesterol (see chapter 2). Because these hormones are lipid-soluble, they are not stored in the adrenal gland cells but diffuse from the cells as they are synthesized. Adrenal cortical hormones are transported in the blood bound to specific plasma proteins; they are metabolized in the liver and excreted in the bile and urine. The hormones of the adrenal cortex bind to nuclear receptors and stimulate the synthesis of specific proteins responsible for producing the target cell's responses.

Mineralocorticoids

As their name suggests, the mineralocorticoids regulate ion balance in the blood. The mineralocorticoids are the major secretory products of the zona glomerulosa of the adrenal cortex. **Aldosterone** (al-DOS-ter-ohn) is produced in the greatest amounts, although other, closely related mineralocorticoids are also secreted. Aldosterone is secreted under low blood pressure conditions. It returns blood pressure to its normal range through modulation of kidney function. Aldosterone increases the rate of sodium reabsorption by the kidneys, which increases blood levels of Na^+. The higher blood Na^+ levels enhance water reabsorption through osmosis. Recall from chapter 3 that osmosis is the diffusion of water toward higher solute areas. This reabsorption of water increases blood volume and thereby increases blood pressure. Aldosterone also stimulates K^+ excretion into the urine by the kidneys, which lowers blood levels of K^+. In addition, aldosterone increases the rate of H^+ excretion into the urine. When aldosterone is secreted in high concentrations, reduced blood K^+ levels and alkalosis (elevated pH of body fluids) may result. The specific effects of aldosterone and the mechanisms controlling aldosterone secretion are discussed along with kidney functions in chapters 26 and 27 and with cardiovascular system functions in chapter 21.

Glucocorticoids

Glucocorticoids help provide energy for cells by stimulating the increased use of lipids and proteins. It is the zona fasciculata of the adrenal cortex that secretes the **glucocorticoid hormones,** primarily **cortisol** (KOR-tih-sol). The numerous target tissues and responses to the glucocorticoids are listed in table 18.8. The responses are classified as metabolic, developmental, or anti-inflammatory. Glucocorticoids cause lipid breakdown, reduce glucose and amino acid uptake in skeletal muscle, stimulate **gluconeogenesis** (GLOO-koh-nee-oh-JEN-eh-sis; the synthesis of new glucose from precursor molecules, such as amino acids in the liver), and increase protein degradation. Glucocorticoids also increase blood glucose levels and glycogen deposits in cells. The glucose and glycogen are a reservoir of molecules that can be metabolized rapidly.

Glucocorticoids are also required for the maturation of tissues, such as fetal lungs, and for the development of

TABLE 18.8 **Target Tissues and Their Responses to Glucocorticoid Hormones**

Target Tissues	Responses
Peripheral tissues, such as skeletal muscle, liver, and adipose tissue	Inhibit glucose use; stimulate the formation of glucose from amino acids and, to some degree, from lipids (gluconeogenesis) in the liver, which results in elevated blood glucose levels; stimulate glycogen synthesis in cells; mobilize lipids by increasing lipolysis, which results in the release of fatty acids into the blood and an increased rate of fatty acid metabolism; increase protein breakdown and decrease protein synthesis
Immune tissues	Anti-inflammatory; depress antibody production, white blood cell production, and the release of inflammatory components in response to injury; suppress the immune system
Target cells for epinephrine	Receptor molecules for epinephrine and norepinephrine decrease without adequate amounts of glucocorticoid hormone

receptor molecules in target tissues for epinephrine and norepinephrine. In addition, glucocorticoids decrease the intensity of the inflammatory and immune responses by decreasing both the number of white blood cells and the secretion of inflammatory chemicals from tissues. This anti-inflammatory effect is important under conditions of stress, when the rate of glucocorticoid secretion is relatively high. Synthetic glucocorticoids are often used to suppress the immune response in people suffering from autoimmune conditions and in transplant recipients (see chapter 22).

ACTH is necessary to maintain the secretory activity of the adrenal cortex, which rapidly atrophies without this hormone. Corticotropin-releasing hormone (CRH) released from the hypothalamus stimulates the anterior pituitary to secrete ACTH. The zona fasciculata is very sensitive to ACTH, and it responds by increasing cortisol secretion. The regulation of ACTH and cortisol secretion is outlined in figure 18.16.

1. Corticotropin-releasing hormone (CRH) is released from hypothalamic neurons in response to stress or low blood glucose and passes, by way of the hypothalamohypophysial portal system, to the anterior pituitary.
2. In the anterior pituitary, CRH binds to and stimulates cells that secrete adrenocorticotropic hormone (ACTH).
3. ACTH binds to membrane-bound receptors on cells of the adrenal cortex and stimulates the secretion of glucocorticoids, primarily cortisol.
4. Cortisol acts on target tissues, resulting in increased lipid and protein breakdown, increased glucose levels, and anti-inflammatory effects.
5. Cortisol has a negative-feedback effect because it inhibits CRH release from the hypothalamus and ACTH secretion from the anterior pituitary.

Stress and hypoglycemia (low levels of glucose in the blood) trigger a large increase in CRH release from the hypothalamus by causing a rapid increase in blood levels of cortisol. In addition, CRH levels vary significantly throughout the day. Table 18.9 outlines several abnormalities associated with the hyposecretion or hypersecretion of adrenal hormones.

Apply **Predict 7**

Cortisone, a drug similar to cortisol, is sometimes given to people who have severe allergies or extensive inflammation or to those who suffer from autoimmune diseases. Taking this substance chronically can damage the adrenal cortex. Explain how this damage can occur.

PROCESS **Figure**

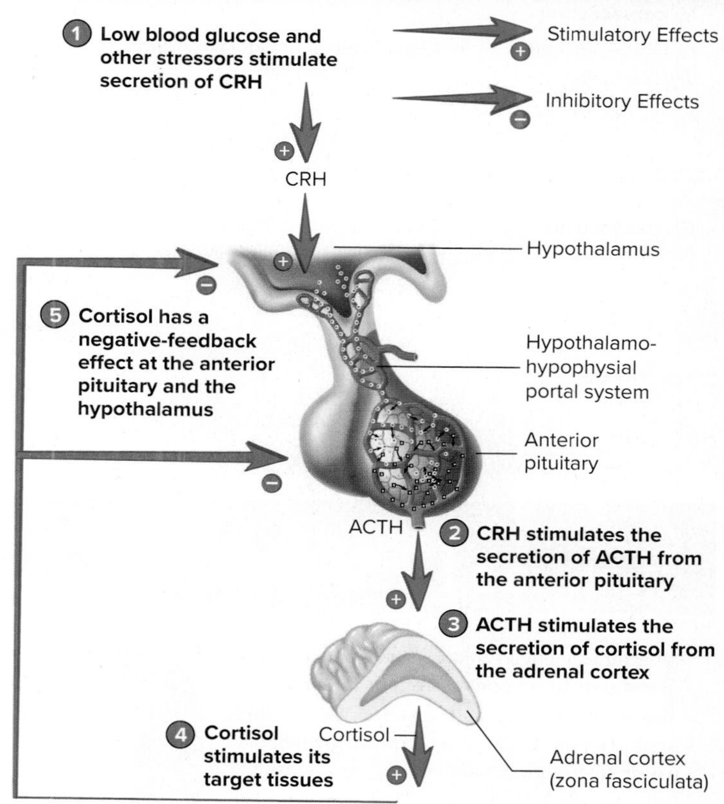

PROCESS **Figure 18.16**

Regulation of Cortisol Secretion

Cortisol secretion is regulated by the hypothalamic hormone, CRH, and the anterior pituitary hormone, ACTH.

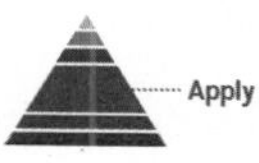

Explain why the drug cortisone (KOR-ti-sohn), a steroid closely related to cortisol, is prescribed to treat joint injuries, allergies, or asthma.

TABLE 18.9 Symptoms of Hyposecretion and Hypersecretion of Adrenal Cortex Hormones

	Cause	Symptoms
Hyposecretion		
Mineralocorticoids (aldosterone)	Removal of gland or loss of function or Addison disease (low levels of aldosterone *and* cortisol)	Hyponatremia (low blood levels of sodium) Hyperkalemia (high blood levels of potassium) Acidosis (pH is too low) Low blood pressure Tremors and tetany of skeletal muscles Polyuria (excess urine production)
Glucocorticoids (cortisol)	Removal of gland or loss of function	Hypoglycemia (low blood glucose levels) Depressed immune system Unused proteins and lipids from diet, resulting in weight loss Loss of appetite, nausea, vomiting Bronzing of skin due to increased pigmentation (if ACTH levels are elevated)
Adrenal Androgens		In females, reduction of pubic and axillary hair
Hypersecretion		
Mineralocorticoids (aldosterone)	Tumor in gland or aldosteronism	Slight hypernatremia (high blood levels of sodium) Hypokalemia (low blood levels of potassium) Alkalosis High blood pressure Weakness of skeletal muscles Acidic urine
Glucocorticoids (cortisol)	Tumor in gland or Cushing syndrome (high cortisol *and* androgens)	Hyperglycemia (high blood glucose levels; adrenal diabetes; leads to diabetes mellitus) Depressed immune system Destruction of tissue proteins, causing muscle atrophy and weakness, osteoporosis, weak capillaries (easy bruising), thin skin, and impaired wound healing; mobilization and redistribution of lipids, causing depletion of adipose tissue from limbs and deposition in face (moon face), neck (buffalo hump), and abdomen (Cushing syndrome) Emotional effects, including euphoria and depression
Androgens	Tumor in gland or adrenogenital syndrome	In females, hirsutism (excessive facial and body hair), acne, increased sex drive, regression of breast tissue, and loss of regular menstruation

Case STUDY 18.2 Cushing Syndrome

Ethan noticed that he had gained a substantial amount of weight over the past few months and that he was feeling weak. His physician observed that the adipose tissue distribution was mainly in his trunk, face, and neck (figure 18.17). There was also evidence of decreased muscle mass, and Ethan had several bruises on his upper and lower limbs. Results of a routine blood test showed elevated blood glucose levels and low blood K^+ levels. There was no observable evidence that Ethan had cancer. His physician suspected that he was suffering from Cushing syndrome.

A second blood sample was taken. Ethan's blood cortisol levels were very high, and his blood ACTH levels were very low. Based on these data, Ethan's physician explained that he was probably suffering from an adrenal gland tumor, which was secreting large amounts of cortisol, and that the tumor was not responding to the negative-feedback mechanisms that normally control cortisol secretion. Subsequently, imaging techniques revealed a tumor in Ethan's left adrenal gland. After his left adrenal gland was surgically removed, Ethan's symptoms decreased dramatically over the next few weeks.

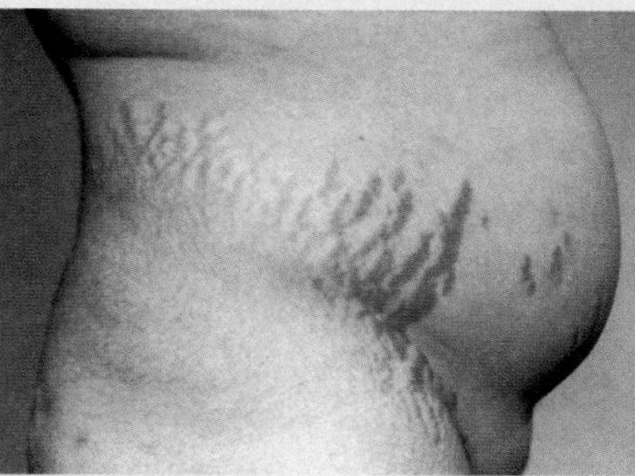

FIGURE 18.17 Cushing Syndrome
Rapid deposition of adipose tissue in the trunk can cause the skin to stretch, which can be seen as stretch marks in this photograph.
Clinical Photography, Central Manchester University Hospitals NHS Foundation Trust, UK/Science Source

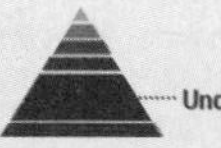

Predict 8

a. *Why did the physician suspect Cushing syndrome?*

b. *Explain why Ethan's physician concluded that a hormone-secreting tumor in one of Ethan's adrenal glands was responsible for his symptoms.*

c. *After surgical removal of his left adrenal gland, how did Ethan's blood cortisol and ACTH levels change?*

d. *How would the data from the second blood sample have been different if Ethan's condition had been due to a hormone-secreting tumor in his anterior pituitary gland?*

Adrenal Androgens

Some adrenal steroids function as weak androgens. *Androgen* is a generic term for steroid hormones that cause the development of male secondary sex characteristics. Most androgens are secreted by the reproductive system (see chapter 28). However, there are adrenal androgens secreted by the zona reticularis. Some adrenal androgens are converted by peripheral tissues to the potent androgen testosterone, while other adrenal androgens are weak androgens such as androstenedione (an-droh-STEEN-die-ohn). Adrenal androgens stimulate pubic and axillary hair growth and sex drive in females. However, the effects of adrenal androgens in males are negligible, in comparison with testosterone secreted by the testes.

ASSESS YOUR PROGRESS

40. *Describe the three layers of the adrenal cortex, and name the hormones produced by each layer.*
41. *Name the target tissue of aldosterone, and list the effects of an increase in aldosterone secretion on the concentration of ions in the blood.*
42. *Describe the effects produced by an increase in cortisol secretion. Starting with the hypothalamus, describe how stress or low blood glucose levels can stimulate cortisol release.*
43. *List the possible causes of hyposecretion of adrenal cortex hormones, and describe the symptoms.*
44. *List the possible causes of hypersecretion of adrenal cortex hormones, and describe the symptoms.*
45. *What effects do adrenal androgens have on males and on females?*

18.6 Pancreas

LEARNING OUTCOMES

After reading this section, you should be able to

A. **Describe the location and structure of the pancreas.**
B. **Name the hormones secreted by the pancreatic islets and describe their effects on their target tissues.**
C. **Explain how pancreatic hormones are regulated.**
D. **Compare and contrast the causes and symptoms of type 1 and type 2 diabetes mellitus.**

The **pancreas** (PAN-kree-as) is both an exocrine gland and an endocrine gland. The exocrine portion consists of acini (AS-i-nie), which produce pancreatic juice, and a duct system, which carries the pancreatic juice to the small intestine (see chapter 24). The endocrine part, consisting of pancreatic islets (islets of Langerhans; figure 18.18), secretes hormones that enter the plasma of the blood. The pancreas lies behind the peritoneum between the greater curvature of the stomach and the duodenum. It is an elongated structure approximately 15 cm long, weighing approximately 85–100 g. The head of the pancreas lies near the duodenum, and its body and tail extend toward the spleen.

Between 500,000 and 1 million pancreatic islets are dispersed among the ducts and acini of the pancreas. Each islet is composed of (1) **alpha (α) cells** (20%), which secrete **glucagon,** a peptide hormone; (2) **beta (β) cells** (75%), which secrete **insulin,** a peptide hormone consisting of two peptide chains bound together; and (3) **delta (δ) cells,** which secrete somatostatin, also a peptide hormone. Nerves from both divisions of the autonomic nervous system innervate the pancreatic islets, and a well-developed capillary network surrounds each islet.

Effect of Insulin and Glucagon on Their Target Tissues

The pancreatic hormones play an important role in regulating the concentration of critical nutrients in the blood, especially glucose and amino acids (table 18.10). The major target tissues of insulin are the (1) liver, (2) adipose tissue, (3) skeletal muscles, and (4) satiety center within the hypothalamus of the brain. The **satiety** (sa-TIE-eh-tee) **center** is a collection of neurons in the hypothalamus that controls appetite. However, insulin does not directly affect most other areas of the nervous system. The specific effects of insulin on these target tissues are listed in table 18.10.

Insulin

Insulin's primary function is to lower blood glucose levels by stimulating glucose transport into body cells. Insulin is secreted when blood glucose is elevated, such as after a meal. Insulin binds to membrane-bound receptors on target cells. Once insulin binds to its receptor, the receptor causes specific proteins in the membrane to become phosphorylated. Part of the cells' response to insulin is to increase the number of transport proteins in the plasma membrane for glucose and amino acids. Finally, insulin and its receptor enter the cell by endocytosis. The insulin is released from the insulin receptor and broken down within the cell, and the insulin receptor returns to the plasma membrane.

In general, the target tissue responds to insulin by increasing its ability to take up and use glucose and amino acids. Glucose molecules that are not needed immediately as an energy source to maintain cell metabolism are stored as glycogen in skeletal muscle, the liver, and other tissues and are converted to lipids in adipose tissue. Amino acids can be broken down and used as an energy source, or they can be converted to protein. Without insulin, the ability of these tissues to take up and use glucose and amino acids is minimal.

The normal regulation of blood glucose levels requires insulin. Blood glucose levels can increase dramatically when too little insulin is secreted or when insulin receptors do not respond to it (see Clinical Impact 18.2). In the absence of insulin, the movement of glucose and amino acids into cells declines dramatically, even though blood levels of these molecules may increase to very high levels. The hypothalamic satiety center requires insulin in order to take up glucose. In the absence of insulin, the satiety center cannot detect the presence of glucose in the extracellular fluid, even when glucose levels are high. The result is an intense sensation of hunger

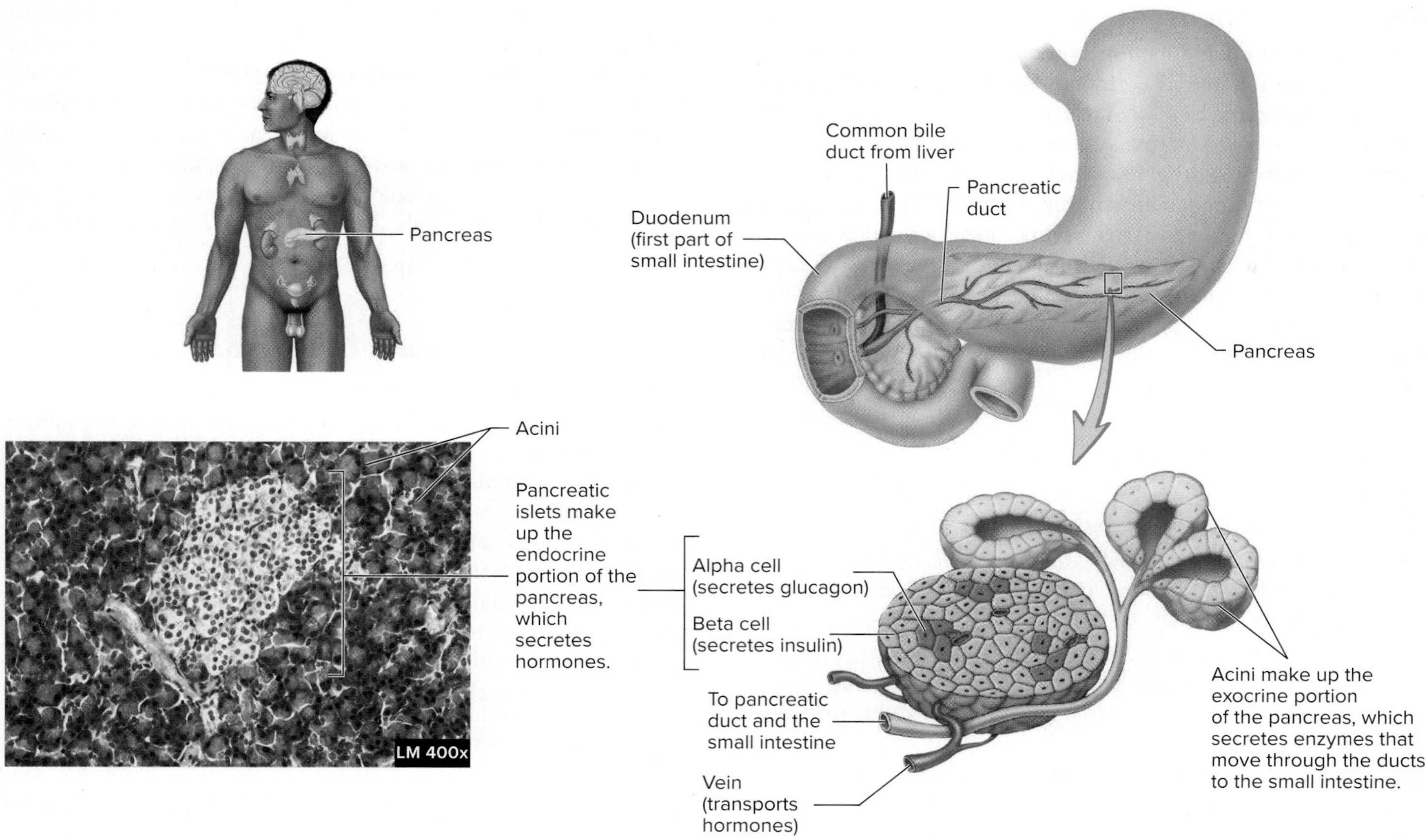

FIGURE 18.18 Histology of the Pancreatic Islets

A pancreatic islet consists of clusters of specialized cells among the acini of the exocrine portion of the pancreas. The stain used for this slide does not distinguish between alpha and beta cells. Biophoto Associates/Science Source APR

TABLE 18.10 Hormones of the Pancreas

Cells in Islets	Hormone	Structure	Target Tissue	Response
Alpha (α)	Glucagon	Peptide	Primarily liver	Increased breakdown of glycogen for release of glucose into the blood; increased production of new glucose
Beta (β)	Insulin	Peptide	Especially liver, skeletal muscle, adipose tissue	Increased uptake and use of glucose and amino acids
Delta (δ)	Somatostatin	Peptide	Alpha and beta cells (some somatostatin is produced in the hypothalamus)	Inhibition of insulin and glucagon secretion

in spite of high blood glucose levels, a condition called *polyphagia* (pol-ee-FAY-jee-ah). High blood glucose levels also cause increased urine volume (*polyuria;* pol-ee-YOO-ree-ah) and loss of water in the urine. Glucose is filtered from the blood into the kidney tubules. There, the glucose creates an osmotic gradient favoring the movement of water into the tubules and its subsequent loss in urine (see chapter 26). Elevated blood glucose levels also increase blood osmolality, resulting in an increased sensation of thirst (*polydipsia;* pol-ee-DIP-see-ah; see chapter 27).

When too much insulin is secreted, blood glucose levels can fall very low because too much insulin causes target tissues to rapidly take up glucose from the blood. Although the nervous system, except for cells of the satiety center, is not a target tissue for insulin, the nervous system depends primarily on blood glucose as an energy source. Consequently, low blood glucose levels cause changes in the function of the CNS, including dizziness, loss of cognitive function, and, in extreme cases, loss of consciousness.

Glucagon

Glucagon is the companion hormone to insulin (see chapter 17). Its secretion is stimulated when blood glucose levels decline. Glucagon promotes the release of glucose from intracellular stores. For example, glucagon primarily influences the liver, although it has some effect on skeletal muscle and adipose tissue (table 18.11). Glucagon binds to membrane-bound receptors, activates G proteins, and increases cAMP synthesis. In general, glucagon causes the breakdown of glycogen and increases glucose synthesis in the liver. It also increases the breakdown of lipids. The amount of glucose released from the liver into the blood increases dramatically after glucagon secretion increases.

Regulation of Pancreatic Hormone Secretion

Regulation of Insulin Secretion

Pancreatic secretion is partially under humoral control. The hormone-secreting cells can directly respond to low blood glucose levels. In addition, blood levels of other nutrients, neural stimulation, and other hormones control the secretion of insulin (figure 18.19).

The following factors increase insulin secretion:

1. *Hyperglycemia,* or elevated blood levels of glucose, directly stimulates insulin secretion from pancreatic β cells.
2. Certain amino acids also stimulate insulin secretion by acting directly on pancreatic β cells.
3. Parasympathetic stimulation associated with food intake acts with elevated blood glucose levels to increase insulin secretion.
4. Gastrointestinal hormones involved with regulating digestion, such as gastrin, secretin, and cholecystokinin (see chapter 24), increase insulin secretion.

Thus, insulin secretion tends to increase after a meal, when glucose and amino acid levels in the blood are their highest.

Insulin secretion decreases under a different set of conditions, which tends to be when glucose and amino acid levels in the blood are their lowest.

The following factors decrease insulin secretion:

1. *Hypoglycemia,* or low blood levels of glucose, directly slows insulin secretion.
2. Activation of the sympathetic nervous system is inhibitory to insulin secretion. This helps prevent a rapid fall in blood glucose levels. Because most tissues, except nervous tissue, require insulin to take up glucose, sympathetic stimulation maintains blood glucose levels in a normal range during periods of physical activity or excitement. This response is important for supplying a constant level of glucose to the brain for normal nervous system function.
3. Somatostatin inhibits both insulin and glucagon secretion, but the factors that regulate somatostatin secretion are not clear. It can be released in response to food intake, in which case somatostatin may prevent the oversecretion of insulin.
4. During periods of fasting, when blood glucose levels are low, the rate of insulin secretion declines.

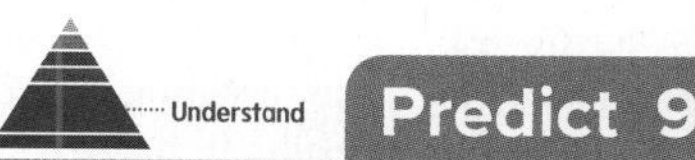

Explain why the increase in insulin secretion in response to parasympathetic stimulation and gastrointestinal hormones is consistent with the maintenance of blood glucose levels in the blood.

Regulation of Glucagon Secretion

Low blood glucose levels stimulate glucagon secretion, and high blood glucose levels inhibit it. Certain amino acids and sympathetic stimulation also increase glucagon secretion. After a

TABLE 18.11 Effect of Insulin and Glucagon on Target Tissues

Target Tissue	Response to Insulin	Response to Glucagon
Skeletal muscle, cardiac muscle, cartilage, bone, fibroblasts, leukocytes, and mammary glands	Increased glucose uptake and glycogen synthesis; increased uptake of certain amino acids	Little effect; skeletal muscle does not have glucagon receptors
Liver	Increased glycogen synthesis; increased use of glucose for energy (glycolysis)	Rapid increase in the breakdown of glycogen to glucose (glycogenolysis) and release of glucose into the blood; increased formation of glucose (gluconeogenesis) from amino acids, pyruvate, lactate, and, to some degree, lipids; increased metabolism of fatty acids, resulting in more ketones in the blood
Adipose cells	Increased glucose uptake, glycogen synthesis, lipid synthesis, and fatty acid uptake; increased glycolysis; inhibits lipase	High concentrations cause breakdown of lipids (lipolysis); probably unimportant under most conditions
Nervous system	Little effect, except increased glucose uptake in the satiety center	No effect

Clinical IMPACT 18.2 Diabetes Mellitus

Diabetes mellitus results primarily from the inadequate secretion of insulin or the inability of tissues to respond to insulin. **Type 1 diabetes mellitus,** also called *insulin-dependent diabetes mellitus (IDDM),* affects approximately 5–10% of people with diabetes mellitus and results from diminished insulin secretion. It develops as a result of autoimmune destruction of the pancreatic islets, and symptoms appear after approximately 90% of the islets have been destroyed. Type 1 diabetes mellitus most commonly develops in young people. Heredity may play a role in the condition, although the initiation of pancreatic islet destruction may involve a viral infection of the pancreas.

Type 2 diabetes mellitus, also called *noninsulin-dependent diabetes mellitus (NIDDM),* results from the inability of tissues to respond to insulin. Type 2 diabetes mellitus usually develops in people older than 40–45 years of age, although it is being observed more frequently in much younger patients.

Type 2 diabetes mellitus is more common than type 1 diabetes mellitus. Approximately 90–95% of people who have diabetes mellitus have type 2. The "thrifty genotype" hypothesis suggests that type 2 diabetes mellitus may be more common today because the genes that make people susceptible to the condition were once beneficial. For example, during periods of famine, the ability to store adipose tissue and to have altered glucose metabolism may have been advantageous, but today, when food is abundant, having these genes increases the likelihood of developing type 2 diabetes mellitus.

People with type 2 diabetes mellitus have a reduced number of functional receptors for insulin, or one or more of the enzymes activated by the insulin receptor are defective. Thus, glucose uptake by cells is very slow, which results in elevated blood glucose after a meal. Obesity is common, although not universal, in patients with type 2 diabetes mellitus. Elevated blood glucose levels cause adipose cells to convert glucose to lipid, even though the rate at which adipose cells take up glucose is impaired. Increased blood glucose and increased urine production lead to hyperosmolality of blood and dehydration of cells. The poor use of nutrients and dehydration of cells lead to lethargy, fatigue, and periods of irritability. Elevated blood glucose levels affect the endothelial tissue of blood vessels, as well as the nervous system's ability to respond to tactile sensation. The combination of these effects results in recurrent injury and infection, especially in distal tissues, such as the feet.

Patients with type 2 diabetes mellitus do not experience sudden, large increases in blood glucose and severe tissue wasting, as occurs with type 1 diabetes mellitus, because a slow rate of glucose uptake does occur, even though the insulin receptors are defective. In some people with type 2 diabetes mellitus, insulin production eventually decreases because pancreatic islet cells atrophy; then type 1 diabetes mellitus develops. Approximately 25–30% of patients with type 2 diabetes mellitus take insulin, 50% take oral medication to increase insulin secretion and improve the efficiency of glucose utilization, and the remainder control blood glucose levels with exercise and diet alone.

Glucose tolerance tests are used to diagnose diabetes mellitus. In general, the test involves feeding the patient a large amount of glucose after a period of fasting and then collecting blood samples for a few hours afterward. A sustained increase in blood glucose levels strongly indicates that the person has diabetes mellitus.

Too much insulin relative to the amount of glucose ingested leads to insulin shock. The high levels of insulin cause target tissues to take up glucose at a very high rate. As a result, the concentration of blood glucose rapidly falls to a low level. Because the nervous system depends on glucose as its major source of energy, neurons malfunction, leading to nervous system responses, such as disorientation, confusion, and convulsions. Too much insulin, too little food intake after an insulin injection, or increased metabolism of glucose due to excess physical exercise can cause insulin shock in a diabetic patient.

Keeping blood glucose within normal levels at all times can prevent damage to blood vessels and reduced nerve function in patients with either type of diabetes mellitus. However, doing so requires increased attention to diet and frequent blood glucose testing to ensure that blood glucose levels do not fall too low and lead to insulin shock.

high-protein meal, amino acids increase both insulin and glucagon secretion. Insulin causes target tissue uptake of amino acids for protein synthesis, and glucagon increases the process of glucose synthesis from amino acids in the liver (gluconeogenesis). Both protein synthesis and the use of amino acids to maintain blood glucose levels result from the low, but simultaneous, secretion of insulin and glucagon induced by meals high in protein.

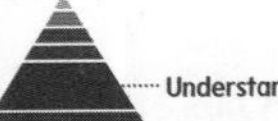

Predict 10

Compare the regulation of glucagon and insulin secretion after a meal high in carbohydrates, after a meal low in carbohydrates but high in proteins, and during physical exercise.

ASSESS YOUR PROGRESS

46. *Where is the pancreas located? Describe the exocrine and endocrine parts of this gland and the secretions produced by each portion.*
47. *Name the target tissues for insulin and glucagon, and list their effects on the target tissues.*
48. *How does insulin affect the satiety center of the hypothalamus?*
49. *What effect do blood glucose levels, blood amino acid levels, the autonomic nervous system, and somatostatin have on insulin and glucagon secretion?*
50. *Describe the causes and symptoms of type 1 diabetes mellitus and type 2 diabetes mellitus.*

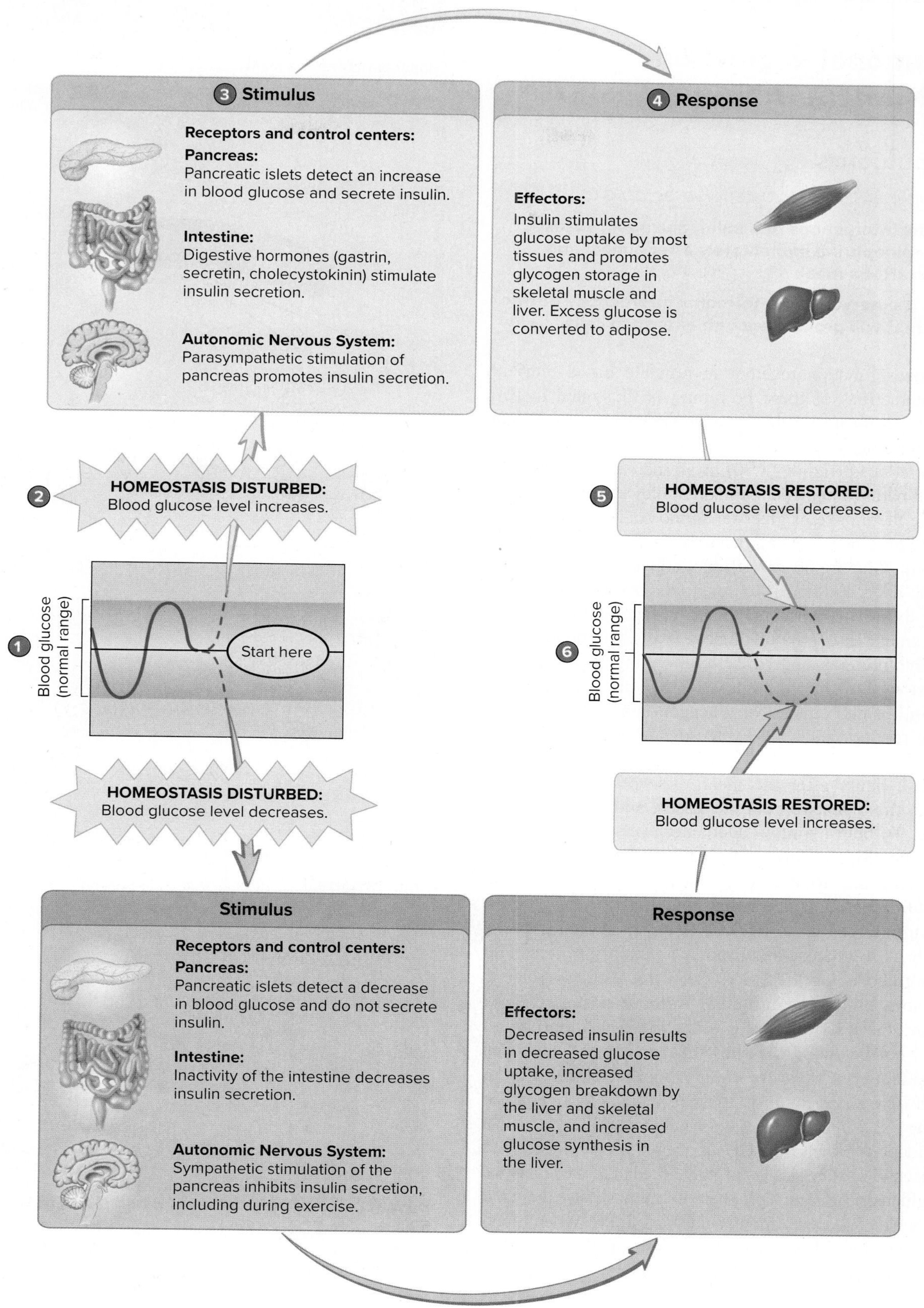

HOMEOSTASIS FIGURE 18.19 Regulation of Insulin Secretion

(1) Blood glucose is within its normal range. (2) Blood glucose level increases outside the normal range. (3) Pancreatic islets secrete insulin in direct response to elevated blood glucose. Digestive hormones and parasympathetic activity also stimulate insulin secretion. (4) Most tissues take up glucose when insulin binds to its receptors on the tissue. Liver and skeletal muscle cells convert glucose to glycogen. (5) Blood glucose level drops back to the normal range. (6) Homeostasis is restored. Observe the response to a drop in blood glucose by following the *lower pink arrows*.

18.7 Hormonal Regulation of Nutrient Utilization

LEARNING OUTCOMES

After reading this section, you should be able to

A. **Explain the interactions of insulin, glucagon, cortisol, GH, and epinephrine immediately after a meal and 1–2 hours after a meal.**

B. **Describe the nervous and hormonal interactions during exercise that will provide enough energy to cells.**

Several hormones function together to regulate blood nutrient levels. The interactions of these hormones is illustrated in two situations—after a meal and during exercise. After a meal and under resting conditions, secretion of glucagon, cortisol, GH, and epinephrine is reduced (figure 18.20). Both increasing blood glucose levels and parasympathetic stimulation elevate insulin secretion to increase the uptake of glucose, amino acids, and lipids by target tissues. Substances not immediately used for cell metabolism are stored. Glucose is converted to glycogen in skeletal muscle and the liver, and it is used for lipid synthesis in adipose tissue and the liver. The rapid uptake and storage of glucose prevent too large an increase in blood glucose levels. Amino acids are incorporated into proteins, and lipids that were ingested as part of the meal are stored in adipose tissue and the liver. If the meal is high in protein, a small amount of glucagon is secreted, thereby increasing the rate at which the liver uses amino acids to form glucose.

Within 1–2 hours after the meal, absorption of digested materials from the digestive tract decreases, and blood glucose levels decline. To help maintain adequate levels of glucose for normal brain function, secretion of glucagon, GH, cortisol, and epinephrine increases soon after a meal. As blood glucose declines, insulin secretion decreases, and the rate of glucose entry into insulin target tissues slows. Glycogen, stored in cells, is converted back to glucose and used as an energy source. The liver releases glucose into the blood. Cells that use less glucose start using more lipids and proteins. Adipose tissue releases fatty acids, and the liver releases triglycerides (in lipoproteins) and ketones into the blood. Tissues take up these substances from the blood and use them for energy. Lipid molecules are a major source of energy for most tissues when blood glucose levels are low.

The interactions of insulin, GH, glucagon, epinephrine, and cortisol are excellent examples of negative-feedback mechanisms. When blood glucose levels are high, these hormones cause the rapid uptake and storage of glucose, amino acids, and lipids. When blood glucose levels are low, they cause the release of glucose and a switch to lipid and protein metabolism as a source of energy for most tissues.

During exercise, skeletal muscles require energy to support the contraction process (see chapter 9). Although metabolism of intracellular nutrients can sustain muscle contraction for a short time, additional energy sources are required during prolonged activity. Sympathetic nervous system activity, which increases during exercise, stimulates the release of epinephrine from the adrenal medulla and the release of glucagon from the pancreas (figure 18.21). These hormones induce the conversion of

FUNDAMENTAL **Figure**

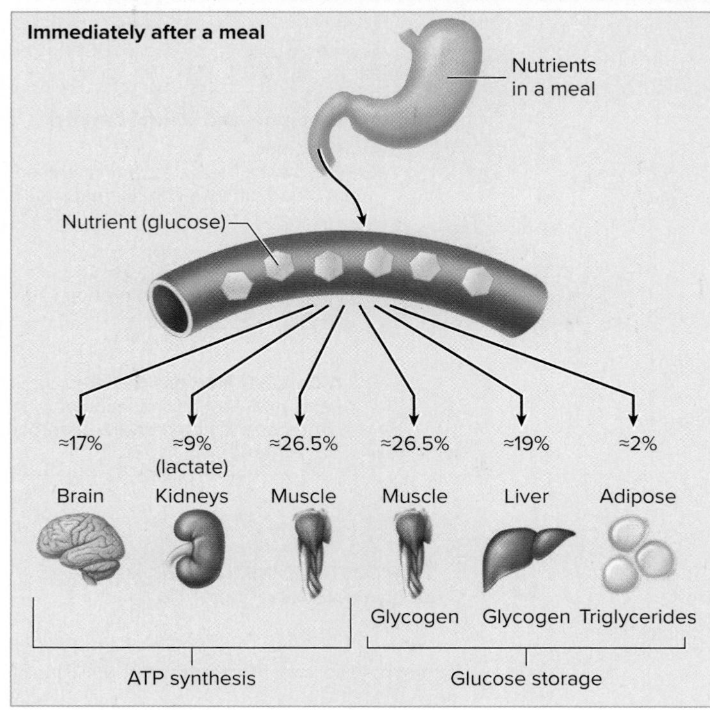

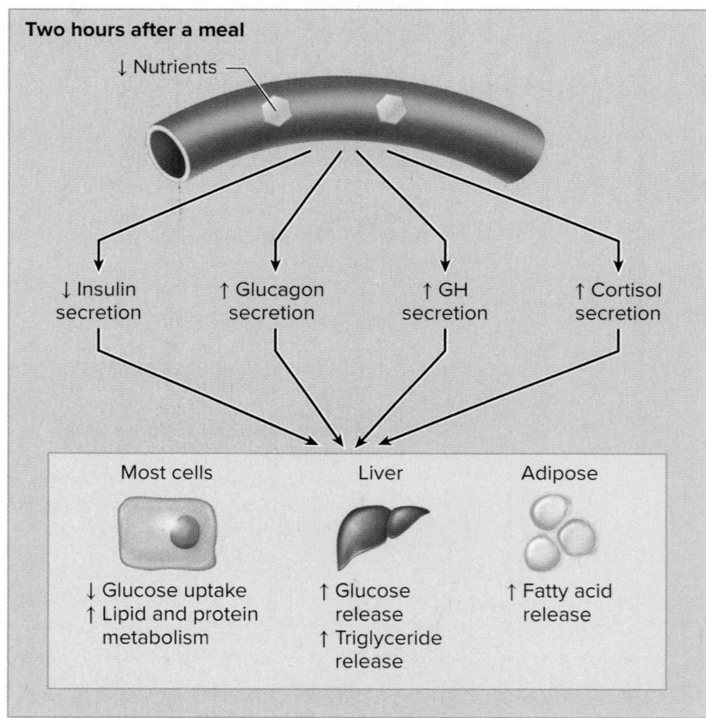

FIGURE 18.20 Regulation of Blood Nutrient Levels After a Meal

Blood nutrient levels are maintained immediately after a meal and for several hours afterward.

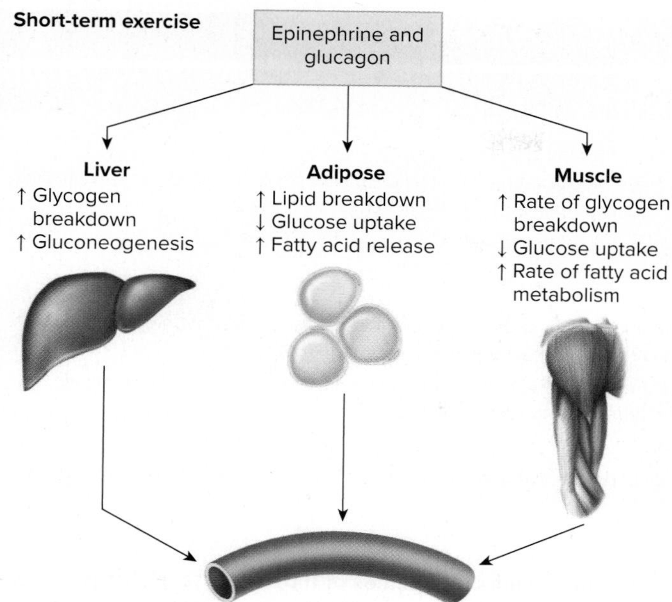

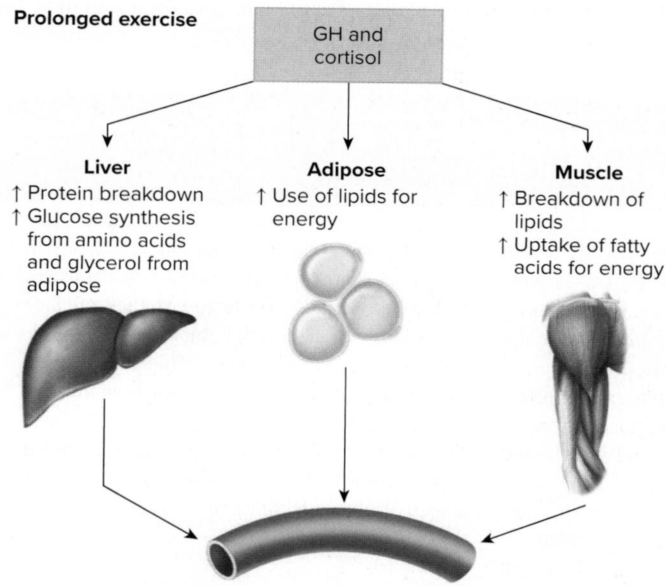

FIGURE 18.21 Regulation of Blood Nutrient Levels During Exercise

Short-term exercise blood nutrient levels are regulated primarily by epinephrine. Prolonged exercise blood nutrient levels are regulated primarily by cortisol and GH.

glycogen to glucose in the liver and the release of glucose into the blood, thus providing skeletal muscles with a source of energy. Because epinephrine and glucagon have short half-lives, they can rapidly adjust blood glucose levels for varying conditions of activity.

During sustained activity, glucose released from the liver and other tissues is not adequate to support muscle activity, and the danger exists that blood glucose levels will become too low to support brain function. A decrease in insulin prevents the uptake of glucose by most tissues, thus conserving glucose for the brain. In addition to other functions, epinephrine, glucagon, cortisol, and GH cause an increase in fatty acids, triglycerides, and ketones in the blood. Because GH increases protein synthesis and slows the breakdown of proteins, muscle proteins are not used as an energy source. Consequently, glucose metabolism decreases, and lipid metabolism in skeletal muscles increases. At the end of a long race, for example, muscles rely to a large extent on lipid metabolism for energy.

Apply **Predict 11**

Explain why long-distance runners may not have much of a "kick" left when they try to sprint to the finish line.

ASSESS YOUR PROGRESS

51. *Describe the hormonal effects that occur immediately after a meal to cause nutrients to move into cells and be stored.*
52. *What occurs hormonally 1–2 hours after a meal that causes stored materials to be released and used for energy?*
53. *During exercise, how does sympathetic nervous system activity regulate blood glucose levels? Name five hormones that interact to ensure that the brain and the muscles have adequate energy sources during exercise, and explain the role of each.*

18.8 Hormones of the Reproductive System

LEARNING OUTCOMES

After reading this section, you should be able to

A. **List and describe the functions of the hormones secreted by the testes and ovaries.**
B. **Explain how the anterior pituitary regulates secretion by the testes and ovaries.**
C. **Explain how the placenta acts as a temporary endocrine gland.**

All aspects of reproduction, including puberty, menstruation, gamete formation, and pregnancy, are under the control of reproductive hormones. Reproductive hormones are secreted primarily from the ovaries, testes, placenta, and pituitary gland (table 18.12). These hormones are discussed in chapter 28. The main endocrine glands of the male reproductive system are the testes. The functions of the testes depend on the secretion of FSH and LH from the anterior pituitary gland. The main hormone secreted by the testes

TABLE 18.12 Hormones of the Reproductive Organs

Hormone	Structure	Target Tissue	Response
Testes			
Testosterone	Steroid	Most cells	Aids in spermatogenesis, development of genitalia, maintenance of functional reproductive organs, secondary sex characteristics, and sexual behavior
Inhibin	Polypeptide	Anterior pituitary gland	Inhibits FSH secretion
Ovaries			
Estrogen	Steroid	Most cells	Aids in uterine and mammary gland development and function, maturation of genitalia, secondary sex characteristics, sexual behavior, and menstrual cycle
Progesterone	Steroid	Most cells	Aids in uterine and mammary gland development and function, maturation of genitalia, secondary sex characteristics, and menstrual cycle
Inhibin	Polypeptide	Anterior pituitary gland	Inhibits FSH secretion
Relaxin	Polypeptide	Connective tissue cells	Increases the flexibility of connective tissue in the pelvic area, especially the symphysis pubis

is testosterone, an androgen. **Testosterone** regulates the production of sperm cells by the testes and the development and maintenance of male reproductive organs and secondary sex characteristics. The testes secrete another hormone, called **inhibin,** which inhibits the secretion of FSH from the anterior pituitary gland.

The main endocrine glands of the female reproductive system are the ovaries. Like the testes, the functions of the ovaries depend on the secretion of FSH and LH from the anterior pituitary gland. The main hormones secreted by the ovaries are **estrogen** and **progesterone.** These hormones, along with FSH and LH, control the female reproductive cycle, prepare the mammary glands for

MICROBES In Your Body 18.1 Hormonal Regulation of Nutrient Metabolism Is Influenced by Gut Microbes

Obesity has increased at an alarming rate over the last three decades. It is estimated that over 1.6 billion adults worldwide are overweight or obese. In the United States, one-third of adults are obese. As obesity rates have increased, so have the rates of obesity-related health conditions such as insulin resistance, diabetes, and cardiovascular disease. Why this dramatic increase? There are two main reasons for obesity: diet/lifestyle and gut bacteria; it seems these two may be related.

The most familiar cause of obesity is diet and lifestyle. The "typical" Western diet consists of frequent large meals high in refined grains, red meat, saturated fats, and sugary drinks. Combined with a reduction in physical activity and less sleep for many Americans, the Western diet and lifestyle can lead to obesity and poor health.

However, could humans' gut microbiota be just as responsible (or even more responsible) for obesity? Comparisons between the gut microbiota of lean versus obese individuals seem to suggest the possibility of an important link between gut microbiota and our weight. The gut in humans, like other animals, is densely populated with microbiota. The majority (90%) of human gut bacteria fall into two groups: *Firmicutes* and *Bacteroidetes.* Lean people have more *Bacteroidetes* than *Firmicutes,* while the opposite is true for obese people.

We now know that gut microbiota affect nutrient processing and absorption, hormonal regulation of nutrient use by body cells, and even our hunger level.

Changes in gut microbiota alter the hormonal regulation of nutrient use. Inflammation-promoting effects of an imbalanced gut microbiota is thought to induce obesity via promoting insulin resistance. Normal gut microbiota metabolism is critical for secretion of several antihunger hormones, and anti-depressive neurotransmitters and neurochemicals. Shifts in normal gut microbiota, as related to diet, may very well disrupt normal antihunger signals and gut permeability leading to overeating and inflammation related to obesity.

Can gut microbiota in obese people be manipulated to cause them to become lean? Several possibilities exist, including the distinct possibility that prescribing antibiotics against bacteria associated with obesity could shift the metabolism of an obese person to become leaner. Another possibility is the use of prebiotics—nondigestible sugars that enhance the growth of beneficial microbiota. Finally, probiotic use is another possible intervention for obesity. Probiotics are nonpathogenic live bacteria that confer a health benefit to the host. This is a rapidly expanding field that holds much promise, but it is still in its beginning stages of our understanding.

Predict 12

Using section 18.7 in this chapter and knowledge you gained about how levels of growth hormone (GH) and cortisol determine nutrient use and metabolic reactions, predict the following relationship. Predict whether GH and cortisol levels are higher or lower in a person whose gut microbiota population has more Firmicutes *than* Bacteroidetes *bacteria. Would this person experience hunger more or less often than an individual with more* Bacteroidetes *bacteria in their gut?*

lactation, and maintain pregnancy. Estrogen and progesterone are also responsible for the development of the female reproductive organs and female secondary sex characteristics. Like the testes, the ovaries secrete inhibin, which inhibits FSH secretion. This information may help you answer this chapter's Learn to Predict question.

During the first one-third of pregnancy, the placenta secretes an LH-like substance that is necessary to maintain pregnancy (see chapter 28). Throughout most of pregnancy, the ovaries and placenta secrete increasing amounts of estrogen and progesterone, which are also necessary to maintain pregnancy. In addition, the ovaries secrete **relaxin,** which increases the flexibility of the connective tissue of the symphysis pubis and helps dilate the cervix of the uterus. This facilitates delivery by making the birth canal larger.

ASSESS YOUR PROGRESS

54. *List the hormones secreted by the testes, and describe their functions.*

55. *List the hormones secreted by the ovaries, and describe their functions.*

56. *What hormones from the anterior pituitary gland regulate secretion by the testes and ovaries? Explain how these hormones function.*

57. *What hormones are secreted by the placenta to help maintain pregnancy and facilitate birth?*

18.9 Hormones of the Pineal Gland

LEARNING OUTCOMES

After reading this section, you should be able to

A. **List the hormones secreted by the pineal gland and describe their possible functions.**

B. **Explain the photoperiod and its relationship to pineal gland secretion.**

The **pineal** (PIN-ee-al) **gland** in the epithalamus of the brain secretes hormones that act on the hypothalamus and the gonads to inhibit reproductive functions, such as by inhibiting the secretion of certain reproductive hormones. Two substances have been proposed as secretory products: (1) **melatonin** (mel-ah-TONE-in) and (2) **arginine vasotocin** (AR-ji-neen vah-soh-TOH-sin; table 18.13). Melatonin can decrease hypothalamic GnRH secretion. This mechanism may inhibit reproductive functions. It may also help regulate sleep cycles by increasing the tendency to sleep.

TABLE 18.13 Other Hormones and Hormonelike Substances

Chemical Messenger	Structure	Target Tissue	Response
Pineal Gland			
Melatonin	Amino acid derivative	At least the hypothalamus	Inhibition of gonadotropin-releasing hormone secretion, thereby inhibiting reproduction; significance is not clear in humans; may help regulate sleep-wake cycles
Arginine vasotocin	Peptide	Possibly the hypothalamus	Possible inhibition of gonadotropin-releasing hormone secretion
Thymus			
Thymosin	Peptide	Immune tissues	Development and function of the immune system
Several Tissues (autocrine and paracrine chemical messengers)			
Eicosanoids			
Prostaglandins	Modified fatty acid	Most tissues	Mediation of the inflammatory response; increased uterine contractions; involved in ovulation, possible inhibition of progesterone synthesis; blood coagulation; other functions
Thromboxanes	Modified fatty acid	Most tissues	Mediation of the inflammatory response; other functions, including blood clotting
Prostacyclins	Modified fatty acid	Most tissues	Mediation of the inflammatory response; other functions, including blood clotting
Leukotrienes	Modified fatty acid	Most tissues	Mediation of the inflammatory response; other functions, including blood clotting
Enkephalins and endorphins	Peptides	Nervous system	Reduction of pain sensation; other functions
Epidermal growth factor	Protein	Many tissues	Stimulation of division in many cell types; embryonic development
Fibroblast growth factor	Protein	Many tissues	Stimulation of cell division in many cell types; embryonic development
Interleukin-2	Protein	Certain immune-competent cells	Stimulation of cell division of T lymphocytes

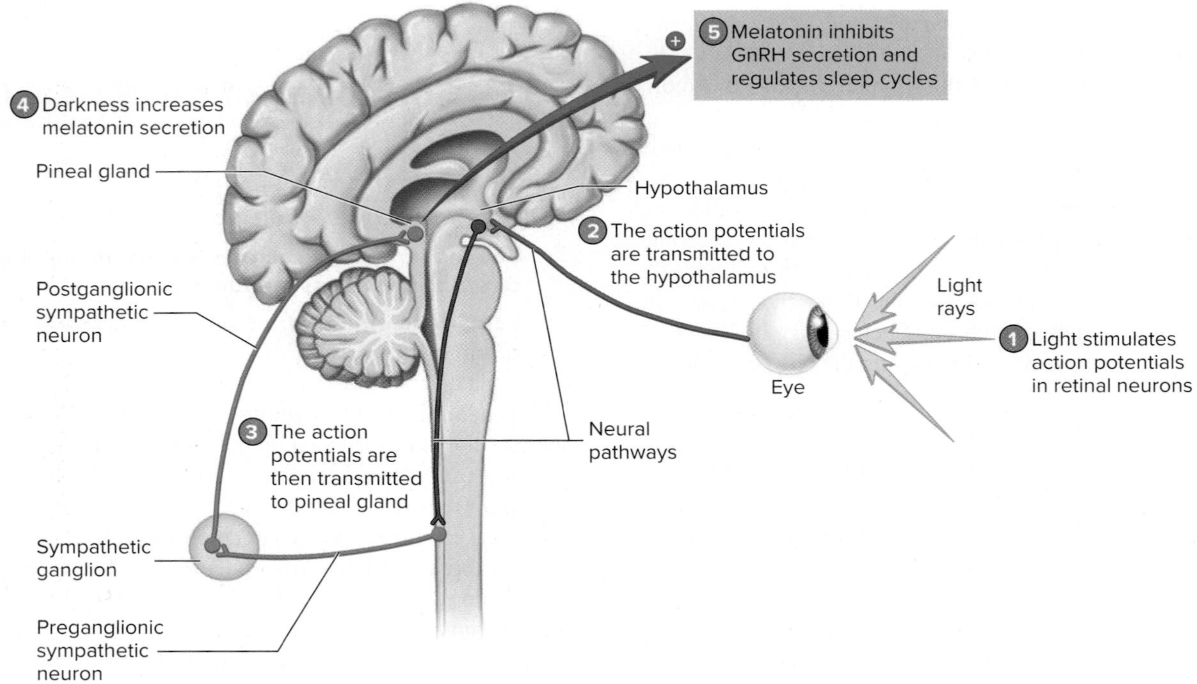

PROCESS Figure 18.22

Regulation of Melatonin Secretion from the Pineal Gland

Light entering the eye inhibits the release of melatonin from the pineal gland, and dark stimulates the release of melatonin.

Joe works the night shift at the hospital and has had trouble sleeping. His doctor suggested taking prescription melatonin for 2–3 months to help regulate Joe's sleep cycle. What time of day did Joe's doctor suggest he take the melatonin? Explain.

Arginine vasotocin works with melatonin to regulate the function of the reproductive system in some animals. Evidence for the role of melatonin is more extensive, however.

In some animals, pineal secretions are regulated by the **photoperiod,** the amount of daylight and darkness that occurs each day and changes with the seasons of the year. Figure 18.22 details the mechanism regulating melatonin secretion.

1. Light entering the eye stimulates neurons in the retina to initiate action potentials.
2. Action potentials are transmitted to the hypothalamus.
3. Action potentials from the hypothalamus are transmitted through the sympathetic division to the pineal gland.
4. A *decrease* in light (an increase in darkness) results in increased sympathetic stimulation of the pineal gland and increased melatonin secretion. An *increase* in light results in decreased sympathetic stimulation of the pineal gland and decreased melatonin secretion.
5. Melatonin inhibits GnRH secretion from the hypothalamus and may help regulate sleep cycles.

Thus, humans secrete larger amounts of melatonin at night than during the day. In animals that breed in the spring, the increasingly longer days as summer approaches reduce pineal secretions. Because pineal secretions inhibit reproductive functions in these species, they experience hypertrophy of the reproductive structures in the summer.

Melatonin's role in regulating reproductive functions in humans is not clear, but some researchers recommend its use to enhance sleep. However, because melatonin causes atrophy of reproductive structures in some species, undesirable side effects on the reproductive system may be possible for people who take supplemental melatonin.

The function of the pineal gland in humans is not clear, but tumors that destroy the pineal gland correlate with early sexual development, and tumors that result in pineal hormone secretion correlate with delayed development of the reproductive system. It is not clear, however, if the pineal gland controls the onset of puberty.

ASSESS YOUR PROGRESS

58. *Where is the pineal gland located? Name the hormones it produces and their possible effects.*
59. *Explain the relationship between the photoperiod and pineal gland secretion.*

18.10 Other Hormones and Chemical Messengers

LEARNING OUTCOMES

After reading this section, you should be able to

A. **Describe the functions of the hormones secreted by the thymus, digestive system, heart, and kidneys.**
B. **Differentiate between autocrine and paracrine chemical messengers.**
C. **Give examples of both autocrine and paracrine chemical messengers and describe their functions.**

Hormones of the Thymus

The **thymus** (THIGH-mus) is important for immune function. It is in the neck and superior to the heart in the thorax. The thymus secretes the hormone **thymosin** (THIGH-moh-sin; see table 18.13). Both the thymus and thymosin play a role in the development and maturation of the immune system (see chapter 22).

Hormones of the Digestive Tract

Several hormones are released from the digestive tract. They regulate digestive functions by influencing the activity of the stomach, intestines, liver, and pancreas (see chapter 24).

Hormones of Adipose Tissue

Adipocytes secrete the hormone **leptin.** Leptin regulates satiety signals in the hypothalamus. In other words, it reduces the urge to eat. When the synthesis of leptin is disabled, animals eat excessively and become obese.

Hormonelike Chemicals

Recall from chapter 17 that some chemical messengers differ from hormones in that they are not secreted from discrete endocrine glands (see table 17.1). The effects of these chemicals are often local rather than systemic, or their functions are not understood adequately to explain their role in the body. **Autocrine chemical messengers** are released from cells that influence the same cell from which they are released. **Paracrine chemical messengers** are released from one cell type, diffuse short distances, and influence the activity of another cell type, which is the target tissue. Certain molecules sometimes function in an autocrine fashion and sometimes in a paracrine fashion. This distinction is similar to that for differentiating when a particular molecule is acting as a neurotransmitter and when it is acting as a hormone. The difference lies in the mode of transport (see chapter 17).

Examples of autocrine chemical messengers include chemical mediators of inflammation derived from the fatty acid arachidonic (ah-rak-ih-DON-ik) acid, such as eicosanoids and modified phospholipids. The eicosanoids include prostaglandins (PROS-tah-GLAN-dinz), thromboxanes (THROM-bok-zanes), prostacyclins (pros-tah-SIGH-klinz), and leukotrienes (loo-koh-TRY-eens). An example of a modified phospholipid is platelet-activating factor (see chapter 19). Paracrine chemical messengers include substances that play a role in modulating the sensation of pain, such as **endorphins, enkephalins** (en-KEF-ah-linz), prostaglandins, and several peptide growth factors, such as **epidermal growth factor, fibroblast growth factor,** and **interleukin-2** (in-ter-LOO-kin; see table 18.13).

Prostaglandins, thromboxanes, prostacyclins, and leukotrienes are released from injured cells and are responsible for initiating some of the symptoms of inflammation (see chapter 22), in addition to being released from certain healthy cells. For example, prostaglandins are involved in the regulation of uterine contractions during menstruation and childbirth, the process of ovulation, the inhibition of progesterone synthesis by the corpus luteum, the regulation of coagulation, kidney function, and the modification of the effect of other hormones on their target tissues. Pain receptors are stimulated directly by prostaglandins and other inflammatory compounds, and prostaglandins cause vasodilation of blood vessels, which is associated with headaches. Anti-inflammatory drugs, such as aspirin, inhibit prostaglandin synthesis and, as a result, reduce inflammation and pain. These examples are paracrine chemical messengers because they are synthesized and secreted by the cells near their target cells. Once prostaglandins enter the blood, they are metabolized rapidly.

Three classes of peptide molecules, which are endogenously produced analgesics, bind to the same receptors as morphine. They include enkephalins, endorphins, and **dynorphins** (DIE-nohr-finz). They are produced in several body sites, such as in parts of the brain, pituitary gland, spinal cord, and intestines. They act as neurotransmitters in some neurons of both the central and the peripheral nervous systems and as hormones or paracrine regulatory substances. In general, they moderate the sensation of pain (see chapter 14). Decreased sensitivity to painful stimuli during exercise and stress may result from the increased secretion of these substances.

Several proteins can be classified as growth factors. They generally function as paracrine chemical messengers because they are secreted near their target tissues. Epidermal growth factor stimulates cell divisions in a number of tissues and plays an important role in embryonic development. Interleukin-2 stimulates the proliferation of T lymphocytes and plays a very important role in immune responses (see chapter 22).

The number of hormonelike substances in the body is large, and only a few of them have been mentioned here. Chemical communication among body cells is complex, well developed, and

Systems PATHOLOGY | Graves Disease (Hyperthyroidism)

Background Information

Grace manages a business, has several employees, and works hard to make time for her husband and two children. Over several months, she slowly noticed that she was sweating excessively and appeared flushed. In addition, she often felt her heart pounding, was much more nervous than usual, and found it difficult to concentrate. Then Grace began to feel weak and lose weight, even though her appetite was greater than normal. Her family recognized some of these changes and noticed that her eyes seemed larger than usual. They encouraged her to see her physician. After an examination and some blood tests, Grace was diagnosed with Graves disease, a type of hyperthyroidism. Graves disease is caused by altered regulation of hormone secretion—specifically, the elevated secretion of thyroid hormones from the thyroid gland. In approximately 95% of Graves disease cases, the immune system produces an unusual antibody type, which binds to receptors on the cells of the thyroid follicle and stimulates them to secrete increased amounts of thyroid hormone. The secretion of the releasing hormone and thyroid-stimulating hormone is inhibited by elevated thyroid hormones. However, the antibody is produced in large amounts and is not inhibited by thyroid hormones. A very elevated rate of thyroid hormone secretion is therefore maintained. In addition, the size of the thyroid gland increases. Enlargement of the thyroid gland is called a goiter. Connective tissue components are deposited behind the eyes, causing them to bulge (figure 18.23).

Grace was treated with radioactive iodine (^{131}I) atoms that were actively transported into thyroid cells, where they destroyed a substantial portion of the thyroid gland. Data indicate that this treatment has few side effects and is effective in treating most cases of Graves disease. Other options include (1) drugs that inhibit the synthesis and secretion of thyroid hormones and (2) surgery to remove part of the thyroid gland. Unfortunately, removal of the thyroid gland normally does not reverse exophthalmos. Figure 18.24 shows the effects Graves disease has on the other systems in the body. Table 18.14 lists some other representative endocrine diseases and disorders.

Predict 13

Explain why removal of part of the thyroid gland is an effective treatment for Graves disease.

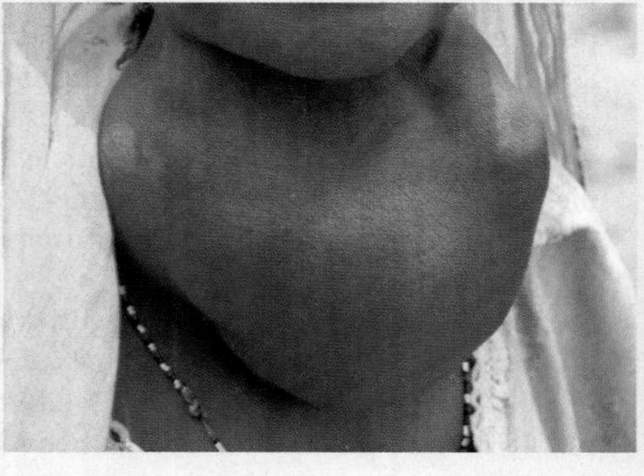

(a)

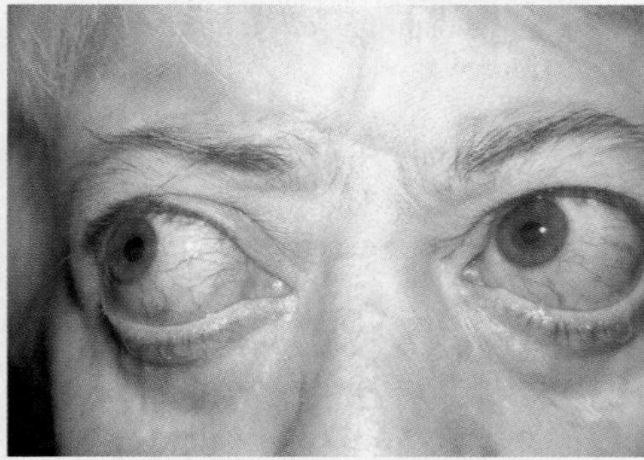

(b)

FIGURE 18.23 Effects of Graves Disease
(*a*) A goiter and (*b*) protruding eyes are symptoms of hyperthyroidism. (a) Mike Goldwater/Alamy Stock Photo; (b) Ralph C. Eagle, Jr./Science Source

necessary to maintain homeostasis. Investigations into chemical regulation increase our knowledge of body functions—knowledge that can be used to develop new treatments for pathological conditions.

ASSESS YOUR PROGRESS

60. *What hormone is secreted by the thymus? What is its function?*

61. *What function do the hormones secreted by the stomach and small intestine perform?*

62. *What is the difference between an autocrine and a paracrine chemical messenger?*

63. *List eicosanoids and modified phospholipids that function as autocrine chemical messengers, and explain how they work.*

64. *List examples of paracrine chemical messengers that play a role in modulating pain or are peptide growth factors.*

65. *Describe the paracrine functions of prostaglandins and how anti-inflammatory drugs can reduce pain and inflammation.*

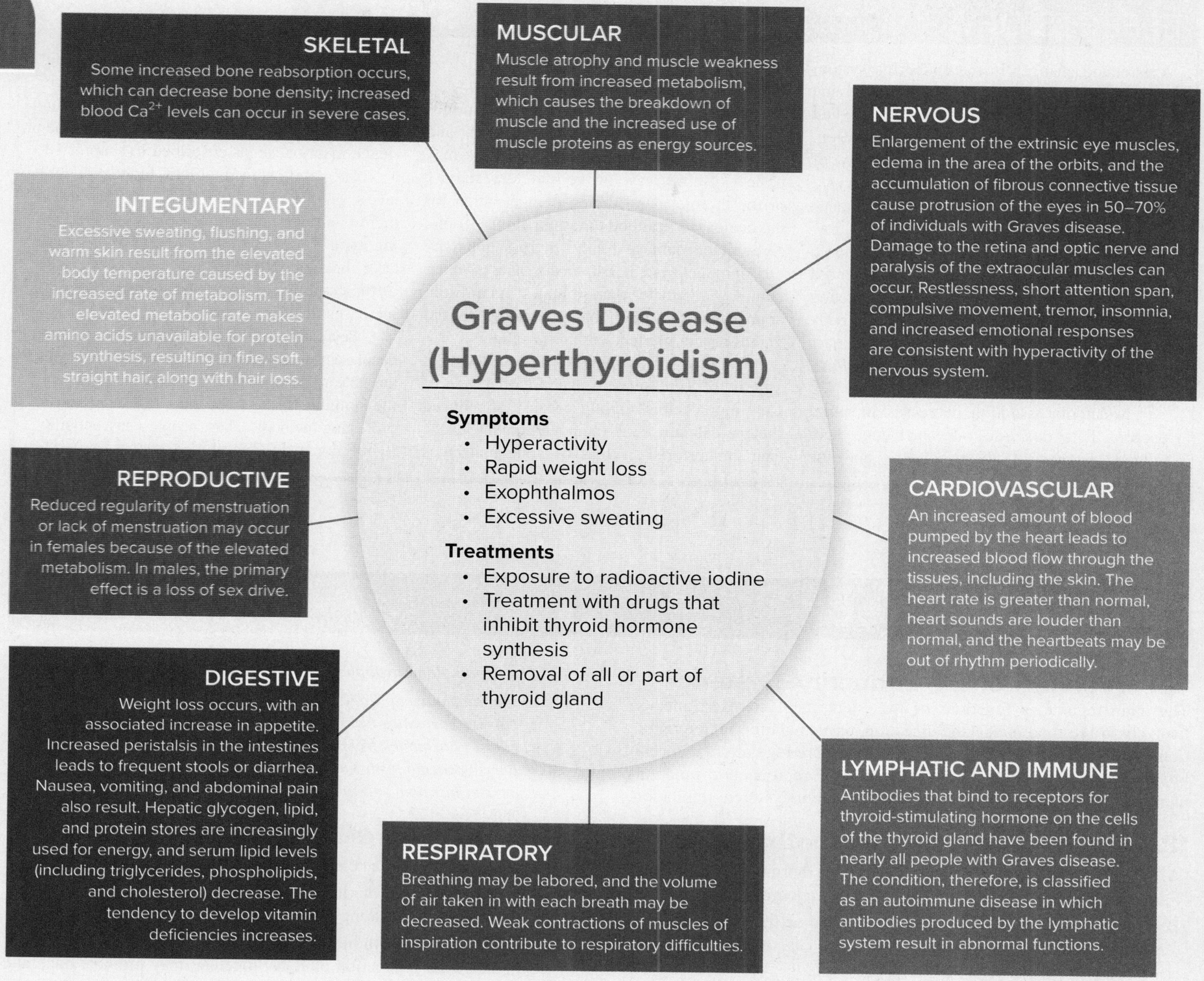

SKELETAL
Some increased bone reabsorption occurs, which can decrease bone density; increased blood Ca^{2+} levels can occur in severe cases.

MUSCULAR
Muscle atrophy and muscle weakness result from increased metabolism, which causes the breakdown of muscle and the increased use of muscle proteins as energy sources.

NERVOUS
Enlargement of the extrinsic eye muscles, edema in the area of the orbits, and the accumulation of fibrous connective tissue cause protrusion of the eyes in 50–70% of individuals with Graves disease. Damage to the retina and optic nerve and paralysis of the extraocular muscles can occur. Restlessness, short attention span, compulsive movement, tremor, insomnia, and increased emotional responses are consistent with hyperactivity of the nervous system.

INTEGUMENTARY
Excessive sweating, flushing, and warm skin result from the elevated body temperature caused by the increased rate of metabolism. The elevated metabolic rate makes amino acids unavailable for protein synthesis, resulting in fine, soft, straight hair, along with hair loss.

Graves Disease (Hyperthyroidism)

Symptoms
- Hyperactivity
- Rapid weight loss
- Exophthalmos
- Excessive sweating

Treatments
- Exposure to radioactive iodine
- Treatment with drugs that inhibit thyroid hormone synthesis
- Removal of all or part of thyroid gland

REPRODUCTIVE
Reduced regularity of menstruation or lack of menstruation may occur in females because of the elevated metabolism. In males, the primary effect is a loss of sex drive.

CARDIOVASCULAR
An increased amount of blood pumped by the heart leads to increased blood flow through the tissues, including the skin. The heart rate is greater than normal, heart sounds are louder than normal, and the heartbeats may be out of rhythm periodically.

DIGESTIVE
Weight loss occurs, with an associated increase in appetite. Increased peristalsis in the intestines leads to frequent stools or diarrhea. Nausea, vomiting, and abdominal pain also result. Hepatic glycogen, lipid, and protein stores are increasingly used for energy, and serum lipid levels (including triglycerides, phospholipids, and cholesterol) decrease. The tendency to develop vitamin deficiencies increases.

RESPIRATORY
Breathing may be labored, and the volume of air taken in with each breath may be decreased. Weak contractions of muscles of inspiration contribute to respiratory difficulties.

LYMPHATIC AND IMMUNE
Antibodies that bind to receptors for thyroid-stimulating hormone on the cells of the thyroid gland have been found in nearly all people with Graves disease. The condition, therefore, is classified as an autoimmune disease in which antibodies produced by the lymphatic system result in abnormal functions.

FIGURE 18.24 Interactions Between Graves Disease and Other Systems in the Body
Patients with Graves disease have higher-than-normal thyroid hormone levels, which increases the activity of most body systems.

TABLE 18.14 Representative Diseases and Disorders of the Endocrine System

Condition	Description
Diabetes insipidus	Due to a lack of ADH from the posterior pituitary; results in excessive urination
Hashimoto thyroiditis	Autoimmune disease in which thyroid hormone secretion can be decreased; metabolic rate is decreased, weight gain is possible, and activity levels are depressed
Addison disease	Low levels of aldosterone and cortisol from the adrenal cortex; low blood Na^+ levels, low blood pressure, and excessive urination
Gestational diabetes	Develops in pregnant females due to actions of the placental hormone, human placental lactogen (HPL); in some females, HPL overly desensitizes the female's insulin receptors; causes elevated blood glucose levels in the mother and, if left untreated, excessive fetal growth

EFFECTS OF AGING ON THE ENDOCRINE SYSTEM

Age-related changes in the endocrine system are not the same for all of the endocrine glands. Some, but not all, undergo a gradual decrease in secretory activity. In addition, some decreases in the secretory activity of endocrine glands appear to be secondary to a decrease in physical activity as people age.

GH secretion decreases as people grow older. The decrease is greater in people who do not exercise, but it may not occur at all in those who exercise regularly. Decreasing GH secretion may explain the gradual decrease in lean body mass. For example, bone mass and muscle mass decrease as GH levels decline. At the same time, the proportion of adipose tissue increases.

Melatonin secretion decreases in aging people. This decrease may influence age-related changes in sleep patterns and the secretory patterns of other hormones, such as GH and testosterone.

The secretion of thyroid hormones decreases slightly with increasing age, and the T_3:T_4 ratio decreases. However, this may be less of a decrease in the secretory activity of the thyroid gland than a compensation for the decreased lean body mass in aging people. Age-related damage to the thyroid gland by the immune system can occur and is more common in females than in males. As a result, approximately 10% of older females' thyroid glands do not produce enough T_3 and T_4.

Parathyroid hormone secretion does not appear to decrease with age. Blood levels of Ca^{2+} may decline slightly because of reduced dietary calcium intake and vitamin D levels. The greatest risk is loss of bone matrix as parathyroid hormone increases to maintain blood levels of Ca^{2+} within their normal range.

Reproductive hormone secretion gradually declines in older males, and females experience menopause, as described in chapter 28.

The ability to regulate blood glucose levels does not decline with age. However, there is an age-related probability of developing type 2 diabetes mellitus for those who have the familial tendency, and the incidence of the condition is correlated with age-related increases in body weight.

Secretion of thymosin from the thymus decreases with age. Fewer immature lymphocytes are able to mature and become functional, and the immune system becomes less effective in protecting the body. Thus, people's susceptibility to infection and to cancer increases.

Concept Check

18.1 Overview of the Endocrine System

The main regulatory functions of the endocrine system are metabolism, control of food intake and digestion, tissue maturation, ion regulation, water balance, heart rate and blood pressure regulation, control of blood glucose and other nutrients, control of reproductive functions, uterine contractions and milk letdown, and immune system regulation.

18.2 Pituitary Gland and Hypothalamus

A. The pituitary gland secretes at least nine hormones that regulate numerous body functions as well as other endocrine glands.
B. The hypothalamus regulates pituitary gland activity through neuropeptides and action potentials.

Structure of the Pituitary Gland

A. The posterior pituitary develops from the floor of the brain and consists of the infundibulum and the neurohypophysis.
B. The anterior pituitary develops from the roof of the mouth.

1. *The pituitary gland* 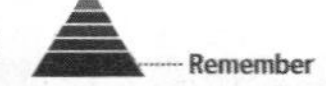

   a. develops from the floor of the brain.
   b. develops from the roof of the mouth.
   c. is stimulated by neuropeptides produced in the midbrain.
   d. secretes only three major hormones.
   e. Both a and b are correct.

Relationship of the Pituitary Gland to the Brain: The Hypothalamus

The hypothalamohypophysial tract connects the hypothalamus and the posterior pituitary. Neuropeptides are produced in hypothalamic neurons and are secreted from the posterior pituitary.

2. *The hypothalamohypophysial portal system* 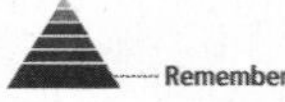

   a. contains one capillary bed.
   b. carries hormones from the anterior pituitary to the body.
   c. carries hormones from the posterior pituitary to the body.
   d. carries hormones from the hypothalamus to the anterior pituitary.
   e. carries hormones from the hypothalamus to the posterior pituitary.

Hormones of the Pituitary Gland

A. ADH promotes water retention by the kidneys.
B. Oxytocin promotes uterine contractions during delivery and causes milk letdown in lactating females.
C. GH stimulates growth in most tissues and regulates metabolism. GH stimulates the production of IGFs; together, they promote bone and cartilage growth. GH is regulated by GHRH and somatostatin.
D. TSH, or thyrotropin, causes the release of thyroid hormones.
E. ACTH is derived from proopiomelanocortin; it stimulates cortisol secretion from the adrenal cortex and increases skin pigmentation.
F. Several hormones in addition to ACTH are derived from proopiomelanocortin.
   - Lipotropins cause lipid breakdown.
   - β endorphins play a role in analgesia.
   - MSH increases skin pigmentation.
G. LH and FSH are major gonadotropins that regulate the production of gametes and reproductive hormones (testosterone in males, estrogen and progesterone in females). GnRH from the hypothalamus stimulates their secretion.
H. Prolactin stimulates milk production in lactating females. Prolactin-releasing hormone (PRH) from the hypothalamus stimulates prolactin secretion.

3. *Which of these hormones is* not *secreted into the hypothalamohypophysial portal system?* Remember
   a. *GHRH*
   b. *TRH*
   c. *PIH*
   d. *GnRH*
   e. *ACTH*

4. *Which of these stimulates the secretion of ADH?* 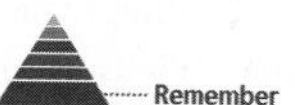

   a. *elevated blood osmolality*
   b. *decreased blood osmolality*
   c. *release of hormones from the hypothalamus*
   d. *ACTH*
   e. *increased blood pressure*

5. *Oxytocin is responsible for* 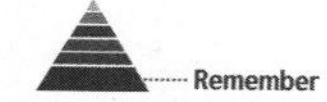

   a. *preventing milk letdown from the mammary glands.*
   b. *preventing goiter.*
   c. *causing contraction of the uterus.*
   d. *maintaining normal calcium levels.*
   e. *increasing the metabolic rate.*

6. *Growth hormone* 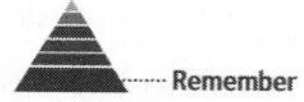

   a. *increases the usage of glucose.*
   b. *increases the breakdown of lipids.*
   c. *decreases the synthesis of proteins.*
   d. *decreases the synthesis of glycogen.*
   e. *All of these are correct.*

7. *Which of these hormones stimulates IGF secretion?* 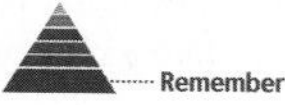

   a. *FSH*
   b. *GH*
   c. *LH*
   d. *prolactin*
   e. *TSH*

8. *Hypersecretion of growth hormone* 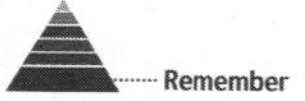

   a. *results in gigantism if it occurs in children.*
   b. *causes acromegaly in adults.*
   c. *increases the probability that a person will develop diabetes.*
   d. *can lead to severe atherosclerosis.*
   e. *All of these are correct.*

9. *LH and FSH* 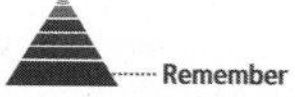

   a. *are produced in the hypothalamus.*
   b. *production is increased by TSH.*
   c. *promote the production of gametes and reproductive hormones.*
   d. *inhibit the production of prolactin.*
   e. *All of these are correct.*

10. *The hypothalamohypophysial portal system connects the hypothalamus with the anterior pituitary. Why is such a special circulatory system advantageous?* Apply

11. *A patient exhibits polydipsia (thirst), polyuria (excess urine production), and urine with a low specific gravity (contains few ions and no glucose). If you wanted to reverse the symptoms, would you administer insulin, glucagon, ADH, or aldosterone? Explain.* Understand

12. *A patient complains of headaches and visual disturbances. A casual glance reveals enlarged finger bones, a heavy deposition of bone over the eyes, and a prominent jaw. The doctor determines that the headaches and visual disturbances result from increased pressure within the skull and that the presence of a pituitary tumor is affecting hormone secretion. Name the hormone causing the problem, and explain why increased pressure exists within the skull.* Apply

18.3 Thyroid Gland

A. The thyroid gland is just inferior to the larynx and is composed of small, hollow balls of cells called follicles, which contain thyroglobulin.

B. Parafollicular cells are scattered throughout the thyroid gland.

Thyroid Hormones

A. T_3 and T_4 synthesis occurs in thyroid follicles. Iodide ions are taken into the follicles by active transport, oxidized, and bound to tyrosine molecules in thyroglobulin. Thyroglobulin is taken into the follicular cells and broken down; T_3 and T_4 are transported into the blood.

B. T_3 and T_4 are transported in the blood bound to thyroxine-binding globulin as well as other plasma proteins. Approximately one-third of the T_4 is converted to active T_3.

C. T_3 and T_4 bind with nuclear receptor molecules and initiate new protein synthesis.

D. T_3 and T_4 affect nearly every tissue in the body. They increase metabolism in many tissues. Normal growth of many tissues is dependent on T_3 and T_4.

E. TRH and TSH regulate T_3 and T_4 secretion.

13. *T_3 and T_4* 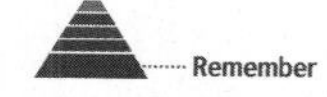

   a. *require iodine for their production.*
   b. *are made from the amino acid tyrosine.*
   c. *are transported in the blood bound to thyroxine-binding globulin.*
   d. *All of these are correct.*

14. *Which of these symptoms is associated with hyposecretion of thyroid hormones?* Remember
   a. *hypertension*
   b. *nervousness*
   c. *diarrhea*
   d. *weight loss with either normal or increased food intake*
   e. *decreased metabolic rate*

15. *Choose the statement that most accurately predicts the long-term effect of exposure to a substance that prevents the active transport of iodide by the thyroid gland.* Remember
   a. *Large amounts of T_3 and T_4 accumulate within the thyroid follicles, but little is released.*
   b. *The person exhibits hypothyroidism.*
   c. *The anterior pituitary secretes smaller amounts of TSH.*
   d. *The circulating levels of T_3 and T_4 increase.*

16. *Most laboratories are able to determine blood levels of TSH, T_3, and T_4. Given that ability, design a method of determining whether hyperthyroidism in a patient results from a pituitary abnormality or from the production of a nonpituitary thyroid stimulatory substance.* Apply

Calcitonin

A. An increase in blood calcium levels stimulates calcitonin secretion by the parafollicular cells.

B. Calcitonin decreases blood calcium and phosphate levels by inhibiting osteoclasts.

17. Calcitonin

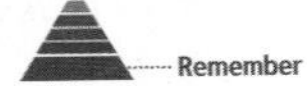

a. is secreted by the parathyroid glands.
b. levels increase when blood calcium levels decrease.
c. causes blood calcium levels to decrease.
d. insufficiency results in weak bones and tetany.

18.4 Parathyroid Glands

A. The parathyroid glands are embedded in the thyroid gland.

B. PTH increases blood calcium levels.

C. A decrease in blood calcium stimulates PTH secretion.

18. Parathyroid hormone secretion increases in response to

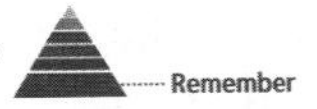

a. a decrease in blood calcium levels.
b. increased production of parathyroid-stimulating hormone from the anterior pituitary.
c. increased secretion of parathyroid-releasing hormone from the hypothalamus.
d. increased secretion of calcitonin.
e. decreased secretion of ACTH.

19. If parathyroid hormone levels increase, which of these conditions is expected? Remember

a. Osteoclast activity increases.
b. Calcium absorption from the small intestine is inhibited.
c. Calcium reabsorption from the urine is inhibited.
d. Less active vitamin D_3 forms in the kidneys.
e. All of these are correct.

20. An anatomy and physiology instructor asks two students to predict a patient's response to chronic vitamin D_3 deficiency. One student claims the person would suffer from hypocalcemia. The other student claims the calcium levels would remain within their normal range, although at the low end, and that bone reabsorption would occur to the point that advanced osteomalacia might occur. With whom do you agree, and why? Understand

18.5 Adrenal Glands

A. The adrenal glands are near the superior poles of the kidneys.

B. The adrenal medulla functions as part of the sympathetic nervous system. The adrenal cortex is divided into three layers: the zona glomerulosa, the zona fasciculata, and the zona reticularis.

21. The adrenal medulla

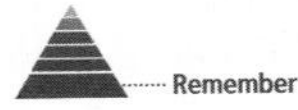

a. produces steroids.
b. secretes cortisol as its major product.
c. decreases its secretions during exercise.
d. forms from a modified portion of the sympathetic division of the ANS.
e. All of these are correct.

Hormones of the Adrenal Medulla

Epinephrine accounts for 80% and norepinephrine for 20% of the adrenal medulla hormones. They prepare the body for physical activity.

- Epinephrine increases blood glucose levels, the use of glycogen and glucose by skeletal muscle, and heart rate and force of contraction. It also causes vasoconstriction in the skin and viscera and vasodilation in skeletal and cardiac muscle.
- Norepinephrine and epinephrine stimulate cardiac muscle and cause the constriction of most peripheral blood vessels.

22. In the condition in which a benign tumor results in hypersecretion of hormones from the adrenal medulla, expected symptoms include Remember

a. hypotension.
b. bradycardia (slow heart rate).
c. pallor (decreased blood flow to the skin).
d. lethargy.
e. hypoglycemia.

Hormones of the Adrenal Cortex

A. The zona glomerulosa secretes the mineralocorticoids, especially aldosterone. Aldosterone acts on the kidneys to increase sodium and to decrease potassium and hydrogen levels in the blood.

B. The zona fasciculata secretes glucocorticoids, especially cortisol.
- Cortisol increases lipid and protein breakdown, increases glucose synthesis from amino acids, decreases the inflammatory response, and is necessary for the development of some tissues.
- ACTH from the anterior pituitary stimulates cortisol secretion. CRH from the hypothalamus stimulates ACTH release. Low blood glucose levels and stress stimulate CRH secretion.

C. The zona reticularis secretes androgens. In females, androgens stimulate axillary and pubic hair growth and sex drive.

23. Which of these is not *a hormone secreted by the adrenal cortex?* Remember

a. aldosterone
b. androgens
c. cortisol
d. epinephrine

24. If aldosterone secretions increase,

a. blood potassium levels increase.
b. blood hydrogen levels increase.
c. acidosis results.
d. blood sodium levels decrease.
e. blood volume increases.

25. Glucocorticoids (cortisol)

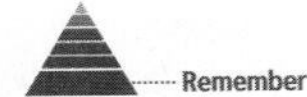

a. increase the breakdown of lipids.
b. increase the breakdown of proteins.
c. increase blood glucose levels.
d. decrease inflammation.
e. All of these are correct.

26. Which of these is (are) expected in Cushing syndrome (hypersecretion of adrenal cortex hormones)? Remember

a. loss of hair in females
b. deposition of adipose tissue in the face, neck, and abdomen
c. low blood glucose
d. low blood pressure
e. All of these are correct.

27. *Over the past year, Julie has gradually gained weight. The increase in adipose tissue is distributed over her trunk, face, and neck, and her muscle mass appears to be decreased. Julie also feels weak and bruises easily. Her physician suspects Cushing syndrome and orders a series of blood tests. The results reveal elevated blood levels of cortisol and ACTH. There is no evidence of an extrapituitary source of ACTH. Predict the cause of Julie's condition and the treatments that are likely to be recommended.* Apply

28. *Predict some of the consequences of exposure to intense and prolonged stress.* Understand

18.6 Pancreas

A. The pancreas, located along the small intestine and the stomach, is both an exocrine and an endocrine gland.

B. The endocrine portion consists of the pancreatic islets. Each islet is composed of alpha cells, which secrete glucagon; beta cells, which secrete insulin; and delta cells, which secrete somatostatin.

29. *Within the pancreas, the pancreatic islets produce*

   a. insulin.
   b. glucagon.
   c. digestive enzymes.
   d. Both a and b are correct.
   e. All of these are correct.

Effect of Insulin and Glucagon on Their Target Tissues

A. Insulin's target tissues are the liver, adipose tissue, muscle, and the satiety center in the hypothalamus. It increases the uptake of glucose and amino acids by cells for energy production.

B. Glucagon's target tissue is mainly the liver. It causes the breakdown of glycogen and lipids for use as an energy source.

30. *Insulin increases*
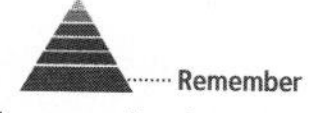

   a. the uptake of glucose by its target tissues.
   b. the breakdown of protein.
   c. the breakdown of lipids.
   d. glycogen breakdown in the liver.
   e. All of these are correct.

31. *Glucagon* Remember
   a. primarily affects the liver.
   b. causes glycogen to be stored.
   c. causes blood glucose levels to decrease.
   d. decreases lipid metabolism.
   e. performs all of these functions.

32. *A patient arrives at the emergency room in an unconscious condition. A medical emergency bracelet reveals that he has diabetes. The patient is in either diabetic coma or insulin shock. How can you tell which, and what treatment do you recommend for each condition?* Apply

33. *Dylan, a 10-year-old boy, was constantly hungry and was losing weight rapidly in spite of his unusually large food intake. Dylan was also constantly thirsty and urinated frequently. In addition, he felt weak and lethargic, and his breath occasionally had a distinctive sweet, or acetone, odor. Dylan's parents tried to make sure he ate a healthy diet, but Dylan was sneaking candy and soft drinks when his parents were not around. What type of hormonal imbalance do you think is responsible for Dylan's symptoms? What effect would eating candy and drinking sugary soda have on Dylan's health?* Apply

Regulation of Pancreatic Hormone Secretion

A. Insulin secretion increases because of elevated blood glucose levels, an increase in some amino acids, parasympathetic stimulation, and gastrointestinal hormones. Sympathetic stimulation decreases insulin secretion.

B. Glucagon secretion is stimulated by low blood glucose levels, certain amino acids, and sympathetic stimulation.

C. Somatostatin inhibits insulin and glucagon secretion.

34. *When blood glucose levels increase, the secretion of which of these hormones increases?* Remember
   a. glucagon
   b. insulin
   c. GH
   d. cortisol
   e. epinephrine

35. *If a person who has diabetes mellitus has forgotten to take an insulin injection, the symptoms that may soon appear include* Remember
   a. acidosis.
   b. hyperglycemia.
   c. increased urine production.
   d. lethargy and fatigue.
   e. All of these are correct.

18.7 Hormonal Regulation of Nutrient Utilization

A. After a meal, the following events take place:

- High glucose levels inhibit glucagon, cortisol, GH, and epinephrine, which reduces the release of glucose from tissues.
- Insulin secretion increases as a result of the high blood glucose levels, thereby increasing the uptake of glucose, amino acids, and lipids, which are used for energy or stored.
- One to two hours after the meal, blood glucose levels drop. Glucagon, GH, cortisol, and epinephrine levels increase, insulin levels decrease, and glucose is released from tissues.
- Adipose tissue releases fatty acids, triglycerides, and ketones, which most tissues use for energy.

B. During exercise, the following events occur:

- Sympathetic activity increases epinephrine and glucagon secretion, causing a release of glucose into the blood.
- Low blood sugar levels, caused by the uptake of glucose by skeletal muscles, stimulate epinephrine, glucagon, GH, and cortisol secretion, causing an increase in fatty acids, triglycerides, and ketones in the blood, all of which are used for energy.

18.8 Hormones of the Reproductive System

The ovaries, testes, placenta, and pituitary gland secrete reproductive hormones.

36. *Which of the following is* not *a hormone produced by the ovaries?*

Remember

   a. *estrogen*
   b. *progesterone*
   c. *prolactin*
   d. *inhibin*
   e. *relaxin*

18.9 Hormones of the Pineal Gland

The pineal gland produces melatonin and arginine vasotocin, which can inhibit reproductive maturation and may regulate sleep-wake cycles.

37. *Melatonin*

   a. *is produced by the posterior pituitary.*
   b. *production increases as day length increases.*
   c. *inhibits the development of the reproductive system.*
   d. *increases GnRH secretion from the hypothalamus.*
   e. *decreases the tendency to sleep.*

18.10 Other Hormones and Chemical Messengers

A. The thymus produces thymosin, which is involved in the development of the immune system.

B. The digestive tract produces several hormones that regulate digestive functions.

C. Autocrine and paracrine chemical messengers are produced by many cells of the body and usually have a local effect on body functions.

D. Eicosanoids, such as prostaglandins, prostacyclins, thromboxanes, and leukotrienes, are derived from fatty acids and mediate inflammation and other functions. Endorphins, enkephalins, and dynorphins are analgesic substances. Growth factors influence cell division and growth in many tissues, and interleukin-2 influences cell division in the T cells of the immune system.

38. *Which of these substances, produced by many body tissues, can promote inflammation, pain, and vasodilation of blood vessels?*

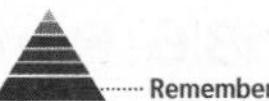

   a. *endorphins*
   b. *enkephalins*
   c. *thymosin*
   d. *epidermal growth factor*
   e. *prostaglandins*

Answers to this chapter's odd-numbered Concept Check questions appear in Appendix F.

19 CHAPTER

Cardiovascular System

BLOOD

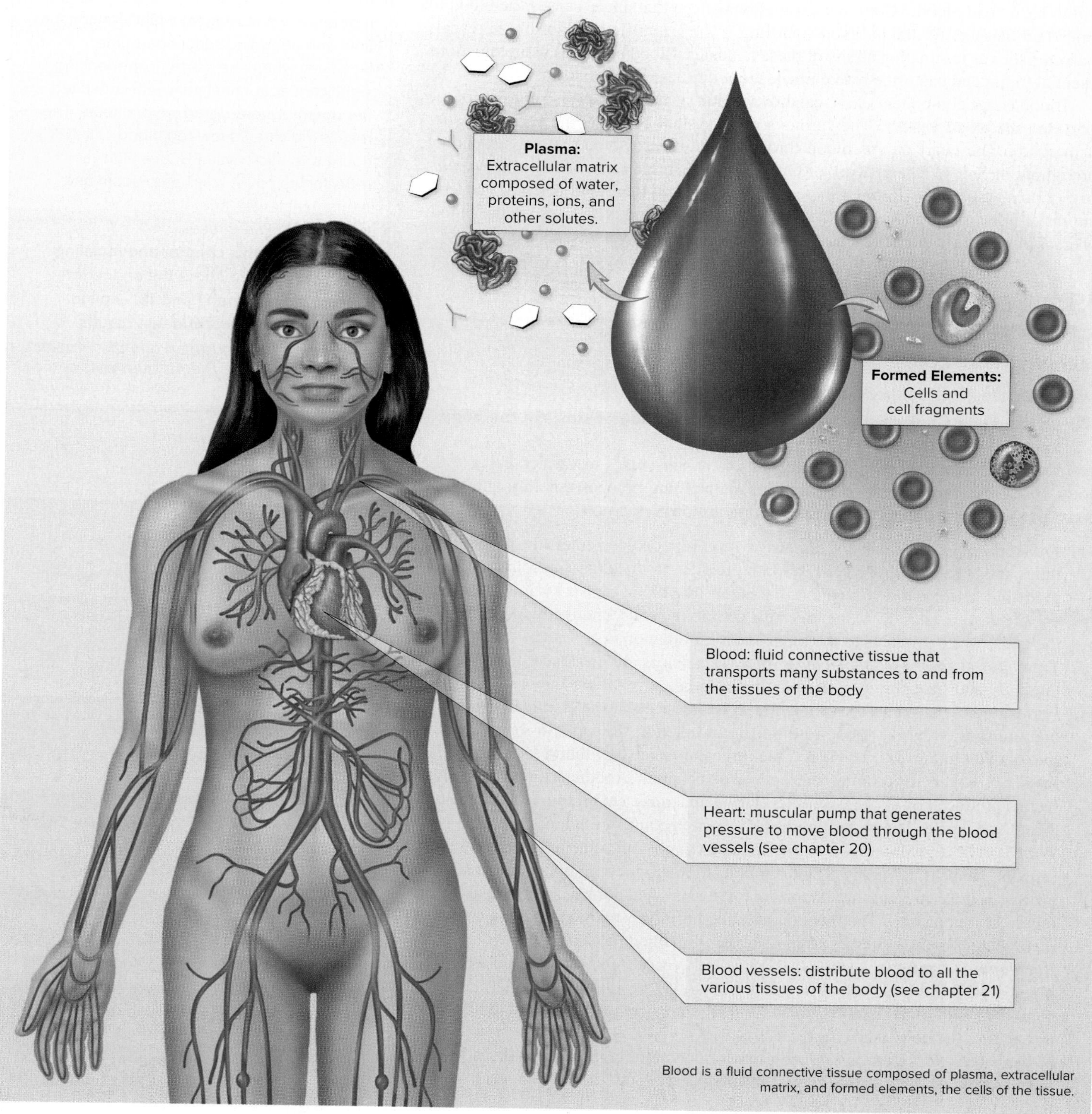

Blood is a fluid connective tissue composed of plasma, extracellular matrix, and formed elements, the cells of the tissue.

Historically, many cultures around the world, both ancient and modern, have believed in the magical qualities of blood. Some societies consider blood the "essence of life" because the uncontrolled loss of it can result in death. Blood has also been thought to define character and emotions. For example, people from prominent families are sometimes described as "bluebloods," whereas criminals are said to have "bad blood." Common expressions allege that anger causes the blood to "boil" and that fear results in blood "curdling." The scientific study of blood reveals characteristics as fascinating as any of these fantasies. Blood performs many functions essential to life and can often reveal much about our health.

Blood is one component of the **cardiovascular system,** which also consists of the heart and the blood vessels. The cardiovascular system connects the various tissues of the body. The heart pumps blood through a network of blood vessels extending throughout the body. This network of blood vessels is often referred to as the *circulatory system.* As it flows through the circulatory system, the blood delivers nutrients and picks up waste products at the body tissues. This chapter focuses on the blood, whereas chapters 20 and 21 discuss the heart and the blood vessels, respectively

Learn to Predict

Frankie didn't have time to be sick. So at first she attributed her extreme tiredness to the stress of being a 40-year-old single mother of two teenagers while working full-time and attending school part-time. However, when she started experiencing significant abdominal pain, she consulted her doctor, who ordered several tests. The results indicated a low red blood cell (RBC) count with microcytic RBCs, a high reticulocyte count, low hemoglobin and hematocrit levels, and evidence of hemoglobin in her feces.

After reading this chapter and recalling what you learned about the endocrine system in chapters 17 and 18, explain Frankie's symptoms and test results.

Answers to this question and the chapter's odd-numbered Predict questions can be found in Appendix E.

19.1 Functions of Blood

LEARNING OUTCOME

After reading this section, you should be able to

A. **List and explain the ways blood helps maintain homeostasis in the body.**

The blood acts as a transport fluid carrying many substances to various parts of the body. By acting this way, blood is vital for maintaining homeostasis throughout the body. Blood helps maintain homeostasis in the following ways:

1. *Transport of gases, nutrients, and waste products.* Oxygen enters the blood in the lungs and is carried to the cells. Carbon dioxide, produced by the cells, is carried in the blood to the lungs, where it is exhaled. The blood transports ingested nutrients, ions, and water from the digestive tract to the cells, and the blood transports the cells' waste products to the kidneys for elimination.
2. *Transport of processed molecules.* Many substances are produced in one part of the body and transported in the blood to another part, where they are modified. For example, the precursor to vitamin D is produced in the skin (see chapter 5) and transported by the blood to the liver and then to the kidneys for processing into active vitamin D_3. The blood then transports active vitamin D_3 to the small intestine, where it promotes the uptake of calcium. Another example involves lactate produced by skeletal muscles during anaerobic respiration (see chapter 9). The blood carries lactate to the liver, where it is converted into glucose.
3. *Transport of regulatory molecules.* Regulatory molecules include chemical messengers, such as hormones, that regulate the activities of many physiological processes. Enzymes that are important for normal metabolism are also considered regulatory molecules. The blood carries the hormones and many of the enzymes that regulate body processes from one part of the body to another.
4. *Regulation of pH and osmosis.* Buffers (see chapter 2), which help keep the blood's pH within its normal range of 7.35–7.45, are in the blood. The osmotic composition of blood is also critical for maintaining normal fluid and ion balance throughout the body (see chapter 27).
5. *Maintenance of body temperature.* Body temperature regulation involves several mechanisms, including the movement of warm blood from the interior of the body to its surface, where heat is released.

Module 9
Cardiovascular System

Platelets

Platelets (table 19.2; see figure 19.8) are minute fragments of cells. They consist of a small amount of cytoplasm surrounded by a plasma membrane. Platelets are roughly disc-shaped and average about 3 μm in diameter. Glycoproteins and proteins on their surface allow platelets to attach to other molecules, such as collagen in connective tissue. Some of these surface molecules, as well as molecules released from granules in the platelet cytoplasm, play important roles in controlling blood loss. The platelet cytoplasm also contains actin and myosin, which can cause contraction of the platelet (see section 19.5).

The life expectancy of platelets is about 5–9 days. Platelets are derived from **megakaryocytes** (MEG-ah-KAIR-ee-oh-sites), which are extremely large cells found in the red bone marrow. Small fragments of these cells break off and enter the blood as platelets (see figure 19.2).

Platelets play an important role in preventing blood loss by (1) forming platelet plugs that seal holes in small vessels and (2) promoting the formation and contraction of clots that help seal off larger wounds in the vessels.

ASSESS YOUR PROGRESS

28. *What is a platelet? How do platelets form?*

29. *What are the two major roles of platelets in preventing blood loss?*

19.5 Hemostasis

LEARNING OUTCOMES

After reading this section, you should be able to

A. **Explain the three processes that can lead to hemostasis: vascular spasm, platelet plug formation, and coagulation.**

B. **Describe the regulation of clot formation and how clots are removed.**

Hemostasis (HEE-moh-stay-sis, hee-MOS-tah-sis), the cessation of bleeding, is very important to the maintenance of homeostasis. If not stopped, excessive bleeding from a cut or torn blood vessel can result in a positive-feedback cycle, consisting of ever-decreasing blood volume and blood pressure that disrupts homeostasis and results in death. Fortunately, when a blood vessel is damaged, a series of events helps prevent excessive blood loss. Hemostasis involves three processes: (1) vascular spasm, (2) platelet plug formation, and (3) coagulation.

Vascular Spasm

Vascular spasm is the immediate but temporary constriction of a blood vessel. Vascular spasm occurs when smooth muscle within the wall of the vessel contracts. This constriction can close small vessels completely and stop the flow of blood through them. Damage to blood vessels can activate nervous system reflexes that cause vascular spasms. Chemicals released by cells of the damaged vessel as well as platelets also stimulate vascular spasms. For example, endothelial cells release the peptide **endothelin** (en-doh-THEE-lin), which leads to constriction of blood vessels. Also, during the formation of a platelet plug, platelets release **thromboxanes** (THROM-bok-zanes), which are derived from certain prostaglandins. Thromboxanes also lead to constriction of blood vessels.

Platelet Plug Formation

A **platelet plug** is an accumulation of platelets that can seal small breaks in blood vessels. A platelet plug is not the same thing as a blood clot, but the formation of the platelet plug is an important step in blood clot formation. Platelet plug formation is very important in maintaining the integrity of the circulatory system. Small tears occur in the smaller vessels and capillaries many times each day, and platelet plug formation quickly closes them. People who lack the normal number of platelets tend to develop numerous small hemorrhages in their skin and internal organs.

The formation of a platelet plug can be described as a series of steps, but in actuality many of the steps take place simultaneously. Figure 19.10 illustrates the process of platelet plug formation.

1. **Platelet adhesion:** Platelets bind to collagen that is exposed when a blood vessel is damaged. Most platelet adhesion is mediated through **von Willebrand factor (vWF),** a protein produced and secreted by blood vessel endothelial cells. Platelets have surface receptors on their membrane. These surface receptors bind to vWF released from damaged blood vessels. vWF also binds to the exposed collagen of the damaged vessel, thereby forming a bridge between exposed collagen and platelets. In addition, other platelet surface receptors can bind directly to collagen.
2. **Platelet release reaction:** After platelets adhere to collagen, they become activated. These activated platelets then release adenosine diphosphate (ADP), thromboxanes, and other chemicals by exocytosis. The ADP and thromboxane bind to their respective receptors on the surfaces of other platelets, activating them. These activated platelets release additional chemicals, thereby producing a cascade of chemical release by the platelets. Thus, more and more platelets become activated. This is an example of positive feedback.
3. **Platelet aggregation:** As platelets become activated, they change shape and express fibrinogen receptors that can bind to fibrinogen, a plasma protein. Fibrinogen forms a bridge between the fibrinogen receptors of different platelets, resulting in a platelet plug.

In addition to forming a platelet plug, activated platelets also release phospholipids (platelet factor III) and coagulation factor V, which are important in clot formation.

Coagulation

Vascular spasms and platelet plugs alone are not sufficient to close large tears or cuts. When a blood vessel is severely damaged, **coagulation** (koh-ag-you-LAY-shun), or blood clotting, results in the formation of a clot. A **blood clot** is a network of threadlike protein fibers, called **fibrin,** that traps blood cells, platelets, and fluid (figure 19.11).

Blood clot formation depends on a number of **clotting factors,** or *coagulation factors,* which are proteins found within plasma (table 19.3). Normally, the clotting factors are in an inactive state and do not cause clotting. After injury, the clotting

PROCESS **Figure**

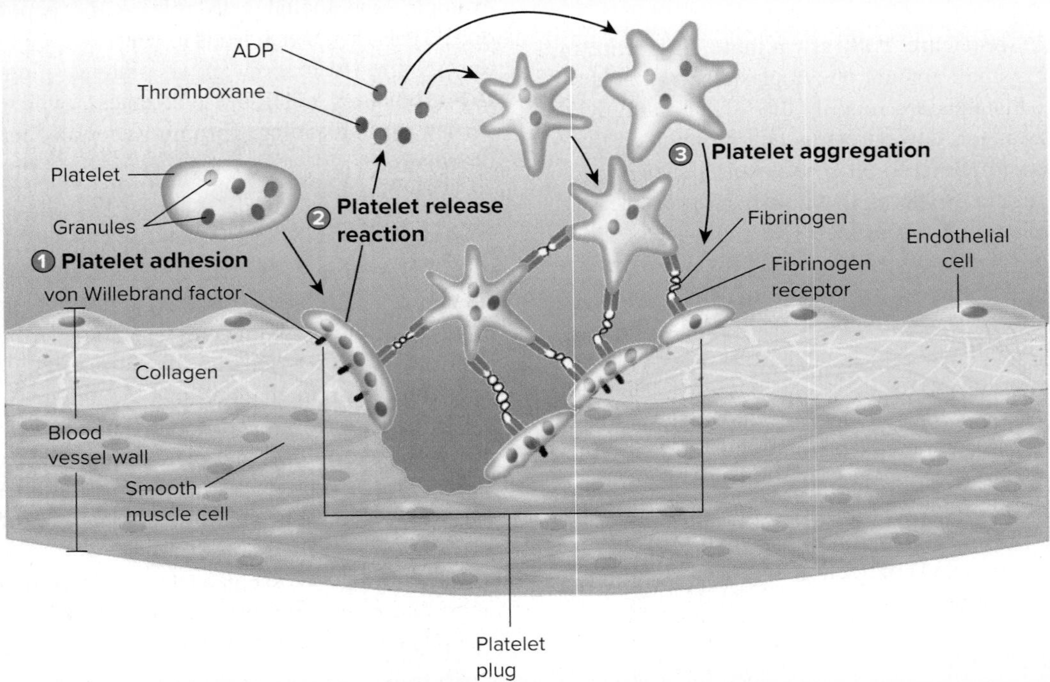

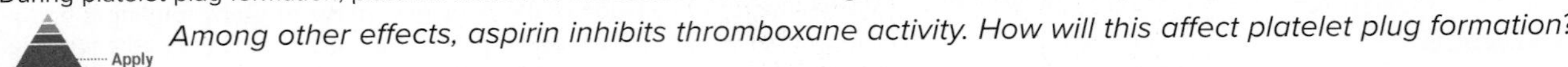

PROCESS **Figure 19.10**

Platelet Plug Formation

During platelet plug formation, platelets adhere to the surface of the damaged vessel and to other platelets, reducing blood loss at the injury site.

Apply *Among other effects, aspirin inhibits thromboxane activity. How will this affect platelet plug formation?*

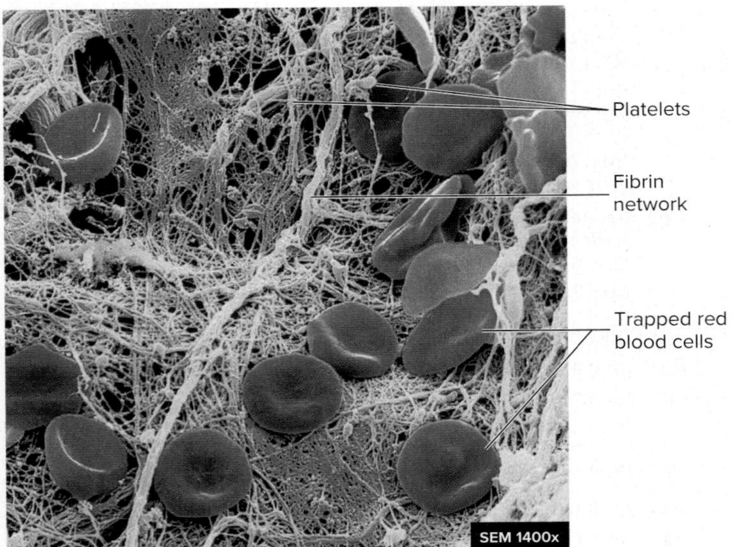

FIGURE 19.11 Blood Clot

A blood clot consists of fibrin, which traps red blood cells, platelets, and fluid.

Eye of Science/Science Source

factors are activated. The activation of clotting factors is a complex process involving many chemical reactions, some of which require calcium ions (Ca^{2+}) and molecules on the surface of activated platelets, such as phospholipids and factor V.

Understand **Predict 5**

Why is it advantageous for clot formation to involve molecules on the surface of activated platelets?

Clotting factors are activated in two ways: (1) the extrinsic pathway and (2) the intrinsic pathway. The extrinsic pathway is so named because it begins with chemicals that are outside, or extrinsic to, the blood, while the intrinsic pathway is so named because it begins with chemicals that are inside, or intrinsic to, the blood. These two pathways converge to form the common pathway, which results in the formation of a fibrin clot.

Figure 19.12 illustrates the process of clot formation.

1. *Extrinsic pathway:* Damaged tissues release a mixture of lipoproteins and phospholipids called **thromboplastin** (throm-boh-PLAS-tin), also known as *tissue factor* (*TF*) or factor III. Thromboplastin, in the presence of Ca^{2+}, forms a complex with factor VII that activates factor X, which is the clotting factor that initiates the common pathway.
2. *Intrinsic pathway*: Damage to blood vessels can expose collagen in the connective tissue beneath the endothelium of the blood vessel. When plasma factor XII comes into contact with collagen, factor XII is activated. Subsequently, activated factor XII stimulates factor XI, which in turn activates factor IX. Activated factor IX joins with factor VIII, platelet phospholipids, and Ca^{2+} to activate factor X, which, as stated in the extrinsic pathway description, initiates the common pathway.

Although the extrinsic and intrinsic pathways were once considered distinct, we now know that the extrinsic pathway can activate

Clinical IMPACT 19.1 Clinical Importance of Taking Aspirin

Platelet activation results in platelet plug formation and the production of chemicals, such as phospholipids, that are important for blood clotting. Alternatively, the inhibition of platelet activation reduces the formation of blood clots. Understanding how this occurs requires knowledge of the chemical behavior of the **eicosanoids,** a group that includes prostaglandins, thromboxanes, and leukotrienes, the compounds involved in platelet activation. In humans, arachidonic acid is the most common precursor molecule for the eicosanoids. The enzyme cyclooxygenase (COX) converts arachidonic acid into a prostaglandin that can be converted into thromboxane. However, the actions of COX are inhibited by aspirin, which inhibits prostaglandin and thromboxane synthesis. As a result, aspirin reduces platelet activation.

Taking aspirin can have harmful or beneficial effects, depending on the circumstances. If an expectant mother ingests aspirin near the end of pregnancy, thromboxane synthesis is inhibited and several effects are possible. The mother can experience excessive bleeding after delivery because of decreased platelet function, and the baby can exhibit numerous localized hemorrhages called **petechiae** (pe-TEE-kee-ee) over the surface of its body as a result of decreased platelet function. If the quantity of ingested aspirin is large, the infant, the mother, or both may die as a result of hemorrhage.

On the other hand, platelet plugs and blood clots can block blood vessels, producing heart attacks and strokes. Therefore, suspected heart attack victims are routinely given aspirin en route to the emergency room to reduce further clotting. The United States Preventive Services Task Force (USPSTF) and the American Heart Association (AHA) recommend low-dose aspirin therapy (75–160 mg/day) for all men and women at high risk for cardiovascular disease. Determining risk involves analyzing many factors and should be done in consultation with a physician. The decreased risk for cardiovascular disease from aspirin therapy must be weighed against the increased risk for hemorrhagic stroke and gastrointestinal bleeding.

The drug Plavix (clopidogrel bisulfate) reduces the activation of platelets by blocking the ADP receptors on the surface of platelets. It is used to prevent clotting and, with other anticlotting drugs, to treat heart attacks.

TABLE 19.3 Clotting Factors

Factor Number	Name (Synonym)	Description and Function
I	Fibrinogen	Plasma protein synthesized in the liver; converted to fibrin in the common pathway
II	Prothrombin	Plasma protein synthesized in the liver (requires vitamin K); converted to thrombin in the common pathway
III	Thromboplastin (tissue factor)	Mixture of lipoproteins released from damaged tissue; required in the extrinsic pathway
IV	Calcium ion	Required throughout the clotting sequence
V	Proaccelerin (labile factor)	Plasma protein synthesized in the liver; activated form functions in the intrinsic and extrinsic pathways
VII	Serum prothrombin conversion accelerator (stable factor, proconvertin)	Plasma protein synthesized in the liver (requires vitamin K); functions in the extrinsic pathway
VIII	Antihemophilic factor (antihemophilic globulin)	Plasma protein synthesized in megakaryocytes and endothelial cells; required in the intrinsic pathway
IX	Plasma thromboplastin component (Christmas factor)	Plasma protein synthesized in the liver (requires vitamin K); required in the intrinsic pathway
X	Stuart factor (Stuart-Prower factor)	Plasma protein synthesized in the liver (requires vitamin K); required in the common pathway
XI	Plasma thromboplastin antecedent	Plasma protein synthesized in the liver; required in the intrinsic pathway
XII	Hageman factor	Plasma protein required in the intrinsic pathway
XIII	Fibrin-stabilizing factor	Protein found in plasma and platelets; required in the common pathway
Platelet Factors (released by platelets during the intrinsic pathway)		
I	Platelet accelerator	Same as plasma factor V
II	Thrombin accelerator	Accelerates thrombin and fibrin production
III		Phospholipids necessary for the intrinsic and extrinsic pathways
IV		Binds heparin, which prevents clot formation

Note: Factor VI was once thought to be involved but is no longer accepted as playing a role in clotting; it is apparently the same as activated factor V.

FUNDAMENTAL **Figure**

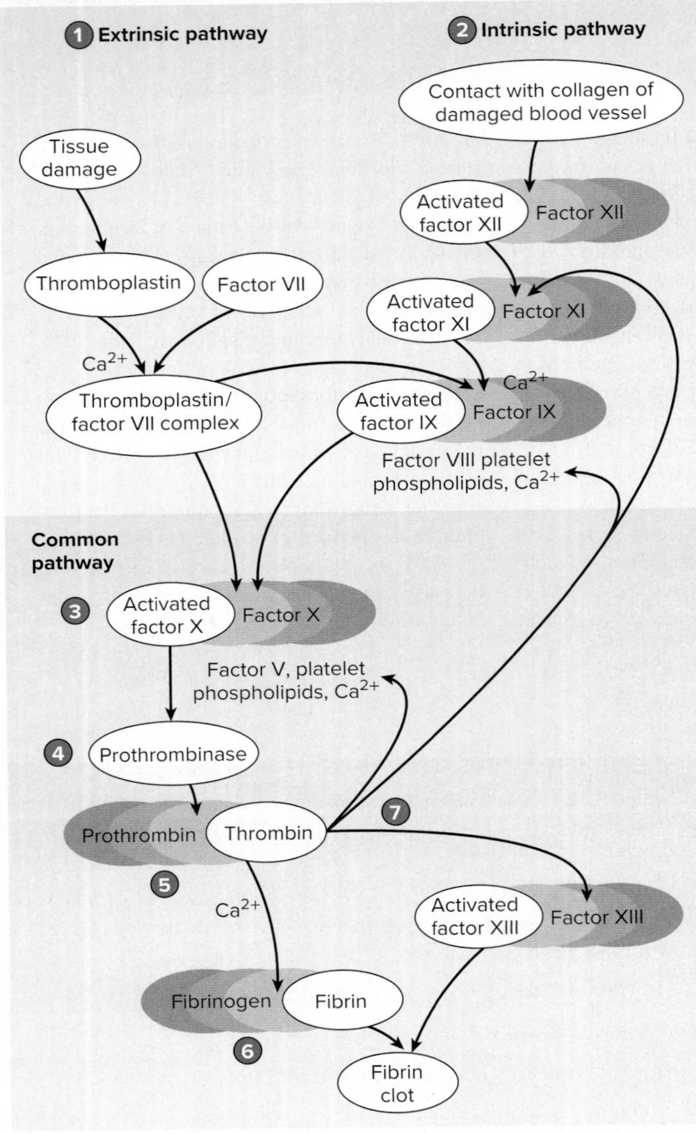

PROCESS **Figure 19.12**

Clot Formation

In a sequence of chemical reactions, activated clotting factors (*white ovals*) activate inactive clotting factors (*purple ovals*). Clot formation begins through either the extrinsic or the intrinsic pathway. The common pathway starts with factor X and results in a fibrin clot.

Heparin is an anticoagulant that activates an enzyme called antithrombin. Based on its name, how would antithrombin disrupt blood clotting?

the clotting factors in the intrinsic pathway. The thromboplastin/factor VII complex from the extrinsic pathway can stimulate the formation of activated factor IX in the intrinsic pathway.

3. *Common pathway initiated*: Activation of the extrinisic and/or intrinsic pathways results in the activation of factor X.
4. *Prothrombinase formed:* On the surface of platelets, activated factor X, factor V, platelet phospholipids, and Ca^{2+} combine to form **prothrombinase,** or *prothrombin activator*.
5. *Thrombin produced*: Prothrombinase converts the soluble plasma protein **prothrombin** to the enzyme **thrombin.**
6. *Fibrin produced*: A major function of thrombin is to convert the soluble plasma protein fibrinogen to the insoluble protein fibrin. Fibrin is the protein that forms the fibrous network of the blood clot.
7. *Positive-feedback effects of thrombin*: In addition, thrombin also stimulates factor XIII activation, which is necessary to stabilize the clot. Thrombin can also activate many of the clotting proteins, such as factor XI and prothrombinase. Thus, a positive-feedback system operates whereby thrombin production stimulates the production of additional thrombin. Thrombin also has a positive-feedback effect on platelet aggregation by stimulating platelet activation.

Vitamin K is required for the formation of many of the factors involved in blood clot formation (table 19.3). Humans rely on two sources for vitamin K. About half comes from the diet, and half comes from gut microbiome, particularly bacteria within the large intestine. Antibiotics taken to fight bacterial infections sometimes kill these intestinal bacteria, thereby reducing vitamin K levels and causing bleeding. Vitamin K supplements may be necessary for patients on prolonged antibiotic therapy. Newborns lack these intestinal bacteria; thus, they routinely receive a vitamin K injection at birth. Infants can also obtain vitamin K from food, such as milk.

The absorption of vitamin K from the large intestine requires the presence of bile because vitamin K is fat-soluble. Therefore, disorders involving an obstruction of bile flow to the intestine can interfere with vitamin K absorption and lead to insufficient blood clotting. Liver diseases that result in the decreased synthesis of clotting factors can also cause insufficient blood clotting.

Control of Clot Formation

Without control, clot formation would spread from the point of initiation through the entire circulatory system. Furthermore, blood vessels in a healthy person contain rough areas that can stimulate clot formation, and small amounts of prothrombin are constantly being converted into thrombin. To prevent unwanted clotting, the blood contains several **anticoagulants** (AN-tee-koh-AG-you-lants). These anticoagulants prevent clotting factors from initiating clot formation under normal concentrations in the blood. Only when clotting factor concentrations exceed a given threshold in a local area does clot formation occur. At the site of injury, so many clotting factors are activated that the anticoagulants are unable to prevent clot formation. However, away from the injury site, the activated clotting factors are diluted in the blood, anticoagulants neutralize them, and clotting is prevented.

Examples of anticoagulants in the blood are antithrombin, heparin, and prostacyclin. **Antithrombin,** a plasma protein produced by the liver, slowly inactivates thrombin. Heparin, produced by basophils and endothelial cells, works with antithrombin to rapidly inactivate thrombin. **Prostacyclin** (pros-tah-SIE-klin) is a prostaglandin derivative produced by endothelial cells. It counteracts the effects of thrombin by causing vasodilation and inhibiting the release of clotting factors from platelets.

Anticoagulants are also important when blood is outside the body. They prevent the clotting of blood used in transfusions and laboratory blood tests. Besides heparin, examples include **ethylenediaminetetraacetic** (ETH-il-een-DIE-ah-meen-tet-rah-ah-SEE-tik) **acid (EDTA)** and sodium citrate. EDTA and sodium

TABLE 19.4 Representative Diseases and Disorders of Blood

Condition	Description
Erythrocytosis	
Relative erythrocytosis	Overabundance of red blood cells due to decreased blood volume, as may result from dehydration, diuretics, or burns
Primary erythrocytosis (polycythemia vera)	Stem cell defect of unknown cause; results in overproduction of red blood cells, granulocytes, and platelets; signs include low erythropoietin levels and enlarged spleen; increased blood viscosity and blood volume can cause clogging of the capillaries and hypertension
Secondary erythrocytosis	Overabundance of red blood cells resulting from decreased O_2 supply, as occurs at high altitudes, in chronic obstructive pulmonary disease, and in congestive heart failure; decreased O_2 delivery to the kidney stimulates the secretion of erythropoietin, resulting in increased blood viscosity and blood volume that can cause clogging of the capillaries and hypertension
Anemia	Deficiency of hemoglobin in the blood
Iron-deficiency anemia	Caused by insufficient intake or absorption of iron or by excessive iron loss; leads to reduced hemoglobin production
Folate-deficiency anemia	Folate is important in DNA synthesis; inadequate folate in the diet results in a reduction in cell division and therefore a reduced number of red blood cells
Pernicious anemia	Secondary folate-deficiency anemia caused by inadequate amounts of vitamin B_{12}, which is important for folate synthesis
Hemorrhagic anemia	Results from blood loss due to trauma, ulcers, or excessive menstrual bleeding
Hemolytic anemia	Occurs when red blood cells rupture or are destroyed at an excessive rate; causes include inherited defects, exposure to certain drugs or snake venom, response to artificial heart valves, autoimmune disease, and hemolytic disease of the newborn
Aplastic anemia	Caused by an inability of the red bone marrow to produce red blood cells, usually as a result of damage to stem cells after exposure to certain drugs, chemicals, or radiation
Thalassemia	Autosomal recessive disease that results in insufficient production of globin part of hemoglobin
Leukemia	Cancers of the red bone marrow in which one or more white blood cell types is produced; cells are usually immature or abnormal and lack normal immunological functions
Thrombocytopenia	Reduction in the number of platelets that leads to chronic bleeding through small vessels and capillaries; causes include genetics, autoimmune disease, infections, and decreased platelet production resulting from pernicious anemia, drug therapy, radiation therapy, or leukemias
Clotting Disorders	
Disseminated intravascular coagulation (DIC)	Clotting throughout the vascular system, followed by bleeding; may develop when normal regulation of clotting by anticoagulants is overwhelmed, as occurs due to massive tissue damage; also caused by alteration of the lining of the blood vessels resulting from infections or snakebites
Von Willebrand disease	Most common inherited bleeding disorder; platelet plug formation and the contribution of activated platelets to blood clotting are impaired; treatments are injection of von Willebrand factor or administration of drugs that increase von Willebrand factor levels in blood, which helps platelets adhere to collagen and become activated
Hemophilia	Genetic disorder in which clotting is abnormal or absent; each of the several types results from deficiency or dysfunction of a clotting factor; most often a sex-linked trait that occurs almost exclusively in males
Infectious Diseases of Blood	
Septicemia (blood poisoning)	Spread of microorganisms and their toxins by the blood; often the result of a medical procedure, such as insertion of an intravenous tube; release of toxins by bacteria can cause septic shock, producing decreased blood pressure and possibly death
Malaria	Caused by a protozoan introduced into blood by *Anopheles* mosquito; symptoms include chills and fever produced by toxins released when the protozoan causes red blood cells to rupture
Infectious mononucleosis	Caused by Epstein-Barr virus, which infects salivary glands and lymphocytes; symptoms include fever, sore throat, and swollen lymph nodes, all probably produced by the immune system response to infected lymphocytes
Acquired immunodeficiency syndrome (AIDS)	Caused by human immunodeficiency virus (HIV), which infects lymphocytes and suppresses immune system

White Blood Count

A **white blood count (WBC)** measures the total number of white blood cells in the blood. Normally, 4500–11,000 white blood cells are present in each microliter of blood. **Leukopenia** (loo-koh-PEE-nee-ah) is a lower-than-normal WBC resulting from depression or destruction of the red marrow. Viral infections, radiation, drugs, tumors, and vitamin deficiencies (B_{12} or folate) can cause leukopenia. **Leukocytosis** (LOO-koh-sigh-TOH-sis) is an abnormally high WBC. **Leukemia** (loo-KEE-mee-ah), a cancer of the red marrow, often results in leukocytosis, but the white blood cells have an abnormal structure and function as well. Bacterial infections can also cause leukocytosis by stimulating neutrophils to increase in number.

Differential White Blood Count

A **differential white blood count** determines the percentage of each of the five kinds of white blood cells. Normally, neutrophils account for 55–70%; lymphocytes, 20–40%; monocytes, 2–8%; eosinophils, 1–4%; and basophils, 0.5–1%. A differential WBC can provide insight into a patient's condition. For example, in patients with bacterial infections the neutrophil count is often greatly increased, whereas in patients with allergic reactions the eosinophil and basophil counts are elevated.

Clotting

The blood's ability to clot can be assessed by the platelet count and the prothrombin time measurement.

Platelet Count

A normal **platelet count** is 150,000–400,000 platelets per microliter of blood. In the condition called **thrombocytopenia** (THROM-boh-sigh-toh-PEE-nee-ah), the platelet count is greatly reduced, resulting in chronic bleeding through small vessels and capillaries. It can be caused by decreased platelet production as a result of hereditary disorders, lack of vitamin B_{12}, drug therapy, or radiation therapy.

Prothrombin Time Measurement

Prothrombin time measurement expresses how long it takes for the blood to start clotting, which is normally 9–12 seconds. Prothrombin time is determined by adding thromboplastin to whole plasma. Thromboplastin is a chemical released from injured tissues that starts the process of clotting (see figure 19.12). Prothrombin time is officially reported as the International Normalized Ratio (INR), which standardizes the time blood takes to clot based on the slightly different thromboplastins used by different labs. Because many clotting factors must be activated to form fibrin, a deficiency of any one of them can cause the prothrombin time to be abnormal. Vitamin K deficiency, certain liver diseases, and drug therapy can increase prothrombin time.

Blood Chemistry

The composition of materials dissolved or suspended in the plasma can be used to assess the functioning of many of the body's systems. For example, high blood glucose levels can indicate that the pancreas is not producing enough insulin; high blood urea nitrogen (BUN) can be a sign of reduced kidney function; increased bilirubin can indicate liver dysfunction or hemolysis; and high cholesterol levels can signify an increased risk for cardiovascular disease. A number of blood chemistry tests are routinely done when a blood sample is taken, and additional tests are available.

Predict 8

When a patient complains of acute pain in the abdomen, the physician suspects appendicitis, which is often caused by a bacterial infection of the appendix. What blood test should be done to support the diagnosis?

ASSESS YOUR PROGRESS

45. *What occurs in a type and crossmatch?*
46. *What tests are included in a CBC? Give the normal value, and name a disorder that would cause an abnormal test result for each.*
47. *What are the normal values for a platelet count and a prothrombin time measurement? Name a disorder that would cause an abnormal result for each test.*
48. *What are some examples of blood chemistry tests?*

Concept Check

19.1 Functions of Blood

A. Blood transports gases, nutrients, waste products, processed molecules, and regulatory molecules.
B. Blood is involved in the regulation of pH, osmosis, and body temperature.
C. Blood protects against disease and initiates tissue repair.

1. *Which of these is a function of blood?*

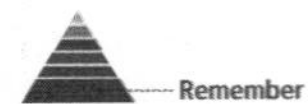

a. clot formation
b. protection against foreign substances
c. maintenance of body temperature
d. regulation of pH and osmosis
e. All of these are correct.

19.2 Composition of Blood

Blood is a type of connective tissue that consists of plasma and formed elements.

19.3 Plasma

A. Plasma is mostly water (91%) and contains proteins, such as albumins (maintains osmotic pressure), globulins (function in transport and immunity), fibrinogen (involved in clot formation), and hormones and enzymes (involved in regulation).
B. Plasma contains ions, nutrients, waste products, and gases.

2. *Which of these is* not *a component of plasma?*

a. nitrogen
b. sodium ions
c. platelets
d. water
e. urea

20.3 Anatomy of the Heart

LEARNING OUTCOMES

After reading this section, you should be able to

A. **Describe the structure of the pericardium.**
B. **List the layers of the heart wall and describe the structure and function of each.**
C. **Relate the large veins and arteries that enter and exit the heart.**
D. **Describe the location and blood flow through the coronary arteries.**
E. **Describe the location and blood flow through the cardiac veins.**
F. **Review the structure and functions of the chambers of the heart.**
G. **Name the valves of the heart and state their locations and functions.**

Pericardium

The **pericardium** (per-ih-KAR-dee-um), or *pericardial sac,* is a double-layered, closed sac that surrounds the heart (figure 20.3; see figure 20.2*c*). It consists of two layers: (1) the outer **fibrous pericardium** and (2) inner **serous pericardium.** The fibrous pericardium is a tough, fibrous connective tissue layer that prevents overdistension of the heart and anchors it within the mediastinum. Superiorly, the fibrous pericardium is continuous with the connective tissue coverings of the great vessels, such as the aorta, and inferiorly it is attached to the surface of the diaphragm (see figure 20.2*b*). The serous pericardium is a layer of simple squamous epithelium.

The serous pericardium is further divided into two parts: (1) the **parietal pericardium** and (2) the **visceral pericardium.** The parietal pericardium is the part lining the fibrous pericardium. The visceral pericardium is the part covering the heart surface (figure 20.3). The term *visceral pericardium* is used when describing this portion of the pericardium. However, this same region is called the *epicardium* when describing this region in the context of the heart wall. The parietal and visceral portions of the serous pericardium are continuous with each other where the great vessels enter or leave the heart. The space between the visceral and parietal pericardia is the **pericardial cavity** and is filled with a thin layer of serous **pericardial fluid.** This fluid helps reduce friction as the heart moves within the pericardial sac.

Even though the pericardium contains fibrous connective tissue, it can accommodate changes in heart size by gradually enlarging. The pericardial cavity can also increase in volume to hold a significant volume of pericardial fluid, such as with certain illnesses.

Predict 1

Over the weekend, Tony, 22 years old, developed severe chest pains that became worse with deep inhalations and when lying down. As his condition worsened over the next day, Tony became anxious and feared that he might be having a heart attack, so he had a friend drive him to the emergency room. The ER physician identified a low-grade fever, tachycardia (increased heart rate), and a weak and rapid pulse. A chest x-ray showed distension of the jugular veins and pericardial space. The ER physician diagnosed pericarditis, which was probably due to a viral infection. The physician performed pericardiocentesis to drain the excess fluid from the pericardium. Explain the manifestations that the physician observed, describe how she drained the excess fluid with a needle, and name the body layers the needle penetrated.

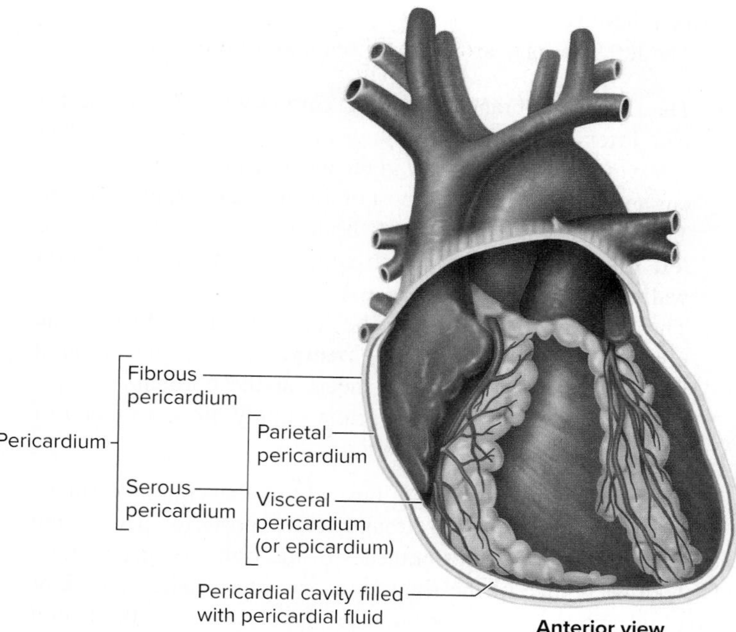

FIGURE 20.3 Heart in the Pericardium
The heart is surrounded by the pericardium, which consists of an outer fibrous pericardium and an inner serous pericardium. The serous pericardium has two parts: The parietal pericardium lines the fibrous pericardium, and the visceral pericardium (epicardium) covers the surface of the heart. The pericardial cavity, between the parietal and visceral pericardia, is filled with a small amount of pericardial fluid.

Heart Wall

The heart wall is composed of three layers of tissue: the epicardium, myocardium, and endocardium (figure 20.4).

1. The **epicardium** (EP-ih-KAR-dee-um), or *visceral pericardium,* is the superficial layer of the heart wall. It is a thin serous membrane that constitutes the smooth, outer surface of the heart.
2. The **myocardium** (MY-oh-KAR-dee-um) is the thick, middle layer of the heart. It is composed of cardiac muscle tissue and is responsible for the heart's ability to contract.
3. The **endocardium** (EN-doh-KAR-dee-um) is deep to the myocardium. It consists of simple squamous epithelium over a layer of connective tissue. The endocardium forms the smooth, inner surface of the heart chambers, which allows blood to move easily through the heart. The endocardium also covers the surfaces of the heart valves.

Ridges formed by the myocardium can be seen on the internal surfaces of the heart chambers. Though the interior surfaces of the atria are mainly flat, the interior of both auricles and a part

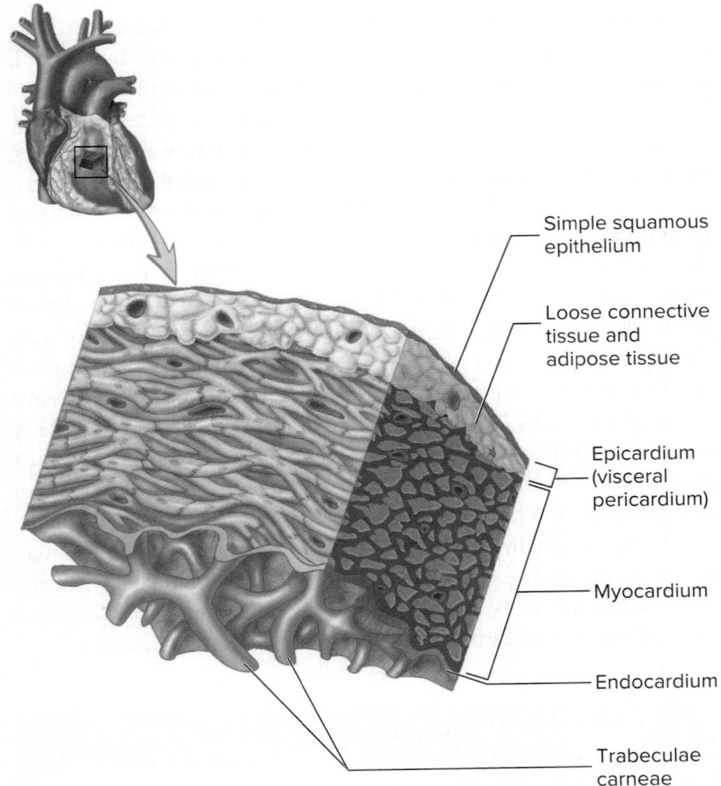

FIGURE 20.4 Heart Wall
Part of the wall of the heart has been removed, enlarged, and rotated so that its inner surface is visible. The enlarged section illustrates the epicardium (visceral pericardium), myocardium, and endocardium. APR

of the right atrial wall contain muscular ridges called **pectinate** (PEK-ti-nate) **muscles.** The pectinate muscles of the right atrium are separated from the larger, smooth portions of the atrial wall by a ridge called the **crista terminalis** (KRIS-tah TER-mi-NAL-is; terminal crest). The interior walls of the ventricles contain larger, muscular ridges and columns called **trabeculae** (trah-BEK-yoo-lee; beams) **carneae** (KAR-nee-ee; flesh). These ridges help with forceful ejection of blood from the ventricles.

External Anatomy and Coronary Circulation

The heart consists of four chambers: two **atria** (AY-tree-ah; sing. atrium) and two **ventricles** (VEN-tri-kulz). The thin-walled atria form the superior and posterior parts of the heart, and the thick-walled ventricles form the anterior and inferior portions (figure 20.5). **Auricles** (AW-ri-kulz; ears) are flaplike extensions of the atria that can be seen anteriorly between each atrium and ventricle. It is interesting to note that the entire atrium used to be called the auricle, and some medical personnel still refer to it as such.

Blood enters the atria of the heart through several large veins. The **superior vena cava** (VEE-nah KAY-vah) and the **inferior vena cava** carry blood from the body to the right atrium. In addition, the smaller coronary sinus carries blood from the walls of the heart to the right atrium. Four **pulmonary veins** carry blood from the lungs to the left atrium.

Blood leaves the ventricles of the heart through two arteries: (1) the **pulmonary trunk** and (2) the **aorta.** The pulmonary trunk carries blood from the right ventricle to the lungs. The aorta carries blood from the left ventricle to the body. Because of their large size, the pulmonary trunk and aorta are often called the great arteries.

The coronary circulation consists of blood vessels that carry blood to and from the tissues of the heart wall. The major vessels of the coronary circulation lie in several grooves, or sulci, on the surface of the heart. A large groove called the **coronary** (KOR-oh-nair-ee; circling like a crown) **sulcus** (SUL-cuss; ditch) runs obliquely around the heart, separating the atria from the ventricles. Two more grooves extend inferiorly from the coronary sulcus, indicating the division between the right and left ventricles. (1) The **anterior interventricular sulcus** is on the anterior surface of the heart, extending from the coronary sulcus toward the apex of the heart (figure 20.5*a,b*). (2) The **posterior interventricular sulcus** is on the posterior surface of the heart, extending from the coronary sulcus toward the apex of the heart (figure 20.5*c*). In a healthy, intact heart, the grooves are covered by adipose tissue, and only after this tissue is removed can they be seen.

The major arteries supplying blood to the tissue of the heart lie within the coronary sulcus and interventricular grooves on the surface of the heart. The **right** and **left coronary arteries** exit the aorta just above the point where the aorta leaves the heart. These vessels lie within the coronary sulcus (figure 20.6*a*). The right coronary artery is usually smaller in diameter than the left one, and it does not carry as much blood as the left coronary artery. Considering your knowledge of the structure and function of the ventricles, why do you think think there is this difference in size between these vessels?

The left coronary artery has three major branches.

1. The first major branch of the left coronary artery is the **anterior interventricular artery,** or the *left anterior descending artery*. It extends inferiorly in the anterior interventricular sulcus and supplies blood to most of the anterior part of the heart.
2. The second major branch of the left coronary artery is the **left marginal artery,** which supplies blood to the lateral wall of the left ventricle.
3. The third major branch of the left coronary artery is the **circumflex** (SER-kum-fleks) **artery,** which extends around to the posterior side of the heart in the coronary sulcus. Branches of the circumflex artery supply blood to much of the posterior wall of the heart.

The right coronary artery lies within the coronary sulcus and extends from the aorta around to the posterior part of the heart. There are two major branches of the right coronary artery. (1) A larger branch of the right coronary artery, called the **right marginal artery,** and other branches supply blood to the lateral wall of the right ventricle. (2) A second branch of the right coronary artery, called the **posterior interventricular artery,** lies in the posterior interventricular sulcus and supplies blood to the posterior and inferior part of the heart.

Most of the myocardium receives blood from more than one arterial branch. In addition, the coronary circulation includes many **anastamoses,** or direct connections between arteries. These

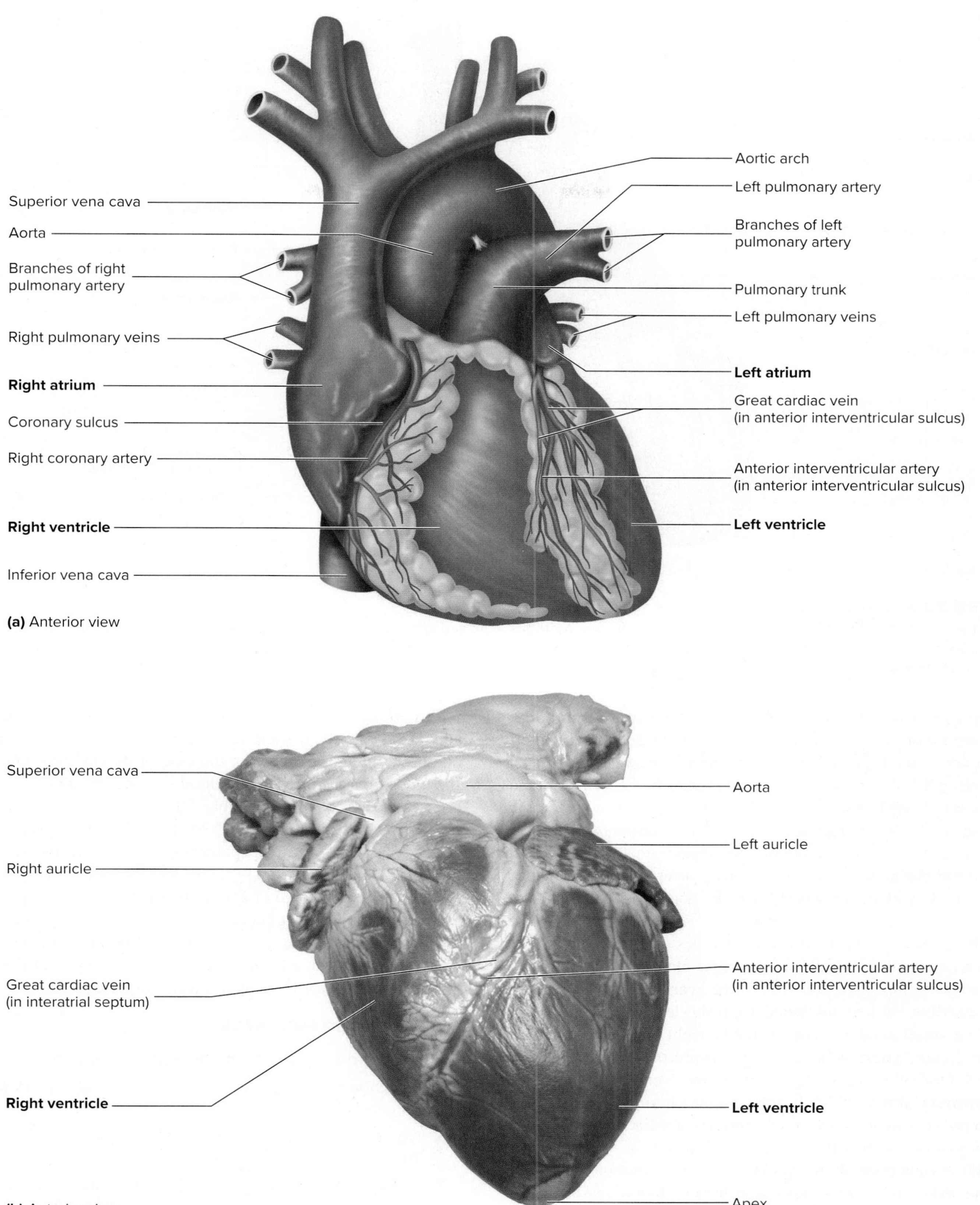

FIGURE 20.5 Surface View of the Heart

(*a*) The two atria (right and left) are located superiorly, and the two ventricles (right and left) are located inferiorly. The superior and inferior venae cavae enter the right atrium. The pulmonary veins enter the left atrium. The pulmonary trunk exits the right ventricle, and the aorta exits the left ventricle. (*b*) Photograph of the anterior surface of the heart. APR

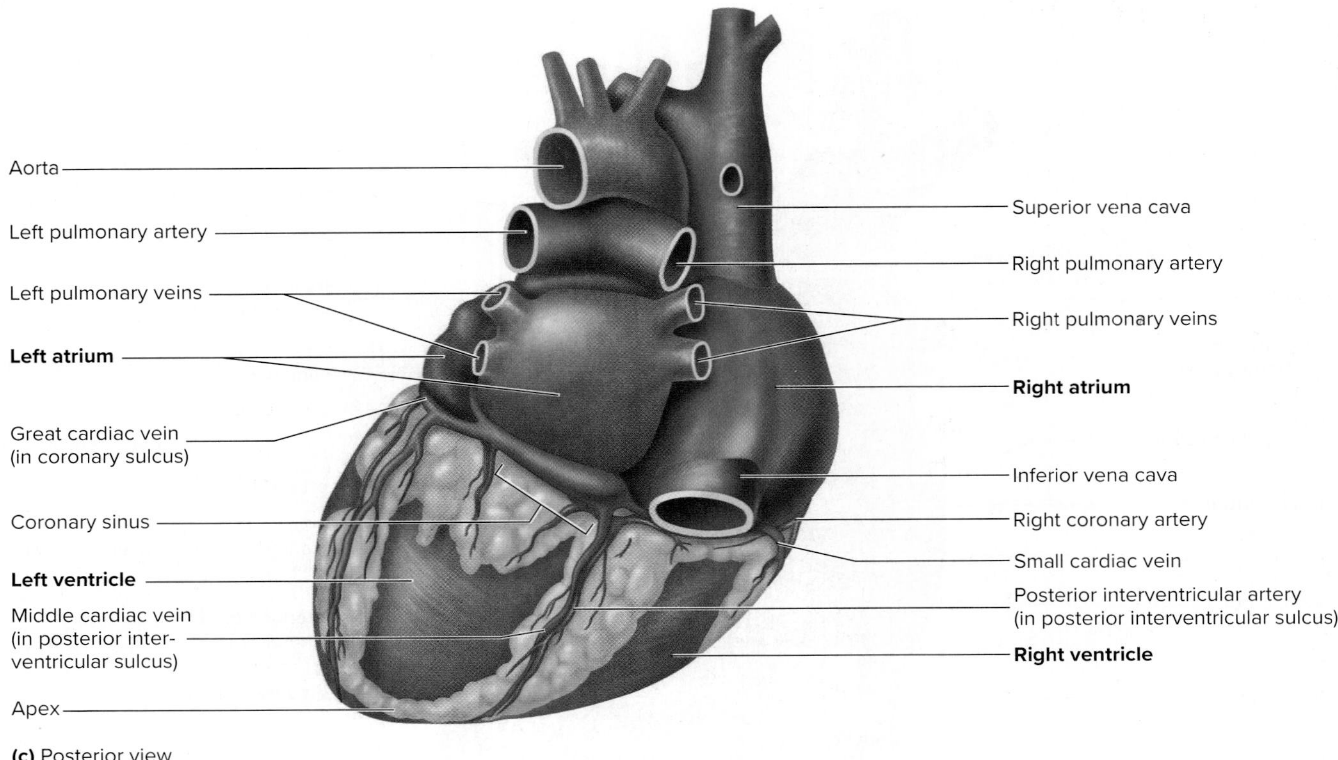

(c) Posterior view

FIGURE 20.5 (continued)
(c) The two atria (right and left) are located superiorly, and the two ventricles (right and left) are located inferiorly. The superior and inferior venae cavae enter the right atrium, and the four pulmonary veins enter the left atrium. The pulmonary trunk divides, forming the left and right pulmonary arteries. (b) A. & F. Michler/Peter Arnold/Getty Images

anastamoses may form either between branches of a given artery or between branches of different arteries. Because of these interconnections, blockage of just one of the coronary arteries in an area does not fully impede blood flow there. The density of blood vessels supplying blood to the myocardium increases with aerobic exercise, as do the number and extent of the anastamoses. Consequently, aerobic exercise increases the chance that a person will survive the blockage of a small coronary artery. The blockage of larger coronary blood vessels still has the potential to permanently damage large areas of the heart wall.

The coronary circulation also includes veins that carry the blood from the heart walls to the right atrium. There are two major veins draining the blood from the heart wall tissue: (1) The **great cardiac vein** drains blood from the left side of the heart, and (2) a **small cardiac vein** drains the right margin of the heart (figure 20.6*b*). These veins converge toward the posterior part of the coronary sulcus and empty into a large venous cavity called the **coronary sinus,** which in turn empties into the right atrium. A number of smaller veins empty into the cardiac veins, into the coronary sinus, or directly into the right atrium.

Blood flow through the coronary blood circulation is not continuous. When the cardiac muscle contracts, blood vessels in the wall of the heart are compressed so blood does not readily flow through them. When the cardiac muscle relaxes, the blood vessels are not compressed, and blood flow through the coronary blood vessels resumes.

As blood flows through tissues, O_2 is released from the blood and moves into the tissues. The amount of O_2 released varies from one tissue to another, even in the case of the different muscle tissue types. In a resting person, blood flowing through the coronary arteries gives up approximately 70% of its O_2. In comparison, blood flowing through arteries to skeletal muscle gives up only about 25% of its O_2. The percentage of O_2 the blood releases to skeletal muscle can increase to 70% or more during exercise. Because the percentage of O_2 delivered to cardiac muscle is near its maximum at rest, it cannot increase substantially during exercise. Therefore, cardiac muscle requires blood to flow through the coronary arteries at a higher rate than its resting level in order to provide an adequate O_2 supply during exercise.

ASSESS YOUR PROGRESS

4. *Describe the parts of the pericardium and their functions.*
5. *Describe the three layers of the heart wall, and state their functions.*
6. *Name the chambers of the heart, and describe their structures. What is an auricle?*
7. *List the major blood vessels that enter and leave the heart. Which chambers do they enter or exit?*
8. *Describe the flow of blood through the coronary arteries and their branches.*
9. *Trace the flow of blood through the cardiac veins.*

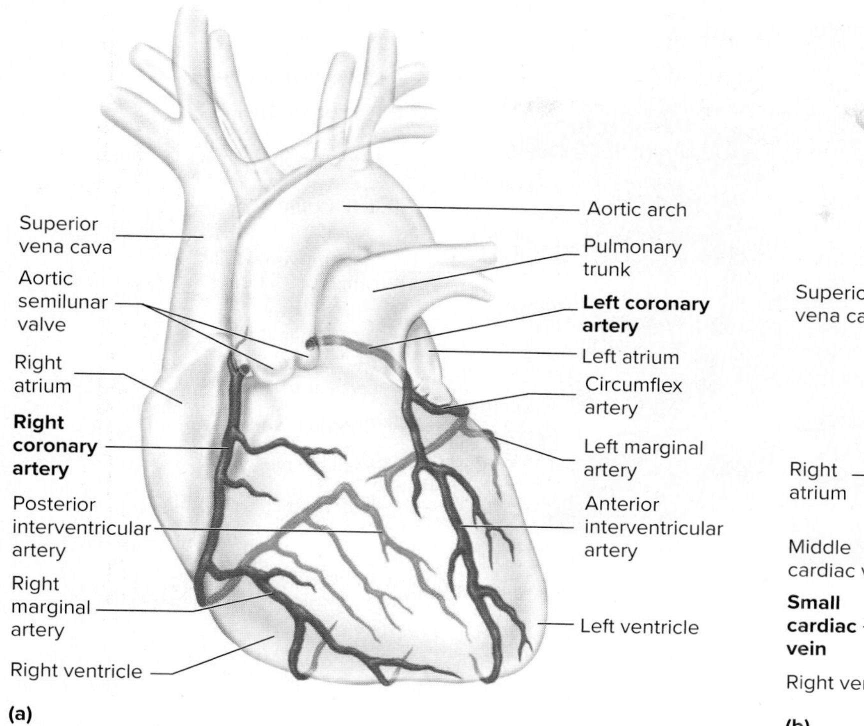

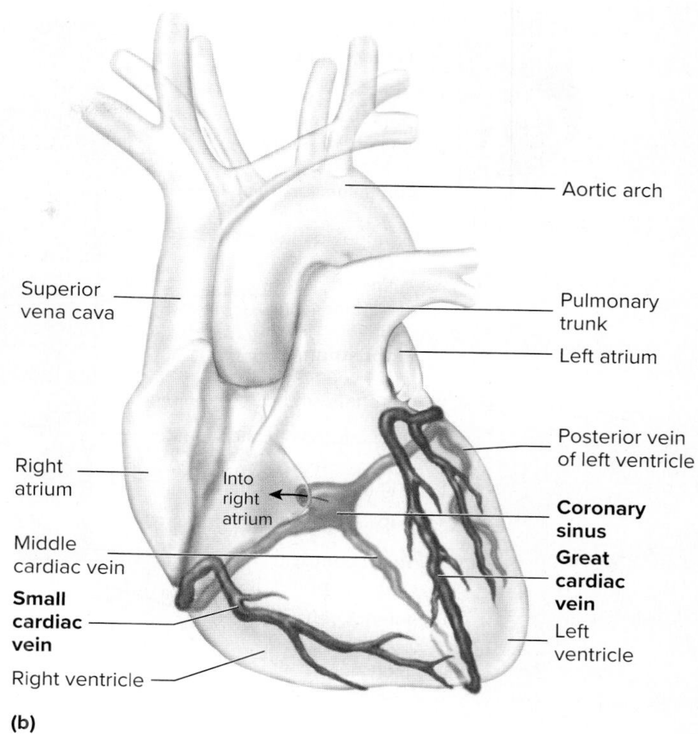

FIGURE 20.6 Coronary Circulation

(*a*) Arteries supplying blood to the heart. The arteries of the anterior surface are seen directly and are darker in color; the arteries of the posterior surface are seen through the heart and are lighter in color. (*b*) Veins draining blood from the heart. The veins of the anterior surface are seen directly and are darker in color; the veins of the posterior surface are seen through the heart and are lighter in color. APR

Heart Chambers and Valves

Right and Left Atria

The **right atrium** has three major openings: (1) an opening from the superior vena cava, (2) an opening from the inferior vena cava, and (3) an opening from the coronary sinus. The openings from the superior vena cava and the inferior vena cava receive blood from the body, and the opening of the coronary sinus receives blood from the heart itself (figure 20.7). The **left atrium** has four relatively uniform openings from the four pulmonary veins that receive blood from the lungs.

The right and left atria are separated from each other by the wall of tissue called the **interatrial septum.** The **fossa ovalis** (FOS-ah oh-VA-lis) is a slight, oval depression on the right side of the interatrial septum marking the former location of the **foramen ovale** (oh-VAL-ee), an opening between the right and left atria in the embryonic and fetal heart. In the fetal heart, this opening allows blood to flow from the right to the left atrium and bypass the pulmonary circulation (see chapter 29).

Right and Left Ventricles

The atria open into the ventricles through **atrioventricular canals** (figure 20.7). Each ventricle has one large, superiorly placed outflow route near the midline of the heart. Blood flows from the **right ventricle** into the pulmonary trunk. Blood flows from the **left ventricle** into the aorta. The two ventricles are separated from each other by the **interventricular septum,** which has a thick, muscular part toward the apex and a thin, membranous part toward the atria. The wall of the left ventricle is much thicker than the wall of the right ventricle (figure 20.7). The thicker wall of the left ventricle allows for stronger contractions to pump blood through the systemic circulation.

Atrioventricular Valves

An **atrioventricular valve** is in each atrioventricular canal and is composed of cusps, or flaps. Atrioventricular valves ensure one-way flow of blood from the atria into the ventricles, preventing blood from flowing back into the atria. The atrioventricular valve between the right atrium and the right ventricle is called the **tricuspid** (try-KUS-pid) **valve** because it consists of three cusps (figure 20.7*a,b*). The atrioventricular valve between the left atrium and the left ventricle is called the **bicuspid** (bi-KUS-pid) **valve** because it has two cusps. Another common term for the bicuspid valve is the *mitral* (MY-tral) *valve* (figure 20.7*a,c*).

Each ventricle contains cone-shaped, muscular pillars called **papillary** (PAP-i-lar-ee; nipple) **muscles.** These muscles are attached to the cusps of the atrioventricular valves by thin, strong connective tissue strings called **chordae tendineae** (KOHR-dee TEN-di-nee-ee; heart strings) (figure 20.7*a,b*). The papillary muscles contract when the ventricles contract and prevent the valves from opening into the atria by pulling on the chordae tendineae attached to the valve cusps, similar to the way parachute cords hold a parachute in place when a skydiver is airborne.

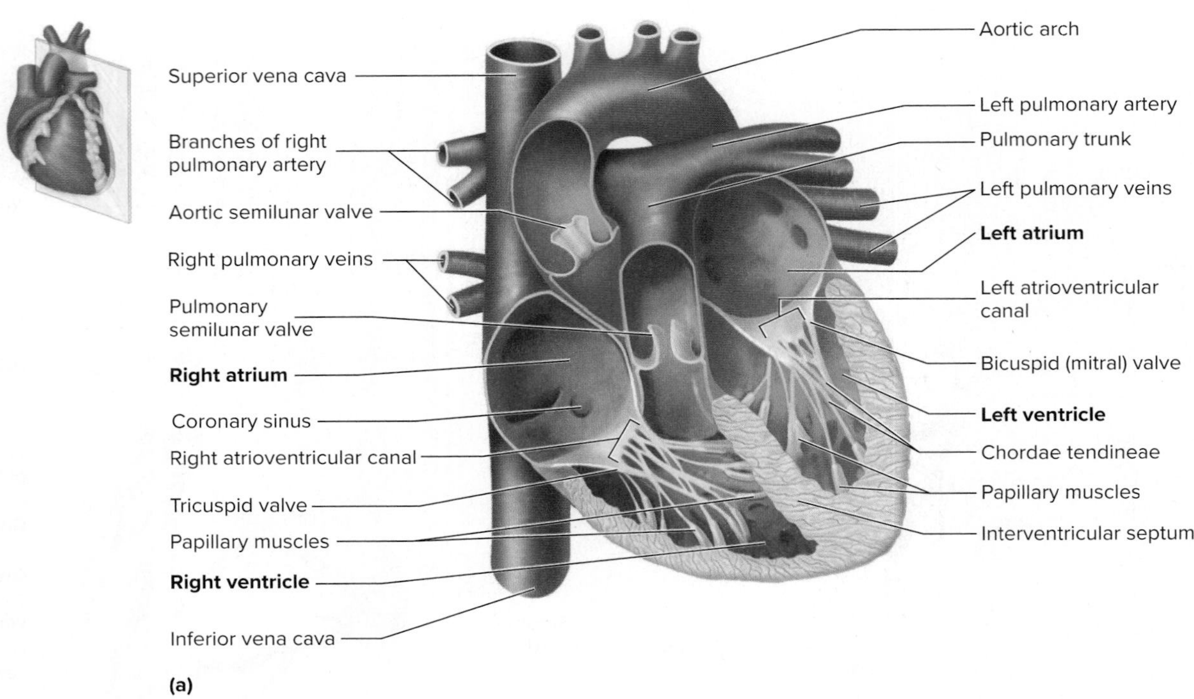

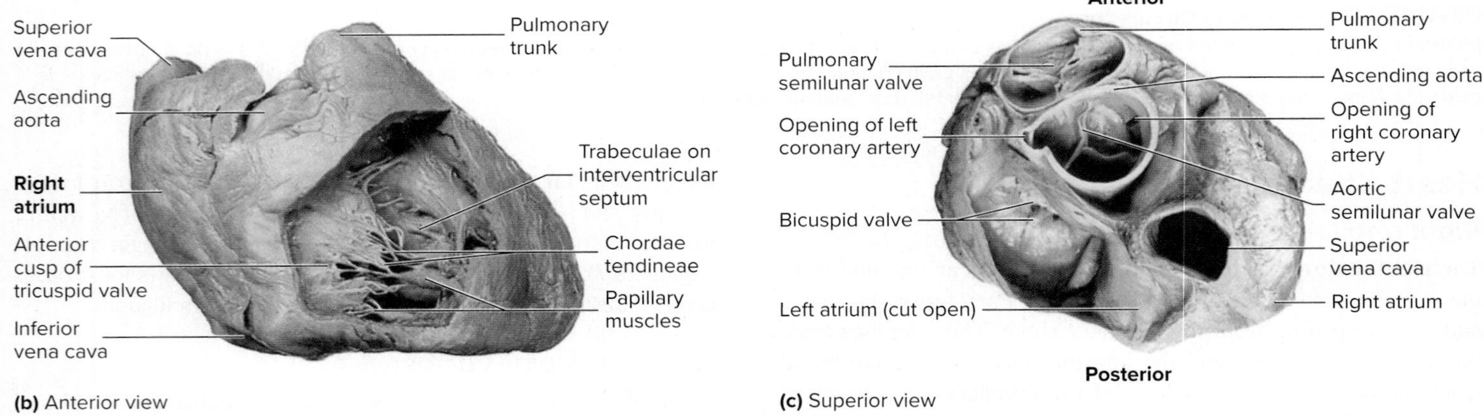

FIGURE 20.7 Internal Anatomy of the Heart

(*a*) The heart is cut in a frontal plane to show the internal anatomy. (*b*) Tricuspid valve, chordae tendineae, and papillary muscles. (*c*) Heart valves. Note the three cusps of each semilunar valve meeting to prevent the backflow of blood. (b, c) R. T. Hutchings APR

Blood flowing from the atrium into the ventricle pushes the valve open into the ventricle (figure 20.8*a*). When the ventricle contracts, blood pushes the valve back toward the atrium. The atrioventricular canal is closed as the valve cusps meet (figure 20.8*b*).

Semilunar Valves

A semilunar (sem-ee-LOO-nar; half-moon-shaped) valve is positioned between each ventricle and its associated great artery. The semilunar valves are identified by the great artery in which each is located and include the **aortic semilunar valve** and **pulmonary semilunar valve.** Each valve consists of three pocketlike, semilunar cusps, the free inner borders of which meet in the center of the artery to block blood flow (see figure 20.7*a*,*c*). Contraction of the ventricles pushes blood against the semilunar valves, forcing them to open, and blood can then enter the great arteries (figure 20.8*b*). However, when blood flows back from the aorta or pulmonary trunk toward the ventricles, it enters the pockets of the cusps, causing the cusps to meet in the center of the aorta or pulmonary trunk. This effectively closes the semilunar valves and prevents blood from flowing back into the ventricles (figure 20.8*a*).

ASSESS YOUR PROGRESS

10. *Why is the wall of the left ventricle thicker than the wall of the right ventricle?*

11. *Describe the openings of the right and left atria. What structure separates the atria from each other?*

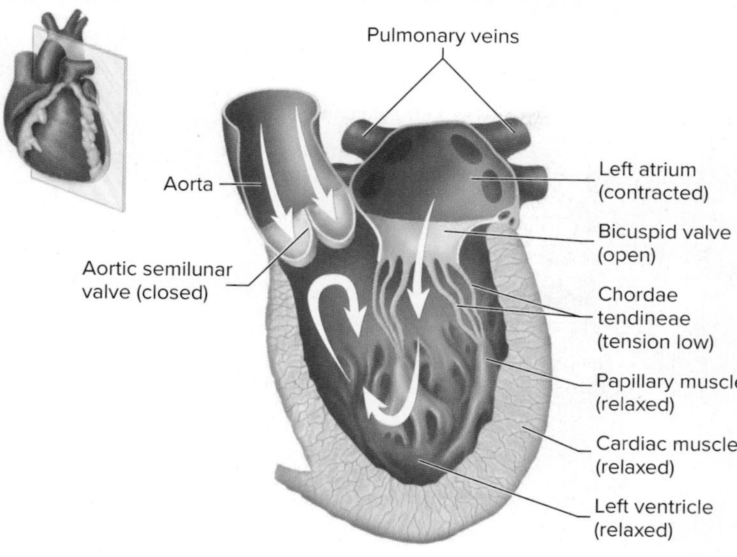

(a) Valve positions when blood is flowing into the left ventricle

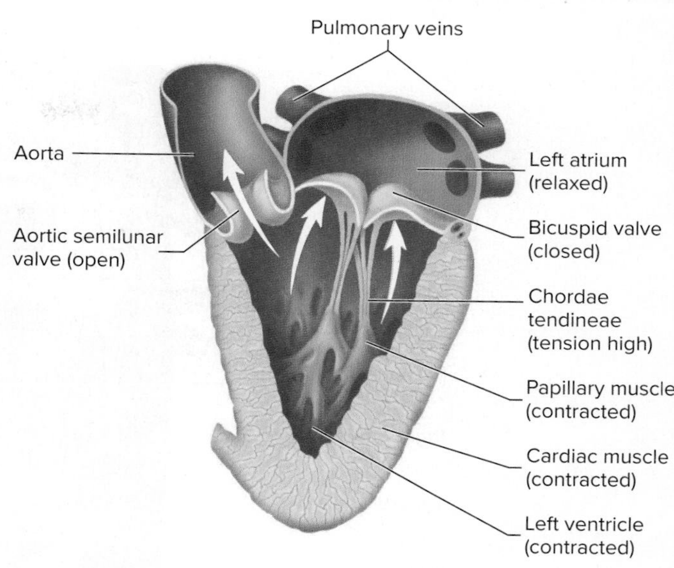

(b) Valve positions when blood is flowing out of the left ventricle

FIGURE 20.8 Function of the Heart Valves
(*a*) When blood is flowing into the left ventricle, the bicuspid valve is open and the aortic semilunar valve is closed. (*b*) When blood is flowing out of the left ventricle, the bicuspid valve is closed and the aortic semilunar valve is open. The tricuspid and pulmonary semilunar valves (not shown) open and close in a similar pattern.

12. *Describe the openings of the right and left ventricles. What structure separates the ventricles from each other?*

13. *Name the valves that separate the atria from the ventricles. What are the functions of the papillary muscles and the chordae tendineae?*

14. *Where are the semilunar valves found?*

20.4 Route of Blood Flow Through the Heart

LEARNING OUTCOME

After reading this section, you should be able to

A. **Relate the flow of blood through the heart, naming the chambers, valves, and vessels in the correct order.**

Blood flow through the heart is depicted in figure 20.9. Even though it is more convenient to discuss blood flow through the heart one side at a time, it is important to understand that blood flows through both sides simultaneously. Both atria contract at about the same time and both ventricles contract at about the same time, therefore blood is moving through both the pulmonary and the systemic circulations with each heartbeat. This concept is particularly important when electrical activity, pressure changes, and heart sounds are discussed later in this chapter.

1. Deoxygenated blood enters the relaxed right atrium from the systemic circulation through the superior and inferior venae cavae and from the heart wall through the coronary sinus.
2. Most of the blood in the right atrium then passes into the relaxed right ventricle. The right atrium then contracts, pushing the remaining blood in the atrium into the right ventricle to complete right ventricular filling.
3. Contraction of the right ventricle pushes blood against the tricuspid valve, forcing it closed. Closing of the tricuspid valve prevents blood from moving back into the right atrium. Blood also pushes against the pulmonary semilunar valve, forcing it open. Blood then flows into the pulmonary trunk.
4. The pulmonary trunk branches to form the **pulmonary arteries** (see figure 20.5), which carry blood to the lungs, where CO_2 is released and O_2 is picked up (see chapters 21 and 23).
5. Blood returning from the lungs enters the left atrium through the four pulmonary veins.
6. Most of the blood passes from the left atrium, through the bicuspid valve, into the relaxed left ventricle. Contraction of the left atrium completes left ventricular filling.
7. Contraction of the left ventricle pushes blood against the bicuspid valve, closing it and preventing blood from moving back into the left atrium. Blood is also pushed against the aortic semilunar valve, opening it and allowing blood to enter the aorta.
8. Blood flowing through the aorta is distributed to all parts of the body, except to the parts of the lungs supplied by the pulmonary blood vessels (see chapter 23).

Recall that in the embryonic and fetal heart the foramen ovale allows for blood to flow between the two atria. This hole closes at birth, separating the right and left sides of the heart. For a more detailed discussion of blood flow through the fetal heart, see chapter 29.

ASSESS YOUR PROGRESS

15. *Starting at the venae cavae and ending at the aorta, trace the flow of blood through the heart.*

FUNDAMENTAL Figure

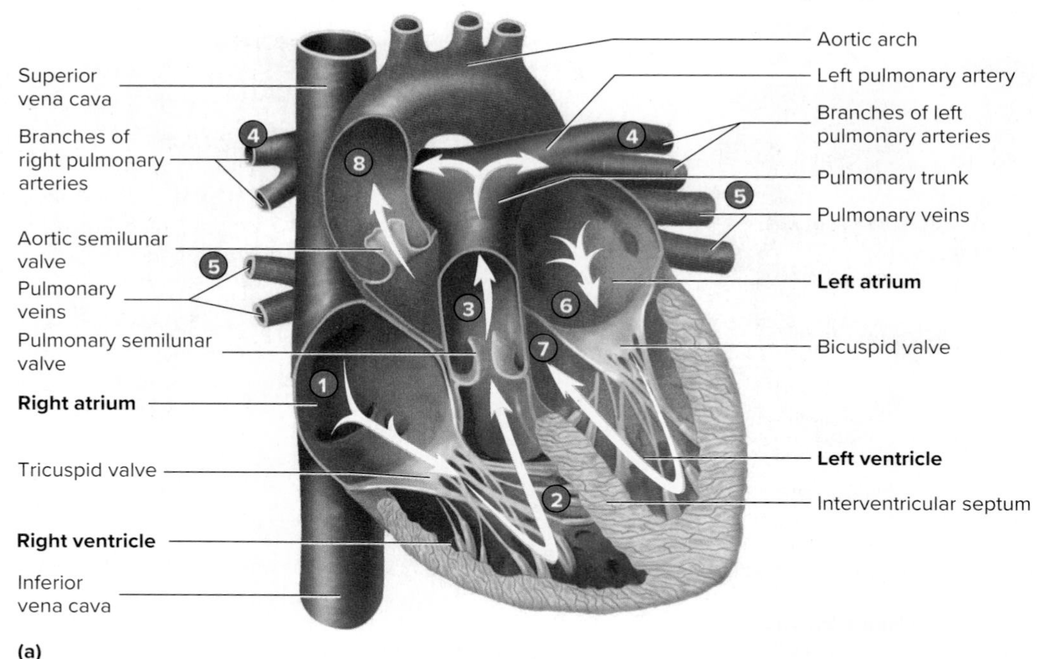

(a)

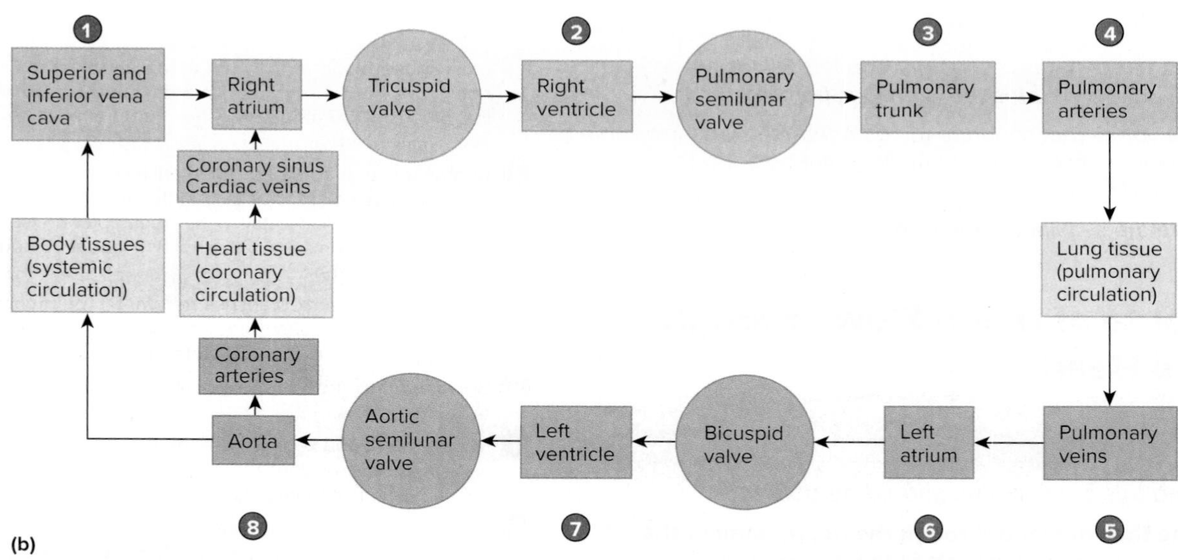

(b)

PROCESS Figure 20.9

Blood Flow Through the Heart

(*a*) Frontal section of the heart revealing the four chambers and the direction of blood flow (*purple numbers*). (*b*) Diagram listing, in order, the structures through which blood flows in the systemic, pulmonary, and coronary circulations. The heart valves are indicated by *circles;* areas containing deoxygenated blood are represented in *blue,* and areas containing oxygenated blood are depicted in *red.*

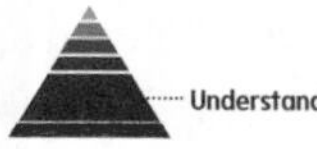

Imagine that you are a red blood cell moving through the circulation. After moving into the right atrium, how many heart valves will you pass through before you first enter the circulation of the lungs? How many heart valves will you pass through before entering the circulation of the brain?

20.5 Histology

LEARNING OUTCOMES

After reading this section, you should be able to

A. **Describe the structure and functions of the heart skeleton.**
B. **Relate the structural and functional characteristics of cardiac muscle cells.**
C. **Compare and contrast cardiac muscle and skeletal muscle.**
D. **Explain the structure and function of the conducting system of the heart.**

Heart Skeleton

The **heart skeleton** consists of a plate of fibrous connective tissue between the atria and the ventricles. This connective tissue plate forms **fibrous rings** around the atrioventricular and semilunar valves and provides solid support for them, reinforcing the valve openings (figure 20.10). The fibrous connective tissue plate also serves as electrical insulation between the atria and the ventricles and provides a rigid site for attachment of the cardiac muscles.

Cardiac Muscle

Cardiac muscle cells are elongated, branching cells that have one, or occasionally two, centrally located nuclei. Cardiac muscle cells contain actin and myosin myofilaments organized to form sarcomeres, which join end-to-end to form myofibrils (see chapter 9). As is the case in skeletal muscle, the actin and myosin myofilaments are responsible for cardiac muscle contraction, and their organization gives cardiac muscle a striated (banded) appearance. However, the striations are less regularly arranged and less numerous than in skeletal muscle (figure 20.11).

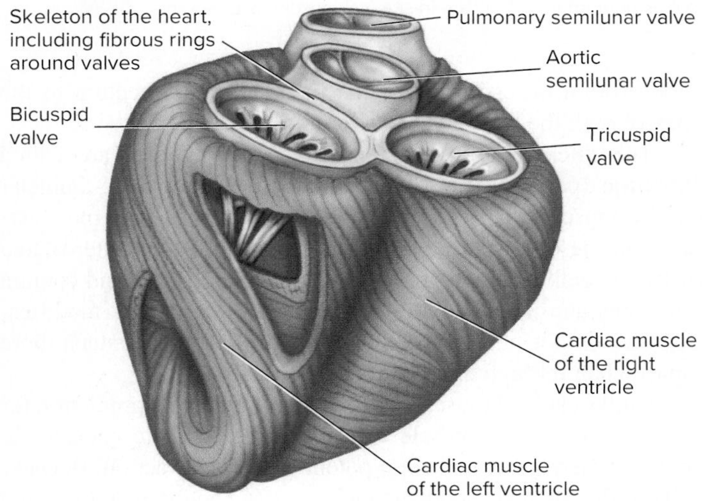

FIGURE 20.10 Heart Skeleton
The skeleton of the heart consists of fibrous connective tissue rings, which surround the heart valves and separate the atria from the ventricles. Cardiac muscle attaches to the fibrous connective tissue. The muscle fibers are arranged so that contraction of the ventricles produces a wringing motion and the distance between the apex and the base of the heart shortens.

Cardiac muscle cell contraction is very similar to that of skeletal muscle; however, the onset of contraction is longer and prolonged in cardiac muscle. These differences in contraction are partially due to differences in cell anatomy. Cardiac muscle has **sarcoplasmic reticulum,** which stores Ca^{2+}, similar to skeletal muscle. But the sarcoplasmic reticulum is not as regularly arranged as in skeletal muscle fibers, and there are no dilated cisternae, as in skeletal muscle.

We learned in chapter 9 that stimulations of the skeletal muscle at the sarcolemma, or plasma membrane, are carried deep into the cell by transverse tubules. Similarly, cardiac muscles have transverse tubules that are in close association with the sarcoplasmic reticulum. However, the T tubules in cardiac muscle are larger in diameter than in skeletal muscle, and extensions of T tubules are not as closely associated with the sarcoplasmic reticulum as in skeletal muscle. Also, the T tubules of cardiac muscle are found near the Z disks of the sarcomeres, instead of where the actin and myosin overlap, as in skeletal muscle. Given these structural differences, depolarizations of the cardiac muscle plasma membrane are not carried from the surface of the cell to the sarcoplasmic reticulum as efficiently as they are in skeletal muscle, and Ca^{2+} must diffuse a greater distance from the sarcoplasmic reticulum to the actin myofilaments. Another important difference between cardiac muscle and skeletal muscle is the sources for Ca^{2+} necessary for contraction. In skeletal muscle, adequate Ca^{2+} for contraction is stored in the sarcoplasmic reticulum, but cardiac muscle requires some Ca^{2+} from the extracellular fluid and from the T tubules.

Cardiac muscle is specialized to meet the high energy requirements needed for proper myocardial function. Adenosine triphosphate (ATP) provides the energy for cardiac muscle contraction. ATP production depends on O_2 availability. Because cardiac muscle must continue to contract and relax in a relatively steady rhythm to maintain life, it cannot develop a large oxygen deficit, which is often seen in skeletal muscle. Cardiac muscle cells are rich in mitochondria, which perform oxidative metabolism at a rate rapid enough to sustain normal myocardial energy requirements. Also, the myocardium has an extensive capillary network that provides an adequate O_2 supply to the cardiac muscle cells.

Another unique characteristic of cardiac muscle is that cardiac muscle cells are organized in spiral bundles or sheets. Additionally, cardiac cells are bound to adjacent cells by specialized cell-to-cell contacts called **intercalated** (in-TER-kah-lay-ted) **disks** (figure 20.11). Intercalated disks are located at the ends of cells, connecting them end-to-end; however, intercalated disks can also connect cells laterally. At intercalated disks, the plasma membranes are folded, and the adjacent cells fit together, thus greatly increasing contact between them. In addition, specialized plasma membrane structures at the intercalated disks increase physical and electrical connections between cells. These plasma membrane structures include desmosomes and gap junctions. **Desmosomes** (DEZ-moh-sohms) hold the cells together, and **gap junctions** allow cytoplasm to flow freely between cells, resulting in areas

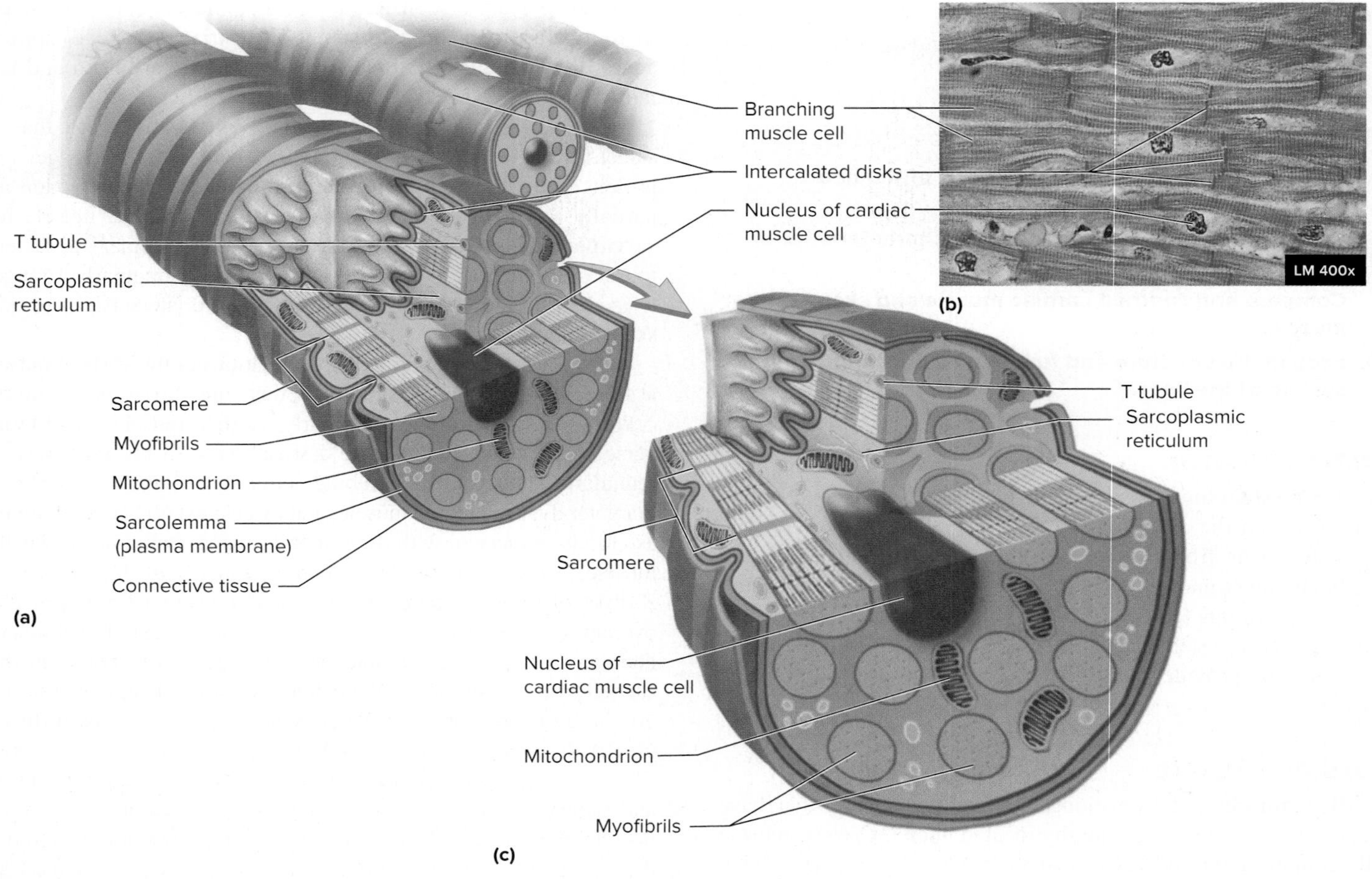

FIGURE 20.11 Histology of the Heart
(*a*) Cardiac muscle cells are branching cells with centrally located nuclei. The cells are joined to one another by intercalated disks. Gap junctions in the intercalated disks allow action potentials to pass from one cardiac muscle cell to the next. (*b*) A light micrograph of cardiac muscle tissue. The cardiac muscle cells appear striated because of the arrangement of the individual myofilaments. (*c*) As in skeletal muscle, sarcomeres join end-to-end to form myofibrils, and mitochondria provide ATP for contraction. Sarcoplasmic reticulum and T tubules are visible but are not as numerous as they are in skeletal muscle. (b) Ed Reschke APR

of low electrical resistance between the cells. This enables action potentials to pass easily from one cell to the next (see figure 4.3). Electrically, the cardiac muscle cells behave as a single unit, and the heart's highly coordinated contractions depend on this functional characteristic.

Conducting System

A conducting system relays action potentials through the heart. This system consists of modified cardiac muscle cells that form two nodes (knots or lumps) and a conducting bundle (figure 20.12). The two nodes are contained within the walls of the right atrium and are named according to their position in the atrium. The **sinoatrial (SA) node** is medial to the opening of the superior vena cava, and the **atrioventricular (AV) node** is medial to the right atrioventricular valve. The AV node gives rise to a conducting bundle of the heart, the **atrioventricular (AV) bundle** (bundle of His). This bundle passes through a small opening in the fibrous skeleton to reach the interventricular septum, where it divides to form the **right** and **left bundle branches,** which extend beneath the endocardium on each side of the interventricular septum to the apex of both the right and the left ventricles.

The inferior terminal branches of the bundles are called **Purkinje** (per-KIN-jee) **fibers.** These fibers are large-diameter cardiac muscle fibers. They have fewer myofibrils than most cardiac muscle cells and do not contract as forcefully. Intercalated disks are well developed between the Purkinje fibers and contain numerous gap junctions. As a result of these structural modifications, action potentials travel along the Purkinje fibers much more rapidly than through other cardiac muscle tissue.

Unlike skeletal muscle cells that require neural stimulation for contraction, cardiac muscle cells have the intrinsic capacity to spontaneously generate action potentials for contraction. Because cells of the SA node spontaneously generate action potentials at a greater frequency than other cardiac muscle cells, these cells are called the **pacemaker** of the heart. The SA node is made up of specialized, small-diameter cardiac muscle cells that merge with the other cardiac muscle cells of the right atrium. It is the activity of the SA node that causes the heart to contract spontaneously and rhythmically.

Figure 20.12 traces an action potential through the conducting system of the heart and illustrates the subsequent pattern of contraction of the heart chambers.

1. The heart is at rest and all chambers are relaxed.
2. Action potentials are generated at the SA node and spread from the SA node to adjacent cardiac cells of the atrium. Preferential pathways conduct action potentials (*dotted arrows*) from the SA node to the AV node at a greater velocity than they are transmitted in the remainder of the atrial muscle tissue; however, such pathways cannot be distinguished structurally from other areas of the atrial wall.
3. Cardiac muscle of the atrial wall contracts in response to the action potentials conducted through the atrial wall.
4. When the heart beats under resting conditions, approximately 0.04 second is required for action potentials to travel from the SA node to the AV node. Action potentials are propagated slowly through the AV node, compared with the remainder of the conducting system. The slow rate of action potential conduction in the AV node is due, in part, to the smaller-diameter muscle cells and fewer gap junctions in their intercalated disks. Like the other specialized conducting cells in the heart, they have fewer myofibrils than most cardiac muscle cells. As a consequence, a delay of 0.11 second occurs from the time action potentials reach the AV node until they pass to the AV bundle. The delay of action potentials at the AV node allows for completion of the atrial contraction before ventricular contraction begins. After action potentials pass from the AV node to the highly specialized conducting bundles, the velocity of conduction increases dramatically. The action potentials pass through the left and right bundle branches and through the individual Purkinje fibers that penetrate the myocardium of the ventricles.
5. Because of the arrangement of the conducting system in the ventricles, the first part of the ventricular myocardium that is stimulated is the inner wall of the ventricles near the apex. Thus, ventricular contraction begins at the apex and progresses throughout the ventricles toward the base of the heart. The spiral arrangement of muscle layers in the wall of the heart results in a wringing action. During the process, the distance between the apex and the base of the heart decreases and blood is forced upward from the apex toward the great vessels at the base of the heart (see figure 20.9).

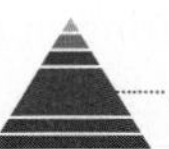

Predict 2

Because of a reduced blood supply to the AV node, the delay in the conduction of action potentials from the SA node to the AV node is increased slightly. All other areas of the conducting system of the heart are functioning normally. Predict how this affects the normal rhythm of the heart.

ASSESS YOUR PROGRESS

16. *What is the heart skeleton composed of? What are its functions?*
17. *Compare and contrast cardiac muscle and skeletal muscle.*
18. *Why does cardiac muscle have slow onset of contraction and prolonged contraction?*
19. *What anatomical features are responsible for the ability of cardiac muscle cells to contract as a unit?*
20. *Identify the parts of the conducting system of the heart. Explain how the conducting system coordinates contraction of the atria and ventricles.*
21. *Explain why Purkinje fibers conduct action potentials more rapidly than other cardiac muscle cells.*
22. *Relate why the SA node is the pacemaker of the heart.*

20.6 Electrical Properties

LEARNING OUTCOMES

After reading this section, you should be able to

A. **Explain what is meant by the autorhythmicity of cardiac muscle and relate it to the pacemaker potential.**
B. **Summarize the characteristics of action potentials in cardiac muscle.**
C. **Explain the importance of a long refractory period in cardiac muscle.**
D. **Describe the waves and intervals of an electrocardiogram.**

In chapter 3, we defined the membrane potential of a cell as the electrical charge difference across the plasma membrane. This charge difference is the result of a cell's regulation of ion movement into and out of the cell. Cardiac muscle cells—like other electrically excitable cells, such as neurons and skeletal muscle fibers—have a **resting membrane potential,** the membrane potential when the cell is relaxed. The resting membrane potential depends on a low permeability of the plasma membrane to Na^+ and Ca^{2+} and a higher permeability to K^+. When neurons, skeletal muscle fibers, and cardiac muscle cells are depolarized to their threshold level, action potentials result (see chapter 11).

Autorhythmicity of Cardiac Muscle

The heart is said to be **autorhythmic** (AW-toh-RITH-mik) because it stimulates itself (*auto*) to contract at regular intervals (*rhythmic*). If the heart is removed from the body and maintained under physiological conditions with the proper nutrients and temperature, it will continue to beat autorhythmically for a long time.

In the SA node, pacemaker cells generate action potentials spontaneously and at regular intervals. These action potentials spread through the conducting system of the heart to other cardiac muscle cells, causing voltage-gated Na^+ channels to open. As a result, action potentials are produced and the cardiac muscle cells contract.

Depolarization of pacemaker cells is dependent on Na^+, K^+, and Ca^{2+}; however, the ways that these ions affect the membrane potential are very different. When a spontaneously developing local potential, called the **pacemaker potential,** reaches threshold, then action potentials are generated in the SA node. Changes in ion movement into and out of the pacemaker cells cause the pacemaker potential. Figure 20.13 illustrates the changes in the membrane potential during the pacemaker potential.

1. Sodium ions cause depolarization by moving into the cells through specialized nongated Na^+ channels. A decreasing permeability to K^+ also causes depolarization as less K^+ moves out of the cells. The decreasing K^+ permeability occurs due to the voltage changes at the end of the previous action potential. As a result of the depolarization, voltage-gated Ca^{2+} channels open, and the movement of Ca^{2+} into the pacemaker cells causes further depolarization.
2. When the pacemaker potential reaches threshold, many voltage-gated Ca^{2+} channels open. In pacemaker cells, the movement of Ca^{2+} into the cells is primarily responsible for the depolarization

PROCESS **Figure**

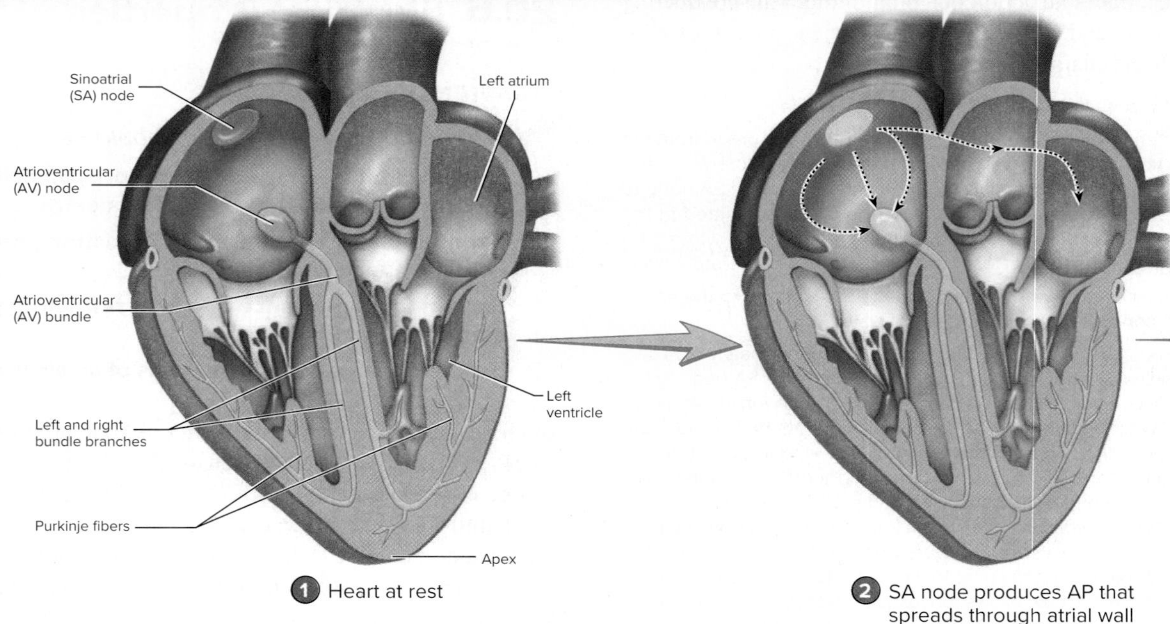

PROCESS Figure 20.12

Conducting System of the Heart: Coordination of Stimulation and Contraction of Myocardium

The conduction system of the heart is composed of specialized cardiac muscle cells that produce spontaneous action potentials. The organization of the conduction system ensures the proper pattern of stimulation and contraction of the atria and ventricle, maintaining normal blood flow. APR

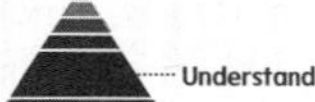

Why is it important for stimulation of the ventricles to begin at the apex and spread toward the base?

phase of the action potential. This is different from other cardiac muscle cells, where the movement of Na^+ into the cells is primarily responsible for depolarization.

3. Repolarization occurs, as in other cardiac muscle cells, when the voltage-gated Ca^{2+} channels close and the voltage-gated K^+ channels open.
4. After the resting membrane potential is reestablished, production of another pacemaker potential starts the generation of the next action potential.

Although most cardiac muscle cells respond to action potentials produced by the SA node, some cardiac muscle cells in the conducting system can also generate spontaneous action potentials. Normally, the SA node controls the rhythm of the heart because its pacemaker cells generate action potentials at a faster rate than other potential pacemaker cells. The SA node produces a heart rate of 70–80 beats per minute (bpm). In some conditions, another area of the conducting system may generate a heartbeat. An **ectopic focus** (ek-TOP-ik FOH-kus; pl. foci, FOH-sigh) is any part of the heart other than the SA node that generates a heartbeat. For example, if the SA node does not function properly, the part of the heart that can produce action potentials at the next highest frequency is the AV node, which produces a heart rate of 40–60 bpm. Another cause of an ectopic focus is blockage of the conducting pathways between the SA node and other parts of the heart. For example, if action potentials do not pass through the AV node, an ectopic focus can develop in an AV bundle, resulting in a heart rate of only 30 bpm.

Ectopic foci can also appear when the rate of action potential generation in cardiac muscle cells outside the SA node becomes enhanced. For example, when cells are injured, their plasma membranes become more permeable, resulting in depolarization. Inflammation or lack of adequate blood flow to cardiac muscle tissue can injure cardiac muscle cells. These injured cells can be the source of ectopic action potentials. Also, alterations in blood levels of K^+ and Ca^{2+} can change the cardiac muscle membrane potential, and certain drugs, such as those that mimic the effect of epinephrine on the heart, can alter cardiac muscle membrane permeability.

Various chemical agents, such as nifedipine and verapamil (ver-AP-ah-mil), block voltage-gated Ca^{2+} channels. Voltage-gated Ca^{2+} channel–blocking agents prevent the movement of Ca^{2+} through voltage-gated Ca^{2+} channels into the cell; for that reason, they are called **calcium channel blockers.** Some calcium channel blockers are widely used to treat various cardiac disorders, including tachycardia and certain arrhythmias (table 20.1). Calcium channel blockers slow the development of the pacemaker potential and thus reduce the heart rate. If action potentials arise prematurely within the SA node or other areas of the heart, calcium channel blockers reduce that tendency. Calcium

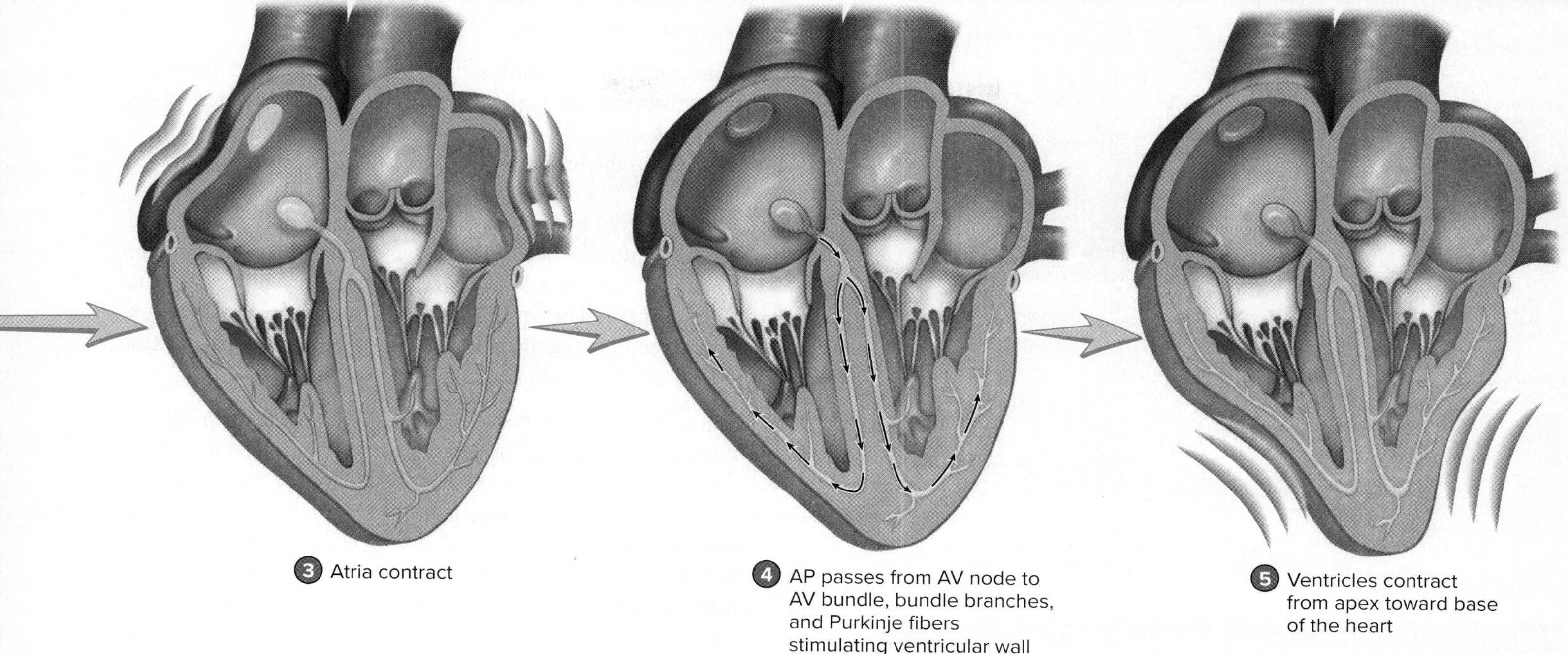

PROCESS **Figure**

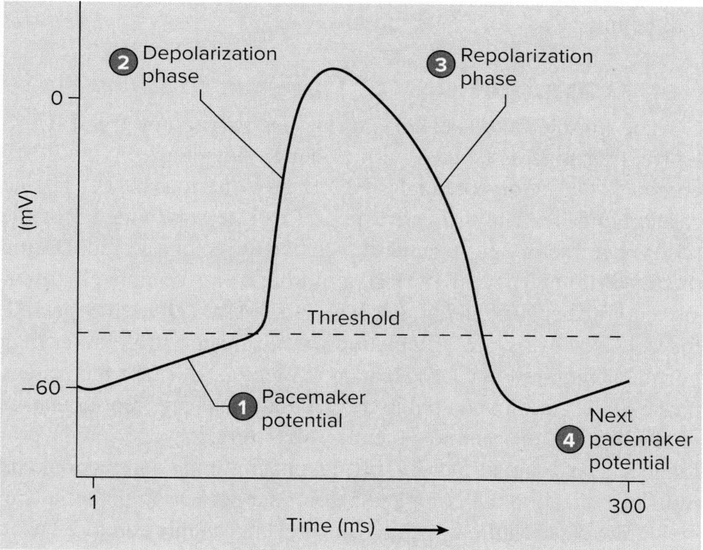

PROCESS **Figure 20.13**

Pacemaker Potential

The production of action potentials by the pacemaker cells of the SA node is responsible for the autorhythmicity of the heart.

When studying action potentials, it is important to recognize not only the major ions involved but also the direction those ions move across the membrane. When the appropriate ion channel is open, which ion(s) is(are) moving into the cell and which ion(s) is(are) moving out the cell?

channel blockers also reduce the amount of work performed by the heart because less Ca^{2+} enters cardiac muscle cells to activate the contractile mechanism. On the other hand, epinephrine and norepinephrine increase the heart rate and its force of contraction by opening voltage-gated Ca^{2+} channels.

Action Potentials in Cardiac Muscle Cells

Like action potentials in skeletal muscle, those in cardiac muscle exhibit depolarization followed by repolarization of the resting membrane potential. Alterations in membrane channels are responsible for the changes in the permeability of the plasma membrane that produce the action potentials. Action potentials in cardiac muscle last longer than those in skeletal muscle, and the membrane channels differ somewhat from those in skeletal muscle. In contrast to action potentials in skeletal muscle, which take less than 2 milliseconds (ms) to complete, action potentials in cardiac muscle take approximately 200–500 ms to complete.

The longer action potentials in cardiac muscle can be divided into four phases, each associated with specific changes in ion movement across the membrane. Figure 20.14 represents the electrical changes that occur during a cardiac muscle action potential.

1. *Depolarization phase:* Rapid depolarization is the result of changes in membrane permeability to Na^+, K^+, and Ca^{2+}; however, membrane permeability to Na^+ is the primary determinant of this phase. Membrane channels, called **voltage-gated Na^+ channels,** open, bringing about the depolarization phase of the action potential. As the voltage-gated Na^+ channels open, Na^+ diffuses into the cell, causing rapid depolarization until the cell is depolarized to approximately +20 millivolts (mV).

   The voltage change occurring during depolarization affects other ion channels in the plasma membrane. Several types of

PROCESS **Figure**

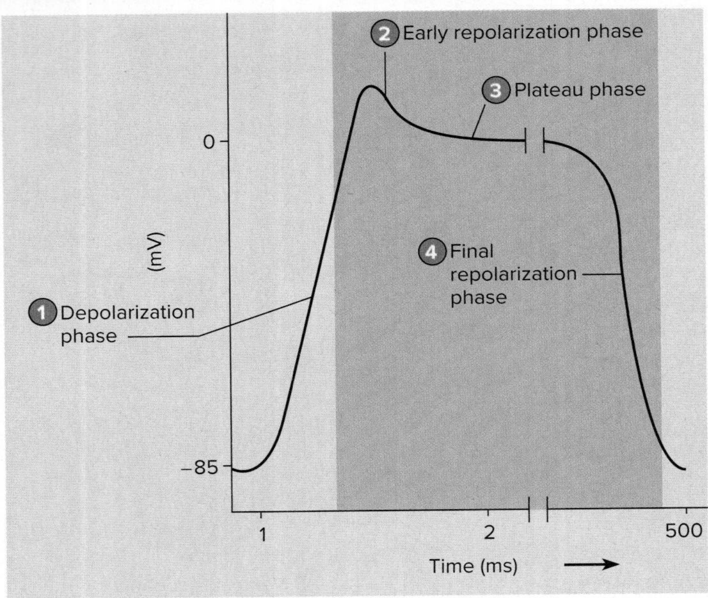

PROCESS **Figure 20.14**

Cardiac Muscle Action Potential in Cardiac Muscle

The action potential consists of four phases: depolarization, early repolarization, plateau phase, and final repolarization.

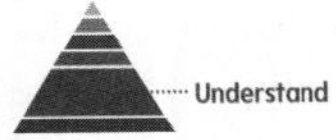

For each phase, identify the ions involved in the change in the membrane potential and the direction the ions are moving.

voltage-gated K^+ channels exist, each of which opens and closes at different membrane potentials, causing changes in membrane permeability to K^+. For example, at rest, the movement of K^+ through open voltage-gated K^+ channels is primarily responsible for establishing the resting membrane potential in cardiac muscle cells. Depolarization causes these voltage-gated K^+ channels to close, thereby decreasing membrane permeability to K^+. Depolarization also causes **voltage-gated Ca^{2+}** channels to begin to open. These changes contribute to depolarization. Compared with Na^+ channels, the Ca^{2+} channels open and close slowly.

2. *Early repolarization phase:* Repolarization is also the result of changes in membrane permeability to Na^+, K^+, and Ca^{2+}. Early repolarization occurs when the voltage-gated Na^+ channels and some voltage-gated Ca^{2+} channels close, and a small number of voltage-gated K^+ channels open. Sodium ion movement into the cell slows, and some K^+ moves out of the cell. At this point, repolarization begins, but in cardiac muscle early repolarization is slow due to the influx of Ca^{2+}, resulting in a plateau phase.
3. *Plateau phase:* The plateau phase occurs as voltage-gated Ca^{2+} channels remain open, and Ca^{2+} and some Na^+ move into the cell through the voltage-gated Ca^{2+} channels. The influx of these ions counteracts the potential change produced by the movement of K^+ out of the cell.
4. *Final repolarization phase:* The plateau phase ends, and final repolarization begins as the voltage-gated Ca^{2+} channels close and many more voltage-gated K^+ channels open. Thus, Ca^{2+} and Na^+ stop diffusing into the cell, and the tendency for K^+ to diffuse out of the cell increases. These permeability changes cause the membrane potential to return to its resting level.

Action potential propagation in cardiac muscle differs from that in skeletal muscle (figure 20.15).

1. Action potentials in cardiac muscle are conducted from cell to cell through the gap junctions of the intercalated disks, whereas action potentials in skeletal muscle fibers are conducted along the length of a single muscle fiber (cell), but not from fiber to fiber.
2. Action potential propagation is slower in cardiac muscle than in skeletal muscle because cardiac muscle cells are smaller in diameter and much shorter than skeletal muscle fibers. Although the gap junctions allow the transfer of action potentials between cardiac muscle cells, they slow the rate of action potential conduction between the cardiac muscle cells.

Another interesting characteristic of cardiac muscle contraction is the need for extracellular Ca^{2+} for contraction to occur. The movement of Ca^{2+} through the plasma membrane, including the membranes of the T tubules, into cardiac muscle cells stimulates the release of Ca^{2+} from the sarcoplasmic reticulum, a process called **calcium-induced calcium release (CICR).** When an action potential occurs in a cardiac muscle cell, Ca^{2+} enters the cell and binds to receptors in the membranes of the sarcoplasmic reticulum, resulting in the opening of Ca^{2+} channels on the membrane of the sarcoplasmic reticulum. Calcium ions then move out of the sarcoplasmic reticulum and activate the interaction between actin and myosin to produce contraction of the cardiac muscle cells. Skeletal muscle contraction does not depend on this mechanism and relies only on intracellular Ca^{2+} for contraction.

Refractory Periods of Cardiac Muscle

Cardiac muscle, like skeletal muscle, has **refractory** (ree-FRAK-tohr-ee) **periods** associated with its action potentials. Figure 20.15 compares the action potentials and refractory periods in skeletal and cardiac muscle. The refractory period can be subdivided into the absolute refractory period and the relative refractory period. During the **absolute refractory period,** a muscle cell is completely insensitive to further stimulation. During the **relative refractory period,** the cell is sensitive to stimulation, but a greater stimulation than normal is required to cause an action potential. Because the plateau phase of the action potential in cardiac muscle delays repolarization to the resting membrane potential, the refractory period is prolonged. The long refractory period ensures that contraction and most of relaxation are complete before another action potential can be initiated (see figure 20.15*b*). This prevents tetanic contractions in cardiac muscle and is responsible for rhythmic contractions.

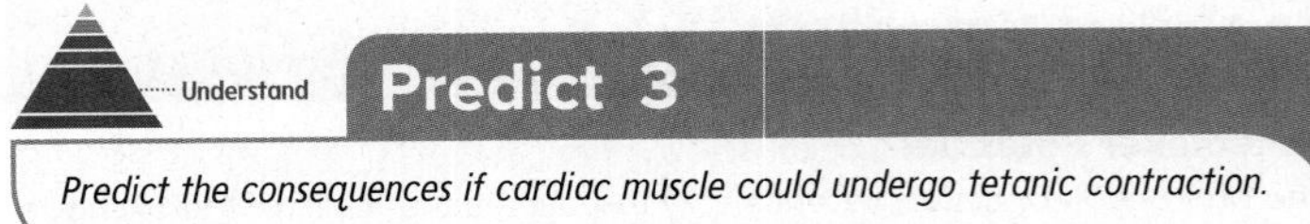

Predict the consequences if cardiac muscle could undergo tetanic contraction.

Electrocardiogram

Action potentials conducted through the myocardium during the cardiac cycle produce electrical currents that can be measured at the body surface. Electrodes placed on the body surface and

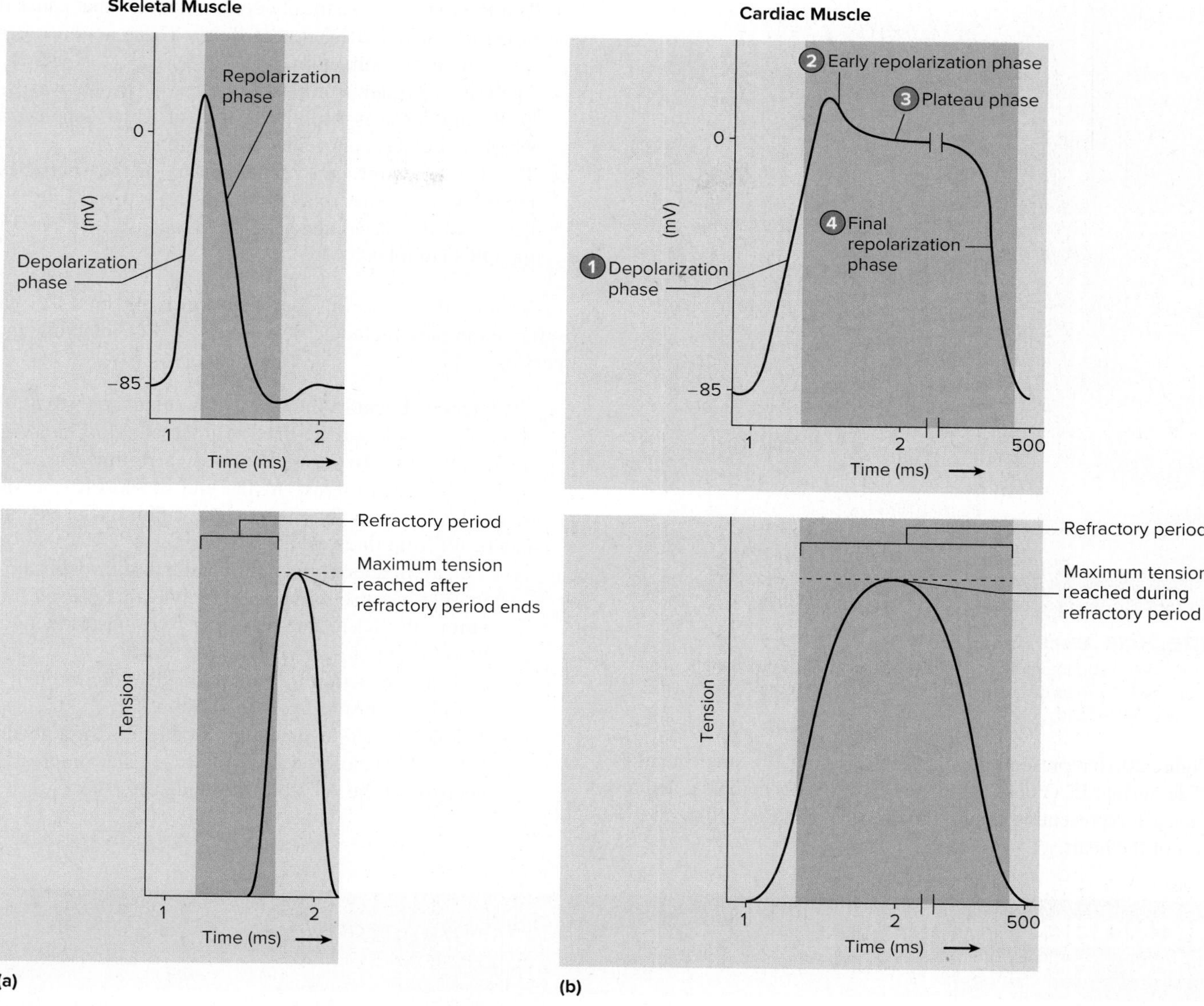

FIGURE 20.15 Comparison of Action Potentials in Skeletal and Cardiac Muscle
(*a*) An action potential in skeletal muscle consists of depolarization and repolarization phases. (*b*) An action potential in cardiac muscle consists of depolarization, early repolarization, plateau, and final repolarization phases. Cardiac muscle does not repolarize as rapidly as skeletal muscle (indicated by the *break in the curve*) because of the plateau phase.

attached to an appropriate recording device can detect small voltage changes resulting from action potentials in the cardiac muscle. The electrodes do not detect individual action potentials; rather, they detect a summation of all the action potentials transmitted by the cardiac muscle cells through the heart at a given time. The summated record of the cardiac action potentials is an **electrocardiogram** (**ECG** or **EKG;** figure 20.16).

The ECG is a record of the electrical activity of the heart. It, however, is not a direct measurement of mechanical events in the heart, and neither the force of contraction nor blood pressure can be determined from it. However, each deflection in the ECG record indicates an electrical event within the heart that is correlated with a subsequent mechanical event. Consequently, electrocardiography is extremely valuable in diagnosing a number of abnormal cardiac rhythms (arrhythmias) and other abnormalities, particularly because it is painless, easy to record, and noninvasive (does not require surgery). In addition to abnormal heart rates and rhythms, ECG analysis can reveal abnormal conduction pathways, hypertrophy or atrophy of portions of the heart, and the approximate location of damaged cardiac muscle. Table 20.1 describes the symptoms and possible causes of major cardiac arrhythmias.

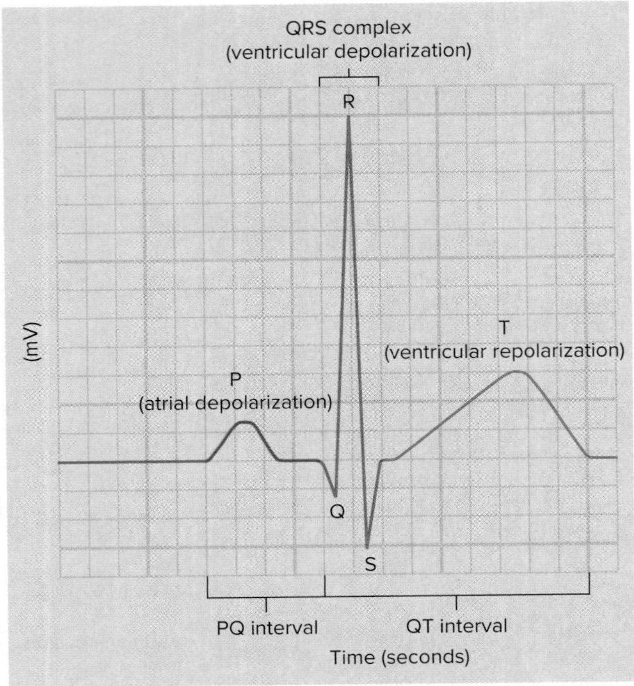

FIGURE 20.16 Electrocardiogram

The major waves and intervals of an electrocardiogram. Each thin, horizontal line on the ECG recording represents 1 mV, and each thin, vertical line represents 0.04 second.

Figure 20.16 represents a typical ECG tracing of a single heartbeat. The normal ECG consists of a P wave, a QRS complex, and a T wave, each representing important electrical changes of the myocardium of the heart.

- The **P wave** is the result of action potentials that cause depolarization of the atrial myocardium. These action potentials result in atrial contraction.
- The **QRS complex,** composed of three individual waves—the Q, R, and S waves—results from ventricular depolarization, which stimulates ventricular contraction.
- The **T wave** represents repolarization of the ventricles and precedes ventricular relaxation. A wave representing repolarization of the atria cannot be seen because it occurs during the QRS complex.

Various time intervals between waves on an ECG can be useful. Examples include PR interval (or PQ interval) and QT interval.

- PR interval. Because the Q wave is often very small, this is more commonly called the PR interval. This interval lasts approximately 0.16 second, during which time the atria contract and begin to relax. At the end of the PR interval, the ventricles begin to depolarize. Elongation of the PR interval can result from three events:
  - (a) a delay in action potential conduction through the atrial muscle because of damage, such as that caused by **ischemia** (ih-SKEE-mee-uh), which is obstruction of the blood supply to the walls of the heart
  - (b) a delay in action potential conduction through atrial muscle because of a dilated atrium
  - (c) a delay in action potential conduction through the AV node and bundle because of ischemia, compression, or necrosis of the AV node or bundle

MICROBES In Your Body 20.1 How Bacteria Affect Cardiac Muscle

You've learned that the majority of bacteria are either harmless or an integral part of our well-being. Unfortunately, there are a handful of pathogenic bacteria that can interfere with the body's homeostasis.

Most people associate bacterial pneumonia with the lungs only. However, in the medical community, it is well known that pneumonia can cause serious heart problems. In fact, cardiac problems cause 70% of the deaths in individuals with other types of severe bacterial infections. Most bacterial pneumonia is caused by the bacterium *Streptococcus pneumoniae,* but until recently the mechanism by which this pathogen damages the heart had not been well understood. It seems that these bacteria induce the cells lining blood vessels to endocytose them and deposit them in cardiac muscle tissue. There, the bacteria release a toxin, called pneumolysin, that kills the cardiac muscle cells. These areas of dead cardiac muscle are called microlesions. In addition, during recovery from the infection, scars may form within the myocardium. Thus, the bacteria physically damage the heart, which interrupts the electrical signal necessary for cardiac muscle contraction. In addition, simply treating pneumonia with the traditional antibiotic ampicillin may actually worsen damage to the heart. Ampicillin causes the bacterial cell walls to burst, which releases a surge of pneumolysin, creating even more microlesions. Use of an antibiotic that does not destroy the bacterial cell walls will help reduce cardiac muscle death. Further, a vaccine against the bacterial molecule that induces the bacterial transport and against pneumolysin has shown great promise in minimizing the tissue damage caused by these bacteria.

Although pathogenic bacteria exist, modern medicine continues to make great strides to reduce their damaging effects on our bodies. In addition, the more we learn about our microbiome, the more effectively we may be able to prevent bacterial infections from occurring in the first place.

Predict 4

Given that S. pneumoniae microlesions interrupt the electrical activity that flows between cardiac muscle cells, the heart can experience severe stress and may malfunction or stop contracting altogether. Using what you learned about skeletal muscle contraction, would microlesions in skeletal muscle cause the same type of reaction as in cardiac muscle?

Clinical IMPACT 20.1 Angina, Infarctions, and the Treatment of Blocked Coronary Arteries

Angina pectoris (an-JYE-na, pain; PEK-toh-ris, in the chest) is chest pain that results from a reduced blood supply to cardiac muscle. The pain is temporary and, if blood flow is restored, little permanent change or damage results. Angina pectoris is characterized by chest discomfort deep to the sternum, often described as heaviness, pressure, or moderately severe pain. It is often mistaken for indigestion. The pain can also be referred to the neck, lower jaw, left arm, and left shoulder (see chapter 14).

Most often, angina pectoris results from narrowed and hardened coronary arterial walls. The reduced blood flow results in a reduced supply of O_2 to cardiac muscle cells. As a consequence, the limited anaerobic respiration of cardiac muscle results in a reduced pH in affected areas of the heart, which stimulates pain receptors. The pain is predictably associated with exercise because the increased pumping of the heart requires more O_2, and the narrowed blood vessels cannot supply it.

Rest and drugs, such as nitroglycerin, frequently relieve angina pectoris. Nitroglycerin dilates the blood vessels, including the coronary arteries. Consequently, the drug increases the O_2 supply to cardiac muscle and reduces the heart's workload. Because peripheral arteries are dilated, the heart has to pump blood against a lower pressure, and the need for O_2 decreases. The heart also pumps less blood because blood tends to remain in the dilated blood vessels and less blood is returned to the heart.

Myocardial infarction (my-oh-KAR-dee-al in-FARK-shun) results when a prolonged lack of blood flow to a part of the cardiac muscle leads to a lack of O_2 and ultimately cellular death. Symptoms of myocardial infarction include chest pain that radiates into the left shoulder and arm, shortness of breath, nausea, vomiting, and sweating. Interestingly, these symptoms are common in males, but females may experience very different symptoms. Over 40% of females who have suffered a myocardial infarction did not experience chest pain. Symptoms for females include sudden fatigue, dizziness, and abdominal pain.

Myocardial infarctions vary in severity, depending on the amount of cardiac muscle and the part of the heart that is affected. If blood supply to cardiac muscle is reestablished within 20 minutes, no permanent damage occurs. If the oxygen deficiency lasts longer, cell death results. However, within 30–60 seconds after blockage of a coronary blood vessel, functional changes are obvious. The electrical properties of the cardiac muscle are altered, and the heart's ability to function properly is lost.

The most common cause of myocardial infarction is thrombus formation that blocks a coronary artery. Coronary arteries narrowed by **atherosclerotic** (ah-ther-oh-skleh-ROT-ik) **lesions** increase the risk for myocardial infarction. Atherosclerotic lesions partially block blood vessels, resulting in turbulent blood flow, and the surfaces of the lesions are rough. These changes increase the probability of thrombus formation.

Blocked blood vessels can be treated using various medical techniques. **Angioplasty** (AN-jee-oh-PLAS-tee) is a process whereby a surgeon threads a small balloon, usually into the femoral artery (see chapter 21), through the aorta and into a coronary artery. After entering the partially occluded coronary artery, the balloon is inflated, flattening the atherosclerotic deposits against the vessel walls and opening the occluded blood vessel. This technique improves the function of cardiac muscle in patients experiencing inadequate blood flow to the cardiac muscle through the coronary arteries. However, some controversy exists about its effectiveness. At least in some patients, dilation of the coronary arteries can reverse within a few weeks or months, and blood clots can form in coronary arteries following angioplasty. To help prevent future blockage, a metal-mesh tube called a **stent** is inserted into the vessel. Although the stent is better able to hold the vessel open, it, too, can eventually become blocked. Small, rotating blades and lasers are also used to remove lesions from coronary vessels.

Coronary bypass is a surgical procedure that relieves the effects of obstructed coronary arteries. This technique involves taking healthy segments of blood vessels from other parts of the patient's body and using them to bypass obstructions in the coronary arteries. The technique is common in cases of severe occlusion in specific parts of coronary arteries.

Enzymes are used to break down blood clots that form in the coronary arteries and cause myocardial infarctions. The major enzyme used is **tissue plasminogen** (plaz-MIN-oh-jen) **activator (t-PA).** This enzyme activates plasminogen, an inactive form of an enzyme in the body that breaks down the fibrin of clots. The strategy calls for administering t-PA to people suffering from myocardial infarctions as soon as possible following the onset of symptoms. Removal of the occlusions produced by clots reestablishes blood flow to the cardiac muscle and reduces the amount of cardiac muscle permanently damaged by the occlusions.

TABLE 20.1 Major Cardiac Arrhythmias

Conditions	Symptoms	Possible Causes
Abnormal Heart Rhythms		
Tachycardia	Heart rate in excess of 100 beats per minute (bpm)	Elevated body temperature; excessive sympathetic stimulation; toxic conditions
Paroxysmal atrial tachycardia	Sudden increase in heart rate to 95–150 bpm for a few seconds or even for several hours; P wave precedes every QRS complex; P wave inverted and superimposed on T wave	Excessive sympathetic stimulation; abnormally elevated permeability of slow channels
Ventricular tachycardia	Frequently causes fibrillation	Often associated with damage to AV node or ventricular muscle

(continued)

TABLE 20.1 Major Cardiac Arrhythmias (continued)

Conditions	Symptoms	Possible Causes
Abnormal Rhythms Resulting from Ectopic Action Potentials		
Atrial flutter	300 P waves/min; 125 QRS complexes/min, resulting in two or three P waves (atrial contraction) for every QRS complex (ventricular contraction)	Ectopic action potentials in the atria
Atrial fibrillation	No P waves; normal QRS complexes; irregular timing; ventricles constantly stimulated by atria; reduced pumping effectiveness and filling time	Ectopic action potentials in the atria
Ventricular fibrillation	No QRS complexes; no rhythmic contraction of the myocardium; many patches of asynchronously contracting ventricular muscle	Ectopic action potentials in the ventricles
Bradycardia	Heart rate less than 60 bpm	Elevated stroke volume in athletes; excessive vagal stimulation; carotid sinus syndrome
Sinus Arrhythmia	Heart rate varies 5% during respiratory cycle and up to 30% during deep respiration	Cause not always known; occasionally caused by ischemia or inflammation or associated with cardiac failure
SA Node Block	Cessation of P wave; new low heart rate due to AV node acting as pacemaker; normal QRS complex and T wave	Ischemia; tissue damage due to infarction; causes unknown
AV Node Block		
First-degree	PR interval greater than 0.2 second	Inflammation of AV bundle
Second-degree	PR interval 0.25–0.45 second; some P waves trigger QRS complexes and others do not; 2:1, 3:1, and 3:2 P wave/QRS complex ratios may occur	Excessive vagal stimulation
Third-degree (complete heart block)	P wave dissociated from QRS complex; atrial rhythm approximately 100 bpm; ventricular rhythm less than 40 bpm P P P P P P P P P P	Ischemia of AV nodal fibers or compression of AV bundle
Premature Atrial Contractions	Occasional shortened intervals between contractions; frequently occurs in healthy people P wave superimposed on QRS complex	Excessive smoking; lack of sleep; too much caffeine; alcoholism
Premature Ventricular Contractions (PVCs)	Prolonged QRS complex; exaggerated voltage because only one ventricle may depolarize; inverted T wave; increased probability of fibrillation PVC PVC	Ectopic foci in ventricles; lack of sleep; too much caffeine, irritability; occasionally occurs with coronary thrombosis

Note: SA = sinoatrial; AV = atrioventricular.

These conditions result in slow conduction of action potentials through the bundle branches.

- QT interval. The QT interval extends from the beginning of the QRS complex to the end of the T wave. It lasts about 0.36 second and represents the approximate length of time required for the ventricles to complete contraction and start to relax. An unusually long QT interval reflects the abnormal conduction of action potentials through the ventricles, which can result from myocardial infarctions or from an abnormally enlarged left or right ventricle.

Altered forms of the electrocardiogram due to cardiac abnormalities include complete heart block, premature ventricular contraction, bundle branch block, atrial fibrillation, and ventricular fibrillation (table 20.1).

ASSESS YOUR PROGRESS

23. *For cardiac muscle action potentials, describe ion movement during the depolarization, early repolarization, plateau, and final repolarization phases.*
24. *Why is cardiac muscle referred to as autorhythmic? What are ectopic foci?*
25. *How does the depolarization of pacemaker cells differ from the depolarization of other cardiac cells? What is the pacemaker potential?*
26. *How is the prolonged refractory period generated in cardiac muscle? What is the advantage of a prolonged refractory period?*
27. *What does an ECG measure? Name the waves and intervals produced by an ECG, and state what events occur during each wave and interval.*

20.7 Cardiac Cycle

LEARNING OUTCOMES

After reading this section, you should be able to

A. **Describe the cardiac cycle and the relationship among the contraction of each of the chambers, the opening and closing of valves, the pressure in each of the chambers, the phases of the electrocardiogram, and the heart sounds.**

B. **Discuss the heart sounds and their significance.**

The right and left halves of the heart can be viewed as two separate pumps that work together. Each pump consists of a "primer pump" (the atrium) and a "power pump" (the ventricle). Both atrial primer pumps complete the filling of the ventricles with blood, and both ventricular power pumps produce the major force that causes blood to flow through the pulmonary and systemic arteries. The term **cardiac cycle** refers to the repetitive pumping process that begins with the onset of cardiac muscle contraction and ends with the beginning of the next contraction (figure 20.17). Blood moves from an area of higher pressure to an area of lower pressure. Pressure changes produced within the heart chambers as a result of cardiac muscle contraction and relaxation move blood along the previously described routes of the pulmonary and systemic circulations.

The duration of the cardiac cycle varies considerably among humans and during an individual's lifetime. It can be as short as 0.25–0.3 second in a newborn or as long as 1 or more seconds in a well-trained athlete. The normal cardiac cycle of 0.7–0.8 second depends on the capability of cardiac muscle to contract and on the functional integrity of the conducting system.

The cardiac cycle involves a predictable pattern of contraction and relaxation of the heart chambers. As you study the events of the cardiac cycle described in this section, keep in mind that the term **systole** (SIS-toh-lee) means to contract, and **diastole** (die-AS-toh-lee) means to dilate, which occurs as the heart wall relaxes. Therefore, **atrial systole** is contraction of the atrial myocardium, and **atrial diastole** occurs as the atrial myocardium relaxes. Similarly, **ventricular systole** is contraction of the ventricular myocardium, and **ventricular diastole** occurs as the ventricular myocardium relaxes. When the terms *systole* and *diastole* are used alone, they refer to ventricular systole and diastole.

Before we begin our discussion of the cardiac cycle, it is important to have a clear image of the state of the heart. At the beginning of the cardiac cycle, the atria and ventricles are relaxed, the AV valves are open, and the semilunar valves are closed. During the cardiac cycle, changes in chamber pressure and the opening and closing of the heart valves determine the direction of blood movement. As the cardiac cycle is described, it is important to focus on these pressure changes and heart valve movements.

Figure 20.17 illustrates the phases of the cardiac cycle, describing the stimulation of the heart chambers, changes in pressure, and opening and closing of the heart valves:

1. *Heart relaxed: passive ventricular filling.* As stated earlier, before a cardiac cycle begins, all chambers are relaxed. At rest, most of the blood movement into the chambers is a passive process resulting from the greater blood pressure in the veins than in the heart chambers. As the blood moves into the atria, much of it flows into the ventricles for two reasons: (a) The AV valves are open and (b) atrial pressure is slightly greater than ventricular pressure. This time period when blood is passively moving into the ventricles is called *passive ventricular filling.*
2. *Atrial systole: active ventricular filling.* The SA node generates an action potential that stimulates atrial contraction. The P wave of an ECG represents this electrical activity. Atrial contraction begins the cardiac cycle. As the atria contract, they carry out the primer pump function by actively forcing more blood into the ventricles.
3. *Ventricular systole: period of isovolumetric contraction.* The action potential passes to the AV node, down the AV bundle, bundle branches, and Purkinje fibers, stimulating ventricular systole. This electrical activity is represented as the QRS complex of an ECG. As the ventricles contract, ventricular pressures increase, causing blood to flow toward the atria and close the AV valves. Recall that the semilunar valves are closed at this point as well. Ventricular contraction continues and ventricular pressures rise; however, because all the valves are closed, no blood flows from the ventricles at this time. This brief interval is called the *period of isovolumetric (iso, same) contraction* because the volume of blood in the ventricles does not change, even though the ventricles are contracting.
4. *Ventricular systole: period of ejection.* Ventricular contraction continues, and ventricular pressure builds until it overcomes the pressures in the pulmonary trunk and aorta. As a result, the semilunar valves are pushed open, and blood flows from the ventricles into those arteries.

FUNDAMENTAL **Figure**

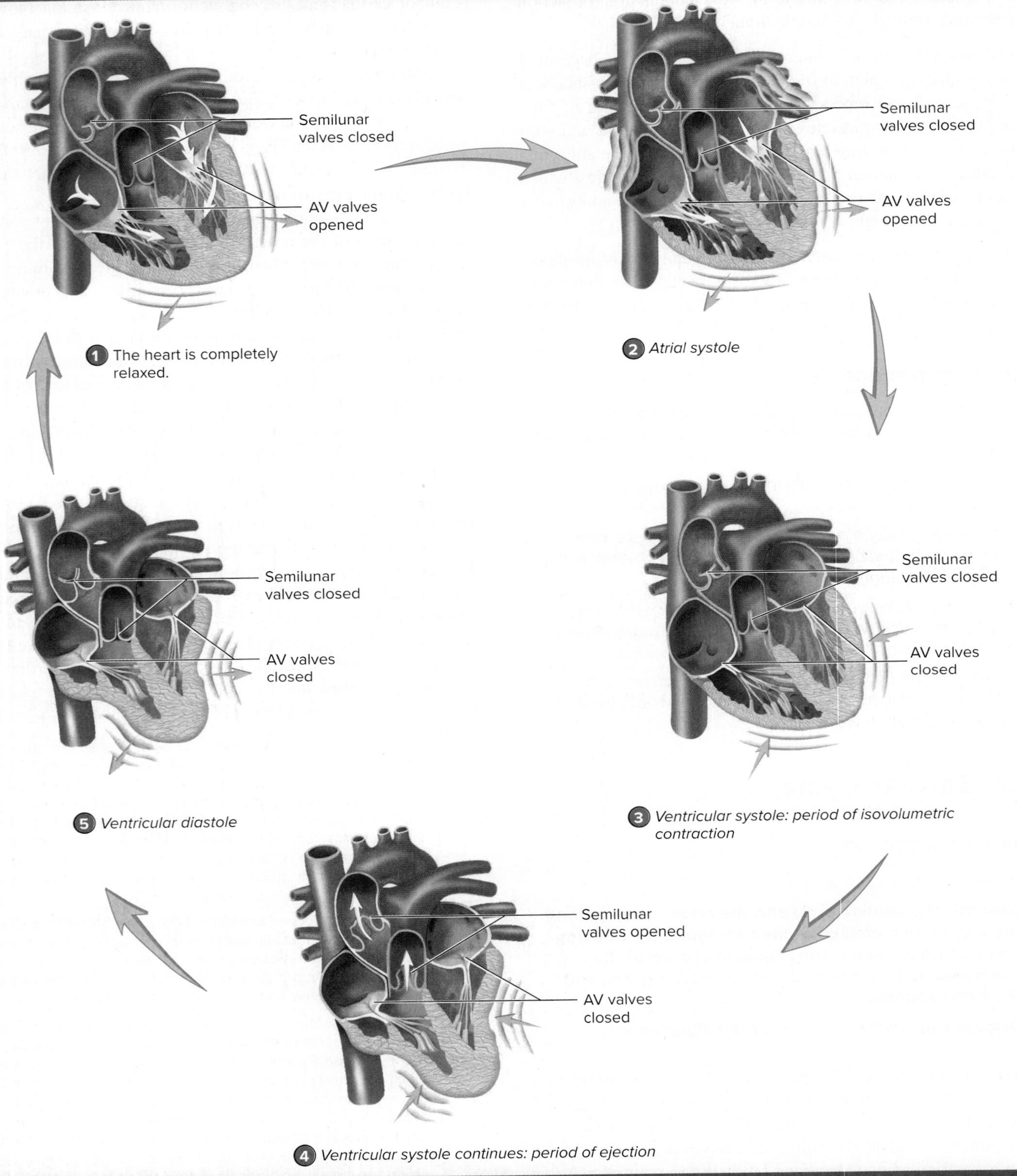

PROCESS **Figure 20.17**

Cardiac Cycle

The cardiac cycle is a repeating series of contraction and relaxation that moves blood through the heart (*AV* = atrioventricular).

Understand *Ventricular systole is divided into two phases: the isovolumetric (same volume) phase and the ventricular ejection phase. Explain the differences between these two phases.*

B. The tricuspid valve separates the right atrium and ventricle. The bicuspid valve separates the left atrium and ventricle. The chordae tendineae attach the papillary muscles to the atrioventricular valves.

C. The semilunar valves separate the aorta and pulmonary trunk from the ventricles.

1. *Which of these structures returns blood to the right atrium?* Remember
   - *a. coronary sinus*
   - *b. inferior vena cava*
   - *c. superior vena cava*
   - *d. Both b and c are correct.*
   - *e. All of these are correct.*

2. *The valve located between the right atrium and the right ventricle is the* Remember
   - *a. aortic semilunar valve.*
   - *b. pulmonary semilunar valve.*
   - *c. tricuspid valve.*
   - *d. bicuspid (mitral) valve.*

3. *The papillary muscles*

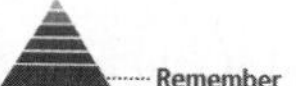

   - *a. are attached to chordae tendineae.*
   - *b. are found in the atria.*
   - *c. contract to close the foramen ovale.*
   - *d. are attached to the semilunar valves.*
   - *e. surround the openings of the coronary arteries.*

4. *The bulk of the heart wall is*

   - *a. epicardium.*
   - *b. pericardium.*
   - *c. myocardium.*
   - *d. endocardium.*
   - *e. exocardium.*

5. *Explain why the walls of the ventricles are thicker than the walls of the atria.* Understand

6. *Explain why it is sufficient to replace the ventricles, but not the atria, in artificial heart transplantation.* Understand

20.4 Route of Blood Flow Through the Heart

A. Blood from the body flows through the right atrium into the right ventricle and then to the lungs.

B. Blood returns from the lungs to the left atrium, enters the left ventricle, and is pumped back to the body.

7. *Given these blood vessels:*

   (1) aorta
   (2) inferior vena cava
   (3) pulmonary trunk
   (4) pulmonary vein

   Choose the arrangement that lists the vessels in the order a red blood cell would encounter them going from the systemic veins to the systemic arteries.
   - *a. 1,3,4,2*
   - *b. 2,3,4,1*
   - *c. 2,4,3,1*
   - *d. 3,2,1,4*
   - *e. 3,4,2,1*

20.5 Histology

Heart Skeleton

The fibrous heart skeleton supports the openings of the heart, electrically insulates the atria from the ventricles, and provides a point of attachment for heart muscle.

Cardiac Muscle

A. Cardiac muscle cells are branched and have a centrally located nucleus. Actin and myosin are organized to form sarcomeres. The sarcoplasmic reticulum and T tubules are not as organized as in skeletal muscle.

B. Cardiac muscle cells are joined by intercalated disks, which allow action potentials to move from one cell to the next. Thus, cardiac muscle cells function as a unit.

C. Cardiac muscle cells have a slow onset of contraction and a prolonged contraction time caused by the length of time required for Ca^{2+} to move to and from the myofibrils.

D. Cardiac muscle is well supplied with blood vessels that support aerobic respiration.

E. Cardiac muscle aerobically uses glucose, fatty acids, and lactate to produce ATP for energy. Cardiac muscle does not develop a significant oxygen deficit.

8. *Cardiac muscle has*

   - *a. sarcomeres.*
   - *b. a sarcoplasmic reticulum.*
   - *c. transverse tubules.*
   - *d. many mitochondria.*
   - *e. All of these are correct.*

9. *Action potentials pass from one cardiac muscle cell to another* Remember
   - *a. through gap junctions.*
   - *b. by a special cardiac nervous system.*
   - *c. because of the large voltage of the action potentials.*
   - *d. because of the plateau phase of the action potentials.*
   - *e. by neurotransmitters.*

Conducting System

A. The SA node and the AV node are in the right atrium.

B. The AV node is connected to the bundle branches in the interventricular septum by the AV bundle.

C. The bundle branches give rise to Purkinje fibers, which supply the ventricles.

D. The SA node is made up of small-diameter cardiac muscle cells that initiate action potentials, which spread across the atria and cause them to contract.

E. Action potentials are slowed in the AV node, allowing the atria to contract and blood to move into the ventricles. Then the action potentials travel through the AV bundles and bundle branches to the Purkinje fibers, causing the ventricles to contract, starting at the apex. The AV node is also made up of small-diameter cardiac muscle fibers.

10. *During the transmission of action potentials through the conducting system of the heart, there is a temporary delay at the* Remember
   - *a. bundle branches.*
   - *b. Purkinje fibers.*
   - *c. AV node.*
   - *d. SA node.*
   - *e. AV bundle.*

11. *Given these structures of the conducting system of the heart:*

   (1) atrioventricular bundle
   (2) AV node
   (3) bundle branches
   (4) Purkinje fibers
   (5) SA node

   Choose the arrangement that lists the structures in the order an action potential passes through them.
   - *a. 2,5,1,3,4*
   - *b. 2,5,3,1,4*
   - *c. 2,5,4,1,3*
   - *d. 5,2,1,3,4*
   - *e. 5,2,4,3,1*

12. *Purkinje fibers* 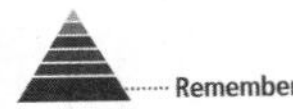

    a. *are specialized cardiac muscle cells.*
    b. *conduct impulses much more slowly than ordinary cardiac muscle.*
    c. *conduct action potentials through the atria.*
    d. *connect the SA node and the AV node.*
    e. *ensure that ventricular contraction starts at the base of the heart.*

20.6 Electrical Properties

Autorhythmicity of Cardiac Muscle

A. Cardiac pacemaker muscle cells are autorhythmic because of the spontaneous development of a pacemaker potential.

B. The pacemaker potential results from the movement of Na^+ and Ca^{2+} into the pacemaker cells.

C. Ectopic foci are areas of the heart that regulate heart rate under abnormal conditions.

Action Potentials in Cardiac Muscle Cells

A. After depolarization and partial repolarization, a plateau is reached, during which the membrane potential only slowly repolarizes.

B. The movement of Na^+ through the voltage-gated Na^+ channels causes depolarization.

C. During depolarization, voltage-gated K^+ channels close, and voltage-gated Ca^{2+} channels begin to open.

D. Early repolarization results from closure of the voltage-gated Na^+ channels and the opening of some voltage-gated K^+ channels.

E. The plateau exists because voltage-gated Ca^{2+} channels remain open.

F. The rapid phase of repolarization results from closure of the voltage-gated Ca^+ channels and the opening of many voltage-gated K^+ channels.

G. The entry of Ca^{2+} into cardiac muscle cells causes Ca^{2+} to be released from the sarcoplasmic reticulum to trigger contractions.

Refractory Periods of Cardiac Muscle

Cardiac muscle has a prolonged depolarization and thus a prolonged refractory period, which allows time for the cardiac muscle to relax before the next action potential causes a contraction.

Electrocardiogram

A. An ECG records only the electrical activities of the heart.
   - Depolarization of the atria produces the P wave.
   - Depolarization of the ventricles produces the QRS complex.
   - Repolarization of the atria occurs during the QRS complex.
   - Repolarization of the ventricles produces the T wave.

B. Based on the magnitude of the ECG waves and the time between waves, ECGs can be used to diagnose heart abnormalities.

13. *T waves on an ECG represent* 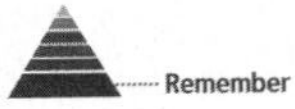

    a. *depolarization of the ventricles.*
    b. *repolarization of the ventricles.*
    c. *depolarization of the atria.*
    d. *repolarization of the atria.*

14. *Predict the consequences for the heart's pumping effectiveness if numerous ectopic foci in the ventricles produce action potentials.* Understand

15. *A patient has tachycardia. Would you recommend a drug that prolongs or shortens the plateau of cardiac muscle cell action potentials?* Apply

16. *A doctor lets you listen to a patient's heart with a stethoscope at the same time that you feel the patient's pulse. Once in a while, you hear two heartbeats very close together, but you feel only one pulse beat. Later, the doctor tells you that the patient has an ectopic focus in the right atrium. Explain why you hear two heartbeats very close together. The doctor also tells you that the patient exhibits a pulse deficit (the number of pulse beats felt is fewer than the number of heartbeats heard). Explain why a pulse deficit occurs.* Apply

17. *A friend tells you an ECG revealed that her son has a slight heart murmur. Should you be convinced that he has a heart murmur? Explain.* Understand

20.7 Cardiac Cycle

A. The cardiac cycle involves repetitive contraction and relaxation of the heart chambers.

B. Blood moves through the circulatory system from areas of higher pressure to areas of lower pressure. Contraction of the heart produces the pressure.

C. The cardiac cycle is divided into five periods:
   - Active ventricular filling results when the atria contract and pump blood into the ventricles.
   - Although the ventricles are contracting, during the period of isovolumetric contraction, ventricular volume does not change because all the heart valves are closed.
   - During the period of ejection, the semilunar valves open, and blood is ejected from the heart.
   - Although the heart is relaxing, during the period of isovolumetric relaxation, ventricular volume does not change because all the heart valves are closed.
   - Passive ventricular filling results when blood flows from the higher pressure in the veins and atria to the lower pressure in the relaxed ventricles.

Events Occurring During the Cardiac Cycle

A. Most ventricular filling occurs when blood flows from the higher pressure in the veins and atria to the lower pressure in the relaxed ventricles.

B. Contraction of the atria completes ventricular filling.

C. Contraction of the ventricles closes the AV valves, opens the semilunar valves, and ejects blood from the heart.

D. The volume of blood in a ventricle just before it contracts is the end-diastolic volume. The volume of blood after contraction is the end-systolic volume.

E. Relaxation of the ventricles results in the closing of the semilunar valves, the opening of the AV valves, and the movement of blood into the ventricles.

18. *The greatest amount of ventricular filling occurs during* Remember
    a. *the first one-third of diastole.*
    b. *the middle one-third of diastole.*
    c. *the last one-third of diastole.*
    d. *ventricular systole.*

19. *While the semilunar valves are open during a normal cardiac cycle, the pressure in the left ventricle is* Understand
    a. *higher than the pressure in the aorta.*
    b. *lower than the pressure in the aorta.*
    c. *the same as the pressure in the left atrium.*
    d. *lower than the pressure in the left atrium.*

20. *Blood flows neither into nor out of the ventricles during*
    a. *the period of isovolumetric contraction.*
    b. *the period of isovolumetric relaxation.*
    c. *diastole.*
    d. *systole.*
    e. *Both a and b are correct.*

Remember

21. *In most tissues, peak blood flow occurs during systole and decreases during diastole. In heart tissue, however, the opposite is true, and peak blood flow occurs during diastole. Explain this difference.*

Apply

22. *Explain why it is more efficient for contraction of the ventricles to begin at the apex of the heart than at the base.*

Understand

Heart Sounds

A. Closure of the atrioventricular valves produces the first heart sound.
B. Closure of the semilunar valves produces the second heart sound.
C. Turbulent flow of blood into the ventricles can be heard in some people, producing a third heart sound.

Aortic Pressure Curve

A. Contraction of the ventricles forces blood into the aorta, producing the peak systolic pressure.
B. Blood pressure in the aorta falls to the diastolic level as blood flows out of the aorta.
C. Elastic recoil of the aorta maintains pressure in the aorta and produces the dicrotic notch and dicrotic wave.

23. *Pressure in the aorta is at its lowest*
    a. *at the time of the first heart sound.*
    b. *at the time of the second heart sound.*
    c. *just before the AV valves open.*
    d. *just before the semilunar valves open.*

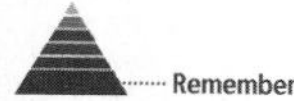

24. *Just after the dicrotic notch on the aortic pressure curve*
    a. *the pressure in the aorta is greater than the pressure in the left ventricle.*
    b. *the pressure in the left ventricle is greater than the pressure in the aorta.*
    c. *the pressure in the left atrium is greater than the pressure in the left ventricle.*
    d. *the pressure in the left atrium is greater than the pressure in the aorta.*
    e. *blood pressure in the aorta is 0 mm Hg.*

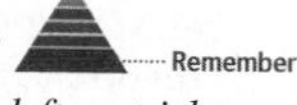

25. *The "lubb" sound (first heart sound) is caused by the*
    a. *closing of the AV valves.*
    b. *closing of the semilunar valves.*
    c. *blood rushing out of the ventricles.*
    d. *filling of the ventricles.*
    e. *ventricular contraction.*

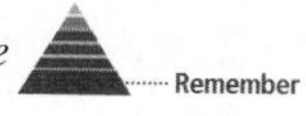

26. *Many endurance-trained athletes have a decreased resting heart rate, compared with that of nonathletes. Explain why an endurance-trained athlete's resting heart rate decreases rather than increases.*

20.8 Mean Arterial Blood Pressure

A. Mean arterial pressure is the average blood pressure in the aorta. Adequate blood pressure is necessary to ensure delivery of blood to the tissues.
B. Mean arterial pressure is proportional to cardiac output (amount of blood pumped by the heart per minute) times peripheral resistance (total resistance to blood flow through blood vessels).
C. Cardiac output is equal to stroke volume times heart rate.
D. Stroke volume, the amount of blood pumped by the heart per beat, is equal to end-diastolic volume minus end-systolic volume.
   - Venous return is the amount of blood returning to the heart. Increased venous return increases stroke volume by increasing end-diastolic volume.
   - Increased force of contraction increases stroke volume by decreasing end-systolic volume.
E. Cardiac reserve is the difference between resting and exercising cardiac output.

27. *Stroke volume is the*
    a. *amount of blood pumped by the heart per minute.*
    b. *difference between end-diastolic and end-systolic volume.*
    c. *difference between the amount of blood pumped at rest and that pumped at maximum output.*
    d. *amount of blood pumped from the atria into the ventricles.*

28. *Cardiac output is defined as*
    a. *blood pressure times peripheral resistance.*
    b. *peripheral resistance times heart rate.*
    c. *heart rate times stroke volume.*
    d. *stroke volume times blood pressure.*
    e. *blood pressure minus peripheral resistance.*

29. *Increased venous return results in*
    a. *increased stroke volume.*
    b. *increased cardiac output.*
    c. *decreased heart rate.*
    d. *Both a and b are correct.*

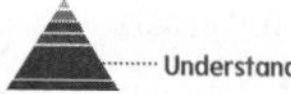

20.9 Regulation of the Heart

Intrinsic Regulation

A. Venous return is the amount of blood that returns to the heart during each cardiac cycle.
B. The Starling law of the heart describes the relationship between preload and the stroke volume of the heart. An increased preload causes the cardiac muscle cells to contract with more force and produce a higher stroke volume.

Extrinsic Regulation

A. The cardioregulatory center in the medulla oblongata regulates parasympathetic and sympathetic nervous control of the heart.
B. Parasympathetic stimulation is supplied by the vagus nerve.
   - Parasympathetic stimulation decreases heart rate.
   - Postganglionic neurons secrete acetylcholine, which increases membrane permeability to K^+, producing hyperpolarization of the membrane.
C. Sympathetic stimulation is supplied by the cardiac nerves.
   - Sympathetic stimulation increases heart rate and force of contraction (stroke volume).
   - Postganglionic neurons secrete norepinephrine, which increases membrane permeability to Na^+ and Ca^{2+} and produces depolarization of the membrane.

D. Epinephrine and norepinephrine are released into the blood from the adrenal medulla as a result of sympathetic stimulation.
   - The effects of epinephrine and norepinephrine on the heart are long-lasting, compared with those of neural stimulation.
   - Epinephrine and norepinephrine increase the rate and force of heart contraction.

20.10 The Heart and Homeostasis

Effect of Blood Pressure

A. Baroreceptors monitor blood pressure.

B. In response to a decrease in blood pressure, the baroreceptor reflexes increase sympathetic stimulation and decrease parasympathetic stimulation of the heart, resulting in increased heart rate and force of contraction.

Effect of pH, Carbon Dioxide, and Oxygen

A. Chemoreceptors monitor blood CO_2, pH, and O_2 levels.

B. In response to increased CO_2 and decreased pH, medullary chemoreceptor reflexes increase sympathetic stimulation and decrease parasympathetic stimulation of the heart.

C. Carotid body chemoreceptor stimulated by low O_2 levels result in decreased heart rate and vasoconstriction.

D. All regulatory mechanisms functioning together in response to low blood pH, high blood CO_2, and low blood O_2 levels usually produce increased heart rate and vasoconstriction. Decreased O_2 levels stimulate an increase in heart rate indirectly by stimulating respiration, and the stretch of the lungs activates a reflex that increases sympathetic stimulation of the heart.

Effect of Extracellular Ion Concentration

A. An increase or a decrease in extracellular K^+ decreases heart rate.

B. Increased extracellular Ca^{2+} increases force of contraction of the heart and decreases heart rate. Decreased Ca^{2+} levels produce the opposite effect.

Effect of Body Temperature

Heart rate increases when body temperature increases, and it decreases when body temperature decreases.

30. *Parasympathetic nerve fibers are found in the ________ nerves and release ________ at the heart.*
   a. *cardiac, acetylcholine*
   b. *cardiac, norepinephrine*
   c. *vagus, acetylcholine*
   d. *vagus, norepinephrine*

31. *Increased parasympathetic stimulation of the heart*

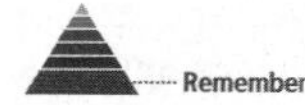

   a. *increases the force of ventricular contraction.*
   b. *increases the rate of depolarization in the SA node.*
   c. *decreases heart rate.*
   d. *increases cardiac output.*

32. *Because of the baroreceptor reflex, when normal arterial blood pressure decreases, the*
   a. *heart rate decreases.*
   b. *stroke volume decreases.*
   c. *frequency of afferent action potentials from baroreceptors decreases.*
   d. *cardioregulatory center stimulates parasympathetic neurons.*

33. *A decrease in blood pH and an increase in blood CO_2 levels result in*
   a. *increased heart rate.*
   b. *increased stroke volume.*
   c. *increased sympathetic stimulation of the heart.*
   d. *increased cardiac output.*
   e. *All of these are correct.*

34. *An increase in extracellular potassium levels can cause*
   a. *an increase in stroke volume.*
   b. *an increase in force of contraction.*
   c. *a decrease in heart rate.*
   d. *Both a and b are correct.*

35. *An experiment on a dog was performed in which the mean arterial blood pressure was monitored before and after the common carotid arteries were partially clamped (at time A). The results are graphed here:*

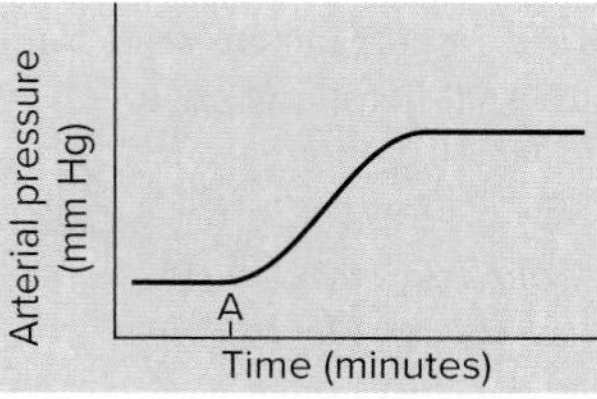

Explain the change in mean arterial blood pressure. (Hint: *Baroreceptors are located in the internal carotid arteries, which are superior to the site of clamping of the common carotid arteries.*)

36. *During hemorrhagic shock (caused by loss of blood), blood pressure may fall dramatically, although the heart rate is elevated. Explain why blood pressure falls despite the increase in heart rate.*

Answers to this chapter's odd-numbered Concept Check questions appear in Appendix F.

CHAPTER 21

Cardiovascular System

BLOOD VESSELS AND CIRCULATION

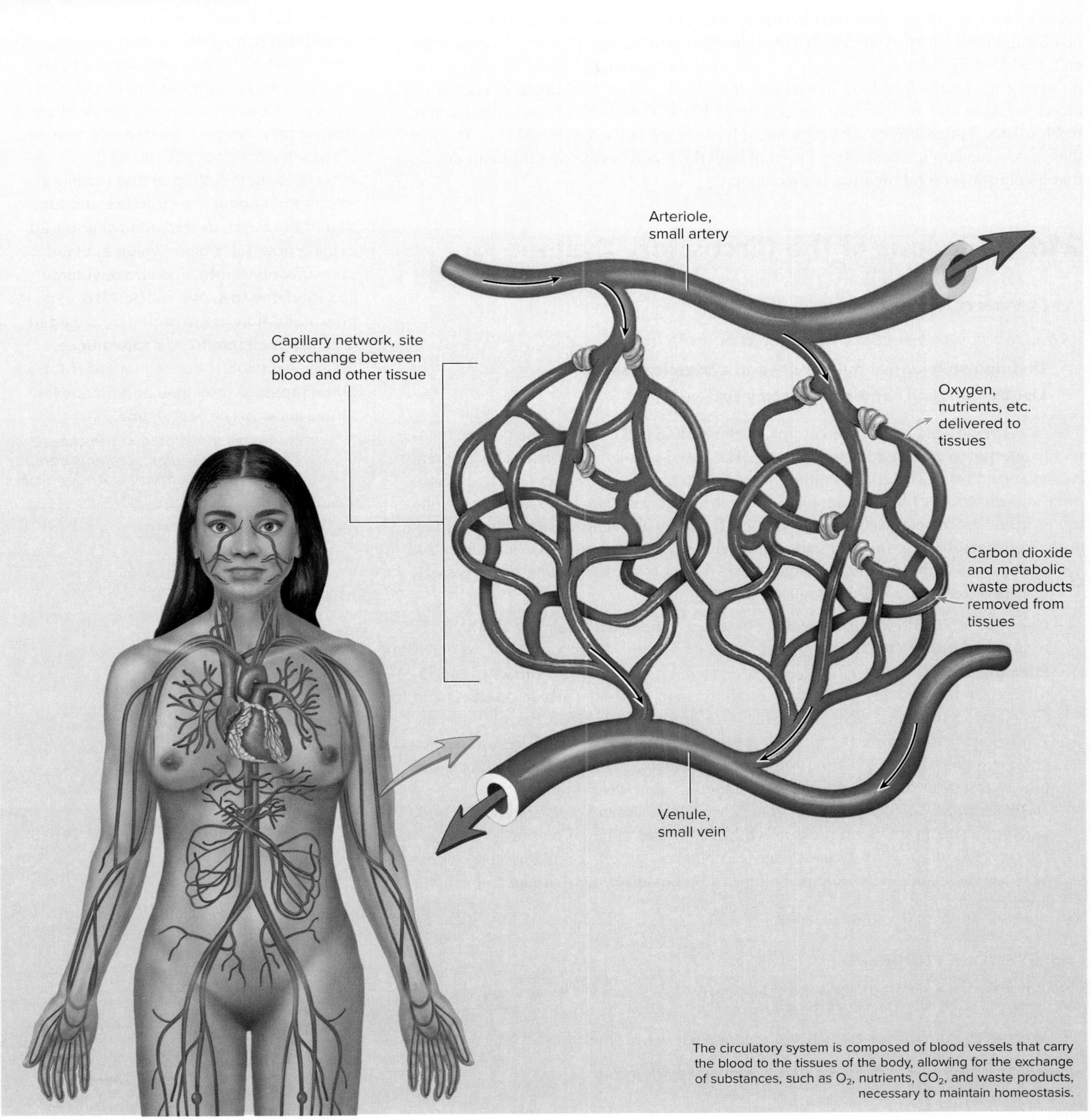

Arteriole, small artery

Capillary network, site of exchange between blood and other tissue

Oxygen, nutrients, etc. delivered to tissues

Carbon dioxide and metabolic waste products removed from tissues

Venule, small vein

The circulatory system is composed of blood vessels that carry the blood to the tissues of the body, allowing for the exchange of substances, such as O_2, nutrients, CO_2, and waste products, necessary to maintain homeostasis.

The complex water systems that move fluid through pipes for the numerous businesses and homes in a city are actually a good analogy for representing the intricacy and coordinated functions of blood vessels. The heart is the pump that provides the major force causing blood to circulate, and the blood vessels are the pipes that carry blood to the body tissues and back to the heart. In the same way the water system distributes water that is vital to normal operations in our homes and businesses, the circulatory system distributes the many substances that are necessary for and produced by the various metabolic activities throughout the body. In addition to providing the routes for blood movement, the blood vessels participate in regulating blood pressure and determining the degree of blood flow to the body's most active tissues. Blood pressure must be high enough to ensure sufficient blood flow to meet the tissues' metabolic needs. Regulation of both the blood vessels and the heart ensure that homeostatic blood pressure is maintained.

Learn to Predict

T.J. and Tyler were building a treehouse. While searching for a board in a pile of used lumber, T.J. stepped on a rusty nail, which penetrated deeply into his foot, causing it to bleed. Neither T.J. nor Tyler wanted to tell their parents about the accident, but after 3 days, T.J. developed septic shock. His foot had become infected, and the infection had spread into his bloodstream.

After reading this chapter and recalling information about the structure and function of the heart, described in chapter 20, explain how T.J.'s blood volume, blood pressure, heart rate, and stroke volume changed due to septic shock. Also, explain how blood flow in the periphery changed and how it affected T.J.'s appearance. Finally, explain the consequences if T.J.'s blood pressure remained abnormally low for a prolonged period of time.

Answers to this question and the chapter's odd-numbered Predict questions can be found in Appendix E.

21.1 Functions of the Circulatory System

LEARNING OUTCOMES

After reading this section, you should be able to

A. **Distinguish between pulmonary and systemic vessels.**

B. **List the functions of the circulatory system.**

The blood vessels are part of the cardiovascular system and comprise the portion commonly referred to as the circulatory system. The blood vessels of the circulatory system are organized into two sets: (1) pulmonary vessels and (2) systemic vessels. **Pulmonary vessels** transport blood from the right ventricle, through the lungs, and back to the left atrium. **Systemic vessels** transport blood from the left ventricle, through all parts of the body, and back to the right atrium (see figure 20.1). As described in chapter 20, the heart provides the major force that causes blood to move through these vessels. The circulatory system has five unique functions:

1. *Carries blood.* Blood vessels carry blood from the heart to almost all the body tissues and back to the heart.
2. *Exchanges nutrients, waste products, and gases with tissues.* Nutrients and O_2 diffuse from blood vessels to cells in all areas of the body. Waste products and CO_2 diffuse from the cells, where they are produced, to blood vessels.
3. *Transports substances.* Hormones, components of the immune system, molecules required for coagulation, enzymes, nutrients, gases, waste products, and other substances are transported in the blood to all areas of the body.
4. *Helps regulate blood pressure.* The circulatory system and the heart work together to maintain blood pressure within a normal range of values.
5. *Directs blood flow to tissues.* The circulatory system regulates the degree of blood flow, and, therefore, the volume of blood delivered to tissues to maintain homeostasis.

ASSESS YOUR PROGRESS

Answers to these questions are found in the section you have just completed. Re-read the section if you need help in answering these questions.

1. *What is the difference between pulmonary and systemic vessels?*
2. *Describe the five functions of the circulatory system.*

Module 9
Cardiovascular System

FUNDAMENTAL **Figure**

21.2 Structural Features of Blood Vessels

LEARNING OUTCOMES

After reading this section, you should be able to

A. **List the types of arteries, capillaries, and veins.**
B. **Describe the structure and function of arteries, capillaries, and veins.**
C. **Describe the innervation of the blood vessel walls.**

Blood vessels are hollow tubes that conduct blood through the tissues of the body. There are three main types of blood vessels: (1) arteries, (2) capillaries, and (3) veins. These vessels form a continuous passageway for blood flow from the heart, through the body tissues, and back to the heart. Blood leaving the heart first passes through arteries. Next, the blood flows through the capillaries, which are the smallest blood vessels. Finally, blood moves through veins as it once again flows into the heart.

Structure of Blood Vessels

General Features

Except for the capillaries and the smallest veins, called venules, the blood vessel walls consist of three relatively distinct tissue layers. These tissue layers are most evident in the muscular arteries and least evident in the veins. From the lumen to the outer wall of the blood vessels, the layers, or **tunics** (TOO-niks), are (1) the tunica intima, (2) the tunica media, and (3) the tunica externa (figure 21.1).

The **tunica intima,** also called the *tunica interna,* is the most internal layer of a blood vessel wall. This tunic consists of four layers: (1) endothelium; (2) a basement membrane; (3) the lamina propria, which is a thin layer of connective tissue; and (4) the **internal elastic membrane,** which is a fenestrated layer of elastic fibers that separates the tunica intima from the next layer, the tunica media.

The **tunica media,** or middle layer, consists of smooth muscle fibers arranged circularly around the blood vessel. The amount of blood flowing through a blood vessel can be regulated by contraction or relaxation of the smooth muscle in the tunica media. **Vasoconstriction** (VAY-soh-con-STRIK-shun) results from smooth muscle contraction and causes a decrease in blood vessel diameter, thereby decreasing blood flow through the vessel. **Vasodilation** (VAY-soh-die-LAY-shun) results from smooth muscle relaxation and causes an increase in blood vessel diameter, thereby increasing blood flow through the vessel.

The tunica media also contains variable amounts of elastic and collagen fibers, depending on the size of the vessel. An **external elastic membrane** separates the tunica media from the tunica externa. It can be identified at the outer border of the tunica media in some arteries. In addition, a few longitudinally oriented smooth muscle fibers occur in some arteries near the tunica intima.

The **tunica externa** is composed of connective tissue, which varies from dense connective tissue near the tunica media to loose

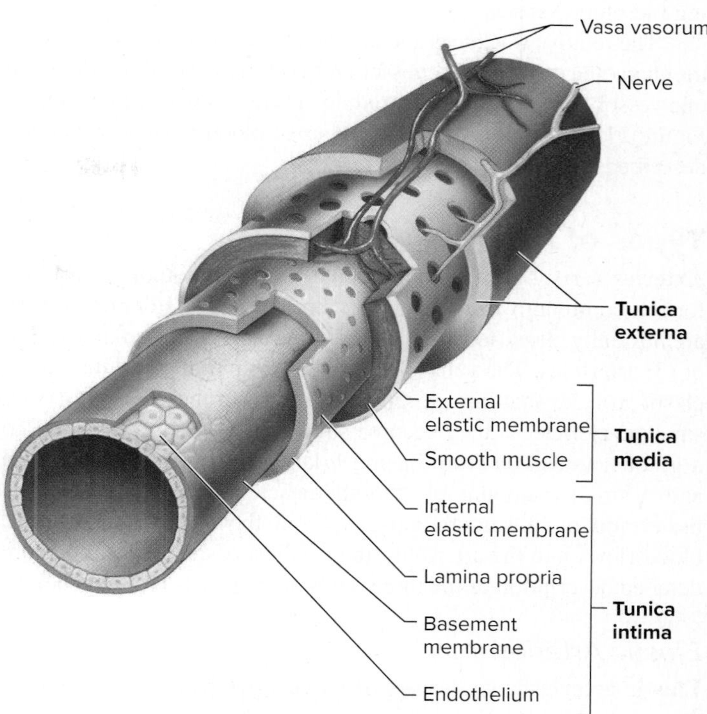

(a)

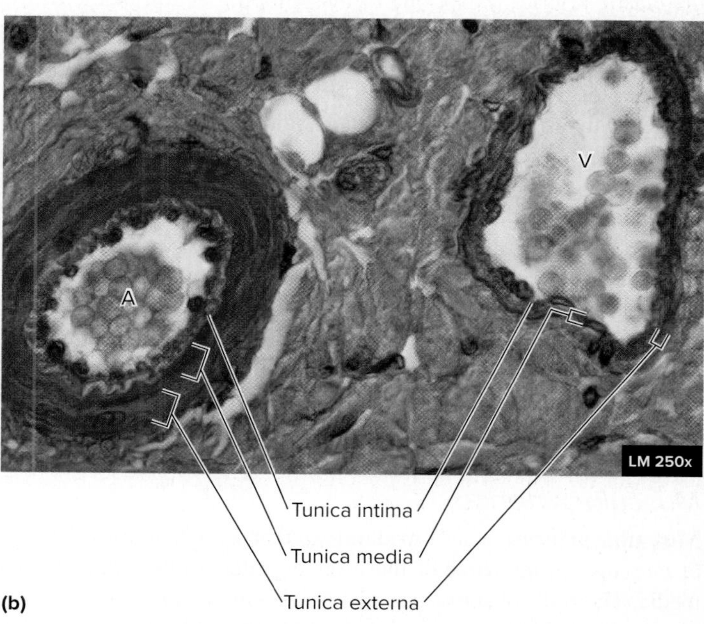

(b)

FIGURE 21.1 Histology of Blood Vessel Walls

(*a*) The layers, or tunics, of the blood vessel wall are the tunica intima, media, and externa. Vasa vasorum are blood vessels that supply blood to the wall of the blood vessel. (*b*) The typical structure of a medium-sized artery (A) and a vein (V). Note that the artery has a thicker wall than the vein. The predominant layer in the wall of the artery is the tunica media, with its circular layers of smooth muscle. The predominant layer in the wall of the vein is the tunica externa, and the tunica media is thinner than in the artery. Ed Reschke/Photolibrary/Getty Images APR

connective tissue that merges with the connective tissue surrounding the blood vessels.

The relative thickness and composition of each layer vary with the diameter of the blood vessel and its type. The transition from one vessel type to another is gradual, as are the structural changes. Figure 21.2 illustrates the major types of blood vessels, which are described below.

Types of Arteries

Arteries carry blood away from the heart. Although the arteries form a continuum from the largest to the smallest branches, they are normally classified as (1) elastic arteries, (2) muscular arteries, or (3) arterioles. The ventricles of the heart pump blood into large, elastic arteries that branch repeatedly to form many progressively smaller arteries. As they become smaller, the artery walls undergo a gradual transition from having a large amount of elastic tissue and a smaller amount of smooth muscle to having less elastic tissue and more smooth muscle. From these muscular arteries, blood flows into the arterioles, the smallest of the arteries. A more detailed description of the three types of arteries is provided below.

Elastic Arteries

Elastic arteries have the largest diameters (figure 21.2*a*) and are often called *conducting arteries*. Because these vessels are the first to receive blood from the heart, blood pressure is relatively high in the elastic arteries. Also, due to the pumping action of the heart, blood pressure in the elastic arteries fluctuates between higher systolic and lower diastolic values. When stretched, the walls of elastic arteries recoil, preventing drastic decreases in blood pressure. Elastic arteries have a greater amount of elastic tissue and a smaller amount of smooth muscle in their walls, compared with other arteries. The elastic fibers are responsible for the elastic characteristics of the blood vessel wall, but collagenous connective tissue determines the degree to which the arterial wall can stretch.

The tunica intima of elastic arteries is relatively thick. The elastic fibers of the internal and external elastic membranes merge and are not recognizable as distinct layers. The tunica media consists of a meshwork of elastic fibers with interspersed, circular smooth muscle fibers and some collagen fibers. The tunica externa is relatively thin.

Muscular Arteries

Muscular arteries include medium-sized and small arteries. The use of *muscular* in the name of these vessels refers to their thick tunica media. The walls of some muscular arteries are relatively thick, compared with their diameter, mainly because the tunica media contains 25–40 layers of smooth muscle (figure 21.2*b*). The tunica intima of the muscular arteries has a well-developed internal elastic membrane. The tunica externa is composed of a relatively thick layer of collagenous connective tissue that blends with the surrounding connective tissue. Muscular arteries are frequently called *distributing arteries* because the smooth muscle fibers allow them to partially regulate blood flow to different body regions by either constricting or dilating.

Smaller muscular arteries range from 40 μm to 300 μm in diameter. Those that are 40 μm in diameter have approximately three or four layers of smooth muscle in their tunica media, whereas arteries that are 300 μm across have essentially the same structure as the larger muscular arteries. The small muscular arteries are adapted for vasodilation and vasoconstriction.

Arterioles

Arterioles (ar-TEER-ee-ohlz) are the smallest arteries in which the three layers can be identified. They transport blood from small arteries to capillaries (figure 21.2*c;* see figure 21.4). They range in diameter from approximately 40 μm, which is less than half the thickness of a sheet of printer paper, to as small as 9 μm. The tunica intima has no observable internal elastic membrane, and the tunica media consists of one or two layers of circular smooth muscle fibers. Arterioles, like the small arteries, are capable of vasodilation and vasoconstriction.

ASSESS YOUR PROGRESS

3. *In which direction, relative to the heart, is blood carried by arteries and veins?*
4. *Name the three layers of a blood vessel wall. What kinds of tissue are in each layer?*
5. *List the types of arteries. Compare the amount of elastic fibers and smooth muscle in each type of artery.*

Capillaries

Blood flows from arterioles into **capillaries** (figure 21.2*d*), the most common type of blood vessel. Capillary walls are the thinnest of all blood vessels. Recall that one of the four layers of the tunica intima is an internal lining of simple squamous endothelial cells called the **endothelium** (en-doh-THEE-lee-um). In the vessels associated with the heart, this endothelial lining is continuous with the endocardium of the heart.

Most of the exchange that occurs between the blood and interstitial spaces occurs across the thin walls of capillaries. The capillary wall consists primarily of a single layer of endothelial cells (figure 21.2*d*) that rests on a basement membrane. Outside the basement membrane is a delicate layer of loose connective tissue that merges with the connective tissue surrounding the capillary.

Scattered along the length of the capillary are **pericapillary cells** closely associated with the endothelial cells. These scattered cells lie between the basement membrane and the endothelial cells and are fibroblasts, macrophages, or undifferentiated smooth muscle fibers.

Most capillaries range from 7 μm to 9 μm in diameter, and they branch without changing in diameter. Capillaries are variable in length, but in general they are approximately 1 mm long. Red blood cells flow through most capillaries single file and are frequently folded as they pass through the smaller-diameter capillaries.

Types of Capillaries

When comparing the many capillaries of the body, it becomes apparent that these vessels show variation in size and permeability, or the degree to which materials enter or leave the blood. Based on these characteristics, capillaries are classified as

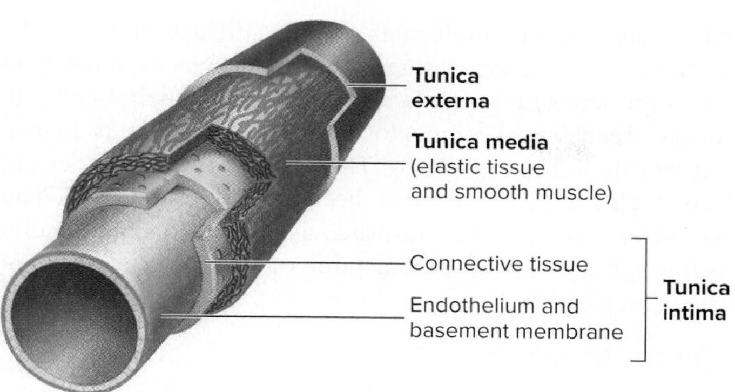

(a) Elastic arteries. The tunica media is mostly elastic connective tissue. Elastic arteries recoil when stretched, which prevents blood pressure from falling rapidly.

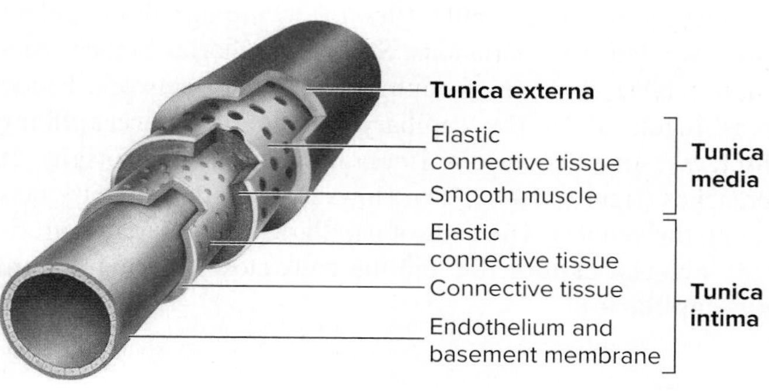

(b) Muscular arteries. The tunica media is a thick layer of smooth muscle. Muscular arteries regulate blood flow to different regions of the body.

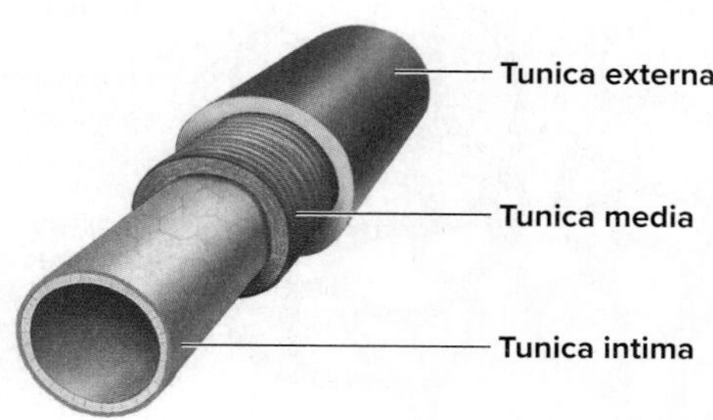

(c) Arterioles. All three tunics are present; the tunica media consists of only one or two layers of circular smooth muscle cells.

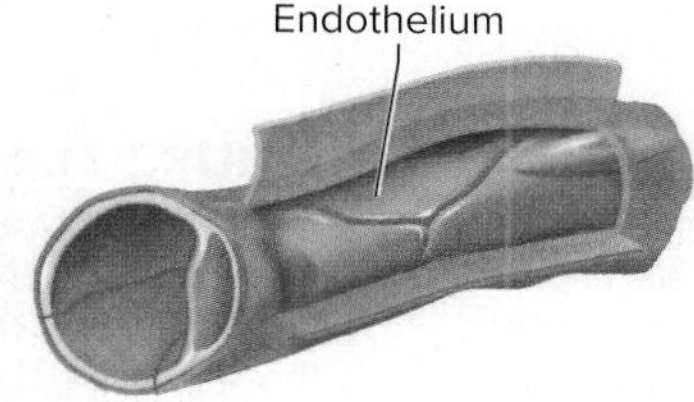

(d) Capillaries. Walls consist of only a simple endothelium surrounded by delicate loose connective tissue.

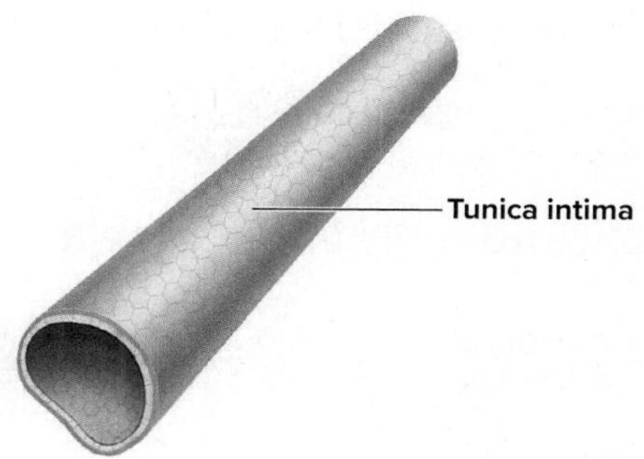

(e) Venules. Only the tunica intima resting on a delicate layer of dense connective tissue is present.

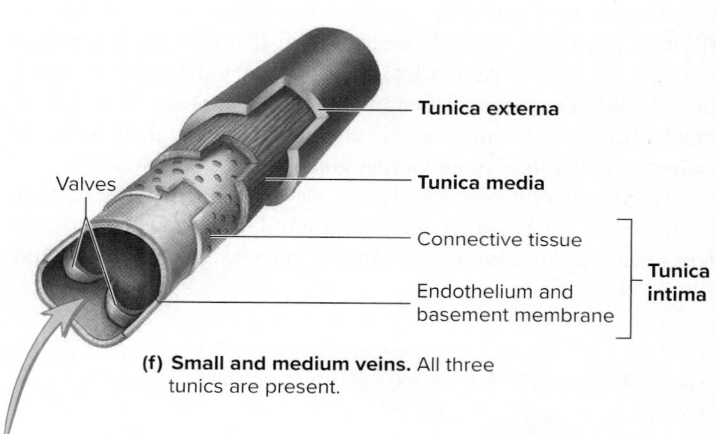

(f) Small and medium veins. All three tunics are present.

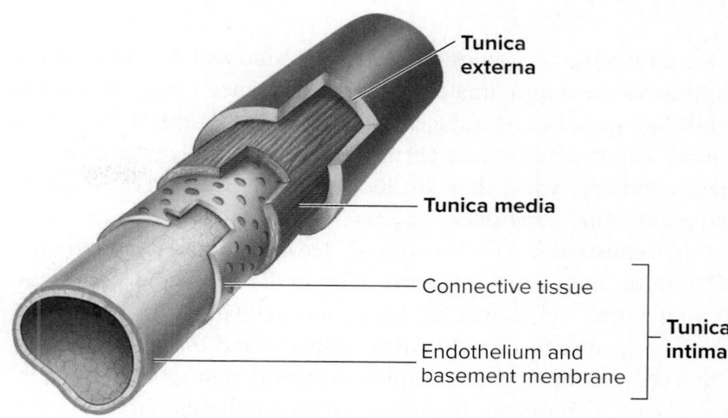

(g) Large veins. All three tunics are present. The tunica media is thin but can regulate vessel diameter because blood pressure in the venous system is low. The predominant layer is the tunica externa.

FIGURE 21.2 Structural Comparison of Blood Vessel Types

Blood vessels include different types of arteries, capillaries, and veins. This figure illustrates structural differences among these vessels. Blood vessel types, arranged as blood flows from the heart to the tissues and back to the heart, include (*a*) elastic arteries, (*b*) muscular arteries, (*c*) arterioles, (*d*) capillaries, (*e*) venules, (*f*) small and medium veins, and (*g*) large veins.

(1) continuous, (2) fenestrated, or (3) sinusoidal. **Continuous capillaries** are approximately 7–9 μm in diameter, and their walls exhibit no gaps between the endothelial cells (figure 21.3*a*). Continuous capillaries are less permeable to large molecules than are other capillary types; they are located in muscle, nervous tissue, and many other locations.

In **fenestrated** (FEN-es-TRAY-ted) **capillaries,** endothelial cells have numerous fenestrae (figure 21.3*b*). The **fenestrae** (feh-NES-tree; windows) are areas approximately 70–100 nm in diameter in which the cytoplasm is absent and the plasma membrane consists of a porous diaphragm that is thinner than the normal plasma membrane. In some capillaries, the diaphragm is not present. Fenestrated capillaries are in tissues where capillaries are highly permeable, such as the intestinal villi, ciliary processes of the eyes, choroid plexuses of the central nervous system, and glomeruli of the kidneys.

Sinusoidal (sigh-nuh-SOY-dal) **capillaries,** also called *sinusoids,* are larger in diameter than either continuous or fenestrated capillaries, and their basement membrane is less prominent (figure 21.3*c*) or completely absent. Their fenestrae are larger than those in fenestrated capillaries, and gaps can exist between endothelial cells. The sinusoidal capillaries occur in places where large molecules or, sometimes, whole cells move across their wall, for example, in the liver or endocrine glands.

Substances cross capillary walls by diffusing either (1) through or between the endothelial cells or (2) through fenestrae. Lipid-soluble substances, such as O_2 and CO_2, and small, water-soluble molecules readily diffuse through the endothelial cells. Larger water-soluble substances must pass through the fenestrae or gaps between the endothelial cells. In addition, transport by pinocytosis occurs, but little is known about its role in the capillaries. The walls of the capillaries are effective permeability barriers because red blood cells and large, water-soluble molecules, such as proteins, cannot readily pass through them, with the exception of some specialized capillaries described earlier.

Capillary Network

Capillaries do not exist individually in tissues but form branching networks. Arterioles supply blood to each capillary network (figure 21.4). Blood flows from arterioles to capillary networks through **metarterioles** (MET-ar-TEER-ee-ohlz), vessels with isolated smooth muscle fibers along their walls. Blood then flows from a metarteriole into a **thoroughfare channel,** a vessel within the capillary network that extends in a relatively direct fashion from a metarteriole to a venule. Blood flow through thoroughfare channels is relatively continuous. Several capillaries branch from the thoroughfare channels, forming the capillary network. Blood flow is regulated in the capillary branches by **precapillary sphincters,** smooth muscle fibers located at the origin of the branches (figure 21.4). Blood flows through the capillary network into the venules. The ends of capillaries closest to the arterioles are **arterial capillaries,** and the ends closest to venules are **venous capillaries.**

(a) Continuous capillary

(b) Fenestrated capillary

Fenestra with diaphragm

Fenestra without a diaphragm

(c) Sinusoidal capillary

Large fenestra

FIGURE 21.3 Structure of Capillary Walls

(*a*) Continuous capillaries have no gaps between endothelial cells and no fenestrae. (*b*) Fenestrated capillaries have fenestrae 7–100 nm in diameter, covered by thin, porous diaphragms, which are not present in some capillaries. (*c*) Sinusoidal capillaries have larger fenestrae without diaphragms and can have gaps between endothelial cells.

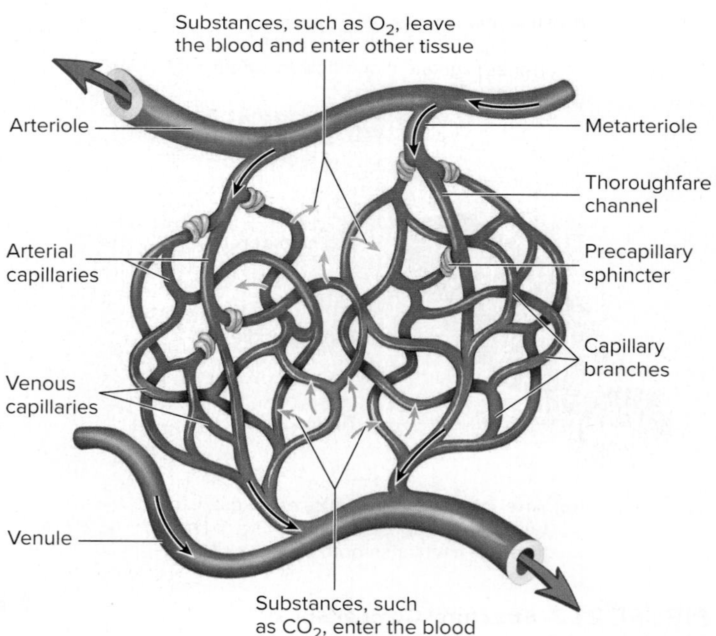

FIGURE 21.4 Capillary Network

A capillary network stems from an arteriole. Blood flows from the arteriole, through metarterioles, through the capillary network, to venules. Smooth muscle fibers, called precapillary sphincters, regulate blood flow through the capillaries. Blood flow decreases when the precapillary sphincters constrict and increases when they dilate. Exchange between the blood and other tissues occurs primarily at capillary networks.

Capillary networks are more numerous and more extensive in highly metabolic tissues, such as in the lungs, liver, kidneys, skeletal muscle, and cardiac muscle. Capillaries in the skin function in thermoregulation, and heat loss results from the flow of a large volume of blood through them. Capillary networks in the dermis of skin have many more thoroughfare channels than capillary networks in cardiac or skeletal muscle. The major function of the capillaries in these muscle tissues is nutrient and waste product exchange.

Arteriovenous Anastomoses

Arteriovenous anastomoses (ah-NAS-toh-MOH-seez) are specialized vascular connections that allow blood to flow directly from arterioles to small veins without passing through capillaries. A **glomus** (GLOH-mus; pl. glomera, GLOM-er-ah) is an arteriovenous anastomosis that consists of arterioles with abundant smooth muscle in their walls. The vessels are branched and coiled and are surrounded by connective tissue sheaths. Glomera are present in large numbers in the sole of the foot, the palm of the hand, the terminal phalanges, and the nail beds. The glomera help regulate body temperature by regulating blood flow through the hands and feet. As body temperature decreases, glomera constrict and less blood flows through them, reducing the rate of heat loss from the body. As body temperature increases, glomera dilate and more blood flows through them, increasing the rate of heat loss from the body. **Pathologic arteriovenous anastomoses** can form in areas of the body as a result of injury or tumors. These abnormal vascular connections allow for the direct flow of blood from arteries to veins. If they are sufficiently large, pathological arteriovenous anastomoses can lead to heart failure because of the tremendous increase in venous return to the heart.

ASSESS YOUR PROGRESS

6. *Describe the general structure of a capillary.*
7. *Compare the structure of the three types of capillaries. Explain the various ways that materials pass through capillary walls.*
8. *Describe a capillary network. Where is the smooth muscle that regulates blood flow into and through the capillary network located? What is the function of a thoroughfare channel?*
9. *Contrast the function of capillaries in the skin with the function of capillaries in muscle tissue.*
10. *Define* arteriovenous anastomosis *and* glomus, *and explain their functions.*

Types of Veins

From capillaries, blood flows into **veins,** vessels that carry blood toward the heart. When compared with arteries, the walls of veins are thinner. Vein walls also contain less elastic tissue and fewer smooth muscle fibers (see figure 21.1*b*). As the blood returns to the heart, it flows through veins with thicker walls and greater diameters. Veins are classified by size as (1) venules, (2) small veins, or (3) medium or large veins.

Venules and Small Veins

Venules (VEN-yools) are the smallest veins (figure 21.2*e*). Their structure is very similar to that of capillaries in that they are tubes composed of endothelium resting on a delicate basement membrane. Venules have diameters up to 50 μm. A few isolated smooth muscle fibers exist outside the endothelial cells, especially in the larger venules. As the vessels increase to 0.2–0.3 mm in diameter, the smooth muscle fibers form a continuous layer; the vessels are then called **small veins** (figure 21.2*f*). In addition to a larger diameter compared to venules, small veins also have a tunica externa composed of collagenous connective tissue.

The venules collect blood from the capillaries (figure 21.4) and transport it to small veins, which in turn transport it to medium veins. Nutrient exchange occurs across the venule walls, but, as the walls of the small veins increase in thickness, the degree of nutrient exchange decreases.

Medium and Large Veins

Most of the veins observed in gross anatomical dissections are **medium veins** and **large veins** (figure 21.2*f,g*). Medium veins collect blood from small veins and deliver it to large veins. The **large veins** transport blood from the medium veins to the heart. In medium and large veins, the tunica intima is thin and consists of endothelial cells, a relatively thin layer of collagenous connective tissue, and a few scattered elastic fibers. The tunica media is also thin and is composed of a thin layer of circularly arranged smooth muscle fibers containing some collagen fibers and a few sparsely distributed elastic fibers. The tunica externa, which is composed of collagenous connective tissue, is the predominant layer.

Portal Veins

In some areas of the body, a capillary network is directly connected to another capillary network by **portal** (POR-tal; door) **veins.** Specifically, portal veins begin in a primary capillary network, extend some distance, and end in a secondary capillary network. This connection is unique in that there is no pumping mechanism like the heart between the two capillary networks. Three portal vein systems are found in humans: (1) The hepatic portal veins carry blood from the capillaries in the gastrointestinal tract and spleen to dilated capillaries, called sinusoidal capillaries, in the liver (see figure 21.10); (2) the hypothalamo-hypophysial portal veins carry blood from the hypothalamus of the brain to the anterior pituitary gland (see chapter 18); and (3) the renal nephron portal systems are associated with the urine-forming structures of the kidneys (see chapter 26).

Valves

Veins that have diameters greater than 2 mm contain **valves,** which allow blood to flow toward the heart, but not in the opposite direction (see figure 21.2*f*). The valves consist of folds in the tunica intima that form two flaps shaped like the semilunar valves of the heart. The two folds overlap in the middle of the vein so that, when blood attempts to flow in a reverse direction, the valves occlude, or block, the vessel. Medium veins contain many valves,

Clinical IMPACT 21.1

Varicose Veins, Phlebitis, and Gangrene

The veins of the lower limbs are subject to certain disorders. **Varicose veins** result when the veins of the lower limbs are stretched to the point that the valves become incompetent. Because of the stretching of the vein walls, the flaps of the valves no longer overlap to prevent the backflow of blood. As a consequence, the venous pressure is greater than normal in the veins of the lower limbs, resulting in edema. Blood flow in the veins can become sufficiently stagnant that the blood clots. This condition can result in **phlebitis** (fleh-BIE-tis), which is inflammation of the veins. If the inflammation is severe and blood flow becomes stagnant in a large area, it can lead to **gangrene** (GANG-green), tissue death caused by a reduction in or loss of blood supply. Some people have a genetic propensity to develop varicose veins. The condition is further encouraged by activities that increase the pressure in the veins. One such condition is pregnancy, in which the venous pressure in the lower limbs increases because of compression by the expanded uterus. Also, standing in place for prolonged periods can lead to varicose veins.

and the number of valves is greater in veins of the lower limbs than in veins of the upper limbs.

Vasa Vasorum

For arteries and veins greater than 1 mm in diameter, nutrients cannot diffuse from the lumen of the vessel to all the layers of the wall. Therefore, nutrients are supplied to the blood vessel walls by way of small blood vessels called the **vasa vasorum** (VAY-sah vay-SOH-rum), which penetrate from the exterior of the vessel to form a capillary network in the tunica externa and the tunica media (see figure 21.1*a*).

ASSESS YOUR PROGRESS

11. *List the types of veins. Compare the vessel wall structure in each type of vein.*
12. *Describe portal veins. Name three examples.*
13. *In which type of blood vessels are valves found? What is their function?*
14. *What is the vasa vasorum? What is its function?*

Neural Innervation of Blood Vessels

The walls of most blood vessels are richly innervated by unmyelinated sympathetic nerve fibers (see figure 21.1*a*). Some blood vessels, such as those in the penis and clitoris, are innervated by parasympathetic fibers. Small arteries and arterioles are innervated to a greater extent than other blood vessel types. The nerve fibers branch to form plexuses in the tunica externa, and nerve terminals containing neurotransmitter vesicles project among the smooth muscle fibers of the tunica media. Synapses consist of several enlargements of each of the nerve fibers among the smooth muscle fibers. Sympathetic stimulation causes blood vessels to constrict; parasympathetic stimulation causes blood vessels in the penis and clitoris to dilate.

The smooth muscle fibers of blood vessels act to some extent in unison. Gap junctions exist between adjacent smooth muscle fibers; as a consequence, stimulation of a few smooth muscle fibers in the vessel wall results in constriction of a relatively large segment of the blood vessel.

A few myelinated sensory neurons innervate some blood vessels and function as baroreceptors. They monitor stretch in the blood vessel wall and detect changes in blood pressure.

ASSESS YOUR PROGRESS

15. *Describe the innervation of blood vessel walls. Which types of vessels have the most innervation?*

21.3 Pulmonary Circulation

LEARNING OUTCOME

After reading this section, you should be able to

A. **Trace the path of blood flow in pulmonary circulation.**

The **pulmonary** (PULL-moh-NAIR-ee; relating to the lungs) **circulation** is the system of blood vessels that carries blood from the right ventricle of the heart to the lungs and back to the left atrium of the heart. The heart pumps deoxygenated blood from the right ventricle into a short artery (about 5 cm long) called the **pulmonary trunk** (figure 21.5). The pulmonary trunk then branches into the right and left **pulmonary arteries,** transporting blood to the right lung and left lung, respectively. Within the lungs, gas exchange occurs between the air in the lungs and the blood. Two **pulmonary veins** exit each lung. All four of the pulmonary veins carry oxygenated blood to the left atrium (see figure 20.9).

ASSESS YOUR PROGRESS

16. *Name, in order, the vessels of pulmonary circulation, beginning with the right ventricle.*

21.4 Systemic Circulation: Arteries

LEARNING OUTCOME

After reading this section, you should be able to

A. **List the major arteries that supply each of the body areas.**

The **systemic circulation** is the system of vessels that carries blood from the left ventricle of the heart to the tissues of the body and back to the right atrium. Oxygenated blood entering the heart from the pulmonary veins passes through the left atrium into the left ventricle. The left ventricle pumps blood into the aorta. Blood flows from the aorta to all parts of the body (figure 21.5).

FUNDAMENTAL **Figure**

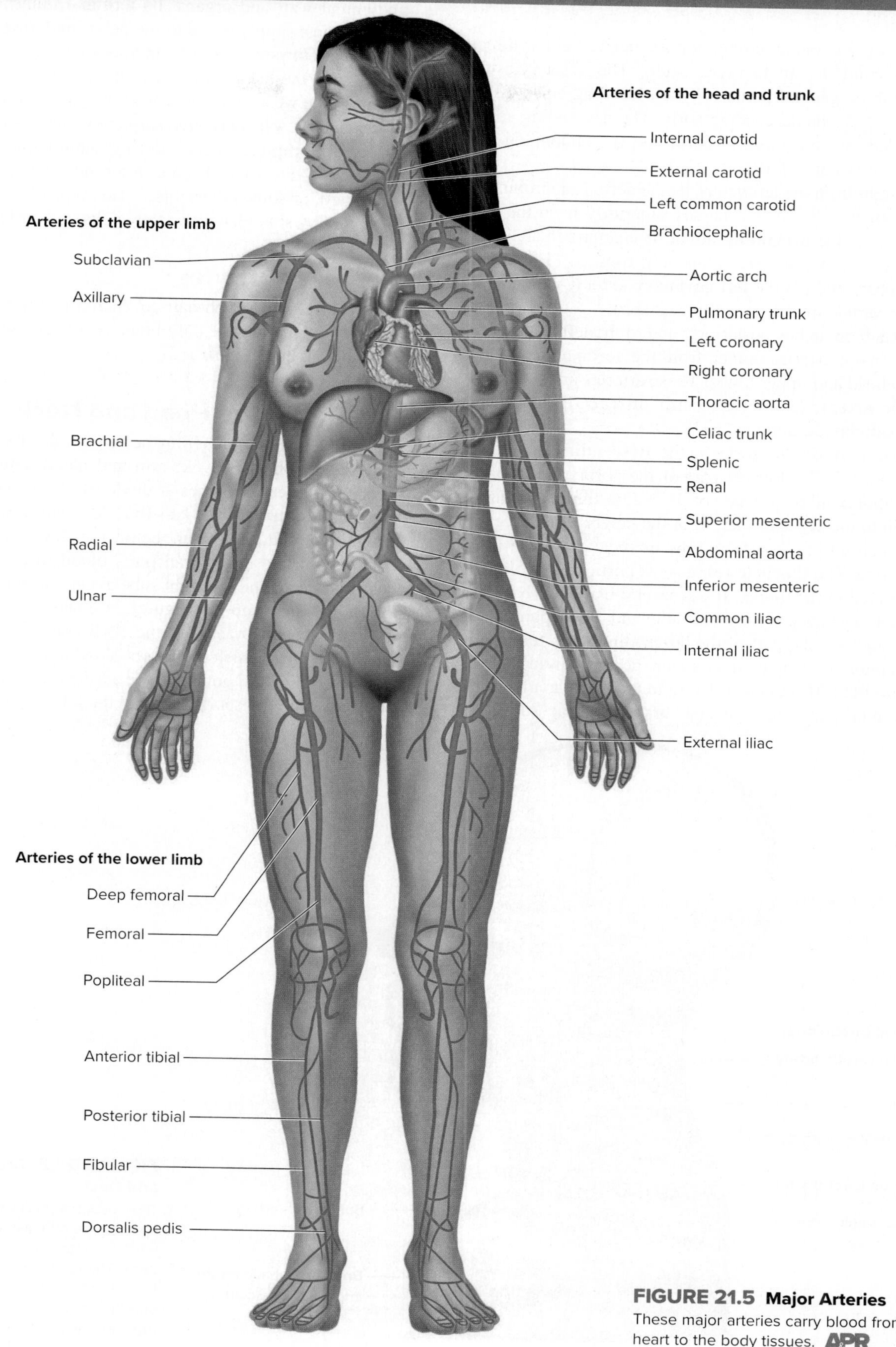

FIGURE 21.5 Major Arteries
These major arteries carry blood from the heart to the body tissues. APR

Aorta

All arteries of the systemic circulation are derived either directly or indirectly from the **aorta** (ay-OR-tuh). The aorta is usually divided into three general parts: (1) the ascending aorta, (2) the aortic arch, and (3) the descending aorta. The descending aorta is further divided into the thoracic aorta and the abdominal aorta (figure 21.5; see figure 21.10).

At its origin from the left ventricle, the aorta is approximately 2.8 cm in diameter. Because it passes superiorly from the heart, this part is called the **ascending aorta.** It is approximately 5 cm long and has only two arteries branching from it: (1) the **right coronary artery** and (2) the **left coronary artery,** which supply blood to the cardiac muscle (see figure 20.6*a*).

The aorta then arches posteriorly and to the left as the **aortic arch.** Three major arteries branch from the aortic arch and carry blood to the head and upper limbs. These arteries are (1) the **brachiocephalic artery,** (2) the **left common carotid artery,** and (3) the **left subclavian artery.**

The next part of the aorta is the **descending aorta.** The descending aorta is the longest part of the aorta, and it extends through the thorax in the left side of the mediastinum and through the abdomen to the superior margin of the pelvis. The descending aorta is divided into two parts: (1) the thoracic aorta and (2) the abdominal aorta. The **thoracic aorta** is the portion of the descending aorta located in the thorax. It has several branches that supply various structures between the aortic arch and the diaphragm. The **abdominal aorta** is the part of the descending aorta that extends from the diaphragm to the point at which the aorta divides into the two **common iliac** (IL-ee-ack; relating to the flank area) **arteries.** The abdominal aorta has several branches that supply the abdominal wall and organs. Its terminal branches, the common iliac arteries, supply blood to the pelvis and lower limbs.

An **aneurysm** (AN-you-rizm) is a weakened spot in the aortic wall. Once the aneurysm forms, it is likely to enlarge and may rupture. The weakened aortic wall may leak blood slowly into the thorax and must be corrected surgically. The majority of traumatic aortic arch ruptures occur during automobile accidents when the body is thrown with great force into the steering wheel, the dashboard, or some other object. This type of injury is effectively prevented by shoulder-type safety belts and air bags.

Coronary Arteries

The **coronary** (KOR-oh-nair-ee; encircling the heart like a crown) **arteries,** which are the only branches of the ascending aorta, are described in chapter 20.

Arteries of the Head and Neck

The first vessel to branch from the aortic arch is the **brachiocephalic** (BRAH-kee-oh-se-FAL-ik; arm and head) **artery** (figure 21.6). This short artery branches at the level of the clavicle to form the **right common carotid** (kah-ROT-id) **artery** and the **right subclavian** (sub-KLAY-vee-an; below the clavicle) **artery.** The right common carotid artery transports blood to the right side of the head and neck, and the right subclavian artery transports blood to the right upper limb (see figures 21.6 and 21.8).

The second branch of the aortic arch is the **left common carotid artery,** which transports blood to the left side of the head and neck. The third branch of the aortic arch is the **left subclavian artery,** which transports blood to the left upper limb.

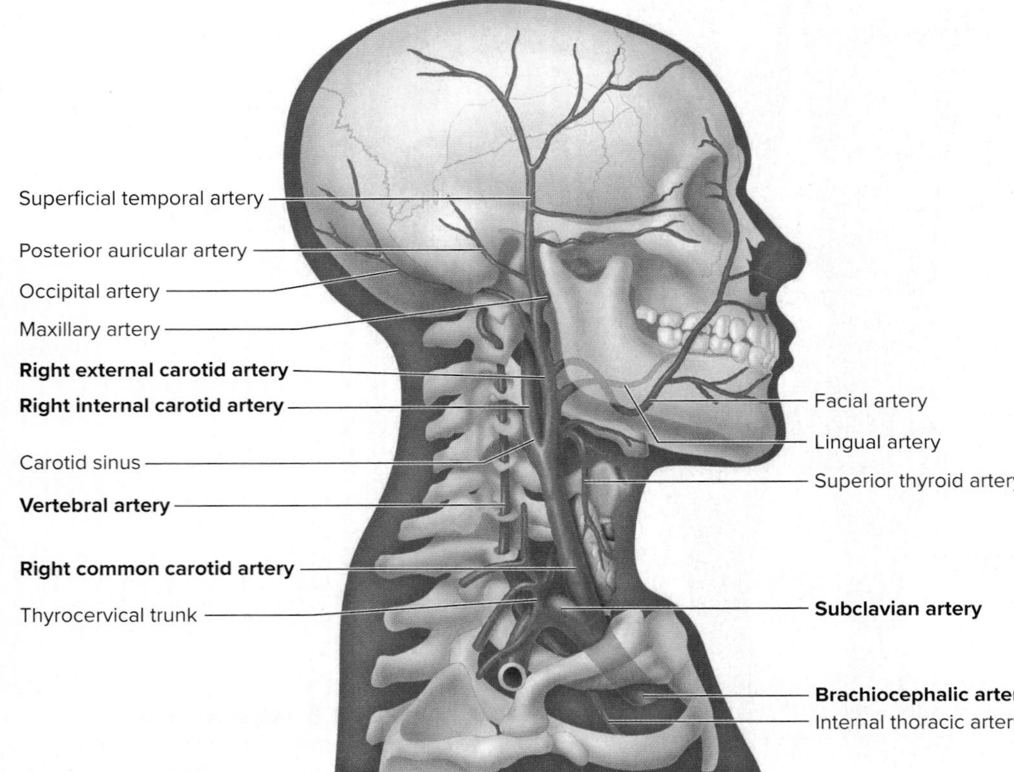

FIGURE 21.6 Arteries of the Head and Neck
The brachiocephalic artery, the right common carotid artery, and the right vertebral artery supply the head and neck. The right common carotid artery branches from the brachiocephalic artery, and the vertebral artery branches from the subclavian artery. APR

The common carotid arteries extend superiorly, without branching, along each side of the neck, from their base to the inferior angle of the mandible. At this point, each common carotid artery branches into **internal** and **external carotid arteries** (figure 21.6; see figure 21.8). At the point of bifurcation on each side of the neck, the common carotid artery and the base of the internal carotid artery are dilated slightly to form the **carotid sinus,** which is important in the baroreceptor reflex (described later in this chapter). The external carotid arteries have several branches that supply the structures of the neck and face (table 21.1; figure 21.6; see figure 21.8). The internal carotid arteries, together with the vertebral arteries, which are branches of the subclavian arteries, supply the brain (see figures 21.6, 21.7, and 21.8; table 21.1).

Apply

Predict 1

The term carotid *means "to put to sleep," implying that, if the carotid arteries are occluded for even a short time, the patient can lose consciousness (go to sleep). The blood supply to the brain is extremely important to brain function. Elimination of this supply for even a relatively short time can result in permanent brain damage because the brain is dependent on oxidative metabolism and quickly malfunctions in the absence of oxygen. What is the physiological significance of arteriosclerosis, which slowly reduces blood flow through the carotid arteries?*

The **left** and **right vertebral arteries** originate from the left and right subclavian arteries, respectively, and pass through the transverse foramina of the cervical vertebrae. They enter the cranial cavity through the foramen magnum. Within the cranial cavity, the left and right vertebral arteries both give off arteries to the cerebellum. The left and right vertebral arteries unite to form a single, midline **basilar** (BAS-ih-lar) **artery** (figures 21.7 and 21.8; table 21.1). The basilar artery gives off branches to the pons and the cerebellum. The left and right vertebral arteries branch to form the **posterior cerebral arteries,** which supply the posterior part of the cerebrum (see figure 21.7).

The internal carotid arteries enter the cranial cavity through the carotid canals and give off branches, including the **middle cerebral arteries** and the **anterior cerebral arteries.** The middle cerebral arteries supply large parts of the lateral cerebral cortex and the anterior cerebral arteries supply blood to the frontal lobes of the cerebrum (see figure 21.7). The two anterior cerebral arteries are connected to each other by an anterior communicating artery. The middle cerebral arteries connect to the posterior cerebral arteries by way of the **posterior communicating arteries.** These connections complete a circle around the pituitary gland and the base of the brain called the **cerebral arterial circle** (circle of Willis; see figures 21.7 and 21.8).

A **stroke** is a sudden neurological disorder, often caused by decreased blood supply to a part of the brain. It can occur as a result of a thrombosis, an embolism, or a hemorrhage. Any one

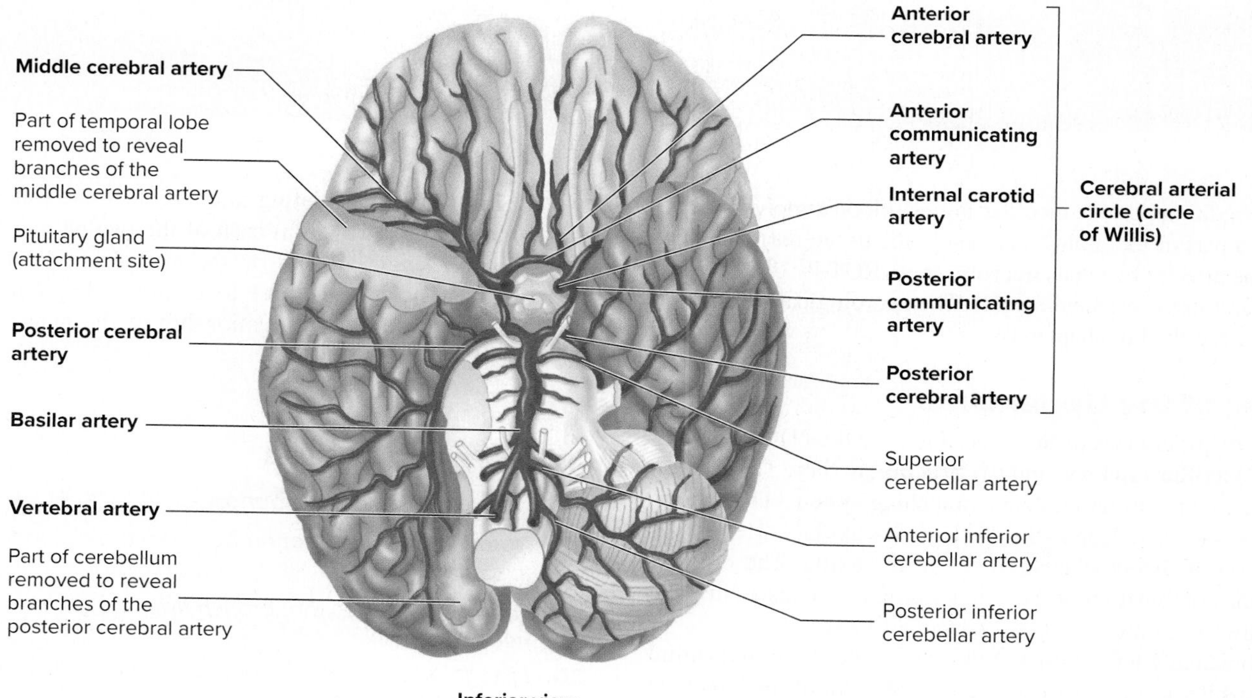

FIGURE 21.7 Cerebral Arterial Circle (Circle of Willis)

The internal carotid and vertebral arteries carry blood to the brain. The vertebral arteries join to form the basilar artery. Branches of the internal carotid arteries and the basilar artery supply blood to the brain and complete a circle of arteries around the pituitary gland and the base of the brain called the cerebral arterial circle (circle of Willis). APR

TABLE 21.1 **Arteries of the Head and Neck (figures 21.6, 21.7, and 21.8)**

Arteries	Tissues Supplied
Common Carotid Arteries	Head and neck by branches listed below
External Carotid	
Superior thyroid	Neck, larynx, and thyroid gland
Lingual	Tongue, mouth, and submandibular and sublingual glands
Facial	Mouth, pharynx, and face
Occipital	Posterior head and neck and meninges around posterior brain
Posterior auricular	Middle and inner ear, head, and neck
Ascending pharyngeal	Deep neck muscles, middle ear, pharynx, soft palate, and meninges around posterior brain
Superficial temporal	Temple, face, and anterior ear
Maxillary	Middle and inner ears, meninges, lower jaw and teeth, upper jaw and teeth, temple, external eye structures, face, palate, and nose
Internal Carotid	
Posterior communicating	Joins the posterior cerebral artery
Anterior cerebral	Anterior portions of the cerebrum; forms the anterior communicating arteries
Middle cerebral	Most of the lateral surface of the cerebrum
Vertebral Arteries (branches of the subclavian arteries)	
Anterior spinal	Anterior spinal cord
Posterior inferior cerebellar	Cerebellum and fourth ventricle
Basilar Artery (formed by junction of vertebral arteries)	
Anterior interior cerebellar	Cerebellum
Superior cerebellar	Cerebellum and midbrain
Posterior cerebral	Posterior portions of the cerebrum

of these conditions can reduce the brain's blood supply or cause trauma to a part of the brain. As a result, the tissue normally supplied by the arteries becomes **necrotic** (ne-KROT-ik; dead), forming an infarct in the affected area(s). The neurological results of a stroke are described in chapter 14.

Arteries of the Upper Limb

The three major arteries of the upper limb are the (1) **subclavian artery,** (2) **axillary artery,** and (3) **brachial artery.** These arteries form a continuum rather than a branching system. The subclavian artery is located deep to the clavicle. The axillary artery is the continuation of the subclavian artery in the axilla. The brachial artery is the continuation of the axillary artery as it passes into the arm (figure 21.9; table 21.2).

The brachial artery divides at the elbow into **ulnar** and **radial arteries,** which form two arches within the palm of the hand: (1) The **superficial palmar arch** is formed by the ulnar artery and is completed by anastomosing with the radial artery; and (2) the **deep palmar arch** is formed by the radial artery and is completed by anastomosing with the ulnar artery. This arch is not only deep to the superficial arch but proximal as well.

Digital (DIJ-i-tal; relating to the digits—the fingers and the thumb) **arteries** branch from each of the two palmar arches and unite to form single arteries on the medial and lateral sides of each digit. It may be helpful to create a diagram similar to figure 21.8 illustrating the relationship of the major arteries of the upper limb.

ASSESS YOUR PROGRESS

17. *Name the parts of the aorta.*

18. *Name the arteries that branch from the ascending aorta to supply the heart.*

19. *Name the arteries that branch from the aorta to supply the head and neck.*

20. *List the arteries that are part of, and branch from, the cerebral arterial circle.*

21. *Name the arteries that branch from the aorta to supply the upper limbs.*

22. *List, in order, the arteries that travel through the upper limb to the digits.*

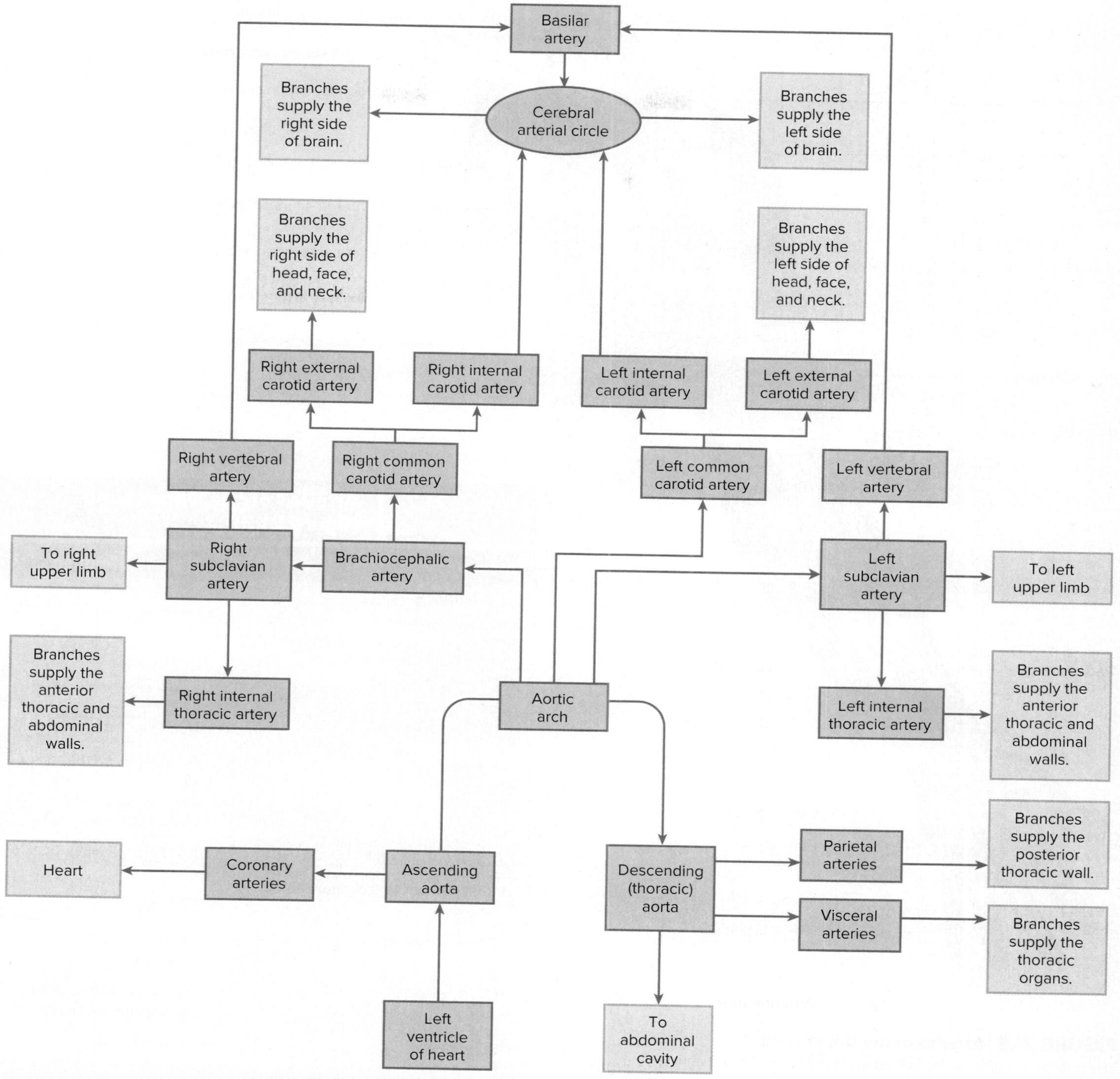

FIGURE 21.8 Major Arteries of the Head and Thorax
The relationships among the major arteries that supply blood to the structures of the head and thorax are illustrated in the diagram with red arrows indicating the direction of blood flow. Compare this diagram with the anatomical representations in figures 21.5, 21.6, and 21.7.

Thoracic Aorta and Its Branches

Recall that the descending aorta is divided into the thoracic aorta of the thoracic cavity and the abdominal aorta of the abdominal cavity. The branches of the thoracic aorta are divided into two groups: (1) the **visceral branches** supplying portions of the thoracic organs and (2) the **parietal branches** supplying portions of the thoracic wall (figure 21.10*a,b;* table 21.3). The visceral branches supply a portion of the lungs, including the bronchi and bronchioles (see chapter 23), as well as the esophagus and the pericardium. Even though a large quantity of blood flows to the lungs through the pulmonary arteries, the bronchi and bronchioles require a separate oxygenated blood supply through small bronchial branches from the thoracic aorta.

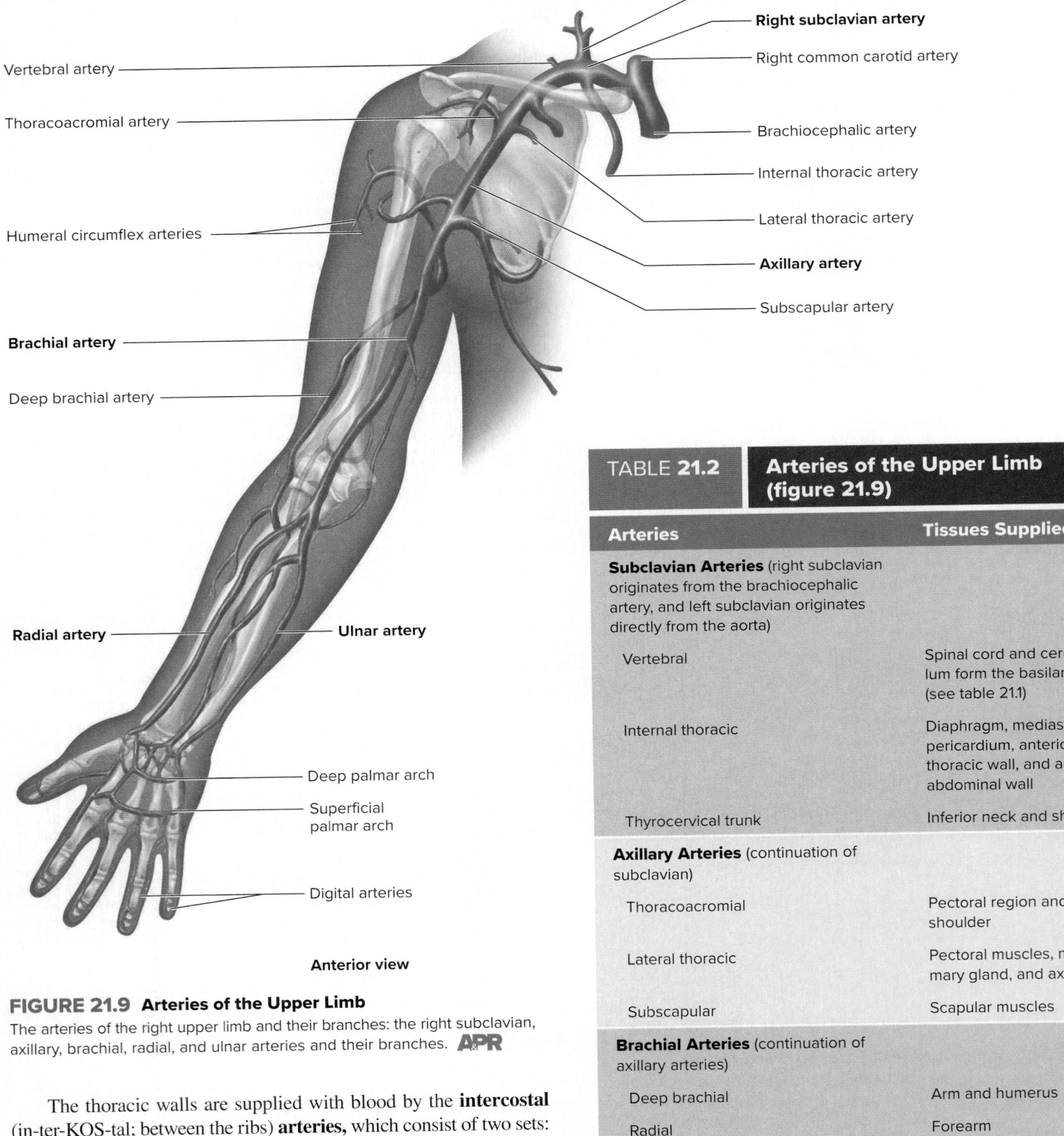

FIGURE 21.9 Arteries of the Upper Limb
The arteries of the right upper limb and their branches: the right subclavian, axillary, brachial, radial, and ulnar arteries and their branches. APR

The thoracic walls are supplied with blood by the **intercostal** (in-ter-KOS-tal; between the ribs) **arteries,** which consist of two sets:

1. The **anterior intercostals** are derived from the **internal thoracic arteries,** which are branches of the subclavian arteries. They lie on the inner surface of the anterior thoracic wall (figure 21.10*a,b;* table 21.3).
2. The **posterior intercostals** are parietal arteries that are derived as bilateral branches directly from the descending aorta. The anterior and posterior intercostal arteries lie along the inferior

TABLE 21.2 Arteries of the Upper Limb (figure 21.9)

Arteries	Tissues Supplied
Subclavian Arteries (right subclavian originates from the brachiocephalic artery, and left subclavian originates directly from the aorta)	
Vertebral	Spinal cord and cerebellum form the basilar artery (see table 21.1)
Internal thoracic	Diaphragm, mediastinum, pericardium, anterior thoracic wall, and anterior abdominal wall
Thyrocervical trunk	Inferior neck and shoulder
Axillary Arteries (continuation of subclavian)	
Thoracoacromial	Pectoral region and shoulder
Lateral thoracic	Pectoral muscles, mammary gland, and axilla
Subscapular	Scapular muscles
Brachial Arteries (continuation of axillary arteries)	
Deep brachial	Arm and humerus
Radial	Forearm
Deep palmar arch	Hand and fingers
Digital arteries	Fingers
Ulnar	Forearm
Superficial palmar arch	Hand and fingers
Digital arteries	Fingers

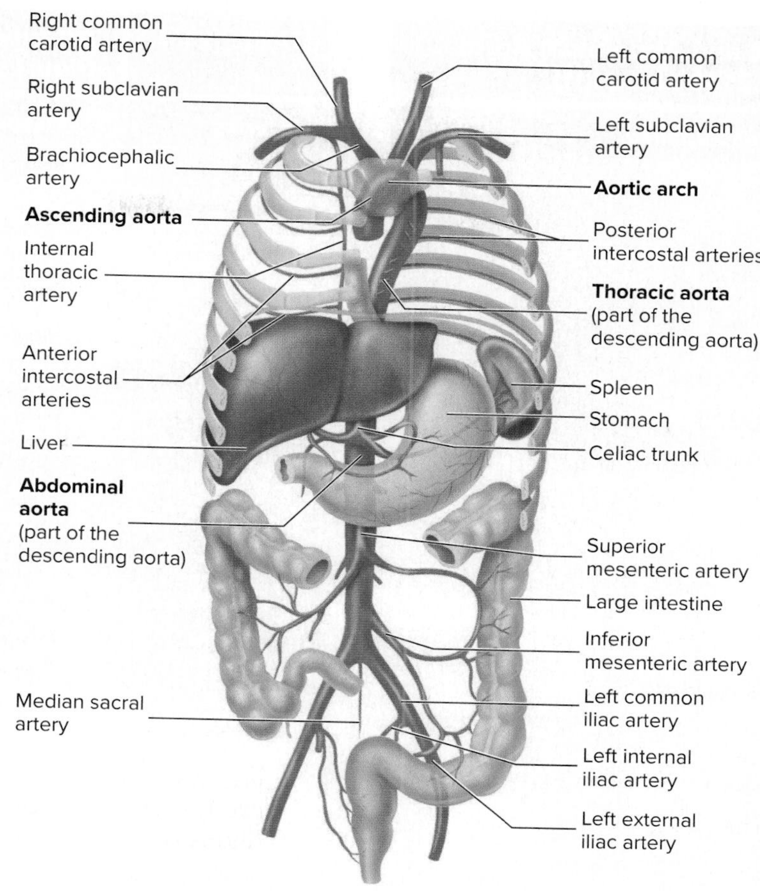

(a) Anterior view

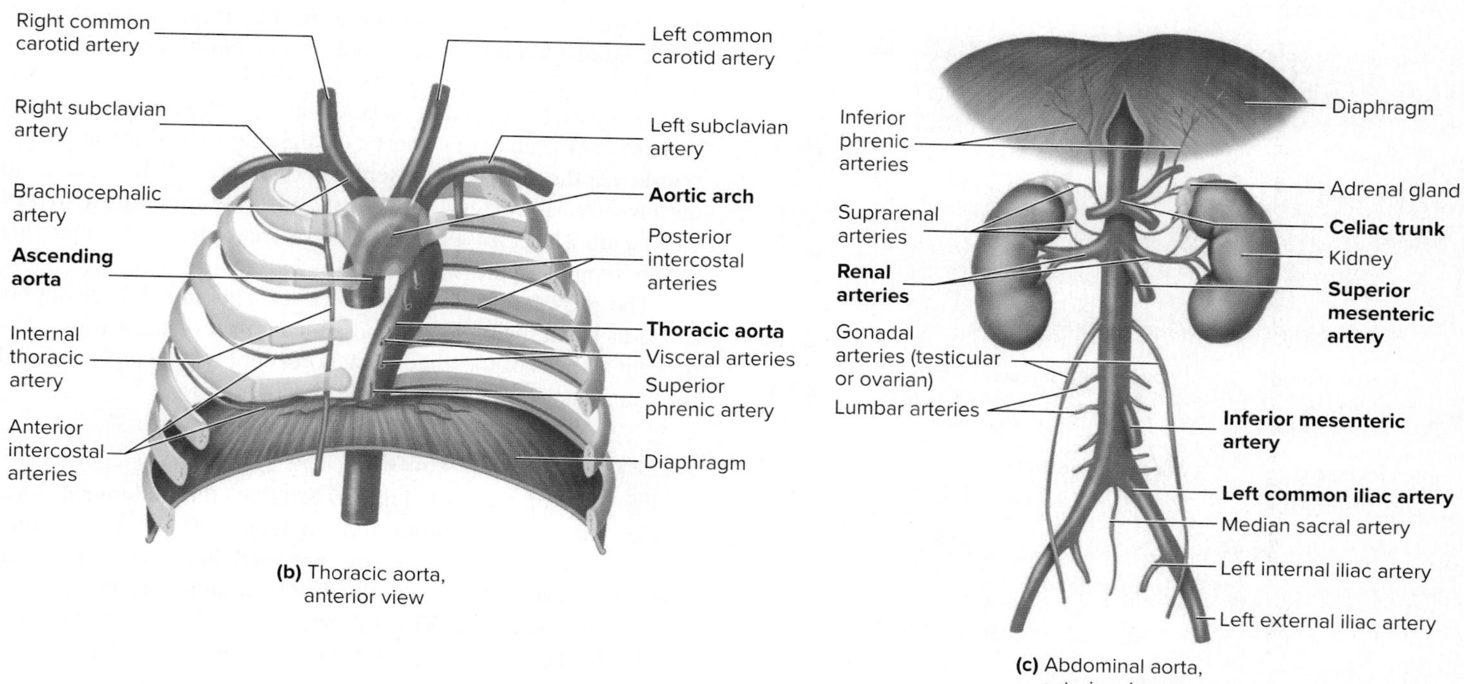

(b) Thoracic aorta, anterior view

(c) Abdominal aorta, anterior view

FIGURE 21.10 Branches of the Aorta

(*a*) The aorta is considered in three portions: the ascending aorta, the aortic arch, and the descending aorta. The descending aorta consists of the thoracic aorta and the abdominal aorta. (*b*) The thoracic aorta. (*c*) The abdominal aorta.

TABLE 21.3 Thoracic and Abdominal Aorta (figures 21.10 and 21.11)

Arteries	Tissues Supplied
Thoracic Aorta	
Visceral Branches	
Bronchial	Lung tissue
Esophageal	Esophagus
Parietal Branches	
Intercostal	Thoracic wall
Superior phrenic	Superior surface of diaphragm
Abdominal Aorta	
Visceral Branches	
Unpaired	
Celiac trunk	
Left gastric	Stomach and esophagus
Common hepatic	
Gastroduodenal	Stomach and duodenum
Right gastric	Stomach
Hepatic	Liver
Splenic	Spleen and pancreas
Left gastroepiploic	Stomach
Superior mesenteric	Pancreas, small intestine, and colon
Inferior mesenteric	Descending colon and rectum
Paired	
Suprarenal	Adrenal gland
Renal	Kidney
Gonadal	
Testicular (male)	Testis and ureter
Ovarian (female)	Ovary, ureter, and uterine tube
Parietal Branches	
Inferior phrenic	Adrenal gland and inferior surface of diaphragm
Lumbar	Lumbar vertebrae and back muscles
Median sacral	Inferior vertebrae
Common iliac	
External iliac	Lower limb (see table 21.5)
Internal iliac	Lower back, hip, pelvis, urinary bladder, vagina, uterus, rectum, and external genitalia (see table 21.4)

TABLE 21.4 Arteries of the Pelvis (figures 21.11 and 21.12)

Arteries	Tissues Supplied
Internal Iliac	Pelvis through the branches listed below
Visceral Branches	
Middle rectal	Rectum
Vaginal	Vagina and uterus
Uterine	Uterus, vagina, uterine tube, and ovary
Parietal Branches	
Lateral sacral	Sacrum
Superior gluteal	Muscles of the gluteal region
Obturator	Pubic region, deep groin muscles, and hip joint
Internal pudendal	Rectum, external genitalia, and floor of pelvis
Inferior gluteal	Inferior gluteal region, coccyx, and proximal thigh

margin of each rib and anastomose with each other approximately midway between the ends of the ribs. **Superior phrenic** (FREN-ik; to the diaphragm) **arteries** supply blood to the diaphragm.

Abdominal Aorta and Its Branches

The branches of the abdominal aorta, like those of the thoracic aorta, are divided into visceral and parietal parts (figures 21.10*a,c* and 21.11; table 21.3). The visceral arteries are in turn divided into paired and unpaired branches. There are three major unpaired branches of the abdominal aorta: (1) the **celiac** (SEE-lee-ak; belly) **trunk,** (2) the **superior mesenteric** (mez-en-TER-ik; relating to the mesenteries) **artery,** and (3) the **inferior mesenteric artery** (see figure 21.10*a,c*). Each has several major branches supplying the abdominal organs.

The paired visceral branches of the abdominal aorta supply the kidneys, adrenal glands, and gonads (testes and ovaries). The parietal arteries of the abdominal aorta supply the diaphragm and the abdominal wall (figure 21.11).

Arteries of the Pelvis

At the level of the fifth lumbar vertebra, the abdominal aorta divides into two **common iliac arteries.** The common iliac arteries then divide to form the **external iliac arteries,** which enter the lower limbs, and the **internal iliac arteries,** which supply the pelvic area. Visceral branches of the abdominal aorta supply the pelvic organs, such as the urinary bladder, rectum, uterus, and vagina. Parietal branches of the abdominal aorta supply blood to the walls and floor of the pelvis; the lumbar, gluteal, and proximal thigh muscles; and the external genitalia (figures 21.11 and 21.12; table 21.4).

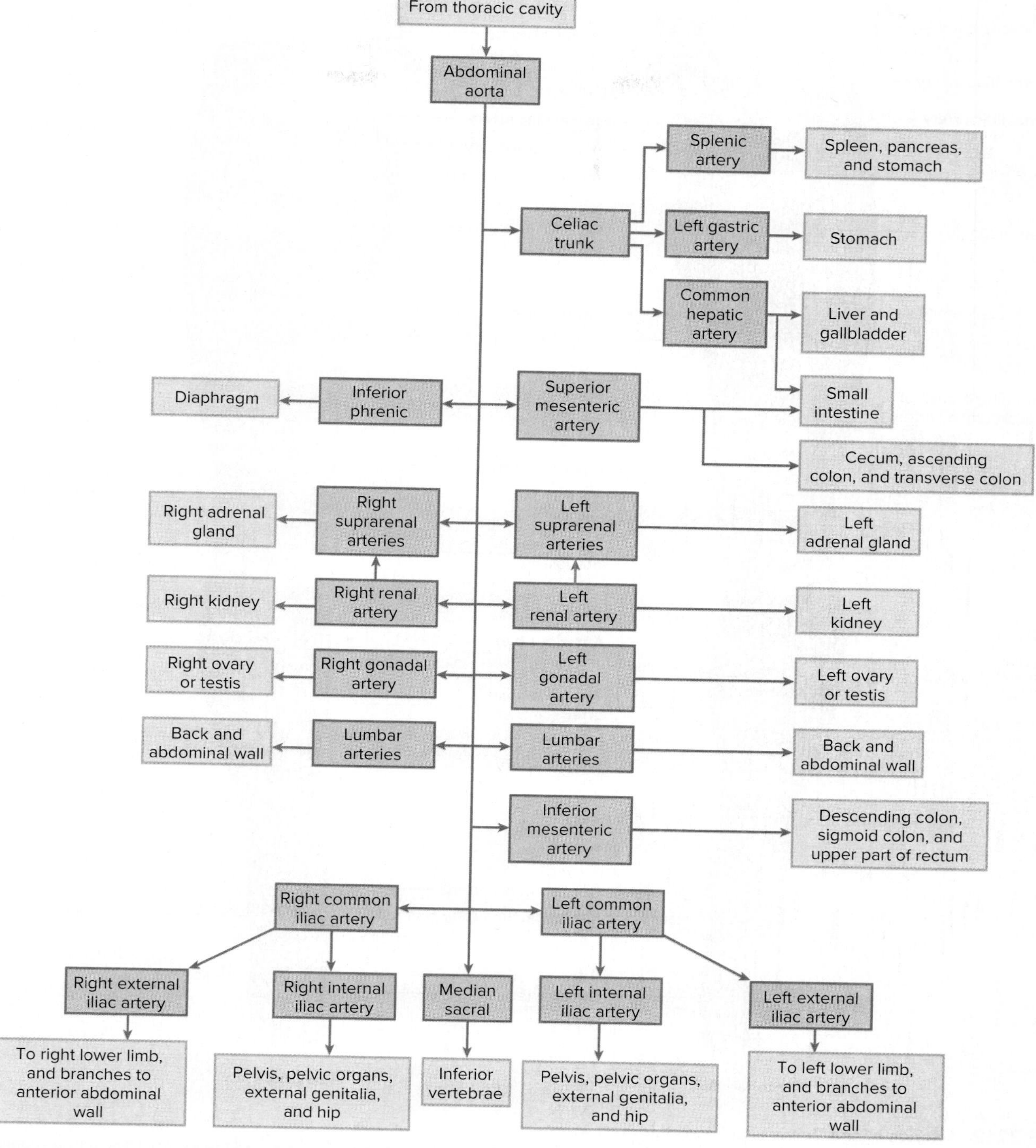

FIGURE 21.11 Major Arteries of the Abdomen and Pelvis

Visceral branches include those that are unpaired (celiac trunk, superior mesenteric, and inferior mesenteric) and those that are paired (renal, suprarenal, testicular, and ovarian). Parietal branches include inferior phrenic, lumbar, and median sacral. The relationships among the arteries of the abdomen and pelvis are illustrated in the diagram with red arrows indicating the direction of blood flow. Compare this diagram with the anatomical representation in figure 21.10*a,c*.

Arteries of the Lower Limb

The arteries of the lower limb form a continuum similar to that of the arteries of the upper limb. The **external iliac artery** becomes the **femoral** (FEM-o-ral; relating to the thigh) **artery** in the thigh, which becomes the **popliteal** (pop-LIT-ee-al; ham, the hamstring area posterior to the knee) **artery** in the popliteal space. The popliteal artery gives off the **anterior tibial artery** just inferior to the knee and then continues as the **posterior tibial artery.**

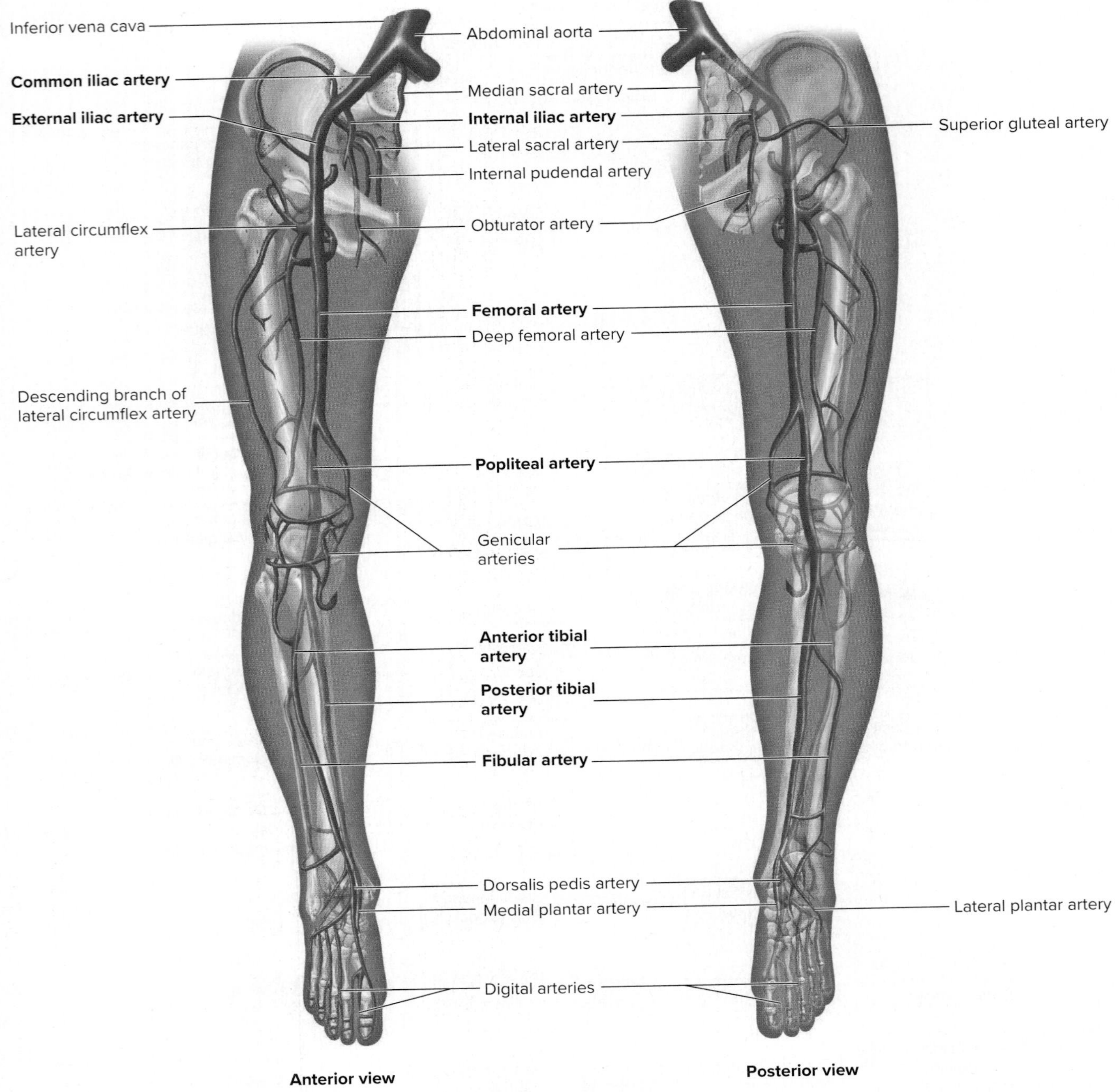

FIGURE 21.12 Arteries of the Pelvis and Lower Limb
The internal and external iliac arteries and their branches. The internal iliac artery supplies the pelvis and hip, and the external iliac artery supplies the lower limb through the femoral artery.

The anterior tibial artery becomes the **dorsalis pedis artery** at the foot. The posterior tibial artery gives off the **fibular artery,** or *peroneal artery,* and then gives rise to **medial** and **lateral plantar** (PLAN-tar; the sole of the foot) **arteries,** which in turn give off **digital branches** to the toes. The arteries of the lower limb are illustrated in figure 21.12 and are listed in table 21.5. It may be helpful to create a diagram similar to figure 21.11 illustrating the relationship of the major arteries of the lower limb.

TABLE 21.5	Arteries of the Lower Limb (figure 21.12)
Arteries	**Tissues Supplied**
Femoral	Thigh, external genitalia, and anterior abdominal wall
Deep femoral	Thigh, knee, and femur
Popliteal (continuation of the femoral artery)	
Posterior tibial	Knee and leg
Fibular (peroneal)	Calf and peroneal muscles and ankle
Medial plantar	Plantar region of foot
Digital	Digits of foot
Lateral plantar	Plantar region of foot
Digital	Digits of foot
Anterior tibial	Knee and leg
Dorsalis pedis	Dorsum of foot
Digital	Digits of foot

ASSESS YOUR PROGRESS

23. *Name the two types of branches arising from the thoracic aorta. What structures are supplied from each group?*
24. *What areas of the body are supplied by the paired arteries that branch from the abdominal aorta? The unpaired arteries? Name the three major unpaired arteries.*
25. *Name the arteries that branch from the aorta to supply the pelvic area. List the organs of the pelvis that are supplied by branches of these arteries.*
26. *List, in order, the arteries that travel from the aorta to the digits of the lower limbs.*

21.5 Systemic Circulation: Veins

LEARNING OUTCOME

After reading this section, you should be able to

A. **List the major veins that carry blood away from each of the body areas.**

Deoxygenated blood from the body is returned to the right atrium through three major veins: (1) the **coronary sinus,** returning blood from the walls of the heart (see figures 20.6*b* and 20.7); (2) the **superior vena cava** (VEE-nah KAY-vah; venous cave), returning blood from the head, neck, thorax, and upper limbs; and (3) the **inferior vena cava,** returning blood from the abdomen, pelvis, and lower limbs (figure 21.13).

In a very general way, the smaller veins follow the same course as the arteries, and many are given the same names. The veins, however, are more numerous and more variable. The larger veins often follow a very different course and have names different from the arteries.

Earlier in the chapter, we categorized veins based on size as venules, small veins, medium veins, and large veins. When describing the specific veins of the body, we often categorize veins based on location. In that situation, there are three major types of veins: (1) superficial veins, (2) deep veins, and (3) sinuses. In general, the superficial veins of the limbs are larger than the deep veins, whereas in the head and trunk the opposite is the case. Venous sinuses occur primarily in the cranial cavity and the heart.

Veins Draining the Heart

The **cardiac veins** transport blood from the walls of the heart and return it through the coronary sinus to the right atrium. A detailed description of the cardiac veins is found in chapter 20.

Veins of the Head and Neck

The two pairs of major veins that drain blood from the head and neck are (1) the **external jugular** (JUG-you-lar; neck) **veins** and (2) the **internal jugular veins.** The external jugular veins are the more superficial of the two sets, and they drain blood primarily from the posterior head and neck. The external jugular vein drains into the subclavian vein. The internal jugular veins are much larger and deeper than the external jugular veins. The internal jugular veins drain blood from the cranial cavity and the anterior head, face, and neck.

The internal jugular vein is formed primarily as the continuation of the **venous sinuses** of the cranial cavity. The venous sinuses are actually spaces within the dura mater surrounding the brain (see chapter 13). They are depicted in figure 21.14 and listed in table 21.6.

Once the internal jugular veins exit the cranial cavity, they receive several venous tributaries that drain the external head and face (figures 21.14 and 21.15; table 21.7). On each side of the body the internal jugular veins merge with the **subclavian veins** to form the **brachiocephalic veins.** Note that there is a single brachiocephalic *artery* (see figure 21.5) and two brachiocephalic *veins.*

Veins of the Upper Limb

The **cephalic** (se-FAL-ik; toward the head), **basilic** (ba-SIL-ik), and **brachial veins** are responsible for draining most of the blood from the upper limbs (figure 21.17; table 21.8). Many of the tributaries of the cephalic and basilic veins in the forearm and hand can be seen through the skin. Because of the considerable variation in

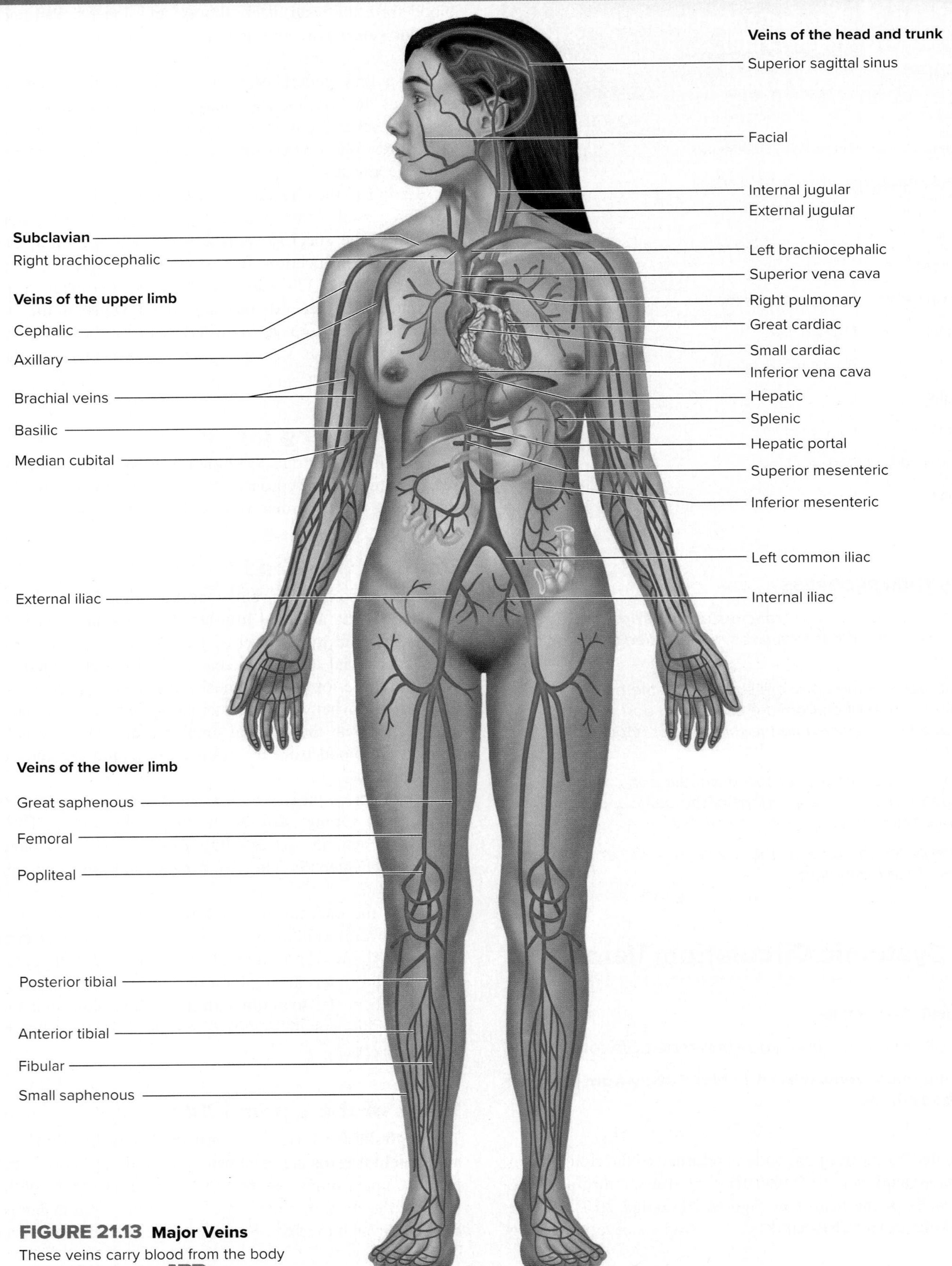

FIGURE 21.13 Major Veins
These veins carry blood from the body tissues to the heart. APR

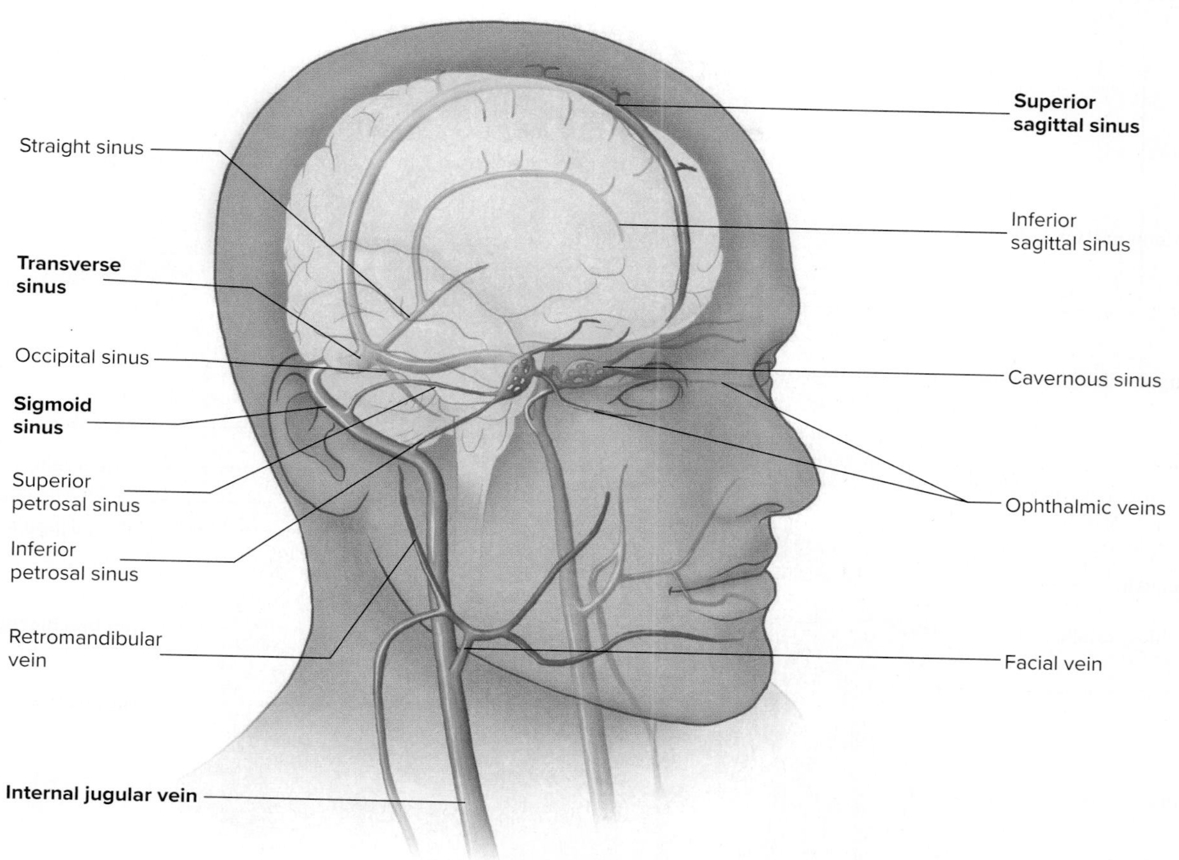

FIGURE 21.14 Venous Sinuses Associated with the Brain
The venous sinuses of the brain are drainage channels formed from the dura mater. These sinuses transport venous blood and cerebrospinal fluid away from the brain. The venous sinuses empty into the internal jugular veins.

TABLE 21.6 Venous Sinuses of the Cranial Cavity (figure 21.14)

Veins	Tissues Drained
Internal Jugular Vein	
Sigmoid sinus	
Superior and inferior petrosal sinuses	Anterior portion of cranial cavity
Cavernous sinus	
Ophthalmic veins	Orbit
Transverse sinus	
Occipital sinus	Central floor of posterior fossa of skull
Superior sagittal sinus	Superior portion of cranial cavity and brain
Straight sinus	
Inferior sagittal sinus	Deep portion of longitudinal fissure

the tributary veins of the forearm and hand, they often are left unnamed. The basilic vein of the arm becomes the **axillary vein** as it passes through the axillary region. The cephalic vein empties into the axillary vein and then becomes the **subclavian vein** at the margin of the first rib.

The **median cubital** (KYOO-bi-tal; pertaining to the elbow) **vein** is a variable vein that usually connects the cephalic vein or its tributaries with the basilic vein. In many people, this vein is quite prominent on the anterior surface of the upper limb at the level of the elbow (cubital fossa); therefore, it is often used as a site for drawing blood from a patient.

The deep veins draining the upper limb follow the same course as the arteries. Thus, the **radial** and **ulnar veins** are named for the arteries they accompany. They are usually paired, with one small vein lying on each side of the artery, and they have numerous connections with one another and with the superficial veins. The radial and ulnar veins empty into the **brachial veins,** which accompany the brachial artery and empty into the axillary vein (see figure 21.14). It may be helpful to create a diagram similar to figure 21.16 illustrating the relationship of the major veins of the upper limb.

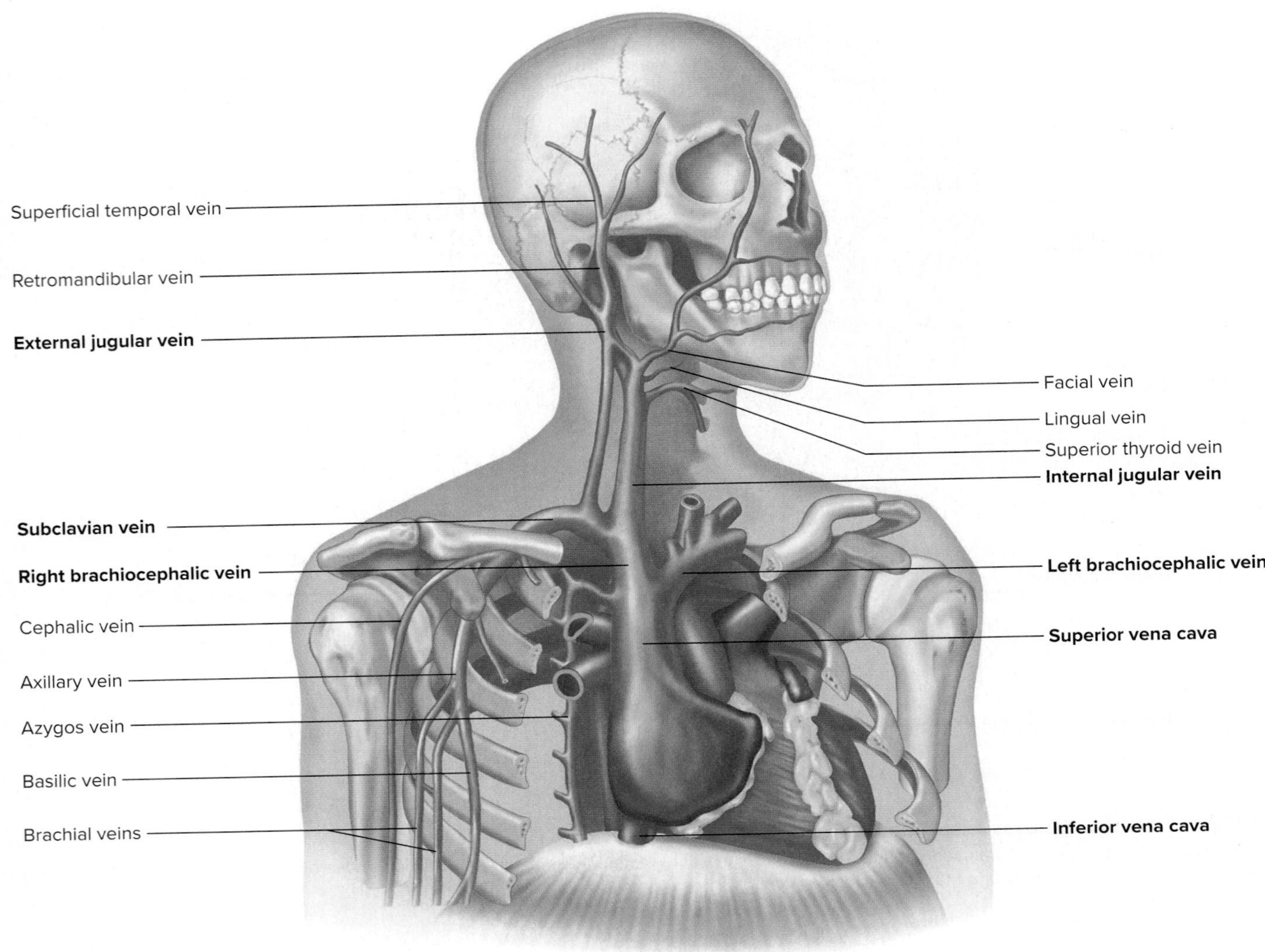

FIGURE 21.15 Veins of the Head and Neck
The right brachiocephalic vein and its tributaries. The major veins draining the head and neck are the internal and external jugular veins. APR

TABLE 21.7 Veins Draining the Head and Neck (figures 21.15 and 21.16)

Veins	Tissues Drained
Brachiocephalic	
Internal jugular	Brain
Lingual	Tongue and mouth
Superior thyroid	Thyroid and deep posterior facial structures (also empties into external jugular)
Facial	Superficial and anterior facial structures
External jugular	Superficial surface of posterior head and neck

Veins of the Thorax

Three major veins return blood from the thorax to the superior vena cava: (1) the right brachiocephalic vein, (2) the left brachiocephalic vein, and (3) the **azygos** (AZ-eye-gos; unpaired) **vein.** The thoracic drainage to the brachiocephalic veins is through the anterior thoracic wall by way of the **internal thoracic veins.** They receive blood from the **anterior intercostal veins.** Blood from the posterior thoracic wall is collected by **posterior intercostal veins** that drain into the azygos vein on the right side of the thorax and the **hemiazygos** (HEM-ee-AZ-eye-gos) **vein** or the **accessory hemiazygos vein** on the left side of the thorax. The hemiazygos and accessory hemiazygos veins empty into the azygos vein, which drains into the superior vena cava. The thoracic veins are listed in table 21.9 and illustrated in figure 21.18 (also see figure 21.16).

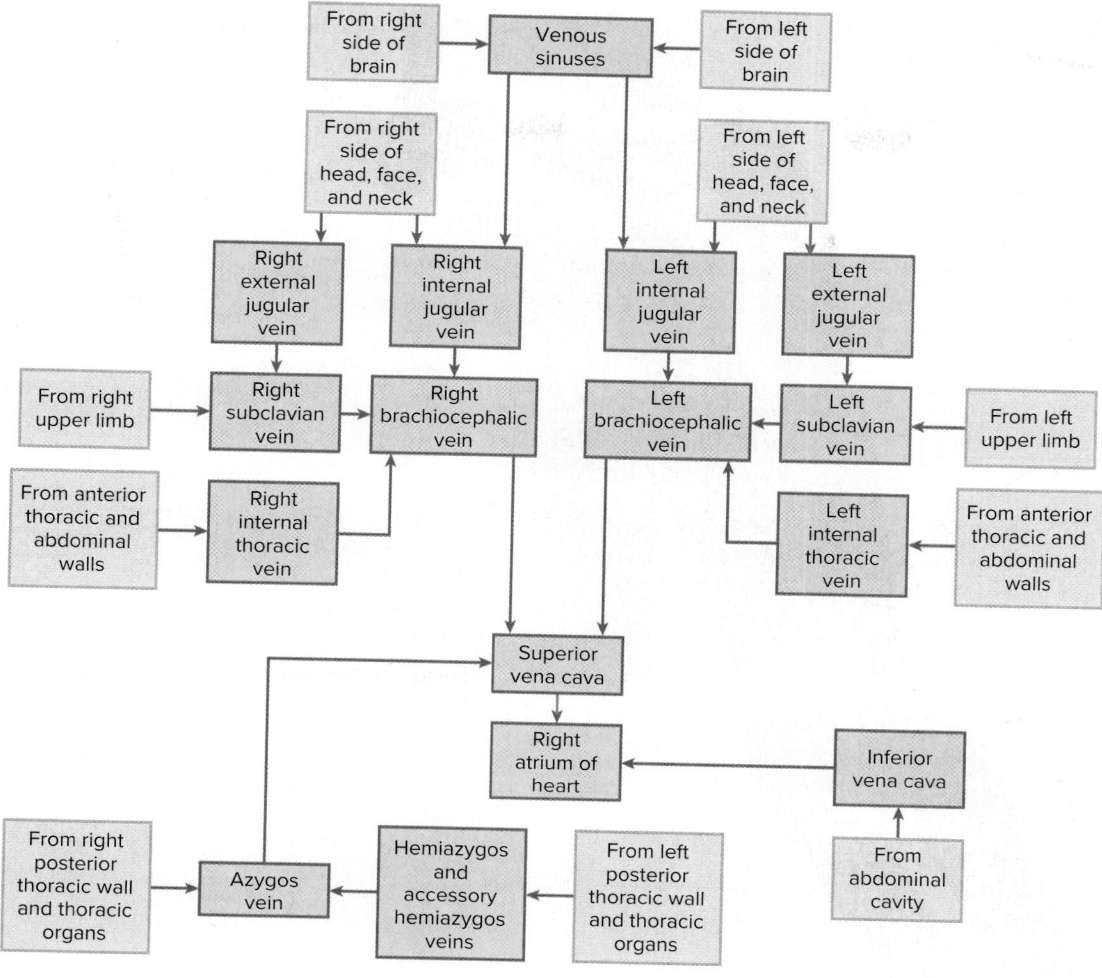

FIGURE 21.16 Major Veins of the Head and Thorax
The relationships among the major veins of the head and thorax are illustrated in the diagram with blue arrows indicating the direction of blood flow. Compare this diagram with the anatomical representation in figures 21.13, 21.14, 21.15, and 21.18.

TABLE 21.8 Veins of the Upper Limb (figure 21.17)

Veins	Tissues Drained
Subclavian (continuation of the axillary vein)	
Axillary (continuation of the basilic vein)	
Cephalic	Lateral arm, forearm, and hand (superficial veins of the forearm and hand are variable)
Brachial (paired, deep veins)	Deep structures of the arm
Radial	Deep forearm
Ulnar	Deep forearm
Basilic	Medial arm, forearm, and hand (superficial veins of the forearm and hand are variable)
Median cubital	Connects basilic and cephalic veins
Deep and superficial palmar venous arches	Drain into superficial and deep veins of the forearm
Digital	Fingers

ASSESS YOUR PROGRESS

27. *What are the three major veins that return blood to the right atrium?*
28. *What veins collect blood from the heart muscle?*
29. *List the two pairs of major veins that drain blood from the head and neck. Describe venous sinuses. To what large vein do the venous sinuses connect?*
30. *List the major deep and superficial veins of the upper limb.*
31. *List the three major veins that return blood from the thorax to the superior vena cava.*

Veins of the Abdomen and Pelvis

Blood from the posterior abdominal wall drains into the **ascending lumbar veins.** These veins are continuous superiorly with the hemiazygos on the left and the azygos on the right. Blood from the rest of the abdomen, pelvis, and lower limbs returns to the heart through the inferior vena cava. The gonads (testes and ovaries), kidneys, and adrenal glands are the only abdominal organs outside the pelvis that drain directly into the inferior vena cava. The

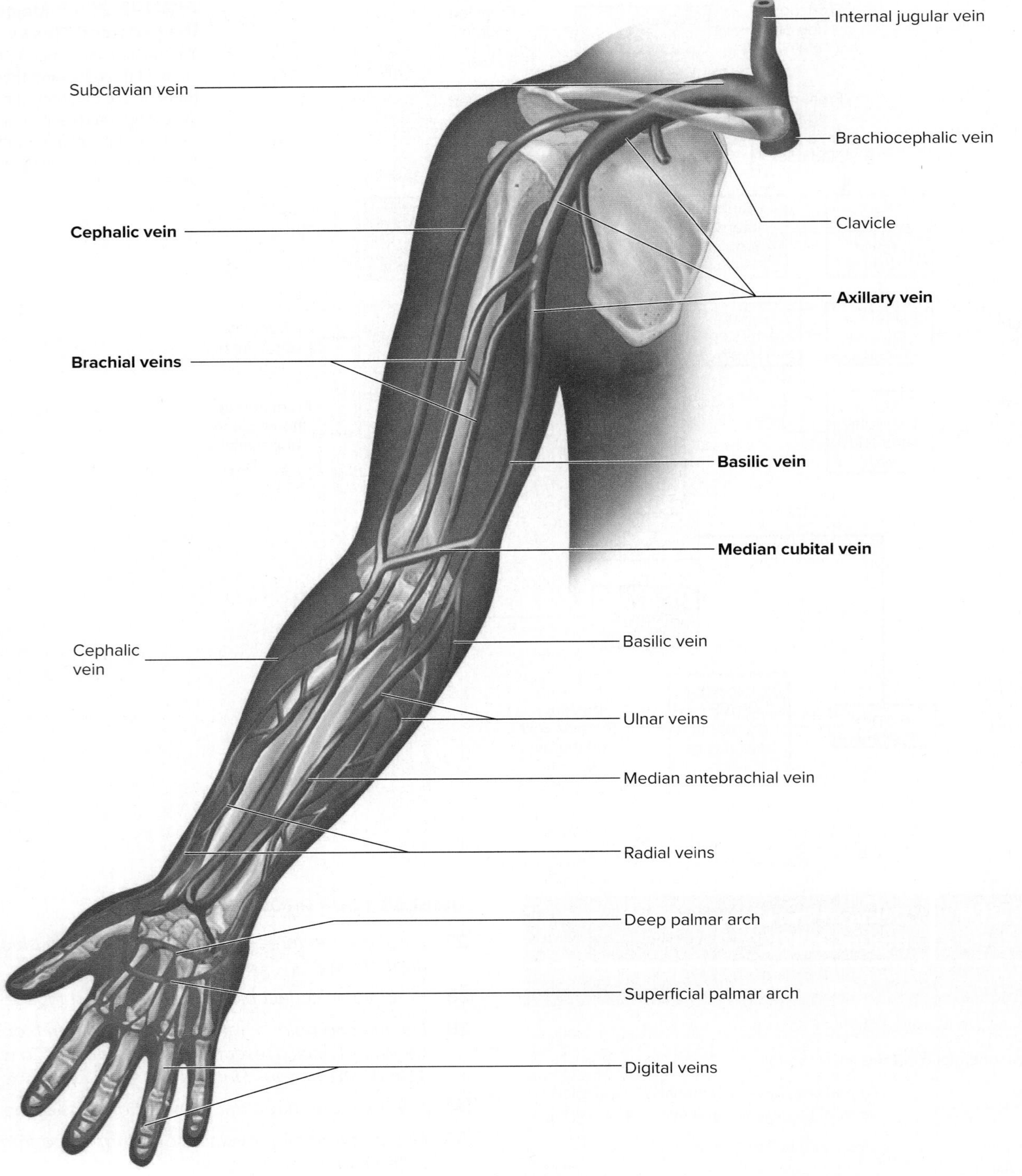

FIGURE 21.17 Veins of the Upper Limb

The subclavian vein and its tributaries. The major veins draining the superficial structures of the limb are the cephalic and basilic veins. The brachial veins drain the deep structures.

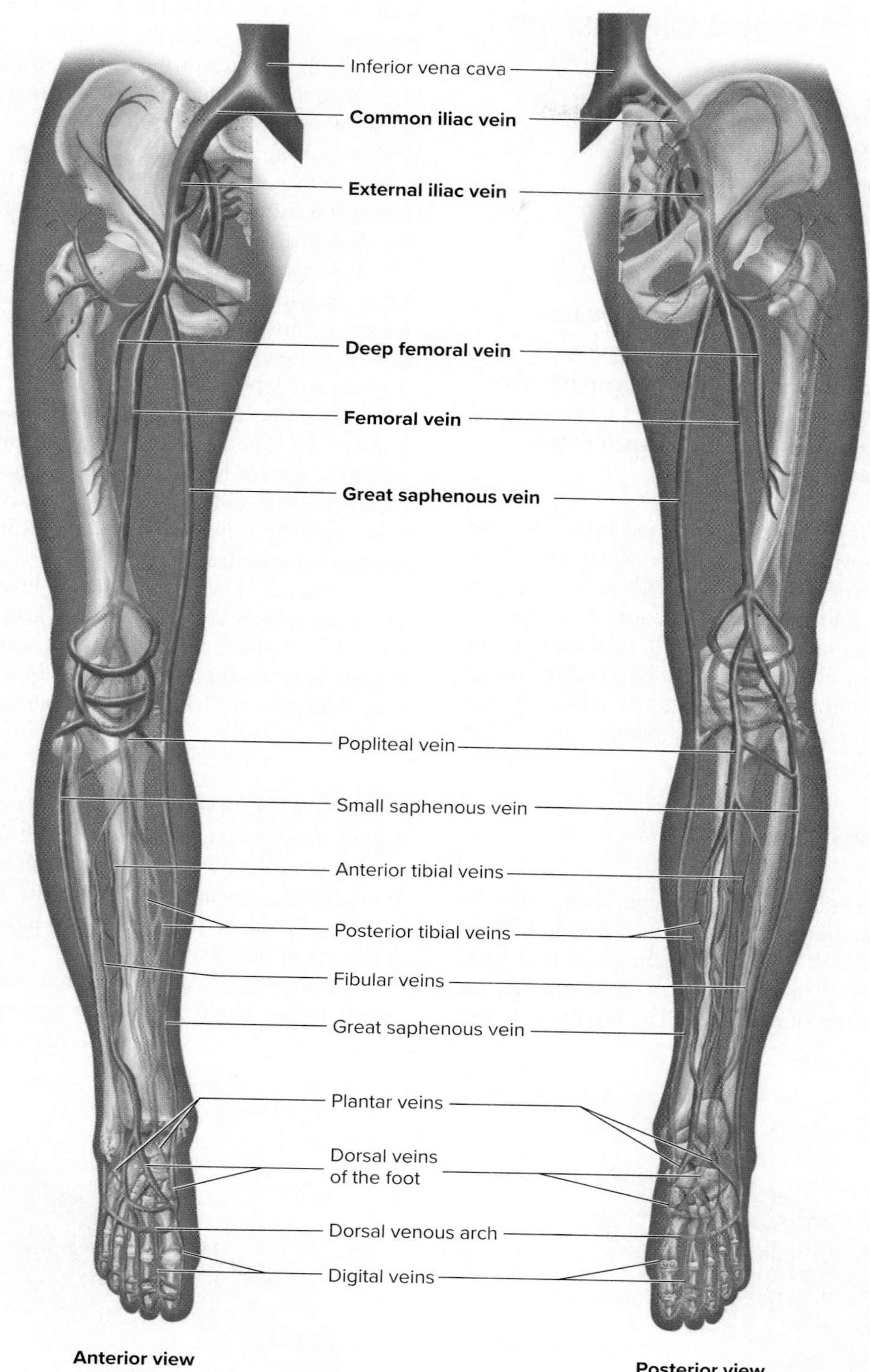

FIGURE 21.22 Veins of the Pelvis and Lower Limb
The right common iliac vein and its tributaries. APR

21.6 Dynamics of Blood Circulation

LEARNING OUTCOMES

After reading this section, you should be able to

A. **Compare laminar and turbulent blood flow.**
B. **Define *blood pressure*.**
C. **Explain how blood pressure is measured.**
D. **Summarize Poiseuille's law.**
E. **Describe the relationship of viscosity to blood flow.**
F. **Relate Laplace's law to critical closing pressure.**
G. **Explain how vessel diameter and vascular compliance affect blood pressure.**
H. **List the percent distribution of blood in each of the systemic vessel types.**

The dynamics of blood circulating through blood vessels are the same as those of water flowing through pipes. Blood movement through the vessels is determined by (1) flow, (2) resistance, and (3) pressure. As we will find in the next section, these factors are closely interrelated, and many of these interrelationships are clinically significant. Control mechanisms that regulate blood pressure and blood flow through the tissues are critical to the functions of the circulatory system and the homeostasis of the whole body.

Laminar and Turbulent Flow in Vessels

Fluid, including blood, tends to flow through long, smooth-walled tubes in a streamlined fashion called **laminar flow** (figure 21.23*a*). Fluid behaves as if it were composed of a large number of concentric layers. The movement of these layers is not the same because of the effect of resistance. The layer nearest the wall of the tube experiences the greatest resistance to flow because it moves against the stationary wall. The innermost layers slip over the surface of the outermost layers and experience less resistance to movement. Thus, flow in a vessel consists of movement of concentric layers, with the outer layer moving most slowly and the layer at the center moving most rapidly. This is similar to water flow in a river, where the movement of water is fastest toward the more central area of the river and slower near the shoreline.

Laminar flow is interrupted and becomes **turbulent flow** when the rate of flow exceeds a critical velocity or when the fluid passes a constriction, a sharp turn, or a rough surface. Turbulent flow is caused by numerous small currents flowing at an angle to the long axis of the vessels. These small currents result in flowing whorls or eddy currents in the blood vessel (figure 21.23*b*). Vibrations of the liquid and blood vessel walls during turbulent flow cause the sounds heard when blood pressure is measured using a blood pressure cuff. Turbulent flow is also common as blood flows past the valves in the heart and is partially responsible for the heart sounds (see chapter 20).

Turbulent flow of blood through vessels occurs primarily in the heart and to a lesser extent where arteries branch. Sounds caused by turbulent blood flow in arteries are not normal and usually indicate that the artery is abnormally constricted, which may indicate an increased probability that thromboses will develop.

Blood Pressure

Blood pressure is a measure of the force blood exerts against blood vessel walls. An instrument called a **mercury (Hg) manometer** measures blood pressure in millimeters of mercury (mm Hg). A blood pressure of 100 mm Hg is great enough to lift a column of mercury 100 mm.

Blood pressure can be measured directly by inserting a **cannula** (tube) into a blood vessel and connecting a manometer or an

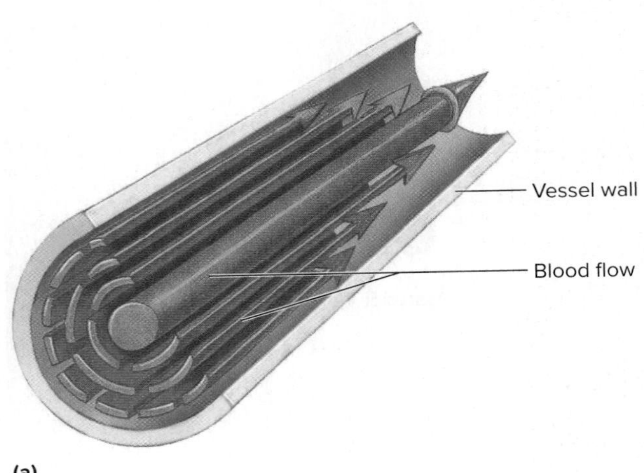

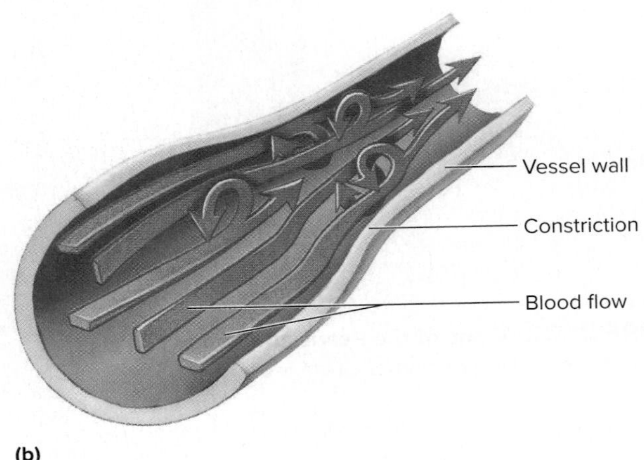

FIGURE 21.23 Laminar and Turbulent Flow
(*a*) In laminar flow, fluid flows in long, smooth-walled tubes as if it were composed of a large number of concentric layers. (*b*) Turbulent flow is caused by numerous small currents flowing crosswise or obliquely to the long axis of the vessel, resulting in flowing whorls and eddy currents.

FUNDAMENTAL **Figure**

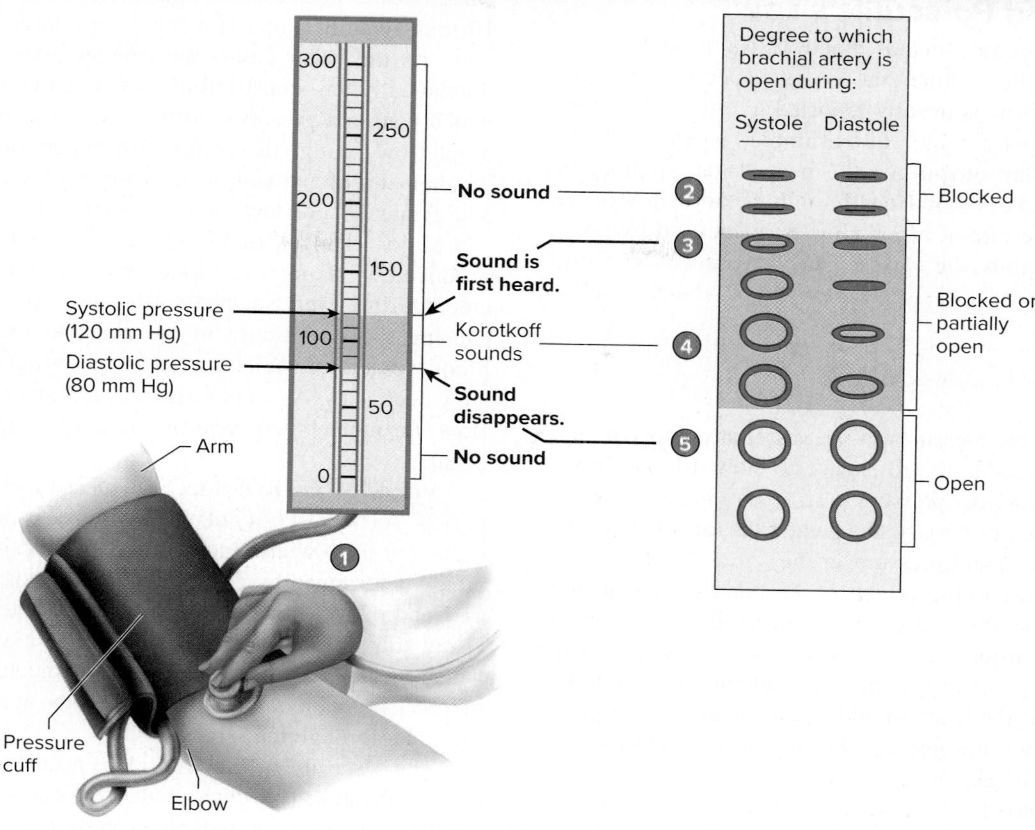

PROCESS **Figure 21.24**

Blood Pressure Measurement

The auscultatory method, illustrated in this figure, allows medical professionals to measure arterial blood pressure.

When the pressure cuff is inflated to close the brachial artery, which arteries in the upper limb will not receive blood flow?

electronic pressure transducer to it. Electronic transducers are very sensitive and can precisely detect rapid fluctuations in pressure.

Placing a catheter into a blood vessel or into a chamber of the heart to monitor pressure changes is possible but not appropriate for routine clinical examinations. Health professionals most often use the **auscultatory** (aw-SKUL-ta-to-ree) **method** to measure blood pressure. Figure 21.24 illustrates the auscultatory method.

1. A blood pressure cuff connected to a **sphygmomanometer** (SFIG-moh-mah-NOM-ih-ter) is wrapped around a patient's arm just above the elbow. A stethoscope is placed over the patient's brachial artery. Some sphygmomanometers have mercury manometers, and others have digital manometers, but they all measure pressure in terms of millimeters of mercury.
2. The blood pressure cuff is inflated until the brachial artery is completely collapsed. Because blood flow through the constricted area is blocked at this point, no sounds can be heard through the stethoscope.
3. The pressure in the cuff is gradually lowered. As soon as it declines below the systolic pressure, blood flows through the constricted area during systole (contraction of the ventricles). The blood flow is turbulent and produces vibrations in the blood and surrounding tissues that can be heard through the stethoscope. These sounds are called **Korotkoff** (koh-ROT-kof) **sounds,** and the pressure at which a Korotkoff sound is first heard represents the **systolic pressure.**
4. As the pressure in the blood pressure cuff is lowered still more, the Korotkoff sounds change tone and loudness.
5. When the pressure has dropped until continuous laminar blood flow is reestablished, the sound disappears completely. The pressure at which continuous laminar flow is reestablished is the **diastolic pressure.** This method for determining systolic and diastolic pressures is not entirely accurate, but its results are within 10% of methods that are more direct.

ASSESS YOUR PROGRESS

35. *Describe laminar flow and turbulent flow through a tube. What conditions cause turbulent flow of blood?*
36. *What creates blood pressure? Describe the auscultatory method of measuring blood pressure.*
37. *What are Korotkoff sounds?*

Blood Flow and Poiseuille's Law

The **rate** at which a liquid, such as blood, flows through a tube can be expressed as the volume that passes a specific point per unit of time. Blood flow is usually reported in either milliliters (mL) or liters (L) per minute. For example, when a person is resting, the **cardiac output** of the heart is approximately 5 L/min; thus, the rate of blood flow through the aorta is approximately 5 L/min. The rate of blood flow is influenced by pressure differences within the vessel and resistance to flow. Mathematically, the rate of blood flow in a vessel can be described by equation (21.1):

$$\text{Flow} = \frac{P_1 - P_2}{R} \quad (21.1)$$

where P_1 and P_2 are the pressures in the vessel at points one and two, respectively, and R is the resistance to flow. Blood always flows from an area of higher pressure to an area of lower pressure; the greater the pressure difference, the greater the rate of flow. For example, the average blood pressure in the aorta (P_1) is greater than the blood pressure in the vessels of the relaxed right atrium (P_2). Therefore, blood flows from the aorta to tissues and from tissues to the right atrium. This is dependent on the pumping action of the heart maintaining a pressure gradient throughout the circulatory system. If the heart should stop contracting, the pressure in the aorta would become equal to that in the right atrium, and blood would no longer flow.

The flow of blood, resulting from a pressure difference between the two ends of a blood vessel, is opposed by a resistance to flow. As such, the degree of blood flow is inversely related to the amount of resistance. Another way to state this is that as resistance increases, blood flow decreases; conversely, as the resistance decreases, blood flow increases. Resistance is affected by several factors including blood viscosity, vessel length, and vessel diameter. Considering these three factors, resistance can be represented mathematically by equation (21.2):

$$\text{Resistance} = \frac{128vl}{\pi D^4} \quad (21.2)$$

where v is the viscosity of blood, l is the length of the vessel, and D is the diameter of the vessel. Both 128 and π are constants and for practical purposes the length of the blood vessel is constant. Thus, the diameter of the blood vessel and the viscosity of the blood determine resistance. The viscosity of blood changes slowly.

When equation (21.1) (flow) is combined with equation (21.2) (resistance), the following relationship, called **Poiseuille's** (pwah-ZUH-yes) **law,** results:

$$\text{Flow} = \frac{P_1 - P_2}{R} = \frac{\pi(P_1 - P_2)\,D^4}{128vl} \quad (21.3)$$

Notice in equation (21.3) that the value for diameter (D) is raised to the fourth power. That indicates that diameter has a great impact on the overall calculation of flow. Specifically, a small change in the diameter of a vessel dramatically changes the resistance to flow, and therefore the amount of blood that flows through it. For example, decreasing the diameter of a vessel by half increases the resistance to flow 16-fold and decreases flow 16-fold. Imagine water flowing from a large tube into a smaller tube. As the water enters the smaller tube, flow will decrease dramatically. Vasoconstriction decreases the diameter of a vessel, which causes a greater resistance to flow and, overall, reduced blood flow through the vessel. Conversely, vasodilation increases the diameter of a vessel, which causes a lower resistance to flow and greater blood flow through the vessel.

Major changes in blood flow through blood vessels are produced by changes in blood pressure and blood vessel diameter. During exercise, heart rate and stroke volume increase, causing blood pressure in the aorta to increase. In addition, blood vessels in skeletal muscles vasodilate, and resistance to flow decreases. As a consequence, a dramatic increase in blood flow through blood vessels in exercising skeletal muscles occurs.

Viscosity (vis-KOS-i-tee) is a measure of a liquid's resistance to flow. As the viscosity of a liquid increases, the pressure required to force it to flow also increases. The viscosity of liquids is commonly determined by considering the viscosity of distilled water as 1 and then comparing the viscosity of other liquids with that. Using this procedure, whole blood has a viscosity of 3.0–4.5, which means that about three times as much pressure is required to force whole blood through a given tube at the same rate as forcing water through the same tube.

The viscosity of blood is influenced largely by **hematocrit** (hee-MAT-oh-krit), which is the percentage of the total blood volume composed of red blood cells (see chapter 19). As the hematocrit increases, the viscosity of blood increases logarithmically. Blood with a hematocrit of 45% has a viscosity about three times that of water, whereas blood with a very high hematocrit of 65% has a viscosity about seven to eight times that of water. The plasma proteins have only a minor effect on the viscosity of blood, but dehydration or uncontrolled production of red blood cells can increase the hematocrit and the viscosity of blood substantially. Viscosity above the normal range increases the workload on the heart. If this workload is great enough, heart failure can result.

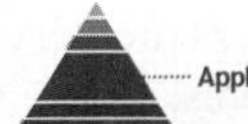

Predict 2

Predict the effect of each of the following conditions on blood flow: (a) vasoconstriction of blood vessels in the skin in response to cold exposure, (b) vasodilation of blood vessels in the skin in response to elevated body temperature, and (c) erythrocytosis, which results in a greatly increased hematocrit.

Critical Closing Pressure and Laplace's Law

The **critical closing pressure** of a blood vessel is the lowest pressure at which the vessel remains open; pressures below critical closing pressure allow the vessel to collapse and blood flow through the vessel stops. Critical closing pressure is of concern in cases such as shock. When a person is in shock, blood pressure can decrease below the critical closing pressure in vessels (see Clinical

Impact 21.6). As a consequence, the blood vessels collapse, and flow ceases. The tissues supplied by those vessels can become necrotic because of the lack of blood supply. (*Note:* This information as well as the information in Clinical Impact 21.6 will be useful in answering the Learn to Predict question at the beginning of the chapter.)

Critical closing pressure is essentially the minimum force necessary to hold open a vessel. This force is dependent on two factors: (1) the diameter of the vessel and (2) blood pressure. **Laplace's** (lah-PLAS-sez) **law** states that the force that stretches the vessel wall is proportional to the diameter of the vessel times the blood pressure. Laplace's law is expressed by the equation (21.4):

$$F = D \times P \tag{21.4}$$

where F is force, D is vessel diameter, and P is pressure. As the pressure in a vessel decreases, the force that stretches the vessel wall also decreases. Conversely, as the pressure in a vessel increases, the force that stretches the vessel wall also increases.

Laplace's law also explains how vessel diameter affects the force applied to the vessel wall. From equation (21.4), we see that as the diameter of a vessel increases, the force applied to the vessel wall increases, even if the pressure remains constant. Sometimes a part of an arterial wall becomes weakened and a bulge, called an aneurysm, forms in it. The vessel diameter increases at the site of the aneursym; therefore, the force applied to the weakened part is greater than at other points along the blood vessel. The greater force causes the weakened vessel wall to bulge even more, further increasing the pressure on it. This positive feedback can proceed until the vessel finally ruptures. Ruptured aneurysms in the blood vessels of the brain or in the aorta are often fatal.

Predict 3

Richard does not know it, but he has an aneurysm at the base of his left middle cerebral artery. One of Richard's favorite activities is to take a hot sauna bath and then jump into cold water. Richard does not realize that this causes rapid vasoconstriction of his cutaneous blood vessels. How will this activity affect Richard's aneurysm?

Vascular Compliance

Compliance (kom-PLY-ans) is the tendency for blood vessel volume to increase as blood pressure increases. Vessels with greater compliance stretch more easily. Vessels with smaller compliance stretch less easily.

An analogy to clarify this relationship is comparing the volume of water a plastic cup can hold with the volume of water a water balloon can hold. The water balloon has the capacity to stretch, or has a greater compliance, compared to a plastic cup.

Compliance is expressed by equation (21.5):

$$\text{Compliance} = \frac{\text{Increase in volume (mL)}}{\text{Increase in pressure (mm Hg)}} \tag{21.5}$$

Vessels with a large compliance exhibit a large increase in volume when the pressure increases a small amount. Vessels with a small compliance do not show a large increase in volume when the pressure increases.

Recall that veins have thinner walls than arteries. This difference also affects the compliance of the vessel. Venous compliance is approximately 24 times greater than arterial compliance. As venous pressure increases, the volume of the veins increases greatly. Consequently, veins act as storage areas, or reservoirs, for blood because their large compliance allows them to hold much more blood than other areas of the circulatory system (table 21.13).

To illustrate this, let's consider the distribution of blood volume in the body. Approximately 84% of the total blood volume is contained in the systemic blood vessels. Because of their larger compliance compared to other vessels, veins can hold a larger volume of blood. So it is not surprising that most of that blood is in the veins (64%). Smaller volumes of blood are in the arteries (15%) and the capillaries (5%; table 21.13).

ASSESS YOUR PROGRESS

38. *Describe the relationship among blood flow, blood pressure, and resistance.*

39. *According to Poiseuille's law, what effects do viscosity, blood vessel diameter, and blood vessel length have on resistance? On blood flow?*

40. *Define* viscosity, *and state the effect of hematocrit on viscosity.*

41. *State Laplace's law. How does it relate to critical closing pressure and aneurysm?*

42. *What is vascular compliance? Do veins or arteries have greater compliance? Explain why.*

TABLE 21.13 Distribution of Blood Volume in Blood Vessels

Vessels		Total Blood Volume (%)
Systemic vessels		
Veins		64
Large veins	(39%)	
Small veins	(25%)	
Arteries		15
Large arteries	(8%)	
Small arteries	(5%)	
Arterioles	(2%)	
Capillaries		5
TOTAL IN SYSTEMIC VESSELS		84
Pulmonary vessels		9
Heart		7
TOTAL BLOOD VOLUME		100

21.7 Physiology of the Systemic Circulation

LEARNING OUTCOMES

After reading this section, you should be able to

A. **Explain the relationship between cross-sectional area of blood vessels and the rate of blood flow.**
B. **Explain how blood pressure and resistance to flow change as blood flows through the blood vessels.**
C. **Define *pulse pressure*.**
D. **List locations on the body surface where the pulse can be detected.**
E. **Describe the exchange of materials across a capillary wall.**
F. **Explain how preload, venous tone, and gravity affect cardiac output.**

The primary function of the circulatory system is distribution, ensuring that O_2, CO_2, nutrients, hormones, and other substances are efficiently moved from one area of the body to other areas. This distribution relies on the constant flow of blood through the circulatory system. Recall from equation (21.3) that flow is determined by several factors, including pressure. In this section we will discuss the factors that affect blood flow and blood pressure as well as how blood flow and blood pressure regulate exchange of substances between the blood and other tissues.

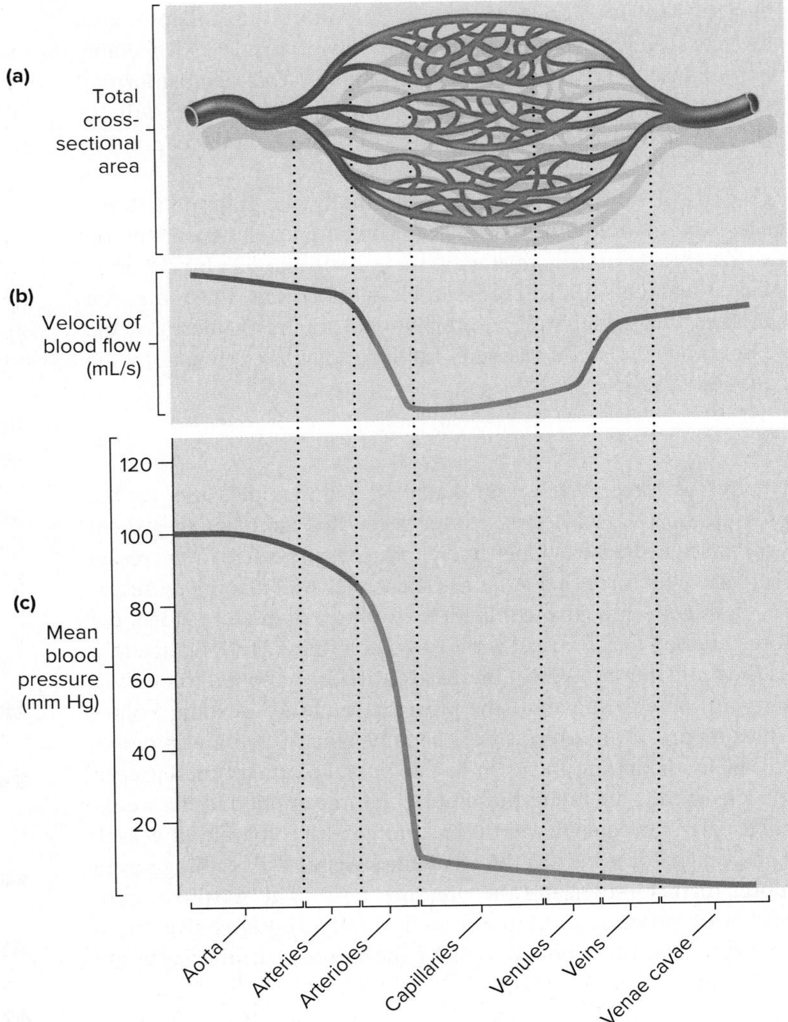

FIGURE 21.25 Blood Vessel Area and Velocity of Blood Flow
(*a*) A schematic representing the total cross-sectional area for each of the major blood vessel types. The total cross-sectional area of all the capillaries is much greater (2500 cm^2) than that of the aorta (5 cm^2), although the cross-sectional area of each capillary is much smaller than that of the aorta. (*b*) Blood velocity decreases dramatically in arterioles, capillaries, and venules and is greater in the aorta and the large veins. As the total cross-sectional area increases, the velocity of blood flow decreases. (*c*) Blood pressure decreases in each part of the systemic circulation. This decrease is proportional to resistance to blood flow.

Cross-Sectional Area of Blood Vessels

Blood flows through the vessels of the body at different velocities. The velocity of blood flow changes relative to the cross-sectional area of each blood vessel type. We can determine the cross-sectional area for each individual blood vessel; however, a more useful number is to determine the total cross-sectional area for all blood vessels of a given type. This can be done by calculating the cross-sectional area of a particular blood vessel type and multiplying by the number of that type of blood vessel in the body (figure 21.25*a*). For example, only one aorta exists, and it has a cross-sectional area of 5 square centimeters (cm^2). An individual capillary has a very small cross-sectional area. However, the total cross-sectional area considers the combined area of all capillaries, which number approximately 10 billion in the body. So the total cross-sectional area of all capillaries is 2500 cm^2, which is much greater than the cross-sectional area of the aorta.

The velocity of blood flow in a particular blood vessel type is inversely proportional to its total cross-sectional area (figure 21.25*b*). The velocity of blood flow is greatest in the aorta, but the total cross-sectional area is small. In contrast, the total cross-sectional area of the capillaries is large, but the velocity of blood flow is low. As the veins become larger in diameter, their total cross-sectional area decreases, and the velocity of blood flow increases. The relationship between total cross-sectional area and velocity of blood flow is much like a stream that flows rapidly through a narrow gorge but more slowly through a broad plane.

Pressure and Resistance

Blood pressure changes as blood moves from one blood vessel type to another. The left ventricle forcefully ejects blood from the heart into the aorta. Because the heart's pumping action is pulsatile, the aortic pressure fluctuates between a systolic pressure of 120 mm Hg and a diastolic pressure of 80 mm Hg. As blood flows through the circulation, from arteries through the capillaries and

TABLE 21.14 Blood Pressure Classification in Adults

	Systolic Blood Pressure (mm Hg)		Diastolic Blood Pressure (mm Hg)
Normal blood pressure	<120	and	<80
Elevated blood pressure	120–129	and	<80
Stage 1 hypertension	130–139	or	80–89
Stage 2 hypertension	≥140	or	≥90
Hypertensive crisis	>180	and/or	>120

Source: Guideline for the Prevention, Detection, Evaluation, and Management of High Blood Pressure in Adults: A Report of the American College of Cardiology/American Heart Association Task Force on Clinical Practice Guidelines. *J Am Coll Cardiol* 2017; Nov 13.

the veins, the pressure falls progressively to a minimum of approximately 0 mm Hg or even slightly lower by the time it returns to the right atrium (figure 21.25*c*). Table 21.14 outlines the clinical classification of blood pressure in adults.

The decrease in blood pressure in each part of the systemic circulation is directly proportional to the resistance to blood flow. In other words, the greater the resistance in a blood vessel, the more rapidly the pressure decreases as blood flows through it. This resistance to flow is associated with the diameter of the vessel. As vessel diameter decreases, resistance to flow increases. When considering the blood vessels of the body, vessels with larger diameters have lower levels of resistance, whereas vessels with smaller diameters have higher levels of resistance.

Resistance to flow also affects the speed at which pressure changes in the different vessels of the body (see figure 21.21*c*). For example, resistance is small in the aorta, so the average pressure at the end of the aorta is nearly the same as at the beginning of the aorta, about 100 mm Hg. The resistance in medium arteries, which are as small as 3 mm in diameter, is also small, so their average pressure is only decreased to 95 mm Hg. In the smaller arteries, however, the resistance to blood flow is greater; by the time blood reaches the arterioles, the average pressure is approximately 85 mm Hg. The resistance to flow is greater in the arterioles than in any other part of the systemic circulation; at their ends, the average pressure is only approximately 30 mm Hg. The resistance is also fairly high in the capillaries. The blood pressure at the arterial end of the capillaries is approximately 30 mm Hg, and it decreases to approximately 10 mm Hg at the venous end. Resistance to blood flow in the veins is small because of their relatively large diameter; by the time the blood reaches the right atrium in the venous system, the average pressure has decreased from 10 mm Hg to approximately 0 mm Hg.

The muscular arteries and arterioles are capable of constricting or dilating in response to autonomic and hormonal stimulation, altering resistance and blood flow. If vessels constrict, resistance to blood flow increases, less blood flows through the constricted blood vessels, and blood is shunted to other, nonconstricted areas of the body. Muscular arteries help control the amount of blood flowing to each body region, and arterioles regulate blood flow through specific tissues. Constriction of an arteriole decreases blood flow through the local area it supplies, and vasodilation increases blood flow.

ASSESS YOUR PROGRESS

43. *List the percent distribution of blood in the large arteries, small arteries, arterioles, capillaries, small veins, and large veins.*

44. *Describe the total cross-sectional areas of the aorta, arteries, arterioles, capillaries, venules, veins, and venae cavae.*

45. *Describe how the velocity of blood flow changes as blood moves through the aorta to the venae cavae.*

46. *Describe the changes in resistance and blood pressure as blood flows through the aorta to the venae cavae.*

47. *Explain how constriction and dilation of muscular arteries shunt blood from one area of the body to another and how constriction and dilation of arterioles change blood flow through local areas.*

Pulse and Pulse Pressure

As blood is ejected from the left ventricle into the aorta, it produces a pressure wave, or **pulse,** that travels rapidly along the arteries. Its rate of transmission is approximately 15 times greater in the aorta (7–10 m/s) and 100 times greater in the distal arteries (15–35 m/s) than the velocity of blood flow.

You are most likely familiar with the practice of "taking a person's pulse" in a clinical situation. The pulse is important clinically because health professionals can determine heart rate, rhythmicity, and other characteristics by detecting it. The pulse can be felt at 10 major locations on each side of the body where large arteries are close to the surface (figure 21.26).

On the head and neck, a pulse can be felt in three arteries: (1) the common carotid artery in the neck, (2) the superficial temporal artery immediately anterior to the ear, and (3) the facial artery at the point where it crosses the inferior border of the mandible approximately midway between the angle and the genu.

On the upper limb, a pulse can also be felt in three arteries: (1) the axillary artery in the axilla, (2) the brachial artery on the medial side of the arm slightly proximal to the elbow, and (3) the radial artery on the lateral side of the anterior forearm just proximal to the wrist. The **radial pulse,** taken at the radial artery, is traditionally used because it is the most easily accessible artery in the body.

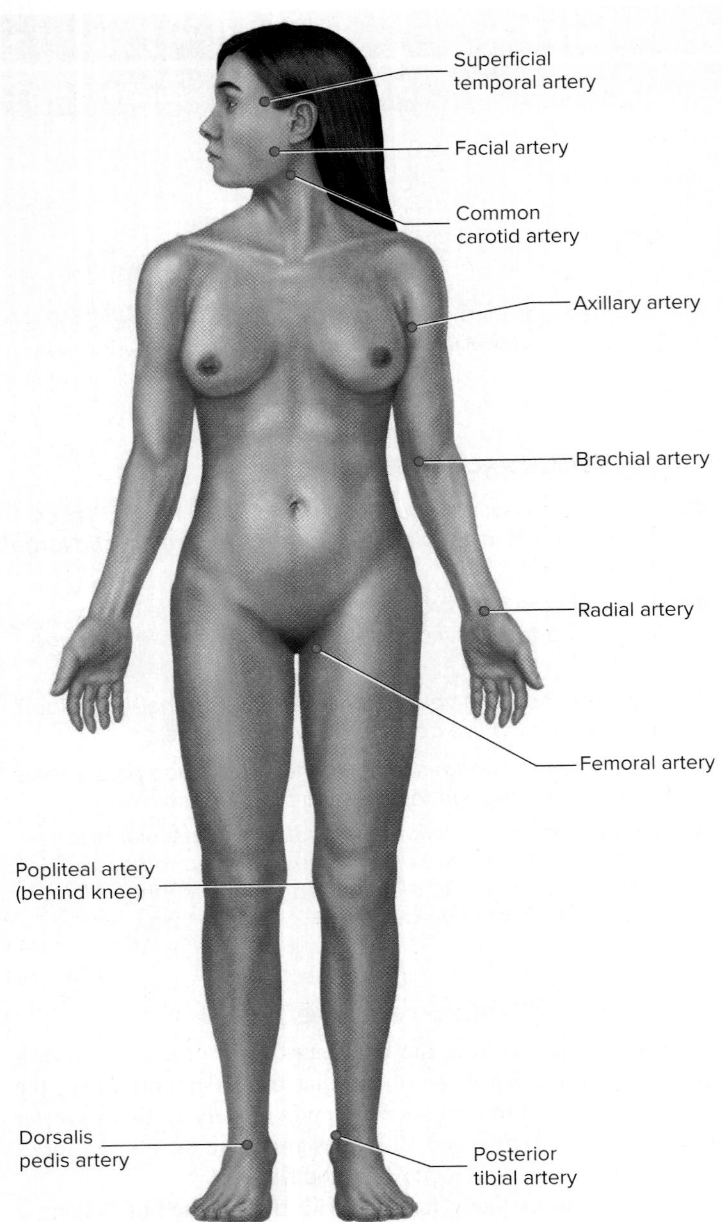

FIGURE 21.26 Major Points at Which the Pulse Can Be Monitored
Each pulse point is named after the artery on which it occurs.

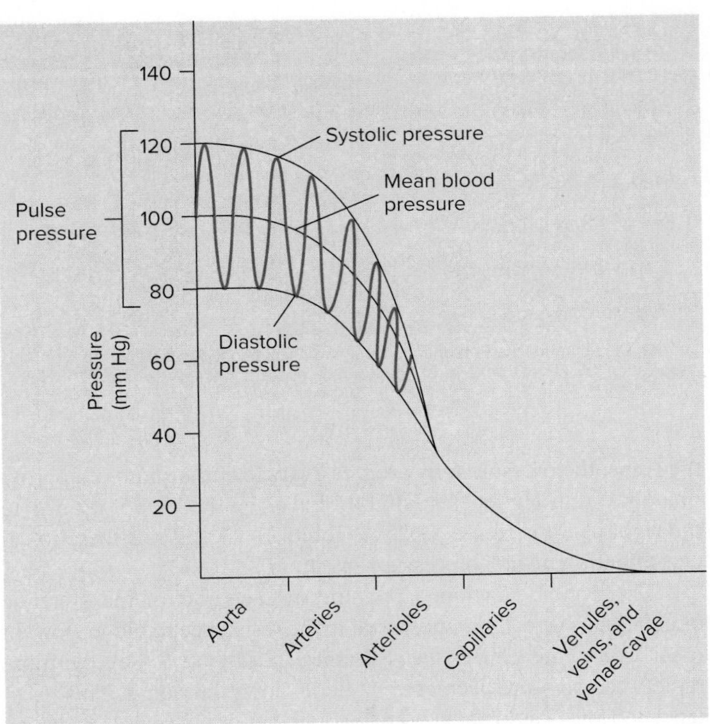

FIGURE 21.27 Blood Pressure in the Major Blood Vessel Types
In small arteries and arterioles, blood pressure fluctuations between systole and diastole are reduced. No fluctuations in blood pressure occur in capillaries and veins.

In the lower part of the body, a pulse can be felt in four locations: (1) the femoral artery in the groin, (2) the popliteal artery just proximal to the knee on the posterior surface, (3) the dorsalis pedis artery at the ankle, and (4) the posterior tibial artery at the ankle.

The pressure wave that we recognize as a pulse is generated by pulse pressure. **Pulse pressure** is the difference between systolic and diastolic pressures (figure 21.27). For example, in a healthy, young adult at rest, systolic pressure is approximately 120 mm Hg, and diastolic pressure is approximately 80 mm Hg; thus, the pulse pressure is approximately 40 mm Hg (= 120 mm Hg − 80 mm Hg). Two major factors influence pulse pressure: (1) stroke volume of the heart and (2) vascular compliance. Pulse pressure is directly related to stroke volume. When stroke volume decreases, pulse pressure also decreases; when stroke volume increases, pulse pressure increases. For example, during exercise, such as running, the stroke volume increases; as a consequence, the pulse pressure also increases. After running, the pulse pressure gradually returns to its resting value as the stroke volume of the heart decreases.

Pulse pressure is inversely related to vascular compliance. As vascular compliance increases, pulse pressure decreases. Conversely, as vascular compliance decreases, pulse pressure increases. The vascular compliance decreases as a person ages. Arteries in older people become less elastic, or arteriosclerotic, causing the pressure in the aorta to rise more rapidly and to a greater degree during systole and to fall more rapidly to its diastolic value. Thus, for a given stroke volume, systolic pressure and pulse pressure are higher as vascular compliance decreases.

As the pulse passes through the smallest arteries and arterioles, it is gradually damped, so that the fluctuation between the systolic and diastolic pressures becomes smaller until the difference is almost absent at the end of the arterioles (figure 21.27). At the beginning of the capillary, there is a steady pressure of close to 30 mm Hg, which is adequate to force blood through the capillaries if the precapillary sphincters dilate.

Capillary Exchange and Regulation of Interstitial Fluid Volume

Approximately 10 billion capillaries exist in the body. The heart and blood vessels maintain blood flow through those capillaries and support **capillary exchange,** which is the movement of substances into and out of capillaries. Capillary exchange is the process by which cells receive everything they need to survive and to eliminate metabolic waste products. If blood flow through capillaries is not maintained, cells cannot survive.

By far, the most important means by which capillary exchange occurs is **diffusion.** Oxygen, hormones, and nutrients, such as glucose and amino acids, diffuse from a higher concentration in capillaries to a lower concentration in the interstitial fluid. Waste products, including CO_2, diffuse from a higher concentration in the interstitial fluid to a lower concentration in the capillaries. Similar to the diffusion into and out of cells (see figure 3.10), how a substance moves into and out of the capillaries depends on its solubility characteristics. Lipid-soluble molecules, such as O_2, CO_2, steroid hormones, and fatty acids, diffuse through the plasma membranes of the endothelial cells of the capillaries. Water-soluble substances, such as glucose and amino acids, diffuse through intercellular spaces or through fenestrations of capillaries (see figure 21.3). In a few areas of the body, such as the spleen and liver, the spaces between the endothelial cells are large enough to allow proteins to pass through them. In other areas, the connections between endothelial cells are extensive, and few molecules pass between the endothelial cells; such is the case in the capillaries of the brain that form the blood-brain barrier. In these capillaries, mediated transport moves water-soluble substances across the capillary walls (see chapter 13 for a description of the blood-brain barrier). The endothelial cells of capillaries appear to take up small pinocytotic vesicles and transport them across the capillary wall. However, the pinocytotic vesicles do not appear to be a major means by which molecules move across the capillary wall.

Blood enters capillaries at their arterial ends and exits the capillaries at their venous ends.

The movement of fluid across a capillary wall is driven by **net filtration pressure (NFP),** which is the difference between net hydrostatic pressure and net osmotic pressure:

$$\text{NFP} = \text{Net hydrostatic pressure} - \text{Net osmotic pressure} \quad (21.6)$$

Hydrostatic pressure is the pressure exerted by fluid, such as blood or interstitial fluid. Osmostic pressure, as defined in chapter 3, is the force required to prevent water from moving by osmosis across a selectively permeable membrane. Note the term *net* is used in each of these pressures, indicating that more than one force affects each of them.

Net hydrostatic pressure is determined by two hydrostatic pressures: (1) **capillary hydrostatic pressure (CHP),** which is the blood pressure within the capillaries; and (2) **interstitial fluid hydrostatic pressure (IHP),** which is the hydrostatic pressure exerted by the interstitial fluid of the tissue surrounding the capillaries. CHP at the arterial end of a capillary is about 30 mm Hg. This pressure results mainly from the force of contraction of the heart, but it can be modified by the effect of gravity on fluids within the body (see "Blood Pressure and the Effect of Gravity," later in this section).

Let's consider how the net hydrostatic pressure changes from the arterial end of the capillary compared to the venous end of the capillary. At the arterial end of capillaries, the net hydrostatic pressure that moves fluid across the capillary walls into the tissue spaces is the difference between CHP and IHP:

$$\begin{aligned} \text{Net hydrostatic pressure} &= \text{CHP} - \text{IHP} \quad (21.7) \\ &= 30 - (-3) \\ &= 33 \text{ mm Hg} \end{aligned}$$

In equation (21.7), IHP is a negative number because of the suction effect produced by the lymphatic vessels as they absorb excess fluid from the tissue spaces. The lymphatic system is described in chapter 22. Here, it is only necessary to understand that excess interstitial fluid enters lymphatic capillaries and is eventually returned to the blood.

The CHP decreases as blood moves through the capillary. The decrease is from about 30 mm Hg at the arterial end of the capillary to 10 mm Hg at the venous end of the capillary. This causes a reduction in the net hydrostatic pressure moving fluid out of the venous end of the capillary. Again, we can demonstrate this using equation (21.7):

$$\begin{aligned} \text{Net hydrostatic pressure} &= \text{CHP} - \text{IHP} \\ &= 10 - (-3) \\ &= 13 \text{ mm Hg} \end{aligned}$$

Net osmotic pressure is the difference in osmotic pressure between the blood and the interstitial fluid. Solutes, such as proteins in the blood and interstitial fluids, will greatly affect the osmotic pressure. **Blood colloid osmotic pressure (BCOP)** is caused by plasma proteins in the blood. **Interstitial colloid osmotic pressure (ICOP)** is caused by proteins in the interstitial fluid. Large proteins do not pass freely through the capillary walls, and the difference in protein concentrations between the blood and the interstitial fluid is responsible for osmosis across the capillary wall. Ions and small molecules do not make a significant contribution to osmosis across the capillary wall because they pass freely through it and their concentrations are approximately the same in the blood as in the interstitial fluid.

The BCOP (28 mm Hg) is several times larger than the ICOP (8 mm Hg) because of the presence of albumin and other proteins in the plasma (see chapter 19). For demonstration purposes, we can calculate the net osmotic pressure using equation (21.8):

$$\begin{aligned} \text{Net osmotic pressure} &= \text{BCOP} - \text{ICOP} \quad (21.8) \\ &= 28 - 8 \\ &= 20 \text{ mm Hg} \end{aligned}$$

The greater the osmotic pressure of a fluid, the greater the tendency for water to move into that fluid (see chapter 3). The net osmotic pressure results in the osmosis of water into the capillary because water has a greater tendency to move into the blood than into the interstitial fluid.

The concentration of proteins within capillaries and the concentration of proteins within interstitial fluid do not change significantly because only a small amount of fluid passes from the capillaries into the tissue spaces. Therefore, when we consider the

PROCESS **Figure**

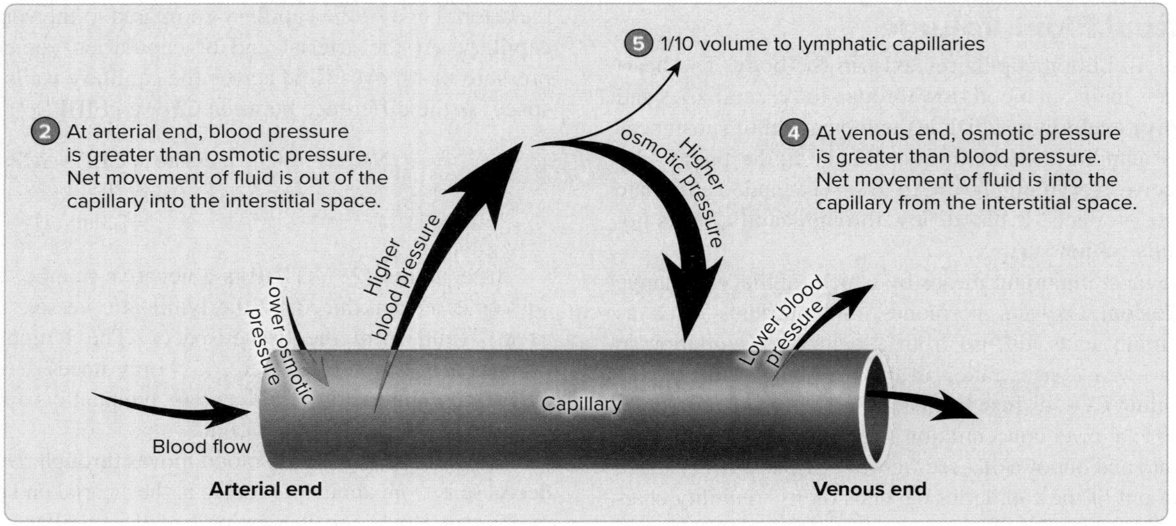

1

33 mm Hg (Net hydrostatic pressure)
− 20 mm Hg (Net osmotic pressure)
13 mm Hg (Net filtration pressure)

3

13 mm Hg (Net hydrostatic pressure)
− 20 mm Hg (Net osmotic pressure)
− 7 mm Hg (Net filtration pressure)

PROCESS **Figure 21.28**

Fluid Exchange Across the Walls of Capillaries

Pressure differences exist between the inside and the outside of capillaries at their arterial and venous ends.

Which pressure would be affected by an obstruction in the capillary? Would this increase or decrease the net filtration pressure?

Clinical IMPACT 21.2

Edema

Increases in the permeability of capillaries allow plasma proteins to move from capillaries into the interstitial fluid. This causes an increase in the interstitial colloid osmotic pressure, which causes a net increase in the amount of fluid moving from capillaries into interstitial spaces. The result is edema, swelling due to excessive fluid accumulation in tissues.

Edema can result from many different conditions. Chemical mediators of inflammation increase the permeability of the capillary walls and can cause edema. Decreases in plasma protein concentration reduce the blood colloid osmotic pressure, so more fluid moves out of the capillary at its arterial end and less fluid moves into the capillary at its venous end. The result once again is edema. Severe liver infections that reduce plasma protein synthesis, loss of protein molecules in urine through the kidneys, and protein starvation all lead to edema. Blockage of veins, as in venous thrombosis, increases blood pressure in capillaries and can cause edema. Either blockage or removal of lymphatic vessels, as occurs when lymph nodes are suspected of being cancerous, allows fluid to accumulate in the interstitial spaces and results in edema.

venous end of the capillary, the net osmotic pressure moving fluid into capillaries by osmosis is still approximately 20 mm Hg.

Now that we have discussed the factors that affect NFR, we can discuss how this affects movement of fluid across a capillary wall, which is illustrated in figure 21.28.

1. Using equation (21.6), we can estimate NFR at the arterial end of the capillary. The net hydrostatic pressure, which moves fluid out of the capillary and into the interstitial space, is greater than the net osmotic pressure, which moves fluid into the capillary.
2. As a result of these differences, there is a net movement of fluid out of the capillary at the arterial end.
3. Again, using equation (21.6), we can estimate the NFR at the venous end of the capillary. In this case, the net hydrostatic pressure is lower than the net osmotic pressure.
4. As a result of these differences, there is a net movement of fluid into the capillary at the venous end.
5. Approximately nine-tenths of the fluid that leaves the capillary at the arterial end reenters the capillary at its venous end. The remaining one-tenth of the fluid enters lymphatic capillaries and is eventually returned to the general circulation (see chapter 22).

Exchange of fluid across the capillary wall and movement of fluid into lymphatic capillaries keep the volume of the interstitial fluid within a narrow range of values. Disruptions in the movement of fluid across the wall of the capillary can result in edema, or swelling, as a result of increased interstitial fluid volume (see Clinical Impact 21.2).

Apply

Predict 4

Edema often results from a disruption in the normal inwardly and outwardly directed pressures across the capillary wall. On the basis of what you know about fluid movement across the wall of the capillary and the regulation of capillary blood pressure, explain why large fluctuations in arterial blood pressure do not cause significant edema, whereas small increases in venous pressure can lead to edema.

ASSESS YOUR PROGRESS

48. *What is a pulse? List the locations on the body where the pulse can easily be detected.*
49. *What is pulse pressure? How do stroke volume and vascular compliance affect pulse pressure?*
50. *What is the most important means by which capillary exchange occurs?*
51. *Describe the factors that influence the movement of fluid from capillaries into the tissues.*
52. *What is the main force for the return of fluids at the venous end of capillaries?*
53. *What happens to the fluid in the tissues? What is edema?*

Functional Characteristics of Veins

In chapter 20, factors that affect cardiac output were described. One of these factors is influenced by veins, specifically preload, which is determined by the volume of blood that enters the heart from the veins (see chapter 20). Therefore, the factors that affect flow in the veins are of great importance to the overall function of the cardiovascular system. If the volume of blood is increased because of a rapid transfusion, the amount of blood flow to the heart through the veins increases. This increases the preload, which causes the cardiac output to increase because of the Starling law of the heart. On the other hand, rapid loss of a large volume of blood decreases venous return to the heart, which decreases the preload and cardiac output.

Venous tone is a continual state of partial contraction of the veins as a result of sympathetic stimulation (see chapter 16). Increased sympathetic stimulation increases venous tone by causing the veins to constrict more, which forces the large venous volume to flow toward the heart. Consequently, venous return and preload increase, causing an increase in cardiac output. Conversely, decreased sympathetic stimulation reduces venous tone, allowing veins to relax and dilate. As the veins fill with blood, venous return to the heart, preload, and cardiac output decrease.

The periodic compression of veins by contracting skeletal muscles forces blood to flow more rapidly through them toward

Case STUDY 21.1 Venous Thrombosis

Harry is a 55-year-old college professor who teaches a night class in a small town about 50 miles from his home. One night, as he walked to his car after class, Harry noticed that his right leg was uncomfortable. When he arrived home, about 90 minutes later, Harry realized that the calf of his right leg had become very swollen. When he extended his knee and plantar flexed his foot, the pain in his right leg increased. Harry thought this might be a serious condition, so he drove to the hospital.

In the emergency room, technicians performed a Doppler test, which monitors the flow of blood through blood vessels. The test confirmed that a thrombus had formed in one of the deep veins of Harry's right leg. His pain and edema were consistent with the presence of a venous thrombosis.

Harry was admitted to the hospital, and his physician prescribed intravenous (IV) heparin. About 4 a.m., Harry experienced an increase in his respiratory rate, his breathing became labored, he felt pain in his chest and back, and his arterial oxygen levels decreased. In response to these changes, Harry's physician increased the amount of heparin. The chest pain subsided, and Harry's respiratory movements improved over the next 24 hours. The next day, a CT scan revealed pulmonary emboli, but no infarctions of the lung. The edema in Harry's leg also slowly improved.

Harry remained in the hospital for several days, during which heparin was continued and then oral coumadin was prescribed. Frequent blood samples were taken to determine Harry's prothrombin time (see chapter 19). After about a week, Harry was released from the hospital. His physician, however, prescribed oral coumadin for at least several months. In addition, Harry was required to have his prothrombin time checked periodically.

Apply

Predict 5

a. Explain why edema and pain developed in response to a thrombus in a deep vein of Harry's right leg.

b. If a thrombus in the posterior tibial vein gave rise to an embolus, name in order the parts of the circulatory system the embolus would pass through before lodging in a blood vessel in the lungs. Explain why the lungs are the most likely places the embolus will lodge.

c. Predict the effect of pulmonary emboli on the right ventricle's ability to pump blood.

d. Predict the effect of pulmonary emboli on blood oxygen levels, on the left ventricle's ability to pump blood, and on systemic blood pressure. What responses would be activated by this change in blood pressure? (Hint: See figure 21.32.)

e. Explain why Harry's physician prescribed heparin and coumadin and why coumadin was continued long after the venous thrombosis and lung emboli had dissolved.

the heart. The valves in the veins prevent flow away from the heart so that, when veins are compressed, blood is forced toward the heart. During exercise, the combination of arterial dilation and compression of the veins by skeletal muscles causes blood to return to the heart more rapidly than under conditions of rest.

Blood Pressure and the Effect of Gravity

Blood pressure is approximately 0 mm Hg in the right atrium and approximately 100 mm Hg in the aorta. However, the pressure in the vessels above and below the heart is affected by gravity. While a person is standing, the pressure in the venules of the feet can be as much as 90 mm Hg, instead of the usual 10 mm Hg. Arterial pressure is influenced by gravity to the same degree; thus, the arterial ends of the capillaries can have a pressure of 110 mm Hg rather than 30 mm Hg. The normal pressure difference between the arterial and the venous ends of capillaries remains the same, so that blood continues to flow through the capillaries. The major effect of the high pressure in the feet and legs when a person stands for a prolonged time without moving is edema. Without skeletal muscle movement, the pressure at the venous end of the capillaries increases. Up to 15–20% of the total blood volume can pass through the walls of the capillaries into the interstitial spaces of the lower limbs during 15 minutes of standing still.

When a person changes position from lying down to standing, the blood pressure in the veins of the lower limbs increases. Because of the structure of their walls, the compliance of veins is approximately 24 times greater than the compliance of arteries. The increased blood pressure causes the distensible (compliant) veins to expand but has little effect on the arteries. As the veins expand and fill with blood, venous return decreases because less blood is returning to the heart. As venous return decreases, cardiac output and blood pressure decrease (see chapter 20). If negative-feedback mechanisms do not compensate and cause blood pressure to increase, the delivery of blood to the brain is not adequate to maintain homeostasis, and the person may feel dizzy or even faint.

ASSESS YOUR PROGRESS

54. *How do blood volume and venous tone affect cardiac output?*
55. *What effect does standing still for a prolonged time have on the blood pressure in the feet and in the head? Explain why this effect occurs.*
56. *Why does a person feel dizzy if they stand up too quickly from sitting or lying down?*

21.8 Control of Blood Flow in Tissues

LEARNING OUTCOMES

After reading this section, you should be able to

A. **Explain how local control regulates blood flow.**
B. **Explain how nervous mechanisms control blood flow.**
C. **Explain how hormonal mechanisms control blood flow.**

Blood flow provided to the tissues by the circulatory system is highly controlled and matched closely to the metabolic needs of tissues. Mechanisms that control blood flow through tissues are classified as (1) local control, (2) nervous control, and (3) hormonal control (table 21.15).

Local Control of Blood Flow in Tissues

Blood flow is not equal in all tissues of the body. Some organs require a greater blood flow than others. For example, blood flow through the brain, kidneys, and liver is relatively high. By contrast, blood flow through resting skeletal muscles is not high, but it is greater than that through other tissue types because skeletal muscle constitutes 35–40% of the total body mass. However, blood flow through exercising skeletal muscles can increase up to 20-fold, and the flow through the viscera, including the kidneys and liver, either remains the same or decreases. Local control of blood flow is achieved by the periodic relaxation and contraction of precapillary sphincters regulating blood flow through capillary networks of the tissues. In most tissues, blood flow is proportional to the metabolic needs of the tissue; therefore, as metabolic needs increase, as is the case when the activity of skeletal muscle increases, blood flow increases to supply the greater need for O_2 and other nutrients. Blood flow also increases in response to a buildup of metabolic end products.

In some tissues, blood flow serves purposes other than delivering nutrients and removing waste products. In the skin, blood flow dissipates heat from the body. In the kidneys, it eliminates metabolic waste products, regulates water balance, and controls the pH of body fluids. Among other functions, blood flow delivers nutrients that enter the blood from the small intestine to the liver for processing.

Functional Characteristics of the Capillary Bed

The rate of blood flow through capillaries is not constant, but fluctuates. The cyclic fluctuation is the result of **vasomotion** (vay-soh-MOH-shun, vas-oh-MOH-shun), the periodic contraction and relaxation of the precapillary sphincters. The innervation of the metarterioles and the precapillary sphincters in capillary networks is sparse. Local factors primarily regulate these structures, and as such the rate of blood flow. As the rate of metabolism increases in a tissue, blood flow through its capillaries increases. The precapillary sphincters relax, allowing blood to flow into the local capillary network. Blood flow can increase sevenfold to eightfold as a result of vasodilation of the metarterioles and the relaxation of precapillary sphincters in response to an increased rate of metabolism.

Figure 21.29 illustrates local control of blood flow through a capillary network.

1. As the rate of metabolism increases in a tissue, **vasodilator substances** are produced in the extracellular fluid. These substances include CO_2, lactate, adenosine, adenosine monophosphate, adenosine diphosphate, endothelium-derived relaxation factor (EDRF), K^+, and H^+. Once produced, the vasodilator substances diffuse from the tissues supplied by the capillary to the area of the precapillary sphincter, the metarterioles, and the arterioles to cause vasodilation and relaxation of the precapillary sphincters.

PROCESS **Figure**

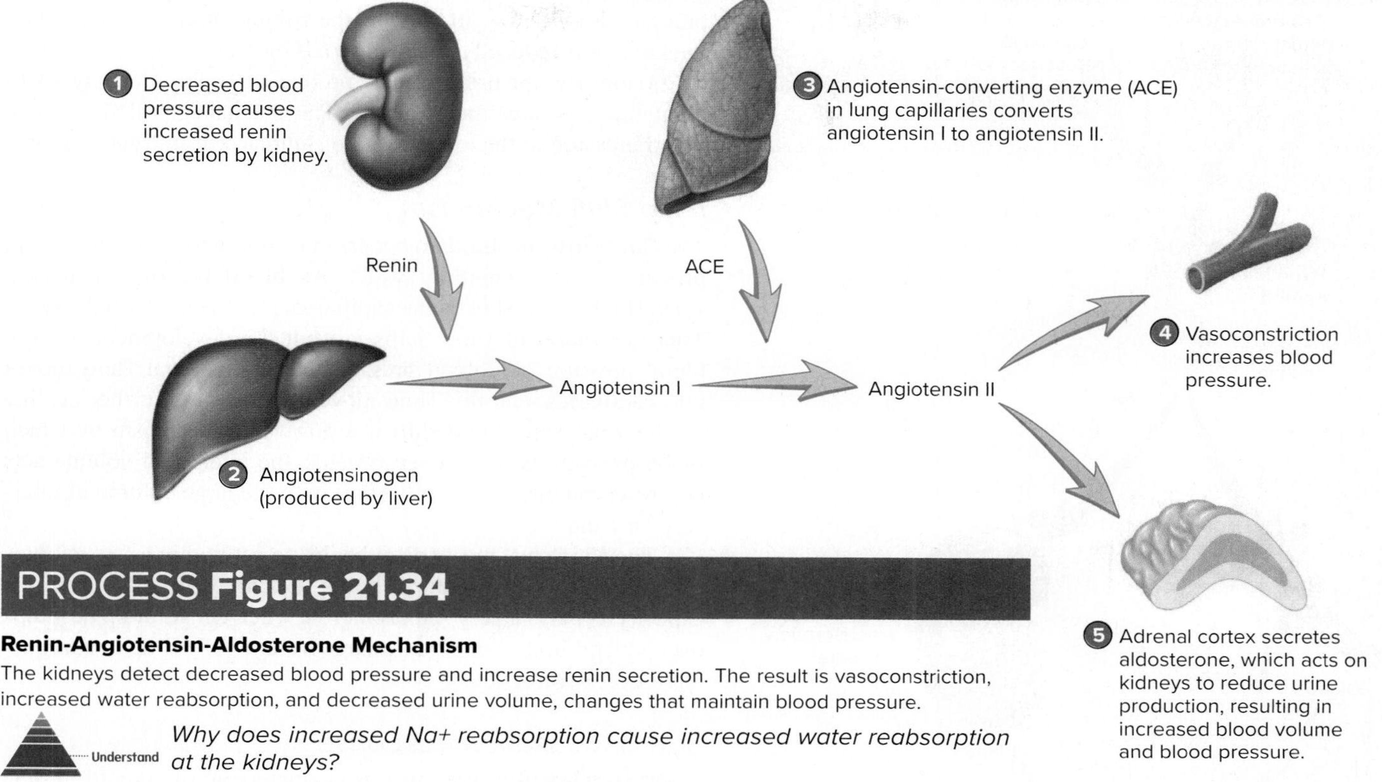

PROCESS **Figure 21.34**

Renin-Angiotensin-Aldosterone Mechanism

The kidneys detect decreased blood pressure and increase renin secretion. The result is vasoconstriction, increased water reabsorption, and decreased urine volume, changes that maintain blood pressure.

Understand *Why does increased Na+ reabsorption cause increased water reabsorption at the kidneys?*

4 Angiotensin II causes vasoconstriction in arterioles and, to some degree, in veins. As a result, it increases peripheral resistance and venous return to the heart, both of which raise blood pressure.

5 Angiotensin II also stimulates aldosterone secretion from the adrenal cortex. **Aldosterone** (al-DOS-ter-ohn) acts on the kidneys to increase the reabsorption of Na^+ and Cl^- from the filtrate into the extracellular fluid. If antidiuretic hormone (ADH; see chapter 18) is present, water moves by osmosis with the Na^+ and Cl^-. Consequently, aldosterone causes the kidneys to retain solutes, such as Na^+ and Cl^-, and water. The result is increased blood volume, causing blood pressure to increase (see chapter 26). Angiotensin II also increases salt appetite, thirst, and ADH secretion.

Secretion of renin is dependent on changes in blood pressure. Decreased blood pressure stimulates renin secretion, and increased blood pressure decreases renin secretion. The renin-angiotensin-aldosterone mechanism is important in maintaining blood pressure on a daily basis. It also reacts strongly under conditions of circulatory shock, but it requires many hours to become maximally effective. Its onset is not as fast as that of nervous reflexes or the adrenal medullary response, but its duration is longer. Once renin is secreted, it remains active for approximately 1 hour, and the effect of aldosterone lasts much longer (many hours).

Angiotensin-converting enzyme (ACE) inhibitors are a class of drugs that inhibit angiotensin-converting enzyme, which converts angiotensin I to angiotensin II. These drugs were first identified as components of the venom of pit vipers. Subsequently, several ACE inhibitors were synthesized. ACE inhibitors are commonly administered to combat hypertension.

Angiotensin II is not the only stimulus for aldosterone secretion. Other stimuli can directly stimulate aldosterone secretion. For example, an increased plasma ion concentration of K^+ and a reduced plasma concentration of Na^+ directly stimulate aldosterone secretion from the adrenal cortex (see chapters 18 and 27). Aldosterone regulates the concentration of these ions in the plasma. A decreased blood pressure and an elevated K^+ concentration occur during plasma loss, during dehydration, and in response to tissue damage, such as burns and crushing injuries.

Antidiuretic Hormone (Vasopressin) Mechanism

The **antidiuretic hormone (vasopressin) mechanism** works in harmony with the renin-angiotensin-aldosterone mechanism in response to changes in blood pressure (figure 21.35). Baroreceptors are sensitive to changes in blood pressure. Decreases in blood pressure detected by the baroreceptors result in the release of antidiuretic hormone (ADH) from the posterior pituitary, although the blood pressure must decrease substantially before the mechanism is activated.

ADH acts directly on blood vessels to cause vasoconstriction, although it is not as potent as other vasoconstrictors. Within minutes after a rapid and substantial decline in blood pressure, ADH is released in sufficient quantities to help reestablish normal blood pressure. ADH also decreases the rate of urine production by the kidneys, thereby helping maintain blood volume and blood pressure.

Neurons of the hypothalamus are sensitive to changes in the solute concentration of the plasma. Even small increases in solute concentrations directly stimulate hypothalamic neurons that increase ADH secretion (figure 21.35; see chapter 26). Increases in the concentration of the plasma, as occur during dehydration, and

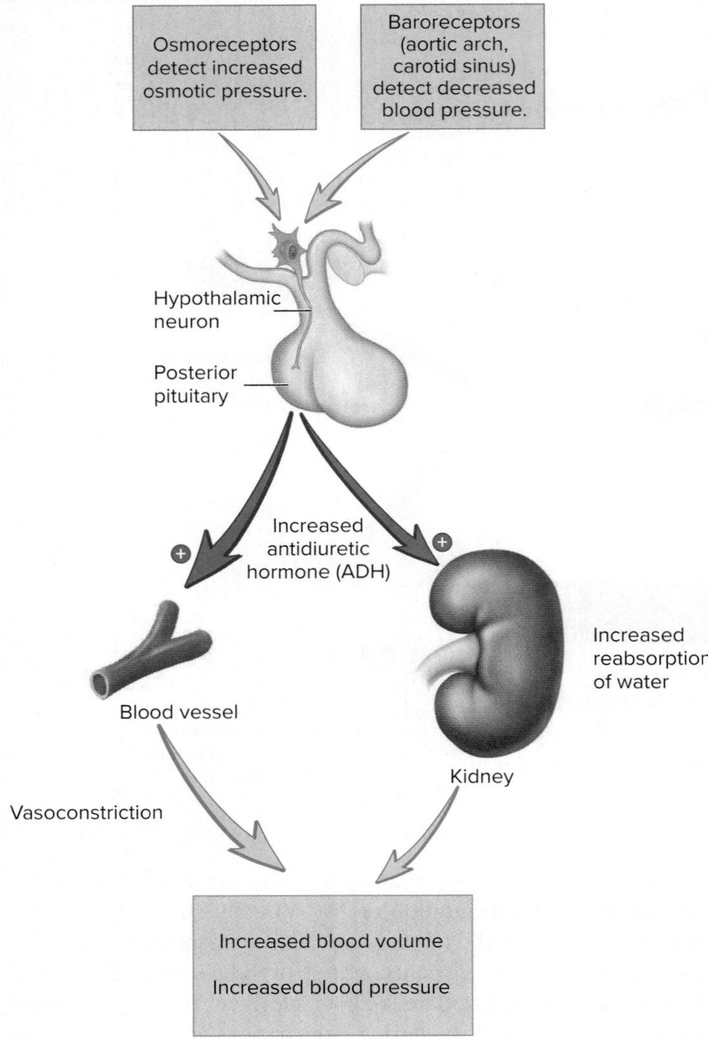

FIGURE 21.35 Antidiuretic Hormone (Vasopressin) Mechanism
Increases in the osmolality of blood or decreases in blood pressure result in antidiuretic hormone (ADH) secretion. ADH increases water reabsorption by the kidneys, and large amounts of ADH result in vasoconstriction. These changes maintain blood pressure.

decreases in blood pressure, as happens after plasma loss, such as in extensive burns or crushing injuries, stimulate ADH secretion.

Atrial Natriuretic Mechanism

A polypeptide called **atrial natriuretic** (AY-tree-al nay-tree-yoo-RET-ik) **hormone (ANH)** is released from cells in the atria of the heart. A major stimulus for its release is increased venous return, which stretches atrial cardiac muscle fibers. Atrial natriuretic hormone acts on the kidneys to increase the rate of urine production and Na^+ loss in the urine. It also dilates arteries and veins. Loss of water and Na^+ in the urine causes the blood volume to decrease, which decreases venous return, and vasodilation results in a decrease in peripheral resistance. These effects cause a decrease in blood pressure.

The renin-angiotensin-aldosterone, ADH, and atrial natriuretic mechanisms work simultaneously to help regulate blood pressure by controlling urine production by the kidneys. If blood pressure drops below 50 mm Hg, the volume of urine produced by the kidneys is reduced to nearly zero. If blood pressure is increased to 200 mm Hg, the urine volume produced is approximately six to eight times greater than normal. The mechanisms that regulate blood pressure in the long term are summarized in figure 21.36.

Fluid Shift Mechanism

The **fluid shift mechanism** occurs in response to small changes in pressures across capillary walls. As blood pressure increases, some fluid is forced from the capillaries into the interstitial spaces. This movement of fluid helps prevent the development of high blood pressure. As blood pressure falls, interstitial fluid moves into capillaries, and this fluid movement resists a further decline in blood pressure. Fluid shift is a powerful mechanism by which blood pressure is maintained because the interstitial volume acts as a reservoir and is in equilibrium with the large volume of intercellular fluid.

The fluid shift mechanism begins to act within a few minutes of a stimulus, but it requires hours to achieve its full functional capacity. It plays a very important role when dehydration develops over several hours, or when a large volume of saline is administered over several hours.

Stress-Relaxation Response

A **stress-relaxation response** is characteristic of smooth muscle fibers (see chapter 9). When blood volume suddenly declines, blood pressure also decreases, reducing the force applied to smooth muscle fibers in blood vessel walls. As a result, during the next few minutes to an hour, the smooth muscle fibers contract, reducing the volume of the blood vessels, and thus resisting a further decline in blood pressure. Conversely, when blood volume increases rapidly, as occurs during a transfusion, blood pressure increases, and smooth muscle fibers of the blood vessel walls relax, resulting in a more gradual increase in blood pressure. The stress-relaxation mechanism is most effective when changes in blood pressure occur over a period of many minutes.

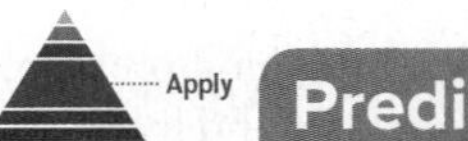

Apply **Predict 8**

Explain the various mechanisms that regulate blood pressure in response to the rapid loss of a large volume of blood, compared with the loss of the same volume of blood over a period of several hours.

ASSESS YOUR PROGRESS

69. *What stimulates renin secretion in the kidneys?*
70. *For each of these chemicals—angiotensin II, aldosterone, antidiuretic hormone, and atrial natriuretic hormone—state where each is produced and how each affects the circulatory system.*
71. *What is fluid shift, and what does it accomplish?*
72. *Describe the stress-relaxation response of a blood vessel.*

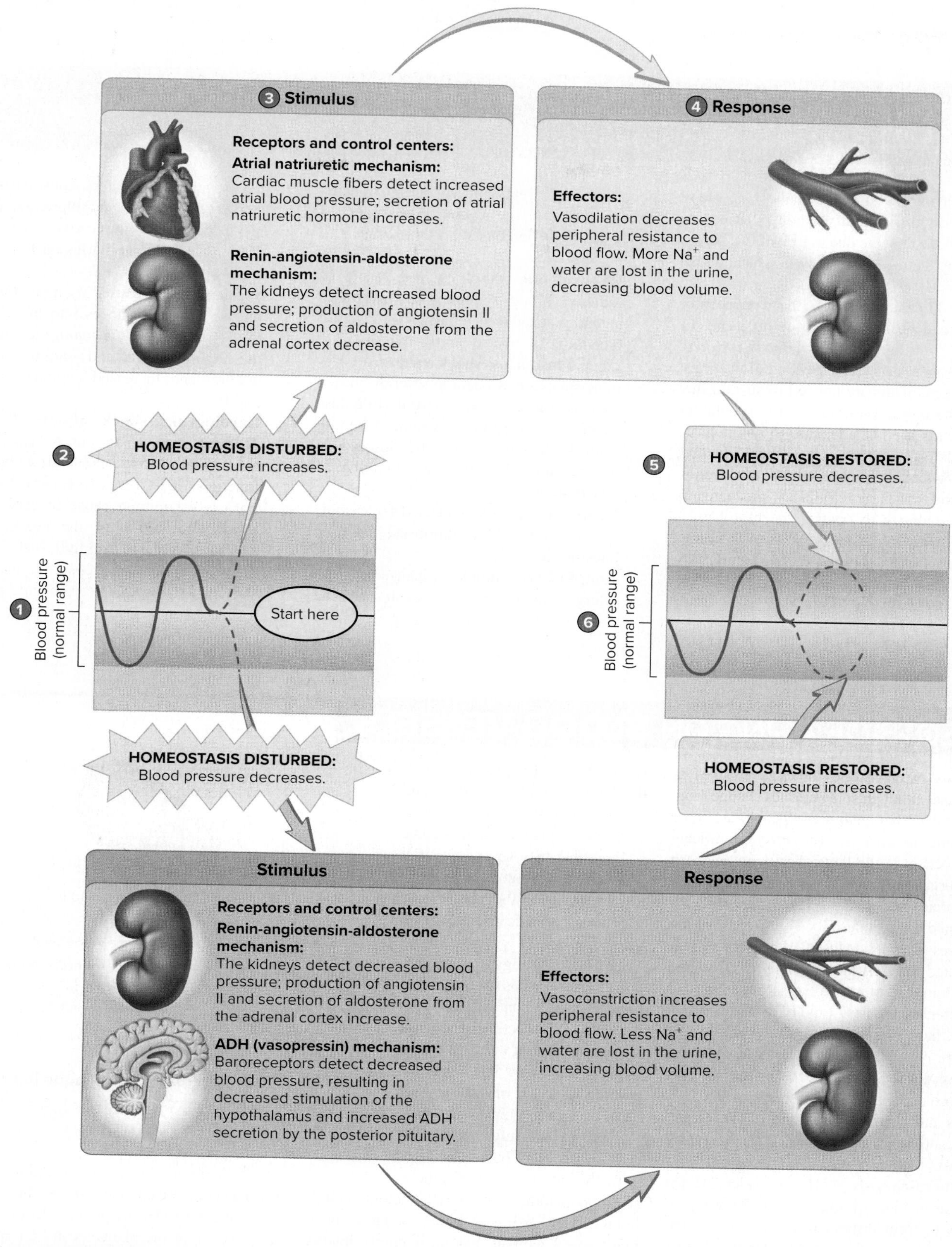

HOMEOSTASIS FIGURE 21.36 Summary of Long-Term (Slow-Acting) Blood Pressure Control Mechanisms

(1) Blood pressure is within its normal range. (2) Blood pressure increases outside the normal range, which causes homeostasis to be disturbed. (3) Increased blood pressure is detected by cardiac muscle fibers and the kidneys (receptors). The heart and kidneys (control center) respond to increased blood pressure by secretion of hormones. (4) Blood vessels of the body and the kidneys (effectors) respond to the hormones by dilating or adjusting blood volume through urine formation. (5) These changes cause blood pressure to decrease. (6) Blood pressure returns to its normal range, and homeostasis is restored. Observe the responses to a decrease in blood pressure outside its normal range by following the *pink arrows*. For more information on the renin-angiotensin-aldosterone mechanism, see figure 21.34; for the antidiuretic hormone mechanism, see figure 21.36; for the atrial natriuretic mechanism, see figure 27.9.

Clinical IMPACT 21.6 Circulatory Shock

Circulatory shock is inadequate blood flow throughout the body that causes tissue damage due to lack of O_2. Severe shock may damage vital body tissues and lead to death.

In mild cases of shock, the baroreceptor reflexes can be adequate to compensate for blood loss until the blood volume is restored. In more severe cases of shock, all of the regulatory mechanisms are needed to sustain life. But in the most severe cases, the regulatory mechanisms are not adequate to compensate for the effects of shock. As a consequence, a positive-feedback cycle begins to develop: The blood pressure regulatory mechanisms lose their ability to control the blood pressure, and shock worsens. As shock becomes worse, the effectiveness of the regulatory mechanisms deteriorates even further. The positive-feedback cycle proceeds until death occurs or until treatment, such as a transfusion, terminates the cycle. Five types of shock are classified based on their cause:

1. **Hypovolemic shock** is the result of reduced blood volume. **Hemorrhagic shock,** caused by internal or external bleeding, is one type of hypovolemic shock. **Plasma loss shock** results from loss of plasma, as may occur in severely burned areas of the body. **Interstitial fluid loss shock** is reduced blood volume resulting from the loss of interstitial fluid, as may occur as a result of diarrhea, vomiting, or dehydration.
2. **Neurogenic shock** is caused by vasodilation in response to emotional upset or anesthesia.
3. **Anaphylactic shock** is caused by an allergic response that results in the release of inflammatory substances that cause vasodilation and increased capillary permeability. Large amounts of fluid then move from capillaries into the interstitial spaces.
4. **Septic shock** is caused by infections that release toxic substances into the circulatory system (*blood poisoning*), depressing the heart's activity and leading to vasodilation and increased capillary permeability.
5. **Cardiogenic shock** results from a decrease in cardiac output caused by events that decrease the heart's ability to function. Heart attack (myocardial infarction) is a common cause of cardiogenic shock. Fibrillation of the heart, which can be initiated by stimuli such as cardiac arrhythmias or exposure to electrical shocks, also results in cardiogenic shock.

EFFECTS OF AGING ON BLOOD VESSELS

The walls of all arteries undergo changes as people age, although some arteries change more rapidly than others and some people are more susceptible to change. The most significant change occurs in the large elastic arteries such as the aorta, in the large arteries that carry blood to the brain, and in the coronary arteries; the age-related changes described here refer to these blood vessel types. Muscular arteries exhibit age-related changes, but these are less dramatic and seldom disrupt normal vessel function.

Arteriosclerosis (ar-TEER-ee-oh-skler-OH-sis; hardening of the arteries) consists of degenerative changes in arteries that make them less elastic, which greatly increases resistance to blood flow. Advanced arteriosclerosis reduces the normal circulation of blood and significantly increases the work performed by the heart.

Atherosclerosis (ATH-er-oh-skler-OH-sis) is the deposition of material in the walls of arteries to form distinct plaques. It is a common type of arteriosclerosis. Atherosclerosis affects primarily medium and larger arteries, including the coronary arteries. The plaques form when macrophages containing cholesterol accumulate in the tunica intima, and smooth muscle fibers of the tunica media proliferate (figure 21.37). The plaques narrow the lumens of blood vessels and make their walls less elastic. Atherosclerotic plaques can become so large that they severely restrict or block blood flow through arteries. In addition, the plaques are sites of thrombosis and embolism formation.

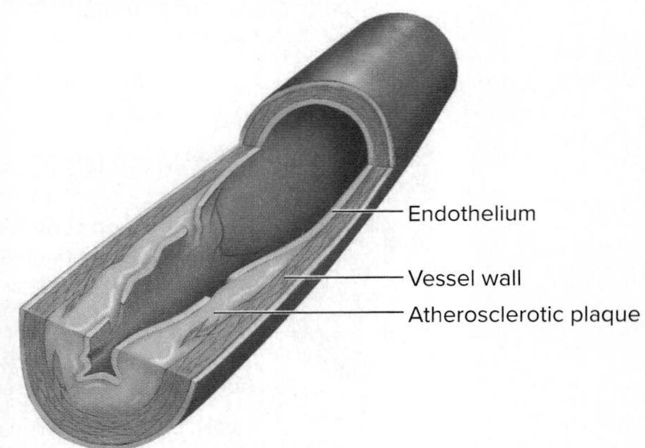

FIGURE 21.37 Atherosclerotic Plaque in an Artery
Atherosclerotic plaques develop within the tissue of the artery wall.

Some investigators propose that arteriosclerosis is not a pathological process but an aging or wearing-out process. Evidence also suggests that arteriosclerosis may be caused by inflammation, possibly a result of autoimmune disease. Atherosclerosis has been studied extensively, and many risk factors have been associated with the development of atherosclerotic plaques. These risk factors include being older, being a male, being a postmenopausal woman, having a family history of atherosclerosis, smoking cigarettes, having hypertension, having diabetes mellitus, having increased blood LDL and cholesterol levels, being overweight, leading a sedentary lifestyle, and having high blood triglyceride levels. Avoiding the environmental factors that influence atherosclerosis slows the development of atherosclerotic plaques. In some cases, the severity of the plaques can be reduced by behavioral modifications and/or drug therapy. For example, regulating blood glucose levels in people with diabetes mellitus and taking drugs that lower high blood cholesterol can provide some protection.

Concept Check

21.1 Functions of the Circulatory System

A. The circulatory system carries blood from the heart to the tissues of the body and returns the blood to the heart.

B. The circulatory system allows for nutrient, waste, and gas exchange with the tissues.

C. The circulatory system transports other substances (hormones, enzymes, etc.) through the body.

D. The circulatory system regulates blood pressure and blood flow to the tissues.

21.2 Structural Features of Blood Vessels

A. Blood flows from the heart through elastic arteries, muscular arteries, and arterioles to the capillaries.

B. Blood returns to the heart from the capillaries through venules, small veins, and large veins.

Structure of Blood Vessels

Except for capillaries and venules, blood vessels have three layers.

A. The inner tunica intima consists of endothelium, a basement membrane, and an internal elastic lamina.

B. The tunica media, the middle layer, contains circular smooth muscle and elastic fibers.

C. The outer tunica externa is connective tissue.

Types of Arteries

A. Large elastic arteries are thin-walled with large diameters. The tunica media has many elastic fibers and little smooth muscle.

B. Muscular arteries are thick-walled with small diameters. The tunica media has abundant smooth muscle and some elastic fibers.

C. Arterioles are the smallest arteries. The tunica media consists of smooth muscle fibers and a few elastic fibers.

Capillaries

A. The entire circulatory system is lined with simple squamous epithelium called endothelium. Capillaries consist only of endothelium.

B. Capillaries are surrounded by loose connective tissue, the externa, that contains pericapillary cells.

C. Three types of capillaries exist.

- The walls of continuous capillaries have no gaps between the endothelial cells.
- Fenestrated capillaries have pores, called fenestrae, that extend completely through the cell.
- Sinusoidal capillaries are large-diameter capillaries with large fenestrae.

D. Materials pass through the capillaries in several ways: between the endothelial cells, through the fenestrae, and through the plasma membrane.

E. Blood flows from arterioles through metarterioles and then through the capillary network. Venules drain the capillary network.

- Smooth muscle in the arterioles, metarterioles, and precapillary sphincters regulates blood flow into the capillaries.
- Blood can pass rapidly through the thoroughfare channel.

F. Arteriovenous anastomoses allow blood to flow from arteries to veins without passing through the capillaries. They function in temperature regulation.

Types of Veins

A. Venules are composed of endothelium surrounded by a few smooth muscle fibers.

B. Small veins are venules covered with a layer of smooth muscle.

C. Medium-sized veins and large veins contain less smooth muscle and fewer elastic fibers than arteries of the same size.

D. Valves prevent the backflow of blood in the veins.

E. Vasa vasorum are blood vessels that supply the tunica externa and tunica media.

1. Given these blood vessels:

(1) arteriole
(2) capillary
(3) elastic artery
(4) muscular artery
(5) vein
(6) venule

Choose the arrangement that lists the blood vessels in the order a red blood cell passes through them as it leaves the heart, travels to a tissue, and returns to the heart.

a. 3,4,2,1,5,6
b. 3,4,1,2,6,5
c. 4,3,1,2,5,6
d. 4,3,2,1,6,5
e. 4,2,3,5,1,6

2. Given these structures:

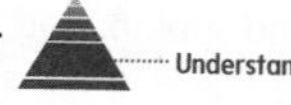

(1) metarteriole
(2) precapillary sphincter
(3) thoroughfare channel

Choose the arrangement that lists the structures in the order a red blood cell encounters them as it passes through a tissue.

a. 1,3,2
b. 2,1,3
c. 2,3,1
d. 3,1,2
e. 3,2,1

3. In which of these blood vessels are elastic fibers present in the largest amounts?

Remember

a. large arteries
b. medium arteries
c. arterioles
d. venules
e. large veins

4. Comparing and contrasting arteries and veins, veins have

Remember

a. thicker walls.
b. a greater amount of smooth muscle than arteries.
c. a tunica media, but arteries do not.
d. valves, but arteries do not.
e. All of these are correct.

5. *The structures that supply the walls of blood vessels with blood are*

Remember

a. venous shunts.
b. tunic channels.
c. arteriovenous anastomoses.
d. vasa vasorum.
e. coronary arteries.

Neural Innervation of Blood Vessels

Sympathetic nerve fibers supply the smooth muscle of the tunica media.

21.3 Pulmonary Circulation

The pulmonary circulation moves blood to and from the lungs. The pulmonary trunk arises from the right ventricle and divides to form the pulmonary arteries, which project to the lungs. From the lungs, the pulmonary veins return to the left atrium.

21.4 Systemic Circulation: Arteries

Arteries carry blood from the left ventricle of the heart to all parts of the body.

Aorta

The aorta leaves the left ventricle to form the ascending aorta, aortic arch, and descending aorta (consisting of the thoracic and abdominal aortae).

Coronary Arteries

Coronary arteries supply the heart.

Arteries of the Head and Neck

A. The brachiocephalic, left common carotid, and left subclavian arteries branch from the aortic arch to supply the head and the upper limbs. The brachiocephalic artery divides to form the right common carotid and the right subclavian arteries. The vertebral arteries branch from the subclavian arteries.

B. The common carotid arteries and the vertebral arteries supply the head.
- The common carotid arteries divide to form the external carotids, which supply the face and mouth, and the internal carotids, which supply the brain.
- The vertebral arteries join within the cranial cavity to form the basilar artery, which supplies the brain.

Arteries of the Upper Limb

A. The subclavian artery continues (without branching) as the axillary artery and then as the brachial artery. The brachial artery divides into the radial and ulnar arteries.

B. The radial artery supplies the deep palmar arch, and the ulnar artery supplies the superficial palmar arch. Both arches give rise to the digital arteries.

Thoracic Aorta and Its Branches

The thoracic aorta has visceral branches that supply the thoracic organs and parietal branches that supply the thoracic wall.

Abdominal Aorta and Its Branches

A. The abdominal aorta has visceral branches that supply the abdominal organs and parietal branches that supply the abdominal wall.

B. The visceral branches are paired and unpaired. The paired arteries supply the kidneys, adrenal glands, and gonads. The unpaired arteries supply the stomach, spleen, and liver (celiac trunk); the small intestine and upper part of the large intestine (superior mesenteric); and the lower part of the large intestine (inferior mesenteric).

Arteries of the Pelvis

A. The common iliac arteries arise from the abdominal aorta, and the internal iliac arteries branch from the common iliac arteries.

B. The visceral branches of the internal iliac arteries supply the pelvic organs, and the parietal branches supply the pelvic wall and floor and the external genitalia.

Arteries of the Lower Limb

A. The external iliac arteries branch from the common iliac arteries.

B. The external iliac artery continues (without branching) as the femoral artery and then as the popliteal artery. The popliteal artery divides to form the anterior and posterior tibial arteries.

C. The posterior tibial artery gives rise to the fibular (peroneal) and plantar arteries. The plantar arteries form the plantar arch, from which the digital arteries arise.

6. *Given these arteries:*

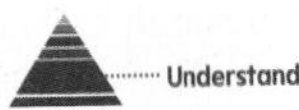

(1) basilar
(2) common carotid
(3) internal carotid
(4) vertebral

Which of these arteries have direct *connections with the cerebral arterial circle (circle of Willis)?*

a. 1,2
b. 2,4
c. 1,3
d. 3,4
e. 2,3

7. *Given these blood vessels:*

(1) axillary artery
(2) brachial artery
(3) brachiocephalic artery
(4) radial artery
(5) subclavian artery

Choose the arrangement that lists the vessels in order, from the aorta to the right hand.

a. 2,5,4,1
b. 5,2,1,4
c. 5,3,1,4,2
d. 3,5,1,2,4
e. 4,5,1,2,3

8. *A branch of the aorta that supplies the liver, stomach, and spleen is the*

Remember

a. celiac trunk.
b. common iliac.
c. inferior mesenteric.
d. superior mesenteric.
e. renal.

9. *Given these arteries:*

(1) common iliac
(2) external iliac
(3) femoral
(4) popliteal

Choose the arrangement that lists the arteries in order, from the aorta to the knee.

a. 1,2,3,4
b. 1,2,4,3
c. 2,1,3,4
d. 2,1,4,3
e. 3,1,2,4

10. *For each of the following destinations, name all the arteries that a red blood cell would encounter if it started its journey in the left ventricle.* Understand
    a. *posterior interventricular groove of the heart*
    b. *anterior neck to the brain (give two ways)*
    c. *posterior neck to the brain (give two ways)*
    d. *external skull*
    e. *tip of the fingers of the left hand (what other blood vessel would be encountered if the trip were through the right upper limb?)*
    f. *anterior compartment of the leg*
    g. *liver*
    h. *small intestine*
    i. *urinary bladder*

21.5 Systemic Circulation: Veins

A. The three major veins returning blood to the heart are the superior vena cava (head, neck, thorax, and upper limbs), the inferior vena cava (abdomen, pelvis, and lower limbs), and the coronary sinus (heart).

B. Veins are of three types: superficial, deep, and sinuses.

Veins Draining the Heart

Coronary veins enter the coronary sinus or the right atrium.

Veins of the Head and Neck

A. The internal jugular veins drain the venous sinuses of the anterior head and neck.

B. The external jugular veins and the vertebral veins drain the posterior head and neck.

Veins of the Upper Limb

A. The deep veins are the small ulnar and radial veins of the forearm, which join the brachial veins of the arm. The brachial veins drain into the axillary vein.

B. The superficial veins are the basilic, cephalic, and median cubital. The basilic vein becomes the axillary vein, which then becomes the subclavian vein. The cephalic vein drains into the axillary vein.

Veins of the Thorax

The left and right brachiocephalic veins and the azygos veins return blood to the superior vena cava.

Veins of the Abdomen and Pelvis

A. Ascending lumbar veins from the abdomen join the azygos and hemiazygos veins.

B. Vessels from the kidneys, adrenal gland, and gonads directly enter the inferior vena cava.

C. Vessels from the stomach, intestines, spleen, and pancreas connect with the hepatic portal vein. The hepatic portal vein transports blood to the liver for processing. Hepatic veins from the liver join the inferior vena cava.

Veins of the Lower Limb

A. The deep veins are the fibular (peroneal), anterior and posterior tibial, popliteal, femoral, and external iliac.

B. The superficial veins are the great and small saphenous veins.

11. *Given these veins:* 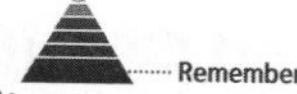

    (1) *brachiocephalic*
    (2) *internal jugular*
    (3) *superior vena cava*
    (4) *venous sinus*

    Choose the arrangement that lists the veins in order, from the brain to the heart.
    a. *1,2,4,3*
    b. *2,4,1,3*
    c. *2,4,3,1*
    d. *4,2,1,3*
    e. *4,2,3,1*

12. *Blood returning from the arm to the subclavian vein passes through which of these veins?* Remember
    a. *cephalic*
    b. *basilic*
    c. *brachial*
    d. *Both a and b are correct.*
    e. *All of these are correct.*

13. *Given these blood vessels:* 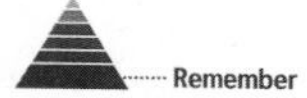

    (1) *inferior mesenteric vein*
    (2) *superior mesenteric vein*
    (3) *hepatic portal vein*
    (4) *hepatic vein*

    Choose the arrangement that lists the vessels in order, from the small intestine to the inferior vena cava.
    a. *1,3,4*
    b. *1,4,3*
    c. *2,3,4*
    d. *2,4,3*
    e. *3,1,4*

14. *Given these veins:* Remember
    (1) *small saphenous*
    (2) *great saphenous*
    (3) *fibular (peroneal)*
    (4) *posterior tibial*

    Which are superficial veins?
    a. *1,2*
    b. *1,3*
    c. *2,3*
    d. *2,4*
    e. *3,4*

15. *For each of the following starting places, name all the veins that a red blood cell would encounter on its way back to the right atrium.* 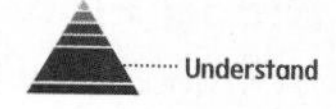

    a. *anterior interventricular groove of the heart (give two ways)*
    b. *venous sinus near the brain*
    c. *external posterior of skull*
    d. *hand (return deep and superficial)*
    e. *foot (return deep and superficial)*
    f. *stomach*
    g. *kidney*
    h. *left inferior wall of the thorax*

16. *In a study of heart valve functions, it is necessary to inject a dye into the right atrium of the heart by inserting a catheter into a blood vessel and moving the catheter into the right atrium. What route would you suggest? If you wanted to do this procedure into the left atrium, what would you do differently?* Understand

21.6 Dynamics of Blood Circulation

The interrelationships among pressure, flow, resistance, and the control mechanisms that regulate blood pressure and blood flow play a critical role in the function of the circulatory system.

Laminar and Turbulent Flow in Vessels

Blood flow through vessels is normally streamlined, or laminar. Turbulent flow is disruption of laminar flow.

Blood Pressure

A. Blood pressure is a measure of the force exerted by blood against the blood vessel wall. Blood moves through vessels because of blood pressure.

B. Blood pressure can be measured by listening for Korotkoff sounds produced by turbulent flow in arteries as pressure is released from a blood pressure cuff.

17. *The resistance to blood flow is greatest in the* 

    a. aorta.
    b. arterioles.
    c. capillaries.
    d. venules.
    e. veins.

18. *All the blood that passes through the aorta, except the blood that flows into the coronary vessels, returns to the heart through the venae cavae.* (Hint: *The diameter of the aorta is 26 mm, and the diameter of a vena cava is 32 mm.) Explain why the resistance to blood flow in the aorta is greater than the resistance to blood flow in the venae cavae. Because the resistances are different, explain why blood flow can be the same.* Apply

19. *As blood vessels increase in diameter, the amount of smooth muscle decreases and the amount of connective tissue increases. Explain why.* (Hint: *Remember Laplace's law.)* Apply

20. *A very short nursing student is asked to measure the blood pressure of a very tall person. She decides to measure the blood pressure at the level of the tall person's foot while he is standing. What artery does she use? After taking the blood pressure, she decides that the tall person is suffering from hypertension because the systolic pressure is 200 mm Hg. Is her diagnosis correct? Why or why not?* Apply

Blood Flow and Poiseuille's Law

A. Blood flow is the amount of blood that moves through a vessel in a given period. Blood flow is directly proportional to pressure differences and inversely proportional to resistance.

B. Resistance is the sum of all the factors that inhibit blood flow. Resistance increases when viscosity increases and when blood vessels become smaller in diameter or increase in length.

C. Viscosity is the resistance of a liquid to flow. Most of the viscosity of blood results from red blood cells. The viscosity of blood increases when the hematocrit increases.

Critical Closing Pressure and Laplace's Law

A. As pressure in a vessel decreases, the force holding it open decreases, and the vessel tends to collapse. The critical closing pressure is the pressure at which a blood vessel closes.

B. Laplace's law states that the force acting on the wall of a blood vessel is proportional to the diameter of the vessel times blood pressure.

Vascular Compliance

A. Vascular compliance is a measure of the change in volume of blood vessels produced by a change in pressure. The venous system has a large compliance and acts as a blood reservoir.

B. The greatest volume of blood is contained in the veins. The smallest volume is in the arterioles.

21. *Vascular compliance is* 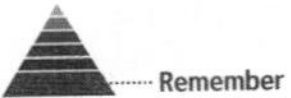

    a. greater in arteries than in veins.
    b. the increase in vessel volume divided by the increase in vessel pressure.
    c. the pressure at which blood vessels collapse.
    d. proportional to the diameter of the blood vessel times pressure.
    e. All of these are correct.

22. *Veins* Remember

    a. increase their volume because of their large compliance.
    b. increase venous return to the heart when they vasodilate.
    c. vasodilate because of increased sympathetic stimulation.
    d. All of these are correct

21.7 Physiology of the Systemic Circulation

Cross-Sectional Area of Blood Vessels

As the diameter of vessels decreases, their total cross-sectional area increases, and the velocity of blood flow through them decreases.

Pressure and Resistance

Blood pressure averages 100 mm Hg in the aorta and drops to 0 mm Hg in the right atrium. The greatest drop occurs in the arterioles, which regulate blood flow through tissues.

Pulse and Pulse Pressure

A. Pulse pressure is the difference between systolic and diastolic pressures. Pulse pressure increases when stroke volume increases or vascular compliance decreases.

B. Pulse pressure waves travel through the vascular system faster than the blood flows.

C. Pulse pressure can be used to take the pulse, which can serve as an indicator of heart rate and rhythm.

Capillary Exchange and Regulation of Interstitial Fluid Volume

A. Blood pressure, capillary permeability, and osmosis affect the movement of fluid from the capillaries.

B. A net movement of fluid occurs from the blood into the tissues. The fluid gained by the tissues is removed by the lymphatic system.

23. *David was suffering from severe cirrhosis of the liver and hepatitis. Over a period of time, he developed severe edema. Explain how decreased liver function can result in edema.* Apply

Functional Characteristics of Veins

Venous return to the heart increases because of an increase in blood volume, venous tone, and arteriole dilation.

Blood Pressure and the Effect of Gravity

In a standing person, hydrostatic pressure caused by gravity increases blood pressure below the heart and decreases pressure above the heart.

21.8 Control of Blood Flow in Tissues

Blood flow through tissues is highly controlled and matched closely to the metabolic needs of tissues.

Local Control of Blood Flow in Tissues

A. Blood flow through a tissue is usually proportional to the tissue's metabolic needs. Exceptions are tissues that perform functions that require additional blood.

B. Control of blood flow by the metarterioles and precapillary sphincters can be regulated by vasodilator substances or by lack of O_2 and nutrients.

C. Only large changes in blood pressure have an effect on blood flow through tissues.

D. If the metabolic activity of a tissue increases, the number and the diameter of capillaries in the tissue increase over time.

E. Autoregulation refers to changes in blood flow in response to changes in O_2, nutrients, and metabolic by-products, which alter vasoconstriction and contraction of precapillary sphincters to adjust blood flow through tissues.

F. Long-term regulation of blood flow results in alteration in capillary diameter and number of capillaries in a tissue.

Nervous and Hormonal Control of Blood Flow in Tissues

A. The sympathetic nervous system (vasomotor center in the medulla) controls blood vessel diameter. Other brain areas can excite or inhibit the vasomotor center.

B. Vasomotor tone is a state of partial contraction of blood vessels.

C. The nervous system is responsible for routing the flow of blood and maintaining blood pressure.

D. Sympathetic action potentials stimulate epinephrine and norepinephrine release from the adrenal medulla, and these hormones cause vasoconstriction in most blood vessels.

24. *Local direct control of blood flow through a tissue*

a. maintains an adequate rate of flow despite large changes in arterial blood pressure.
b. results from relaxation and contraction of precapillary sphincters.
c. occurs in response to a buildup in CO_2 in the tissues.
d. occurs in response to a decrease in oxygen in the tissues.
e. All of these are correct.

21.9 Regulation of Mean Arterial Pressure

Mean arterial pressure (MAP) is proportional to cardiac output times peripheral resistance.

Short-Term Regulation of Blood Pressure

A. Baroreceptors are sensory receptors sensitive to stretch.
- Baroreceptors are located in the carotid sinuses and the aortic arch.
- The baroreceptor reflex changes peripheral resistance, heart rate, and stroke volume in response to changes in blood pressure.

B. Chemoreceptors are sensory receptors sensitive to O_2, CO_2, and pH levels in the blood.

C. Epinephrine and norepinephrine are released from the adrenal medulla as a result of sympathetic stimulation. They increase heart rate, stroke volume, and vasoconstriction.

D. The CNS ischemic response, which results from high CO_2 or low pH levels in the medulla, increases peripheral resistance.

25. *An increase in mean arterial pressure can result from*

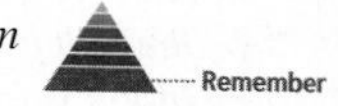

a. an increase in peripheral resistance.
b. an increase in heart rate.
c. an increase in stroke volume.
d. All of these are correct.

26. *When blood O_2 levels markedly decrease, the chemoreceptor reflex causes* (Remember)

a. peripheral resistance to decrease.
b. mean arterial blood pressure to increase.
c. vasomotor tone to decrease.
d. vasodilation.
e. All of these are correct.

27. *During hyperventilation, CO_2 is "blown off," and CO_2 levels in the blood decrease. What effect does this decrease have on blood pressure? Explain. What symptoms do you expect to see as a result?* (Apply)

28. *Epinephrine causes vasodilation of blood vessels in cardiac muscle but vasoconstriction of blood vessels in the skin. Explain why this is a beneficial arrangement.* (Apply)

Long-Term Regulation of Blood Pressure

A. In the renin-angiotensin-aldosterone mechanism, renin is released by the kidneys in response to low blood pressure. Renin promotes the production of angiotensin II, which causes vasoconstriction and an increase in aldosterone secretion.

B. The antidiuretic hormone (vasopressin) mechanism causes ADH release from the posterior pituitary in response to a substantial decrease in blood pressure. ADH acts directly on blood vessels to cause vasoconstriction.

C. The atrial natriuretic mechanism causes atrial natriuretic hormone release from the cardiac muscle fibers when atrial blood pressure increases. It stimulates an increase in urine production, causing a decrease in blood volume and blood pressure.

D. The fluid shift mechanism causes fluid shift, which is the movement of fluid between the interstitial spaces and capillaries in response to changes in blood pressure to maintain blood volume.

E. The stress-relaxation response is an adjustment of the smooth muscles of blood vessels in response to a change in blood volume.

29. *When blood pressure is suddenly decreased a small amount (10 mm Hg), which of these mechanisms are activated to restore blood pressure to normal levels?* (Remember)

a. chemoreceptor reflexes
b. baroreceptor reflexes
c. CNS ischemic responses
d. All of these are correct.

30. *A sudden release of epinephrine from the adrenal medulla* Remember
    a. *increases heart rate.*
    b. *increases stroke volume.*
    c. *causes vasoconstriction in visceral blood vessels.*
    d. *All of these are correct.*

31. *In response to a decrease in blood pressure*

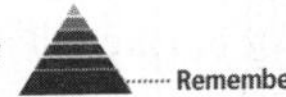

    a. *ADH secretion increases.*
    b. *the kidneys decrease urine production.*
    c. *blood volume increases.*
    d. *All of these are correct.*

32. *In response to a decrease in blood pressure*

    a. *more fluid than normal enters the tissues (fluid shift mechanism).*
    b. *smooth muscles in blood vessels relax (stress-relaxation response).*
    c. *the kidneys retain more salts and water than normal.*
    d. *All of these are correct.*

33. *A patient is found to have severe arteriosclerosis of the renal arteries, which has reduced renal blood pressure. Which of these is consistent with that condition?* Understand
    a. *hypotension*
    b. *hypertension*
    c. *decreased vasomotor tone*
    d. *exaggerated sympathetic stimulation of the heart*
    e. *Both a and c are correct.*

34. *During exercise, the blood flow through skeletal muscle may increase up to 20-fold. However, the cardiac output does not increase that much. This occurs because of* Understand
    a. *vasoconstriction in the viscera.*
    b. *vasoconstriction in the skin (at least temporarily).*
    c. *vasodilation of skeletal muscle blood vessels.*
    d. *Both a and b are correct.*
    e. *All of these are correct.*

35. *While Jack and Eliza were backpacking on a trail in Yellowstone Park, they encountered a grizzly bear cub that seemed amazingly tame. However, while Jack tried to feed the cub, its mother appeared and attacked him. Eliza escaped by climbing a tree, but Jack received several deep lacerations (cuts) and lost a lot of blood over the next several hours. Eliza helped him reach medical aid, and he survived. Which of the following mechanisms was (were) activated to help keep Jack alive? Explain your choice.* Apply
    (1) *baroreceptor mechanism*
    (2) *CNS ischemic response*
    (3) *renin-angiotensin-aldosterone mechanism*
    (4) *fluid shift mechanism*
    (5) *antidiuretic hormone mechanism*
    (6) *adrenal medullary response*
    a. *1,2,3,4,5,6*
    b. *1,3,4,5,6*
    c. *1,6*
    d. *1,4,6*
    e. *1*

36. *Mr. Wilson, age 85, lives in a care facility, where he is not very mobile and is often lethargic. One day an aide noticed that he was sitting in his usual chair but appeared to be unconscious. She took his pulse, which was 140 beats/minute and then took his blood pressure, which was 190/130. Which of the following conditions is (are) consistent with these observations?* Apply
    a. *stroke*
    b. *activation of the CNS ischemic response*
    c. *heart attack*
    d. *shock*
    e. *Both a and b are correct.*

Answers to this chapter's odd-numbered Concept Check questions appear in Appendix F.

CHAPTER 22

Lymphatic System and Immunity

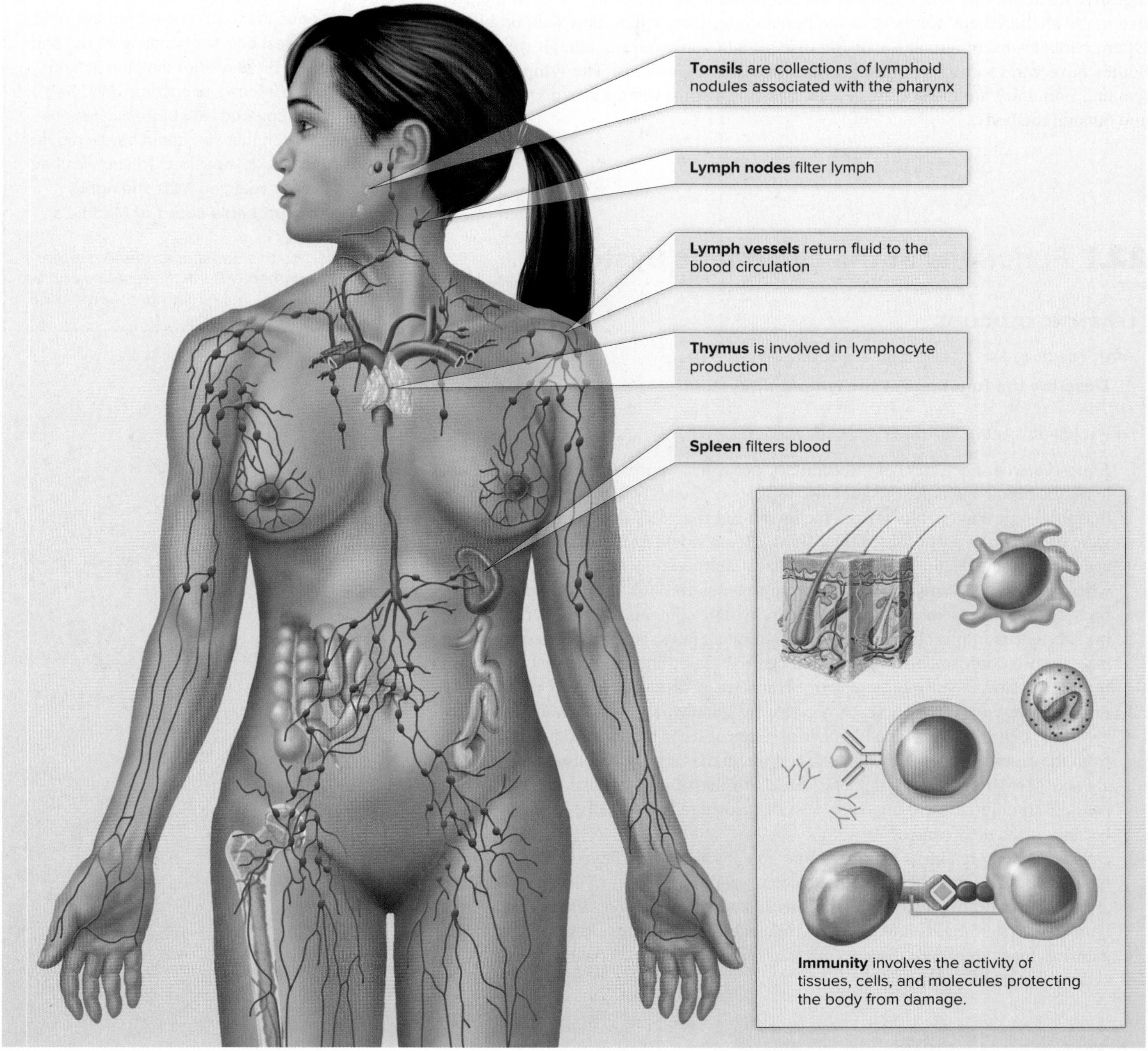

The lymphatic system is important to the defense of the body, but it also plays a role in maintaining the fluid balance as well as in the absorption of lipids in the digestive tract. Immunity involves many structural levels of the body (organ, tissue, cell, chemical) working together to protect the body.

One of the basic themes of life is that many organisms consume other organisms—or use them to survive. For example, a parasite lives on or in another organism, called the host. The host provides the parasite with the conditions and food necessary for survival. Humans are host to many kinds of organisms, including microorganisms (bacteria, viruses, fungi, and protozoans), insects, and worms. Some of these microorganisms are beneficial, like the microbiota of the digestive tract, but that is not the case with all of them. Hookworms, for example, can live in the sheltered environment of the human intestines, where they feed on blood. Often, parasites harm humans, causing disease and sometimes death. However, our bodies have ways to resist or destroy harmful microorganisms. The lymphatic system and immunity are the body's defense systems against threats arising both inside and outside the body.

Learn to Predict

The next time Jake suggests clearing an area for a new flowerbed, Maddie may just say no. While clearing a rather overgrown area of their backyard, Maddie pulled up several vines that had grown onto the fence. The next day, her hands were red and itchy, and by the day after that, the itching had become intense. In addition, Maddie's hands were covered with blisterlike lesions and so swollen that she could hardly move her fingers. Maddie suspected she was having an allergic reaction. Was she right? **Explain the probable cause of Maddie's symptoms.**

Answers to this question and the chapter's odd-numbered Predict questions can be found in Appendix E.

22.1 Functions of the Lymphatic System

LEARNING OUTCOME

After reading this section, you should be able to

A. **Describe the functions of the lymphatic system.**

The lymphatic system has three main functions:

1. *Fluid balance*. Each day, in the capillary networks, approximately 30 L of fluid leave the blood and enter the interstitial spaces of the body. However, only 27 L of that fluid return to the blood from the interstitial spaces. If those extra 3 L of fluid were to remain as part of interstitial fluid, edema would result, causing tissue damage and eventual death. Instead, lymphatic capillaries collect the 3 L of clear fluid, where it is called **lymph** (LIMF). Lymph passes through the lymphatic vessels back to the blood. In addition to water, lymph contains solutes derived from (a) substances in plasma, such as ions, nutrients, gases, and some proteins, which pass from blood capillaries into the interstitial fluid; and (b) substances derived from cells, such as hormones, enzymes, and waste products.
2. *Lipid absorption*. **Lacteals** (LAK-tee-alz) are lymphatic vessels located in the lining of the digestive tract. The lymphatic system absorbs lipids and other substances from the digestive tract (see chapter 24) through the lacteals. Lipids enter the lacteals and pass through the lymphatic vessels to the venous circulation. The lymph passing through these lymphatic vessels, called **chyle** (KILE), appears white because of its lipid content.
3. *Defense*. Microorganisms and other foreign substances are filtered from lymph by lymph nodes and from blood by the spleen. In addition, lymphocytes and other cells are capable of destroying microorganisms and other foreign substances. Because the lymphatic system fights infections, and filters blood and lymph to remove microorganisms, many infectious diseases produce symptoms associated with the lymphatic system (see table 22.6).

ASSESS YOUR PROGRESS

Answers to these questions are found in the section you have just completed. Re-read the section if you need help in answering these questions.

1. *Describe the three functions of the lymphatic system.*

Module 10
Lymphatic System

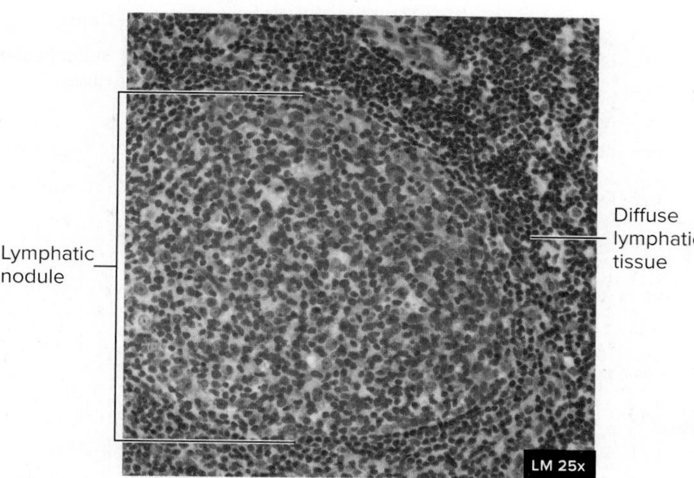

FIGURE 22.5 Diffuse Lymphatic Tissue and a Lymphatic Nodule
Diffuse lymphatic tissue surrounding a lymphatic nodule in the small intestine. STEVE GSCHMEISSNER/Science Photo Library/Alamy Stock Photo APR

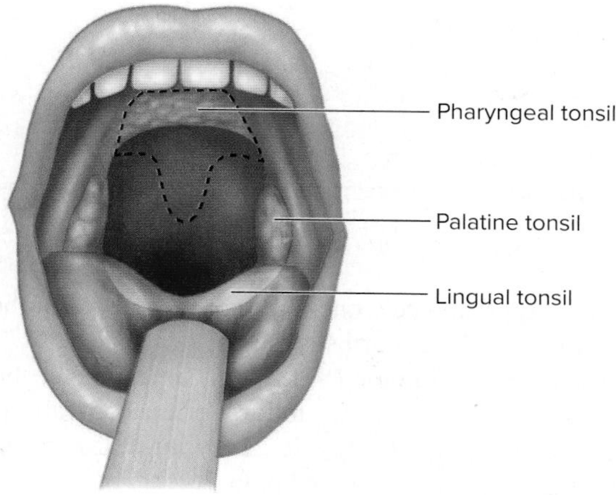

FIGURE 22.6 Tonsils
Anterior view of the oral cavity, showing the tonsils. Part of the palate is removed (*dotted line*) to show the pharyngeal tonsil. APR

tonsil is a collection of somewhat closely aggregated lymphatic nodules near the junction between the nasal cavity and the pharynx. When the pharyngeal tonsil is enlarged, it is commonly called the **adenoid** (ADD-eh-noyd; glandlike) or **adenoids.** An enlarged pharyngeal tonsil can interfere with normal breathing. The **lingual tonsil** is a loosely associated collection of lymphatic nodules on the posterior surface of the tongue.

Sometimes the palatine tonsils and/or the pharyngeal tonsil become chronically infected and must be removed. The lingual tonsil becomes infected less often than the other tonsils and is more difficult to remove.

ASSESS YOUR PROGRESS

8. *What are the primary lymphatic organs? What are the secondary lymphatic organs and tissues?*
9. *What is mucosa-associated lymphoid tissue (MALT)? In what way is the location of MALT beneficial?*
10. *Distinguish among lymphatic tissue, lymphatic nodules, lymphatic follicles, and Peyer patches.*
11. *Describe the structure, function, and location of the tonsils.*

Lymph Nodes

Lymph nodes are small, round or bean-shaped structures ranging from 1 mm to 25 mm long. They are distributed along the course of the lymphatic vessels (figure 22.7; see figure 22.1). An important function of lymph nodes is to filter the lymph, removing bacteria and other materials. In addition, lymphocytes congregate and proliferate as well as carry out their protective functions within lymph nodes.

Lymph nodes are categorized as superficial or deep. **Superficial lymph nodes** are in the subcutaneous tissue beneath the skin, and **deep lymph nodes** are everywhere else. Most superficial and deep lymph nodes are located near or on blood vessels. Approximately 450 lymph nodes are distributed throughout the body.

- Cervical and head lymph nodes (about 70) filter lymph from the head and neck.
- Axillary lymph nodes (about 30) filter lymph from the upper limbs and superficial thorax.
- Thoracic lymph nodes (about 100) filter lymph from the thoracic wall and organs.
- Abdominopelvic lymph nodes (about 230) filter lymph from the abdomen and pelvis.
- Inguinal and popliteal lymph nodes (about 20) filter lymph from the lower limbs and the superficial pelvis.

A dense connective tissue **capsule** surrounds each lymph node (figure 22.7). Extensions of the capsule, called **trabeculae** (trah-BEK-yoo-lee), form a delicate internal skeleton in the lymph node. Reticular fibers extend from the capsule and trabeculae to form a fibrous network throughout the lymph node. In some areas of the lymph node, lymphocytes and macrophages are packed around the reticular fibers to form lymphatic tissue; in other areas, the reticular fibers extend across open spaces to form **lymphatic sinuses.** The lymphatic tissue and sinuses within the lymph node are arranged into two somewhat indistinct layers, an outer cortex and an inner medulla. The **cortex** consists of a subcapsular sinus, beneath the capsule, and cortical sinuses, which are separated by diffuse lymphatic tissue, trabeculae, and lymphatic nodules. The inner **medulla** is organized into branching, irregular strands of diffuse lymphatic tissue, called the **medullary cords,** separated by medullary sinuses (see figure 22.7*b*).

Lymph nodes are the only structures that filter lymph. **Afferent lymphatic vessels** carry lymph to the lymph nodes, where it is filtered, and **efferent lymphatic vessels** carry lymph away from the lymph nodes. Lymph from afferent lymphatic vessels enters the subcapsular sinus, filters through the cortex and medulla, and exits the lymph node through efferent lymphatic vessels. The efferent vessels of one lymph node may become the afferent vessels of another lymph node or may converge to form lymphatic trunks, which carry lymph to the blood at thoracic veins.

Macrophages lining the lymphatic sinuses remove bacteria and other foreign substances from the lymph as it slowly filters through the sinuses. Microorganisms and other foreign substances in the lymph can stimulate lymphocytes throughout the lymph node to

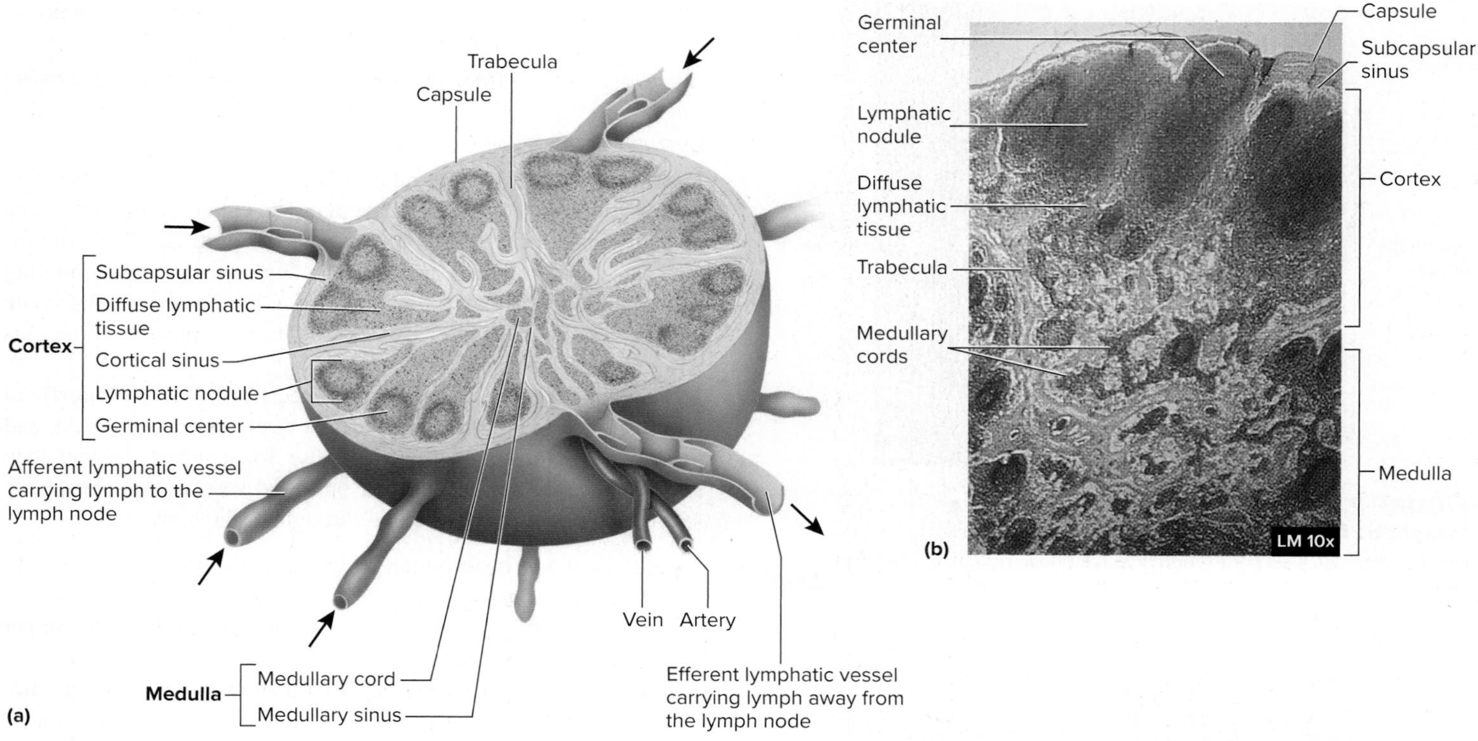

FIGURE 22.7 Lymph Node

(*a*) *Arrows* indicate the direction of lymph flow. As lymph moves through the sinuses, phagocytic cells remove foreign substances. The germinal centers are sites of lymphocyte production. (*b*) Histology of a lymph node. (b) Trent Stephens

undergo cell division, with proliferation especially evident in the lymphatic nodules of the cortex. These areas of rapid lymphocyte division are called **germinal centers.** The newly produced lymphocytes are released into the lymph and eventually reach the bloodstream, where they circulate. Subsequently, the lymphocytes can leave the blood and enter other lymphatic tissues.

Spleen

The **spleen** is roughly the size of a clenched fist and is located on the left, superior part of the abdominal cavity (figure 22.8). The average weight of the adult spleen is 180 g in males and 140 g in females. The size and weight of the spleen tend to decrease in older people, but in certain diseases the spleen can achieve a weight of 2000 g or more. For example, about 50% of individuals who have infectious mononucleosis develop an enlarged spleen as a result of increased numbers of defense cells. Usually, the spleen will reduce in size following the infection.

The spleen has an outer capsule of dense irregular connective tissue and a small amount of smooth muscle. Bundles of connective tissue fibers from the capsule form trabeculae, which extend into the organ, subdividing it into small, interconnected compartments. Arteries, veins, and lymphatic vessels extend through the trabeculae to supply the compartments, which are filled with white pulp and red pulp. **White pulp** is lymphatic tissue surrounding the arteries within the spleen. **Red pulp** is associated with the veins within the spleen. Red pulp consists of a fibrous network, filled with macrophages and red blood cells, and enlarged capillaries that connect to the veins. Approximately one-fourth of the volume of the spleen is white pulp, and three-fourths is red pulp.

Branches of the **splenic** (SPLEN-ik) **artery** enter the spleen at the **hilum,** and their branches follow the various trabeculae into the spleen (figure 22.8*a,b*). Figure 22.8*c* illustrates the pattern of blood flow through white and red pulp.

1. From the trabeculae, arterial branches extend into the white pulp, which consists of the periarterial lymphatic sheath and lymphatic nodules. The **periarterial lymphatic sheath** is composed of diffuse lymphatic tissue surrounding arteries and arterioles extending to lymphatic nodules.
2. Arterioles enter lymphatic nodules and give rise to capillaries. Blood flows from the capillaries into the red pulp, which consists of the splenic cords and the venous sinuses. The **splenic cords** are a network of reticular cells that produce reticular fibers (see chapter 4). The spaces between the reticular cells are occupied by splenic macrophages and blood cells that have come from the capillaries. The **venous sinuses** are enlarged capillaries between the splenic cords.
3. Some capillaries connect directly with a venous sinus.
4. The ends of most capillaries are separated from the venous sinuses, though blood rapidly crosses the gap.
5. Some capillaries empty into the splenic cords. Blood percolates through the splenic cords and passes through the walls of the venous sinuses.
6. The venous sinuses typically connect to trabecular veins, which unite to form vessels that leave the spleen to form the **splenic vein.**

Although blood flow through the spleen can take from a few seconds to an hour or more, most blood flows through the spleen rapidly. The rapid flow results from the movement of blood from the ends of capillaries into the beginning of the venous sinuses.

PROCESS **Figure**

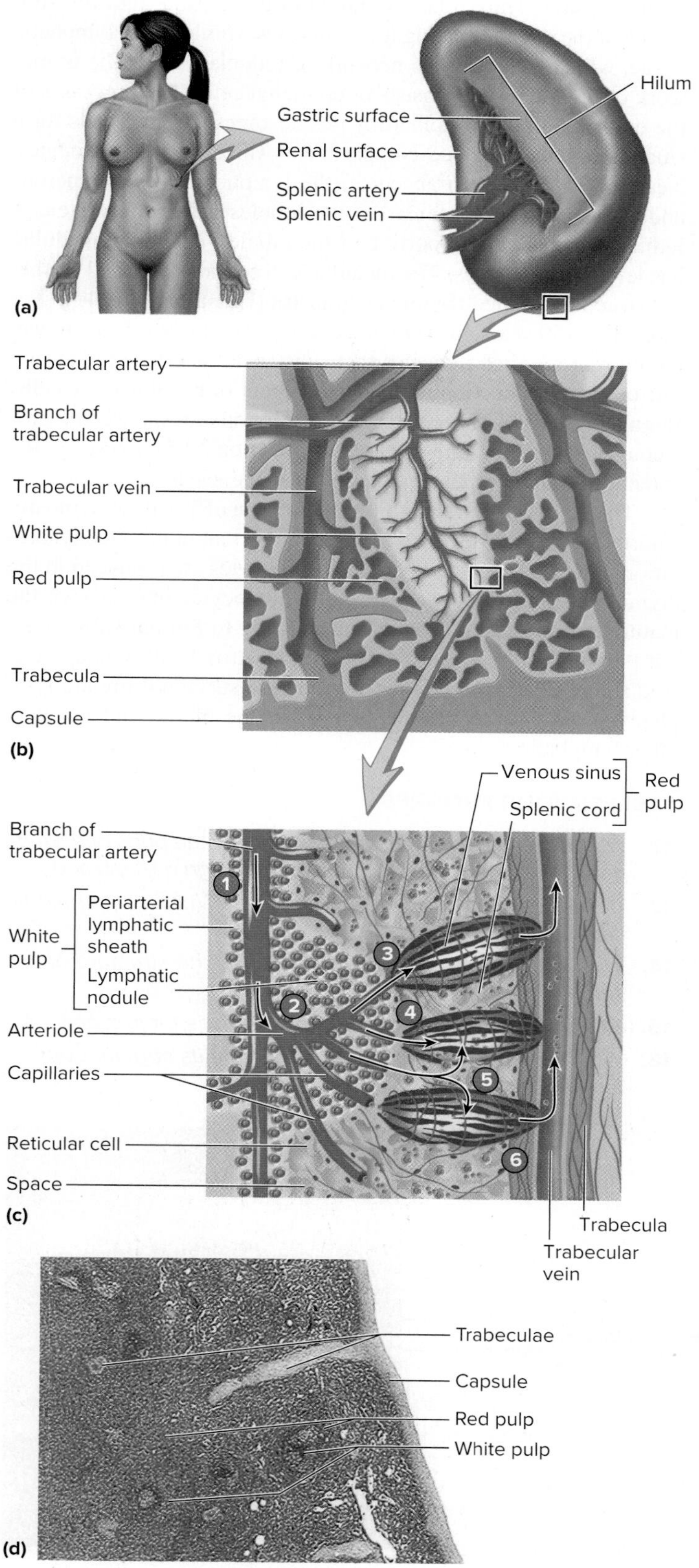

Recall that though a few capillaries connect directly to venous sinuses, most capillaries are separated by a small gap (figure 22.8*c*, *step 4*). Slower blood flow occurs when blood leaves the ends of the capillaries, enters the splenic cords, percolates through them, and passes through the walls of the venous sinuses.

The spleen has several functions, including destroying defective red blood cells, detecting and responding to foreign substances in the blood, and acting as a blood reservoir. As red blood cells age, they lose their ability to bend and fold. Consequently, the cells can rupture as they pass slowly through the meshwork of the splenic cords or the intercellular slits of the venous sinus walls. Splenic macrophages then phagocytize the cellular debris.

Foreign substances in the blood passing through the spleen can stimulate an immune response because of the presence of specialized lymphocytes in the white pulp (see section 22.5). There are high concentrations of T cells in the periarterial lymphatic sheath and B cells in the lymphatic nodules.

The splenic cords of the spleen are a limited reservoir for blood. For example, during exercise splenic volume can be reduced by 40–50%. The resulting small increase in circulating red blood cells can promote better O_2 delivery to muscles during exercise or emergency situations. Physiologists do not presently know if this reduction results from the contraction of smooth muscle within the capsule, from the contraction of smooth muscle (myofibroblast) within the trabeculae, or from the reduced blood flow through the spleen caused by the constriction of blood vessels.

Although the ribs protect the spleen, it is often ruptured in traumatic abdominal injuries. A ruptured spleen can cause severe bleeding, shock, and death. Surgical intervention may stop the bleeding. Cracks in the spleen are repaired using sutures and blood clotting agents. Mesh wrapped around the spleen can hold it together. If these techniques do not stop the bleeding, a **splenectomy** (splee-NEK-toh-mee), removal of the spleen, may be necessary. After removal of the spleen, other lymphatic organs and the liver compensate for the loss of its functions.

Thymus

The **thymus** (THIGH-mus) is a bilobed gland (figure 22.9) located in the superior mediastinum, the partition dividing the thoracic cavity into the left and right parts. The thymus increases in size until the first year of life, after which it remains approximately the same size until 60 years of age, when it decreases in size.

PROCESS **Figure 22.8**

Spleen

(*a*) Inferior view of the spleen. (*b*) Section of the spleen, showing the arrangement of arteries, veins, white pulp, and red pulp. White pulp is associated with arteries, and red pulp is associated with veins. (*c*) Steps 1–6 trace blood flow through the white and red pulp. (*d*) Histology of the spleen. (d) Dennis Strete/McGraw Hill APR

Which step of blood flow from the trabecular artery to the trabecular vein shown in the figure is responsible for slow blood flow through the spleen?

Case STUDY 22.1 Lymphedema

Cindy is a 40-year-old woman who has been diagnosed with breast cancer. Before removing the cancerous tumor from her left breast, her surgeon injected a dye and a radioactive tracer, technetium-99, at the tumor site. The dye and tracer enabled the surgeon to find **sentinel lymph nodes,** those lymph nodes closest to the tumor. The sentinel lymph nodes were sampled for cancer. When cancer cells were found in all of them, the surgeon removed the axillary lymph nodes from under Cindy's left arm.

A few days after the surgery, Cindy noticed that the skin on her left arm felt tight and the arm felt heavy. In addition, her wedding ring was tighter than usual. These symptoms were due to an abnormal accumulation of fluid in Cindy's upper limb, called **lymphedema** (LIMF-e-DEE-mah), caused by the removal of her axillary lymph nodes. In the United States, the most common cause of lymphedema is removal of or damage to lymph nodes and vessels as a result of cancer surgery or radiation treatment. Approximately 10–20% of women whose axillary lymph nodes have been removed develop lymphedema.

Predict 1

a. *What is the rationale for testing sentinel lymph nodes for cancer?*

b. *What was the rationale for removing Cindy's axillary lymph nodes?*

c. *Why does removing the axillary lymph nodes result in lymphedema?*

d. *Exercise can help reduce lymphedema. Explain.*

e. *A compression bandage or garment can help reduce lymphedema. Explain.*

f. *In intermittent pneumatic pump compression therapy, the pressure of a garment enclosing a limb increases and decreases periodically. In addition, the pressure increases sequentially from the distal part to the proximal part of a limb. How does this therapy help reduce lymphedema?*

Each lobe of the thymus is surrounded by a thin connective tissue capsule. Trabeculae extend from the capsule into the substance of the gland, dividing it into **lobules.** Unlike other lymphatic tissue, which has a fibrous network of reticular fibers, the framework of thymic tissue consists of epithelial cells. The processes of the epithelial cells are joined by desmosomes, and the cells form small, irregularly shaped compartments filled with lymphocytes. Near the capsule and trabeculae, the lymphocytes are numerous and form dark-staining areas of the lobules called the cortex. A lighter-staining, central portion of the lobules, called the medulla, has fewer lymphocytes. The medulla also contains rounded epithelial structures, called **thymic corpuscles** (Hassall corpuscles). For more than 150 years, the function of these structures was unknown, but current research indicates that substances associated with thymic corpuscles function in the development of **regulatory T cells.** Regulatory T cells suppress the body's immune response and protect against autoimmune diseases (see section 22.5). However, the extent of thymic corpuscle function is still unclear.

The thymus is the site for the maturation of T cells. **Thymosin,** a hormone secreted by the thymus, is important in the T-cell maturation process. Large numbers of lymphocytes are produced in the thymus, but most degenerate. The lymphocytes that survive the maturation process are capable of reacting to foreign substances, but they normally do not react to and destroy healthy body cells (see figure 22.4 and section 22.5). These surviving thymic lymphocytes migrate to the medulla, enter the blood, and travel to other lymphatic tissues.

ASSESS YOUR PROGRESS

12. *Where are lymph nodes found? Describe the parts of a lymph node, and explain how lymph flows through a lymph node.*

13. *Describe the function of lymph nodes. What is a germinal center?*

14. *Where is the spleen located? Describe the structure of the spleen.*

15. *Explain how the spleen performs its three main functions.*

16. *Where is the thymus located? Describe its structure and function.*

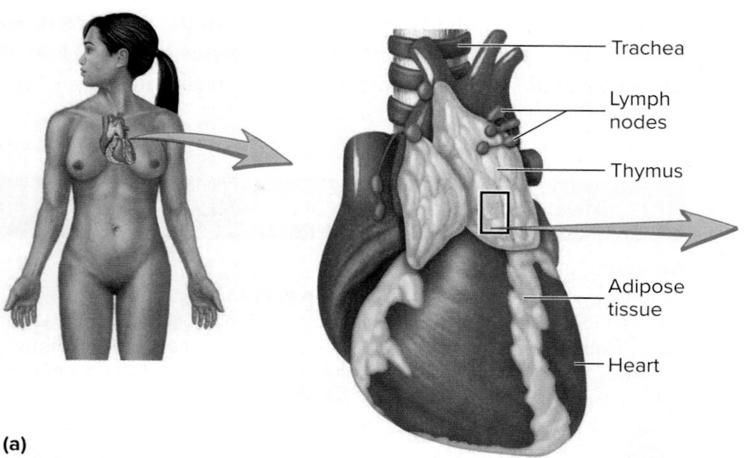

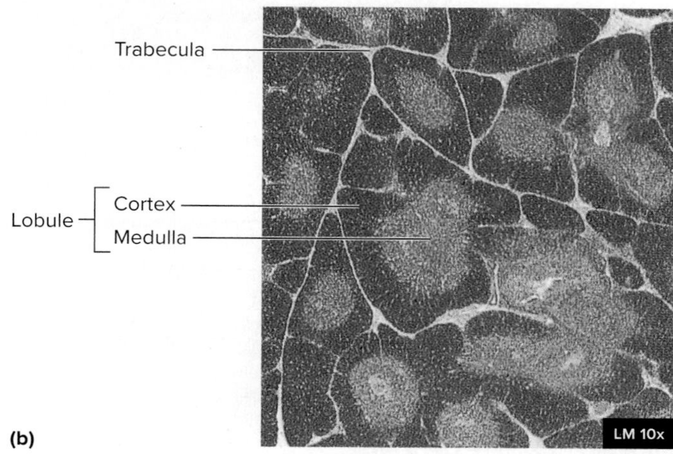

FIGURE 22.9 Thymus
(*a*) Location and shape of the thymus in relation to the heart. (*b*) Histology of thymic lobules, showing the outer cortex and the inner medulla. (b) Trent Stephens APR

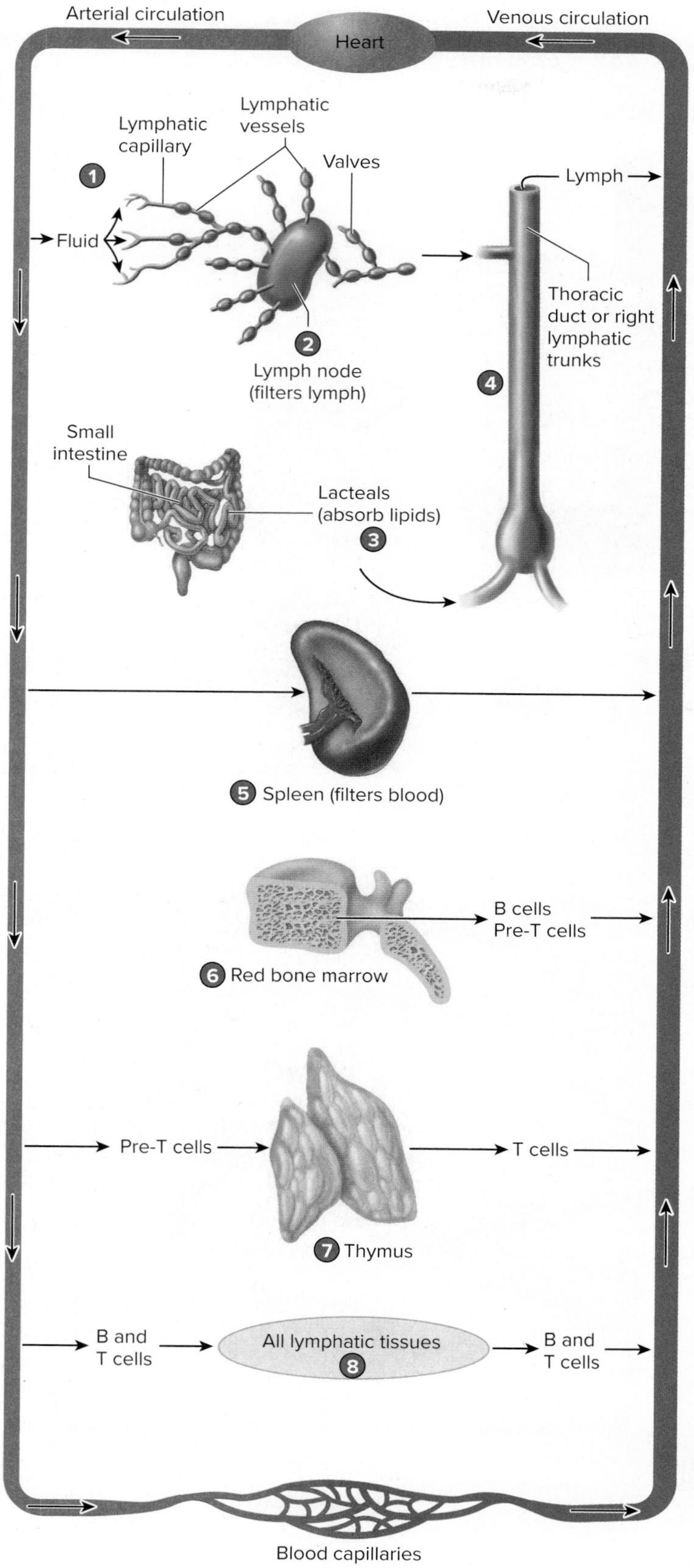

Overview of the Lymphatic System

Figure 22.10 summarizes the processes performed by the lymphatic system.

1. Lymphatic capillaries and vessels remove excess fluid from tissues forming lymph, a clear fluid.
2. Lymph nodes filter lymph and are sites where lymphocytes respond to infections.
3. Lacteals in the small intestine absorb lipids, forming chyle, which is lymph containing lipids.
4. Lymph, including chyle, from the body passes through the thoracic duct or right lymphatic trunks before entering the blood.
5. The spleen filters blood and is a site where lymphocytes respond to infections.
6. Lymphocytes (pre-B and pre-T cells) originate from stem cells in bone marrow (see figure 22.4). The pre-B cells become mature B cells in the red bone marrow and are released into the blood. The pre-T cells enter the blood and migrate to the thymus.
7. The thymus is where pre-T cells increase in number and become mature T cells that are released into the blood.
8. B cells and T cells from the blood enter and populate all lymphatic tissues. These lymphocytes can remain in tissues or pass through them and return to the blood to respond to infections.

B cells and T cells are responsible for much of immunity. In response to infections, B cells and T cells increase in number and circulate to lymphatic and infected tissues. How B cells and T cells protect the body is discussed in section 22.5.

22.3 Immunity

LEARNING OUTCOMES

After reading this section, you should be able to

A. **Define the concepts of specificity and memory as they apply to immunity.**

B. **Distinguish between the general characteristics of innate immunity and adaptive immunity.**

Immunity is the ability to resist damage from foreign substances, such as microorganisms; harmful chemicals, such as toxins released by microorganisms; and internal threats, such as cancer cells. Immunity is categorized as **innate immunity** (also called *nonspecific resistance*) and **adaptive immunity** (also called *specific immunity*), although the two systems are fully integrated in the body (figure 22.11). In innate immunity, the body recognizes and destroys certain foreign substances, but the response to them is the same each time the body is exposed. In adaptive immunity, the body recognizes and destroys foreign substances, but the response to them is faster and stronger than the first time the foreign substance was encountered.

PROCESS **Figure**

Arterial circulation
Heart
Venous circulation
Lymphatic capillary
Lymphatic vessels
Valves
1
Fluid
Lymph
Thoracic duct or right lymphatic trunks
2 Lymph node (filters lymph)
4
Small intestine
Lacteals (absorb lipids)
3
5 Spleen (filters blood)
B cells
Pre-T cells
6 Red bone marrow
Pre-T cells
T cells
7 Thymus
B and T cells
All lymphatic tissues 8
B and T cells
Blood capillaries

PROCESS **Figure 22.10**

Overview of the Lymphatic System

The lymphatic system helps regulate fluid levels in the tissue and provides protection against pathogens. APR

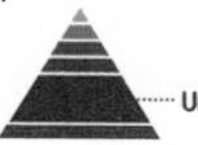

Understand *The lymph nodes and spleen both function as filters. How do they differ in this filtration role?*

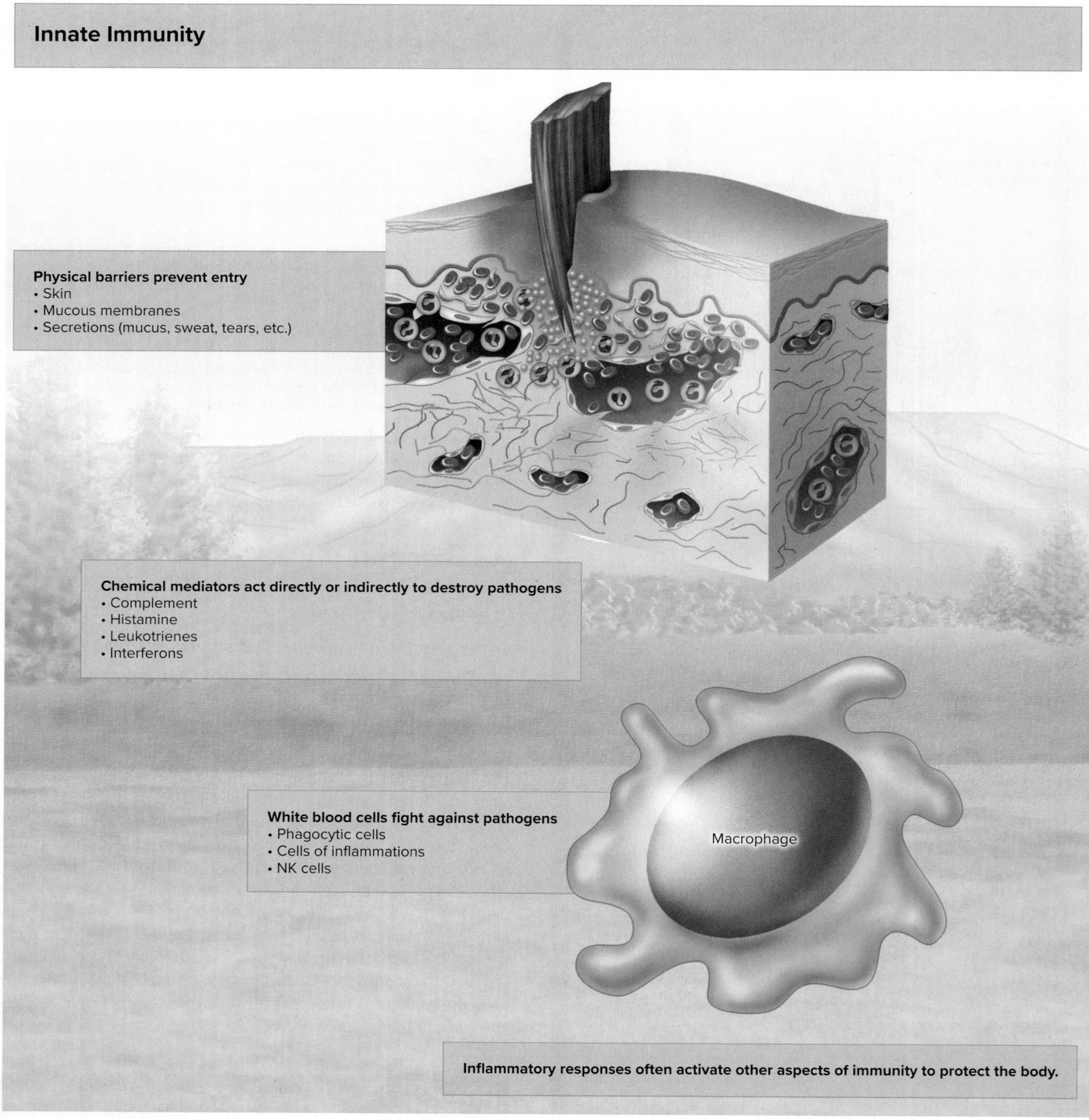

FIGURE 22.11 Components of Immunity
The body is protected by many different lines of defense. We organize these into two major divisions: innate immunity and adaptive immunity.

Adaptive Immunity

Cell-mediated immunity involves cytotoxic T lymphocytes directly destroying pathogens and diseased cells.

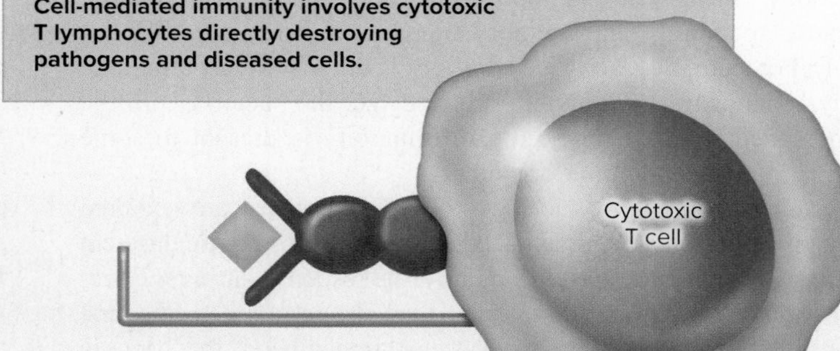

Antibody-mediated immunity involves B lymphocytes and the production of antibodies to fight against extracellular antigens.

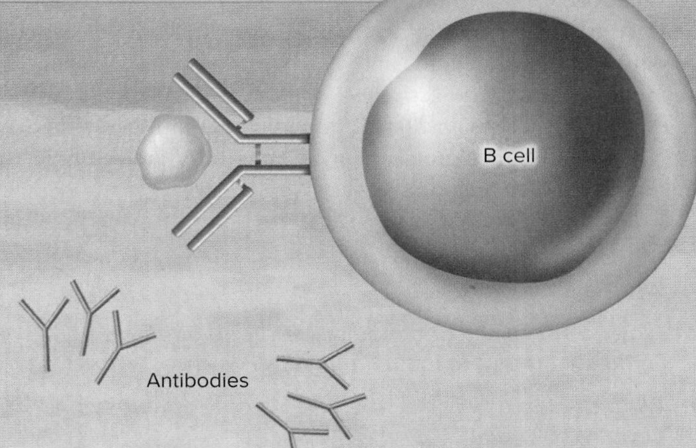

Specificity and memory are characteristics of adaptive immunity, but not of innate immunity. **Specificity** is the ability of adaptive immunity to recognize a particular substance. For example, innate immunity can act against bacteria in general, whereas adaptive immunity can distinguish among various kinds of bacteria. **Memory** is the ability of adaptive immunity to "remember" previous encounters with a particular substance. As a result, the response is faster, stronger, and longer lasting.

Innate immunity includes body defenses that are present at birth and genetically determined. In innate immunity, each time the body is exposed to a substance, the response is the same because specificity and memory of previous encounters do not apply. For example, each time a bacterial cell is introduced into the body, cells of innate immunity phagocytize the bacteria with the same speed and efficiency. Innate immunity is present to some degree in all multicellular organisms.

Adaptive immunity includes body defenses that are acquired through a person's lifetime, depending on exposure to different microorganisms. In adaptive immunity, the response during the second exposure is faster and stronger than the response to the first exposure because the immune system "remembers" the bacteria from the first exposure. For example, following the first exposure to the bacteria, the body can take many days to destroy them. During this time, the bacteria damage tissues and produce the symptoms of disease. Following the second exposure to the same bacteria, the response by the cells of adaptive immunity is rapid and effective. Bacteria are destroyed before any symptoms develop, and the person is said to be **immune.** Adaptive immunity is unique to vertebrates.

Although the immune system can be described in terms of innate and adaptive, these categories are artificial divisions used to emphasize particular aspects of immunity. Actually, there is only one immune system, but its responses often involve components of more than one type of immunity. For example, although adaptive immunity can recognize and remember specific antigens, once recognition has occurred, the antigen is destroyed with the help of many innate immunity activities, including inflammation and phagocytosis. Innate and adaptive immunity are intimately linked. Most importantly, mediators of innate immunity are required to initiate and regulate adaptive immunity.

ASSESS YOUR PROGRESS

17. *What is immunity?*
18. *Why do specificity and memory relate to adaptive immunity but not to innate immunity?*
19. *What are the differences between innate immunity and adaptive immunity?*

22.4 Innate Immunity

LEARNING OUTCOMES

After reading this section, you should be able to

A. **Describe the three components of innate immunity.**
B. **Describe the chemical mediators involved with innate immunity.**
C. **List the types of white blood cells involved in innate immunity.**
D. **List the events of the inflammatory response and explain their significance.**

Innate immunity includes body defenses that are present at birth and genetically determined. The main components of innate immunity are (1) physical barriers that prevent microbes from entering the body or that physically remove them from body surfaces; (2) chemical mediators that act directly against microorganisms or activate other mechanisms, leading to the destruction of the microorganisms; and (3) cells involved in phagocytosis and the production of chemicals that participate in the immune response.

Physical Barriers

One of the best defenses of the body is to prevent entry of disease-causing agents into the body. If these microorganisms or foreign substances do not enter the body, they cannot cause damage. **Physical barriers,** such as the skin and mucous membranes, prevent microorganisms and chemicals from entering the body. They also remove microorganisms and other substances from the body surface in several ways. The substances are washed from the eyes by tears, from the mouth by saliva, and from the urinary tract by urine. In the respiratory tract, ciliated mucous membranes sweep microbes trapped in the mucus to the back of the throat, where they are swallowed. Coughing and sneezing also remove microorganisms from the respiratory tract.

Chemical Mediators

Chemical mediators are molecules responsible for many aspects of innate immunity (table 22.1). Some chemical mediators on the surface of cells kill microorganisms or prevent them from entering the cells. For example, lysozyme in tears destroys microorganisms while mucus traps them, preventing them from reaching the epithelial tissues that secrete the mucus. Other chemical mediators, such as histamine, complement, and eicosanoids (e.g., prostaglandins and leukotrienes), promote other defense mechanisms such as inflammation by causing vasodilation and increasing vascular permeability, as well as attract white blood cells, and stimulate phagocytosis. **Cytokines** (SIGH-toh-kines) are proteins or peptides secreted by cells that bind to receptors on cell surfaces, stimulating a response. They usually bind to receptors on neighboring cells, but sometimes they bind to receptors on the secreting cell. Cytokines regulate the intensity and duration of immune responses and stimulate the proliferation and differentiation of cells. Examples of cytokines are interferons, interleukins, and lymphokines.

Complement

Complement is a group of about 20 proteins that protect the body by destroying abnormal cells or enhancing other components of immunity. Complement proteins make up approximately 10% of the globulin part of plasma proteins. They include proteins named C1–C9 and factors B, D, and P (properdin). Normally, complement proteins circulate in the blood in an inactive, nonfunctional form. They become activated in the **complement cascade,** a series of reactions in which each component of the series activates the

TABLE 22.1 Chemical Mediators of Innate Immunity and Their Functions

Chemical	Description
Surface chemicals	Lysozymes (in tears, saliva, nasal secretions, and sweat) lyse cells; acid secretions (sebum in the skin and hydrochloric acid in the stomach) prevent microbial growth or kill microorganisms; mucus on the mucous membranes traps microorganisms until they can be destroyed.
Histamine	Histamine is an amine released from mast cells, basophils, and platelets; histamine causes vasodilation, increases vascular permeability, stimulates gland secretions (especially mucus and tear production), causes smooth muscle contraction of airway passages (bronchioles) in the lungs, and attracts eosinophils.
Kinins	Kinins are polypeptides derived from plasma proteins; kinins cause vasodilation, increase vascular permeability, stimulate pain receptors, and attract neutrophils.
Interferons	Interferons are proteins, produced by most cells, that interfere with virus production and infection.
Complement	Complement is a group of plasma proteins that increase vascular permeability, stimulate the release of histamine, activate kinins, lyse cells, promote phagocytosis, and attract neutrophils, monocytes, macrophages, and eosinophils.
Prostaglandins	Prostaglandins are a group of lipids (PGEs, PGFs, thromboxanes, and prostacyclins), some of which cause smooth muscle relaxation and vasodilation, increase vascular permeability, and stimulate pain receptors.
Leukotrienes	Leukotrienes are a group of lipids, produced primarily by mast cells and basophils, that cause prolonged smooth muscle contraction (especially in the lung bronchioles), increase vascular permeability, and attract neutrophils and eosinophils.
Pyrogens	Pyrogens are chemicals, released by neutrophils, monocytes, and other cells, that stimulate fever production.

Note: PGE = prostaglandin E; PGF = prostaglandin F.

next component. The complement cascade begins with either the classic pathway or the alternative pathway, both of which are illustrated in figure 22.12.

1. The classical pathway, which is part of adaptive immunity, begins when an antigen-antibody complex (discussed in more detail in section 22.5) binds to C1. The C1-antigen–antibody complex activates C4.
2. Activated C4 forms a molecular complex with C2 that in turn activates C3. The complement cascade begins through either the alternative pathway or the classical pathway.
3. The **alternative pathway,** which is part of innate immunity, is initiated when the complement protein C3 becomes spontaneously active. If activated C3 does not interact with a microorganism, it is quickly inactivated by proteins on the surface of the body's cells.
4. However, in the event of an infection, activated C3 can become stabilized by combining with some foreign substances, such as part of a bacterial cell or virus.
5. Once C3 is stablized by either the classical or alternative pathway, it stimulates the complement cascade by activating C5, which in turn activates C6, which then activates C7. Continuing the cascade, C7 activates C8, which then activates C9.
6. Activated C3, C4, C5, and C7 promote inflammation, chemotaxis, and phagocytosis.
7. Activated C5–C9 combine to form a membrane attack complex (MAC).

As shown in figure 22.12, activated complement proteins provide protection in several ways. They can form a **membrane attack complex (MAC,** figure 22.12, *step 7*) that produces a channel through a cell's plasma membrane. The formation of MACs ultimately destroys the cell. MAC formation begins when activated C3 attaches to a plasma membrane, stimulating a series of reactions activating C5–C9. The main component of a MAC is activated C9 molecules, which change shape, attach to each other, and form a channel through the membrane. Cell death as a consequence of MACs is different in nucleated cells versus bacterial cells. When MACs form in the plasma membrane of a nucleated cell, Na^+ and water enter the cell through the channel and cause the cell to lyse. When MACs form in the outer membrane of certain bacteria (Gram negative), an enzyme called lysozyme passes through the channel and digests the bacterial cell wall. When the wall breaks apart, the bacterial cell undergoes lysis.

Complement proteins also enhance other aspects of immunity (figure 22.12, *step* 6). Complement proteins can cause inflammation, which increases blood flow to the site of infection. Immune cells often demonstrate chemotaxis, or the movement toward chemical signals. Complement proteins act as the chemical signals attracting different immune system cells to the sites of injury or infection. Complement proteins can also attach to the surface of bacterial cells and stimulate macrophages to phagocytize the bacteria. This process is called **opsonization.**

Interferons

Interferons (in-ter-FEER-onz) are proteins that protect the body against viral infection and perhaps some forms of cancer. After a virus infects a cell, viral replication can occur. Viral nucleic acids and proteins, which are produced using the infected cell's organelles, are assembled into new viruses. The new viruses are released from the infected cell to infect other cells. Because infected cells usually stop their normal functions or die during viral replication, viral infections are clearly harmful to the body. Fortunately, viruses and other substances can stimulate infected cells to produce interferons, which neither protect the cell that produces them nor act directly against viruses. Instead, interferons bind to the surface of neighboring cells and stimulate them to produce antiviral proteins. In this way, interferon acts as a "save yourself" signal from an infected cell to its neighboring cells. These antiviral proteins stop viral reproduction in the neighboring cells by preventing the production of viral nucleic acids and proteins.

Interferon viral resistance is innate rather than adaptive, and the same interferons act against many different viruses. Infection

PROCESS **Figure**

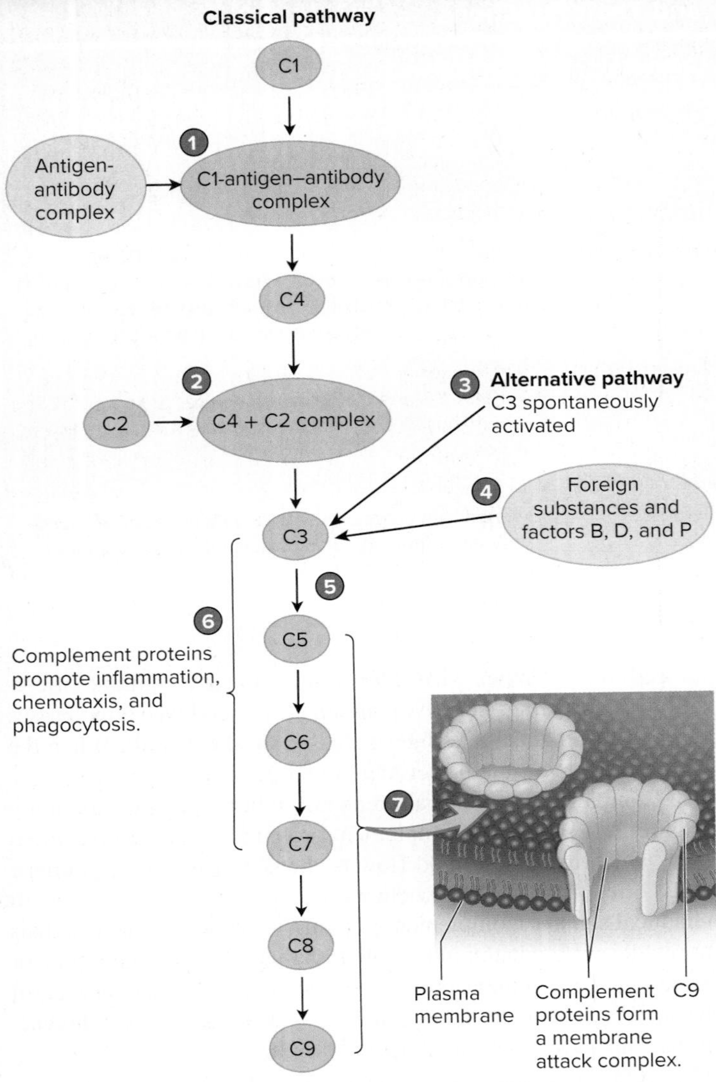

PROCESS **Figure 22.12**

Complement Cascade

Complement proteins circulate in the blood in an inactive form. Only the activated proteins are shown. The complement cascade begins with either the alternative pathway or the classical pathway.

What is the benefit of the complement proteins promoting inflammation, chemotaxis, and phagocytosis?

by one kind of virus can actually protect against infection by other kinds of viruses. Some interferons also play a role in activating immune cells, such as macrophages and natural killer cells.

Because viruses induce some cancers, interferons may play a role in controlling cancers. Interferons activate macrophages and natural killer cells (a type of lymphocyte) that attack tumor cells. Through genetic engineering, interferons are produced in sufficient quantities for clinical use and, along with other therapies, have been effective in treating certain viral infections and cancers. For example, interferons are used to treat hepatitis C, a viral disorder that can cause cirrhosis and cancer of the liver, and to treat genital warts caused by the herpes virus. Interferons are also approved to treat Kaposi sarcoma, a cancer that can develop in AIDS patients.

ASSESS YOUR PROGRESS

20. *List the three components of innate immunity.*

21. *Name two physical barriers that prevent microorganisms from entering the body. In what ways are microorganisms removed from body surfaces?*

22. *What roles do cytokines play as chemical mediators?*

23. *What is complement? In what two ways is it activated? How does complement provide protection?*

24. *What are interferons? How do they protect against viral infection?*

White Blood Cells

White blood cells and the cells derived from them (see table 19.2) are the most important cellular components of the immune system. White blood cells are produced in red bone marrow and lymphatic tissue and are released into the blood, where they are transported throughout the body. To be effective, white blood cells must move into the tissues where they are needed. White blood cells are attracted to chemical signals called **chemotactic** (kee-moh-TAK-tik) **factors.** Chemotactic factors include parts of microbes as well as chemicals released by cells of the body, including complement, leukotrienes, kinins, and histamine. Chemotactic factors diffuse from the area from which they are released. White blood cells can detect small differences in chemotactic factor concentration and move from areas of lower chemotactic factor concentration to areas of higher concentration. Thus, they move toward the source of these substances, an ability called **chemotaxis.** White blood cells can move by ameboid motion over the surface of cells, can squeeze between cells, and can sometimes pass directly through other cells.

Phagocytosis (FAG-oh-sigh-TOH-sis) is the endocytosis and destruction of particles by cells called **phagocytes** (see figure 3.17). The particles can be microorganisms or their parts, foreign substances, or dead cells from the body. Several types of cells play roles in innate immunity (table 22.2). The most important phagocytic cells are neutrophils and macrophages.

Neutrophils

Neutrophils are small, phagocytic cells produced in large numbers in red bone marrow and released into the blood, where they circulate for a few hours. Approximately 126 billion neutrophils per day leave the blood and pass through the wall of the digestive tract, where they provide phagocytic protection. The neutrophils are then eliminated as part of the feces. Neutrophils are usually the first cells to enter infected tissues in large numbers. They release chemical signals, such as cytokines and chemotactic factors, that increase the inflammatory response by recruiting and activating other immune cells. Neutrophils often die after a single phagocytic event.

Neutrophils also release lysosomal enzymes that kill microorganisms and cause tissue damage and inflammation. **Pus** is an accumulation of dead neutrophils, dead microorganisms, debris from dead tissue, and fluid.

TABLE 22.2 Cells of Innate Immunity and Their Primary Functions

Cell	Primary Function
Neutrophil	Phagocytosis and inflammation; usually the first cell to leave the blood and enter infected tissues
Monocyte	Leaves the blood and enters tissues to become a macrophage
Macrophage	Most effective phagocyte; important in later stages of infection and in tissue repair; located throughout the body to "intercept" foreign substances; processes antigens; involved in the activation of B cells and T cells
Basophil	Motile cell that leaves the blood, enters tissues, and releases chemicals that promote inflammation
Mast cell	Nonmotile cell in connective tissues that promotes inflammation through the release of chemicals
Eosinophil	Enters tissues from the blood and defends against parasitic infections; participates in inflammation associated with asthma and allergies
Natural killer cell	Lyses tumor and virus-infected cells

Macrophages

Macrophages are large phagocytic cells. Macrophages are derived from **monocytes,** one of the classes of white blood cells described in chapter 19. When monocytes leave the blood and enter tissues, they mature into macrophages by enlarging about fivefold and increasing their number of lysosomes and mitochondria. Though neutrophils and macrophages are both phagocytic cells, macrophages have longer life spans than neutrophils. In addition, they can ingest more and larger particles than neutrophils. Macrophages usually accumulate in tissues after neutrophils do, and they are responsible for most of the phagocytic activity in the late stages of an infection, including cleaning up dead neutrophils and other cellular debris. In addition to their phagocytic role, macrophages produce a variety of chemicals, such as interferons, prostaglandins, and complement, that enhance the immune response (see table 22.1).

Macrophages are beneath the free surfaces of the body, such as in the skin (dermis), subcutaneous tissue, mucous membranes, and serous membranes. They are also found around blood and lymphatic vessels. Macrophages provide protection in these areas by trapping and destroying microorganisms entering the tissues.

If microbes do gain entry to the blood or lymphatic system, macrophages are waiting within enlarged spaces, called **sinuses,** to phagocytize them. Blood vessels in the spleen, bone marrow, and liver have sinuses, as do lymph nodes. Within the sinuses, reticular cells produce a fine network of reticular fibers that slows the flow of blood or lymph and provides a large surface area for the attachment of macrophages. In addition, macrophages are on the endothelial lining of the sinuses.

Based on their location and structure, macrophages may be referred to by various names. Because macrophages on the reticular fibers and endothelial lining of the sinuses were among the first macrophages studied, these cells are referred to as the **reticuloendothelial system.** However, researchers now recognize that macrophages are derived from monocytes and are in locations other than the sinuses. Because monocytes and macrophages have a single, unlobed nucleus, they are also called the **mononuclear phagocytic system.** Sometimes macrophages are given specific names—for instance, *dust cells* in the lungs, *Kupffer cells* in the liver, and *microglia* in the central nervous system.

Basophils and Mast Cells

Basophils and mast cells play important roles in stimulating inflammation. **Basophils,** which are white blood cells derived from red bone marrow, are motile cells that can leave the blood and enter infected tissues. **Mast cells,** which are also derived from red bone marrow, are nonmotile cells in connective tissue, especially near capillaries. Like macrophages, mast cells are located at points where microorganisms may enter the body, such as the skin, lungs, digestive tract, and urogenital tract.

Basophils and mast cells can be activated through innate immunity (e.g., by complement) or through adaptive immunity (see "Effects of Antibodies" in section 22.5). When activated, they release chemicals—for example, histamine and leukotrienes—that produce an inflammatory response or activate other mechanisms, such as smooth muscle contraction in the lungs.

Eosinophils

Eosinophils are produced in red bone marrow, enter the blood, and within a few minutes enter tissues. Eosinophil numbers increase in response to parasitic infections. Eosinophils secrete enzymes that effectively kill some parasites. Also, eosinophil numbers greatly increase in the case of an allergic reaction with much inflammation.

Natural Killer (NK) Cells

Natural killer (NK) cells are a type of lymphocyte produced in red bone marrow and account for up to 15% of lymphocytes. Though these are lymphocytes, they are not part of adaptive immunity. NK cells recognize classes of cells, such as tumor cells or virus-infected cells in general, rather than specific tumor cells or cells infected by a specific virus. For this reason, and because NK cells do not exhibit a memory response, they are classified as part of innate immunity. NK cells use a variety of methods to kill their target cells, including releasing chemicals that damage plasma membranes and cause the cells to lyse.

PROCESS **Figure**

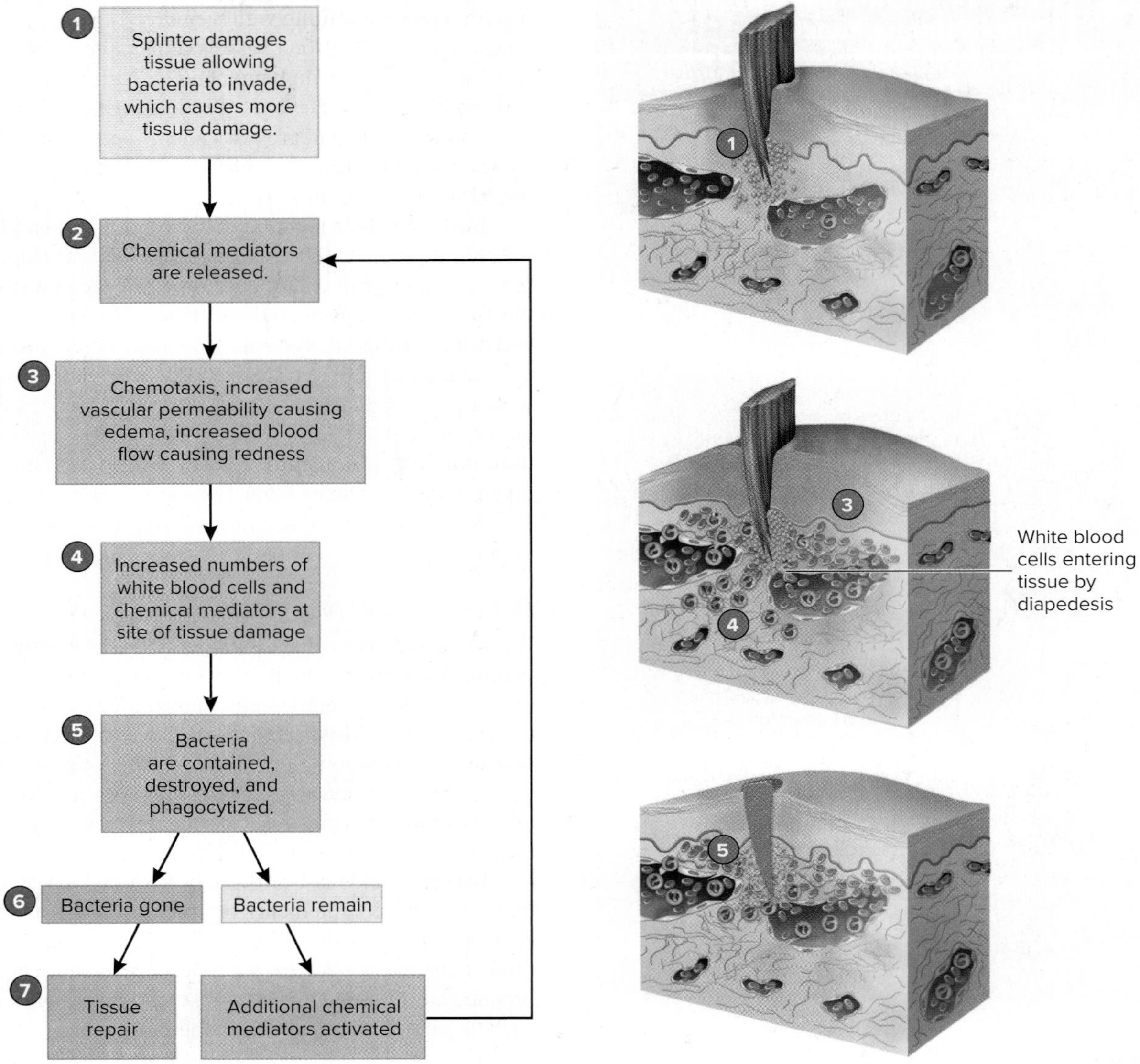

1. Splinter damages tissue allowing bacteria to invade, which causes more tissue damage.
2. Chemical mediators are released.
3. Chemotaxis, increased vascular permeability causing edema, increased blood flow causing redness
4. Increased numbers of white blood cells and chemical mediators at site of tissue damage
5. Bacteria are contained, destroyed, and phagocytized.
6. Bacteria gone → 7. Tissue repair

Bacteria remain → Additional chemical mediators activated (→ back to 2)

White blood cells entering tissue by diapedesis

PROCESS **Figure 22.13**

Inflammatory Response

Bacteria cause tissue damage and the release of chemical mediators, which initiate inflammation and phagocytosis, resulting in the destruction of the bacteria. If any bacteria remain, additional chemical mediators are activated. After all the bacteria have been destroyed, the tissue is repaired. APR

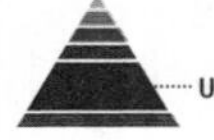

Predict what might happen if the bacteria could not be destroyed and a large number remained in the body.

ASSESS YOUR PROGRESS

25. *Define* chemotactic factor, chemotaxis, *and* phagocytosis.

26. *What are the functions of neutrophils and macrophages? What is pus?*

27. *What effects are produced by the chemicals released from basophils, mast cells, and eosinophils?*

28. *How do NK cells function?*

Inflammatory Response

The **inflammatory response** is a complex sequence of events involving many of the chemical mediators and cells of innate immunity. Trauma, burns, chemicals, and infections can damage tissues, resulting in inflammation. In figure 22.13 we use a bacterial infection to illustrate an inflammatory response.

1. As a result of injury, such as a splinter piercing the skin, bacteria enter the tissue, causing additional damage.

2 This damage stimulates the release or activation of chemical mediators, such as histamine, complement, kinins, and eicosanoids (e.g., prostaglandins and leukotrienes).

3 The chemical mediators cause vasodilation, which increases blood flow, bringing phagocytes and other white blood cells to the area, as well as increased vascular permeability that allows fibrinogen and complement to enter the tissue from the blood. The increase in blood flow and vascular permeability results in redness and swelling, two of the cardinal signs of inflammation.

4 White blood cells increase in number at the injury site as they move from the blood into the tissue by diapedesis.

5 Chemical mediators, such as fibrin and complement, increase at the injury site as well. Fibrinogen is converted to fibrin, which walls off the infected area, preventing the spread of infection. Complement further enhances the inflammatory response and attracts additional phagocytes.

6 The process of releasing chemical mediators and attracting phagocytes and other white blood cells continues until the bacteria are destroyed.

7 Phagocytes, such as neutrophils and macrophages, remove microorganisms and dead tissue, and the damaged tissues are repaired.

Inflammation can be local or systemic. **Local inflammation** is an inflammatory response confined to a specific area of the body (see chapter 4). Symptoms of local inflammation include redness, heat, and swelling due to increased blood flow and increased vascular permeability, as well as pain caused by swelling and by chemical mediators acting on pain receptors. The tissue destruction, swelling, and pain lead to loss of function.

Systemic inflammation is an inflammatory response that occurs in many parts of the body. In addition to the local symptoms at the sites of inflammation, three additional features can be present:

1. Red bone marrow produces and releases large numbers of neutrophils, which promote phagocytosis.
2. Fever is induced by the release of pyrogens. **Pyrogens** (PIE-roh-jenz; fire-producing) are chemicals released by microorganisms, macrophages, neutrophils, and other cells. These chemicals in turn stimulate fever production by affecting the body's temperature-regulating mechanism in the hypothalamus. As a consequence, heat production and heat conservation increase, raising body temperature. Fever promotes the activities of the immune system, such as phagocytosis, and inhibits the growth of some microorganisms.
3. In severe cases of systemic inflammation, increased vascular permeability is so widespread that large amounts of fluid are lost from the blood into the tissues. The decreased blood volume can cause shock and death.

ASSESS YOUR PROGRESS

29. *What kinds of tissue damage can result in inflammation?*
30. *Describe the events that take place during an inflammatory response.*
31. *What are the symptoms of local inflammation and of systemic inflammation?*

22.5 Adaptive Immunity

LEARNING OUTCOMES

After reading this section, you should be able to

A. **Define *antigen*.**
B. **Describe the two groups of antigens.**
C. **Explain the role of haptens in allergic reactions.**
D. **Describe the origin, development, activation, proliferation, and inhibition of lymphocytes.**
E. **Describe the function of major histocompatibility complex (MHC) molecules in immunity.**
F. **Distinguish between MHC class I molecules and MHC class II molecules.**
G. **Define *antibody-mediated immunity* and name the cell involved.**
H. **Define *cell-mediated immunity* and name the cells involved.**
I. **Diagram the structure of an antibody.**
J. **Describe the effects produced by antibodies.**
K. **Discuss the primary and secondary responses to an antigen and explain the basis for long-lasting immunity.**
L. **Describe the types and functions of T cells.**

Adaptive immunity is the ability of lymphcytes to recognize, respond to, and "remember" a particular substance. Substances that stimulate adaptive immunity are called **antigens** (AN-tih-jens). They are usually large molecules with a molecular weight of 10,000 or more.

Adaptive immunity involves two major types of lymphocytes: B cells and T cells, each of which carries out defense of the body in different ways (table 22.3). Adaptive immunity can be divided into antibody-mediated immunity and cell-mediated immunity. **Antibody-mediated immunity** involves proteins called **antibodies,** which are found in extracellular fluids, such as the plasma of blood, interstitial fluid, and lymph. B cells give rise to cells that produce antibodies. **Cell-mediated immunity** involves the actions of T cells. Several subpopulations of T cells exist, each responsible for a particular aspect of cell-mediated immunity. For example, **cytotoxic T cells** are responsible for producing the effects of cell-mediated immunity. **Helper T cells** and **regulatory T cells** can promote or inhibit the activities of both antibody-mediated immunity and cell-mediated immunity.

Table 22.4 summarizes and contrasts the main features of innate immunity and the two categories of adaptive immunity.

Antigens

Antigens are divided into two groups: foreign antigens and self-antigens. **Foreign antigens** are not produced by the body but are introduced from outside it. Components of bacteria, viruses, and other microorganisms are examples of foreign antigens. Other foreign antigens include pollen, animal dander (scaly, dried skin), feces of house dust mites, foods, and drugs. Many of these trigger an **allergic reaction,** an overreaction of the immune system in some

TABLE 22.3 Cells of Adaptive Immunity and Their Primary Functions

Cell	Primary Function
B cell	After activation, differentiates to become plasma cell or memory B cell
Plasma cell	Produces antibodies that are directly or indirectly responsible for destroying the antigen
Memory B cell	Quick and effective response to an antigen against which the immune system has previously reacted; responsible for adaptive immunity
Cytotoxic T cell	Responsible for destroying cells by lysis or by producing cytokines
Helper T cell	Activates B cells and cytotoxic T cells
Regulatory T cell	Inhibits B cells, helper T cells, and cytotoxic T cells
Memory T cell	Quick and effective response to an antigen against which the immune system has previously reacted; responsible for adaptive immunity
Dendritic cell	Processes antigen and is involved in the activation of B cells and T cells

people. Transplanted tissues and organs that contain foreign antigens cause rejection of the transplant. **Self-antigens** are molecules the body produces to stimulate an adaptive immune system response. The response to self-antigens can be beneficial or harmful. For example, the recognition of tumor antigens can result in tumor destruction, whereas **autoimmune disease** can develop when self-antigens stimulate unwanted tissue destruction. An example is rheumatoid arthritis, which destroys the tissues within joints.

ASSESS YOUR PROGRESS

32. *Define* antigen. *Distinguish between a foreign antigen and a self-antigen.*
33. *What are allergic reactions and autoimmune diseases?*
34. *What are the two types of adaptive immunity?*

Antigenic Determinants and Antigen Receptors

For an adaptive immunity response to occur, lymphocytes must interact with and recognize an antigen. Recall that antigens are large molecules, but lymphocytes do not interact with the entire antigen. Instead, lymphocytes interact with specific regions of the antigen called **antigenic determinants,** or *epitopes* (EP-i-tohps). Each antigen has many different antigenic determinants (figure 22.14). The lymphocytes of a given clone have, on their surfaces, identical proteins called **antigen receptors.** These antigen

TABLE 22.4 Comparison of Innate and Adaptive Immunity

		ADAPTIVE IMMUNITY	
Characteristics	**INNATE IMMUNITY**	**Antibody-Mediated Immunity**	**Cell-Mediated Immunity**
Primary cells	Neutrophils, eosinophils, basophils, mast cells, monocytes, and macrophages	B cells	T cells
Origin of cells	Red bone marrow	Red bone marrow	Red bone marrow
Site of maturation	Red bone marrow (neutrophils, eosinophils, basophils, and monocytes) and tissues (mast cells and macrophages)	Red bone marrow	Thymus
Location of mature cells	Blood, connective tissue, and lymphatic tissue	Blood and lymphatic tissue	Blood and lymphatic tissue
Primary secretory products	Histamine, kinins, complement, prostaglandins, leukotrienes, and interferons	Antibodies	Cytokines
Primary actions	Inflammatory response and phagocytosis	Protection against extracellular antigens (bacteria, toxins, parasites, and viruses outside cells)	Protection against cytoplasmic antigens (viruses, cytoplasmic bacteria, and cytoplasmic fungi) and tumors; regulates antibody-mediated immunity and cell-mediated immunity responses (helper T and regulatory T cells)
Hypersensitivity reactions	None	Immediate hypersensitivity (atopy, anaphylaxis, cytotoxic reactions, and immune complex disease)	Delayed hypersensitivity (allergic reaction to infection or contact hypersensitivity)

Clinical IMPACT 22.1

Haptens and Allergic Reactions

Haptens (HAP-tenz), often referred to as incomplete antigens, are small molecules (of low molecular weight) that can combine with large molecules, such as blood proteins, to stimulate an adaptive immune response. In many cases, however, haptens lead to allergic reactions (see table 22.6). For example, penicillin, a common antibiotic prescribed to combat bacterial infections, is a hapten that can break down and bind to other molecules in the blood. The combined molecule can then stimulate an allergic reaction that ranges from a rash and fever to severe symptoms that can lead to death. It is estimated that 20% of patients have allergic reactions when administered penicillin. Research indicates that the likelihood of a reaction increases with subsequent prescriptions. Skin tests are available to determine a patient's susceptibility to an allergic reaction to penicillin. (*Note:* Information in this Clinical Impact may be helpful in answering the Learn to Predict question at the beginning of the chapter.)

receptors combine with a specific antigenic determinant of a given antigen. The immunity response to an antigen with a particular antigenic determinant is similar to the lock-and-key model for enzymes (see chapter 2), and any given antigenic determinant can combine only with a specific antigen receptor.

Antigen receptor structure is different for T cells and B cells. **T-cell antigen receptors** consist of two polypeptide chains, which are subdivided into a variable region and a constant region (figure 22.15). The variable region can bind to an antigen. There are many different types of T-cell receptors, each of which responds to a different antigen. The variety of different T-cell receptors is possible because they have different variable regions. **B-cell antigen receptors** consist of four polypeptide chains with two identical variable regions. As you will see later in the text, B-cell antigen receptors are essentially antibodies on the surface of B cells.

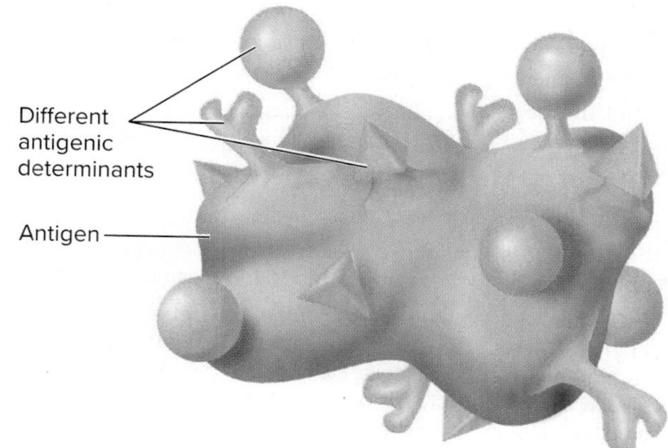

FIGURE 22.14 Antigenic Determinants
An antigen has many antigenic determinants to which lymphocytes can respond.

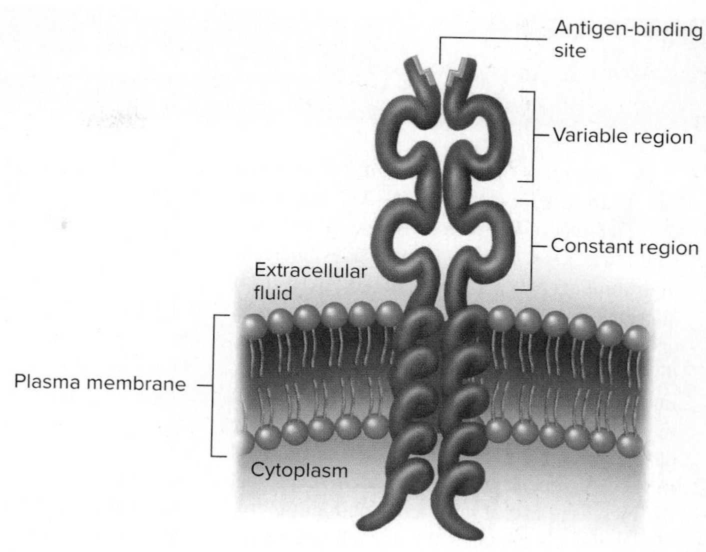

FIGURE 22.15 T-Cell Receptor
A T-cell receptor consists of two polypeptide chains. The variable region of each type of T-cell receptor is specific for a given antigen. The constant region attaches the T-cell receptor to the plasma membrane.

Major Histocompatibility Complex Molecules

A major responsibility of immune cells is to "verify" the identify of the cells found in the body. They are able to do this through the recognition of foreign antigens versus self-antigens. Just as important, immune cells must verify the health of self-cells. Cells infected by a virus or bacteria or mutated cells that may become cancerous are risks to the overall homeostatic condition of the body. Immune cells must be able to detect if a self-cell has been compromised by infection or mutation. Most lymphocyte activation involves interaction with **major histocompatibility complex (MHC) molecules.** MHC molecules are glycoproteins found on the plasma membranes of most of the body's cells. Each MHC molecule has a variable region that can bind antigens found inside the cell. MHC molecules display antigens produced in or processed by the cell on the cell's plasma membrane. As MHC molecules are formed in the cell, they combine with fragments of other molecules in the cytoplasm. The MHC molecules are then moved to the plasma membrane, where these fragments are displayed to immune cells.

Note that there was a distinction made that these antigens are either *produced in* or *processed by* the cell. Antigens that are produced in the cell are commonly referred to as **endogenous antigens.** Often these are proteins produced through genetic expression and protein synthesis. Antigens that are *processed by* a cell are substances that are obtained from the external environment, usually by phagocytosis, and then broken down within the cytoplasm. These antigens are referred to as **exogenous antigens.** Two classes of MHC molecules are present in the body, each responsible for displaying one of these two types of antigens: (1) MHC class I molecules display endogenous antigens and (2) MHC class II molecules display exogenous antigens.

MICROBES In Your Body 22.1

Do Our Gut Bacteria Drive Immune Development and Function?

"All disease begins in the gut." This quote from Hippocrates (460–377 B.C.), the father of Western medicine, is still relevant today. Over the last four decades, increasing numbers of people have suffered from allergies and autoimmune disorders. Researchers hypothesize that the increase in these conditions stems from inadequate development of immune function. In turn, they hypothesize that underdeveloped immune function is due to deficiencies in our gut microbiota. This has led to the Hygiene Hypothesis, which states that the increased use of antibiotics and antimicrobial chemicals damages the normal gut microbiota and other microbiota that are critical for immune system development and function.

Could the Hygiene Hypothesis explain the observed increases in allergies and autoimmune disorders? Much of the evidence for the importance of gut microbiota for immune function is derived from studies with germ-free mice. These lab-raised mice lack the natural microorganisms in their gut and in their body. As a result, the mice have multiple defects with their lymphatic tissues, such as fewer and smaller Peyer patches in the gut and fewer B and T lymphocytes. However, if scientists place intestinal or fecal microbiota from normal mice into the gut of germ-free mice, the immune tissues of the germ-free mice begin developing and functioning normally.

The importance of the gut in immune development is further supported by the fact that it contains the largest concentration of lymphatic tissue and microbiota in the human body. In the gut there are between 500 and 1000 species of bacteria, compared with a few hundred associated with the skin or fewer than 10 species associated with the conjunctiva of the eye. In humans, the gut microbiota begin to appear just before birth. As the baby passes through the birth canal, more microorganisms are transferred from the mother to the baby. The makeup of a baby's microbiota is influenced by many factors, including genetics, the mode of delivery (vaginal or C-section), antibiotic use, stress, and the mother's diet during late pregnancy. The first year of life is the most critical for the accumulation of gut bacteria, but this process continues through childhood. At about 10 years of age, a person's gut microbiota are established and remain similar in composition throughout life. Humans and their gut microbiota have a symbiotic relationship, in that the gut provides space and nutrients for the microbiota, which in turn provide their host with specialized nutrition, physiological regulators, and protection against pathogens. Because of these ever-present microbiota ("good" bacteria), human gut epithelial and immune cells must maintain tolerance to them yet still protect against invading gut pathogens ("bad" bacteria).

How do our cells distinguish between "good" and "bad" bacteria? As it turns out, gut microbiota help stimulate the development of immune cells by triggering the production of different receptors. These receptors are found in the plasma membranes of white blood cells, such as macrophages and neutrophils, as well as in the plasma membranes of intestinal epithelial cells. The surface of all bacterial cells has bacteria-specific molecules that can be recognized by the receptors of defense cells, which is what allows for distinction between "good" and "bad" microorganisms. Activation of the receptors triggers a cascade of events, which result in immune responses such as T-lymphocyte activation and the production of immunity chemicals. In addition, the "good" bacteria attack invading "bad" bacteria by secreting antimicrobial substances against them and competing with them for nutrients and space. Thus, without appropriate amounts and/or types of gut microbiota, the body's immune system may not have all of the messages that are essential for producing specific immune cells and chemicals that kill pathogenic intestinal microorganisms.

Medical professionals are interested in manipulating gut microbiota to reduce allergies and other diseases and to promote healing. First, and perhaps most importantly, is to get the desired population of gut microbiota started immediately in infancy through breastfeeding. Human breast milk contains carbohydrates that stimulate the growth of specific intestinal microbiota while preventing infection by some pathogens. And the use of prebiotics (nondigestible carbohydrates that promote the growth of healthy microbiota) and probiotics (live normal gut microbiota) is being actively explored for the treatment of problems that arise later in life. However, there is still much work to be done before we fully understand the extent to which gut microbiota are involved in human immune function.

Predict 2

In some underdeveloped countries, children are nutritionally deprived. Studies of twins in these countries have demonstrated that sometimes one of the twins thrives, whereas the other twin is malnourished. In the malnourished twin, the gut microbiota population is far less diverse and much smaller than that of the thriving twin. Using what you have learned about the role of gut microbiota in immune function, predict a possible developmental repercussion in the malnourished twin. Propose some possible solutions that might result in both twins having a normal gut microbe population.

MHC class I molecules are found on nucleated cells; they display endogenous antigens on the cell's plasma membrane. Figure 22.16 illustrates the production and display of an MHC class I molecule displaying an endogenous antigen in a virally infected cell.

1. When a virus reproduces inside a cell, viral proteins are produced within the cell.
2. Some of these viral proteins are broken down in the cytoplasm.
3. The protein fragments enter the rough endoplasmic reticulum and combine with MHC class I molecules to form complexes.
4. The MHC class I/antigen complexes then move through the Golgi apparatus to be further transported to the plasma membrane.
5. MHC class I/antigen complexes on the cell's plasma membrane can bind to T-cell receptors on the surface of T cells. This combination is a signal that activates T cells. Activated T cells can destroy infected cells, which effectively stops viral replication (see "Cell-Mediated Immunity," later in this section).

Thus, the MHC class I/antigen complex functions as a signal, or "red flag," that prompts the immune system to destroy the displaying cell. In essence, the cell is displaying a sign that says,

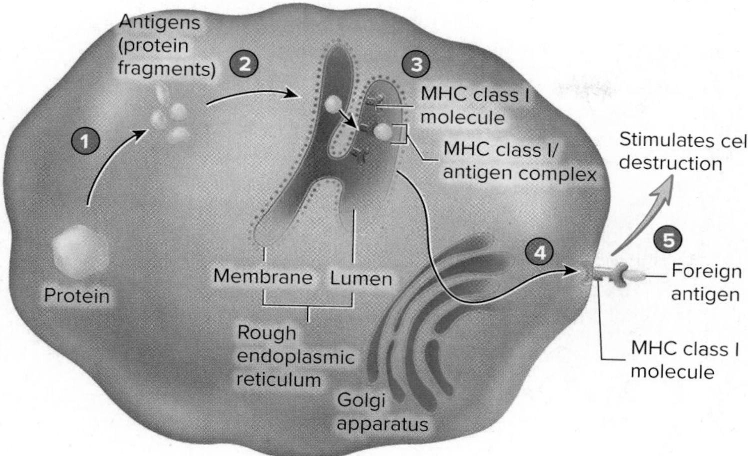

PROCESS Figure 22.16

MHC Class I Molecule and Endogenous Antigen

Foreign proteins, such as viral proteins, or self-proteins in the cytosol are processed and presented at the cell surface by MHC class I molecules. APR

Understand *Describe the events that must occur for an MHC class I molecule to display a self-protein.*

"Kill me!" This process is said to be **MHC-restricted** because both the antigen and the individual organism's own MHC molecule are required.

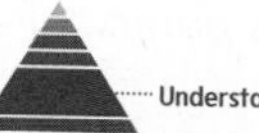
Understand

Predict 3

In mouse A, T cells can respond to virus X. If these T cells are transferred to mouse B, which is infected with virus X, will the T cells respond to the virus? Explain.

The same process that moves foreign protein fragments to the cell's plasma membrane can also inadvertently transport self-protein fragments. As part of normal protein metabolism, cells continually break down old proteins and synthesize new ones. Some self-protein fragments that result from protein breakdown can combine with MHC class I molecules and be displayed on the surface of the cell, thus becoming self-antigens. Normally, the immune system does not respond to self-antigens in combination with MHC molecules because the lymphocytes that could respond have been eliminated or inactivated (see "Inhibition of Lymphocytes," later in this section).

MHC class II molecules display exogenous antigens and are found on phagocytic cells called **antigen-presenting cells.** Antigen-presenting cells engulf substances encountered in the extracellular environment and process them within the cytoplasm. These "found" substances are exogenous antigens. Examples of antigen-presenting cells include B cells, macrophages, monocytes, and dendritic cells. **Dendritic** (den-DRIT-ik) **cells** are large, motile cells with long cytoplasmic extensions. These cells are scattered throughout most tissues (except the brain), with their highest concentrations in lymphatic tissues and the skin. Dendritic cells in the skin are often called **Langerhans cells.**

Figure 22.17 illustrates the production of an MHC class II molecule displaying an exogenous antigen.

1. Antigen-presenting cells can take in foreign antigens by endocytosis.
2. Within the endocytotic vesicle, the antigen is broken down into fragments to form processed antigens.
3. Vesicles from the Golgi apparatus containing MHC class II molecules combine with the endocytotic vesicles. The MHC class II molecules and processed antigens combine.
4. The MHC class II/antigen complexes are transported to the plasma membrane, where they are displayed to other immune cells.
5. The displayed MHC class II/antigen complex can stimulate immune cells.

MHC class II/antigen complexes on the cell's surface can bind to T-cell receptors on the T cells. The presentation of an antigen using MHC class II molecules is MHC-restricted because both the antigen and the individual's own MHC class II molecule are required. Unlike MHC class I molecules, however, this display does not result in the destruction of the antigen-presenting cell. Instead, the MHC class II/antigen complex is a "rally around the flag" signal that stimulates other immune system cells to respond to the antigen. The displaying cell is like Paul Revere, who spread the alarm for the militia to arm and organize. The militia then went out and fought the enemy. For example, when the specific lymphocytes that can recognize the antigen come into contact with the MHC class II/antigen complex, they are stimulated to divide. The activities of these lymphocytes, such as the production of antibodies, then destroy the antigen.

It can be difficult to remember the difference between the two classes of MHC molecules, particularly when it seems that both are displaying material "picked up" from the cytoplasm. There are a few differences to remember.

1. MHC class I molecules are found on nucleated cells, whereas MHC class II molecules are found on a special group of phagocytic cells, the antigen-presenting cells.
2. MHC class I molecules display endogenous antigens, meaning molecules that the cell produces; however, MHC class II molecules display exogenous antigens, meaning molecules that are "found."

MHC molecules are genetically determined. Due to the complexity of the genes involved in MHC protein production, there is a great amount of variation in MHC molecules in the population. As a result, it is rare for two people to have exactly the same MHC molecules, except in the case of identical twins. MHC molecule differences are of major concern when tissue is transplanted from one individual to another. Genetically similar individuals (siblings or parent and offspring) are more likely to have similar MHC molecules and, therefore, be a better "match" for tissue transplants (see Clinical Impact 22.2).

Understand

Predict 4

Antibodies bind to a foreign antigen, resulting in removal of that foreign antigen from the body. Explain what happens to antibody production as the foreign antigens decrease.

PROCESS **Figure**

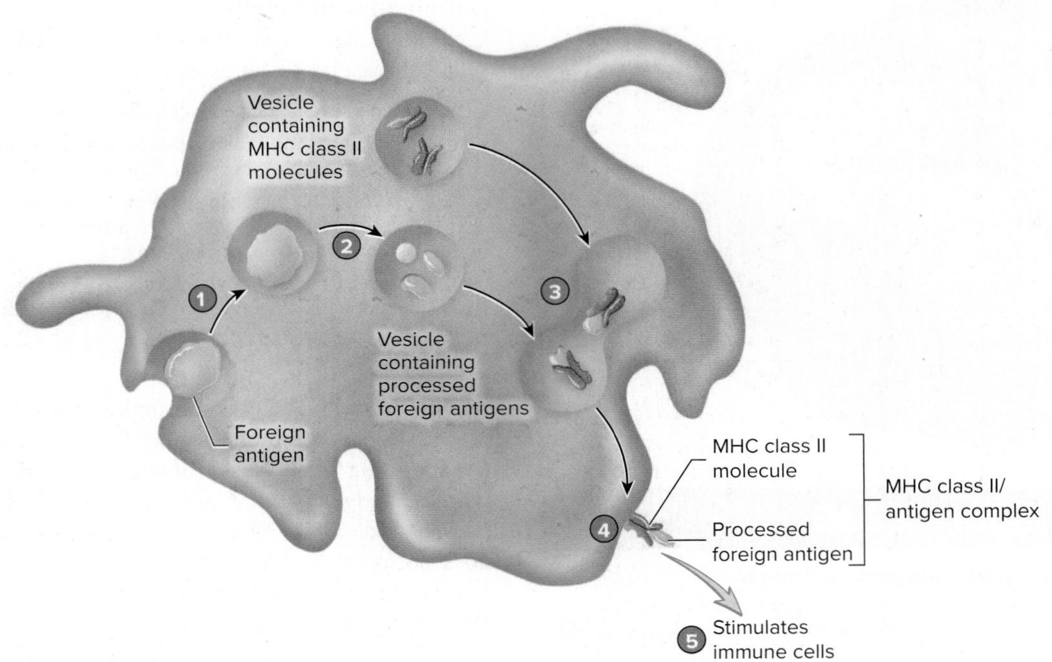

PROCESS **Figure 22.17**

MHC Class II Molecule and Exogenous Antigens

A molecule from the extracellular environment is taken into an antigen-presenting cell, processed, and presented at the plasma membrane by MHC class II molecules.

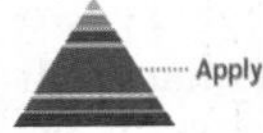

Imagine that a cell experiences a mutation that results in the production of an abnormal protein. On which of the MHC class molecules would fragments of this abnormal protein most likely be displayed? Why did you select this particular MHC class?

ASSESS YOUR PROGRESS

35. *Define* antigenic determinant *and* antigen receptor. *How are they related to each other?*

36. *What types of cells display MHC class I and class II antigen complexes, and what happens as a result?*

37. *What types of antigens are displayed by MHC class I molecules? By MHC class II molecules?*

38. *What does MHC-restricted mean?*

Clonal Selection

Clonal selection is the mechanism that results in a large population of identical lymphocytes, called **clones.** Clonal selection occurs when a lymphocyte **proliferates** (divides repeatedly) and **differentiates** (becomes specialized) when exposed to a *specific* antigen.

All blood cells, including lymphocytes, are derived from stem cells in the red bone marrow (see chapter 19). The process of blood cell formation begins during embryonic development and continues throughout life. Some stem cells give rise to pre-T cells, which migrate through the blood to the thymus, where they divide and are processed into T cells (see figures 22.4 and 22.10). The thymus produces hormones, such as **thymosin,** which stimulate T-cell maturation. Other stem cells produce pre-B cells, which are processed in the red bone marrow into B cells. A **positive selection** process results in the survival of pre-B and pre-T cells that are capable of an immune response. Cells that are incapable of an immune response die.

The B cells and T cells are members of **clones,** small groups of identical lymphocytes. All lymphocytes of a given clone respond to the same specific antigen. Although each clone can respond only to a particular antigen, such a large number of clones exist that the immune system can react to most molecules. Some of the clones can also respond to self-antigens, causing the destruction of body cells. A **negative selection** process eliminates or suppresses clones acting against self-antigens, thereby preventing the destruction of a person's own cells. Although the negative selection process occurs mostly during prenatal development, it continues throughout life. Inhibition of lymphocytes will be discussed in more detail later in this section.

B cells are released from red bone marrow, T cells are released from the thymus, and both types of cells move through the blood to lymphatic tissue. T cells are more numerous than B cells; there are approximately five T cells for every B cell in the blood. Lymphocytes live for a few months to many years and continually circulate between the blood and the lymphatic tissues. Antigens can come

Clinical IMPACT 22.2

Transplant Rejection

Genes that code for the production of MHC molecules are generally called major histocompatibility complex genes. Histocompatibility is the tissues' ability (Gr. *histo*) to "get along" (compatibility) when tissues are transplanted from one individual to another. In humans, the major histocompatibility complex genes are often referred to as **human leukocyte antigen (HLA) genes** because they were first identified in leukocytes. The HLA genes control the production of MHC antigens, which are found on the plasma membrane of cells. Millions of possible combinations of the HLA genes exist, and it is very rare for two individuals (except identical twins) to have the same set of HLA genes. The closer the relationship between two people, the greater the likelihood they share the same HLA genes.

The immune system can distinguish between self cells and foreign cells because they are both marked with MHCs. Rejection of a transplanted tissue is caused by a normal immune system response to the foreign MHCs. **Acute rejection** occurs several weeks after transplantation and results from a delayed hypersensitivity reaction and cell lysis. Lymphocytes and macrophages infiltrate the area, a strong inflammatory response occurs, and the foreign tissue is destroyed. If acute rejection does not develop, **chronic rejection** may occur at a later time. In chronic rejection, immune complexes form in the arteries supplying the graft, the blood supply fails, and the transplanted tissue is rejected.

Graft rejection can occur in two different directions. In **host-versus-graft rejection,** the recipient's (host's) immune system recognizes the donor's (graft) tissue as foreign and rejects the transplant. In **graft-versus-host rejection,** the donor tissue (graft) recognizes the recipient's (host's) tissue as foreign, and the transplant rejects the recipient, causing destruction of the recipient's tissues and death.

To reduce graft rejection, a tissue match is performed. Only tissues with MHCs similar to the recipient's have a chance of acceptance. Even when the match is close, immunosuppressive drugs must be administered throughout the person's life to prevent rejection. Unfortunately, the person then has a drug-produced immunodeficiency and is more susceptible to infections. An exact match is possible only for a graft from one part to another part of a person's body or between identical twins.

into contact with and activate lymphocytes, resulting in cell divisions that increase the number of lymphocytes able to recognize the antigen. These lymphocytes can circulate in blood and lymph to reach antigens in tissues throughout the body.

Activation of Lymphocytes

Antigens activate lymphocytes in different ways, depending on the type of lymphocyte and the type of antigen involved. Despite these differences, however, two general principles of lymphocyte activation exist: (1) Lymphocytes must be able to recognize the antigen; (2) after recognition, the lymphocytes must increase in number to destroy the antigen. In the following section we describe how the interactions of antigens with helper T cells lead to activation and proliferation of the cells that carry out adaptive immunity responses.

Costimulation

The combination of an MHC class II/antigen complex with an antigen receptor is usually only the first signal necessary to produce a response from a B cell or a T cell. In many cases, **costimulation** by additional signals is also required. Costimulation is accomplished by cytokines released from cells as well as molecules attached to the surfaces of cells (figure 22.18*a*). Cytokines produced by lymphocytes are often called **lymphokines** (LIM-foh-kynez). Table 22.5 lists important cytokines and their functions.

Certain pairs of surface molecules can also be involved in costimulation (figure 22.18*b*). When the surface molecule on one cell combines with the surface molecule on another, the

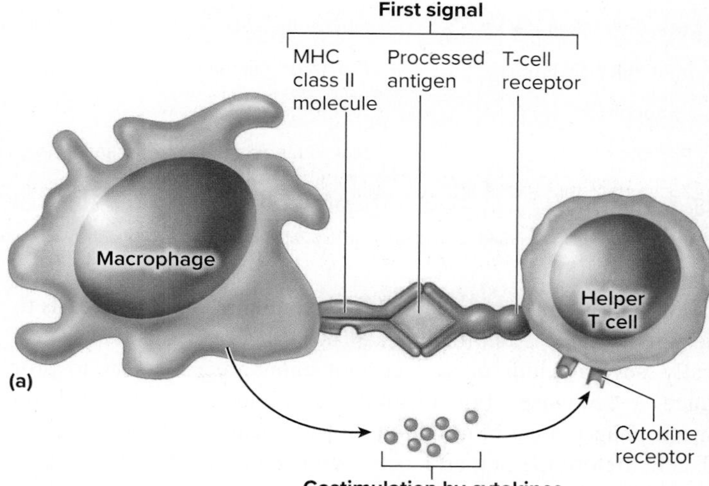

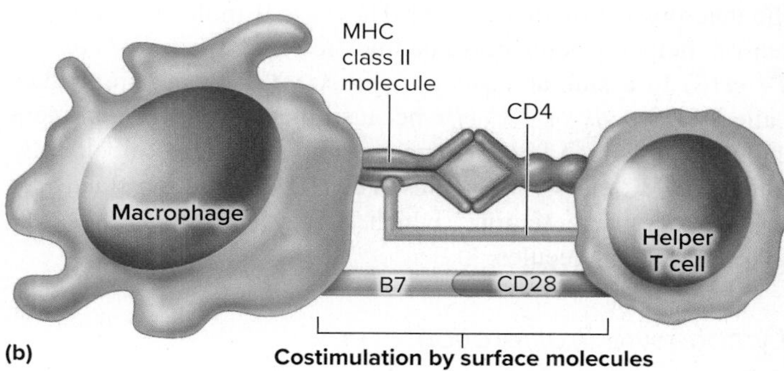

FIGURE 22.18 Costimulation

Activation of lymphocytes requires multiple signals, including the binding of MHC complex molecules/antigen complex as well as other costimulatory signals. (*a*) A helper T cell activated a first signal, the binding of the MHC class II/antigen complex to the T-cell receptor, and costimulation by cytokines released by another cell, in this case a macrophage. (*b*) Other costimulatory signals involve the combining of surface molecules, such as the binding of a B7 molecule of the macrophage with a CD28 molecule of the helper T cell and the combination of a CD4 marker from the helper T cell and the MHC class II molecule of the macrophage.

TABLE 22.5 Cytokines and Their Functions

Cytokine*	Description
Interferon alpha (IFNα)	Prevents viral replication and inhibits cell growth; secreted by virus-infected cells
Interferon beta (IFNβ)	Prevents viral replication, inhibits cell growth, and decreases the expression of major histocompatibility complex (MHC) class I and II molecules; secreted by virus-infected fibroblasts
Interferon gamma (IFNγ)	About 20 different proteins that activate macrophages and natural killer (NK) cells, stimulate adaptive immunity by increasing the expression of MHC class I and II molecules, and prevent viral replication; secreted by helper T, cytotoxic T, and NK cells
Interleukin-1 (IL-1)	Costimulation of B cells and T cells; promotes inflammation through prostaglandin production and induces fever acting through the hypothalamus (pyrogen); secreted by macrophages, B cells, and fibroblasts
Interleukin-2 (IL-2)	Costimulation of B cells and T cells and activation of macrophages and NK cells; secreted by helper T cells
Interleukin-4 (IL-4)	Plays a role in allergic reactions by activation of B cells, resulting in the production of immunoglobulin E (IgE); secreted by helper T cells
Interleukin-5 (IL-5)	Part of the response against parasites by stimulating eosinophil production; secreted by helper T cells
Interleukin-8 (IL-8)	Chemotactic factor that promotes inflammation by attracting neutrophils and basophils; secreted by macrophages
Interleukin-10 (IL-10)	Inhibits the secretion of interferon gamma and interleukins; secreted by regulatory T cells
Interleukin-15 (IL-15)	Promotes inflammation and activates memory T cells and natural killer cells
Lymphotoxin	Kills target cells; secreted by cytotoxic T cells
Perforin	Makes a hole in the membrane of target cells, resulting in lysis of the cell; secreted by cytotoxic T cells
Tumor necrosis factor α (TNFα)	Activates macrophages and promotes fever (pyrogen); secreted by macrophages

*Some cytokines were named according to the laboratory test first used to identify them; however, these names are rarely an accurate description of the actual function of the cytokine.

combination can act as a signal that stimulates one of the cells to respond, or the combination can hold the cells together. Typically, several kinds of surface molecules are necessary to produce a response. For example, a molecule called B7 on macrophages must bind with a molecule called CD28 on helper T cells before the helper T cells can respond to the antigen presented by the macrophage. In addition, helper T cells have a glycoprotein called CD4, which helps connect helper T cells to the macrophage by binding to MHC class II molecules. For this reason, helper T cells are sometimes referred to as *CD4 cells* or *T4 cells*. In a similar fashion, cytotoxic T cells are sometimes called *CD8 cells* or *T8 cells* because they have a glycoprotein called CD8, which helps connect cytotoxic T cells to cells displaying MHC class I molecules. The CD designation stands for "cluster of differentiation," which is a system used to classify many surface molecules.

Lymphocyte Proliferation

Before exposure to an antigen, the number of lymphocytes in a clone is too small to produce an effective response against the antigen. Exposure to an antigen results in an increase in lymphocyte number. The first lymphocytes to increase in number are the helper T cells. This is important because the increased number of helper T cells responding to the antigen can find and stimulate B cells or cytotoxic T cells. Subsequently, the number of B cells or cytotoxic T cells increases. This is important because the B cells and cytotoxic T cells are responsible for the immune response that destroys the antigen.

Figure 22.19 illustrates the activation and proliferation of helper T cells, a process that is important for immunity responses, including both antibody-mediated and cell-mediated.

1. An antigen-presenting cell, such as a macrophage, engulfs, processes, and displays an antigen on its plasma membrane by way of an MHC class II molecule (see figure 22.17).
2. A helper T cell interacts with the macrophage through its T-cell receptor.
3. Costimulation occurs by a CD4 glycoprotein of the helper T cell or by cytokines, such as interleukin-1 released by the macrophage.
4. Interleukin-1 binds to interleukin-1 receptors and stimulates the helper T cell to secrete cytokine interleukin-2 and to produce interleukin-2 receptors.
5. The helper T cell stimulates itself to divide when interleukin-2 binds to interleukin-2 receptors.
6. The "daughter" helper T cells can be stimulated to divide again if they are exposed to the same antigen that stimulated the "parent" cell. This greatly increases the number of helper T cells specific to this antigen.
7. The increased number of helper T cells can facilitate the activation of B cells or cytotoxic T cells.
8. Some "daughter" cells will become memory helper T cells, which become active in future encounters with the same antigen.

Inhibition of Lymphocytes

Lymphocyte activity is regulated. Though activation and proliferation of lymphocytes are necessary for maintaining the health of the body, these same lymphocytes should not respond to normal cells. **Tolerance** is a state of unresponsiveness of lymphocytes to a specific antigen. The most important function of tolerance is to prevent

PROCESS **Figure**

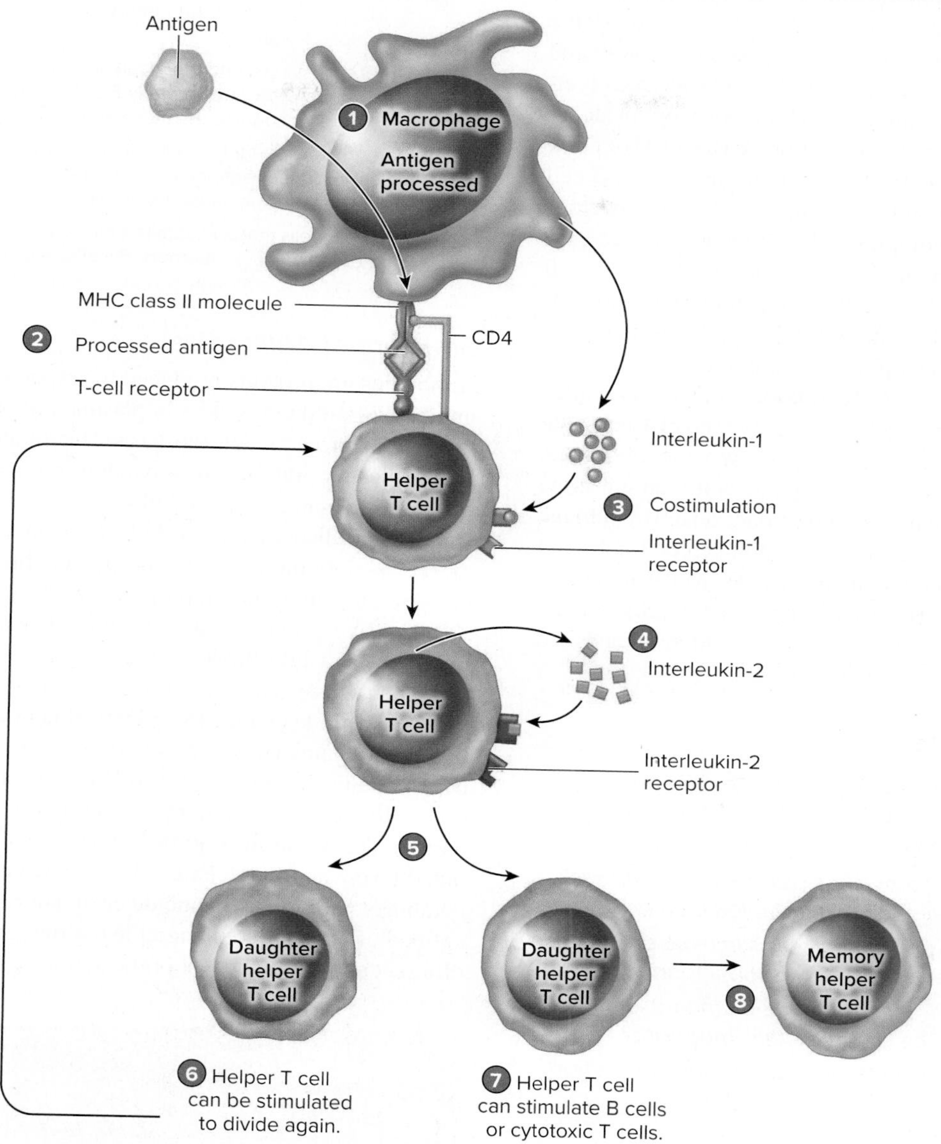

PROCESS **Figure 22.19**

Proliferation of Helper T Cells

An antigen-presenting cell (macrophage) stimulates helper T cells to divide and produce cytokines.

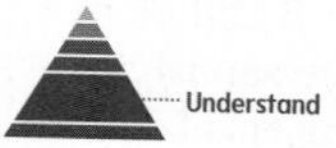

Cellular communication is an important aspect of immunity. In this figure, paracrine communication and autocrine communication are both shown. Identify the step for each type of communication (paracrine and autocrine) and the chemical mediator associated with each. (See table 17.1 for descriptions of cellular communication.)

the immune system from responding to self-antigens, although foreign antigens can also induce tolerance. The need to maintain tolerance and to avoid the development of autoimmune disease is obvious. Tolerance can be induced in three primary ways:

1. *Deletion of self-reactive lymphocytes.* During prenatal development and after birth, stem cells in red bone marrow and the thymus give rise to immature lymphocytes that develop into mature lymphocytes capable of an immune response. When immature lymphocytes are exposed to their specific antigen, instead of responding in ways that cause elimination of the antigen, they respond by dying. Because immature lymphocytes are exposed to self-antigens, this process eliminates self-reactive lymphocytes. In addition, if immature lymphocytes escape deletion during their development and become mature, these self-reacting lymphocytes can still be deleted most likely by the activities of regulatory T cells.

2. *Prevention of the activation of lymphocytes.* For lymphocytes to be activated, two signals are usually required: (1) the MHC/antigen complex binding with an antigen receptor and (2) costimulation. Preventing either of these events stops lymphocyte activation. For example, blocking, altering, or deleting an antigen receptor prevents activation. **Anergy** (AN-er-jee; without working) is a condition of inactivity in which a B cell or a T cell does not respond to an antigen. Anergy develops when an MHC-antigen complex binds to an antigen receptor and no costimulation occurs. For example, if a helper T cell encounters a self-antigen on a cell that cannot provide costimulation, the helper T cell is turned off. It is likely that only antigen-presenting cells can provide costimulation.
3. *Activation of regulatory T cells.* **Regulatory T cells,** also called *suppressor T cells,* are a poorly understood group of T cells that are defined by their ability to suppress immune responses. Regulatory T cells develop in the thymus and then enter the tissues of the body. Regulatory T cells reduce adaptive immune responses by releasing cytokines that inhibit helper T cells and cytotoxic T cells. By inhibiting helper T cells, which are necessary for the activation of B cells, and cytotoxic T cells, regulatory T cells control the activities of both antibody-mediated immunity and cell-mediated immunity.

ASSESS YOUR PROGRESS

39. *What are lymphocyte clones? What is the difference between positive and negative lymphocyte selection?*

40. *What is costimulation? State two ways it can happen.*

41. *Why are helper T cells sometimes called CD4 or T4 cells? Why are cytotoxic T cells sometimes called CD8 or T8 cells?*

42. *Describe how antigen-presenting cells stimulate an increase in the number of helper T cells. Why is this important?*

43. *Describe how helper T cells stimulate an increase in the number of B cells or T cells. Why is this important?*

44. *What is tolerance? Explain three ways it is accomplished.*

Antibody-Mediated Immunity

Antibody-mediated immunity involves the production of antibodies in response to extracellular antigens. Exposure of the body to an antigen can lead to the activation of B cells and to the production of antibodies, which are responsible for destroying the antigen. Because antibodies occur in body fluids, antibody-mediated immunity is effective against extracellular antigens, such as bacteria, viruses, protozoans, fungi, parasites, and toxins, when they are outside cells. Antibody-mediated immunity can also cause immediate hypersensitivity reactions (see table 22.7).

Typically, the proliferation and activation of B cells involve helper T cells. Figure 22.20 illustrates the proliferation and activation of a B cell.

1. Before a B cell can be activated by a helper T cell, the B cell must take in and process the same antigen that activated the helper T cell. The antigen binds to a B-cell receptor and both the receptor and antigen are taken into the cell.
2. The B cell uses an MHC class II molecule to present the processed antigen to a T-cell receptor on the helper T cell.
3. Costimulation of the B cell occurs through surface molecules, such as CD4, as well as through the release of interleukins (cytokines) by the helper T cell.
4. The B cell divides, and the resulting "daughter" B cells divide, and so on, eventually producing many B cells (only four are shown in figure 22.20) that recognize the same antigen.
5. Many of the daughter cells differentiate to become **plasma cells,** which produce antibodies. Antibodies are part of the immune response that eliminates the antigen.
6. Daughter cells that do not differentiate to become plasma cells reduce in size and become **memory B cells.** Memory B cells may become active in future encounters with the same antigen.

Structure of Antibodies

Antibodies are proteins produced in response to an antigen. Large numbers of antibodies exist in plasma, although plasma also contains other proteins. On the basis of protein type and associated lipids, plasma proteins are separated into albumin and alpha-(α), beta-(β), and gamma-(γ) globulin parts. As a group, antibodies are sometimes called *gamma globulins* because they are found mostly in the γ-globulin part of plasma, or **immunoglobulins (Ig),** because they are globulin proteins involved in immunity.

The five general classes of antibodies are denoted IgG, IgM, IgA, IgE, and IgD (table 22.6). All classes of antibodies have a similar structure. This structure is a Y-shaped protein consisting of four polypeptide chains: two identical heavy chains and two identical light chains (figure 22.21). Each light chain is attached to a heavy chain. An antibody is organized into two major regions, each with specific function: (1) variable region and (2) constant region. The **variable region** is formed by the ends of the combined heavy and light chains. This is the part of the antibody that combines with the antigenic determinant of the antigen. Different antibodies have different variable regions, and they are specific for different antigens. The rest of the antibody is the **constant region.**

Clinical IMPACT 22.3

Uses of Monoclonal Antibodies

A **monoclonal antibody** is a pure antibody preparation that is specific for only one antigen. A monoclonal antibody preparation can be produced by injecting a laboratory animal with a specific antigen. The antigen activates a B-cell clone against the antigen. The B cells are removed from the animal and fused with tumor cells, which divide to form large numbers of cells. The tumor cells of a given clone produce only one kind of antibody.

Monoclonal antibodies are used for determining pregnancy and for diagnosing diseases, such as gonorrhea, syphilis, hepatitis, rabies, and cancer. These tests are specific and rapid because the monoclonal antibodies bind only to the antigen being tested. Monoclonal antibodies have been used to treat some autoimmune diseases and reduce the chances of tissue rejection after transplant. They may also be used as treatments for certain cancers, such as breast cancer (see section 22.8). Monoclonal antibodies were also approved by the U.S. FDA in the treatment of COVID-19.

FUNDAMENTAL **Figure**

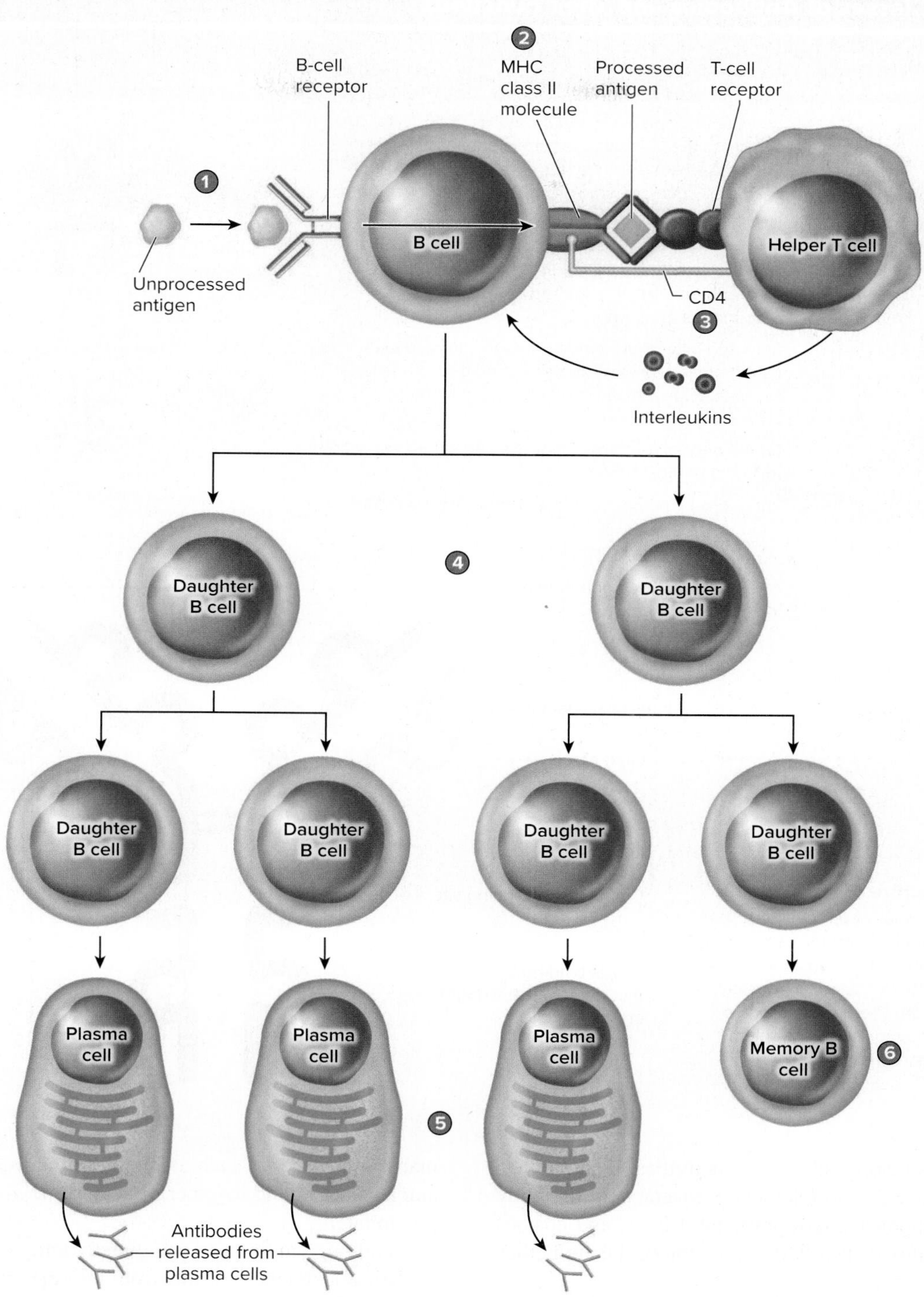

B-cell receptor
MHC class II molecule
Processed antigen
T-cell receptor
1
2
Unprocessed antigen
B cell
Helper T cell
CD4
3
Interleukins
4
Daughter B cell
Daughter B cell
Daughter B cell
Daughter B cell
Daughter B cell
Daughter B cell
Plasma cell
Plasma cell
Plasma cell
Memory B cell
5
6
Antibodies released from plasma cells

PROCESS **Figure 22.20**

Proliferation of B Cells

A helper T cell stimulates a B cell to divide. Most daughter cells (only two shown here) differentiate to become plasma cells that produce antibodies. A few may reduce in size and become memory B cells.

Considering that antibodies are proteins that will be released from the cell, which types of cytoplasmic organelles are likely to be found in high numbers in plasma cells? (See table 3.1 for a summary of organelles and their functions.)

TABLE 22.6 Classes of Antibodies and Their Functions

Antibody	Total Serum Antibody (%)	Description	Structure
IgG	80–85	Activates complement and promotes phagocytosis; can cross the placenta and provide immune protection to the fetus and newborn; responsible for Rh reactions, such as hemolytic disease of the newborn	
IgM	5–10	Activates complement and acts as an antigen-binding receptor on the surface of B cells; responsible for transfusion reactions in the ABO blood system; often the first antibody produced in response to an antigen	
IgA	15	Secreted into saliva, into tears, and onto mucous membranes to provide protection on body surfaces; found in colostrum and milk to provide immune protection to newborns	
IgE	0.002	Binds to mast cells and basophils and stimulates the inflammatory response	
IgD	0.2	Functions as antigen-binding receptors on B cells	

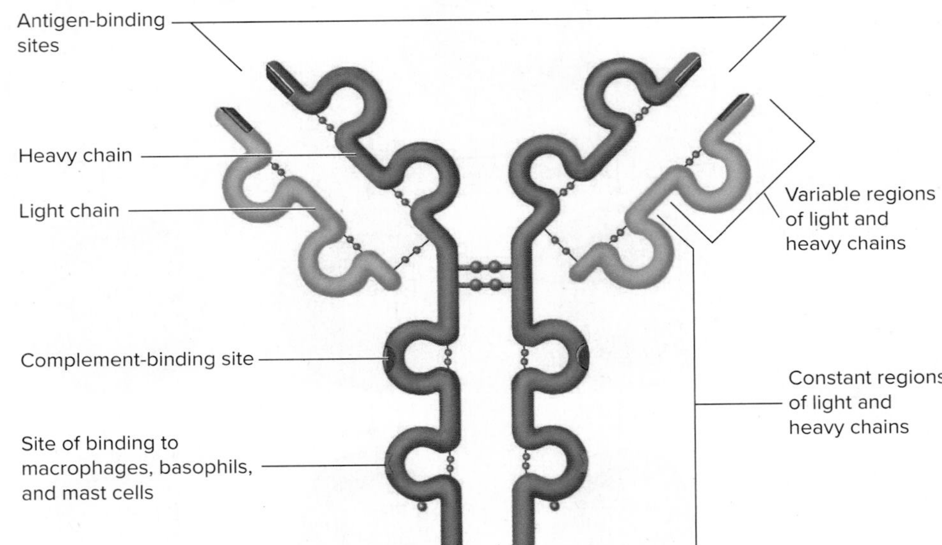

FIGURE 22.21 Structure of an Antibody
Antibodies consist of two heavy and two light polypeptide chains. The variable region of the antibody binds to the antigen. The constant region of the antibody can activate the classical pathway of the complement cascade. The constant region can also attach the antibody to the plasma membrane of cells such as macrophages, basophils, and mast cells.

The constant region is responsible for the activities of antibodies, such as the ability to activate complement or to attach the antibody to cells such as macrophages, basophils, mast cells, and eosinophils. The constant region is nearly the same for all the antibodies of a particular class.

Effects of Antibodies

The effects of antibodies can be described as direct effects or indirect effects. Direct effects of antibodies include the following: (1) The antibody can bind to the antigenic determinant and interfere with the antigen's ability to function (figure 22.22*a*) or (2) the antibody can combine with an antigenic determinant on two different antigens, rendering the antigens ineffective (figure 22.22*b*). The ability of antibodies to join antigens together is the basis for many clinical tests, such as blood typing, because, when enough antigens are bound together, they become visible as a clump or a precipitate.

Although antibodies can directly alter antigen function, most of their effectiveness results from indirect mechanisms:

1. When an antibody (IgG or IgM) combines with an antigen through the variable region, the constant region can activate the complement cascade through the classical pathway (figure 22.22*c;* see figure 22.11). Activated complement stimulates inflammation; attracts neutrophils, monocytes, macrophages, and eosinophils to sites of infection; and kills bacteria by lysis.
2. Antibodies (IgE) can initiate an inflammatory response (figure 22.22*d*). The antibodies attach to mast cells or basophils through their constant region. When antigens combine with

FUNDAMENTAL **Figure**

Direct Antibody Effects

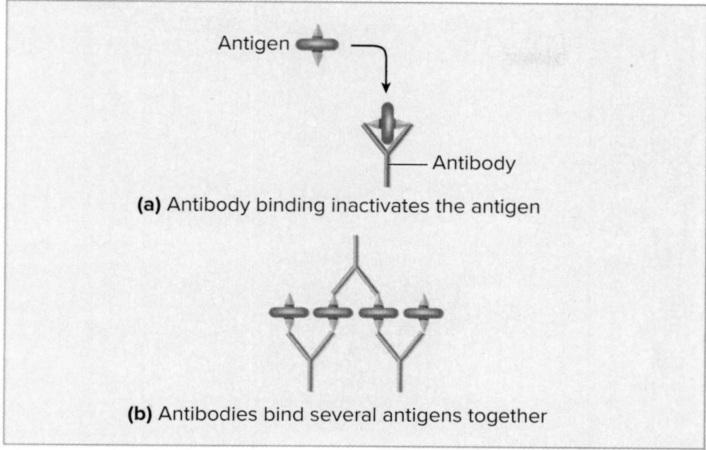

Indirect Antibody Effects

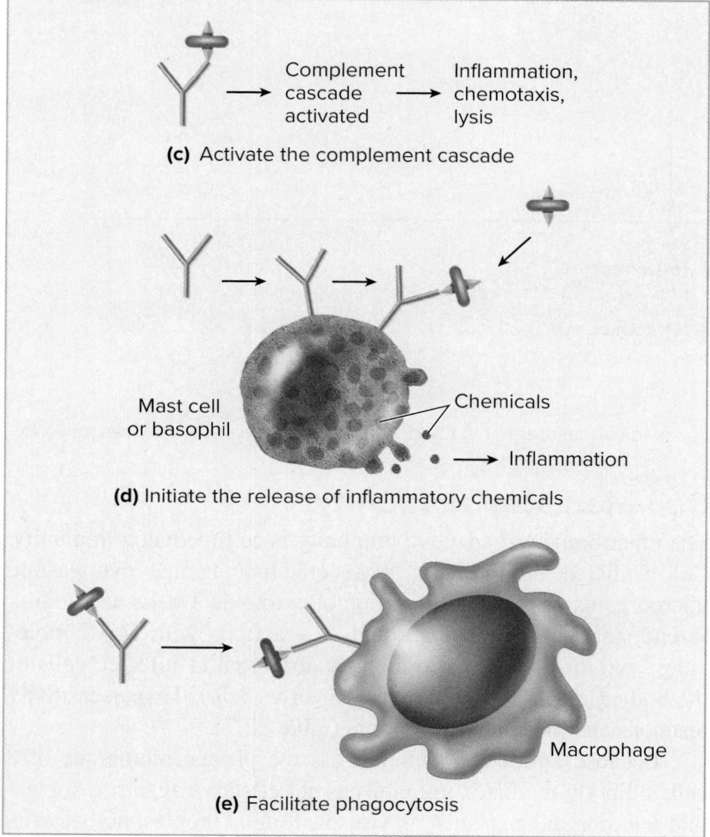

FIGURE 22.22 Effects of Antibodies

Antibodies directly affect antigens by (*a*) inactivating the antigens or (*b*) binding the antigens together. Antibodies indirectly affect antigens by activating other mechanisms through the constant region of the antibody. Indirect mechanisms include (*c*) activation of complement, (*d*) increased inflammation resulting from the release of inflammatory chemicals from mast cells or basophils, and (*e*) increased phagocytosis resulting from antibody attachment to macrophages.

the variable region of the antibodies, the mast cells or basophils release chemicals through exocytosis, and inflammation results. For example, people who have hay fever inhale antigens (usually, plant pollen), which are then absorbed through the respiratory mucous membrane. The combination of the antigens with antibodies stimulates mast cells to release inflammatory chemicals, such as histamine. The resulting localized inflammatory response produces swelling and increased mucus production in the respiratory tract.

3. **Opsonins** (OP-soh-ninz) are substances that make an antigen more susceptible to phagocytosis. An antibody (IgG) acts as an opsonin by connecting to an antigen through the variable region of the antibody and to a macrophage through the constant region of the antibody. The macrophage then phagocytizes the antigen and the antibody (figure 22.22*e*).

Antibody Production

Figure 22.22 illustrates the activation of B lymphocytes and subsequent production of antibodies by plasma cells. It is important to note that antibody production after the first exposure to an antigen is different from that after a second or subsequent exposure (figure 22.23). The first exposure of a B cell to an antigen for which it is specific causes the **primary response.** This primary response includes a series of cell divisions, cell differentiation, and antibody production (see figure 22.20). The B-cell receptors on the surface of B cells are actually antibodies, usually IgM and IgD. The receptors have the same variable region as the antibodies that are eventually produced by the B cell. Usually, IgM is the first antibody produced in response to an antigen, but later other classes of antibodies are produced as well. The primary response normally takes 3–14 days to produce enough antibodies to be effective against the antigen. In the meantime, disease symptoms usually develop because the antigen has had time to cause tissue damage (figure 22.23*a*).

The **secondary response,** or *memory response,* occurs when the immune system is exposed to an antigen against which it has already produced a primary response (figure 22.23*b*). When exposed to the antigen, memory B cells rapidly divide to produce plasma cells, which produce large amounts of antibody. The secondary response provides better protection than the primary response for two reasons: (1) The time required to start producing antibodies is less (hours to a few days), and (2) the amount of antibody produced is much larger. As a consequence, the antigen is quickly destroyed, no disease symptoms develop, and the person is immune.

The secondary response also includes the formation of new memory B cells, which protect against additional exposures to the antigen. Memory B cells are the basis for adaptive immunity. After destruction of the antigen, plasma cells die, the antibodies they released are degraded, and antibody levels decline to the point at which they can no longer provide adequate protection. Memory B cells persist for many years—for life, in some cases. However, if memory cell production is not stimulated or if the memory B cells produced are short-lived, repeated infections of the same disease are possible. For example, the same cold virus can cause the common cold more than once in the same person.

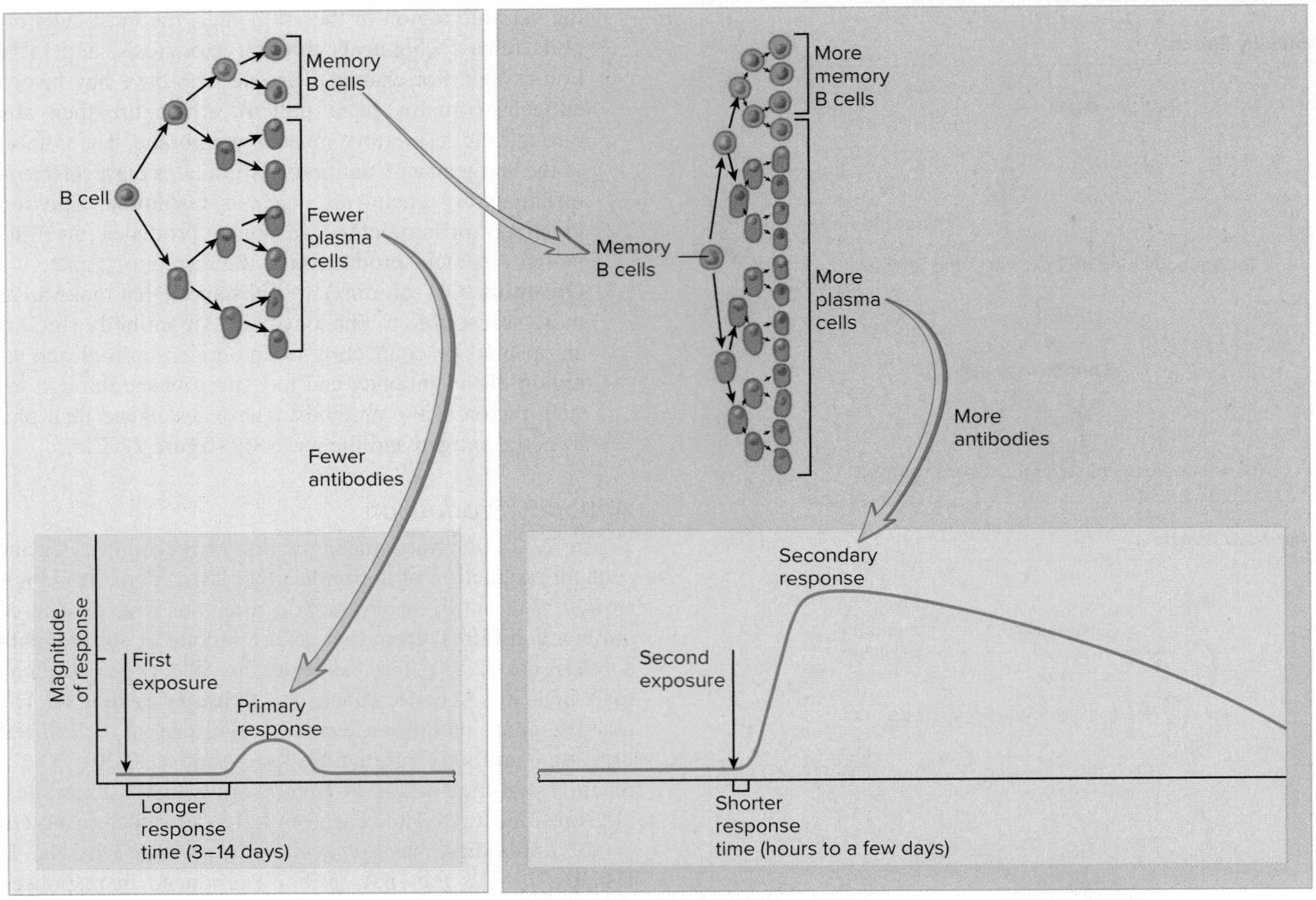

(a) Primary response

(b) Secondary response

FIGURE 22.23 Antibody Production
Antibody production in a primary response (*a*) has a longer response time and produces lower numbers of antibodies compared to a secondary response (*b*).

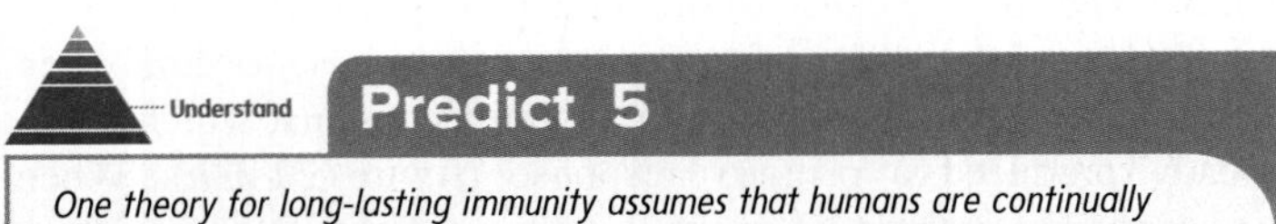

One theory for long-lasting immunity assumes that humans are continually exposed to the disease-causing agent. Explain how this exposure can produce lifelong immunity.

ASSESS YOUR PROGRESS

45. *What type of lymphocyte is responsible for antibody-mediated immunity? What are the functions of antibody-mediated immunity?*

46. *What are the functions of the variable and constant regions of an antibody?*

47. *List the five classes of antibodies, and state their functions.*

48. *Describe the different ways that antibodies participate in destroying antigens.*

49. *What are plasma cells and memory B cells, and how do they function?*

50. *What are the primary and secondary antibody responses? Why doesn't the primary response prevent illness, whereas the secondary response does?*

Cell-Mediated Immunity

The other branch of adaptive immunity is cell-mediated immunity. Cell-mediated immunity is most effective against cytoplasmic microorganisms through the action of cytotoxic T cells responding to endogenous antigens. Through interactions with MHC molecules, cytotoxic T cells can identify abnormal or infected cells of the body. Cell-mediated immunity involves delayed hypersensitivity reactions and the control of tumors (table 22.7).

Because antibodies cannot cross the plasma membrane of a cell, antibody-mediated immunity is not effective against cytoplasmic microorganisms, such as viruses, fungi, cytoplasmic bacteria, and parasites. However, cell-mediated immunity is effective against these cytoplasmic microorganisms because it destroys the cells in which the microorganisms are located. For example, viruses enter cells and direct those cells to make new viruses. The newly produced viruses are then released to infect other cells. Thus, cells are turned into virus-manufacturing cells. Cell-mediated immunity fights viral infections by destroying virally infected cells, reducing the chance that the virus can spread to other cells of the body.

Cytotoxic T cells become activated when exposed to their specific antigen, leading to cell proliferation and subsequent destruction of the infected cell. Figure 22.24 illustrates the proliferation

TABLE 22.7 Representative Diseases and Disorders of the Lymphatic System and Immunity

Condition	Description
LYMPHATIC SYSTEM	
Infections	
Lymphadenitis (lim-FAD-ee-NIE-tis)	Inflammation of the lymph nodes; lymph nodes become enlarged and tender as microorganisms are trapped and destroyed
Lymphangitis (lim-fan-JIE-tis)	Inflammation of the lymphatic vessels; often results in visible red streaks in the skin that extend from the site of infection
Bubonic (byoo-BON-ik) plague	Enlarged lymph nodes caused by bacterial infection (transferred by flea bites from rats); without treatment, bacteria enter the blood, and death occurs rapidly due to septicemia; known as the Black Death in the Middle Ages
Lymphedema (LIMF-e-DEE-mah)	
Abnormal accumulation of lymph in tissues, often the limbs; 70–90% of cases in females; can be inherited or caused by developmental defects (primary lymphedema), disease, or damage to the lymphatic system (secondary lymphedema)	
Elephantiasis (el-ee-fan-TIE-ah-sis)	Caused by long, slender roundworms transferred to humans by mosquito bites; adult worms lodge in lymphatic vessels and block lymph flow, so that a limb can become permanently swollen and enlarged; major cause of lymphedema worldwide
Lymphedema following cancer treatment	Caused by removal of lymph nodes near a tumor by surgery or radiation therapy; sentinel lymph nodes (those nearest the tumor) are first examined for cancer cells
Lymphoma (lim-FOH-mah)	Cancer of lymphocytes that often begins in lymph nodes; immune system becomes depressed, with increased susceptibility to infections
IMMUNITY	
Immediate Hypersensitivities	
Symptoms occur within a few minutes of exposure to an antigen because antibodies are already present from prior exposure.	
Hay fever	Often caused by inhalation of plant pollen antigens
Asthma (AZ-mah)	Antigen combines with antibodies on mast cells or basophils in the lungs, which then release inflammatory chemicals that cause constriction of the air tubes, so that the patient has trouble breathing
Immune complex disease	Caused by excessive formation of immune complexes (combinations of antigens and IgG or IgM), which activate too much complement; results in acute inflammatory response and tissue damage; examples include serum sickness, some autoimmune diseases, chronic graft rejection, and Arthus reactions (localized reactions)
Urticaria (ER-ti-KAR-i-ah)	Skin rash or localized swelling; can be caused by an ingested antigen; also called hives
Anaphylaxis (AN-ah-fi-LAK-sis, AN-ah-fih-LAK-sis)	Systemic allergic reaction, often resulting from insect sting or drugs, such as penicillin; chemicals released from mast cells and basophils cause systemic vasodilation, increased vascular permeability, drop in blood pressure, and possibly death
Delayed Allergic Reactions	
Symptoms occur in hours to days following exposure to the antigen because these types of reactions involve migration of T cells to the antigen, followed by release of cytokines.	
Poison ivy and poison oak	Antigen absorbed by epithelial cells, which are then destroyed by T cells, causing inflammation and tissue destruction; itching can be intense
Autoimmune Diseases	
Similar to allergic reactions, except that the immune system incorrectly treats self-antigens as foreign antigens. Many types of autoimmune diseases exist, including type 1 diabetes, gluten-sensitive enteropathy, rheumatoid arthritis, multiple sclerosis, systemic lupus erythematosus, and Graves disease.	
Congenital Immunodeficiencies	
They usually involve failure of the fetus to form adequate numbers of B cells, T cells, or both.	
Severe combined immunodeficiency (SCID)	Both B cells and T cells fail to form; unless patient is kept in a sterile environment or provided with a compatible bone marrow transplant, death from infection results
Acquired Immunodeficiencies	
They have many causes—for example, diseases, stress, and drugs.	
Acquired immunodeficiency syndrome (AIDS)	Life-threatening disease caused by the human immunodeficiency virus (HIV); HIV is transmitted in body fluids; infection begins when the virus binds to the CD4 protein found primarily on helper T cells; without helper T cells, cytotoxic T-cell and B-cell activation is impaired, and adaptive immunity is suppressed; course of HIV infection varies, with most people surviving 10 or more years
Transplanted tissue rejection	Caused by a normal immune response to foreign antigens encoded by the major histocompatilbility complex genes, also called human leukocyte antigen (HLA) genes; drugs that suppress the immune system must be administered for life to prevent graft rejection

PROCESS **Figure**

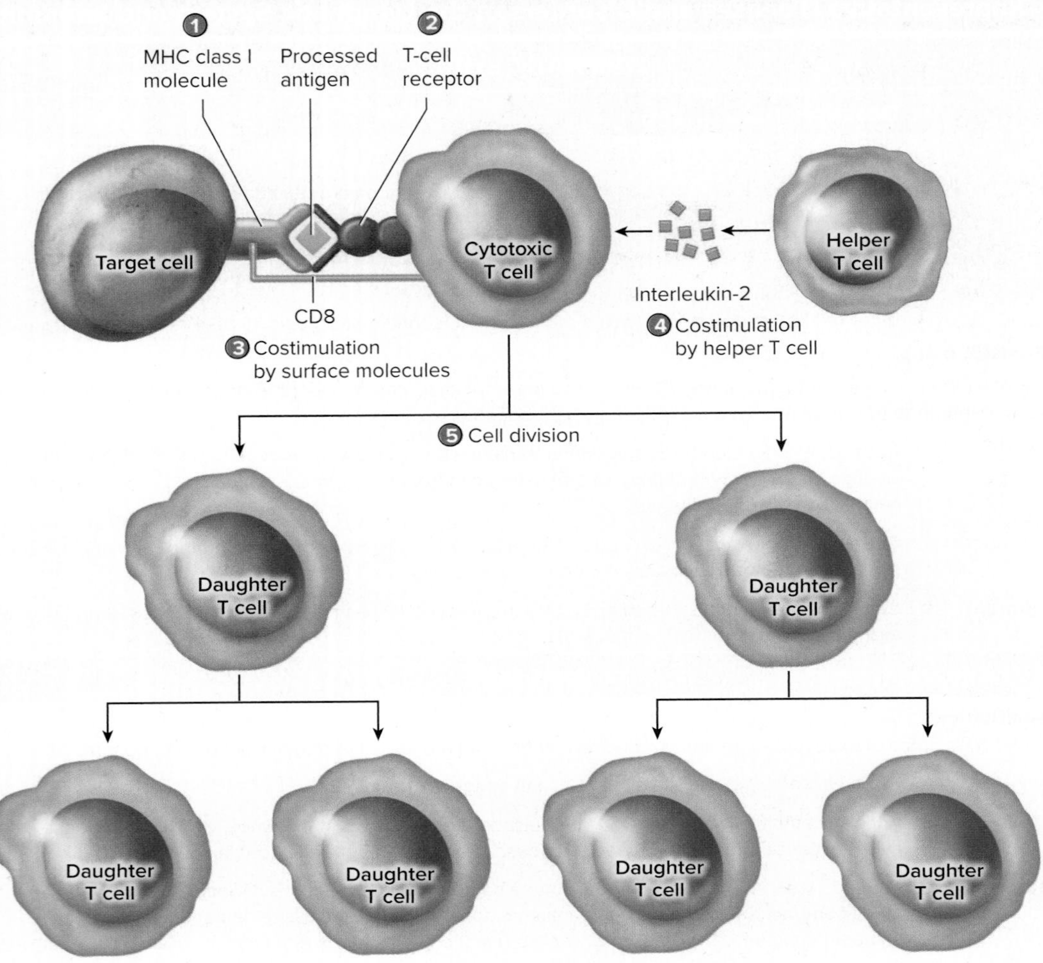

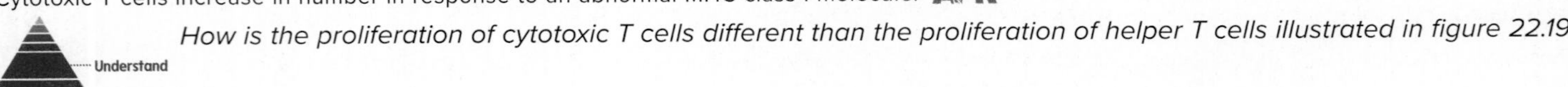

PROCESS **Figure 22.24**

Proliferation of Cytotoxic T Cells

Cytotoxic T cells increase in number in response to an abnormal MHC class I molecule. APR

Understand *How is the proliferation of cytotoxic T cells different than the proliferation of helper T cells illustrated in figure 22.19?*

of cytotoxic T cells in response to a virally infected cell. Effects of activated cytotoxic T cells is illustrated in figure 22.25.

1. When viruses infect cells, some viral proteins are broken down and become processed endogenous antigens that are combined with MHC class I molecules and displayed on the surface of the infected cells. T cells can distinguish between virally infected cells and non-infected cells because MHC class I/antigen complexes are on the surface of infected cells, but not on the surface of uninfected cells.
2. Binding of the T-cell receptor to the MHC class I/antigen complex is a signal for activating cytotoxic T cells.
3. Costimulation by other surface molecules, such as CD8, also occurs.
4. Helper T cells provide costimulation by releasing cytokines, such as interleukin-2, which activates cytotoxic T cells. However, unlike their interactions with macrophages and B cells, helper T cells do not connect to cytotoxic T cells through MHC class II/antigen complexes or other surface molecules.
5. The activated cytotoxic T cell divides, the resulting daughter cells divide, and so on, eventually producing many cytotoxic T cells (only four are shown in Figure 22.24).

An increased number of helper T cells results in greater stimulation of cytotoxic T cells. In cell-mediated responses, helper T cells are activated and stimulated to divide in the same fashion as in antibody-mediated responses (see figure 22.19).

The response of activated cytotoxic T cells is illustrated in figure 22.25.

1. After T cells are activated by an antigen on the surface of a target cell, they undergo a series of divisions to produce cytotoxic T cells and memory T cells.
2. Memory T cells can provide a secondary response and long-lasting immunity in the same fashion as memory B cells.

PROCESS **Figure**

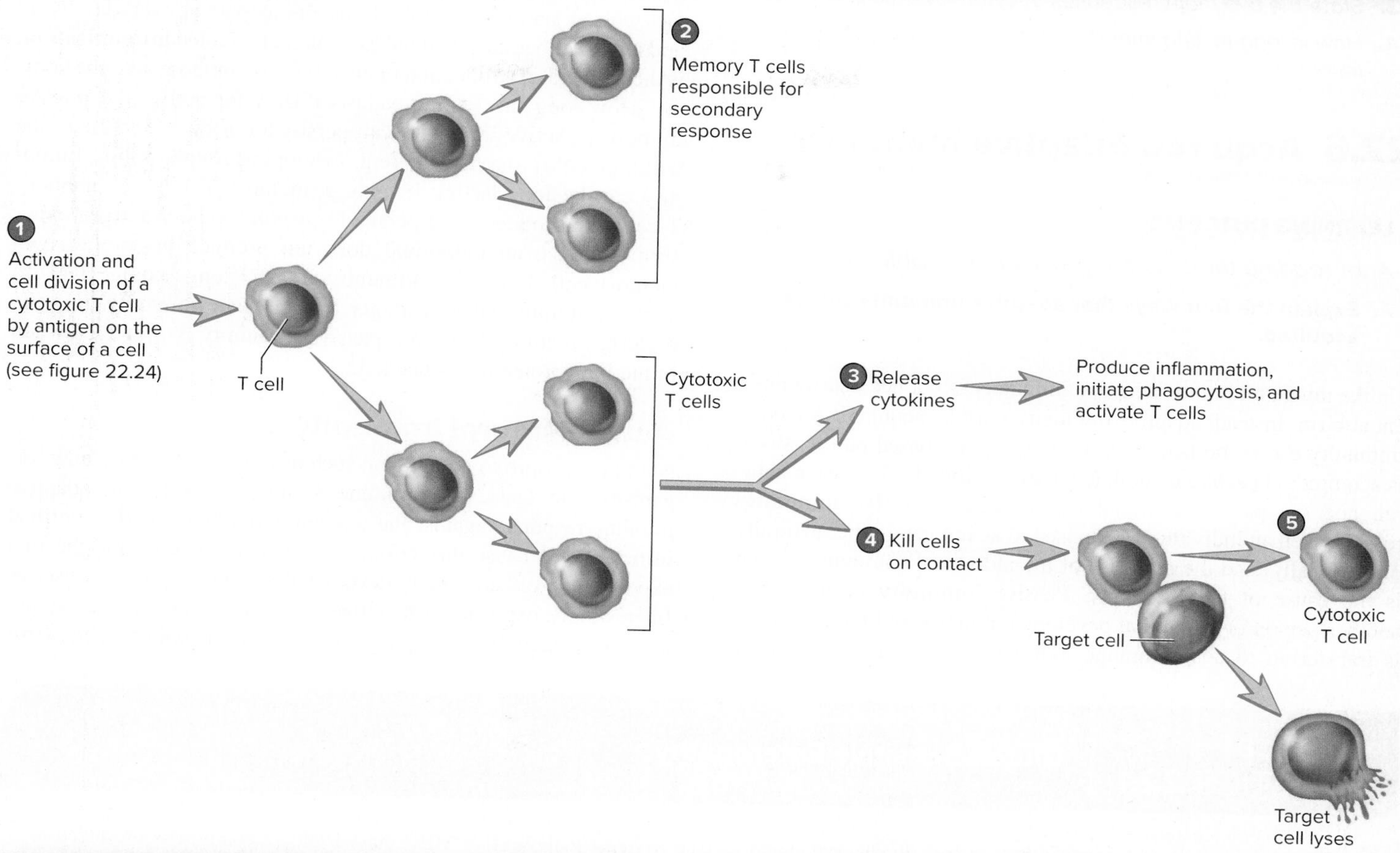

1 Activation and cell division of a cytotoxic T cell by antigen on the surface of a cell (see figure 22.24)

T cell

2 Memory T cells responsible for secondary response

Cytotoxic T cells

3 Release cytokines

Produce inflammation, initiate phagocytosis, and activate T cells

4 Kill cells on contact

5

Target cell

Cytotoxic T cell

Target cell lyses

PROCESS **Figure 22.25**

Stimulation and Effects of T Cells

When activated, cytotoxic T cells form many additional cytotoxic T cells, as well as memory T cells. The cytotoxic T cells release cytokines that promote the destruction of the antigen or cause the lysis of target cells, such as virus-infected cells, tumor cells, or transplanted cells. The memory T cells are responsible for the secondary response.

Which cells are most likely responsible for handling the target cell once it has lysed?

3 One effect of cytotoxic T cells is the release of cytokines that activate additional components of the immune system. For example, one important function of cytokines is the recruitment of cells, such as macrophages. These cells are then responsible for phagocytosis and inflammation.

4 Another effect of cytotoxic T cells is the destruction of target cells. Cytotoxic T cells can come into contact with other cells and cause them to lyse. Virally infected cells have viral antigens, tumor cells have tumor antigens, and tissue transplants have foreign antigens on their surfaces that can stimulate cytotoxic T-cell activity. A cytotoxic T cell binds to a target cell and releases chemicals that cause the target cell to lyse. The major method of lysis involves a protein called **perforin,** which is similar to the complement protein C9 (see figure 22.11). Perforin released by cytotoxic T cells forms a channel in the plasma membrane of the target cell. Water enters the cell through the channel, causing the cell to swell and lyse.

5 The cytotoxic T cell then moves on to destroy additional target cells.

Predict 6

In patients with acquired immunodeficiency syndrome (AIDS), the HIV virus infects and destroys helper T cells. Patients often die of pneumonia caused by a cytoplasmic fungus (Pneumocystis carinii) *or of Kaposi sarcoma, which is characterized by tumorous growths in the skin and lymph nodes. Explain what is happening.*

ASSESS YOUR PROGRESS

51. *What type of lymphocyte is responsible for cell-mediated immunity? What are the functions of cell-mediated immunity?*

52. *How do cytoplasmic microorganisms stimulate cytotoxic T cells? What role do helper T cells play in this process?*

53. *State the two main responses of cytotoxic T cells.*
54. *How is long-lasting immunity achieved in cell-mediated immunity?*

22.6 Acquired Adaptive Immunity

LEARNING OUTCOME

After reading this section, you should be able to

A. **Explain the four ways that adaptive immunity can be acquired.**

Unlike innate immunity, adaptive immunity is not necessarily present at birth. Instead, adaptive immunity must be acquired. Adaptive immunity can be broken down into four types, based on the way it is acquired: (1) active natural, (2) active artificial, (3) passive natural, and (4) passive artificial (figure 22.26). **Active immunity** results when an individual is exposed to an antigen (either naturally or artificially) and the response of the individual's immune system is the cause of the immunity. **Passive immunity** occurs when another person or an animal develops immunity and the immunity is transferred to a nonimmune individual. *Natural* and *artificial* refer to the method of exposure. *Natural exposure* implies that contact with an antigen or antibody occurs as part of everyday living and is not deliberate. Artificial exposure, also called **immunization,** is the deliberate introduction of an antigen or antibody into the body.

How long the immunity lasts differs for active and passive immunity. Active immunity can persist for a few weeks (e.g., the common cold) to a lifetime (e.g., whooping cough, polio). Immunity can be long-lasting if enough memory B cells or memory T cells are produced and persist to respond to later antigen exposure. Because an individual does not produce his or her own memory cells in passive immunity, it is not long-lasting. Because active immunity can last longer than passive immunity, it is the preferred method. However, passive immunity is preferred when immediate protection is needed.

Active Natural Immunity

Natural exposure to an antigen, such as a disease-causing microorganism, can cause the immune system to mount an adaptive immune response against the antigen and achieve **active natural immunity.** Because the individual is not immune during the first exposure, he or she usually develops the symptoms of the disease. Interestingly, exposure to an antigen does not always produce symptoms. For example, many people exposed to the poliomyelitis virus

Clinical GENETICS 22.1 Gluten-Sensitive Enteropathy

Gluten-sensitive enteropathy, also called *celiac* (SEE-lee-ak) *disease,* is a malabsorption disorder, meaning that nutrients are poorly absorbed. Gluten-sensitive enteropathy results from damage to the lining of the small intestine, specifically the fingerlike projections, called villi, that increase the surface area for nutrient absorption (see chapter 24). In a healthy intestine, the lining resembles a shag carpet. In gluten-sensitive enteropathy, the epithelium has become damaged, and the intestinal villi are flattened and inflamed.

Gluten-sensitive enteropathy is usually characterized by gastrointestinal symptoms, such as diarrhea, painful abdominal cramping, bloating, and intestinal gas. Prolonged gluten-sensitive enteropathy leads to additional complications, including anemia, osteoporosis, and neurological problems, in part due to nutritional deficiencies.

Gluten-sensitive enteropathy occurs in about 1 in 133 people, but the frequency may actually be even higher because the widely varying symptoms and severity of the disease make diagnosis difficult.

Gluten-sensitive enteropathy is an autoimmune disease and is often associated with other autoimmune diseases, such as systemic lupus erythematosus (see Systems Pathology, later in this chapter). The damage to the intestinal lining is caused by an inappropriate immune response, which is triggered by the gluten proteins in wheat, barley, and rye. Although neither rice nor corn contains gluten proteins, gluten is often hidden as an additive in prepared foods and sauces.

Gluten-sensitive enteropathy has a genetic component. Most patients have mutated variants of some of the MHC class II genes. As a result, abnormal MHC class II molecules are produced and can bind to digested fragments of gluten. However, the genetics of gluten-sensitive enteropathy are complex and not fully understood. For example, the variant MHC alleles alone are not sufficient to cause the disease because many people who have the variant alleles do not develop gluten-sensitive enteropathy. Furthermore, the genetic expression of the disease is influenced by variable environmental factors because the onset and severity of the disease can be triggered by unknown factors at any time in life.

Gluten-sensitive enteropathy results from both adaptive and innate immune responses. On the surface of antigen-presenting cells, the MHC class II/gluten complex is presented to helper T cells to initiate an adaptive immune response (see figure 22.18). The adaptive immune response includes antibody production and the activation of cytotoxic T cells. The innate immune response promotes inflammation through the activation of the alternative complement pathway and the release of cytokines, such as interleukin-15 (IL-15), from macrophages, dendritic cells, and other cells. In addition, exposure to gluten can activate natural killer cells and dendritic cells. The result of these immune responses is a deleterious attack on the epithelial lining of the small intestine, leading to the damaged villi common to gluten-sensitive enteropathy.

The only treatment for gluten-sensitive enteropathy is a strict, gluten-free diet. Before embarking on a lifelong gluten-free diet, however, it is important to have a definitive diagnosis. Tests for higher-than-normal levels of antibodies produced in gluten-sensitive enteropathy, such as anti-tissue transglutaminase, and a biopsy of the small intestine to examine the villi are recommended. In the future, early genetic diagnosis and manipulation of the immune response may be able to reduce the sensitivity to gluten.

FUNDAMENTAL Figure

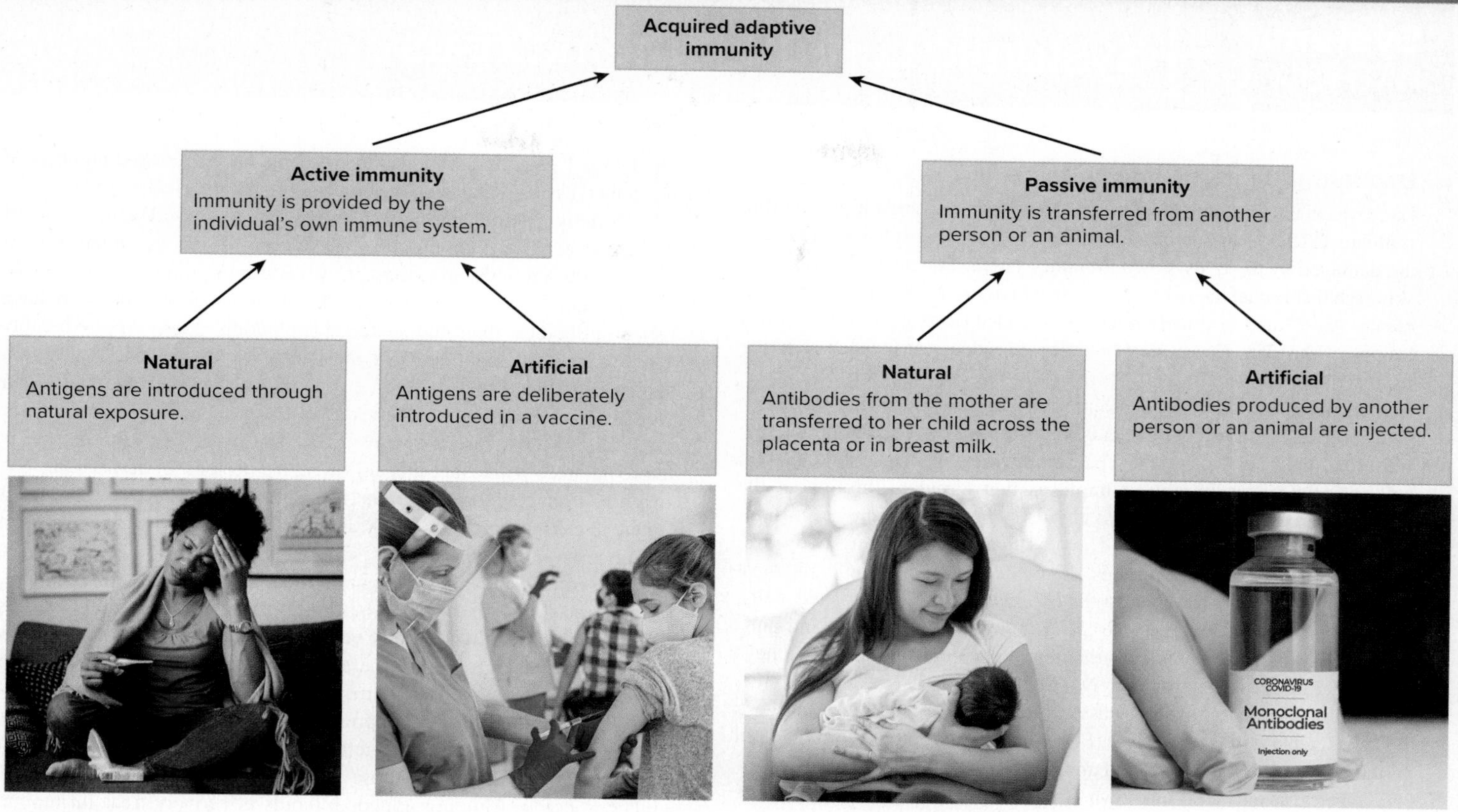

Acquired adaptive immunity

Active immunity
Immunity is provided by the individual's own immune system.

Natural
Antigens are introduced through natural exposure.

Artificial
Antigens are deliberately introduced in a vaccine.

Passive immunity
Immunity is transferred from another person or an animal.

Natural
Antibodies from the mother are transferred to her child across the placenta or in breast milk.

Artificial
Antibodies produced by another person or an animal are injected.

FIGURE 22.26 Ways to Acquire Adaptive Immunity
Adaptive immunity can be acquired actively or passively. Each of these pathways also involves natural and artificial means of acquiring adaptive immunity.
(Young woman feeling) Brothers91/Getty Images; (Doctor vaccinating girl) valentinrussanov/Getty Images; (Breastfeeding Mother) FatCamera/Getty Images; (Doctor holds a vial of monoclonal antibodies) Cristian Storto/Alamy Stock Photo

at an early age have an immune system response, produce poliomyelitis antibodies, but do not exhibit any disease symptoms.

Active Artificial Immunity

In **active artificial immunity,** an antigen is deliberately introduced into a person's body to stimulate the immune system. This process is called immunization, or **vaccination,** and the introduced antigen is a **vaccine.** A vaccine is usually administered by injection. Examples of vaccinations are the DPT injection against diphtheria, pertussis (whooping cough), and tetanus and the MMR injection against mumps, measles, and rubella (German measles).

A vaccine usually consists of a part of a microorganism, a dead microorganism, or a live, altered microorganism. The antigen has been changed so that it will stimulate an immune response but will not cause the disease symptoms. Because active artificial immunity produces long-lasting immunity without disease symptoms, it is the preferred method of acquiring adaptive immunity.

Understand

Predict 7

Some vaccination procedures require a booster shot, another dose of the original vaccine given sometime after the original dose was administered. Why are booster shots administered?

Passive Natural Immunity

Passive natural immunity results when antibodies are transferred from a mother to her child across the placenta before birth or through the mother's milk after the child is born. During her life, the mother has been exposed to many antigens, either naturally or artificially, and she has antibodies against many of these antigens that protect her and the developing fetus against disease. Some of the antibodies (IgG) can cross the placenta and enter the fetal blood. Following birth, the antibodies protect the baby for the first few months. Eventually, the antibodies break down, and the baby must rely on his or her own immune system. If the mother nurses her baby, antibodies (IgA) in the breast milk also provide some protection for the baby.

Passive Artificial Immunity

Achieving **passive artificial immunity** usually begins with vaccinating an animal, such as a horse. After the animal's immune system responds to the antigen, antibodies (and sometimes T cells) are removed from the animal and injected into the human requiring immunity. In some cases, a human who has developed immunity through natural exposure or vaccination can serve as a source of antibodies. Passive artificial immunity provides immediate protection for the individual receiving the antibodies and is

Systems PATHOLOGY | Systemic Lupus Erythematosus

Background Information

Lucy was diagnosed with lupus when she was 25. **Systemic lupus erythematosus (SLE)** is an autoimmune disease, meaning that tissues and cells are damaged by the body's own immune system. The name describes the skin rash that is characteristic of the disease (figure 22.27). The term *lupus* means "wolf" and originally referred to eroded (as if gnawed by a wolf) lesions of the skin. *Erythematosus* refers to redness of the skin resulting from inflammation.

In SLE, a large variety of antibodies are produced that recognize self-antigens, such as nucleic acids, phospholipids, coagulation factors, red blood cells, and platelets. The combination of the antibodies with self-antigens forms immune complexes that circulate throughout the body and are deposited in various tissues, where they stimulate inflammation and tissue destruction. Thus, SLE can affect many body systems, as the term *systemic* implies (figure 22.28). For example, the most common antibodies act against DNA released from damaged cells. Normally, the liver removes the DNA, but sometimes DNA and antibodies form immune complexes that tend to be deposited in the kidneys and other tissues. Approximately 40–50% of individuals with SLE develop renal disease. In some cases, the antibodies can bind to antigens on cells, causing the cells to lyse. For example, antibodies binding to red blood cells cause hemolysis and anemia.

The cause of SLE is unknown. The most popular hypothesis suggests that a viral infection disrupts the function of regulatory T cells, resulting in loss of tolerance to self-antigens. The picture is probably more complicated, however, because not all SLE patients have reduced numbers of regulatory T cells. In addition, some patients have decreased numbers of the helper T cells that normally stimulate regulatory T-cell activity.

Genetic factors probably contribute to the development of the disease. The likelihood of developing SLE is much higher if a family member also has it. In addition, family members of SLE patients who do not have SLE are much more likely to have DNA antibodies than the general population does. Approximately 1 of every 2000 individuals in the United States has SLE. The first symptoms usually appear between 15 and 25 years of age and affect women approximately nine times as often as men. A low-grade fever is present in most cases of active SLE. The progress of the disease is unpredictable, with flare-ups followed by periods of remission. The survival after diagnosis is greater than 90% after 10 years. The most frequent causes of death are kidney failure, central nervous system dysfunction, infections, and cardiovascular disease.

No cure for SLE exists, nor is there one standard of treatment, because the course of the disease is highly variable and patient histories differ widely. Treatment usually begins with mild medications and proceeds to increasingly potent therapies as conditions warrant. Aspirin and nonsteroidal anti-inflammatory drugs are used to suppress inflammation. Antimalarial drugs are prescribed to treat skin rash and arthritis in SLE, but the mechanism of action is unknown. Patients who do not respond to these drugs and those who have severe SLE are helped by glucocorticoids. Although glucocorticoids effectively treat inflammation, they can produce undesirable side effects, including suppression of normal adrenal gland functions. In patients with life-threatening SLE, very high doses of glucocorticoids are used.

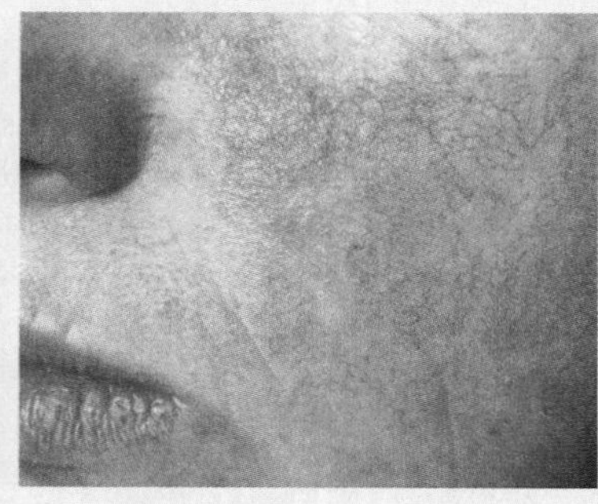

FIGURE 22.27 Systemic Lupus Erythematosus

The butterfly rash results from inflammation in the skin. BSIP/Science Source

Predict 8

The red lesions common to SLE are called purpura (PUR-poo-rah) and are caused by bleeding into the skin. The lesions gradually change color and disappear in 2-3 weeks. Explain how SLE produces purpura.

therefore preferred when time might not be available for the individual to develop his or her own immunity. However, this technique provides only temporary immunity because the antibodies are used or eliminated by the recipient.

Antiserum is the general term for the injection that contains antibodies responsible for passive artificial immunity. Antiserum is essentially blood serum, which is plasma minus the clotting factors. Antisera are available against microorganisms that cause diseases, such as rabies, hepatitis, and measles; bacterial toxins, such as those that cause tetanus, diphtheria, and botulism; and venoms from poisonous snakes and black widow spiders.

ASSESS YOUR PROGRESS

55. *Distinguish between active and passive immunity.*

56. *State four general ways of acquiring adaptive immunity. Which two provide the longest-lasting immunity?*

57. *What type of immunity occurs when a child is given the chickenpox vaccine? What type of immunity does a nursing baby obtain?*

58. *What type of immunity occurs when a person is given the rabies antisera? What type of immunity occurs if a person had the chickenpox as a child?*

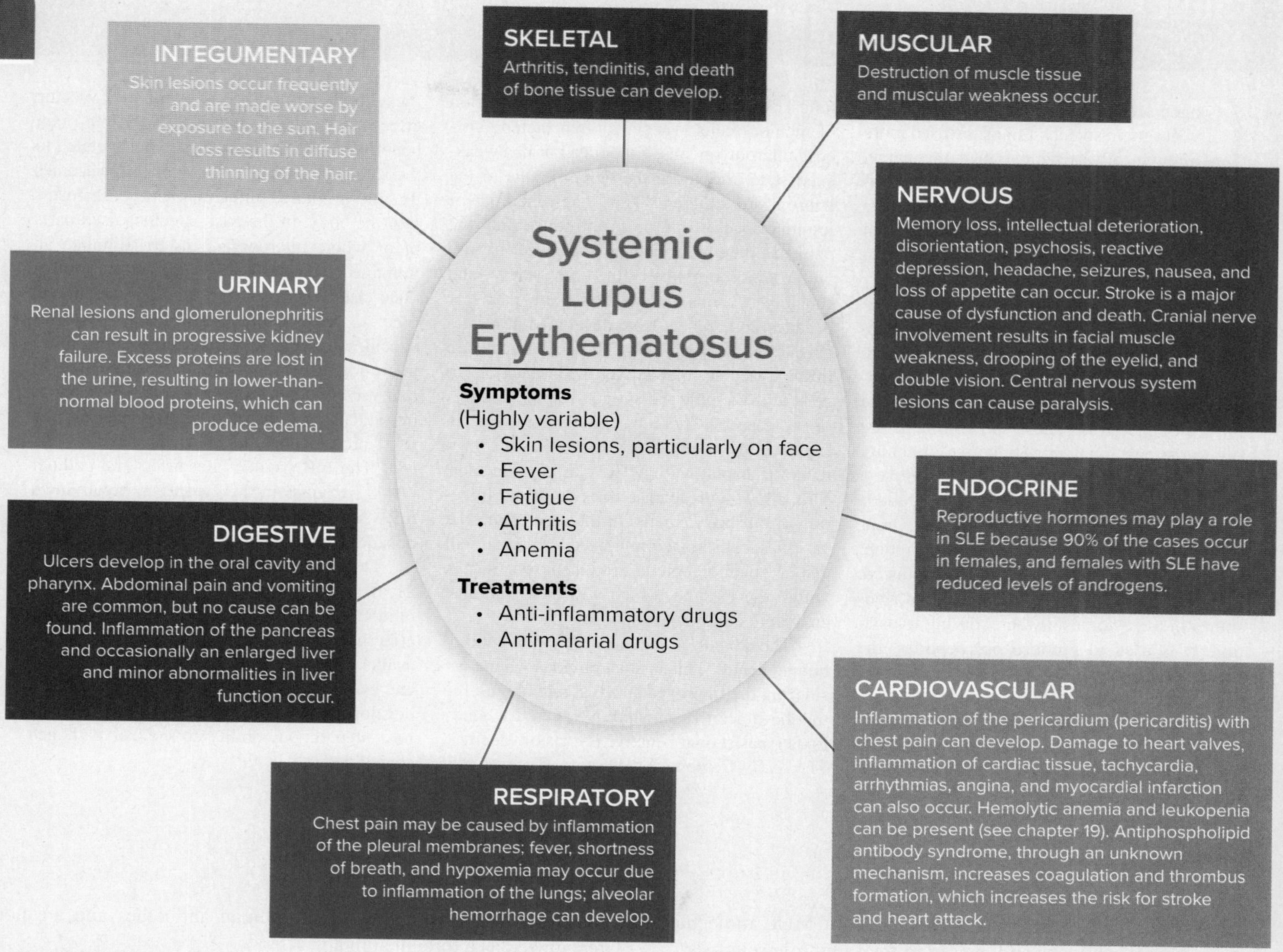

INTEGUMENTARY
Skin lesions occur frequently and are made worse by exposure to the sun. Hair loss results in diffuse thinning of the hair.

SKELETAL
Arthritis, tendinitis, and death of bone tissue can develop.

MUSCULAR
Destruction of muscle tissue and muscular weakness occur.

URINARY
Renal lesions and glomerulonephritis can result in progressive kidney failure. Excess proteins are lost in the urine, resulting in lower-than-normal blood proteins, which can produce edema.

Systemic Lupus Erythematosus

Symptoms
(Highly variable)

- Skin lesions, particularly on face
- Fever
- Fatigue
- Arthritis
- Anemia

Treatments

- Anti-inflammatory drugs
- Antimalarial drugs

NERVOUS
Memory loss, intellectual deterioration, disorientation, psychosis, reactive depression, headache, seizures, nausea, and loss of appetite can occur. Stroke is a major cause of dysfunction and death. Cranial nerve involvement results in facial muscle weakness, drooping of the eyelid, and double vision. Central nervous system lesions can cause paralysis.

DIGESTIVE
Ulcers develop in the oral cavity and pharynx. Abdominal pain and vomiting are common, but no cause can be found. Inflammation of the pancreas and occasionally an enlarged liver and minor abnormalities in liver function occur.

ENDOCRINE
Reproductive hormones may play a role in SLE because 90% of the cases occur in females, and females with SLE have reduced levels of androgens.

RESPIRATORY
Chest pain may be caused by inflammation of the pleural membranes; fever, shortness of breath, and hypoxemia may occur due to inflammation of the lungs; alveolar hemorrhage can develop.

CARDIOVASCULAR
Inflammation of the pericardium (pericarditis) with chest pain can develop. Damage to heart valves, inflammation of cardiac tissue, tachycardia, arrhythmias, angina, and myocardial infarction can also occur. Hemolytic anemia and leukopenia can be present (see chapter 19). Antiphospholipid antibody syndrome, through an unknown mechanism, increases coagulation and thrombus formation, which increases the risk for stroke and heart attack.

FIGURE 22.28 System Interactions: Systemic Lupus Erythematosus (SLE)
SLE is an autoimmune disease that is not isolated to one system. The diagram illustrates how the systems of the body are affected by SLE.

22.7 Immunotherapy

LEARNING OUTCOME

After reading this section, you should be able to

A. **Define and give examples of *immunotherapy*.**

Knowledge of how the immune system operates has produced two fundamental benefits: (1) an understanding of the cause and progression of many diseases and (2) the development or proposed development of methods to prevent, stop, or even reverse diseases. In this section, we discuss the second benefit, **immunotherapy,** which treats disease by altering immune system function or by directly attacking harmful cells. Some types of immunotherapy attempt to boost immune system function in general. For example, administering cytokines or other agents can promote inflammation and activate immune cells, which can help destroy tumor cells. On the other hand, sometimes inhibiting the immune system is helpful. For example, multiple sclerosis is an autoimmune disease in which the immune system treats self-antigens as foreign antigens, thereby destroying the myelin that covers axons. The cytokine

Clinical IMPACT 22.4 COVID-19 and mRNA Vaccines

Logos are so important to a company's visibility in society. Logos are used more often in advertisement than the name. Whether you consider advertisements for athletic shoes or luxury automobiles, logos have become so prominent in our lives that we often see them on other items, such as t-shirts or backpacks. It is the logo that we use to identify the product. Similarly, our defense cells recognize pathogens by a "logo"—a small surface-bound component called an antigen. For some viruses, such as COVID-19, the "logo" (antigen) for recognition is a spike protein on the surface of the virus. These spike proteins are key to the development of adaptive immunity against the specific virus.

Recall from chapter 3 that cells produce proteins through a two-phase process: transcription and translation. During transcription, an mRNA copy of a DNA gene is produced. This mRNA moves from the nucleus to ribosomes in the cytoplasm where, during translation, it is used to produce polypeptides, the precursors to proteins.

Vaccines are used to induce adaptive immunity by exposing defense cells to antigens in a way that prevents or reduces disease symptoms but allows for the development of long-lasting immunity through the production of memory cells. Vaccines often include specific microorganisms, either dead or in a weakened state, to expose the defense cells to the appropriate antigen. The ideal method of immunization would be to introduce only the antigen, thereby reducing the need to use whole microorganism for both safety and financial reasons. Indeed, over the past few decades, researchers have developed new vaccines that do just that. These vaccines are mRNA vaccines that deliver the instructions to cells to make only the antigen—spike proteins in the case of COVID-19. As we can see in figure 22.16, cells process cytoplasmic proteins for display with MHC class I molecules. This allows our defense cells to detect infection of our body's cells. In the case of mRNA vaccines, cells in an immunized individual will display specific proteins produced from mRNA within the vaccine, which will then stimulate an adaptive immune response.

The advent of vaccines is monumental to human health. This is most obvious when considering the improved survival rate of children that have been vaccinated. No scientific study to date has shown negative effects of vaccines. The U.S. Centers for Disease Control and Prevention and the U.S. FDA monitor vaccine effects to ensure their safety. Two important benefits of mRNA vaccines are both related to the safety of their use. First, mRNA vaccines do not introduce infectious microorganisms into the body. In the past, vaccines used parts of or whole microorganisms to stimulate an immune response. Using vaccines that introduce dead or weakened microorganisms in order to prevent infection limits the types of vaccines that can be produced to only those microorganisms that can be manipulated in that way. Second, the use of mRNA vaccines introduces the instructions for making the right protein into only the cytoplasm of the cell. The mRNA does not affect the cellular DNA. Enzymes in the cytoplasm break down mRNA molecules, including the ones introduced through mRNA vaccines.

During the COVID-19 pandemic of 2020–21, the decades-old ground-breaking research of mRNA vaccines took front stage as multiple effective vaccines for the disease became available. Other mRNA vaccines for flu, HIV, and even treatments for cancer have also been developed. The use of mRNA vaccines is the next step in our ability to control pathogen spread and reduce disease.

interferon beta (IFNβ) blocks the expression of MHC molecules that display self-antigens and is used to treat multiple sclerosis.

Some immunotherapy methods take a more specific approach. For example, vaccination can prevent many diseases (see section 22.6). The ability to produce monoclonal antibodies can result in effective treatments for tumors. If an antigen unique to tumor cells can be found, monoclonal antibodies can deliver radioactive isotopes, drugs, toxins, enzymes, or cytokines that kill the tumor cell directly or activate the immune system to kill the cell. Unfortunately, so far researchers have found no antigen on tumor cells that is not also present on normal cells. Nonetheless, this approach may be useful if damage to normal cells is minimal. For example, tumor cells may have more surface antigens of a particular type than normal cells, resulting in greater treatment delivery. Tumor cells may also be more susceptible to damage, or normal cells may be better able to recover from the treatment.

In the past, a problem with monoclonal antibody delivery systems is that the immune system recognizes the monoclonal antibody as a foreign antigen. To avoid destruction by the patient's immune system, the therapeutic monoclonal antibodies are humanized so that they resemble human antibodies and are not recognized as a foreign antigen.

Some uses of monoclonal antibodies to treat tumors are yielding promising results. For example, monoclonal antibodies with radioactive iodine (^{131}I) have caused the regression of B-cell lymphomas with few side effects. Herceptin, a monoclonal antibody, binds to a growth factor that is overexpressed in 25–30% of primary breast cancers. The antibodies "tag" cancer cells, which are then lysed by natural killer cells. Herceptin slows disease progression and increases survival time, but it is not a cure for breast cancer. Most recently, monoclonal antibodies have been used for **checkpoint therapy** of several types of cancer. In this type of therapy, antibodies target proteins that normally serve as checkpoints that prevent the immune system from attacking the body's cells. In cancer, however, those same proteins allow cancer cells to evade the immune system. When monoclonal antibodies are used to block avoidance of the immune system checkpoints, the cancer cells undergo programmed cell death and the tumor shrinks.

Many other immunotherapy approaches are being studied, and more treatments that use the immune system are sure to be developed. There are now nearly 100 monoclonal antibodies approved for therapies ranging from cancer to rheumatoid arthritis. With hundreds of clinical trials currently underway, there are likely to be many more therapeutic uses of monoclonal antibodies in the near future.

ASSESS YOUR PROGRESS

59. *What is immunotherapy? Give some examples.*

EFFECTS OF AGING ON THE LYMPHATIC SYSTEM AND IMMUNITY

Aging appears to have little effect on the lymphatic system's ability to remove fluid from tissues, absorb lipids from the digestive tract, or remove defective red blood cells from the blood. However, aging has a severe impact on the adaptive immune system.

The thymus atrophies as a person ages, so it loses the ability to produce new T cells. By age 40, much of the thymus has been replaced with adipose tissue and, after age 60, the thymus decreases in size to the point that it can be difficult to detect. Although the number of T cells remains stable in most individuals due to the replication (not maturation) of T cells in secondary lymphatic tissues, the T cells are less functional. In many individuals, the ability of helper T cells to proliferate in response to antigens decreases. Thus, antigen exposure produces fewer helper T cells, which results in less stimulation of B cells and cytotoxic T cells. Consequently, responses to antigens decrease in both antibody-mediated immunity and cell-mediated immunity.

Recall that immunity increases greatly in the early years of our life, as we are exposed to different antigens. Memory cells allow for faster and greater responses to these antigens, and therefore we say we are immune to many types of diseases. As a person ages, particularly after about age 60, both primary and secondary antibody responses decrease. This reduction in response is due to many factors. More antigen is required to produce a response, the response is slower, less antibody is produced, and fewer memory cells result. Thus, a person's ability to resist infections and develop immunity decreases. Because these declines are most evident after age 60, it is recommended that regular vaccinations be given well before that age. However, vaccinations can be beneficial at any age, especially if the individual has reduced resistance to infection. For example, older people are more susceptible to influenza (flu) and should be vaccinated every year.

The ability of cell-mediated immunity to resist cytoplasmic pathogens also decreases with age. Some pathogens cause disease but are not eliminated from the body; with age, decreased immunity can lead to reactivation of the pathogen. An example is the virus that causes chickenpox in children, which can remain latent within neurons, even if the disease seems to have disappeared. Later in life, the virus can leave the neurons and infect skin cells, causing painful lesions known as herpes zoster, or shingles.

Autoimmune disease occurs when immune responses destroy otherwise healthy tissue. There is very little increase in the number of new-onset autoimmune diseases in older individuals. However, the chronic inflammation and immune responses that begin earlier in life have a cumulative, damaging effect. Likewise, the increased incidence of cancer is likely to be caused primarily by repeated exposure to and damage from cancer-causing agents rather than by decreased immunity.

Concept Check

22.1 Functions of the Lymphatic System

The lymphatic system maintains fluid balance in tissues, absorbs lipids from the small intestine, and defends against microorganisms and foreign substances.

1. *The lymphatic system* Remember
   a. *removes excess fluid from tissues.*
   b. *absorbs lipids from the digestive tract.*
   c. *defends the body against microorganisms and other foreign substances.*
   d. *All of these are correct*

22.2 Anatomy of the Lymphatic System

The lymphatic system consists of lymph, lymphatic vessels, lymphatic tissue, lymphatic nodules, lymph nodes, the tonsils, the spleen, and the thymus.

Lymphatic Vessels

A. Lymphatic vessels carry lymph away from tissues.

B. Lymphatic capillaries lack a basement membrane and have loosely overlapping epithelial cells. Fluids and other substances easily enter lymphatic capillaries.

C. Lymphatic capillaries join to form lymphatic vessels.
- Lymphatic vessels have valves that ensure a one-way flow of lymph.
- Contraction of lymphatic vessel smooth muscle, contraction of skeletal muscle, and thoracic pressure changes move the lymph.

D. Lymph nodes are found along the lymphatic vessels. After passing through lymph nodes, lymphatic vessels form lymphatic trunks and lymphatic ducts.

E. Lymphatic trunks and ducts empty into the blood at thoracic veins (junctions of the internal jugular and subclavian veins).
- Lymph from the right thorax, the right-upper limb, and the right side of the head and the neck enters the right thoracic veins.
- Lymph from the lower limbs, pelvis, and abdomen; the left thorax; the left-upper limb; and the left side of the head and the neck enters the left thoracic veins.

F. The jugular, subclavian, and bronchomediastinal trunks may unite to form the right lymphatic duct.

G. The thoracic duct is the largest lymphatic vessel.

H. The intestinal and lumbar trunks may converge on the cisterna chyli, a sac that joins the inferior end of the thoracic duct.

Lymphatic Tissue and Organs

A. Lymphatic tissue is reticular connective tissue that contains lymphocytes and other cells.

B. The primary lymphatic organs (red bone marrow and the thymus) are where lymphocytes mature into functional cells. Secondary lymphatic organs and tissues are where lymphocytes produce an immune response.

C. Lymphatic organs are encapsulated (lymph nodes, spleen, thymus).

D. Lymphatic tissue is nonencapsulated (diffuse lymphatic tissue, lymphatic nodules, tonsils). Mucosa-associated lymphoid tissue (MALT) is nonencapsulated lymphatic tissue located in and below the mucous membranes of the digestive, respiratory, urinary, and reproductive tracts.

E. Diffuse lymphatic tissue consists of dispersed lymphocytes and has no clear boundaries.

F. Lymphatic nodules are small aggregates of lymphatic tissue (e.g., Peyer patches in the small intestine and the tonsils in the pharynx).

G. The tonsils
- The tonsils are large groups of lymphatic nodules in the oral cavity and nasopharynx.
- The three groups of tonsils are the palatine, pharyngeal, and lingual tonsils.

H. Lymph nodes
- Lymphatic tissue in the lymph node is organized into the cortex and the medulla. Lymphatic sinuses extend through the lymphatic tissue.
- Substances in lymph are removed by phagocytosis, or they stimulate lymphocytes (or both).
- Lymphocytes leave the lymph nodes and circulate to other tissues.

I. The spleen
- The spleen is in the left superior side of the abdomen.
- Foreign substances stimulate lymphocytes in the white pulp of the spleen (periarterial lymphatic sheath and lymphatic nodules).
- Foreign substances and defective red blood cells are removed from the blood by phagocytes in the red pulp of the spleen (splenic cords and venous sinuses).
- The spleen is a limited reservoir for blood.

J. The thymus
- The thymus is a gland in the superior mediastinum and is divided into a cortex and a medulla.
- Lymphocytes in the cortex are separated from the blood by reticular cells.
- Lymphocytes produced in the cortex migrate through the medulla, enter the blood, and travel to other lymphatic tissues, where they can proliferate.

Overview of the Lymphatic System

See figure 22.10.

2. *Which of the following statements is correct?* Understand
   a. *Lymphatic vessels do not have valves.*
   b. *Lymphatic vessels empty into lymph nodes.*
   c. *Lymph from the right-lower limb passes into the right jugular or subclavian vein.*
   d. *Lymph from the jugular and subclavian trunks empties into the cisterna chyli.*
   e. *All of these are correct.*

3. *The tonsils* 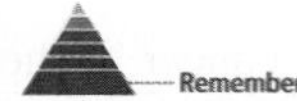

   a. *consist of large groups of lymphatic nodules.*
   b. *protect against bacteria.*
   c. *can become chronically infected.*
   d. *decrease in size in adults.*
   e. *All of these are correct.*

4. *Lymph nodes* 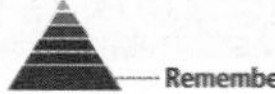

   a. *filter lymph.*
   b. *are where lymphocytes divide and increase in number.*
   c. *contain a network of reticular fibers.*
   d. *contain lymphatic sinuses.*
   e. *All of these are correct.*

5. *Which of these statements about the spleen is* not *correct?* 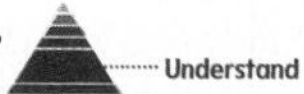

   a. *The spleen has white pulp associated with the arteries.*
   b. *The spleen has red pulp associated with the veins.*
   c. *The spleen destroys defective red blood cells.*
   d. *The spleen is surrounded by trabeculae located outside the capsule.*
   e. *The spleen is a limited reservoir for blood.*

6. *The thymus* 

   a. *increases in size in adults.*
   b. *produces lymphocytes that move to other lymphatic tissue.*
   c. *is located in the abdominal cavity.*
   d. *All of these are correct.*

7. *A patient is suffering from edema in the right-lower limb. Explain why elevating and massaging the limb help remove the excess fluid.* Apply

8. *If the thymus of an experimental animal is removed immediately after its birth, the animal exhibits the following characteristics: (a) an increased susceptibility to infections, (b) decreased numbers of lymphocytes in lymphatic tissue, and (c) a greatly decreased ability to reject grafts. Explain these observations.* Apply

9. *If the thymus of an adult experimental animal is removed, the following observations can be made: (a) No immediate effect occurs, and (b) after 1 year, decreases occur in the number of lymphocytes in the blood, the ability to reject grafts, and the ability to produce antibodies. Explain these observations.* Apply

10. *Adjuvants are substances that slow but do not stop the release of an antigen from an injection site into the blood. Suppose injection A is given without an adjuvant and injection B of the same amount of antigen is given with an adjuvant that causes antigen to be released over a period of 2–3 weeks. Does injection A or injection B result in the greater amount of antibody production? Explain.* Apply

22.3 Immunity

A. Immunity is the ability to resist the harmful effects of microorganisms and other foreign substances.

B. Innate immunity and adaptive immunity can function together to eliminate an antigen.

22.4 Innate Immunity

Physical Barriers

Physical barriers prevent the entry of microbes (skin and mucous membranes) or remove them (tears, saliva, and mucus).

Chemical Mediators

A. Chemical mediators promote phagocytosis and inflammation.

B. Complement can be activated by either the alternative or the classical pathway. Complement lyses cells, increases phagocytosis, attracts immune system cells, and promotes inflammation.

C. Interferons prevent viral replication. Interferons are produced by virally infected cells and move to other cells, which are then protected.

White Blood Cells

A. Chemotactic factors are parts of microorganisms or chemicals that are released by damaged tissues. Chemotaxis is the ability of white blood cells to move to tissues that release chemotactic factors.

B. Phagocytosis is the ingestion and destruction of materials.

C. Neutrophils are small phagocytic white blood cells.

D. Macrophages are large phagocytic white blood cells.
- Macrophages can engulf more than neutrophils can.
- Macrophages in connective tissue protect the body at locations where microbes are likely to enter, and macrophages clean blood and lymph.

E. Basophils and mast cells release chemicals that promote inflammation.

F. Eosinophils defend against parasitic worms.

G. Natural killer cells lyse tumor cells and virus-infected cells.

Inflammatory Response

A. The inflammatory response can be initiated in many ways.
- Chemical mediators cause vasodilation and increase vascular permeability, which allows the entry of other chemical mediators.
- Chemical mediators attract phagocytes.
- The numbers of chemical mediators and phagocytes increase until the cause of the inflammation is destroyed. Then the tissue undergoes repair.

B. Local inflammation produces redness, heat, swelling, pain, and loss of function. Symptoms of systemic inflammation include an increase in neutrophil numbers, fever, and shock.

11. Which of these is an example of innate immunity?

a. Tears and saliva wash away microorganisms.
b. Basophils release histamine and leukotrienes.
c. Neutrophils phagocytize a microorganism.
d. The complement cascade is activated.
e. All of these are correct.

12. Neutrophils

a. enlarge to become macrophages.
b. account for most of the dead cells in pus.
c. are usually the last cell type to enter infected tissues.
d. are usually located in lymphatic and blood sinuses.

13. Macrophages

a. are large, phagocytic cells that outlive neutrophils.
b. develop from mast cells.
c. often die after a single phagocytic event.
d. have the same function as eosinophils.
e. All of these are correct.

14. Which of these cells is the most important in the release of histamine, which promotes inflammation? Remember

a. monocyte
b. macrophage
c. eosinophil
d. mast cell
e. natural killer cell

15. Which of these conditions does not *occur during the inflammatory response?* Understand

a. release of histamine and other chemical mediators
b. chemotaxis of phagocytes
c. entry of fibrinogen into tissues from the blood
d. vasoconstriction of blood vessels
e. increased permeability of blood vessels

16. Josie developed a poison ivy rash after a camping trip. Her doctor prescribed a cortisone ointment to relieve the inflammation. A few weeks later, Josie scraped her elbow, which became inflamed. Because she had some of the cortisone ointment left over, she applied it to the scrape. Was the ointment an effective treatment for the poison ivy? Was the ointment an appropriate treatment for the scrape? Apply

17. Billie was riding her skateboard down a newly paved road from the top of a hill. Part of the way down, she fell and skinned her knees on the asphalt. From the following list, choose the immune response(s) that occurred in the next several hours. Apply

(1) increased capillary permeability
(2) chemotaxis of neutrophils
(3) coagulation
(4) release of mediators of inflammation
(5) increased mitosis of B lymphocytes

a. 1,2,3,4,5 *b. 1,2,3,4* *c. 1,2,3* *d. 1,2*

22.5 Adaptive Immunity

A. Antigens are large molecules that stimulate an adaptive immune response.

B. B cells are responsible for antibody-mediated immunity. T cells are involved with cell-mediated immunity.

Antigens

A. The antigenic determinant is the specific part of the antigen to which the lymphocyte responds. The antigen receptor (T-cell receptor or B-cell receptor) on the surface of lymphocytes combines with the antigenic determinant.

B. MHC class I molecules display antigens on the surface of nucleated cells, resulting in the destruction of the cells.

C. MHC class II molecules display antigens on the surface of antigen-presenting cells, resulting in the activation of immune cells.

D. MHC-antigen complex and costimulation are usually necessary to activate lymphocytes. Costimulation involves cytokines and certain surface molecules.

E. Antigen-presenting cells stimulate the proliferation of helper T cells, which stimulate the proliferation of B cells or cytotoxic T cells.

Clonal Selection

A. B cells and T cells originate in red bone marrow. T cells are processed in the thymus, and B cells are processed in bone marrow.
B. Positive selection ensures the survival of lymphocytes that can react against antigens, and negative selection eliminates lymphocytes that react against self-antigens.
C. A clone is a group of identical lymphocytes that can respond to a specific antigen.
D. B cells and T cells move to lymphatic tissue from their processing sites. They continually circulate from one lymphatic tissue to another.
E. Tolerance is suppression of the immune system's response to an antigen.
F. Tolerance is produced by the deletion of self-reactive cells, by the prevention of lymphocyte activation, and by the activation of regulatory T cells.

18. *Antigens* 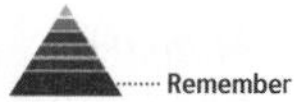

    a. *are foreign substances introduced into the body.*
    b. *are molecules produced by the body.*
    c. *stimulate an adaptive immune system response.*
    d. *All of these are correct.*

19. *MHC molecules* 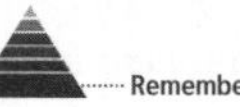

    a. *are glycoproteins.*
    b. *attach to the plasma membrane.*
    c. *have a variable region that can bind to foreign antigens and self-antigens.*
    d. *may form an MHC-antigen complex that activates T cells.*
    e. *All of these are correct.*

20. *Antigen-presenting cells can* 

    a. *take in foreign antigens.*
    b. *process antigens.*
    c. *use MHC class II molecules to display the antigens.*
    d. *stimulate other immune system cells.*
    e. *All of these are correct.*

21. *B cells* 

    a. *are processed in the thymus.*
    b. *originate in red bone marrow.*
    c. *once released into the blood remain in the blood.*
    d. *are responsible for cell-mediated immunity.*
    e. *All of these are correct.*

22. *Which of these participates in costimulation?* 

    a. *cytokines*
    b. *complement*
    c. *antibodies*
    d. *histamine*
    e. *natural killer cells*

23. *Helper T cells* 

    a. *respond to antigens from macrophages.*
    b. *respond to cytokines from macrophages.*
    c. *stimulate B cells with cytokines.*
    d. *All of these are correct.*

24. *The most important function of tolerance is to* 

    a. *increase lymphocyte activity.*
    b. *increase complement activation.*
    c. *prevent the immune system from responding to self-antigens.*
    d. *prevent excessive immune response to foreign antigens.*
    e. *process antigens.*

25. *Upon first exposure to an antigen, a sequence of events results in antigen processing and an increase in the number of helper T cells. Given the following list of events, select the sequence that results in an increased number of helper T cells.* Understand
    (1) *Unprocessed extracellular antigen is ingested by a macrophage.*
    (2) *The MHC II complex is presented at the cell surface.*
    (3) *Costimulation occurs.*
    (4) *Interleukin-1 is released from macrophages, and interleukin-2 is released from T lymphocytes.*
    (5) *A specific helper T cell recognizes and binds to the MHC II complex.*
    (6) *Mitosis of helper T cells takes place.*
    (7) *The ingested antigen is broken down to fragments.*
    (8) *The processed antigen and MHC II molecules are joined and transported to the cell surface.*

    a. *1,7,8,2,5,3,4,6*
    b. *1,7,8,5,2,3,4,6*
    c. *7,8,1,2,5,3,4,6*
    d. *1,2,3,4,5,6,7,8*
    e. *1,8,7,2,3,5,6,4*

Antibody-Mediated Immunity

A. Antibodies are proteins.
    - The variable region of an antibody combines with the antigen. The constant region activates complement or binds to cells.
    - Five classes of antibodies exist: IgG, IgM, IgA, IgE, and IgD.
B. Antibodies affect the antigen in many ways.
    - Antibodies bind to the antigen and interfere with antigen activity or bind the antigens together.
    - Antibodies act as opsonins (substances that increase phagocytosis) by binding to the antigen and to macrophages.
    - Antibodies can activate complement through the classical pathway.
    - Antibodies attach to mast cells or basophils and cause the release of inflammatory chemicals when the antibody combines with the antigen.
C. The primary response results from the first exposure to an antigen. B cells form plasma cells, which produce antibodies, and memory B cells.
D. The secondary response results from exposure to an antigen after a primary response, and memory B cells quickly form plasma cells and additional memory B cells.

Cell-Mediated Immunity

A. Cells infected with cytoplasmic microorganisms process antigens that combine with MHC class I molecules.
B. Cytotoxic T cells are stimulated to divide, producing more cytotoxic T cells and memory T cells, when MHC class I/antigen complexes are presented to T-cell receptors. Cytokines released from helper T cells also stimulate cytotoxic T cells.
C. Cytotoxic T cells lyse virus-infected cells, tumor cells, and tissue transplants.
D. Cytotoxic T cells produce cytokines, which promote phagocytosis and inflammation.

26. *Variable amino acid sequences on the arms of the antibody molecule* Remember
    a. *make the antibody specific for a given antigen.*
    b. *enable the antibody to activate complement.*
    c. *enable the antibody to attach to basophils and mast cells.*
    d. *are part of the constant region.*
    e. *All of these are correct.*

27. *Antibodies* Remember
    a. *prevent antigens from binding together.*
    b. *promote phagocytosis.*
    c. *inhibit inflammation.*
    d. *block complement activation.*
    e. *block the function of opsonins.*

28. *The secondary antibody response* 

    a. *is slower than the primary response.*
    b. *produces fewer antibodies than the primary response.*
    c. *prevents disease symptoms from occurring.*
    d. *occurs because of cytotoxic T cells.*

29. *The type of lymphocyte responsible for the secondary antibody response is the* Remember
    a. *memory B cell.*
    b. *B cell.*
    c. *T cell.*
    d. *helper T cell.*

30. *The largest percentage of antibodies in the blood are* 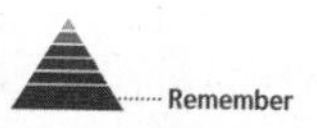

    a. *IgA.*
    b. *IgD.*
    c. *IgE.*
    d. *IgG.*
    e. *IgM.*

31. *Antibody-mediated immunity* 

    a. *works best against cytoplasmic antigens.*
    b. *regulates the activity of T cells.*
    c. *cannot be transferred from one person to another.*
    d. *is responsible for immediate hypersensitivity reactions.*

32. *The activation of cytotoxic T cells can result in* 

    a. *lysis of virus-infected cells.*
    b. *production of cytokines.*
    c. *production of memory T cells.*
    d. *All of these are correct.*

33. *An infant appears healthy until about 9 months of age, when he develops severe bacterial infections, one after another. Fortunately, the infections are treated successfully with antibiotics. When infected with the measles and other viral diseases, the infant recovers without unusual difficulty. Explain the different immune responses to these infections. Why did it take so long for this disorder to become apparent?* (Hint: *Consider IgG.)* Apply

34. *A patient has many allergic reactions. As part of the treatment scheme, doctors try to identify the allergen that stimulates the immune system's response. A series of solutions, each containing an allergen that commonly causes a reaction, is composed. Each solution is injected into the skin at different locations on the patient's back. The following results are obtained: (a) At one location, the injection site becomes red and swollen within a few minutes; (b) at another injection site, swelling and redness appear 2 days later; and (c) no redness or swelling develops at the other sites. Explain what happened for each observation by describing what part of the immune system was involved and what caused the redness and swelling.* Apply

22.6 Acquired Adaptive Immunity

A. Active natural immunity results from natural exposure to an antigen.
B. Active artificial immunity results from deliberate exposure to an antigen.
C. Passive natural immunity results from the transfer of antibodies from a mother to her fetus or baby.
D. Passive artificial immunity results from the transfer of antibodies (or cells) from an immune animal to a nonimmune animal.

35. *Tetanus is caused by bacteria that enter the body through wounds in the skin. The bacteria produce a toxin that causes spastic muscle contractions. Death often results from failure of the respiratory muscles. A patient goes to the emergency room after stepping on a nail. If the patient has been vaccinated against tetanus, he or she is given a tetanus booster shot, which consists of the toxin altered so that it is harmless. A patient who has never been vaccinated against tetanus is given an antiserum shot against tetanus. Explain the rationale for this treatment strategy. Sometimes both a booster and an antiserum shot are given, but at different locations on the body. Explain why both vaccinations are given and why they are injected in different locations.* Apply

22.7 Immunotherapy

Immunotherapy treats diseases by stimulating or inhibiting the immune system.

Answers to this chapter's odd-numbered Concept Check questions appear in Appendix F.

23 CHAPTER

Respiratory System

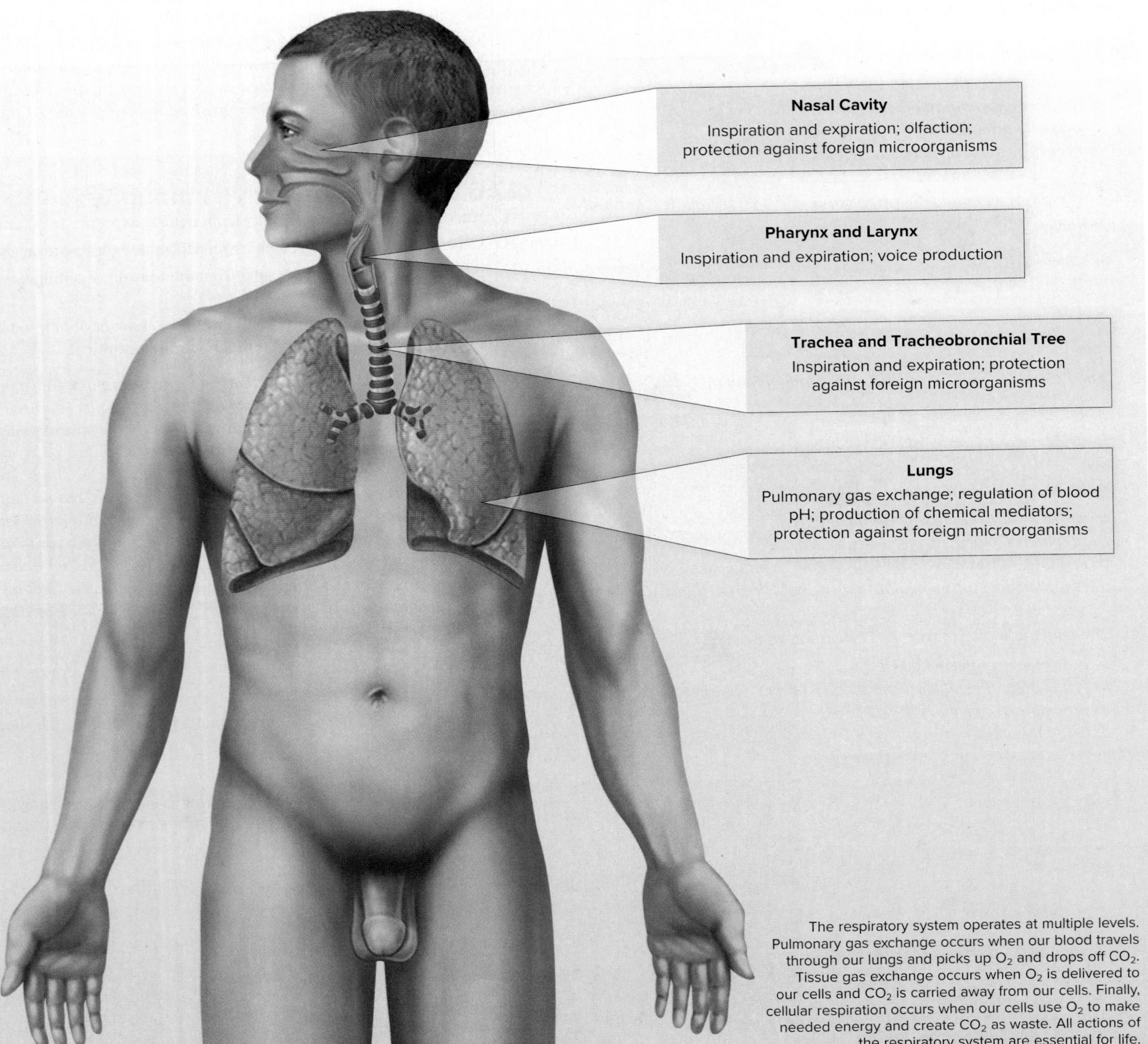

The respiratory system operates at multiple levels. Pulmonary gas exchange occurs when our blood travels through our lungs and picks up O_2 and drops off CO_2. Tissue gas exchange occurs when O_2 is delivered to our cells and CO_2 is carried away from our cells. Finally, cellular respiration occurs when our cells use O_2 to make needed energy and create CO_2 as waste. All actions of the respiratory system are essential for life.

If you've ever had a severe chest cold, bronchitis, or pneumonia, you might be able to relate to what Mr. Theron of this chapter's Learn to Predict experienced when his left lung collapsed. If we stop breathing, or breathing becomes difficult, within seconds we feel a strong need for air. From our first breath at birth, the rate and depth of our breathing are unconsciously matched to our activities, whether studying, sleeping, talking, eating, or exercising. Breathing is so characteristic of life that, along with the pulse, it is one of the first vital signs checked to determine whether an unconscious person is alive.

Breathing is necessary because all living cells of the body require O_2 and produce CO_2. The respiratory system exchanges these gases between the air and the blood, and the cardiovascular system transports them between the lungs and the body cells. Without healthy respiratory and cardiovascular systems, the capacity to carry out normal activity is reduced.

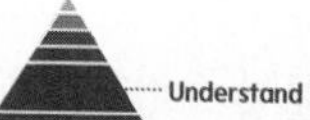

Learn to Predict

Flashing lights at 2 a.m. alerted the neighbors that something was wrong at the Theron home. Mr. Theron, who has moderate emphysema, could not stop coughing, so his wife called 911. In the emergency room, a physician listened to Mr. Theron's respiratory sounds and concluded that his left lung had collapsed.

Explain how emphysema affected Mr. Theron's breathing, what caused his lung to collapse, and how the physician was able to detect the collapsed lung.

Answers to this question and the chapter's odd-numbered Predict questions can be found in Appendix E.

23.1 Anatomy of the Respiratory System

LEARNING OUTCOMES

After reading this section, you should be able to

A. **List the structures that compose the respiratory system.**

B. **Describe the structural and functional anatomy of the respiratory system.**

The respiratory system consists of the structures used to acquire oxygen (O_2) and remove carbon dioxide (CO_2) from the blood. Oxygen is required for the body's cells to synthesize the chemical energy molecule ATP. Carbon dioxide is a by-product of ATP production and must be removed from the blood. Otherwise, increased levels of CO_2 will lower the pH of the blood. The blood pH must be maintained within relatively narrow limits to maintain homeostasis.

There are seven structures that make up the respiratory system (figure 23.1). They include the following:

1. *External nose.* The external nose encloses the chamber for air inspiration. Although air can be inspired through the mouth, the mouth is part of the digestive system rather than the respiratory system.
2. *Nasal cavity.* The nasal cavity is a cleaning, warming, and humidifying chamber for inspired air.
3. *Pharynx.* The pharynx is commonly called the throat. It serves as a common passageway for food and air.
4. *Larynx.* The larynx is frequently called the voice box. Its rigid structure helps keep the airway constantly open, or patent.
5. *Trachea.* The trachea is commonly known as the windpipe. It serves as an air-cleaning tube to funnel inspired air to each lung.
6. *Bronchi.* The bronchi are tubes that direct air into the lungs.
7. *Lungs.* Each lung is a labyrinth of air tubes and a complex network of air sacs, called alveoli, and capillaries. The air sacs are separated by walls of connective tissue containing both collagenous and elastic fibers. Each air sac is the site of gas exchange between the air and the blood.

In this chapter, we will discuss the detailed anatomy of each component of the respiratory system and the mechanisms that control breathing and gas exchange.

ASSESS YOUR PROGRESS

Answers to these questions are found in the section you have just completed. Re-read the section if you need help in answering these questions.

1. *List the components of the respiratory system.*

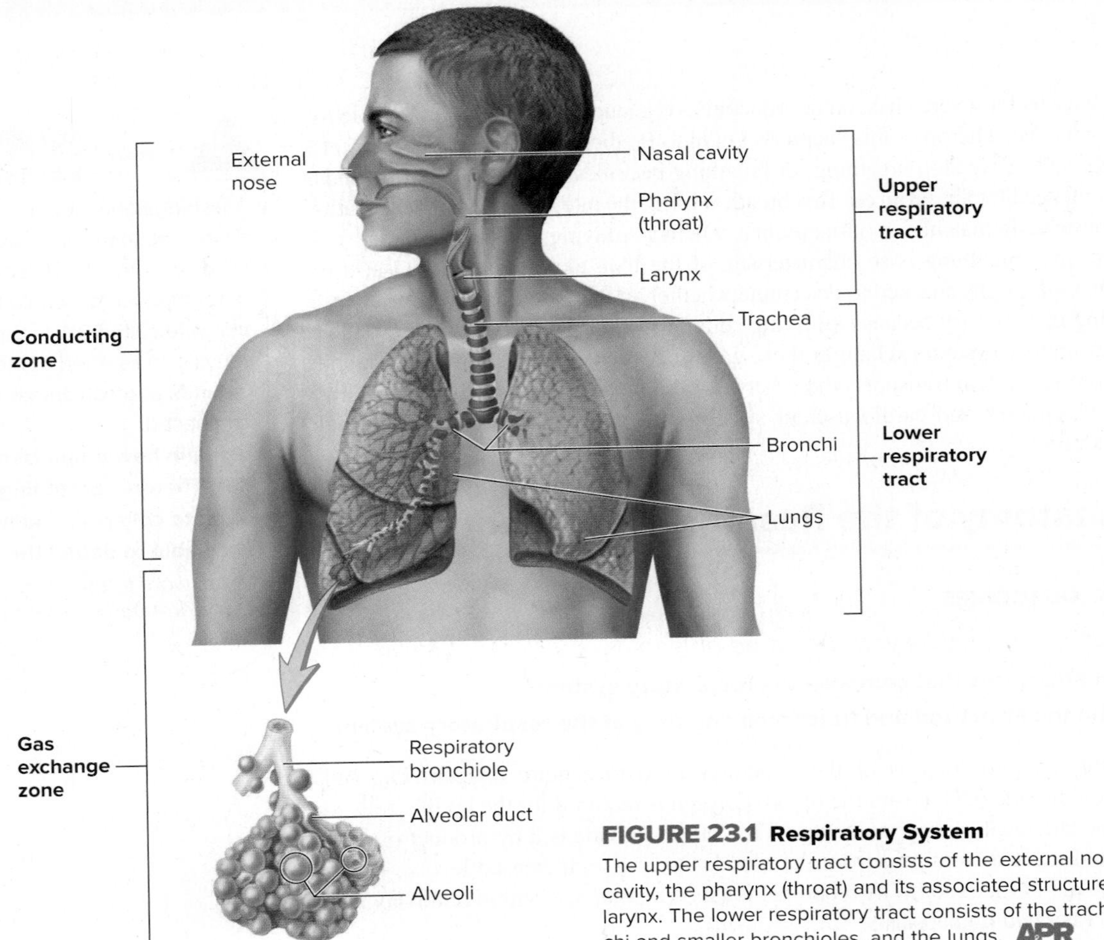

FIGURE 23.1 Respiratory System
The upper respiratory tract consists of the external nose, the nasal cavity, the pharynx (throat) and its associated structures, and the larynx. The lower respiratory tract consists of the trachea, the bronchi and smaller bronchioles, and the lungs. APR

23.2 Functions of the Respiratory System

LEARNING OUTCOME

After reading this section, you should be able to

A. **Describe the functions of the respiratory system.**

Respiration is critical for homeostasis and consists of two broad aspects: (1) **breathing,** which is simply movement of air into and out of the lungs, and (2) **gas exchange,** which is the diffusion of gases across membranes. There are two major types of gas exchange within the body: (1) **pulmonary gas exchange,** which is the movement of gases between atmospheric air in the lungs and the blood, and (2) **tissue gas exchange,** which is the movement of gases between the blood and the body's cells.

Breathing, also called **pulmonary ventilation,** and gas exchange occur in different regions of the respiratory tract. Commonly, the respiratory tract is separated into two regions: (1) the **upper respiratory tract,** which includes the structures from the nose to the larynx, and (2) the **lower respiratory tract,** which includes the structures from the trachea through the alveoli in the lungs. Infections of the upper respiratory tract are among the top five reasons patients in the United States see their doctor. The upper and lower respiratory tracts can be further subdivided between structures used strictly for pulmonary ventilation and structures used for gas exchange. The **conducting zone** encompasses the structures from the nose to the smallest air tubes within the lungs and is strictly for pulmonary ventilation. The **respiratory zone** is solely within the lungs and includes some specialized small air tubes and the alveoli. Gas exchange occurs within the respiratory zone.

For the respiratory system to accomplish gas exchange between the air and the blood, there are four simultaneous processes:

1. *Pulmonary ventilation.* This is what we more commonly refer to as breathing. Air moves into and out of the respiratory passages.
2. *Pulmonary gas exchange.* At the terminal portion of the air tubes are tiny air sacs called alveoli. O_2 moves out of the alveolar air and into the blood. At the same time, CO_2 diffuses out of the blood and joins the air in the alveoli.
3. *Gas transport.* Carbon dioxide and O_2 travel in the blood to and from cells.
4. *Tissue gas exchange.* Gas exchange with the tissues involves the exit of O_2 from the blood into cells, while CO_2 exits cells to enter the blood.

Sometimes, it could be confusing to hear the term *respiration* alone because it also refers to cellular metabolism, or **cellular respiration** (discussed in chapter 25); in fact, the two processes are related. They are linked by the processes of pulmonary ventilation and gas exchange. Pulmonary gas exchange provides the O_2 needed by cells to perform cellular respiration, which makes ATP from glucose. Pulmonary gas exchange then rids the body of potentially toxic CO_2 produced during cellular respiration.

In addition to gas exchange, the respiratory system performs the following functions:

1. *Regulation of blood pH.* The respiratory system can alter blood pH by changing blood CO_2 levels.
2. *Production of chemical mediators.* The lungs produce an enzyme called angiotensin-converting enzyme (ACE), which is an important component of blood pressure regulation (discussed in chapter 26).
3. *Voice production.* Air moving past the vocal folds makes sound and speech possible.
4. *Olfaction.* The sensation of smell occurs when airborne molecules are drawn into the nasal cavity (discussed in chapter 15).
5. *Protection.* The respiratory system provides protection against some microorganisms by preventing them from entering the body and removing them from respiratory surfaces.

ASSESS YOUR PROGRESS

2. *What are the four steps of gas exchange?*
3. *Explain the functions of the respiratory system.*

23.3 Structures and Histology of the Respiratory Tract

LEARNING OUTCOMES

After reading this section, you should be able to

A. **Describe the anatomy of the respiratory passages, beginning at the nose and ending with the alveoli.**
B. **State the parts of the respiratory membrane.**
C. **Explain the role of the thoracic wall in pulmonary ventilation.**
D. **Describe the structure of the lungs, including the blood and lymphatic supply.**
E. **Explain the role of the pleura in pulmonary ventilation.**

Structures of the upper and lower respiratory tracts are well adapted for the conduction of air through the respiratory tract. These structures move, clean, warm, and humidify the air. In the upper respiratory tract, air is moved from the external environment toward the alveoli. Once air is in the alveoli, the respiratory function of the lower respiratory tract is readily carried out due to the close contact of the alveoli with blood capillaries.

The Upper Respiratory Tract

Nose and Nasal Cavity

The **nose,** or *nasus* (NAY-sus), consists of the external nose and the nasal cavity. The **external nose** is the visible structure that forms a prominent feature of the face. The largest part of the external nose is composed of hyaline cartilage plates (see figure 7.12*b*). The nasal bones plus extensions of the frontal and maxillary bones constitute the *bridge* of the nose, which is where eyeglasses would rest.

The **nasal cavity** is the open chamber inside the nose where air first enters the respiratory system. The nasal cavity begins at the anterior external openings called the **nares** (NAY-rees; sing. naris), or *nostrils.* It extends to posterior openings into the pharynx. These openings are called **choanae** (KOH-an-ee; figure 23.2*b*). Just inside each naris, in the anterior part of the nasal cavity, is a region called the **vestibule** (VES-tih-byul; entry room). The vestibule is lined with stratified squamous epithelium, which is continuous with the stratified squamous epithelium of the skin.

The floor of the nasal cavity, which separates it from the oral cavity in the mouth, is called the **hard palate** (PAL-uht). The hard palate is formed by the palatine process of the maxillae and the palatine bone. Within the nasal cavity, the hard palate is covered by a highly vascular mucous membrane. It is this mucous membrane that helps warm and humidify inspired air. The nasal cavity is divided into right and left halves. The two halves are separated by a wall of tissue called the **nasal septum.** The anterior part of the nasal septum is composed of cartilage, while the posterior part consists of the vomer bone and the perpendicular plate of the ethmoid bone. A deviated nasal septum occurs when the septum bulges to one side and is a common cause of snoring (see figure 7.12*a*).

On each side of the nasal cavity, there are three lateral bony ridges called **conchae** (KON-kee; resembling a conch shell). The conchae used to be named the turbinate bones because they act as "wind turbines," helping the air churn through the nasal cavity. In fact, people with chronic nasal congestion may have a turbinate reduction in which a surgeon performs a procedure to reduce the size of the nasal conchae. The air passes through tunnels beneath each concha. Each of these tunnels is called a **meatus** (mee-AY-tus; tunnel or passageway). Within the superior and middle meatuses are openings from the various **paranasal sinuses** (see figure 7.13). Each inferior meatus also contains the opening of a **nasolacrimal** (NAY-zoh-LAK-rim-al) **duct** for tear drainage from the surface of the eye (see figure 15.8).

The nasal cavity is a critical component of the respiratory system. Its primary function is as the air intake portion of the respiratory system. It is here where the majority of the warming, cleaning, and humidifying of air occurs, which is critical for effective gas exchange within the lungs. In total, the nasal cavity has five functions:

1. *Serves as a passageway for air.* The nasal cavity remains open even when the mouth is full of food.
2. *Cleans the air.* The vestibule is lined with hairs, which trap some of the large particles of dust in the air. The nasal septum and nasal conchae increase the surface area of the nasal cavity and make airflow within the cavity more turbulent, thereby increasing the likelihood that air will come into contact with the mucous membrane lining the nasal cavity. This mucous membrane consists of pseudostratified ciliated columnar epithelium with goblet cells. The goblet cells secrete mucus, which traps debris in the air. The cilia on the surface of the

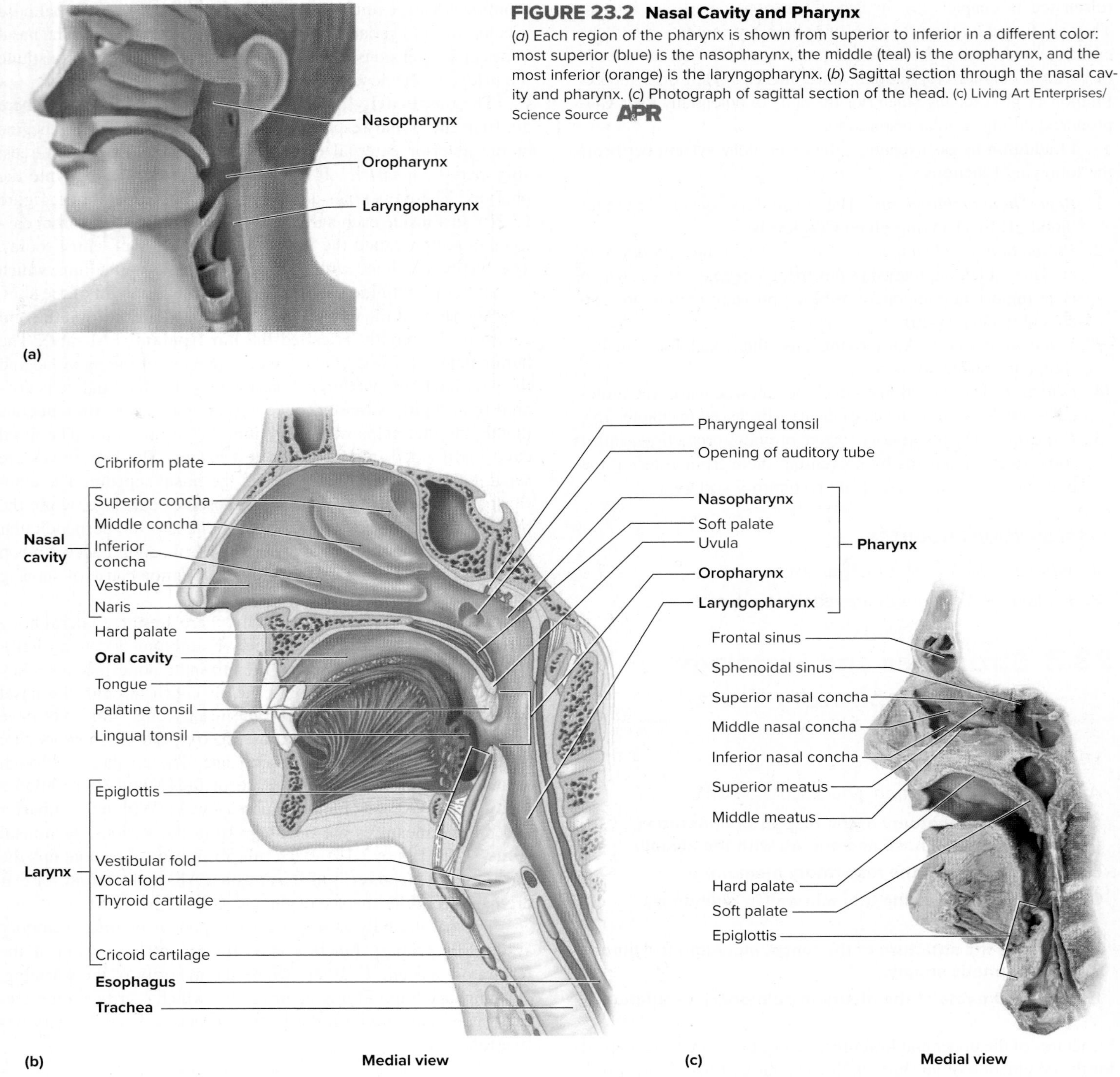

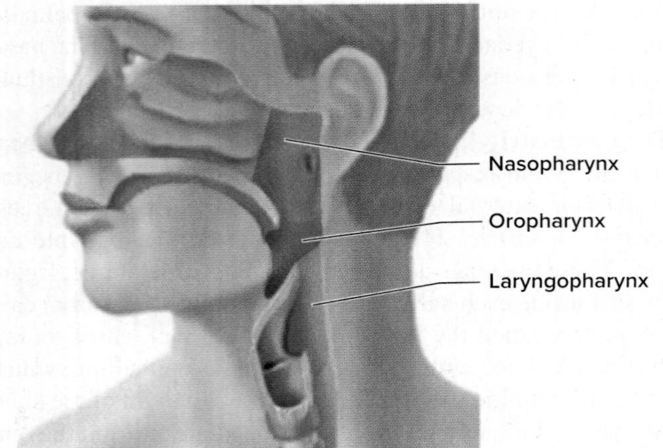

(a)

FIGURE 23.2 Nasal Cavity and Pharynx

(*a*) Each region of the pharynx is shown from superior to inferior in a different color: most superior (blue) is the nasopharynx, the middle (teal) is the oropharynx, and the most inferior (orange) is the laryngopharynx. (*b*) Sagittal section through the nasal cavity and pharynx. (*c*) Photograph of sagittal section of the head. (c) Living Art Enterprises/ Science Source APR

Cribriform plate
Nasal cavity: Superior concha, Middle concha, Inferior concha, Vestibule, Naris
Hard palate
Oral cavity
Tongue
Palatine tonsil
Lingual tonsil
Larynx: Epiglottis, Vestibular fold, Vocal fold, Thyroid cartilage, Cricoid cartilage
Esophagus
Trachea
Pharyngeal tonsil
Opening of auditory tube
Pharynx: **Nasopharynx**, Soft palate, Uvula, **Oropharynx**, **Laryngopharynx**

(b) **Medial view**

Frontal sinus
Sphenoidal sinus
Superior nasal concha
Middle nasal concha
Inferior nasal concha
Superior meatus
Middle meatus
Hard palate
Soft palate
Epiglottis

(c) **Medial view**

mucous membrane sweep the mucus posteriorly to the pharynx, where it is swallowed and eliminated by the acidic secretions of the stomach.

3. *Humidifies and warms the air.* Moisture is added to the air as it passes through the nasal cavity. There are two major sources for the moisture: (1) the mucous epithelium and (2) tears that drain into the nasal cavity through the nasolacrimal duct. Warm blood flowing through the mucous membrane warms the air within the nasal cavity before it passes into the pharynx, thus preventing damage to the rest of the respiratory passages due to cold air.
4. *Contains the olfactory epithelium.* The olfactory epithelium, the sensory organ for smell, is located in the most superior part of the nasal cavity (see figure 15.1).
5. *Helps determine voice sound.* The nasal cavity and paranasal sinuses are resonating chambers for speech. For example, most people know immediately when you have a cold because your voice sounds different.

Clinical IMPACT 23.1

Sinusitis

Sinusitis (sigh-nuh-SIGH-tis), commonly referred to as a sinus infection, is inflammation of sinus mucous membranes, especially those of the paranasal sinuses. Viral infections, such as the common cold, can cause mucous membranes to become inflamed and swollen and to produce excess mucus. As a result, the sinus opening into the nasal cavity is partially or completely blocked, allowing mucus to accumulate within the sinus, which can promote a bacterial infection. Treatments include taking antibiotics and using decongestants, hydration, and steam inhalation to promote sinus drainage. Sinusitis can also result from swelling caused by allergies or by polyps that obstruct the sinus opening into the nasal cavity.

Pharynx

The **pharynx** (FAIR-inks), or throat, is the common opening of both the digestive and the respiratory systems. The pharynx receives air from the nasal cavity and receives air, food, and drink from the oral cavity. Inferiorly, the pharynx is connected to the respiratory system at the larynx and to the digestive system at the esophagus. There are three regions of the pharynx: (1) the nasopharynx, (2) the oropharynx, and (3) the laryngopharynx (figure 23.2*a*).

Nasopharynx

The **nasopharynx** (NAY-zoh-FAIR-inks) is the most superior portion of the pharynx. It is immediately posterior to the nasal cavity. Specifically, it is a continuation of the nasal cavity from the choanae. The nasopharynx is superior to the **soft palate.** The soft palate is an incomplete partition composed of muscle and connective tissue. It separates the nasopharynx from the middle portion of the pharynx, the oropharynx. The extension of the soft palate is called the **uvula** (YOU-vyu-lah; grape). The soft palate prevents swallowed materials from entering the nasopharynx and nasal cavity. It pushes food and other materials toward the back of the pharynx. The nasopharynx is lined with a mucous membrane that traps debris such as dust, as well as microbes. This debris-laden mucus from the nasal cavity is moved through the nasopharynx and swallowed. Any swallowed pathogens are likely killed by the acid in the stomach. The nasopharynx is continuous with the middle ear through the auditory tubes, openings on each side of the nasopharynx (figure 23.2*b;* see chapter 15). Air passes through the auditory tubes to equalize air pressure between the atmosphere and the tympanic membrane. The posterior wall of the nasopharynx houses the pharyngeal tonsil, or *adenoids* (AD-eh-noydz), which helps defend the body against infection (see chapter 22). An enlarged pharyngeal tonsil can interfere with normal pulmonary ventilation and airflow through the auditory tubes.

Oropharynx

The **oropharynx** (OR-oh-FAIR-inks) is a continuation of the nasopharynx. The oropharynx is the middle portion of the pharynx. It is immediately posterior to the mouth and begins at the soft palate. From there, it descends to the superior portion of the larynx. A region called the **fauces** (FAW-seez) joins the mouth's oral cavity and the oropharynx. Thus, air, food, and drink all pass through the oropharynx. Moist stratified squamous epithelium lines the oropharynx and protects it against abrasion. Two groups of tonsils, called the palatine tonsils and the lingual tonsil, are located near the fauces.

Laryngopharynx

The **laryngopharynx** (lah-RING-oh-FAIR-inks) is a continuation of the oropharynx. The laryngopharynx spans the posterior length of the larynx: from the most superior larynx structure, the epiglottis, to the esophagus. Food and drink pass through the laryngopharynx to the esophagus. Although most air passes from the laryngopharynx into the larynx, a small amount of air may be swallowed with food and drink. The laryngopharynx is lined with moist stratified squamous epithelium.

ASSESS YOUR PROGRESS

4. *Name the parts of the upper and lower respiratory tracts.*
5. *Explain how the conducting zone differs from the gas exchange zone.*
6. *Describe the structures of the nasal cavity.*
7. *What are the five functions of the nasal cavity?*
8. *Name the three regions of the pharynx. With what other structures does each part communicate?*

Larynx

The **larynx** (LAIR-inks) is commonly known as the voice box. It is located in the anterior part of the laryngopharynx and extends from the base of the tongue to the trachea. The larynx is held in place by membranes and muscles superior to the hyoid bone (figure 23.2*b*). The rigid walls of the larynx maintain an open passageway between the pharynx and the trachea. Its rigidity is due to an outer casing of nine cartilages connected to one another by muscles and ligaments (figure 23.3). Six of the nine cartilages are paired, and three are unpaired. The following is a list of the cartilages composing the larynx:

1. *Thyroid cartilage.* The **thyroid** (shield) **cartilage** is the largest of the cartilages. It is a single shield-shaped piece of cartilage, which is also known as the *Adam's apple.*
2. *Cricoid cartilage.* The **cricoid** (CRY-koyd; ring-shaped) **cartilage** forms the base of the larynx. It is a single piece of cartilage upon which the other cartilages rest.
3. *Epiglottis.* The **epiglottis** (ep-ih-GLOT-is; on the glottis) is a single piece of cartilage that is attached to the thyroid cartilage and projects superiorly. The epiglottis is unique among the larynx cartilages because it is a freely movable flap and is constructed of elastic cartilage rather than hyaline cartilage. It helps divert food away from the trachea opening during swallowing.
4. *Arytenoid cartilages.* The paired **arytenoid** (ar-ih-TEE-noyd; ladle-shaped) **cartilages** articulate with the superior border on the posterior of the cricoid cartilage.

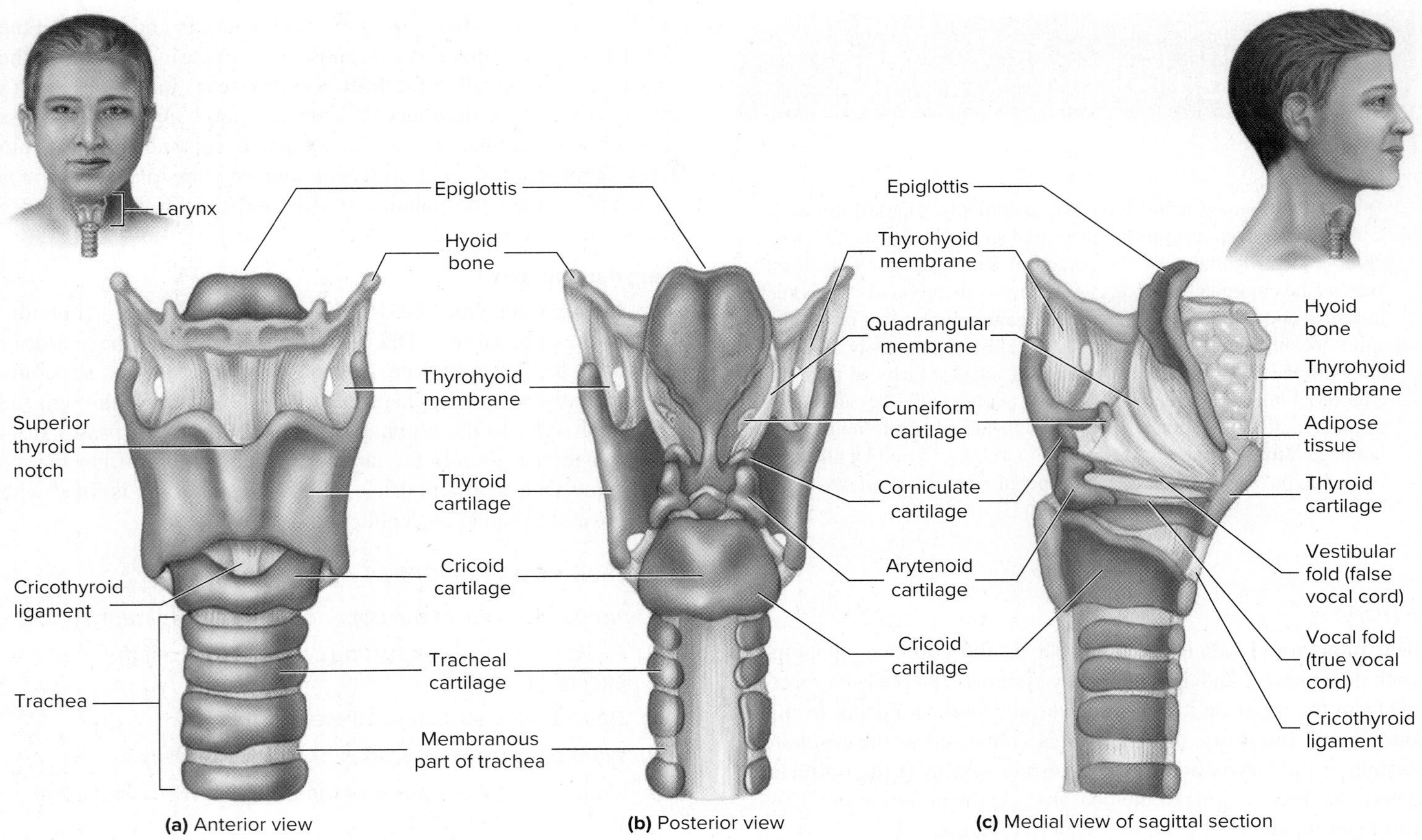

FIGURE 23.3 Anatomy of the Larynx

The larynx helps keep the airway open. (*a*) In the anterior view, the thyroid cartilage is visible. This is also known as the Adam's apple. (*b*) The posterior view shows the epiglottis, which moves inferiorly to prevent food and other swallowed materials from entering the trachea. (*c*) The medial view shows the vestibular and vocal folds, which are important in swallowing, speech, and other functions. APR

5. *Corniculate cartilages.* The paired **corniculate** (kor-NIK-you-late; horn-shaped) **cartilages** are attached to the superior tips of the arytenoid cartilages.
6. *Cuneiform cartilages.* The paired **cuneiform** (KYU-nee-ih-form; wedge-shaped) **cartilages** are contained in a mucous membrane anterior to the corniculate cartilages.

The larynx is called the voice box because it houses the ligaments used for speech as well as for swallowing and other functions (figure 23.4). Both pairs of ligaments are covered by a mucous membrane. These ligaments are found within two separate structures: (1) the vestibular folds and (2) the vocal folds. The **vestibular folds,** or *false vocal cords,* contain the superior pair of ligaments that extend from the anterior surface of the arytenoid cartilages to the posterior surface of the thyroid cartilage. The **vocal folds,** or *true vocal cords,* contain the inferior ligaments. At the junction of the vocal folds is an opening; this opening, in combination with the vocal folds, is called the **glottis** (GLOT-is). The epithelium covering the vestibular and vocal folds is stratified squamous. The remainder of the larynx is lined with pseudostratified ciliated columnar epithelium. If the vocal folds become inflamed, **laryngitis** (lair-in-JIE-tis) occurs and the person "loses" their voice.

The larynx wall contains two sets of skeletal muscles: (1) intrinsic muscles and (2) extrinsic muscles. The **intrinsic muscles** attach to the arytenoid and corniculate cartilages and aid in closing and opening the glottis. The **extrinsic muscles** include the sternohyoid and sternothyroid (see chapter 10), which elevate the larynx during swallowing.

The larynx, with its cartilages and the vestibular and vocal folds, performs four main functions:

1. Maintains an open passageway for air movements.
2. Prevents swallowed materials from entering the larynx and lower respiratory tract.
3. Produces sound for speech.
4. Protects the lower respiratory tract from foreign materials.

Functions of the Vestibular and Vocal Folds

The vocal folds are the primary source of sound production. Air moving past the vocal folds causes them to vibrate and produce sound. The force of air moving past the vocal folds determines the amplitude of the vibration and the loudness of the sound: the greater the amplitude of the vibration, the louder the sound. The frequency of vibrations determines pitch: Higher-frequency vibrations produce higher-pitched sounds and lower-frequency

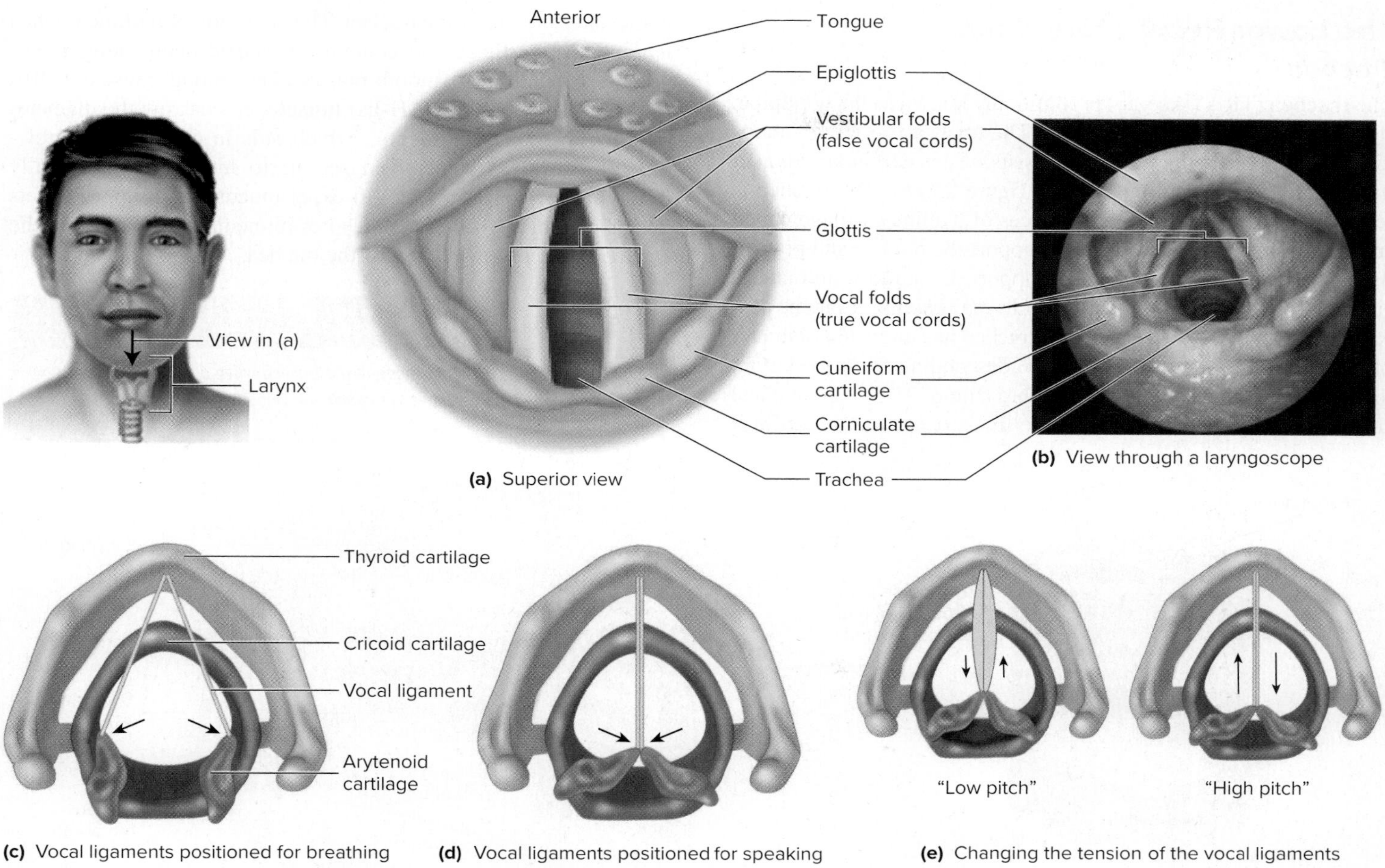

(a) Superior view

(b) View through a laryngoscope

(c) Vocal ligaments positioned for breathing

(d) Vocal ligaments positioned for speaking

(e) Changing the tension of the vocal ligaments

FIGURE 23.4 Vestibular Vocal Folds and Sound Production

(*a*) Relationship of the vestibular folds to the vocal folds and the laryngeal cartilages. (*b*) Laryngoscopic view of the vestibular and vocal folds. (*c*) Lateral rotation of the arytenoid cartilages moves the vocal ligaments laterally for pulmonary ventilation. (*d*) Medial rotation of the arytenoid cartilages moves the vocal ligaments medially for speaking. (*e*) Anterior/posterior movement of the arytenoid cartilages changes the length and tension of the vocal ligaments, altering the pitch of sounds. Arrows show the direction of viewing the vestibular and vocal ligaments. A lower pitch is created when the vocal ligaments are thickened and a higher pitch is created when the vocal ligaments are stretched thin. (b) CNRI/Science Source

vibrations produce lower-pitched sounds. Variations in the length of the vibrating segments of the vocal folds affect the frequency of the vibrations. Higher-pitched tones are produced when only the anterior parts of the folds vibrate, and progressively lower tones result when longer sections of the folds vibrate. Because males usually have longer vocal folds than females, most males have lower-pitched voices. The sound produced by the vibrating vocal folds is modified by the tongue, lips, teeth, and other structures to form words. Interestingly, a person whose larynx has been removed due to carcinoma of the larynx can produce sound by swallowing air and causing the esophagus to vibrate.

Movement of the arytenoid and other cartilages is controlled by the intrinsic and extrinsic muscles of the larynx, thereby changing the position and length of the vocal folds. When a person is simply breathing, lateral rotation of the arytenoid cartilages opens the vocal folds, which allows greater movement of air (figure 23.4*c*). Medial rotation of the arytenoid cartilages closes the vocal folds, places them in position for producing sounds, and changes the tension on them (figure 23.4*d*). Anterior movement of the arytenoid cartilages decreases the length and tension of the vocal folds, lowering pitch. Posterior movement of the arytenoid cartilages increases the length and tension of the vocal folds, increasing pitch (figure 23.4*e*).

In addition to sound production, the vestibular and vocal folds provide the most important method for preventing swallowed materials from entering the larynx. During swallowing, food passes over the epiglottis toward the esophagus and the vestibular and vocal folds move together medially, closing the glottis. The closure of the vestibular and vocal folds can also prevent the passage of air, as when a person holds their breath or increases air pressure within the lungs prior to coughing or sneezing.

Predict 1

Jake told his girlfriend that the roller coaster did not bother him, but during the ride he let loose with a long, high-pitched scream. Explain how the muscles that control the vocal folds and the muscles that move the epiglottis helped produce Jake's scream.

The Lower Respiratory Tract

Trachea

The **trachea** (TRAY-kee-ah) is commonly known as the windpipe. It allows air to flow into the lungs. The trachea is a membranous tube attached to the larynx and consists of dense regular connective tissue and smooth muscle (see figure 23.2*b*). The trachea is reinforced with 15–20 C-shaped pieces of hyaline cartilage called **tracheal rings.** The tracheal rings support the trachea and prevent it from collapsing. The cartilages support the anterior and lateral sides of the trachea to protect it while maintaining a patent passageway for air (figure 23.5*a*). The trachea has an inside diameter of 12 mm and a length of 10–12 cm, descending from the larynx to the level of the fifth thoracic vertebra (figure 23.6). The tracheal rings are incomplete circles with the thickest portion of cartilage at the anterior wall of the trachea. The posterior wall of the trachea is devoid of cartilage and contains an elastic ligamentous membrane and bundles of smooth muscle. The smooth muscle, called the **trachealis** (tray-kee-AH-lis) **muscle,** can narrow the diameter of the trachea by contracting, which aids in coughing. Narrowing the trachea's diameter causes air to move more forcefully through the trachea, helping to expel mucus and foreign objects during coughing. The esophagus lies immediately posterior to the cartilage-free posterior wall of the trachea.

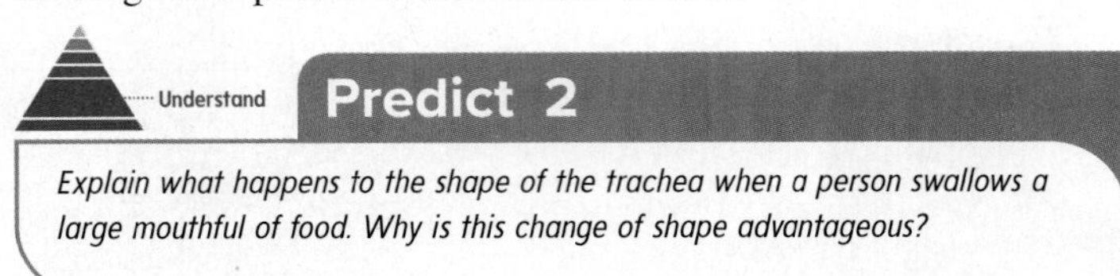

Understand **Predict 2**

Explain what happens to the shape of the trachea when a person swallows a large mouthful of food. Why is this change of shape advantageous?

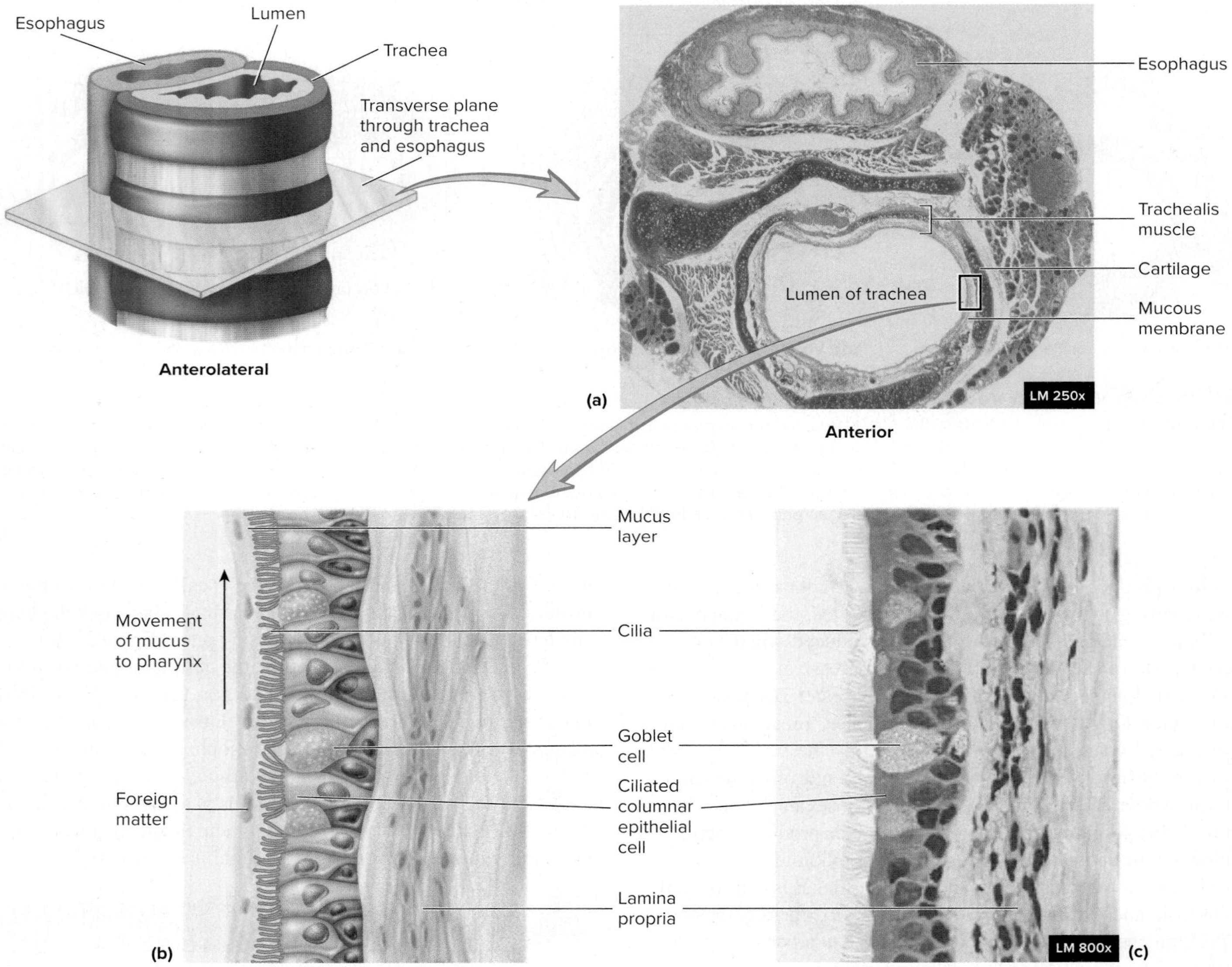

Esophagus
Lumen
Trachea
Transverse plane through trachea and esophagus
Anterolateral
(a)
Esophagus
Trachealis muscle
Cartilage
Lumen of trachea
Mucous membrane
LM 250x
Anterior
Mucus layer
Movement of mucus to pharynx
Cilia
Goblet cell
Foreign matter
Ciliated columnar epithelial cell
Lamina propria
(b)
LM 800x
(c)

FIGURE 23.5 Trachea

(*a*) Light micrograph of a transverse section of the trachea. The esophagus is posterior to the trachea, next to the smooth muscle connecting the ends of the C-shaped cartilages of the trachea. (*b*) Mucus, produced by the goblet cells, traps foreign matter in the air. Movement of the cilia moves the mucus and foreign matter to the laryngopharynx. (*c*) Light micrograph of the surface of the mucous membrane lining the trachea. Goblet cells are interspersed between ciliated cells. (a) Biophoto Associates/Science Source; (c) Ed Reschke/Photolibrary/Getty Images APR

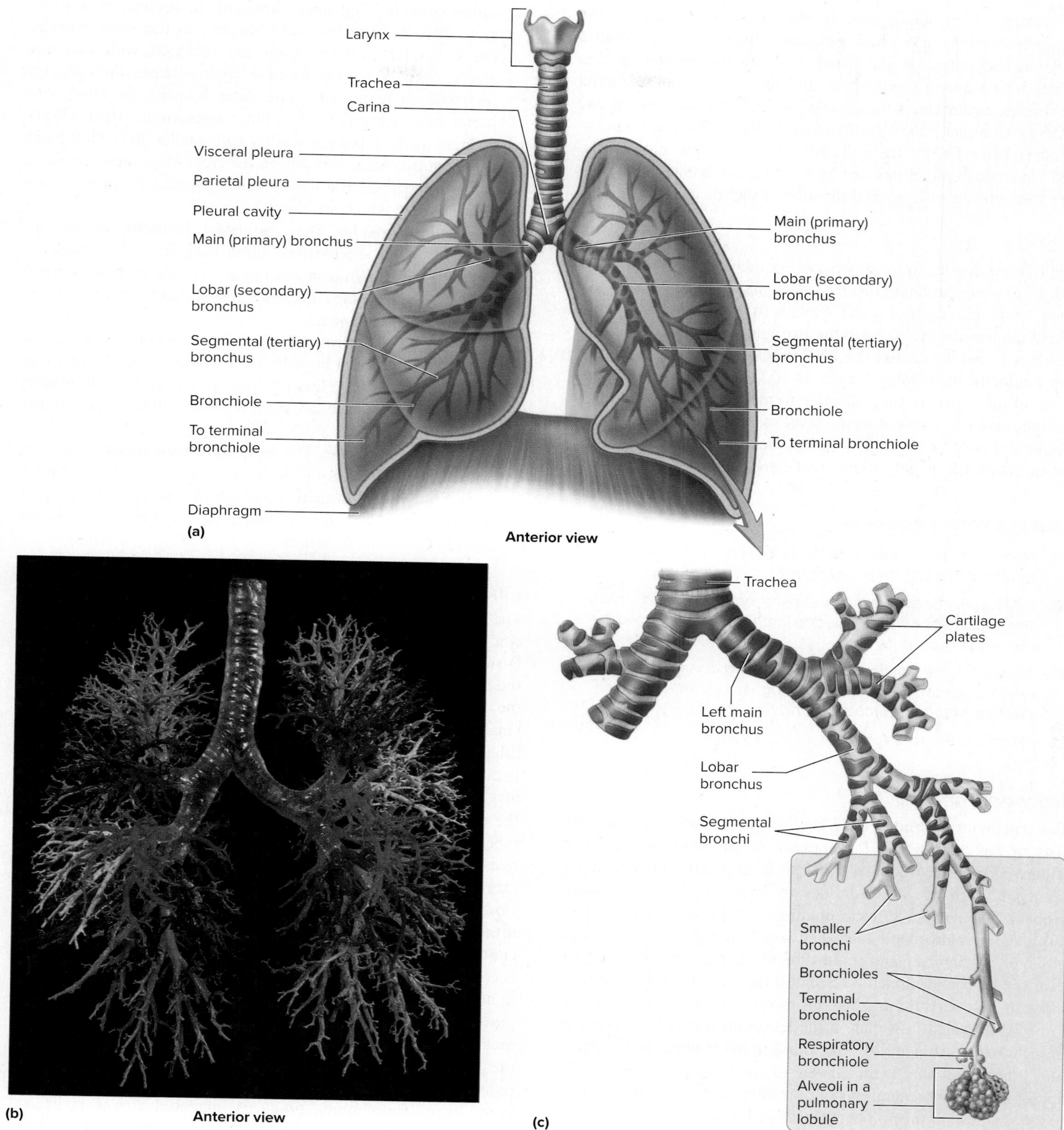

FIGURE 23.6 Tracheobronchial Tree

(*a*) The conducting zone of the tracheobronchial tree begins at the trachea and ends at the terminal bronchioles. (*b*) A cast of the tracheobronchial tree demonstrating the magnitude of branching. (*c*) A more detailed look at the branching pattern of bronchi. Note that the walls of bronchioles do not contain cartilage; rather, they are composed of smooth muscle. (b) Mediscan/Alamy Stock Photo APR

A mucous membrane lines the trachea (see figure 23.5*b*). The membrane's goblet cells produce mucus, which traps inspired dust, bacteria, and other foreign matter. The ciliated epithelium then moves the mucus and foreign matter into the larynx. From the larynx the foreign matter enters the pharynx and is swallowed (see figure 23.5*b,c*). Constant, long-term irritation to the trachea, as occurs in smokers, can cause the tracheal epithelium to become moist stratified squamous epithelium that lacks cilia and goblet cells. This transition prevents the normal function of the tracheal epithelium.

Bronchi

The trachea divides to form two smaller tubes called **main bronchi,** or *primary bronchi* (BRONG-kye; sing. bronchus, BRONG-kuss; windpipe), each of which extends to a lung. At the location where the trachea divides into the two main bronchi is a ridge of cartilage called the **carina** (ka-RYE-nah). The carina is an important landmark for reading x-rays. In addition, the mucous membrane of the carina is very sensitive to mechanical stimulation. If foreign matter is inspired to the level of the carina, it stimulates a powerful cough reflex. Materials in the air passageways beyond the carina do not usually stimulate a cough reflex.

ASSESS YOUR PROGRESS

9. *Name and describe the three single cartilages of the larynx. What are their functions?*
10. *Distinguish between the vestibular and vocal folds. How are sounds of different loudness and pitch produced by the vocal ligaments?*
11. *How does the position of the arytenoid cartilages change when a person is simply breathing versus making low-pitched and high-pitched sounds?*
12. *What are the four functions of the larynx?*

Tracheobronchial Tree

The **tracheobronchial** (TRAY-kee-oh-BRONG-kee-al) **tree** consists of the trachea and the network of air tubes in the lungs (figure 23.6). The trachea divides to form a left and right main bronchus, each of which divides to form smaller and smaller bronchi. The smaller bronchi continue getting smaller until they terminate in microscopic tubes and sacs. The right main bronchus is larger in diameter and more directly in line with the trachea than the left main bronchus. Because the right main bronchus is more in line with the trachea, an inspired object is more likely to become lodged in it than in the left main bronchus. The main bronchi have cartilage rings like those in the trachea. Within each lung, there are four main classes of air passageways. Overall, approximately 16 generations of branching occur from the trachea to the smallest air tubes. The walls of each class of air passageway are supported by cartilage and smooth muscle, giving way to all smooth muscle in the smallest air passageways. In addition, each class of air passageway is lined with a type of ciliated epithelium, which functions as a mucus-cilia escalator, trapping debris from the air and moving it to the larynx. The four classes of air passageways, listed from largest to smallest, are the following:

1. *Lobar bronchi.* The **lobar bronchi,** or *secondary bronchi,* arise directly from the main bronchi. In the lobar bronchi, the C-shaped cartilage rings are replaced with cartilage plates. Smooth muscle forms a layer between the cartilage and mucous membrane. The lobar bronchi are lined with pseudostratified ciliated columnar epithelium, which slowly changes as the tubes get smaller and smaller. In the left lung, there are two lobar bronchi. In the right lung, there are three lobar bronchi. Each lobar bronchus supplies its own section of each lung, which are called lobes.
2. *Segmental bronchi.* The **segmental bronchi,** or *tertiary bronchi,* supply subdivisions within each lung lobe, which are called bronchopulmonary segments. As the bronchi become smaller, the cartilage becomes sparse, and smooth muscle becomes more abundant.
3. *Bronchioles.* The **bronchioles** result from continued branching of the segmental bronchi. Bronchioles are less than 1 mm in diameter and have less cartilage and more smooth muscle. The larger bronchioles are lined with ciliated simple columnar epithelium.
4. *Terminal bronchioles.* The **terminal bronchioles** arise from several subdivisions of bronchioles. The terminal bronchioles have no cartilage in their walls, but the smooth muscle layer is prominent. The terminal bronchioles are lined with ciliated simple cuboidal epithelium.

Changes in Air Passageway Diameter

The bronchi and bronchioles are capable of changing their diameter. The smooth muscle layer in them can relax and contract. **Bronchodilation** occurs when the smooth muscle relaxes, making the bronchiole diameter larger. **Bronchoconstriction** occurs when the smooth muscle contracts, making the bronchiole diameter smaller. This works in the same way as vasoconstriction and vasodilation. The flow of air decreases when the resistance to airflow is increased by conditions that reduce the diameter of the respiratory passageways. According to Poiseuille's law (see chapter 21), the resistance to airflow is proportional to the diameter (D) of a tube. Thus, a small change in diameter results in a large change in resistance, which greatly decreases airflow. For example, during exercise bronchodilation occurs, reducing the resistance to airflow, which increases air movement. However, during an **asthma attack,** the release of inflammatory chemicals, such as leukotrienes, causes severe bronchoconstriction. The bronchoconstriction decreases the diameter of the airways, which increases resistance to airflow and greatly reduces air movement. In severe cases, air movement can be so restricted that the patient dies. Fortunately, medications, such as **albuterol** (al-BYU-ter-ol), help counteract the effects of an asthma attack by promoting smooth muscle relaxation in the walls of terminal bronchioles so that air can flow more freely. Emphysema produces increased airway resistance because the bronchioles are obstructed as a result of inflammation and because damaged bronchioles collapse during expiration, thus trapping air within the alveoli. Cancer can also occlude respiratory passages as the tumor replaces lung tissue. When there is increased resistance, increasing the pressure difference between alveoli and the atmosphere can help maintain airflow. Within

Clinical GENETICS 23.1 Emphysema

Emphysema (em-fi-ZEE-mah) is a condition in which lung alveoli become progressively enlarged as the walls between them are destroyed. Individuals who have emphysema experience shortness of breath and coughing.

Cigarette smoking is the major risk factor for emphysema. Chemicals in cigarette smoke damage lung tissues and stimulate inflammation. As part of the inflammatory response, neutrophils and macrophages release **proteases,** which are enzymes that break down proteins. Proteases in the lungs protect against some bacteria and foreign substances, but too much protease activity can result in the breakdown of lung tissue proteins, especially elastin in elastic fibers. **Alpha-1 anti-trypsin (AAT),** which is synthesized in the liver, is a **protease inhibitor.** Normally, AAT inhibits protease activity, preventing the destruction of lung tissue. However, excess protease production stimulated by cigarette smoke can cause lung damage, leading to emphysema. Approximately 1–2% of emphysema cases are due to a deficiency of AAT caused by defects in the AAT gene. The mutated gene reduces the amount of secreted AAT. Multiple alleles for AAT have been identified. Individuals who are homozygous for the normal allele produce normal levels of AAT. Individuals with one copy of the normal allele and one copy of the most common abnormal allele have about 60% of normal levels of AAT. This is sufficient activity to prevent protease damage. However, individuals with two copies of the *abnormal* allele produce only about 15–20% of normal AAT levels. If these individuals smoke, the development of emphysema is accelerated by 10–15 years. Other variant alleles cause different levels of AAT. The most severe form results in no AAT and the development of emphysema by age 30, even in nonsmokers. Treatment of AAT deficiency follows the normal course of treatment for emphysema. Stopping smoking reduces the destruction of lung tissue by removing the stimulus for excess protease activity. Drugs, such as danazol and tamoxifen, can stimulate increased AAT production in the liver. In addition, patients may receive intravenous infusions of AAT, a process called alpha-1 antitrypsin augmentation.

5. The basement membrane of the capillary endothelium
6. The capillary endothelium, which is a single layer of simple squamous cells

ASSESS YOUR PROGRESS

13. *Explain the branching of the tracheobronchial tree.*
14. *Describe the arrangement of cartilage, smooth muscle, and epithelium in the tracheobronchial tree. Explain why pulmonary ventilation becomes more difficult during an asthma attack.*
15. *How is debris removed from the tracheobronchial tree?*
16. *Name the two types of cells in the alveolar wall, and state their functions.*
17. *List the individual layers of the respiratory membrane.*

Thoracic Wall and Muscles of Pulmonary Ventilation

The thoracic wall consists of the (1) thoracic vertebrae, (2) ribs, (3) costal cartilages, (4) sternum, and (5) associated muscles (see chapters 7 and 10). The **thoracic cavity** is the space enclosed by the thoracic wall and the **diaphragm** (DIE-ah-fram; partition). Recall from chapter 10 that the diaphragm is a sheet of skeletal muscle separating the thoracic cavity from the abdominal cavity. The diaphragm and other skeletal muscles associated with the thoracic wall change thoracic volume during pulmonary ventilation (figure 23.8). We will discuss the specific roles of the muscles of ventilation in section 23.4.

Lungs

The **lungs** are the primary organs of gas exchange. Based on their volume, they are among the largest organs of the body. Each lung is conical in shape and extends from the diaphragm to a point approximately 2.5 cm superior to the clavicle. The portion of the lungs in contact with the diaphragm is the **base.** The portion of the lungs that extends above the clavicle is called the **apex.** The right lung is larger than the left and weighs an average of 620 g, whereas the left lung weighs an average of 560 g.

The **hilum** (HIGH-lum) is an indentation on the medial surface of the lung. The hilum is where structures, such as the main bronchus, blood vessels, nerves, and lymphatic vessels, enter or exit the lung. All the structures passing through the hilum are referred to as the **root of the lung.**

The right lung has three large sections called **lobes,** while the left lung has two lobes. The lung lobes are separated by deep, prominent **fissures** on the surface of the lung. Each lung lobe is supplied by a lobar bronchus. The left lung also has a medial indentation called the **cardiac notch** (figure 23.9). This structural arrangement provides room for the heart to lie between the lungs. The lung lobes are further subdivided into **bronchopulmonary segments.** Each bronchopulmonary segment is supplied by the segmental bronchi. There are 9 bronchopulmonary segments in the left lung and 10 in the right lung. The bronchopulmonary segments are separated from each other by connective tissue partitions, which are not visible as surface fissures. Individual diseased bronchopulmonary segments can be surgically removed because major blood vessels and bronchi do not cross the connective tissue partitions. This leaves the rest of the lung relatively intact. The bronchopulmonary segments are even further subdivided into

FUNDAMENTAL **Figure**

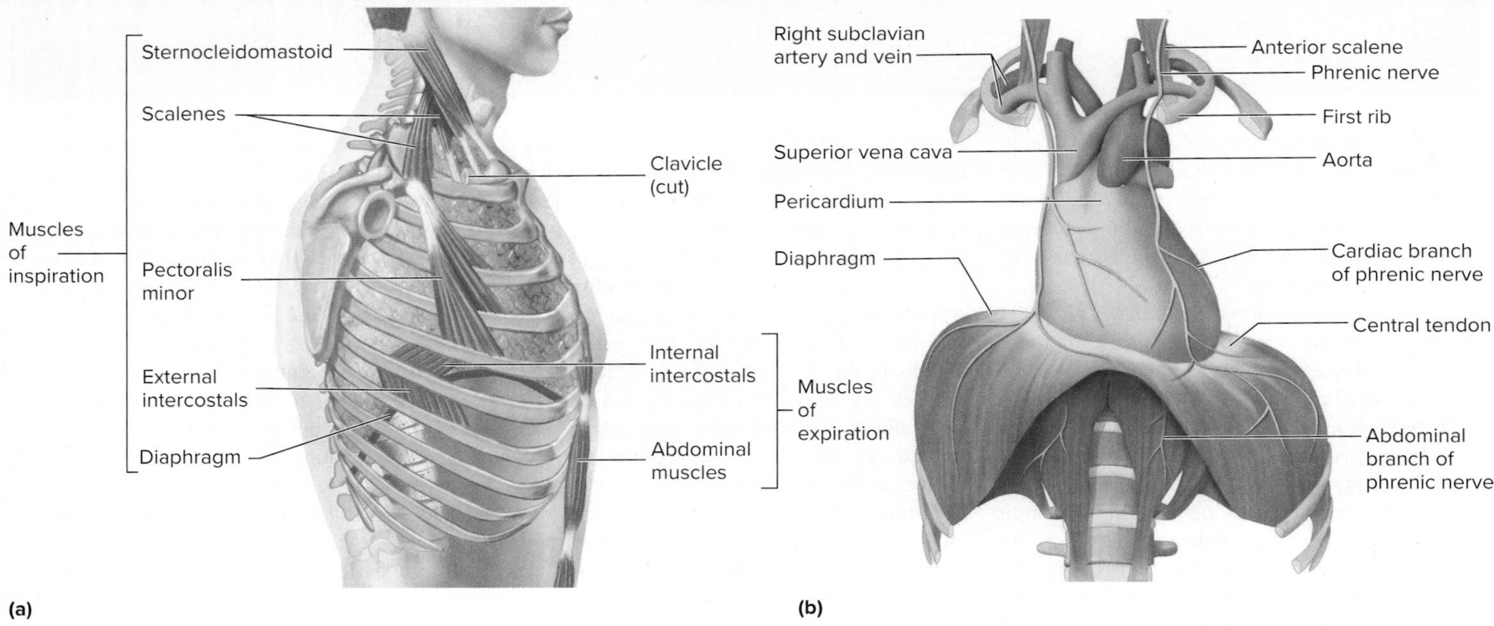

FIGURE 23.8 Muscles of Ventilation

(*a*) Muscles of ventilation at the end of expiration. (*b*) The diaphragm is one of the principal muscles of inspiration. The phrenic nerve (see section 23.7) sends impulses to contract the diaphragm during inspiration.

lobules by partial walls of connective tissue. Bronchioles supply each lobule.

Blood Supply to the Lungs

Blood that has passed through the lungs and picked up O_2 is called **oxygenated blood,** and blood that has passed through the tissues and released some of its O_2 is called **deoxygenated blood.** There are two blood flow routes to the lungs: (1) blood flow to the alveoli and (2) blood flow to the tissues of the bronchial tree. The major route takes deoxygenated blood to the alveoli in the lungs, where it is oxygenated (see chapter 21). To get to the alveoli, the deoxygenated blood flows through pulmonary arteries to pulmonary capillaries. In the capillaries, the blood becomes oxygenated and returns to the heart through pulmonary veins. The second route takes oxygenated blood to the tissues of the bronchi down to the respiratory bronchioles. The oxygenated blood flows from the thoracic aorta through bronchial arteries to capillaries, where O_2 is released. Deoxygenated blood from the proximal part of the bronchi returns to the heart through the bronchial veins and the azygos venous system (see chapter 21). More distally, the venous drainage from the bronchi enters the pulmonary veins. Thus, the oxygenated blood returning from the alveoli in the pulmonary veins is mixed with a small amount of deoxygenated blood returning from the bronchi. However, the available O_2 is not significantly reduced.

Lymphatic Supply to the Lungs

The lungs have two lymphatic supplies: (1) the superficial lymphatic vessels and (2) the deep lymphatic vessels. The **superficial lymphatic vessels** are deep to the connective tissue that surrounds each lung, called the **visceral pleura.** These vessels drain lymph from the superficial lung tissue and the visceral pleura. The **deep lymphatic vessels** follow the bronchi. These vessels drain lymph from the bronchi and associated connective tissues. There are no lymphatic vessels located in the walls of the alveoli. Both the superficial and deep lymphatic vessels exit the lung at the hilum.

Phagocytic cells within the lungs phagocytize carbon particles and other debris from inspired air and move them to the lymphatic vessels. In an older person, especially one who smokes or has lived most of their life in a city with air pollution, these particles accumulate and cause the surface of the lungs to become gray or black. Though the lymphatic vessels primarily serve as a way to remove harmful substances from the lung tissue, cancer cells from the lungs can spread to other parts of the body through the lymphatic vessels.

Pleura

The lungs are contained within the thoracic cavity. There are two pleural cavities within the thoracic cavity. Each pleural cavity houses one lung. The **pleural** (PLUR-al; relating to the ribs) **cavities** are lined with a serous membrane (figure 23.10). Recall from chapter 20 that separating the two pleural cavities is a central region called the **mediastinum** (MEE-dee-ah-STY-num). The mediastinum houses the heart, trachea, esophagus, and other structures, such as blood vessels and the thymus. The serous membrane that covers the inner thoracic wall, the superior surface of the diaphragm, and the mediastinum is called the **parietal pleura.** At the hilum, the parietal pleura is continuous with the visceral pleura, which covers the surface of the lung.

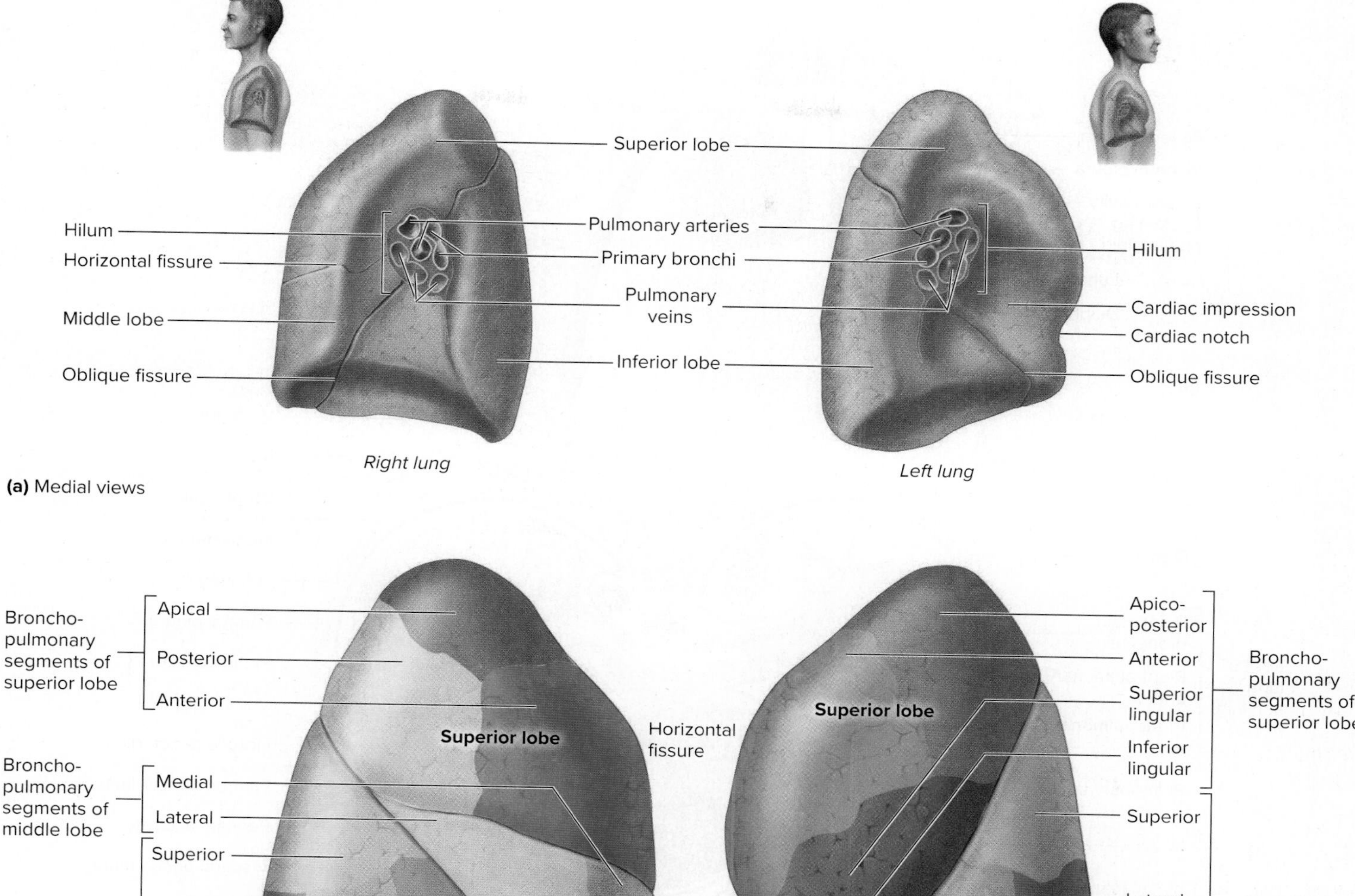

FIGURE 23.9 Lobes and Bronchopulmonary Segments of the Lungs
(*a*) Gross anatomy of the lungs, showing the lung lobes and bronchi. The right lung is divided into three lobes by the horizontal and oblique fissures. The left lung is divided into two lobes by the oblique fissure. A main bronchus supplies each lung. (*b*) Each lobe consists of several bronchopulmonary segments.

ASSESS YOUR PROGRESS

18. *Distinguish among a lung, a lung lobe, a bronchopulmonary segment, and a lobule. How are they related to the tracheobronchial tree?*

19. *How many lobes are in the right lung and in the left lung? Why is there a difference in the number of lobes?*

20. *What are the two major routes of blood flow to and from the lungs? What is the function of each route?*

21. *Describe the lymphatic supply of the lungs.*

22. *Name the pleurae of the lungs. What is their function?*

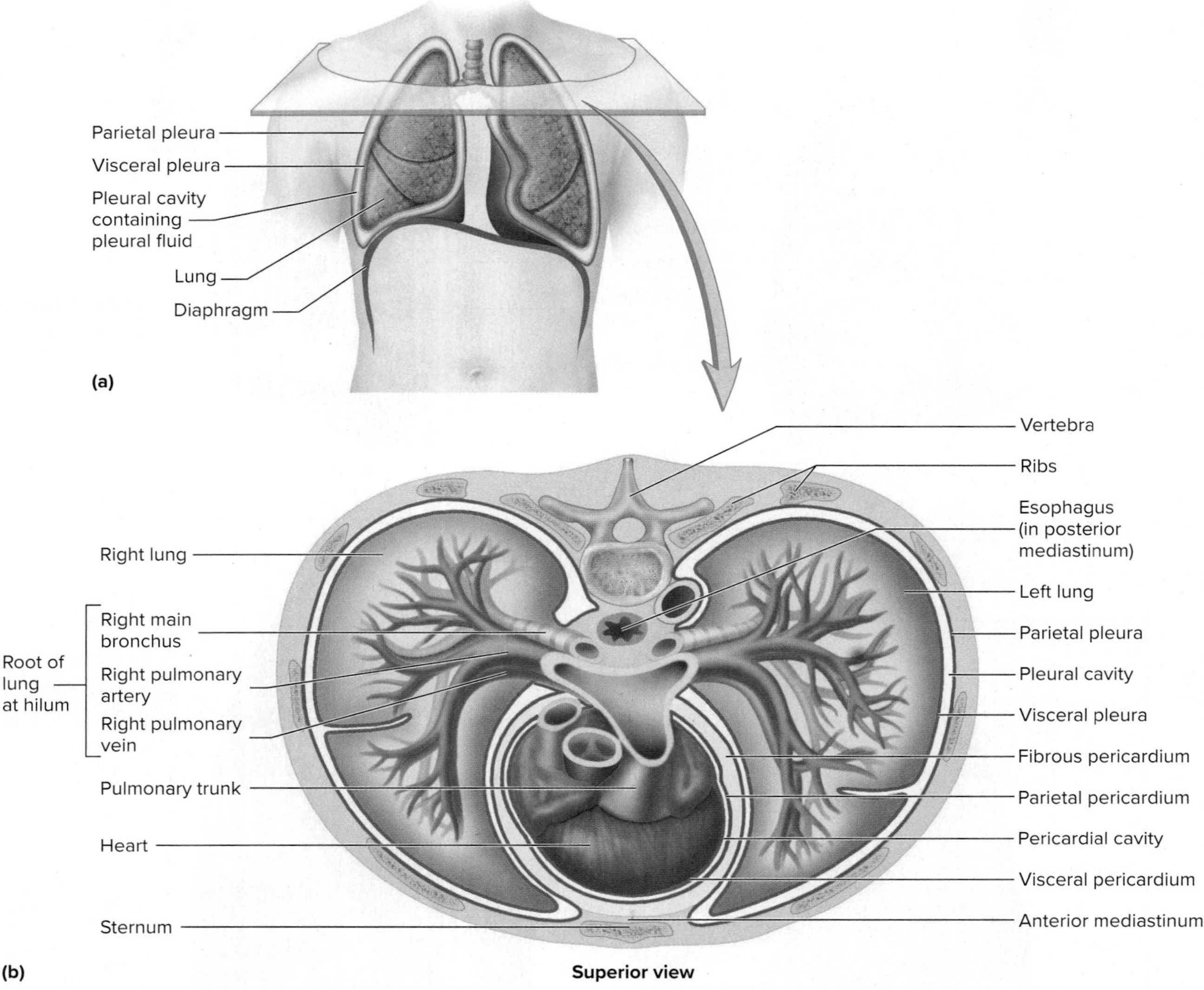

FIGURE 23.10 Pleural Cavities and Membranes
(*a*) Anterior view of the thorax and the pleural cavity. (*b*) Transverse section of the thorax, showing the relationship of the pleural cavities to the thoracic organs. Each lung is surrounded by a pleural cavity. The parietal pleura lines the wall of each pleural cavity, and the visceral pleura covers the surface of the lungs. The space between the parietal and visceral pleurae is small and filled with pleural fluid.

23.4 Behavior of Gases

LEARNING OUTCOMES

After reading this section, you should be able to

A. **Explain the role of the muscles of respiration in pulmonary ventilation.**
B. **Explain partial pressure and its relationship to the concentration of gases in the body.**
C. **List the pulmonary volumes and capacities, and define each of them.**
D. **Distinguish between anatomical dead space and physiological dead space.**
E. **Define *compliance, minute volume,* and *alveolar ventilation.***

As we've stated, the process of breathing is twofold: pulmonary ventilation and gas exchange. To understand each of these mechanisms, we must examine the relationships governing the movement of gases.

Behavior of Gases and Pulmonary Ventilation

Pulmonary ventilation, as we described earlier, is simply the movement of air into and out of the lungs. There are two primary aspects to pulmonary ventilation: (1) actions of the muscles of ventilation and (2) air pressure gradients.

Muscles of Ventilation

The function of the muscles of ventilation is to change the volume of the thoracic cavity, which allows for air to flow into and out of the lungs. There are several **muscles of inspiration** that act to increase the volume of the thoracic cavity. They include the (1) diaphragm, (2) external intercostals, (3) pectoralis minor, and (4) scalene muscles. The **muscles of expiration** are the muscles that decrease thoracic volume by depressing the ribs and sternum. These are the (1) internal intercostals and (2) transverse thoracis, with assistance from the abdominal muscles. Although the internal intercostals and the transverse thoracis are most active during expiration, and the external intercostals are most active during inspiration, the primary function of these muscles is to stiffen the thoracic wall by contracting at the same time. In this way, they prevent the thoracic cage from collapsing inward during inspiration.

Muscles of Inspiration

During inspiration, the thoracic cavity volume increases. Downward movement of the diaphragm upon contraction is responsible for approximately two-thirds of the thoracic volume increase. The diaphragm is dome-shaped, and the base of the dome attaches to the inner circumference of the inferior thoracic cage (see figure 10.16). The top of the dome is a flat sheet of connective tissue called the **central tendon.** In normal, quiet inspiration, contraction of the diaphragm causes the central tendon to move downward. There is very little change in the overall shape of the diaphragm. This downward movement is facilitated by relaxation of the abdominal muscles, which moves the abdominal organs out of the way. This is noticeable when your hands rest on your stomach. However, as the depth of inspiration increases, the abdominal organs prevent the central tendon from moving inferiorly. Continued contraction of the diaphragm causes it to flatten as the lower ribs are elevated.

The remaining muscles of inspiration, such as the external intercostals, increase thoracic volume by elevating the ribs. As the ribs are elevated, the costal cartilages allow lateral rib movement and lateral expansion of the thoracic cavity (figure 23.11). The ribs slope inferiorly from the vertebrae to the sternum, and elevation of the ribs also increases the anterior-posterior dimension of the thoracic cavity.

Muscles of Expiration

During expiration, the thoracic cavity volume decreases. During quiet pulmonary ventilation, expiration is a passive process due to significant amounts of elastic tissue in the thorax wall and the lungs. When tension is removed, the thorax wall and the lungs spring back into a smaller, relaxed state. In addition, the diaphragm relaxes, which causes it to move upward. Also, the external intercostals relax and the ribs move downward. Contractions of abdominal muscles also cause the thoracic cavity volume to decrease and push the abdominal organs upward into the diaphragm, which moves it superiorly.

Muscles of Ventilation in Quiet Pulmonary Ventilation Compared with Labored Pulmonary Ventilation

Several differences can be recognized between normal, quiet pulmonary ventilation and labored pulmonary ventilation. During labored inspiration, more air moves into the lungs because all of the inspiratory muscles are active. They contract more forcefully than during quiet pulmonary ventilation, which causes a greater increase in thoracic volume (see figure 23.8). During labored expiration, more air moves out of the lungs due to the forceful contraction of the internal intercostals and the abdominal muscles. This produces a more rapid and greater decrease in thoracic volume than would be produced by the passive recoil of the thorax and lungs.

The Relationship Between Pressure Gradients and Pulmonary Ventilation

In order to fully understand why increasing thoracic cavity volume allows inspiration to occur, it is necessary to recognize the relationship between pressure and volume.

Pressure and Volume

The relationship between pressure and volume is an inverse one. That is to say, as the volume of a container increases, the pressure in that container decreases. The pressure of a gas in a container at a constant temperature follows **Boyle's law:**

$$P = k/V \qquad (23.1)$$

where P is gas pressure, k is a constant for a given temperature, and V is the volume of the container. Body temperature in humans can be considered a constant. Thus, Boyle's law explains why, upon inspiration, the air pressure within the thoracic cavity decreases. Conversely, upon expiration, the air pressure within the thoracic cavity increases because the volume of the thoracic cavity decreases (figure 23.12).

Pressure Gradients and Airflow

During inspiration, air flows into the lungs down its pressure gradient. During expiration, air flows out of the lungs down its pressure gradient. This pressure gradient is provided, in part, by atmospheric pressure—the combined force of all the gases that make up the air we breathe. The physics of airflow in tubes, such as the ones that make up the respiratory passages, is the same as that of the flow of blood in blood vessels (see chapter 21):

$$F = \frac{P1 - P2}{R} \qquad (23.2)$$

where F is airflow (milliliters per minute) in a tube, $P1$ is pressure at point 1, $P2$ is pressure at point 2, and R is resistance to airflow.

Air moves through tubes because of a pressure difference: Air moves from areas of higher pressure to areas of lower pressure. Thus, when $P1$ is greater than $P2$, gas flows from $P1$ to $P2$. For example, during inspiration, air pressure outside the body is greater than air pressure in the alveoli, and air flows into the body through the trachea and bronchi to the alveoli.

In addition, as we will discuss, the greater the pressure difference, the faster the flow rate. If the pressure difference decreases, the flow rate also decreases. For example, at higher altitudes, atmospheric pressure is lower than at sea level, making the pressure difference less. The decrease in the pressure gradient between the atmospheric air and our alveoli is why it seems harder to breathe at high altitudes.

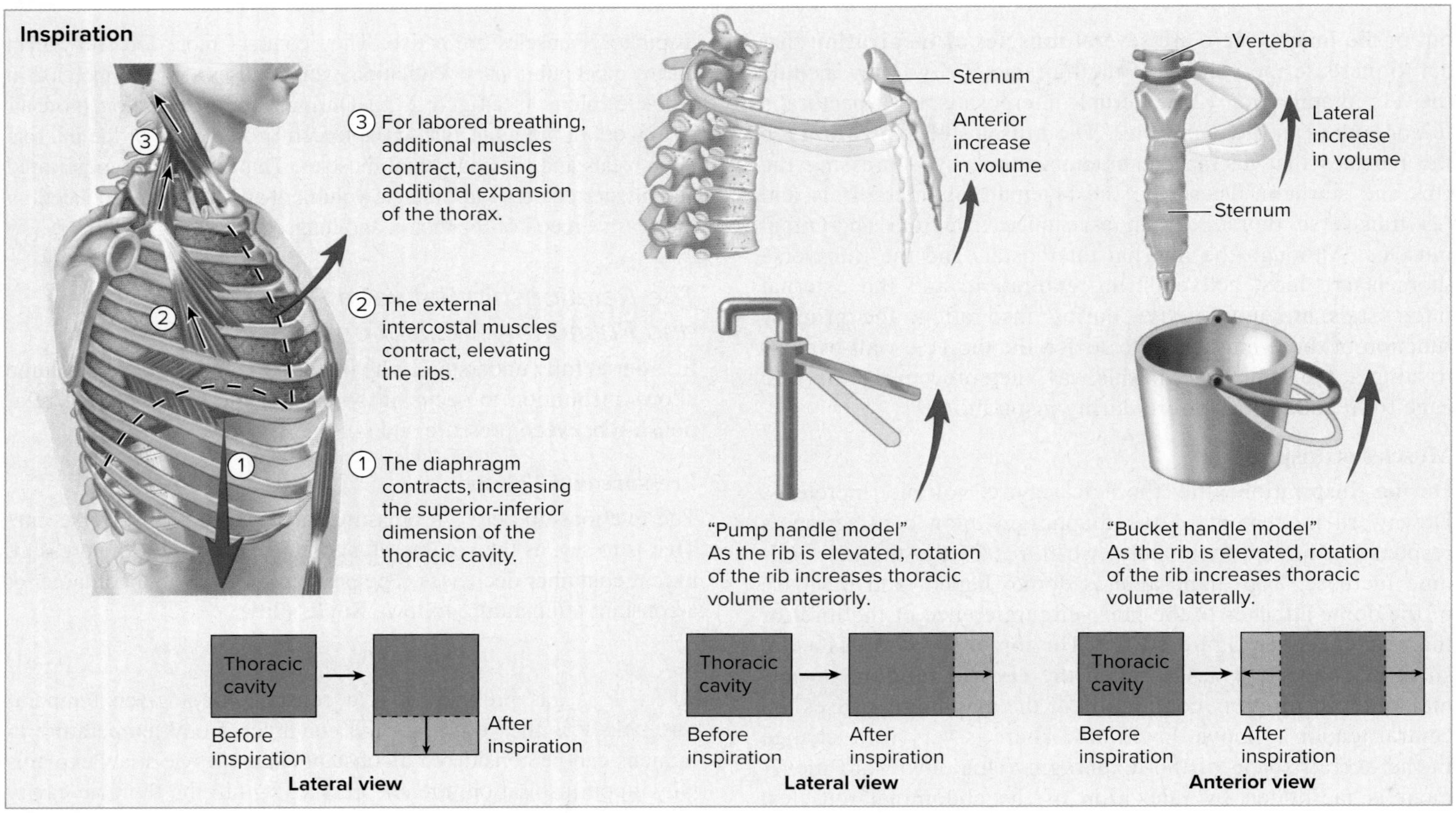

Inspiration

③ For labored breathing, additional muscles contract, causing additional expansion of the thorax.

② The external intercostal muscles contract, elevating the ribs.

① The diaphragm contracts, increasing the superior-inferior dimension of the thoracic cavity.

Thoracic cavity

Before inspiration

After inspiration

Lateral view

Sternum

Anterior increase in volume

"Pump handle model"
As the rib is elevated, rotation of the rib increases thoracic volume anteriorly.

Thoracic cavity

Before inspiration

After inspiration

Lateral view

Vertebra

Lateral increase in volume

Sternum

"Bucket handle model"
As the rib is elevated, rotation of the rib increases thoracic volume laterally.

Thoracic cavity

Before inspiration

After inspiration

Anterior view

(a)

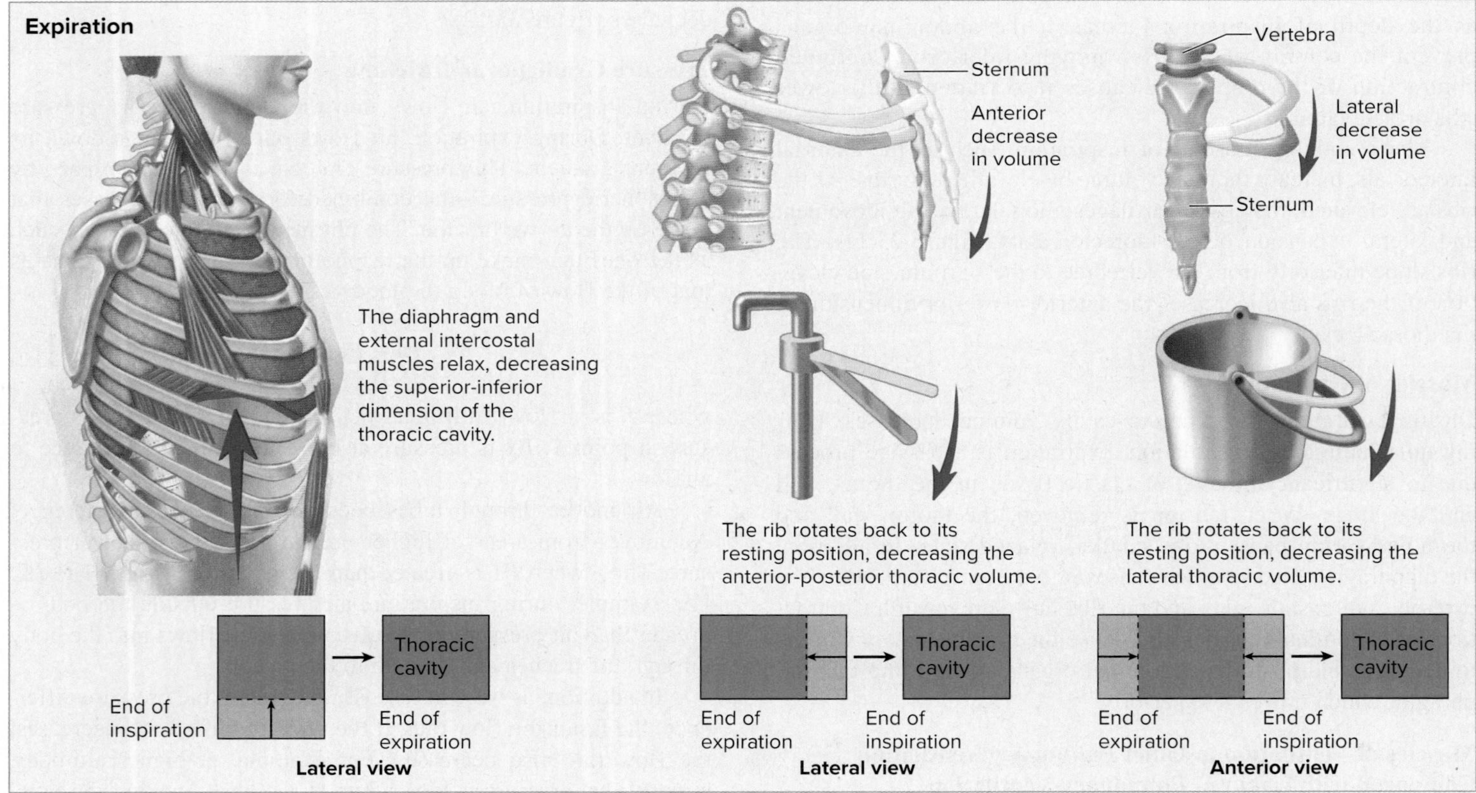

FIGURE 23.11 Changes in Thoracic Volume

(*a*) Elevation of the rib in the "bucket-handle" movement increases thoracic volume laterally and in the "pump-handle" movement it increases thoracic volume anteriorly. (*b*) As the rib rotates back to its resting position in the "bucket-handle" movement, it decreases the lateral thoracic volume, and in the "pump-handle" movement, it decreases anterior-posterior thoracic volume. APR

Boyle's Law

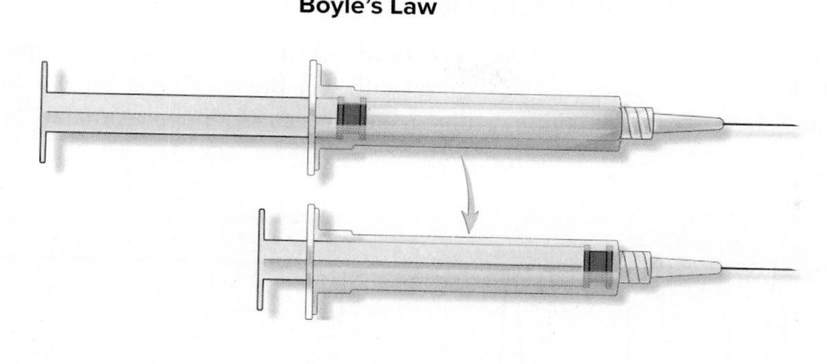

P=1/V

Pressure and volume are inversely related at a given temperature. Just as pushing the plunger on this syringe (decrease in volume) will cause the fluid to be ejected (increase in pressure), the recoil of the diaphragm upon expiration decreases the volume of the thoracic cavity. This causes intra-alveolar pressure to increase above atmospheric pressure and air to flow out of the lungs. When the next inspiration occurs, the diaphragm will contract downward. This increases the volume of the thoracic cavity, causing intra-alveolar pressure to decrease below atmospheric pressure and air to flow into the lungs.

Dalton's Law

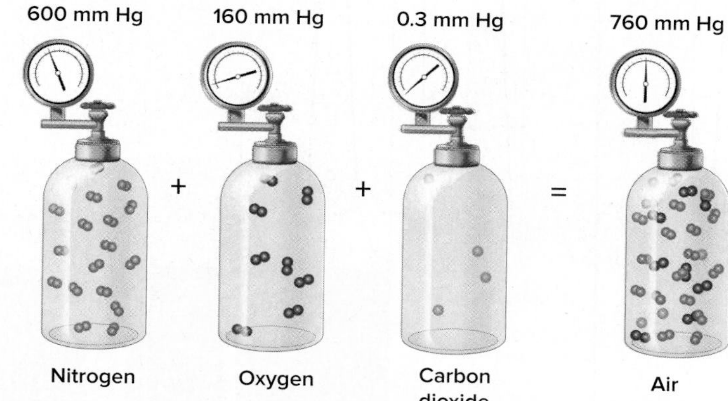

Partial pressure of a gas = % of gas × total pressure

The partial pressure of a gas in a mixture of gases is the percentage of the gas in the mixture. Gases move down their partial pressure gradients. The greater the difference in partial pressure between two areas, the faster the rate of gas movement. Atmospheric air is a mixture of N_2, O_2, and CO_2.

Henry's Law

Concentrate of dissolved gas = Pressure of gas × Solubility coefficient

The concentration of a gas dissolved in a liquid is equal to the partial pressure of the gas times the solubility coefficient of the gas. Only a small amount of the gases in air dissolves in the fluid lining the alveoli. Carbon dioxide, however, is 24 times more soluble than O_2; therefore, CO_2 exits through the respiratory membrane more readily than O_2 enters. A common example of Henry's law is opening a carbonated drink. When the drink is put into the container, it is under pressure and CO_2 dissolves in the solution. Opening the bottle releases the pressure and the dissolved CO_2 leaves the solution.

FIGURE 23.12 Gas Laws

The gas laws help explain movement of air into and out of the lungs.

ASSESS YOUR PROGRESS

23. *List the muscles of inspiration, and describe their role in quiet inspiration. List the muscles of expiration, and describe their role in quiet expiration. How does this change during labored pulmonary ventilation?*

24. *What is pulmonary ventilation?*

25. *How do pressure differences and resistance affect airflow through a tube?*

26. *What happens to the pressure within a container when the volume of the container increases? Whose law describes this relationship?*

27. *Describe the process of making intra-alveolar pressure changes that occurs during quiet resting pulmonary ventilation.*

Measurement of Lung Function

Sometimes, a person's lungs do not move sufficient amounts of air to support normal activities. In that case, several types of medical tests can be performed to determine what might be causing the lung malfunction. The patient's measurements are then used to diagnose specific diseases and to track recovery.

Pulmonary Volumes and Capacities

Spirometry (spy-ROM-eh-tree) is the process of measuring volumes of air that move into and out of the respiratory system, and a **spirometer** (spy-ROM-eh-ter) is the device used to measure these pulmonary volumes. There are four different pulmonary volumes measured in spirometry (figure 23.13). The four pulmonary volumes for a young adult male are:

1. *Tidal volume.* The **tidal volume** is the normal volume of air inspired and expired with each breath. At rest, quiet pulmonary ventilation results in a tidal volume of approximately 500 mL.

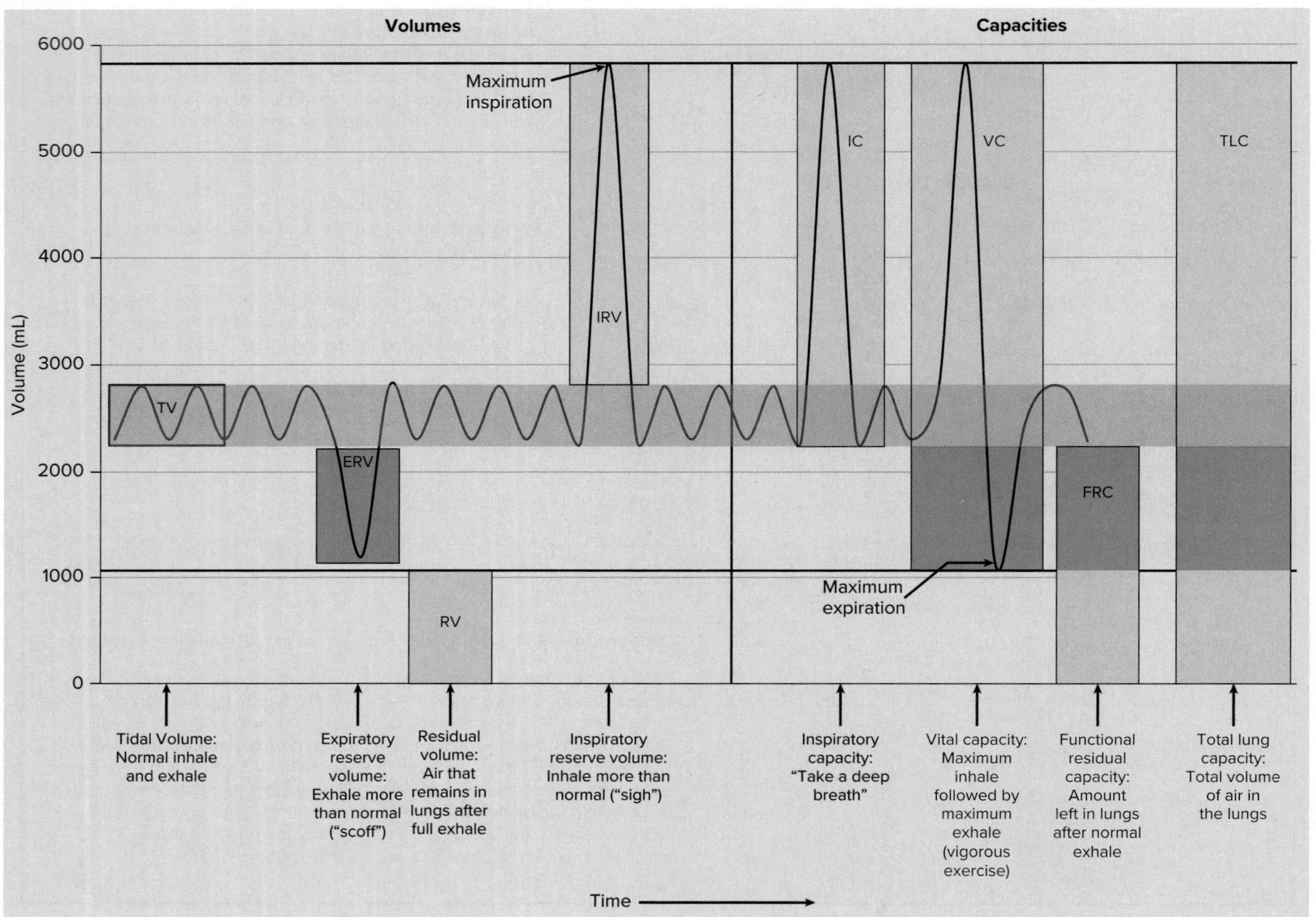

Volume/Capacity	Abbreviation	Average Value (young adult male)
Tidal Volume	TV	500 mL
Expiratory Reserve Volume	ERV	1100 mL
Residual Volume	RV	1200 mL
Inspiratory Reserve Volume	IRV	3000 mL
Inspiratory Capacity (IRV + TV)	IC	3500 mL
Vital Capacity (IRV + TV + ERV)	VC	4600 mL
Functional Residual Capacity (ERV + RV)	FRC	2300 mL
Total Lung Capacity (IRV + TV + ERV + RV)	TLC	5800 mL

FIGURE 23.13 Lung Volumes and Lung Capacities
The tidal volume during resting conditions is represented.

2. *Inspiratory reserve volume.* The **inspiratory reserve volume** is the amount of air that can be inspired forcefully after a normal inspiration (approximately 3000 mL at rest).
3. *Expiratory reserve volume.* The **expiratory reserve volume** is the amount of air that can be forcefully expired after a normal expiration (approximately 1100 mL at rest).
4. *Residual volume.* The **residual volume** is the volume of air still remaining in the respiratory passages and lungs after the most forceful expiration (approximately 1200 mL).

The tidal volume increases when a person is more active. Because the maximum volume of the respiratory system does not change from moment to moment, an increase in tidal volume causes a decrease in the inspiratory and expiratory reserve volumes.

Pulmonary capacities are the sum of two or more pulmonary volumes (figure 23.13). Examples of pulmonary capacities are the following:

1. **Inspiratory capacity** is the tidal volume plus the inspiratory reserve volume. It is the amount of air a person can inspire maximally after a normal expiration (approximately 3500 mL at rest).
2. **Functional residual capacity** is the expiratory reserve volume plus the residual volume. It is the amount of air remaining in the lungs at the end of a normal expiration (approximately 2300 mL at rest).
3. **Vital capacity** is the sum of the inspiratory reserve volume, the tidal volume, and the expiratory reserve volume. It is the maximum volume of air a person can expel from the respiratory tract after a maximum inspiration (approximately 4600 mL).
4. **Total lung capacity** is the sum of the inspiratory and expiratory reserve volumes plus the tidal volume and the residual volume (approximately 5800 mL).

A functional measure of lung performance is the **forced vital capacity.** This is a simple and clinically important pulmonary test. In conditions such as chronic obstructive pulmonary disease (COPD), emphysema, and chronic bronchitis, the vital capacity may not be dramatically affected, but how rapidly air is expired can be greatly decreased. The **forced expiratory volume in 1 second (FEV_1)** is the amount of air expired within the first second of the test. A lower FEV_1 measure indicates that the severity of the disease has worsened. The patient inspires maximally and then expires maximally into a spirometer as rapidly as possible. The volume of air expired at the end of the test is the vital capacity. The spirometer also records the volume of air expired per second.

Minute Volume

The **respiratory rate** is the number of breaths per minute. This is one of the vital signs health professionals measure in clinics and hospitals. The **minute volume** is a measure of the amount of air moved through the respiratory system per minute. The minute volume can be calculated by multiplying the tidal volume by the respiratory rate. For example, the average minute volume for a young adult male would be:

$$\text{Tidal Volume} \times \text{Respiratory Rate} = \text{Minute Volume} \tag{23.3}$$

$$\underset{\text{(tidal volume)}}{500 \text{ mL}} \times \underset{\text{(respiratory rate)}}{12 \text{ breaths/minute}} = \underset{\text{or 6 L/min}}{6000 \text{ mL/min}}$$

Although minute volume measures the amount of air moving into and out of the respiratory system per minute, it is not a measure of the amount of air available for gas exchange. However, minute volume is clinically important because it is an indication of CO_2 levels, an important physiological parameter (see section 23.5).

Alveolar Ventilation

Alveolar ventilation is the measure of the volume of air available for gas exchange per minute. Recall that part of the respiratory system functions solely to move air. Only a portion of each breath reaches the alveoli for gas exchange. The remaining areas where no gas exchange occurs is called the dead space. There are two types of dead space within the respiratory system: (1) anatomical dead space and (2) physiological dead space. The **anatomical dead space** areas include all the structures of the upper respiratory tract, and structures of the lower respiratory tract to the terminal bronchioles. These are all of the conducting zone areas. The volume of air in the anatomical dead space is approximately 1 mL per pound of an individual's ideal body weight. The **physiological dead space** is the combination of the anatomical dead space and the volume of any alveoli with lower than normal gas exchange. To calculate alveolar ventilation, the following formula is used:

$$\dot{V}_A = f(V_T - V_D) \tag{23.4}$$

where $\dot{V}_A$ is alveolar ventilation (milliliters per minute), f is respiratory rate (frequency; breaths per minute), V_T is tidal volume (milliliters per breath), and V_D is dead space (milliliters per breath). The dot over the letter V means that this is a *per minute* measure. Thus, for each breath, physiologically relevant air is only that volume inside healthy alveoli. Predict question 4 provides an opportunity to calculate a representative alveolar ventilation rate.

Predict 4

What is the alveolar ventilation of a resting person with a tidal volume of 500 mL, a dead space of 150 mL, and a respiratory rate of 12 breaths per minute? Suppose the person exercises so that tidal volume increases to 4000 mL, dead space increases to 300 mL due to dilation of the respiratory passageways, and respiratory rate increases to 24 breaths per minute. What is the alveolar ventilation then? How is the change in alveolar ventilation beneficial for doing exercise?

Factors Affecting Pulmonary Ventilation

Gender, Age, Body Size, and Physical Fitness

Factors such as gender, age, body size, and physical conditioning cause variations in respiratory volumes and capacities from one individual to another. For example, the vital capacity of adult females is usually 20–25% less than that of adult males. The vital capacity reaches its maximum amount in young adults and gradually decreases in the elderly. Taller people usually have a greater vital capacity than people with a shorter stature, and slender people have a greater vital capacity than obese individuals. Well-trained athletes can have a vital capacity 30–40% above that of people with a sedentary lifestyle. In patients whose respiratory muscles are paralyzed by spinal cord injury or diseases such as poliomyelitis or muscular dystrophy, vital capacity can be reduced to values not consistent with survival (less than 500–1000 mL).

Disease States

In a healthy person, anatomical and physiological dead spaces are nearly the same, meaning that most alveoli are functional. However, in patients with emphysema, alveolar walls degenerate, and small alveoli combine to form larger alveoli. The result is not only fewer alveoli but also alveoli with an increased volume and decreased surface area. Although the enlarged alveoli are still ventilated, their surface area is inadequate for complete gas exchange, and the physiological dead space increases.

Compliance of the Lungs and Thorax

Compliance is a measure of the ease with which the lungs and thorax expand. The compliance of the lungs and thorax is the volume by which they increase for each unit of change in intra-alveolar pressure. It is usually expressed in liters (volume of air) per mm Hg (pressure), and for a normal person the compliance of the lungs and thorax is 0.18 L/mm Hg. That is, for every 1 mm Hg change in intra-alveolar pressure, the volume changes by 0.18 L. A lower-than-normal compliance means that it is harder to expand the lungs and thorax. There are many conditions that could decrease compliance. These include the deposition of inelastic fibers in lung tissue (pulmonary fibrosis), the collapse of the alveoli (infant respiratory distress syndrome and pulmonary edema), increased resistance to airflow caused by airway obstruction (asthma, bronchitis, and lung cancer), and deformities of the thoracic wall that reduce its ability to expand and allow the thoracic volume to increase (kyphosis and scoliosis). Pulmonary diseases that result in decreased compliance can markedly affect the total amount of energy required for pulmonary ventilation and increase the total amount of energy expended by the body by up to 30%.

On the other hand, if the lungs and thorax have lost some of their elasticity, the compliance will be greater. If this becomes the case, it is easier to expand the lungs and thorax. For example, emphysema sometimes causes the destruction of elastic lung tissue. This reduces the elastic recoil force of the lungs, thereby making expansion of the lungs easier and resulting in a higher-than-normal compliance. However, because the elastic recoil of the lungs is reduced, expiration is not as efficient.

ASSESS YOUR PROGRESS

28. *Distinguish among tidal volume, inspiratory reserve volume, expiratory reserve volume, and residual volume.*
29. *Differentiate among inspiratory capacity, functional residual capacity, vital capacity, and total lung capacity.*
30. *What is forced expiratory volume in 1 second, and why is it clinically important?*
31. *What is the difference between minute volume and alveolar ventilation?*
32. *What is compliance? What is the effect on lung expansion when compliance increases or decreases?*
33. *What is dead space? Contrast anatomical dead space with physiological dead space.*

Behavior of Gases and Gas Exchange

Pulmonary ventilation supplies atmospheric air to the alveoli. Pulmonary gas exchange is the diffusion of gases between the alveoli and the blood in the pulmonary capillaries. The molecules of gas move down their partial pressure gradient from the air into the blood for O_2 and from the blood into the air for CO_2.

Partial Pressure

To understand the mechanism behind the movement of O_2 into the blood and CO_2 out of the blood, we must first discuss how the amount of a gas in a mixture of gases is measured. Atmospheric pressure is due to a mixture of gases, each of which is present in a different amount. The term *pressure* is used to express the amount of each gas in a mixture. This is comparable to using the term *concentration* for solutes. According to **Dalton's law,** the total pressure of a gas is the sum of the individual pressures of each gas (see figure 23.12). The individual pressure of each gas is called the **partial pressure.** At sea level, the pressure of all the gases in the air, or atmospheric pressure, is approximately 760 mm Hg (table 23.1).

To determine the partial pressure of each gas, its percentage is multiplied by the total pressure. The partial pressure of each gas in dry atmospheric air is as follows:

Nitrogen:
(79%) $P_{N_2} = 0.79 \times 760$ mm Hg $= 600$ mm Hg

Oxygen:
(21%) $P_{O_2} = 0.21 \times 760$ mm Hg $= 160$ mm Hg

Carbon Dioxide:
(0.04%) $P_{CO_2} = 0.04 \times 760$ mm Hg $= 0.3$ mm Hg

Water Vapor:
(0.0%) $P_{H_2O} = 0.0 \times 760$ mm Hg $= 0.0$ mm Hg

Thus, atmospheric pressure of dry air at sea level is calculated using the following:

Atmospheric air: $P_{N_2} + P_{O_2} + P_{CO_2} + P_{H_2O} = 760.3$ mm Hg

$$\begin{aligned} P_{N_2} &= 600 \text{ mm Hg} \\ P_{O_2} &= 160 \text{ mm Hg} \\ P_{CO_2} &= 0.3 \text{ mm Hg} \\ P_{H_2O} &= 0.0 \text{ mm Hg} \\ \hline & 760.3 \text{ mm Hg} \end{aligned} \quad (23.5)$$

A common misconception is that at higher altitudes there is "less" O_2 in the air. However, this is not the case. Rather, it is total atmospheric pressure that is lower at higher altitudes than at sea level. For example, the atmospheric pressure at an elevation of 14,000 ft above sea level, the elevation of Pike's Peak in Colorado, is about 430 mm Hg. The percentage of the air that is O_2 remains at 21%. Thus,

$$0.21 \times 430 \text{ mm Hg} = 90 \text{ mm Hg}$$

Therefore, at high altitudes your body does, in fact, react as if there were "less" O_2. However, it is the O_2 partial pressure gradient that has reduced, causing less O_2 to enter the lungs per breath. The normal initial adaptation to high altitudes is an increased pulmonary ventilation rate per minute, thereby allowing a sufficient amount of O_2 delivery to the lungs.

TABLE 23.1 Partial Pressures of Gases at Sea Level

	Dry Air		Humidified Air		Alveolar Air		Expired Air	
Gases	mm Hg	%	mm Hg	%	mm Hg	%	mm Hg	%
Nitrogen	600	79	562.4	74	569	74.9	566	74.5
Oxygen	160	21	152	20	104	13.6	120	15.7
Carbon dioxide	0.3	0.04	0.3	0.04	40	5.3	27	3.6
Water vapor	0.0	0.00	47	6.20	47	6.2	47	6.2

Three factors cause differences in the composition among alveolar air, expired air, and atmospheric air: (1) Air entering the respiratory system is humidified; (2) O_2 diffuses from the alveoli into the blood, while CO_2 diffuses from the blood into the alveoli; (3) the alveolar air is only partially replaced with atmospheric air during each inspiration.

Diffusion of Gases into and out of Liquids

Gas molecules move from the air into a liquid, or from a liquid into the air, down their partial pressure gradients. Gases move from a higher partial pressure to a lower partial pressure. When partial pressures of gases are equal between the air and a liquid, they are in equilibrium. However, to calculate the amount of a gas in a liquid, the partial pressure alone is not sufficient. The amount of the gas is also dependent on how readily a gas dissolves in the liquid, which is called the **solubility coefficient.** Thus, at a given temperature, **Henry's law** describes the concentration of a gas at equilibrium in a liquid (see figure 23.12):

$$\text{Concentration of dissolved gas} = \text{Pressure of gas} \times \text{Solubility coefficient} \quad (23.6)$$

In water, the solubility coefficient for O_2 is 0.024; for CO_2 it is 0.57. Thus, CO_2 is approximately 24 times more soluble in water than O_2 is.

Predict 5

As a scuba diver descends, the pressure of the water on the body prevents normal expansion of the lungs. To compensate, the diver breathes pressurized air, which has a greater pressure than air at sea level. What effect does the increased pressure have on the amount of gas dissolved in the diver's body fluids? A scuba diver who suddenly ascends to the surface from a great depth can develop decompression sickness (the bends), in which bubbles of nitrogen gas form. The expanding bubbles damage tissues or block blood flow through small blood vessels. Explain why the bubbles develop.

Diffusion Coefficient

To determine the rate at which a gas diffuses into and out of a liquid or tissue, two factors must be considered: (1) the solubility coefficient of the gas and (2) the molecular weight of the gas. This rate is called the **diffusion coefficient.** For example, if the diffusion coefficient of O_2 is assigned a value of 1, the relative diffusion coefficient of CO_2 is 20, which means CO_2 diffuses through the respiratory membrane about 20 times more readily than O_2 does. The diffusion coefficient of CO_2 compared to O_2 is 20:1. The diffusion coefficient becomes very important when the respiratory membrane becomes progressively damaged as a result of disease. The capacity of the respiratory membrane for allowing O_2 to move into the blood is often so impaired that death from O_2 deprivation results. If life is being maintained by extensive O_2 therapy, which increases the concentration of O_2 in the lung alveoli, the reduced capacity for the diffusion of CO_2 across the respiratory membrane can result in substantial increases in CO_2 in the blood. Increased CO_2 levels in the blood can be very toxic (see section 23.6).

ASSESS YOUR PROGRESS

34. *According to Dalton's law, what is the partial pressure of a mixture of gases? What is water vapor pressure?*

35. *Why are the compositions of inspired, alveolar, and expired air different?*

36. *According to Henry's law, how do partial pressure and solubility of a gas affect its concentration in a liquid?*

23.5 Physiology of the Respiratory System

LEARNING OUTCOMES

After reading this section, you should be able to

A. **Describe the changes in alveolar pressure that are responsible for the movement of air into and out of the lungs.**
B. **Explain how surfactant and pleural pressure prevent the collapse of the lungs.**
C. **Explain how changes in pleural pressure cause changes in alveolar volume.**
D. **Describe the partial pressure gradients for O_2 and CO_2.**
E. **Explain the factors that affect gas movement through the respiratory membrane.**

Now that we've established that the major driving force of pulmonary ventilation is a pressure difference between atmospheric air and the thoracic cavity, let's look more closely at the step-by-step mechanisms of alveolar ventilation.

Mechanisms of Alveolar Ventilation

As we step through one respiratory cycle, or one breath, we will track the relative pressure difference between the atmosphere and the alveoli (figure 23.14). Atmospheric air pressure outside the body is about 760 mm Hg. Air pressure in the alveoli is called **intra-alveolar pressure.** When a person inspires, the intra-alveolar pressure decreases because the alveolar volume has increased. Conversely, when a person expires, the intra-alveolar pressure increases because the alveolar volume has decreased. It is the pressure difference between atmospheric pressure and intra-alveolar pressure that results in air movement during one respiratory cycle. The details of this process during quiet resting pulmonary ventilation are shown in figure 23.14 and are as follows:

1. *Alveolar pressure equals atmospheric pressure.* At the end of expiration, before the next respiratory cycle starts, atmospheric pressure and intra-alveolar pressure are equal and no air moves into or out of the lungs.
2. *Alveolar pressure is less than atmospheric pressure.* As inspiration begins, contraction of inspiratory muscles increases thoracic volume, which results in expansion of the lungs and an increase in alveolar volume. The increased alveolar volume causes a decrease in intra-alveolar pressure below atmospheric pressure to approximately −1 mm Hg. Air flows into the lungs because atmospheric pressure is greater than intra-alveolar pressure.
3. *Alveolar pressure again equals atmospheric pressure.* At the end of inspiration, the thorax stops expanding, the alveoli stop expanding, and intra-alveolar pressure becomes equal to atmospheric pressure because of airflow into the lungs. No movement of air occurs after intra-alveolar pressure becomes equal to atmospheric pressure, but the volume of the lungs is larger than it was at the end of expiration.
4. *Alveolar pressure is greater than atmospheric pressure.* During expiration, the volume of the thorax decreases as the diaphragm relaxes, and the thorax and lungs recoil. Because thoracic volume determines alveolar volume, the smaller thoracic volume results in a corresponding decrease in alveolar volume. Thus, intra-alveolar pressure rises over atmospheric pressure to approximately +1 mm Hg. Because intra-alveolar pressure is greater than atmospheric pressure, air flows out of the lungs. As expiration ends, the decrease in thoracic volume stops, and the alveoli stop changing size. The process repeats, beginning at step 1.

Factors Affecting Alveolar Ventilation

While changes in pressure differences are the principal factors in driving alveolar ventilation, there are two other factors that influence the ability of alveoli to increase and decrease in volume. These two factors are (1) lung recoil and (2) pleural pressure.

Lung Recoil

Lung recoil is the tendency for the lungs to decrease in size after they are stretched. Imagine a stretched rubber band snapping back to its original size when released. Similarly, upon expiration, the tension on the lungs is released and they return to their original, smaller size, which compresses the alveoli. Lung recoil occurs for two reasons: (1) elastic recoil and (2) surface tension. Elastic recoil occurs because elastic fibers within the lungs and thoracic wall return to their original shape and size once the tension on them is released, just like the rubber band.

Lung recoil due to surface tension is because of hydrogen bonding within the alveoli. Alveoli are lined with an aqueous alveolar fluid, which adheres to the wall of the alveoli. However, the water molecules in the alveolar fluid are also attracted to each other toward the center of each alveolus. As hydrogen bonds form,

Clinical IMPACT 23.3 — COVID-19 and Lung Inflammation

In January 2020, the first U.S. case of the pandemic of coronavirus disease 2019 (COVID-19) was reported. COVID-19 is caused by the severe acute respiratory syndrome corona virus 2 (SARS-CoV-2). SARS-CoV-2 is a cytopathic virus, meaning that as part of its replication cycle, it induces injury and death of infected cells. SARS-CoV-2 infects cells by binding to the receptor for angiotensin converting enzyme 2 (ACE 2). The virus uses this receptor to enter many cell types in the body. In addition, when SARS-CoV-2 occupies the ACE 2 receptor, ACE 2 cannot prevent the damaging effects of angiotensin II, including inflammation and death of alveolar cells. As of now, it remains unclear how much of the damage in COVID-19 is caused by angiotensin II independent of other viral actions.

The majority of people (81%) diagnosed with COVID-19 experience mild to moderate symptoms, including mild pneumonia. However, a small percentage of people (5%) experience critical symptoms, such as respiratory failure, shock, and multiorgan dysfunction. Infection with SARS-CoV-2 damages alveoli as they become fluid-filled, leading to the development of acute respiratory distress syndrome (ARDS; see section 23.5). ARDS patients have difficulty breathing and experience low O_2 levels, which for some individuals, the lung damage is permanent and requires lung transplants for survival. In 70% of fatal COVID-19 cases, secondary bacterial and fungal infections occurred. These secondary infections could be a direct cause of respiratory failure. In about 28% of fatal COVID-19 cases, a massive release of the immune cell signal molecules, cytokines, resulted in a cytokine storm leading to unrestricted levels of inflammation and the attraction of other immune cells, including monocytes and T lymphocytes, to the lungs. The immune cells secrete excessive amounts of proteases, which damage the alveoli. In addition, the patients experienced pulmonary edema, as well as formation of a hyaline membrane. A hyaline membrane consists of secreted proteins and dead cells that line alveoli, thereby blocking gas diffusion. Across the body, there is a domino effect from the cytokine storm, which includes septic shock and multiorgan failure, especially that of the heart and kidneys. Treatment of COVID-19 is focused on preventing the damaging effects of the cytokine storm. Vaccination against SARS-CoV-2 is the best approach to control the pandemic.

PROCESS **Figure**

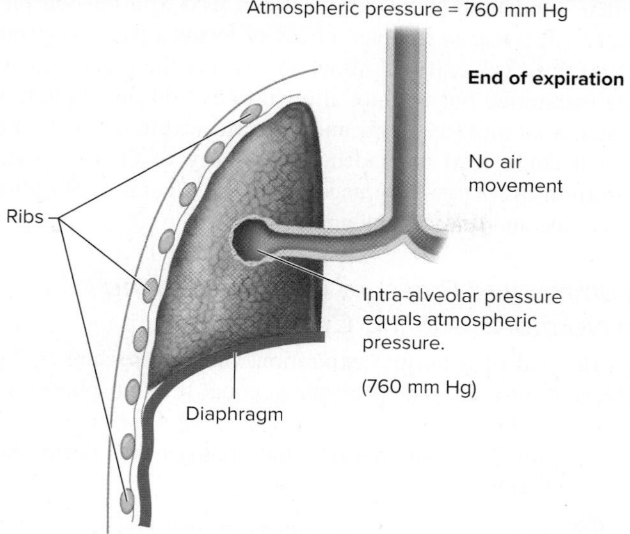

1. At the end of expiration, alveolar pressure is equal to atmospheric pressure, and there is no air movement.

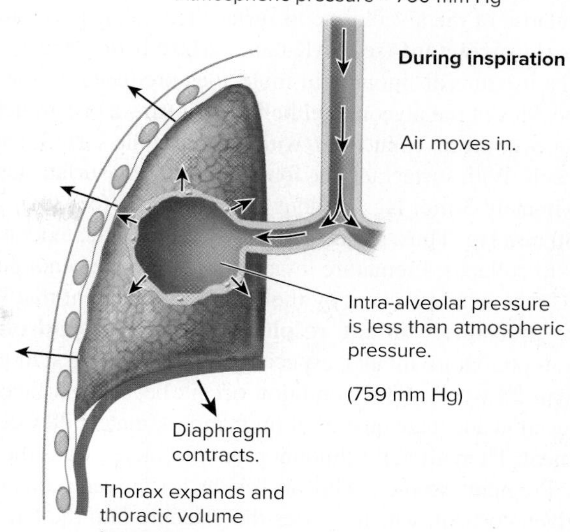

2. During inspiration, increased thoracic volume results in increased alveolar volume and decreased alveolar pressure. Atmospheric pressure is greater than alveolar pressure, and air moves into the lungs.

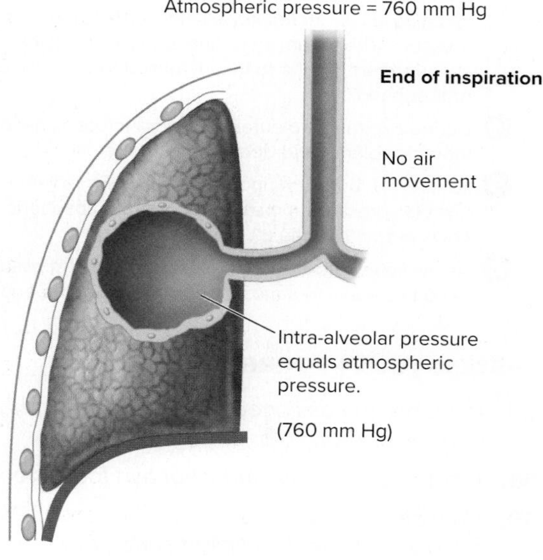

3. At the end of inspiration, alveolar pressure is equal to atmospheric pressure, and there is no air movement.

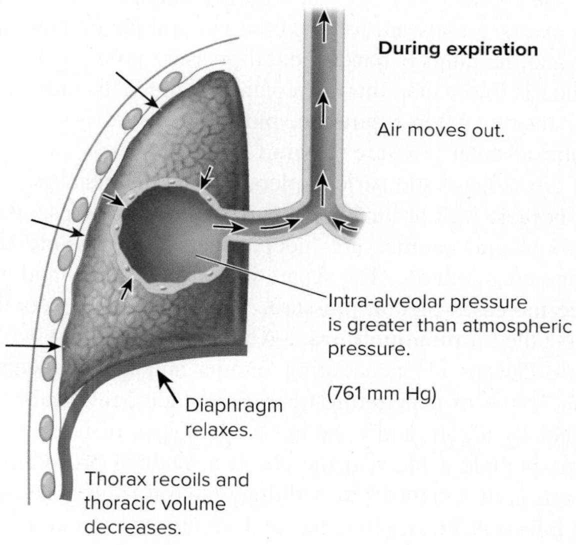

4. During expiration, decreased thoracic volume results in decreased alveolar volume and increased alveolar pressure. Alveolar pressure is greater than atmospheric pressure, and air moves out of the lungs.

PROCESS **Figure 23.14**

Intra-alveolar Pressure Changes During Inspiration and Expiration

The combined space of all the alveoli is represented by a large "bubble" (*blue*). The alveoli are actually microscopic and would not be visible at the scale of this illustration. APR

How would traveling to higher altitude, where atmospheric pressure is lower, affect step 2?

the walls of each alveolus are pulled inward, which causes it to collapse. Collapse of the alveoli due to surface tension is prevented by the molecule **surfactant** (ser-FAK-tant; surface acting agent). Surfactant is a mixture of lipoprotein molecules produced by the type II pneumocytes of the alveolar epithelium. It forms a one-molecule-thick layer over the alveolar fluid, which reduces the surface tension in the alveoli. With surfactant, the force produced by surface tension is approximately 3 mm Hg; without surfactant, the force can be as high as 30 mm Hg. Thus, surfactant greatly reduces the tendency of the lungs to collapse. Premature infants do not produce enough surfactant. This is what is meant by the common statement that "their lungs are immature." **Infant respiratory distress syndrome** is common in premature infants, especially those with a gestation age of less than 28 weeks. This condition occurs because surfactant is not produced in adequate quantities until approximately 28 weeks of development. Thereafter, the amount produced increases as the fetus matures. Pregnant women who are likely to deliver prematurely can be given cortisol, which crosses the placenta into the fetus and stimulates surfactant synthesis.

Pleural Pressure

Pleural pressure is the pressure within the pleural cavity between the parietal pleura and the visceral pleura. Recall that the parietal and visceral pleurae are adhered to each other by pleural fluid. The pleural fluid is analogous to a thin film of water between two sheets of glass (the visceral and parietal pleurae); the glass sheets can easily slide over each other, but it is difficult to separate them. When the thoracic wall expands during inspiration, the parietal pleura exerts an outward force on the visceral pleura covering the lungs, and the lungs expand. Pleural pressure pulls the lungs outward and is lower than intra-alveolar pressure. This aids in alveolar expansion. After expiration, pleural pressure is −4 mm Hg and intra-alveolar pressure is 0 mm Hg.

If the visceral and parietal pleurae become separated, such as if the thoracic wall or lung is pierced, the lungs collapse. Because the two pleural cavities are independent, it is possible to have only one lung collapse. The separation of the visceral and parietal pleurae increases pleural pressure. This increase in pleural pressure is called a **pneumothorax.** A pneumothorax has two major possible causes: (1) penetrating trauma and (2) nonpenetrating trauma. Types of penetrating traumas include being stabbed, getting shot by a gun, and breaking a rib. Types of nonpenetrating traumas include a blow to the chest; a medical procedure, such as insertion of a catheter to withdraw pleural fluid; disease, such as an infection or emphysema; and severe, spastic coughing. A pneumothorax may be treated by inserting a chest tube that aspirates the pleural cavity and restores a negative pressure, which can cause reexpansion of the lung. Surgery may also be necessary to close the opening into the pleural cavity. When an area of the lungs experiences reduced airflow, such as with a pneumothorax, there is vasoconstriction in vessels leading to the affected area. At the same time, vasodilation occurs to areas of the lungs continuing to receive adequate airflow. In this way, the body can compensate, up to a point, for damage to the lungs (see section 23.7).

In a **tension pneumothorax,** the pressure within the pleural cavity is always higher than atmospheric pressure. Any situation where a pneumothorax occurred can lead to a tension pneumothorax. If a tear in the pleural cavity forms a tissue flap that acts as a flutter valve, it will allow air to enter the pleural cavity during inspiration but will not allow it to exit during expiration. The result is an increase in air and pressure within the pleural cavity, which could lead to inadequate delivery of O_2 to tissues. The insertion of a large-bore needle into the pleural cavity allows air to escape and releases the pressure.

Summary of Pressure Changes During a Normal Breathing Cycle

At the end of a normal expiration, pleural pressure is 756 mm Hg, and intra-alveolar pressure is equal to atmospheric pressure (760 mm Hg).

Figure 23.15 summarizes the changes that occur during a normal breathing cycle.

1. During normal, quiet inspiration, pleural pressure decreases to −7 mm Hg.
2. Consequently, the alveolar volume increases, intra-alveolar pressure decreases below atmospheric pressure, and air flows into the lungs.
3. As air flows into the lungs, intra-alveolar pressure increases and becomes equal to atmospheric pressure at the end of inspiration. The decrease in pleural pressure during inspiration occurs for two reasons. First, because changing volume affects pressure (Boyle's law), the increased volume of the thoracic cavity causes decreased pleural pressure. Second, as the thoracic cavity expands, the lungs expand because they adhere to the inner thoracic wall through the pleurae. As the lungs expand, their tendency to recoil increases, resulting in an increased suction effect and a lowering of pleural pressure. The tendency for the lungs to recoil increases as the lungs are stretched, similar to the increased force generated in a stretched rubber band.
4. During expiration, pleural pressure increases because of decreased thoracic volume and decreased lung recoil.
5. As pleural pressure increases, alveolar volume decreases, intra-alveolar pressure increases above atomospheric pressure, and air flows out of the lungs.
6. As air flows out of the lungs, intra-alveolar pressure decreases and becomes equal to atmospheric pressure at the end of expiration.

ASSESS YOUR PROGRESS

37. *What are the assigned values for atmospheric pressure and for intra-alveolar pressure?*
38. *What is lung recoil, and what two factors cause it?*
39. *How does surfactant reduce lung recoil? What happens if the alveoli have insufficient surfactant?*
40. *What is pleural pressure? What happens to alveolar volume when pleural pressure decreases? What causes pleural pressure to be lower than intra-alveolar pressure?*
41. *How does a pneumothorax cause a lung to collapse? How does a pneumothorax affect the chest cavity?*
42. *During inspiration, what causes pleural pressure to decrease? What effect does this have on intra-alveolar pressure and air movement?*
43. *During expiration, what causes pleural pressure to increase? What effect does this have on intra-alveolar pressure and air movement?*

Adult hemoglobin consists of four subunits, each containing one iron-based heme group. It is the heme group to which O_2 binds, so one hemoglobin can carry up to four O_2 molecules.

The fourth type of hemoglobin is the altered form found in individuals with sickle-cell disease. This hemoglobin is called hemoglobin-S. Recall from chapter 19 that under low O_2 conditions, the hemoglobin-S molecules aggregate together inside red blood cells, causing them to become sickle-shaped. The sickle-shaped red blood cells become lodged inside small capillaries and block blood flow.

Transport of O_2

Once O_2 diffuses through the respiratory membrane into the blood, it is transported to all the cells of the body. Approximately 98.5% of O_2 is transported reversibly bound to hemoglobin within red blood cells, and the remaining 1.5% is dissolved in the plasma. Cells use O_2 in aerobic cellular respiration to synthesize ATP (see chapter 25).

Transport of CO_2

Carbon dioxide is formed as a by-product of the breakdown of glucose when cells use O_2 to produce ATP. The CO_2 diffuses out of individual cells into the blood. The blood concentration of CO_2 needs to be very tightly regulated because too much CO_2 in the blood causes the blood to become acidic. There are three ways CO_2 is transported in the blood: (1) dissolved in the plasma, (2) bound to hemoglobin, and (3) converted to bicarbonate ion (HCO_3^-).

Transport of CO_2 in the Plasma

About 7% of CO_2 dissolves directly in the plasma as it diffuses out of the cells and into the blood. The remaining CO_2 diffuses into the red blood cells, where it either binds to hemoglobin or is converted to HCO_3^-.

Transport of CO_2 by Hemoglobin

Approximately 23% of CO_2 is transported bound to hemoglobin. Many CO_2 molecules bind in a reversible fashion to the α- and β-globin chains of hemoglobin molecules. Carbon dioxide's ability to bind to hemoglobin is affected by the amount of O_2 bound to hemoglobin. The smaller the amount of O_2 bound to hemoglobin, the greater the amount of CO_2 able to bind to it, and vice versa. This relationship is called the **Haldane effect.** In tissues, as hemoglobin binds CO_2, the affinity of hemoglobin for O_2 is reduced. This is beneficial because tissues with higher levels of CO_2 demand more O_2 in order to continue aerobic cellular respiration, our cells' most efficient means of producing ATP.

Transport of CO_2 as Bicarbonate Ions

About 70% of blood CO_2 is transported in the form of HCO_3^-, dissolved in either the cytoplasm of red blood cells or the plasma of the blood. Within red blood cells, an enzyme called **carbonic anhydrase** catalyzes a reversible reaction (see chapter 2). Carbonic anhydrase catalyzes the production of carbonic acid (H_2CO_3) from CO_2 and H_2O. The H_2CO_3 then dissociates into H^+ and HCO_3^- shown by the following equation:

$$\underset{\text{Carbon dioxide}}{CO_2} + \underset{\text{Water}}{H_2O} \xrightleftharpoons{\text{Carbonic anhydrase}} \underset{\text{Carbonic acid}}{H_2CO_3} \rightleftharpoons \underset{\text{Hydrogen ion}}{H^+} + \underset{\text{Bicarbonate ion}}{HCO_3^-} \tag{23.7}$$

As CO_2 levels increase, more H^+ is produced. Recall from chapter 2 that higher concentrations of H^+ cause the pH to decrease and the solution becomes acidic. However, because this is a reversible reaction, if CO_2 levels decrease, carbonic anhydrase creates H_2CO_3 upon the combining of H^+ and HCO_3^-. The H_2CO_3 then dissociates to form CO_2 and H_2O, which lowers H^+ concentration, and pH increases into a more basic (alkaline) range.

At the tissues, where CO_2 levels are higher, HCO_3^- is removed from the red blood cell by an HCO_3^-/Cl^- antiporter. This process is called the **chloride shift.** In the chloride shift, HCO_3^- diffuses out of the red blood cell while Cl^- diffuses in through the antiporter. This exchange maintains electrical neutrality in the red blood cells and plasma. Removing HCO_3^- from inside the red blood cells also promotes greater CO_2 transport. As HCO_3^- concentrations decrease within the red blood cell, more CO_2 reacts with water to form additional HCO_3^- and H^+.

Although elevated H^+ levels usually create an acidic environment, there are mechanisms within the red blood cells that dampen the effect of increased H^+. Hemoglobin serves as a buffer within the red blood cell cytoplasm. Hemoglobin binds to H^+, preventing an increase in H^+ concentration.

Summary of Gas Transport

Figure 23.17 summarizes the event in the transport of both O_2 from the lungs to the tissues and CO_2 from the tissues to the lungs. Figure 23.17*a* summarizes the events as O_2 enters the blood from the alveoli and CO_2 exits the blood.

1. In the lungs, carbon dioxide (CO_2) diffuses from red blood cells and plasma into the alveoli.
2. Carbonic anhydrase catalyzes the formation of CO_2 and H_2O from H_2CO_3.
3. Bicarbonate ions and H+ combine to replace H_2CO_3.
4. In the chloride shift, a membrane transport protein allows HCO_3^- to diffuse into the red blood cells and chloride ions (Cl^-) to diffuse out of them, which maintains their electrical neutrality.
5. Oxygen diffuses into the plasma and into red blood cells. Some of the O_2 remains in the plasma. Oxygen binds to hemoglobin.
6. Hydrogen ions are released from hemoglobin, which promotes the uptake of O_2 by hemoglobin.
7. Carbon dioxide is released from hemoglobin. Hemoglobin that is bound to O_2 readily releases CO_2.

Figure 23.17*b* summarizes the events as O_2 is delivered to the tissues and CO_2 is transported away from the tissues.

1. In the tissues, carbon dioxide (CO_2) diffuses into the plasma and into red blood cells. Some of the carbon dioxide remains in the plasma.

PROCESS Figure

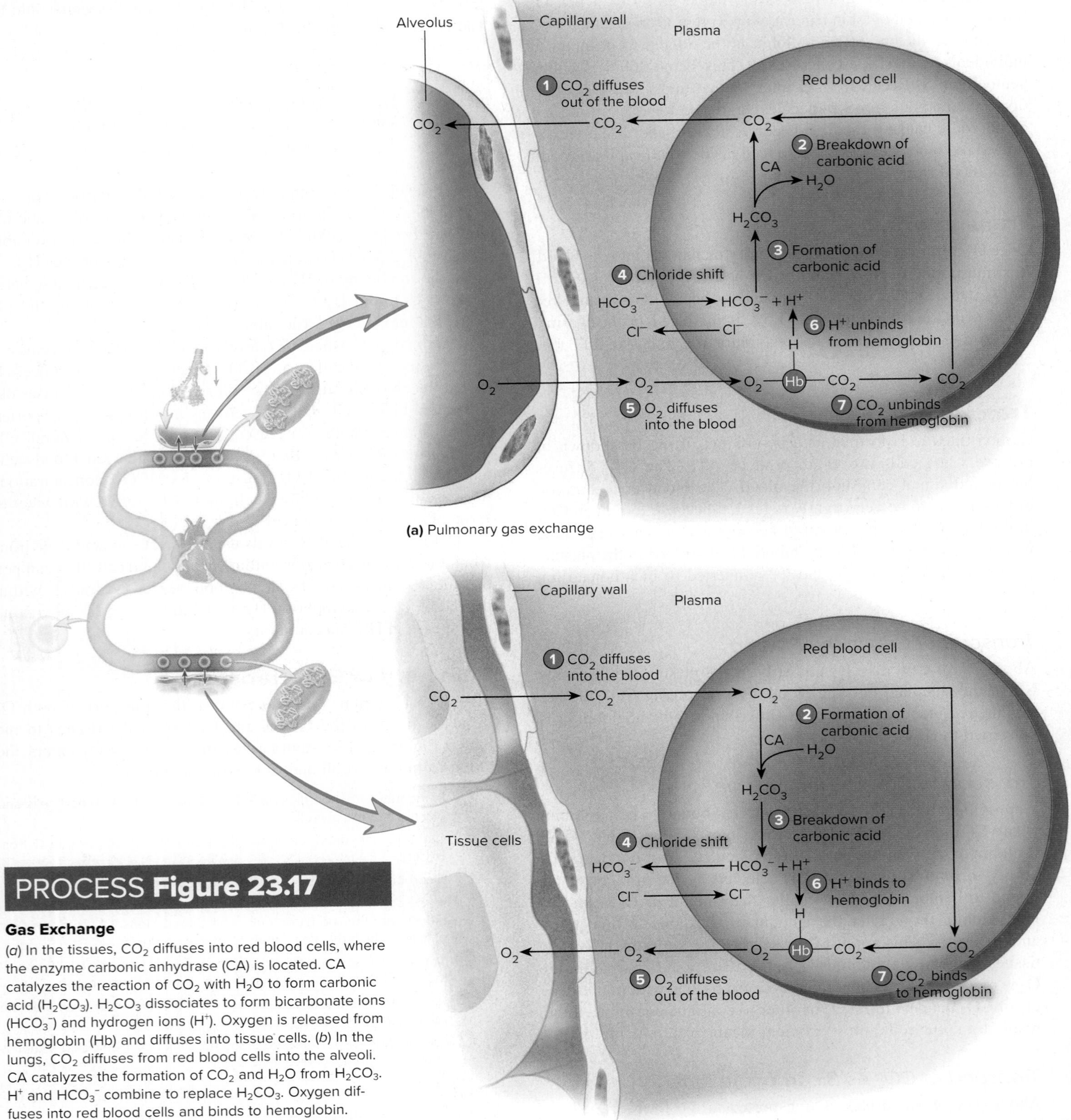

PROCESS Figure 23.17

Gas Exchange

(*a*) In the tissues, CO_2 diffuses into red blood cells, where the enzyme carbonic anhydrase (CA) is located. CA catalyzes the reaction of CO_2 with H_2O to form carbonic acid (H_2CO_3). H_2CO_3 dissociates to form bicarbonate ions (HCO_3^-) and hydrogen ions (H^+). Oxygen is released from hemoglobin (Hb) and diffuses into tissue cells. (*b*) In the lungs, CO_2 diffuses from red blood cells into the alveoli. CA catalyzes the formation of CO_2 and H_2O from H_2CO_3. H^+ and HCO_3^- combine to replace H_2CO_3. Oxygen diffuses into red blood cells and binds to hemoglobin.

Apply *How would the cytoplasmic pH of red blood cells be affected by anemia that is caused by reduced hemoglobin levels?*

2. In red blood cells, carbon dioxide reacts with water (H_2O) to form carbonic acid (H_2CO_3) in a reaction catalyzed by the enzyme carbonic anhydrase (CA).
3. Carbonic acid dissociates to form bicarbonate ions (HCO_3^-) and hydrogen ions (H^+).
4. In the chloride shift, a membrane transporter allows HCO_3^- to diffuse out of the red blood cells and chloride ions (Cl^-) to diffuse into them, which maintains their electrical neutrality.
5. Oxygen (O_2) is released from hemoglobin (Hb). Oxygen diffuses out of red blood cells and plasma into the tissue.
6. Hydrogen ions combine with hemoglobin, which promotes the release of oxygen from hemoglobin.
7. Carbon dioxide combines with hemoglobin. Hemoglobin that has released oxygen readily combines with carbon dioxide. HCO_3^- + H^+.

There are many physiological factors that modulate the affinity of hemoglobin for both O_2 and CO_2. For example, under conditions of increased O_2 demand, the affinity of hemoglobin for O_2 is reduced. A discussion of some of these conditions follows.

Physiological Factors Affecting Gas Transport

The respiratory system maintains blood O_2 and CO_2 concentrations and blood pH within normal values. Changes in these levels out of their normal range have a noticeable influence on the relationship between hemoglobin, O_2, and CO_2. **Chemoreceptors** are specialized neurons that detect changes in the concentration of specific chemicals. The chemoreceptors involved in regulating pulmonary ventilation respond to changes in pH, changes in P_{O_2}, P_{CO_2}, or all three. **Central chemoreceptors** are located bilaterally and ventrally in the **chemosensitive area** of the medulla oblongata, and they are connected to the respiratory center. **Peripheral chemoreceptors** are found in the carotid and aortic bodies. These structures are small, vascular sensory organs encapsulated in connective tissue and located near the carotid sinuses and the aortic arch (see chapter 21).

Effect of P_{O_2} on O_2 Transport

The relationship between O_2 and hemoglobin is similar to that of a ligand and its receptor in that hemoglobin has specific binding sites for O_2. These binding sites are the heme groups of the hemoglobin. Hemoglobin is 100% saturated with O_2 when four O_2 molecules are bound to each hemoglobin molecule in the red blood cells. When there is an average of two O_2 molecules bound to each hemoglobin molecule, hemoglobin is 50% saturated. The **oxygen-hemoglobin dissociation curve** describes the percent saturation of hemoglobin in the blood at different blood P_{O_2} values. The degree of hemoglobin saturation is determined by many factors that affect the "attraction" of hemoglobin for O_2. This attraction is called affinity. The first factor we will consider is the effect of P_{O_2} on hemoglobin's affinity for O_2.

Normally, the P_{O_2} in the blood leaving the lungs is 104 mm Hg. At that partial pressure, hemoglobin is 98% saturated (figure 23.18). Decreases in the P_{O_2} in the pulmonary capillaries have a relatively small effect on hemoglobin saturation, as shown by the fairly

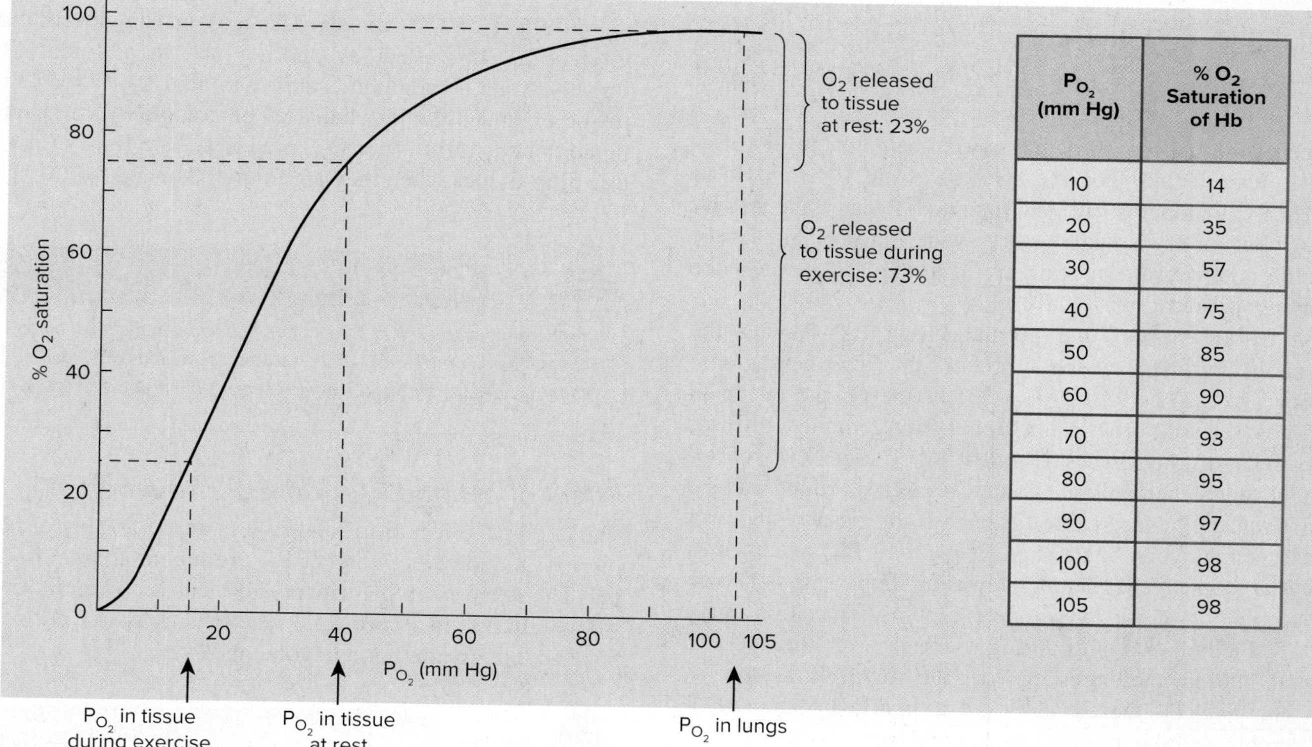

P_{O_2} (mm Hg)	% O_2 Saturation of Hb
10	14
20	35
30	57
40	75
50	85
60	90
70	93
80	95
90	97
100	98
105	98

FIGURE 23.18 Oxygen-Hemoglobin Dissociation Curve
The oxygen-hemoglobin dissociation curve shows the percent saturation of hemoglobin as a function of P_{O_2}. When hemoglobin becomes less saturated, it is typically because the O_2 that was bound to the hemoglobin has been delivered to the tissues.

Clinical IMPACT 23.4

Importance of Reduced P_{O_2}

Carbon dioxide is much more important than O_2 as a regulator of normal alveolar ventilation, but under certain circumstances a reduced P_{O_2} in the arterial blood plays an important stimulatory role. During conditions of shock when blood pressure is very low, the P_{O_2} in arterial blood can drop low enough to strongly stimulate carotid and aortic body sensory receptors. At high altitudes, where atmospheric pressure is low, the P_{O_2} in arterial blood can also drop to levels low enough to stimulate the carotid and aortic bodies. Although P_{O_2} levels in the blood are reduced, the respiratory system's ability to eliminate CO_2 is not greatly affected by low barometric air pressure. Thus, blood CO_2 levels become lower than normal because of the increased alveolar ventilation initiated in response to low P_{O_2}.

In people with emphysema, the destruction of the respiratory membrane allows less O_2 to move into the blood. The resulting low arterial P_{O_2} levels stimulate an increased rate and depth of pulmonary ventilation. At first, arterial P_{CO_2} levels may be unaffected by the reduced surface area of the respiratory membrane because CO_2 diffuses across the respiratory membrane 20 times more readily than does O_2. However, if alveolar ventilation increases to the point that CO_2 exchange increases above normal, arterial CO_2 becomes lower than normal. More severe emphysema, in which the surface area of the respiratory membrane is reduced to a minimum, can decrease CO_2 exchange to the point that arterial CO_2 becomes elevated.

flat shape of the upper part of the oxygen-hemoglobin dissociation curve. Even if the blood P_{O_2} decreases from 104 mm Hg to 60 mm Hg, hemoglobin is still 90% saturated. Because the affinity of hemoglobin for O_2 is stable over a wide range of P_{O_2} levels, hemoglobin is effective at picking up O_2 in the lungs even if the P_{O_2} drops significantly.

In a resting person, the normal blood P_{O_2} leaving the tissues is 40 mm Hg, which correlates to 75% hemoglobin saturation. Thus, 23% (98 − 75 = 23) of the O_2 picked up in the lungs is released from hemoglobin. Oxygen then diffuses into the cells of the tissues (figure 23.18). The 75% of O_2 still bound to the hemoglobin is an O_2 reserve, which can be released if blood P_{O_2} decreases further. In the tissues, at lower P_{O_2} levels, a relatively small change in blood P_{O_2} results in a relatively large change in hemoglobin saturation. This is shown by the steep slope of the oxygen-hemoglobin dissociation curve (figure 23.18). For example, during vigorous exercise, the P_{O_2} in skeletal muscle capillaries can decline to levels as low as 15 mm Hg. Skeletal muscle cells use a significant amount of O_2 for aerobic cellular respiration (see chapter 9). At a P_{O_2} of 15 mm Hg, hemoglobin is only 25% saturated, resulting in the release of 73% (98 − 25 = 73) of the O_2 picked up in the lungs (figure 23.18). Thus, as tissues use more O_2, hemoglobin releases more O_2 to those tissues.

Predict 6

In carbon monoxide (CO) poisoning, CO binds to hemoglobin, thereby decreasing the uptake of O_2 by hemoglobin. In addition, when CO binds to hemoglobin, the oxygen-hemoglobin dissociation curve shifts to the left. How does this shift affect the ability of tissues to get O_2? Explain.

Effect of P_{O_2} on CO_2 Transport

The largest effect of P_{O_2} on CO_2 transport is at low P_{O_2} levels. Recall that when P_{O_2} levels are low, the Haldane effect allows hemoglobin to bind more CO_2. In turn, as more CO_2 binds to hemoglobin, the affinity of hemoglobin for O_2 decreases.

Effect of pH and P_{CO_2} on O_2 Transport

In addition to P_{O_2}, other factors, such as blood pH and P_{CO_2}, influence the saturation of hemoglobin (figure 23.19). As the pH of the blood drops (due to higher H^+ levels), the affinity of hemoglobin for O_2 at any given P_{O_2} is much lower. The higher H^+ levels bind to nonheme portions of hemoglobin, which changes its overall shape. Following the concept of form following function, changing the shape of hemoglobin would change its affinity for O_2. Conversely, an increase in blood pH results in an increased affinity of hemoglobin for O_2. This effect of pH on the oxygen-hemoglobin dissociation curve is called the **Bohr effect,** after its discoverer, Christian Bohr. An increase in P_{CO_2} also decreases hemoglobin's ability to bind O_2 due to the effect of CO_2 on pH. Changes in CO_2 levels indirectly produce a Bohr effect by altering pH. In addition, CO_2 can directly affect hemoglobin's ability to bind O_2. When CO_2 binds to the α- and β-globin chains of hemoglobin (see chapter 19), hemoglobin's affinity for O_2 is reduced. The Bohr effect is beneficial to tissues when they are in high demand for O_2.

Predict 7

How does the movement of CO_2 from fetal blood into maternal blood increase the movement of O_2 from maternal blood into fetal blood? (Hint: Consider the shift of the oxygen-hemoglobin dissociation curve.)

Effect of pH and P_{CO_2} on CO_2 Transport

The principal effect of pH and P_{CO_2} is on the affinity of hemoglobin for O_2. However, a higher P_{CO_2} results in a larger decrease in pH. The decrease in pH triggers an increased respiratory rate, as we will discuss in section 23.7. The sensitivity to CO_2 is valuable for maintaining appropriate blood pH levels.

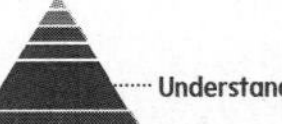

Predict 8

Explain the effect of (1) hyperventilation and (2) holding one's breath on blood pH.

FUNDAMENTAL **Figure**

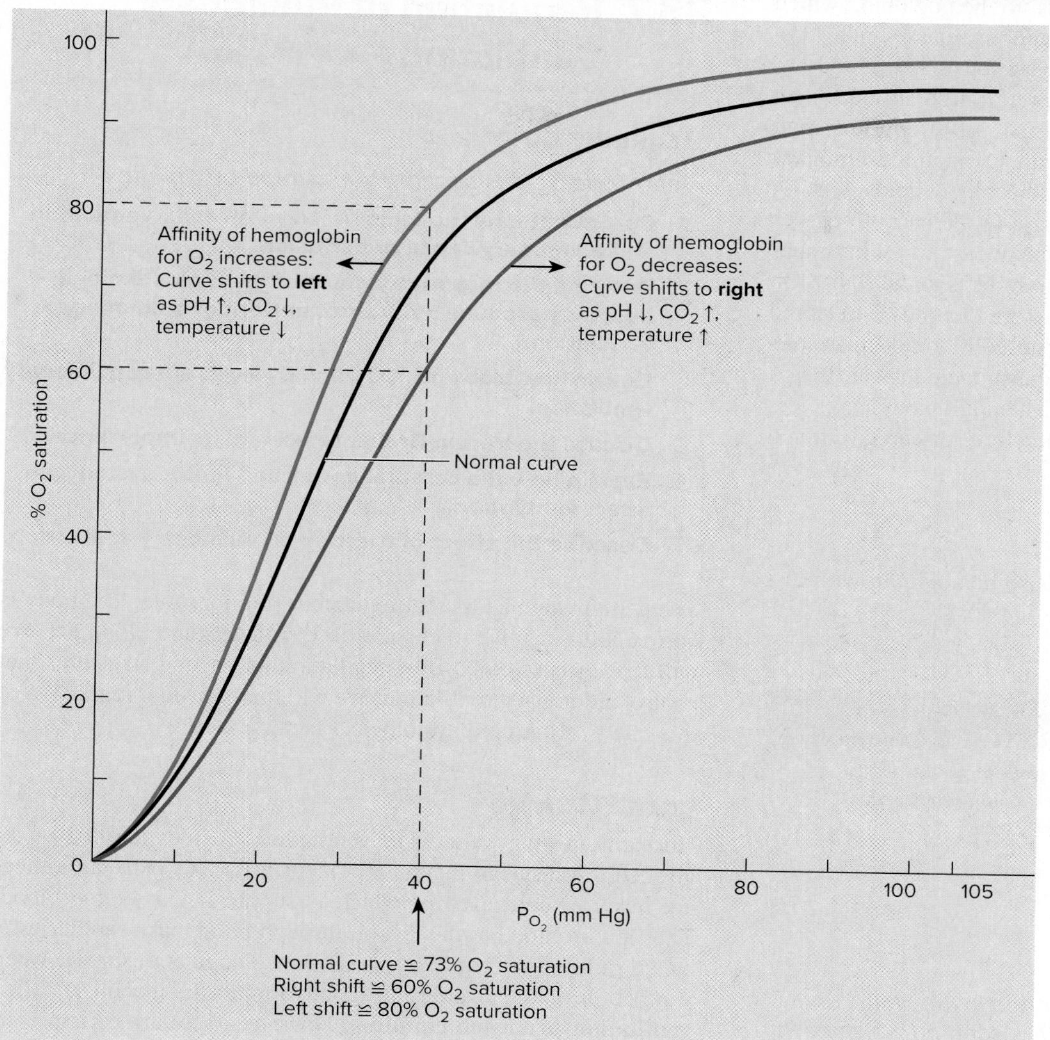

FIGURE 23.19 Shifting the Oxygen-Hemoglobin Dissociation Curve

Tissues that are producing more ATP than when at rest release more CO_2, which lowers the pH. In addition, the increased activity raises the temperature in the tissues. The right shift under these conditions is advantageous to the tissues because more O_2 is needed to support the increased ATP production. A left shift can be advantageous in the lungs because the hemoglobin will attract O_2 with a stronger affinity, which will encourage its diffusion into the blood.

Effect of Temperature on O_2 Transport

An increase in temperature also decreases O_2's tendency to remain bound to hemoglobin. Therefore, elevated temperatures resulting from increased metabolism increase the amount of O_2 released into the tissues by hemoglobin. In less metabolically active tissues in which the temperature is lower, less O_2 is released from hemoglobin.

When hemoglobin's affinity for O_2 decreases, the oxygen-hemoglobin dissociation curve is shifted to the right, and hemoglobin releases more O_2 (figure 23.19). During exercise, when CO_2 and acidic substances accumulate and the temperature increases in the tissue spaces, the oxygen-hemoglobin curve shifts to the right. Under these conditions, as much as 75–85% of the O_2 is released from the hemoglobin. In the lungs, however, the curve shifts to the left because of the lower CO_2 levels, lower temperature, and lower acid levels. Therefore, hemoglobin's affinity for O_2 increases, and it becomes easily saturated (figure 23.19).

During resting conditions, approximately 5 mL of O_2 are transported to the tissues in each 100 mL of blood, and cardiac output is approximately 5000 mL/min. Consequently, 250 mL of O_2 are delivered to the tissues each minute. During exercise, this value can increase up to 15 times. Oxygen transport can be increased threefold because of a greater degree of O_2 release from hemoglobin in the tissue capillaries, and the rate of O_2 transport is increased another five times because of the increase in cardiac output. Consequently, the volume of O_2 delivered to the tissues can be as high as 3750 mL/min (15 × 250 mL/min). Highly trained athletes can increase this volume to as high as 5000 mL/min.

Effect of Temperature on CO_2 Transport

Typically, when body temperature increases, the rate of ATP production is increased. Thus, more CO_2 enters the blood and eventually is converted into H^+ and HCO_3^-, lowering the pH. As we discussed, the response is often an increased respiratory rate, which removes excess CO_2 from the body.

Effect of BPG on O_2 Transport

As red blood cells metabolize glucose for energy, they produce a by-product called **2,3-bisphosphoglycerate** (**BPG;** formerly called diphosphoglycerate). BPG binds to hemoglobin, which reduces its affinity for O_2. Thus, hemoglobin releases more O_2. A potent trigger for increased BPG production is low blood O_2. For example, atmospheric pressure is lower at high altitudes than at sea level, causing both the partial pressure of O_2 in the alveoli and the percent saturation of blood with O_2 in the pulmonary capillaries to be lower. Consequently, the blood holds less O_2 for delivery to tissues. BPG helps increase O_2 delivery to tissues because higher levels of BPG increase the release of O_2 in tissues (the oxygen-hemoglobin dissociation curve shifts to the right). On the other hand, when blood is removed from the body and stored in a blood bank, the BPG levels in the stored blood decrease. As BPG levels decrease, the blood becomes unsuitable for transfusion after approximately 6 weeks because the hemoglobin releases less O_2 to the tissues. Banked blood is, therefore, discarded after 6 weeks of storage.

Effect of BPG on CO_2 Transport

BPG enhances the Haldane effect because hemoglobin with less O_2 bound can transport more CO_2.

Apply **Predict 9**

If a person lacks the enzyme necessary for BPG synthesis, do they exhibit anemia (a lower-than-normal number of red blood cells) or erythrocytosis (a higher-than-normal number of red blood cells)? Explain.

ASSESS YOUR PROGRESS

49. *Name the two ways O_2 is transported in the blood, and state the percentage of total O_2 transport for which each method is responsible.*
50. *How does the oxygen-hemoglobin dissociation curve explain the uptake of O_2 in the lungs and the release of O_2 in tissues?*
51. *What is the Bohr effect? How is it related to blood CO_2?*
52. *Why is it advantageous for the oxygen-hemoglobin dissociation curve to shift to the left in the lungs and to the right in tissues?*
53. *How does temperature affect O_2's tendency to bind to hemoglobin?*
54. *How does BPG affect the release of O_2 from hemoglobin?*
55. *Why is fetal hemoglobin's affinity for O_2 greater than that of maternal hemoglobin?*
56. *How does the lowering HCO_3^- concentrations inside red blood cells affect CO_2 transport?*
57. *What is the chloride shift, and what does it accomplish?*
58. *Name three effects produced by H^+ binding to hemoglobin.*
59. *What is the Haldane effect?*
60. *What effect does blood CO_2 level have on blood pH?*

23.7 Regulation of Pulmonary Ventilation

LEARNING OUTCOMES

After reading this section, you should be able to

A. **Describe the relationship between alveolar ventilation and pulmonary capillary perfusion.**
B. **Describe the respiratory areas of the brainstem and how they produce a rhythmic pattern of pulmonary ventilation.**
C. **Explain how blood pH, CO_2, and O_2 levels affect pulmonary ventilation.**
D. **Discuss the Hering-Breuer reflex and its importance.**
E. **Explain how the cerebral cortex and limbic system can affect ventilation.**
F. **Describe the effect of exercise on pulmonary ventilation.**

There are many factors that regulate respiratory rate. The body is particularly sensitive to changes in CO_2 levels and blood pH. We will first discuss blood flow regulation and neural structures that control pulmonary ventilation. We will then consider regulation of this rate by different physiological factors.

Local Control

Normally, resting pulmonary ventilation provides the body with all the O_2 it needs to maintain homeostasis. This is because there are many alveoli, each of which is supplied with ample blood. The flow of blood to the alveoli through pulmonary capillaries is called **pulmonary capillary perfusion.** The relationship between ventilation of the alveoli and blood flow to the alveoli is called **ventilation-perfusion coupling.** However, there are certain conditions that disrupt normal ventilation-perfusion coupling.

First, it is important to realize that even with normal ventilation-perfusion coupling, not 100% of cardiac output is fully saturated with O_2. Blood that is not completely oxygenated is called shunted blood. There are two types of shunts in the lungs: (1) an anatomical shunt and (2) a physiological shunt. The **anatomical shunt** is due to deoxygenated blood from the bronchi and bronchioles mixing with blood in the pulmonary veins (see section 23.2). Blood that passes through pulmonary capillaries without becoming fully oxygenated is also shunted blood. The **physiological shunt** is the combination of the anatomical shunt and incompletely oxygenated blood from the alveoli. Normally, the physiological shunt makes up 1–2% of cardiac output.

There are two main situations that can cause normal ventilation-perfusion coupling to be disrupted: (1) if there is insufficient blood flow to the alveoli and (2) if there is insufficient air flow to the alveoli. Sometimes alveolar ventilation is sufficient, but blood flow to the alveoli has been reduced. For example, this can happen because of inadequate cardiac output after a heart attack. Another factor that influences differences in blood flow to different areas of the lung is body position. When a person is standing, greater blood flow and pulmonary ventilation occur in the base of the lung than in the top of the lung because gravity tends to pull the blood down toward the base of the lungs. Thus, when standing, more gas exchange occurs at the base of the lungs.

In other instances, alveolar ventilation is severely reduced and the blood in the pulmonary capillaries does not become fully oxygenated. This happens during an asthma attack when bronchioles become constricted. In pneumonia or pulmonary edema, a buildup of fluid in the alveoli results in poor gas diffusion and less oxygenated blood.

Although gravity is the major factor affecting regional blood flow in the lung, under certain circumstances alveolar P_{O_2} can also have an effect. In most tissues, low P_{O_2} results in increased blood flow through the tissues (see chapter 21). However, in the lung, low P_{O_2} has the opposite effect. Low P_{O_2} causes arterioles to constrict, which reduces blood flow. This response helps keep gas exchange in the lungs efficient. Blood is routed away from areas of low O_2 toward parts of the lung that are better oxygenated. Because the function of the lungs is to acquire O_2 for the body, it is more efficient to avoid low O_2 areas in the lungs. For example, if a bronchus becomes partially blocked, ventilation of alveoli past the blockage site decreases, which in turn decreases gas exchange between the air and blood. The effect of this decreased gas exchange is diminished by rerouting the blood to better-ventilated alveoli.

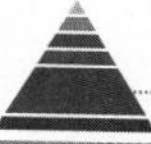

Understand **Predict 10**

Even people in "good shape" may have trouble breathing at high altitudes. Explain how this can happen, even when pulmonary ventilation of the lungs increases.

Neural Control

Regulation of pulmonary ventilation is surprisingly complex. Pulmonary ventilation can be regulated voluntarily such as when speaking or chewing food; yet, during sleep or when focused on other tasks, pulmonary ventilation is regulated involuntarily. The brainstem is the site of automatic regulation of pulmonary ventilation. However, unlike regulation of the heart, which involves a specific set of pacemaker cells, there is not a known single set of neurons functioning as the pacemaker for pulmonary ventilation. Rather, the respiratory center is a complex network of neurons. The most recent evidence actually points away from a pacemaker model and instead points toward a self-inhibiting network of multiple groups of neurons. The brainstem neurons control the basic rhythm of pulmonary ventilation through stimulation of the muscles of ventilation. The recruitment of muscle fibers and the more frequent stimulation of muscle fibers result in stronger muscle contractions and increased depth of pulmonary ventilation. The rate of pulmonary ventilation is determined by how frequently the respiratory muscles are stimulated.

Respiratory Areas in the Brainstem

Neurons involved with pulmonary ventilation are aggregated in certain parts of the brainstem. Scientists have learned that neurons that are active during inspiration are intermingled with those that are active during expiration.

The **medullary respiratory center** in the medulla oblongata consists of two sets of neurons: (1) the ventral respiratory group and (2) the dorsal respiratory group. The **ventral respiratory group (VRG)** forms a longitudinal column of cells located in the ventral part of each half of the medulla oblongata. The **dorsal respiratory group (DRG)** forms a longitudinal column of cells in the dorsal part of each half of the medulla oblongata (figure 23.20). Communication occurs between the two halves of the medulla within a respiratory group so that respiratory movements are symmetrical. Communication also occurs between the dorsal and ventral respiratory groups.

The VRG is responsible for generating the normal, involuntary rhythm of breathing, called **eupnea** (YOOP-nee-ah). In addition, within the VRG is a collection of neurons that are active during both inspiration and expiration. A part of the VRG, the **pre-Bötzinger** (pree-BOUGHT-zeen-ger) **complex,** is believed to establish the basic rhythm of pulmonary ventilation.

The **pontine respiratory group,** formerly called the pneumo-taxic center, is a collection of neurons in the pons that helps modulate pulmonary ventilation rate (figure 23.20). Some of the neurons are active only during inspiration, some only during expiration, and others during both inspiration and expiration. The precise function of the pontine respiratory group is unknown, but it has connections with the medullary respiratory center and appears to play a role in switching between inspiration and expiration, thus fine-tuning the pulmonary ventilation pattern. It is not considered essential for the generation of the respiratory rhythm.

Generation of Rhythmic Pulmonary Ventilation

Eupnea has three distinct phases: (1) an inspiratory phase, (2) a postinspiratory phase, and (3) an expiratory phase.

1. *Inspiratory phase.* The pre-Bötzinger complex drives the continuous inspiratory rhythm, which lasts about 2 seconds. The fundamental action of this inspiratory phase is generation of action potentials in the phrenic and intercostal nerves to drive contraction of the diaphragm and external intercostal muscles. The pre-Bötzinger complex appears to also coordinate other groups of neurons in order to adjust the rate of inspiration based upon conditions in the body such as levels of CO_2 or O_2. It is also thought that the pre-Bötzinger complex influences emotion and cognitive functions as well, but this is not as completely understood.
2. *Postinspiratory phase.* During this phase, which is transient, the extrinsic laryngeal muscle contraction ceases and the contraction of the diaphragm is prolonged to prevent elastic recoil of the thorax. This is beneficial for gas exchange because the length of time air stays in the lungs is increased. The postinspiratory phase is related to lung mechanoreceptor and pontine group functions.
3. *Expiratory phase.* A group of expiratory neurons within the VRG drive this phase, which lasts about 3 seconds. These neurons inhibit the inspiratory neurons of the VRG, resulting in relaxation of the diaphragm and external intercostal muscle. Expiration occurs due to elastic recoil of the thorax.

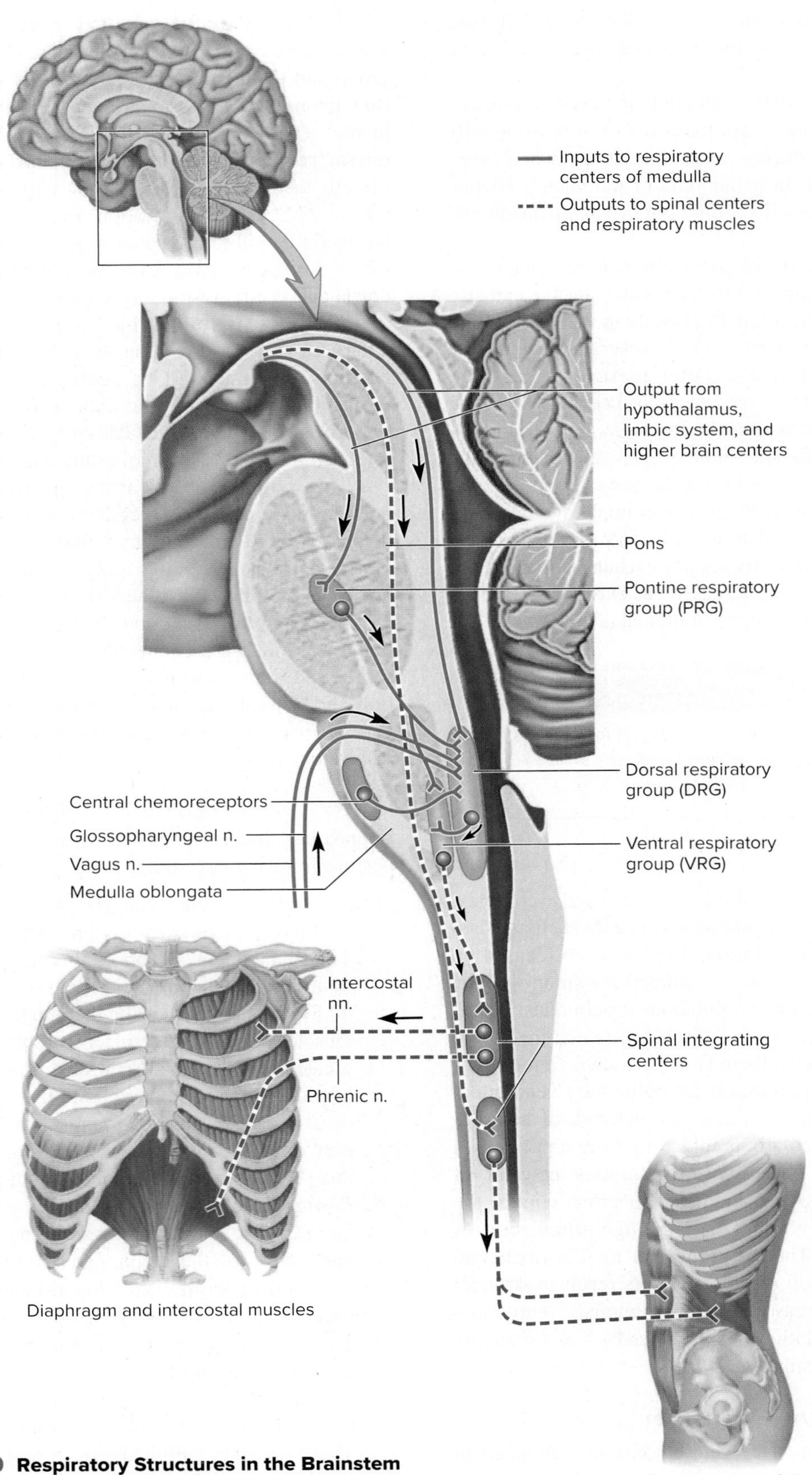

FIGURE 23.20 Respiratory Structures in the Brainstem

This figure shows the relationship of respiratory structures to each other and to the nerves innervating the muscles of ventilation on the left side of the body.

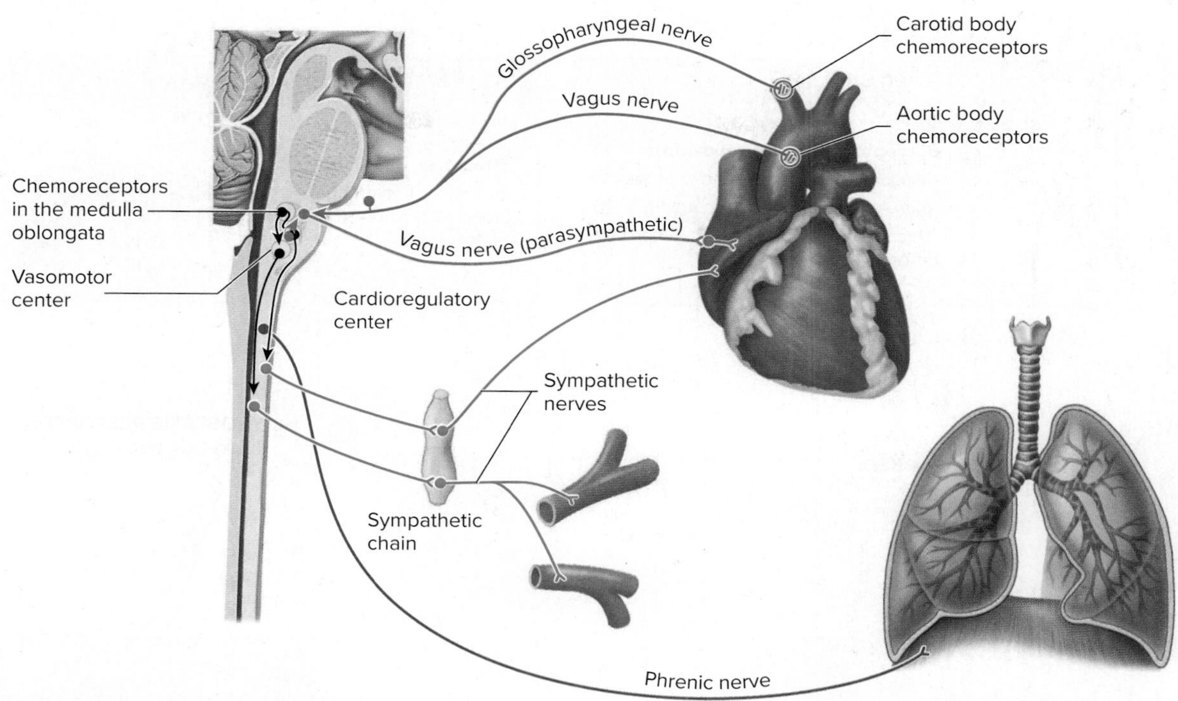

FIGURE 23.21 Chemoreceptor Reflex
An increase in blood CO_2 and a decrease in pH and O_2 result in an increase in heart rate and vasoconstriction and an increased rate and depth of pulmonary ventilation.

Intercommunication among the VRG, DRG, and pontine respiratory group work to modify the rate and depth of breathing. The DRG receives sensory input from chemoreceptors and mechanoreceptors as well as other sources. The DRG integrates this information and then communicates with the VRG for any modifications to the respiratory rhythm.

Chemoreceptors

Effect of P_{O_2} on Respiratory Rate

Carbon dioxide is the principal regulator of respiratory rate. However, changes in P_{O_2} can also affect pulmonary ventilation (figure 23.21). A decrease in O_2 below its normal values is called **hypoxia** (high-POK-see-ah). If P_{O_2} levels in the arterial blood are markedly reduced while the pH and P_{CO_2} are held constant, an increase in pulmonary ventilation rate occurs. However, within a normal range of P_{O_2} levels, the effect of O_2 on the regulation of pulmonary ventilation is small. Only after arterial P_{O_2} decreases to approximately 50% of its normal value does it begin to have a large stimulatory effect on respiratory movements.

At first, it is somewhat surprising that small changes in Po_2 do not cause changes in respiratory rate. But the reason becomes clear if we consider the oxygen-hemoglobin dissociation curve (see figure 23.18). At any P_{O_2} above 80 mm Hg, nearly all of the hemoglobin is saturated with O_2. If P_{O_2} levels decrease below 80 mm Hg, the oxygen-carrying capacity of the blood is significantly reduced.

When P_{O_2} levels are low, the carotid and aortic body chemoreceptors stimulate the respiratory center. This keeps it active despite decreasing O_2 levels. However, if P_{O_2} decreases sufficiently, the respiratory center can fail, resulting in death.

Effect of P_{CO_2} on Respiratory Rate

Blood CO_2 levels are a major regulator of pulmonary ventilation during both resting conditions and intense exercise. Even a small increase in CO_2 in the bloodstream triggers a large increase in the rate and depth of pulmonary ventilation. For example, an increase in P_{CO_2} of only 5 mm Hg causes an increase in pulmonary ventilation of 100%. A greater-than-normal amount of CO_2 in the blood is called **hypercapnia** (HIGH-per-KAP-nee-ah) and a lower-than-normal CO_2 level is called **hypocapnia** (HIGH-poh-KAP-nee-ah). Hypocapnia results in periods when the pulmonary ventilation rate is reduced or does not occur at all.

The chemoreceptors in the chemosensitive area of the medulla oblongata and in the carotid and aortic bodies respond to changes in CO_2 primarily because of the effects of CO_2 on blood pH (see figure 23.21; figure 23.22). The chemosensitive area in the medulla oblongata is far more important in regulating P_{CO_2} and pH than either the carotid or the aortic body. The carotid and aortic bodies are responsible for, at most, 15–20% of the total response to changes in P_{CO_2} or pH. During intense exercise, however, the carotid bodies respond more rapidly to changes in blood pH than does the chemosensitive area of the medulla.

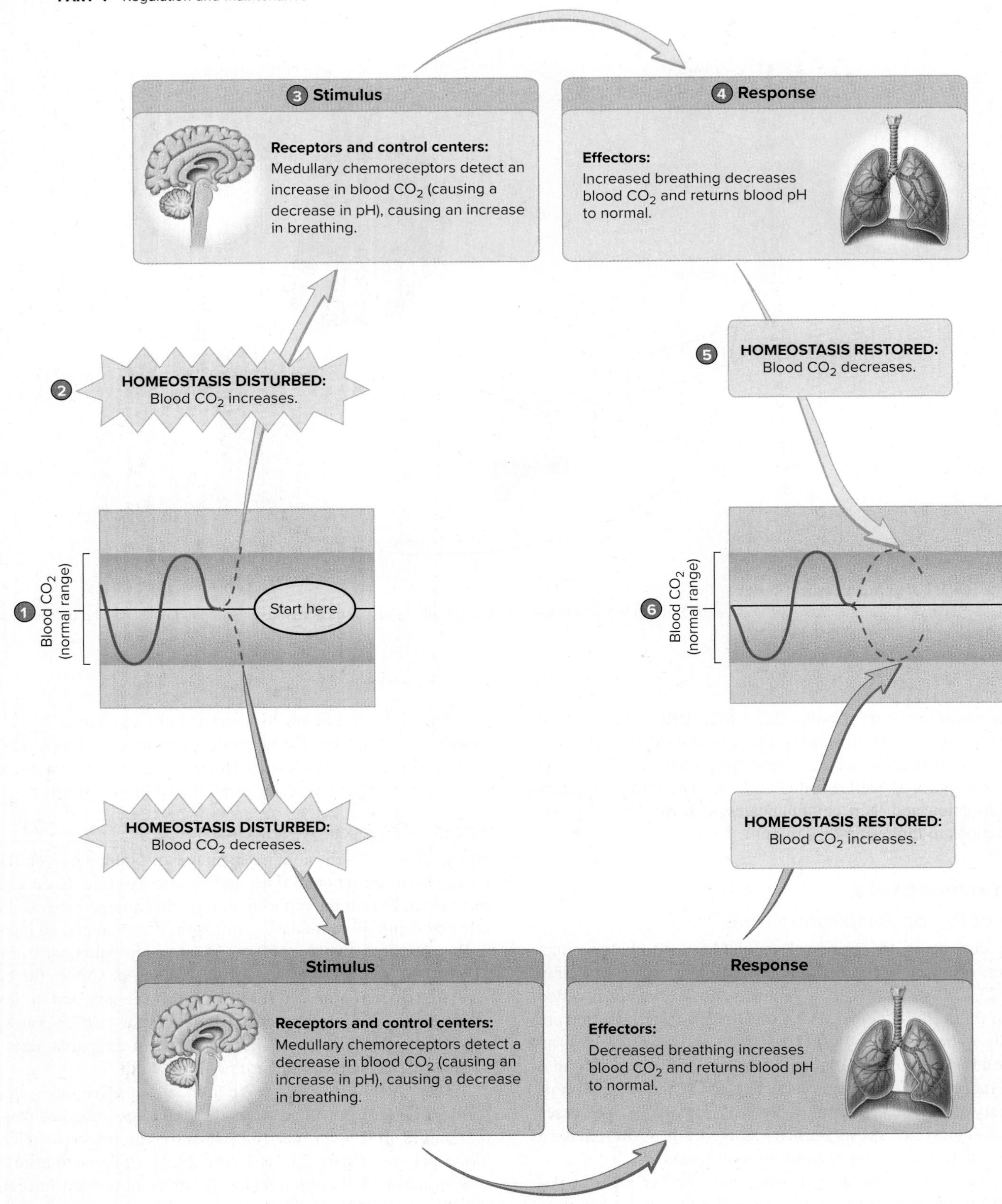

HOMEOSTASIS FIGURE 23.22 Regulation of Blood CO_2

(1) Blood CO_2 is in its normal range. (2) Blood CO_2 increases outside its normal range, which disturbs homeostasis. (3) The control centers for blood CO_2, the medullary chemoreceptors, detect an decrease in blood pH (blood becomes more acidic) and respond to the decreased pH by signaling an increased breathing rate. (4) The effectors, the diaphragm and other respiratory muscles, respond by increasing their contraction rate, which raises the rate of breathing. (5) As a result, more CO_2 is removed, which causes pH to go up (blood becomes more basic). (6) Blood CO_2 returns to its normal range and homeostasis is maintained. Observe the responses to an decrease in blood CO_2 by following the lower *pink* arrows.

Effect of pH on Respiratory Rate

The central chemoreceptors in the medulla oblongata detect changes in blood pH due to changes in CO_2. The carotid and aortic bodies detect changes in pH due to changes in H^+ concentrations. Because H^+ does not easily cross the blood-brain barrier or the blood-cerebrospinal fluid barrier (see chapter 11), the central chemoreceptors detect changes in blood pH through changes in blood CO_2. Carbon dioxide easily diffuses across the blood-brain barrier and the blood-cerebrospinal fluid barrier. The lower pH then stimulates the respiratory center, resulting in a greater rate and depth of pulmonary ventilation reducing CO_2 levels, and blood pH increases to normal levels.

Maintaining body pH levels within normal limits is necessary for the proper functioning of cells. Because changes in CO_2 levels can change pH, the respiratory system plays an important role in acid-base balance. The respiratory system's role in maintaining pH is considered in greater detail in chapter 27.

Mechanoreceptors

The Hering-Breuer Reflex and Respiratory Rate

The Hering-Breuer (HER-ing BROY-er) reflex limits the depth of inspiration and prevents overinflation of the lungs (see figure 23.23*d*). This reflex depends on stretch receptors in the walls of the bronchi and bronchioles of the lungs. Action potentials are initiated in these stretch receptors when the lungs are inflated and are passed along sensory neurons within the vagus nerves to the medulla oblongata. The action potentials have an inhibitory influence on the respiratory center and result in expiration. As expiration proceeds, the stretch receptors are no longer

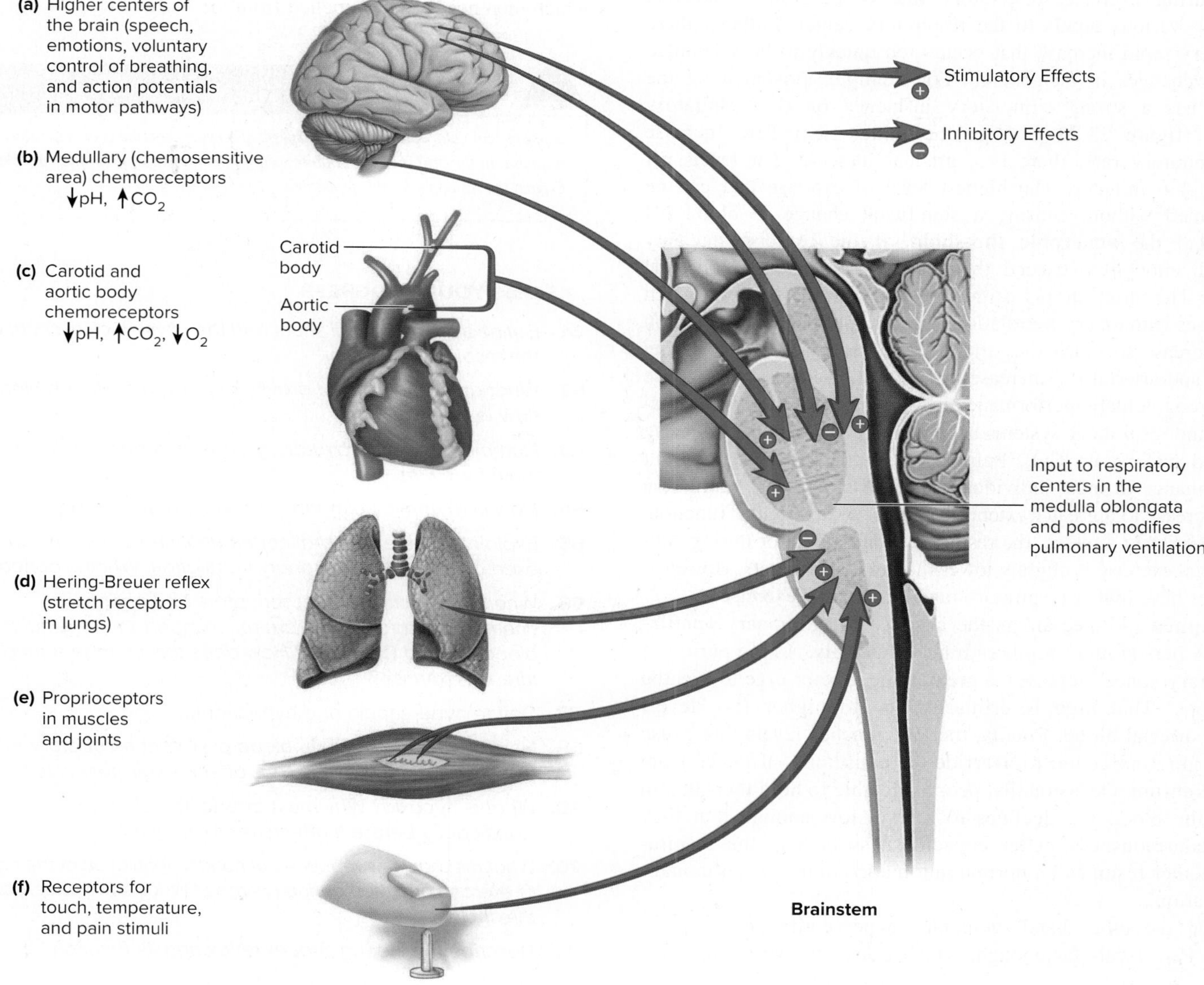

FIGURE 23.23 Major Regulatory Mechanisms of Pulmonary Ventilation
A plus sign indicates an increase in pulmonary ventilation, and a minus sign indicates a decrease in pulmonary ventilation.

stimulated, and the decreased inhibitory effect on the respiratory center allows inspiration to begin again.

In infants, the Hering-Breuer reflex plays a role in regulating the basic rhythm of pulmonary ventilation and in preventing overinflation of the lungs. In adults, however, the reflex is important only when the tidal volume is large, such as during exercise.

Voluntary Influences

Cerebral and Limbic System Control of Respiratory Rate

The rate and depth of pulmonary ventilation is controlled both voluntarily and involuntarily by the cerebral cortex (see figure 23.23). For example, during talking or singing, air movement is controlled to produce sounds, as well as to facilitate gas exchange.

During exercise, respiratory rate changes are controlled through various inputs to the respiratory center. Initially, there is a very rapid increase that occurs too quickly to be accounted for by changes in metabolism. For example, movement of the limbs has a strong stimulatory influence on the respiratory center (figure 23.23*e*). After the initial immediate increase in respiratory rate, there is a gradual increase that levels off within 4–6 minutes. The highest level of exercise that can be performed without causing a significant change in blood pH is called the **anaerobic threshold.** If the exercise intensity is high enough to exceed the anaerobic threshold, blood pH drops. The drop in pH stimulates the carotid bodies, which increases pulmonary ventilation. In fact, pulmonary ventilation can increase so much that arterial P_{CO_2} decreases below resting levels and arterial P_{O_2} increases above resting levels. In response to training, athletic performance increases because the cardiovascular and respiratory systems become more efficient at delivering O_2 and picking up CO_2. Pulmonary ventilation does not limit performance in most individuals because pulmonary ventilation can increase to a greater extent than does cardiovascular function. In conditioned athletes, the respiratory rate at rest or during submaximal exercise is slightly lower than in a non athlete. However, athletes have higher respiratory rates at maximal exercise.

Apnea (AP-nee-ah) is the absence of pulmonary ventilation. A person may stop breathing voluntarily. As the period of voluntary apnea increases, a greater and greater urge to breathe develops. That urge is primarily due to higher P_{CO_2} levels in the arterial blood. Finally, the P_{CO_2} reaches levels that cause the respiratory center to override the conscious influence from the cerebrum. Occasionally, people are able to hold their breath until the blood P_{O_2} declines to a level low enough that they lose consciousness. After consciousness is lost, the respiratory center resumes its normal automatic control of pulmonary ventilation.

On the other hand, voluntary hyperventilation decreases blood P_{CO_2} levels far enough, which causes vasodilation of the peripheral blood vessels and a corresponding drop in blood pressure (see chapter 21). Dizziness or a giddy feeling can result because the decreased blood pressure results in a decreased rate of blood flow to the brain, and therefore less O_2 is delivered to the brain.

Emotions acting through the limbic system of the brain can also affect the respiratory center (figure 23.23*a*). For example, strong emotions can cause hyperventilation or produce the sobs and gasps of crying.

Other Modifications of Pulmonary Ventilation

Higher brain centers control the respiratory system when touch, thermal, or pain receptors are activated (see figure 23.23*f*). For example, irritants in the nasal cavity can initiate a sneeze reflex, and irritants in the lungs can stimulate a cough reflex. An increase in body temperature can stimulate increased pulmonary ventilation because metabolism is elevated and more CO_2 is produced, which then needs to be expelled from the body.

Understand

Predict 11

Suppose that cold water is suddenly splashed on you. Describe your respiratory response. In the past, newborn babies were sometimes swatted on the buttocks. Explain the rationale for this procedure.

ASSESS YOUR PROGRESS

61. *Define the anatomical shunt and the physiological shunt of the respiratory system.*
62. *What are the effects of gravity and alveolar P_{O_2} on blood flow in the lung?*
63. *Name the three respiratory groups, and describe their main functions.*
64. *How is rhythmic pulmonary ventilation generated?*
65. *Explain how the cerebral cortex and limbic system can exert control over pulmonary ventilation. What is apnea?*
66. *Where are central chemoreceptors and peripheral chemoreceptors? Which are most important for regulating blood pH and CO_2 level? How does this change during intense exercise?*
67. *Define* hypercapnia *and* hypocapnia.
68. *How does a decrease in blood pH affect respiratory rate? How does a decrease in CO_2 affect respiratory rate?*
69. *What is hypoxia? Why must arterial P_{O_2} change significantly before it affects respiratory rate?*
70. *What mechanisms regulate pulmonary ventilation at the onset of exercise and then during exercise? What is the anaerobic threshold?*
71. *Describe the Hering-Breuer reflex and its function.*

TABLE 23.2 Representative Diseases and Disorders of the Respiratory System

Condition	Description
RESPIRATORY DISORDERS	
Bronchi and Lungs	
Bronchitis (brong-KIGH-tis)	Inflammation of the bronchi caused by irritants, such as cigarette smoke or infection; swelling impairs breathing; bronchitis can progress to emphysema
Emphysema	Destruction of alveolar walls; increased coughing increases pressure on the alveoli, causing rupture and destruction; loss of alveoli decreases surface area for gas exchange and decreases the lungs' ability to expel air; progression can be slowed, but there is no cure; in combination with bronchitis, the condition is known as chronic obstructive pulmonary disease (COPD)
Adult respiratory distress syndrome (ARDS)	Caused by damage to the respiratory membrane, which promotes inflammation; amount of surfactant is reduced, and fluid fills the alveoli, lessening gas exchange; ARDS usually develops after an injurious event, such as inhaling smoke from a fire or breathing toxic fumes
Cystic fibrosis (figh-BROH-sis)	Genetic disorder that affects mucous secretions throughout the body due to an abnormal transport protein; mucus is much more viscous and accumulates in ducts and tubes, such as the bronchioles; airflow is restricted, and infections are more likely
Pulmonary fibrosis	Replacement of lung tissue with fibrous connective tissue, making the lungs less elastic; exposure to asbestos or coal dust is a common cause
Lung cancer	Occurs in the epithelium of the respiratory tract; can easily spread to other parts of the body because of the rich blood and lymphatic supply to the lungs
Asthma	See Systems Pathology, later in this chapter
Circulatory System	
Thrombosis of the pulmonary arteries	Blood clot in lung blood vessels, causing inadequate blood flow through the pulmonary capillaries, which affects respiratory function
Anemia	Reduced hemoglobin lowers oxygen-carrying capacity of blood
Carbon monoxide poisoning	Carbon monoxide binds more strongly to hemoglobin than O_2 does and prevents already-bound O_2 from entering tissues
Nervous System	
Sudden infant death syndrome (SIDS)	Most frequent cause of death of infants between 2 weeks and 1 year of age; cause is still unknown, but at-risk babies can be placed on monitors that warn if breathing stops
Paralysis of the respiratory muscles	Damage to the spinal cord in the cervical or thoracic region interrupts nervous signals to the muscles of ventilation
Thoracic Wall	Decreased elasticity of the thoracic wall prevents it from expanding to full capacity and reduces air movement; two spinal curvature conditions that reduce elasticity of the thoracic wall are scoliosis (skoh-lee-OH-sis) and kyphosis (kie-FOH-sis)
INFECTIOUS DISEASES OF THE RESPIRATORY SYSTEM	
Upper Respiratory Tract	
Strep throat	Caused by streptococcal bacteria (*Streptococcus pyogenes*); characterized by inflammation of the pharynx and fever
Diphtheria (dif-THEER-ee-ah)	Caused by the bacterium *Corynebacterium diphtheriae;* a grayish membrane forms in the throat and can completely block respiratory passages; DTaP immunization for children partially targets diphtheria
Common cold	Results from a viral infection
Lower Respiratory Tract	
Whooping cough (pertussis; per-TUS-is)	Caused by the bacterium *Bordetella pertussis,* which destroys cilia lining the respiratory epithelium, allowing mucus to accumulate; leads to a very severe cough; DTaP immunization for children targets pertussis
Tuberculosis (too-BER- kyoo-LOH-sis)	Caused by the bacterium *Clostridium tuberculosis,* which forms small, lumplike lesions called tubercles; immune system targets tubercles and causes larger lesions; certain strains of tuberculosis are resistant to antibiotics
Pneumonia (noo-MOH-nee-ah)	Can be caused by a number of bacterial or viral infections of the lungs that cause fever, difficulty in breathing, and chest pain; edema in the lungs decreases their inflation ability and reduces gas exchange
Flu (influenza; in-floo-EN-zah)	Viral infection of the respiratory system; does not affect the digestive system, as is commonly misunderstood; causes chills, fever, headache, and muscle aches
Fungal diseases	Fungal spores enter the respiratory tract attached to dust particles, usually resulting in minor respiratory infections that in some cases can spread to other parts of the body; examples are histoplasmosis and coccidioidomycosis

Systems PATHOLOGY | Asthma

Background Information

Will is an 18-year-old track athlete in seemingly good health. Despite suffering from a slight cold, Will went jogging one morning with his running buddy, Al. After a few minutes of exercise, Will felt that he could hardly get enough air. Even though he stopped jogging, he continued to breathe rapidly and wheeze forcefully. Because his condition was not improving, Al took him to the emergency room of a nearby hospital.

The emergency room doctor used a stethoscope to listen to Will's lungs and noted that air movement was poor. Will inhaled a bronchodilator drug, which rapidly improved his condition.

Asthma (AZ-mah; difficult breathing) is characterized by abnormally increased constriction of the trachea and bronchi in response to various stimuli, which results in narrowed air passageways and decreased pulmonary ventilation efficiency. Symptoms include rapid and shallow breathing, wheezing, coughing, and shortness of breath (figure 23.24*a*). In contrast to many other respiratory disorders, the symptoms of asthma typically reverse either spontaneously or with therapy.

There is no definitive pathological feature or diagnostic test for asthma, but three important characteristics of the disease are chronic airway inflammation, airway hyperreactivity, and airflow obstruction. The inflammation results in tissue damage, edema, and mucous buildup, which can block airflow through the bronchi. Airway hyperreactivity means that the smooth muscle in the trachea and bronchi contracts greatly in response to a stimulus, thus decreasing the diameter of the airway and increasing resistance to airflow. The effects of inflammation and airway hyperreactivity combine to cause airflow obstruction (figure 23.24*b* and *c*).

Many cases of asthma appear to be associated with a chronic inflammatory response by the immune system. The number of immune cells in the bronchi, including mast cells, eosinophils, neutrophils, macrophages, and lymphocytes, increases. Inflammation appears to be linked to airway hyperreactivity by some chemical mediators released by immune cells (e.g., leukotrienes, prostaglandins, and interleukins), which increase the airway's sensitivity to stimulation and cause smooth muscle contraction.

The stimuli that prompt airflow obstruction in asthma vary from one individual to another. Some asthmatics react to particular allergens, which are foreign substances that evoke an inappropriate immune system response (see chapter 22). Examples include inhaled pollen, animal dander, and dust mites. Many cases of asthma are caused by an allergic reaction to substances in the droppings and carcasses of cockroaches, which may explain the higher rate of asthma in poor, urban areas. However, other inhaled substances, such as chemicals in the workplace or cigarette smoke, can provoke an asthma attack without stimulating an allergic reaction. Over 200 substances have been associated with occupational asthma. An asthma attack can also be stimulated by ingested substances, such as aspirin; nonsteroidal anti-inflammatory compounds, such as ibuprofen (eye-byoo-PROH-fen); sulfites in food preservatives; and tartrazine (TAR-trah-zeen) in food colorings. Asthmatics can substitute acetaminophen (as-et-ah-MEE-noh-fen; e.g., Tylenol) for aspirin.

Other stimuli, such as strenuous exercise (especially in cold weather) can precipitate an asthma attack. Such episodes can often be avoided by using a bronchodilator prior to exercise. Viral infections, emotional upset, stress, air pollution, and even reflux of stomach acid into the esophagus are known to elicit an asthma attack.

Treatment of asthma involves avoiding the causative stimulus and taking medications. Steroids and mast cell–stabilizing agents, which prevent the release of chemical mediators from mast cells, can reduce airway inflammation. Bronchodilators are used to increase airflow. Figure 23.25 illustrates the widespread effects of asthma on the body's other organ systems.

Predict 12

It is not usually necessary to assess arterial blood gases when diagnosing and treating asthma. However, this information can sometimes be useful in severe asthma attacks. Suppose that Will had a P_{O_2} of 60 mm Hg and a P_{CO_2} of 30 mm Hg when he first went to the emergency room. Explain how that could happen.

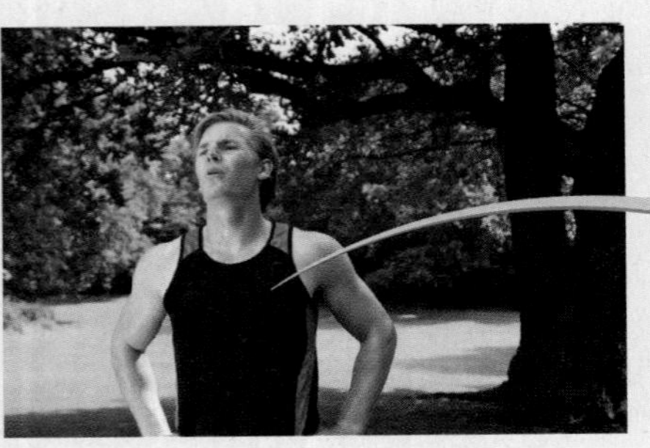

(a)

(b) Asthmatic bronchiole: Note how constricted it is.

(c) Normal bronchiole: Note how clear it is.

FIGURE 23.24

(*a*) Strenuous exercise is one of the many factors that can bring on an asthma attack. (*b*) Changes in bronchiole diameter during an asthma attack. The diameter of the bronchioles is dramatically reduced during an asthma attack, slowing airflow. (*c*) The diameter of the bronchioles is normally sufficient to allow air to flow into and out of the lungs freely. (a) Ammentorp Photography/Alamy Stock Photo; (b) Travis G. Brown, MD/McGraw Hill; (c) Biophoto Associates/Science Source

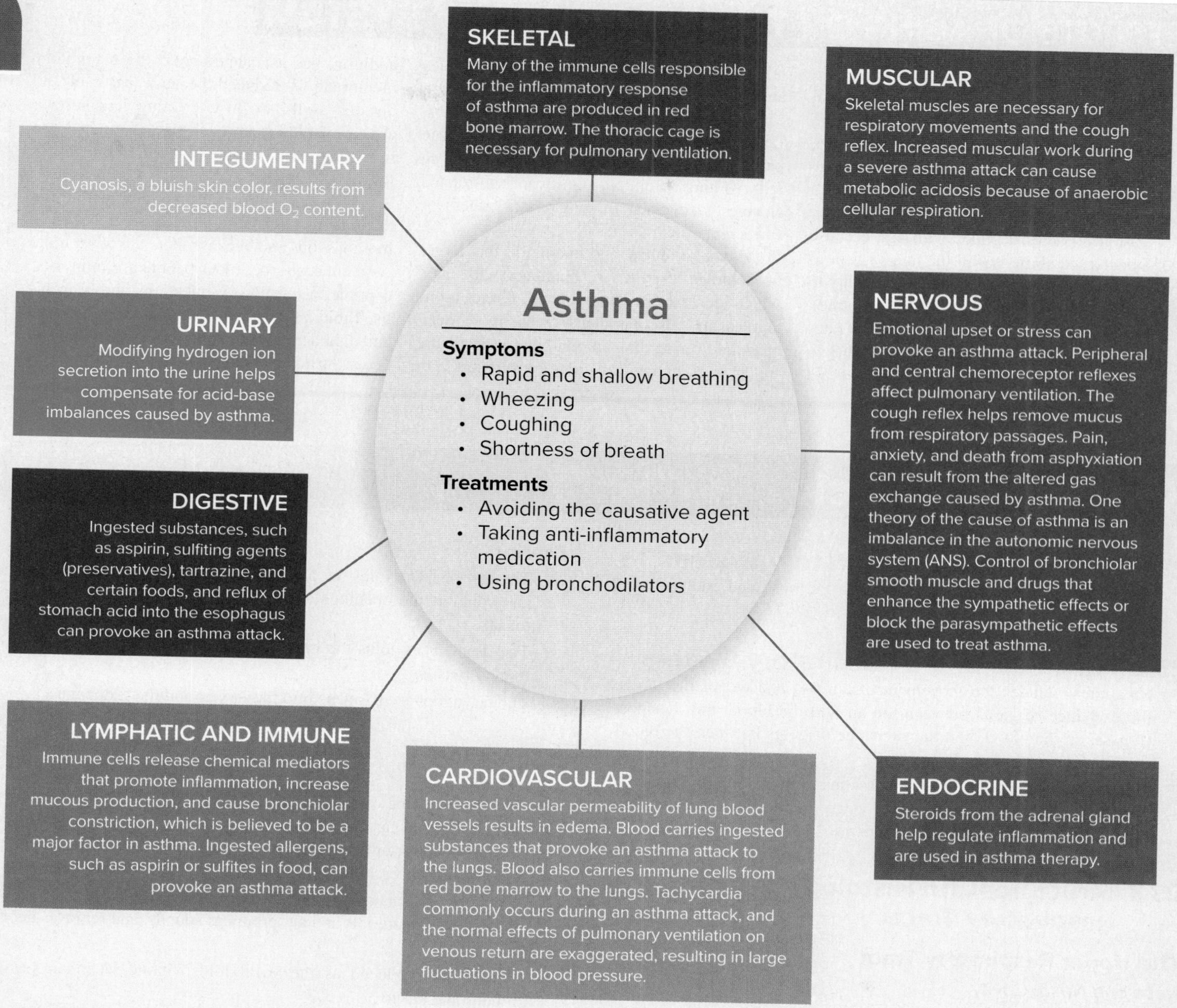

SKELETAL
Many of the immune cells responsible for the inflammatory response of asthma are produced in red bone marrow. The thoracic cage is necessary for pulmonary ventilation.

MUSCULAR
Skeletal muscles are necessary for respiratory movements and the cough reflex. Increased muscular work during a severe asthma attack can cause metabolic acidosis because of anaerobic cellular respiration.

INTEGUMENTARY
Cyanosis, a bluish skin color, results from decreased blood O_2 content.

URINARY
Modifying hydrogen ion secretion into the urine helps compensate for acid-base imbalances caused by asthma.

Asthma

Symptoms

- Rapid and shallow breathing
- Wheezing
- Coughing
- Shortness of breath

Treatments

- Avoiding the causative agent
- Taking anti-inflammatory medication
- Using bronchodilators

NERVOUS
Emotional upset or stress can provoke an asthma attack. Peripheral and central chemoreceptor reflexes affect pulmonary ventilation. The cough reflex helps remove mucus from respiratory passages. Pain, anxiety, and death from asphyxiation can result from the altered gas exchange caused by asthma. One theory of the cause of asthma is an imbalance in the autonomic nervous system (ANS). Control of bronchiolar smooth muscle and drugs that enhance the sympathetic effects or block the parasympathetic effects are used to treat asthma.

DIGESTIVE
Ingested substances, such as aspirin, sulfiting agents (preservatives), tartrazine, and certain foods, and reflux of stomach acid into the esophagus can provoke an asthma attack.

LYMPHATIC AND IMMUNE
Immune cells release chemical mediators that promote inflammation, increase mucous production, and cause bronchiolar constriction, which is believed to be a major factor in asthma. Ingested allergens, such as aspirin or sulfites in food, can provoke an asthma attack.

CARDIOVASCULAR
Increased vascular permeability of lung blood vessels results in edema. Blood carries ingested substances that provoke an asthma attack to the lungs. Blood also carries immune cells from red bone marrow to the lungs. Tachycardia commonly occurs during an asthma attack, and the normal effects of pulmonary ventilation on venous return are exaggerated, resulting in large fluctuations in blood pressure.

ENDOCRINE
Steroids from the adrenal gland help regulate inflammation and are used in asthma therapy.

FIGURE 23.25 Interactions of Asthma with Other Body Systems
During an asthma attack, the body cannot get sufficient O_2, nor can it eliminate adequate amounts of CO_2. The lack of O_2 causes many complications, for example, blood vessel permeability to increase, which can result in edema throughout the body. The inability to eliminate adequate CO_2 causes the body fluid pH to become more acidic, and many processes cannot proceed normally.

EFFECTS OF AGING ON THE RESPIRATORY SYSTEM

Most aspects of the respiratory system are affected by aging. However, even though vital capacity, maximum pulmonary ventilation rates, and gas exchange decrease with age, older people can engage in light to moderate exercise because the respiratory system has a large reserve capacity.

Vital capacity declines with age because of a decreased ability to fill the lungs (inspiratory reserve volume) and a decreased ability to empty the lungs (expiratory reserve volume). As a result, maximum minute volume rates are reduced, which in turn limits the ability to perform intense exercise. These changes are related to weakening of respiratory muscles and to reduced compliance of the thoracic cage caused by the stiffening of cartilage and ribs. Lung compliance increases with age because parts of the alveolar walls are lost, which reduces lung recoil. No significant age-related changes take place in lung elastic fibers or surfactant.

Alveolar ducts and many of the larger bronchioles expand in diameter with age, which increases residual volume. Larger bronchioles and alveolar ducts create more dead space, lowering the amount of air available for gas exchange (alveolar ventilation). In addition, gas exchange across the respiratory membrane is reduced because parts of the alveolar walls are lost, creating less surface area available for gas exchange. A gradual rise in resting tidal volume with age compensates for these changes.

With age, mucus accumulates within the respiratory passageways because it becomes more viscous and because there are fewer cilia. As a consequence, older people are more susceptible to respiratory infections and bronchitis. Table 23.2 describes several other diseases and disorders of the respiratory system that can occur during any stage of life.

Concept Check

23.1 Anatomy of the Respiratory System

The respiratory system structures start with the nose and end with the alveoli in the lungs.

23.2 Functions of the Respiratory System

A. Breathing includes the movement of air into and out of the lungs, the exchange of gases between the air and the blood, the transport of gases in the blood, and the exchange of gases between the blood and tissues.

B. Other functions of the respiratory system are regulation of blood pH, production of chemical mediators, voice production, olfaction, and protection against some microorganisms.

23.3 Structures and Histology of the Respiratory Tract

The Upper Respiratory Tract

Nose and Nasal Cavity

A. The nose consists of the external nose and the nasal cavity.

B. The bridge of the nose is bone, and most of the external nose is cartilage.

C. Openings of the nasal cavity
- The nares open to the outside, and the choanae lead to the pharynx.
- The paranasal sinuses and the nasolacrimal duct open into the nasal cavity.

D. Parts of the nasal cavity
- The nasal cavity is divided by the nasal septum.
- The anterior vestibule contains hairs that trap debris.
- The nasal cavity is lined with pseudostratified ciliated columnar epithelium that traps debris and moves it to the pharynx.
- The superior part of the nasal cavity contains the olfactory epithelium.

E. The nasal cavity serves as a passageway for air; cleans and humidifies air; is the location for the sense of smell; and, with the paranasal sinuses, functions as a resonating chamber for speech.

Pharynx

A. The nasopharynx joins the nasal cavity through the internal choanae and contains the openings to the auditory tube and the pharyngeal tonsils.

B. The oropharynx joins the oral cavity and contains the palatine and lingual tonsils.

C. The laryngopharynx opens into the larynx and the esophagus.

Larynx

A. Cartilage

Three of the nine cartilages are single cartilages. The thyroid cartilage and cricoid cartilage form most of the larynx. The epiglottis covers the opening of the larynx during swallowing. Six of the cartilages are paired. The vocal folds attach to the arytenoid cartilages.

B. The larynx maintains an open air passageway, regulates the passage of swallowed materials and air, produces sounds, and removes debris from the air.

C. Sounds are produced as the vocal folds vibrate when air passes through the larynx.

Tightening the folds produces sounds of different pitches by controlling the length of the fold, which is allowed to vibrate.

1. *The nasal cavity* 

   a. has openings for the paranasal sinuses.
   b. has a vestibule, which contains the olfactory epithelium.
   c. is connected to the pharynx by the nares.
   d. has passageways called conchae.
   e. is lined with squamous epithelium, except for the vestibule.

2. *The larynx* 

   a. connects the oropharynx to the trachea.
   b. has three single and six paired cartilages.
   c. contains the vocal folds.
   d. contains the vestibular folds.
   e. All of these are correct.

The Lower Respiratory Tract

Trachea

A. The trachea connects the larynx to the main bronchi.

B. The trachealis muscle regulates the diameter of the trachea.

Bronchi

The trachea divides to form two main bronchi, which extend to the lungs.

Tracheobronchial Tree

A. The main bronchi divide to form lobar bronchi, which divide to form segmental bronchi, which divide to form bronchioles, which divide to form terminal bronchioles.

B. The trachea to the terminal bronchioles is a passageway for air movement.

- The area from the trachea to the terminal bronchioles is ciliated to facilitate the removal of inspired debris.
- Cartilage helps hold the tube system open (from the trachea to the bronchioles).
- Smooth muscle controls the diameter of the tubes (terminal bronchioles).

Alveoli

A. Terminal bronchioles divide to form respiratory bronchioles, which give rise to alveolar ducts. Air-filled chambers called alveoli open into the respiratory bronchioles and alveolar ducts. The alveolar ducts end as alveolar sacs, which are chambers that connect to two or more alveoli.

B. Gas exchange occurs between the respiratory bronchioles and the alveoli.

C. The components of the respiratory membrane are a film of water, the walls of the alveolus and the capillary, and an interstitial space.

3. *Terminal bronchioles branch to form*

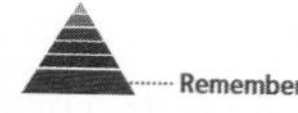

   a. the alveolar duct.
   b. alveoli.
   c. bronchioles.
   d. respiratory bronchioles.

4. *During an asthma attack, a person has difficulty breathing because of constriction of the* Remember

   a. trachea.
   b. bronchi.
   c. terminal bronchioles.
   d. alveoli.
   e. respiratory membrane.

Thoracic Wall and Muscles of Pulmonary Ventilation

The thoracic wall consists of vertebrae, ribs, the sternum, and muscles that allow expansion of the thoracic cavity.

5. *During quiet expiration, the* Remember

   a. abdominal muscles relax.
   b. diaphragm moves inferiorly.
   c. external intercostal muscles contract.
   d. thorax and lungs passively recoil.
   e. All of these are correct.

6. *Suppose that the thoracic wall is punctured at the end of a normal expiration, producing a pneumothorax. Does the thoracic wall move inward, move outward, or not move at all?* Understand

7. *The left phrenic nerve supplies the left side of the diaphragm, and the right phrenic nerve supplies the right side. Damage to the left phrenic nerve results in paralysis of the left side of the diaphragm. During inspiration, does the left side of the diaphragm move superiorly, move inferiorly, or stay in place?* Apply

Lungs

A. The thoracic cavity contains two lungs.

B. The lungs are divided into lobes, bronchopulmonary segments, and lobules.

C. There are three lung lobes on the right and two lung lobes on the left.

D. Each lung lobe is further subdivided into bronchopulmonary segments.

8. *The parietal pleura*

   a. covers the surface of the lung.
   b. covers the inner surface of the thoracic cavity.
   c. is the connective tissue partition that divides the thoracic cavity into right and left pleural cavities.
   d. covers the inner surface of the alveoli.
   e. is the membrane across which gas exchange occurs.

9. *Contraction of the bronchiolar smooth muscle has which of these effects?* Remember

   a. A smaller pressure gradient is required to get the same rate of airflow, compared with normal bronchioles.
   b. It increases airflow through the bronchioles.
   c. It increases resistance to airflow.
   d. It increases alveolar ventilation.

10. *During expiration, the intra-alveolar pressure is*

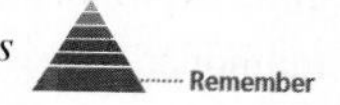

   a. lower than the pleural pressure.
   b. greater than the atmospheric pressure.
   c. lower than the atmospheric pressure.
   d. unchanged.

Blood Supply to the Lungs

A. Deoxygenated blood is transported to the lungs through the pulmonary arteries, and oxygenated blood leaves through the pulmonary veins.

B. Oxygenated blood is mixed with a small amount of deoxygenated blood from the bronchi.

Lymphatic Supply to the Lungs

The superficial and deep lymphatic vessels drain lymph from the lungs.

Pleura

The pleural membranes surround the lungs and protect against friction.

23.4 Behavior of Gases

Behavior of Gases and Pulmonary Ventilation

Pulmonary ventilation is the movement of air into and out of the lungs.

Muscles of Ventilation

A. Contraction of the diaphragm increases thoracic volume.
B. Muscles can elevate the ribs and increase thoracic volume or depress the ribs and decrease thoracic volume.

The Relationship Between Pressure Gradients and Pulmonary Ventilation

A. Air moves from an area of higher pressure to an area of lower pressure.
B. Pressure is inversely related to volume.

11. *Normally, which of the following keeps the lungs from collapsing?* Remember
    a. surfactant
    b. pleural pressure
    c. elastic recoil
    d. Both a and b are correct.

12. *Immediately after the creation of an opening through the thorax into the pleural cavity* Remember
    a. air flows through the hole and into the pleural cavity.
    b. air flows through the hole and out of the pleural cavity.
    c. air flows neither out nor in.
    d. the lung protrudes through the hole.

13. *Compliance of the lungs and thorax* 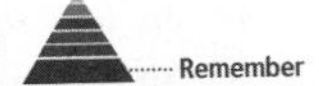

    a. is the volume by which the lungs and thorax change for each unit change of intra-alveolar pressure.
    b. increases in emphysema.
    c. decreases because of lack of surfactant.
    d. All of these are correct.

Measurement of Lung Function

Pulmonary Volumes and Capacities

A. Four pulmonary volumes exist: tidal volume, inspiratory reserve volume, expiratory reserve volume, and residual volume.
B. Pulmonary capacities are the sum of two or more pulmonary volumes and include inspiratory capacity, functional residual capacity, vital capacity, and total lung capacity.
C. The forced expiratory vital capacity measures vital capacity while the individual expires as rapidly as possible.

Minute Volume

A. Minute volume is the total amount of air moved into and out of the respiratory system per minute.
B. Dead space is the part of the respiratory system where gas exchange does not take place.

Alveolar Ventilation

Alveolar ventilation is how much air per minute enters the parts of the respiratory system where gas exchange takes place.

Factors Affecting Pulmonary Ventilation

A. Gender, age, body size, and physical fitness all affect the degree of pulmonary ventilation.
B. Pulmonary ventilation is typically reduced in certain disease states.
C. Compliance is a measure of lung expansion caused by intra-alveolar pressure.
D. Reduced compliance means that it is more difficult than normal to expand the lungs.

14. *Given these lung volumes:* 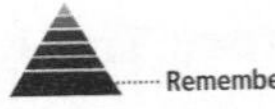

    (1) tidal volume = 500 mL
    (2) residual volume = 1000 mL
    (3) inspiratory reserve volume = 2500 mL
    (4) expiratory reserve volume = 1000 mL
    (5) dead space = 1000 mL
    The vital capacity is
    a. 3000 mL.
    b. 3500 mL.
    c. 4000 mL.
    d. 5000 mL.
    e. 6000 mL.

15. *Alveolar ventilation is the* 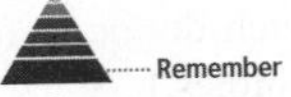

    a. tidal volume times the respiratory rate.
    b. minute volume plus the dead space.
    c. amount of air available for gas exchange in the lungs.
    d. vital capacity divided by the respiratory rate.
    e. inspiratory reserve volume times minute volume.

16. *A person's vital capacity is measured while standing and while lying down. What difference, if any, in the measurement do you predict and why?* Understand

17. *Jenny wanted to do some underwater exploration. Instead of buying expensive SCUBA equipment, she obtained a long hose and an innertube. She attached one end of the hose to the innertube so that the end was always out of the water, and she inserted the other end of the hose in her mouth and went diving. What happened to her alveolar ventilation and why? How can she compensate for this change? How does diving affect lung compliance and the work of pulmonary ventilation?* Apply

Behavior of Gases and Gas Exchange

Partial Pressure

A. Partial pressure is the contribution of a gas to the total pressure of a mixture of gases (Dalton's law).
B. Water vapor pressure is the partial pressure produced by water.
C. Atmospheric air, alveolar air, and expired air have different compositions.

Diffusion of Gases into and out of Liquids

The concentration of a dissolved gas in a liquid is determined by its pressure and by its solubility coefficient (Henry's law).

23.5 Physiology of the Respiratory System

Mechanisms of Alveolar Ventilation

Changes in thoracic volume cause changes in pleural pressure, resulting in changes in alveolar volume, intra-alveolar pressure, and airflow.

Factors Affecting Alveolar Ventilation

Lung Recoil

- Lung recoil results from elastic fibers and water surface tension.
- Surfactant reduces water surface tension.

Pleural Pressure

- A negative pleural pressure can cause the alveoli to expand.
- Pneumothorax is an opening between the pleural cavity and the air that causes a loss of pleural pressure.

Summary of Pressure Changes During a Normal Breathing Cycle

A. Pleural pressure is −4 mm Hg at the end of a normal expiration; air stops flowing out of the lungs.

B. Pleural pressure decreases to −7 mm Hg during inspiration; air flows into the lungs.

18. *One technique for artificial ventilation is mouth-to-mouth resuscitation. The rescuer takes a deep breath, blows air into the patient's mouth, and then lets air flow out. The process is repeated. Explain the following:* Apply

(1) *Why do the patient's lungs expand?*

(2) *Why does air move out of the patient's lungs?*

(3) *What effect do the P_{O_2} and the P_{CO_2} of the rescuer's air have on the victim?*

Factors Affecting Diffusion Through the Respiratory Membrane

The respiratory membrane is thin and has a large surface area that facilitates gas exchange.

Partial Pressure Gradients

A. Oxygen moves from the alveoli (P_{O_2} = 104 mm Hg) into the blood (P_{O_2} = 40 mm Hg). Blood is almost completely saturated with O_2 when it leaves the capillary.

B. The P_{O_2} in the blood decreases (P_{O_2} = 95 mm Hg) when it mixes with deoxygenated blood.

C. Oxygen moves from the tissue capillaries (P_{O_2} = 95 mm Hg) into the tissues (P_{O_2} = 40 mm Hg).

D. Carbon dioxide moves from the tissues (P_{CO_2} = 45 mm Hg) into tissue capillaries (P_{CO_2} = 40 mm Hg).

E. Carbon dioxide moves from the pulmonary capillaries (P_{CO_2} = 45 mm Hg) into the alveoli (P_{CO_2} = 40 mm Hg).

Respiratory Membrane Thickness

The rate of diffusion of gases through the respiratory membrane depends on its thickness, the diffusion coefficient of the gas.

Respiratory Membrane Surface Area

The surface area of the membrane and the partial pressure of the gases in the alveoli and the blood affect the rate of gas diffusion.

19. *The rate of diffusion of a gas across the respiratory membrane increases as the* Remember

a. *respiratory membrane becomes thicker.*
b. *surface area of the respiratory membrane decreases.*
c. *partial pressure gradient of the gas across the respiratory membrane increases.*
d. *diffusion coefficient of the gas decreases.*
e. *All of these are correct.*

20. *During normal, quiet breathing, when does the maximum rate of diffusion of O_2 in the pulmonary capillaries occur? When does the maximum rate of diffusion of CO_2 occur?* Understand

21. *The bacteria that cause gangrene* (Clostridium perfringens) *are anaerobic microorganisms that do not thrive in the presence of O_2. Hyperbaric oxygenation (HBO) treatment places a person in a chamber containing O_2 at three to four times normal atmospheric pressure. Explain how HBO helps treat gangrene.* Apply

23.6 Oxygen and Carbon Dioxide Transport in the Blood

Hemoglobin

A. There are four types of hemoglobin—embryonic, fetal, adult, hemoglobin-S.

B. Fetal hemoglobin has a higher affinity for O_2 than maternal hemoglobin does.

C. Adult hemoglobin is fully saturated when four O_2 are bound to it.

D. Hemoglobin-S is found in individuals with sickle-cell disease.

22. *Experimental evidence suggests that the overuse of erythropoietin (EPO; see chapter 19) reduces athletic performance. What side effects of EPO abuse reduce exercise stamina?*

Transport of O_2

Oxygen is transported by hemoglobin (98.5%) and is dissolved in plasma (1.5%).

23. *Oxygen is mostly transported in the blood* Remember

a. *dissolved in plasma.*
b. *bound to blood proteins.*
c. *within HCO_3^-.*
d. *bound to the heme portion of hemoglobin.*

Transport of CO_2

Transport of CO_2 in the Plasma

Carbon dioxide is transported dissolved in plasma (7%).

Transport of CO_2 by Hemoglobin

In the Haldane effect, the smaller the amount of O_2 bound to hemoglobin, the greater the amount of CO_2 bound to it, and vice versa.

Transport of CO_2 as Bicarbonate Ions

In tissue capillaries, the following events occur:

- Carbon dioxide combines with water inside red blood cells to form carbonic acid, which dissociates to form HCO_3^-. Decreasing HCO_3^- concentrations promote CO_2 transport.
- Exchange of Cl^- for HCO_3^- occurs between plasma and red blood cells; this is called the chloride shift.
- Hydrogen ions binding to hemoglobin promote CO_2 transport, prevent a pH change in red blood cells, and produce a Bohr effect.

24. *Carbon dioxide is mostly transported in the blood*

a. *dissolved in plasma.*
b. *bound to blood proteins.*
c. *within HCO_3^-.*
d. *bound to the heme portion of hemoglobin.*
e. *bound to the globin portion of hemoglobin.*

25. *The chloride shift*

a. *promotes the transport of CO_2 in the blood.*
b. *occurs when Cl^- replaces HCO_3^- within red blood cells.*
c. *maintains electrical neutrality in red blood cells and the plasma.*
d. *All of these are correct.*

Summary of Gas Transport

Affinity of hemoglobin for O_2 decreases as O_2 demand increases.

Physiological Factors Affecting Gas Transport

The affinity of hemoglobin for O_2 is altered by several parameters including pH, temperature, and CO_2 levels.

Effect of P_{O_2} on O_2 Transport

The oxygen-hemoglobin dissociation curve shows that hemoglobin is almost completely saturated when P_{O_2} is 80 mm Hg or above. At lower partial pressures, the hemoglobin releases O_2.

Effect of P_{O_2} on CO_2 Transport

At low P_{O_2} levels, hemoglobin binds more CO_2.

Effect of pH and P_{CO_2} on O_2 Transport

A. Hemoglobin's ability to hold O_2 decreases because of a shift of the oxygen-hemoglobin dissociation curve to the right due to decreased pH (Bohr effect) or increased CO_2.
B. Hemoglobin's ability to hold O_2 increases because of a shift of the oxygen-hemoglobin dissociation curve to the left due to increased pH (Bohr effect), decreased CO_2, or decreased temperature.

Effect of pH and P_{CO_2} on CO_2 Transport

There is little effect of pH on CO_2 transport.

Effect of Temperature on O_2 Transport

An increase in temperature decreases the affinity of hemoglobin for O_2. This is seen as a right shift of the oxygen-hemoglobin dissociation curve.

Effect of Temperature on CO_2 Transport

At higher body temperatures, more CO_2 is produced, which results in an increased respiratory rate.

Effect of BPG on O_2 Transport

The substance 2,3-bisphosphoglycerate increases hemoglobin's ability to release O_2.

Effect of BPG on CO_2 Transport

BPG enhances the Haldane effect.

26. *The oxygen-hemoglobin dissociation curve is adaptive because it*

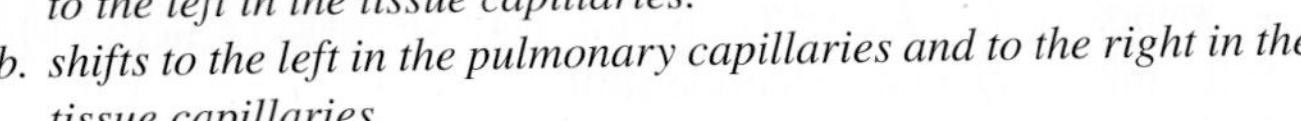

a. shifts to the right in the pulmonary capillaries and to the left in the tissue capillaries.
b. shifts to the left in the pulmonary capillaries and to the right in the tissue capillaries.
c. does not shift.

23.7 Regulation of Pulmonary Ventilation

Local Control

A. Increased alveolar ventilation or increased pulmonary capillary perfusion increases gas exchange.
B. The physiological shunt is the deoxygenated blood returning from the lungs.

Neural Control

Respiratory Areas in the Brainstem

A. The medullary respiratory center consists of the dorsal and ventral respiratory groups.
- The dorsal respiratory groups stimulate the diaphragm.
- The ventral respiratory groups stimulate the intercostal and abdominal muscles.

B. The pontine respiratory group is involved with switching between inspiration and expiration.

Generation of Rhythmic Pulmonary Ventilation

A. Neurons in the medullary respiratory center establish the basic rhythm of pulmonary ventilation.
B. When stimuli from receptors or other parts of the brain exceed a threshold level, inspiration begins.
C. As respiratory muscles are stimulated, neurons that stop inspiration are stimulated. When the stimulation of these neurons exceeds a threshold level, inspiration is inhibited.

Effect of P_{O_2} on Respiratory Rate

Oxygen levels in the blood affect pulmonary ventilation when a 50% or greater decrease from normal exists. Decreased O_2 is detected by receptors in the carotid and aortic bodies, which then stimulate the respiratory center.

Effect of P_{CO_2} on Respiratory Rate

Carbon dioxide is the major regulator of pulmonary ventilation. An increase in CO_2 or a decrease in pH can stimulate the chemosensitive area, causing a greater rate and depth of pulmonary ventilation.

Effect of pH on Respiratory Rate

A low pH stimulates an increased respiratory rate, which expels excess CO_2. A lower level of CO_2 returns pH to normal levels.

The Hering-Breuer Reflex and Respiratory Rate

Stretch of the lungs during inspiration can inhibit the respiratory center and contribute to a cessation of inspiration.

Cerebral and Limbic System Control of Respiratory Rate

A. Pulmonary ventilation can be voluntarily controlled and can be modified by emotions.
B. Collateral fibers from motor neurons and from proprioceptors stimulate the respiratory centers during exercise.
C. Chemosensitive mechanisms and learning fine-tune the effects produced through the motor neurons and proprioceptors during exercise.

Other Modifications of Pulmonary Ventilation

Touch, thermal, and pain sensations can modify pulmonary ventilation.

27. *Which of these parts of the brainstem is correctly matched with its main function?*

Remember

a. ventral respiratory groups—stimulate the diaphragm
b. dorsal respiratory groups—limit inflation of the lungs
c. pontine respiratory group—is involved in the switch between inspiration and expiration
d. All of these are correct.

28. *The chemosensitive area*

a. stimulates the respiratory center when blood CO_2 levels increase.
b. stimulates the respiratory center when blood pH increases.
c. is located in the pons.
d. stimulates the respiratory center when blood O_2 levels increase.
e. All of these are correct.

29. *Blood O_2 levels*

a. are more important than CO_2 levels in the regulation of pulmonary ventilation.
b. need to change only slightly to cause a change in pulmonary ventilation.
c. are detected by sensory receptors in the carotid and aortic bodies.
d. All of these are correct.

30. *Predict what would happen to tidal volume if* Apply
    a. *the vagus nerves were cut,*
    b. *the phrenic nerves were cut, or*
    c. *the intercostal nerves were cut.*

31. *You and your physiology instructor are trapped in an overturned ship. To escape, you must swim under water a long distance. You tell your instructor it would be a good idea to hyperventilate before making the escape attempt. Your instructor calmly replies, "What good would that do because your pulmonary capillaries are already 100% saturated with oxygen?" What should you do, and why?* Apply

32. *Stephanie was hysterical and hyperventilating, so a doctor made her breathe into a paper bag. An especially astute student said to the doctor, "When Stephanie was hyperventilating, she was reducing blood CO_2 levels; when she breathed into the paper bag, CO_2 was trapped in the bag, and she was rebreathing it, thus causing blood CO_2 levels to increase. As Stephanie's blood CO_2 levels increased, her urge to breathe should have increased. Instead, she began to breathe more slowly. Please explain." How do you think the doctor responded?* (Hint: *Recall that the effect of decreased blood CO_2 on the vasomotor center results in vasodilation and a sudden decrease in blood pressure.)* Apply

Answers to this chapter's odd-numbered Concept Check questions appear in Appendix F.

24 CHAPTER

Digestive System

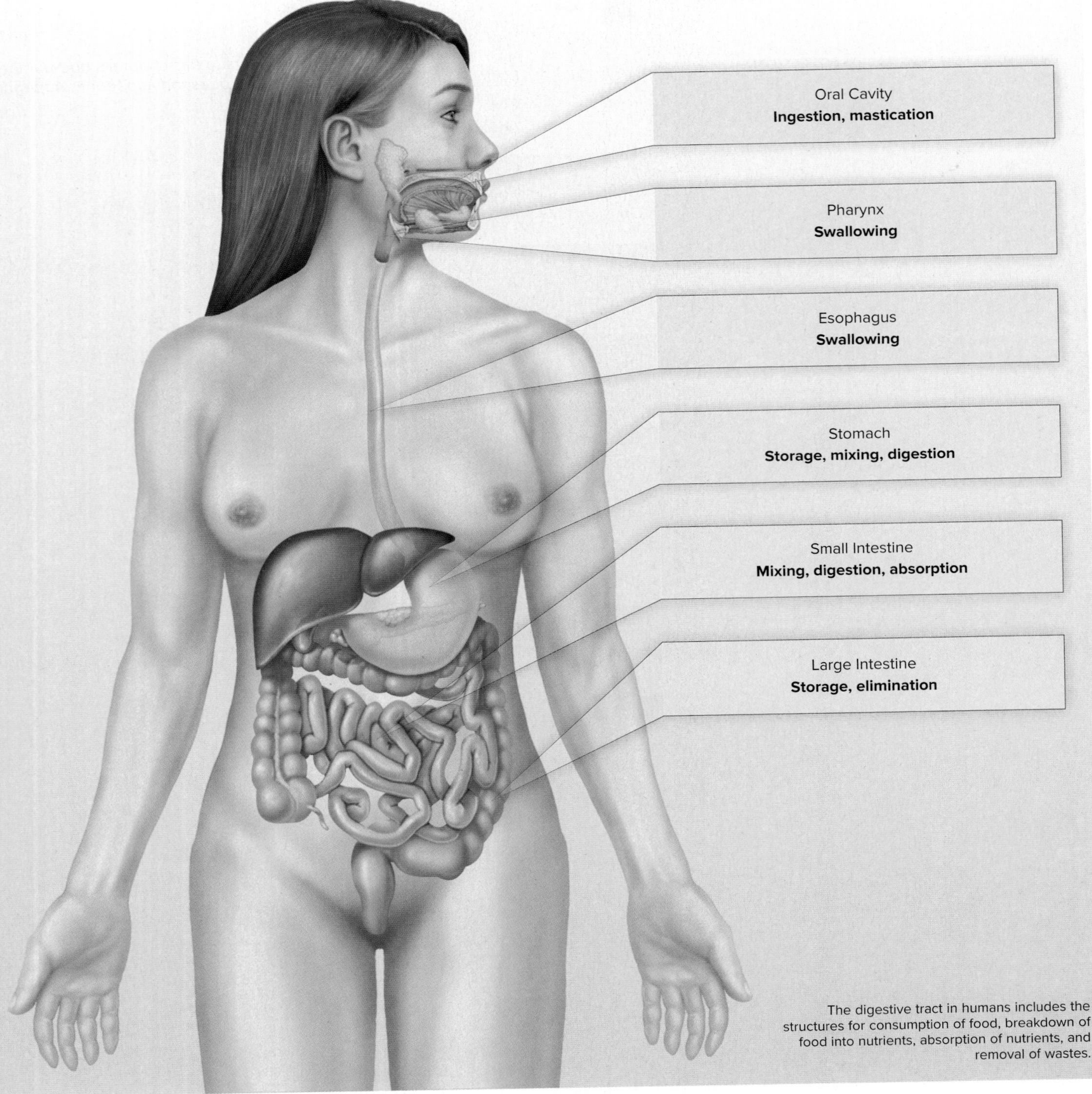

The digestive tract in humans includes the structures for consumption of food, breakdown of food into nutrients, absorption of nutrients, and removal of wastes.

Almost everyone loves to eat, and we all must eat to stay alive. Throughout history, food and drink have provided not only nourishment but also the foundation for many social gatherings. Although it's not something we often think about while enjoying our pizza and favorite beverage, the body has an amazing digestive system that includes its own quality control and waste disposal methods.

Every cell of the body needs nourishment, yet most cells cannot leave their position in the body and travel to a food source. Therefore, the food must be converted to a usable form and delivered. To do this, the digestive system is specialized to ingest food, propel it through the digestive tract, digest it, and absorb water, electrolytes, and nutrients. The digestive process involves a choreographed mixing of food with digestive juices that include strong acids, detergent-like bile salts, and activated enzymes. The body then maximizes absorption of digested nutrients. Once these useful substances are absorbed, they are transported through the blood to cells, which use them for energy or as new molecules for building and maintaining tissues and organs. Indeed, the digestive system is the body's "Grubhub."

Learn to Predict

Rebecca kept attributing her recurring abdominal pain to "something I ate"—and she was partly right about that. Several times during the past year, eating high-fat meals had led to episodes of serious abdominal pain. During the most recent attack, the discomfort became so intense that Rebecca went to the emergency room, where she was given medication to relieve the pain. Still, over the next few hours, her skin took on a yellowish tint, and the next morning she had diarrhea and clay-colored feces. Following lab tests and ultrasonography, a physician diagnosed gallstones and recommended the removal of Rebecca's gallbladder.

Explain how gallstones led to Rebecca's pain and other symptoms.

Answers to this question and the chapter's odd-numbered Predict questions can be found in Appendix E.

24.1 Anatomy of the Digestive System

LEARNING OUTCOME

After reading this section, you should be able to

A. **List the regions of the digestive tract.**

The **digestive system** consists of the digestive tract and accessory organs (figure 24.1). The **digestive tract** is a tube extending from the mouth to the anus. It is also called the **gastrointestinal** (GAS-troh-in-TESS-tin-al; **GI**) **tract** and the *alimentary canal.* The associated **accessory organs** include the tongue, teeth, salivary glands, liver, gallbladder, and pancreas. These organs include glands that secrete fluids into the digestive tract.

The digestive tract and associated accessory organs include the following:

1. *Oral cavity,* including the tongue, teeth, and salivary glands as accessory organs
2. *Pharynx*
3. *Esophagus*
4. *Stomach*
5. *Small intestine,* consisting of the duodenum, jejunum, and ileum, with the liver, gallbladder, and pancreas as accessory organs
6. *Large intestine,* including the cecum, colon, rectum, anal canal, and anus

ASSESS YOUR PROGRESS

Answers to these questions are found in the section you have just completed. Re-read the section if you need help in answering these questions.

1. *List the regions of the digestive tract, from beginning to end.*

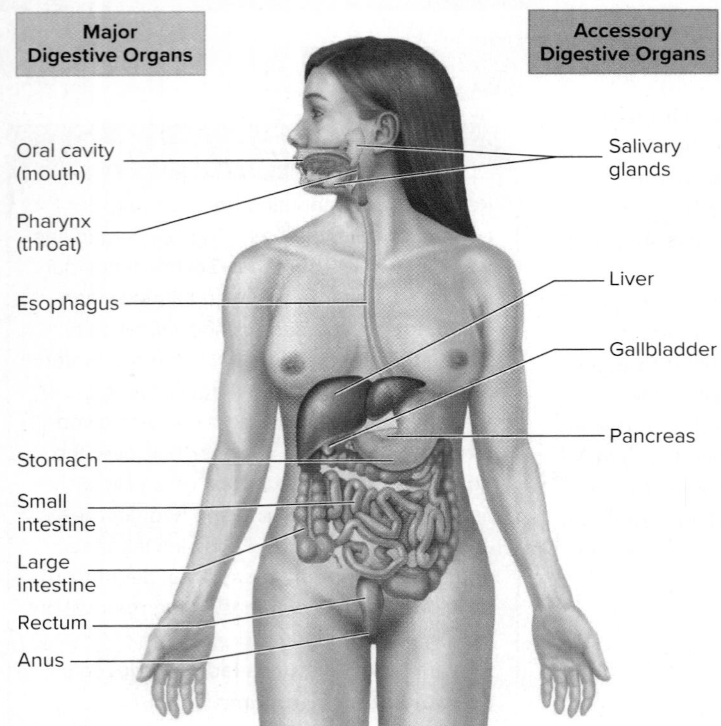

FIGURE 24.1 Digestive System
The digestive system consists of the digestive tract from the oral cavity to the anus, and the associated accessory organs: salivary glands, liver, gallbladder, and pancreas.

24.2 Functions of the Digestive System

LEARNING OUTCOMES

After reading this section, you should be able to

A. **Describe the major functions of the digestive system.**
B. **State which digestive functions occur in the different regions of the digestive tract.**

The six major functions of the digestive system are (1) ingestion and mastication, (2) propulsion and mixing, (3) secretion, (4) digestion, (5) absorption, and (6) elimination. These are described here and in figure 24.2:

1. *Ingestion and Mastication.* Ingestion is the intake of solids or liquids. The normal route of ingestion is through the oral cavity. Mastication is the process by which the teeth chew food in the mouth to begin the process of digestion. Digestive enzymes cannot easily penetrate solid food particles and are effective only on the outer surface of food particles. It is vital, therefore, that solid foods be mechanically broken down by mastication to increase total surface area for digestion.
2. *Propulsion and Mixing.* Propulsion is the movement of food from one end of the digestive tract to the other. Mixing is the movement of food back and forth in the digestive tract, without forward movement. The total time it takes food to travel the length of the digestive tract is usually about 24–36 hours. Each segment of the digestive tract is specialized to assist in moving food undergoing digestion from its oral end to its anal end. The propulsive movements begin with swallowing, followed by peristalsis, and finally mass movements. Characteristics of these propulsive movements are:
   a. **Swallowing,** or *deglutition* (dee-glue-TISH-un), moves liquids or a soft mass of food and liquid, called a **bolus** (BOH-lus), from the oral cavity into the esophagus.
   b. **Peristalsis** (per-i-STAL-sis), outlined in figure 24.3*a,* propels material through most of the digestive tract.
      1. **Peristaltic** (per-ih-STAL-tik) **waves** are muscular contractions consisting of a wave of relaxation of the circular muscles in front of the mass of undigested food (now called chyme).
      2. This is followed by a wave of strong contraction of the circular muscles behind the mass of chyme, which force the bolus along the digestive tract. Each peristaltic wave travels the length of the esophagus in about 10 seconds. Peristaltic waves in the small and large intestines usually travel only short distances.
   c. **Mass movements** are contractions that move material in the distal parts of the large intestine to the anus.

   Mixing contractions blend food with digestive fluids in the stomach and small intestine. These contractions aid with mechanical digestion. There are two major types of mixing contractions:
   a. **Mixing waves** are gentle contractions in the stomach that churn the food with gastric secretions. Ingested food is stored and mixed in the stomach, from where it is slowly released into the small intestine as chyme.
   b. **Segmental contractions** mix food particles with digestive secretions in the small intestine. Figure 24.3*b* shows the sequence of segmental contractions.
      1. A mass of chyme within the tract begins at one location.
      2. Segments of the digestive tract alternate between contraction and relaxation.
      3. The mass of chyme spreads out in both directions.
3. *Secretion.* Secretions are added to lubricate, liquefy, buffer, and digest the food as it moves through the digestive tract. **Mucus,** secreted along the entire digestive tract, lubricates the food and the lining of the tract. The mucus coats and protects the epithelial cells of the digestive tract from mechanical abrasion, stomach acid, and digestive enzymes. The secretions also contain large amounts of **water,** which liquefies the food, making it easier to digest and absorb. Water also moves into the intestine by osmosis. Liver secretions break large lipid droplets into much smaller droplets, which makes the digestion and absorption of lipids possible. **Enzymes** secreted by the oral cavity, stomach, small intestine, and pancreas break down large food molecules into smaller molecules that can be absorbed by the intestinal wall.
4. *Digestion.* Digestion is the breakdown of large organic molecules into their individual components. Digestion consists of **mechanical digestion,** which involves the mastication and mixing of food, and **chemical digestion,** which is

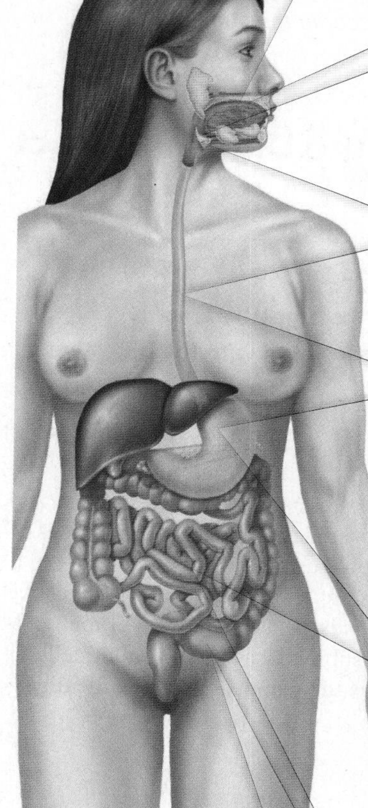

Oral Cavity

Ingestion and Mastication. Solid food and fluids are taken into the digestive tract through the oral cavity. The teeth break food into smaller pieces.

Propulsion and Mixing. The tongue forms food into a bolus and pushes the bolus into the pharynx to begin the swallowing reflex.

Digestion and Secretion. Mastication begins mechanical digestion of food. Amylase in saliva begins carbohydrate (starch) digestion.

Absorption. There is no absorption of nutrients in the mouth, although some drugs can be absorbed across the oral mucosa.

Pharynx

Propulsion and Mixing. Swallowing moves the bolus from the oral cavity to the esophagus. Materials are prevented from entering the nasal cavity by the soft palate and kept out of the lower respiratory tract by the epiglottis and vestibular folds.

Secretion. Mucus provides lubrication.

Esophagus

Propulsion and Mixing. Peristaltic contractions move the bolus from the pharynx to the stomach. The lower esophageal sphincter limits reflux of the stomach contents into the esophagus.

Secretion. Mucus provides lubrication and protects the inferior esophagus from stomach acid.

Stomach

Propulsion and Mixing. Mixing waves churn ingested materials and stomach secretions into chyme. Rugae allow the stomach to expand and store food. Peristaltic waves move the chyme into the small intestine.

Secretion. Release of hydrochloric acid creates the acidic stomach environment. The acid kills most microorganisms and activates the precursor of the proteolytic enzyme pepsin. Mucus provides lubrication and prevents digestion of the stomach wall.

Digestion. Mechanical digestion occurs as food is churned in the stomach by mixing waves. Protein digestion begins as a result of the actions of hydrochloric acid and pepsin.

Absorption. Absorption of only a few substances (e.g., water, alcohol, aspirin) takes place in the stomach.

Small Intestine

Propulsion and Mixing. Segmental contractions mix the chyme, and peristaltic contractions move the chyme into the large intestine.

Secretion. Bicarbonate ions from the pancreas and bile from the liver neutralize stomach acid to form a pH environment suitable for pancreatic and intestinal enzymes. Mucus provides lubrication, prevents digestion of the intestinal wall, and protects the small intestine from stomach acid.

Digestion. Segmental contractions aid mechanical digestion. Enzymes from the pancreas and the lining of the small intestine complete the breakdown of food molecules. Bile salts from the liver emulsify lipids to allow lipid digestion.

Absorption. The circular folds, villi, and microvilli increase surface area. Most nutrients are actively or passively absorbed. Most of the ingested water or the water in digestive tract secretions is absorbed.

Large Intestine

Propulsion and Mixing. Slight segmental mixing occurs. Mass movements propel feces toward the anus, and defecation eliminates the feces.

Secretion. Mucus provides lubrication; mucus and bicarbonate ions protect against acids produced by bacteria.

Absorption. The first half of the colon absorbs salts (e.g., NaCl), water, and vitamins (e.g., K) produced by bacteria.

Elimination. The second half of the colon holds feces until they are eliminated.

FIGURE 24.2 Digestive Functions of the Digestive Tract
Each portion of the digestive tract plays a different role in the breakdown of food and the absorption of nutrients.

accomplished by digestive enzymes secreted along the digestive tract. Large organic molecules must be digested into their individual components before they can be absorbed by the digestive tract. Carbohydrates are broken into monosaccharides. Proteins are broken into amino acids, and triglycerides into fatty acids and glycerol. Minerals and water are not broken down before being absorbed. Vitamins are also absorbed without digestion; in fact, they lose their function if their structure is altered by digestion.

5. *Absorption.* Absorption is the movement of molecules out of the digestive tract and into the blood or into the lymphatic system. The mechanism by which absorption occurs

PROCESS Figure

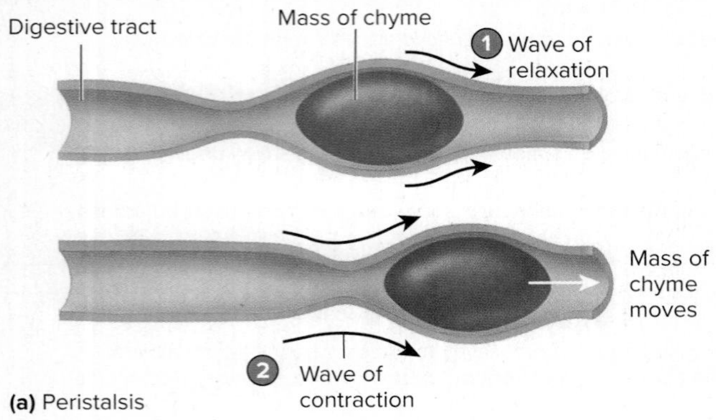

(a) Peristalsis

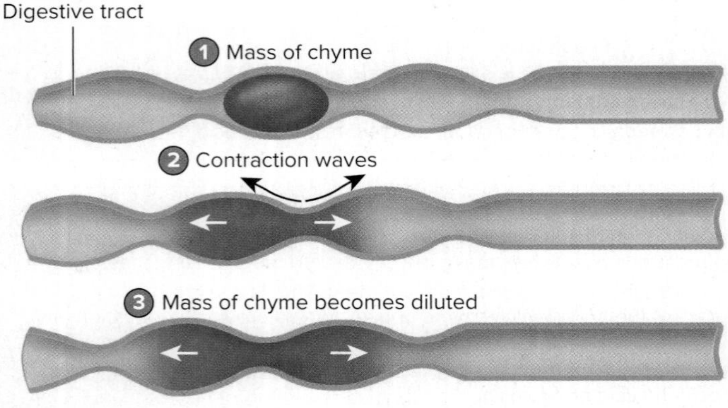

(b) Segmental contractions

PROCESS Figure 24.3

Peristalsis and Segmental Contractions

(*a*) Waves of smooth muscle contraction push food and waste through the digestive tract. (*b*) Smooth muscle contractions in the wall of the small intestine disperse food undergoing digestion throughout its lumen.

Some agents that cause diarrhea increase peristalsis of the intestine. Explain how medications that slow intestinal motility relieve symptoms of diarrhea (see this chapter's Systems Pathology). How might reduced segmental contractions affect the digestive process?

depends on the type of molecule involved. Molecules pass out of the digestive tract by diffusion, facilitated diffusion, active transport, symport, or endocytosis (see chapter 3; section 24.12).

6. *Elimination.* Elimination is the process by which the waste products of digestion are removed from the body. During this process, which occurs primarily in the large intestine, water and salts are absorbed, changing the material in the digestive tract from liquefied to semisolid. These semisolid waste products, called **feces** (FEE-sees), are stored in the distal large intestine, and then eliminated by the process of **defecation.**

ASSESS YOUR PROGRESS

2. *Describe each of the functions involved in the normal functions of the digestive system.*
3. *Explain the three types of propulsion through the digestive tract.*
4. *What is the difference between mechanical digestion and chemical digestion?*
5. *What digestive functions occur in the stomach? In the small intestine?*

24.3 Histology of the Digestive Tract

LEARNING OUTCOMES

After reading this section, you should be able to

A. **Describe the histology of the digestive tract.**
B. **List the types of glands associated with the digestive tract.**

The digestive tract consists of four major tunics, or layers (figure 24.4). From the innermost layer to the outermost layer, the four tunics are (1) mucosa, (2) submucosa, (3) muscularis, and (4) serosa or adventia. These four tunics are present in all areas of the digestive tract, from the esophagus to the anus.

Three major types of glands are associated with the digestive tract: (1) unicellular mucous glands in the mucosa, (2) multicellular glands in the mucosa and submucosa, and (3) multicellular glands (accessory glands, such as the pancreas) outside the digestive tract.

Mucosa

The innermost tunic, the **mucosa** (myu-KOH-sah), or *mucous membrane,* consists of three separate layers:

1. the inner **mucous epithelium,** which is nonkeratinized stratified squamous epithelium in the mouth, oropharynx, esophagus, and anal canal and simple columnar epithelium in the remainder of the digestive tract;
2. a loose connective tissue called the **lamina propria** (PROH-pree-ah); and
3. a thin outer layer of smooth muscle called the **muscularis mucosae.**

The epithelium extends deep into the lamina propria in many places to form **intestinal glands** and **crypts.** Two types of specialized cells in the mucosa are mechanoreceptors involved in peristaltic reflexes and chemoreceptors that detect the chemical composition of food.

Submucosa

Beneath the mucosa lies the **submucosa,** a thick connective tissue layer. This tunic contains nerves, blood vessels, lymphatic vessels, and small glands. A network of neurons and glial cells in the submucosa forms a portion of the enteric nervous system (see next

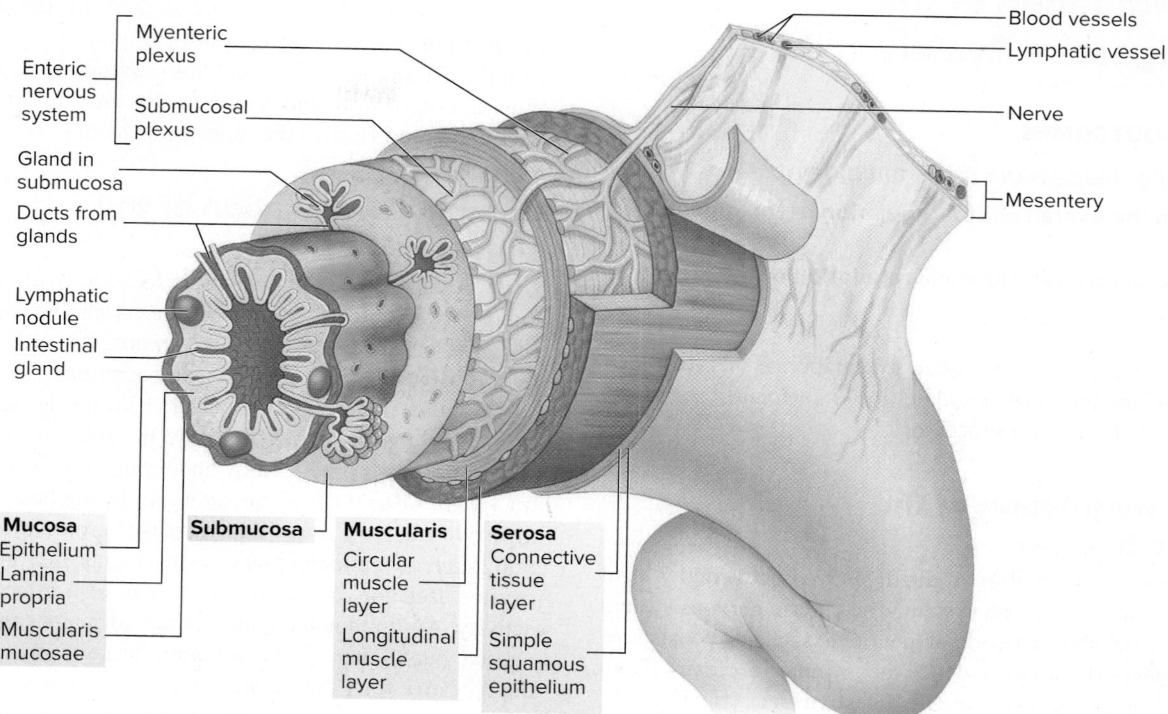

FIGURE 24.4 Digestive Tract Histology

The four tunics are the mucosa, the submucosa, the muscularis, and a serosa or an adventitia. In this image, the serosa is also called the visceral peritoneum, which forms part of the mesentery. Glands may exist along the digestive tract as part of the epithelium, as glands within the submucosa, or as large glands outside the digestive tract.

section) called the **submucosal plexus** (PLEK-sus), or *Meissner plexus*. Axons from the submucosal plexus extend to cells in epithelial intestinal glands, stimulating their secretion. The esophagus and stomach lack a submucosal plexus, but the plexus is extensive throughout the rest of the digestive tract.

Muscularis

The next tunic is the **muscularis,** a muscular layer. The muscularis consists of an inner layer of circular smooth muscle and an outer layer of longitudinal smooth muscle. Two exceptions are the upper esophagus, where the muscles are skeletal, and the stomach, which has three layers of smooth muscle. Between the two muscle layers is a second portion of the enteric nervous system called the **myenteric** (my-en-TER-ik) **plexus,** or *Auerbach plexus* (figure 24.4). The myenteric plexus is much more extensive than the submucosal plexus and controls the motility of the intestinal tract. This function is in contrast with the submucosal plexus, which controls secretions.

Within the myenteric plexus, specialized **interstitial cells** form a network of pacemakers, which promote rhythmic contractions of smooth muscle along the digestive tract. These cells also help transmit signals from neurons to muscles to regulate movement. Dysfunction of these pacemakers decreases motility in the digestive tract.

Together, the submucosal and myenteric plexuses constitute the **enteric** (en-TER-ik) **nervous system (ENS),** or the *enteric plexus,* which is extremely important in controlling secretion and movement (see section 24.4).

Serosa or Adventitia

The fourth layer of the digestive tract is either a **serosa** or an **adventitia** (ad-ven-TISH-ah; foreign or coming from outside), depending on the structure of the layer. Parts of the digestive tract located within the peritoneal cavity have a serosa as the outermost layer. This serosa, or serous membrane, is called the visceral peritoneum. It consists of a thin layer of connective tissue and a simple squamous epithelium (figure 24.4). When the outer layer of the digestive tract is derived from adjacent connective tissue, the tunic is called the adventitia and consists of a connective tissue covering that blends with the surrounding connective tissue. These areas include the esophagus and the retroperitoneal organs (see section 24.5).

ASSESS YOUR PROGRESS

6. *What are the major tunics of the digestive tract wall, listed from inside to outside?*
7. *What types of tissue are found in each tunic?*
8. *In what tunics of the digestive tract are the submucosal and myenteric plexuses found? What are their functions?*
9. *How do the serosa and adventitia differ?*

24.4 Regulation of the Digestive System

LEARNING OUTCOMES

After reading this section, you should be able to

A. **Describe the overall neural regulation of the digestive system.**

B. **Describe the overall chemical regulation of the digestive system.**

The digestive system is controlled by elaborate nervous and chemical mechanisms that regulate the movement, secretion, absorption, and elimination processes.

Nervous Regulation of the Digestive System

Most of the nervous regulation of the digestive tract is under local control by the enteric nervous system. The enteric nervous system (ENS) is an extensive network of neural tissue and consists of (1) the submucosal plexus and (2) the myenteric plexus. Both plexuses are within the walls of the digestive tract (figure 24.4). This network of neurons and associated glial cells is a division of the autonomic nervous system (see chapter 16). It seems incredible, but the ENS contains more neurons than the spinal cord! In addition to local reflexes within the ENS, there is also control mediated by autonomic innervation from the CNS. This innervation is largely by the parasympathetic division of the ANS through the vagus nerves and to a lesser extent by sympathetic nerves (see chapter 16).

There are three major types of enteric neurons: (1) Enteric sensory neurons that detect changes in the chemical composition of digestive tract contents or detect mechanical changes, such as stretch of the digestive tract wall; (2) enteric motor neurons that stimulate or inhibit smooth muscle contraction and glandular secretion in the digestive system; and (3) enteric interneurons that connect enteric sensory and motor neurons. The ENS functions through **local reflexes** to control activities within specific, short regions of the digestive tract. The ENS is capable of controlling the complex peristaltic and mixing movements, as well as blood flow to the digestive tract, without any outside influences. The importance of the ENS is highlighted by the poor intestinal motility observed in patients with **Hirschprung disease,** or *megacolon,* who lack a subset of enteric neurons (see Clinical Impact 24.1).

Although the ENS can control the activities of the digestive tract independently of the CNS, the two systems normally work together. Autonomic innervation from the CNS can increase or decrease ENS activity.

Control of the digestive system by the CNS occurs when reflexes are activated by stimuli originating either in the digestive tract or in the CNS. From within the digestive system, action potentials are carried by sensory neurons in the vagus and sympathetic nerves to the CNS, where the reflexes are integrated. Reflexes within the CNS can be activated by the sight, smell, or taste of food; for example, the smell of your neighbor's cookout increases the secretion of both saliva and pancreatic fluids. All of these reflexes influence activity in parasympathetic neurons of the CNS. Parasympathetic neurons extend to the digestive tract through the vagus nerves to control responses or alter the activity of the ENS and local reflexes. Some sympathetic neurons inhibit muscle contraction and secretion in the digestive system and decrease blood flow to the digestive system.

Chemical Regulation of the Digestive System

Over 30 neurotransmitters are associated with the ENS. Two major ENS neurotransmitters are acetylcholine and norepinephrine. In general, acetylcholine *stimulates* and norepinephrine *inhibits* digestive tract motility and secretions.

Another major ENS neurotransmitter is serotonin, which stimulates digestive tract motility. In addition to neural release, serotonin is also produced by endocrine cells within the digestive tract wall. Over 95% of the serotonin in the body is found in the digestive tract, so drugs that increase serotonin levels and function, such as antidepressants (see chapter 11) and chemotherapeutics used for cancer treatment, can also affect digestive tract activity. An unintended consequence of many cancer therapies is nausea, due to increased serotonin release from endocrine cells in the digestive tract. Serotonin binds to a subset of serotonin receptors on sensory terminals of the vagus nerves, which stimulates the vomiting center in the brain. This results in the nausea and vomiting associated with chemotherapy and radiotherapy. Serotonin receptor blockers, such as ondansetron (on-DAN-see-tron) (e.g., Zofran®), are commonly used to alleviate nausea.

A number of hormones, such as gastrin and secretin, are secreted by endocrine cells in the digestive system and are carried through the blood to target organs of the digestive system or to

Clinical IMPACT 24.1

Enteric Neurons

Hirschprung disease, also called *megacolon,* is a painful developmental disorder caused by the absence of enteric neurons in the distal large intestine. Mutations in the *RET* gene have been identified in patients with Hirschprung disease. The *RET* gene encodes a receptor that is normally activated by the growth factors required for the survival and differentiation of a subset of enteric neurons. The mutations in *RET* that lead to loss of receptor function result in loss of enteric neurons, which results in poor intestinal motility and severe constipation. Conversely, a different set of mutations in the *RET* gene is linked to an inherited cancer called **multiple endocrine neoplasia type 2 (MEN2).** In contrast to the loss of function due to Hirschprung mutations, the MEN2 mutations cause a gain of RET receptor function, so that it is active even in the absence of growth factors. Hence, two types of mutations in the same gene result in two very different syndromes. Rapid DNA tests are used to screen patients and family members for suspected Hirschprung and MEN2 mutations.

target tissues in other systems. These hormones help regulate many digestive tract functions, as well as the secretions of associated glands, such as the liver and pancreas.

In addition to the hormones produced by the digestive system that enter the blood, other paracrine chemicals, such as histamine, are released locally within the digestive tract, where they influence the activity of nearby cells. These localized chemical regulators help local reflexes within the ENS control local digestive tract environments, such as pH levels.

ASSESS YOUR PROGRESS

10. *Describe the roles of the ENS, CNS, and ANS in controlling the digestive system.*

11. *What chemical mechanisms regulate the digestive system?*

24.5 Peritoneum

LEARNING OUTCOME

After reading this section, you should be able to

A. **Describe the peritoneum and its function.**

The walls and organs of the abdominal cavity are lined with a continuous **serous membrane** sheet called the **peritoneum** (PER-i-toh-NEE-um; to stretch over; figure 24.5). Serous membranes are very smooth and secrete a serous fluid, which provides a lubricating film between the layers of membranes. The membrane and fluid reduce friction as organs move within the abdominal cavity. The portion of the peritoneum that covers the organs is the

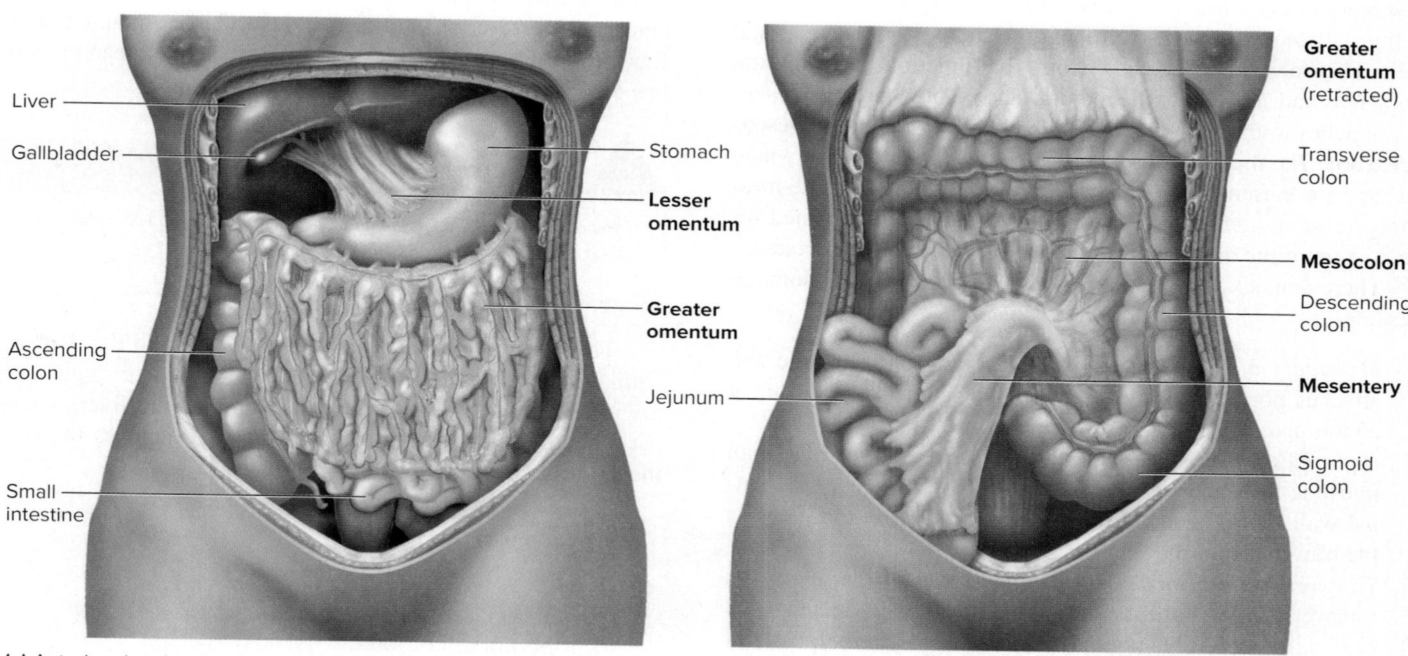

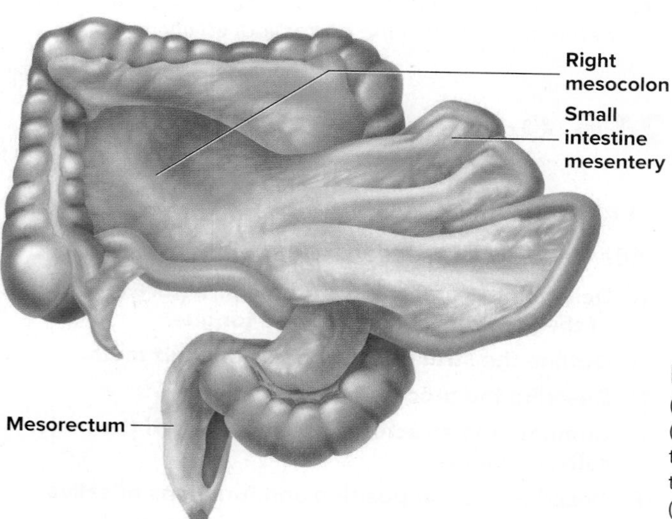

FIGURE 24.5 Mesentery and Omenta

(*a*) Anterior view of the peritoneal cavity with the greater omentum in place. (*b*) Anterior view of the peritoneal cavity with the greater omentum retracted to reveal the small intestine mesentery. (*c*) A view of the mesentery showing the right mesocolon. The left mesocolon is adjacent to the left colic flexure (curve). The mesentery is a contiguous set of connective tissues anchoring the digestive organs in place within the peritoneal cavity. APR

visceral peritoneum, which merges with the portion that covers the interior surface of the wall of the abdominal cavity called the **parietal peritoneum** (figure 24.5). Serous membranes also surround other organs of the body.

Peritonitis is a potentially life-threatening inflammation of the peritoneum. The inflammation can result from chemical irritation by substances, such as bile, that have escaped from a damaged digestive tract or from infection originating in the digestive tract, as when the appendix ruptures. The main symptoms of peritonitis are acute abdominal pain and tenderness that are worsened by movement. An accumulation of excess serous fluid in the peritoneal cavity, called **ascites** (ah-SIGH-teez), can occur in peritonitis. Ascites can also accompany starvation, alcoholism, or liver cancer.

All digestive organs within the abdominal cavity are held in place by a structure called the **mesentery** (MESS-en-ter-ree). The mesentery is a continuous, double layer of epithelial tissue (mesothelium) attached along its full length to the posterior abdominal wall. The mesentery extends from the junction between the esophagus and stomach to the rectum. The point where the mesentery attaches to the posterior abdominal wall is called the **mesenteric root.** The mesenteric root corresponds to the location where the superior mesenteric artery branches from the aorta. The mesentery is subdivided into multiple regions, which are named for the portion of the digestive tract with which they are associated.

There are six contiguous regions of the adult abdominal mesentery:

1. *Mesentery of the small intestine*. This region is mobile and attaches portions of the jejunum and ileum to the posterior abdominal wall.
2. *Right mesocolon*. This region is a continuation of the small intestine mesentery and is anchored to the posterior abdominal wall. At the hepatic (right colic) flexure, it continues as the transverse mesocolon.
3. *Transverse mesocolon*. This is mobile and runs along the transverse colon until it continues at the splenic flexure.
4. *Left mesocolon*. This region is also anchored to the posterior abdominal wall and extends from the splenic (left colic) flexure to the mesosigmoid.
5. *Mesosigmoid*. The mesosigmoid is both anchored and mobile. The mobile region is attached to the sigmoid colon.
6. *Mesorectum*. The mesorectum is formed by the convergence of the mobile and anchored portions of the mesosigmoid. The mesorectum anchors the rectum as it descends through the pelvic floor.

Historically, the mesentery was considered to be simply a fragmented collection of double-folded peritoneal membranes. However, it is has recently been considered to be a single, continuous organ within the abdominal cavity. The mesentery is the organ within which the abdominal digestive organs develop in the embryo. In adults, the mesentery keeps the abdominal digestive organs connected to each other and to the posterior abdominal wall. Considering the mesentery, the abdomen can be subdivided into two domains: (1) a mesenteric domain and (2) a nonmesenteric domain. The mesenteric domain correlates to the visceral peritoneum. This is the location where all of the abdominal digestive organs are embedded and interconnected. The nonmesenteric domain correlates to the parietal peritoneum and includes structures that are posterior to the mesentery such as the inferior vena cava, kidneys, and ureters. Nonmesenteric structures have traditionally been referred to as *retroperitoneal* (behind the peritoneum).

The portion of the mesentery connecting the lesser curvature of the stomach and the proximal end of the duodenum to the liver and diaphragm is called the **lesser omentum** (oh-MEN-tum; membrane of the bowels). The region of the mesentery extending as a fold from the greater curvature of the stomach and then to the transverse colon is called the **greater omentum** (figure 24.5). The greater omentum forms a long, double fold of mesentery that extends inferiorly from the stomach over the surface of the small intestine. Because of this folding, a cavity called the **omental bursa** (BURR-sah; pocket) forms between the two layers of mesentery. The greater omentum can house a large amount of adipose tissue as well as many B and T lymphocytes. The greater omentum has considerable mobility in the abdomen.

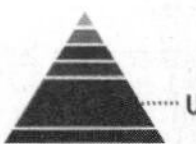

Predict 1

If you placed a pin through the greater omentum, through how many layers of simple squamous epithelium would the pin pass?

The **coronary ligament** attaches the liver to the diaphragm. Unlike other regions of the mesentery, the coronary ligament has a wide space in the center, the bare area of the liver, where no peritoneum exists. The **falciform ligament** attaches the liver to the anterior abdominal wall.

ASSESS YOUR PROGRESS

12. *Where are the visceral peritoneum and parietal peritoneum found? Define and give examples of retroperitoneal organs.*
13. *What is the function of the peritoneum?*
14. *What is the mesentery? Name and describe the location of the mesentery in the abdominal cavity.*

24.6 Oral Cavity

LEARNING OUTCOMES

After reading this section, you should be able to

A. **Describe the oral cavity and the structure and function of the lips, cheeks, palate, and tongue.**
B. **Outline the structure and types of adult teeth.**
C. **Describe the process of mastication.**
D. **Compare the structures and locations of the major salivary glands.**
E. **Describe the composition and functions of saliva.**
F. **Describe the control of the release of saliva.**

The **oral cavity** (figure 24.6), or *mouth,* is divided into two regions: (1) The **vestibule** (VES-tih-byul; entry) is the space between the lips or cheeks and the teeth, and (2) the **oral cavity proper** lies medial to the teeth. The oral cavity is lined with nonkeratinized stratified squamous epithelium, which protects against abrasion.

Lips, Cheeks, and Palate

The lips and cheeks are important in mastication and speech. They help manipulate food and hold it in place within the oral cavity. They also help form words when we speak. A large number of the muscles of facial expression are involved in moving the cheeks and lips (see chapter 10).

The **lips,** or *labia* (LAY-bee-ah), form the anterior boundary of the vestibule (figure 24.6). They are muscular structures formed mostly by the **orbicularis oris** (or-BIK-yoo-LAY-ris OR-is) **muscle** and connective tissue. The skin on the outer surfaces of the upper and lower lips is not highly keratinized and is more transparent than the epithelium over the rest of the body (see chapter 5). The underlying blood vessels give the lips a reddish tint. At the internal margin of the lips, the epithelium is continuous with the nonkeratinized stratified squamous epithelium of the mucosa in the oral cavity.

Each lip has a central mucosal fold called a **labial frenulum** (FREN-you-lum) by which it is attached to the gingiva in its portion of the vestibule.

The **cheeks** form the lateral walls of the oral cavity. They are lined with nonkeratinized stratified squamous epithelium and covered by skin. Within each cheek are the **buccinator muscle**, which flattens the cheek against the teeth, and the **buccal fat pad,** which acts as a gliding pad for the muscles of mastication (see chapter 10). The buccal fat pads change considerably throughout a person's lifetime, especially during weight gain or loss.

The roof of the oral cavity is called the **palate.** The palate separates the oral and nasal cavities and prevents food from passing into the nasal cavity during chewing and swallowing. The palate consists of two parts (figure 24.6; see chapter 7): (1) the **hard palate**, the anterior, bony part; and (2) the **soft palate,** the posterior, nonbony part consisting of skeletal muscle and connective tissue. The **uvula** (YOU-vyu-lah; a grape) is a posterior projection from the soft palate. The posterior boundary of the

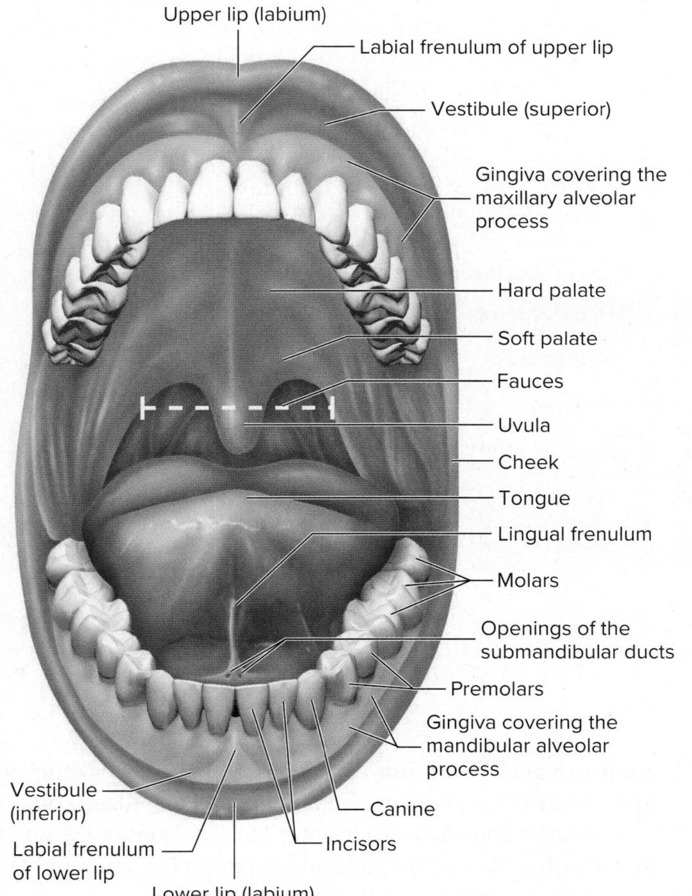

(a) Anterior view of oral cavity

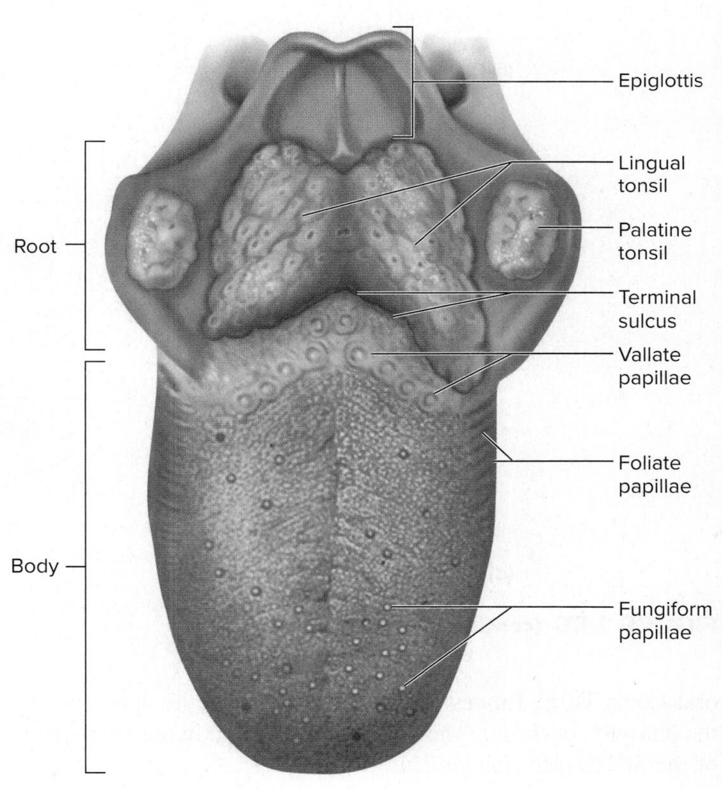

(b) Superior view of tongue

FIGURE 24.6 Oral Cavity, Tongue, and Teeth

(*a*) The oral cavity is the normal location for ingestion of liquid and solid food. (*b*) The tongue consists of the body and the root. The body contains papillae with taste buds and the root contains the lingual tonsil. (*c*) Permanent teeth. (*d*) Deciduous teeth. Dental professionals have developed a "universal" numbering and lettering system for convenience in identifying individual teeth. APR

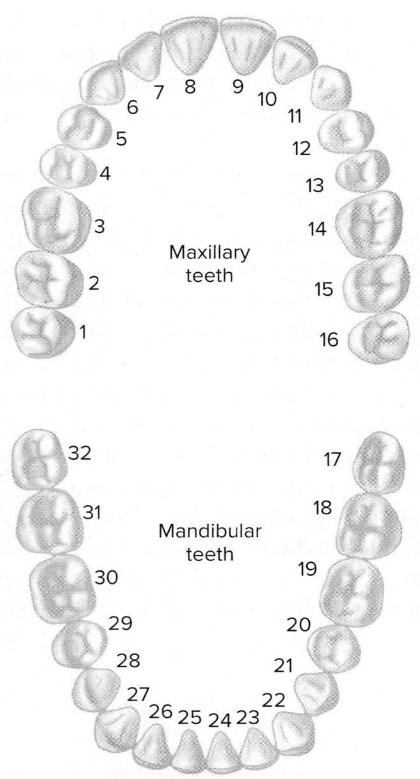

(c) Permanent teeth

Permanent teeth

Tooth Numbers	Name of Tooth
1, 16, 17, 32	Third molar (wisdom tooth)
2, 15, 18, 31	Second molar
3, 14, 19, 30	First molar
4, 13, 20, 29	Second premolar
5, 12, 21, 28	First premolar
6, 11, 22, 27	Canine
7, 10, 23, 26	Lateral incisor
8, 9, 24, 25	Central incisor

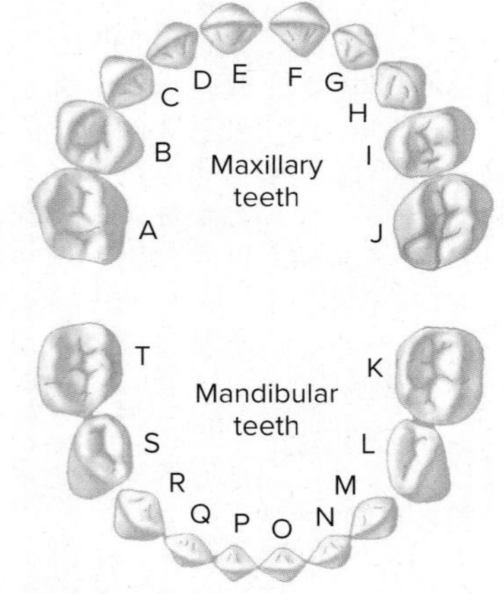

(d) Deciduous teeth

Deciduous teeth

Tooth Letters	Name of Tooth	Time of Eruption/Time of Loss
A, J, K, T	Second molar	20–24 months/9–11 years
B, I, L, S	First molar	10–16 months/9–11 years
C, H, M, R	Canine	16–20 months/8–11 years
D, G, N, Q	Lateral incisor	8–11 months/6–8 years
E, F, O, P	Central incisor	6–8 months/5–7 years

FIGURE 24.6 (continued)

oral cavity is the **fauces** (FAW-seez), which is the opening into the pharynx, or *throat*. The **palatine tonsils** are in the lateral wall of the fauces (see chapter 22).

Tongue

The **tongue** is a large, muscular organ that occupies most of the oral cavity proper when the mouth is closed. A groove called the **terminal sulcus** divides the tongue into two parts: (1) the body and (2) the root (see figure 24.6*b*). The anterior **body** is found within the oral cavity and is relatively free, except for attachment to the floor of the mouth by a thin fold of tissue called the **lingual** (tongue) **frenulum.** The body is covered by nonkeratinized stratified squamous epithelium and papillae, some of which contain taste buds (see chapter 15). The **root** of the tongue is found within the oropharynx and contains a few scattered taste buds and the **lingual tonsil** (see chapter 22).

The muscles associated with the tongue are divided into two categories: (1) **intrinsic muscles** and (2) **extrinsic muscles.** The intrinsic muscles are within the tongue itself and are largely responsible for changing the shape of the tongue, such as flattening and elevating it during drinking and swallowing. The extrinsic tongue muscles are outside the tongue but are attached to it. These muscles protrude and retract the tongue, move it from side to side, and change its shape (see chapter 10).

The tongue moves food in the mouth and, in cooperation with the lips and gums, holds the food in place during mastication. It also plays a major role in swallowing. In addition, the tongue is the location of the taste buds (see chapter 15) and one of the primary organs of speech. Patients with cancer of the tongue often have part or all of their tongue removed. These patients can speak well but may have difficulty chewing and swallowing.

Teeth

The teeth, collectively called the **dentition** (den-TISH-shun), function to *masticate* (chew) food in the oral cavity and assist in speech. Adults normally have 32 **teeth,** which are distributed in two **dental arches:** the maxillary arch and the mandibular arch. The teeth in the right and left halves of each dental arch are roughly mirror images of each other. As a result, the teeth are apportioned into four quadrants: (1) right-upper, (2) left-upper, (3) right-lower, and (4) left-lower. The teeth in each quadrant include one central and one lateral **incisor;** one **canine;** first and second **premolars;** and first, second, and third **molars** (see figure 24.6*c*). The third molars are often called *wisdom teeth* because they usually appear in the late teens or early twenties, when a person is old enough to have acquired some wisdom. In people with small dental arches, the third molars may not have room to erupt into the oral cavity and remain embedded within the jaw. Embedded wisdom teeth are referred to as impacted and may cause pain or irritation. Usually, the impacted wisdom teeth are surgically removed.

The teeth of the adult mouth are called **permanent teeth,** or *secondary teeth.* Most of them are replacements for **deciduous** (dee-SID-yoo-us) **teeth** (*primary teeth or milk teeth),* which are lost during childhood (see figure 24.6*d*). The deciduous teeth erupt (the crowns appear within the oral cavity) between about 6 months and 24 months of age (see figure 24.6*d*). The permanent teeth begin replacing the deciduous teeth at about 5 years, and the process is completed by about 11 years.

Each tooth consists of (1) a crown, (2) a neck, and (3) a root (figure 24.7). The **crown** is the part of the tooth exposed in the oral cavity and covered by enamel. The crown can have one or more **cusps** (points). The **neck** is the small region between the crown and root. The **root** is the largest region of the tooth. It anchors the tooth in the bone.

Within the center of the tooth, in the neck and root, is a **pulp cavity,** which is filled with **pulp,** a collection of blood vessels, nerves, and connective tissue. The portion of the pulp cavity within the root is called the **root canal.** The nerves and blood vessels of the tooth enter and exit the pulp through a hole at the point of each root called the **apical foramen.** It is common to see roots of molars that are noticeably curved rather than straight. In addition, it is common to have branches of a root canal rather than one single root canal. The pulp cavity is surrounded by living, cellular, calcified tissue called **dentin.** The dentin of the tooth crown is covered by an extremely hard, nonliving, acellular substance called **enamel,** which protects the tooth against abrasion and acids produced by bacteria in the mouth. The surface of the dentin in the root is covered with a bonelike substance called **cementum,** which helps anchor the tooth to the periodontal ligament in the jaw.

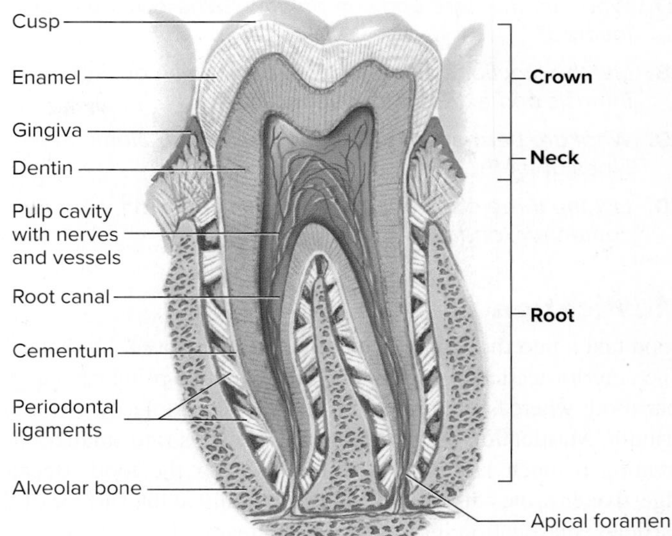

FIGURE 24.7 Molar Tooth in Place in the Alveolar Bone
A tooth consists of a crown, a neck, and a root. The root is covered with cementum, and the tooth is held in the socket by periodontal ligaments. Nerves and vessels enter and exit the tooth through the apical foramen.

The teeth are anchored in **alveoli** (al-VEE-oh-lie; sockets) along the alveolar processes of the mandible and maxilla. Dense fibrous connective tissue and stratified squamous epithelium, referred to as the **gingiva** (JIN-jih-vah; gums), cover the alveolar processes (figure 24.7). **Periodontal** (PER-ee-oh-DON-tal; around a tooth) **ligaments** secure the teeth in the alveoli.

Several conditions can affect the health of the tooth and the structures associated with it, such as the periodontal ligament and gingiva. **Dental caries,** or tooth decay, is a breakdown of enamel by bacterial acids on the tooth surface. Because the enamel is nonliving and cannot repair itself, a dental filling is necessary to prevent further damage. If the decay reaches the pulp cavity, with its rich supply of nerves, a toothache may result. Sometimes, when decay has reached the pulp cavity, a dentist must perform a procedure called a root canal, which consists of removing the pulp from the tooth. **Gingivitis** (jin-ji-VIE-tis) is an inflammation of the gingiva, often caused by food deposited in gingival crevices and not promptly removed by brushing and flossing. Gingivitis may eventually lead to periodontal disease. **Periodontal disease** is the inflammation and degradation of the periodontal ligaments, gingiva, and alveolar bone. This disease is the most common cause of tooth loss in adults. **Halitosis** (hal-i-TOH-sis), or "bad breath," often occurs with periodontal disease.

ASSESS YOUR PROGRESS

15. *What is the difference between the vestibule and the oral cavity proper?*

16. *What are the functions of the lips and cheeks? What muscle forms the substance of the lips? The cheeks?*

17. *What are the hard and soft palates? Where is the uvula located?*
18. *List the functions of the tongue. Distinguish between intrinsic and extrinsic tongue muscles.*
19. *What are permanent and deciduous teeth? Name the types of teeth.*
20. *List the three parts of a tooth. What are dentin, enamel, cementum, and pulp?*

Mastication

Food taken into the mouth is **masticated,** or *chewed,* by the teeth. The anterior teeth (the incisors and the canines) primarily cut and tear food, whereas the premolars and molars primarily crush and grind it. Mastication breaks large food particles into smaller ones, creating a much larger total surface area of the food. Because digestive enzymes digest food molecules only at the surface of the particles, mastication increases the efficiency of digestion.

Four pairs of muscles move the mandible during mastication: (1) **temporalis,** (2) **masseter,** (3) **medial pterygoid,** and (4) **lateral pterygoid** muscles (see chapter 10). The temporalis, the masseter, and the medial pterygoid act to close the jaw. The lateral ptyerygoid is the only one of the four that acts to open the jaw. In addition, the medial and lateral pterygoids, as well as the masseter muscle, accomplish protraction and lateral and medial excursion of the jaw. The temporalis retracts the jaw. All these movements are involved in tearing, crushing, and grinding food.

The **mastication reflex,** or *chewing reflex,* is integrated in the medulla oblongata and controls the basic movements of chewing. The presence of food in the mouth stimulates sensory receptors, which activate a reflex that relaxes the muscles of mastication. As the mandible is lowered, the muscles stretch and activate a reflex that causes the muscles of mastication to contract. Once the mouth is closed, the food again stimulates the muscles of mastication to relax, and the cycle repeats. Descending pathways from the cerebrum strongly influence the mastication reflex so that chewing can be consciously initiated or stopped. The rate and intensity of chewing movements can also be influenced by the cerebrum.

Salivary Glands

A considerable number of **salivary glands** are scattered throughout the oral cavity. There are three pairs of large, multicellular salivary glands: (1) parotid glands, (2) submandibular glands, and (3) sublingual glands (figure 24.8). In addition to these large salivary glands, numerous small, coiled, tubular salivary glands are located (1) deep to the epithelium of the tongue (lingual glands), (2) in the palate (palatine glands), (3) in the cheeks (buccal glands), and (4) in the lips (labial glands).

All of the major large salivary glands are compound **acinar glands,** which are branching glands with clusters of acini resembling grapes (see chapter 4). They produce thin serous secretions or thicker mucous secretions. **Saliva** is a combination of serous and mucous secretions from the various salivary glands.

The largest salivary glands, the **parotid** (pah-ROT-id; beside the ear) **glands,** are serous glands, which produce mostly watery saliva; they are located just anterior to the ear on each side of the head. Each **parotid duct** exits the gland on its anterior margin, crosses the lateral surface of the masseter muscle, pierces the buccinator muscle, and enters the oral cavity adjacent to the second upper molar (figure 24.8*a*). A viral infection can cause the parotid glands to become inflamed and swollen, making the cheeks quite large. Before the measles/mumps/rubella (MMR) vaccination program was begun in the United States, **mumps** was a common childhood disease caused by the mumps virus. Now mumps is very rare in the United States. The virus causing mumps can also infect other tissues, including the testes, which can result in sterility in an adult male.

The **submandibular** (below the mandible) **glands** are mixed glands with more serous than mucous acini. Each gland can be felt as a soft lump along the inferior border of the posterior half of the mandible. A submandibular duct exits each gland, passes anteriorly deep to the mucous membrane on the floor of the oral cavity, and opens into the oral cavity beside the frenulum of the tongue (see figure 24.6*a*).

The **sublingual** (below the tongue) **glands,** the smallest of the three large, paired salivary glands, are mixed glands containing some serous acini but consisting primarily of mucous acini. They lie immediately below the mucous membrane in the floor of the oral cavity. These glands do not have single, well-defined ducts like those of the submandibular and parotid glands. Instead, each sublingual gland opens into the floor of the oral cavity through 10–12 small ducts.

Saliva

Saliva is composed of fluid and proteins and has three main roles (figure 24.9): (1) it helps keep the oral cavity moist, which is needed for normal speech and for tasting food; (2) it has protective functions; and (3) it begins the process of digestion.

Approximately 1–1.5 L/day of saliva are secreted. The serous portion of saliva, secreted primarily by the parotid and submandibular glands, provides the moistening function of saliva. The mucous secretions of the submandibular and sublingual glands contain a large amount of **mucin** (MYU-sin), a proteoglycan that gives a lubricating quality to saliva.

There are several protective functions of saliva.

1. The large volume of saliva helps prevent bacterial infection in the mouth by continually washing the oral surface.
2. Bicarbonate ions (HCO_3^-) in saliva act as a buffer to neutralize the acids produced by oral bacteria. This reduces the harmful effects of bacterial acids on tooth enamel.
3. Saliva contains the proteins **lysozyme** and **immunoglobulin A.** Lysozyme is an enzyme that has a weak antibacterial action, and immunoglobulin A helps prevent bacterial infection.
4. The mucous in saliva helps protect the digestive tract from physical irritation and enzymatic digestion. Any reduction in salivary gland secretion increases the risk for ulceration and infection of the oral mucosa and for caries (cavities) in the teeth.

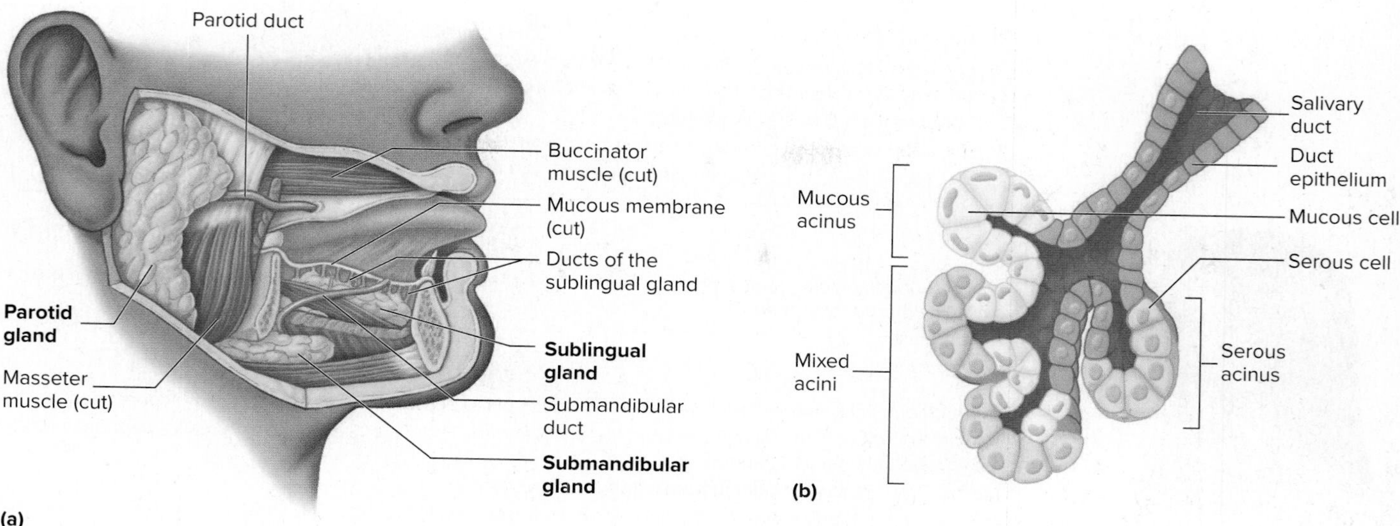

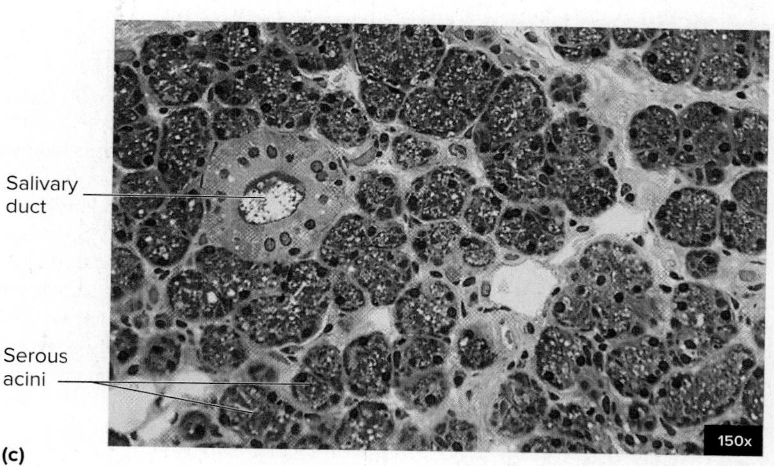

FIGURE 24.8 Salivary Glands
(*a*) The large salivary glands are the parotid glands, the submandibular glands, and the sublingual glands. The parotid duct extends anteriorly from the parotid gland. (*b*) An idealized schematic illustrates the histology of the large salivary glands. The figure is representative of all the glands and does not depict any specific salivary gland. (*c*) Photomicrograph of the parotid gland.
(c) Ed Reschke

The digestive functions of saliva are relatively minor compared with digestion later in the tract. The serous part of saliva contains a digestive enzyme called **salivary amylase** (AM-il-ace; starch-splitting enzyme), which breaks the covalent bonds between glucose molecules in starch and other polysaccharides to produce the disaccharides maltose and isomaltose (figure 24.9). These sugars can give starches a sweet taste. However, food spends very little time in the mouth, so only about 3–5% of the total carbohydrates are digested there. In addition, most starchy foods come from plants and are therefore covered by cellulose, making them inaccessible to salivary amylase. Cooking and thoroughly chewing food destroy the cellulose covering and increase the efficiency of the digestive process. In addition to carbohydrate digestion, there is a small amount of lipid digestion initiated by **lingual lipase** in saliva.

Salivary gland secretion is stimulated by both the parasympathetic and the sympathetic nervous systems, but the parasympathetic system is more prevalent. Salivary nuclei in the brainstem increase salivary secretions by sending action potentials through parasympathetic fibers of the facial (VII) and glossopharyngeal (IX) cranial nerves in response to a variety of stimuli, such as tactile stimulation in the oral cavity or certain tastes, especially sour. Higher centers of the brain also affect salivary gland activity. Odors that trigger thoughts of food or the sensation of hunger can increase saliva secretion as well.

ASSESS YOUR PROGRESS

21. *List the muscles of mastication and the actions they produce. Describe the mastication reflex.*
22. *Name and give the location of the three largest salivary glands. What are the other types of salivary glands called?*
23. *What are the functions of saliva? What substances are contained in saliva?*
24. *What is the difference between serous and mucous saliva?*
25. *Describe the stimuli that stimulate the release of saliva. What nerves are involved?*

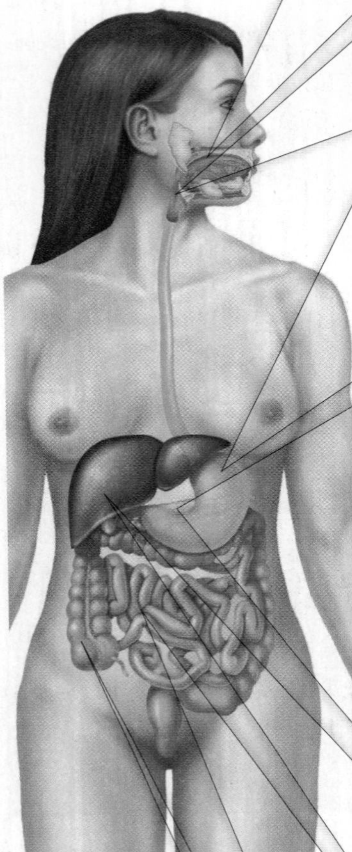

Oral Cavity

Serous saliva. Composed mostly of water, HCO_3^-; moistens food and mucous membrane; neutralizes bacterial acids; flushes bacteria from oral cavity; has weak antibacterial activity

Salivary amylase. Digests carbohydrates

Mucus. Lubricates food; protects digestive tract from digestion

Lingual lipase. Digests a minor amount of lipids

Pharynx

Mucus. Lubricates esophagus; protects lining of esophagus from abrasion and allows food to move more smoothly through esophagus

Gastric

Hydrochloric acid. Antibacterial; decreases stomach pH to activate pepsinogen to pepsin conversion

Pepsin. Secreted in an inactive form and then activated by HCl; digests protein into smaller peptide chains; activates additional pepsinogen

Mucus. Protects stomach lining from acids and digestion

Intrinsic factor. Binds to vitamin B_{12} and aids in its absorption in the small intestine

Gastric lipase. Digests a minor amount of lipids

Pancreas

Zymogens:

Trypsin. Digests proteins (breaks bonds at amino acids lysine or arginine); activates additional trypsinogen as well as other digestive enzymes

Chymotrypsin. Digests proteins (breaks bonds at hydrophobic amino acids)

Carboxypeptidase. Digests proteins (breaks bonds between amino acids at carboxyl end of proteins)

Other enzymes and components:

Pancreatic amylase. Digests carbohydrates (hydrolyzes starches and glycogen to form maltose and isomaltose

Pancreatic lipase. Digests lipids (breaks down triglycerides into monoglycerides and free fatty acids)

Cholesterol esterase. Digests cholesteryl esters (breaks them down into cholesterol and a free fatty acid)

Ribonuclease. Digests ribonucleic acid (breaks phosphodiester bonds)

Deoxyribonuclease. Digests deoxyribonucleic acid (breaks phosphodiester bonds)

HCO_3^-. Neutralizes acid from stomach to provide optimal pH for pancreatic enzymes

Liver

Bile. Bile salts in bile emulsify lipids, making them available to lipases, and help make end products soluble and available for absorption by the intestinal mucosa; many of the other bile contents are waste products, such as bile pigments, that are transported to the intestine for disposal

Small Intestine

Mucus. Protects duodenum from acidic chyme and intestinal wall from digestive enzymes

Brush border enzymes:

Peptidases. Break peptide bonds between amino acids of polypeptides

Enterokinase. Converts trypsinogen to trypsin

Sucrase. Breaks apart sucrose into glucose and fructose

Maltase. Breaks apart maltose into two glucose molecules

Isomaltase. Breaks apart isomaltose into two glucose molecules

Lactase. Breaks apart lactose into glucose and galactose

Large Intestine

Mucus. Provides adhesion for fecal matter; protects intestinal wall from bacterial acids and actions

FIGURE 24.9 Functions of Major Digestive System Secretions
Secretions from each area of the digestive tract are listed. Some enzyme secretions, such as from in the stomach and pancreas, are secreted in an inactive form and then activated within the target organ.

24.7 Swallowing

LEARNING OUTCOMES

After reading this section, you should be able to

A. **List the parts of the pharynx involved with digestion.**
B. **Describe the structure of the esophagus.**
C. **Explain the three phases of swallowing.**

Swallowing involves distinct phases in the pharynx and esophagus (see figure 24.10).

Pharynx

The **pharynx,** described in detail in chapter 23, consists of three parts: (1) nasopharynx, (2) oropharynx, and (3) laryngopharynx. Normally, only the oropharynx and laryngopharynx transmit food. The **oropharynx** communicates with the nasopharynx superiorly, with the larynx and **laryngopharynx** inferiorly, and with the mouth anteriorly. The laryngopharynx extends from the oropharynx to the esophagus and is posterior to the larynx. The epiglottis covers the opening of the larynx and keeps food and drink from entering the larynx. The posterior walls of the oropharynx and laryngopharynx consist of three muscles: the superior, middle, and inferior **pharyngeal constrictors,** which are arranged like three stacked flowerpots, one inside the other. The oropharynx and the laryngopharynx are lined with nonkeratinized stratified squamous epithelium, and the nasopharynx is lined with ciliated pseudostratified columnar epithelium.

Esophagus

The **esophagus** is the part of the digestive tract that extends between the pharynx and the stomach. It is about 25 cm long and lies in the mediastinum, anterior to the vertebrae and posterior to the trachea. It passes through the esophageal hiatus (opening) of the diaphragm and ends at the stomach. The esophagus transports food from the pharynx to the stomach.

The esophagus has thick walls consisting of the four tunics common to the digestive tract: (1) mucosa, (2) submucosa, (3) muscularis, and (4) adventitia. The muscularis has an outer longitudinal layer and an inner circular layer, as is true of most parts of the digestive tract. However, the esophagus differs from other regions by having skeletal muscle fibers in the superior one-third, a mixture of skeletal and smooth muscle fibers in the middle one-third, and smooth muscle fibers in the inferior one-third. An

PROCESS **Figure 24.10**

Phases of Swallowing

The three phases of swallowing are voluntary, pharyngeal, and esophageal.

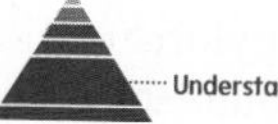

During which part of the swallowing reflex is it not possible to talk or even breathe? Why?

PROCESS **Figure**

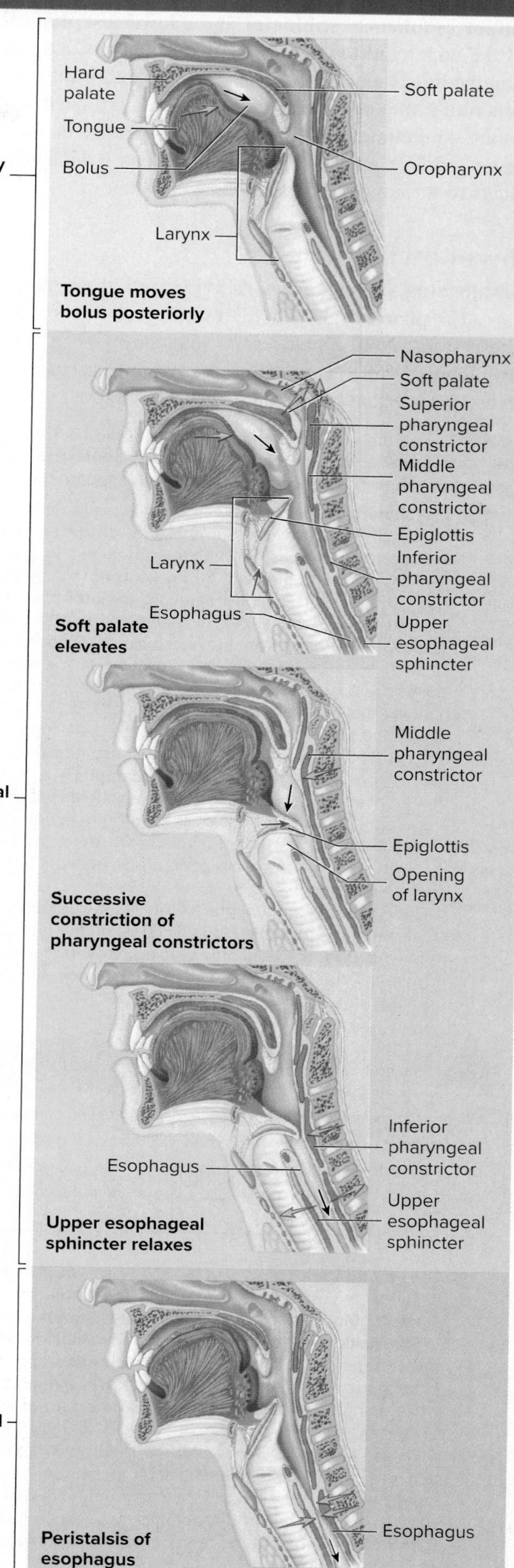

upper esophageal sphincter and a **lower esophageal sphincter,** at the upper and lower ends of the esophagus, respectively, regulate the movement of materials into and out of the esophagus. The mucosal lining of the esophagus is nonkeratinized stratified squamous epithelium. Numerous mucous glands in the submucosal layer produce a thick, lubricating mucus, which passes through ducts to the surface of the esophageal mucosa.

Swallowing Phases

Swallowing, or *deglutition,* is divided into three phases: (1) voluntary, (2) pharyngeal, and (3) esophageal. Figure 24.10 outlines these steps. Note that over 20 separate muscles are involved in swallowing. Here, we discuss the overall process without listing every muscle that contributes to swallowing.

1. During the **voluntary phase,** a bolus of food is formed in the mouth and pushed by the tongue against the hard palate, until it is forced toward the posterior part of the mouth and into the oropharynx.

2. The **pharyngeal phase** of swallowing is a reflex initiated by the stimulation of tactile receptors in the area of the oropharynx. Sensory action potentials travel through the trigeminal (V) and glossopharyngeal (IX) nerves to the **swallowing center** in the medulla oblongata. There, they initiate action potentials in motor neurons, which pass through the trigeminal (V), glossopharyngeal (IX), vagus (X), and accessory (XI) nerves to the soft palate and pharynx. This phase of swallowing begins with the elevation of the soft palate, which closes the passage between the nasopharynx and oropharynx. The pharynx elevates to receive the bolus of food from the mouth and moves the bolus down the pharynx into the esophagus. The superior, middle, and inferior pharyngeal constrictor muscles contract in succession, forcing the food through the pharynx. At the same time, the upper esophageal sphincter relaxes, the elevated pharynx opens the esophagus, and food is pushed into the esophagus. This phase of swallowing is controlled involuntarily, even though the muscles involved are skeletal. The pharyngeal phase of swallowing lasts about 1–2 seconds.

   During the pharyngeal phase, the vestibular folds and vocal cords close, and the **epiglottis** (ep-ih-GLOT-is; on the glottis) is tipped posteriorly, so that the epiglottic cartilage covers the opening into the larynx, and the larynx is elevated. These movements prevent food from passing into the larynx.

Understand

Predict 2

Why is it important to close the opening between the nasopharynx and the oropharynx during swallowing? What may happen if a person emits an explosive burst of laughter while trying to swallow a liquid? Predict the consequences of trying to swallow and speak at the same time.

3. The **esophageal phase** of swallowing, which takes about 5–8 seconds, is responsible for moving food from the pharynx to the stomach. Muscular contractions in the wall of the esophagus occur in peristaltic waves. Gravity helps move liquids and watery food through the esophagus. However, the peristaltic contractions in the esophagus are forceful enough to allow a person to swallow even while doing a headstand or floating in the zero-gravity environment of space.

   As the peristaltic waves and the food bolus approach the stomach, the lower esophageal sphincter in the esophagus relaxes. This sphincter is not anatomically distinct from the rest of the esophagus, but it can be identified physiologically because it remains tonically constricted to prevent the reflux of stomach contents into the lower part of the esophagus.

   The presence of food in the esophagus stimulates the myenteric plexus, which controls the peristaltic waves. Food in the esophagus also stimulates tactile receptors, which send sensory impulses to the medulla oblongata through the vagus nerves. Motor impulses, in turn, pass along the vagal efferent fibers to the skeletal and smooth muscles within the esophagus, thereby stimulating their contractions and reinforcing the peristaltic contractions.

ASSESS YOUR PROGRESS

26. *Name the parts of the pharynx involved with digestion. What are pharyngeal constrictors?*
27. *Where is the esophagus located? Describe the tunics of the esophageal wall and the esophageal sphincters.*
28. *What are the three phases of swallowing? Sequentially list the processes involved in the last two phases and describe how they are regulated.*

24.8 Stomach

LEARNING OUTCOMES

After reading this section, you should be able to

A. **Outline the anatomical and histological characteristics of the stomach.**
B. **Describe stomach secretions.**
C. **Describe stomach secretion function.**
D. **Describe stomach secretion regulation.**
E. **Describe gastric movements.**
F. **Describe gastric movement regulation.**

The **stomach** is an enlarged segment of the digestive tract that primarily functions as a storage and mixing chamber. It is located in the left superior part of the abdomen (see figure 24.1). Its shape and size vary from person to person, even within the same individual from time to time, depending on food content and body posture. Nonetheless, several general anatomical features can be described.

Anatomy of the Stomach

The stomach is divided into four regions: (1) cardia, (2) fundus, (3) body, and (4) pylorus (figure 24.11). The esophagus opens into the **cardia** of the stomach at the gastroesophageal opening. The **lower esophageal sphincter,** also called the *cardiac sphincter,* surrounds the opening. Recall that, although this is an important structure in the normal function of the stomach, it is a physiological constrictor only and cannot be seen anatomically. The part of the stomach to the left of the cardia, the **fundus** (FUN-dus), is actually superior to the cardiac opening. The largest part of the stomach is the **body,** which turns to the right, creating a *greater curvature* and a *lesser curvature.* The body narrows to form the funnel-shaped **pylorus** (pie-LOHR-us; gatekeeper) of the stomach. The wider part of the funnel, toward the body of the stomach, is the **pyloric antrum.** The narrow part of the funnel is the **pyloric canal.** The pyloric canal opens through the pyloric orifice into the small intestine. The pyloric orifice is surrounded by the

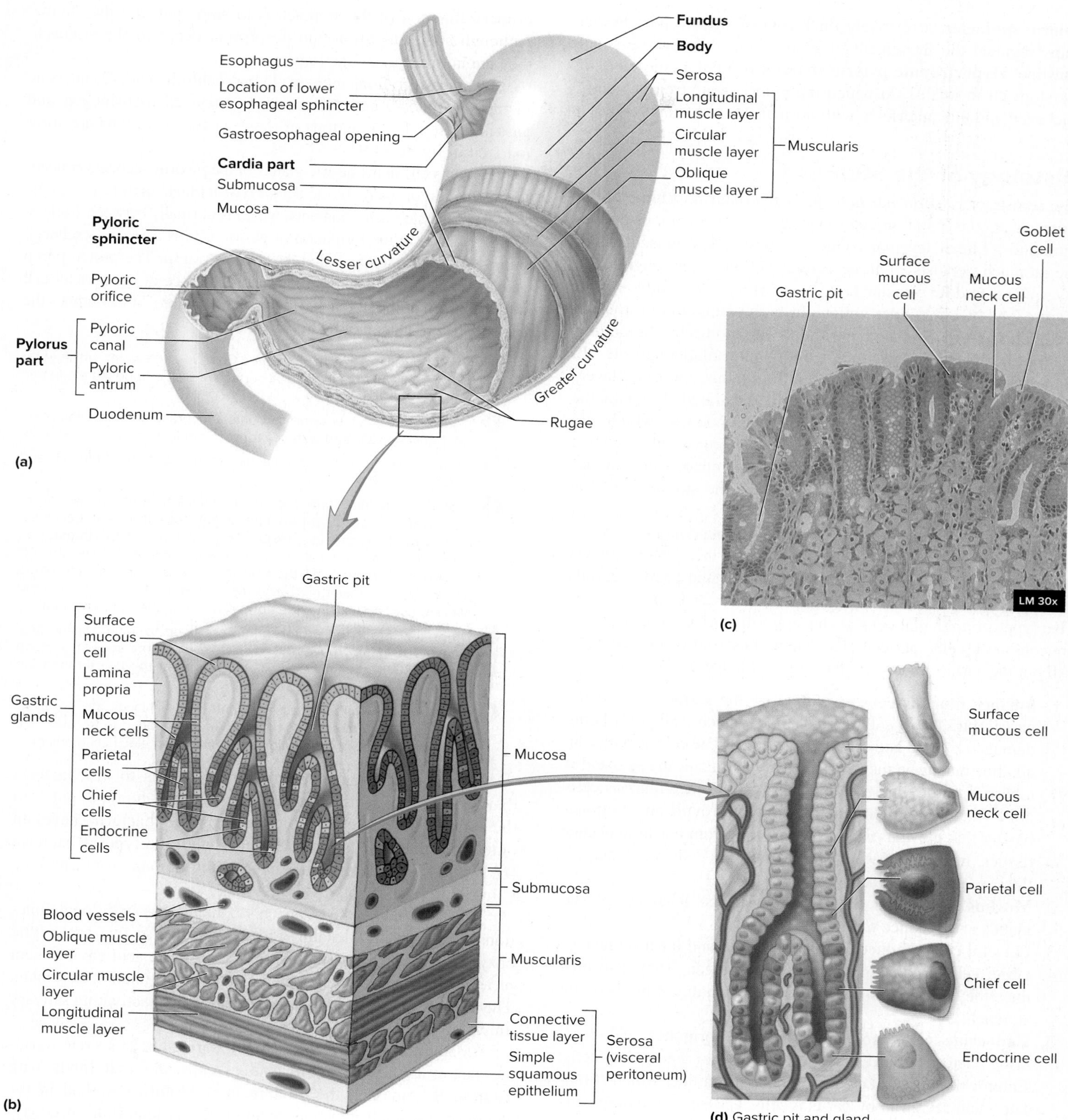

FIGURE 24.11 Anatomy and Histology of the Stomach

(*a*) Cutaway section reveals the muscular layers and internal anatomy of the stomach. (*b*) A section of the stomach wall illustrates its histology, including several gastric pits and glands. (*c*) Photomicrograph of gastric glands. (*d*) Gastric glands contain surface and neck mucous cells that secrete mucus, parietal cells that secrete HCl and intrinsic factor, chief cells that secrete pepsinogen and gastric lipase, as well as endocrine cells that secrete hormones such as gastrin and paracrine factors such as histamine. (c) ©Victor Eroschenko APR

pyloric sphincter, a relatively thick ring of smooth muscle that helps regulate the movement of gastric contents into the small intestine. **Hypertrophic pyloric stenosis** is a common defect of the stomach in infants, in which the pyloric sphincter is greatly thickened and thus interferes with normal stomach emptying.

Histology of the Stomach

The serosa, or *visceral peritoneum,* is the outermost tunic of the stomach. It consists of an outer layer of simple squamous epithelium and an inner layer of connective tissue. The muscularis of the stomach consists of three layers: (1) an outer longitudinal layer, (2) a middle circular layer, and (3) an inner oblique layer (figure 24.11*a*). The inner oblique layer is unique to the stomach wall. This layer helps generate the strong stomach contractions that physically break down ingested food into smaller particles. In some areas of the stomach, such as the fundus, the three layers blend with one another and cannot be separated. Deep to the muscularis are the submucosa and the mucosa, which are arranged in large folds called **rugae** (ROO-gee; wrinkles) when the stomach is empty. These folds allow the mucosa and submucosa to stretch, and the folds disappear as the stomach volume increases as it is filled.

The mucous lining of the stomach is simple columnar epithelium. The epithelium forms numerous, tubelike invaginations called **gastric pits.** Gastric pits are the openings for the **gastric glands** that secrete acid and other substances (figure 24.11*d*). There are five types of epithelial cells of the stomach: surface mucous cells, mucous neck cells, parietal cells, chief cells, and endocrine cells. All but the surface mucous cells are found in the gastric glands.

1. **Surface mucous cells** are found on the surface around the gastric pit. These cells protect the stomach wall from being damaged by acid and digestive enzymes. The cells produce an alkaline mucus on their surface that neutralizes the acid and is a barrier to the digestive enzymes. The surface mucous cells are connected by tight junctions, which provide an additional barrier that prevents acids and enzymes from reaching deeper tissues. In addition, when surface mucous cells are damaged, they are rapidly replaced.
2. **Mucous neck cells** are located near the openings of the glands and produce mucus.
3. **Parietal cells** produce hydrochloric acid and intrinsic factor.
4. **Chief cells** produce the enzyme pepsinogen. They also produce the enzyme gastric lipase, which can digest lipids in the stomach.
5. **Endocrine cells** produce regulatory hormones and paracrine factors. There are several types of endocrine cells. Enterochromaffin-like cells produce histamine, which stimulates acid secretion by parietal cells. Gastrin-containing cells secrete gastrin, and somatostatin-containing cells secrete somatostatin, which inhibits gastrin and insulin secretion.

Secretions of the Stomach

Once food enters the stomach, it is mixed with stomach secretions to form a semifluid material called **chyme** (KIME; juice). The primary function of the stomach is to store and mix the chyme. Although some digestion and absorption occur in the stomach, they are not its major functions.

Stomach secretions include (1) hydrochloric acid, (2) intrinsic factor, (3) mucus, and (4) digestive enzymes (pepsinogen and gastric lipase). The functions of these gastric secretions are summarized in figure 24.9.

Parietal cells in the gastric glands of the pylorus secrete a concentrated solution of hydrochloric acid. **Hydrochloric acid** produces the low pH of the stomach's contents, which is normally between 1 and 3. The key player in the formation of gastric acid is a H^+–K^+ exchange pump that is commonly called the **proton pump.** The proton pump actively transports H^+ across the mucosal surface of the parietal cell into the lumen of the stomach (figure 24.12). Figure 24.12 outlines the steps in the production of hydrochloric acid.

1. The process begins with H^+ derived from CO_2 and water, which enter the parietal cell from its serosal surface (the side opposite the lumen of the gastric pit).
2. Inside the cell, the enzyme carbonic anhydrase catalyzes the reaction between CO_2 and water to form carbonic acid.
3. Some of the carbonic acid molecules then dissociate to form H^+ and HCO_3^-.
4. While H^+ is pumped into the stomach lumen, HCO_3^- moves down its concentration gradient from the parietal cell into the extracellular fluid. During this process, HCO_3^- is exchanged for Cl^- through an antiporter, which is located in the plasma membrane, and the Cl^- subsequently moves into the cell. This results in an elevated blood pH in the veins that carry blood away from the stomach, called the alkaline tide. An alkaline tide normally occurs after eating a meal.
5. Drugs that block the proton pump are used to lower gastric acid levels. The pump moves H^+ by active transport against a steep concentration gradient, and Cl^- diffuses from the cell through ion channels in the plasma membrane.
6. Diffusion of Cl^- into the gastric gland duct balances the positively charged H^+ to reduce the amount of energy needed to transport the H^+ against both a concentration gradient and an electrical gradient.

A major function of hydrochloric acid is to kill bacteria that are ingested with essentially everything humans put into their mouths. However, some pathogenic bacteria have an outer coat that resists stomach acids, and one type of bacteria (*H. pylori*) is normally present in many human stomachs (see Clinical Impact 24.2).

The low pH of the stomach's contents has additional functions. Stomach acid denatures many proteins, so that proteolytic enzymes can reach internal peptide bonds. The acid environment provides the proper pH for the activation and function of pepsin. The acid also stops carbohydrate digestion by inactivating salivary amylase.

In addition to hydrochloric acid, parietal cells secrete intrinsic factor. **Intrinsic factor** is a glycoprotein that binds with vitamin B_{12}, making the vitamin more readily absorbed in the ileum of the small intestine. Vitamin B_{12} is important in deoxyribonucleic acid (DNA) synthesis, which is especially important for continual red blood cell production. A lack of vitamin B_{12} absorption leads to pernicious anemia (see chapter 19). Deficiency of vitamin B_{12} also leads to neurological symptoms, including peripheral neuropathy because vitamin B_{12} is required for maintaining myelin in the peripheral nervous system.

PROCESS **Figure**

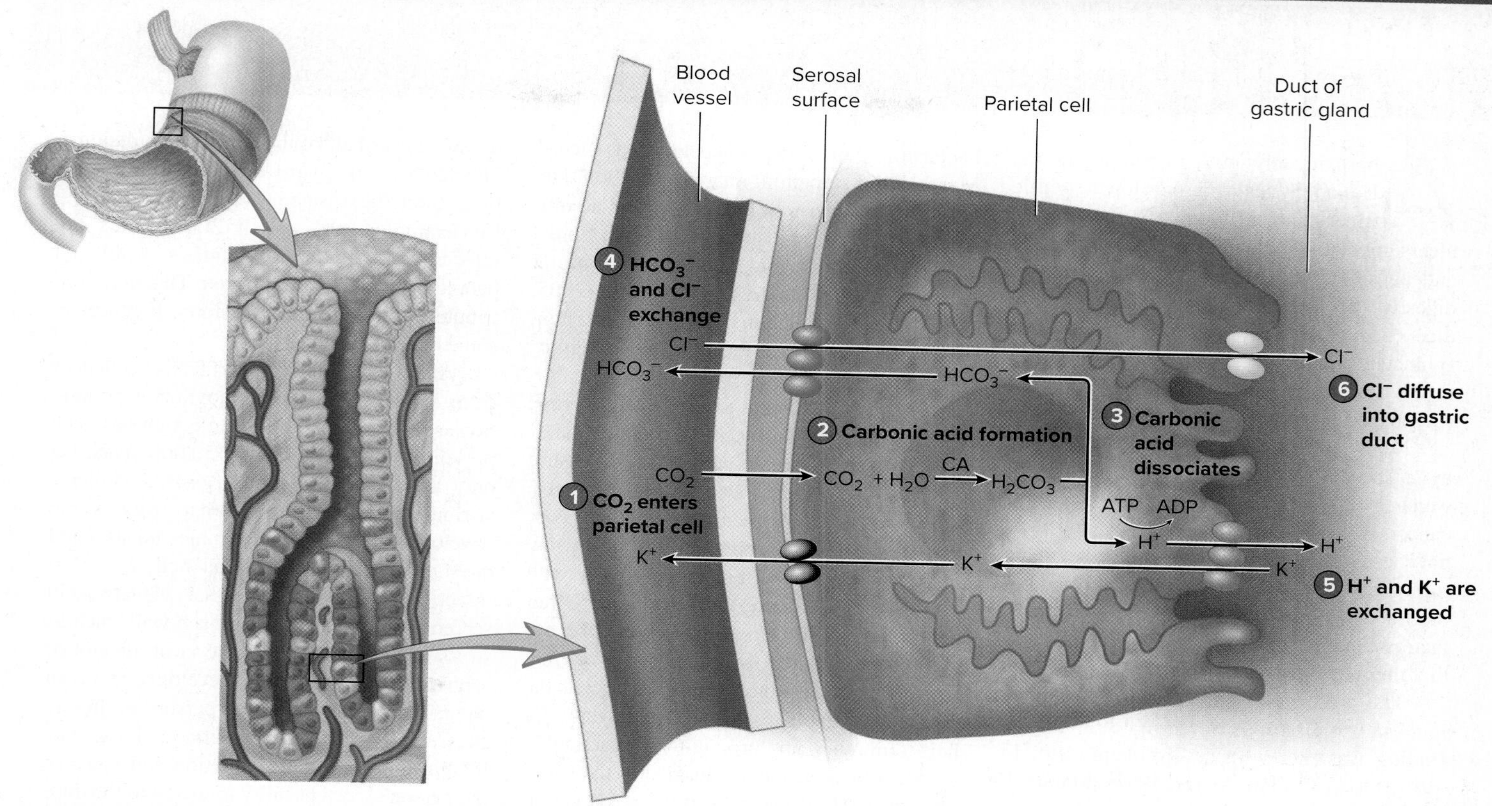

Blood vessel

Serosal surface

Parietal cell

Duct of gastric gland

4 **HCO_3^- and Cl^- exchange**

Cl^- → Cl^-

HCO_3^- ← HCO_3^-

6 **Cl^- diffuse into gastric duct**

2 **Carbonic acid formation**

3 **Carbonic acid dissociates**

CO_2 → $CO_2 + H_2O \xrightarrow{CA} H_2CO_3$

1 **CO_2 enters parietal cell**

ATP ADP

H^+ → H^+

K^+ ← K^+ ← K^+

5 **H^+ and K^+ are exchanged**

PROCESS **Figure 24.12**

Hydrochloric Acid Production by Parietal Cells in the Gastric Glands of the Stomach

A series of steps involving carbonic anhydrase, a proton pump, and a HCO_3^-–Cl^- antiporter produce HCl in the gastric gland. APR

Predict what happens to the pH of blood in the veins leaving the stomach if someone has repeated episodes of vomiting.

Chief cells within the gastric glands secrete **pepsinogen** (pep-SIN-oh-jen). Pepsinogen is packaged in **zymogen** (ZIE-moh-jen) **granules,** which are released by exocytosis when pepsinogen secretion is stimulated. *Zymogen* is the term for an inactive enzyme. Once pepsinogen enters the lumen of the stomach, hydrochloric acid and previously formed pepsin molecules convert it to **pepsin.** Pepsin exhibits optimal enzymatic activity at a pH of 3 or less. Pepsin catalyzes the cleavage of some covalent bonds in proteins, thus breaking them into smaller peptide chains. Chief cells also secrete the enzyme gastric lipase, which can digest lipids even in an acidic environment.

The surface mucous cells and mucous neck cells secrete a viscous, alkaline mucus that covers the surface of the epithelial cells, forming a layer 1–1.5 mm thick. The thick layer of mucus lubricates and protects the epithelial cells of the stomach wall from the damaging effect of the acidic chyme and pepsin. Irritation of the stomach mucosa stimulates the secretion of a greater volume of mucus.

Regulation of Stomach Secretion

Approximately 2–3 L of gastric secretions (gastric juice) are produced each day. The amount and type of food entering the stomach and small intestine dramatically affect the quantity of gastric secretions, but up to 700 mL are secreted as a result of a typical meal. Both nervous and hormonal mechanisms regulate gastric secretions. The neural mechanisms involve reflexes integrated within the medulla oblongata and local reflexes integrated within the ENS. In addition, higher brain centers influence the reflexes. The chemical messengers that regulate stomach secretions include the hormones gastrin, secretin, and cholecystokinin (table 24.1), as well as the paracrine chemical messenger histamine.

The regulation of stomach secretion is divided into three phases: (1) cephalic, (2) gastric, and (2) intestinal. The **cephalic phase** can be viewed as the "get started" phase, when stomach secretions are increased in anticipation of incoming food. This is followed by the "go for it" **gastric phase,** when most of the

Clinical IMPACT 24.2 Peptic Ulcer

Approximately 10% of people in the United States will develop a **peptic ulcer** during their lifetime. Peptic ulcers are caused when the gastric juices (acid and pepsin) digest the mucosal lining of the digestive tract. Approximately 80% of peptic ulcers occur on the duodenal side of the pyloric sphincter, but peptic ulcers can also occur in the stomach (gastric ulcers) or esophagus (esophageal ulcers).

Nearly all peptic ulcers are due to infection by a specific bacterium, *Helicobacter pylori,* which is also linked to gastritis and gastric cancer. Because stress, diet, smoking, and alcohol cause excess acid secretion in the stomach, these lifestyle patterns were deemed responsible for ulcers for many years. Although these factors can contribute to ulcers, it is now clear that the root cause is *H. pylori.*

The presence of bacteria in the stomach mucosa was first discovered in 1892, but the finding was met with severe skepticism. In 1982, an Australian doctor, Barry Marshall, was finally able to culture an unusual bacterium, *H. pylori,* from stomach biopsies. To provide evidence for his belief that this bacterium can cause gastritis and ulcers, Marshall did something that no one should do at home (or even in a lab). He drank a solution of *H. pylori* and subsequently developed gastric inflammation. Luckily, antibiotic treatment was able to cure him. In 2005, along with his colleague, Dr. Robin Warren, he received the Nobel Prize in Physiology or Medicine for his discovery.

Antibiotic treatment to eradicate *H. pylori* is the best therapy for ulcers. A combination of antibiotics and antacids cures 95% of gastric and 74% of duodenal ulcers within 2 months, with less than a 10% recurrence rate. By contrast, the previous conventional treatment using antacids yields only temporary relief, with about 90% recurrence within a year. Other treatments involve drugs that prevent histamine-stimulated acid secretion or that directly inhibit the proton pumps that secrete the acid. Such treatments are effective only for short-term relief, not for long-term treatment.

Most bacteria cannot survive in the stomach. Hence, *H. pylori* is one of the most pervasive of human pathogens because it inhabits a niche without competition. Estimates suggest that well over half of the world's population is infected with *H. pylori.* The infection rate in the United States is about 1% per year of age—for example, 30% of all 30-year-olds are infected. In developing countries, nearly all people over age 25 are infected. This may contribute to the high rates of stomach cancer in some of those countries.

Analyses of the *H. pylori* DNA sequences from various ethnic and geographic populations suggest that *H. pylori* infection has been present in humans for over 150,000 years, yet only about 15–20% exhibit gastric problems attributed to *H. pylori.* What triggers the development of ulcers is a major unanswered question. It seems likely that both *H. pylori* infection and conditions that elevate acid secretion or damage the stomach wall, such as stress or the excessive ingestion of alcohol or aspirin, contribute to the development of an ulcer. For example, if a person is highly stressed, elevated sympathetic activity may inhibit duodenal gland secretion and increase the person's susceptibility to ulcers in the duodenum by reducing the protective coating of mucus on the duodenal wall.

TABLE 24.1 Functions of the Major Gastrointestinal Hormones

Site of Production	Method of Stimulation	Secretory Effects	Motility Effects
Gastrin			
Stomach	Distension; partially digested proteins, autonomic stimulation, ingestion of alcohol or caffeine	Increases gastric secretion	Causes a minor increase in gastric motility
Secretin			
Duodenum	Acidity of chyme	Decreases gastric secretion; stimulates pancreatic and bile secretions high in HCO_3^-	Decreases gastric motility
Cholecystokinin			
Duodenum	Fatty acids and peptides	Slightly decreases gastric secretion; stimulates pancreatic secretions high in digestive enzymes; causes contraction of the gallbladder and relaxation of the hepatopancreatic ampullar sphincter	Strongly decreases gastric motility

stimulation of secretion occurs. Finally, the **intestinal phase** is the "slow down" phase, during which stomach secretion decreases. Figure 24.13 details the steps that regulate each phase of stomach secretion.

 *Cephalic phase.* "Get started!" The cephalic phase is the brain phase of stomach secretion. It is controlled by the CNS. It begins even before the bolus of food enters the stomach. Several types of stimuli act on the centers within the medulla oblongata to influence gastric secretions (figure 24.13*a*). These stimuli include the taste and smell of food, the stimulation of tactile receptors during the process of chewing and swallowing, and pleasant thoughts of food. Action potentials are sent from the medulla oblongata along parasympathetic neurons within the vagus (X) nerves to the stomach. Within the stomach wall, the preganglionic neurons stimulate the postganglionic neurons in the ENS. The postganglionic neurons, which are primarily cholinergic, stimulate secretory activity in the cells of the stomach mucosa.

Parasympathetic stimulation of the stomach mucosa results in the release of the neurotransmitter acetylcholine, which increases the secretory activity of both the parietal and the chief cells and stimulates the secretion of **gastrin** (GAS-trin) and **histamine** from endocrine cells. The gastrin released into the circulation travels to the parietal cells, where it stimulates additional hydrochloric acid and pepsinogen secretion. In addition, gastrin stimulates enterochromaffin-like cells to release histamine, which stimulates parietal cells to secrete hydrochloric acid. Histamine acts as both a local paracrine chemical messenger and a hormone in the blood to stimulate gastric gland secretory activity. Acetylcholine, histamine, and gastrin working together cause a greater secretion of hydrochloric acid than any of them does separately. Of the three, histamine has the greatest stimulatory effect. Drugs that block the actions of histamine are used to lower acid levels.

2 *Gastric phase.* "Go for it!" The gastric phase of stomach secretion produces the greatest volume of gastric secretions. The presence of food in the stomach initiates the gastric phase (figure 24.13*b*). The primary stimuli are distension of the stomach and the presence of amino acids and peptides in the stomach.

Distension of the stomach wall, especially in the body or fundus, stimulates mechanoreceptors. Action potentials generated by these receptors initiate reflexes that involve both the CNS and the ENS. These reflexes result in acetylcholine release and the cascade of events that increase secretion, as in the cephalic phase. The presence of partially digested proteins or moderate amounts of alcohol or caffeine in the stomach also stimulates gastrin secretion.

When the pH of the stomach contents falls below 2, increased gastric secretion produced by distension of the stomach is blocked. This negative-feedback mechanism limits the secretion of gastric juice. This is a great example of one of our key concepts: feedback loops.

3 *Intestinal phase.* "Slow down!" The intestinal phase of gastric secretion inhibits gastric secretions (figure 24.13*c*). It is initiated by acidic chyme entering the duodenum of the small intestine, which activates both neural and hormonal mechanisms. Secretions are inhibited when the pH of the chyme entering the duodenum drops to 2 or below. In addition, when the chyme contains lipid digestion products, gastric secretions are inhibited. There are two hormones involved in the intestinal phase: (1) secretin and (2) cholecystokinin.

Secretin (se-KREE-tin) is released in response to acidic solutions in the duodenum. Secretin inhibits gastric secretions by inhibiting both parietal and chief cells.

Cholecystokinin (KOH-leh-sis-toh-KIE-nin) is released in response to fatty acids, other lipids, and to a lesser degree protein digestion products in the duodenum and the proximal jejunum. Cholecystokinin inhibits gastric secretions.

The inhibition of gastric secretion is also under nervous control. The **enterogastric reflex** consists of a local reflex and a reflex integrated within the medulla oblongata that reduce gastric secretion. Distension of the duodenal wall, the presence of irritating substances in the duodenum, reduced pH, and hypertonic or hypotonic solutions in the duodenum activate the enterogastric reflex.

Cephalic Phase

Taste, smell, or thought of food (chemoreceptors)
Tactile sensation in mouth
1
Hypothalamus
Medulla oblongata
Vagus nerves carry action potentials to the stomach
2
3
Secretions stimulated
4
Histamine
Gastrin
Blood
Gastrin and histamine secretion
Stomach
(a)

Gastric Phase

Vagus nerves
Medulla oblongata
Distention of stomach
1
Secretions stimulated
2
Secretions stimulated
4
Distention
3
Local reflexes
Histamine
Gastrin
Blood
Stomach
(b)

Intestinal Phase

Vagus nerves
Medulla oblongata
Vagus nerves
Chemoreceptors in duodenum stimulated 2
Chyme with pH <2 or lipids inhibit gastric secretions
1
Decreased gastric secretions
Secretions inhibited
4
Local reflexes
3
Blood
Secretin and cholecystokinin
(c)

PROCESS Figure 24.13

Regulation of Stomach Secretions

There are three phases of stomach secretions: cephalic, gastric, and intestinal.

Why is it advantageous to the overall digestive process for secretin and cholecystokinin to slow stomach emptying upon initiation of the intestinal phase?

Clinical IMPACT 24.3

Gastroesophageal Reflux

Gastroesophageal reflux is the reflux of acidic chyme from the stomach into the esophagus. Gastroesophageal reflux is commonly called *heartburn* because the refluxed acid causes a painful, burning sensation in the chest. The pain is usually short-lived but may be confused with the pain of an ulcer or a heart attack. The lower esophageal sphincter normally prevents acid reflux. Overeating (especially fatty and fried foods); lying down immediately after a meal; consuming too much alcohol or caffeine; overuse of nonsteroidal anti-inflammatory drugs, such as aspirin and ibuprofen; and smoking can all cause gastroesophageal reflux. Gastroesophageal reflux commonly occurs in infants, but they usually outgrow it by their first birthday.

Chronic reflux more than twice a week in infants or adults is more serious and is called **gastroesophageal reflux disease (GERD).** GERD in young infants can be difficult to diagnose. Women commonly experience GERD during pregnancy because of increased abdominal pressure from the fetus and higher levels of the hormone progesterone, which relaxes the lower esophageal sphincter.

For most adults, lifestyle changes and medications that decrease gastric acid secretion are sufficient to relieve the symptoms of GERD. Antacids that buffer gastric acid can also alleviate minor discomfort. One class of drugs acts by blocking the H_2 histamine receptors on parietal cells. H_2 receptors are different from the H_1 receptors involved in allergic reactions. Drugs that block allergic reactions do not affect histamine-mediated stomach acid secretion, and vice versa. The most effective inhibitors of gastric acid secretion are the proton pump inhibitors, such as omeprazole. These drugs inhibit the proton pumps on parietal cells, thus preventing acid secretion into the stomach. If not treated, GERD can lead to serious complications, including esophageal ulcers, scarring that constricts the esophagus, and esophageal cancer.

To summarize, gastric acid secretion is controlled by negative-feedback loops involving nerves and hormones. During the gastric phase, high acid levels in the stomach trigger a decrease in additional acid secretion. Then, during the intestinal phase, acidic chyme entering the duodenum triggers a decrease in stomach acid secretion. These negative-feedback loops ensure that the acidic chyme entering the duodenum is neutralized, which is required for the digestion of food by pancreatic and brush-border enzymes in the intestine, and for the prevention of peptic ulcer formation.

Predict 3

Alice, age 85, reported periods of laryngitis that began when she awakened in the morning and lasted a few days. Alice's physician used a laryngoscope to examine her vocal folds and upper trachea, which appeared inflamed. He prescribed an antacid and a drug to decrease H^+ secretion and told her to take the medications prior to going to bed at night. He also advised Alice to avoid eating just before bedtime. Explain the cause of her laryngitis and why the medications should relieve the symptoms.

Movements of the Stomach

Stomach Filling

As food enters the stomach, the rugae flatten and the stomach volume increases up to 20-fold. This expansion allows the stomach to accommodate a large amount of food with very little increased pressure, until the stomach nears maximum capacity. Relaxation of the rugae is mediated by a reflex integrated within the medulla oblongata that inhibits muscle tone, and pressure is further minimized by the ability of smooth muscle to stretch without an increase in tension (see chapter 9).

Mixing of Stomach Contents

Ingested food is thoroughly mixed with stomach gland secretions to form chyme. Two types of stomach movement aid digestion and help move chyme through the digestive tract: (1) mixing waves and (2) peristaltic waves. **Mixing waves** are contractions that occur about every 20 seconds proceeding from the body of the stomach toward the pyloric sphincter. **Peristaltic waves** occur less frequently, are significantly more powerful than mixing waves, and force the chyme near the periphery of the stomach toward the pyloric sphincter. The more solid material near the center of the stomach is pushed superiorly toward the cardia for further digestion (figure 24.14). Roughly 80% of the contractions are mixing waves, and 20% are peristaltic waves. The back-and-forth movement of the chyme effectively mixes the ingested food with gastric juice. Figure 24.14 illustrates the types of movement in the stomach.

1. Relatively weak contractions result in **mixing waves,** which thoroughly mix ingested food with stomach secretions to form chyme.
2. In the mixing wave, the more fluid part of the chyme is pushed toward the pyloric sphincter, whereas the more solid center moves back toward the body of the stomach.
3. Stronger contractions result in **peristaltic waves,** which force the chyme toward and through the pyloric sphincter. The pyloric sphincter usually remains closed because of mild tonic contraction.
4. Again, the more fluid part of the chyme is pushed toward the pyloric region, whereas the more solid center of the chyme squeezes past the peristaltic constriction back toward the body of the stomach.
5. Each peristaltic contraction is sufficiently strong to cause partial relaxation of the pyloric sphincter and to pump a few milliliters of chyme through the pyloric opening and into the duodenum. Increased motility leads to increased emptying.

Stomach Emptying

The amount of time food remains in the stomach depends on a number of factors, including the type and volume of food. Liquids begin exiting the stomach within minutes. Depending on the volume ingested, their exit is usually complete within about 2 hours. The exit of a typical meal is usually complete within 3–4 hours. The pyloric sphincter normally remains partially closed because of mild tonic contraction. Each peristaltic contraction is strong enough to force a small amount of chyme through the pyloric opening and into the duodenum. The peristaltic contractions responsible for moving chyme through the partially closed pyloric opening are called the **pyloric pump.** In general, increased motility leads to increased emptying. In an empty stomach, peristaltic contractions that approach tetanic contractions can occur for about

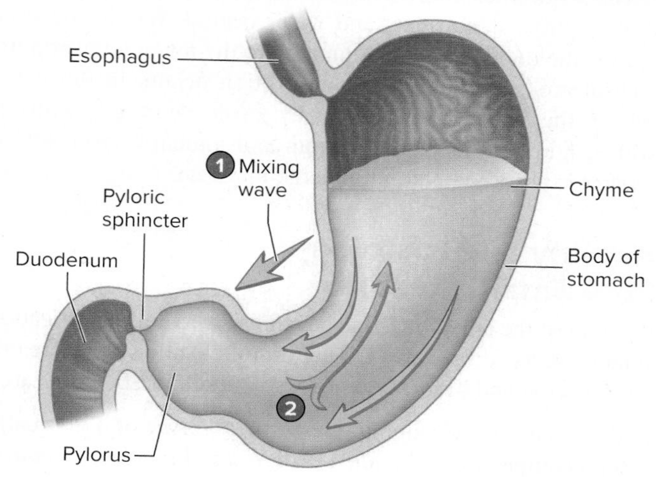

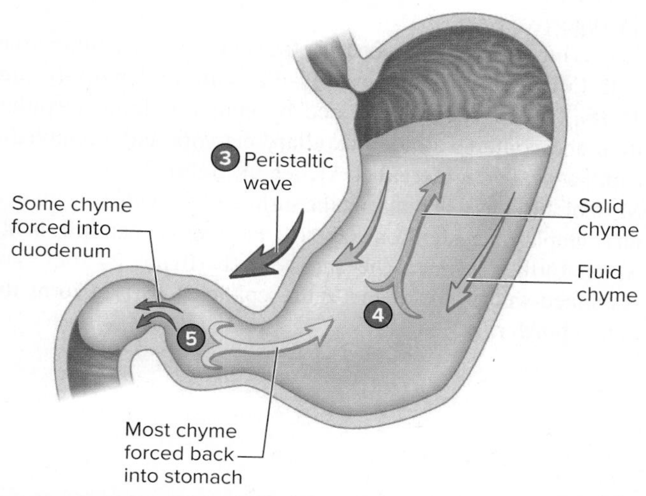

PROCESS **Figure 24.14**

Movements in the Stomach

Food is mixed with hydrochloric acid and other secretions in the stomach to create chyme.

In a person suffering from heartburn, the gastroesophageal opening is weakened and stomach acid can be forced from the stomach back into the esophagus. Explain why medications that slow stomach movements and emptying may worsen heartburn symptoms.

2–3 minutes. The contractions are increased by low blood glucose levels and are strong enough to create uncomfortable sensations called **hunger pangs.** Hunger pangs usually begin 12–24 hours after a meal, in less time for some people. If nothing is ingested, hunger pangs reach their maximum intensity within 3–4 days and then become progressively weaker.

Regulation of Stomach Emptying

If the stomach empties too fast, the efficiency of digestion and absorption is reduced, and acidic gastric contents entering the duodenum may damage its lining. However, if the rate of emptying is too slow, then digestion and absorption in the small intestine are reduced and the stomach wall could be damaged by the acid. To prevent these two extremes, stomach emptying is regulated.

The neural mechanisms that stimulate stomach secretions are also involved with increasing stomach motility. The major stimulus for both motility and secretion is distension of the stomach wall. Increased stomach motility increases stomach emptying. Conversely, the hormonal and neural mechanisms associated with the duodenum that decrease gastric secretions also decrease gastric motility and prevent relaxation of the pyloric sphincter. The enterogastric reflex and the hormone cholecystokinin are major inhibitors of gastric motility. The result is a reduced rate of stomach emptying.

A meal of polysaccharide carbohydrates (starch and glycogen) has the fastest clearance time from the stomach, typically 1 hour. For comparison, a meal rich in dietary lipids and proteins takes up to 6 hours to clear from the stomach. The key to this difference is cholecystokinin-mediated inhibition of stomach emptying. Cholecystokinin secretion increases as lipid content of ingested food increases. The benefit of the reduction in emptying time is allowing lipase adequate time to digest lipids in the meal.

Vomiting is usually a protective mechanism against the ingestion of toxic or harmful substances. Vomiting can result from irritation (e.g., overdistension or overexcitation) anywhere along the digestive tract. Action potentials travel through the vagus nerves and spinal visceral sensory nerves to the vomiting center in the medulla oblongata. Once the vomiting center is stimulated and the reflex is initiated, the following events occur: (1) A deep breath is taken; (2) the hyoid bone and larynx are elevated, opening the upper esophageal sphincter; (3) the opening of the larynx is closed; (4) the soft palate is elevated, closing the connection between the oropharynx and the nasopharynx; (5) the diaphragm and abdominal muscles are forcefully contracted, strongly compressing the stomach and increasing the intragastric pressure; (6) the lower esophageal sphincter is relaxed; and (7) the gastric contents are forced out of the stomach, through the esophagus and oral cavity, to the outside.

ASSESS YOUR PROGRESS

29. *Describe the parts of the stomach. List the tunics of the stomach wall. How is the stomach wall different from the esophagus wall?*

30. *What are gastric pits and gastric glands?*

31. *Name the types of cells in the stomach and the secretions they produce. What are the functions of the secretions?*

32. *Describe the three phases of regulation of stomach secretion.*

33. *How are gastric secretions inhibited? Why is this inhibition necessary?*

34. *As the stomach fills, why does the pressure not greatly increase until maximum volume is reached?*

35. *Name the two kinds of stomach movements. How are stomach movements regulated by hormones and nervous control?*

24.9 Small Intestine

LEARNING OUTCOMES

After reading this section, you should be able to

A. **List the sections of the small intestine.**
B. **Describe the characteristics that account for the large surface area of the small intestine.**
C. **Name the four major cell types of the duodenal mucosa.**
D. **Describe the functions of the cells of the duodenal mucosa.**
E. **Describe the secretions of the small intestine.**
F. **Describe the movements of the small intestine.**

The **small intestine** consists of three segments: (1) duodenum, (2) jejunum, and (3) ileum (figure 24.15). The entire small intestine averages 6 m in length, although there are reports of as much as 9 m in length (6 m is approximately 20 feet–most two-story homes are 20–25 feet tall). The region connected to the stomach, the duodenum, is about 25 cm long (Gr. *dodeka daktulon*, 12 fingers in width). The duodenum merges with the jejunum, which constitutes about two-fifths of the total length of the small intestine, and is about 2.5 m long (approximately 8 feet). The jejunum merges with the ileum, which constitutes three-fifths of the small intestine, and is about 3.5 m long (approximately 11 feet). The ileum merges with the large intestine. Two major accessory glands, the liver and the pancreas, release their secretions into the duodenum.

The small intestine is where the greatest amount of digestion and absorption of nutrients and water occurs. Within the small intestine, the duodenum and jejunum are the major sites of nutrient absorption, although some absorption occurs in the ileum. Most of the water is absorbed by osmosis, along with the absorbed nutrients in the duodenum and jejunum. Over 90% of the water is absorbed before the large intestine.

Anatomy and Histology of the Small Intestine

The lining of the small intestine has three structural modifications that increase its surface area about 600-fold to allow for more efficient digestion and absorption of food. These modifications are:

1. The mucosa and submucosa form a series of folds called the **circular folds,** or *plicae* (PLY-see; PLY-kee) *circulares* (figure 24.16*a*), which run perpendicular to the long axis of the digestive tract.
2. Tiny, fingerlike projections of the mucosa form numerous **villi** (VIL-eye), which are 0.5–1.5 mm in length (figure 24.16*c*). Each villus is covered by simple columnar epithelium and contains a blood capillary network and a lymphatic capillary called a **lacteal** (LAK-tee-al; figure 24.16*d*).
3. Most of the cells that make up the surface of the villi have numerous cytoplasmic extensions (about 1 μm long) called **microvilli,** which further increase the surface area (figure 24.16*e*). The combined microvilli on the entire epithelial surface form the **brush border.**

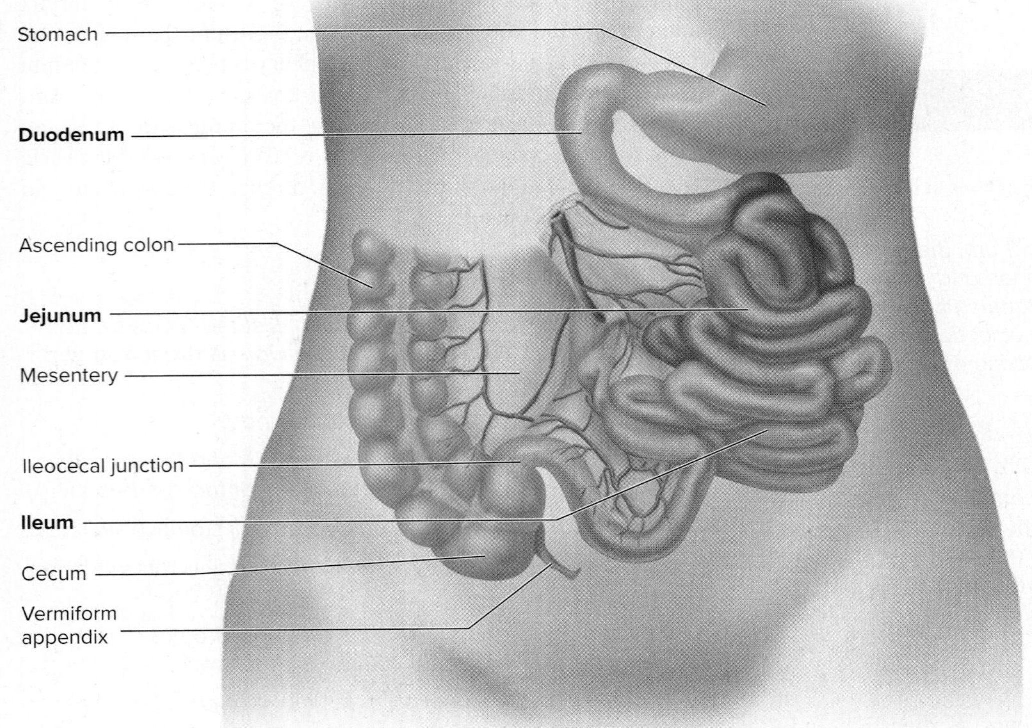

FIGURE 24.15 Small Intestine
The small intestine consists of three segments: the duodenum, jejunum, and ileum. APR

FUNDAMENTAL **Figure**

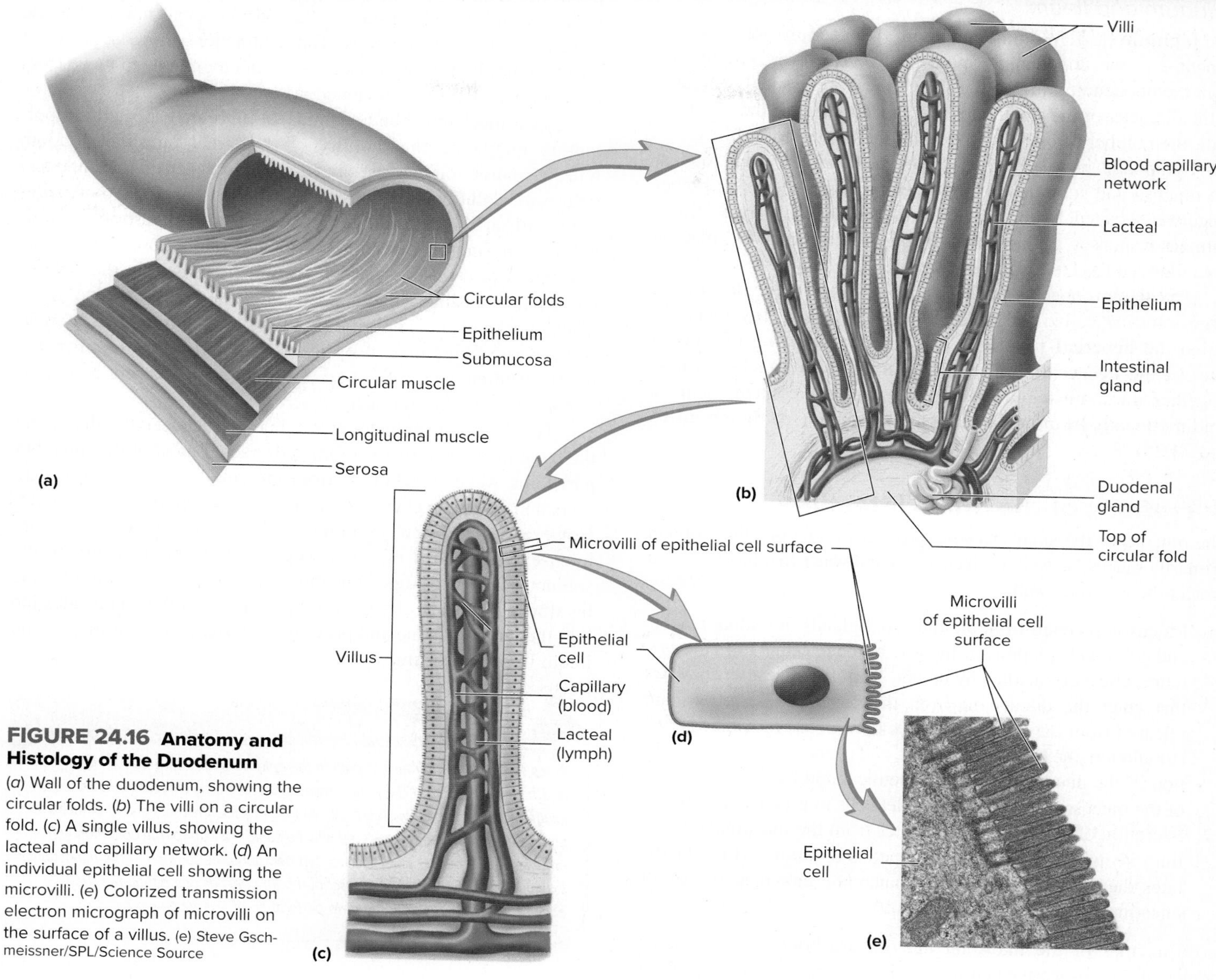

FIGURE 24.16 Anatomy and Histology of the Duodenum
(*a*) Wall of the duodenum, showing the circular folds. (*b*) The villi on a circular fold. (*c*) A single villus, showing the lacteal and capillary network. (*d*) An individual epithelial cell showing the microvilli. (*e*) Colorized transmission electron micrograph of microvilli on the surface of a villus. (e) Steve Gschmeissner/SPL/Science Source

The mucosa of the small intestine is simple columnar epithelium with four major cell types: absorptive cells, goblet cells, granular cells, and endocrine cells.

1. **Absorptive cells** are cells with microvilli that produce digestive enzymes and absorb digested food.
2. **Goblet cells** produce a protective mucus.
3. **Granular cells,** or *Paneth cells,* may help protect the intestinal epithelium from bacteria.
4. **Endocrine cells** produce many regulatory hormones. For example, the hormones secretin and cholecystokinin stimulate hepatic and pancreatic secretions (see table 24.1, figures 24.21 and 24.24).

The epithelial cells are produced within tubular invaginations of the mucosa, called **intestinal glands,** or *crypts of Lieberkühn,* at the base of the villi. The absorptive and goblet cells migrate from the intestinal glands to cover the surface of the villi and are eventually shed from its tip. The granular and endocrine cells remain in the bottom of the glands. The submucosa of the duodenum contains coiled, tubular mucous glands called **duodenal glands,** or *Brunner glands,* which open into the base of the intestinal glands.

Duodenum

The **duodenum** (doo-oh-DEE-num) is the shortest part of the small intestine. The structure of the duodenum begins with a nearly 180-degree arc from where it leaves the stomach and curves around the head of the pancreas within the abdominal cavity (see figure 24.18). This short, superior part ends in a sharp bend, where it joins the jejunum. Within the descending portion of the duodenum are two small projections: (1) the **major duodenal papilla** and (2) the **minor duodenal papilla.** These papillae are the location of ducts from the liver and the pancreas.

Jejunum and Ileum

The **jejunum** (je-JEW-num) and **ileum** (ILL-ee-um) are similar in structure to the duodenum (figure 24.16). However, progressing from the duodenum through the ileum, there are gradual decreases in the diameter of the small intestine, the thickness of the intestinal wall, the number of circular folds, and the number of villi.

Lymphatic nodules called **Peyer patches** are numerous in the mucosa and submucosa of the ileum. Peyer patches and other mucosa-associated lymphoid tissue in the digestive tract initiate immune responses against microorganisms that enter the mucosa from ingested food (see chapter 22).

The ileum connects to the large intestine at a region of the large intestine called the cecum. The site where they merge is called the **ileocecal junction.** The junction is a ring of smooth muscle, the **ileocecal sphincter,** and a one-way **ileocecal valve.** Together, the sphincter and valve allow intestinal contents to move unidirectionally from the ileum in to the cecum (see figures 24.15 and 24.25).

Secretions of the Small Intestine

The mucosa of the small intestine produces secretions that contain primarily mucus, as well as electrolytes and water that lubricate and protect the intestinal wall.

1. Mucus is secreted from the duodenal glands, intestinal glands, and goblet cells. It protects the wall of the intestine from the irritating effects of acidic chyme and from the digestive enzymes that enter the duodenum from the pancreas. Secretions are released from the duodenal glands in response to vagus nerve, stimulation, the hormone secretin, and chemical or tactile irritation of the duodenal mucosa. Chemical and tactile stimulation of the mucosa also stimulate goblet cells to produce mucus.
2. Secretion of electrolytes and water from the intestinal epithelium keeps the chyme in an aqueous solution, which facilitates the digestive process by pancreatic enzymes and small intestine enzymes (see figure 24.9).

Enzymes of the intestinal mucosa are bound to the membranes of the absorptive cell microvilli and are collectively called **brush-border enzymes.** The brush-border enzymes include **disaccharidases,** which break down disaccharides to monosaccharides, and **peptidases,** which hydrolyze the peptide bonds between small amino acid chains (see figure 24.9). The large surface area of the intestinal epithelium brings these enzymes into contact with the chyme. Small molecules, which are breakdown products of digestion, are absorbed through the microvilli and enter the circulatory or lymphatic system.

Movement in the Small Intestine

Movement in the small intestine involves mixing of the chyme and slow propulsion down the digestive tract. Segmental contractions mix the intestinal contents, and peristaltic contractions primarily propel the intestinal contents along the digestive tract (see figure 24.3*a,b*). The peristaltic contractions are generally propagated for only short distances, but a few may proceed the entire length of the intestine. Frequently, intestinal peristaltic contractions are continuations of peristaltic contractions that begin in the stomach. These contractions both mix and propel substances through the small intestine as the wave of contraction proceeds. The contractions move at a rate of about 1 cm/min. It usually takes 3–5 hours for chyme to move from the pylorus to the ileocecal junction.

Local mechanical and chemical stimuli are especially important in regulating the motility of the small intestine. Smooth muscle contraction increases in response to distension of the intestinal wall. Solutions that are either hypertonic or hypotonic, solutions with a low pH, and certain products of digestion, such as amino acids and peptides, also stimulate contractions of the small intestine. Local reflexes, which are integrated within the ENS of the small intestine, mediate the intestine's response to these mechanical and chemical stimuli. Stimulation through parasympathetic nerve fibers may also increase the intestine's motility, but the parasympathetic influences in the intestine are not as important as those in the stomach.

The ileocecal sphincter at the juncture between the ileum and the large intestine remains mildly contracted most of the time, but peristaltic waves reaching it from the small intestine cause it to relax and allow the chyme to move from the ileum into the cecum. However, cecal distension initiates a local reflex that causes more intense constriction of the ileocecal sphincter. Closure of the sphincter facilitates digestion and absorption in the small intestine by slowing the rate of chyme movement from the small intestine into the large intestine and prevents material from returning to the ileum from the cecum.

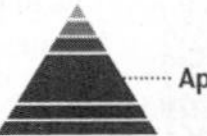

Predict 4

Amos suffers from intermittent pain in the epigastric area that begins about 2 or 3 hours after eating. The pain is relieved by taking an antacid. An endoscopic exam identified duodenal ulcers, and Amos's physician recommended antacids and an antibiotic. Amos wondered why he could not control the condition with antacids alone, but his physician was worried about perforation of the duodenum. Explain why Amos's physician prescribed both antacids and antibiotics. How could the lack of antibiotics lead to perforation of the duodenum?

ASSESS YOUR PROGRESS

36. *Name and describe the three parts of the small intestine.*

37. *What are the circular folds, villi, and microvilli in the small intestine? What are their functions?*

38. *Name the four types of cells found in the duodenal mucosa, and state their functions.*

39. *What are the functions of the intestinal glands and duodenal glands? State the factors that stimulate secretion from the duodenal glands and from goblet cells.*

40. *List the enzymes of the small intestine wall, and give their functions.*

41. *What are the two kinds of movement of the small intestine? How are they regulated?*

42. *What is the function of the ileocecal sphincter and valve?*

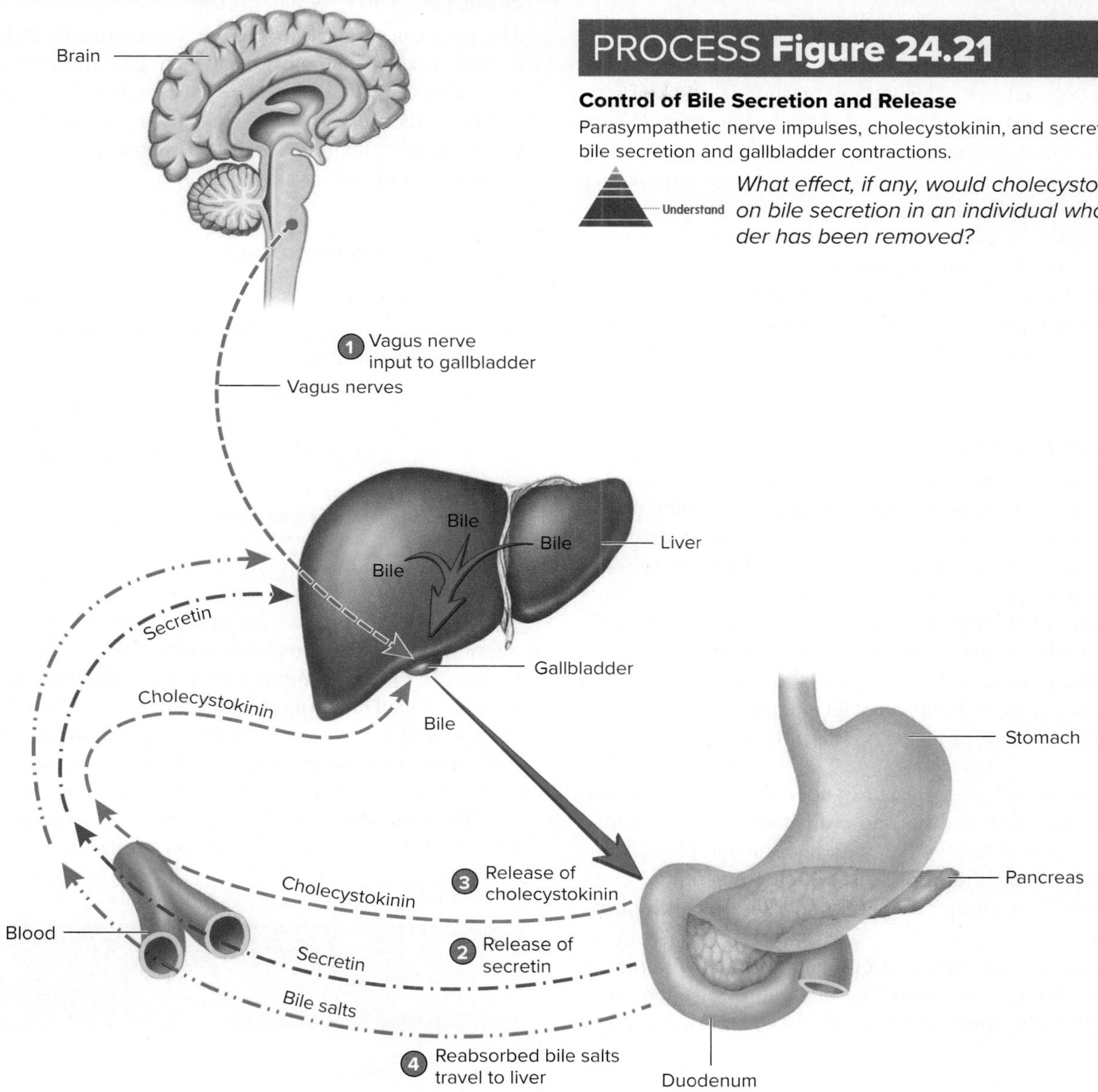

PROCESS Figure 24.21

Control of Bile Secretion and Release

Parasympathetic nerve impulses, cholecystokinin, and secretin all stimulate bile secretion and gallbladder contractions.

Understand *What effect, if any, would cholecystokinin have on bile secretion in an individual whose gallbladder has been removed?*

Bile Production for Digestion and Excretion

The liver produces and secretes about 600–1000 mL of bile each day (see figure 24.9). Bile is a complex solution that contains (1) bile salts, (2) bile pigments, (3) cholesterol, (4) lipids, (5) lipid-soluble hormones, and (6) lecithin (a mixture of phospholipids). Bile contains no digestive enzymes, but it plays a role in digestion because it neutralizes stomach acid and emulsifies lipids. The relative alkaline pH of bile helps neutralize the acidic chyme entering the duodenum. This is important because the pancreatic enzymes cannot function at the acidic pH of the chyme leaving the stomach. **Bile salts** emulsify lipids, which is necessary for subsequent digestion by lipase. Bile pigments are not required for any digestive function but rather are excretory products. Bile pigments have greenish-yellow to brown colors and give feces their characteristic color. One common bile pigment is bilirubin, which results from the breakdown of hemoglobin (see chapter 19).

Figure 24.21 describes the regulation of bile secretion and release from the gall bladder. Both neural and hormonal signals stimulate the secretion and release of bile.

1. Parasympathetic stimulation through the vagus nerves increases bile secretion from the liver.
2. Two hormones released from the duodenum increase bile in the digestive tract: (a) secretin and (b) cholecystokinin. Secretin stimulates bile secretion from the liver, primarily by increasing the water and HCO_3^- content of bile.
3. Cholecystokinin stimulates gallbladder contractions to release bile into the duodenum.
4. Bile salts increase bile secretion through a positive-feedback system. Over 90% of bile salts are reabsorbed in the ileum and carried in the blood by the hepatic portal circulation. Upon their return to the liver, the bile salts stimulate further bile secretion and are once again secreted into the bile. This recycling process reduces the loss of bile salts in the feces. Bile secretion into the duodenum continues until the duodenum empties.

Storage of Nutrients

Hepatocytes can remove glucose from the blood and store it in the form of **glycogen.** They can also store lipids, vitamins (A, B_{12}, D, E, and K), copper, and iron. This storage function is usually short-term, and the amount of stored material in the hepatocytes—hence their size—fluctuates during the day.

Hepatocytes help maintain blood glucose levels within very narrow limits. If a large amount of glucose enters the general circulation after a meal, it will result in hyperglycemia. Under normal conditions, this is prevented because the blood from the small intestine passes through the hepatic portal vein to the liver, where hepatocytes remove glucose and other substances from the blood, store them, and then secrete them back into the circulation when needed.

Processing of Nutrients

The processing, or interconversion, of nutrients is another important function of the liver. Our food choices are not always in line with the nutrient requirements of the body (candy bars for breakfast, for example). If this is the case, the liver can convert some nutrients into others. For example, if a person is on a diet that is excessively high in protein, an oversupply of amino acids and an undersupply of lipids and carbohydrates may be delivered to the liver. The hepatocytes break down the amino acids and cycle many of them through metabolic pathways so that they can be used to produce ATP, lipids, and glucose (see chapter 25).

Hepatocytes also transform substances that cannot be used by most cells into more readily usable substances. For example, they combine ingested dietary fats with choline and phosphorus in the liver to produce phospholipids, which are essential components of plasma membranes. In addition, vitamin D is hydroxylated in the liver hepatocytes. The hydroxylated form of vitamin D, which is the major circulating form of vitamin D, is transported through the blood to the kidneys, where it is again hydroxylated to form active Vitamin D_3, a hormone regulating Ca^{2+}.

Detoxification

Many ingested substances are harmful to body cells. In addition, the body itself produces many by-products of metabolism that, if accumulated, are toxic. The liver forms a major line of defense by altering the structure of many of these harmful substances to make them less toxic or to make their elimination easier. Ammonia, for example, a by-product of amino acid metabolism, is toxic and not readily removed from the blood by the kidneys. Hepatocytes remove ammonia from the blood and convert it to urea, which is less toxic than ammonia. Urea is then secreted into the blood and eliminated by the kidneys in the urine. The liver hepatocytes also remove other substances from the blood and excrete them into the bile.

Hepatic phagocytic cells (Kupffer cells), which lie along the sinusoid walls of the liver, phagocytize "worn-out" and dying red and white blood cells, some bacteria, and other debris that enters the liver through the blood vessels.

Synthesis of New Molecules

The liver can produce its own new compounds, including plasma proteins such as albumins, fibrinogen, globulins, heparin, and clotting factors, which are released into the blood (see chapter 19). In addition, the liver is the major site of cholesterol synthesis. Cholesterol is important for plasma membrane structure and steroid hormone synthesis, for example.

ASSESS YOUR PROGRESS

43. *Describe the lobes of the liver. What is the porta hepatis?*
44. *Diagram the duct system from the liver, gallbladder, and pancreas that empties into the major duodenal papilla.*
45. *Describe the flow of blood to and through the liver. Describe the flow of bile away from the liver.*
46. *Explain and give examples of the major functions of the liver.*
47. *What stimulates bile secretion from the liver?*

Gallbladder

The **gallbladder** is a saclike structure for bile storage. It is on the inferior surface of the liver; it is about 8 cm long and 4 cm wide (see figure 24.18). Three tunics form the gallbladder wall: (1) an inner mucosa folded into rugae that allow the gallbladder to expand; (2) a muscularis, which is a layer of smooth muscle that allows the gallbladder to contract; and (3) an outer covering of serosa. The cystic duct connects the gallbladder to the common bile duct.

The function of the gallbladder is to store and concentrate bile. The liver continually secretes bile, which flows to the

Clinical IMPACT 24.4

Cystic Fibrosis

Cystic fibrosis is a hereditary disorder that occurs in 1 of every 2000 births and affects 33,000 people in the United States; it is the most common lethal genetic disorder among Caucasians. The most critical effects of the disease, accounting for 90% of the deaths, are on the respiratory system. Several other problems occur, however, in affected people. Because the disease is a disorder in a Cl^- transport channel protein—which affects chloride transport and, as a result, the movement of water—all exocrine glands are affected. The buildup of thick mucus in the pancreatic and hepatic ducts causes blockage of the ducts so that bile salts and pancreatic digestive enzymes are prevented from reaching the duodenum. As a result, digestion is reduced, and fat-soluble vitamins are poorly absorbed due to the lack of bile to form micelles. The person suffers from vitamin A, D, E, and K deficiencies, which result in conditions such as night blindness, skin disorders, rickets, and excessive bleeding. Therapy includes administering the missing vitamins to the person and reducing dietary fat intake.

gallbladder, where 40–70 mL of bile are stored. While the bile is in the gallbladder, water and electrolytes are absorbed. Thus, bile salts and pigments become as much as 5–10 times more concentrated than when secreted by the liver. Bile is released from the gallbladder by contractions stimulated by cholecystokinin and, to a lesser degree, by vagal stimulation. In this way, large amounts of concentrated bile are dumped into the small intestine shortly after a meal (figure 24.21).

Gallstones are insoluble aggregates formed in the gallbladder. They are often caused by precipitation of excess cholesterol, which can be the result of a high-cholesterol diet or other causes. Cholesterol is not soluble in water and is ordinarily kept in solution by bile salts. Occasionally, a gallstone passes out of the gallbladder and enters the cystic duct, blocking the release of bile. This condition interferes with normal digestion, and often the gallstone must be surgically removed. If the gallstone moves far enough down the duct, it can also block the pancreatic duct, resulting in pancreatitis. This information may help you answer this chapter's Learn to Predict question.

ASSESS YOUR PROGRESS

48. *Describe the three tunics of the gallbladder wall.*
49. *What is the function of the gallbladder? What stimulates the release of bile from the gallbladder?*

Anatomy of the Pancreas

The **pancreas** is a complex organ composed of both endocrine and exocrine tissues that perform several functions. The pancreas is located behind the stomach. The head of the pancreas is nestled within the curvature of the duodenum (figure 24.22*a*). The body and tail extend to the spleen.

The endocrine part of the pancreas consists of **pancreatic islets,** or *islets of Langerhans* (figure 24.22*b*). The islet cells produce three

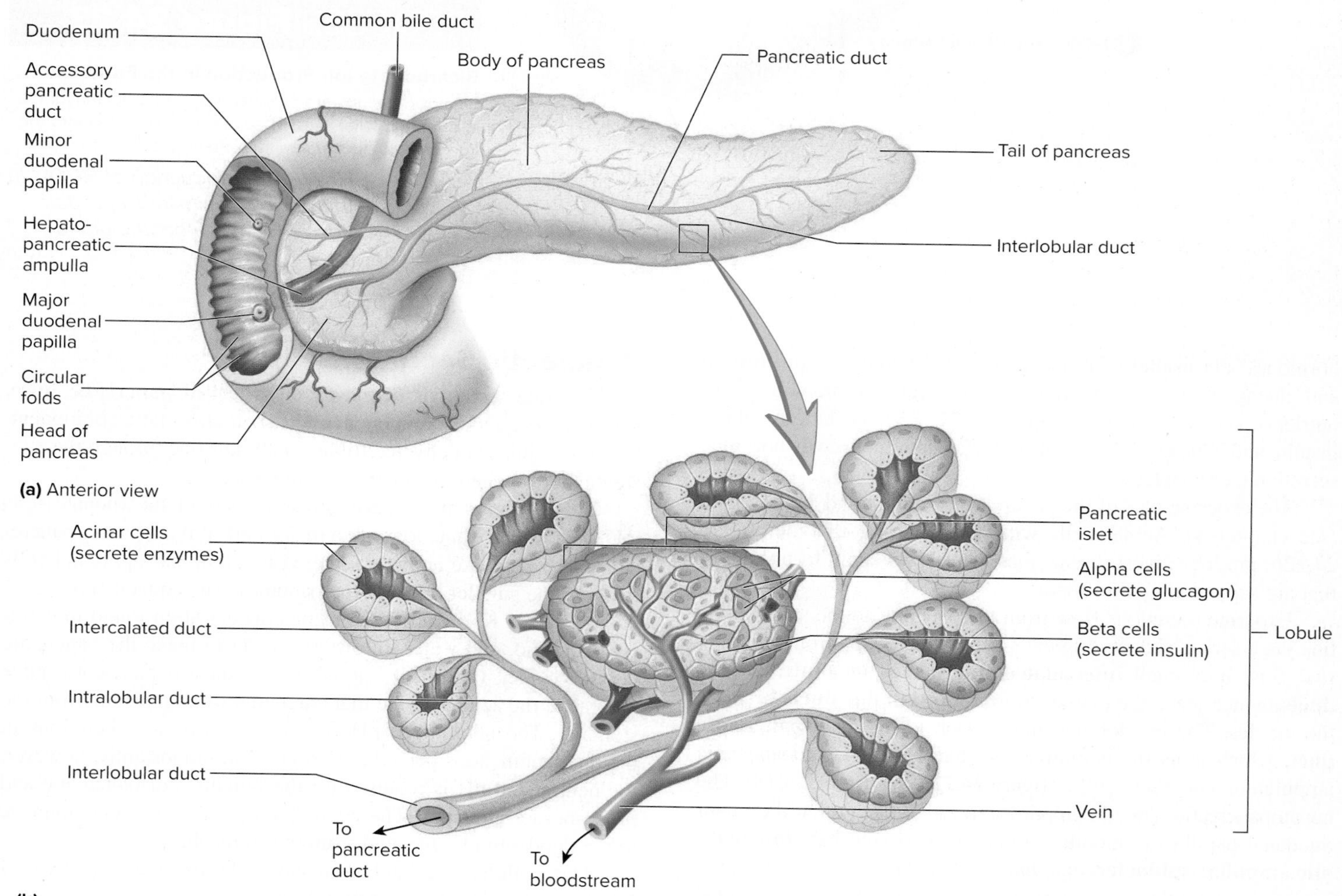

FIGURE 24.22 Anatomy and Histology of the Duodenum and Pancreas
(*a*) The head of the pancreas lies within the duodenal curvature, with the pancreatic duct emptying into the duodenum. (*b*) Histology of the pancreas, showing both the acinar cells and the pancreatic duct system. APR

PROCESS **Figure**

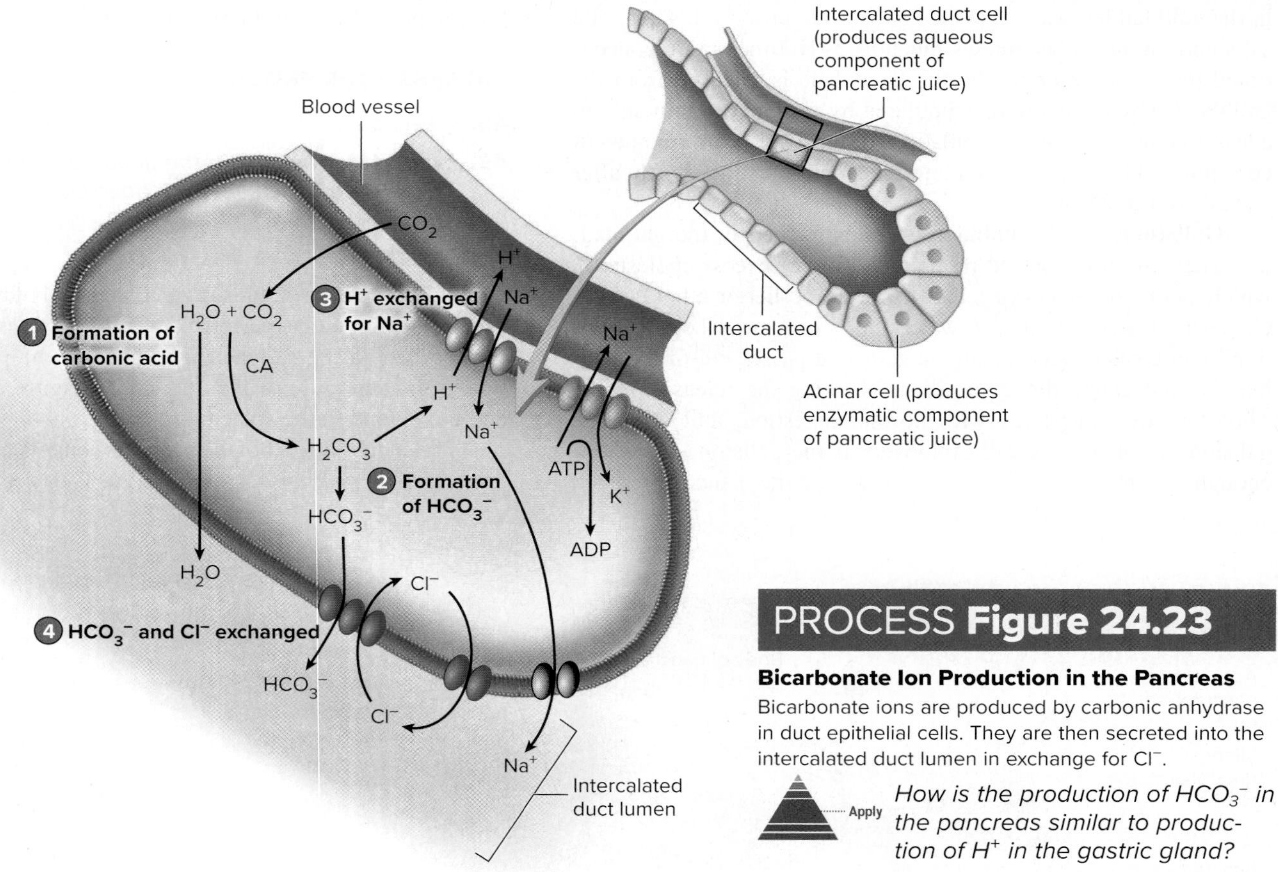

PROCESS **Figure 24.23**

Bicarbonate Ion Production in the Pancreas

Bicarbonate ions are produced by carbonic anhydrase in duct epithelial cells. They are then secreted into the intercalated duct lumen in exchange for Cl^-.

Apply *How is the production of HCO_3^- in the pancreas similar to production of H^+ in the gastric gland?*

hormones: (1) insulin, (2) glucagon, and (3) somatostatin. Insulin and glucagon are very important in controlling the blood levels of nutrients, such as glucose and amino acids. Somatostatin regulates insulin and glucagon secretion and may inhibit growth hormone secretion (see chapter 18).

The exocrine part of the pancreas is a compound acinar gland (see chapter 4). Acinar cells within the **acini** (AS-i-nie; figure 24.22*b*) produce digestive enzymes. Clusters of acini form lobules that are separated by thin septa.

Exocrine secretions flow from the pancreas to the small intestine via a series of ducts (figure 24.22*b*). Secretions from the acini first flow into small **intercalated ducts,** then into **intralobular ducts,** which leave the lobules to join **interlobular ducts** between the lobules. The interlobular ducts attach to the main **pancreatic duct,** which joins the common bile duct at the hepatopancreatic ampulla, or *Vater's ampulla* (figure 24.22*a*; see figure 24.18). The hepatopancreatic ampulla empties into the duodenum at the major duodenal papilla. A smooth muscle sphincter, the **hepatopancreatic ampullar sphincter,** or *sphincter of Oddi,* regulates the opening of the ampulla. In most people, an accessory pancreatic duct opens at the minor duodenal papilla. The ducts are lined with simple cuboidal epithelium, and the epithelial cells of the acini are pyramid-shaped. A smooth muscle sphincter surrounds the pancreatic duct where it enters the hepatopancreatic ampulla.

Pancreatic Secretions

The exocrine secretions of the pancreas, called **pancreatic juice,** have (1) an aqueous component and (2) an enzymatic component. Pancreatic juice is delivered to the small intestine through the pancreatic ducts, where it functions in digestion.

The **aqueous pancreatic juice** is rich in bicarbonate ions (HCO_3^-). Bicarbonate ions are a major part of the aqueous pancreatic juice. They are actively secreted by columnar epithelial cells that line the smaller ducts of the pancreas. The aqueous juice contains Na^+ and K^+ in about the same concentration found in extracellular fluid, and water follows passively to make the pancreatic juice isotonic. The HCO_3^- ions of the aqueous pancreatic juice neutralize the acidic chyme that enters the small intestine from the stomach. The neutralized pH caused by pancreatic secretions in the duodenum stops pepsin digestion. More importantly, however, the neutralized pH is required for the functions of pancreatic and brush-border enzymes. The neutralized pH also prevents damage to the duodenum by the acid from the stomach.

The cellular mechanism responsible for the secretion of HCO_3^- is diagrammed in figure 24.23.

1. The enzyme carbonic anhydrase is present in duct epithelial cells.
2. Carbonic anhydrase forms carbonic acid, which dissociates into H^+ and HCO_3^-.

PROCESS **Figure**

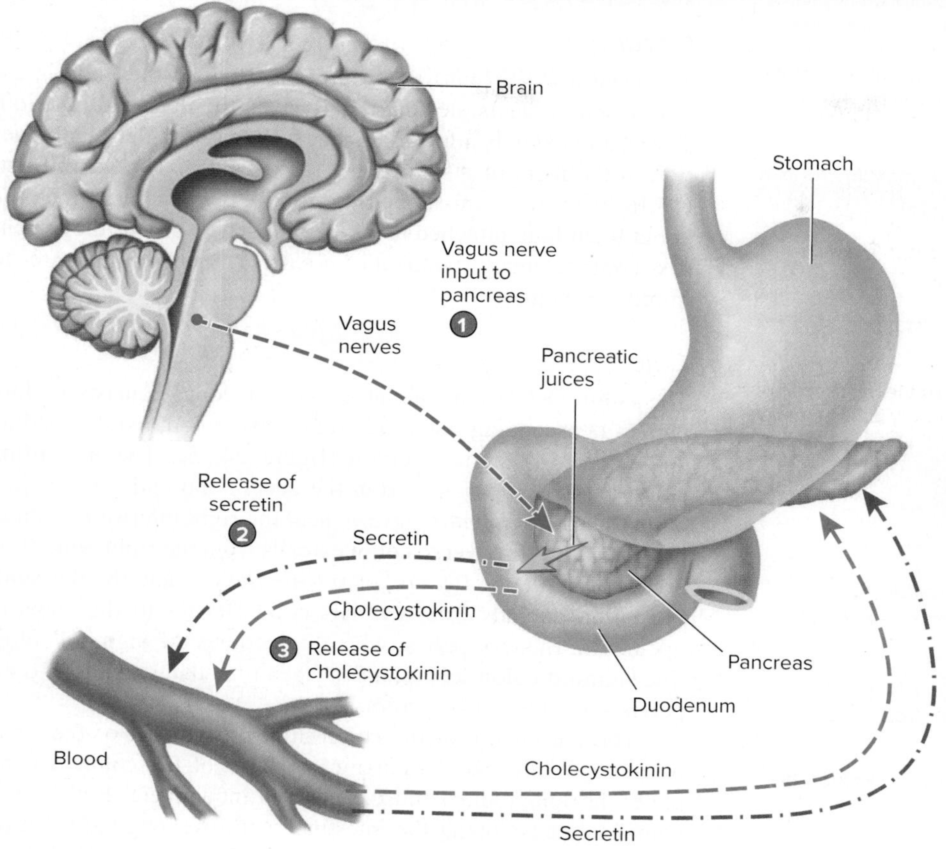

PROCESS Figure 24.24

Control of Pancreatic Secretion

Cholecystokinin and parasympathetic impulses stimulate pancreatic enzyme secretion. Secretin stimulates secretion of HCO_3^- from the pancreas.

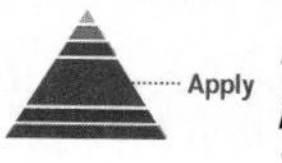

Blockage of the pancreatic duct prevents pancreatic enzymes from being delivered to the small intestine. What effect would you expect this to have on cholecystokinin and secretin levels in the blood?

3. The H^+ are exchanged for Na^+, which are removed from the cell by the **Na^+–K^+ pump.** The Na^+–K^+ pump is an ATPase that moves Na^+ out and K^+ into the cell. It generates a Na^+ gradient that is important in many cellular processes, including intestinal nutrient and water absorption described later in this chapter.
4. The HCO_3^- are then transported into the intercalated duct lumen in exchange for Cl^-. The result is an aqueous pancreatic juice rich in HCO_3^-.

The production of HCO_3^- in the pancreas is similar to the production of H^+ in the gastric gland (see figure 24.12). The major difference is that an alkaline solution is produced in the pancreas, whereas an acidic solution is produced in the stomach.

The **enzyme-rich pancreatic juice** contains enzymes that digest all major classes of food. This enzyme-rich secretion is produced by the acinar cells of the pancreas. Without the enzymes produced by the pancreas, lipids, proteins, and carbohydrates cannot be adequately digested (see figures 24.2 and 24.9).

The three major proteolytic enzymes are (1) **trypsin,** (2) **chymotrypsin,** and (3) **carboxypeptidase.** In the same manner as pepsin, these protein-digesting enzymes are secreted in inactive forms, whereas many of the other enzymes are secreted in active form. The inactive forms are called trypsinogen, chymotrypsinogen, and procarboxypeptidase. They are activated by proteolytic removal of certain peptides from the precursor proteins. The proteolytic enzyme **enterokinase** (EN-teer-oh-KIE-nase), which is attached to the brush border of the small intestine, activates trypsinogen. Trypsin then activates more trypsinogen, as well as chymotrypsinogen and procarboxypeptidase. This process of releasing inactive enzymes is necessary because if the enzymes were produced in their active forms, they would start to digest the pancreas itself. Inappropriate activation causes **pancreatitis,** which is a painful inflammation of the pancreas. Pancreatitis can result from alcoholism, the use of certain drugs, pancreatic duct blockage, cystic fibrosis, viral infection, or pancreatic cancer. Symptoms can range from mild abdominal pain to systemic shock and coma.

Enzyme-rich pancreatic juice also contains other enzymes that digest carbohydrate, lipids, and nucleic acids. The enzyme **pancreatic amylase** continues the polysaccharide digestion initiated in the oral cavity. The lipid-digesting enzyme **pancreatic lipase** breaks down lipids into monoglycerides and free fatty acids. In addition to lipase, the pancreas also secretes the enzyme cholesterol esterase, which digests cholesteryl esters (the dietary form of cholesterol) into cholesterol and free fatty acids. Deoxyribonucleases and ribonucleases are enzymes that degrade DNA and RNA, respectively.

Regulation of Pancreatic Secretion

The mechanism regulating pancreatic secretion is outlined in figure 24.24.

1. Parasympathetic stimulation through the vagus (X) nerves also stimulates the secretion of enzyme-rich pancreatic juices. Sympathetic impulses inhibit secretion. The effect of vagal stimulation on pancreatic juice secretion is greatest during the cephalic and gastric phases of stomach secretion.

2 Both hormonal and neural mechanisms control secretion of pancreatic juice. The hormones secretin and cholecystokinin are released from the duodenum in response to specific stimuli. Each hormone stimulates secretion of a specific type of pancreatic juice. Secretin stimulates secretion of the HCO_3^--rich aqueous juice. An acidic chyme in the duodenum stimulates the release of secretin.

Predict 5

Explain why secretin production in response to acidic chyme and its stimulation of HCO_3^- secretion constitute a negative-feedback mechanism.

3 Cholecystokinin stimulates the secretion of the enzyme-rich pancreatic juice. Recall that cholecystokinin also stimulates the release of bile from the gallbladder, which aids in the digestion of lipids. The major stimulus for the release of cholecystokinin is the presence of fatty acids and other lipids in the duodenum.

ASSESS YOUR PROGRESS

50. *Describe the parts of the pancreas responsible for endocrine and exocrine secretions. Diagram the duct system of the pancreas.*

51. *Name the two kinds of exocrine secretions produced by the pancreas. What stimulates their production, and what is their function?*

52. *What enzymes are present in pancreatic juice? Explain the function of each.*

24.11 Large Intestine

LEARNING OUTCOMES

After reading this section, you should be able to

A. **List the parts of the large intestine and describe its anatomy and histology.**
B. **Describe the major functions of the large intestine.**
C. **Explain how defecation is regulated.**

The **large intestine** is the portion of the digestive tract extending from the ileocecal junction to the anus. It consists of four parts: (1) cecum, (2) colon, (3) rectum, and (4) anal canal. Normally, 18–24 hours are required for material to pass through the large intestine, in contrast to the 3–5 hours required for chyme to move through the small intestine. Thus, the movements of the large intestine are more sluggish than those of the small intestine. While in the large intestine, chyme is converted to feces. The formation of **feces** involves the absorption of water and salts, secretion of mucus, and extensive action of microorganisms. The large intestine stores the feces until they are eliminated by defecation. About 1500 mL of chyme enter the cecum each day, but more than 90% of the volume is reabsorbed, so that only 80–150 mL of feces are normally eliminated by defecation.

Anatomy of the Large Intestine

Cecum

The **cecum** (SEE-kum) is the proximal end of the large intestine, where it meets the small intestine at the ileocecal junction. The cecum extends inferiorly about 6 cm past the ileocecal junction in the form of a blind sac (figure 24.25). The **vermiform** (VER-mi-form; worm-shaped) **appendix** is a smaller, blind tube about 9 cm long attached to the cecum. The walls of the appendix contain many lymphatic nodules, which contribute to immune functions.

Colon

The **colon** (KOH-lon), about 1.5–1.8 m long, consists of four parts: (1) ascending colon, (2) transverse colon, (3) descending colon, and (4) sigmoid colon (figure 24.25). The **ascending colon** extends superiorly from the cecum and ends at the right colic flexure, or *hepatic flexure,* near the right inferior margin of the liver. The **transverse colon** extends from the right colic flexure to the left colic flexure, or *splenic flexure*, and the **descending colon** extends from the left colic flexure to the superior opening of the true pelvis, where it becomes the sigmoid colon. The **sigmoid colon** forms an S-shaped tube that extends into the pelvis and ends at the rectum.

The muscularis of the colon differs from that of the small intestine. While the circular muscle layer of the colon is complete, the longitudinal muscle layer is incomplete. Rather than completely enveloping the intestinal wall, the longitudinal layer forms three bands, called the **teniae coli** (TEE-nee-aye KOH-lye). The teniae coli run the length of the colon (figure 24.26*a*;

Clinical IMPACT 24.5

Appendicitis

Appendicitis is an inflammation of the vermiform appendix that usually occurs because of an obstruction of the appendix. Secretions from the appendix cannot pass the obstruction and accumulate, resulting in enlargement and pain. Bacteria in the area can cause infection of the appendix. Symptoms include sudden abdominal pain, particularly in the right-lower portion of the abdomen; slight fever; loss of appetite; constipation or diarrhea; nausea; and vomiting. In the right-lower quadrant of the abdomen, about one-third the distance along a line from the right anterior superior iliac spine to the umbilicus, is an area called the McBurney point. This area of the body surface becomes very tender in patients with acute appendicitis because of pain referred from the inflamed appendix. Each year, 500,000 people in the United States experience appendicitis. The usual treatment is surgical removal of the appendix, called an appendectomy. If the appendix bursts, the infection can spread throughout the peritoneal cavity, causing peritonitis, with life-threatening results.

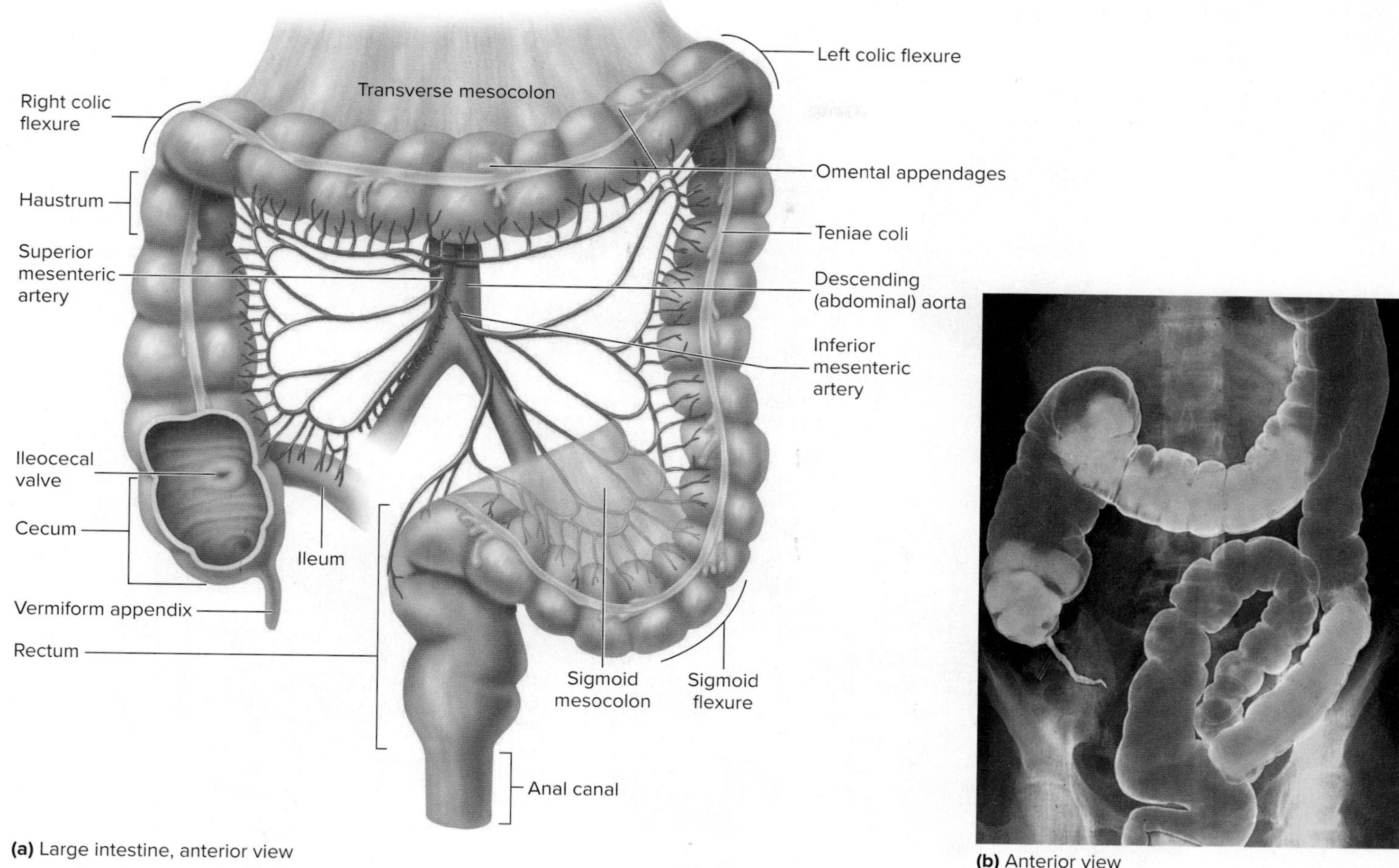

(a) Large intestine, anterior view

(b) Anterior view

FIGURE 24.25 Large Intestine

(*a*) The large intestine consists of the cecum, colon, rectum, and anal canal. The teniae coli and omental appendages are along the length of the colon. (*b*) Radiograph of the large intestine following a barium enema. (b) CNRI/Science Source APR

see figure 24.25). Contractions of the teniae coli cause pouches called **haustra** (HAW-strah; to draw up) to form along the length of the colon, giving it a puckered appearance. Small, lipid-filled connective tissue pouches called **omental appendages** are attached to the outer surface of the colon along its length.

The mucosal lining of the large intestine consists of simple columnar epithelium. This epithelium is not formed into folds or villi like that of the small intestine but has numerous, straight, tubular glands called **crypts** (figure 24.26*b–d*). The crypts, which are somewhat similar to the intestinal glands of the small intestine, are composed of three cell types: (1) absorptive, (2) goblet, and (3) granular. The major difference is that, in the large intestine, goblet cells predominate, and the other two cell types are greatly reduced in number.

Rectum

The **rectum** is a straight, muscular tube that begins at the distal end of the sigmoid colon and ends at the anal canal (see figure 24.25). The mucosal lining of the rectum is simple columnar epithelium, and the muscular tunic is relatively thick, compared with the rest of the digestive tract.

Anal Canal

The last 2–3 cm of the digestive tract is the **anal canal** (see figure 24.25). It begins at the inferior end of the rectum and ends at the **anus** (external digestive tract opening). The smooth muscle layer of the anal canal is even thicker than that of the rectum and forms the **internal anal sphincter** at its superior end. Skeletal muscle forms the **external anal sphincter** at the inferior end of the canal. The epithelium of the superior part of the anal canal is simple columnar, and that of the inferior part is stratified squamous. Rectal veins that supply the anal canal can become enlarged or inflamed, a condition known as **hemorrhoids.** Hemorrhoids cause pain, itching, and bleeding around the anus. They can usually be treated by changes in diet or medications.

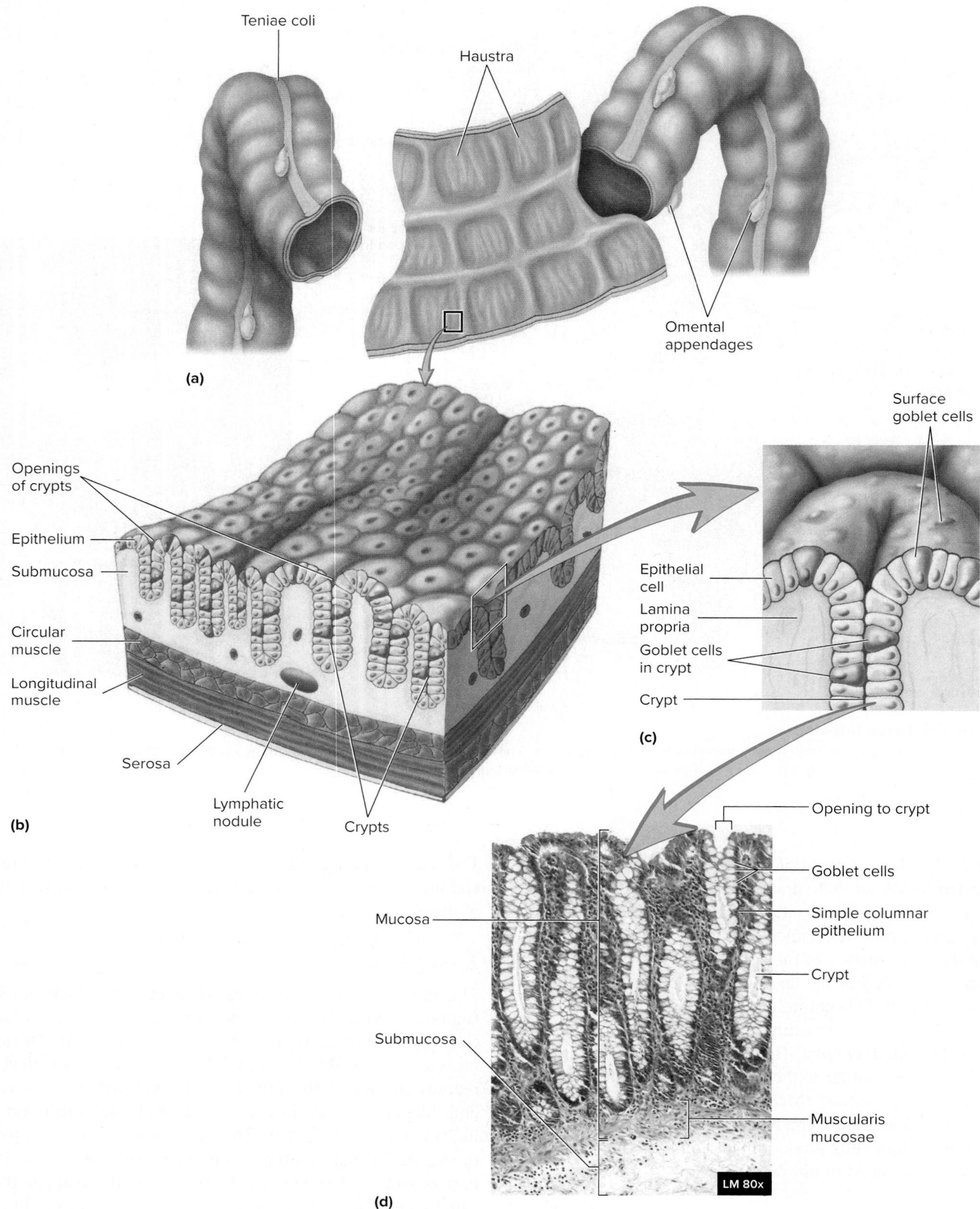

FIGURE 24.26 Histology of the Large Intestine

(*a*) Section of the transverse colon cut open to show the inner surface. (*b*) Enlargement of the inner surface, showing openings of the crypts. (*c*) Higher magnification of a single crypt. (*d*) Photomicrograph showing the histology of the large intestine wall. (d) Al Telser/McGraw Hill

MICROBES In Your Body 24.1 Fecal Transplants

Would you be shocked if your doctor said the one thing that could save your life is feces? Unfortunately, we are in the midst of a global, hospital-acquired diarrhea epidemic. The cause of this epidemic is a bacterium called *Clostridium difficile* (commonly referred to as *C. diff*), a pathogen that is normally found in the large intestine, but is controlled by the normal microbiota. One of the most critical functions of the normal gut microbiota is prevention of infections through competition with pathogens. As a consequence, when a patient takes antibiotics, *C. diff* can flourish and cause life-threatening diarrhea. Treatment of *C. diff* infections with specific antibiotics will often stop the diarrhea initially. However, *C. diff* are spore-forming bacteria. Spores are very stable structures that allow bacteria to withstand harsh conditions until favorable conditions return and the bacteria can regrow. Thus, antibiotics kill only the *C. diff* cells, not the spores. Hence, it is very common for patients to suffer multiple recurrences of diarrhea for months, which can lead to death in some patients. Additionally, a more virulent, resistant strain of *C. diff* has emerged. This strain is resistant to certain antibiotics and makes a greater number of spores and more of the toxins responsible for the diarrhea.

So, where do feces come into play? Because antibiotic treatments are not effective (65% infection recurrence), physicians are considering an old treatment: fecal transplants. The first documented case of transplanting feces from a healthy donor into a diseased recipient was in 1958. Fecal transplantation has since been used successfully in veterinary medicine for decades. However, due to the unappealing nature of this treatment, it has only recently been considered an option in humans. Now more commonly known as intestinal fecal transplantation (IFT), it has been shown to effectively treat diarrhea in over 90% of *C. diff* infections. The idea is that a healthy donor—usually a close family household member such as a spouse or significant partner—donates their feces. The feces are mixed with physiological saline, filtered, and then introduced into the recipient's gastrointestinal (GI) tract by one of two ways: the upper GI tract route or the lower GI tract route. The upper GI tract route uses either a gastroscope or nasogastric tube to transfer the material to the recipient's intestine. Of the two, this one is easier and costs less. However, there is the possibility the donor microbiota may not reach the end of the large intestine or that the patient may vomit the fecal material. The lower GI tract route uses a colonoscope or enema and is sometimes the preferred approach, but does run the risk of perforating the large intestine. Thus, as yet, there is no standardized method for transferring the donor feces. But research is showing that more and more patients may overcome their initial reluctance when presented with a predictable success rate and greater reliability than other protocols. In addition, the recent "RePOOPulating" study shows promise that doctors may soon be able to treat *C. diff* infections simply by prescribing a pill that contains normal microbiota.

Predict 6

Predict the mechanism by which ingestion of a capsule filled with dried normal microbiota could treat a C. diff *infection. Would the pill be able to be swallowed, or would it have to be administered directly into the intestine? Explain.*

Secretions of the Large Intestine

The major secretion product of the large intestine is mucus (see figures 24.2 and 24.9). Mucus is secreted from the numerous goblet cells scattered along the length of the mucosa of the large intestine. In addition, there are numerous crypts lined almost entirely with goblet cells. Little enzymatic activity is associated with secretions of the large intestine. Mucus lubricates the wall of the large intestine and helps the fecal matter stick together. Tactile stimuli and irritation of the large intestine wall trigger local enteric reflexes that increase mucous secretion. Parasympathetic stimulation also increases the secretory rate of the goblet cells.

The feces that leave the digestive tract consist of water, solid substances (e.g., undigested food), microorganisms, and sloughed-off epithelial cells. An abnormally frequent discharge of watery feces is called **diarrhea** (see this chapter's Systems Pathology).

Numerous microorganisms inhabit the large intestine, and are referred to as **normal microbiota** of the gut. They reproduce rapidly and ultimately constitute about 30% of the dry weight of the feces. An important function of normal microbiota is to synthesize vitamin K, which is passively absorbed in the large intestine. Acids are secreted by normal microbiota as metabolic by-products. An antiporter exchanges HCO_3^- for Cl^- in epithelial cells of the large intestine in response to acid produced by the normal microbiota. Another antiporter exchanges Na^+ for H^+. Movement of Na^+ into the epithelial cells via this exchanger and other Na^+ channels is driven by the Na^+ gradient established by the Na^+–K^+ pump. Water leaves the lumen of the large intestine through osmosis as Na^+ and Cl^- move into the epithelial cells. Normal microbiota also break down a small amount of cellulose to glucose. However, the glucose cannot be absorbed in the large intestine. Bacterial actions in the large intestine produce gases called **flatus** (FLAY-tus; blowing). The amount of flatus depends partly on the specific bacterial population in the large intestine and partly on the type of food consumed. For example, beans, which contain certain complex carbohydrates, are well known for their flatus-producing effect.

Movement in the Large Intestine

Segmental mixing movements occur in the large intestine much less often than in the small intestine. Peristaltic waves are largely responsible for moving chyme along the ascending

PROCESS **Figure**

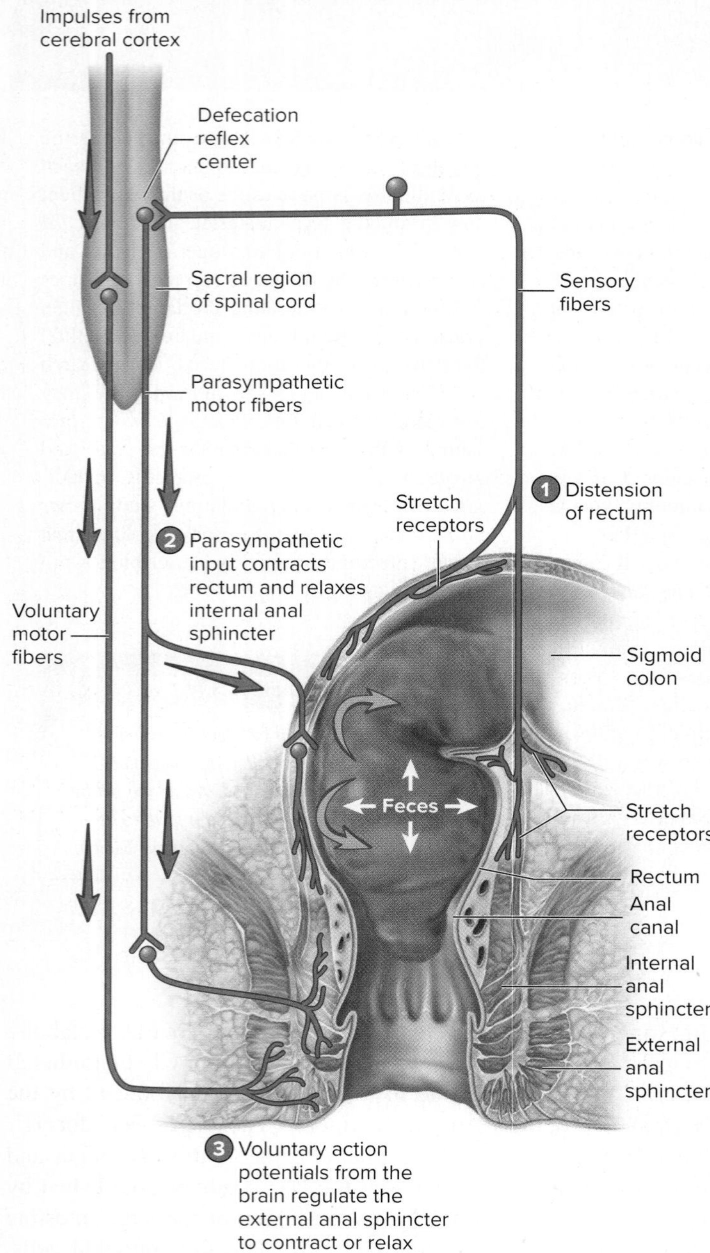

PROCESS **Figure 24.27**

Control of Defecation

Defecation involves both reflex and voluntary neural signals that are triggered by distension of the rectum.

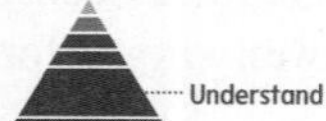

What would be the consequence of a spinal cord injury above the defecation reflex center?

colon. At widely spaced intervals (normally three or four times each day), large parts of the transverse and descending colon undergo several strong contractions, called **mass movements.** Each mass movement contraction extends over a much longer part of the digestive tract (≥20 cm) than does a peristaltic contraction and propels the large intestine contents a considerable distance toward the anus (figure 24.27). Mass movements are very common after meals because they are initiated by the presence of food in the stomach or duodenum. Mass movements are most common about 15 minutes after breakfast. They usually persist for 10–30 minutes and then stop for perhaps half a day.

Mass movements are coordinated by two reflexes in the ENS: (a) gastrocolic and (b) duodenocolic. **Gastrocolic reflexes** are initiated by distension in the stomach, and **duodenocolic reflexes** are initiated by distension in the duodenum. The gastrocolic and duodenocolic reflexes promote peristalsis of the small and large intestines, including mass movements. These reflexes are mediated by parasympathetic reflexes, local reflexes, and hormones, such as cholecystokinin and gastrin. The thought or smell of food, distension of the stomach, and the movement of chyme into the duodenum can stimulate them.

During defecation, the contractions that move feces toward the anus must be coordinated with the relaxation of the internal and external anal sphincters. Parasympathetic reflexes are responsible for most of the defecation reflex.

The internal and external **anal sphincters** prevent defecation. Resting sphincter pressure results from tonic muscle contractions, mostly of the internal anal sphincter. In response to increased abdominal pressure, reflexes mediated through the spinal cord cause contractions of the external anal sphincter. Thus, the untimely expulsion of feces during coughing or exertion is avoided.

There is also conscious control of the defecation reflex. Action potentials from the sacral spinal cord are propagated to the brain, where parts of the brainstem and hypothalamus inhibit or facilitate reflex activity in the spinal cord. In addition, action potentials are also propagated to the cerebrum, where awareness of the need to defecate is realized. The external anal sphincter is composed of skeletal muscle and is under conscious cerebral control. If this sphincter is relaxed voluntarily, feces are expelled. On the other hand, increased contraction of the external anal sphincter prevents defecation. The defecation reflex persists for only a few minutes and quickly declines. Generally, the reflex is reinitiated after a period that may be as long as several hours. Mass movements in the large intestine are usually the reason for reinitiation of the defecation reflex. The **defecation reflex** consists of local and parasympathetic reflexes. Local reflexes cause weak contractions of the distal colon and rectum and relaxation of the internal anal sphincter. The steps are summarized in figure 24.27.

1. Distension of the rectum by feces stimulates local defecation reflexes that cause contractions of the large intestine and rectum, which move feces toward the anus.
2. Distension of the rectum stimulates parasympathetic reflexes. Action potentials are propagated to the defecation reflex center. Input from the defecation reflex center causes contraction of the large intestine and rectum, but causes relaxation of the internal anal sphincter.
3. Voluntary control of the external anal sphincter from motor nerve fibers contracts it or relaxes it, depending on whether defecation is initiated.

Defecation can be initiated by voluntary actions that stimulate a defecation reflex, called the Valsalva maneuver. This "straining" includes a large inspiration of air, followed by closure of the larynx and forceful contraction of the abdominal muscles. As a consequence, the pressure in the abdominal cavity increases and forces feces into the rectum. Stretch of the rectum initiates a defecation reflex, and input from the brain overrides the reflexive contraction of the external anal sphincter stimulated by increased abdominal pressure. The increased abdominal pressure also helps push feces through the rectum. The Valsalva maneuver is also employed during urination and childbirth. Individuals with heart disease are discouraged from initiating the Valsalva maneuver as it can decrease heart rate due to the release of acetylcholine from the vagus nerves.

ASSESS YOUR PROGRESS

53. *Describe the parts of the large intestine. What are teniae coli, haustra, and crypts?*
54. *Explain the difference in structure between the internal anal sphincter and the external anal sphincter.*
55. *Name the substances secreted and absorbed in the large intestine.*
56. *What is the role of microorganisms in the large intestine?*
57. *What kinds of movements occur in the large intestine? Describe the defecation reflex.*

24.12 Digestion and Absorption

LEARNING OUTCOMES

After reading this section, you should be able to

A. **Describe the chemical digestion and absorption of carbohydrates, lipids, and proteins.**
B. **Explain the transport of water and ions through the intestinal wall.**

Digestion is the breakdown of food to molecules small enough to be absorbed into the blood. **Mechanical digestion** breaks large food particles apart into smaller ones, such as during chewing for example. **Chemical digestion** is the breaking of covalent chemical bonds in organic molecules by digestive enzymes. Carbohydrates break down into monosaccharides, lipids break down into fatty acids and monoglycerides, and proteins break down into amino acids (figure 24.28). However, some molecules (e.g., vitamins, minerals, and water) are not broken down. A relatively small amount of digestion begins in the oral cavity, and some occurs in the stomach, but the vast majority of digestion occurs in the proximal end of the small intestine, especially in the duodenum.

Absorption is the means by which molecules are moved out of the digestive tract into the blood for distribution throughout the body. Nearly all absorption of nutrients occurs in the duodenum and jejunum of the small intestine. Some absorption also occurs in the ileum. A few chemicals, such as nitroglycerin, can be absorbed

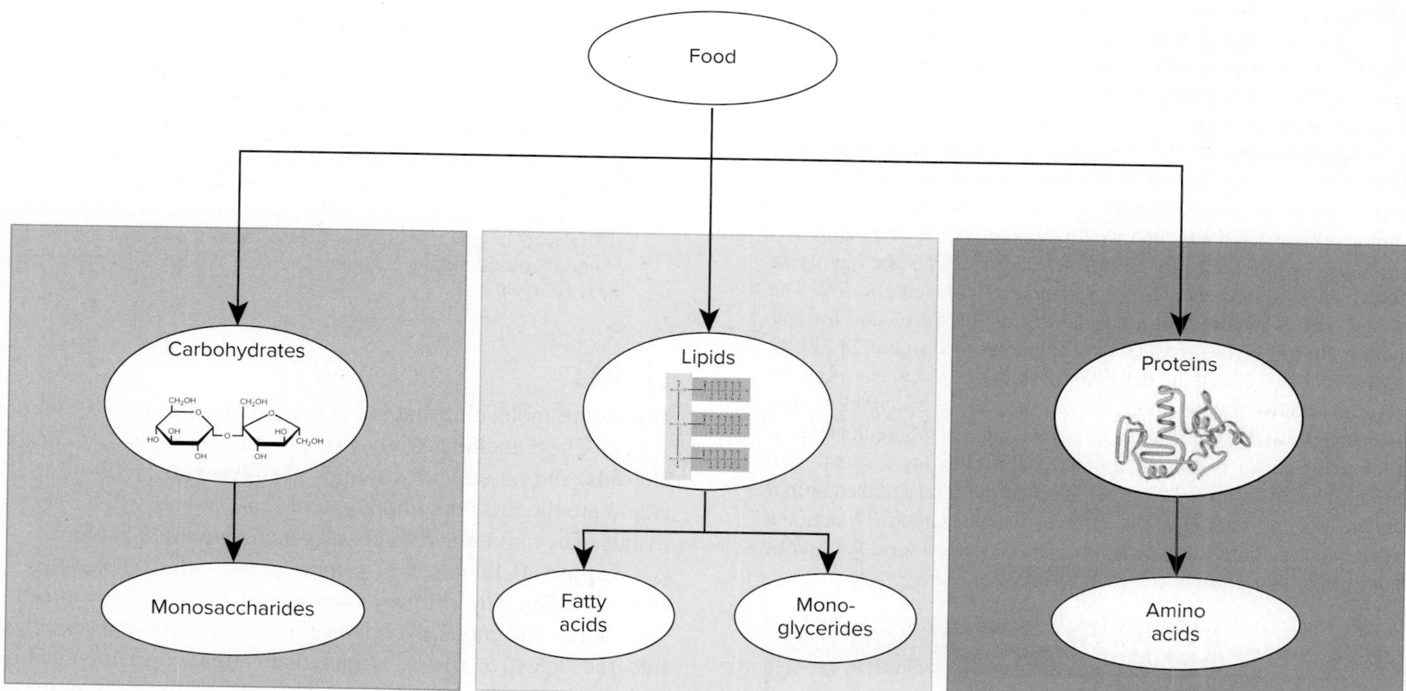

FIGURE 24.28 Digestion
Food consists primarily of carbohydrates, lipids, and proteins. Carbohydrates are broken down into monosaccharides, lipids into fatty acids and monoglycerides, and proteins into amino acids. APR

through the thin mucosa of the oral cavity below the tongue. Some small molecules (e.g., alcohol and aspirin) can diffuse through the stomach epithelium into the blood.

Some molecules can be absorbed by diffusion, whereas others must be transported across the intestinal wall. Transport requires transport proteins, which work by facilitated diffusion, active-transport, or secondary-transport mechanisms, such as symport and antiport. The epithelial cells that form the intestinal wall have two distinct sides with different transport proteins on each side. The side that faces the digestive tract lumen is called the **apical membrane,** and the side that faces the blood vessels is called the **basolateral membrane.** The transport proteins in these membranes are responsible for the one-way movement of molecules from the digestive tract to the rest of the body.

Once the digestive products have been absorbed, they are transported to other parts of the body by two routes.

1. Water, ions, and water-soluble digestion products, such as glucose and amino acids, enter the hepatic portal system and travel to the liver.
2. The products of lipid metabolism are coated with proteins and transported into lymphatic capillaries called lacteals (see figure 24.16*c,d*). The lacteals are connected by lymphatic vessels to the thoracic duct (see chapter 22), which empties into the left subclavian vein. The protein-coated lipid products then travel in the blood to adipose tissue or to the liver.

Case STUDY 24.1 Spinal Cord Injury and Defecation

Dan, a 17-year-old male, was driving home late at night after a ski trip when he missed a sharp curve and crashed. He suffered traumatic injury at the T11 level of the spinal cord, with complete paralysis of both lower limbs. As a result, Dan became incontinent and unable to control his bowel movements.

Approximately 10,000 new spinal cord injuries occur per year in the United States. About 80% of those injuries involve men, usually in their late teens or twenties. The most common cause is motor vehicle accidents, followed by violence, falls, and sports.

Loss of the ability to control defecation affects the quality of life of most spinal cord injury patients, at least temporarily. The spinal cord is required for a normal defecation reflex and for voluntary control of the external anal sphincter (see figure 24.27). In terms of their effect on defecation, spinal cord injuries can be divided into two groups: injuries that occur above the conus medullaris and those that damage the conus medullaris, where the defecation reflex center is located. Immediately following a spinal cord injury, loss of reflexes below the level of the injury, called **spinal shock,** occurs. However, the reflexes usually become functional again, and the defecation reflex may be depressed for a few weeks but eventually returns.

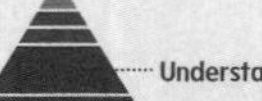

Predict 7

Explain how an enema involving the injection of fluid into the rectum can stimulate defecation.

Carbohydrates

Ingested **carbohydrates** consist primarily of polysaccharides, such as starches; disaccharides, such as sucrose (table sugar) and lactose (milk sugar); and monosaccharides, such as glucose and fructose (the sugar found in many fruits). During digestion, polysaccharides break down first into smaller chains and some disaccharides and monosaccharides. Disaccharides then break down into monosaccharides.

A minor amount of carbohydrate digestion begins in the oral cavity with the partial digestion of starches by **salivary amylase** (AM-il-ace). Digestion continues in the stomach until the food is well mixed with acid, which inactivates salivary amylase. Carbohydrate digestion is resumed in the small intestine by **pancreatic amylase** (figure 24.29). Pancreatic amylase in the small intestine is responsible for the majority of carbohydrate digestion. However, many of the digested carbohydrates at this point are disaccharides, which cannot be absorbed. The final step in carbohydrate digestion is performed by a series of **disaccharidases** that are bound to the microvilli of the intestinal epithelium. Disaccharidases generate three important monosaccharides: (1) glucose, (2) galactose, and (3) fructose. The major monosaccharide is glucose.

Figure 24.30 outlines the process of glucose transport.

1. The monosaccharides glucose and galactose are taken up into intestinal epithelial cells by symport, powered by a Na^+ gradient.
2. The Na^+ gradient is generated by the **Na^+–K^+ pump** located on the basolateral membrane. Diffusion of Na^+ down its concentration gradient provides the energy to transport glucose or galactose across the plasma membrane. In contrast to glucose and galactose, the monosaccharide fructose is taken up by facilitated diffusion.
3. Once inside the intestinal epithelial cell, monosaccharides are transported by facilitated diffusion to the capillaries of the intestinal villi.
4. The monosaccharides are then carried by the hepatic portal system to the liver, where the nonglucose monosaccharides are converted to glucose. Glucose enters the cells through facilitated diffusion. The rate of glucose transport into most types of cells is greatly influenced by **insulin** and may increase 10-fold in its presence (see chapter 18).

Lipids

Lipids are molecules that are insoluble or only slightly soluble in water. They include triglycerides, phospholipids, cholesterol, steroids, and fat-soluble vitamins. **Triglycerides** (trie-GLISS-eh-ridez) are the most common type of lipid and are often referred to as fats. They consist of three fatty acids bound to glycerol.

Lipase (LIE-pase) enzymes digest lipid molecules (see figure 24.29). The primary products of lipase digestion are free fatty acids and monoglycerides. There are three lipases released into the digestive tract: (1) pancreatic lipase, (2) lingual lipase, and (3) gastric lipase. The vast majority of lipase is **pancreatic lipase,** which is secreted by the pancreas and digests lipids in the small intestine. A minor amount of **lingual lipase** is secreted in the oral cavity and swallowed with food. It digests a small amount

Clinical IMPACT 24.6 — Lactose Intolerance

Lactose intolerance is the inability to digest the lactose in milk and other dairy products. The majority of adults in most regions of the world are lactose intolerant, although infants are not. Why can infants digest milk, whereas their parents cannot? The reason is that many adults lack the enzyme lactase. Lactase, present on the surface of absorptive cells in the intestinal mucosa, digests the disaccharide lactose down to two monosaccharides. Lactase is made at birth but is no longer synthesized after about age 6 in 5–15% of Europeans and 80–90% of Africans and Asians. Therefore, these people can no longer digest lactose. The major exceptions are people of northern European ancestry and some pastoral nomadic tribes in Africa and the Middle East. In these populations, a mutation in the promoter (see chapter 3) of the lactase gene permits the continued expression of lactase into adulthood. Normally, lactase production stops because the promoter is "turned off" as the infant ages, but the mutation allows the promoter to ignore this developmental switch.

Researchers believe that the dietary reliance on milk and milk products in some societies provided a selective advantage for lactase persistence. In the United States, most people are lactose tolerant, but intolerance is still one of the most common digestive tract disorders seen by primary care physicians. The main symptom of lactose intolerance is diarrhea due to fluid loss as water follows lactose through the digestive tract. In addition, a considerable amount of gas is generated from lactose metabolism by normal microbiota in the large intestine. Even though the normal microbiota metabolize lactose to monosaccharides, it is too late for the monosaccharides to be absorbed. Gene therapy has proven successful in animal models of lactose intolerance, although at present the best treatment is simply to avoid foods containing lactose.

(<10%) of lipid in the stomach. The stomach also produces very small amounts of **gastric lipase.** Lingual and gastric lipase are most important in neonatal infants, while pancreatic lipase is the major enzyme in adults.

Pancreatic lipase alone cannot efficiently digest lipids. A key step in lipid digestion is **emulsification** (ih-MUL-sih-fih-KAY-shun), by which bile salts transform large lipid droplets into much smaller droplets. Bile salts mix with lipids and act as detergents to disrupt lipid droplets. By decreasing the droplet size, emulsification increases the surface area of the lipid exposed to lipase and other digestive enzymes. This is necessary because lipase is water-soluble and can digest lipids only at the surface of the droplets. The bile salts are secreted by the liver and stored in the gallbladder until needed in the duodenum. Lingual and gastric lipase, which work in the acidic environment of the stomach, do not require bile salts.

Try performing some of your own emulsification. First, mix some cooking oil and food coloring. After shaking or stirring, does the food coloring mix well with the oil? Now, to emulsify the cooking oil, add a drop or two of dish detergent and shake or stir again. Does the food coloring mix with the oil better than before?

Lipid Transport

Figure 24.31 illustrates the process by which lipids are absorbed.

1. Once lipids are digested in the intestine, bile salts aggregate around the small droplets. Lipid droplets surrounded by bile salts are called **micelles** (MYE-selz; small morsels). The hydrophobic ends of the bile salts are directed toward the free fatty acids, cholesterol, and monoglycerides at the center of the micelle; the hydrophilic ends are directed outward toward the water environment.
2. When a micelle comes in contact with the epithelial cells of the small intestine, the lipid contents of the micelle pass by simple diffusion through the plasma membrane of the epithelial cells. The bile salts are not absorbed until they reach the epithelium of the distal ileum.
3. Within the smooth endoplasmic reticulum of the intestinal epithelial cells, free fatty acids are combined with monoglyceride molecules to form triglycerides. Proteins synthesized in the epithelial cells attach to droplets of triglycerides, phospholipids, and cholesterol called **chylomicrons** (kye-lo-MY-kronz). Chylomicrons contain about 90% triglyceride, 5% cholesterol, 4% phospholipid, and 1% protein (figure 24.32).
   The chylomicrons leave the epithelial cells by exocytosis and enter the lacteals of the lymphatic system within the villi.
4. Chylomicrons enter the lymphatic capillaries rather than the blood capillaries because the lymphatic capillaries lack a basement membrane and are more permeable to large particles, such as chylomicrons, which are about 0.3 mm in diameter. They travel through the lymphatic system via the thoracic duct to the bloodstream and then by the blood to adipose tissue.

Before entering adipocytes, triglycerides break back down into fatty acids and glycerol, which enter the adipocytes and are once more converted to triglycerides. Triglycerides are stored in adipose tissue until an energy source is needed elsewhere in the body. In the liver, the chylomicron lipids are stored, converted into other molecules, or used as energy. The chylomicron remnant, minus the triglyceride, is conveyed through the blood to the liver, where it breaks up.

Because lipids are either insoluble or only slightly soluble in water, they are transported through the blood in combination with proteins, which are water-soluble. Lipids combined with proteins are called **lipoproteins** and are categorized as high- or low-density (figure 24.32). *Density* describes the compactness of a substance and is the ratio of mass to volume. Lipids are less dense than water and tend to float in water. Proteins, which are denser than water, tend to sink in water. A lipoprotein with a high lipid content has a very low density, whereas a lipoprotein with a high protein content has a relatively high density. Chylomicrons, which are made up of 99% lipid and only 1% protein, are lipoproteins with an extremely low density. The other major transport

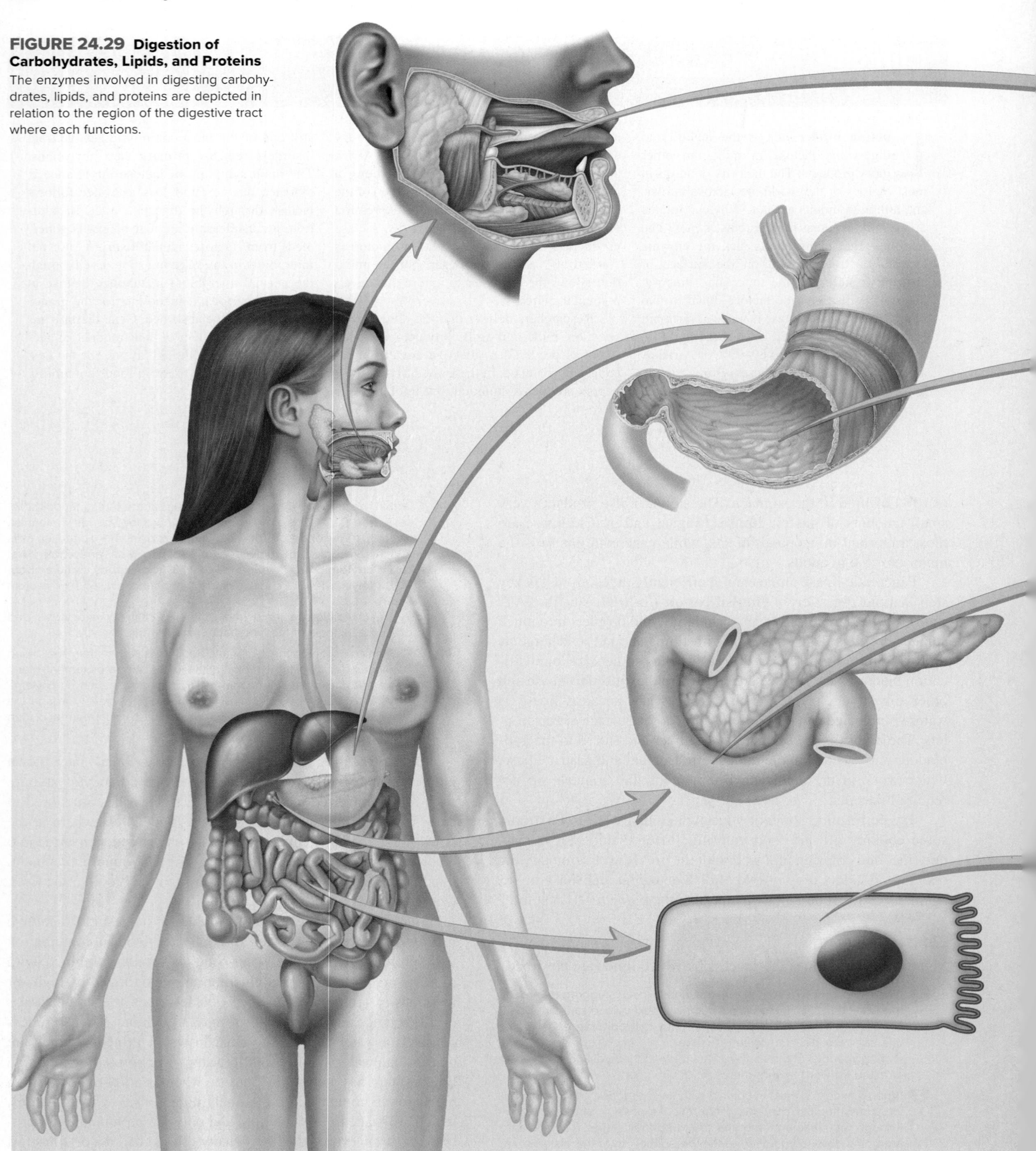

FIGURE 24.29 Digestion of Carbohydrates, Lipids, and Proteins
The enzymes involved in digesting carbohydrates, lipids, and proteins are depicted in relation to the region of the digestive tract where each functions.

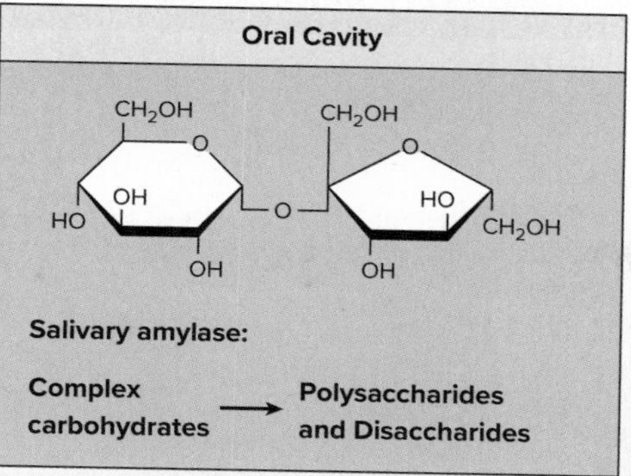
Oral Cavity
CH_2OH
CH_2OH
OH
HO
HO
O
CH_2OH
OH
OH
Salivary amylase:
Complex carbohydrates ⟶ Polysaccharides and Disaccharides

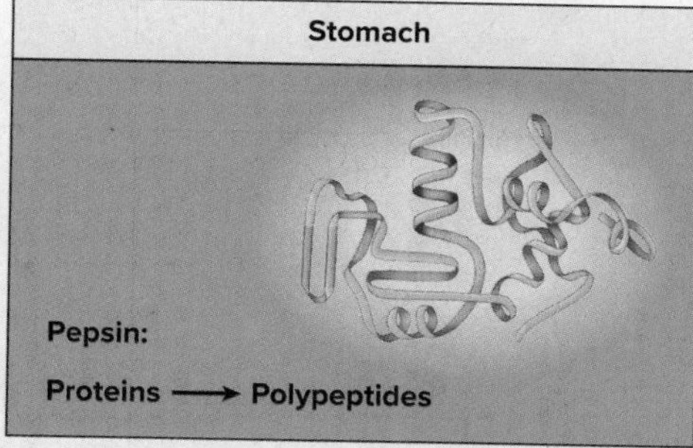
Stomach
Pepsin:
Proteins ⟶ Polypeptides

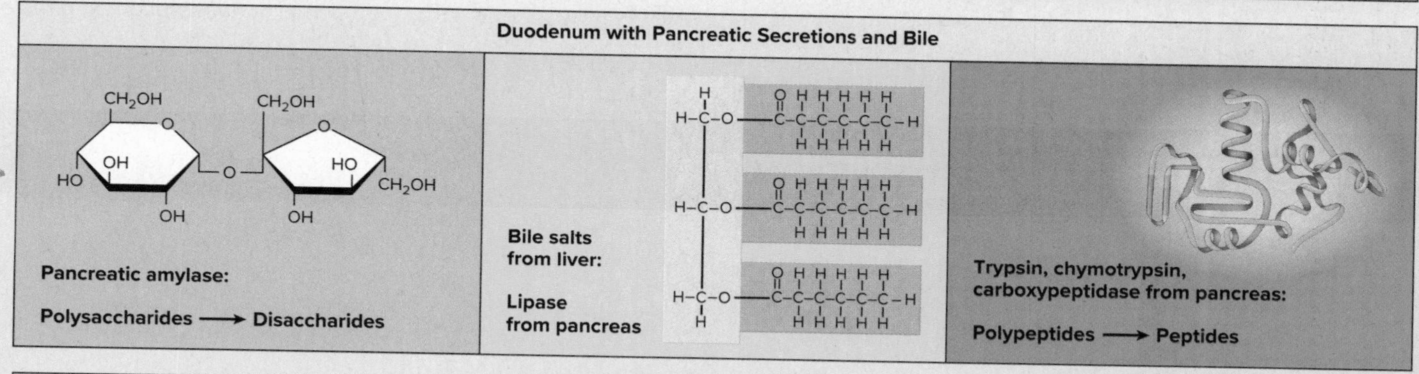
Duodenum with Pancreatic Secretions and Bile
Pancreatic amylase:
Polysaccharides ⟶ Disaccharides
Bile salts from liver:
Lipase from pancreas
Trypsin, chymotrypsin, carboxypeptidase from pancreas:
Polypeptides ⟶ Peptides

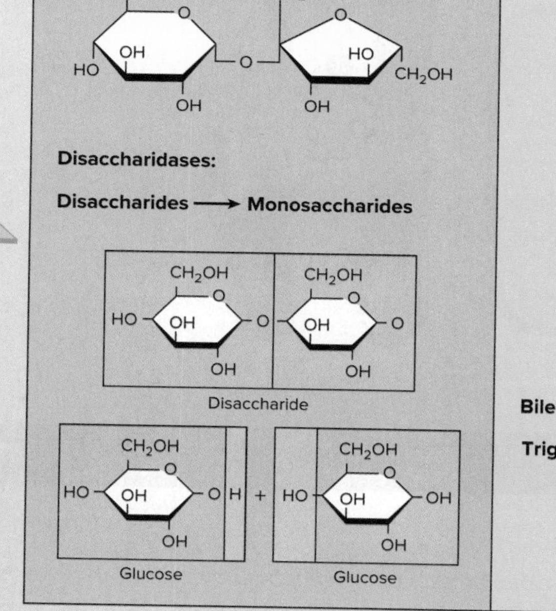
Epithelium of Small Intestine
Disaccharidases:
Disaccharides ⟶ Monosaccharides
Disaccharide
Glucose
Glucose

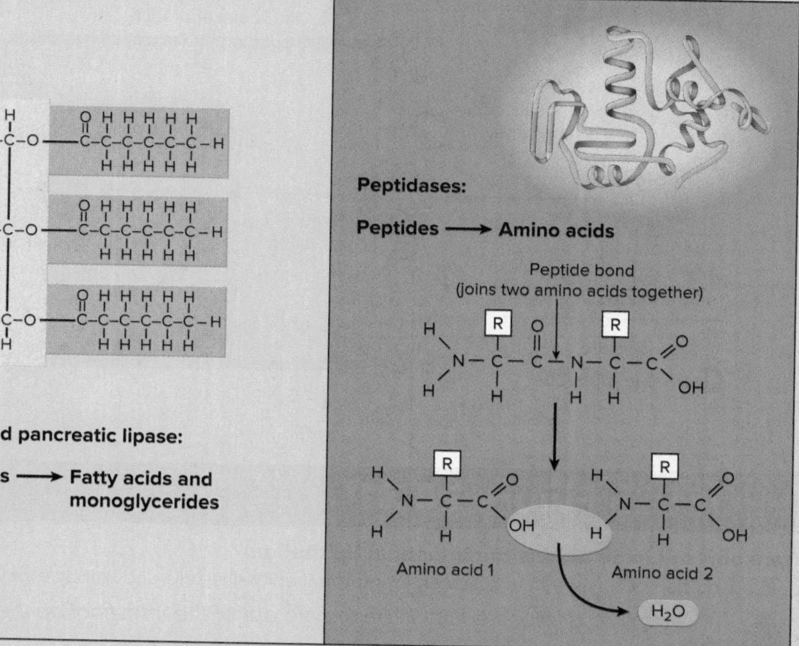
Bile salts and pancreatic lipase:
Triglycerides ⟶ Fatty acids and monoglycerides
Peptidases:
Peptides ⟶ Amino acids
Peptide bond
(joins two amino acids together)
Amino acid 1
Amino acid 2
H_2O

FUNDAMENTAL **Figure**

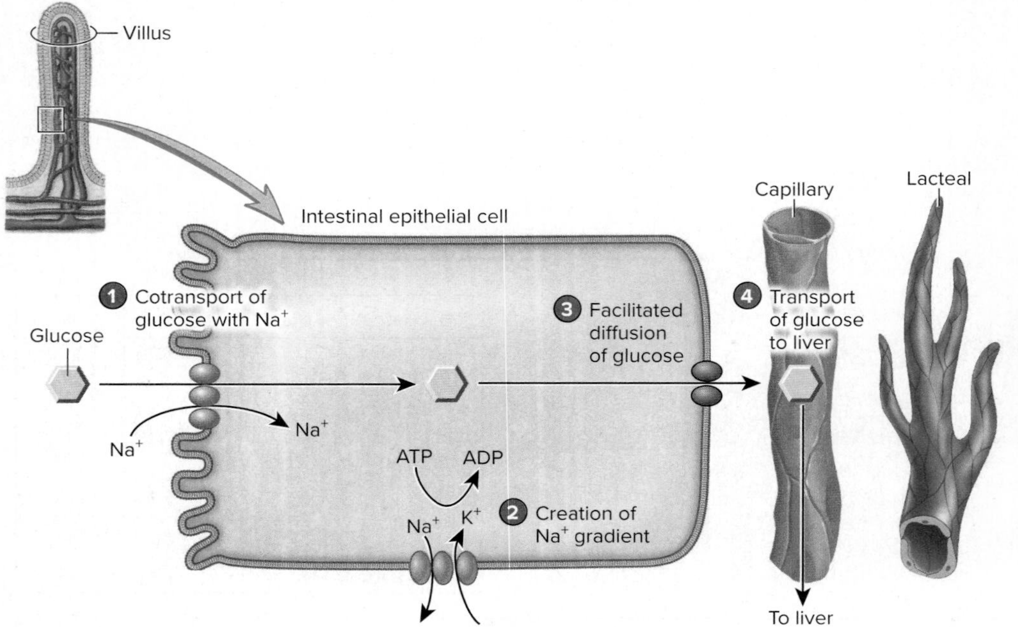

PROCESS **Figure 24.30**

Transport of Glucose Across the Intestinal Epithelium

Glucose absorption occurs by symport powered by a Na^+ gradient.

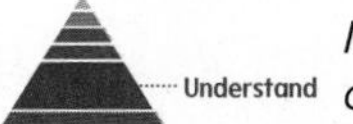

If a drug is given that specifically inhibits the Na^+–K^+ pump in intestinal epithelial cells, how will glucose absorption be affected?

PROCESS **Figure**

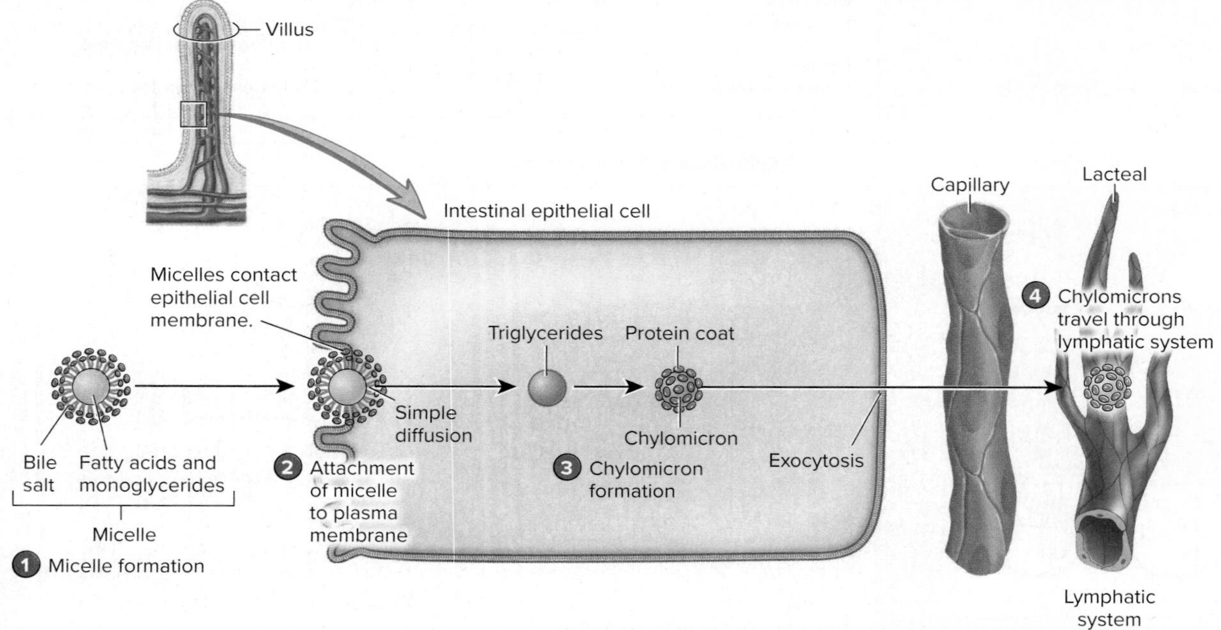

PROCESS **Figure 24.31**

Transport of Lipids Across the Intestinal Epithelium

Lipid absorption occurs when micelles enter intestinal epithelial cells and exit by exocytosis.

Why must digested lipids be moved out of the intestinal epithelial cells into lacteals of the lymphatic system by exocytosis?

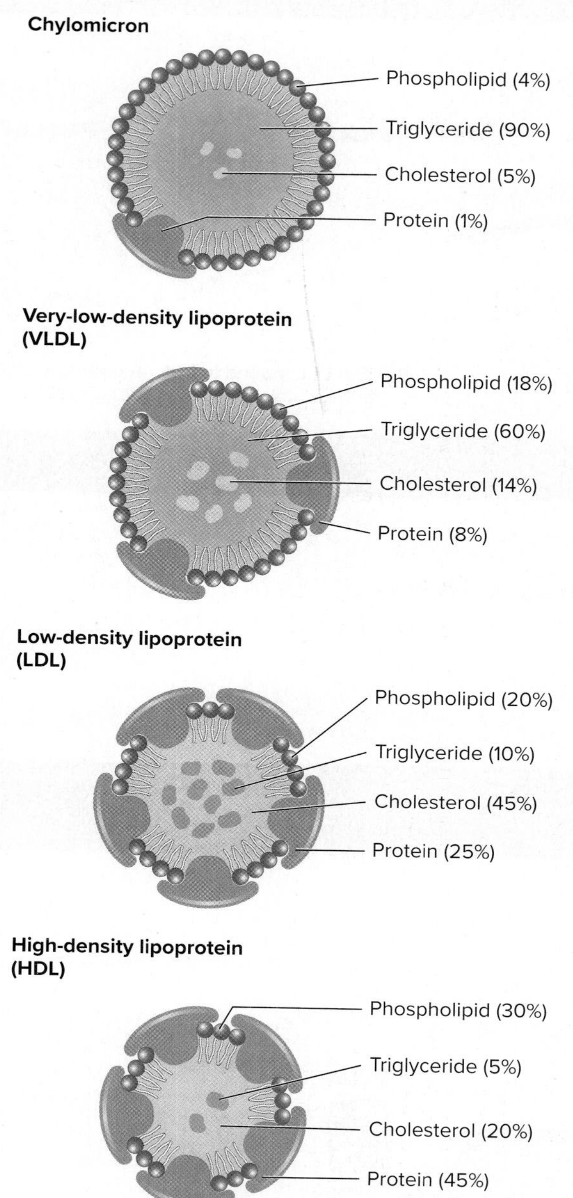

FIGURE 24.32 Lipoproteins

Cholesterol and lipids are transported through the blood by lipoproteins that are classified based on their density. A low protein content results in a low density. Chylomicrons are lipoproteins with extremely low density.

lipoproteins are **very low-density lipoprotein (VLDL),** which is 92% lipid and 8% protein; **low-density lipoprotein (LDL),** which is 75% lipid and 25% protein; and **high-density lipoprotein (HDL),** which is 55% lipid and 45% protein (figure 24.32).

About 15% of the cholesterol in the body is ingested in the food we eat. Eating foods containing saturated fatty acids can raise plasma cholesterol levels by stimulating LDL production and inhibiting LDL receptor production. Conversely, ingesting unsaturated fatty acids lowers plasma cholesterol. Replacing fats with carbohydrates in the diet can also reduce blood cholesterol. The remaining 85% is manufactured in body cells, mostly in the liver and intestinal mucosa. Most of the cholesterol and other lipids taken into or manufactured in the liver leave the liver in the form of VLDL. Most of the triglycerides are removed from the VLDL to be stored in adipose tissue; as a result, VLDL becomes LDL.

The cholesterol in LDL is critical for the production of steroid hormones and bile salts in the liver. It is also an important component of plasma membranes. Abnormally low cholesterol levels may lead to weakened blood vessel walls and an increased risk for cerebral hemorrhage.

Figure 24.33 details the process of LDL transport into cells.

1. LDL is delivered to cells of various tissues through the blood. Cells have **LDL receptors** in "pits" on their surfaces, which bind the LDL.
2. Once LDL is bound to the receptors, the pits on the cell surface become endocytotic vesicles.
3. The cell takes in LDL by receptor-mediated endocytosis. For example, each fibroblast has 20,000–50,000 LDL receptors on the surface. However, those receptors are confined to cell surface pits, which occupy only 2% of the cell surface. Once inside the cell, the endocytotic vesicle combines with a lysosome, and the LDL components are separated for use in the cell.

Cells not only take in cholesterol and other lipids from LDLs but also make their own cholesterol. When the combined intake and manufacture of cholesterol exceeds a cell's needs, a negative-feedback system reduces the amount of LDL receptors and cholesterol manufactured by the cell. Excess lipids are also packaged into HDLs by the cells. These are transported back to the liver for recycling or excretion in bile.

LDL is commonly considered "bad" because, when in excess, it deposits cholesterol in arterial walls. On the other hand, HDL is considered "good" because it transports cholesterol from the tissues via blood to the liver for removal from the body in the bile. A high HDL/LDL ratio in the blood is related to a lower risk for heart disease. Low HDL levels are linked to obesity, and weight reduction increases HDL levels. Aerobic exercise can decrease LDL levels and increase HDL levels.

Proteins

Proteins are taken into the body from a number of dietary sources. Digestion of proteins begins in the stomach. **Pepsin** secreted by the stomach catalyzes the cleavage of covalent bonds in proteins to produce smaller polypeptide chains. Pepsin digests as much as 10–20% of the total ingested protein. Once the proteins and polypeptide chains leave the stomach, **pancreatic proteases** continue the digestive process to produce small peptide chains (see figure 24.29). There are three major pancreatic proteases: (1) trypsin, (2) chymotrypsin, and (3) carboxypeptidase. The protein digestion products are finally broken down into tripeptides, dipeptides, and amino acids by **peptidases** bound to the microvilli of the small intestine. Each peptidase is specific for a certain peptide chain length or for a certain amino acid sequence.

Figure 24.34 describes the process of amino acid transport.

1. Basic, acidic, and neutral amino acids are transported into the epithelial cells by separate carrier molecules.
2. Acidic and most neutral amino acids enter by symport with a Na^+ gradient, similar to the mechanism used for glucose transport. Basic amino acids enter the epithelial cells by facilitated diffusion.

PROCESS **Figure**

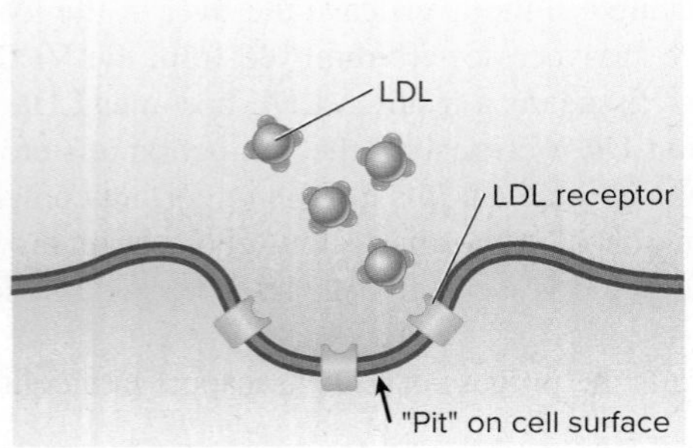

1 Cells have pits on the surface, which contain LDL receptors.

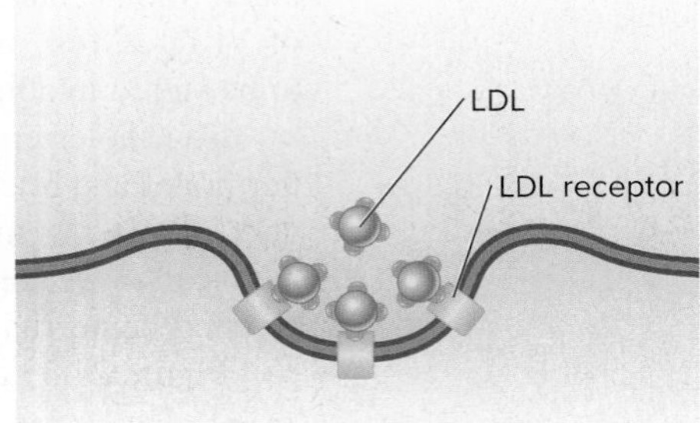

2 LDL binds to the LDL receptors in the pits.

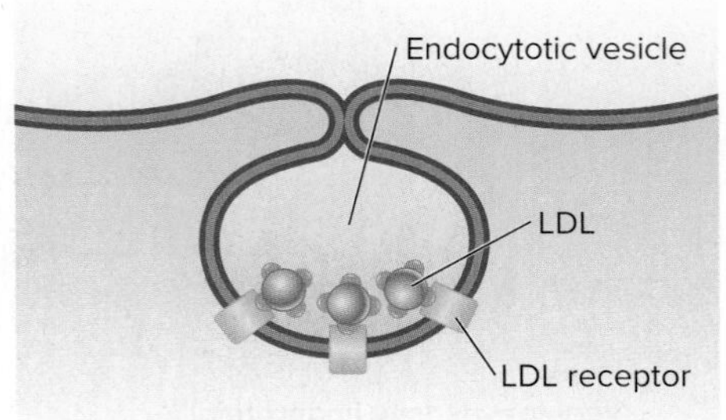

3 The LDL, bound to LDL receptors, is taken into the cell by endocytosis.

PROCESS **Figure 24.33**

Transport of LDL into Cells

The LDL receptor transports LDL into cells by endocytosis.

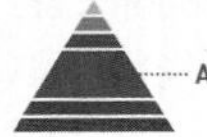

Predict the consequence of a mutation that prevents endocytosis of LDL receptors.

PROCESS **Figure**

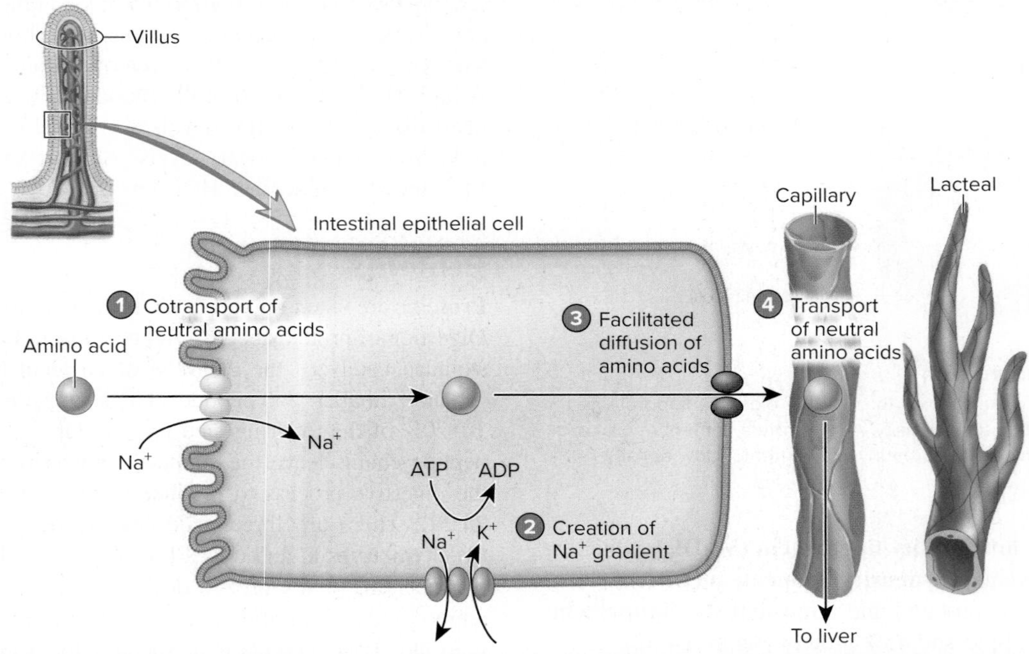

PROCESS **Figure 24.34**

Amino Acid Transport Across the Intestinal Epithelium

Most amino acid absorption occurs by symport powered by a Na^+ gradient.

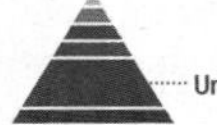

How is transport of acidic and neutral amino acids across the intestinal epithelia similar to transport of glucose and galactose?

Clinical GENETICS 24.1 Familial Hypercholesterolemia

Familial hypercholesterolemia (FH) is a common genetic disorder in Europe and North America that affects 1 out of 500 people. The clinical sign of the disease is increased blood levels of LDL cholesterol. The elevated cholesterol levels accelerate the development of atherosclerosis, which often leads to coronary artery disease and heart attacks among people in their forties and fifties. Another common feature of FH is the presence of **xanthomas** (zan-THOH-mas), which are nodules of cholesterol and other lipids just under the skin, especially at joints.

FH is caused by mutations in the LDL receptor gene that result in defective LDL receptors. The LDL receptor normally removes cholesterol from the blood by transporting LDL cholesterol into cells. Once inside the cell, LDL cholesterol is metabolized, and cholesterol synthesis is inhibited by a negative-feedback mechanism. When less LDL cholesterol is transported into cells, blood LDL cholesterol rises for two reasons: (1) The normal removal of LDL cholesterol does not occur, and (2) there is less inhibition of cholesterol synthesis. The usual treatment for FH is statin drugs, which lower blood LDL levels by inhibiting the synthesis of cholesterol.

The severity of FH depends on whether a person is homozygous or heterozygous. Homozygous individuals have two mutant alleles and completely lack LDL receptors. These patients have the most severe form of FH, with very high blood LDL cholesterol levels, and they often have heart attacks in their teens. Most FH patients are heterozygous, with one normal and one mutant allele. These patients have half the number of normal LDL receptors and are at increased risk for heart attacks at midlife. Although genetic testing is not yet standard, automated assays are available for the more common mutations in the LDL receptor, and they can allow early diagnosis and treatment before life-threatening symptoms develop. In the future, FH will be an excellent candidate for gene therapy because it is a severe but well-studied single-gene defect.

Dipeptides and tripeptides enter intestinal epithelial cells by a H^+ symport mechanism analogous to Na^+ symport. The total amount of each amino acid that enters the intestinal epithelial cells as dipeptides or tripeptides is considerably more than the amount that enters as single amino acids. Once inside the cells, dipeptidases and tripeptidases split the dipeptides and tripeptides into their component amino acids.

3. Individual amino acids then leave the epithelial cells.
4. Amino acids then enter the hepatic portal system, which transports them to the liver. The amino acids may be modified in the liver or released into the bloodstream and distributed throughout the body.

Amino acids are actively transported into the various cells of the body. This transport is stimulated by growth hormone and insulin. Most amino acids serve as building blocks to form new proteins (see chapter 2), but some amino acids may be used for energy.

Water

About 9 L of **water** enter the digestive tract each day as a combination of ingested and secreted fluids. Of this 9 L, about 92% is absorbed in the small intestine, and another 6–7% is absorbed in the large intestine (figure 24.35). Water moves in either direction across the wall of the small intestine by osmosis. Osmotic gradients across the epithelium determine the direction of this diffusion. When the chyme is dilute, water is absorbed by osmosis across the intestinal wall into the blood. When the chyme is very concentrated and contains very little water, water moves by osmosis into the lumen of the small intestine. As nutrients are absorbed in the small intestine, its osmotic pressure decreases; as a consequence, water moves from the small intestine into the surrounding extracellular fluid. Water in the extracellular fluid can then enter the blood. Because of the osmotic gradient produced as nutrients are absorbed in the small intestine, nearly all the water that enters the small intestine by way of the oral cavity, stomach, or intestinal secretions is reabsorbed.

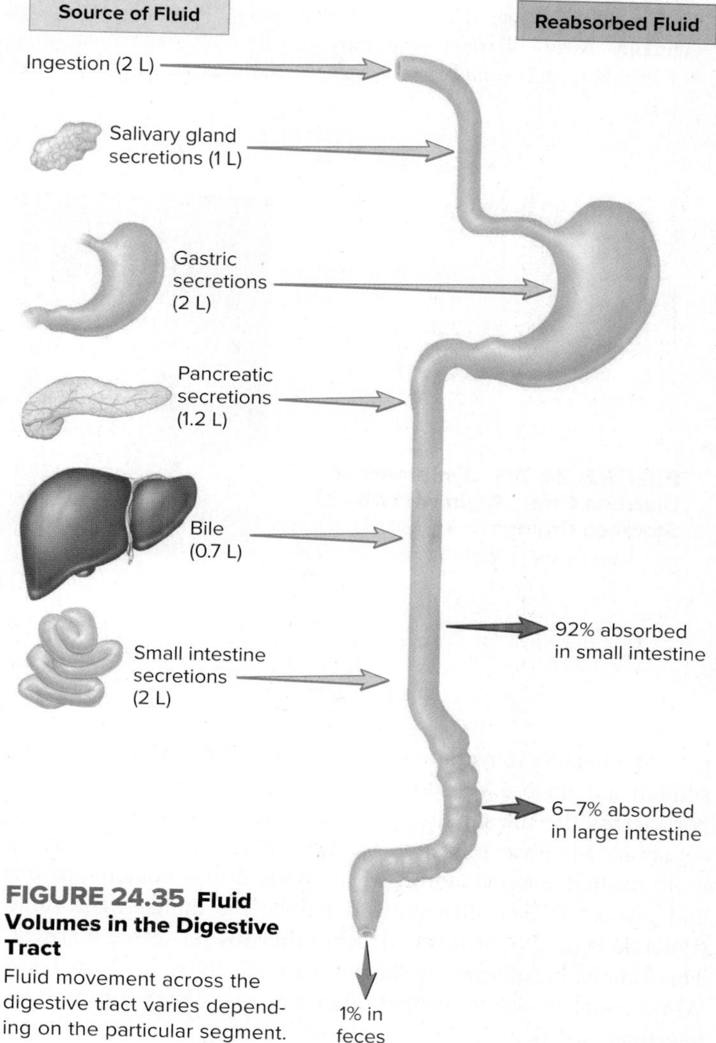

FIGURE 24.35 Fluid Volumes in the Digestive Tract

Fluid movement across the digestive tract varies depending on the particular segment.

Systems PATHOLOGY | Diarrhea

Background Information

Tom, a tourist visiting a developing country, started to experience sharp pains in his abdominal region. He also began to feel hot and sweaty and felt an extreme urge to defecate. Tom anxiously inquired about the nearest facility. Once the immediate crisis was taken care of, Tom and his wife went back to their hotel room, where they remained while Tom recovered. During the next 2 days, his stools were frequent and watery. He also vomited a couple of times. Tom was encouraged to rest and drink plenty of fluids. He was feeling much better, although a little weak, in a couple of days. Diarrhea is one of the most common complaints in clinical medicine. Diarrhea affects more than half the tourists in developing countries (figure 24.36), where it may result from eating food to which the digestive tract is not accustomed or from ingesting food or water contaminated with microorganisms.

Diarrhea is any change in bowel habits involving increased stool frequency or fluidity (figure 24.37). It is not a disease in itself, but it can be a symptom of a wide variety of disorders. Diarrhea that lasts less than 2–3 weeks is acute diarrhea; diarrhea lasting longer is considered chronic. Acute diarrhea is usually self-limiting, but some forms of diarrhea can be fatal if not treated. Diarrhea results from either a decrease in fluid absorption in the intestine or an increase in fluid secretion. It can also be caused by increased bowel motor activity that moves chyme rapidly through the small intestine, so that more water enters the large intestine. Normally, about 600 mL of fluid enter the large intestine each day, and all but 150 mL are reabsorbed. The loss of more than 200 mL of fluid per day in the stool is considered abnormal.

Secretion of mucus by the large intestine increases dramatically in response to diarrhea. This mucus contains large quantities of HCO_3^-, which come from dissociation of carbonic acid into HCO_3^- and H^+ within the blood supply to the large intestine. The HCO_3^- enter the mucus secreted by the large intestine, whereas the H^+ remain in the circulation; as a result, the blood pH decreases. Thus, a condition called metabolic acidosis can develop (see chapter 27).

Diarrhea is usually caused by bacteria, viruses, amoebic parasites, or chemical toxins. Symptoms can begin from as little as 1–2 hours after bacterial toxins are ingested to as long as 24 hours or more for some strains of bacteria. Nearly any bacterial species is capable of causing diarrhea. Some types of bacterial diarrhea are associated with severe vomiting, whereas others are not. Some bacterial toxins also induce fever. Identifying the causal organism usually requires laboratory analysis of the food or stool but, in cases of acute diarrhea, the infectious agent is seldom identified.

Treatment of diarrhea involves replacing lost fluids and ions (figure 24.37). The diet should be limited to clear fluids during at least the first day or so. Medicines that may help combat diarrhea include bismuth subsalicylate (sub-sah-LIS-ih-late), which increases mucus and HCO_3^- secretion and decreases pepsin activity, and loperamide (loh-PER-ah-myde), which slows intestinal motility. Patients should avoid milk and milk products. Breads, rice, and baked fish or chicken can be added to the diet as the person's condition improves. A normal diet can be resumed after 2–3 days.

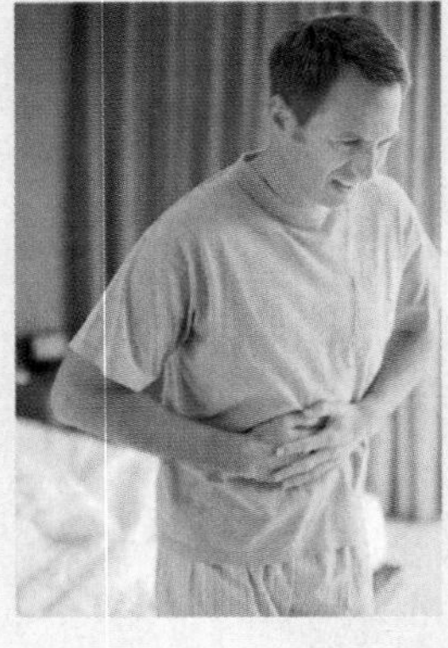

FIGURE 24.36 Symptoms of Diarrhea Often Begin with Sharp Stomach Cramps

Paul Bradbury/age fotostock

Predict 8

Predict the effects of prolonged diarrhea.

An effective rehydration strategy is to drink water containing sodium and glucose. As sodium and glucose are absorbed by symport across the intestinal epithelium, water follows by osmosis. As an added value, this strategy also replaces ions and provides an immediate energy source. Most sports drinks contain sodium and glucose, which efficiently rehydrate the athlete. The same principle is used in **oral rehydration therapy** for severe diarrhea. This simple, inexpensive treatment is especially valuable in Third World countries where people often die from diarrhea caused by intestinal infections.

Ions

Ions are predominantly absorbed by active transport in the small intestine. Active transport mechanisms drive the absorption of (1) $\mathbf{Na^+}$, (2) $\mathbf{K^+}$, (3) $\mathbf{Ca^{2+}}$, (4) $\mathbf{Mg^{2+}}$, and (5) $\mathbf{PO_4^-}$. **Chloride** ions move passively through the intestinal wall of the duodenum and the jejunum following the positively charged Na^+, but Cl^- is actively transported from the ileum. Although Ca^{2+} is actively transported along the entire length of the small intestine, vitamin D_3 is required for that transport process. The absorption of Ca^{2+} is under hormonal control, as are its excretion and storage.

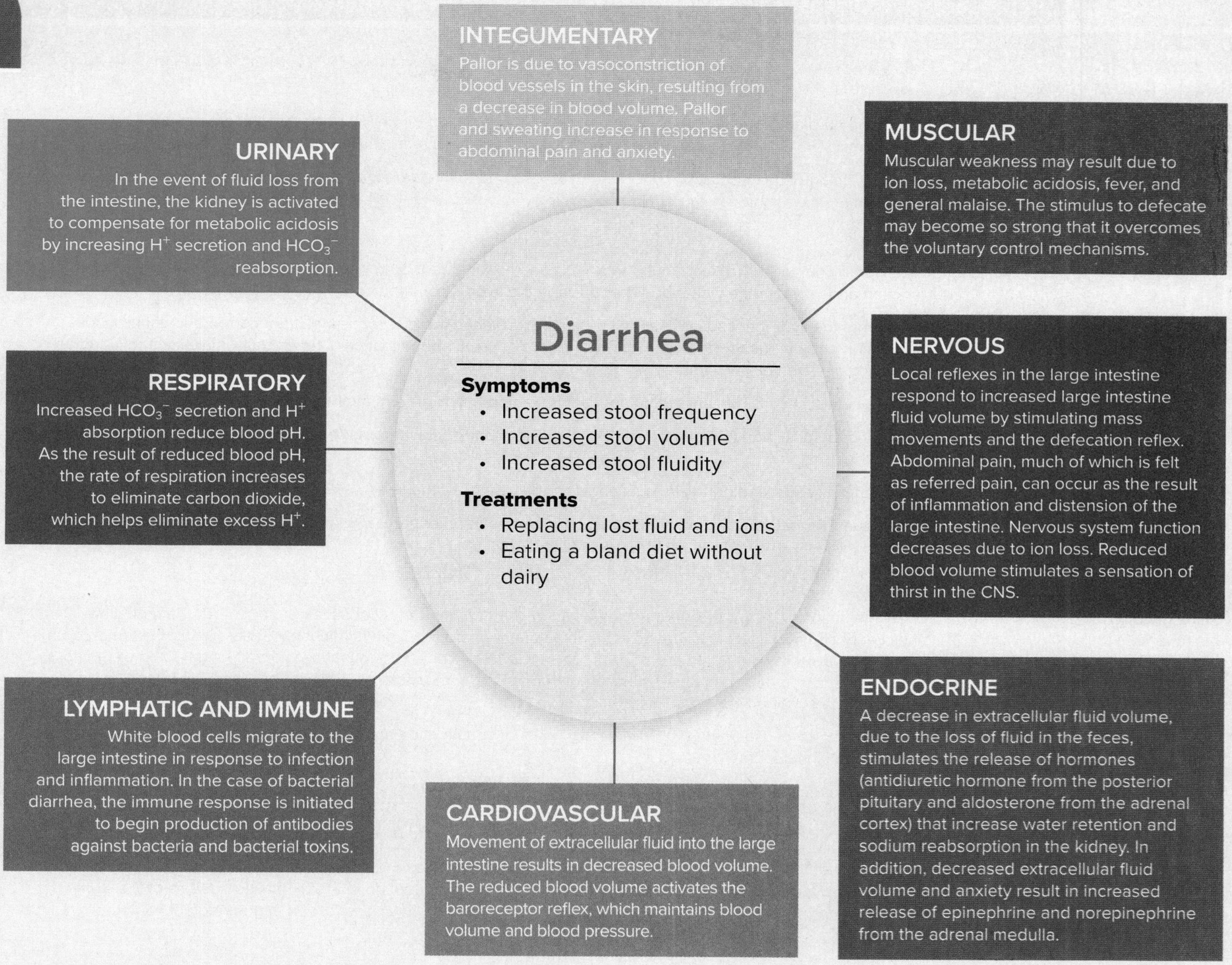

INTEGUMENTARY
Pallor is due to vasoconstriction of blood vessels in the skin, resulting from a decrease in blood volume. Pallor and sweating increase in response to abdominal pain and anxiety.

URINARY
In the event of fluid loss from the intestine, the kidney is activated to compensate for metabolic acidosis by increasing H^+ secretion and HCO_3^- reabsorption.

MUSCULAR
Muscular weakness may result due to ion loss, metabolic acidosis, fever, and general malaise. The stimulus to defecate may become so strong that it overcomes the voluntary control mechanisms.

Diarrhea

Symptoms
- Increased stool frequency
- Increased stool volume
- Increased stool fluidity

Treatments
- Replacing lost fluid and ions
- Eating a bland diet without dairy

RESPIRATORY
Increased HCO_3^- secretion and H^+ absorption reduce blood pH. As the result of reduced blood pH, the rate of respiration increases to eliminate carbon dioxide, which helps eliminate excess H^+.

NERVOUS
Local reflexes in the large intestine respond to increased large intestine fluid volume by stimulating mass movements and the defecation reflex. Abdominal pain, much of which is felt as referred pain, can occur as the result of inflammation and distension of the large intestine. Nervous system function decreases due to ion loss. Reduced blood volume stimulates a sensation of thirst in the CNS.

LYMPHATIC AND IMMUNE
White blood cells migrate to the large intestine in response to infection and inflammation. In the case of bacterial diarrhea, the immune response is initiated to begin production of antibodies against bacteria and bacterial toxins.

CARDIOVASCULAR
Movement of extracellular fluid into the large intestine results in decreased blood volume. The reduced blood volume activates the baroreceptor reflex, which maintains blood volume and blood pressure.

ENDOCRINE
A decrease in extracellular fluid volume, due to the loss of fluid in the feces, stimulates the release of hormones (antidiuretic hormone from the posterior pituitary and aldosterone from the adrenal cortex) that increase water retention and sodium reabsorption in the kidney. In addition, decreased extracellular fluid volume and anxiety result in increased release of epinephrine and norepinephrine from the adrenal medulla.

FIGURE 24.37 Symptoms and Treatments of Diarrhea
Multiple systems are affected by diarrhea.

Parathyroid hormones, calcitonin, and vitamin D_3 all play a role in regulating blood levels of Ca^{2+} (see chapters 6, 18, and 27).

ASSESS YOUR PROGRESS

58. *Describe the mechanism of absorption and the route of transport for water-soluble and lipid-soluble molecules.*

59. *Describe the enzymatic digestion of carbohydrates, lipids, and proteins. List where each step of digestion occurs and the breakdown products of each step.*

60. *Explain how lipids are emulsified. Describe the role of micelles, chylomicrons, VLDLs, LDLs, and HDLs in the absorption and transport of lipids in the body.*

61. *Explain how tripeptides, dipeptides, and amino acids enter intestinal epithelial cells.*

62. *Describe the movement of water through the intestinal wall.*

63. *When and where are various ions absorbed?*

TABLE 24.2 Representative Diseases and Disorders of the Digestive System

Condition	Description
Stomach	
Vomiting	Contraction of the diaphragm and abdominal muscles and relaxation of the esophageal sphincters to forcefully expel gastric contents; vomiting reflex is initiated by irritation of the stomach or small intestine
Peptic ulcer	Lesions in the lining of the stomach or duodenum, usually due to infection by the bacterium *Helicobacter pylori;* stress, diet, smoking, or alcohol may be a predisposing factor; antibiotic therapy is the accepted treatment
Liver	
Cirrhosis (sir-OH-sis)	Characterized by damage and death of hepatic cells and replacement by connective tissue; results in loss of normal liver function and interference with blood flow through the liver; a common consequence of alcoholism
Hepatitis (hep-ah-TYE-tis)	Inflammation of the liver that causes liver cell death and replacement by scar tissue; if not corrected, results in loss of liver function and eventually death; symptoms include nausea, abdominal pain, fever, chills, malaise, and jaundice; caused by any of seven distinct viruses
Hepatitis A	Infectious hepatitis; usually transmitted by poor sanitation practices or from mollusks living in contaminated waters
Hepatitis B	Serum hepatitis; usually transmitted through blood or other body fluids through either sexual contact or contaminated hypodermic needles
Hepatitis C	Often a chronic disease leading to cirrhosis and possibly cancer of the liver
Gallstones	Most often due to excess cholesterol in the bile; gallstones can enter the cystic duct, where they block the release of bile and/or pancreatic enzymes, which interferes with digestion
Intestine	
Inflammatory bowel disease (IBD)	Localized inflammatory degeneration that may occur anywhere along the digestive tract but most commonly involves the distal ileum and proximal large intestine; the intestinal wall often becomes thickened, constricting the lumen, with ulcers and fissures in the damaged areas; symptoms include diarrhea, abdominal pain, fever, fatigue, and weight loss; cause is unknown; treatments involve anti-inflammatory drugs, avoidance of foods that produce symptoms, and surgery in some cases; also called Crohn disease or ulcerative colitis
Irritable bowel syndrome (IBS)	Disorder of unknown cause marked by alternating bouts of constipation and diarrhea; may be linked to stress or depression; high familial incidence
Gluten enteropathy (celiac disease)	Malabsorption in the small intestine due to the effects of gluten, a protein in certain grains, especially wheat; the reaction can destroy newly formed epithelial cells, causing the intestinal villi to become blunted and decreasing the intestinal surface, which reduces absorption of nutrients
Constipation (kon-sti-PAY-shun)	Slow movement of feces through the large intestine, causing the feces to become dry and hard because of increased fluid absorption while being retained; often results from inhibiting normal defecation reflexes; spasms of the sigmoid colon resulting from irritation can also result in slow feces movement and constipation; high-fiber diet can be preventive
Infections of the Digestive Tract	
Food poisoning	Caused by ingesting bacteria or toxins, such as *Staphylococcus aureus, Salmonella,* or *Escherichia coli;* symptoms include nausea, abdominal pain, vomiting, and diarrhea; in severe cases, death can occur
Typhoid (TIE-foyd) fever	Caused by a virulent strain of the bacterium *Salmonella typhi,* which can cross the intestinal wall and invade other tissues; symptoms include severe fever, headaches, and diarrhea; usually transmitted through poor sanitation practices; leading cause of death in many developing countries
Cholera (KOL-er-a)	Caused by a bacterium, *Vibrio cholerae,* in contaminated water; bacteria produce a toxin that stimulates the secretion of chloride, HCO_3^-, and water into the large intestine, resulting in severe diarrhea; the loss of as much as 12–20 L of fluid per day causes shock and even death; still a major health problem in parts of Asia
Giardiasis (jee-ar-DYE-a-sis)	Caused by a protozoan, *Giardia lamblia,* invading the large intestine; symptoms include nausea, abdominal cramps, weakness, weight loss, and malaise; the protozoans are transmitted in the feces of humans and other animals, often by drinking from contaminated wilderness streams
Intestinal parasites	Common under conditions of poor sanitation; parasites include tapeworms, pinworms, hookworms, and roundworms
Diarrhea (die-ah-REE-ah)	Intestinal mucosa secretes large amounts of water and ions due to irritation, inflammation, or infection; diarrhea moves feces out of the large intestine more rapidly and speeds recovery
Dysentery (DIS-en-tair-ee)	Severe form of diarrhea with blood or mucus in the feces; can be caused by bacteria, protozoa, or amoebae

EFFECTS OF AGING ON THE DIGESTIVE SYSTEM

There are a variety of diseases and disorders associated with the digestive system (table 24.2). As a person ages, gradual changes occur throughout the digestive tract. The connective tissue layers of the digestive tract—the submucosa and serosa—tend to thin. The blood supply to the digestive tract decreases. The number of smooth muscle cells in the muscularis also decreases, resulting in reduced motility in the digestive tract. In addition, goblet cells within the mucosa secrete less mucus. Glands along the digestive tract, such as the gastric glands, the liver, and the pancreas, also tend to secrete less with age. However, these changes by themselves do not appreciably decrease the function of the digestive system.

Through the years, the digestive tract, like the skin and lungs, is directly exposed to materials from the outside environment. Some of those substances can cause mechanical damage to the digestive tract, and others are toxic to the tissues. Because the connective tissue of the digestive tract becomes thin with age and because the protective mucous covering is reduced, an older person's digestive tract becomes less and less protected from these outside influences. In addition, the mucosa of older people tends to heal more slowly following injury. Declines also occur in the liver's ability to detoxify certain chemicals, the hepatic phagocytic cells' ability to remove particulate contaminants, and the liver's ability to store glycogen. These problems worsen in people who smoke.

The overall decline in the defenses of the digestive tract leaves older people more susceptible to infections and toxic agents. Older people are therefore more likely to develop ulcerations and cancers of the digestive tract. Colorectal cancers, for example, are the second-leading cause of cancer deaths in the United States, with an estimated 135,000 new cases and 57,000 deaths each year.

Gastroesophageal reflux disorder increases with advancing age. It is probably the main reason that older people take antacids, H_2 antagonists, and proton pump inhibitors. Disorders that are not necessarily age-induced, such as hiatal hernia and irregular or inadequate esophageal motility, can be worsened by the effects of aging because of general decreased motility in the digestive tract.

The enamel on the surface of older people's teeth becomes thinner with age and may expose the underlying dentin. In addition, the gingiva covering the tooth root recedes, exposing additional dentin. Exposed dentin may become painful and change the person's eating habits. Many older people also lose teeth, which can have a marked effect on eating habits unless they are fitted with artificial teeth. The muscles of mastication tend to become weaker; as a result, older people tend to chew their food less before swallowing.

Another age-related complication in the digestive system involves the way medications and other chemicals are absorbed from the digestive tract. The decreased mucous covering and the thinned connective tissue layers allow chemicals to pass more readily from the digestive tract into the blood. However, a decline in the blood supply to the digestive tract hinders the absorption of such chemicals. Drugs administered to treat cancer, which occurs in many older people, may irritate the mucosa of the digestive tract, resulting in nausea and loss of appetite.

Concept Check

24.1 Anatomy of the Digestive System

A. The digestive system consists of the digestive tract and its associated accessory organs.

B. The digestive tract includes the oral cavity, pharynx and esophagus, stomach, small intestine, and large intestine.

C. Accessory organs include the salivary glands, tonsils, liver, gallbladder, and pancreas.

24.2 Functions of the Digestive System

The functions of the digestive system are ingestion, propulsion and mixing, secretion, digestion, absorption, and storage and elimination.

24.3 Histology of the Digestive Tract

The digestive tract is composed of four tunics: mucosa, submucosa, muscularis, and serosa or adventitia.

Mucosa

A. The mucosa consists of a mucous epithelium, a lamina propria, and a muscularis mucosae.

B. The epithelium extends into the lamina propria to form intestinal glands.

Submucosa

The submucosa is a connective tissue layer containing the submucosal plexus, blood vessels, and small glands.

Muscularis

A. The muscularis consists of an inner layer of circular smooth muscle and an outer layer of longitudinal smooth muscle.

B. The myenteric plexus is between the two muscle layers.

C. Interstitial pacemaker cells are located throughout the myenteric plexus.

Serosa or Adventitia

The serosa or adventitia forms the outermost layer of the digestive tract.

1. *Which layer of the digestive tract is in direct contact with the food that is consumed?* Remember

   a. mucosa
   b. muscularis
   c. serosa
   d. submucosa

24.4 Regulation of the Digestive System

Nervous, hormonal, and local chemical mechanisms regulate digestion.

Nervous Regulation of the Digestive System

Nervous regulation involves the ENS and CNS reflexes.

Chemical Regulation of the Digestive System

A. Over 30 neurotransmitters are associated with the ENS.
B. The digestive tract produces hormones that regulate digestion.
C. Other chemicals produced by the digestive tract exercise local control of digestion.

2. *The ENS is found in*
   a. the submucosa layer.
   b. the muscularis layer.
   c. the serosa layer.
   d. Both a and b are correct.
   e. All of these are correct.

24.5 Peritoneum

A. The peritoneum is a serous membrane that lines the abdominal cavity and organs.
B. The mesentery is a contiguous organ that maintains the position of the abdominal digestive organs within the abdominal cavity. Portions of the mesentery are named for the organs with which it is associated.
C. Retroperitoneal (nonmesenteric) organs are located behind the peritoneum.

24.6 Oral Cavity

The oral cavity includes the vestibule and the oral cavity proper.

Lips, Cheeks, and Palate

A. The lips and cheeks are involved in facial expression, mastication, and speech.
B. The roof of the oral cavity is divided into the hard and soft palates.
C. The palatine tonsils are located in the lateral wall of the fauces.

Tongue

A. The tongue is involved in speech, taste, mastication, and swallowing.
B. The intrinsic tongue muscles change the shape of the tongue, and the extrinsic tongue muscles move the tongue.
C. The anterior two-thirds of the tongue is covered with papillae; the posterior one-third is devoid of papillae.

Teeth

A. Twenty deciduous teeth are replaced by 32 permanent teeth.
B. The types of teeth are incisors, canines, premolars, and molars.
C. A tooth consists of a crown, a neck, and a root.
D. The root is composed of dentin. Within the dentin of the root is the pulp cavity, which is filled with pulp, blood vessels, and nerves. The crown is dentin covered by enamel.
E. Periodontal ligaments hold the teeth in the alveoli.

3. *Dentin*
   a. forms the surface of the crown of the teeth.
   b. holds the teeth to the periodontal ligaments.
   c. is found in the pulp cavity.
   d. makes up most of the structure of the teeth.
   e. is harder than enamel.

4. *The number of premolar deciduous teeth is*

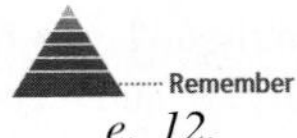

   a. 0. *b. 2.* *c. 4.* *d. 8.* *e. 12.*

Mastication

The muscles of mastication are the temporalis, masseter, medial pterygoid, and lateral pterygoid.

Salivary Glands

A. Salivary glands produce serous and mucous secretions.
B. The three pairs of large salivary glands are the parotid, submandibular, and sublingual.

5. *Which of these glands does* not *secrete saliva into the oral cavity?*
   a. submandibular gland
   b. pancreas
   c. sublingual gland
   d. parotid gland

6. *The portion of the digestive tract in which digestion begins is the*
   a. oral cavity.
   b. esophagus.
   c. stomach.
   d. duodenum.
   e. jejunum.

24.7 Swallowing

Swallowing involves the pharynx and esophagus. It is divided into three phases.

Pharynx

The pharynx consists of the nasopharynx, oropharynx, and laryngopharynx.

Esophagus

A. The esophagus connects the pharynx to the stomach. The upper and lower esophageal sphincters regulate movement.
B. The esophagus consists of an outer adventitia, a muscular layer (longitudinal and circular), a submucosal layer (with mucous glands), and a stratified squamous epithelium.

Swallowing Phases

A. During the voluntary phase of swallowing, a bolus of food is moved by the tongue from the oral cavity to the pharynx.
B. The pharyngeal phase is a reflex caused by the stimulation of stretch receptors in the pharynx.
   - The soft palate closes the nasopharynx, and the epiglottis and vestibular folds close the opening into the larynx.
   - Pharyngeal muscles move the bolus to the esophagus.
C. The esophageal phase is a reflex initiated by the stimulation of stretch receptors in the esophagus. A wave of contraction (peristalsis) moves the food to the stomach.

7. *During swallowing*

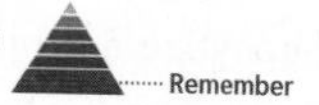

a. the movement of food results primarily from gravity.
b. the swallowing center in the medulla oblongata is activated.
c. food is pushed into the oropharynx during the pharyngeal phase.
d. the soft palate closes off the opening into the larynx.

8. *While anesthetized, patients sometimes vomit. Given that the anesthetic eliminates the swallowing reflex, explain why it is dangerous for an anesthetized patient to vomit.*

24.8 Stomach

Anatomy of the Stomach

The openings of the stomach are the gastroesophageal (to the esophagus) and the pyloric (to the duodenum).

9. *The stomach*

a. has large folds in the submucosa and mucosa called rugae.
b. has two layers of smooth muscle in the muscularis tunic.
c. opening from the esophagus is the pyloric opening.
d. has an area closest to the duodenum called the fundus.
e. All of these are correct.

Histology of the Stomach

A. The wall of the stomach consists of an external serosa, a muscle layer (longitudinal, circular, and oblique), a submucosa, and simple columnar epithelium (surface mucous cells).
B. Rugae are the folds in the stomach when it is empty.
C. Gastric pits are the openings to the gastric glands, which contain mucous neck cells, parietal cells, chief cells, and endocrine cells.

10. *Which of these stomach cell types is* not *correctly matched with its function?*

a. surface mucous cells—produce mucus
b. parietal cells—produce hydrochloric acid
c. chief cells—produce intrinsic factor
d. endocrine cells—produce regulatory hormones

Secretions of the Stomach

A. Hydrochloric acid promotes pepsin activity and kills microorganisms.
B. Intrinsic factor is necessary for vitamin B_{12} absorption in the small intestine.
C. Mucus protects the stomach lining.
D. Pepsinogen is converted to pepsin, which digests proteins. Gastric lipase digests lipids.
E. The sight, smell, taste, or thought of food initiates the cephalic phase. Nerve impulses from the medulla stimulate hydrochloric acid, pepsinogen, gastrin, and histamine secretion.
F. Distension of the stomach, which stimulates gastrin secretion and activates CNS and local reflexes that promote secretion, initiates the gastric phase.
G. Acidic chyme, which enters the duodenum and stimulates neuronal reflexes and the secretion of hormones that inhibit gastric secretions, initiates the intestinal phase.

11. *Why doesn't the stomach digest itself?*

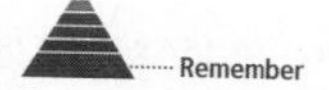

a. The stomach wall is not composed of protein, so it is not affected by proteolytic enzymes.
b. The digestive enzymes of the stomach are not strong enough to digest the stomach wall.
c. The lining of the stomach wall has a protective layer of epithelial cells.
d. The stomach wall is protected by large amounts of mucus.

12. *Which of these hormones stimulates stomach secretions?*

a. cholecystokinin
b. insulin
c. gastrin
d. secretin

13. *Achlorhydria is a condition in which the stomach stops producing hydrochloric acid and other secretions. What effect would achlorhydria have on the digestive process? On red blood cell count?*

14. *Victor experienced the pain of a duodenal ulcer during final examination week. Explain what habits worsened the ulcer, and recommend possible remedies.*

Movements of the Stomach

A. The stomach stretches and relaxes to increase volume.
B. Mixing waves mix the stomach contents with stomach secretions to form chyme.
C. Peristaltic waves move the chyme into the duodenum.
D. Gastrin and stretching of the stomach stimulate stomach emptying.
E. Chyme entering the duodenum inhibits movement through neuronal reflexes and the release of hormones.

24.9 Small Intestine

The small intestine is divided into the duodenum, jejunum, and ileum.

Anatomy and Histology of the Small Intestine

A. Circular folds, villi, and microvilli greatly increase the surface area of the intestinal lining.
B. Absorptive, goblet, and endocrine cells are in intestinal glands. Duodenal glands produce mucus.

15. *Which of these structures increase the mucosal surface of the small intestine?*

a. circular folds
b. villi
c. microvilli
d. length of the small intestine
e. All of these are correct.

Secretions of the Small Intestine

A. Mucus protects against digestive enzymes and stomach acids.
B. Digestive enzymes (disaccharidases and peptidases) are bound to the intestinal wall.
C. The vagus nerves, secretin, and chemical or tactile irritation stimulate intestinal secretion.

16. *Which cells in the small intestine have digestive enzymes attached to their surfaces?* Remember

    a. *mucous cells*
    b. *goblet cells*
    c. *endocrine cells*
    d. *absorptive cells*

17. *The bacterium* Vibrio cholerae *produces cholera toxin, which activates a chloride channel in the intestinal epithelium. In contrast, mutations that inactivate the same channel cause cystic fibrosis. Explain how increased chloride channel activity causes severe diarrhea, whereas decreased activity causes the intestinal symptoms of cystic fibrosis.* Apply

Movement in the Small Intestine

A. Segmental contractions mix intestinal contents. Peristaltic contractions move materials distally.

B. Stretch of smooth muscles, local reflexes, and the parasympathetic nervous system stimulate contractions. Distension of the cecum initiates a reflex that inhibits peristalsis.

24.10 Accessory Organs: Liver, Gallbladder, and Pancreas

Anatomy of the Liver

A. The liver has four lobes: right, left, caudate, and quadrate.

B. The liver is divided into lobules.

- The hepatic cords are composed of columns of hepatocytes separated by the bile canaliculi.
- The sinusoids are enlarged spaces filled with blood and lined with endothelium and hepatic phagocytic cells.

18. *The hepatic sinusoids*

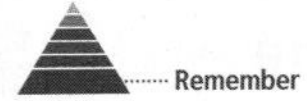

    a. *receive blood from the hepatic artery.*
    b. *receive blood from the hepatic portal vein.*
    c. *empty into the central veins.*
    d. *All of these are correct.*

Histology of the Liver

A. The portal triads supply the lobules.

- The hepatic arteries and the hepatic portal veins take blood to the lobules and empty into the sinusoids.
- The sinusoids empty into central veins, which join to form the hepatic veins, which leave the liver.
- Bile canaliculi converge to form hepatic ducts, which leave the liver.

B. Bile leaves the liver through the hepatic duct system.

- The hepatic ducts receive bile from the lobules.
- The cystic duct from the gallbladder joins the hepatic duct to form the common bile duct.
- The common bile duct joins the pancreatic duct at the point at which it empties into the duodenum.

Functions of the Liver

A. The liver produces bile, which contains bile salts that emulsify lipids.

B. The liver stores and processes nutrients, detoxifies harmful chemicals, and synthesizes new molecules.

C. Hepatic phagocytic cells phagocytize red blood cells, bacteria, and other debris.

D. The liver produces blood proteins.

19. *Which of the following might occur if a person suffers from a severe case of hepatitis that impairs liver function?* Remember

    a. *Lipid digestion is difficult.*
    b. *By-products of hemoglobin breakdown accumulate in the blood.*
    c. *Plasma proteins decrease in concentration.*
    d. *Toxins in the blood increase.*
    e. *All of these occur.*

Gallbladder

A. The gallbladder is a small sac on the inferior surface of the liver.

B. The gallbladder stores and concentrates bile.

C. Cholecystokinin stimulates gallbladder contraction.

20. *The gallbladder* Remember

    a. *produces bile.*
    b. *stores bile.*
    c. *contracts and releases bile in response to secretin.*
    d. *contracts and releases bile in response to sympathetic stimulation.*
    e. *Both b and c are correct.*

21. *Gallstones sometimes obstruct the common bile duct. What are the consequences of such a blockage?* Understand

Anatomy of the Pancreas

A. The pancreas is both an endocrine and an exocrine gland. Its exocrine function is the production of digestive enzymes.

B. The pancreas is divided into lobules that contain acini. The acini connect to a duct system that eventually forms the pancreatic duct, which empties into the duodenum.

Pancreatic Secretions

A. Digestive enzymes, including inactive proteolytic enzymes that are activated in the small intestine.

B. A watery HCO_3^- solution that neutralizes acidic chyme.

22. *The aqueous pancreatic juice*

    a. *is secreted by the pancreatic islets.*
    b. *contains HCO_3^-.*
    c. *is released primarily in response to cholecystokinin.*
    d. *passes directly into the blood.*
    e. *All of these are correct.*

Regulation of Pancreatic Secretion

Cholecystokinin and the vagus nerves stimulate the release of digestive enzymes. Secretin stimulates release of HCO_3^- and water.

24.11 Large Intestine

Anatomy of the Large Intestine

A. The cecum forms a blind sac at the junction of the small and large intestines. The vermiform appendix is a blind tube off the cecum.

B. The ascending colon extends from the cecum superiorly to the right colic flexure. The transverse colon extends from the right to the left colic flexure. The descending colon extends inferiorly to join the sigmoid colon.

C. The sigmoid colon is an S-shaped tube that ends at the rectum.

D. Longitudinal smooth muscles of the large intestine wall are arranged into bands, called teniae coli, that contract to produce pouches called haustra.

E. An internal anal sphincter (smooth muscle) and an external anal sphincter (skeletal muscle) surround the anal canal.

Secretions of the Large Intestine

A. Mucus protects the intestinal lining.

B. Epithelial cells secrete HCO_3^-. Sodium is absorbed by active transport driven by the Na^+–K^+ ATPase pump, and water is absorbed by osmosis.

C. Microorganisms are responsible for vitamin K production, gas production, and much of the bulk of feces.

23. *Which of these is* not *a function of the large intestine?*

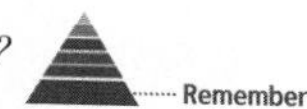

a. absorption of glucose
b. absorption of certain vitamins
c. absorption of water and salts
d. production of mucus

Movement in the Large Intestine

A. Segmental movements mix the large intestine's contents.

B. Mass movements are strong peristaltic contractions that occur three or four times a day.

C. Defecation is the elimination of feces. Reflex activity moves feces through the internal anal sphincter. Voluntary activity regulates movement through the external anal sphincter.

24. *Defecation* Remember

a. can be initiated by stretch of the rectum.
b. can occur as a result of mass movements.
c. involves local reflexes.
d. involves parasympathetic reflexes mediated by the spinal cord.
e. All of these characteristics are true of defecation.

25. *A patient has a spinal cord injury at level L2. How does this injury affect the patient's ability to defecate? What components of the defecation response are still present, and which are lost?* Apply

24.12 Digestion and Absorption

A. Digestion is the breakdown of organic molecules into their components.

B. Absorption is the means by which molecules are moved out of the digestive tract and distributed throughout the body.

C. Transport from the intestinal epithelium occurs by two routes.

- Water, ions, and water-soluble products of digestion are transported to the liver through the hepatic portal system.
- The products of lipid digestion are transported through the lymphatic system to the circulatory system.

Carbohydrates

A. Carbohydrates consist of starches, glycogen, sucrose, lactose, glucose, and fructose.

B. Polysaccharides are broken down into monosaccharides by a number of different enzymes.

C. Monosaccharides are taken up by intestinal epithelial cells by symport that is powered by a Na^+ gradient or by facilitated diffusion.

D. The monosaccharides are carried to the liver, where the nonglucose monosaccharides are converted to glucose.

E. Glucose is transported to the cells that require energy.

F. Insulin influences the rate of glucose transport.

26. *Which of these structures produces enzymes that digest carbohydrates?*

a. salivary glands
b. pancreas
c. lining of the small intestine
d. Both a and b are correct.
e. All of these are correct.

Lipids

A. Lipids include triglycerides, phospholipids, steroids, and fat-soluble vitamins.

B. Lipase digests lipid molecules to form free fatty acids and monoglycerides.

C. Emulsification, the transformation of large lipid droplets into smaller droplets, is accomplished by bile salts.

D. Within the epithelial cells, free fatty acids are combined with a monoglyceride to form triglycerides.

E. Chylomicrons, VLDL, LDL, and HDL enter lacteals within intestinal villi and are carried through the lymphatic system to the bloodstream. LDL transports cholesterol to cells, and HDL transports it from cells to the liver.

F. Triglycerides are stored in adipose tissue, converted into other molecules, or used as energy.

27. *Bile* Remember

a. is an important enzyme for the digestion of lipids.
b. is made by the gallbladder.
c. contains breakdown products from hemoglobin.
d. emulsifies lipids.
e. Both c and d are correct.

28. *Micelles are* Remember

a. lipids surrounded by bile salts.
b. produced by the pancreas.
c. released into lacteals.
d. stored in the gallbladder.
e. reabsorbed in the colon.

29. *If the thoracic duct were tied off, which of these classes of nutrients would* not *enter the blood at their normal rate?* Remember

a. amino acids
b. glucose
c. lipids
d. fructose
e. nucleotides

30. *Which of these lipoprotein molecules transports excess lipids from cells back to the liver?* Remember

    a. *high-density lipoprotein (HDL)*
    b. *low-density lipoprotein (LDL)*
    c. *very low-density lipoprotein (VLDL)*

31. *Would a patient with familial hypercholesterolemia (FH) benefit from dietary changes?* Understand

Proteins

A. Pepsin in the stomach breaks proteins into polypeptide chains.
B. Trypsin and other proteolytic enzymes from the pancreas produce smaller peptides.
C. Peptidases, bound to the microvilli of the small intestine, break down peptides.
D. Amino acids are transported to the liver, where the amino acids can be modified or released into the bloodstream.
E. Amino acids are actively transported into cells under the stimulation of growth hormone and insulin.

Water

Water moves in either direction across the wall of the small intestine, depending on the osmotic gradients across the epithelium.

Ions

A. Sodium, potassium, calcium, magnesium, and phosphate are actively transported.
B. Chloride ions move passively through the wall of the duodenum and jejunum but are actively transported from the ileum.
C. Calcium ions are actively transported, but vitamin D is required for transport, and the transport is under hormonal control.

32. *Discuss why the most effective oral rehydration therapy is water containing sodium and glucose instead of water alone or water with fructose.* Understand

Answers to this chapter's odd-numbered Concept Check questions appear in Appendix F.

25 CHAPTER Nutrition, Metabolism, and Temperature Regulation

Photo: Nutrients include the different substances the body needs to function. Some of these substances must be digested before they are absorbed into the blood, whereas others are absorbed in their original form. Anna Kucher/Shutterstock

"You are what you eat" is a common phrase we all hear. Health claims about foods and food supplements bombard us every day. Meanwhile, obesity rates in U.S. children and adults have soared. Nutrition and weight maintenance are subjects of constant discussion on television, in newspapers, and around the water cooler. When choosing food, many of us are more concerned about its taste than its nutritional value. What happens if we do not obtain enough vitamins, or if we eat too much sugar and fat? Which new diets or diet supplements are ridiculous, and which ones have merit? A basic understanding of nutrition can answer these and other questions so that we can develop a healthful diet. It also allows us to know which nutrition questions currently do not have good answers.

Learn to Predict

Sadie and David loved it when their mothers planned a picnic at the park. They enjoyed running and playing on the jungle gym. Today, Sadie begged her mom to pack a snack of chocolate chip cookies and grape soda. This snack was packed with calories that would give the children lots of energy, but otherwise, it had very little nutritional value. Sadie's mom explained that a snack of fruits, whole-wheat crackers, and water would be much better for everyone.

Predict the outcome if Sadie's mom allowed them to bring Sadie's suggested snack, rather than the snack her mother suggested they take to the park.

Answers to this question and the chapter's odd-numbered Predict questions can be found in Appendix E.

25.1 Nutrition

LEARNING OUTCOMES

After reading this section, you should be able to

A. **Define *nutrition, nutrients, essential nutrients,* and *kilocalorie*.**
B. **Describe MyPlate and its use.**
C. **For carbohydrates, describe their dietary sources, their uses in the body, and the daily recommended amounts of each in the diet.**
D. **For lipids, describe their dietary sources, their uses in the body, and the daily recommended amounts of each in the diet.**
E. **For proteins, describe their dietary sources, their uses in the body, and the daily recommended amounts of each in the diet.**
F. **List and describe the function of the important vitamins and minerals for body health.**
G. **Describe the symptoms of deficiency for each of the important vitamins and minerals for body health.**
H. **Discuss the Reference Daily Intake.**
I. **Explain the Daily Reference Value of food.**

Most us of think *nutrition* refers to the evaluation of food and drink requirements for normal body functions. Though this is an important area of focus when deciding on what to eat and drink, **nutrition** is the process by which the body obtains and uses certain components of food. In this definition of *nutrition,* the process includes (1) digestion, (2) absorption, (3) transportation, and (4) cell metabolism.

Nutrients

Nutrients are the substances taken into the body that are used by the cells of the body to produce energy, to provide building blocks for new molecules, and to function in other chemical reactions. Some substances in food, such as nondigestible plant fibers, are not nutrients per se because the cells of the body do not use them; however, these substances can still serve important functions for the body as a whole. For example, fiber is considered an important component of our diet even though we cannot digest it. Instead, fiber adds to the bulk of feces, which stimulates normal motility of the large intestine.

Nutrients are divided into six major classes: (1) carbohydrates, (2) lipids, (3) proteins, (4) vitamins, (5) minerals, and (6) water. Carbohydrates, lipids, and proteins are the major organic nutrients. They must be broken down by enzymes into their components during digestion before they can be absorbed by the small intestine. Vitamins, minerals, and water are absorbed by the digestive tract without being

Module 12
Digestive System

digested. Many of the subunits or the organic nutrients are broken down further by the body's cells to supply energy, whereas others are used by the cells as building blocks for new carbohydrates, lipids, and proteins. Carbohydrates, lipids, proteins, and water are required in fairly substantial quantities. Vitamins and minerals, on the other hand, are required in only small amounts.

A balanced diet consists of enough nutrients in the correct proportions to support normal body function. Our body has the ability to produce many of the substances necessary for normal cellular activity from the nutrients we ingest. Interestingly, when some nutrient levels are low, our cells have the ability to convert other substances to the nutrient that is lacking. For example, if glucose levels are low, the body can convert some lipids to glucose through a specific metabolic pathway. **Essential nutrients,** also called *indispensable nutrients,* are substances that must be ingested because the body cannot manufacture them at all or cannot manufacture adequate amounts of them. The essential nutrients include certain amino acids and fatty acids, most vitamins, minerals, water, and a few carbohydrates. However, the term *essential* does not mean that the body requires only the essential nutrients. Other nutrients are necessary; if they are not part of the diet, they can be synthesized from the essential nutrients. Most of this synthesis takes place in the liver, which has a remarkable ability to transform and manufacture molecules.

Kilocalories

The body uses the energy stored within the chemical bonds of certain nutrients. A **calorie** (KAL-oh-ree; **cal**) is the amount of energy (heat) necessary to raise the temperature of 1 g of water 1°C. A **kilocalorie** (KIL-oh-KAL-oh-ree; **kcal**) is 1000 calories and is used to express the larger amounts of energy supplied by foods and released through metabolism.

A kilocalorie is often called a *Calorie* (with a capital *C*). Unfortunately, this usage has been confused with the term *calorie* (with a lowercase *c*). Food labels and nutrition books commonly use *calorie* when *Calorie* (*kilocalorie*) is the proper term.

Most of the kilocalories supplied by food come from carbohydrates, proteins, or lipids (fats). The number of kilocalories per gram of each of these nutrients is well established. For each gram of carbohydrate or protein the body metabolizes, about 4 kcal of energy are released. Fats contain more energy per unit of weight than carbohydrates and proteins and yield about 9 kcal/g. Table 25.1 lists the kilocalories supplied by some common foods. A typical diet in the United States consists of 50–60% carbohydrates, 35–45% fats, and 10–15% proteins. Table 25.1 also lists the carbohydrate, fat, and protein composition of some foods.

MyPlate

Every 5 years, the U.S. Department of Health and Human Services (HHS) and the Department of Agriculture (USDA) jointly recommend the types and amounts of food Americans should eat to be healthy. In light of the increasing problem of obesity in the United States, the past two cycles of updates focused on guidelines to help Americans make healthful choices. *The Dietary Guidelines for Americans, 2010* focused on two concepts: (1) balancing calorie intake to obtain and maintain a healthy weight and (2) increasing consumption of healthful, nutrient-rich foods. The USDA also introduced MyPlate, a new food icon to replace the former food guide icon, called MyPyramid. MyPlate (figure 25.1) is a simple visual reminder of how to build a healthful meal. The MyPlate icon shows a plate and glass with portions representing foods from the fruits, vegetables, grains, proteins, and dairy food groups. To emphasize the importance of making healthful food choices, half the plate is fruits and vegetables. In addition to the MyPlate icons, the USDA also launched ChooseMyPlate.gov, a website that includes information on how to make healthful dietary choices.

The latest recommendations, the *Dietary Guidelines for Americans, 2020–2025,* focus on developing healthy dietary patterns at all stages of life by selecting nutrient-dense foods and limiting added sugars, saturated fats, sodium, and alcoholic beverages. This is the first time the *Dietary Guidelines for Americans* provided specific guidelines for different life stages, from birth to older adults. This emphasis on life stages emphasizes that eating healthy is important for all life stages.

ASSESS YOUR PROGRESS

Answers to these questions are found in the section you have just completed. Re-read the section if you need help in answering these questions.

1. *What is nutrition, and what processes does it include?*
2. *Distinguish between a nutrient and an essential nutrient.*
3. *List the six major classes of nutrients.*
4. *Define* kilocalorie. *State the number of kilocalories supplied by a gram of carbohydrate, a gram of lipid, and a gram of protein.*
5. *List the five food groups shown in MyPlate. How is the importance of eating fruits and vegetables indicated in MyPlate?*

Carbohydrates

Sources in the Diet

Carbohydrates include monosaccharides, disaccharides, and polysaccharides (see chapter 2). Most of the carbohydrates humans ingest come from plants. An exception is lactose, which is found in milk and other dairy products.

Glucose and fructose are the most common monosaccharides in the diet. Plants capture the energy in sunlight and use it to produce glucose, which can be found in vegetables. Fructose (fruit sugar) and galactose are isomers of glucose (see figure 2.16). Fructose is in fruits, berries, honey, and high-fructose corn syrup, which is used to sweeten soft drinks and desserts. Galactose is found in milk.

When most of us think of sugar, we are probably thinking of the sugar you can buy in big bags in the grocery store. This is commonly referred to as table sugar. Table sugar is actually the disaccharide sucrose. As a disaccharide, each molecule of sucrose is composed of two monosaccharides, a glucose molecule and a fructose molecule joined together (see figure 2.17). The principal sources of sucrose are sugarcane, sugar beets, maple sugar, and honey. Two other common dietary disaccharides are maltose and lactose. Maltose (malt sugar), derived from germinating cereals, is composed of two glucose molecules, and lactose (milk sugar) consists of a glucose and a galactose molecule (see figure 2.16).

TABLE 25.1 Nutrient Content of Some Typical Foods

Food	Quantity	Food Energy (kcal)	Carbohydrate (g)	Fat (g)	Protein (g)
Dairy Products					
Whole milk (3.3% fat)	1 cup	150	11	8	8
Low-fat milk (2% fat)	1 cup	120	12	5	8
Butter	1 tablespoon	100	—	12	—
Grains					
Bread, white enriched	1 slice	75	24	1	2
Bread, whole-wheat	1 slice	65	14	1	3
Fruits					
Apple	1	80	20	1	—
Banana	1	100	26	—	1
Orange	1	65	16	—	1
Vegetables					
Corn, canned	1 cup	140	33	1	4
Peas, canned	1 cup	150	29	1	8
Lettuce	1 cup	5	2	—	—
Celery	1 cup	20	5	—	1
Potato, baked	1 large	145	33	—	4
Meat, Fish, and Poultry					
Lean ground beef (10% fat)	3 ounces	185	—	10	23
Shrimp, french fried	3 ounces	190	9	9	17
Tuna, canned	3 ounces	170	—	7	24
Chicken breast, fried	3 ounces	160	1	5	26
Bacon	2 slices	85	—	8	4
Hot dog	1	170	1	15	7
Fast Foods					
McDonald's Egg McMuffin	1	300	30	12	18
McDonald's Big Mac	1	540	45	29	25
Taco Bell beef burrito	1	420	53	15	17
Arby's roast beef	1	360	37	14	22
Pizza Hut Super Supreme	1 slice	245	29	17	14
Long John Silver fish	2 pieces	520	32	34	24
Dairy Queen Oreo Cookie Blizzard, medium	1	680	100	25	14
Desserts					
Chocolate chip cookie	1	50	7	2	1
Apple pie	1 piece	135	49	14	3
Soft ice cream	1 cup	377	38	23	7
Beverages					
Cola	12 ounces	145	37	—	—
Beer	12 ounces	144	13	—	1
Wine	3-½ ounces	73	2	—	—
Hard liquor (86 proof)	1-½ ounces	105	—	—	—
Miscellaneous					
Egg	1	80	1	6	6
Mayonnaise	1 tablespoon	100	—	11	—
Sugar	1 tablespoon	45	12	—	—

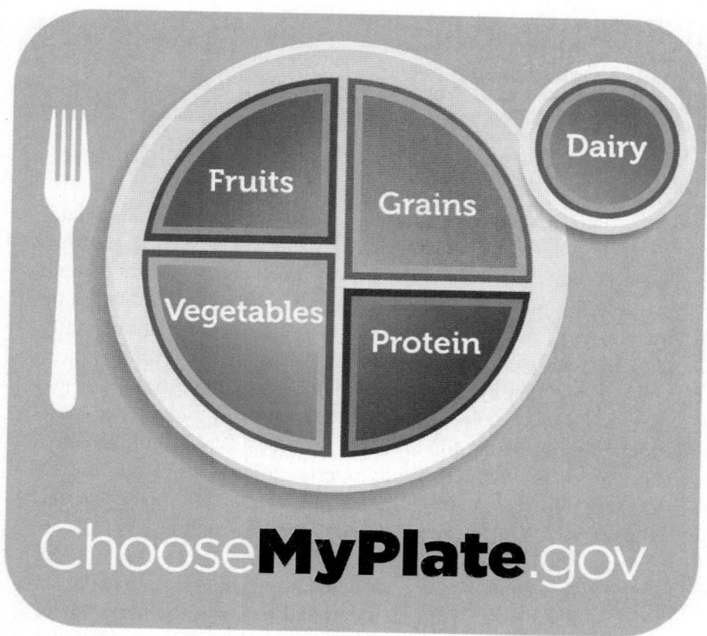

FIGURE 25.1 MyPlate
The MyPlate icon provides a visual reminder for making choices at mealtime, by selecting healthful foods from five food groups. Half the meal should be fruits and vegetables. *Source:* U.S. Department of Agriculture

Complex carbohydrates are polysaccharides, which consist of many glucose molecules bound together to form long chains. Examples of common dietary polysaccharides include starch, glycogen, and cellulose. Starch is an energy-storage molecule found primarily in plants (vegetables, fruits, and grains). Glycogen is an energy-storage molecule in animals and is located primarily in muscle and in the liver. Cellulose forms plant cell walls.

Uses of Carbohydrates in the Body

During digestion, polysaccharides and disaccharides are split into monosaccharides, which are absorbed into the blood (see chapter 24). Humans can digest starch and glycogen because our bodies produce enzymes that break the bonds between the glucose molecules of starch and glycogen. Digestion of certain polysaccharides requires specific enzymes that can break the bonds linking the monosaccharides in the molecule. Humans are unable to digest cellulose because our bodies do not produce the enzymes that break the bonds between its glucose molecules. As a consequence, the digestive tract is unable to absorb cellulose. Instead, cellulose provides fiber, or "roughage," thereby increasing the bulk of feces and making it easier to defecate.

As stated earlier, the liver has the ability to chemically alter many of the absorbed nutrients, providing the cells of the body with the molecules necessary for normal function. The liver converts fructose, galactose, and other monosaccharides absorbed by the small intestine into glucose. Glucose, whether absorbed from the digestive tract or synthesized in the liver, provides energy to produce **adenosine triphosphate (ATP)** molecules (see section 25.3). Because the brain relies almost entirely on glucose for its energy, the body carefully regulates blood glucose levels (see chapter 18).

Muscle and liver cells convert excess glucose into glycogen for storage. Cells can store only a limited amount of glycogen; therefore, any additional glucose is converted into lipids and stored in adipose tissue. Glycogen can be rapidly converted back to glucose when energy is needed. For example, during exercise, muscles convert glycogen to glucose, and between meals the liver helps maintain blood sugar levels by converting glycogen to glucose, which is released into the blood.

In addition to serving as a source of energy, sugars have other functions. They form part of deoxyribonucleic acid (DNA), ribonucleic acid (RNA), and ATP molecules (see chapter 2). They also combine with proteins to form glycoproteins, such as the glycoprotein receptor molecules on the outer surface of the plasma membrane (see chapter 3).

Recommended Consumption of Carbohydrates

According to the Dietary Guidelines Advisory Committee, the **Acceptable Macronutrient Distribution Range (AMDR)** for carbohydrates is 45–65% of total kilocalories. Although a minimum level of carbohydrates has not been established, researchers believe that amounts of 100 g or less per day result in overuse of the body's proteins and lipids for energy. Because muscles are primarily protein, the use of proteins for energy can result in the breakdown of muscle tissue. The extensive use of lipids for energy can lead to acidosis (see chapter 27).

Complex carbohydrates are recommended in the diet because many starchy foods contain other valuable nutrients, such as vitamins and minerals, making them "nutrient dense." Complex carbohydrates are also recommended over simple sugars because the slower rate of digestion and absorption of complex carbohydrates does not cause large increases and decreases in blood glucose levels, as the consumption of large amounts of simple sugars does. Foods primarily composed of simple sugars, such as soft drinks and candy, are rich in carbohydrates but have few other nutrients. For example, a typical soda is mostly sucrose, containing 9 teaspoons of sugar per 12 oz can. Consuming these kinds of foods in excess usually results in obesity and tooth decay. (*Note:* This information may be useful in answering the Learn to Predict question at the beginning of this chapter.)

ASSESS YOUR PROGRESS

6. *What are the most common monosaccharides in the diet? What are the sources of the three common disaccharides: sucrose, maltose, and lactose?*
7. *Give three examples of complex carbohydrates. How does the body use them?*
8. *How does the body use glucose and other monosaccharides?*
9. *What is the recommended daily consumption of carbohydrates?*

Lipids

Sources in the Diet

About 95% of the lipids in the human diet are **triglycerides** (try-GLIS-eh-ridez), Triglycerides, which are sometimes called *triacylglycerols* (try-AS-il-GLIS-er-olz), consist of three fatty acids attached to a glycerol molecule (see chapter 2). Triglycerides are often referred to as fats, which are solid at room temperature, or oils, which are liquid at room temperature. Fats and oils can be categorized as saturated or unsaturated depending on the types of bonds in the fatty acid. **Saturated fats and oils** have only single covalent bonds between the carbon atoms of their fatty acids (see figure 2.19). These types of fatty acids are found in the fats of meat (e.g., beef, pork), dairy products (e.g., whole milk, cheese, butter), eggs, coconut oil, and palm oil. **Unsaturated fats and oils** have one or more double covalent bonds between the carbon atoms of their fatty acids (see figure 2.19). **Monounsaturated fats** have one double bond, and **polyunsaturated fats** have two or more double bonds. Monounsaturated fats include olive and peanut oils; polyunsaturated fats are in fish, safflower, sunflower, and corn oils.

Unsaturated fatty acids can also be classified according to the location of the first double bond in the carbon chain. The "starting" point for determining the location of the double bonds is the omega (methyl) end of the fatty acid. The first double bond of an omega-3 fatty acid starts three carbon atoms after the omega end; an omega-6 fatty acid starts after six carbons; and an omega-9 fatty acid starts after nine carbons (see figure 2.19).

The remaining 5% of lipids include cholesterol and phospholipids, such as **lecithin** (LES-ih-thin). Cholesterol is a steroid (see chapter 2) found in high concentrations in liver and egg yolks, but it is also present in whole milk, cheese, butter, and meats. Cholesterol is not in plants. Phospholipids, major components of plasma membranes, are found in a variety of foods, including egg yolks.

Uses of Lipids in the Body

Triglycerides are important sources of energy that can be used to produce ATP. A gram of triglyceride delivers more than twice as many kilocalories as a gram of carbohydrate. Some cells, such as skeletal muscle cells, derive most of their energy from triglycerides.

After a meal, excess triglycerides that are not immediately used are stored in adipose tissue or the liver. Later, when energy is required, the triglycerides are broken down, and their fatty acids are released into the blood to be taken up and used by various tissues. In addition to storing energy, adipose tissue surrounds and pads organs. Adipose tissue located under the skin is an insulator, which prevents heat loss.

Cholesterol is an important molecule that has many functions in the body. It can be either obtained in food or manufactured by the liver and most other tissues. Cholesterol is a component of the plasma membrane, and it can be modified to form other useful molecules, such as bile salts and steroid hormones. Bile salts are necessary for lipid digestion and absorption. Steroid hormones include the reproductive hormones estrogen, progesterone, and testosterone.

The eicosanoids (EYE-koh-sah-noyds), which include prostaglandins and leukotrienes, are derived from fatty acids. The molecules are involved in activities such as inflammation, blood clotting, tissue repair, and smooth muscle contraction. Phospholipids, such as lecithin, are part of the plasma membrane and are used to construct the myelin sheath around the axons of neurons. Lecithin is also found in bile and helps emulsify lipids.

Clinical IMPACT 25.1

What Are "*Trans*" Fats?

Solid fats, mainly shortening and margarine, work better than liquid oils for preparing some foods, such as pastries. Polyunsaturated vegetable oils can be changed from a liquid to a solid by making them more saturated—that is, by decreasing the number of double covalent bonds in their polyunsaturated fatty acids. To saturate an unsaturated oil, the oil can be *hydrogenated,* which means that hydrogen gas is bubbled through the oil to produce a change in molecular shape that solidifies the oil. The more saturated the product, the harder it becomes at room temperature. These processed fats are usually referred to as ***trans*** **fats.**

Unprocessed polyunsaturated fats are found mostly in the ***cis*** **form,** which means the hydrogen atoms are on the same side of the carbon-carbon double bond in their fatty acids (see figure 2.19). During hydrogenation, some of the hydrogen atoms are transferred to the opposite side of the double bond to make the ***trans*** **form,** characterized by one hydrogen atom on one side of the double bond and another on the opposite side. Processed foods and oils account for most of the *trans* fats in the American diet, although some *trans* fats occur naturally in food from animal sources. *Trans* fatty acids raise the concentration of low-density lipoproteins and lower the concentration of high-density lipoproteins in the blood (see chapter 24). These changes are associated with a greater risk for cardiovascular disease. The Food and Drug Administration (FDA) requires that food labels include a detailed list of the amounts of saturated and *trans* fats, allowing the consumer to make better dietary choices.

Recommended Consumption of Lipids

The AMDR for lipids is 20–35% for adults, 25–35% for children and adolescents 4 to 18 years of age, and 30–35% for children 2 to 3 years of age. Saturated fats should amount to no more than 10% of total kilocalories or be as low as possible. Most dietary fat should come from sources of polyunsaturated and monounsaturated fats. Nutritionists recommend that people limit their cholesterol intake to 300 mg (the amount in one egg yolk) or less per day and keep their *trans* fat consumption as low as possible. These guidelines reflect the belief that excess fats, especially saturated fats, *trans* fats, and cholesterol, contribute to cardiovascular disease. The typical American diet derives 35–45% of its kilocalories from lipids, indicating that most Americans need to reduce their dietary fat consumption.

Most of the lecithin consumed in the diet is broken down in the digestive tract. The liver can manufacture all the lecithin necessary to meet the body's needs, so taking lecithin supplements is not necessary.

The **essential fatty acids** in the human diet include **alpha-linolenic** (lin-oh-LEN-ik) **acid,** an omega-3 fatty acid, and **linoleic** (lin-oh-LEE-ik) **acid,** an omega-6 fatty acid. These fatty acids must be ingested because humans lack the enzymes necessary to synthesize them. Seeds, nuts, and legumes are good sources of alpha-linolenic and linoleic acids. Alpha-linolenic acid is in the green leaves of plants, and linoleic acid is in grains. Other fatty acids, such as omega-9 fatty acids, can be synthesized from essential fatty acids.

Essential fatty acids are used to synthesize prostaglandins that affect blood clotting. Linoleic acid can be converted to **arachidonic** (ah-rak-ih-DON-ik) **acid,** an omega-6 fatty acid used to produce thromboxanes, which increase blood clotting. Alpha-linolenic acid can be converted to **eicosapentaenoic** (EYE-koh-sah-pen-tah-NOH-ik) **acid (EPA)** and **docosahexaenoic** (DOH-koh-sah-heks-ah-NOH-ik) **acid (DHA),** omega-3 fatty acids that can be used to synthesize prostaglandins, which decrease blood clotting. People who eat foods rich in EPA and DHA, such as herring, salmon, tuna, and sardines, increase the synthesis of prostaglandins from EPA and DHA. Those who eat these fish two or more times per week have a lower risk for heart attack than those who do not, possibly because of reduced blood clotting. EPA and DHA are also known to reduce blood triglyceride levels. People who do not like to eat fish can take fish oil supplements as a source of EPA and DHA. People who have bleeding disorders, take anticoagulants, or anticipate surgery should follow their physicians' advice regarding the use of these supplements because they can increase the risk for bleeding and hemorrhagic stroke.

ASSESS YOUR PROGRESS

10. *What is the major source of lipids in the diet? What are some other sources?*
11. *Distinguish between saturated and unsaturated fats. What are trans fats?*
12. *How does the body use triglycerides, cholesterol, prostaglandins, and lecithin?*
13. *Describe the recommended dietary intake of lipids. List the essential fatty acids, and state food sources that contain them.*

Proteins

Sources in the Diet

Proteins are chains of amino acids (see chapter 2). Proteins in the body are constructed of 20 kinds of amino acids, which are divided into two groups: essential and nonessential. The body cannot synthesize **essential amino acids,** also called *indispensable amino acids,* so they must be obtained in the diet. The nine essential amino acids are histidine, isoleucine, leucine, lysine, methionine, phenylalanine, threonine, tryptophan, and valine. Other amino acids are referred to as conditionally essential or nonessential. **Conditionally essential amino acids** can be synthesized by the body under normal conditions, but not in situations such as premature birth or certain metabolic diseases. Conditionally essential amino acids include arginine, cysteine, glutamine, glycine, proline, and tyrosine. **Nonessential amino acids,** also called *dispensable amino acids,* which are necessary to construct our proteins, do not necessarily need to be ingested because they can be synthesized from essential amino acids. The nonessential amino acids include alanine, aspartic acid, asparagine, glutamic acid, and serine.

A **complete protein** is a food that contains adequate amounts of all nine essential amino acids, whereas an **incomplete protein** does not. Examples of complete protein foods are meat, fish, poultry, milk, cheese, eggs, soy, and the grain quinoa; incomplete proteins include leafy green vegetables, grains, and legumes (peas and beans). If two incomplete proteins, such as rice and beans, are ingested together, the amino acid composition of each complements the other, and a complete protein is created. Thus, a vegetarian diet, if balanced correctly, provides all the essential amino acids.

Uses of Proteins in the Body

The body uses amino acids to synthesize proteins. Proteins perform numerous functions in the body. For example, collagen provides structural strength in connective tissue, as does keratin in the skin. The interactions of actin and myosin make muscle contraction possible. Enzymes regulate the rate of chemical reactions, and protein hormones regulate many physiological processes (see chapter 18). Proteins in the blood prevent changes in pH (buffers), promote blood clotting (coagulation factors), and transport O_2 and CO_2 (hemoglobin). Transport proteins (see chapter 3) move materials across plasma membranes, and other proteins in the plasma membrane function as receptor molecules. Antibodies, lymphokines, and complement are part of the immune system response that protects against microorganisms and other foreign substances.

The body also uses proteins for energy. As an energy source, proteins yield the same amount of kilocalories as carbohydrates. If excess proteins are ingested, the energy in the proteins can be stored by converting their amino acids into glycogen or lipids.

Recommended Consumption of Proteins

The AMDR for protein is 10–35% of total kilocalories. When protein intake is adequate, the synthesis and breakdown of proteins in a healthy adult occur at the same rate.

The amino acids of proteins contain nitrogen, so saying that a person is in **nitrogen balance** means that the nitrogen content of ingested protein is equal to the nitrogen excreted in urine and feces. A starving person is in negative nitrogen balance because the nitrogen gained in the diet is less than that lost by excretion. In other words, when proteins are broken down for energy, more nitrogen is lost than is replaced in the diet. On the other hand, a growing child or a healthy pregnant woman is in positive nitrogen balance because more nitrogen is going into the body to produce new tissues than is lost by excretion.

ASSESS YOUR PROGRESS

14. *Distinguish between essential, conditionally essential, and nonessential amino acids. Explain the difference between complete and incomplete protein foods.*
15. *Describe the functions of proteins in the body.*
16. *What is the AMDR of proteins? What is nitrogen balance? What would place a person in negative nitrogen balance?*

Vitamins

Vitamins (VITE-ah-minz; life-giving chemicals) are organic molecules that exist in very small quantities in food. These molecules are essential to normal metabolism (table 25.2). **Essential**

vitamins cannot be produced by the body and must be obtained through the diet. Because no single food or nutrient provides all the essential vitamins, people should maintain a balanced diet by eating a variety of foods. The absence of an essential vitamin in the diet can result in a deficiency disease.

A few vitamins, such as vitamin K, are produced by intestinal bacteria, and a few others can be formed by the body from substances called provitamins. A **provitamin** is a part of a vitamin that the body can convert into a functional vitamin. For example, beta carotene is a provitamin that the body can form into vitamin A. The other provitamins are **7-dehydrocholesterol** (dee-HIGH-dro-koh-LES-ter-ol), which can be converted to vitamin D, and **tryptophan** (TRIP-toh-fan), which can be converted to niacin.

Rather than breaking down vitamins by catabolism, the body uses them in their original or slightly modified forms. If the chemical structure of a vitamin is destroyed, its function is usually lost. For example, the chemical structure of many vitamins is destroyed by heat, as when food is overcooked. This is another example of the key concept of the relationship between form and function.

Many vitamins function as **coenzymes,** which combine with enzymes to make the enzymes functional (see chapter 2). Without enzymes and their coenzymes, many chemical reactions would occur too slowly to support good health and life. For example, vitamins B_2 and B_3, and biotin (BY-oh-tin) and pantothenic (pan-toh-THEN-ik) acid are critical for some of the chemical reactions involved in producing ATP. Folate (FOH-late) and vitamin B_{12} are required for nucleic acid synthesis. Vitamins A, B_1, B_6, B_{12}, C, and D are necessary for growth. Vitamin K is necessary for the synthesis of proteins involved in blood clotting (table 25.2).

Vitamins are classified as either fat-soluble or water-soluble. **Fat-soluble vitamins,** which include vitamins A, D, E, and K, dissolve in lipids and are absorbed from the intestine along with lipids. Some of them can be stored in the body for a long time. Because they can be stored, these vitamins can accumulate in the body to the point of toxicity. **Water-soluble vitamins,** which include the B vitamins and vitamin C, dissolve in water. They are absorbed from the water in the intestinal tract and typically remain in the body only a short time before being excreted in the urine.

Vitamins were discovered at the beginning of the twentieth century. They were found to be associated with certain foods known to protect people from diseases such as rickets and beriberi. In 1941, the first Food and Nutrition Board established the **Recommended Dietary Allowances (RDAs),** which are the nutrient intakes sufficient to meet the needs of nearly all people in certain age and gender groups. RDAs were established for different-aged males and females, starting with infants and continuing on to adults. RDAs were also set for pregnant and lactating women. The RDAs have been reevaluated every 4–5 years and updated when necessary on the basis of new information.

The RDAs establish a minimum intake of vitamins and minerals that should protect almost everyone (97%) in a given group from diseases caused by vitamin or mineral deficiencies. Although personal requirements can vary, the RDAs are a good benchmark. The farther below the RDAs an individual's dietary intake is, the more likely that person is to develop a nutritional deficiency. On the other hand, consuming too much of some vitamins and minerals can be harmful. For example, the long-term ingestion of 3–10 times the RDA for vitamin A can cause bone and muscle pain, skin disorders, hair loss, and an enlarged liver. Consuming 5–10 times the RDA of vitamin D over the long term can result in calcium deposits in the kidneys, heart, and blood vessels, and consuming more than 2 g of vitamin C daily can cause stomach inflammation and diarrhea.

Clinical IMPACT 25.2

Free Radicals and Antioxidants

Free radicals are molecules, produced as part of normal metabolism, that are missing an electron. The loss of an electron from a molecule is called oxidation. Free radicals can replace the missing electron by taking an electron from cell molecules, such as lipids, proteins, or DNA, resulting in damage to the cell. Damage from free radicals may contribute to aging and certain diseases, such as atherosclerosis and cancer. However, substances called **antioxidants** may counteract these effects by donating an electron to free radicals and thus preventing the oxidation of cell components. Examples of antioxidants are beta carotene (provitamin A), vitamin C, and vitamin E.

Many studies have attempted to determine whether taking large doses of antioxidants is beneficial. The best evidence presently available does not support the claim that large doses of antioxidants can prevent chronic disease or otherwise improve health. On the other hand, the amount of antioxidants normally found in a balanced diet (including fruits and vegetables rich in antioxidants), combined with the complex mix of other chemicals found in food, can be beneficial.

Predict 1

What would happen if vitamins were broken down during digestion rather than being absorbed intact into the circulation?

ASSESS YOUR PROGRESS

17. *What are vitamins, essential vitamins, and provitamins?*

18. *Name the fat-soluble vitamins and the water-soluble vitamins.*

19. *List some of the functions of vitamins in the body.*

20. *What are Recommended Dietary Allowances (RDAs)? Why are they useful?*

21. *What are some symptoms of specific vitamin deficiencies?*

Minerals

Minerals (MIN-er-aulz) are inorganic nutrients that are necessary for normal metabolic functions. The minerals are divided into two groups, major minerals and trace minerals, based on the amount required in the diet for good health. The daily requirement for

TABLE **25.2** **Principal Vitamins**

Vitamin	Fat-Soluble (F) or Water-Soluble (W)	Source	Function	Symptoms of Deficiency	Reference Daily Intake (RDI)*
A (retinol)	F	From provitamin beta carotene found in yellow and green vegetables: preformed in liver, egg yolk, butter, and milk	Necessary for rhodopsin synthesis, normal health of epithelial cells, and bone and tooth growth	Rhodopsin deficiency, night blindness, delayed growth, skin disorders, and increased infection risk	5000 IU
B_1 (thiamine)	W	Yeast, grains, and milk	Involved in carbohydrate and amino acid metabolism, necessary for growth	Beriberi—muscle weakness (including cardiac muscle), neuritis, and paralysis	1.5 mg
B_2 (riboflavin)	W	Green vegetables, liver, wheat germ, milk, and eggs	Component of flavin adenine dinucleotide, involved in citric acid cycle	Eye disorders and skin cracking, especially at corners of the mouth	1.7 mg
B_3 (niacin)	W	Fish, liver, red meat, yeast, grains, peas, beans, and nuts	Component of nicotinamide adenine dinucleotide, involved in glycolysis and citric acid cycle	Pellagra—diarrhea, dermatitis, and nervous system disorders	20 mg
Pantothenic acid	W	Liver, yeast, green vegetables, grains, and intestinal bacteria	Constituent of coenzyme-A, glucose production from lipids and amino acids, and steroid hormone synthesis	Neuromuscular dysfunction and fatigue	10 mg
Biotin	W	Liver, yeast, eggs, and intestinal bacteria	Fatty acid and nucleic acid synthesis, movement of pyruvic acid into citric acid cycle	Mental and muscle dysfunction, fatigue, and nausea	30 µg
B_6 (pyridoxine)	W	Fish, liver, yeast, tomatoes, and intestinal bacteria	Involved in amino acid metabolism	Dermatitis, delayed growth, and nausea	2.0 mg
Folate	W	Liver, leafy green vegetables, and intestinal bacteria	Nucleic acid synthesis, hemopoiesis, and prevention of birth defects	Macrocytic anemia (enlarged red blood cells) and neural tube defects	0.4 mg
B_{12} (cobalamins)	W	Liver, red meat, milk, and eggs	Necessary for red blood cell production, some nucleic acid and amino acid metabolism	Pernicious anemia and nervous system disorders	6.0 µg
C (ascorbic acid)	W	Citrus fruit, tomatoes, and green vegetables	Collagen synthesis, general protein metabolism	Scurvy—defective bone formation and poor wound healing	60 mg
D (cholecalciferol, ergosterol)	F	Fish liver oil, enriched milk, and eggs; provitamin D converted by sunlight to cholecalciferol in the skin	Promotes calcium and phosphorus use, normal growth and bone and tooth formation	Rickets—poorly developed, weak bones; osteomalacia; and bone reabsorption	400 IU
E (tocopherol, tocotrienols)	F	Wheat germ; cottonseed, palm, and rice oils; grain; liver; and lettuce	Prevents oxidation of plasma membranes and DNA	Hemolysis of red blood cells	30 IU
K (phylloquinone)	F	Alfalfa, liver, spinach, vegetable oils, cabbage, and intestinal bacteria	Required for synthesis of a number of clotting factors	Excessive bleeding due to slow blood clotting	80 µg

*Reference Daily Intakes for people over 4 years of age; IU = international units.

TABLE 25.3 Important Minerals

Mineral	Function	Symptoms of Deficiency	Reference Daily Intake (RDI)*
Calcium	Bone and teeth formation, blood clotting, muscle activity, nerve function	Spontaneous action potential generation in neurons, tetany	1000 mg
Chlorine	Blood acid-base balance; hydrochloric acid production in stomach	Acid-base imbalance	2.3 g†
Chromium	Associated with enzymes in glucose metabolism	Unknown	35 μg
Cobalt	Component of vitamin B_{12}, red blood cell production	Anemia	Unknown
Copper	Hemoglobin and melanin production, electron-transport system	Anemia and loss of energy	0.9 mg
Fluorine	Provides extra strength in teeth, prevents dental caries	No real pathology	4 mg
Iodine	Thyroid hormone production; maintenance of normal metabolic rate	Goiter and decrease in normal metabolism	150 μg
Iron	Component of hemoglobin; ATP production in electron-transport system	Anemia, decreased O_2 transport, energy loss	18 mg
Magnesium	Coenzyme constituent, bone formation, muscle and nerve function	Increased nervous system irritability, vasodilation, arrhythmias	420 mg
Manganese	Hemoglobin synthesis, growth, activation of several enzymes	Tremors, convulsions	2.3 mg
Molybdenum	Enzyme component	Unknown	45 μg
Phosphorus	Bone and teeth formation; energy transfer (ATP); component of nucleic acids	Loss of energy and cellular function	1250 mg
Potassium	Muscle and nerve function	Muscle weakness, abnormal electrocardiogram, alkaline urine	3.5 g
Selenium	Component of many enzymes	Unknown	55 μg
Sodium	Osmotic pressure regulation; nerve and muscle function	Nausea, vomiting, exhaustion, dizziness	1.5 g†
Sulfur	Component of hormones, several vitamins, proteins	Unknown	Unknown
Zinc	Component of several enzymes; CO_2 transport and metabolism; protein metabolism	Deficient CO_2 transport, deficient protein metabolism	11 mg

*Reference Daily Intakes for people over 4 years of age, except for sodium.

†3.8 g sodium chloride (table salt).

major minerals is 100 mg or more daily. The daily requirement for **trace minerals** is less than 100 mg daily. The trace minerals are needed in such low amounts that the required amount for some is unknown. Minerals constitute about 4–5% of total body weight, much of which is Ca^{2+} stored in the bones. Some minerals are components of other important molecules in the body, such as coenzymes, a few vitamins, and hemoglobin. Minerals are involved in a number of important functions, including establishing resting membrane potentials and generating action potentials, adding mechanical strength to bones and teeth, combining with organic molecules, and acting as coenzymes, buffers, and regulators of osmotic pressure. Table 25.3 lists important minerals and their functions.

People ingest minerals alone or in combination with organic molecules, as well as obtain them from both animal and plant sources. However, mineral absorption from plants can be limited because the minerals tend to bind to plant fibers. Refined breads and cereals contain hardly any minerals or vitamins because the seeds used to make them are crushed, and the outer parts of the seeds housing most of the minerals and vitamins are discarded. Minerals and vitamins are often added to refined breads and cereals to compensate for their loss during the refinement process.

A balanced diet can provide all the vitamins and minerals required for good health for most people. Some nutritionists, however, recommend taking a once-a-day multiple vitamin and mineral supplement as insurance because many people's diets are not balanced.

ASSESS YOUR PROGRESS

22. *What are minerals? What is the daily requirement for major minerals?*
23. *List several minerals the body needs and a function of each.*

Daily Values for Nutrients

Daily Values are dietary values that appear on food labels to help consumers plan a healthful diet. Daily Values are based on two other sets of reference values: Reference Daily Intakes and Daily Reference Values.

- **Reference Daily Intakes (RDIs)** are based on the 1968 RDAs for certain vitamins and minerals. RDIs have been set for four categories of people: infants, toddlers, people over 4 years of age, and pregnant or lactating women. Generally, the RDIs are set to the highest 1968 RDA value of an age category. For example, the highest RDA for iron in males over 4 years of age is 10 mg/day and for females over 4 years of age, 18 mg/day. Thus, the RDI for iron is set at 18 mg/day.
- **Daily Reference Values (DRVs)** are set for total fat, saturated fat, cholesterol, total carbohydrate, dietary fiber, sodium, potassium, and protein.

Having two standards on food labels, RDIs for vitamins and minerals and DRVs for other nutrients, was thought to be more confusing for consumers than having one standard. Therefore, the RDIs and DRVs were combined to form the Daily Values.

The Daily Values appearing on food labels are based on a 2000 kcal reference diet, which approximates the weight maintenance requirements of postmenopausal women, women who exercise moderately, teenage girls, and sedentary men (figure 25.2). On large food labels, additional information is listed based on a daily intake of 2500 kcal, which is adequate for young men. However, government standards do not require that all possible Daily Values be listed on food labels.

The Daily Values for energy-producing nutrients are determined as a percentage of daily kilocalorie intake: 60% for carbohydrates, 30% for total fats, 10% for saturated fats, and 10% for proteins. The Daily Value for fiber is 14 g for each 1000 kcal of intake. The Daily Values for a nutrient in a 2000 kcal/day diet can be calculated on the basis of the recommended daily percentage of the nutrient and the kilocalories in a gram of the nutrient. For example, carbohydrates should compose 60% of a 2000 kcal/day diet, or 1200 kcal/day (0.60 × 2000). Because there are 4 kcal in a gram of carbohydrate, the Daily Value for carbohydrate is 300 g/day (1200/4).

Nutrition Facts

4 servings per container

Serving size	**1 cup (227g)**
Amount per serving	
Calories	**280**
	% Daily Value*
Total Fat 9g	**12%**
Saturated Fat 4.5g	**23%**
Trans Fat 0g	
Cholesterol 35mg	**12%**
Sodium 850mg	**37%**
Total Carbohydrate 34g	**12%**
Dietary Fiber 4g	**14%**
Total Sugars 6g	
Includes 0g Added Sugars	**0%**
Protein 15g	
Vitamin D 0mcg	0%
Calcium 320mg	25%
Iron 1.6mg	8%
Potassium 510mg	10%

* The % Daily Value (DV) tells you how much a nutrient in a serving of food contributes to a daily diet. 2,000 calories a day is used for general nutrition advice.

FIGURE 25.2 Food Label

The food label highlights calorie counts prominently and includes the amount and % Daily Value of different nutrients, vitamins, and minerals, allowing the consumer to make an informed dietary choice. *Source:* U.S. Food and Drug Administration

The Daily Values for some nutrients are limited due to their link to certain diseases. Thus, the Daily Values for total fats are less than 65 g; for saturated fats, less than 20 g; and for cholesterol, less than 300 mg because these nutrients are associated with increased risk for heart disease. The Daily Value for sodium is less than 2400 mg because of its association with high blood pressure in some people.

For a particular food, the Daily Value is used to calculate the **Percent Daily Value (% Daily Value)** for some of the nutrients in one serving of the food (figure 25.2). For example, if a serving of food has 3 g of fat and the Daily Value for total fat is 65 g, the % Daily Value is 5% (3/65 = 0.05, or 5%). The Food and Drug Administration (FDA) requires % Daily Values to be on food labels so that the public has useful and accurate dietary information.

The FDA provides specific requirements for food nutrition labels. The current nutrition label (figure 25.2) has calorie counts displayed prominently, representing reasonable serving sizes. Manufacturers are required to list the actual amounts of vitamin D, calcium, iron, and potassium; however, listing the amounts of other vitamins is optional. Manufacturers are also required to list the amounts of added sugar, to assist consumers in making better choices about total sugar intake, which has been linked to the current increase in obesity in the United States. Saturated fat and *trans* fat information must also be included. This reflects the current view of nutritionists that the types of fats we ingest are more important than the amount.

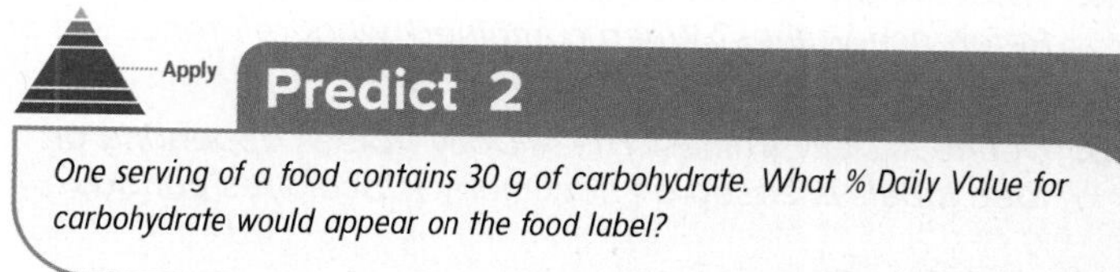

The % Daily Values for nutrients related to energy consumption are based on a 2000 kcal/day diet. For people who maintain their weight on a 2000 kcal/day diet, the total of the % Daily Values for each of these nutrients should be no more than 100%. However, for individuals consuming more or fewer than 2000 kcal/day, the total % Daily Values can be more or fewer than 100%. For example, for a person consuming 2200 kcal/day, the total of the % Daily Values for each of these nutrients should be no more than 110% because 2200/2000 = 1.10, or 110%.

When using the % Daily Values of a food to determine how the amounts of its nutrients fit into the overall diet, the number of servings in a container or package needs to be considered. For example, suppose a small (2.25-ounce) bag of corn chips has a % Daily Value of 16% for total fat. A person might suppose that eating the bag of chips accounts for 16% of total fat for the day. The bag, however, contains 2.5 servings. Therefore, if all the chips in

PROCESS **Figure**

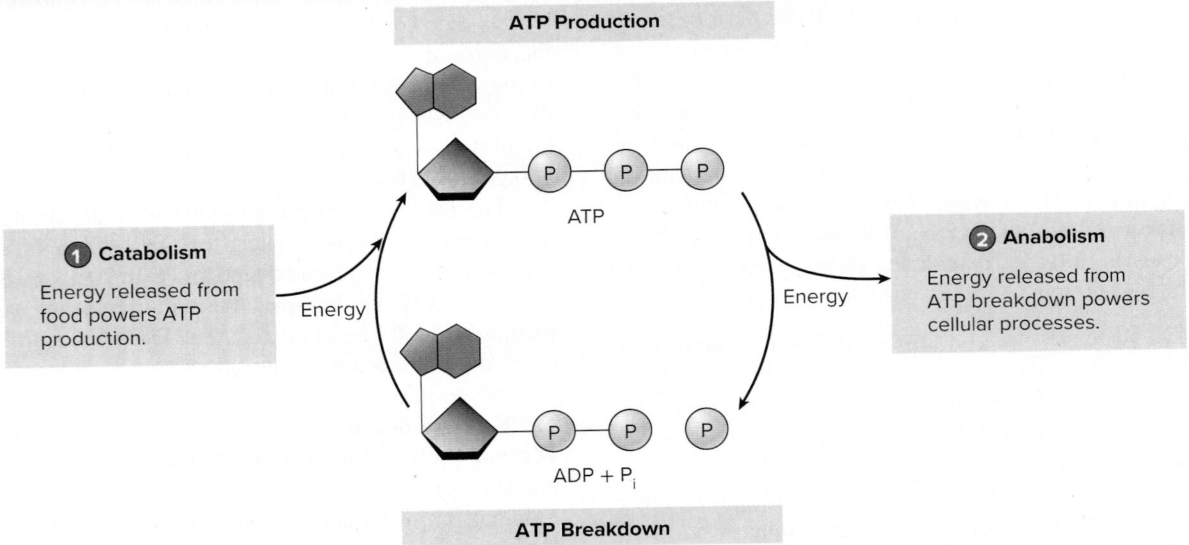

PROCESS **Figure 25.3**

ATP Derived from Catabolic Reactions Drives Anabolic Reactions

Energy released by catabolism is required to form ATP from ADP and phosphate (P_i). Energy and a phosphate are given off when ATP is converted back to ADP during anabolism.

Which organelles in a cell are more likely to be involved in anabolic reactions? (Hint: *A review of table 3.1 may be helpful in answering this question.)*

1. Catabolism of nutrients begins during digestion when large molecules, such as polysaccharides and fats, are broken down for absorption by the small intestine. The process of catabolism continues in the cells when the absorbed nutrients are further broken down for ATP production.
2. The energy derived from catabolism is used to drive anabolic reactions and processes such as active transport and muscle contraction. Anabolism occurs in all the body cells as they divide to form new cells, maintain their own intracellular structure, and produce molecules, such as hormones, neurotransmitters, and extracellular matrix molecules, for export.

the bag are consumed, they account for 40% (16% × 2.5) of the maximum recommended total fat.

ASSESS YOUR PROGRESS

24. *What are the Reference Daily Intakes and the Daily Reference Values? When combined, what reference set of values is established?*
25. *Define* % Daily Values. *The % Daily Values appearing on food labels is based on how many kilocalories per day?*

25.2 Metabolism

LEARNING OUTCOMES

After reading this section, you should be able to

A. **Define *metabolism, anabolism,* and *catabolism.***
B. **Relate hydrogen atoms to energy.**

Metabolism (meh-TAB-oh-lizm; change) is the total of all the chemical reactions that occur in the body. It consists of catabolism and anabolism. **Catabolism** (kah-TAB-oh-lizm) includes the energy-releasing process by which large molecules are broken down into smaller molecules. **Anabolism** (ah-NAB-oh-lizm) includes the energy-requiring process by which small molecules are joined to form larger molecules.

Figure 25.3 illustrates the integration of catabolism and anabolism.

Large nutrient molecules, such as carbohydrates, lipids, and proteins, are broken down by digestion into smaller molecules, such as glucose, amino acids, and fatty acids, which are absorbed from the digestive tract into the blood (see chapter 24). These smaller molecules are taken into cells, where they are catabolized, and the energy from them is used to combine adenosine diphosphate (ADP) and an inorganic phosphate group (P_i) to form ATP:

$$ADP + P_i + Energy \rightarrow ATP$$

The energy in small nutrient molecules is used to produce many ATP molecules, each of which stores a small amount of energy. These smaller amounts of energy are more readily available for use in cells than is the larger amount of energy stored in nutrient molecules. Figure 25.4 provides an overview of the biochemical pathway for ATP production, focusing on each of the major nutrients. Each pathway will be discussed in further detail later in this chapter.

PROCESS **Figure**

PROCESS **Figure 25.4**

Overview of Biochemical Pathways of ATP Production

Carbohydrates, lipids, and proteins enter biochemical pathways to produce energy in the cell. Anna Kucher/Shutterstock

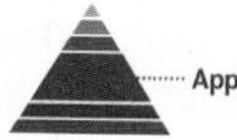

If a toxin blocked the process of glycolysis, which nutrients, and specifically which components, might still be metabolized for ATP production?

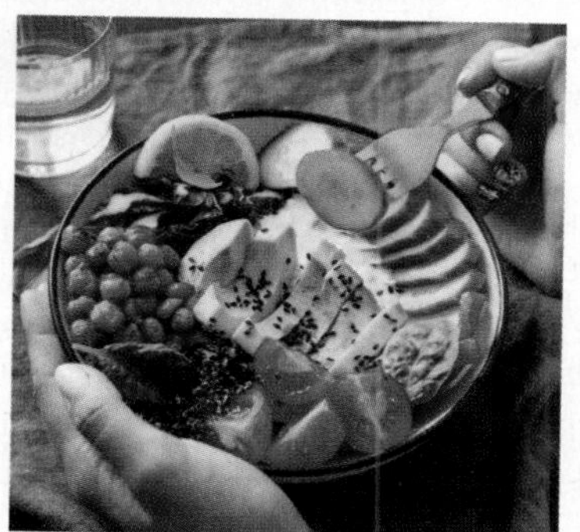

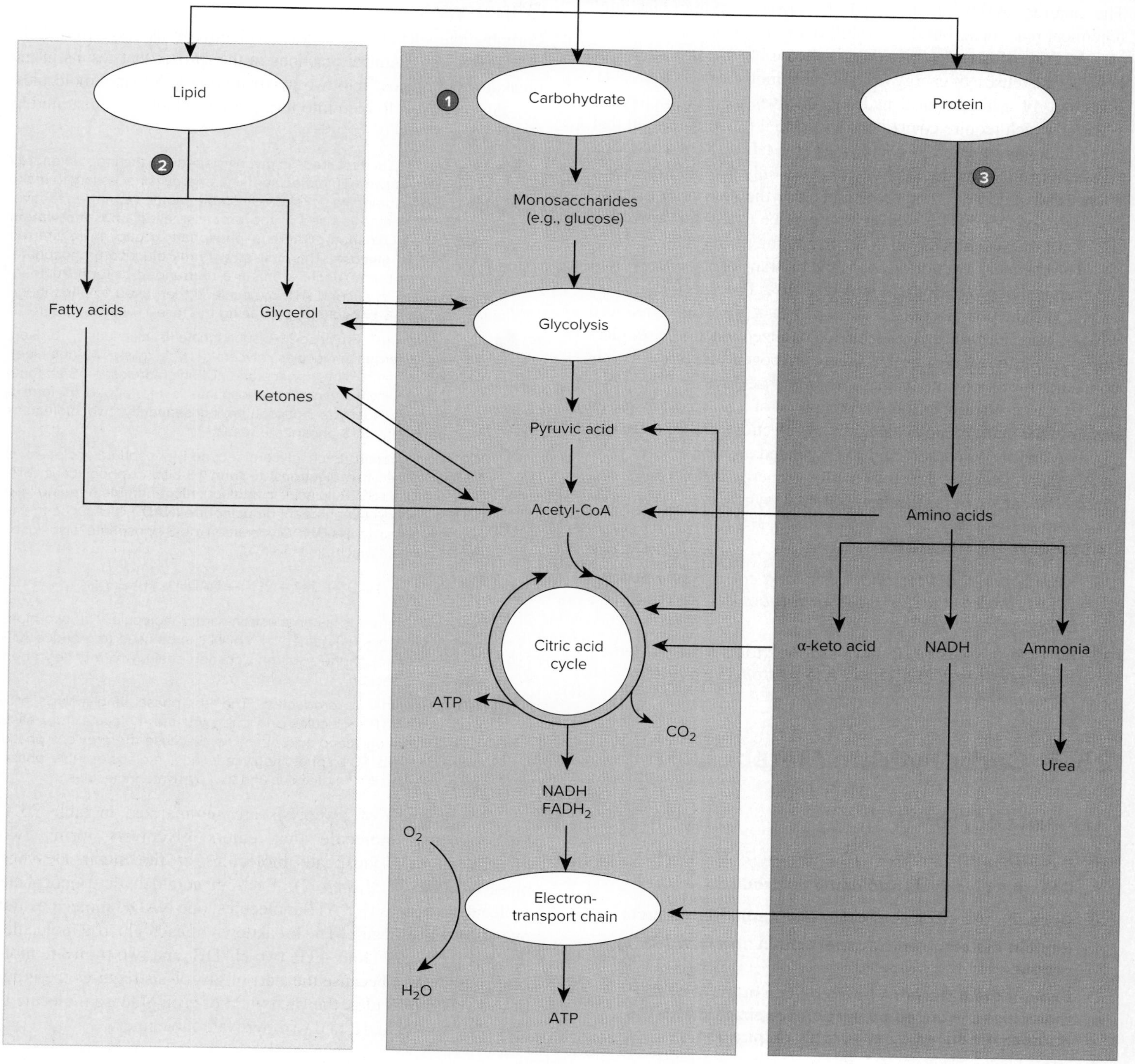

Lipid

2

Fatty acids

Glycerol

Ketones

1

Carbohydrate

Monosaccharides
(e.g., glucose)

Glycolysis

Pyruvic acid

Acetyl-CoA

Citric acid
cycle

ATP

CO_2

NADH
$FADH_2$

O_2

Electron-
transport chain

H_2O

ATP

Protein

3

Amino acids

α-keto acid

NADH

Ammonia

Urea

1. Carbohydrates are digested to monosaccharides, such as glucose. Cells can further break down the monosaccharides to produce ATP.
2. Lipids, such as triglycerides, are broken down into fatty acids and glycerol, which then can enter a pathway similar to the pathway by which carbohydrates generate ATP.
3. Proteins are digested into amino acids. Amino acids either enter the pathway that resembles carbohydrate breakdown or are broken down further. The breakdown products can then be used to generate ATP.

ATP is often called the energy currency of the cell because, when it is spent, or broken down to ADP, energy becomes available for use by the cell. As a comparison, if a quarter represents an ATP molecule, then a $20 bill is analogous to a small nutrient molecule. The quarter (ATP) can be used in various vending machines (chemical reactions), but the $20 bill (nutrient molecule) cannot.

A series of chemical reactions, called a biochemical pathway, controls the release of energy from nutrient molecules (figure 25.4). Each step of a biochemical pathway involves a specific enzyme, some of which require coenzymes for normal function. Recall that some vitamins function as coenzymes (see table 25.2). Therefore, proper nutrition provides the body with not only the fuel to produce energy and build new components, but also the molecular machinery to do so. (*Note:* This information may be useful for answering the Learn to Predict question at the beginning of the chapter.)

The chemical reactions responsible for transferring energy from the chemical bonds of nutrient molecules to ATP molecules involve oxidation-reduction reactions (see chapter 2). A molecule is reduced when it gains electrons. A molecule is oxidized when it loses electrons. A nutrient molecule has many hydrogen atoms covalently bonded to the carbon atoms that form the "backbone" of the molecule. Because a hydrogen atom is composed of a H^+ (proton) and an electron, the nutrient molecule has many electrons and is, therefore, highly reduced. When a H^+ and an associated electron are lost from the nutrient molecule, the molecule loses energy and becomes oxidized. The energy in the electron is used to synthesize ATP.

ASSESS YOUR PROGRESS

26. *How are metabolism, anabolism, and catabolism related? How is the energy derived from catabolism used to drive anabolic reactions?*

27. *How does the removal of hydrogen atoms from nutrient molecules result in a loss of energy from the nutrient molecule?*

25.3 Carbohydrate Metabolism

LEARNING OUTCOMES

After reading this section, you should be able to

A. **Describe glycolysis and name its products.**
B. **Describe the citric acid cycle and name its products.**
C. **Explain the electron-transport chain and how ATP is produced in the process.**
D. **Explain the difference between the number of ATP molecules produced by aerobic respiration and the number produced by anaerobic respiration.**

Monosaccharides are the breakdown products of carbohydrate digestion. Glucose is the most important monosaccharide in terms of cellular metabolism for humans. Glucose is transported in the blood to all the tissues of the body, where it serves as a source of energy. Any excess glucose in the blood following a meal can be used to form glycogen, or glucose can be partially broken down and the components used to form lipids. Glycogen is a short-term energy-storage molecule that the body can store in limited amounts, whereas lipids are long-term energy-storage molecules that the body can store in large amounts. Most of the body's glycogen is in skeletal muscle and in the liver.

Glycolysis

Carbohydrate metabolism begins with **glycolysis** (glye-KOHL-ih-sis), a series of chemical reactions in the cytosol that results in the breakdown of glucose into two **pyruvate** (pie-ROO-vate) molecules.

Glycolysis is divided into four phases, which are illustrated in figure 25.5.

1. *Input of ATP.* The first steps in glycolysis require the input of energy in the form of two ATP molecules. The energy is necessary to make the glucose molecule, a relatively stable molecule, more reactive. An ATP molecule is used in the process called **phosphorylation** (FOS-fohr-ih-LAY-shun), where a phosphate group is transferred from ATP to glucose. This first step forms glucose-6-phosphate. The glucose-6-phosphate atoms are rearranged to form fructose-6-phosphate. A second ATP molecule is then used to phosphorylate fructose-6-phosphate, producing fructose-1,6-bisphosphate.
2. *Sugar cleavage.* Fructose-1,6-bisphosphate is cleaved, or broken, into two 3-carbon molecules, glyceraldehyde (glis-er-AL-deh-hide)-3-phosphate and dihydroxyacetone (DIE-high-drok-see-AS-eh-tone) phosphate. Dihydroxyacetone phosphate is rearranged to form a second glyceraldehyde-3-phosphate; consequently, two molecules of glyceraldehyde-3-phosphate result.
3. *NADH production.* Each glyceraldehyde-3-phosphate molecule is oxidized (loses two electrons) to form 1,3-bisphosphoglyceric (BIZ-phos-foh-GLIH-SEER-ik) acid. In addition, **nicotinamide adenine** (nik-oh-TIN-ah-mide AD-eh-neen) **dinucleotide (NAD^+)** is reduced (gains two electrons) to **NADH.** Glyceraldehyde-3-phosphate also loses two H^+, one of which binds to NAD^+:

$$NAD^+ + 2e^- + 2H^+ \rightarrow NADH + H^+$$

NADH is referred to as an electron-carrier molecule. The two high-energy electrons (e^-) gained by NADH can be used to produce ATP molecules through the electron-transport chain, which is described later in this section.

4. *ATP and pyruvate production.* The last phase of glycolysis produces two ATP molecules and one pyruvate molecule from each 1,3-bisphosphoglyceric acid molecule. Because the previous phase produced two 1,3-bisphosphoglyceric acid molecules, this phase produces four ATP molecules and two pyruvate molecules.

The products of glycolysis are summarized in table 25.4. Each glucose molecule that enters glycolysis forms two glyceraldehyde-3-phosphate molecules at the sugar cleavage phase (figure 25.5, *step* 2). Each glyceraldehyde-3-phosphate molecule produces two ATP molecules, one NADH molecule, and one pyruvate molecule. The breakdown of each glucose molecule, therefore, produces four ATP, two NADH, and two pyruvate molecules. However, because the start of glycolysis requires the input of two ATP molecules, the final yield of each glucose molecule is two ATP, two NADH, and two pyruvate molecules.

1 Input of ATP

Glucose

ATP → ADP

Glucose-6-phosphate

Fructose-6-phosphate

ATP → ADP

Fructose-1,6-bisphosphate

2 Sugar cleavage

CH_2-OH / C / CH_2-O-Ⓟ

Dihydroxyacetone phosphate

CH_2-O-Ⓟ / $CH-OH$ / $H-C=O$

Glyceraldehyde-3-phosphate (two molecules)

To step 3 (top of next column)

3 NADH production

2 NAD^+ → 2 NADH

CH_2-O-Ⓟ / $CH-OH$ / Ⓟ$-O-C=O$

1,3-bisphosphoglyceric acid (two molecules)

4 ATP and pyruvate production

2 ADP → 2 ATP

CH_2-O-Ⓟ / $CH-OH$ / COOH

3-phosphoglyceric acid (two molecules)

CH_2-OH / $CH-O-$Ⓟ / COOH

2-phosphoglyceric acid (two molecules)

→ H_2O

CH_2 / $C-O-$Ⓟ / COOH

Phosphoenolpyruvic acid (two molecules)

2 ADP → 2 ATP

CH_3 / $C=O$ / COO^-

Pyruvate (two molecules)

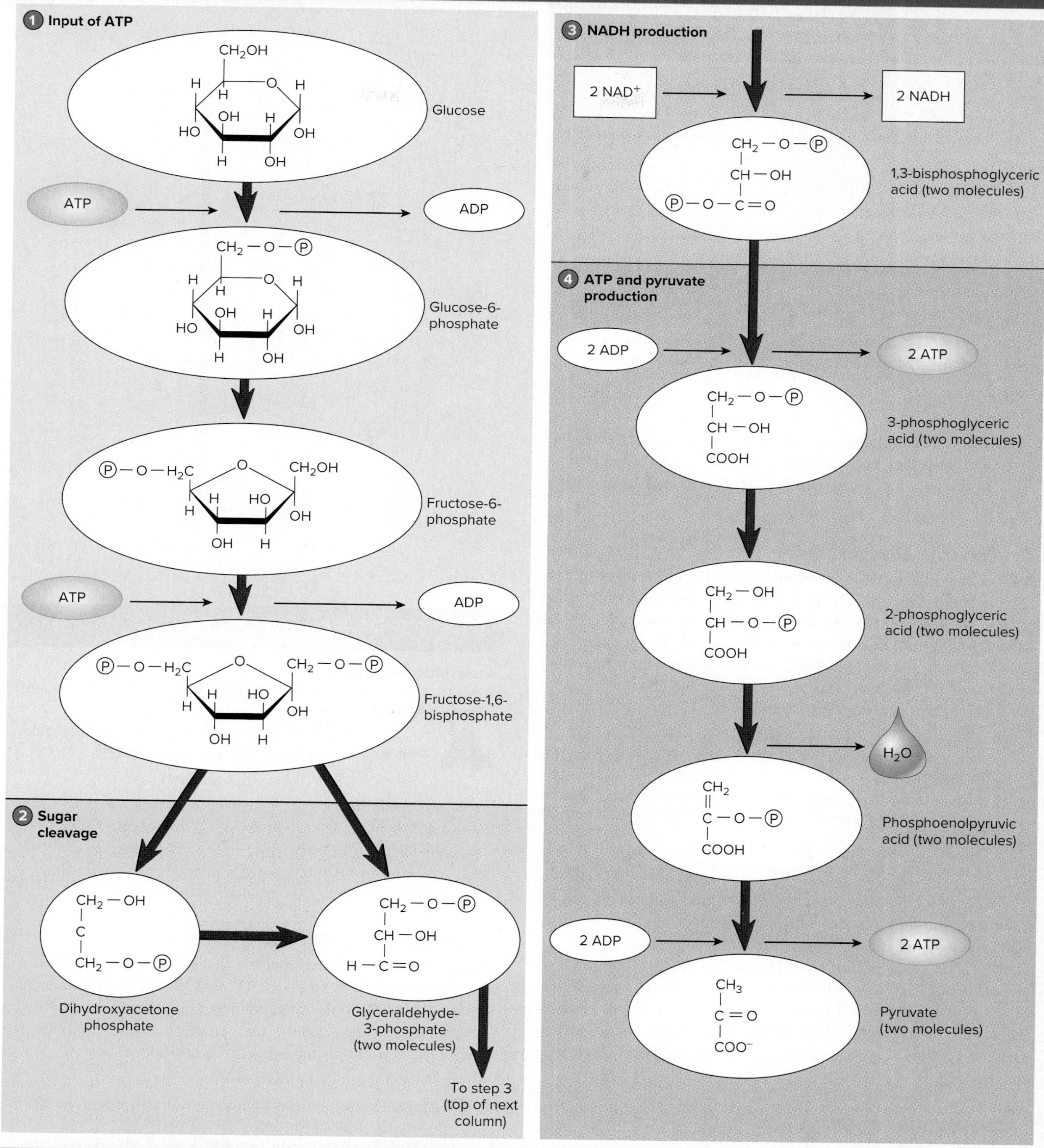

PROCESS **Figure 25.5**

Glycolysis

During glycolysis, glucose is broken down to pyruvate. This series of chemical reactions takes place in the cytosol.

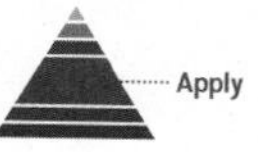

What is the net yield of ATP if 10 glucose molecules undergo glycolysis?

TABLE 25.4 **ATP Production from One Glucose Molecule**

Process	ATP Produced*	Other Products
Glycolysis	2 ATP (4 ATP produced minus 2 ATP used in the process)	2 NADH, 2 pyruvate
Acetyl-CoA production		2 NADH
Citric acid cycle	2 ATP	6 NADH, 2 $FADH_2$
Electron-transport chain	28 ATP	Water molecules
Total ATP	32 ATP	

*NADH and $FADH_2$ are used in the production of ATP in the electron-transport chain.
Abbreviations: ATP = adenosine triphosphate; NADH = reduced nicotinamide adenine dinucleotide; $FADH_2$ = reduced flavin adenine diphosphate; acetyl-CoA = acetyl coenzyme A.

If the cell has adequate amounts of O_2, the NADH and pyruvate molecules are used in aerobic respiration to produce ATP. In the absence of sufficient O_2, they are used in anaerobic respiration.

Anaerobic Respiration

Anaerobic (an-air-OH-bik) **respiration** is the breakdown of glucose in the absence of O_2. In human cells, the breakdown of a glucose molecule in the absence of O_2 produces two molecules of **lactate** and two molecules of ATP. The ATP thus produced is a source of energy during activities such as intense exercise, when insufficient O_2 is delivered to tissues. Anaerobic glycolysis can be divided into two phases, which are illustrated in figure 25.6.

1. *Glycolysis.* Glucose undergoes several reactions to produce two pyruvate molecules and two NADH. There is also a net gain of two ATP molecules.
2. *Lactate formation.* Pyruvate is first converted to **lactic acid,** a reaction that requires the input of energy from the NADH produced in step 3 of glycolysis. In cells, lactic acid usually releases a H^+ and is converted to lactate, the ionized form of lactic acid. Lactate is released from the cells that produce it, and blood transports it to the liver.

When O_2 becomes available, the lactate in the liver can be converted through a series of chemical reactions into glucose. The glucose then can be released from the liver and transported in the blood to cells that use glucose for energy. This process of converting lactate to glucose is called the **Cori cycle.** Some of the reactions involved in this process require energy derived from ATP that is produced by aerobic respiration. The O_2 necessary for synthesizing the ATP is part of the **oxygen deficit** (see chapter 9).

ASSESS YOUR PROGRESS

28. *Describe the four phases of glycolysis. What are the products of glycolysis?*
29. *What determines whether the pyruvate produced in glycolysis is used in aerobic respiration or anaerobic respiration?*

PROCESS **Figure**

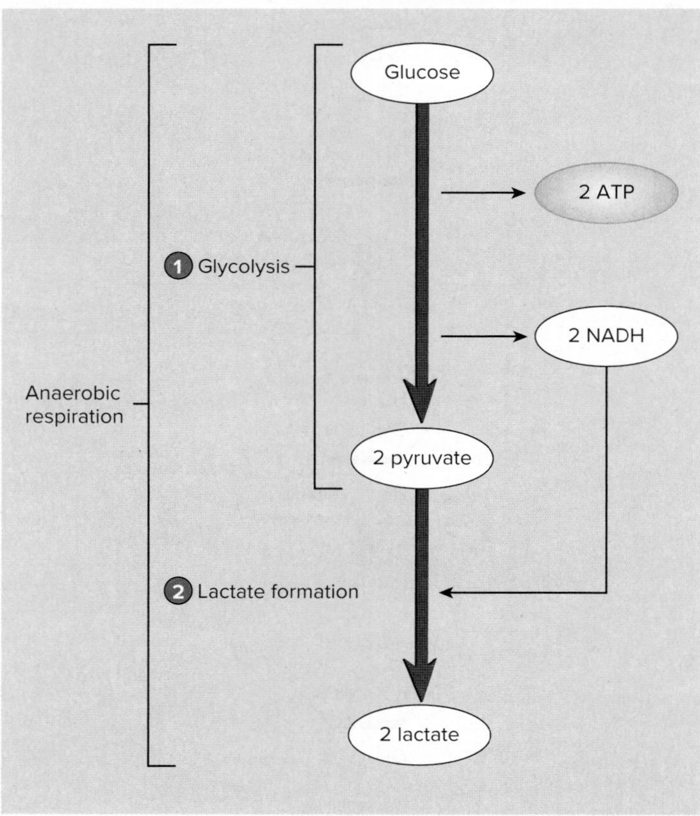

PROCESS **Figure 25.6**

Anaerobic Respiration

When O_2 is not readily available, the pyruvate produced from glycolysis is converted to lactate.

How many carbon atoms does a lactate molecule contain? Explain your answer.

30. *Describe the two phases of anaerobic respiration. How many ATP molecules result from anaerobic respiration?*
31. *What happens to the lactate produced in anaerobic respiration once O_2 becomes available?*

Aerobic Respiration

Aerobic (air-OH-bik) **respiration** is the breakdown of glucose in the presence of O_2 to produce CO_2, water, and 32 ATP molecules. Most of the ATP molecules required to sustain life are produced through aerobic respiration. This process is quite complex. For simplicity, aerobic respiration can be considered in four phases, which are summarized in figure 25.7.

1. *Glycolysis:* Glycolysis in the cytosol converts glucose to two pyruvate molecules and produces two ATP and two NADH. The two NADH can move to the inner mitochondrial membrane to participate in step 4.
2. *Acetyl-CoA formation:* The two pyruvate molecules produced in glycolysis are converted to two acetyl-CoA molecules, producing CO_2 and NADH. The NADH can move to the inner mitochondrial membrane to participate in step 4.

FUNDAMENTAL **Figure**

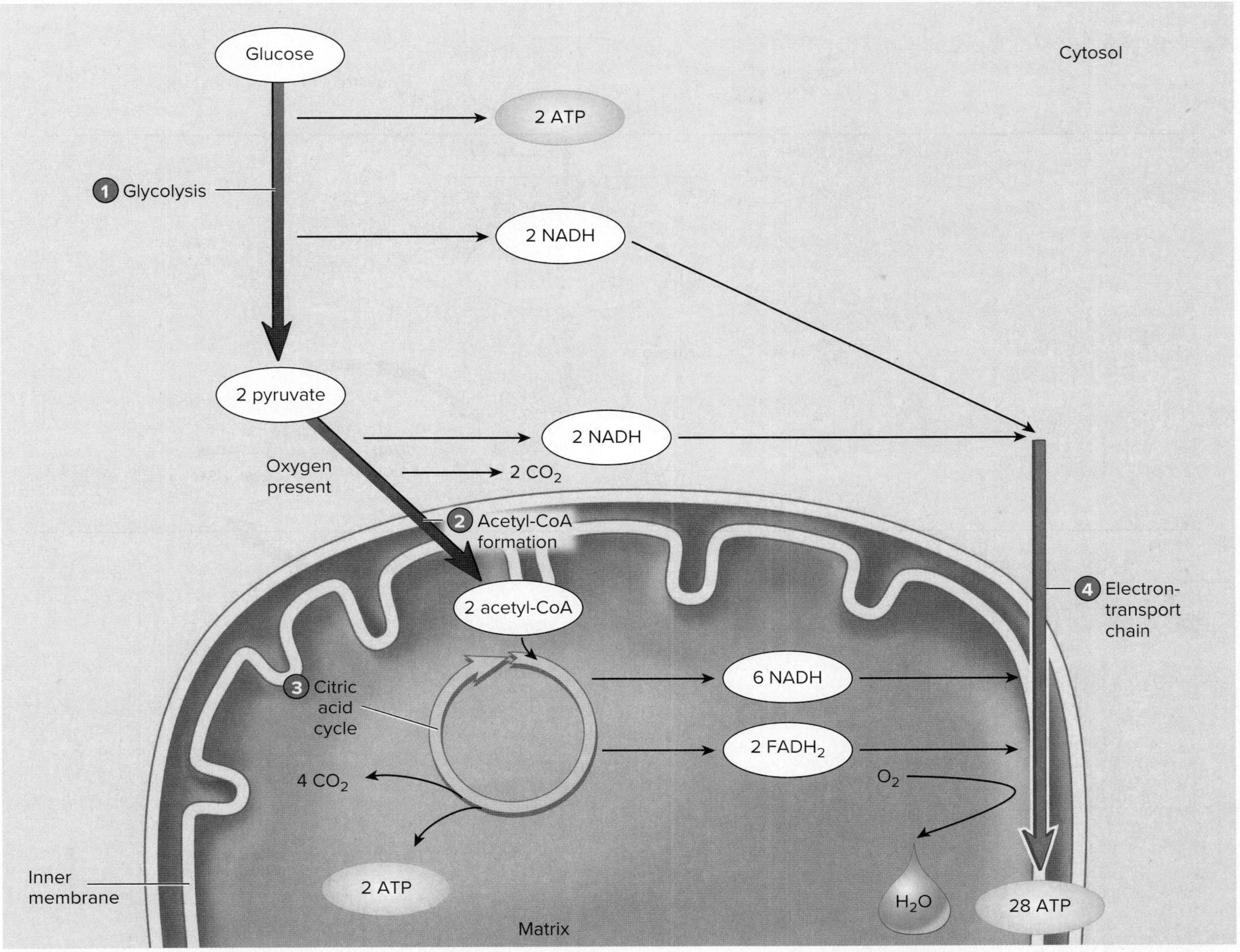

Glucose

Cytosol

2 ATP

1 Glycolysis

2 NADH

2 pyruvate

2 NADH

Oxygen present

$2\ CO_2$

2 Acetyl-CoA formation

2 acetyl-CoA

4 Electron-transport chain

3 Citric acid cycle

6 NADH

$2\ FADH_2$

$4\ CO_2$

O_2

Inner membrane

2 ATP

H_2O

28 ATP

Matrix

PROCESS **Figure 25.7**

Aerobic Respiration

Aerobic respiration involves four phases: (1) glycolysis, (2) acetyl-CoA formation, (3) the citric acid cycle, and (4) the electron-transport chain. The number of carbon atoms in a molecule is indicated after the molecule's name. As glucose is broken down, the carbon atoms from glucose are incorporated into carbon dioxide.

The CO_2 that is produced in steps 2 and 3 eventually is eliminated from the body; however, it does have an important homeostatic role. What is that homeostatic role?

3 *Citric acid cycle:* Within the mitochondrial matrix, the two acetyl-CoA molecules enter the citric acid cycle, which produces four CO_2, six NADH, two $FADH_2$, and two ATP. The NADH and $FADH_2$ can move to the inner mitochondrial membrane to participate in step 4.

4 *Electron-transport chain:* At the inner mitochondrial membrane, the electron-transport chain uses NADH and $FADH_2$ to produce 28 ATP. This process requires O_2, which combines with H^+ to form H_2O.

Recall that glycolysis, the first phase of aerobic respiration, produces pyruvate. Figure 25.8 details the reduction of pyruvate through the process of acetyl-CoA formation and the citric acid cycle.

1 The pyruvate moves from the cytosol into a mitochondrion. A mitochondrion is separated into the intermembrane space and the matrix by the inner mitochondrial membrane (see figure 3.29).

2 Within the matrix, enzymes remove a carbon and two oxygen atoms from the 3-carbon pyruvate molecule to form CO_2 and a 2-carbon acetyl (AS-eh-til) group. During this reaction, H^+ and electrons are also released and used to reduce NAD^+ to NADH. The acetyl group combines with coenzyme A (CoA) to form acetyl-CoA. For each two pyruvate molecules from glycolysis, two acetyl-CoA molecules, two CO_2 molecules, and two NADH are formed during this phase (see figure 25.7).

3 The third phase of aerobic respiration is the **citric acid cycle,** which is named after the 6-carbon citric acid molecule formed in the first step of the cycle. It is also called the *Krebs cycle* after its discoverer, British biochemist Sir Hans Krebs. The citric acid cycle begins with the production of citric acid. This occurs when the 2-carbon acetyl-CoA, produced in the second phase, combines with a 4-carbon molecule called **oxaloacetic** (OK-sah-loh-ah-SEE-tik) **acid.** A series

PROCESS **Figure**

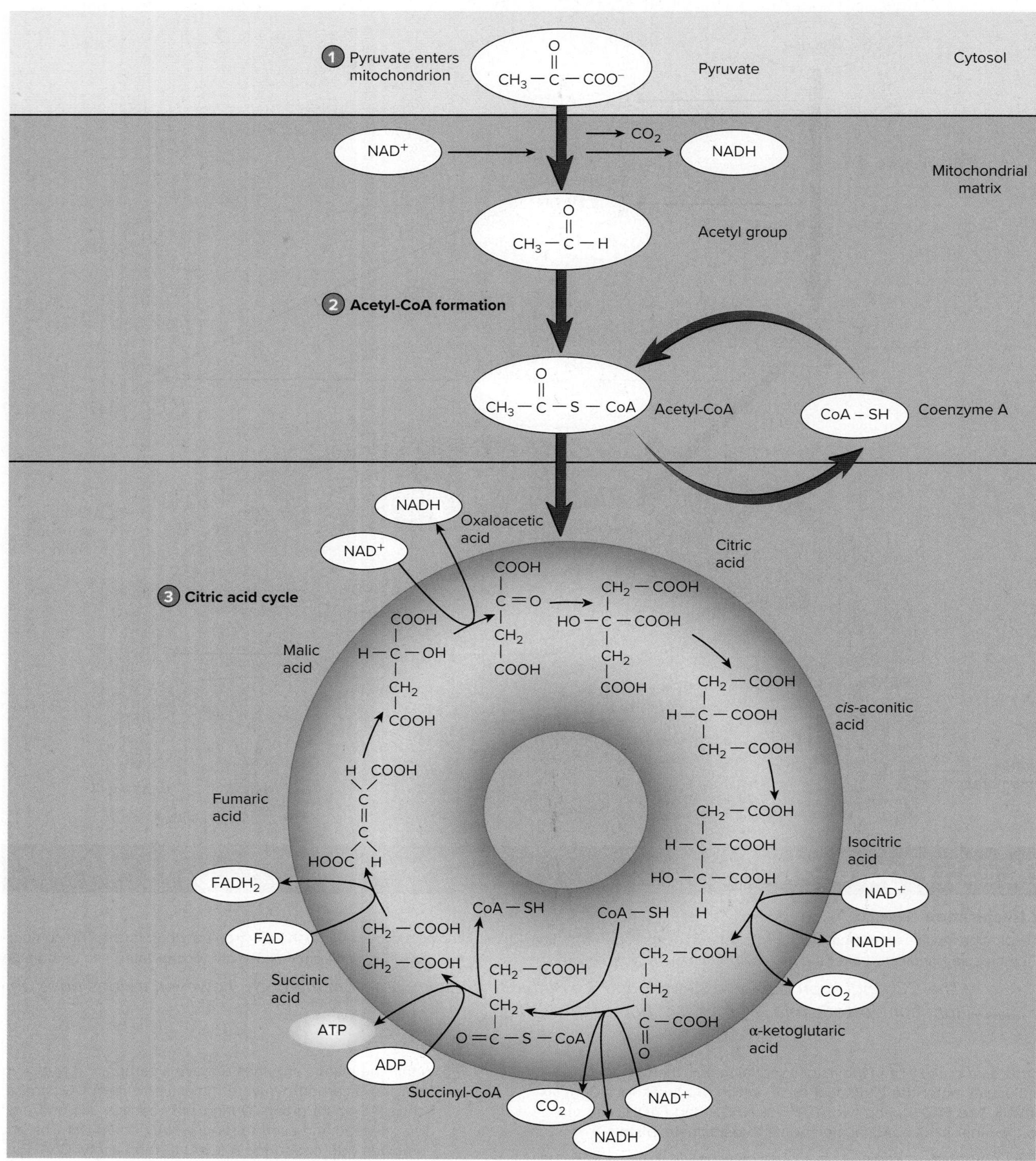

PROCESS **Figure 25.8**

Acetyl-CoA and the Citric Acid Cycle

Pyruvate from the cytosol is converted to acetyl-CoA in mitochondria. The acetyl-CoA enters the citric acid cycle.

Understand *One molecule is needed to begin the process of the citric acid cycle and is also a product of the process. Which molecule is this? Explain your answer.*

FUNDAMENTAL **Figure**

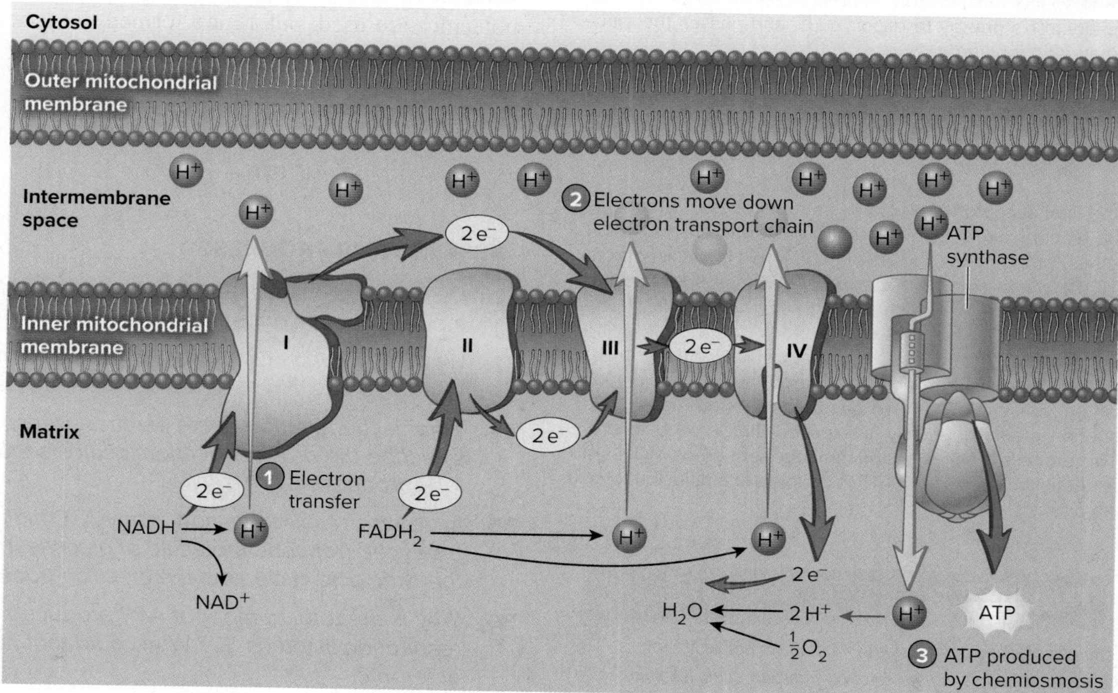

PROCESS Figure 25.9

Electron-Transport Chain

The electron-transport chain in the mitochondrial inner membrane consists of four protein complexes (*purple;* numbered I to IV) with carrier proteins.

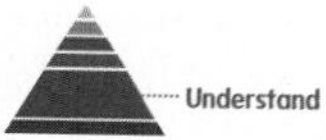

Electronegativity is the ability for an atom or molecule to attract electrons (see chapter 2). Considering the components of the electron-transport chain, with protein I being the beginning of the chain and protein IV the end of the chain, which end has the higher electronegativity? Explain your answer.

of reactions occurs in which the citric acid molecule is modified, producing ATP, electron carriers (NADH and $FADH_2$), and CO_2. As the cycle proceeds, another oxaloacetic acid molecule is produced. This new oxaloacetic acid can start the cycle again by combining with another acetyl-CoA.

The citric acid cycle involves the reduction of citric acid molecules, formed from acetyl-CoA and oxaloacetic acid, as just described. During the reactions of the citric acid cycle, three important events occur:

1. *ATP production.* For each citric acid molecule, one ATP is formed.
2. *NADH and $FADH_2$ production.* For each citric acid molecule, three NAD^+ molecules are converted to NADH molecules, and one flavin (FLAY-vin) adenine dinucleotide (FAD) molecule is converted to $FADH_2$. The NADH and $FADH_2$ molecules are electron carriers that enter the electron-transport chain and are used to produce ATP.
3. *Carbon dioxide production.* Each 6-carbon citric acid molecule at the start of the cycle becomes a 4-carbon oxaloacetic acid molecule at the end of the cycle. Two carbon and four oxygen atoms from the citric acid molecule are used to form two CO_2 molecules. Thus, some of the carbon and oxygen atoms that make up food molecules, such as glucose, are eventually eliminated from the body as CO_2. Humans literally breathe out part of the food they eat.

Before moving to the last phase, let's summarize the reactions in the first three phases. For each glucose molecule that begins aerobic respiration, two pyruvate molecules are produced in glycolysis, and they are converted into two acetyl-CoA molecules, each of which then enters the citric acid cycle. To determine the number of molecules produced from glucose by the citric acid cycle, two "turns" of the cycle must be counted; the results are two ATP, six NADH, two $FADH_2$, and four CO_2 molecules (see figure 25.7, table 25.4).

Figure 25.9 illustrates the activity of the **electron-transport chain,** which is a series of electron carriers in the inner mitochondrial membrane.

1. At the beginning of this phase, electrons are transferred from NADH and $FADH_2$ to the electron-transport carriers. Electrons and H^+ are released from NADH and $FADH_2$. After the loss of the electrons and the H^+, the oxidized NAD^+ and FAD are reused to transport additional electrons from the citric acid cycle to the electron-transport chain.
2. The electrons released from NADH and $FADH_2$ pass from one electron carrier to the next through a series of oxidation-reduction reactions. Three of the electron carriers also function as proton pumps, which move the H^+ from the mitochondrial matrix into the

intermembrane space. Each proton pump accepts an electron, uses some of the electron's energy to export a H^+, and passes the electron to the next electron carrier.

3 The last electron carrier in the series collects the electrons and combines them with O_2 and H^+ to form water:

$$\frac{1}{2} O_2 + 2\,H^+ + 2\,e^- \rightarrow H_2O$$

Oxygen is the final acceptor of electrons in this process. Without O_2 to accept the electrons, the reactions of the electron-transport chain cease, effectively stopping aerobic respiration. The H^+ released from NADH and $FADH_2$ is moved from the intermembrane space to the matrix by active transport. As a result, the concentration of H^+ in the intermembrane space exceeds that of the matrix and a H^+ concentration gradient is established. The H^+ cannot simply diffuse down the concentration gradient but must pass through certain channels formed by an enzyme called **ATP synthase.** As the H^+ diffuses down the concentration gradient, energy is released that is used to produce ATP. This process is called **chemiosmosis** (kem-ee-os-MOH-sis) because the chemical formation of ATP is coupled to a diffusion force similar to osmosis.

Predict 3

Many poisons function by blocking certain steps in metabolic pathways. For example, cyanide blocks the last step in the electron-transport chain. Explain why this blockage causes death.

Summary of ATP Production

As stated earlier, the process of aerobic respiration is complex. The major product of this process is ATP, so it is helpful to now summarize the combined yield of ATP from all phases. For each glucose molecule, aerobic respiration produces a net gain of 32 ATP molecules: 2 from glycolysis, 2 from the citric acid cycle, and 28 from the NADH molecules and $FADH_2$ molecules that pass through the electron-transport chain (table 25.4).

The number of ATP molecules produced from each glucose molecule is a theoretical number. The calculations that predict 32 ATP molecules per glucose molecule assume that 2 H^+ are necessary for the formation of each ATP. If more than 2 are required, the efficiency of aerobic respiration decreases. In addition, the 2 NADH molecules produced by glycolysis in the cytosol cannot cross the inner mitochondrial membrane; thus, their electrons are donated to a shuttle molecule, which carries the electrons to the electron-transport chain. The actual number of ATP produced from the glycolytic NADH varies depending on the shuttle molecule used to move the NADH into the mitochondrion. In skeletal muscle and the brain, fewer ATP molecules are produced for each NADH molecule, resulting in a total number of 30 ATP molecules; however, in the liver, kidneys, and heart, more ATP molecules may be produced for each NADH molecule, and the total number of ATP molecules formed may be higher. Also, it costs energy to get ADP and phosphates into the mitochondria and to get ATP out. Considering all these factors, each glucose molecule yields about 25 ATP molecules instead of 32.

In addition to ATP, aerobic respiration also produces CO_2 and water. Specifically, aerobic respiration produces 6 CO_2 molecules. Water molecules are reactants in some of the chemical reactions of aerobic respiration and products in others. Six water molecules are used, but 12 are formed, for a net gain of 6 water molecules. Thus, aerobic respiration can be summarized as follows:

$$C_6H_{12}O_6 + 6\,O_2 + 6\,H_2O + 32\,ADP + 32\,P_i \rightarrow$$
$$6\,CO_2 + 12\,H_2O + 32\,ATP$$

ASSESS YOUR PROGRESS

32. *Define aerobic respiration, and list its products. Describe the four phases of aerobic respiration.*

33. *Why is the citric acid cycle a cycle? What molecules are produced as a result of the citric acid cycle?*

34. *What is the function of the electron-transport chain? Describe the process of chemiosmosis that occurs during ATP production.*

35. *In aerobic respiration, how many ATP molecules are produced from one molecule of glucose through glycolysis, the citric acid cycle, and the electron-transport chain?*

36. *Why is the total number of ATP produced in aerobic respiration listed as 32? Why could that number be different?*

37. *Write the summary equation for the aerobic breakdown of one glucose molecule.*

25.4 Lipid Metabolism

LEARNING OUTCOME

After reading this section, you should be able to

A. **Describe the basic steps involved in using lipids as an energy source.**

Lipids are the body's main energy-storage molecules. In a healthy person, lipids are responsible for about 99% of the body's energy storage, and glycogen accounts for about 1%. Although proteins serve as an energy source, they are not considered storage molecules because their breakdown normally involves the loss of molecules that perform other functions.

Triglycerides are the main lipid stored in adipose tissue. Synthesis and breakdown of triglycerides occur constantly; thus, the lipids present in adipose tissue today are not the same lipids that were there a few weeks ago. Between meals, when triglycerides are broken down in adipose tissue, some of the fatty acids produced are released into the blood, where they are called **free fatty acids.** Other tissues, especially skeletal muscle and the liver, use the free fatty acids as a source of energy.

The metabolism of fatty acids occurs by **beta-oxidation,** a series of reactions in which two carbon atoms are removed from the end of a fatty acid chain to form acetyl-CoA. The process of beta-oxidation continues to remove two carbon atoms at a time until the entire fatty acid chain is converted into acetyl-CoA molecules. Acetyl-CoA can enter the citric acid cycle and be used to generate ATP (figure 25.10; see figure 25.4).

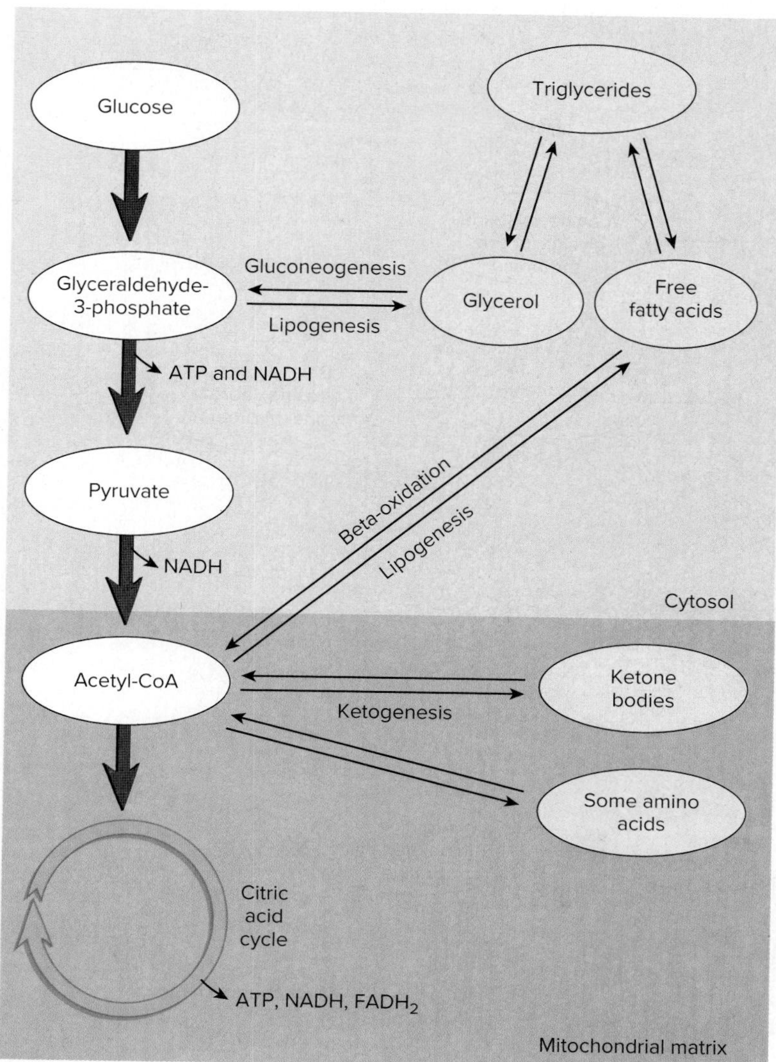

FIGURE 25.10 Lipid Metabolism
Triglycerides are broken down into glycerol and fatty acids. Glycerol enters glycolysis to produce ATP. The fatty acids are broken down by beta-oxidation into acetyl-CoA, which enters the citric acid cycle to produce ATP and electron carriers. Acetyl-CoA can also be used to produce ketone bodies (ketogenesis). Lipogenesis is the production of lipids. Glucose is converted to glycerol, and amino acids are converted to acetyl-CoA molecules. Acetyl-CoA molecules can combine to form fatty acids. Glycerol and fatty acids join to form triglycerides.

Acetyl-CoA is also used in **ketogenesis** (kee-toh-JEN-eh-sis), the formation of ketone bodies. In the liver, when large amounts of acetyl-CoA are produced, not all of the acetyl-CoA enters the citric acid cycle. Instead, two acetyl-CoA molecules combine to form a molecule of acetoacetic (AS-eh-toh-ah-SEE-tik) acid, which is converted mainly into β-hydroxybutyric (high-DROHK-see-byoo-TIR-ik) acid and a smaller amount of acetone (AS-eh-tone). Acetoacetic acid, β-hydroxybutyric acid, and acetone are called **ketone** (KEE-tone) **bodies;** they are released into the blood, where they travel to other tissues, especially skeletal muscle. In the cells of these tissues, the ketone bodies are converted back into acetyl-CoA, which enters the citric acid cycle to produce ATP.

The presence of small amounts of ketone bodies in the blood is normal and beneficial, but excessive production of ketone bodies is called **ketosis** (kee-TOH-sis). Because ketone bodies are acidic, if the increased number of ketone bodies exceeds the capacity of the body's buffering systems, acidosis, a decrease in blood pH, can occur (see chapter 27). Because ketone bodies are derived from the breakdown of fatty acids, conditions that increase lipid metabolism can speed the rate of ketone body formation, thus increasing the possibility of ketosis. Examples of conditions that increase lipid metabolism are starvation (see Clinical Impact 25.4), diets consisting mainly of proteins and lipids with few carbohydrates, and untreated diabetes mellitus. Ketone bodies are excreted by the kidneys and diffuse into the alveoli of the lungs. Because ketone bodies are excreted by the kidneys and lungs, the characteristics of untreated diabetes mellitus include ketone bodies in the urine and "acetone breath."

ASSESS YOUR PROGRESS

38. *What is beta-oxidation? Explain how it results in ATP production.*
39. *What are ketone bodies, how are they produced, and for what are they used? What occurs when there is an excess?*

25.5 Protein Metabolism

LEARNING OUTCOME

After reading this section, you should be able to

A. **Describe the basic steps involved in using proteins as an energy source.**

Recall that proteins are polymers of amino acids. During digestion and absorption in the small intestine, proteins are broken down to individual amino acids. Once absorbed into the blood, amino acids are quickly taken up by cells, especially in the liver. Amino acids are used primarily to synthesize needed proteins (see chapter 3), and only secondarily as a source of energy (figure 25.11; see figure 25.4). Unlike glycogen and triglycerides, amino acids are not stored in the body.

As stated earlier in the chapter, the body can manufacture some amino acids. The synthesis of nonessential amino acids usually begins with keto acids. A keto acid can be converted into an amino acid by replacing its oxygen atom with an amine group (figure 25.12). Usually, this conversion is accomplished by transferring an amine group from an amino acid to the keto acid, a reaction called **transamination** (trans-AM-ih-NAY-shun). For example, α-ketoglutaric acid (a keto acid) reacts with an amino acid to form glutamic acid (an amino acid; figure 25.13*a*). Most amino acids can undergo transamination to produce glutamic acid. The glutamic acid provides an amine group that is used to synthesize most of the nonessential amino acids. A few nonessential amino acids are formed from the essential amino acids by other chemical reactions.

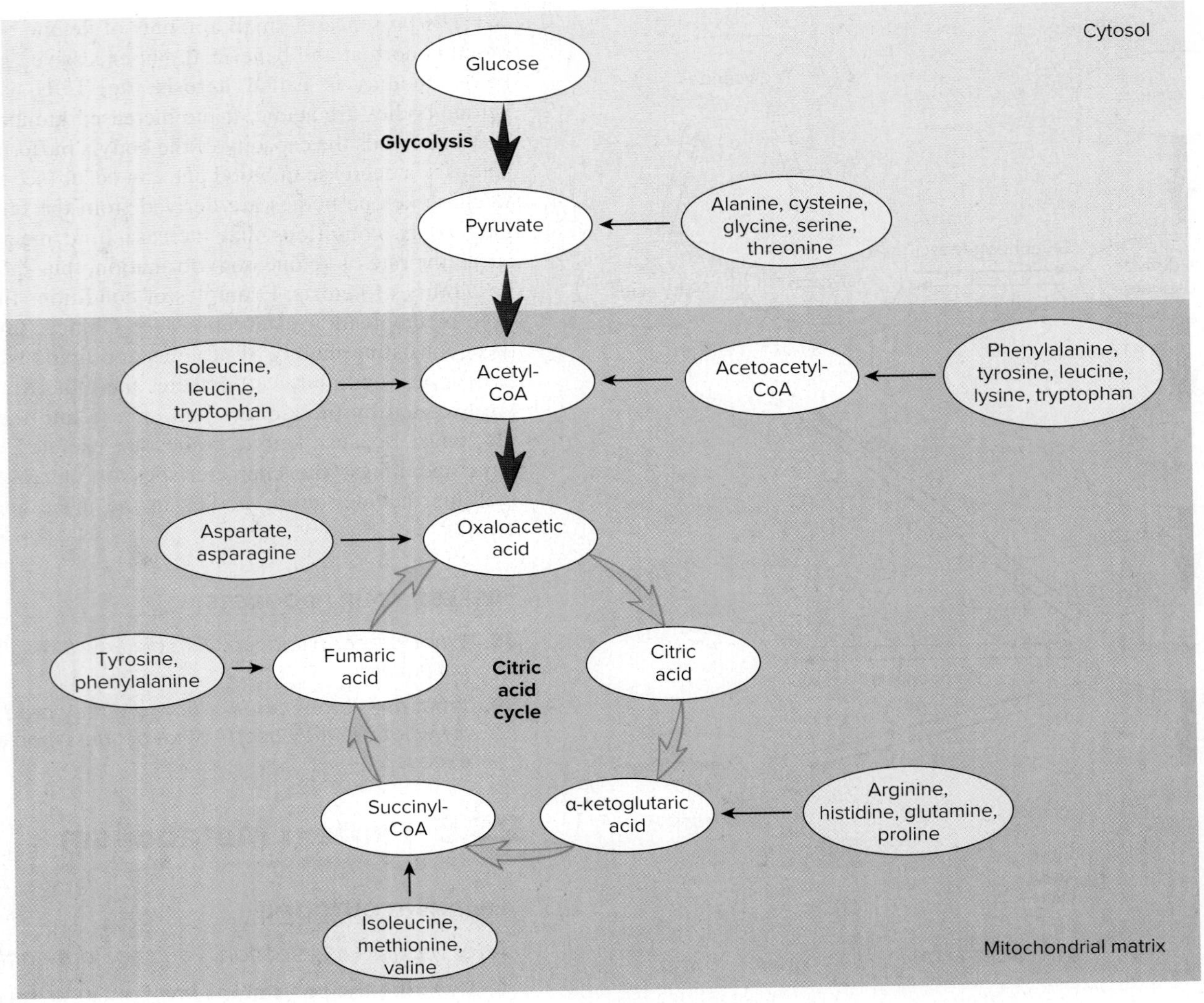

FIGURE 25.11 Amino Acid Metabolism
Amino acids (*pink ovals*) can enter carbohydrate metabolism at various points.

If serving as a source of energy, amino acids can be used in two ways:

- In **oxidative deamination** (dee-am-ih-NAY-shun), or *deamination* (dee-AM-ih-ni-ZAY-shun), an amine group is removed from an amino acid (usually glutamic acid), leaving ammonia and a keto acid (figure 25.13*b*). In the process, NAD^+ is reduced to NADH, which can enter the electron-transport chain to produce ATP. Although ammonia is toxic to cells, it does not accumulate to toxic levels because the liver converts it to urea, which the blood carries to the kidneys for elimination (figure 25.13*c;* see chapter 26).
- Amino acids can also be converted into the intermediate molecules of carbohydrate metabolism (see figure 25.11). These molecules are then metabolized to yield ATP. The conversion of an amino acid often begins with a transamination or oxidative deamination reaction, in which the amino acid is converted into a keto acid (see figure 25.12). The keto acid enters the citric acid cycle or is converted into pyruvate or acetyl-CoA.

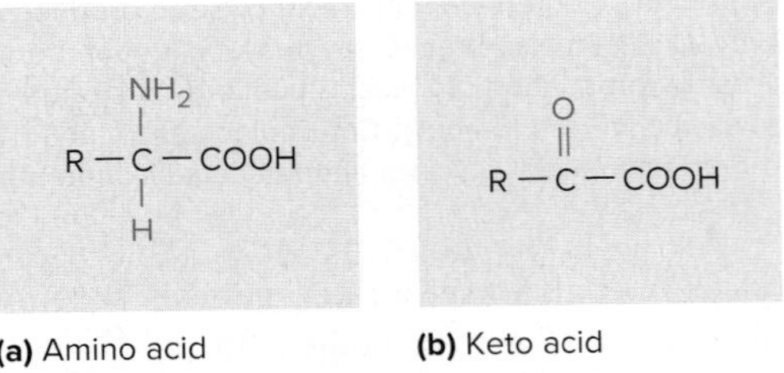

FIGURE 25.12 General Formulas of an Amino Acid and a Keto Acid
(*a*) Amino acid with a carboxyl group (—COOH), an amine group (NH_2), a hydrogen atom (H), and a group called "R," which represents the rest of the molecule. (*b*) Keto acid with a double-bonded oxygen replacing the amine group and the hydrogen atom of the amino acid.

ASSESS YOUR PROGRESS

40. *What is accomplished by transamination and oxidative deamination?*

41. *How are proteins (amino acids) used to produce energy?*

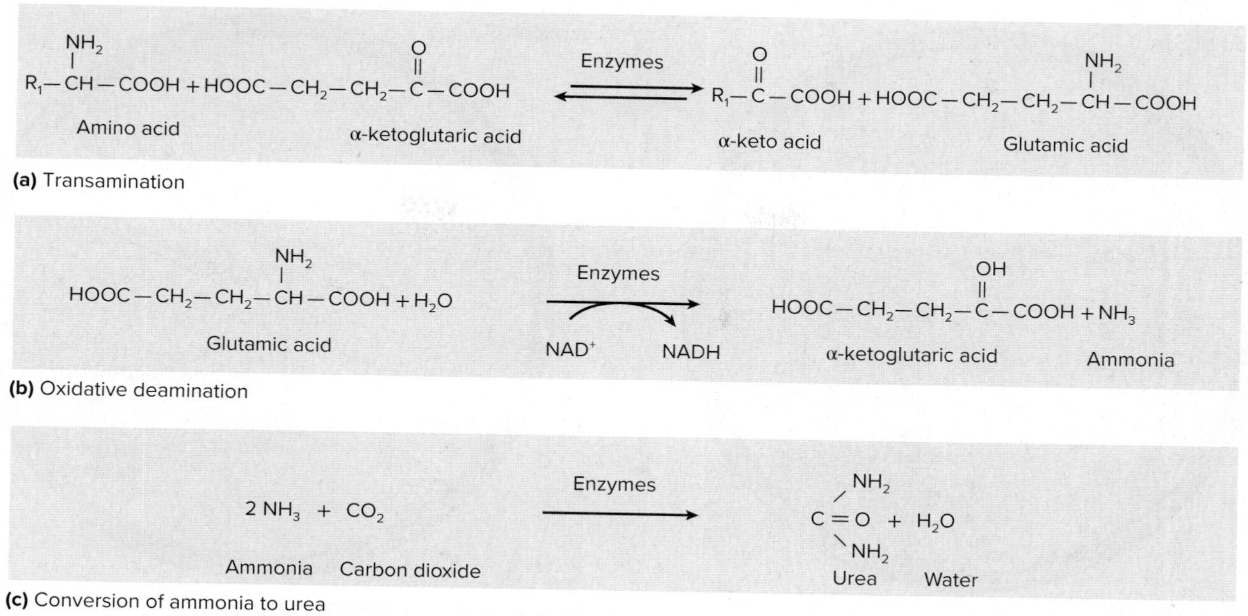

$$R_1-\underset{}{\overset{NH_2}{\overset{|}{CH}}}-COOH + HOOC-CH_2-CH_2-\overset{O}{\overset{||}{C}}-COOH \xrightleftharpoons{\text{Enzymes}} R_1-\overset{O}{\overset{||}{C}}-COOH + HOOC-CH_2-CH_2-\overset{NH_2}{\overset{|}{CH}}-COOH$$

Amino acid · α-ketoglutaric acid · α-keto acid · Glutamic acid

(a) Transamination

$$HOOC-CH_2-CH_2-\overset{NH_2}{\overset{|}{CH}}-COOH + H_2O \xrightarrow[NAD^+ \ \to \ NADH]{\text{Enzymes}} HOOC-CH_2-CH_2-\overset{OH}{\overset{||}{C}}-COOH + NH_3$$

Glutamic acid · NAD⁺ · NADH · α-ketoglutaric acid · Ammonia

(b) Oxidative deamination

$$2\,NH_3 + CO_2 \xrightarrow{\text{Enzymes}} C(=O)(NH_2)_2 + H_2O$$

Ammonia · Carbon dioxide · Urea · Water

(c) Conversion of ammonia to urea

FIGURE 25.13 Amino Acid Reactions

(*a*) Transamination reaction in which an amine group is transferred from an amino acid to a keto acid to form a different amino acid. (*b*) Oxidative deamination reaction in which an amino acid loses an amine group to become a keto acid and to form ammonia. In the process, NADH, which can be used to generate ATP, is formed. (*c*) Ammonia is converted to urea in the liver. (The actual conversion of ammonia to urea is more complex, involving a number of intermediate reactions that constitute the urea cycle.)

25.6 Interconversion of Nutrient Molecules

LEARNING OUTCOME

After reading this section, you should be able to

A. ***Define glycogenesis, lipogenesis, glycogenolysis, and gluconeogenesis.***

The body relies on homeostatic levels of nutrients in the blood. In maintaining these levels, the cells of the body can store nutrients or convert one type of nutrient molecule to another. This interconversion of nutrient molecules includes several processes. We will focus our discussion on blood glucose and four processes involved with glucose use and storage: glycogenesis, lipogenesis, glycogenolysis, and gluconeogenesis.

1. *Glycogenesis.* As blood glucose levels increase, insulin stimulates the movement of glucose from the blood into the cells. Glucose enters most cells by facilitated diffusion and is immediately converted to glucose-6-phosphate, which cannot recross the plasma membrane (figure 25.14*a*). Glucose-6-phosphate then continues through glycolysis to produce ATP. However, if excess glucose is present (e.g., after a meal), it is used to form glycogen through a process called **glycogenesis** (GLY-koh-JEN-eh-sis). Most of the body's glycogen is contained in skeletal muscle and the liver. Glycogenesis, therefore, allows cells to store glucose in the form of glycogen, thereby regulating blood glucose levels.
2. *Lipogenesis.* Once glycogen stores, which are quite limited, are filled, excess glucose, as well as amino acids, are used to synthesize lipids through a process called **lipogenesis** (lip-oh-JEN-eh-sis; see figure 25.10). Triglycerides are the common lipid produced by lipogenesis. Recall that a triglyceride is composed of glycerol and fatty acid chains; therefore, lipogenesis requires the production of these components. Glucose molecules can be used to form glyceraldehyde-3-phosphate, which can then be converted to glycerol. Glucose and amino acids can be used to form acetyl-CoA molecules. These 2-carbon acetyl-CoA molecules can then join together to form fatty acid chains. Glycerol and three fatty acid chains then combine to form triglycerides.
3. *Glycogenolysis.* When blood glucose levels decrease, cells can "tap into their stores" by the breakdown of glycogen into glucose-6-phosphate through a set of reactions called **glycogenolysis** (GLY-koh-jeh-NOL-ih-sis; figure 25.14*b*). In skeletal muscle, glucose-6-phosphate continues through glycolysis to produce ATP. The liver can use glucose-6-phosphate for energy or can convert it to glucose, which diffuses into the blood. Although the liver can release glucose into the blood, skeletal muscle cannot because it lacks the necessary enzymes to convert glucose-6-phosphate into glucose.
4. *Gluconeogenesis.* The release of glucose from the liver is necessary to maintain blood glucose levels between meals. Maintaining these levels is especially important to the brain, which normally uses only glucose for an energy source and consumes about two-thirds of the total glucose used each day. When liver glycogen levels are inadequate to supply glucose, the liver can synthesize glucose from molecules other than carbohydrates, such as amino acids and glycerol. The process of synthesizing glucose from noncarbohydrate sources is called **gluconeogenesis** (GLOO-koh-nee-oh-JEN-eh-sis). Most amino acids can

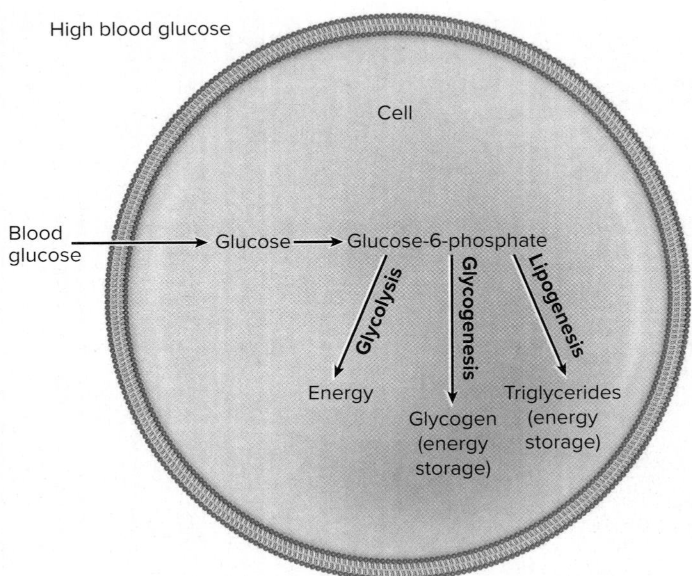

(a) When blood glucose levels are high, glucose enters the cell and is phosphorylated to form glucose-6-phosphate, which can enter glycolysis or glycogenesis.

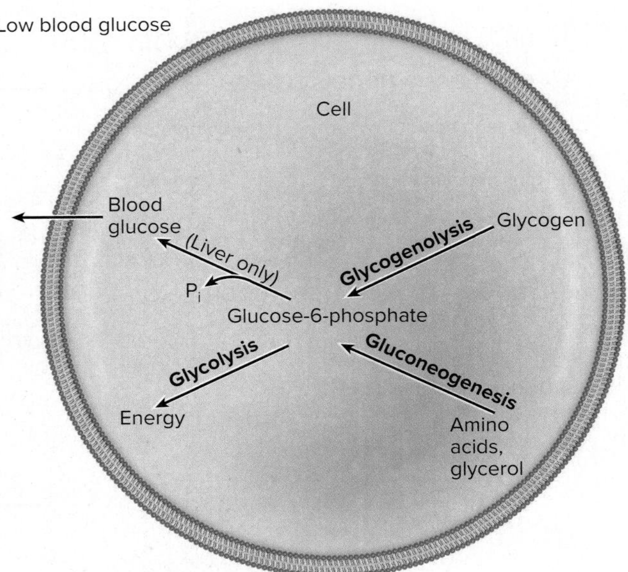

(b) When blood glucose levels drop, glucose-6-phosphate can be produced through glycogenolysis or gluconeogenesis. Glucose-6-phosphate can enter glycolysis, or in the liver, the phosphate group can be removed, forming glucose which is released into the blood.

FIGURE 25.14 Interconversion of Nutrient Molecules
(*a*) Cells either use glucose or store it, usually in the form of glycogen. (*b*) Glucose-6-phosphate is an important intermediate to many biochemical pathways, such as gluconeogenesis, glycogenolysis, and glycolysis.

be converted into citric acid cycle molecules, acetyl-CoA, or pyruvate (see figure 25.11). Through a series of chemical reactions, these molecules are converted into glucose. Glycerol can be converted to glyceraldehyde-3-phosphate, which in turn can be converted to glucose.

ASSESS YOUR PROGRESS

42. *Distinguish among the processes of glycogenesis, lipogenesis, glycogenolysis, and gluconeogenesis.*

Clinical IMPACT 25.3

Alcoholism and Cirrhosis of the Liver

Chronic alcohol abuse can result in **cirrhosis** (sir-OH-sis) **of the liver,** which involves lipid deposition, cell death, inflammation, and scar tissue formation. Enzymes in the liver convert ethanol (beverage alcohol) into acetyl-CoA; in the process, two NADH molecules are produced. The NADH molecules enter the electron-transport chain and are used to produce ATP molecules. Each gram of ethanol provides 7 kcal of energy. A high level of NADH in the cell results from the metabolism of ethanol, thereby inhibiting the production of NADH by glycolysis and the citric acid cycle. Consequently, carbohydrates and amino acids do not break down but are converted into lipids, which accumulate in the liver. Because the liver is unable to carry out its normal functions, death can result.

25.7 Metabolic States

LEARNING OUTCOME

After reading this section, you should be able to

A. **Differentiate between the absorptive and postabsorptive metabolic states.**

Metabolism refers to the collection of chemical reactions that take place in the cells of the body. These reactions vary depending on levels of activity and availability of nutrients. The body experiences two major metabolic states: the absorptive state and the postabsorptive state. The regulation of these states is discussed in chapter 18 (see section 18.7). The **absorptive state** is the period immediately after a meal, when nutrients are being absorbed through the intestinal wall into the circulatory and lymphatic systems (figure 25.15). The absorptive state usually lasts about 4 hours after each meal, though the rate of absorption declines after 1–2 hours. During this time the cells use most of the glucose that enters the blood for the energy they require. The remainder of the glucose is converted into glycogen or lipids. Most of the absorbed lipids are deposited in adipose tissue. Many of the absorbed amino acids are used by cells in protein synthesis, some are used for energy, and still others enter the liver and are converted into lipids or carbohydrates.

The **postabsorptive state** occurs late in the morning, late in the afternoon, or during the night after each absorptive state is concluded (figure 25.16). The maintenance of normal blood glucose levels is vital to the body's homeostasis, especially for

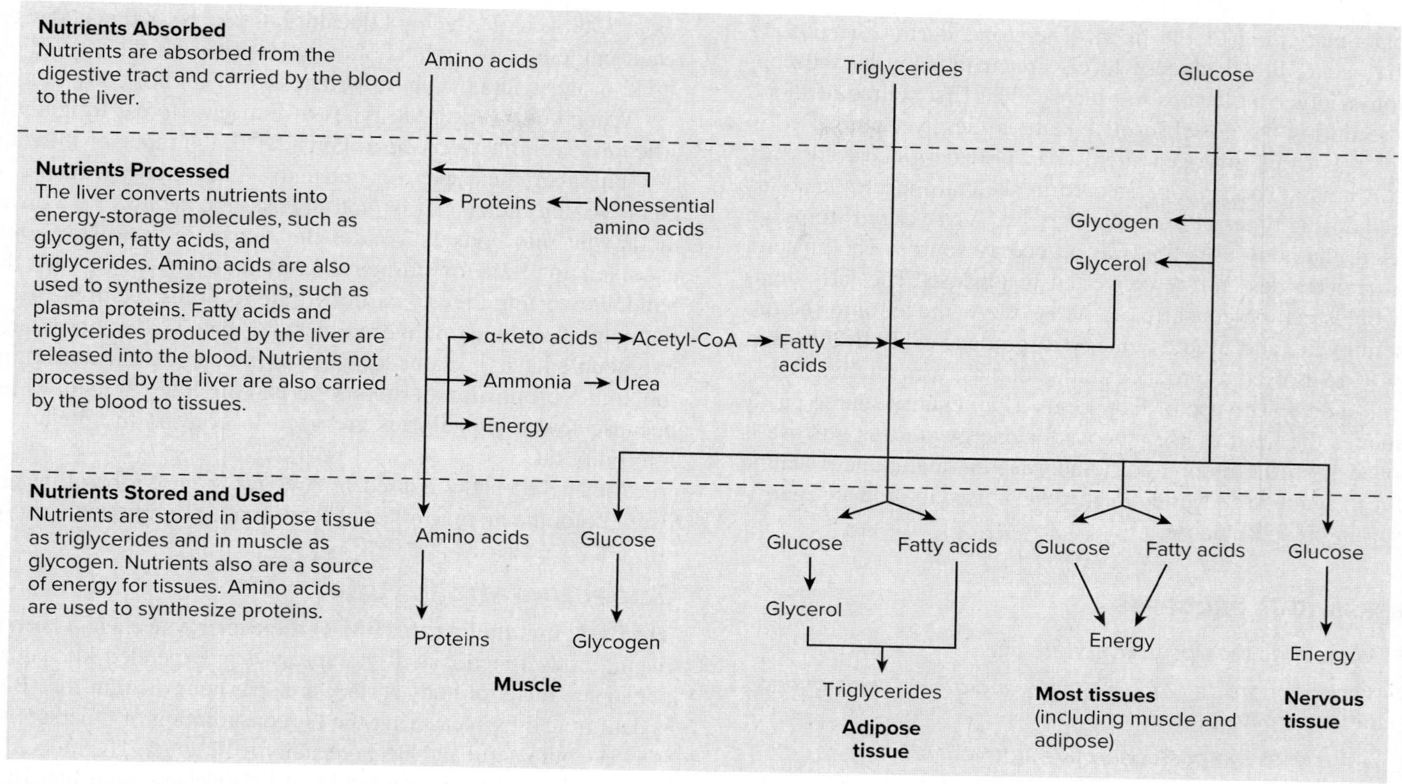

FIGURE 25.15 Events of the Absorptive State

Absorbed molecules, especially glucose, are used as sources of energy. Molecules not immediately needed for energy are stored: Glucose is converted to glycogen or triglycerides, triglycerides are deposited in adipose tissue, and amino acids are converted to triglycerides or carbohydrates.

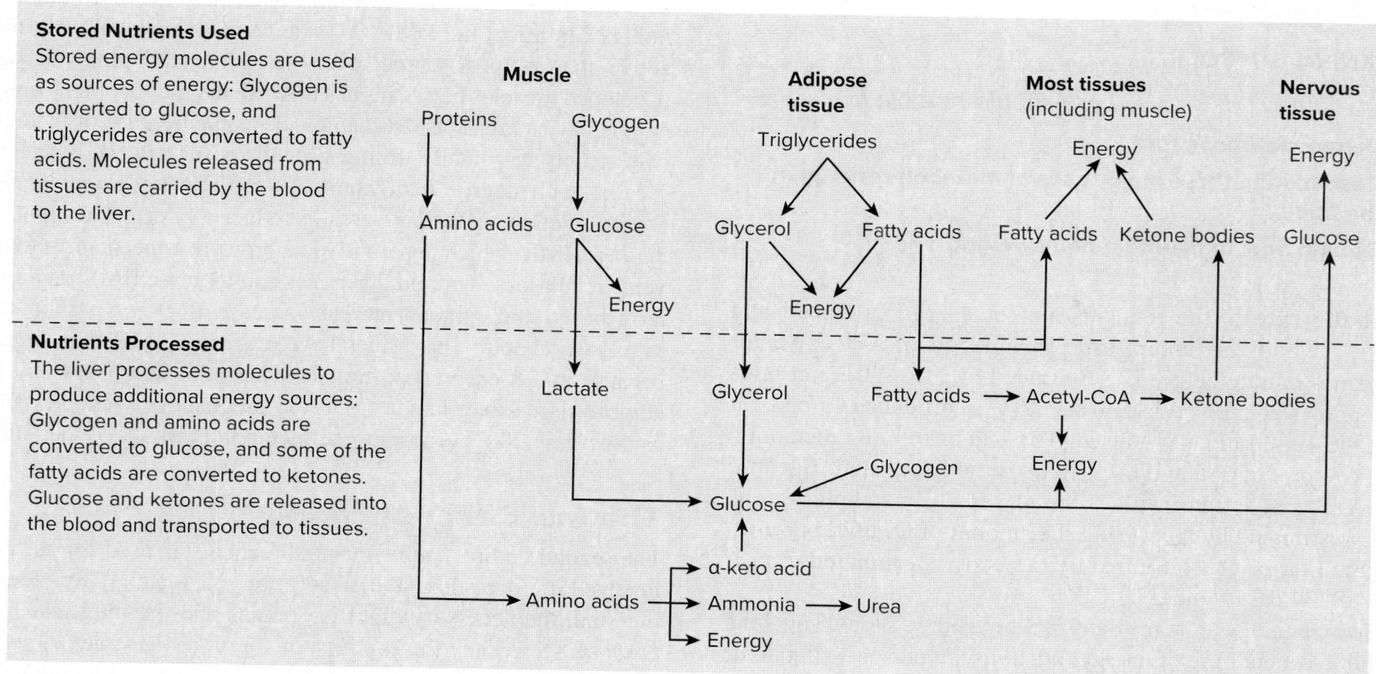

FIGURE 25.16 Events of the Postabsorptive State

Stored energy molecules are used as sources of energy: Glycogen is converted to glucose; triglycerides are broken down to fatty acids, some of which are converted to ketones; and proteins are converted to glucose.

normal functioning of the brain. Therefore, during the postabsorptive state, blood glucose levels are maintained by the conversion of other molecules to glucose. The first source of blood glucose during the postabsorptive state is the glycogen stored in the liver, but this glycogen supply can provide glucose for only about 4 hours. The glycogen stored in skeletal muscles can also be used during times of vigorous exercise. As glycogen stores are depleted, the body uses lipids as an energy source. The glycerol from triglycerides can be converted to glucose. The fatty acids from lipids can be converted to acetyl-CoA, moved into the citric acid cycle, and used as energy to produce ATP. In the liver, acetyl-CoA is used to produce ketone bodies, which other tissues use for energy. The use of fatty acids as an energy source partly eliminates the need to use glucose for energy, so less glucose is removed from the blood and homeostasis is maintained. Amino acids can again be converted to glucose or used to produce energy, conserving blood glucose.

ASSESS YOUR PROGRESS

43. *When does the absorptive state occur?*
44. *What happens to glucose, lipids, and amino acids during the absorptive state?*
45. *When does the postabsorptive state occur?*
46. *Why is it important to maintain blood glucose levels during the postabsorptive state? Name three sources of this glucose.*

25.8 Metabolic Rate

LEARNING OUTCOMES

After reading this section, you should be able to

A. **Define *metabolic rate.***
B. **Describe the three major uses of metabolic energy in the body.**
C. **Explain how to maintain body weight.**

Metabolic rate is the total amount of energy produced and used by the body per unit of time. A molecule of ATP exists for less than 1 minute before it is degraded back to ADP and inorganic phosphate. For this reason, ATP is produced in cells at about the same rate as it is used. Thus, in examining metabolic rate, ATP production and use can be roughly equated. Because most ATP production involves the use of O_2, metabolic rate is usually estimated by measuring the amount of O_2 used per minute. One liter of O_2 consumed by the body is estimated to produce 4.825 kcal of energy.

To maintain weight, the daily input of energy should equal the metabolic expenditure of energy; otherwise, a person will gain or lose weight. For a typical 23-year-old, 70-kg (154-pound) male to maintain his weight, the daily input should be 2700 kcal/day; for a typical 58-kg (128-pound) female of the same age, 2000 kcal/day is sufficient. A pound of body fat (adipose tissue) provides about 3500 kcal. Reducing kilocaloric intake by 500 kcal/day can result in the loss of 1 pound of body fat per week. Clearly, adjusting kilocaloric input is an important way to control body weight.

When considering the types of nutrients to eat to maintain a healthy weight, we need to consider the number of kilocalories but also the types of nutrients. The energy expense of metabolizing nutrients is not always the same. To convert dietary fat into body fat, 3% of the energy in the dietary fat is used, leaving 97% for storage as body fat deposits. On the other hand, converting dietary carbohydrate to lipids requires 23% of the energy in the carbohydrate, leaving just 77% as body fat. If two people have the same kilocaloric intake, the one consuming the higher proportion of dietary fat is more likely to gain weight because fewer kilocalories are used to convert the dietary fat into body fat.

Metabolic energy is used in three ways: (1) for basal metabolism, (2) for the thermic effect of food, and (3) for muscular activity.

Basal Metabolic Rate

The **basal metabolic rate (BMR)** is the energy needed to keep the resting body functional. It is expressed in expended kilocalories per square meter of body surface area per hour (kcal/m^2/hr). BMR is determined by measuring the O_2 consumption of a person who is awake but restful and has not eaten for 12 hours. The liters of O_2 consumed are then multiplied by 4.825 because each liter of O_2 used results in 4.825 kcal of energy. A typical BMR for a 70-kg (154-pound) male is 38 kcal/m^2/h.

In the average person, basal metabolism accounts for about 60% of energy expenditure. Basal metabolism supports active-transport mechanisms, muscle tone, maintenance of body temperature, beating of the heart, and other activities. A number of factors can affect the BMR. Muscle tissue is metabolically more active than adipose tissue, even at rest, so people with well-developed muscles have a higher BMR than other people. Younger people have a higher BMR than older people because of increased cell activity, especially during growth. Fever can increase BMR 7% for each degree Fahrenheit elevation in body temperature. During dieting or fasting, greatly reduced kilocaloric input can depress BMR, which apparently is a protective mechanism to prevent weight loss. Thyroid hormones can increase BMR on a long-term basis, and epinephrine can increase BMR on a short-term basis (see chapter 18). Males have a greater BMR than females because males have proportionately more muscle tissue and less adipose tissue than females. During pregnancy, a female's BMR can increase 20% because of the metabolic activity of the fetus.

Thermic Effect of Food

The second component of metabolic energy is used for activities involved in digestion and absorption of food. When food is ingested, the accessory digestive organs and the intestinal lining produce secretions, the motility of the digestive tract increases, active transport increases, and the liver is involved in synthesizing new molecules. The energy cost of these events, called the **thermic effect of food,** accounts for about 10% of the body's energy expenditure.

Clinical GENETICS 25.1 Newborn Screening of Metabolic Disorders

Metabolic disorders, sometimes called inborn errors of metabolism, are a large class of genetic disorders that result in biochemical defects. Metabolic disorders affect the body's ability to break down or use nutrients needed for energy, growth, and repair. Too little synthesis of certain substances or a buildup of toxic compounds can cause significant health problems. Although the frequency of any given individual disorder is rare, the overall incidence of metabolic disorders is estimated to be up to 1 in 1000 births.

Early detection through newborn screening is vital. Metabolic disorders can hinder early mental and physical development. Depending on the disorder, specific treatment can prevent or limit harm if it is started early. In the United States, most states require the screening of newborns. However, there is no national standard for newborn screening, so the specific disorders for which tests are performed vary from state to state. Although over several hundred genetic disorders are known, most are so rare that it is not cost-effective to test for them.

Table 25.5 lists the most common blood tests performed for metabolic disorders. All of the disorders listed are autosomal recessive.

TABLE 25.5 Metabolic Disorders

Disorder	Description	Effect	Treatment
Phenylketonuria (PKU)	Inability to metabolize the amino acid phenylalanine (see chapter 29)	Intellectual disability	Restrict dietary phenylalanine.
Galactosemia	Inability to convert the sugar galactose to glucose, resulting in a buildup of galactose	Intellectual disability, growth deficiency, cataracts, severe infections, death	Eliminate milk and other dairy products from the diet. Galactose is one of two sugars in lactose (milk sugar).
Biotinidase deficiency	Inability to separate the vitamin biotin from other chemicals, resulting in a biotin deficiency	Seizures, hearing loss, optic atrophy, intellectual disability, poor muscle control	Take oral biotin supplements.
Maple syrup urine disease	Deficiency in an enzyme complex, resulting in an inability to metabolize the amino acids leucine, isoleucine, and valine	Intellectual disability in those surviving past 3 months of age	Restrict dietary intake of the affected amino acids.
Homocystinuria	Defect in methionine metabolism, leading to an accumulation of homocysteine	Dislocated lenses of the eyes, intellectual disability, skeletal abnormalities, abnormal blood clotting	Take high doses of vitamin B_6; eat methionine-restricted diet supplemented with cysteine.
Tyrosinemia	Deficiency in a series of enzymes that break down the amino acid tyrosine	Mild intellectual disability, language skill difficulties, liver and kidney failure	Restrict dietary tyrosine and phenylalanine.

Muscular Activity

Muscular activity consumes about 30% of the body's energy. Therefore, physical activity resulting from skeletal muscle movement requires the expenditure of energy. In addition, energy is needed for the increased contraction of the heart and muscles of respiration. The number of kilocalories expended in an activity depends almost entirely on the amount and duration of muscular work performed. Despite the fact that studying can make a person feel tired, intense mental concentration produces little change in BMR.

Energy loss through muscular activity is the only component of energy expenditure that a person can reasonably control. Comparing the number of kilocalories gained from food with the number of kilocalories lost in exercise reveals why losing weight can be difficult. For example, if brisk walking uses 225 kcal/h, it takes 20 minutes of brisk walking to burn off the 75 kcal in one slice of bread (75/225 = 0.33 h). Research suggests that a combination of appropriate physical activity and appropriate kilocaloric intake is the best way to maintain a healthy body composition and weight.

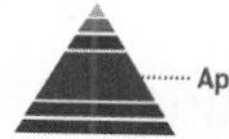

Predict 4

If watching TV uses 95 kcal/h, how long does it take to burn off the kilocalories in one cola or beer (see table 25.1)? If jogging at a pace of 6 mph uses 580 kcal/h, how long does it take to use the kilocalories in one cola or beer?

Clinical IMPACT 25.4 Starvation and Obesity

Starvation

Starvation is the inadequate intake of nutrients or the inability to metabolize or absorb nutrients. Starvation can be caused by a number of factors, such as prolonged fasting, anorexia, deprivation, or disease.

Symptoms of starvation, in addition to weight loss, include apathy, listlessness, withdrawal, and increased susceptibility to infectious diseases. Few people die directly from starvation because they usually die of an infectious disease first. Other signs of starvation include changes in hair color, flaky skin, and massive edema in the abdomen and lower limbs, causing the abdomen to appear bloated.

During starvation, the body's ability to consume normal volumes of food also decreases. Foods high in bulk but low in protein content often cannot reverse the process of starvation. Intervention involves feeding the starving person low-bulk foods containing ample protein, calories, vitamins, and minerals. Starvation also results in dehydration; thus, rehydration is an important part of intervention. Even with intervention, a victim may be so affected by disease or weakness that he or she cannot recover.

Obesity

Obesity is the storage of excess fat, and it results from the ingestion of more food than is necessary for the body's energy needs. Obesity can be defined on the basis of body weight, body mass index, or body fat. "Desirable body weight" is listed in a table produced by the Metropolitan Life Insurance Company and indicates, for any height, the weight associated with a maximum life span. Overweight is defined as 10% more than the desirable weight, and obesity is 20% more than the desirable weight. **Body mass index (BMI)** can be calculated by dividing a person's weight (Wt) in kilograms by the square of his or her height (Ht) in meters:

$$\text{BMI} = \text{Wt}/\text{Ht}^2$$

A BMI greater than 25 is overweight, and a value greater than 30 is defined as obese. About 26% of Americans have a BMI of 30 or greater. In terms of the percent of total body weight contributed by fat, 15% body fat in men and 25% body fat in women is associated with reduced health risks. Obesity is defined as more than 25% body fat in men and 30–35% in women.

The distribution of fat in obese individuals can vary. Fat can accumulate mainly in the upper body, such as in the abdominal region, or it can be associated with the hips and buttocks. These distribution differences can be clinically significant because upper body obesity is associated with an increased likelihood of diabetes mellitus, cardiovascular disease, stroke, and death.

In some cases, obesity is caused by a medical condition. For example, a tumor in the hypothalamus can stimulate overeating. In most cases, however, no specific cause can be recognized. In fact, obesity can occur for many reasons and can have more than one cause in the same individual. There seems to be a genetic component for obesity; if one or both parents are obese, their children are more likely to be obese. Environmental factors, such as eating habits, can also play an important role. For example, adopted children can exhibit obesity similar to that of their adoptive parents. In addition, psychological factors, such as overeating as a way to deal with stress, can contribute to obesity.

In **hypertrophic** (high-per-TROF-ik; *hyper,* above normal + *trophe,* nourishment) **obesity,** the number of adipose cells is usually normal, but the amount of lipids contained in each adipose cell is increased. This type of obesity is characteristic of adult-onset obesity. People who were thin or of average weight and quite active when young become less active as they age. Although they no longer use as many kilocalories, they still consume the same amount of food as when they were younger. The excess kilocalories (see section 25.8) are used to synthesize fat. In this type of obesity, the amount of lipids in each adipose cell increases, and if the amount of stored lipids continues to increase, the total number of adipose cells may also increase. It is estimated that the average U.S. resident gains 1.25–1.5 lb of body fat per year after age 25 and, at the same time, loses 0.25–0.5 lb of lean body weight (muscle mass) per year.

In **hyperplastic** (high-per-PLAS-tik; *hyper* + *plasis,* a molding) **obesity,** which is characteristic of juvenile-onset obesity, the number of adipose cells is increased. This condition may also be accompanied by an increase in cell size (hypertrophic obesity). Hyperplastic obesity has a very strong hereditary component, but family eating habits can also have a great influence. People with hyperplastic obesity are obese as children and become more obese with age. This type of obesity is a major health problem in school-age children.

ASSESS YOUR PROGRESS

47. *What is metabolic rate? How is it measured?*
48. *What is BMR? What factors can alter BMR?*
49. *What is the thermic effect of food?*
50. *BMR, the thermic effect of food, and muscular activity each accounts for what percentage of total energy expenditure?*
51. *How are kilocaloric input and output adjusted to maintain body weight?*

25.9 Body Temperature Regulation

LEARNING OUTCOME

After reading this section, you should be able to

A. **Describe heat production and regulation in the body.**

Humans can maintain a relatively constant internal body temperature despite changes in the temperature of the surrounding environment. This is the result of heat production during normal metabolic activity. A constant body temperature is very important for homeostasis. For example, environmental temperatures are too low for normal enzyme function, so the heat produced by metabolism helps maintain body temperature at a steady level that is high enough for normal enzyme function. Excessively high body temperatures, on the other hand, can alter enzyme structure, resulting in loss of the enzyme's function.

Free energy is the total amount of energy liberated by the complete catabolism of food. It is usually expressed in terms of kilocalories (kcal) per mole of food consumed. For example, the complete catabolism of 1 mole of glucose (168 g; see chapter 2) releases 686 kcal of free energy. About 43% of the total energy released by catabolism is used to produce ATP and to accomplish biological work, such as anabolism, muscular contraction, and other cellular activities. The remaining energy is lost as **heat.**

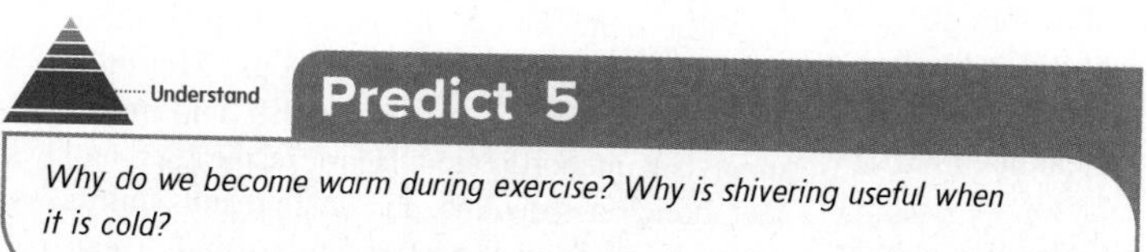

Predict 5

Why do we become warm during exercise? Why is shivering useful when it is cold?

The average normal body temperature is considered to be 37°C (98.6°F) when measured orally and 37.6°C (99.7°F) when measured rectally. Rectal temperature comes closer to the true core body temperature, but an oral temperature is more easily obtained in older children and adults and therefore is the preferred measure.

Our bodies exchange heat with the environment in a number of ways (figure 25.17), including radiation, conduction, convection, and evaporaton.

1. **Radiation** is the gain or loss of heat between two objects that are not in physical contact. For example, the body can gain heat by radiation from the sun, a hot coal, or the hot sand of a beach. On the other hand, the body can lose heat by radiation to cool vegetation or snow on the ground.
2. **Conduction** is the exchange of heat between objects in direct contact with each other, such as the bottoms of the feet and the floor.
3. **Convection** is a transfer of heat between the body and the air or water, as the air or water moves across the surface of the skin. A cool breeze causes air to move over the body, allowing body heat to be lost.
4. **Evaporation** is the conversion of water from a liquid to a gas, a process that requires heat. The evaporation of 1 g of water from the body surface results in the loss of 580 cal of heat.

Body temperature is maintained by balancing heat gain with heat loss. If heat gain exceeds heat loss, body temperature increases; if heat loss exceeds heat gain, body temperature decreases. The body generates heat through normal metabolism as well as through the muscle contractions. This is why shivering (fast cycles of muscle contractions) occurs when we are cold. The body also exchanges heat with the environment by radiation, conduction, or convection, depending on skin temperature and the environmental temperature. In addition, the body can lose heat to the environment through evaporation of perspiration from the skin.

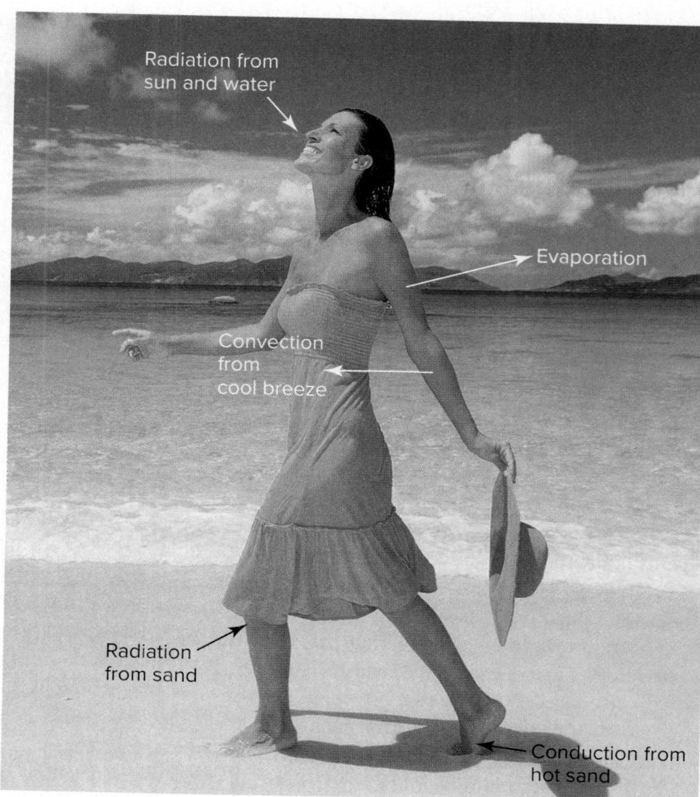

FIGURE 25.17 Heat Exchange
Heat exchange between a person and the environment occurs by radiation, conduction, convection, and evaporation. Arrows show the direction of net heat gain or loss in this environment. M.M. Sweet/Moment/Flickr/Getty Images

The difference in temperature between the body and the environment determines the amount of heat exchanged between the two. The greater the temperature difference, the greater the rate of heat exchange. Control of the temperature difference is used to regulate body temperature. For example, if the environmental temperature is very cold, as on a cold winter day, a large temperature difference exists between the body and the environment, and therefore a large loss of heat occurs. Behaviorally, we can reduce the heat loss by seeking a warmer environment—for example, by going inside a heated house or putting on extra clothes.

Physiologically, the body controls temperature difference through the dilation and constriction of blood vessels in the skin and the activity of sweat glands. When the environmental temperature is greater than body temperature, vasodilation brings warm blood to the skin, causing an increase in skin temperature. This reduces the heat gradient between the environment and skin and therefore decreases heat gain from the environment. At the same time, sweat glands increase secretion and evaporation carries away excess heat to prevent heat gain and overheating. Conversely, when the environmental temperature is less than body temperature, vasoconstriction reduces blood flow to the skin and skin temperature decreases. This reduces the amount of heat that is lost to the environment.

Clinical IMPACT 25.5 Hyperthermia and Hypothermia

Hyperthermia

Hyperthermia, elevated body temperature, develops when heat gain exceeds the body's ability to lose heat. Hyperthermia can result from exercise, exposure to hot environments, fever, or anesthesia.

Exercise increases body temperature because heat is a by-product of muscle activity (see chapter 9). Normally, while a person is exercising, vasodilation and increased sweating prevent harmful body temperature increases. However, in a hot, humid environment, the evaporation of sweat decreases, and exercise must be curtailed to prevent overheating.

Exposure to a hot environment normally activates heat-loss mechanisms so that body temperature is maintained within the normal range, a negative-feedback mechanism. However, with prolonged exposure to a hot environment, the normal negative-feedback mechanisms are unable to keep body temperature from increasing above normal, resulting in **heat exhaustion.** Heavy sweating causes dehydration, decreased blood volume, decreased blood pressure, and increased heart rate. Heat exhaustion is characterized by wet, cool skin due to heavy sweating. In addition, the person usually feels weak, dizzy, and nauseated. Treatment includes moving to a cooler environment to allow heat loss, ceasing activity to reduce the heat produced by muscle metabolism, and restoring blood volume by drinking fluids.

Heat stroke is more severe than heat exhaustion because it results from a breakdown in the normal negative-feedback mechanisms of temperature regulation. If the temperature of the hypothalamus becomes too high, it no longer functions appropriately. Sweating stops, and the skin becomes dry and flushed. The person becomes confused, irritable, or even comatose. Treatment is the same as for heat exhaustion, except that efforts to promote heat loss from the skin should be increased—for example, by applying wet cloths to the skin or by immersing the person in a cool bath.

Fever is the development of a higher-than-normal body temperature due to invasion of the body by microorganisms or other foreign substances. Lymphocytes, neutrophils, and macrophages release chemicals called **pyrogens** (PIE-roh-jenz), such as certain interleukins, interferons, and tissue necrosis factor. Pyrogens increase the synthesis of prostaglandins, which stimulate a rise in the temperature set point of the hypothalamus. Consequently, body temperature and metabolic rate increase. Physiologists believe fever is beneficial because it speeds the chemical reactions of the immune system (see chapter 22) and inhibits the growth of some microorganisms. However, body temperatures greater than 41°C (106°F) can be harmful. To lower body temperature, physicians prescribe aspirin, nonsteroidal anti-inflammatory drugs (NSAIDs), and acetaminophen, which act by inhibiting the synthesis of prostaglandins.

In people who have the inherited muscle disorder **malignant hyperthermia,** certain general anesthetics cause sustained, uncoordinated muscle contractions. Consequently, body temperature increases.

Therapeutic hyperthermia is an induced elevation in local or general body temperature sometimes used to treat tumors and infections.

Hypothermia

If heat loss exceeds the body's ability to produce heat, body temperature falls below normal. **Hypothermia** is a decrease in body temperature to 35°C (95°F) or below. Hypothermia usually results from prolonged exposure to a cold environment. At first, body temperature is maintained by normal negative-feedback mechanisms—that is, heat loss is decreased by constricting blood vessels in the skin, and heat production is increased by shivering. However, if body temperature decreases despite these mechanisms, hypothermia develops. The individual's thinking becomes sluggish, and movements are uncoordinated. Heart, respiratory, and metabolic rates decline, and death results unless body temperature is restored to normal. Treatment for hypothemia calls for rewarming the body a few degrees per hour.

Frostbite is damage to the skin and deeper tissues resulting from prolonged exposure to the cold. Specifically, damage results from direct cold injury to cells, injury from ice crystal formation, and reduced blood flow to affected tissues. The fingers, toes, ears, nose, and cheeks are most commonly affected. The consequences of frostbite can range from redness and discomfort to loss of the affected part due to death of the tissue. The best treatment is immersion in a warm-water bath. Patients should avoid rubbing the affected area or applying local dry heat.

Therapeutic hypothermia is sometimes used to slow the metabolic rate during surgical procedures, such as heart surgery. Due to the decreased metabolic rate, the tissues do not require as much oxygen as normal and are less likely to be damaged.

Body temperature regulation is an example of a negative-feedback system controlled by a set point. A small area in the anterior part of the hypothalamus detects slight increases in body temperature through changes in blood temperature (figure 25.18). As a result, mechanisms that cause heat loss, such as vasodilation and sweating, are activated, and body temperature decreases. Alternatively, a small area in the posterior hypothalamus can detect slight decreases in body temperature and can initiate heat gain by increasing muscular activity (shivering) and vasoconstriction.

Under some conditions, the set point of the hypothalamus changes. For example, during a fever, the set point is raised, heat-conserving and heat-producing mechanisms are stimulated, and body temperature increases. To recover from a fever, the set point is lowered to normal, heat-loss mechanisms are initiated, and body temperature decreases.

ASSESS YOUR PROGRESS

52. *What is free energy? How much free energy is lost as heat from the body?*
53. *What are four ways that heat is exchanged between the body and the environment?*
54. *How is body temperature maintained behaviorally in a cold environment? How is body temperature maintained physiologically in a hot environment?*
55. *How does the hypothalamus regulate body temperature?*

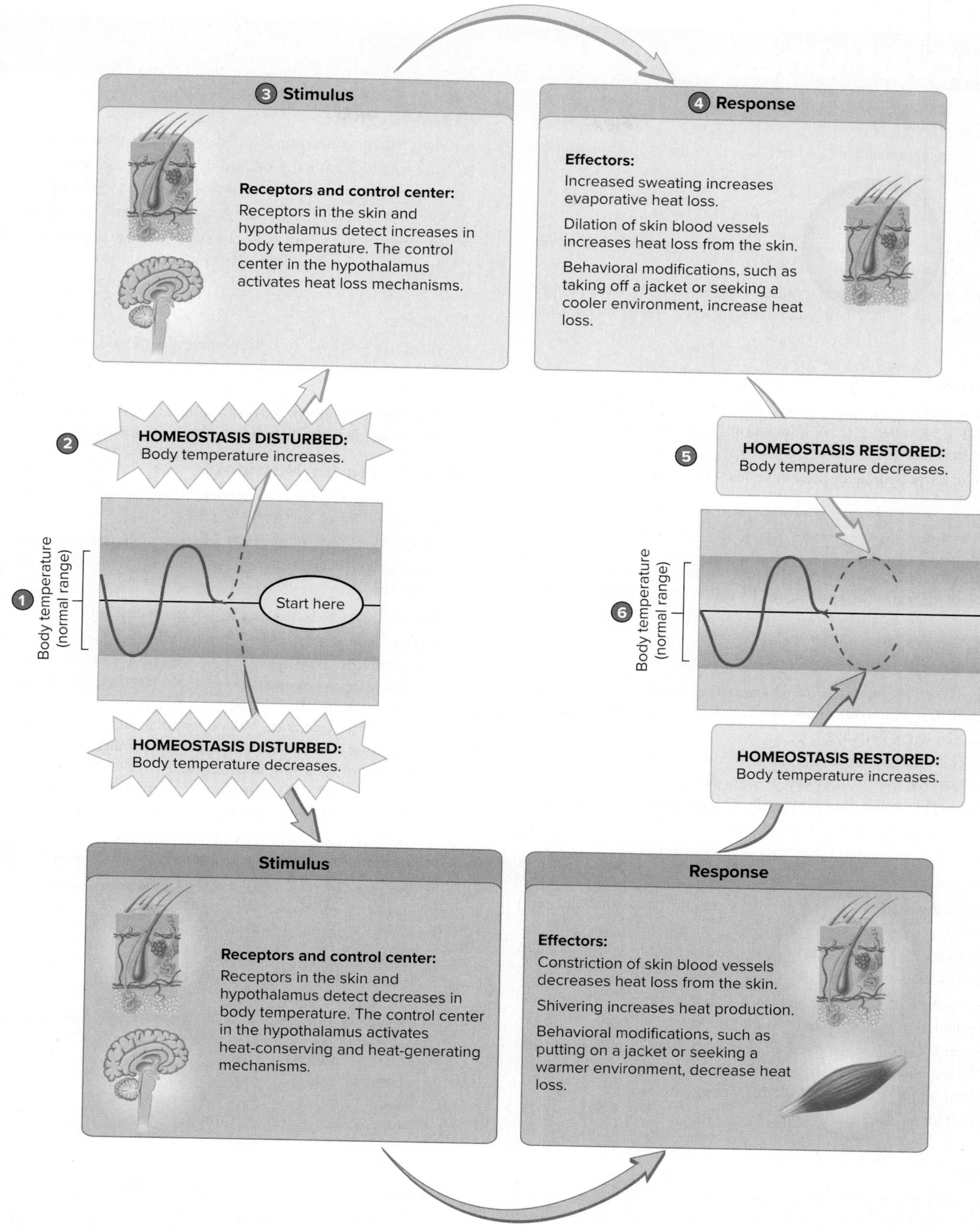

HOMEOSTASIS FIGURE 25.18 Summary of Temperature Regulation

(1) Body temperature is within normal range. (2) Body temperature increases outside the normal range, which causes homeostasis to be disturbed. (3) Receptors in the skin and hypothalamus detect the increase in body temperature, and the control center in the hypothalamus responds to the change in body temperature. (4) The effectors are activated. Blood vessels in the skin dilate, and sweating increases to promote heat loss and evaporative cooling. (5) Body temperature decreases. (6) Body temperature returns to its normal range, and homeostasis is restored. Observe the responses to a decrease in body temperature by following the lower *pink* arrows.

Concept Check

25.1 Nutrition

Nutrition is the ingestion and use of food, as well as the evaluation of food and drink requirements.

Nutrients

A. Nutrients are the chemicals used by the body: carbohydrates, lipids, proteins, vitamins, minerals, and water.

B. Essential nutrients must be ingested because the body either cannot manufacture them at all or cannot manufacture them in adequate amounts.

Kilocalories

A. A calorie (cal) is the heat (energy) necessary to raise the temperature of 1 g of water 1°C. A kilocalorie (kcal), or Calorie (Cal), is 1000 calories.

B. A gram of carbohydrate or protein yields 4 kcal, and a gram of lipids yields 9 kcal.

MyPlate

The MyPlate icon provides a visual reminder for making choices at mealtime, by selecting healthful foods from five food groups. Half the meal should be fruits and vegetables.

Carbohydrates

A. Carbohydrates are ingested as monosaccharides (glucose, fructose), disaccharides (sucrose, maltose, lactose), and polysaccharides (starch, glycogen, cellulose).

B. Polysaccharides and disaccharides are converted to glucose, which can be used for energy or stored as glycogen or lipids.

C. The Acceptable Macronutrient Distribution Range (AMDR) for carbohydrates is 45–65% of total kilocalories.

Lipids

A. Lipids are ingested as triglycerides (95%) or cholesterol and phospholipids (5%).

B. Monounsaturated fats and oils have one double bond, and polyunsaturated fats and oils have two or more double bonds.

C. Most unprocessed polyunsaturated oils occur in the *cis* form, whereas hydrogenated polyunsaturated oils are in the *trans* form.

D. Triglycerides are used for energy or stored in adipose tissue. Cholesterol forms other molecules, such as steroid hormones. Cholesterol and phospholipids are part of the plasma membrane.

E. The AMDR for lipids is 20–35%.

Proteins

A. Proteins are ingested and broken down into amino acids.

B. Proteins function in protection (antibodies), regulation (enzymes, hormones), structure (collagen), muscle contraction (actin and myosin), and transportation (hemoglobin, transport proteins); they also act as receptor molecules.

C. The AMDR for protein is 10–35% of total kilocalories.

Vitamins

A. Many vitamins function as coenzymes or as parts of coenzymes.

B. Most vitamins are not produced by the body and must be obtained in the diet. Some vitamins can be formed from provitamins.

C. Vitamins are classified as either fat-soluble or water-soluble.

D. Recommended Dietary Allowances (RDAs) are a guide for estimating the nutritional needs of groups of people based on their age, gender, and other factors.

Minerals

A. Minerals contribute to normal metabolism, add mechanical strength to bones and teeth, function as buffers, and are involved in osmotic balance.

B. The daily requirement for major minerals is 100 mg or more daily; for trace minerals, less than 100 mg daily is sufficient.

Daily Values for Nutrients

A. Daily Values are dietary references that can be used to plan a healthful diet.

B. Daily Values for vitamins and minerals are based on Reference Daily Intakes, which are generally the highest 1968 RDA values of age categories.

C. Daily Values are based on Daily Reference Values.

- The Daily Reference Values for energy-producing nutrients (carbohydrates, total fat, saturated fat, and proteins) and dietary fiber are recommended percentages of the total kilocalories ingested daily for each nutrient.
- The Daily Reference Values for total fats, saturated fats, cholesterol, and sodium are the uppermost limits considered desirable because of their link to diseases.

D. The % Daily Value is the percent of the recommended Daily Value of a nutrient found in one serving of a particular food.

1. *Which of these statements concerning kilocalories is true?* 

   a. *A kilocalorie is the amount of energy required to raise the temperature of 1 g of water 1°C.*
   b. *There are 9 kcal in a gram of protein.*
   c. *There are 4 kcal in a gram of lipids.*
   d. *A pound of body fat contains 3500 kcal.*

2. *What type of nutrient is recommended as the primary energy source in the diet?* Remember
   a. *carbohydrates*
   b. *lipids*
   c. *proteins*
   d. *cellulose*

3. *A source of monounsaturated fats is* 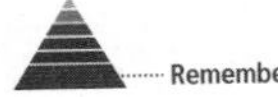

   a. *fat associated with meat.*
   b. *egg yolks.*
   c. *whole milk.*
   d. *fish oil.*
   e. *olive oil.*

4. *A complete protein food* 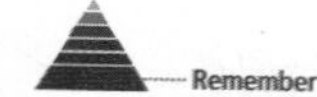

   a. *provides the daily amount (grams) of protein recommended for a healthful diet.*
   b. *can be used to synthesize the nonessential amino acids.*
   c. *contains all 20 amino acids.*
   d. *includes beans, peas, and leafy green vegetables.*

5. *Concerning vitamins,* 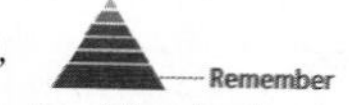

   a. *most can be synthesized by the body.*
   b. *they are normally broken down before they can be used by the body.*
   c. *A, D, E, and K are water-soluble vitamins.*
   d. *many function as coenzymes.*

6. *Minerals* 

   a. *are inorganic nutrients.*
   b. *compose about 4–5% of total body weight.*
   c. *act as buffers and osmotic regulators.*
   d. *are components of enzymes.*
   e. *All of these are correct.*

7. *One serving of a food contains 2 g of saturated fat. What % Daily Value for saturated fat would appear on the food label for this food?* Apply

8. *An active teenage boy has a daily intake of 3000 kcal. What is the maximum amount (weight) of total fats he should consume, according to the Daily Values?* Apply

9. *If the teenager in question 8 eats a serving of food that has a total fat content of 10 g/serving, what is his % Daily Value for total fat?* Apply

10. *Why does a vegetarian usually have to be more careful about his or her diet than a person who eats meat?* Understand

11. *Explain why a person suffering from copper deficiency feels tired all the time.* Apply

12. *Why can some people lose weight on a 1200 kcal/day diet, whereas others cannot?* Apply

13. *After learning that sweat evaporation results in loss of calories, an anatomy and physiology student enters a sauna to try to lose weight. He reasons that a liter (about a quart) of water weighs 1000 g, which is equivalent to 580,000 cal, or 580 kcal, of heat when lost as sweat. Therefore, instead of reducing his diet by 580 kcal/day, he believes that losing a liter of sweat every day in the sauna will cause him to lose about a pound of fat a week. Will this approach work? Explain.* Apply

25.2 Metabolism

A. Metabolism consists of catabolism and anabolism. Catabolism breaks down molecules and gives off energy. Anabolism builds up molecules and requires energy.

B. The energy in carbohydrates, lipids, and proteins is used to produce ATP through oxidation-reduction reactions.

25.3 Carbohydrate Metabolism

Glycolysis

Glycolysis is the breakdown of glucose into two pyruvate molecules. Also produced are two NADH molecules and two ATP molecules.

Anaerobic Respiration

A. Anaerobic respiration is the breakdown of glucose in the absence of O_2 into two lactate molecules. Two ATP molecules are also produced.

B. Lactate can be converted to glucose (Cori cycle) using aerobically produced ATP (oxygen deficit).

Aerobic Respiration

A. Aerobic respiration is the breakdown of glucose in the presence of O_2 to produce CO_2, water, and 32 ATP molecules.

B. The first phase is glycolysis, which produces two ATP, two NADH, and two pyruvate molecules.

C. The second phase is the conversion of the two pyruvate molecules into two molecules of acetyl-CoA. These reactions also produce two NADH and two CO_2 molecules.

D. The third phase is the citric acid cycle, which produces two ATP, six NADH, two $FADH_2$, and four CO_2 molecules.

E. The fourth phase is the electron-transport chain. The high-energy electrons in NADH and $FADH_2$ enter the electron-transport chain and are used in the synthesis of ATP and water.

14. *Glycolysis* 

   a. *is the breakdown of glucose to two pyruvate molecules.*
   b. *requires the input of two ATP molecules.*
   c. *produces two NADH molecules.*
   d. *does not require O_2.*
   e. *All of these are correct.*

15. *Anaerobic glycolysis* __________ *O_2 and produces* __________ *energy (ATP) for the cell than aerobic respiration.* 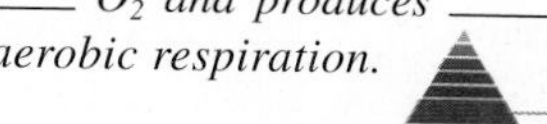

   a. *does not require, more*
   b. *does not require, less*
   c. *requires, more*
   d. *requires, less*

16. *The molecule that moves electrons from the citric acid cycle to the electron-transport chain is* 

   a. *tRNA.*
   b. *mRNA.*
   c. *ADP.*
   d. *NADH.*
   e. *pyruvic acid.*

17. *The CO_2 you breathe out comes from* 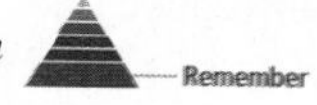

   a. *glycolysis.*
   b. *the electron-transport chain.*
   c. *anaerobic glycolysis.*
   d. *the food you eat.*

25.4 Lipid Metabolism

A. Triglycerides are broken down and released as free fatty acids.

B. Free fatty acids are taken up by cells and broken down by beta-oxidation into acetyl-CoA.
   - Acetyl-CoA can enter the citric acid cycle.
   - Acetyl-CoA can be converted into ketone bodies.

18. *Lipids are*
    a. *stored primarily as triglycerides.*
    b. *synthesized by beta-oxidation.*
    c. *broken down by oxidative deamination.*
    d. *All of these are correct.*

25.5 Protein Metabolism

A. New amino acids are formed by transamination, the transfer of an amine group to a keto acid.

B. Amino acids are used to synthesize proteins. If used for energy, ammonia is produced as a by-product of oxidative deamination. Ammonia is converted to urea and excreted.

19. *Amino acids* 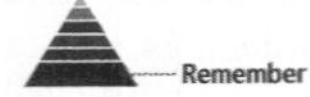
    a. *are classified as essential or nonessential.*
    b. *can be synthesized in a transamination reaction.*
    c. *can be used as a source of energy.*
    d. *can be converted to keto acids.*
    e. *All of these are correct.*

20. *Ammonia is* 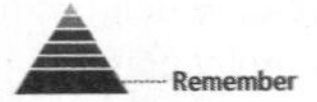
    a. *a by-product of lipid metabolism.*
    b. *formed during ketogenesis.*
    c. *converted into urea in the liver.*
    d. *produced during lipogenesis.*
    e. *converted to keto acids.*

25.6 Interconversion of Nutrient Molecules

A. Glycogenesis is the formation of glycogen from glucose.

B. Lipogenesis is the formation of lipids from glucose and amino acids.

C. Glycogenolysis is the breakdown of glycogen to glucose.

D. Gluconeogenesis is the formation of glucose from amino acids and glycerol.

21. *The conversion of amino acids and glycerol into glucose is called*
    a. *gluconeogenesis.*
    b. *glycogenesis.*
    c. *glycogenolysis.*
    d. *ketogenesis.*

25.7 Metabolic States

A. In the absorptive state, nutrients are used as energy or stored.

B. In the postabsorptive state, stored nutrients are used for energy.

22. *Which of these events takes place during the absorptive state?*
    a. *Glycogen is converted into glucose.*
    b. *Glucose is converted into lipids.*
    c. *Ketones are produced.*
    d. *Proteins are converted into glucose.*

25.8 Metabolic Rate

Metabolic rate is the total energy expenditure per unit of time, and it has three components.

Basal Metabolic Rate

Basal metabolic rate, the energy used at rest, is 60% of the metabolic rate.

Thermic Effect of Food

The energy used to digest and absorb food, called the thermic effect of food, is 10% of the metabolic rate.

Muscular Activity

Muscular energy, that used for muscle contraction, is 30% of the metabolic rate.

23. *Thyroid hormone increases the activity of the sodium-potassium pump. If a person produced excess amounts of thyroid hormone, how would basal metabolic rate, body weight, and body temperature be affected? How would the body attempt to compensate for the changes in body weight and temperature?*

25.9 Body Temperature Regulation

A. Body temperature is maintained by balancing heat gain and heat loss.
   - Heat is produced through metabolism.
   - Heat is exchanged with the environment through radiation, conduction, convection, and evaporation.

B. The greater the temperature difference between the body and the environment, the greater the rate of heat exchange.

C. Body temperature is regulated by a set point in the hypothalamus.

24. *Loss of heat resulting from loss of water from the body's surface is*
    a. *radiation.*
    b. *conduction.*
    c. *evaporation.*
    d. *convection.*

25. *In some diseases, an infection causes a high fever, resulting in a crisis state. Once body temperature begins to return to normal, the person is on the way to recovery. If you were looking for symptoms in a person who had just passed through the crisis state, would you look for dry, pale skin or flushed, wet skin? Explain.*

Answers to this chapter's odd-numbered Concept Check questions appear in Appendix F.

26 CHAPTER

Urinary System

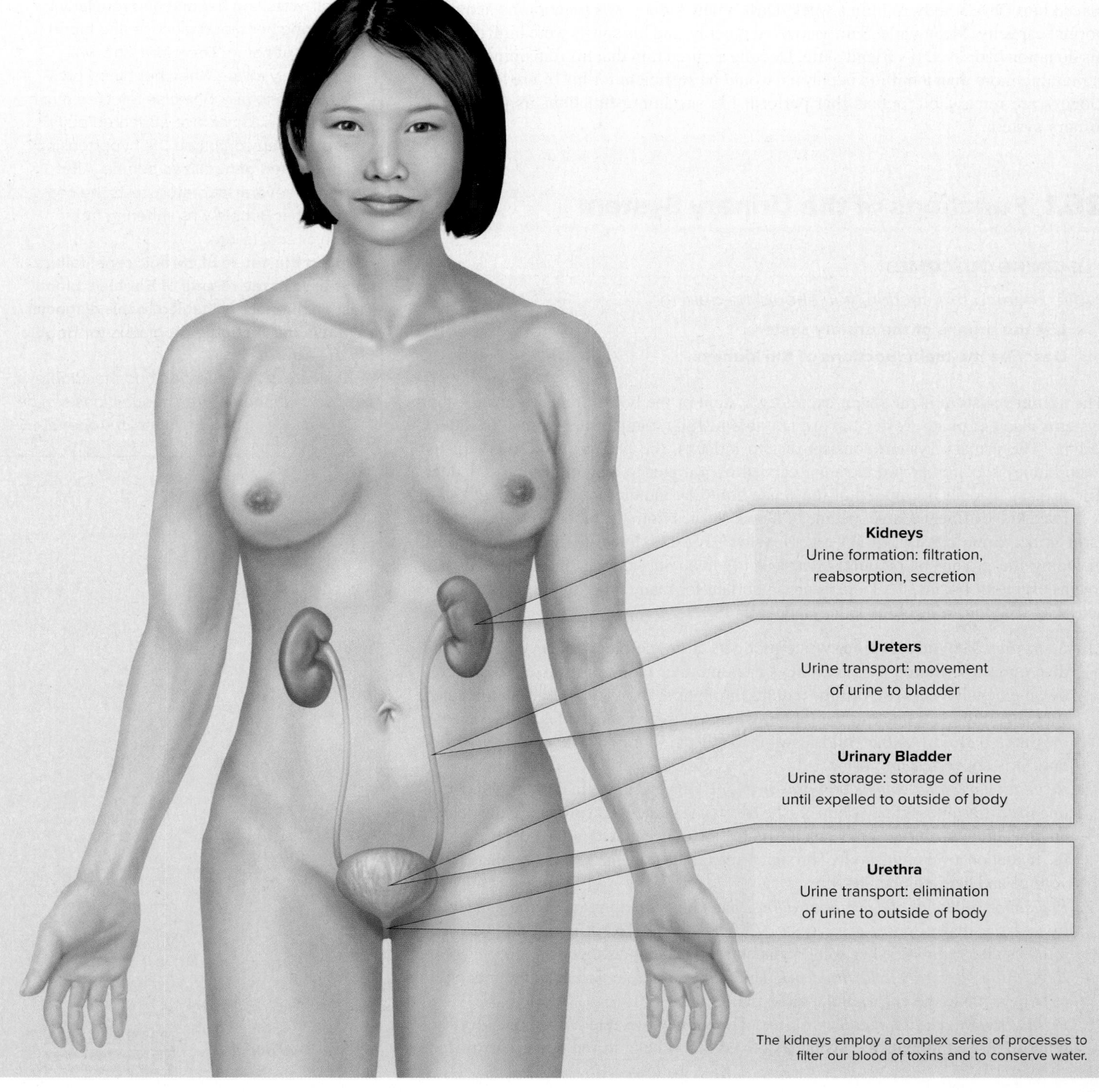

The kidneys employ a complex series of processes to filter our blood of toxins and to conserve water.

It must have been fate. Sam met Dave when they played on the same softball team, and the two became great friends. A few years later, Dave was diagnosed with a fatal, progressive kidney disease. Like Bobbie in this chapter's Learn to Predict, Dave began feeling tired and suffering from generalized edema. Without a kidney transplant, Dave could expect to live only a few more years. Immediately, Sam volunteered to be tested as a possible kidney donor and, amazingly, he was a nearly perfect match. After months of testing and planning, one of Sam's kidneys was removed and placed into Dave's body. Within a week, Dave's new kidney was functioning at almost normal capacity. Meanwhile, Sam recovered quickly, and his spirits were high because his donation had saved his friend's life. Doctors assured him that his remaining kidney, containing more than a million nephrons, would be sufficient for his future needs. The kidneys are remarkable organs that perform life-sustaining functions as part of the urinary system.

Learn to Predict

Fifty-seven-year-old Bobbie is living proof that a person can live with type 2 diabetes. Since being diagnosed with the condition 15 years ago, she has taken good care of herself, watching her diet and regularly monitoring her blood glucose and blood pressure at home. Therefore, she was immediately aware when her blood pressure began to rise. She also felt tired much of the time, and her face appeared puffy. Her physician confirmed the hypertension and detected generalized edema. After ordering several laboratory tests, he concluded that Bobbie was suffering from chronic renal failure.

Explain the cause of chronic renal failure and predict the results of Bobbie's blood test and urinalysis that led to this diagnosis. What is the probable prognosis for Bobbie in the future?

Answers to this question and the chapter's odd-numbered Predict questions can be found in Appendix E.

26.1 Functions of the Urinary System

LEARNING OUTCOMES

After reading this section, you should be able to

A. **List the organs of the urinary system.**

B. **Describe the main functions of the kidneys.**

The **urinary system** is the major excretory system of the body. Some organs in other systems also eliminate wastes but are not able to fully compensate in case of kidney failure. The urinary system consists of two kidneys, the primary excretory organs. Each kidney's excretory products are carried by a ureter to a single urinary bladder. The urinary bladder is emptied of the waste liquid by the urethra (figure 26.1).

Each kidney filters a large volume of blood. Wastes from the blood are collected and form urine. Urine consists of (1) excess water; (2) excess ions; (3) metabolic wastes, including the protein by-product, urea; and (4) toxic substances. In addition to their role as excretory organs, the kidneys are important for many other important metabolic activities. The functions of the kidneys include:

1. *Excretion.* The kidneys filter waste products from the blood. Nearly 21% of cardiac output is filtered by the kidneys each minute. Fluid and waste are captured by an extensive network of tubes found throughout the kidney. Large molecules, such as proteins, remain in the blood, whereas smaller molecules and ions enter the filtered fluid. As the fluid flows through the kidneys, it is slowly modified until it is converted into urine.
2. *Regulation of blood volume and pressure.* The kidneys play a major role in controlling the extracellular fluid volume in the body. The kidneys can produce either a large volume of dilute urine or a small volume of concentrated urine, depending on the hydration level of the body. Through urine production, the kidneys regulate blood volume and hence blood pressure.
3. *Regulation of blood solute concentrations.* The kidneys help regulate the concentration of the major ions, such as Na^+, Cl^-, K^+, Ca^{2+}, HCO_3^-, and HPO_4^{2-}. The kidneys also regulate other solute concentrations, such as urea.
4. *Regulation of extracellular fluid pH.* The kidneys secrete variable amounts of H^+ to help regulate the extracellular fluid pH.
5. *Regulation of red blood cell synthesis.* The kidneys secrete a hormone, erythropoietin, that stimulates the synthesis of red blood cells in red bone marrow (see chapter 19).

Module 13
Urinary System

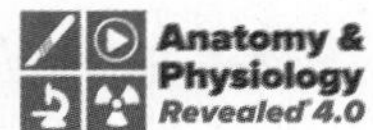

of juxtamedullary nephrons and are closer to the outer edge of the cortex (figure 26.4).

The Renal Corpuscle

The filtration portion of the nephron is housed in the renal corpuscle. The renal corpuscle consists of (1) the glomerulus and (2) the glomerular capsule (or, *Bowman capsule*). The **glomerulus** (glo-MER-you-lus; ball of yarn) is a network of capillaries twisted around each other like a ball of yarn (figure 26.5*a,b*). Fluid filtered from the glomerular capillaries is called the filtrate. The **glomerular capsule** is an indented, double-walled chamber surrounding the glomerulus. From the glomerular capsule, the filtered fluid flows into the proximal convoluted tubule region of the renal tubule.

A glomerular capsule consists of two layers: (1) an outer parietal layer and (2) an inner visceral layer (figure 26.5*b*). The outer layer is the **parietal layer.** It is constructed of simple squamous epithelial cells. The epithelial cells become cube-shaped at the beginning of the proximal convoluted tubule. The inner layer is the **visceral layer.** It is constructed of specialized cells called **podocytes,** which wrap around the glomerular capillaries.

The renal corpuscle has several unique characteristics that make it particularly efficient at filtration—the main function of the kidneys.

1. *Porous capillaries.* The glomerular capillaries are highly permeable due to the presence of **fenestrae** (fe-NES-tree; windows). Recall from chapter 21 that capillaries have different levels of permeability, depending on the size of their pores. In the case of fenestrae, neither large proteins nor blood cells can fit through them.
2. *Porous visceral layer.* Gaps, called **filtration slits,** are between the cell processes of the podocytes of the visceral layer (figure 26.5*c*). A basement membrane lies sandwiched between the endothelial cells of the glomerular capillaries and the podocytes of the glomerular capsule.
3. *High pressure.* An **afferent** (AF-eh-rent; *aff-*, toward) **arteriole** supplies blood to the glomerulus for filtration. An **efferent** (EF-eh-rent; *eff-*, away from) **arteriole** transports the filtered blood away from the glomerulus (figure 26.5*a*). The glomerular capillaries have much higher pressure than other capillaries due to the smaller diameter of the efferent arteriole compared to the afferent arteriole.

Together, the structures in the corpuscle make up the **filtration membrane.** The filtration membrane consists of capillary endothelium, the basement membrane, and the podocytes of the glomerular capsule (figure 26.5*d*). We will discuss the filtration membrane in greater detail in section 26.3. The filtration membrane performs the first major step in urine production. Urine production begins when the filtration membrane filters the blood. The filtered fluid, called **filtrate,** then enters the lumen, or capsular space, inside the glomerular capsule.

An important regulatory structure, called the **juxtaglomerular apparatus,** is located next to the glomerulus (figure 26.5*b*).

The juxtaglomerular apparatus consists of a unique set of afferent arteriole cells and specialized cells in the distal convoluted tubule that are in close contact with each other. These specialized cells include the following:

1. At the point where the afferent arteriole enters the renal corpuscle, it has a cuff of specialized smooth muscle cells around it. These cells are called **juxtaglomerular cells.**
2. A part of the distal convoluted tubule of the nephron lies between the afferent and efferent arterioles next to the renal corpuscle. In this section of the distal convoluted tubule, there is a group of specialized cells called the **macula** (MAK-you-lah) **densa.**

Secretion of the enzyme **renin** (REE-nin) by the juxtaglomerular apparatus plays an important role in the regulation of filtrate formation and blood pressure (see section 26.4).

The Renal Tubule

Once the blood is filtered, the resulting fluid is modified to form urine as it passes through each section of the renal tubule. The first section is the **proximal convoluted tubule.** It is approximately 14 mm long and 60 μm in diameter. The wall of the proximal convoluted tubule is composed of simple cuboidal epithelium. The proximal convoluted tubule cells rest on a basement membrane, which forms the outer surface of the tubule. These cells have many microvilli projecting from the luminal (next to the filtrate) surface of the cells (figure 26.6*a,b*). The microvilli substantially increase the surface area of the epithelial cells.

As the proximal convoluted tubule continues descending toward the medulla, the cell type begins to change. At this point, the renal tubule is called the nephron loop. Every nephron loop has two limbs: (1) the **descending limb** and (2) the **ascending limb.**

Clinical GENETICS 26.1 Polycystic Kidney Disease

Polycystic kidney disease is the third-leading cause of renal failure (after diabetes mellitus and high blood pressure). Approximately 90% of patients inherit the condition as an autosomal dominant trait. Consequently, if one parent carries an allele for this disorder, each child has a 50% chance of also having the disorder (see chapter 29). The gene for this condition codes for a protein that may regulate cell-to-cell interactions.

In people affected by polycystic kidney disease, the kidneys are enlarged and often contain large, fluid-filled cysts varying in size from a few millimeters to centimeters. The cysts increase in number and enlarge as the person ages. Development of the cysts results from abnormal cell-to-cell interactions and causes excess proliferation of the epithelial cells that make up the kidney nephrons and collecting ducts.

Polycystic kidney disease is often detected using ultrasound techniques. The condition is usually diagnosed when patients are between 30 and 50 years of age. Approximately 50% of patients require hemodialysis (see this chapter's Systems Pathology) by 70 years of age.

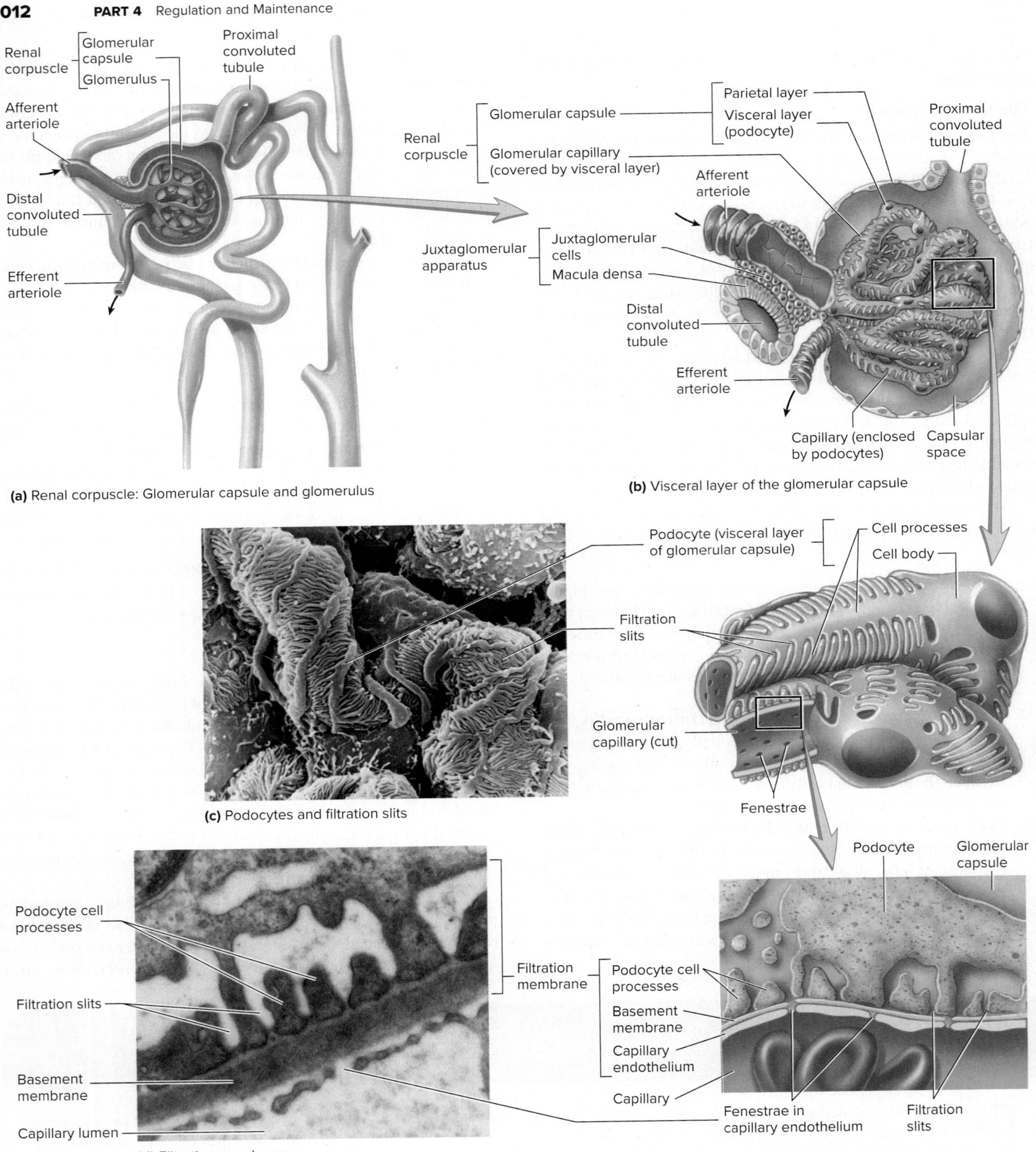

FIGURE 26.5 Renal Corpuscle

Filtration of the blood occurs in the renal corpuscle. (*a*) The renal corpuscle consists of the glomerular capsule and the glomerulus. The glomerular capsule is indented to form a double-walled chamber and surrounds the glomerulus, a network of capillaries. Blood flows from the afferent arteriole into the glomerulus and leaves the glomerulus through the efferent arteriole. (*b*) The visceral layer of the glomerular capsule covers the glomerular capillaries. Fluid from the blood enters the glomerular capsule and passes into the proximal convoluted tubule of the nephron. The juxtaglomerular apparatus consists of cells from the wall of the afferent arteriole and the distal convoluted tubule. (*c*) The glomerulus is composed of fenestrated capillaries. The visceral layer of the glomerular capsule consists of specialized cells called podocytes. Spaces between the podocyte cell processes are called filtration slits. (*d*) The filtration membrane consists of the fenestrated glomerular capillary endothelium, a basement membrane, and the podocyte cell processes. (c) David M. Phillips/Science Source; (d) Biophoto Associates/Science Source

FUNDAMENTAL **Figure**

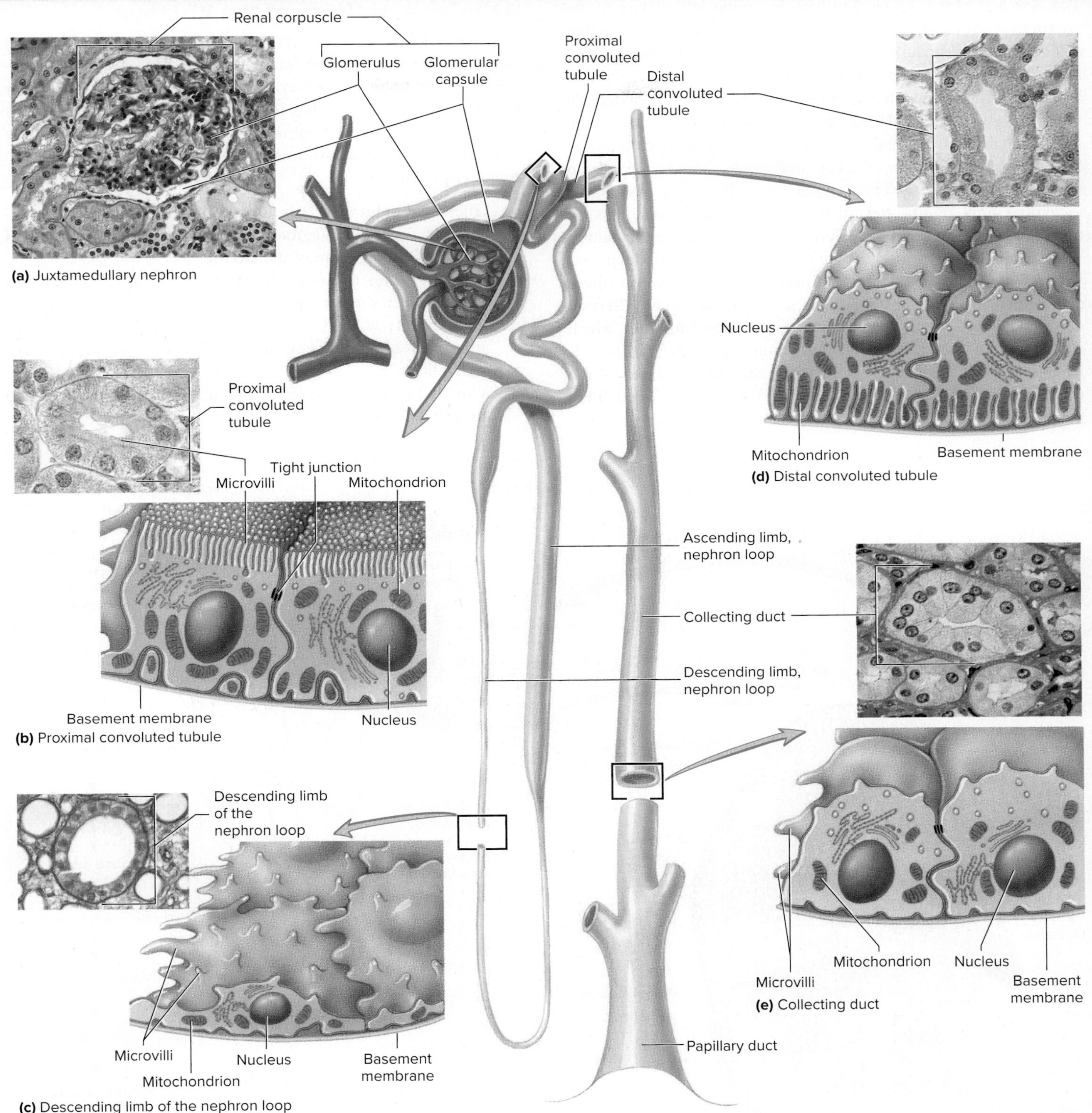

FIGURE 26.6 Histology of the Nephron

The function of each region of the renal tubule is evident based on the type of epithelial tissue found there. (*a*) Juxtamedullary nephrons have longer nephron loops than cortical nephrons. (*b*) The luminal surface of the epithelial cells in the proximal convoluted tubule is lined with numerous microvilli. The basal surface of each cell rests on a basement membrane, and each cell is bound to the adjacent cells by tight junctions. Active reabsorption and secretion are major functions. (*c*) The thin segment of the descending limb of the nephron loops is composed of simple squamous epithelial cells that have microvilli and contain a relatively small number of mitochondria. Water easily difuses from the thin segment into the interstitial fluid. (*d*) The cells of the distal convoluted tubule have sparse microvilli and numerous mitochondria, and they actively reabsorb Na^+, K^+, and Cl^-. (*e*) The cells of the collecting duct have some microvilli and numerous mitochondria, and they actively reabsorb Na^+, K^+, and Cl^-. (a) MICROSCAPE/Science Source; (b) JOSE CALVO/Science Source; (c) Alvin Telser/Science Source; (d) JOSE CALVO/Science Source; (e) M. I. Walker/Science Source

The first part of the descending limb is similar in structure to the proximal convoluted tubule. The portion of the nephron loop that extends into the medulla becomes very thin near the bend of the loop (figure 26.6*a,c*). The lumen in the thin part narrows, and an abrupt transition occurs from simple cuboidal epithelium to simple squamous epithelium. Like the descending limb, the first part of the ascending limb is thin and made of simple squamous epithelium. Soon, however, it becomes thicker, and simple cuboidal epithelium replaces the simple squamous epithelium. The thick part of the ascending limb returns toward the renal corpuscle and ends by transitioning to the distal convoluted tubule near the macula densa.

The **distal convoluted tubule** is shorter than the proximal convoluted tubule. Its epithelium is simple cuboidal. However, these cells are smaller and have fewer microvilli (figure 26.6*d*). Several distal convoluted tubules connect to a single **collecting duct,** which is composed of simple cuboidal epithelium (figure 26.6*e*). The collecting duct, which is larger in diameter than the segments of the nephron, form much of the medullary rays and extend through the medulla toward the tips of the renal pyramids.

Arteries and Veins of the Kidneys

A system of blood vessels allows the exchange of materials that occurs in the kidneys. The renal arteries branch off the abdominal aorta and enter the kidneys (figure 26.7). As the renal artery extends deep into the kidney, it branches into smaller and smaller blood vessels. The following is a list of arteries, in order, starting with renal artery and progressing to the blood vessels that surround each nephron.

1. The **renal artery** delivers approximately 21% of cardiac output per minute. The **segmental arteries** branch from the renal artery to each portion of the kidney.
2. The **interlobar** (in-ter-LOH-bar; between the lobes) **arteries** pass between the renal pyramids.
3. The **arcuate** (AR-kyu-ate; arched) **arteries** branch from the interlobar arteries. They arch between the cortex and the medulla.
4. **Cortical radiate arteries** branch off the arcuate arteries and project into the cortex.

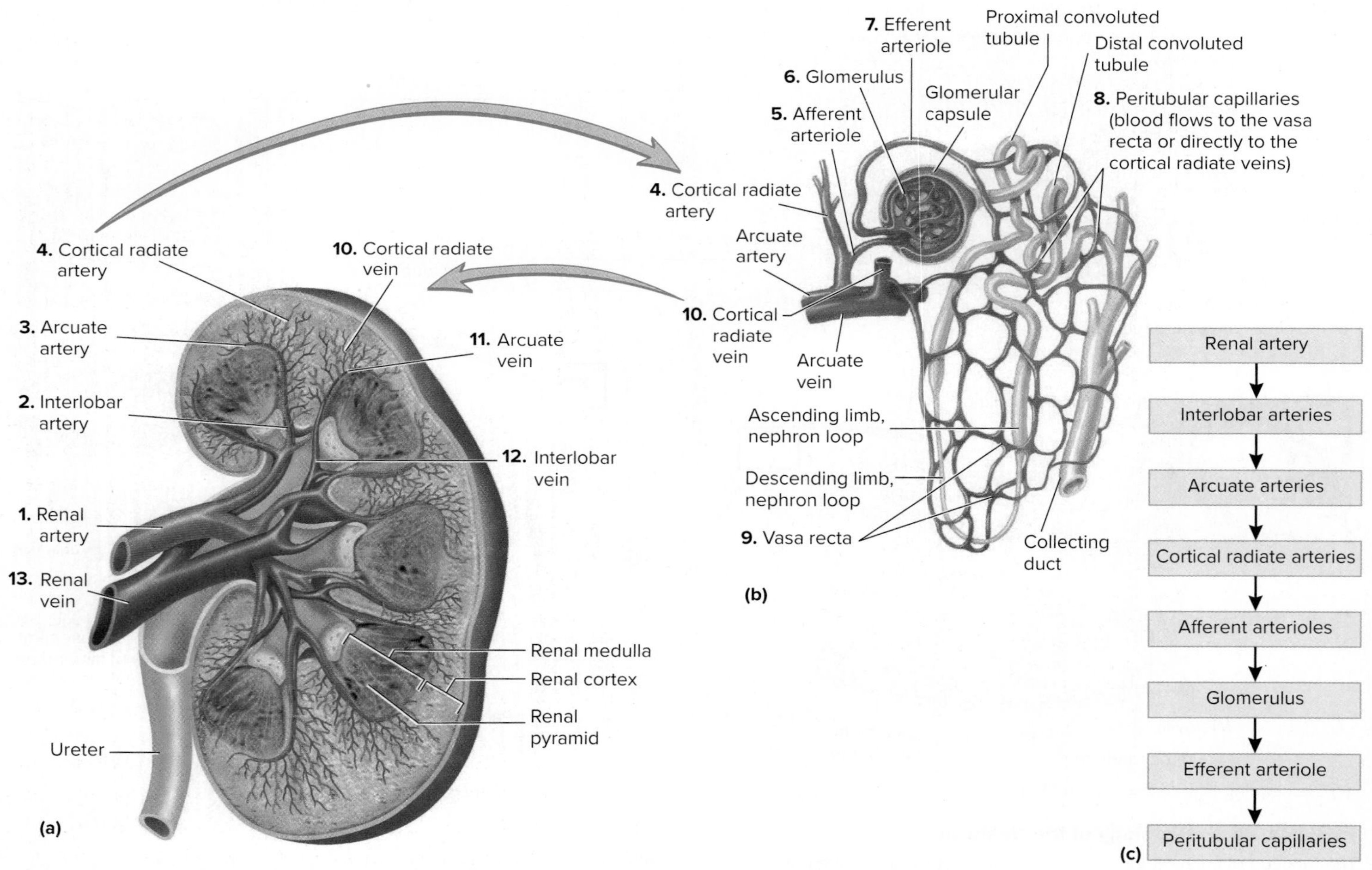

FIGURE 26.7 Blood Flow Through the Kidney

Numbers 1–13 show the sequence of blood flow through the kidney. (*a*) Blood flow through the larger arteries and veins of the kidney. Vessels are listed in order from entry of blood into the kidney to exit of blood from the kidney. (*b*) Blood flow through the arteries, capillaries, and veins that provide circulation to the nephrons. Vessels are listed in order from blood flowing into the glomerulus and blood exiting the nephron circulation. (c) Blood flow pathway from entry into the kidney and through vessels of the nephron. APR

5. **The afferent arterioles** arise from branches of the cortical radiate arteries. The afferent arterioles carry blood into the glomerular capillaries.
6. The **glomerular capillaries** are the locations of filtration.
7. **Efferent arterioles** carry blood away from the glomerular capillaries.
8. The **peritubular** (around the tubes) **capillaries** branch from the efferent arterioles. They surround the proximal convoluted tubules, the distal convoluted tubules, and the nephron loops.
9. The **vasa recta** (VAH-sah REK-tah; straight vessels) are specialized portions of the peritubular capillaries that extend deep into the medulla of the kidney and surround the nephron loops and collecting ducts.

Blood from the peritubular capillaries, including the vasa recta, will return to the general circulation through the veins of the kidneys (see numbers 10-13 in figure 26.7*a,b*).

ASSESS YOUR PROGRESS

6. *What is the functional unit of the kidney? Name its parts.*
7. *Distinguish between cortical and juxtamedullary nephrons.*
8. *List the components of a renal corpuscle.*
9. *Describe the structure of the glomerular capsule, the glomerulus, and the filtration membrane.*
10. *Describe the structure of the afferent and efferent arterioles and the juxtaglomerular apparatus. What is the function of the juxtaglomerular apparatus?*
11. *Describe the structure and location of the proximal convoluted tubule, nephron loop, distal convoluted tubule, collecting duct, and papillary duct.*
12. *Explain the blood supply for the kidney.*

26.3 Urine Production

LEARNING OUTCOMES

After reading this section, you should be able to

A. **Briefly describe the three processes necessary for urine production.**
B. **Identify the principal factors that influence filtration and explain how they affect the rate of filtrate formation.**
C. **Explain how filtration is regulated.**
D. **Describe the role of the various regions of the kidney tubule in the process of reabsorption.**
E. **Explain how substances are able to move across the wall of the tubule.**
F. **Relate the types of substances that are moved during tubular secretion and explain how those substances are moved.**
G. **Describe the three mechanisms that explain the kidney's ability to concentrate urine.**

The primary function of the kidney is regulation of body fluid composition. The kidney is the organ that sorts the substances from the blood for either removal in the urine or return to the blood. Substances that are waste products, toxins, and excess materials are permanently removed from the body, whereas other substances need to be preserved to maintain homeostasis. The structural components that perform this sorting are the nephrons, the functional units of the kidney. If you have ever decided to organize your "junk" drawer in your desk or kitchen, you may realize just how difficult it is to quickly sort through all its contents. In fact, you may have found yourself simply emptying the drawer onto a table and then sorting the contents one by one as you place objects into a "save group" or a "throw away group." In a sense, the kidney uses the same approach when regulating blood composition. The "throw away" items end up in the urine, and the "save" items go back into the blood.

Figure 26.8 details the three major steps in urine production: (1) filtration, (2) tubular reabsorption, and (3) tubular secretion.

1. *Filtration.* Blood pressure in the glomerular capillaries forces fluid and small molecules out of the blood. The filtered fluid is now called filtrate. Filtration is nonselective and separates based only on size or charge of molecules. Filtration is comparable to emptying your "junk" drawer of everything except large, permanent items. Filtration does not remove everything in the blood—it removes only those substances small enough to fit through the filtration membrane.
2. *Tubular reabsorption.* Cells in the renal tubules contain many transport proteins. These transport proteins move water and some filtered molecules from the filtrate back into the blood in the peritubular capillaries. This prevents them from being lost from the body as components of urine (these are the "saved" items from your junk drawer). Most of the filtered water and useful solutes have been returned to the blood by the time the filtrate has been modified to urine, whereas the remaining waste or excess substances and a small amount of water form urine (table 26.1).
3. *Tubular secretion.* Certain tubule cells transport additional solutes from the blood into the filtrate. Some of these solutes may not have been filtered by the filtration membrane (these are some "throw away" items that had been left behind in your junk drawer).

Urine consists of substances filtered directly from the blood and those that are secreted into the renal tubule, minus any reabsorbed substances.

Filtration

Filtration is a nonspecific process whereby materials are separated based on size or charge. A simple example of size filtration is demonstrated by a coffee maker in which coffee grounds are too large to pass through the coffee filter. In this case, the driving force of filtration is gravity. The kidneys also demonstrate size filtration by filtering the blood, but here, the driving force of filtration is blood pressure. Filtration is the first step in urine production. All blood components except blood cells and most proteins can leave the glomerular capillaries and enter the glomerular capsule as filtrate. It is the filtrate that will be modified into urine.

The importance of filtration is indicated by the large percentage of cardiac output, or blood, sent through the kidneys each minute. This percentage of cardiac output that flows through the kidneys is called the **renal fraction.** It varies from 12% to 30% of

FUNDAMENTAL **Figure**

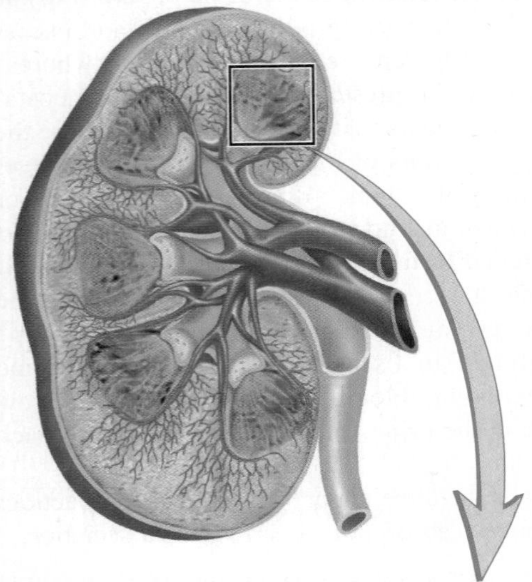

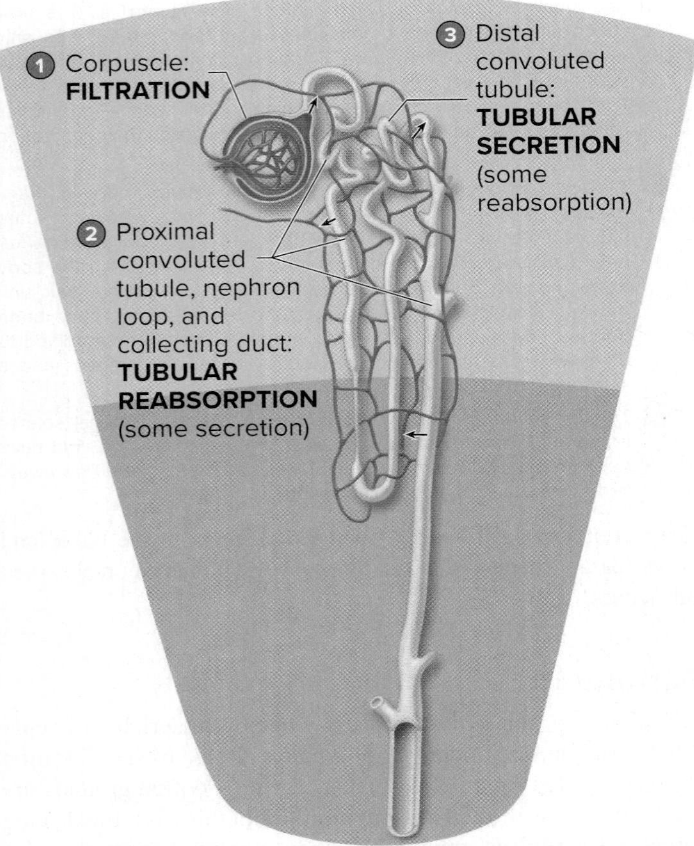

PROCESS **Figure 26.8**

Urine Production

Urine formation involves three major processes. Filtration occurs within the renal corpuscle. Reabsorption happens primarily in the proximal convoluted tubule and the nephron loop, although there is some reabsorption in the distal convoluted tubule. Secretion occurs mostly in the distal convoluted tubule, but may also occur in the proximal convoluted tubule. APR

What would happen to water reabsorption if the osmotic pressure of the blood were to increase above normal?

the cardiac output in healthy, resting adults, but it averages 21% (table 26.2).

There are several measurements of filtration that can be calculated as an indication of proper kidney function. These calculations can measure either (1) rate of whole blood flow or (2) rate of plasma flow.

To calculate the rate of whole blood flow through the kidneys, called **renal blood flow rate,** two pieces of information are necessary: (1) the renal fraction, or 21%, and (2) the cardiac output, or 5600 mL/min. The following equation (26.1) is used:

$$\begin{aligned}\text{Renal blood flow rate} &= \text{Cardiac output} \times \text{Renal fraction} \qquad (26.1)\\ 1176 \text{ mL/min} &= 5600 \text{ mL/min} \times 0.21\end{aligned}$$

To calculate the rate of plasma flow through the kidneys, called the **renal plasma flow rate,** we must account for the percentage of whole blood made up by plasma, which is approximately 55%. The equation is the following:

$$\begin{aligned}\text{Renal plasma flow rate} &= \text{Renal blood flow rate}\\ &\quad \times \text{\% of whole blood that is plasma} \qquad (26.2)\\ 650 \text{ mL/min} &= 1176 \text{ mL/min} \times 0.55\end{aligned}$$

To calculate the rate of filtrate formed per minute, called the **glomerular filtration rate (GRF),** you first need to know what percentage of plasma is filtered from the blood. This is called the **filtration fraction.** The filtration fraction is approximately 19%. Thus, to calculate the GFR, the following equation is used.

$$\begin{aligned}\text{GFR} &= \text{Renal plasma flow rate}\\ &\quad \times \text{Filtration fraction} \qquad (26.3)\\ 123.5 \text{ mL plasma/min} &= 650 \text{ mL/min} \times 0.19\end{aligned}$$

In other words, the GFR indicates that the kidneys form approximately 125 mL/min of filtrate. When calculated over the entire day, there are about 180,000 mL, or 180 L, of filtrate produced daily.

This enormous volume is equal to about ninety 2-liter soft drink bottles per day. Because a healthy person produces only 1000–2000 milliliters (1–2 liters) of *urine* each day, the equivalent of one 2-liter soft drink bottle, it is readily apparent that not all of the filtrate becomes urine. In fact, about 99% of the filtrate volume is reabsorbed into the blood as it travels through the renal tubule, and less than 1% becomes urine. Although it may seem pointless to remove so much material from the blood only to return it right away, it is important that filtration remains continuous so that waste products can be removed from the blood as quickly as possible.

Filtration Membrane

Recall that the renal corpuscles in the renal cortex house the filtration structures, each of which is called a **filtration membrane.** It separates materials on the basis of size and charge of the blood components. Thus, the filtration membrane allows water and small molecules to leave the blood while preventing blood cells and most proteins from leaving the blood. Several structures make up the filtration membrane:

1. The fenestrated glomerular capillaries
2. The basement membrane between the capillary wall and the visceral layer of the glomerular capsule
3. Podocytes of the visceral layer of the glomerular capsule (see figure 26.5*d*)

TABLE **26.1** **Concentrations of Major Solutes in Urine**

Substance	Plasma	Filtrate	Net Movement of Solute*	Urine	Urine Concentration/ Plasma Concentration‡
Water (L)	180	180	178.6	1.4	—
Organic molecules (mg/100 mL)					
Protein	3900–5000	6–11	−100.0	0†	0
Glucose	100	100	−100.0	0	0
Urea	26	26	−11.4	1820	70
Uric acid	3	3	−2.7	42	14
Creatinine	1.1	1.1	0.5	196	180
Ions (mEq/L)					
Na^+	142	142	−141.0	128	0.9
K^+	5	5	−4.5	60	12.0
Cl^-	103	103	−101.9	134	1.3
HCO_3^-	28	28	−27.9	14	0.5

*In many cases, solute moves into and out of the nephron. Numbers indicate net movement. Negative numbers are net movement out of the filtrate, and positive numbers are net movement into the filtrate.

†Trace amounts of protein can be found in the urine. A value of zero is assumed here.

‡Represents solute added to urine via secretion from the interstitial fluid.

TABLE **26.2** **Calculation of Renal Flow Rates**

	Amount per Minute (mL)	Calculation
Renal Blood Flow	1176	Amount of blood flowing through the kidneys per minute = cardiac output × the percentage of cardiac output that enters the kidneys 5600 mL blood/min × 0.21 = 1176 mL blood/min
Renal Plasma Flow	650	Amount of plasma flowing through the kidneys per minute = renal blood flow × % of the blood that is plasma 1176 mL blood/min × 0.55 ≈ 650 mL plasma/min
Glomerular Filtration Rate (GFR)	125	Amount of plasma (filtrate) that enters the glomerular capsule per minute = renal plasma flow × % of the plasma that enters the renal capsule 650 mL plasma/min × 0.19 ≈ 125 mL filtrate/min
Urine	1	Nonreabsorbed filtrate that leaves the kidneys per minute = glomerular filtration rate × % of the filtrate that is not reabsorbed into the blood 125 mL filtrate/min × 0.008 = 1 mL urine/min Milliliters of urine per minute can be converted to liters of urine per day by multiplying by 1.44. 1 mL urine/min × 1.44 = 1.4 L/day

Together, these components prevent molecules larger than 7 nm in diameter or those having a molecular mass equal to or greater than 40,000 daltons from passing through. For comparison, an antibody molecule is 12 nm, glucose is 0.9 nm, and the amino acid methionine is 0.7 nm in diameter. The exclusion of molecules larger than 7 nm is partially due to the fact that the fenestrae are about 7 nm in size. Most plasma proteins are slightly larger than 7 nm in diameter and are retained in the glomerular capillaries. However, albumin, which has a diameter just slightly less than 7 nm, enters the filtrate only in small amounts. Therefore, the filtrate is not protein-free but, rather, contains about 0.03% protein. In addition, some protein hormones, such as thyrotropin-releasing hormone, oxytocin, and antidiuretic hormone, are small enough to pass through the filtration membrane. Any protein that is filtered is actively reabsorbed by endocytosis and metabolized by the cells in the proximal convoluted tubule. The basement membrane and the podocytes further contribute to filtration through charge exclusions. They contain negatively charged glycoproteins, which repel negatively charged plasma proteins and prevent them from exiting the blood. In summary, the combined effect of the filtration membrane components prevents most proteins from exiting the blood on the basis of size and charge, and only a small amount of protein is found in the urine of healthy people.

PROCESS **Figure**

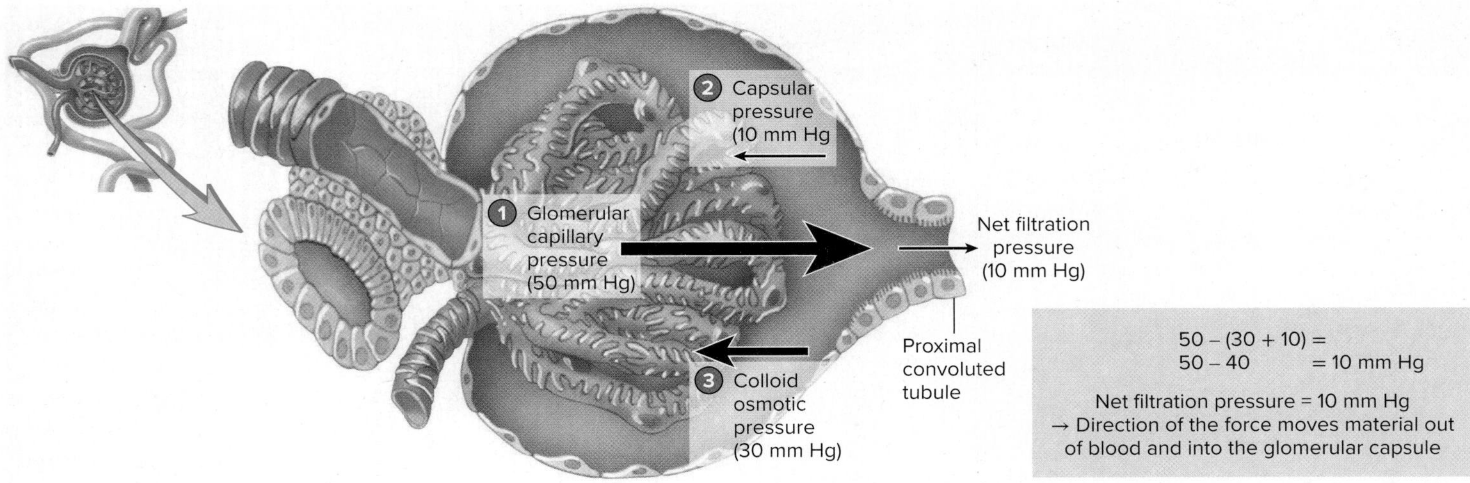

PROCESS **Figure 26.9**

Filtration Pressure

Filtration pressure across the filtration membrane is equal to the glomerular capillary pressure (GCP) minus the blood colloid osmotic pressure (BCOP) in the glomerular capillary minus the capsular hydrostatic pressure (CHP) in the glomerular capsule.

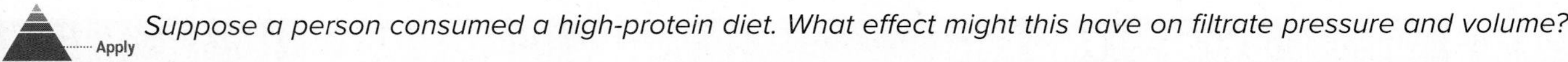

Suppose a person consumed a high-protein diet. What effect might this have on filtrate pressure and volume?

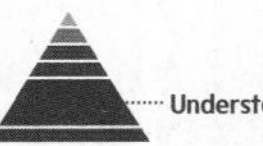

Predict 1

A hemoglobin molecule has a smaller diameter than an albumin molecule, but very little hemoglobin passes from the blood into the filtrate. Explain why. Under what circumstances do large amounts of hemoglobin enter the filtrate?

Filtration Pressure

No matter the type of size-based filter, there is one commonality: They all require a force to cause movement through it. For example, for a coffee maker, as noted earlier, the force is gravity. For the filtration membrane, three forces, or pressures, determine the amount of filtrate formed. The combination of these three pressures is called **filtration pressure.** Figure 26.9 details the three pressures contributing to filtration pressure.

1. **Glomerular capillary pressure (GCP).** The GCP is essentially the blood pressure inside the glomerular capillaries. It is an *outward pressure* from blood pressing on the fenestrated capillary walls. The GCP forces fluid and solutes out of the blood into the glomerular capsule. This GCP is higher than that in other capillaries of the body. The higher GCP is due to the smaller diameter of the efferent arteriole compared to that of the afferent arteriole and glomerular capillaries. As you learned in chapter 21, when the diameter of a vessel decreases, the resistance to blood flow through the vessel is greater. Thus, as the blood flows from the larger-diameter afferent arteriole through the glomerular capillaries to the smaller-diameter efferent arteriole, the blood pressure increases in the glomerular capillaries. Consequently, filtrate is forced across the filtration membrane into the lumen of the glomerular capsule. The GCP is approximately 50 mm Hg compared with approximately 30 mm Hg at the arterial end of other capillary networks.
2. **Capsular hydrostatic pressure (CHP).** The CHP is an *inward pressure* that opposes filtration. CHP is due to pressure from the filtrate fluid in the capsular space. The CHP is about 10 mm Hg.
3. **Blood colloid osmotic pressure (BCOP).** The BCOP is also an *inward pressure* that opposes filtration. It is due to the osmotic pressure of plasma proteins in the glomerular capillaries. Through osmosis, these proteins draw fluid back into the glomerular capillary from the glomerular capsule. The BCOP is greater at the end of the glomerular capillary than at its beginning because there is a higher protein concentration at the end of the glomerulus. The average BCOP is approximately 30 mm Hg.

To calculate filtration pressure, all three filtration pressures are summed. In a normal kidney, GCP is greater than the combination of CHP and BCOP. The filtration pressure is a net *outward* pressure of approximately 10 mm Hg:

$$\begin{array}{ccccccc} \text{Filtration pressure} & = & \text{Glomerular capillary pressure} & - & \text{Capsular hydrostatic pressure} & - & \text{Blood colloid osmotic pressure} \\ 10\text{ mm Hg} & = & 50\text{ mm Hg} & - & 10\text{ mm Hg} & - & 30\text{ mm Hg} \end{array} \quad (26.4)$$

Normally, the filtrate does not exert an osmotic force on fluid movement out of the glomerular capillaries because the solute concentration of the filtrate is very low. This is because few proteins cross the filtration membrane. However, in a disease such as **glomerular nephritis,** the filtration membrane becomes more permeable, allowing more protein than normal to enter the filtrate. The elevated protein in the filtrate increases the colloid osmotic pressure of the filtrate. This results in elevated filtration pressure, thereby increasing the filtrate volume.

Prolonged elevated blood pressure, or **hypertension,** can be very damaging to the glomerular capillaries. The persistent outward force on these delicate vessels can cause microtears, weakening their walls, which eventually leads to scarring of the glomerular capillaries. Over time, the available surface area for filtration and removal of excess fluid and wastes is dramatically reduced, leading to even higher blood pressure and further damage to remaining healthy vessels. An extended period of untreated hypertension could result in such severe damage to kidneys that the only treatment option is a kidney transplant. To prevent such damage, patients with hypertension can employ lifestyle habits to keep blood pressure from becoming excessively elevated.

Regulation of Glomerular Filtration Rate

The glomerular filtration rate (GFR) is very stable. It does not significantly change even if systemic blood pressure drops as low as 90 mm Hg or rises as high as 180 mm Hg. There are two ways through which the GFR is regulated: (1) intrinsic mechanisms and (2) extrinsic mechanisms. The intrinsic mechanisms are collectively referred to as **autoregulation** and are due to properties inherent to structures of the renal corpuscle. The extrinsic mechanisms are governed by the autonomic nervous system and particular hormones.

Intrinsic Mechanisms: Autoregulation

Autoregulation is achieved through two processes: (1) the myogenic mechanism and (2) tubuloglomerular feedback. The **myogenic mechanism** is associated with intrinsic properties of smooth muscle cells. In the afferent and efferent arterioles, smooth muscle cells act as stretch receptors. These stretch receptors detect changes in blood pressure. Elevated blood pressure causes increased stretch of the smooth muscle cells in the wall of the afferent arteriole. The smooth muscle cells contract in direct response to stretch. This causes vasoconstriction of the afferent arteriole. On the other hand, smooth muscle cells in the wall of the afferent arteriole relax when blood pressure decreases. Relaxation of the smooth muscle cells causes vasodilation of the afferent arteriole. In this way, blood supply to the glomerulus, and thus GFR, fluctuates very little, even when the mean arterial pressure changes.

Tubuloglomerular feedback matches filtrate flow past the macula densa cells of the juxtaglomerular apparatus to GFR. When the macula densa cells detect an increased flow rate, they send a signal to the juxtaglomerular cells of the afferent arteriole to constrict. Thus, glomerular filtration rate decreases due to a decreased glomerular capillary pressure.

Extrinsic Mechanisms: Sympathetic Nervous System and Hormones

Autoregulation maintains renal blood flow and filtrate formation at a relatively constant rate unless sympathetic stimulation is intense. In severe conditions such as hemorrhage or dehydration, the mean arterial pressure can drop below 90 mm Hg, and the sympathetic nervous system causes a dramatic decrease in renal blood flow and GFR to maintain homeostatic blood pressure. Because norepinephrine-secreting sympathetic neurons innervate the blood vessels of the kidneys, sympathetic stimulation constricts the small arteries and afferent arterioles, thereby decreasing renal blood flow and filtrate formation. Intense sympathetic stimulation, as may occur during shock or intense exercise, decreases the rate of filtrate formation to only a few milliliters per minute; however, small changes in sympathetic stimulation have a minimal effect on renal blood flow and filtrate formation.

Severe stress or circulatory shock causes dramatic vasoconstriction of the afferent arterioles. This lowers renal blood flow so severely that the blood supply to the kidney is inadequate to maintain normal kidney metabolism. As a consequence, kidney tissues can be damaged and thus unable to perform their normal functions if blood flow is not reestablished. Therefore, shock should be treated quickly. On the other hand, reduced blood flow to the kidneys during stress or shock is consistent with homeostasis. Intense vasoconstriction maintains blood pressure at levels adequate to sustain blood flow to organs such as the heart and brain. A reduction in blood flow to organs such as the kidneys is only harmful if the lack of blood flow is prolonged.

Under low blood pressure conditions, the juxtaglomerular cells in the juxtaglomerular apparatus secrete the enzyme renin. Recall from chapter 21 that secretion of this enzyme results in the activation of the potent vasoconstrictor angiotensin II. By stimulating vasoconstriction, angiotensin II helps maintain GFR at normal levels. This mechanism is discussed in greater detail in section 26.4.

ASSESS YOUR PROGRESS

13. *Name the three general processes involved in producing urine.*
14. *Contrast the rates of renal blood flow, renal plasma flow, and glomerular filtration. How do they affect urine production?*
15. *Describe the filtration membrane. What substances do not pass through it?*
16. *What is filtration pressure? How does glomerular capillary pressure affect filtration pressure and the amount of urine produced?*
17. *How do systemic blood pressure and afferent arteriole diameter affect glomerular capillary pressure?*
18. *Describe autoregulation.*
19. *Explain the effect of sympathetic stimulation on the kidney and the GFR during rest, exercise, and shock.*

Tubular Reabsorption

The process of tubular reabsorption entails nearly every type of cell transport mechanism you learned in chapter 3. **Tubular reabsorption** is the transport of water and solutes from the filtrate into the blood. Principally, water movement in the kidney is governed by osmosis. Recall that osmosis is the movement of water toward solutions with higher solute concentrations, or high osmotic pressure. Solute movement is quite often through diffusion across the renal tubule cells. Diffusion is the net movement of solutes down their concentration gradient. However, some molecules are too large to pass through the plasma membrane, or the cell may need to move a molecule against its concentration gradient. In these instances, cells use transport proteins. There are several types of transport proteins used by renal tubule cells. For example, symporters move two molecules or ions in the same direction. Occasionally, the energy from Na^+ diffusion drives the movement of a second ion or molecules. This process is secondary active transport.

Proper tubular reabsorption is critical in preventing the body from becoming overly dehydrated and deficient in important materials. Nearly all (99%) of the water and solutes are rapidly returned to the blood via the renal tubules, and because of this, toxins are quickly removed from the blood. The filtrate leaves the lumen of the glomerular capsule and flows first through the proximal convoluted tubule, into the nephron loop and the distal convoluted tubule, and then finally into the collecting ducts. As the filtrate passes through these structures, many of the substances in the filtrate are removed. Inorganic salts, organic molecules, and about 99% of the filtrate volume leave the renal tubule and enter the interstitial fluid. Because the pressure is low in the peritubular capillaries, these substances enter the peritubular capillaries and flow through the renal veins to enter the general circulation (see figure 26.8).

Solutes reabsorbed from the lumen of the renal tubule to the interstitial fluid include amino acids, glucose, and fructose, as well as Na^+, K^+, Ca^{2+}, HCO_3^-, and Cl^-. A more complete list is provided in table 26.3 for each part of the nephron.

The small volume of the filtrate (approximately 1%) that forms urine contains urea, uric acid, creatinine, K^+, and other substances. The regulation of solute reabsorption and the permeability characteristics of portions of the nephron allow for the production of a small volume of very concentrated urine or a large volume of very dilute urine.

Reabsorption in the Proximal Convoluted Tubule

The proximal convoluted tubule is the site of the majority of reabsorption. The mechanisms underlying reabsorption can be better understood by considering the cells found there. The cells of the proximal convoluted tubule have numerous microvilli, which dramatically increase the surface area available for reabsorption. To establish the portion of each proximal convoluted tubule cell where a particular process for reabsorption occurs, these portions are named. The portions of each cell are the following:

1. **Basal membrane.** The basal membranes form the outer wall of the renal tubules.
2. **Apical membrane.** The apical membranes make up the inside surface of the renal tubule wall. It is the apical membrane of the proximal convoluted tubule that houses the microvilli.
3. **Lateral surface.** The lateral surfaces bind the renal tubule cells to adjacent cells in the renal tubule.

Figure 26.10 describes the process of reabsorption in the proximal convoluted tubule.

TABLE 26.3 Reabsorption of Major Solutes from the Nephron

Apical Membrane	Basal Membrane
Proximal Convoluted Tubule	
Substances Symported with Na^+	*Active Transport*
	Na^+ (exchanged for K^+)
K^+	*Facilitated Diffusion*
Cl^-	K^+
Ca^{2+}	Cl^-
Mg^{2+}	Ca^{2+}
HCO_3^-	HCO_3^-
PO_4^{3-}	PO_4^{3-}
Amino acids	Amino acids
Glucose	Glucose
Fructose	Fructose
Galactose	Galactose
Lactate	Lactate
Succinate	Succinate
Citrate	Citrate
Diffusion Between Tubule Cells	
K^+	
Ca^{2+}	
Mg^{2+}	
Thick Ascending Limb of the Nephron Loop	
Substances Symported with Na^+	*Active Transport*
	Na^+ (exchanged for K^+)
K^+	*Facilitated Diffusion*
Cl^-	K^+
	Cl^-
Diffusion Between Tubule Cells	
K^+	
Ca^{2+}	
Mg^{2+}	
Distal Convoluted Tubule and Collecting Duct	
Substances Symported with Na^+	*Active Transport*
	Na^+ (exchanged for K^+)
Cl^-	*Facilitated Diffusion*
K^+	K^+
	Cl^-

1. Reabsorption of most solutes is linked to the diffusion of Na^+ into the cells of the proximal convoluted tubule. There is a steep concentration gradient for Na^+ from the filtrate into the cytoplasm of the cells of the proximal convoluted tubule. This concentration gradient is established by active transport of Na^+ across the basal membrane of the cells of the proximal convoluted tubule. The Na^+–K^+ pump actively transports Na^+ out of these cells and into the interstitial fluid, which keeps the concentration of Na^+ low in their cytoplasm. Thus, Na^+ moves by facilitated diffusion through a symporter from the filtrate into the cytoplasm of the cells of the proximal convoluted tubule. This movement of Na^+ into these cells is responsible for the secondary active transport of many other solutes from the lumen of the proximal convoluted tubule into the cytoplasm of the tubule cells.
2. Carrier proteins that transport amino acids, glucose, and other solutes are located within the **apical membrane,** which separates the lumen of the proximal convoluted tubule from the cytoplasm of the cells of the proximal convoluted tubule. Each of these carrier proteins binds specifically to one of those substances to be transported and

Blood flow

Solutes

H_2O

Peritubular capillary

1 Reabsorption of solutes

2 Reabsorption of 65% of volume of filtrate

3 Osmosis of water

Interstitial fluid

Filtrate flow

Proximal convoluted tubule

Active transport

Symport

Osmosis

Facilitated diffusion

Active transport

Symport

Solutes and water move into the interstitial fluid and then into the peritubular capillaries.

Na^+ K^+ Cl^- K^+ Glucose Amino acids H_2O

ATP

K^+ ADP

Active transport

Symport

Facilitated diffusion

Osmosis

Interstitial fluid

Basal membrane

Tubule cell

Na^+ Cl^- Na^+ Glucose Na^+ Amino acids H_2O

Apical membrane

Filtrate flow

Symport

Osmosis

Solutes move from the filtrate into the tubule cell, and water follows by osmosis.

Lumen of tubule containing filtrate

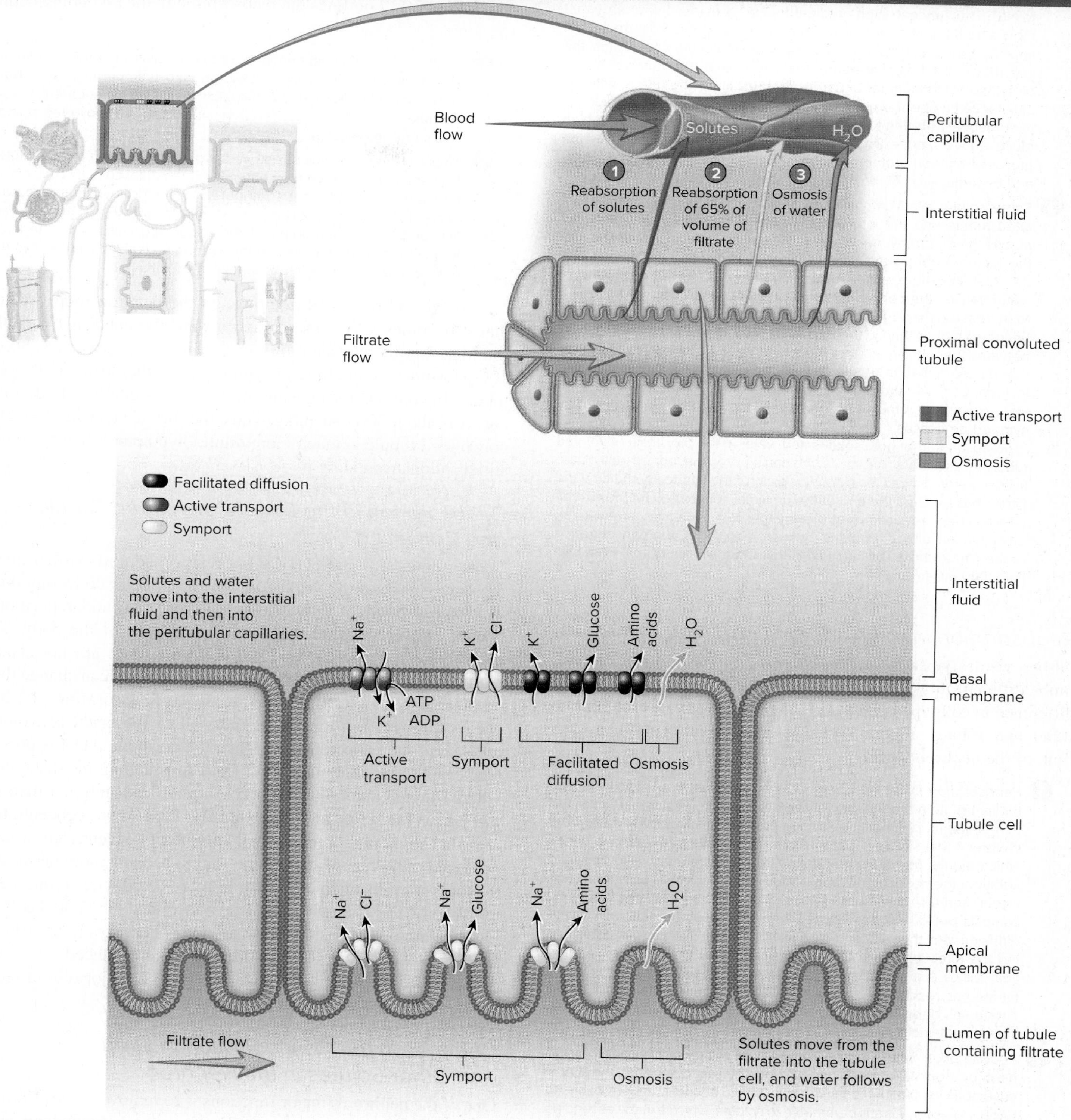

PROCESS Figure 26.10

Reabsorption of Solutes in the Proximal Convoluted Tubule

The symport of molecules and ions across the epithelial lining of the proximal convoluted tubule depends on the active transport of Na^+, in exchange for K^+, across the basal membrane. Symport is the process by which carrier proteins move molecules or ions with Na^+ across the apical membrane. The Na^+ concentration gradient provides the energy for symport. Amino acids, glucose, K^+, Cl^-, and most other solutes are transported into the tubule cells with Na^+. Water enters and leaves the cell by osmosis. Glucose, amino acids, Na^+, Cl^-, and many other solutes leave the cells across the basal membrane by facilitated diffusion.

You learned that the epithelial cells of the proximal convoluted tubule have numerous microvilli. Why are the microvilli beneficial for the process of reabsorption?

to Na^+. The concentration gradient for Na^+ provides the energy that moves both the Na^+ and the other molecules or ions from the lumen into the tubule cell. Once the symported molecules are inside the cell, they cross the basal membrane of the cell by facilitated diffusion or symport. The number of carrier proteins limits the rate at which a substance can be transported. For example, the high blood glucose in someone with untreated diabetes mellitus can lead to such high glucose levels in the filtrate that not all of it can be removed by the glucose transport proteins. The excess glucose remains in the filtrate and becomes part of the urine (see section 26.5).

3. Some solutes also diffuse from the lumen of the proximal convoluted tubule into the interstitial fluid by moving *between* the cells across their lateral surfaces. As other solutes are transported out of the lumen, through the proximal convoluted tubule cells, and into the interstitial fluid, water follows by osmosis. The reabsorption of water causes the concentration of solutes that remain in the lumen to increase. When the concentration of these solutes in the lumen becomes higher than in the interstitial fluid, these solutes will diffuse between the tubule cells into the interstitial fluid. Examples of solutes that diffuse between tubule cells of the proximal convoluted tubule include K^+, Ca^{2+}, and Mg^{2+}. These solutes are reabsorbed by diffusion, even though the same ions are also sometimes reabsorbed by symport processes.

   Reabsorption of both solutes and water in the proximal convoluted tubule is extensive. As solute molecules are transported out of the filtrate, water also moves by osmosis out of the filtrate. By the time the filtrate has reached the end of the proximal convoluted tubule, its volume has been reduced by approximately 65%. However, because the proximal convoluted tubule is permeable to water, the concentration of the filtrate there remains about the same as that of the interstitial fluid (300 mOsm/kg).

Reabsorption in the Nephron Loop

Earlier, we described the nephron loop and its two limbs. The two limbs differ in the type of epithelial tissue present in each. This difference in cell type is linked to the permeability of each limb to water and solutes. Figure 26.11 describes reabsorption in each limb of the nephron loop.

1. *Reabsorption in the descending limb of the nephron loop.* The epithelial tissue in the majority of the descending limb, in particular the thin segment, is simple squamous epithelial tissue. Remember from chapter 4 that simple squamous cells are highly permeable to water, which means the descending limb is highly permeable to water. In addition, the descending limb is moderately permeable to ions such as Na^+ and Cl^-, as well as molecules such as urea. Water moves by osmosis out of the descending limb, while some solutes move by diffusion into the descending limb. The particular factors determining the direction of water and solute movement in the descending limb will be discussed later in this section. Ultimately, by the time the filtrate has reached the end of the thin segment, the volume of the filtrate has been reduced by another 15% and its concentration has significantly increased to 1200 mOsm/L.

2. *Reabsorption in the ascending limb of the nephron loop.* As the nephron loop makes its hairpin turn into the ascending limb, the simple squamous epithelium persists, but it has become impermeable to water. However, it is still permeable to solutes, which exit the ascending limb, thereby again reducing the concentration of the filtrate.

   As the ascending limb continues, the epithelial tissue transitions to become simple cuboidal. This portion of the ascending limb is now called the thick segment. The thick segment of the ascending limb is impermeable to both water and solutes. Instead, the cells of the thick segment house multiple types of transport proteins including ATP-powered pumps and symporters. These transport proteins remove a significant portion of the solutes from the filtrate, which then enters the interstitial fluid. It is this active transport of solutes that contributes to the kidneys' ability to conserve water.

Figure 26.12 outlines the reabsorption in the ascending nephron loop.

1. As the ascending limb continues, it is now called the thick segment. The thick segment of the ascending limb is impermeable to both water and solutes. Instead, the cells of the thick segment house multiple types of transport proteins, including ATP-powered pumps and carrier molecules.

2. These carrier molecules remove a significant portion of the solutes from the filtrate, which then enters the interstitial fluid. It is this active transport of solutes that contributes to the kidneys' ability to conserve water. Cotransport is responsible for moving K^+ and Cl^- with Na^+ across the membrane of the ascending limb of the nephron loop. Once inside the cells of the ascending limb, Cl^- and K^+ exit the cells of the ascending limb via facilitated diffusion.

As we follow the filtrate through the nephron loop, we see that it becomes very concentrated toward the bend of the nephron loop, but the concentration of the filtrate is reduced to about 100 mOsm/kg by the time the fluid reaches the distal convoluted tubule. In contrast, the concentration of the interstitial fluid in the cortex is about 300 mOsm/kg. Thus, the filtrate entering the distal convoluted tubule is much more dilute (hypotonic) than the interstitial fluid surrounding it.

Reabsorption in the Distal Convoluted Tubule and Collecting Duct

Some solutes (K^+ and H^+) are not reabsorbed until farther along the renal tubule in the distal convoluted tubule or collecting duct. The reabsorption of these solutes is generally under hormonal control and depends on the current conditions of the body. The distal convoluted tubule and the collecting duct are not always permeable to water; however, hormone regulation can change their permeability to water (see section 26.4). Reabsorption of water occurs through osmosis across the wall of the distal convoluted tubule and the collecting duct when the hormone ADH is present (see chapter 18). The interstitial fluid surrounding the distal convoluted tubule and collecting duct is more concentrated than the filtrate, so the water moves toward the high solute concentration area. In these conditions, a small volume of concentrated urine is produced. ADH causes the tubule wall to become more permeable to water, a mechanism discussed in more detail later in this chapter. When ADH is absent, the distal convoluted tubule and collecting duct are not permeable to water and water stays in the filtrate. In this case, a large volume of dilute urine is produced.

The distal convoluted tubule also plays a major role in secretion, which is discussed later in this section.

Changes in the Concentration of Urea and Other Solutes in the Nephron

One of the nephron's major functions is to remove wastes from the body. For example, **urea** (yoo-REE-ah), a protein breakdown product, enters the glomerular filtrate at the same concentration as in the plasma. Renal tubules are only moderately permeable to urea, which slows the reabsorption of urea. As the volume of filtrate decreases in the renal tubule, the concentration of urea increases. Only 40–60% of the urea is passively reabsorbed by the renal tubule, although about 99% of the water is reabsorbed. In addition to urea, urate ions, creatinine, sulfates, phosphates, and nitrates are

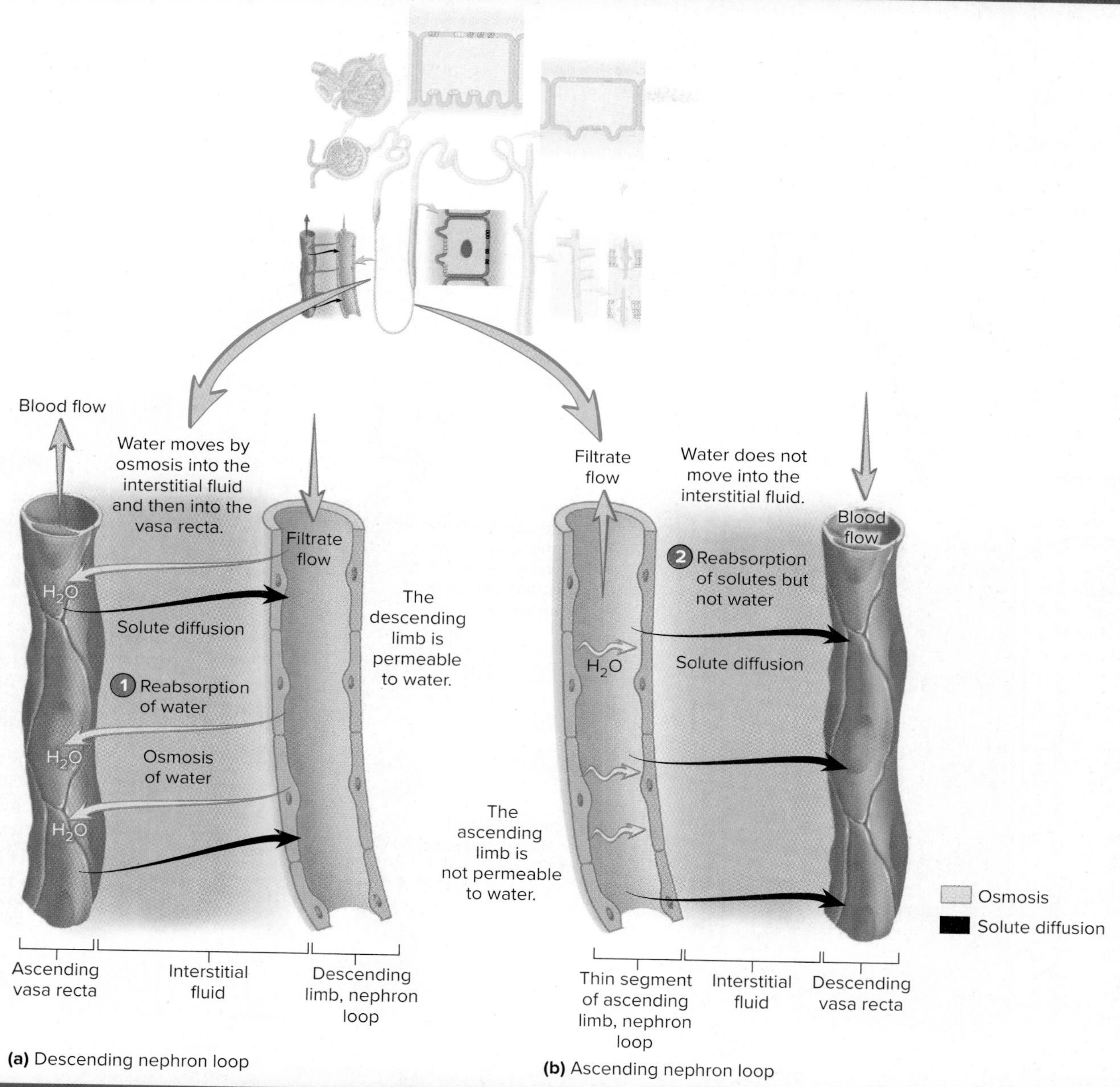

Blood flow

Water moves by osmosis into the interstitial fluid and then into the vasa recta.

Filtrate flow

H_2O

Solute diffusion

The descending limb is permeable to water.

1 Reabsorption of water

H_2O

Osmosis of water

H_2O

Ascending vasa recta

Interstitial fluid

Descending limb, nephron loop

(a) Descending nephron loop

Filtrate flow

Water does not move into the interstitial fluid.

Blood flow

2 Reabsorption of solutes but not water

H_2O

Solute diffusion

The ascending limb is not permeable to water.

Osmosis

Solute diffusion

Thin segment of ascending limb, nephron loop

Interstitial fluid

Descending vasa recta

(b) Ascending nephron loop

PROCESS **Figure 26.11**

Reabsorption in the Nephron Loop: The Descending Limb and the Thin Segment of the Ascending Limb

(*a*) The wall of the thin segment of the descending limb of the nephron loop is permeable to water and, to a lesser extent, to solutes. The interstitial fluid in the medulla of the kidney and the blood in the vasa recta have a high solute concentration (high osmolality). Water therefore moves by osmosis from the tubule into the interstitial fluid and into the vasa recta. An additional 15% of the filtrate volume is reabsorbed. To a lesser extent, solutes diffuse from the vasa recta and interstitial fluid into the tubule. (*b*) The thin segment of the ascending limb of the nephron loop is not permeable to water but is permeable to solutes. The solutes diffuse out of the tubule and into the more dilute interstitial fluid as the ascending limb projects toward the cortex. Then the solutes diffuse into the descending vasa recta.

What is the advantage of producing 180 L of filtrate each day only to reabsorb 178 L (99%) of the filtered material?

reabsorbed, but not to the same extent as water. Therefore, they also become more concentrated in the filtrate as the volume of the filtrate becomes smaller. These substances are toxic if they build up in the body, so their accumulation in the filtrate and elimination in urine help maintain homeostasis (see table 26.1).

Tubular Secretion

Tubular secretion is the movement of nonfiltered substances from the blood into the filtrate. These substances include toxic by-products of metabolism and drugs or molecules not normally produced by the body (table 26.4). As with tubular reabsorption, tubular

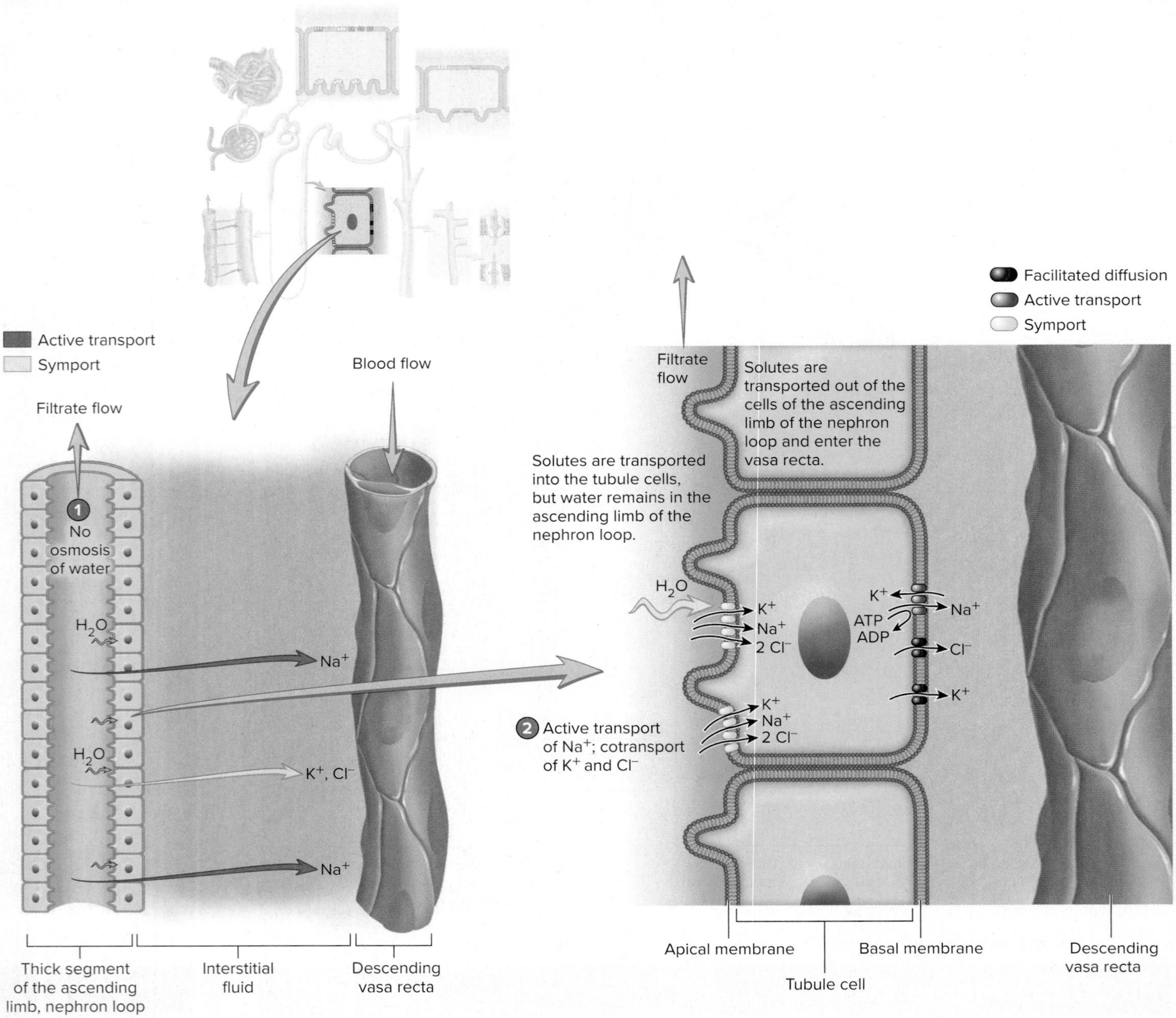

Active transport
Symport
Filtrate flow
Blood flow
1 No osmosis of water
H_2O
Na^+
H_2O
K^+, Cl^-
Na^+
Thick segment of the ascending limb, nephron loop
Interstitial fluid
Descending vasa recta

Facilitated diffusion
Active transport
Symport
Filtrate flow
Solutes are transported out of the cells of the ascending limb of the nephron loop and enter the vasa recta.
Solutes are transported into the tubule cells, but water remains in the ascending limb of the nephron loop.
H_2O
K^+
Na^+
2 Cl^-
K^+
ATP
ADP
Na^+
Cl^-
K^+
K^+
Na^+
2 Cl^-
2 Active transport of Na^+; cotransport of K^+ and Cl^-
Apical membrane
Basal membrane
Tubule cell
Descending vasa recta

PROCESS **Figure 26.12**

Reabsorption in the Thick Segment of the Ascending Limb of the Nephron Loop

The wall of the ascending limb of the nephron loop is not permeable to water. Sodium ions move across the wall of the basal membrane by active transport, establishing a concentration gradient for Na^+. Potassium ions and Cl^- are symported with Na^+ across the apical membrane, and ions pass by facilitated diffusion across the basal membrane of the tubule cells.

What would happen to the concentration of solutes in the medulla if active transport of Na^+ in this segment of the nephron loop were prevented?

TABLE 26.4 Secretion of Substances into the Renal Tubule

Transport Process	Substance Transported
Proximal Convoluted Tubule	
Antiport	H^+
Active transport	Hydroxybenzoates
	Para-aminohippuric acid
	Neurotransmitters
	Dopamine
	Acetylcholine
	Epinephrine
	Bile pigments
	Uric acid
	Drugs and toxins
	Penicillin
	Atropine
	Morphine
Diffusion	Ammonia
Distal Convoluted Tubule	
Antiport	K^+
	H^+
Active transport	K^+

secretion can be either active or passive. For example, ammonia is a toxic by-product of protein metabolism. It is produced when the epithelial cells of the renal tubule remove amino groups from amino acids, which diffuse into the lumen of the renal tubule. On the other hand, H^+, K^+, penicillin, and ***para*-aminohippuric acid** (PAR-ah-a-MEE-noh-hih-PURE-ik; p-aminohippuric acid; **PAH;** a medical diagnostic chemical) are actively secreted by either active transport or antiport processes into the renal tubule. An example of an antiport process in the kidney is the secretion of H^+, which plays a major role in regulating body fluid pH and is discussed in more detail in chapter 27. If blood pH is too acidic, the kidney secretes H^+. The secreted H^+ is produced when CO_2 and water react to form H^+ and HCO_3^-. A Na^+/H^+ antiporter in the tubule cells will move Na^+ into the proximal and distal convoluted tubule cells and move H^+ out of the proximal and distal convoluted tubule cells (figure 26.13). More specifically, Na^+ and HCO_3^- are symported across the basal membrane of the tubule cells and enter the peritubular capillaries. Hydrogen ions are secreted into the lumens of the proximal and distal convoluted tubules. By secreting H^+, the blood pH stays in its normal range and does not become too acidic.

ASSESS YOUR PROGRESS

20. *What is the direction of movement of substances in tubular reabsorption?*
21. *Describe what happens to most of the filtrate that enters the renal tubule.*
22. *On what side of the renal tubule cell does active transport take place during reabsorption of materials?*
23. *Describe how symport works in the renal tubule.*
24. *Name the substances that are moved by active and passive transport. In what part of the renal tubule does this movement take place?*
25. *Explain the differences between the descending limb and the ascending limb of the nephron loop.*
26. *Where does tubular secretion take place? What is the direction of movement?*
27. *What substances are secreted? List the mechanisms by which these substances are transported.*

Urine Concentration Mechanism

As you have just read, the kidneys are remarkable at regulating blood composition. The kidneys are able to produce urine with concentrations ranging from a minimum of 65 mOsm/kg to a maximum of 1200 mOsm/kg while maintaining the extracellular fluid concentration very close to 300 mOsm/kg. But how does the kidney move such a large volume of fluid from the blood into the filtrate and then back into the blood? The kidneys' ability to control the volume and concentration of the urine depends on several factors: (1) countercurrent mechanisms, (2) a medullary concentration gradient, and (3) hormonal mechanisms.

Countercurrent Mechanisms

The kidneys utilize a **countercurrent mechanism.** A countercurrent mechanism is one where fluid in separate structures flows in opposite directions relative to each other. As the fluids pass by each other, materials can be exchanged between the fluids. There are two types of countercurrent mechanisms in the kidney that are critical for either conserving or eliminating water in the body (figure 26.14). These two mechanisms are (1) a countercurrent multiplier and (2) a countercurrent exchanger.

The **countercurrent multiplier** in the nephron loop is responsible for a large percentage of a very high concentration of solutes that is found in the interstitial fluid within the medulla of the kidney. The permeability changes in the nephron loop are responsible for its role as the countercurrent multiplier.

The **countercurrent exchanger** in the vasa recta maintains the high solute concentration in the interstitial fluid. Because the flow rate and blood pressure in the vasa recta are so slow and very low, the blood and the interstitial fluid are always in equilibrium and solutes are not carried away from the interstitial fluid by the blood in the vasa recta.

Countercurrent Mechanisms: Medullary Concentration Gradient

The interstitial fluid in the medulla of the kidney has a very high solute concentration compared with that of the cortex. This is called the **medullary concentration gradient.** The high solute concentration of the interstitial fluid develops from (1) the actions of the two countercurrent mechanisms and (2) the recycling of the protein breakdown product, urea. The concentration of solutes in the medulla increases from 300 mOsm/kg to 1200 mOsm/kg deep in the medulla at the tip of the renal pyramid (figure 26.14).

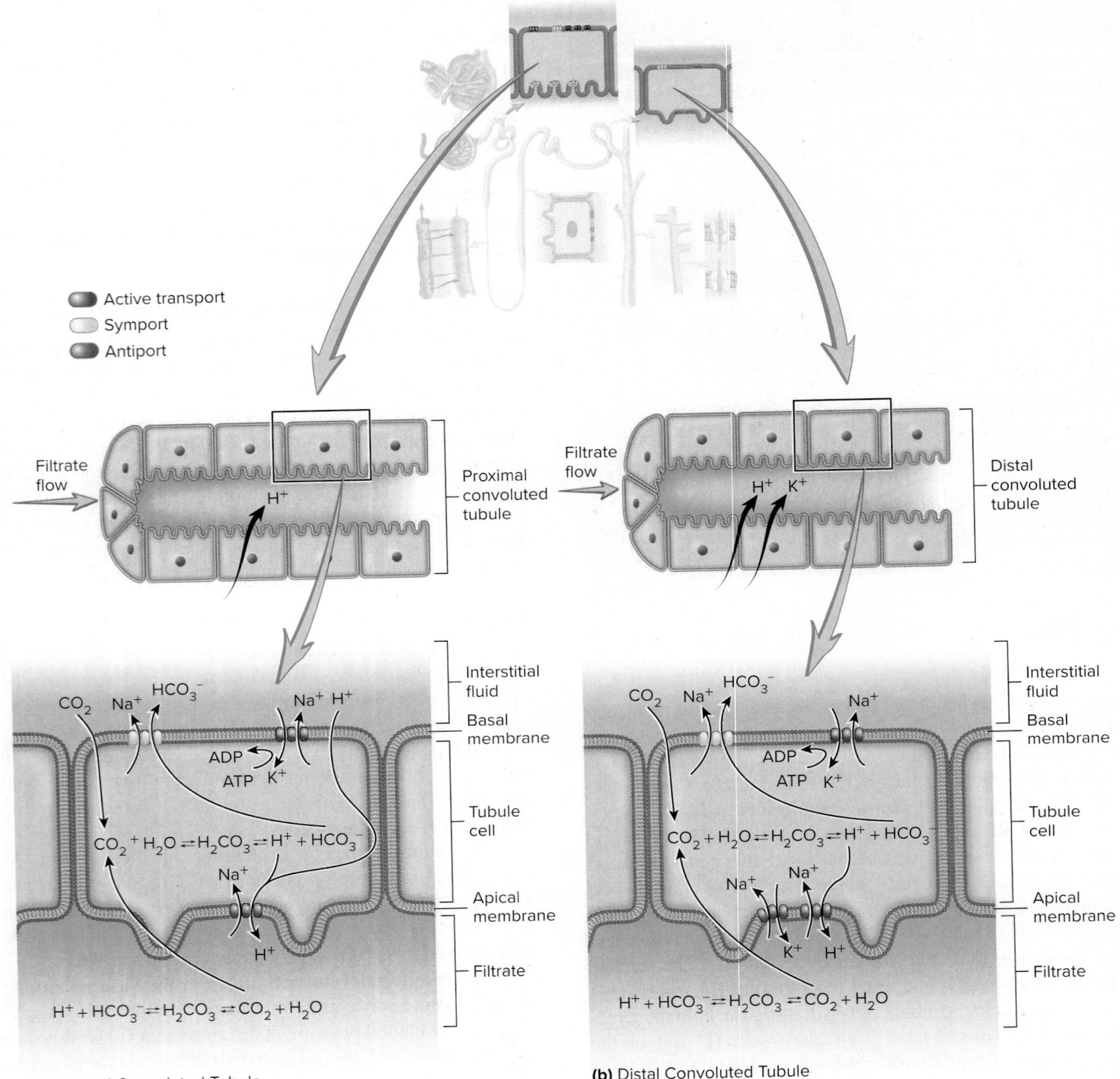

(a) Proximal Convoluted Tubule

(b) Distal Convoluted Tubule

FIGURE 26.13 Secretion of H^+ and K^+ into the Renal Tubule

(*a*) Hydrogen ions are secreted into the filtrate by an antiport mechanism in the proximal convoluted tubule, in which H^+ are exchanged for Na^+. The H^+ are derived from two sources. They diffuse from the peritubular capillaries into the interstitial fluid and then into epithelial cells of the tubule, or they are derived from the reaction between CO_2 and water in the cells of the tubule. Sodium ions and HCO_3^- are symported across the basal membrane into the interstitial fluid and then diffuse into the peritubular capillaries. (*b*) Hydrogen ions and K^+ are secreted into the filtrate by antiport mechanisms in the distal convoluted tubule. Sodium ions and K^+ are moved by active transport across the basal membrane of the tubule cell. Sodium ions and HCO_3^- are symported across the basal membrane into the interstitial fluid and then diffuse into the peritubular capillaries.

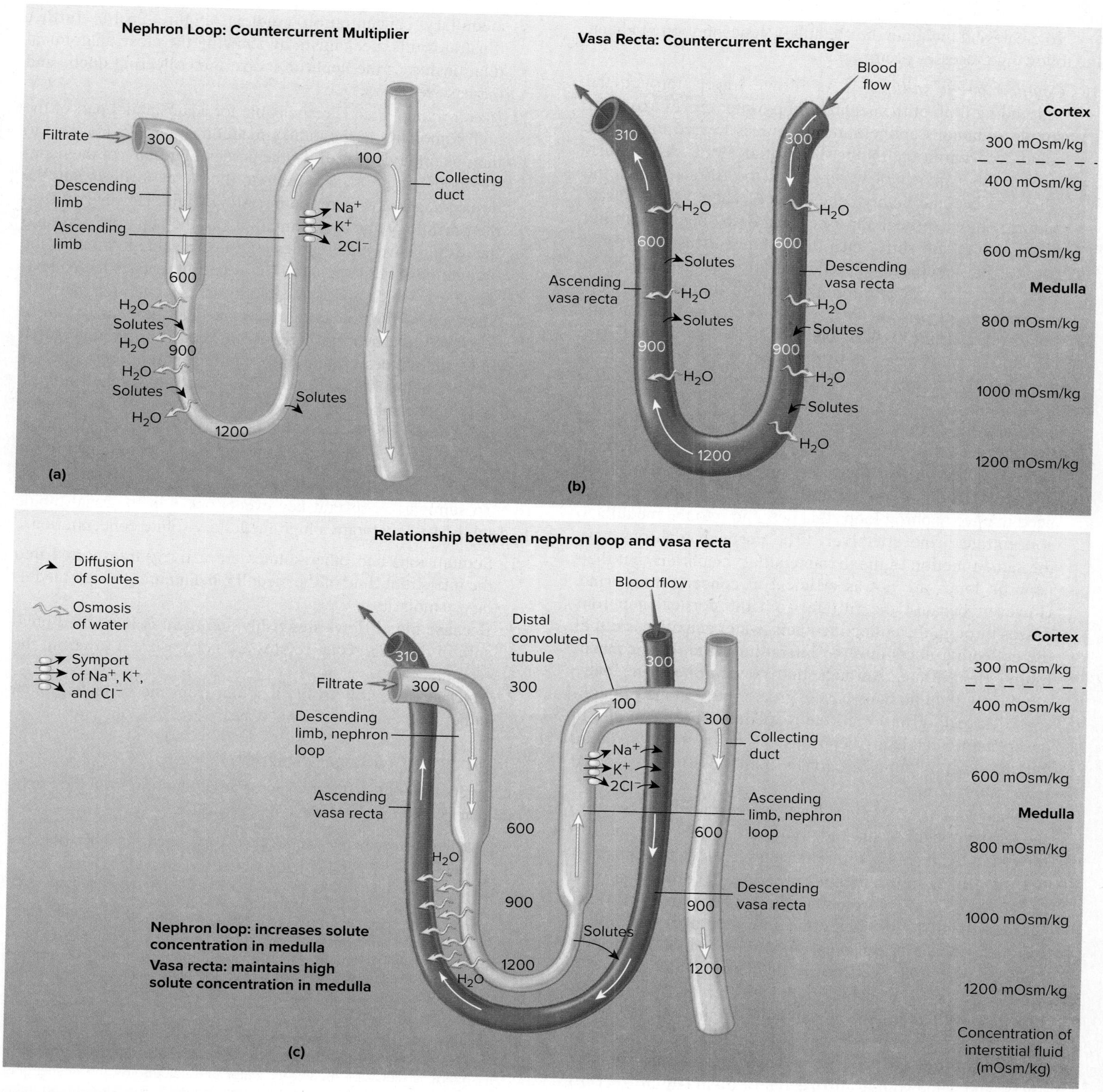

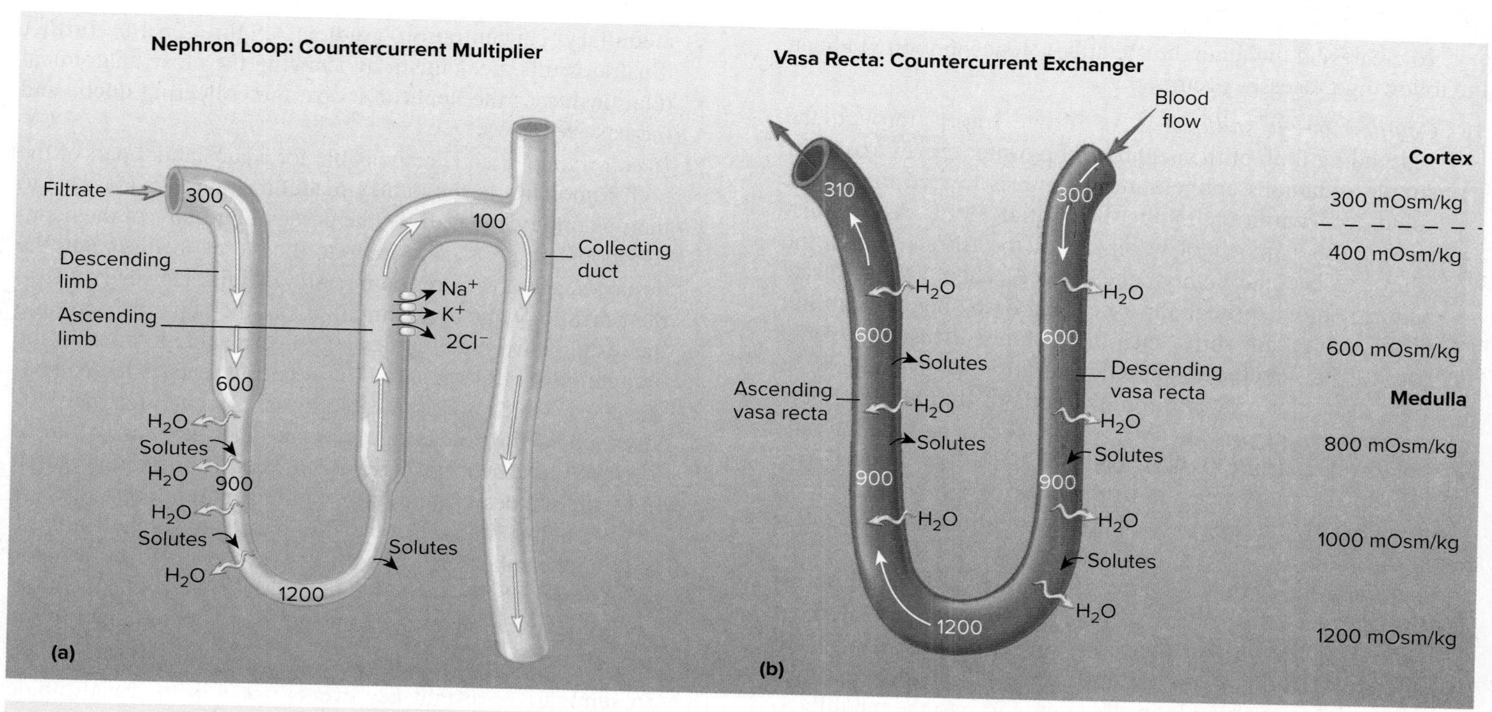

FIGURE 26.14 Filtrate Concentration and the Medullary Concentration Gradient
The nephron loop and the vasa recta function together to maintain a high concentration of solutes in the medulla of the kidney. (*a*) In the nephron loop, the filtrate is concentrated in the descending limb and then diluted in the ascending limb. (*b*) In the vasa recta, the osmolality of the blood does not change appreciably due to its low pressure and slow flow. (*c*) The water that diffuses out of the nephron loop is returned to the general circulation by way of the vasa recta.

To create and maintain the medullary concentration gradient, the following processes occur:

1a. *Countercurrent multiplier.* As filtrate travels through the descending limb of the nephron loop, water moves across its simple squamous epithelium by osmosis toward the higher solute concentration in the interstitial fluid. As we discussed, this osmosis of water out of the filtrate causes the filtrate to become highly concentrated. Then, as the filtrate begins to move through the ascending limb, the permeability of the epithelium shifts such that solutes diffuse out of the filtrate. This increases the concentration of the interstitial fluid even more. In addition, the cells of the thick segment of the ascending limb actively pump solutes into the interstitial fluid, causing a very concentrated solution to form. Hence, the movement of solutes out of the nephron loop dramatically increases the solute concentration of the interstitial fluid.

Only the juxtamedullary nephrons have nephron loops that descend deep into the medulla, but enough of them exist to maintain the high concentration of solutes in the interstitial fluid of the medulla. Not all of the nephrons need to have nephron loops that descend into the medulla to concentrate urine effectively. The cortical nephrons have the same function as the juxtamedullary nephrons, but their nephron loops are not as efficient at concentrating urine. However, because the filtrate from the cortical nephrons passes through the collecting ducts, water can diffuse out of the collecting ducts into the interstitial fluid, thus concentrating the filtrate. Animals that concentrate urine more effectively than humans have a greater percentage of nephrons descending into the kidney medulla. For example, in desert mammals, many nephrons descend into the medulla, and the renal pyramids are longer than those in humans and most other mammals.

1b. *Countercurrent exchanger.* The vasa recta supply blood to the kidney medulla, and they remove excess water and solutes from the medulla without changing the high concentration of solutes in the medullary interstitial fluid. The vasa recta have a countercurrent mechanism because blood flows through them to the kidney medulla, and after the vessels turn near the tip of the renal pyramid, the blood flows the opposite direction, back toward the cortex. The walls of the vasa recta are permeable to both water and solutes. As blood flows toward the medulla, water moves out of the vasa recta, and some solutes diffuse into them. As blood flows back toward the cortex, water moves into the vasa recta, and some solutes diffuse out of them (figure 26.14*b*). The directions of diffusion are such that the vasa recta carry slightly more water and solute from the medulla than to it. Thus, the composition of the blood at both ends of the vasa recta is nearly the same, with the volume and osmolality slightly greater as the blood once again reaches the cortex. In addition, blood pressure in the vasa recta is very low and blood flow rate is extremely slow, even sluggish. This encourages ready diffusion of solutes into and back out of the vasa recta, ensuring the maintenance of the high medullary concentration gradient. Figure 26.14*c* further illustrates this mechanism by showing the close anatomical relationship of the nephron loops, the collecting ducts, and the vasa recta.

2. *Urea cycling.* Urea is responsible for a substantial part of the high osmolality in the kidney medulla (figure 26.15). Due to their histology, the walls of the descending limbs of the nephron loops are permeable to urea; thus, urea diffuses into the descending limbs from the interstitial fluid. However, due to their histology, the ascending limbs of the nephron loops and the distal convoluted tubules are impermeable to urea, so the urea remains in the nephron loops until it reaches the collecting ducts, which are permeable to urea. Some urea then diffuses out of the collecting ducts into the interstitial fluid of the medulla. Therefore, urea is recycled from the interstitial fluid into the descending limbs of the nephron loops, through the ascending limbs, through the distal convoluted tubules, and into the collecting ducts. Most urea then diffuses from the collecting ducts back into the interstitial fluid of the medulla. Consequently, a high urea concentration is maintained in the medulla of the kidney.

To summarize, several key events occur in the renal tubule to establish and maintain a high medullary solute concentration:

1. Sodium ions and other solutes are actively transported into the interstitial fluid of the medulla, maintaining a high medullary osmolarity.
2. Because blood flows sluggishly and there is low blood pressure in the vasa recta, solutes are not washed away from the medulla.
3. Much urea returns to the medulla from the collecting duct, rather than exiting with the urine.

Summary of Urine Formation

Figure 26.16 outlines the steps in urine production from the proximal convoluted tubule to the collecting duct.

1. In the average person, about 180 L of filtrate enter the proximal convoluted tubules daily.
2. Glucose, amino acids, Na^+, Ca^{2+}, K^+, Cl^-, water, and other substances (see table 26.3) move from the lumens of the proximal convoluted tubules into the interstitial fluid. The excess solutes and water then enter the peritubular capillaries. Consequently, cells of the proximal convoluted tubule reabsorb approximately 65% of the filtrate, which moves solutes and water into the interstitial fluid. The osmolality of both the interstitial fluid and the filtrate is maintained at about 300 mOsm/kg.
3. As the filtrate continues to flow through the renal tubule, it enters the descending limbs of the nephron loops. This portion of the nephron loops is highly permeable to water and solutes. As the descending limbs penetrate deep into the kidney medulla, the surrounding interstitial fluid has a progressively greater osmolality. Water diffuses out of the nephron loops as solutes slowly diffuse into them. By the time the filtrate reaches the deepest part of the nephron loops, its volume has been reduced by an additional 15% of the original volume, at least 80% of the filtrate volume has been reabsorbed, and its osmolality has increased to about 1200 mOsm/kg.
4. Both the thin and thick segments are impermeable to water, but solutes diffuse out of the thin segment, and Na^+, Cl^-, and K^+ are symported from the filtrate into the interstitial fluid in the thick segments. The movement of solutes, but not water, across the wall of

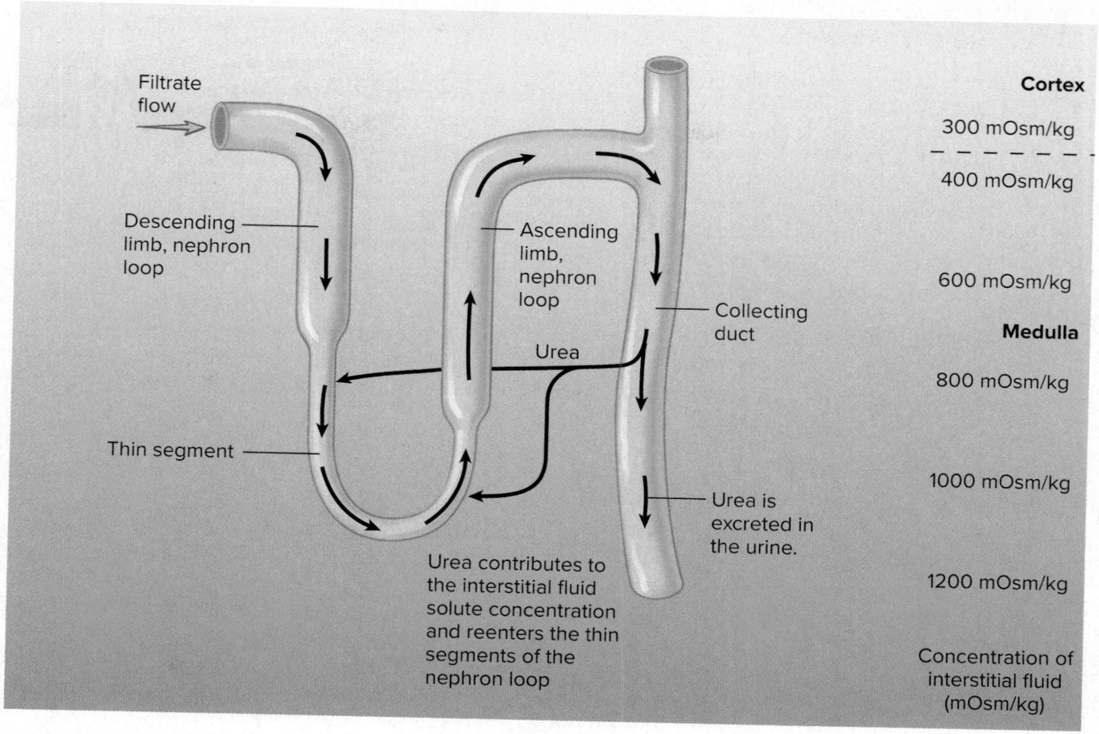

FIGURE 26.15 Medullary Concentration Gradient and Urea Cycling
The concentration of urea in the medulla of the kidney is high and contributes to the overall high concentration of solutes there. The wall of the collecting duct is permeable to urea. Urea diffuses out of the collecting duct into the interstitial fluid of the medulla. The wall of the descending limb of the nephron loops is also permeable to urea. Urea diffuses from the interstitial fluid into the descending limb. Thus, a cycle is produced: Urea flows into the descending limb, through the ascending limb, through the distal convoluted tubule, through the collecting duct, out of the collecting duct, and back into the descending limb.

the ascending limbs causes the osmolality of the filtrate to decrease from 1200 to about 100 mOsm/kg by the time the filtrate again reaches the kidney cortex.

5. The volume of the filtrate does not change as it passes through the ascending limbs. As a result, the filtrate entering the distal convoluted tubules is dilute, compared with the concentration of the surrounding interstitial fluid, which has an osmolality of about 300 mOsm/kg.
6. The distal convoluted tubule and collecting duct are permeable to water when under hormonal regulation.
7. Around 1% or less of the filtrate remains as urine, when the body is conserving water.

The changes just described are *obligatory;* that is, they occur regardless of the concentration and volume of urine that the kidney finally produces. The mechanisms by which the kidney forms concentrated and dilute urine are described in section 26.4.

ASSESS YOUR PROGRESS

28. *List the major mechanisms that create and maintain the high solute concentration in the renal medulla.*
29. *Describe the roles of the nephron loop, the vasa recta, and urea cycling in maintaining a high interstitial solute concentration in the kidney medulla.*
30. *Describe how the filtrate volume and concentration change as filtrate flows through the renal tubules and collecting ducts.*

26.4 Regulation of Urine Concentration and Volume

LEARNING OUTCOME

After reading this section, you should be able to

A. **Explain how antidiuretic hormone, the renin-angiotensin-aldosterone hormone mechanism, and atrial natriuretic hormone influence the concentration and volume of urine.**

Urine can be dilute or very concentrated, and it can be produced in large or small amounts. Mechanisms that maintain the kidneys' extracellular fluid and volume keep the urine concentration and volume within narrow limits.

Filtrate reabsorption in the proximal convoluted tubules and the descending limbs of the nephron loops is obligatory and therefore remains relatively constant. However, filtrate reabsorption in the distal convoluted tubules and collecting ducts is tightly regulated and can change dramatically, depending on the conditions to which the body is exposed. If homeostasis requires the elimination of a large volume of dilute urine, the dilute filtrate can pass through the distal convoluted tubules and collecting ducts with little change in concentration. On the other hand, if water must be conserved to maintain homeostasis, water is reabsorbed from the filtrate as it passes through the distal convoluted tubules and

PROCESS **Figure**

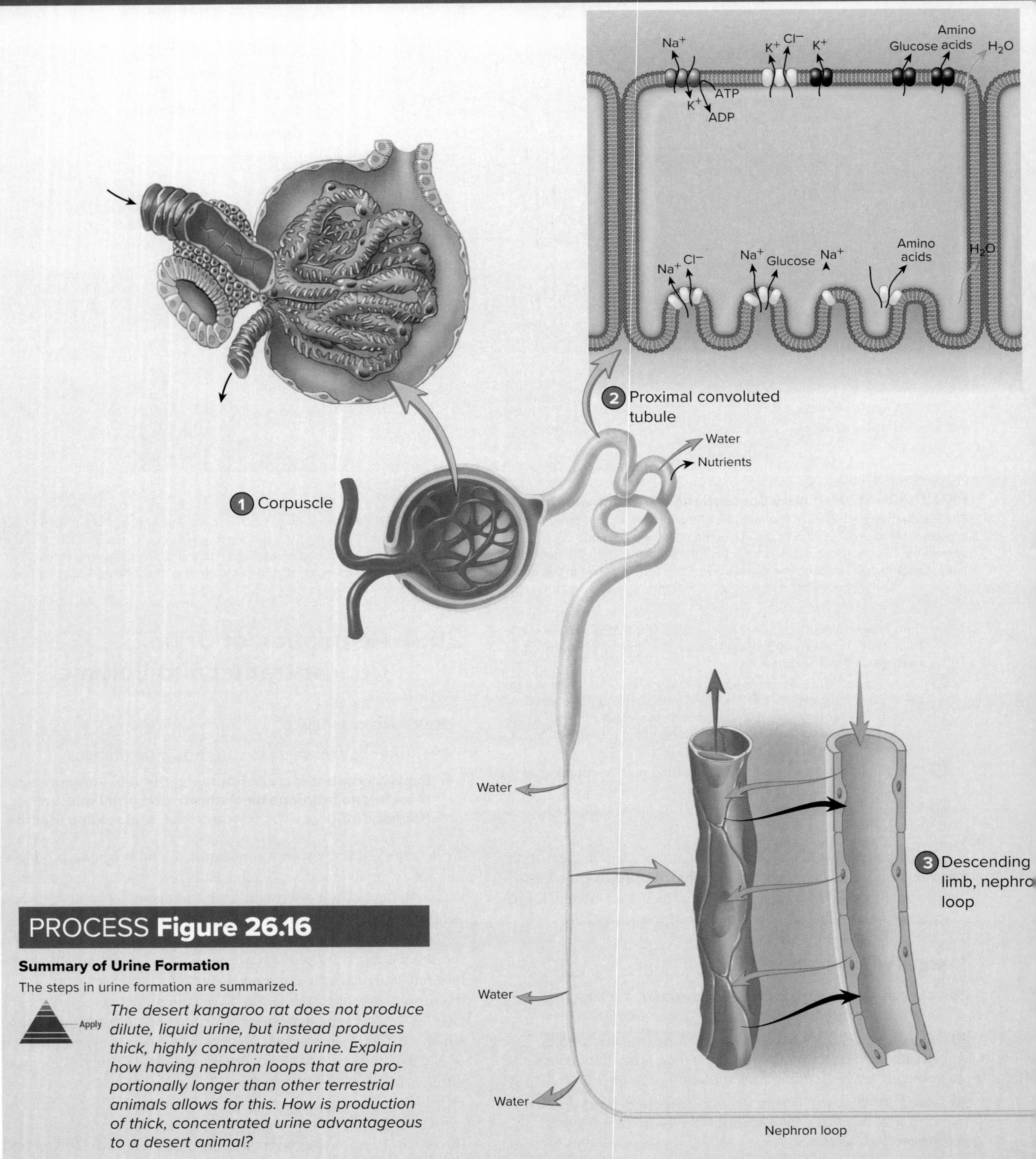

PROCESS **Figure 26.16**

Summary of Urine Formation

The steps in urine formation are summarized.

Apply *The desert kangaroo rat does not produce dilute, liquid urine, but instead produces thick, highly concentrated urine. Explain how having nephron loops that are proportionally longer than other terrestrial animals allows for this. How is production of thick, concentrated urine advantageous to a desert animal?*

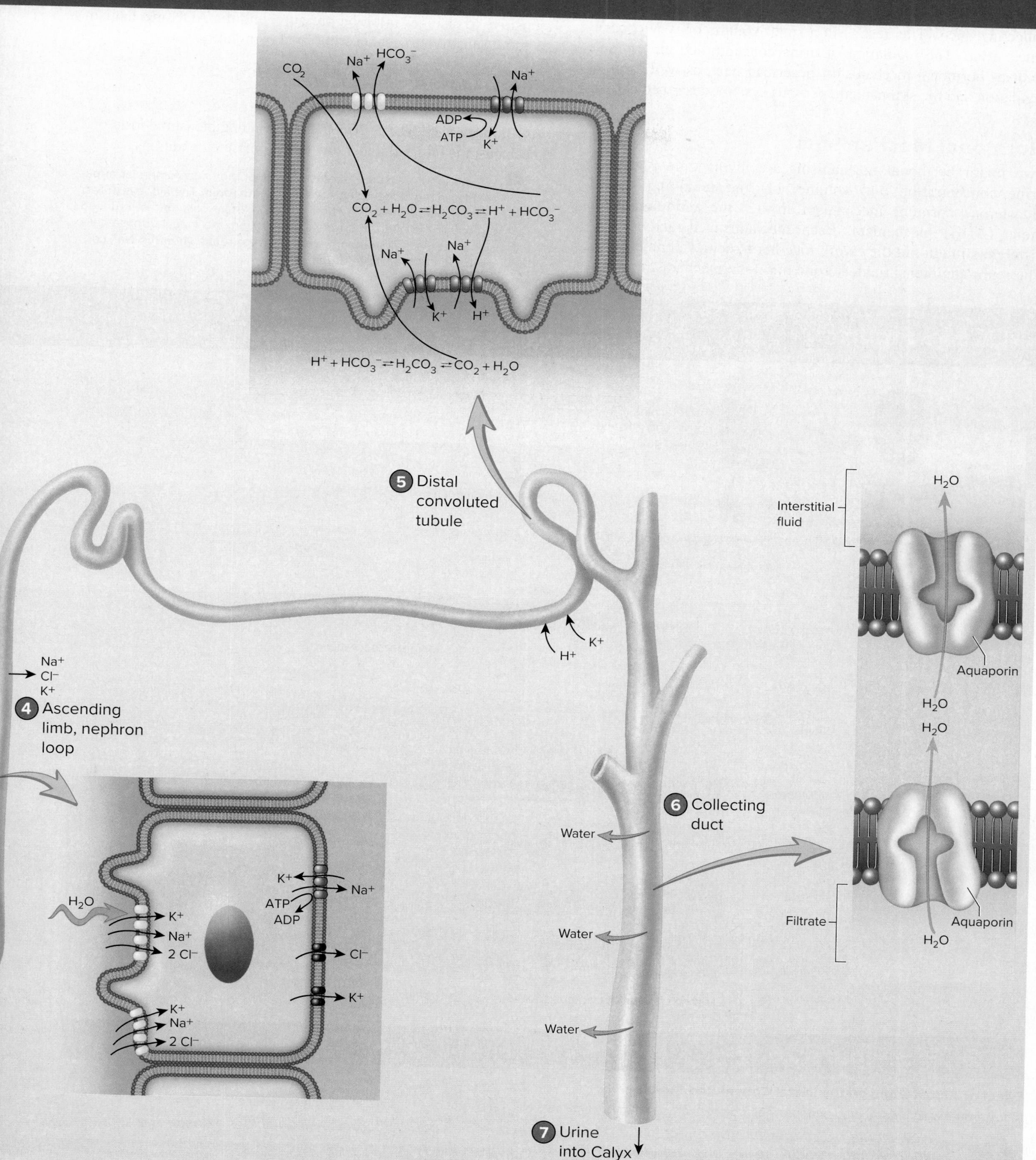

Na^+
HCO_3^-
CO_2
Na^+
ADP
ATP
K^+
$CO_2 + H_2O \rightleftharpoons H_2CO_3 \rightleftharpoons H^+ + HCO_3^-$
Na^+
Na^+
K^+
H^+
$H^+ + HCO_3^- \rightleftharpoons H_2CO_3 \rightleftharpoons CO_2 + H_2O$
5 Distal convoluted tubule
K^+
H^+
Na^+
Cl^-
K^+
4 Ascending limb, nephron loop
H_2O
K^+
Na^+
2 Cl^-
K^+
Na^+
ATP
ADP
Cl^-
K^+
K^+
Na^+
2 Cl^-
6 Collecting duct
Water
Water
Water
7 Urine into Calyx
H_2O
Interstitial fluid
Aquaporin
H_2O
H_2O
Filtrate
Aquaporin
H_2O

collecting ducts. This results in a small volume of very concentrated urine. The regulation of urine concentration and volume involves hormonal mechanisms, described next, as well as autoregulation and the sympathetic nervous system, described earlier.

Hormonal Mechanisms

Two major hormonal mechanisms are involved in regulating urine concentration and volume: (1) the renin-angiotensin-aldosterone hormone mechanism and (2) the antidiuretic hormone (ADH) mechanism. Each mechanism is activated by different stimuli, but they work together to achieve homeostasis. The renin-angiotensin-aldosterone hormone mechanism is more sensitive to changes in blood pressure, and the ADH mechanism is more sensitive to changes in blood osmolality.

Renin-Angiotensin-Aldosterone Hormone Mechanism

As illustrated in figure 26.17, the renin-angiotensin-aldosterone mechanism is initiated under low blood pressure conditions.

1. When blood pressure decreases, cells of the juxtaglomerular apparatuses in the kidneys secrete the enzyme **renin.** The kidneys detect the low blood pressure when juxtaglomerular cells detect reduced stretch of the afferent arteriole. In addition, the macula densa cells signal the juxtaglomerular cells to secrete renin when the Na^+ concentration of the filtrate drops.

PROCESS **Figure**

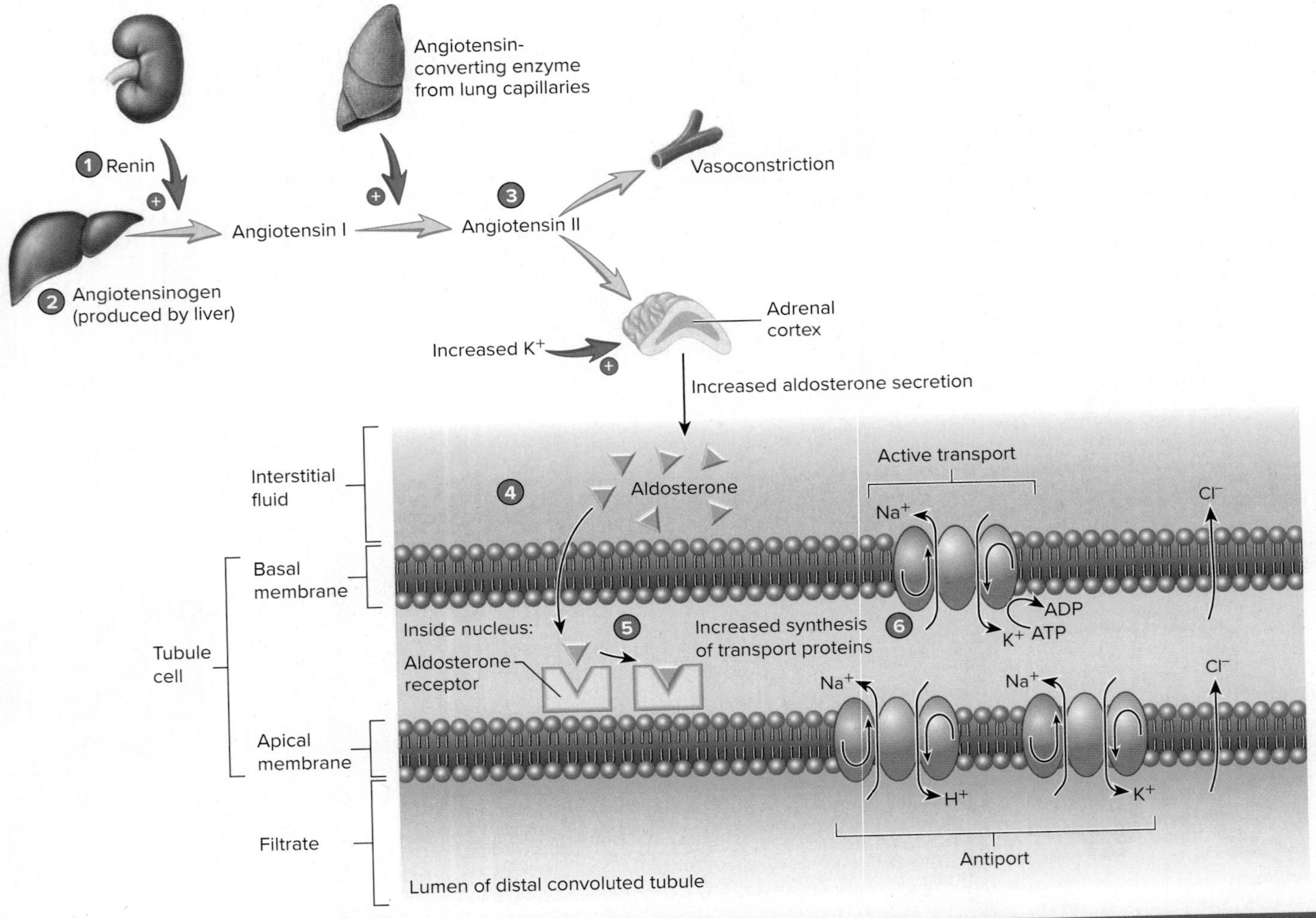

Angiotensin-converting enzyme from lung capillaries

1 Renin

Vasoconstriction

3 Angiotensin II

Angiotensin I

2 Angiotensinogen (produced by liver)

Adrenal cortex

Increased K^+

Increased aldosterone secretion

Interstitial fluid

4 Aldosterone

Active transport

Na^+

Cl^-

Basal membrane

ADP

Inside nucleus:

5

Increased synthesis of transport proteins

6

K^+ ATP

Tubule cell

Aldosterone receptor

Na^+

Na^+

Cl^-

Apical membrane

H^+

K^+

Filtrate

Antiport

Lumen of distal convoluted tubule

PROCESS **Figure 26.17**

Effect of Aldosterone on the Distal Convoluted Tubule

Aldosterone, which is secreted under low blood pressure conditions, stimulates Na^+ reabsorption in the distal convoluted tubule.

How would blood pressure be affected if a person suffered from hypoaldosteronism (insufficient aldosterone secretion)? Would blood K^+ levels also be affected? If so, how?

2 Upon secretion, renin enters the blood and converts **angiotensinogen,** a plasma protein produced by the liver, to **angiotensin I.**

3 **Angiotensin-converting enzyme (ACE)** is a proteolytic enzyme produced by capillaries of organs such as the lungs. ACE converts angiotensin I to **angiotensin II.** Angiotensin II is a potent vasoconstricting hormone that increases peripheral resistance, causing blood pressure to increase. However, angiotensin II is rapidly broken down, so its effect lasts for only a short time. Angiotensin II also increases the rate of aldosterone secretion, the sensation of thirst, salt appetite, and ADH secretion.

The rate of renin secretion decreases if blood pressure in the afferent arteriole increases, or if the Na^+ concentration of the filtrate increases as it passes by the macula densa of the juxtaglomerular apparatuses.

4 A large decrease in the concentration of Na^+ in the interstitial fluid acts directly on the aldosterone-secreting cells of the adrenal cortex to increase the rate of aldosterone secretion. However, angiotensin II is much more important than the blood level of Na^+ for regulating aldosterone secretion. In addition, angiotensin II is critical for returning GFR to normal levels.

Aldosterone is a steroid hormone secreted by the cortex of the adrenal glands (see chapter 18).

5 Aldosterone binds to its receptor in both the distal convoluted tubules and the collecting ducts. Aldosterone molecules diffuse through the plasma membranes and bind to their nuclear receptors.

6 Binding of aldosterone to its receptor increases synthesis of the Na^+–K^+ pump and other Na^+ transport proteins. The Na^+–K^+ pump increases the reabsorption of Na^+ and the secretion of K^+ across the basal membrane of tubule cells, while the other Na^+ transport proteins increase the transport of Na^+ across the apical membrane of tubule cells. As a result, the rate of Na^+ reabsorption increases. Simultaneously, because of the action of the Na^+–K^+ pump, K^+ *secretion increases,* rather than its reabsorption.

Reduced secretion of aldosterone decreases the rate of Na^+ reabsorption. Reduced Na^+ reabsorption keeps the concentration of Na^+ in the distal convoluted tubules and the collecting ducts elevated. Because the concentration of filtrate passing through the distal convoluted tubules and the collecting ducts has a greater-than-normal concentration of solutes, water's capacity to move by osmosis from the distal convoluted tubules and the collecting ducts is diminished, urine volume increases, and the urine has a greater concentration of Na^+.

Because increases in the number of Na^+–K^+ pumps increases the rate of K^+ secretion, increases in blood K^+ levels stimulate aldosterone secretion. Conversely, decreases in blood K^+ levels decrease aldosterone secretion (see chapter 27).

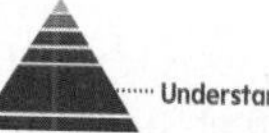

Predict 2

Drugs that increase urine volume are called diuretics. Some diuretics inhibit the active transport of Na^+ in the renal tubule. Explain how these diuretic drugs cause increased urine volume.

ASSESS YOUR PROGRESS

31. *What factors stimulate the release of renin? What will decrease the rate of renin secretion?*
32. *How is angiotensin II activated? What effects does it produce?*

Clinical IMPACT 26.1 Diabetic Nephropathy and Renal Failure

Diabetic nephropathy (neh-FROP-ah-thee) is a disease of the kidneys associated with diabetes mellitus, and it is the principal cause of chronic renal failure. This condition damages renal glomeruli and ultimately destroys functional nephrons through progressive scar tissue formation, mediated in part by an inflammatory response. The damaged glomeruli no longer filter the blood effectively, allowing proteins to pass through the filtration membrane and be excreted in the urine. The presence of protein in the urine of people who have type 2 diabetes strongly suggests significant diabetic nephropathy, which can lead to end-stage renal failure. About 1 in 14 Americans over age 30 has some degree of type 2 diabetes mellitus, and most hemodialysis patients have type 2 diabetes mellitus.

The development of diabetic nephropathy is complex. Although the mechanism is not completely understood, the level of angiotensin II is elevated in diabetes mellitus. This causes exaggerated efferent arteriole vasoconstriction and consequently increased glomerular capillary pressure. The increased glomerular capillary pressure damages the glomerular basement membrane, causing it to thicken and become more permeable. The glomerular basement membrane is also damaged by the production of glycoproteins called **advanced glycosylation end products (AGEs).** AGEs are produced when glucose forms irreversible cross-links with kidney and plasma proteins. The AGEs stimulate the secretion of growth factors from glomerular cells, which promote glomerular basement membrane thickening.

Because the glomerular basement membrane in patients with diabetes mellitus is more permeable than normal, plasma proteins cross the filtration membrane and enter the urine. The initial amount of protein entering the urine is small, a condition called microalbuminuria (MY-kroh-al-boo-min-YOO-ree-ah). However, as the number of functional nephrons in the kidney decreases, microalbuminuria eventually progresses to overt proteinuria (proh-tee-NOO-ree-ah), the secretion of more than 300 mg albumin/day. By the time overt proteinuria has developed, which may take 10–15 years, the number of functional nephrons has decreased to less than 10% of normal, and the kidneys are no longer able to excrete adequate amounts of waste products. This condition is called **end-stage renal disease (ESRD).** In ESRD, renal failure has worsened to the point that kidney function is less than 10% of normal. Unless ESRD is treated by hemodialysis or kidney transplantation, the patient dies.

The use of **angiotensin-converting enzyme (ACE) inhibitors** slows or, in some cases, even halts the progression of proteinuria and end-stage renal disease. ACE inhibitors prevent the formation of angiotensin II; consequently, arterial blood pressure and glomerular capillary pressure remain within their normal ranges. When ACE inhibitors are used in combination with drugs called **angiotensin receptor blockers (ARBs),** which prevent angiotensin II molecules from binding to their receptors, proteinuria decreases up to 45%. People with type 2 diabetes who maintain their blood glucose within normal levels have a much lower incidence of diabetic nephropathy and ESRD.

PROCESS **Figure**

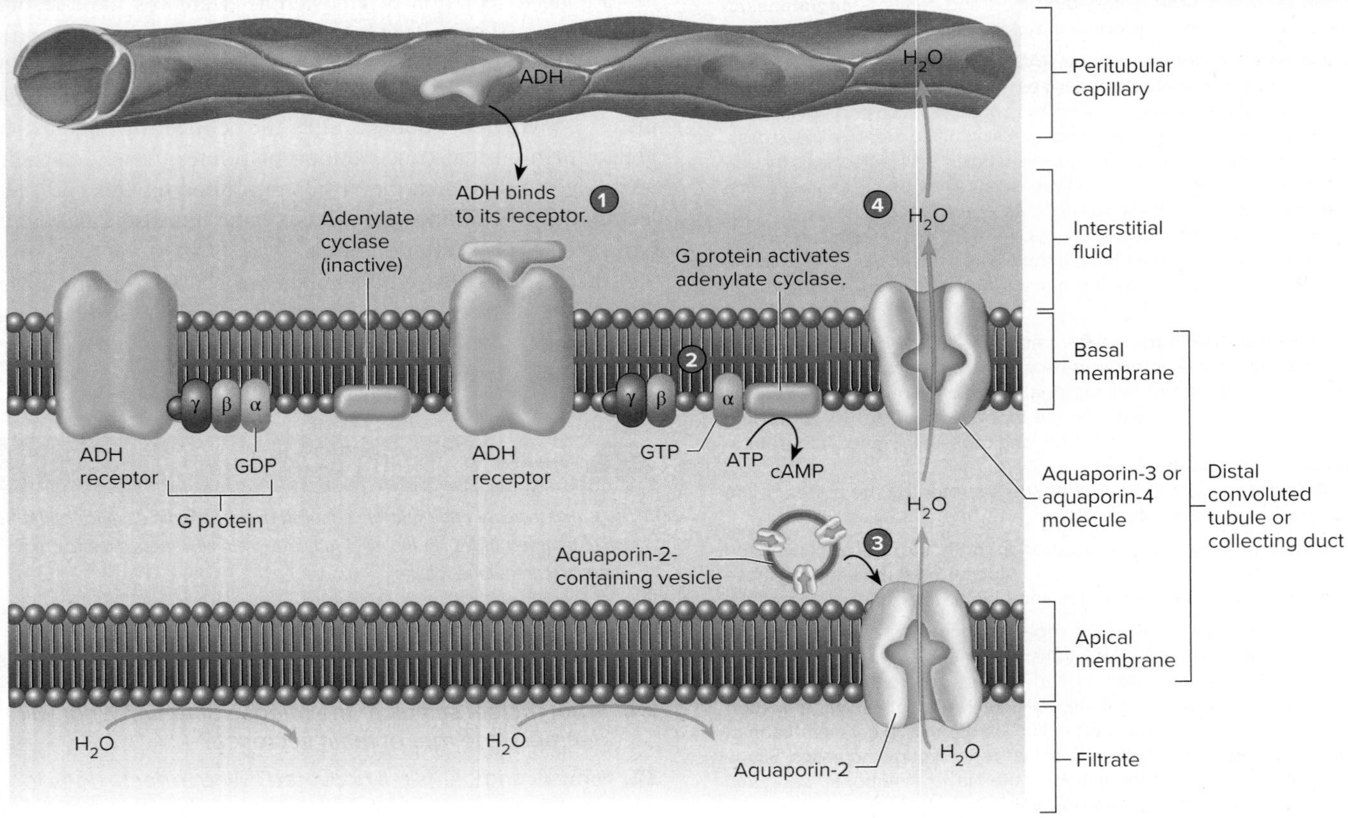

PROCESS **Figure 26.18**

Effect of Antidiuretic Hormone (ADH) on Renal Tubule Water Movement

Increased blood solute concentration affects hypothalamic neurons, and decreased blood pressure affects baroreceptors. In response to either of these stimuli, the posterior pituitary secretes ADH, which increases water reabsorption by the kidneys. Note: The aquaporin-2-containing vesicle is not to scale.

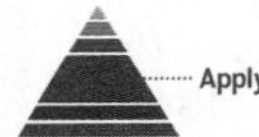

In response to severely low blood pressure, ADH is secreted. How does ADH secretion help return blood pressure to its set point? How might blood pressure respond in an individual who has excess ADH secretion, a condition known as syndrome of inappropriate ADH secretion?

33. *Where is aldosterone produced? What factors stimulate its secretion?*

34. *What are the effects of aldosterone on Na^+ and Cl^- transport? How does aldosterone affect urine concentration, urine volume, and blood pressure?*

Antidiuretic Hormone Mechanism

Neurons of the supraoptic nucleus of the hypothalamus produce **antidiuretic hormone (ADH),** also known as *vasopressin,* which is stored in the posterior pituitary gland (see chapter 18). ADH is released into the blood from the posterior pituitary. Cells called osmoreceptor cells in the supraoptic nucleus are very sensitive to even slight changes in the osmolality of the interstitial fluid. If the osmolality of the blood and interstitial fluid increases, these cells stimulate the ADH-secreting neurons. Action potentials are then propagated along the axons of the ADH-secreting neurons to the posterior pituitary gland, where the axons release ADH from their ends. Reduced osmolality of the interstitial fluid within the supraoptic nucleus inhibits ADH secretion from the posterior pituitary gland (see figure 18.5). Baroreceptors that monitor blood pressure in the atria of the heart, large veins, carotid sinuses, and aortic arch also influence ADH secretion when the blood pressure changes by more than 5–10%. Decreases in blood pressure are detected by baroreceptors when there is reduced stretch of the blood vessel wall. This reduced stretch of the baroreceptors causes them to send a lower frequency of action potentials to the hypothalamus along afferent pathways. These pathways terminate in the supraoptic nucleus of the hypothalamus (see chapter 13). As a result, the hypothalamus triggers secretion of more ADH. Figure 26.18 details the mechanism of ADH effects on water conservation.

1 ADH moves from the peritubular capillaries and binds to ADH receptors in the plasma membranes of the distal convoluted tubule cells and the collecting duct cells.

2. When ADH binds to its receptor, a G protein mechanism is activated, which in turn activates adenylate cyclase.
3. Adenylate cyclase increases the rate of cAMP synthesis. Cyclic AMP promotes the insertion of aquaporin-2-containing cytoplasmic vesicles into the apical membranes of the distal convoluted tubules and collecting ducts, thereby increasing their permeability to water. Water then moves by osmosis out of the distal convoluted tubules and collecting ducts into the tubule cells through the aquaporin-2 water channels.
4. Water exits the tubule cells and enters the interstitial fluid through aquaporin-3 and aquaporin-4 water channels in the basal membranes.

The distal convoluted tubules and collecting ducts remain relatively impermeable to water in the absence of ADH. More urine is produced when little ADH is secreted. A large part of the 19% of the filtrate that is normally reabsorbed in the distal convoluted tubules and the collecting ducts becomes part of the urine.

Insufficient ADH secretion results in a condition called **diabetes insipidus** (die-ah-BEE-teez in-SIP-i-dus); the word *diabetes* refers to the production of a large volume of urine, and the word *insipidus* means the urine is clear, tasteless, and dilute. People who secrete insufficient ADH often produce 10–20 L of urine per day and develop major problems, such as dehydration and ion imbalances. In contrast to diabetes insipidus, **diabetes mellitus** (MEL-ih-tus) refers to the production of a large volume of urine that contains a high concentration of glucose (*mellitus,* honeyed, sweet).

ADH secretion promotes increased water reabsorption by the distal convoluted tubule when blood osmolality increases or when blood pressure declines significantly. Water reabsorption lowers blood osmolality. It also increases blood volume, which elevates blood pressure. Conversely, when blood osmolality decreases or when blood pressure goes up, ADH secretion declines. The reduced ADH levels cause the kidneys to reabsorb less water and to produce a larger volume of dilute urine. The greater loss of water in the urine raises blood osmolality and lowers blood pressure. ADH secretion occurs in response to small changes in osmolality, whereas a substantial change in blood pressure is required to alter ADH secretion. Thus, ADH is more important in regulating blood osmolality than it is in regulating blood pressure.

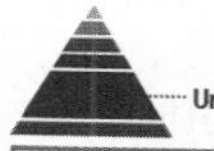

Predict 3

Ethyl alcohol inhibits ADH secretion. Given this information, describe the mechanism by which alcoholic beverages affect urine production.

Clinical IMPACT 26.2 Diuretics

Diuretics (die-yoo-RET-iks) are chemicals that increase the rate of urine production. Although the definition is simple, a number of physiological mechanisms are involved.

Diuretics are used to treat hypertension, as well as several types of edema caused by congestive heart failure, cirrhosis of the liver, and other anomalies. However, treatment with diuretics can lead to complications, including dehydration and electrolyte imbalances.

The varying degree of diuretic chemical types is outlined in the following descriptions, along with their physiological mechanisms. The action of **carbonic anhydrase** (kar-BON-ik an-HIGH-drase) **inhibitors** reduces the rate of H^+ secretion and the reabsorption of bicarbonate ion (HCO_3^-). As H^+ is secreted into the renal tubule, it combines with HCO_3^- to form carbonic acid. Carbonic acid dissociates into water and CO_2, which can diffuse across the wall of the renal tubule. Reduced H^+ secretion causes HCO_3^- to remain in the renal tubule. The HCO_3^- increases tubular osmotic pressure, causing osmotic diuresis. The diuretic effect is useful in treating conditions such as glaucoma and altitude sickness. However, with long-term use, carbonic anhydrase inhibitors tend to lose their diuretic effect.

Sodium ion reabsorption inhibitors include thiazide-type diuretics. They promote the loss of Na^+, Cl^-, and water in the urine. These diuretics are sometimes given to people who have hypertension. The increased loss of water in the urine lowers blood volume and thus blood pressure. Other inhibitors of Na^+ reabsorption, such as bumetanide, furosemide, and ethacrynic acid, specifically inhibit transport in the ascending limb of the nephron loop. These diuretics are frequently used to treat congestive heart failure, cirrhosis of the liver, and renal disease. A possible side effect of these drugs is increased excretion of K^+ in the urine.

Certain **potassium-sparing diuretics** act on the distal convoluted tubules and the collecting ducts to reduce the exchange between Na^+ and K^+. Potassium-sparing diuretics are used to diminish the loss of K^+ in the urine, thereby preserving, or "sparing," these ions. Some potassium-sparing diuretic drugs act by competitive inhibition of aldosterone, whereas others inhibit the symporters for Na^+ in apical membranes of cells in the distal convoluted tubules and collecting ducts. Both types result in Na^+ diuresis and K^+ retention. A side effect of prolonged treatment with certain diuretics is K^+ depletion. These diuretics are inhibitors of Na^+–Cl^- symporters in the ascending limb of the nephron loop. To prevent K^+ depletion, potassium-sparing diuretics are commonly used in combination with Na^+–Cl^- symport inhibitors.

Osmotic diuretics freely pass into the filtrate and undergo limited reabsorption by the renal tubule. These diuretics increase urine volume by elevating the osmotic concentration of the filtrate, thus reducing the amount of water moving by osmosis out of the renal tubule. Urea, mannitol, and glycerine have been used as osmotic diuretics and can be effective in treating patients who have cerebral edema and edema in acute renal failure (see table 26.5).

Xanthines (ZAN-theenz), including caffeine and related substances, act as diuretics partly because they increase renal blood flow and the rate of glomerular filtrate formation. They also influence the renal tubule by decreasing Na^+ and Cl^- reabsorption.

Alcohol acts as a diuretic, although it is not used clinically for that purpose. It inhibits ADH secretion from the posterior pituitary and results in increased urine volume.

Case STUDY 26.1 Diabetes Insipidus

Two infants were born to different families within the same week. Not long after the newborns arrived home from the hospital, their respective parents noticed that their diapers were excessively wet hour after hour throughout the day and night. In addition, both infants were irritable, had slight fevers, and had vomited, even though they had not eaten for several feedings. The parents took the babies to their pediatricians. Subsequently, blood tests indicated that both infants had high blood Na^+ levels. Following water deprivation tests, which monitor plasma levels of ADH, the physicians diagnosed nephrogenic diabetes insipidus. One infant was found to have an ADH receptor abnormality, whereas the other was diagnosed with an aquaporin-2 abnormality.

The term *diabetes* refers to a disease state characterized by polyuria, excess production of urine. There are two major causes of diabetes: (1) inadequate production of or response to insulin, called diabetes mellitus (see chapter 18), and (2) inadequate production of or response to ADH, called diabetes insipidus. Diabetes insipidus is a relatively rare disease that occurs in two varieties: **Central diabetes insipidus (CDI)** is caused by failure of ADH secretion, and **nephrogenic diabetes insipidus (NDI)** results when ADH secretion is normal but the ADH receptor, or the response to ADH, in the kidney is abnormal. Consequently, the G protein mechanism, which normally functions in the insertion of the aquaporin-2 water channel protein in the apical membranes, does not operate. In most cases, NDI results from an inherited condition that affects the function of the ADH receptor. NDI can also be acquired, but that usually happens later in life and can be due to several factors, including the use of certain prescription drugs or the existence of an underlying systemic disease.

Treatment of NDI includes ensuring a plentiful supply of water, following a low-sodium and sometimes a low-protein diet, and using thiazide diuretics (Na^+ reabsorption inhibitors) in combination with a potassium-sparing diuretic.

Predict 4

Use your knowledge of kidney physiology and figure 26.18 to answer the following questions.

a. *Why did the two infants have high blood Na^+ levels and dilute urine?*

b. *Predict how the infants' plasma levels of ADH changed during the water deprivation test, given the diagnosis of NDI.* (Hint: *See section 26.4.*)

c. *Why does an abnormal aquaporin-2 gene result in excessive urine production?*

d. *Predict plasma levels of ADH following a water deprivation test in an individual with central diabetes insipidus.*

e. *Why is treatment with a thiazide diuretic helpful to patients with NDI?* (Hint: *See Clinical Impact 26.2.*)

Production of Concentrated Urine

Filtrate enters the distal convoluted tubules after passing through the nephron loops. From the distal convoluted tubule, filtrate then passes through the collecting ducts. ADH increases the permeability of the distal convoluted tubule and the collecting ducts to water. When ADH is present, water moves by osmosis out of the distal convoluted tubule and collecting duct into the more concentrated interstitial fluid.

ADH increases the permeability of the apical membranes of the distal convoluted tubules and collecting ducts to water by binding to membrane-bound receptors. This activates a G protein mechanism that increases cAMP synthesis inside these cells. Cyclic AMP promotes the insertion of aquaporins into the apical membrane (figure 26.18). **Aquaporins** are water channel proteins that increase the permeability of the distal convoluted tubule and the collecting duct to water. There are multiple forms of aquaporins. In cells of the distal convoluted tubules and collecting ducts, the basal membranes contain aquaporin molecules—aquaporin-3 and aquaporin-4—that are insensitive to ADH. These aquaporin molecules provide channels for water to exit from the collecting duct cells into the interstitial fluid. Aquaporin-2 molecules regulate water movement into the cells. In cells that have not been exposed to ADH, the aquaporin-2 molecules are found in the membranes of vesicles in the cytoplasm (see figure 3.1). In response to ADH, the

Clinical GENETICS 26.2 Nephrogenic Diabetes Insipidus

There are three types of inherited nephrogenic diabetes insipidus (NDI). X-linked NDI, the most common form, affects more males than females. X-linked NDI is caused by a mutation in the V_2 ADH receptor gene on the X chromosome. Mutations in this gene result in defective ADH receptors, which prevent a normal response to ADH in the kidneys.

Autosomal recessive NDI is more rare than the X-linked form, and it affects males and females equally. This form of NDI requires both parents to be carriers for an abnormal aquaporin-2 gene. For children to have autosomal recessive NDI, they must inherit a recessive allele from each parent. In autosomal recessive NDI, there is a 25% chance that each child of heterozygous parents will have NDI.

Autosomal dominant NDI is the most rare form of NDI, and it affects males and females equally. With this form, only one parent must have a dominant allele for an abnormal aquaporin-2 gene, but that parent will also have symptoms of NDI. There is a 50% chance that each child will have NDI.

increased cAMP initiates the incorporation of the membranes of vesicles containing aquaporin-2 channels into the apical membrane. Thus, when ADH is present, water moves by osmosis out of the distal convoluted tubules and collecting ducts; conversely, when ADH is absent, water remains in the distal convoluted tubules and collecting ducts to become urine (figure 26.19). Abnormal aquaporin-2 genes can result in excessive urine production because these genes code for abnormal aquaporin-2 molecules that do not function normally. Thus, the number of functional aquaporins decreases, and water remains in the renal tubule.

The filtrate flows into the distal convoluted tubules and collecting ducts that pass through the kidney medulla with its high concentration of solutes. When ADH is present, water moves by osmosis from the distal convoluted tubules and the collecting ducts into the interstitial fluid. By the time the filtrate has reached the end of the collecting ducts, another 19% of the filtrate has been reabsorbed. Thus, 1% of the filtrate remains as urine, and 99% of the filtrate has been reabsorbed. The osmolality of the filtrate at the ends of the collecting ducts is approximately 1200 mOsm/kg (see figure 26.16).

In addition to the dramatic decrease in filtrate volume and the increase in filtrate osmolality, a marked alteration occurs in the filtrate composition. Waste products, such as creatinine and urea, and excess ions, such as K^+, H^+, phosphate, and sulfate, are at a much higher concentration in urine than in the original filtrate because water has been removed from the filtrate. Overall, the processes of reabsorption and secretion are selective so that, in the end, beneficial substances are retained in the body and toxic substances are eliminated.

Production of Dilute Urine

If ADH is not present or its concentration is low, the distal convoluted tubules and collecting ducts are less permeable to water. This lowered permeability dampens water reabsorption. The concentration of the urine produced is less than 1200 mOsm/kg, and the volume is increased. The volume of this more dilute urine can be much larger than 1% of the filtrate formed each day. If no ADH is secreted, the osmolality of the urine may be close to the osmolality of the filtrate in the distal convoluted tubule, and the volume of urine may approach 20–30 L/day, which is the same volume as ten to fifteen 2-liter soda bottles per day (figure 26.19).

In a healthy person, even when the kidneys produce dilute urine, the concentration of waste products in the urine is large enough to maintain homeostasis. Again, as with the production of

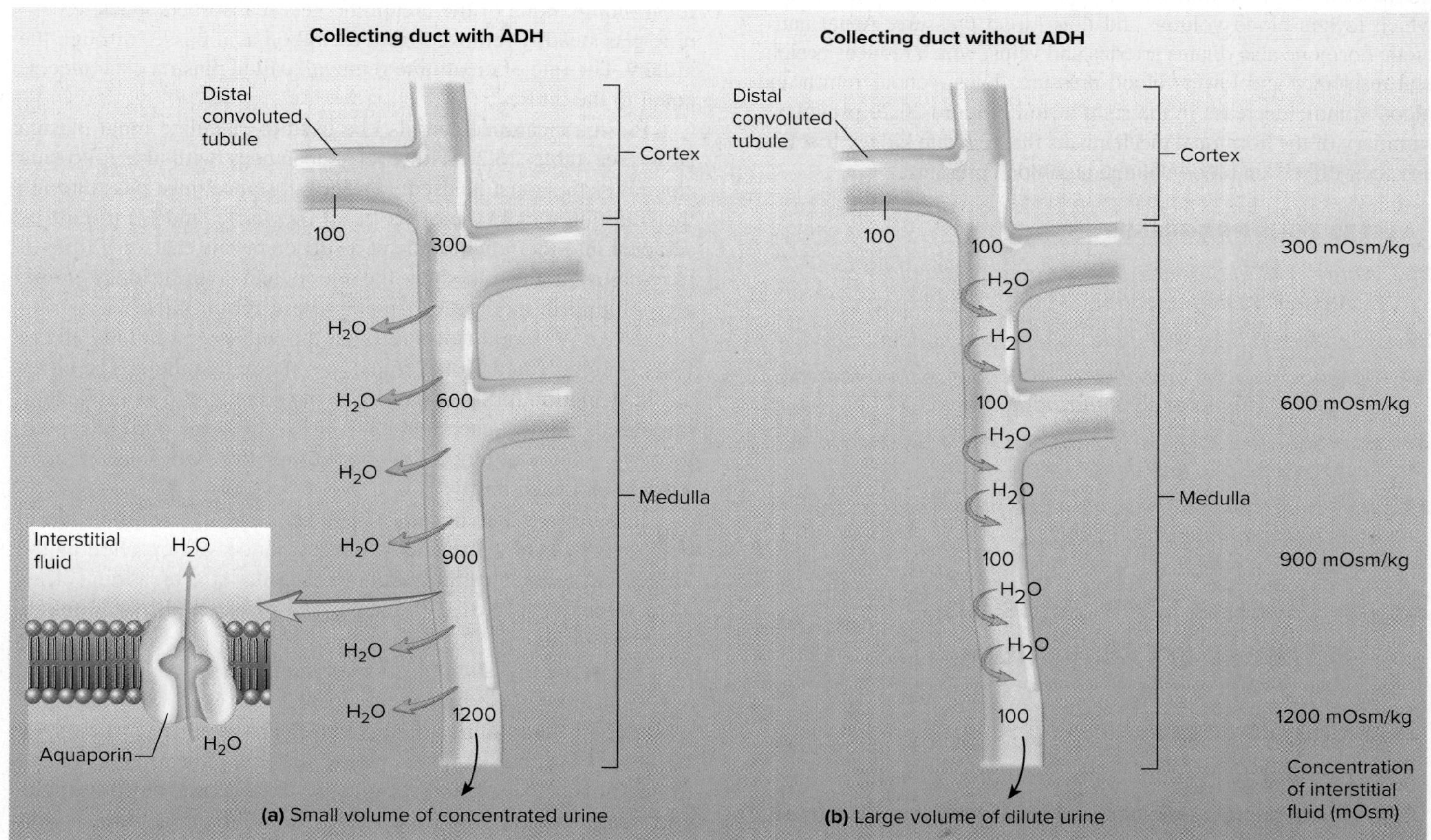

FIGURE 26.19 Effect of ADH on Urine Concentration and Volume

(*a*) In the presence of ADH, the collecting duct is permeable to water and water is reabsorbed into the interstitial fluid. The result is the production of a small volume of concentrated urine. (*b*) In the absence of ADH, the collecting duct is impermeable to water and water remains in the collecting duct. The result is the production of a large volume of dilute urine.

concentrated urine, beneficial substances are retained, and both toxic substances and excess water are eliminated.

Predict 5

Amanda, an inexperienced runner, competed in her first marathon last spring in Phoenix, Arizona. During the run, the temperature reached 35°C (95°F) with 30% humidity. Amanda drank very little water during the race. When she finished 4½ hours later, she was dizzy and disoriented and had an increased heart rate. She was also very pale. Friends took her to a hospital, where the doctor diagnosed severe dehydration and prescribed IV fluids. Amanda did not urinate until nearly 12 hours later. Explain the physiological responses that resulted in her reduced urine production. (Hint: *See section 21.9.*)

Atrial Natriuretic Hormone

Atrial natriuretic (AY-tree-al nay-tree-yoo-RET-ik) **hormone (ANH)** is a hormone secreted by cells in the right atrium of the heart when they are stretched more than normal. Increased stretch of the right atrium occurs when blood volume is higher than usual (see chapter 21). Atrial natriuretic hormone decreases blood volume through inhibition of Na^+ reabsorption in the kidney tubules. ANH also inhibits ADH secretion from the posterior pituitary gland. Increased ANH secretion increases the volume of urine produced, which lowers blood volume and thus blood pressure. Atrial natriuretic hormone also dilates arteries and veins, which reduces peripheral resistance and lowers blood pressure. Thus, venous return and blood volume decrease in the right atrium. Figure 26.20 provides a summary of the hormonal mechanisms that regulate kidney function and their effects on blood volume and blood pressure.

ASSESS YOUR PROGRESS

35. *Where is ADH produced? What factors stimulate an increase in ADH secretion?*
36. *How does ADH affect urine volume and concentration?*
37. *Describe how the presence of ADH causes the production of a small volume of concentrated urine.*
38. *How does the absence of ADH cause the production of a large volume of dilute urine?*
39. *Where is atrial natriuretic hormone produced, and how does it affect urine production?*

26.5 Plasma Clearance and Transport Maximum

LEARNING OUTCOMES

After reading this section, you should be able to

A. **Define *plasma clearance* and show how it is calculated.**
B. **Describe why creatinine is used to estimate GFR through plasma clearance.**
C. **Explain how plasma clearance is used to calculate renal plasma flow.**
D. **Define *renal threshold* and *transport maximum*.**

A clinician who is concerned that a patient's kidney function is declining will measure the GFR by determining plasma clearance. **Plasma clearance** is a calculated value representing the volume of plasma that is cleared of a specific substance each minute. For example, if the clearance value is 100 mL/min for a substance, the substance is completely removed from 100 mL of plasma each minute. The plasma clearance can be calculated for any substance that enters the blood according to the following formula:

$$\text{Plasma clearance (mL/min)} = \text{Quantity of urine (mL/min)} \times \frac{\text{Concentration of substance in urine}}{\text{Concentration of substance in plasma}} \quad (26.5)$$

Plasma clearance can be used to estimate GFR if the appropriate substance is monitored (see table 26.2). Such a substance must have the following characteristics: (1) It must pass through the filtration membrane of the renal corpuscle as freely as water or other small molecules, (2) it must not be reabsorbed, (3) it must not be secreted into the renal tubule, and (4) it must not be either metabolized or produced in the kidneys. **Creatinine** (kree-AH-tun-neen) is a naturally occurring metabolite that has these characteristics. As filtrate forms, the filtrate has the same concentration of creatinine as plasma; however, as the filtrate flows through the renal tubule, none of the creatinine gets reabsorbed. Thus, creatinine gets steadily removed from the blood as it passes through the kidney. The rate of creatinine removal, called plasma clearance, is equal to the GFR.

Plasma clearance can also be used to calculate renal plasma flow (see table 26.2). However, substances with the following characteristics must be used: (1) The substance must pass through the filtration membrane of the renal corpuscle, and (2) it must be secreted into the renal tubule at a sufficient rate that very little of it remains in the blood as the blood leaves the kidney. *Para*-aminohippuric acid (PAH) meets these requirements (see section 26.3). As blood flows through the kidney, essentially all the PAH is either filtered or secreted into the renal tubule. The clearance calculation for PAH is equal to the volume of plasma flowing through the kidney each minute. Also, if the hematocrit is known, the total volume of blood flowing through the kidney each minute can be calculated easily.

In addition, the concept of plasma clearance can be used to help determine how drugs or other substances are excreted by the kidney. A plasma clearance value greater than the creatinine clearance value suggests that the substance is secreted by the tubule into the filtrate.

The **renal threshold** is the maximum plasma concentration of a substance before it begins to appear in the urine. For example, glucose is usually almost completely reabsorbed from the tubule by active transport. However, one of the first indications of diabetes mellitus is the presence of glucose in the urine, or **glucosuria.** Glucosuria occurs when the renal threshold for glucose is surpassed and not all of the filtered glucose is reabsorbed, which leaves excess glucose to be excreted in the urine.

The **transport maximum** is the maximum rate at which a substance can be actively reabsorbed from the filtrate. Different substances have different transport maximum levels. This is

3 Stimulus

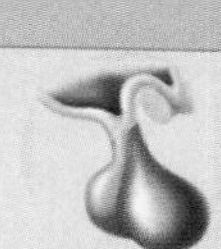

Receptors and control centers:

Pituitary:
Baroreceptors inhibit posterior pituitary ADH secretion when blood volume increases.

Kidney:
Juxtaglomerular apparati inhibit renin release when blood volume increases, which decreases aldosterone secretion.

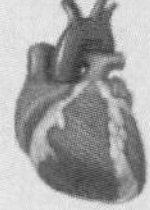

Heart:
Atrial cardiac muscle cells secrete ANH when blood volume increases.

Blood vessels:
Sympathetic division baroreceptors detect increased blood volume, which causes vasodilation of renal arteries.

4 Response

Effectors:

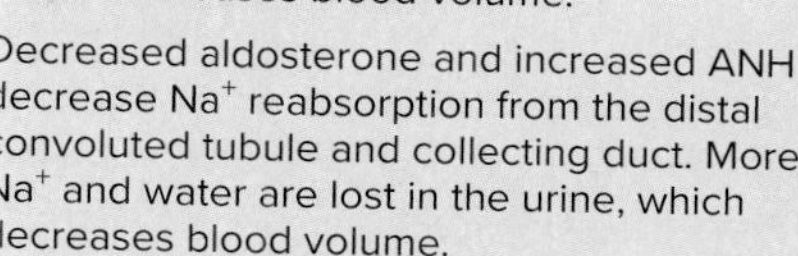

Decreased ADH decreases water reabsorption by the distal convoluted tubules and collecting ducts. Less water returns to the blood and more water is lost in the urine, which decreases blood volume.

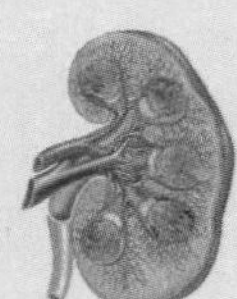

Decreased aldosterone and increased ANH decrease Na^+ reabsorption from the distal convoluted tubule and collecting duct. More Na^+ and water are lost in the urine, which decreases blood volume.

Increased renal blood flow increases the rate of filtrate formation, and more water is lost in the urine.

2 **HOMEOSTASIS DISTURBED:**
High blood volume induces elevated blood pressure.

5 **HOMEOSTASIS RESTORED:**
Reduced blood volume due to loss of water and Na^+ in the urine lowers blood pressure.

1

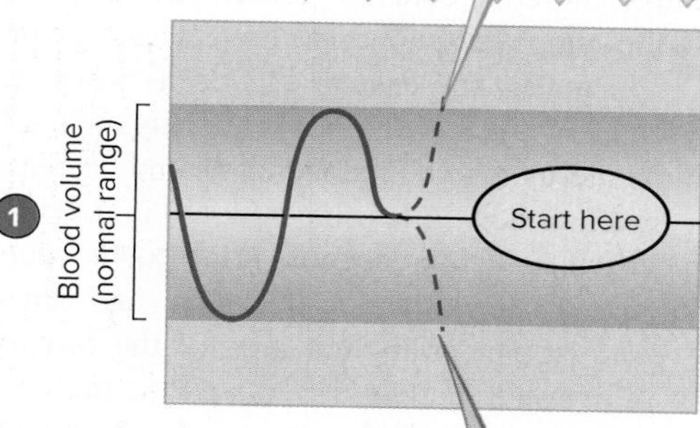

6

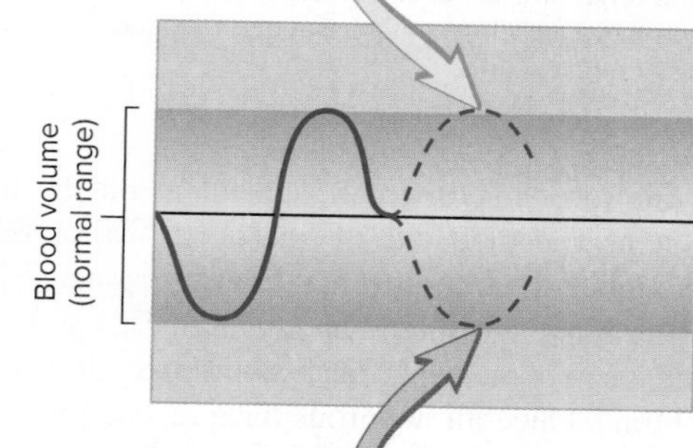

HOMEOSTASIS DISTURBED:
Low blood volume induces lowered blood pressure.

HOMEOSTASIS RESTORED:
Increased blood volume due to decreased Na^+ and water loss in the urine raises blood pressure.

Stimulus

Receptors and control centers:

Blood vessels:
Sympathetic division baroreceptors detect decreased blood volume, which causes vasoconstriction of renal arteries.

Heart:
Atrial cardiac muscle cells do not secrete ANH when blood volume decreases.

Kidney:
Juxtaglomerular apparati stimulate renin release when blood volume decreases, which increases aldosterone secretion.

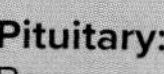

Pituitary:
Baroreceptors stimulate posterior pituitary ADH secretion when blood volume decreases.

Response

Effectors:

Decreased renal blood flow decreases filtrate formation, and less water is lost in urine, which increases blood volume.

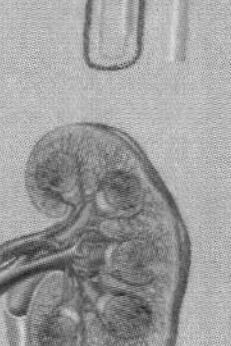

Increased aldosterone and decreased ANH increase Na^+ reabsorption in the distal convoluted tubule and the collecting duct. Less Na^+ and water are lost in the urine, which increases blood volume.

Increased ADH increases the permeability of the distal convoluted tubule and the collecting duct to water. Increased ADH also increases the sensation of thirst. Less water is lost in the urine.

HOMEOSTASIS FIGURE 26.20 Regulation of Blood Pressure

(1) Blood volume is in the normal range. (2) Blood volume increases outside the normal range, which causes homeostasis to be disturbed. (3) The control centers respond to the change in blood volume. (4) The control centers cause ADH and aldosterone secretion to decrease, which reduce water reabsorption. The control centers also cause dilation of renal arteries, which increases urine production. The heart secretes ANH, which also increases urine production. (5) These changes cause blood volume to decrease. (6) Blood volume returns to the normal range and homeostasis is restored. Observe the responses to a decrease in blood volume outside the normal range by following the pink arrows.

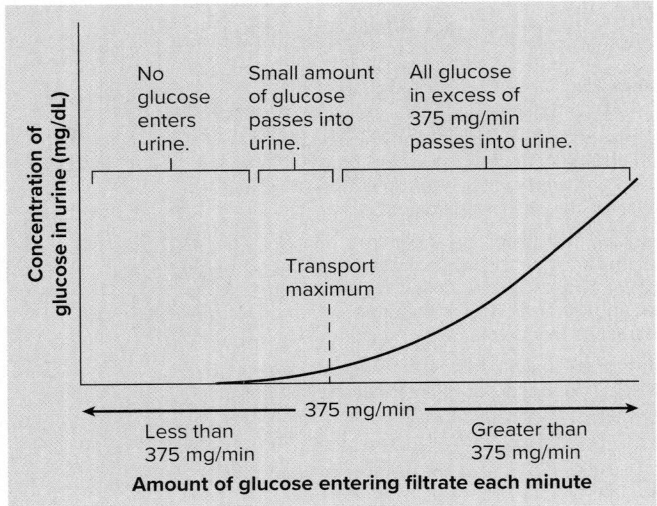

FIGURE 26.21 Transport Maximum for Glucose

As the concentration of glucose increases in the filtrate, it reaches a point that exceeds the renal tubule's ability to actively reabsorb it. That concentration is called the transport maximum. Beyond that concentration, the excess glucose enters the urine.

because the transport maximum is dependent on the number of transport proteins and their rate of transport for a particular substance. For example, the transport maximum for glucose is actually higher than the renal threshold for glucose. This is because the transport proteins in some nephrons become saturated before those in other nephrons. Once all nephrons have reached their maximal capacity to reabsorb glucose, the transport maximum for the kidneys is reached. Thus, glucose will appear in the urine before the transport maximum is reached (figure 26.21). Urine volume in people with glucosuria is also greater than normal because the glucose molecules in the filtrate increase the osmolality of the filtrate in the tubule and reduce the effectiveness of water reabsorption by osmosis.

Predict 6

A person is suspected of having chronic renal failure. To assess kidney function, urea clearance is measured and found to be very low. Explain what a very low urea clearance indicates for this patient. Compare that with the effect of chronic renal failure on the tendency for the blood K^+ level to be higher than normal and the blood Na^+ level to be lower than normal.

ASSESS YOUR PROGRESS

40. *What is plasma clearance, and how is it calculated?*

41. *Explain why plasma clearance of creatinine can be used to estimate GFR.*

42. *Describe how PAH is used to determine renal plasma flow.*

43. *Explain the significance of renal threshold and transport maximum.*

26.6 Urine Movement

LEARNING OUTCOMES

After reading this section, you should be able to

A. **Describe the anatomy and histology of the ureters, urinary bladder, and urethra.**

B. **Explain the flow of urine from the nephron to the urinary bladder.**

C. **Discuss the micturition reflex.**

Anatomy and Histology of the Ureters and Urinary Bladder

The **ureters** are tubes through which urine flows from the kidneys to the urinary bladder. The ureters extend inferiorly and medially from the renal pelvis and exit the kidney at the renal hilum. The ureters descend through the abdominal cavity and enter the urinary bladder (figure 26.22; see figures 26.1 and 26.2). The **urinary bladder** is a hollow, muscular container that lies in the pelvic cavity just posterior to the symphysis pubis. The ureters enter on its posterolateral surface. In males, the urinary bladder is just anterior to the rectum; in females, it is just anterior to the vagina and inferior and anterior to the uterus. Its volume increases and decreases, depending on how much or how little urine is stored in it.

The **urethra,** which transports urine to the outside of the body, exits the urinary bladder inferiorly and anteriorly (figure 26.22, *center*). The triangular area of the urinary bladder's posterior wall between the two ureters and the urethra on the urinary bladder's anterior wall is called the **trigone** (TRY-gohn). This region is histologically unique. The trigone does not expand with the urinary bladder wall as it fills. This causes the trigone to act as a funnel for emptying the urinary bladder. **Cystitis** (sis-TIE-tis) is an inflammation of the urinary bladder, which usually results from a bacterial infection. Typically, bacteria from outside the body enter the bladder. Infection by the bacterium *E. coli* is the most common cause of cystitis.

Transitional epithelium lines both the ureters and the urinary bladder. Transitional epithelium is specialized so that the cells slide past one another, and the number of cell layers decreases as the volume of the ureters and urinary bladder increases (see chapter 4). The rest of the walls of these structures consists of a lamina propria, a muscular coat, and a fibrous adventitia (figure 26.22*b,c*). The wall of the urinary bladder is much thicker than the wall of a ureter because it consists of layers of primarily smooth muscle, sometimes called the **detrusor** (dee-TROO-ser) **muscle.** Contraction of this smooth muscle forces urine out of the urinary bladder. The epithelium itself ranges from four or five cells thick when the urinary bladder is empty to two or three cells thick when it is distended. The urethra is lined with stratified or pseudostratified columnar epithelium.

At the junction of the urinary bladder and the urethra, smooth muscle forms an **internal urethral sphincter** that prevents urine leakage from the urinary bladder. In males, the internal urethral sphincter contracts to keep semen from entering the urinary bladder during sexual intercourse (see chapter 28). The specific anatomy and

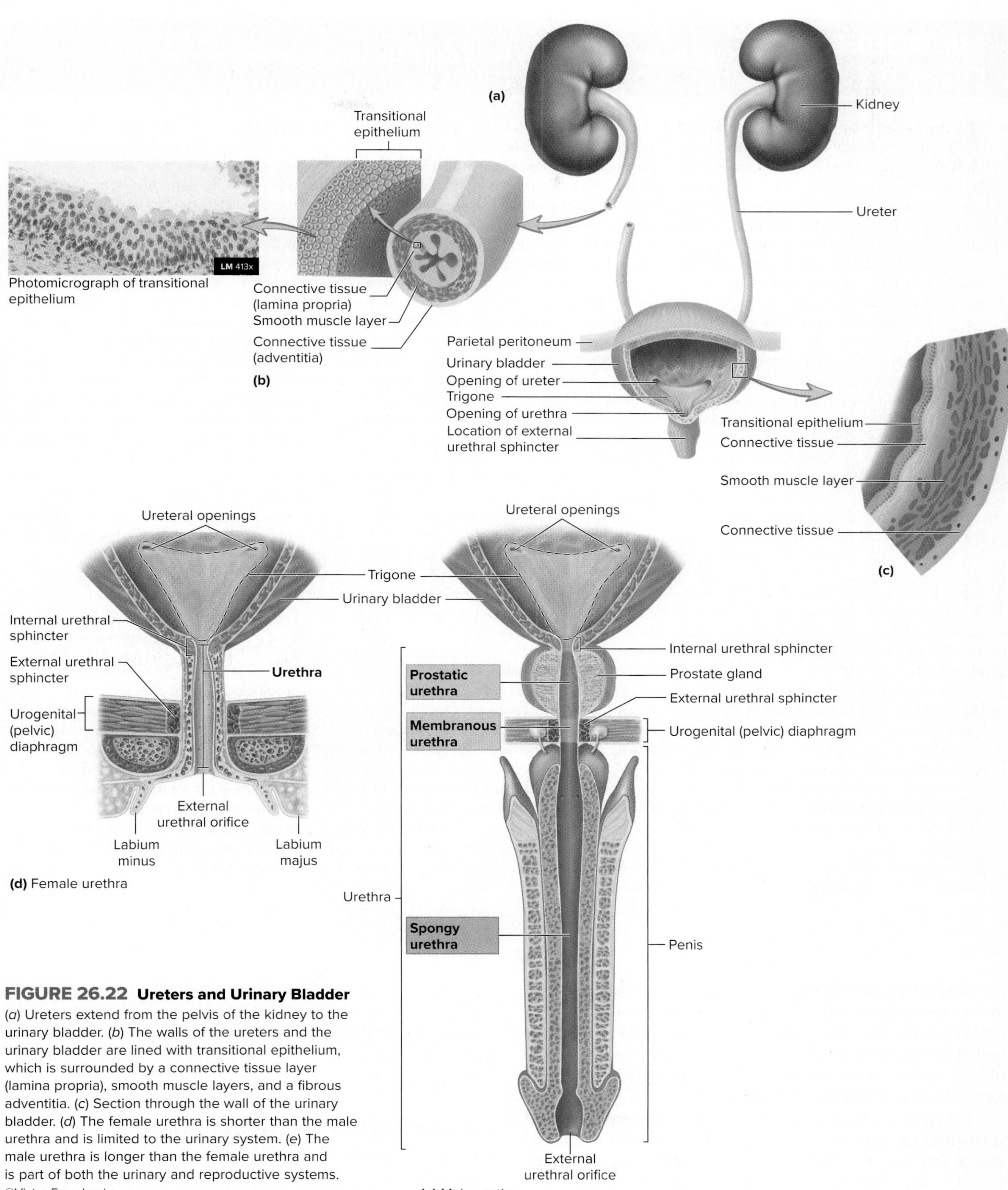

FIGURE 26.22 Ureters and Urinary Bladder
(*a*) Ureters extend from the pelvis of the kidney to the urinary bladder. (*b*) The walls of the ureters and the urinary bladder are lined with transitional epithelium, which is surrounded by a connective tissue layer (lamina propria), smooth muscle layers, and a fibrous adventitia. (*c*) Section through the wall of the urinary bladder. (*d*) The female urethra is shorter than the male urethra and is limited to the urinary system. (*e*) The male urethra is longer than the female urethra and is part of both the urinary and reproductive systems.

MICROBES In Your Body 26.1 — Can Bacteria Actually Help Cure Urinary Bladder Cancer?

In the United States, there are more than 60,000 new cases of urinary bladder cancer diagnosed each year; it is the ninth-leading type of cancer. The majority of urinary bladder cancer is transitional cell carcinoma, which is cancer of the endothelial cell lining of the urinary bladder. However, if the cancer is detected and treated before it penetrates the urinary bladder's muscular wall or spreads to other areas of the body, the 5-year survival rate is 77%. Reliable treatments can resolve these cases relatively quickly. Surprisingly, the most common treatment for early-stage urinary bladder cancer tumors is the introduction of a fluid containing live tuberculosis-causing bacteria into the urinary bladder. We will examine the causes of and screening tests for urinary bladder cancer and explore how a bacterium serves as an anticancer treatment for urinary bladder cancer.

At least 50% of urinary bladder cancer cases can be attributed to cigarette smoking, even 10 years or more after a person has quit smoking. About 30% of cases are due to exposure to environmental carcinogens, such as certain industrial dyes or hair dyes used by professional hair stylists. The remaining cases are often due to a combination of factors, none of which are well understood.

In about 80–90% of urinary bladder cancer cases, the first sign is blood in the urine, called macrohematuria. Sometimes, pain with urination or a change in urination frequency is also an indicator of possible cancer. However, confirmation is usually done with a procedure called **cystoscopy** (sis-TOS-kuh-pee), in which a catheter is inserted into the urinary bladder to view the wall and collect cells, which are then examined under a microscope to look for abnormalities in appearance.

The treatments for urinary bladder cancer are dependent on how deeply the tumor has penetrated into the urinary bladder wall. In earlier stages, treatment is more effective. If the tumor is quite small and shallow in the endothelium, a process called transurethral resection of the bladder tumor (TURBT) can be used to scrape the cancerous cells off the urinary bladder wall. In other cases, in which the tumor is superficial but somewhat more advanced than the earliest stage, immunotherapy with intravesicular (inside the urinary bladder) delivery of a medicine known as Bacillus Calmette-Guérin (BCG) is used. BCG was originally developed in 1906 as a vaccine against the bacterial disease tuberculosis. BCG is a live, attenuated (weakened) strain of *Myocobacterium bovis,* the bacterium that causes tuberculosis in cattle, but it can infect other organisms, including humans. BCG was used as an anticancer therapeutic after results from animal experiments demonstrated its effectiveness.

Tuberculosis and humans have a long history together. The disease was originally called "consumption" because one of its side effects in untreated patients is extreme weight loss. Human tuberculosis is caused by the bacterium *Mycobacterium tuberculosis*. Due to their cellular composition, members of the *Mycobacterium* genus are notoriously difficult to kill, including destruction by our body's immune system. Ironically, this characteristic is what makes tuberculosis bacteria effective at helping kill cancer cells. Urinary bladder cancer is the only cancer treated with BCG. Because the BCG fluid is isolated within the urinary bladder, other organs in the body are not usually exposed to the bacteria.

Members of the *Mycobacterium* genus have cell walls with higher lipid content than other bacteria. It is this lipid content that protects them once they are phagocytosed by macrophages or taken up by cancer cells. Once the infected cells have the bacteria inside, these cells then display the bacterial antigens. Display of the bacterial antigens induces destruction of the infected cells by the immune system (see chapter 22). Because the bacteria used in BCG are live, although attenuated, they can infect other body tissues if they enter the blood. If this happens, patients develop an illness called acute disseminated (widespread) tuberculosis and become contagious to others. Fortunately, development of tuberculosis is a rare occurrence for BCG recipients. Treatments are terminated once white blood cells are detectable in the patient's urine, indicating that an immunological reaction is occurring in the urinary bladder. The average treatment time is about 6 weeks. The BCG urinary bladder cancer treatment is an elegant example of how knowledge of body systems can be applied in an unexpected way: purposefully infecting a patient with bacteria so cancer cells are destroyed by the patient's immune system.

Predict 7

Based on your knowledge of the micturition reflex and using figure 26.23, predict how treatment with BCG and induction of an immunological response in the urinary bladder might affect action potential frequency in sensory neurons located in the wall of the urinary bladder. Would there be a higher or lower frequency of action potentials? How would a patient interpret a change in action potential frequency in relation to the urge to urinate?

physiology of the internal urethral sphincter is more clearly detailed for the male urethra. For the female urethra, the details are not as well established. Females clearly have smooth muscle fibers within the wall of the urethra at the neck of the bladder. These smooth muscle fibers assist with preventing urine leakage, but whether these fibers form a distinct sphincter is still under scrutiny.

Both males and females have a well-defined **external urethral sphincter.** The external urethral sphincter is formed of skeletal muscle that surrounds the urethra as the urethra extends through the pelvic floor. The external urethral sphincter allows a person to voluntarily start or stop the flow of urine through the urethra.

In males, the urethra extends to the end of the penis, where it opens to the outside. The female urethra is much shorter (approximately 4 cm) than the male urethra (approximately 20 cm) and opens into the vestibule anterior to the vaginal opening (see figure 26.22*d,e*).

Urine Flow Through the Nephron and Ureters

Pressure decreases in the renal tubule as filtrate moves along it during urine production. Hydrostatic pressure from filtrate averages 10 mm Hg in the glomerular capsule and drops to nearly 0 mm Hg in the renal pelvis. This pressure gradient forces the filtrate to flow from the glomerular capsule through the renal tubule into the renal pelvis. Because the hydrostatic pressure is 0 mm Hg in the renal pelvis, no pressure gradient exists to force urine to flow through the ureters to the urinary bladder. However, the circular smooth muscle in the walls of the ureters undergoes peristaltic waves of contractions (see chapter 24), which force urine through the ureters. The peristaltic waves progress from the region of the renal pelvis to the urinary bladder. They occur from once every few seconds to once every 2–3 minutes. Parasympathetic stimulation increases their frequency, and sympathetic stimulation decreases it. The peristaltic contractions of each ureter proceed at a velocity of approximately 3 cm/s and can generate pressures in excess of 50 mm Hg.

The ureters penetrate the urinary bladder at an oblique angle through the trigone, creating a valvelike formation at the junction of the ureter and the urinary bladder. Once urine enters the bladder, its backward flow into the ureters is prevented when increased pressure inside the bladder compresses the ureter opening.

When no urine is present in the urinary bladder, internal pressure is about 0 mm Hg; even when the urine volume is 100 mL, pressure rises to only 10 mm Hg. Pressure continues to rise slowly as volume increases to approximately 300 mL, but above volumes of 400 mL the pressure rises rapidly.

Micturition Reflex

The flow of urine from the kidney to the urinary bladder through the ureter is relatively continuous. The urinary bladder acts as a reservoir for urine until it can be eliminated relatively quickly at an appropriate time and place. The urinary bladder can stretch to hold a large urine volume. At its maximum volume, the urinary bladder can contain 1 L (about 1 quart) of urine, but discomfort becomes noticeable when urine volume exceeds approximately 500 mL. The urinary bladder's capacity to distend is due to three factors:

1. The wall of the urinary bladder contains large folds, similar to those of the stomach, which unfold to enlarge the lumen.
2. The lining of the urinary bladder is transitional epithelium, which stretches.
3. The smooth muscle wall of the urinary bladder, with the exception of the trigone, also stretches to accommodate fluid. As urine enters the urinary bladder, it lifts and expands superiorly to accommodate the fluid.

Urination is called **micturition** (mik-choo-RISH-un). The **micturition reflex** is activated when the urinary bladder wall is stretched as urine fills the urinary bladder. Integration of the micturition reflex occurs in the sacral region of the spinal cord and is modified by centers in the pons and cerebrum.

Figure 26.23 shows the steps in the micturition reflex.

1. Urine filling the urinary bladder stimulates stretch receptors, which produce action potentials.
2. The action potentials are carried by sensory neurons to the sacral segments of the spinal cord through the pelvic nerves.

PROCESS **Figure**

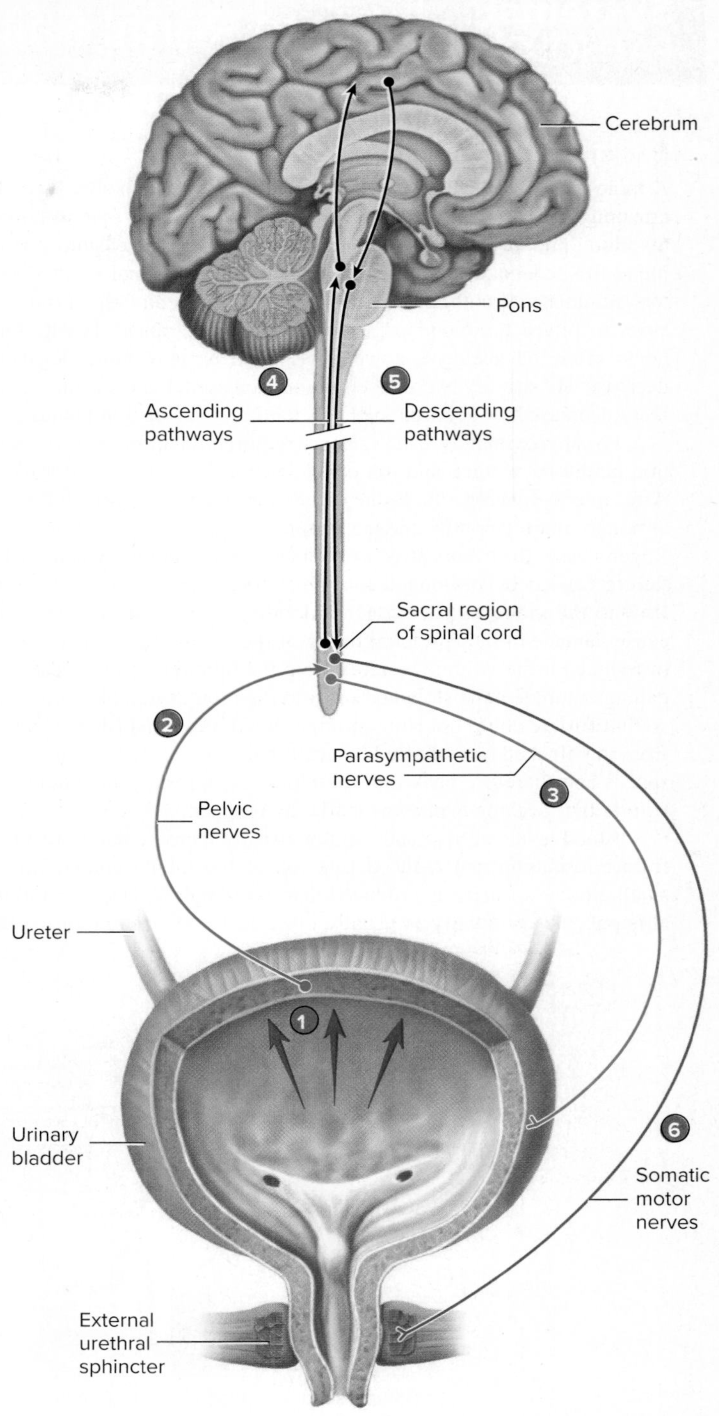

PROCESS **Figure 26.23**

Micturition Reflex

The micturition reflex is under parasympathetic regulation. APR

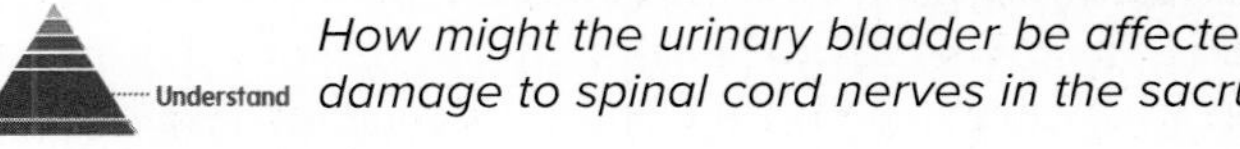

How might the urinary bladder be affected by damage to spinal cord nerves in the sacrum?

Systems PATHOLOGY | Acute Renal Failure

Background Information

A large piece of machinery overturned at a construction site, severely crushing Roger's legs. Because Roger was trapped for several hours, his blood pressure decreased to very low levels (hypotension) due to blood loss, edema in the inflamed tissues, and emotional shock. Doctors administered both intravenous saline solutions and blood transfusions to return his blood pressure to its normal range. Twenty-four hours after the accident, however, Roger's urine volume began to decrease. His urinary Na^+ concentration increased, but his urine osmolality decreased. In addition, cellular debris was evident in his urine.

For approximately 7 days, Roger required renal dialysis to maintain his blood volume and ion concentrations within normal ranges. After about 3 weeks, his kidney function slowly began to improve, although many months passed before it was back to normal. In Roger's case, the events after 24 hours are consistent with acute renal failure caused by prolonged low blood pressure and lack of blood flow to the kidneys. The reduced blood flow was severe enough to cause damage to the epithelial lining of the renal tubules. The period of reduced urine volume resulted from the tubule damage. Dead and damaged tubule cells sloughed off into the tubules and blocked them so that filtrate could not flow through. In addition, the filtrate leaked from the blocked or partially blocked tubules back into the interstitial spaces and therefore back into the blood. As a result, the amount of filtrate that became urine was markedly reduced.

Blood levels of urea and creatine usually increase due to reduced filtrate formation and reduced function of the tubule epithelium. A small amount of urine is produced that has a high Na^+ concentration, although the osmolality is usually close to the concentration of the body fluids. The kidney is not able to reabsorb Na^+, nor can it effectively concentrate urine.

Treatments for Renal Failure

Hemodialysis (HEE-moh-dye-AL-ih-sis) is used when a person is suffering from severe acute or chronic kidney failure. The procedure substitutes for the excretory functions of the kidney. Hemodialysis is based on blood flow through tubes composed of a selectively permeable membrane. Blood is usually taken from an artery, passed through tubes of the dialysis machine, and then returned to a vein (figure 26.24). On the outside of the dialysis tubes is a fluid, called dialysis fluid, which contains the same concentration of solutes as normal plasma, except for the metabolic waste products. As a consequence, the metabolic wastes diffuse from the blood to the dialysis fluid. The dialysis membrane has pores that are too small to allow plasma proteins to pass through them, and because the dialyis fluid contains the same beneficial solutes as the plasma, the net movement of these substances is zero. **Peritoneal** (per-ih-toh-NEE-al) **dialysis** is sometimes used to treat kidney failure. The principles by which peritoneal dialysis works are the same as for hemodialysis, but the dialysis fluid flows through a tube inserted into the peritoneal cavity. The visceral and parietal peritonea act as the dialysis membrane. Waste products diffuse from the blood vessels beneath the peritoneum, across the peritoneum, and into the dialysis fluid.

Kidney transplants are sometimes performed on people who have severe renal failure. Often, the donor has suffered an accidental death and had granted permission to have his or her kidneys used for transplantation. The major cause of kidney transplant failure is rejection by the recipient's immune system. Physicians therefore attempt to match the

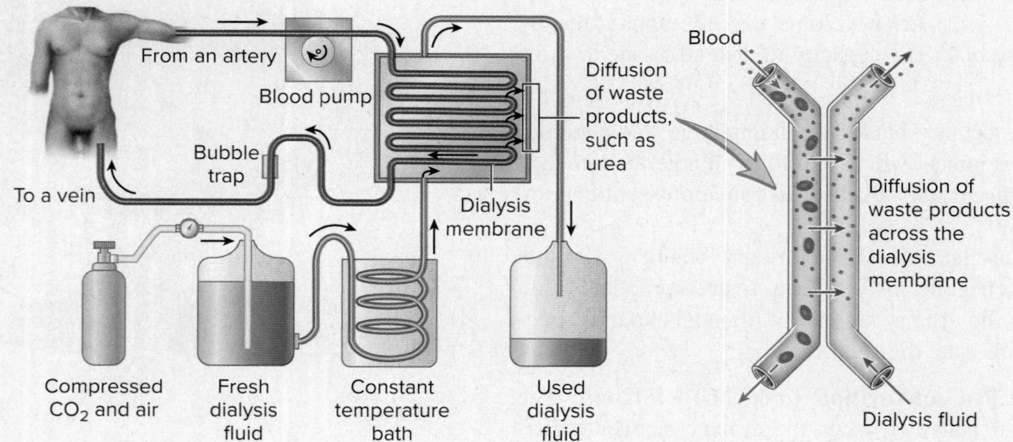

FIGURE 26.24 Hemodialysis
During hemodialysis, blood flows through a system of tubes composed of a selectively permeable membrane. Dialysis fluid, which has a composition similar to that of normal blood (except that the concentration of waste products is very low), flows in the opposite direction on the outside of the dialysis tubes. Waste products, such as urea, diffuse from the blood into the dialysis fluid. Other substances, such as Na^+, K^+, and glucose, can diffuse from the blood into the dialysis fluid if they are present in higher-than-normal concentrations because these substances are present in the dialysis fluid at the same concentrations found in normal blood.

Acute Renal Failure

Symptoms
- Decreased urine volume
- Increased Na^+ in urine
- Decreased urine osmolality

Treatments
- Hemodialysis
- Kidney transplant

INTEGUMENTARY
Anemia causes pallor, and bruising results from clotting proteins lacking in the blood because they are lost in the urine. Accumulation of urinary pigments changes skin tone. High urea gives a yellow cast to light-skinned people, and white crystals of urea, called uremic frost, may appear on areas of the skin where there is heavy perspiration.

SKELETAL
Bone resorption can result because of excessive loss of Ca^{2+} in the urine. Vitamin D levels may be reduced.

DIGESTIVE
Decreased appetite, mouth infections, nausea, and vomiting result from altered digestive tract functions due to the effects of ionic imbalances on the nervous system.

MUSCULAR
Neuromuscular irritability results from the toxic effect of metabolic wastes on the central nervous system and ionic imbalances, such as elevated blood K^+ levels. Involuntary jerking and twitching may occur as neuromuscular irritability develops.

RESPIRATORY
Early during acute renal failure, the depth of breathing increases, and breathing becomes labored as acidosis develops because the kidneys are not able to secrete H^+. Pulmonary edema often develops because of water and Na^+ retention as a result of reduced urine production. The likelihood of pulmonary infection increases as a result of pulmonary edema.

NERVOUS
Elevated blood K^+ levels and the toxic effects of metabolic wastes result in the depolarization of neurons. Slowing of action potential conduction, burning sensations, pain, numbness, or tingling results. Also, decreased mental acuity, reduced ability to concentrate, apathy, and lethargy occur. Or in severe cases, confusion and coma occur.

LYMPHATIC
There are no major direct effects on the lymphatic system, except that increased lymph flow happens as a result of edema.

CARDIOVASCULAR
Water and Na^+ retention may cause edema in peripheral tissues and in the lungs, leading to increased blood pressure and congestive heart failure. Elevated blood K^+ levels result in dysrhythmias and can cause cardiac arrest. Anemia due to decreased erythropoietin production by the damaged kidney exists.

ENDOCRINE
Major hormone deficiencies include vitamin D deficiency. In addition, secretion of reproductive hormones decreases due to the effects of metabolic wastes and ionic imbalances on the hypothalamus.

FIGURE 26.25 Acute Renal Failure
Acute renal failure has significant effects on other organ systems in the body, as this diagram illustrates.

immune characteristics of the donor and recipient to reduce the tendency for rejection. Even with careful matching, recipients have to take medication for the rest of their lives to suppress their immune reactions. In most cases, the transplanted kidney functions well, and the tendency of the recipient's immune system to reject the transplanted kidney can be controlled. Figure 26.25 demonstrates the effects on other organ systems of acute renal failure.

Predict 8

Nine days after the accident, Roger began to appear pale, became dizzy on standing, and was very weak and lethargic. His hematocrit was elevated and his heart was arrhythmic. Explain these manifestations.

3. In response, action potentials travel to the urinary bladder through parasympathetic fibers in the pelvic nerves. The parasympathetic action potentials cause the smooth muscle of the urinary bladder (the detrusor muscle) to contract. In addition, decreased somatic motor action potentials cause the external urethral sphincter, which consists of skeletal muscle, to relax. Urine flows from the urinary bladder when the pressure there is great enough to force the urine through the urethra while the external urethral sphincter is relaxed. The micturition reflex normally produces a series of contractions of the urinary bladder.
4. Action potentials carried by sensory neurons from stretch receptors in the urinary bladder wall also ascend the spinal cord to a micturition center in the pons and to the cerebrum.
5. The micturition reflex integrated in the spinal cord is automatic, but it is either stimulated or inhibited by descending action potentials sent to the sacral region of the spinal cord. For example, higher brain centers prevent micturition by sending action potentials from the cerebrum and pons through spinal pathways to inhibit the spinal micturition reflex. Consequently, parasympathetic stimulation of the urinary bladder is inhibited, and somatic motor neurons that keep the external urethral sphincter contracted are stimulated. The micturition reflex, integrated in the spinal cord, predominates in infants. The ability to inhibit micturition voluntarily develops at the age of 2–3 years; subsequently, the influence of the pons and cerebrum on the spinal micturition reflex predominates.
6. The brain voluntarily controls the external urethral sphincter through somatic motor nerves, causing the sphincter to relax or constrict.

The slow increase in internal pressure helps explain why there is little urge to urinate when the urinary bladder contains less than 300 mL. As stated previously, though, the pressure in the urinary bladder increases rapidly once its volume exceeds approximately 400 mL. In addition, the frequency of action potentials conducted by the ascending spinal pathways to the pons and cerebrum also increases, resulting in a stronger urge to urinate.

Voluntary initiation of micturition requires an increase in action potentials sent from the cerebrum to facilitate the micturition reflex and to voluntarily relax the external urethral sphincter. In addition, voluntary contraction of the abdominal muscles increases abdominal pressure and thereby enhances the micturition reflex by increasing the pressure applied to the urinary bladder wall.

Clinical IMPACT 26.3

Kidney Stones

Kidney stones are hard objects usually found in the pelvis of the kidney. They are typically 2–3 mm in diameter, with either a smooth or a jagged surface, but occasionally a large, branching kidney stone, called a **staghorn stone,** forms in the renal pelvis. About 1% of all autopsies reveal kidney stones, and many stones never cause symptoms. The symptoms associated with kidney stones occur when a stone passes into the ureter, resulting in referred pain down the back, side, and groin area. The ureter contracts around the stone, causing the stone to irritate the epithelium and produce bleeding, which appears as blood in the urine, a condition called **hematuria.** In addition to causing intense pain, kidney stones can block the ureter, cause ulceration in the ureter, and increase the probability of bacterial infection.

About 65% of all kidney stones are composed of calcium oxylate mixed with calcium phosphate, whereas another 15% are magnesium ammonium phosphate and 10% are uric acid or cystine; approximately 2.5% of each kidney stone is composed of mucoprotein.

The cause of kidney stones is usually obscure. Predisposing conditions include concentrated urine and an abnormally high calcium concentration in the urine, although the cause of the high calcium concentration is usually unknown. Magnesium ammonium phosphate stones are often found in people with recurrent kidney infections, and uric acid stones are common in people suffering from gout. Severe kidney stones must be surgically removed from the kidney. However, traditional surgical procedures have mainly been replaced by **lithotripsy** (LITH-oh-trip-see), in which kidney stones are pulverized using ultrasound or lasers.

TABLE 26.5 Representative Diseases and Disorders of the Urinary System

Kidney Disorders	Description
Inflammation of the Kidneys	
Glomerulonephritis (gloh-MARE-yoo-loh-neh-FRY-tis)	Inflammation of the filtration membrane within the renal corpuscle, causing an increase in the filtration membrane's permeability; plasma proteins and blood cells enter the filtrate, which increases urine volume due to increased osmotic concentration of the filtrate
Acute glomerulonephritis	Often occurs 1–3 weeks after a severe bacterial infection, such as "strep throat"; normally subsides after several days
Chronic glomerulonephritis	Long-term, progressive process whereby the filtration membrane thickens and is eventually replaced by connective tissue; the kidneys become nonfunctional
Pyelonephritis (PIE-eh-loh-neh-FRY-tis)	Often begins as a bacterial, usually *E. coli,* infection of the renal pelvis, which spreads to the rest of the kidney; the infection can destroy nephrons, dramatically reducing the kidney's ability to concentrate urine
Renal Failure	Can result from any condition that interferes with kidney function
Acute renal failure	Occurs when damage to the kidney is rapid and extensive; leads to accumulation of wastes in the blood; if renal failure is complete, death can occur in 1–2 weeks
Chronic renal failure	Caused by permanent damage to so many nephrons that the remaining nephrons are inadequate for normal kidney function; can result from chronic glomerulonephritis, trauma to the kidneys, tumors, or kidney stones

Normally, the urge to urinate results from stretch of the urinary bladder wall, but irritation of the urinary bladder or the urethra by a bacterial infection or some other condition can also initiate the urge to urinate, even if the urinary bladder is nearly empty.

If the spinal cord is damaged *above* the sacral region, no micturition reflex exists for a time; however, if the urinary bladder is emptied frequently, the micturition reflex eventually regains the ability to cause the urinary bladder to empty. Although a typical micturition reflex may exist, the person has no conscious control over its onset or duration. This condition is called **automatic bladder.**

On the other hand, if the spinal cord is damaged *in* the sacral region of the spinal cord, it eliminates the micturition reflex altogether. The urinary bladder is unable to contract even though the external urethral sphincter is relaxed. The urinary bladder fills to capacity, and urine is forced in a slow dribble through the external urethral sphincter.

In older people and in patients with damage to the brainstem or spinal cord, there is a reduction in inhibitory action potentials to the sacral region of the spinal cord. Without this inhibition, the sacral centers are hyperexcitable, and even a small amount of urine in the urinary bladder can elicit an uncontrollable micturition reflex.

ASSESS YOUR PROGRESS

44. *What are the functions of the ureters, urinary bladder, and urethra? Describe their structure, including the epithelial lining of their inner surfaces.*
45. *What is the trigone?*
46. *What force moves urine through the nephron and ureters?*
47. *Explain the ability of the urinary bladder to distend.*
48. *Describe the micturition reflex. How is voluntary control of micturition accomplished?*

EFFECTS OF AGING ON THE URINARY SYSTEM

Aging causes the kidneys to gradually decrease in size. This decrease can begin as early as age 20 but becomes obvious by age 50 and continues throughout the remainder of life. The decrease in kidney size appears to be related to changes in the blood vessels of the kidney. The amount of blood flowing through the kidneys gradually decreases. Starting at age 20, there appears to be an approximately 10% decrease every 10 years. Small arteries, including the afferent and efferent arterioles, become irregular and twisted. Functional glomeruli are destroyed. By age 80, 40% of the glomeruli are not functioning. About 30% of the glomeruli that stop functioning no longer have a lumen through which blood flows. Other glomeruli thicken and assume a structure similar to that of arterioles. Some renal tubules and collecting ducts become thicker, shorter, and more irregular in structure. The capacity to secrete and absorb declines, and whole nephrons stop functioning. The kidney's ability to concentrate urine gradually declines. Eventually, changes in the kidney increase the risk for dehydration because of the kidney's reduced ability to produce a concentrated urine. The ability to eliminate uric acid, urea, creatine, and toxins from the blood also decreases.

An age-related loss of responsiveness to ADH and to aldosterone occurs. The kidney decreases renin secretion and has a reduced ability to participate in vitamin D synthesis, which contributes to Ca^{2+} deficiency, osteoporosis, and bone fractures.

Recall that one-third of one kidney is required to maintain homeostasis, and the additional kidney tissue beyond this constitutes a reserve capacity. Therefore, the age-related changes in the kidney reduce the kidney's reserve capacity. As the functional kidney mass is reduced substantially in older people, high blood pressure, atherosclerosis, and diabetes have greater adverse effects.

Concept Check

26.1 Functions of the Urinary System

A. The urinary system consists of the kidneys, ureters, urinary bladder, and urethra.

B. The urinary system eliminates wastes; regulates blood volume, ion concentration, and pH; and is involved with red blood cell and vitamin D production.

1. *Which of these is* not *a general function of the kidneys?*

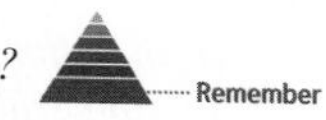

a. regulation of blood volume
b. regulation of solute concentration in the blood
c. regulation of the pH of the extracellular fluid
d. regulation of vitamin A synthesis
e. regulation of red blood cell synthesis

26.2 Kidney Anatomy and Histology

Location and External Anatomy of the Kidneys

A. A kidney lies behind the peritoneum on the posterior abdominal wall on each side of the vertebral column.

B. The renal capsule surrounds each kidney, and adipose tissue and the renal fascia engulf each kidney and anchor it to the abdominal wall.

C. Blood vessels and nerves enter and exit the kidney at the hilum, on the medial side of each kidney, which opens into the renal sinus, containing fat and connective tissue.

2. *The cortex of the kidney contains the*

a. hilum.
b. glomeruli.
c. adipose tissue.
d. renal pyramids.
e. renal pelvis.

Internal Anatomy and Histology of the Kidneys

A. The two major regions of the kidney are the cortex and the medulla.
  - The renal columns extend toward the medulla between the renal pyramids.
  - The renal pyramids of the medulla project to the minor calyces.

B. The minor calyces open into the major calyces, which open into the renal pelvis. The renal pelvis leads to the ureter.

C. The functional unit of the kidney is the nephron. The parts of a nephron are the renal corpuscle, the proximal convoluted tubule, the nephron loop, and the distal convoluted tubule.
  - The renal corpuscle consists of the glomerular capsule and the glomerulus. Materials leave the blood in the glomerulus and enter the glomerular capsule through the filtration membrane.
  - The renal tubule empties through the distal convoluted tubule into a collecting duct.

D. The juxtaglomerular apparatus consists of the macula densa (part of the distal convoluted tubule) and the juxtaglomerular cells of the afferent arteriole.

3. *Given these structures:* Remember

   (1) major calyx
   (2) minor calyx
   (3) renal papilla
   (4) renal pelvis

   Choose the arrangement that lists the structures in order as urine leaves the collecting duct and travels to the ureter.

   a. 1,4,2,3 *b. 2,3,1,4* *c. 3,2,1,4* *d. 4,1,3,2* *e. 4,3,2,1*

4. *Which of these structures contain(s) blood?*

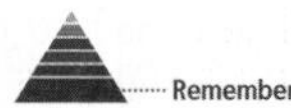

   a. glomerulus
   b. vasa recta
   c. distal convoluted tubule
   d. glomerular capsule
   e. Both a and b are correct.

5. *The juxtaglomerular cells of the ________ and the macula densa cells of the ________ form the juxtaglomerular apparatus.* Remember

   a. afferent arteriole, proximal convoluted tubule
   b. afferent arteriole, distal convoluted tubule
   c. efferent arteriole, proximal convoluted tubule
   d. efferent arteriole, distal convoluted tubule

Arteries and Veins of the Kidneys

A. Arteries branch as follows: renal artery to segmental artery to interlobar artery to arcuate artery to cortical radiate artery to afferent arteriole.

B. Afferent arterioles supply the glomeruli.

C. Efferent arteries from the glomeruli supply the peritubular capillaries and vasa recta.

D. Veins form from the peritubular capillaries as follows: cortical radiate vein to arcuate vein to interlobar vein to renal vein.

6. *Given these blood vessels:*

   (1) afferent arteriole
   (2) efferent arteriole
   (3) glomerulus
   (4) peritubular capillaries

   Choose the correct order as blood passes from a cortical radiate artery to a cortical radiate vein.

   a. 1,2,3,4 *b. 1,3,2,4* *c. 2,1,4,3* *d. 3,2,4,1* *e. 4,3,1,2*

26.3 Urine Production

Urine is produced by filtration, tubular reabsorption, and tubular secretion.

7. *Which of these processes is responsible for kidney function?* Remember

   a. filtration
   b. secretion
   c. reabsorption
   d. Both a and b are correct.
   e. All of these are correct.

Filtration

A. The renal filtrate is plasma minus blood cells and blood proteins. Most (99%) of the filtrate is reabsorbed.

B. The filtration membrane is composed of a fenestrated endothelium, a basement membrane, and the slitlike pores formed by podocytes.

C. Filtration pressure is responsible for filtrate formation.
  - Filtration pressure is glomerular capillary pressure minus capsular hydrostatic pressure minus blood colloid osmotic pressure.
  - Filtration pressure changes are primarily caused by changes in glomerular capillary pressure.

8. *The amount of plasma that enters the glomerular capsule per minute is the* Remember

   a. GFR.
   b. renal plasma flow.
   c. renal fraction.
   d. renal blood flow.

9. *If the glomerular capillary pressure is 40 mm Hg, the capsular hydrostatic pressure is 10 mm Hg, and the blood colloid osmotic pressure within the glomerulus is 30 mm Hg, the filtration pressure is* Remember

   a. −20 mm Hg. *b. 0 mm Hg.* *c. 20 mm Hg.* *d. 60 mm Hg.* *e. 80 mm Hg.*

Regulation of Glomerular Filtration Rate

A. Two important mechanisms regulating GFR are autoregulation and sympathetic stimulation.

B. Autoregulation dampens systemic blood pressure changes by altering afferent arteriole diameter.

C. Sympathetic stimulation decreases afferent arteriole diameter.

10. *Which of these conditions reduces filtration pressure in the glomerulus?* Remember

    a. elevated blood pressure
    b. constriction of the afferent arterioles
    c. decreased plasma protein in the glomerulus
    d. dilation of the afferent arterioles
    e. decreased capsular hydrostatic pressure

11. *If blood pressure increases by 50 mm Hg*

    a. the afferent arterioles constrict.
    b. glomerular capillary pressure increases by 50 mm Hg.
    c. GFR increases dramatically.
    d. efferent arterioles constrict.
    e. All of these are correct.

12. *Propose 3–4 ways to decrease the GFR.*

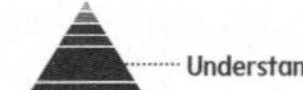

Tubular Reabsorption

A. Filtrate is reabsorbed by passive transport, including simple diffusion and facilitated diffusion. Filtrate is also reabsorbed through active transport and symport. Materials move from the renal tubule into the peritubular capillaries.

B. Specialization of tubule segments
- The thin segment of the nephron loop is specialized for passive transport.
- The rest of the renal tubules and collecting ducts perform active transport, symport, and passive transport.

C. Substances transported
- Active transport moves mainly Na^+ across the wall of the renal tubule. Other ions and molecules are moved primarily by symport.
- Passive transport moves water, urea, and lipid-soluble, nonpolar compounds.

13. *Glucose is usually completely reabsorbed from the filtrate by the time the filtrate has reached the* Remember
    a. end of the proximal convoluted tubule.
    b. bend of the nephron loop.
    c. end of the distal convoluted tubule.
    d. end of the collecting duct.
    e. glomerular capsule.

14. *The greatest volume of water is reabsorbed from the renal tubule by the* Remember
    a. proximal convoluted tubule.
    b. nephron loop.
    c. distal convoluted tubule.
    d. collecting duct.

15. *Water leaves the renal tubule by*

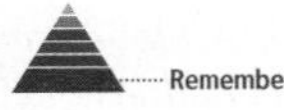

    a. active transport.
    b. filtration into the capillary network.
    c. osmosis.
    d. facilitated diffusion.
    e. symport.

16. *Potassium ions enter the ________ by ________.*

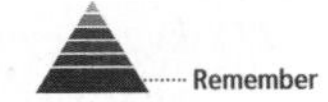

    a. proximal convoluted tubule, diffusion
    b. proximal convoluted tubule, active transport
    c. distal convoluted tubule, diffusion
    d. distal convoluted tubule, antiport

17. *Reabsorption of most solute molecules from the proximal convoluted tubule is linked to the active transport of Na^+ across the* Remember
    a. apical membrane and out of the cell.
    b. apical membrane and into the cell.
    c. basal membrane and out of the cell.
    d. basal membrane and into the cell.

18. *Which of these ions is used to symport amino acids, glucose, and other solutes through the apical membrane of tubule cells?* Remember

    a. K^+ b. Na^+ c. Cl^- d. Ca^{2+} e. Mg^{2+}

Tubular Secretion

A. Substances enter the proximal or distal convoluted tubules and the collecting ducts.

B. Hydrogen ions, K^+, and some substances not produced in the body are secreted by antiport mechanisms.

19. *Which of the following would help compensate for low pH of body fluids?* Apply
    a. increased respiration
    b. increased HCO_3^- reabsorption
    c. increased H^+ secretion
    d. All of these are correct.
    e. Both a and b are correct.

Urine Concentration Mechanism

A. The vasa recta, the nephron loop, and the distribution of urea are responsible for the concentration gradient in the medulla. The concentration gradient is necessary for the production of concentrated urine.

B. Production of urine
- In the proximal convoluted tubule, Na^+ and other substances are removed by active transport. Water follows passively, filtrate volume is reduced 65%, and the filtrate concentration is 300 mOsm/L.
- In the descending limb of the nephron loop, water exits passively and solute enters. The filtrate volume is reduced 15%, and the osmolality of the filtrate concentration is 1200 mOsm/kg.
- In the ascending limb of the nephron loop, Na^+, Cl^-, and K^+ are actively transported out of the filtrate, but water remains because this segment of the renal tubule is impermeable to water. The osmolality of the filtrate concentration is 100 mOsm/kg.

20. *Which of the following contributes to the formation of a hyperosmotic environment in the medulla of the kidney?* Remember
    a. the effects of ADH on water permeability of the ascending limb of the nephron loop
    b. the impermeability of the ascending limb of the nephron loop to water
    c. the symport of Na^+, K^+, and Cl^- out of the ascending limb of the nephron loop
    d. Both a and c are correct.
    e. Both b and c are correct.

21. *At which of these sites is the osmolality of the filtrate at its lowest (lowest concentration)?* Remember
    a. glomerular capillary
    b. proximal convoluted tubule
    c. bend of the nephron loop
    d. initial section of the distal convoluted tubule
    e. collecting duct

26.4 Regulation of Urine Concentration and Volume

Hormonal Mechanisms

A. Aldosterone, produced in the adrenal cortex, affects Na^+ and Cl^- transport in the distal convoluted tubule and collecting ducts.
- A decrease in aldosterone results in less Na^+ reabsorption and an increase in urine concentration and volume. An increase in aldosterone results in greater Na^+ reabsorption and a decrease in urine concentration and volume.
- Aldosterone production is stimulated by angiotensin II, increased blood K^+ concentration, and decreased blood Na^+ concentration.

B. Renin, produced by the kidneys, causes the production of angiotensin II.
- Angiotensin II acts as a vasoconstrictor and stimulates aldosterone secretion, causing a decrease in urine production and an increase in blood volume.
- Decreased blood pressure or decreased Na^+ concentration stimulates renin production.

C. ADH, secreted by the posterior pituitary, increases water permeability in the distal convoluted tubules and collecting ducts.
   - ADH decreases urine volume, increases blood volume, and thus increases blood pressure.
   - ADH release is stimulated by increased blood osmolality or decreased blood pressure.
   - Water movement out of the distal convoluted tubules and collecting ducts is regulated by ADH. If ADH is absent, water is not reabsorbed, and a dilute urine is produced. If ADH is present, water moves out, and a concentrated urine is produced.

D. Atrial natriuretic hormone, produced by the heart when blood pressure increases, inhibits ADH production and reduces the kidney's ability to concentrate urine.

22. *Increased aldosterone causes* 

    a. *increased reabsorption of Na^+.*
    b. *decreased blood volume.*
    c. *decreased reabsorption of Cl^-.*
    d. *increased permeability of the distal convoluted tubule to water.*
    e. *increased volume of urine.*

23. *Juxtaglomerular cells are involved in the secretion of* 

    a. *ADH.*
    b. *angiotensin.*
    c. *aldosterone.*
    d. *renin.*

24. *Angiotensin II* Remember
    a. *causes vasoconstriction.*
    b. *stimulates aldosterone secretion.*
    c. *stimulates ADH secretion.*
    d. *increases the sensation of thirst.*
    e. *All of these are correct.*

25. *ADH governs the* 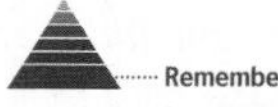

    a. *Na^+ pump of the proximal convoluted tubules.*
    b. *water permeability of the nephron loop.*
    c. *Na^+ pump of the vasa recta.*
    d. *water permeability of the distal convoluted tubules and collecting ducts.*
    e. *Na^+ reabsorption in the proximal convoluted tubule.*

26. *A decrease in blood osmolality results in* 

    a. *increased ADH secretion.*
    b. *increased permeability of the collecting ducts to water.*
    c. *decreased urine osmolality.*
    d. *decreased urine output.*
    e. *All of these are correct.*

27. *To relax after an anatomy and physiology examination, Rob goes to a local bistro and drinks 2 quarts of low-sodium beer. What effect does this beer have on urine concentration and volume? Explain the mechanisms involved.* Apply

28. *Harry is doing yard work one hot summer day and refuses to drink anything until he is finished. He then drinks glass after glass of plain water. Assuming that he drinks enough water to replace all the water he lost as sweat, how does this much water affect urine concentration and volume? Explain the mechanisms involved.* Understand

29. *A patient has the following symptoms: slight increase in extracellular fluid volume, large decrease in plasma sodium concentration, very concentrated urine, and cardiac fibrillation. An imbalance of what hormone is responsible for these symptoms? Are the symptoms caused by oversecretion or undersecretion of the hormone?* Apply

30. *Design a kidney that can produce hyposmotic urine, which is less concentrated than plasma, or hyperosmotic urine, which is more concentrated than plasma, by the active transport of water instead of Na^+. Assume that the kidney's anatomical structure is the same as that in humans, but feel free to change anything else you choose.* Apply

31. *If only a very small amount of urea, instead of its normal concentration, were present in the interstitial fluid of the kidney, how would the kidney's ability to concentrate urine be affected?* Apply

32. *Some patients with hypertension are kept on a low-salt (low-sodium) diet. Propose an explanation for this therapy.* Understand

33. *Marvin was driving too fast on a remote mountain road at 3 a.m. when his car left the road and rolled down a steep hill. Marvin sustained numerous cuts and bruises. When medical help arrived 2 hours later, his systolic blood pressure was 70 mm Hg, and his pulse was weak (thready). Intravenous saline was administered immediately, and plasma and then whole blood were administered in the emergency room. After another hour, Marvin's blood pressure had returned to normal and he no longer appeared pale. While he was in the hospital, Marvin's urine volume decreased to less than 30 mL/h (<400 mL/day). A blood sample indicated elevated blood levels of urea, creatinine, and uric acid. He also exhibited hyperkalemia and some cardiac arrhythmia, and his arterial pH was <7.35 (below normal). Over the next few days, his red blood cell count decreased and he bruised easily. His jugular veins were distended, and there was some peripheral and pulmonary edema. From the following list, select the conditions that applied to Marvin at this time.* Apply
    (1) *hypoxic injury to the kidney*
    (2) *increased reabsorption of wastes*
    (3) *decreased H^+ secretion*
    (4) *decreased K^+ secretion*
    (5) *increased HCO_3^- reabsorption*
    (6) *decreased erythropoietin secretion*

    a. *1,2,3,4,5,6*
    b. *2,3,4,5*
    c. *1,2,3,4*
    d. *1,2,3,4,6*
    e. *1,2,6*

34. *Renin-secreting tumors are usually found in the kidneys but rarely in other organs, such as the liver, lungs, pancreas, and ovaries. Predict the effects of renin-secreting tumors on blood K^+ levels, and explain the effects on action potential conduction in nerves and muscle tissues.* Apply

35. *Even though mutations of aquaporin-3 and aquaporin-4 in the collecting duct have not been described in the literature, if mutations occurred that resulted in a reduced number of these aquaporins in the cells of the collecting ducts, how would urine volume and concentration be affected? Would ADH be an effective treatment?* Apply

26.5 Plasma Clearance and Transport Maximum

A. Plasma clearance is the volume of plasma that is cleared of a specific substance each minute.

B. Renal threshold is the total amount of a substance that enters the renal tubule each minute.

C. Transport maximum is the fastest rate at which a substance is reabsorbed from the renal tubule.

36. The amount of a substance that passes through the filtration membrane into the renal tubule per minute is the Remember

a. renal plasma flow.
b. renal threshold.
c. plasma clearance.
d. transport maximum.

26.6 Urine Movement

Anatomy and Histology of the Ureters and Urinary Bladder

A. Structure

- The walls of the ureter and urinary bladder consist of the epithelium, the lamina propria, a muscular coat, and a fibrous adventitia.
- The transitional epithelium permits changes in size.

B. Function

- The ureters transport urine from the kidney to the urinary bladder.
- The urinary bladder stores urine.

37. The urinary bladder Remember

a. is composed of skeletal muscle.
b. is lined by simple columnar epithelium.
c. is connected to the outside of the body by the ureter.
d. is located in the pelvic cavity.
e. has two urethras and one ureter attached to it.

Urine Flow Through the Nephron and Ureters

A. Hydrostatic pressure forces urine through the nephron.

B. Peristalsis moves urine through the ureters.

Micturition Reflex

A. Stretch of the urinary bladder stimulates a reflex that causes the urinary bladder to contract and inhibits the urethral sphincters.

B. Higher brain centers can stimulate or inhibit the micturition reflex.

Answers to this chapter's odd-numbered Concept Check questions appear in Appendix F.

CHAPTER 27

Fluid, Electrolyte, and Acid-Base Balance

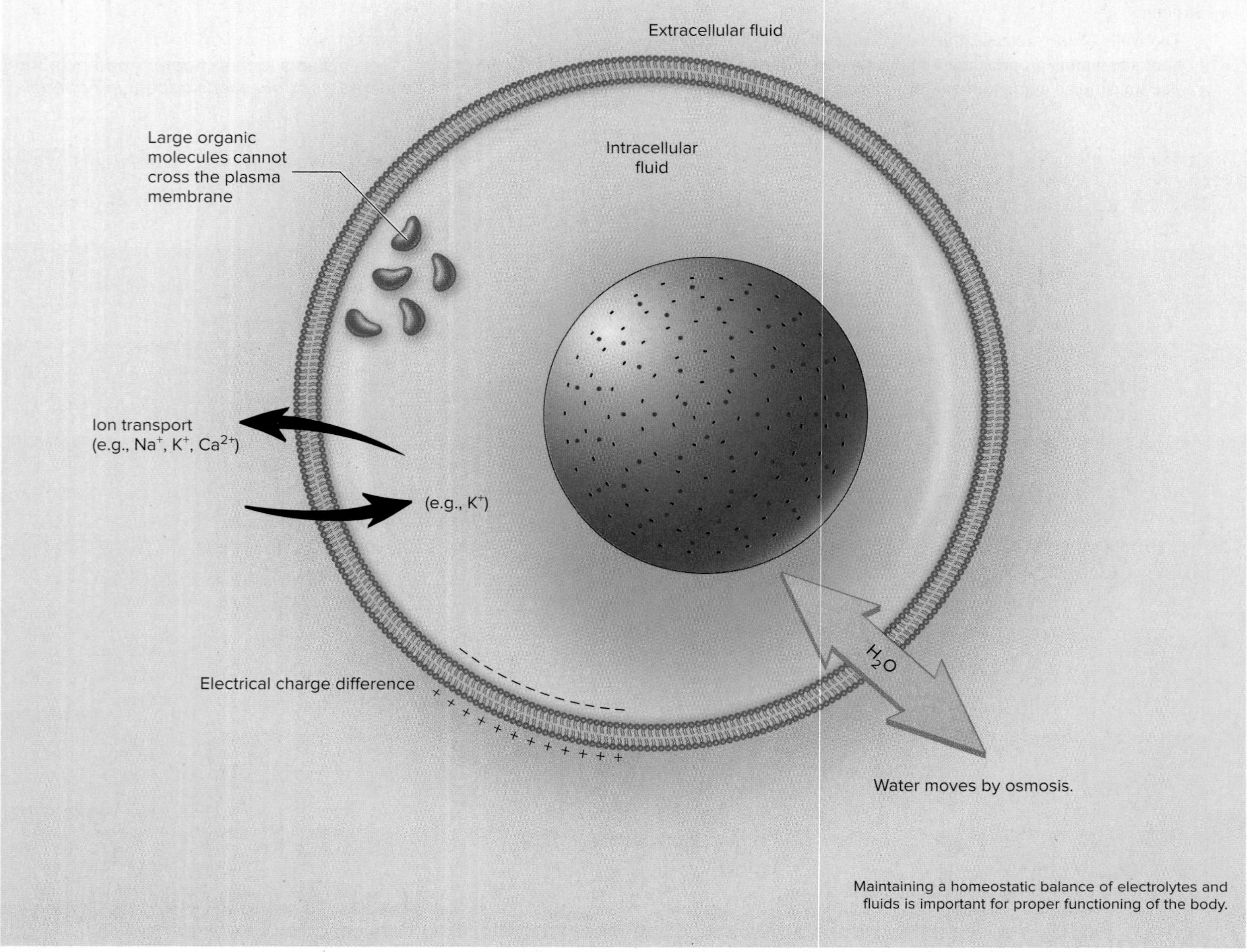

Maintaining a homeostatic balance of electrolytes and fluids is important for proper functioning of the body.

Maintaining appropriate levels of fluid in the body is a crucial component of homeostasis. We can consider our bodies to be simply large containers of water and solutes, including ions (electrolytes). When we eat an extremely salty meal, a few hours later we often feel very thirsty. On the other hand, if we drink several large glasses of water in a short amount of time, we will need to visit the restroom quite frequently over the next few hours. Proper fluid levels help your body maintain adequate blood pressure—too little fluid could cause a person to faint or become disoriented. This chapter's Learn to Predict question describes what happens when the body receives too *little* fluid. Too *much* fluid can also cause an imbalance in electrolyte levels. Proper electrolyte levels help your body's nervous and muscle systems work correctly—overly dilute blood causes malfunctions such as coma, or even death (see Clinical Impact 27.1). In this chapter, you will learn how, under normal circumstances, the balance of electrolytes and body fluids is maintained within a very narrow range.

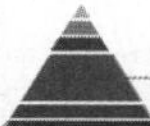

Learn to Predict

Satish and Kiran, two college students in search of adventure, embarked on an orienteering exercise—but it almost turned out to be their last adventure. Their compass malfunctioned, and they became lost in desert terrain during the hottest days of summer. One week later, they were discovered, near death, in a dry ravine. Rescuers estimated that the students had gone without water for 24 hours.

Explain the students' dehydration, the homeostatic mechanisms that would have tried to compensate for this condition, and the specific physiological cause of their illness.

Answers to this question and the chapter's odd-numbered Predict questions can be found in Appendix E.

27.1 Body Fluid Balance

LEARNING OUTCOMES

After reading this section, you should be able to

A. **Identify the major fluid compartments of the body and their subdivisions.**
B. **List the dominant cations and anions in the major fluid compartments.**
C. **Describe the causes of edema.**
D. **Explain how water content of the body is maintained.**
E. **Discuss how body fluid osmolality is achieved and held in homeostatic balance.**
F. **Explain the mechanisms that regulate extracellular fluid volume.**
G. **Describe how intracellular fluid composition is maintained.**

Water accounts for at least half of the total weight of the human body (figure 27.1; table 27.1). This percentage varies with developmental stage, biological sex, and body composition. For example, in infants, 75% of their total weight is water. Also, because males have, on average, a lower percentage of adipose tissue than females, a greater percentage of a male's body weight is due to water than it is for a female. Adipose tissue has a relatively low water content.

Fluid Compartments

The total amount of water in the body is separated into two fluid compartments: (1) the intracellular fluid compartment and (2) the extracellular fluid compartment. Each fluid compartment is composed of water, ions called electrolytes, and other solutes. There are specific electrolyte distributions in the intracellular fluid compared with the extracellular fluid, such as higher K^+ and protein concentrations in the intracellular fluid and higher Na^+ and Cl^- concentrations in the extracellular fluid (figure 27.2; table 27.2). The **osmolality** of a solution is determined by the number of solutes in a particular volume of a solution. Adding water to the solution dilutes its concentration. On the other hand, letting water evaporate from the solution would concentrate it. Body fluid osmolality can also change but is maintained between 285 and 300 mOsm/kg.

Module 13
Urinary System

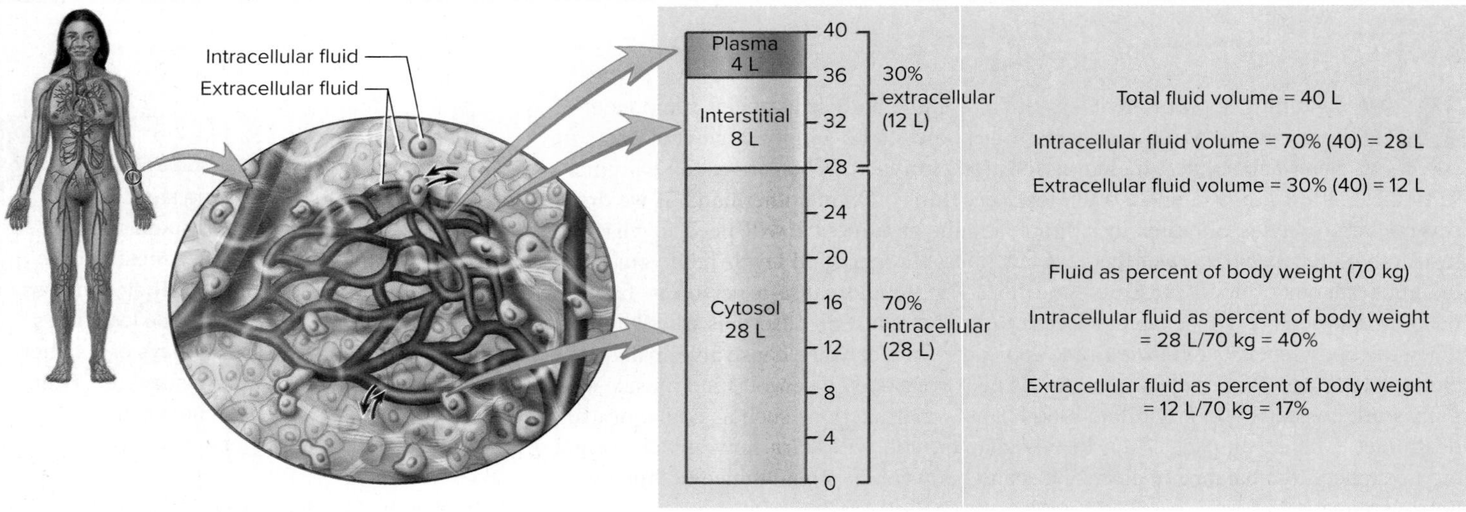

FIGURE 27.1 Body Fluid Volumes
To calculate the amount of fluid in each compartment for an average male weighing 70 kg, the total fluid volume (40 L) is multiplied by the percentage in each compartment. To express fluid volume as percentage of body weight, the volume of each compartment is divided by the body weight. Intracellular fluid comprises more than half of all body fluids. Of extracellular fluid, interstitial fluid comprises more than half.

TABLE 27.1 Approximate Volumes of Body Fluid Compartments*

			EXTRACELLULAR FLUID		
	Total Body Water	Intracellular Fluid	Plasma	Interstitial Fluid	Total
Infants	75	45	4	26	30
Adult Males	60	40	5	15	20
Adult Females	50	35	5	10	15

*Expressed as percentage of body weight.

TABLE 27.2 Approximate Concentration of Major Solutes in Body Fluids*

Solute	Plasma	Interstitial Fluid	Intracellular Fluid†
Cations			
Sodium (Na^+)	153.2	145.1	12.0
Potassium (K^+)	4.3	4.1	150.0
Calcium (Ca^{2+})	3.8	3.4	4.0
Magnesium (Mg^{2+})	1.4	1.3	34.0
TOTAL	162.7	153.9	200.0
Anions			
Chloride (Cl^-)	111.5	118.0	4.0
Bicarbonate (HCO_3^-)	25.7	27.0	12.0
Phosphate (HPO_4^{2-} plus HPO_4^-)	2.2	2.3	40.0
Protein	17.0	0.0	54.0
Other	6.3	6.6	90.0
TOTAL	162.7	153.9	200.0

*Expressed as milliequivalents per liter (mEq/L).
†Data are from skeletal muscle.

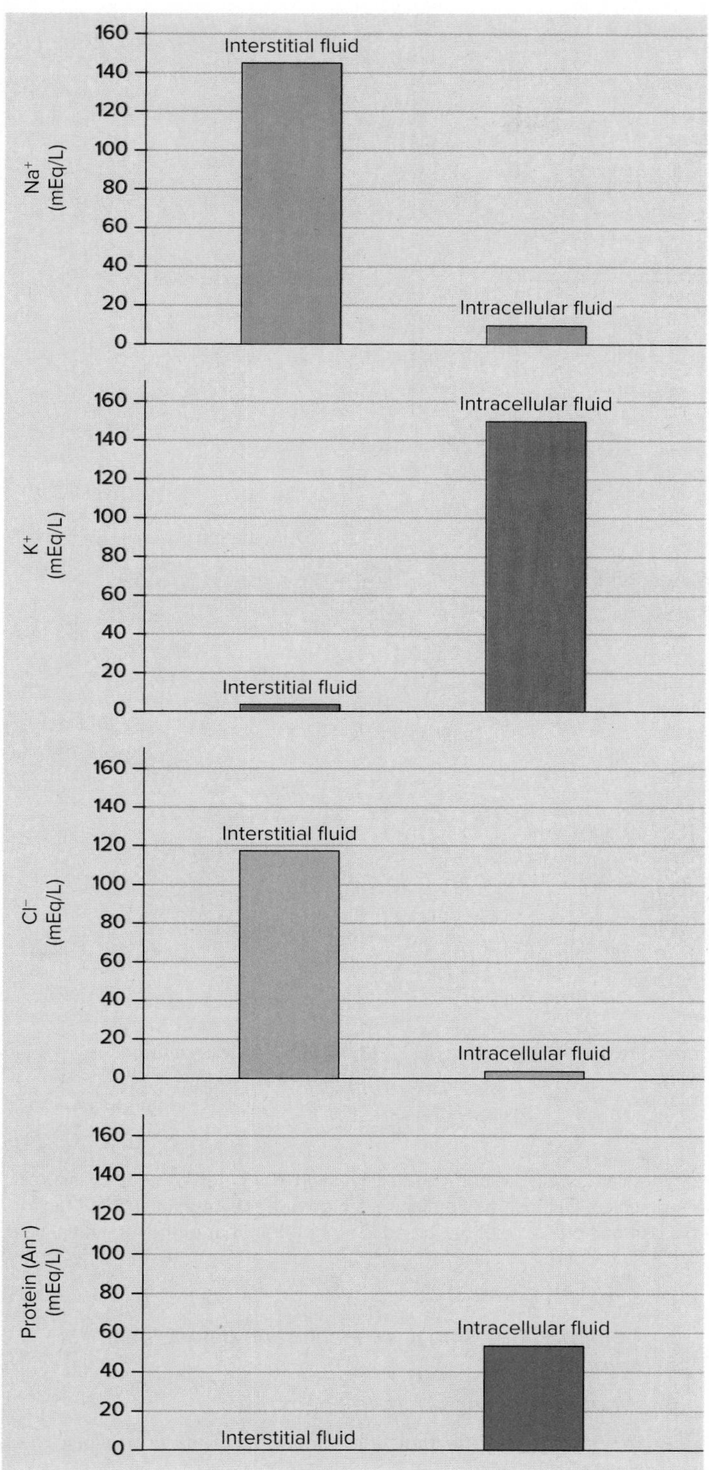

FIGURE 27.2 Concentration of Major Solutes

The concentration, expressed in mEq/L, of particular ions in the interstitial fluid compared to the concentration in the intracellular fluid. Sodium and Cl^- are the major extracellular ions, while K^+ and proteins are the major intracellular ions.

The **intracellular fluid compartment** consists of all the fluid inside the cells the body. This fluid is part of the cytoplasm of the cell and has a similar composition among all the cells of the body. The intracellular fluid compartment accounts for the majority of the water in the body, or about 70%. This equals approximately 40% of the body's total weight.

The **extracellular fluid compartment** accounts for around 30% of all the water in the body, which is equal to about 20% of the body's total weight. This fluid consists of the fluid outside all the cells of the body. The extracellular fluid is distributed throughout the body and is divided into multiple subcompartments, including (1) interstitial fluid between cells, (2) plasma of the blood, (3) lymph within lymphatic vessels, (4) cerebrospinal fluid of the brain and spinal cord, and (5) synovial fluid within synovial joints. However, the interstitial fluid and plasma constitute the vast majority of the extracellular fluid. The **interstitial** (in-ter-STISH-al) **fluid** is the fluid found surrounding the cells of the body and filling the extracellular spaces. **Plasma** (PLAZ-mah) is the liquid portion of the blood inside all the blood vessels in the body.

Exchange Between Compartments

The two major forces that determine fluid movement into and out of the blood are hydrostatic pressure and osmotic pressure (figure 27.3*a*). Under normal conditions, the total osmotic pressure in each compartment is approximately equal, which allows for a continuous, extensive exchange of water and electrolytes between the compartments (figure 27.3*b*).

One of the greatest influences on the maintenance of homeostatic fluid balance between extracellular fluid compartments is osmosis. Osmosis is the diffusion of water toward a solution with a higher solute concentration. For example, during an inflammatory response to an infection, the permeability of the capillary wall increases. The increased permeability allows proteins to exit the plasma and enter the interstitial fluid. Water will then move by osmosis out of the plasma and into the interstitial fluid, which results in swelling, or edema (figure 27.3*c*). However, if the blood osmolarity becomes greater than that of the interstitial fluid, such as with dehydration, water will move by osmosis into the plasma (figure 27.3*d*).

The composition of intracellular fluid is very different from that of extracellular fluid. Recall from chapter 3 that the plasma membrane is selectively permeable. Large and polar molecules cannot easily diffuse across plasma membranes, whereas small and nonpolar molecules can easily diffuse across plasma membranes. One major reason for the different composition of the intracellular fluid is that many of the molecules synthesized inside the cell are large proteins that cannot exit the cell. Another factor contributing to the differences between the intracellular fluid and the extracellular fluid is that cells have transport proteins embedded in the plasma membrane. Some of these transport proteins expend ATP to create a concentration gradient of certain ions. The Na^+–K^+ ATP pump is present in the plasma membranes of all cells. It pumps K^+ into the cell and pumps Na^+ out of the cell. The uneven distribution of molecules and ions creates a charge difference across the plasma membrane. Figure 27.4 illustrates that this difference in charge can also influence the concentration of ions as well as the degree of osmosis across the plasma membrane.

 Large organic molecules, such as proteins, which cannot cross the plasma membrane, are synthesized inside cells and influence the concentration of solutes inside the cells.

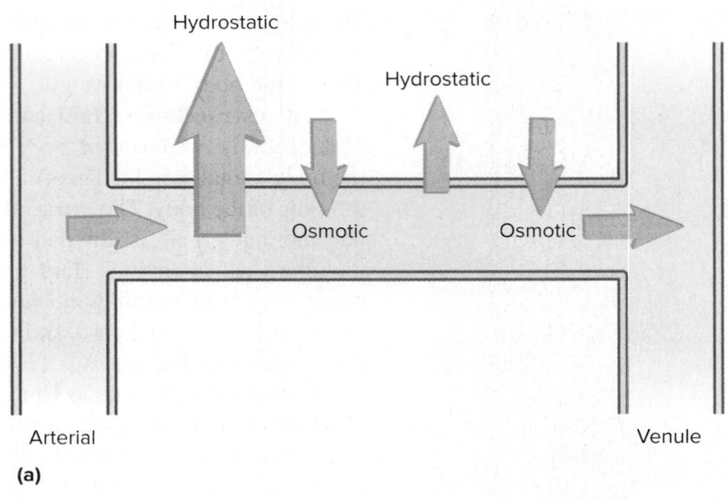

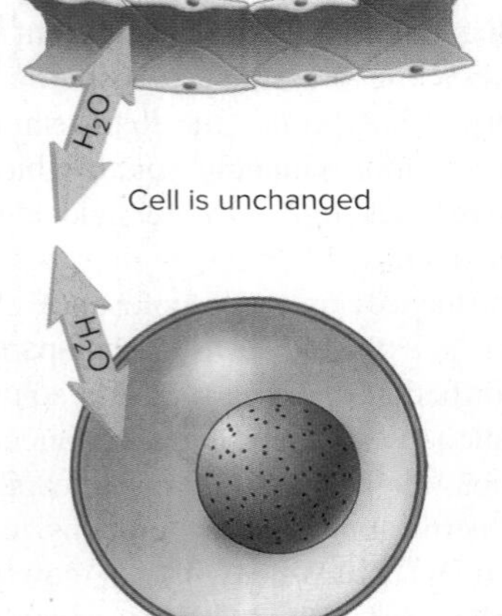

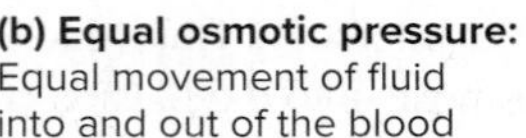

(b) **Equal osmotic pressure:** Equal movement of fluid into and out of the blood

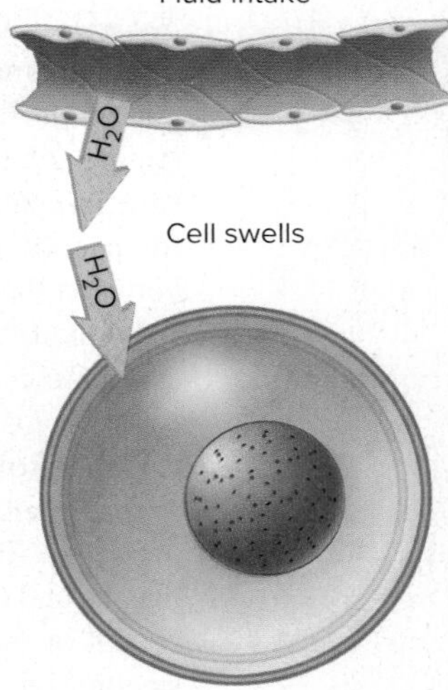

(c) **High osmotic pressure in interstitial fluid:** Movement of fluid out of the blood

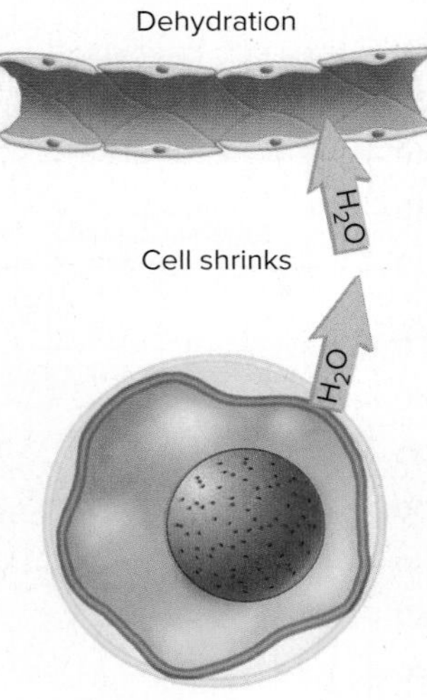

(d) **High osmotic pressure in the blood:** Movement of fluid into the blood

FIGURE 27.3 Influence of Osmotic Pressure on Fluid Movement

(*a*) The two main forces that regulate fluid movement into and out of the blood are hydrostatic pressure and osmotic pressure. (*b*) When osmotic pressures on each side of a plasma membrane are equal, there is no net movement of water molecules. (*c*) If osmotic pressure is higher in the interstitial fluid than that in the blood, there is a net movement of water by osmosis out of the blood. (*d*) If osmotic pressure of the blood is higher than that of the interstitial fluid, there is net movement of water by osmosis into the blood.

2. The transport of ions, such as Na^+, K^+, and Ca^{2+}, across the plasma membrane influences the concentration of ions inside and outside the cell.
3. An electrical charge difference across the plasma membrane influences the distribution of ions inside and outside the cell.
4. The distribution of water inside and outside the cell is determined by osmosis.

ASSESS YOUR PROGRESS

Answers to these questions are found in the section you have just completed. Re-read the section if you need help in answering these questions.

1. *What are the two major fluid compartments of the body? Name the subdivisions of the extracellular fluid compartment.*
2. *What cations and anions occur with the higher percentage in each major compartment?*
3. *Compare the osmotic concentration among most fluid compartments.*
4. *What factors contribute to edema?*
5. *What factors determine the composition of intracellular fluid?*
6. *What characteristic of the plasma membrane is responsible for maintaining the differences between intracellular and extracellular fluid?*

Fluid Input

The body regulates its water content so that the total volume remains constant. The volume of water entering the body equals the volume exiting the body each day. Changes in the total water

PROCESS **Figure**

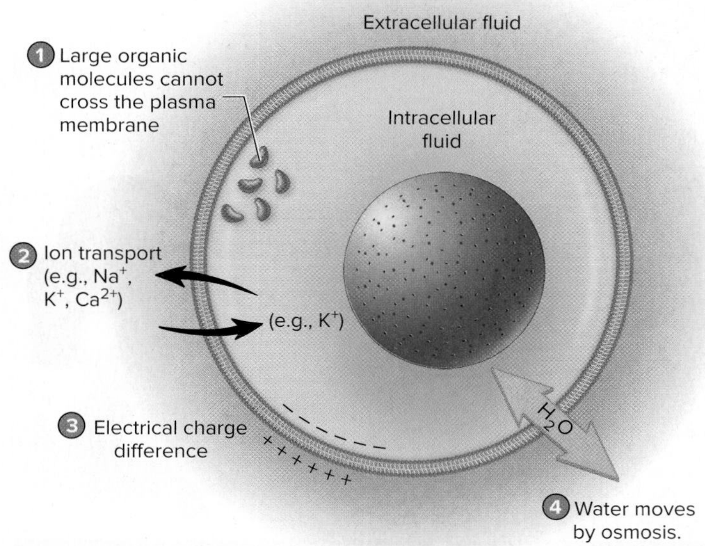

PROCESS **Figure 27.4**

Regulation of Intracellular Fluid

The compositions of the intracellular fluid and the extracellular fluid are different due to the permeability characteristics of the plasma proteins. This uneven distribution of ions is a key feature of electrically excitable cells.

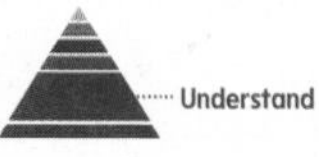

The uneven distribution of ions across the plasma membrane is regulated, in part, by transport proteins. The result is a net negative charge on the inside of the plasma membrane and a net positive charge on the outside of the plasma membrane. How do you explain the net negative charge inside the plasma membrane when the predominant intracellular ion is K^+?

volume alter several factors in the body, such as the solute concentration of body fluids, blood pressure, and interstitial fluid pressure.

The two primary sources of fluid input are (1) food and beverages (90%) and (2) cellular respiration (10%) (table 27.3; see chapter 24). Combined, these two sources bring in around 1500–3000 mL (1.5–3.0 L) of water each day.

TABLE **27.3** **Summary of Water Input and Loss**

Sources of Water	Routes by Which Water Is Lost
Ingestion (90%)	Urine (61%)
Cellular metabolism (10%)	Evaporation: perspiration and respiratory passages (35%)
	Feces (4%)

Fluid Output

Water loss from the body occurs through three routes: (1) from the kidneys as urine (61%), (2) from the skin and respiratory passages by evaporation (35%), and (3) from the digestive tract in feces (4%) (table 27.3).

1. *Kidneys.* The greatest amount of water is excreted through the urine (see chapter 26).
2. *Evaporation.* The amount of water lost through the respiratory passages depends on factors such as air temperature and humidity, as well as body temperature and breathing rate. **Insensible perspiration** is water lost through the skin (see chapter 25), and it regulates heat loss. For each degree that the body temperature rises above normal, an increased volume of 100–150 mL of water is lost each day in the form of insensible perspiration.

   Sensible perspiration is sweat and is secreted by the sweat glands (see chapters 5 and 25). In contrast to insensible perspiration, sweat contains solutes. Sweat resembles extracellular fluid in its composition, with sodium chloride (NaCl) as the major component, but it also contains some K^+, ammonia, and urea (table 27.4). The volume of sweat produced is determined primarily by neural mechanisms that regulate body temperature, although some sweat is produced as a result of sympathetic stimulation in response to stress. Sweat losses of as much as 8–10 L/day have been measured in outdoor workers during the summer.

   Adequate fluid replacement during extensive sweating is important. Because sweat is hyposmotic to plasma, extensive sweating decreases the volume of body fluid but increases the concentration of body fluid. During severe dehydration, an elevation in the hematocrit (blood cell percentage of whole blood) increases blood viscosity, placing an excessive workload on the heart, potentially resulting in heart failure.
3. *Feces.* Relatively little water is lost by way of feces from the digestive tract. Although the total volume of fluid secreted into the digestive tract is large, nearly all the fluid is reabsorbed under normal conditions (see chapter 24). Exceptions are severe vomiting and diarrhea, which can result in a large volume of fluid loss.

TABLE **27.4** **Composition of Sweat**

Solute	Concentration (mM*)
Sodium	9.8–77.2
Potassium	3.9–9.2
Chloride	5.5–65.1
Ammonia	1.7–5.6
Urea	6.5–12.1

*1 mM is 1/1000 of a mole of solute in 1 liter of solution (see appendix C).

PROCESS **Figure**

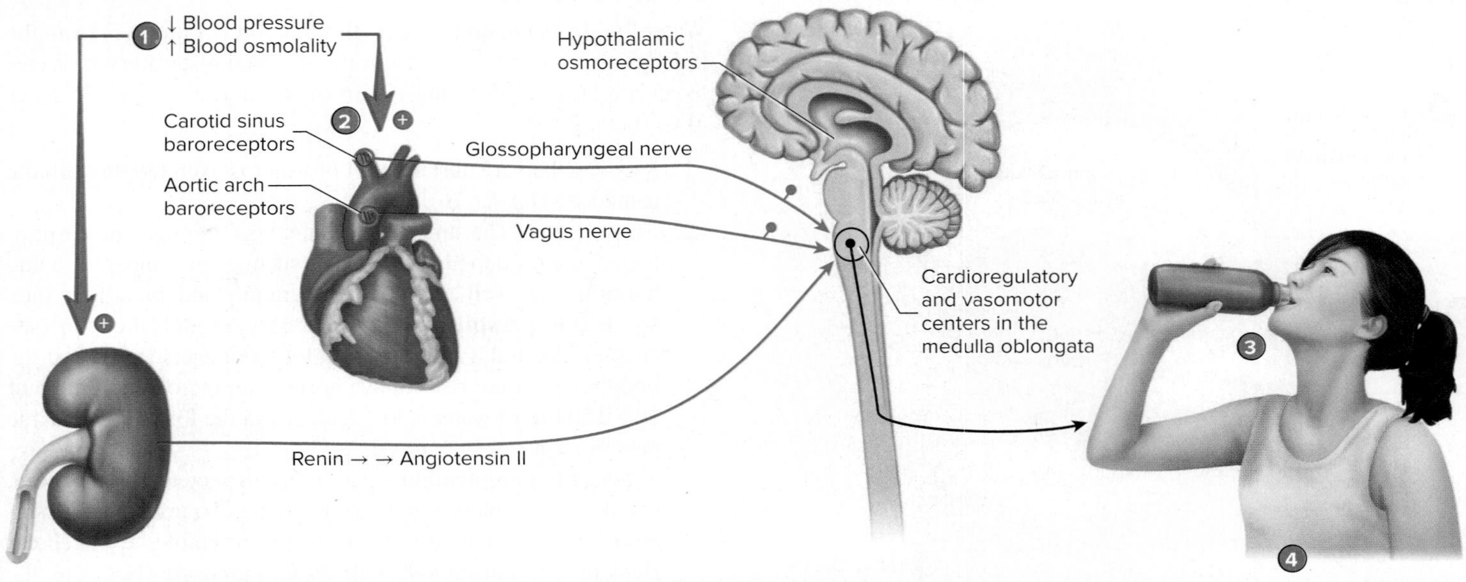

PROCESS **Figure 27.5**

Effect of Blood Pressure on Thirst

Large decreases in blood pressure affect baroreceptors. These stimuli cause an increase in thirst, which increases water intake. APR

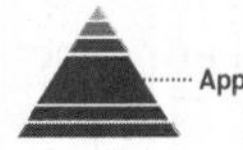

Patients who have experienced significant blood loss by hemorrhage (30–40% of total blood volume) often feel intensely thirsty. Which mechanism has been activated in these patients?

Regulation of Fluid Balance

Thirst is the sensation that induces an urge to drink liquids. An increase in thirst is usually associated with a reduction in the water content of the body, whereas a decrease in thirst is associated with adequate water content of the body.

There are four mechanisms that act to increase thirst or to decrease thirst: (1) hypothalamic osmoreceptors, (2) arterial and juxtaglomerular apparatus baroreceptors, (3) dryness of the mouth, and (4) distension of the stomach.

Regulation of Fluid Input

When blood volume decreases, or blood osmolality increases, the total water content of the blood has been reduced. Thus, an urge to drink is initiated to increase the total water content in the body. Figure 27.5 outlines the steps that increase thirst.

1. *Hypothalamic osmoreceptors.* Neurons in the supraoptic nucleus of the hypothalamus function as osmoreceptors by detecting increases in the concentration of the extracellular fluid. When the solute concentration of the extracellular fluid increases, water moves out of these osmoreceptors by osmosis, shrinking them. When they shrink, they are triggered to send action potentials, which result in the thirst sensation.
2. *Arterial and juxtaglomerular apparatus baroreceptors.* Baroreceptors are sensitive to the degree of stretch on blood vessel walls. Low blood pressure reduces the stretch on the walls of blood vessels. In response to low blood pressure, arterial baroreceptors send action potentials to the thirst center in the hypothalamus, which increases the sensation of thirst. In the kidney, the juxtaglomerular apparatus baroreceptors stimulate the juxtaglomerular cells to secrete the enzyme renin when blood pressure drops. Renin activates the steps in the formation of the hormone angiotensin II. Angiotensin II, in addition to other mechanisms that raise blood pressure, stimulates thirst.
3. *Mouth dryness.* A reduction in saliva production results when the amount of water in the body decreases. The lack of saliva dries the mouth and stimulates sensory neurons in the mouth to send action potentials to the thirst center in the hypothalamus.
4. *Stomach distension.* Stomach distention is also influential in decreasing thirst.

Too much water consumption can be just as dangerous as too little (see Clinical Impact 27.1). Thus, when the total water content in the body is adequate, the thirst sensation decreases.

Once the extracellular solute concentration has returned to its normal range, the hypothalamic osmoreceptors cease action potential conduction and thirst subsides. As blood volume increases, the stretch on the arterial baroreceptors as well as the afferent arteriole of the juxtaglomerular apparatus increases, which suppresses thirst. In addition, thirst is reduced after a person drinks a small amount of liquid and the previously dry mucosa becomes wet and the wall of the stomach is stretched. Because the absorption of water from the stomach takes time, mechanisms that temporarily suppress thirst prevent a person from consuming extreme volumes of fluid. Usually, a healthy person drinks a little more than the minimum volume of fluid needed by the body.

Regulation of Fluid Output

In addition to mechanisms that decrease thirst, fluid volume is regulated by influencing urine output. This is important because, as you learned in chapter 21, blood volume and blood pressure are directly proportional. The carotid sinus and aortic arch baroreceptors monitor blood pressure in the carotid arteries and the aorta; receptors in the juxtaglomerular apparatus monitor pressure changes in the afferent arterioles of the kidneys; and receptors in the walls of the atria of the heart and large veins monitor slight blood pressure changes there. These receptors activate neural and hormonal mechanisms that regulate extracellular fluid volume. We will recap the hormonal mechanisms regulating blood composition in section 27.3.

ASSESS YOUR PROGRESS

7. *Describe three routes for the loss of water from the body. Contrast insensible and sensible perspiration.*
8. *What are the primary organs that regulate the composition and volume of body fluids?*
9. *What two mechanisms are triggered by an increase in the osmolality of the extracellular fluid?*
10. *List three factors that stimulate thirst. Name two factors that inhibit the sense of thirst.*

Fluid Imbalances

Changes in the volume of the extracellular fluid can occur for multiple reasons. For example, upon extended periods of profuse sweating or excess alcohol consumption, water loss is elevated above normal, reducing fluid volume. This triggers thirst and hormonal mechanisms. An increase in extracellular fluid volume can occur when excess water is present, such as when drinking a large volume of water or some other dilute fluid. The increased volume of the extracellular fluid inhibits thirst and hormone secretion, which causes less water to be consumed or reabsorbed from the filtrate in the kidneys. Consequently, more water is excreted with large volumes of dilute urine, which returns fluid volume to its normal range. But what happens when these regulatory mechanisms are temporarily overwhelmed? Two examples when this might occur are dehydration and hyperhydration.

Dehydration

Dehydration occurs when the body fluid volume drops below its set point, increasing its osmolality. The first sign of dehydration is thirst. As dehydration develops, the concentration of solutes in the extracellular fluid increases, allowing water to move by osmosis out of the cell and into the extracellular fluid. If dehydration is severe, the cells can shrink and will function abnormally. If water intake increases after a period of dehydration, the consumed water will be absorbed from the intestine and enter the extracellular fluid. In addition, hormones act on the distal convoluted tubules and collecting ducts of the kidneys to increase the reabsorption of water from the filtrate. The increase in the amount of water entering the extracellular fluid increases fluid volume. Hormonal and thirst mechanisms are sensitive to even small changes in extracellular fluid volume, and the response is fast (from minutes to a few hours). Severe dehydration should be treated with fluids containing electrolytes and not just plain water to avoid overdilution of the body fluids.

Hyperhydration

Hyperhydration, also known as hypotonic hydration, water intoxication, or water poisoning, results from overconsumption of water such that the levels of electrolytes in the blood become overly diluted. Fortunately, accidentally drinking excessive amounts of water is extremely rare. Typically, water intoxication occurs in a few different instances, such as after extreme physical exertion, especially in very hot or humid environments. In these cases, consuming too much plain water afterward can cause plasma Na^+ levels to drop 10% below the normal concentration of 150 mEq/L. There have also been cases of hypotonic hydration when an unconscious patient has received intravenous fluids, a treatment called **fluid replacement therapy.** Typically, the intravenous fluids are hypertonic to body fluids so water is often given along with the fluids. If electrolyte levels in the patient's blood are not carefully monitored while the fluids are being given, the patient could experience hyponatremia (low Na^+ levels). Fortunately, hyponatremia from fluid replacement therapy is rare. Normally, fluid replacement therapy is essential to recovering from severe vomiting, diarrhea, or dehydration. The danger of water intoxication results from water moving into the body's cells via osmosis. The abnormal influx of water into the cells causes them to swell, which, in the brain, causes an increase in intracranial pressure. The symptoms include severe headache, confusion, drowsiness, nausea, seizures, coma, and potentially death. Water intoxication can be avoided in most circumstances by drinking fluids with electrolytes and eating a small amount of food.

27.2 Electrolyte Balance

LEARNING OUTCOMES

After reading this section, you should be able to

A. **Discuss how sodium ion concentration is achieved.**
B. **Describe the regulation of chloride ions.**
C. **Explain potassium ion homeostasis.**
D. **Demonstrate an understanding of calcium ion homeostasis.**
E. **Relate the mechanisms governing magnesium ion concentration.**
F. **Explain the regulation of phosphate ions.**
G. **Describe the causes and symptoms of abnormal plasma levels of selected electrolytes.**

As you have learned, the composition of the fluid in each of the body's fluid compartments consists of water, electrolytes, and other solutes. Specifically, **electrolytes** (ee-LEK-troh-lights) are simply ions derived from salts, acids, and bases, as well as some proteins. The remaining solutes consist of mostly **nonelectrolytes,** which are molecules that do not dissociate into ions in water. These are primarily organic molecules formed with covalent bonds and include lipids, urea, and glucose.

Electrolytes, especially Na^+, are the component of the body's fluids that contribute the greatest influence to their osmolality and can be either cations or anions. The major extracellular ions are Na^+, Cl^-, K^+, Ca^{2+}, Mg^{2+}, and phosphate ions (PO_4^{3-}). Electrolytes are in the food and water we ingest. Organs—such as the kidneys and, to a lesser degree, the liver, skin, and lungs—remove them from the body. The concentration of electrolytes in the body is regulated and does not change significantly unless the individual is growing, gaining weight, or losing weight. The regulation of each electrolyte involves the coordinated participation of several organ systems.

Sodium

Function

Sodium ions are the dominant extracellular cations, and they exert substantial **osmotic pressure.** Osmotic pressure is the force that causes the net movement of water molecules toward an area with a higher solute concentration. Solutions with a higher solute concentration have a greater osmotic pressure than solutions with a lower solute concentration. Approximately 90–95% of the osmotic pressure of the extracellular fluid is caused by Na^+ and the negative ions associated with it. In the United States, most people consume 10–20 times the amount of NaCl (salt) the body needs. Although less than 0.5 g is required to maintain homeostasis, the average individual ingests approximately 3–5 g of NaCl daily. With this level of sodium chloride ingestion, regulation of the body's Na^+ content depends primarily on the excretion of excess quantities of Na^+. On the other hand, when Na^+ intake is very low, the mechanisms for conserving Na^+ in the body take effect.

Regulation

The kidneys are the major route by which Na^+ is excreted. Sodium ions readily pass from the glomerulus into the lumen of the glomerular capsule and are present in the same concentration in the filtrate as in the plasma. The concentration of Na^+ excreted in the urine is determined by the amount of Na^+ and water reabsorbed from filtrate in the renal tubule. If Na^+ reabsorption from the tubule decreases, large quantities are excreted in the urine. If Na^+ reabsorption from the tubule increases, only small quantities are excreted in the urine.

The rate of Na^+ transport in the proximal convoluted tubule is relatively constant, but the Na^+ transport mechanisms of the distal convoluted tubule and the collecting duct are under hormonal control. **Aldosterone** increases Na^+ reabsorption from the distal convoluted tubule and collecting duct. As little as 0.1 g of Na^+ is excreted in the urine each day in the presence of high blood levels of aldosterone. When aldosterone is absent, Na^+ reabsorption in the renal tubule is greatly reduced, and as much as 30–40 g of Na^+ can be lost in the urine daily.

Sodium ions are also excreted from the body in sweat. Normally, only a small quantity of Na^+ is lost each day in the form of sweat, but the amount increases during heavy exercise in warm environments. The mechanisms that regulate sweating control the quantity of Na^+ excreted through the skin. As body temperature increases, thermoreceptor neurons within the hypothalamus respond by increasing the rate of sweat production. As the rate of sweat production increases, the quantity of Na^+ lost in the urine decreases to keep the extracellular concentration of Na^+ constant. Because of this mechanism, the loss of Na^+ in sweat is rarely physiologically significant.

The primary mechanisms that regulate Na^+ concentrations in the extracellular fluid are sensitive to changes in extracellular fluid osmolality or blood pressure (see section 27.3 for summary figure 27.11). These mechanisms do not directly monitor Na^+ levels. The quantity of Na^+ in the body has a dramatic effect on extracellular osmotic pressure and extracellular fluid volume. For example, if the quantity of Na^+ in the extracellular fluid increases, its osmolality also increases. This promotes ADH secretion. ADH stimulates both water reabsorption in the kidneys and thirst. Overall, ADH is a water conservation hormone. A decrease in the quantity of Na^+ in the body causes an opposite set of responses. ADH secretion decreases, which allows a large volume of dilute urine to be produced and decreases the sensation of thirst. As a result of these changes, extracellular osmolality increases. By regulating extracellular fluid osmolality and extracellular fluid volume, the concentration of Na^+ in the body fluids is maintained within a narrow range of values.

Elevated blood pressure under resting conditions increases Na^+ and water excretion. When blood pressure is increased, the walls of the heart, particularly in the right atrium, are stretched. The increased stretch causes specialized cells in the right atrium to secrete the hormone ANH. ANH acts on the kidneys to increase urine production by inhibiting the reabsorption of Na^+ (see figure 27.9). It also inhibits the effect of ADH on the distal convoluted tubules and collecting ducts and inhibits ADH secretion (see chapter 26).

If blood pressure is low, the total Na^+ content of the body is usually also low. In response to low blood pressure, mechanisms such as the renin-angiotensin-aldosterone hormone mechanism are activated, increasing Na^+ concentration and water volume in the extracellular fluid.

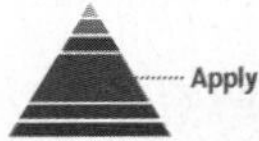

Predict 1

In response to hemorrhagic shock, the kidneys produce a small volume of very concentrated urine. Explain how the rate of filtrate formation changes and how Na^+ transport is altered in the distal convoluted tubule in response to hemorrhagic shock.

Imbalances

Deviations from the normal concentration range for Na^+ in body fluids result in significant symptoms. Low plasma Na^+ levels cause **hyponatremia** (HIGH-poh-nah-TREE-mee-ah). Hyponatremia, such as that caused by overdilution of the blood from drinking too much water after exercise, can lead to mental confusion, seizures, and coma. High plasma Na^+ levels cause

TABLE 27.5 Consequences of Abnormal Plasma Levels of Sodium Ions

HYPONATREMIA		HYPERNATREMIA	
Causes	Inadequate dietary intake of sodium Extrarenal losses Excess water consumption Hyperglycemia	**Causes**	High dietary sodium (rarely causes symptoms) Administration of hypertonic saline solutions Oversecretion of aldosterone Water loss
Symptoms	Lethargy, confusion, apprehension, seizures, and coma When accompanied by reduced blood volume: reduced blood pressure, tachycardia, and decreased urine output When accompanied by increased blood volume: weight gain, edema, and distension of veins	**Symptoms**	Thirst, fever, dry mucous membranes, and restlessness Most serious symptoms are convulsions and pulmonary edema When occurring with increased water volume: weight gain, edema, elevated blood pressure, and bounding pulse

hypernatremia (HIGH-per-nah-TREE-mee-ah). Hypernatremia, such as that caused by excess aldosterone secretion, can cause pulmonary edema and muscle convulsions (see table 27.5).

ASSESS YOUR PROGRESS

11. *Name the substance responsible for most of the osmotic pressure of the extracellular fluid.*
12. *How does aldosterone affect the concentration of Na^+ in the urine?*
13. *What role does sweating play in Na^+ balance?*
14. *How does increased blood pressure result in a loss of water and salt? What happens when blood pressure decreases?*
15. *What effect does ANH have on Na^+ and water loss in urine?*
16. *What are the causes of hypernatremia and hyponatremia? List the symptoms of both conditions.*

Chloride

Function

Chloride ions are the predominant anions in the extracellular fluid. Certain neurotransmitters allow Cl^- entry into the intracellular fluid, which has an inhibitory effect on electrically excitable cells such as neurons and skeletal muscle fibers.

Regulation

Because anions and cations are strongly attracted to each other, the regulatory mechanisms that influence the concentration of cations, including Na^+, K^+, and Ca^{2+} in the extracellular fluid, also influence the concentration of anions. Because Na^+ is the predominant cation, the regulation of Na^+ is the most important factor in the regulation of extracellular Cl^-.

Imbalances

High plasma Cl^- levels cause **hyperchloremia**. This is usually an indication of dehydration but also occurs under conditions causing high blood Na^+ such as Cushing syndrome (see chapter 18). Movement of Cl^- across the plasma membrane follows that of Na^+ due to charge differences. Low plasma Cl^- levels cause **hypochloremia** and may indicate heart failure or Addison disease (see chapter 18).

ASSESS YOUR PROGRESS

17. *What mechanisms regulate Cl^- concentrations?*

Potassium

Function

Potassium ion concentration across the plasma membrane is very tightly regulated because K^+ is the critical factor for determining the resting membrane potential for electrically excitable cells. If extracellular K^+ concentrations increase, the cell depolarizes, whereas if extracellular K^+ concentrations decrease, the cell hyperpolarizes.

Regulation

The principal mechanism regulating K^+ levels is secretion of aldosterone. Elevated levels of K^+ stimulate aldosterone secretion, which increases Na^+ reabsorption and K^+ secretion by way of the Na^+–K^+ pump in the distal convoluted tubules of the kidneys.

Imbalances

Hypokalemia (HIGH-poh-kah-LEE-mee-ah) is due to an abnormally low level of K^+ in the extracellular fluid. Potassium ions are readily filtered out of the blood in the renal corpuscle. They are also actively secreted in the distal convoluted tubules and collecting ducts. This secretion is responsible for controlling the extracellular concentration of K^+. Hypokalemia can be caused by excess K^+ secretion in the kidney due to abnormally elevated aldosterone levels. Aldosterone increases the rate of K^+ secretion in the kidney, which lowers levels of K^+ in the blood (figure 27.6; see chapter 26). Hypokalemia can also be caused by insulin administration. Insulin activates the Na^+–K^+ pump in cells, which causes a decrease in extracellular K^+. Low K^+ levels in the blood can cause fatigue, muscle cramps, or temporary paralysis. **Hyperkalemia** (HIGH-per-kah-LEE-mee-ah) is due to an abnormally high level of K^+ in the extracellular fluid. Hyperkalemia, such as that due to reduced renal excretion, can lead to intestinal cramping, diarrhea, and temporary paralysis (see table 27.6).

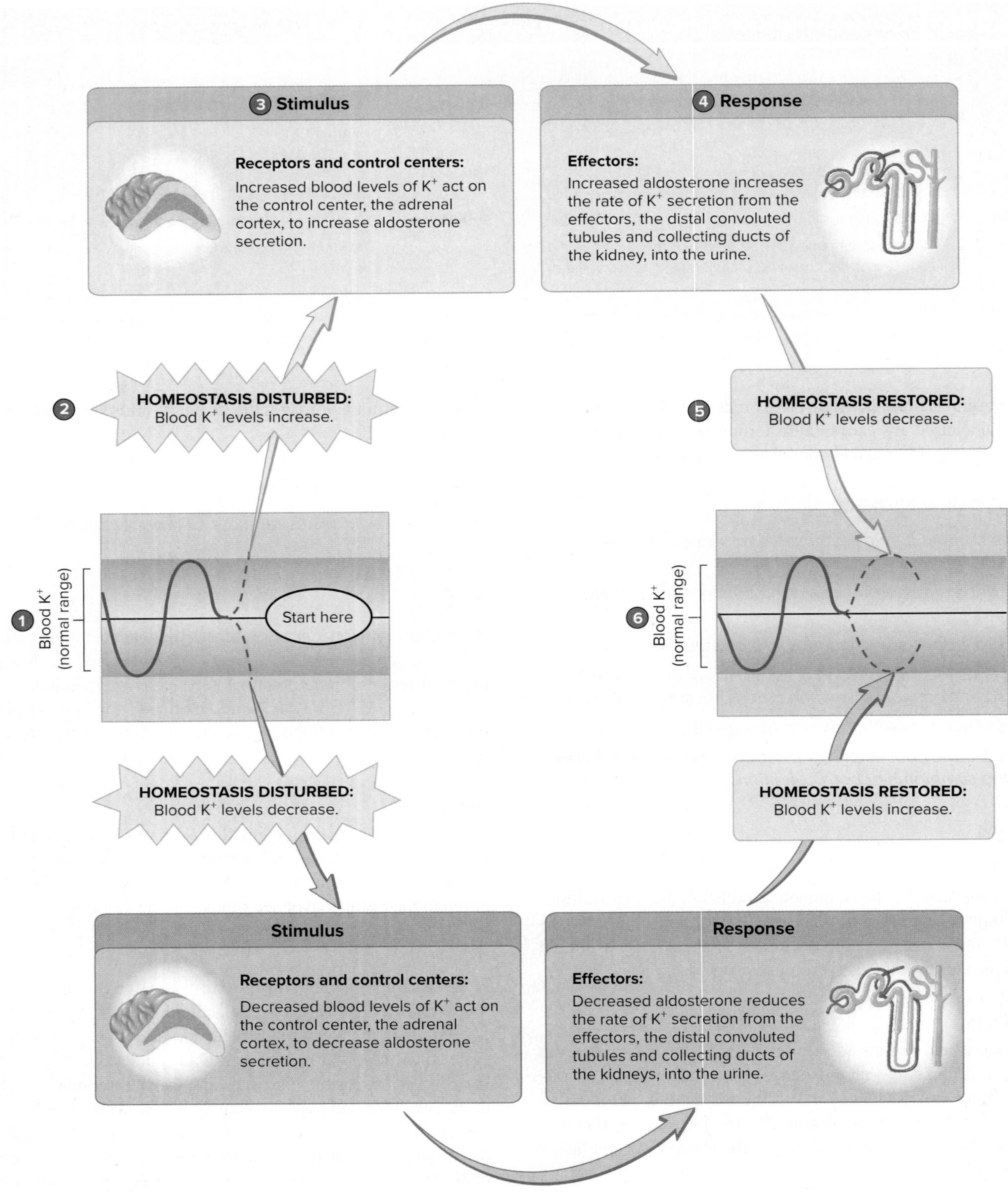

HOMEOSTASIS FIGURE 27.6 Summary of Blood K^+ Regulation

(1) Blood K^+ is in the normal range. (2) Blood K^+ increases outside the normal range, which causes homeostasis to be disturbed. (3) The control center responds to the change in blood K^+. (4) The control center causes aldosterone to be secreted, which increases K^+ secretion at the distal convoluted tubule and the collecting duct. (5) These changes cause blood K^+ to decrease. (6) Blood K^+ returns to the normal range and homeostasis is restored. Observe the responses to a decrease in blood K^+ outside the normal range by following the *pink arrows*.

TABLE 27.6 Consequences of Abnormal Concentrations of Potassium Ions

HYPOKALEMIA		HYPERKALEMIA	
Causes	Alkalosis Insulin administration Reduced K^+ intake Increased renal loss	**Causes**	Loss of intracellular K^+ due to cell trauma or reduced permeability of plasma membrane Reduced renal excretion
Symptoms	Decreased neuromuscular excitability Decreased smooth muscle tone Delayed ventricular depolarization Bradycardia Atrioventricular block	**Symptoms**	
		Mild	Increased neuromuscular irritability Intestinal cramping and diarrhea Rapid cardiac repolarization
		Severe	Muscle weakness Loss of muscle tone and paralysis Reduced rate of cardiac action potential conduction

ASSESS YOUR PROGRESS

18. *What effect does an increase or a decrease in extracellular K^+ concentration have on resting membrane potential?*
19. *In what portion of the renal tubule is K^+ secreted?*
20. *How is the secretion of K^+ regulated?*

Calcium

Function

As with other ions, the extracellular concentration of **calcium ions** is regulated within a narrow range. Calcium ions play numerous critical roles in the body's physiology. As you've learned, Ca^{2+} is important for exocytosis, including that of neurotransmitters. Calcium is the key to muscle contraction for all three muscle types. In cardiac muscle in particular, Ca^{2+} is a major regulator of the action potential.

Regulation

There are three major sites in the body for regulation of Ca^{2+} levels in the extracellular fluid: (1) kidneys, (2) digestive tract, and (3) bones. Almost 99% of total body calcium is contained in bone. Calcium ion regulation partly involves the regulation of Ca^{2+} deposition into and reabsorption from bone (see chapter 6). However, long-term regulation of Ca^{2+} levels depends on maintaining a balance between Ca^{2+} absorption across the intestinal wall and Ca^{2+} excretion by the kidneys.

There are three major hormones that regulate blood levels of Ca^{2+}: (1) parathyroid hormone, (2) vitamin D_3, and (3) calcitonin.

Parathyroid hormone (PTH) is secreted by the parathyroid glands when blood Ca^{2+} levels are too low. PTH increases blood Ca^{2+} through three principal means:

1. *Osteoclasts.* PTH stimulates mechanisms that cause osteoclasts to reabsorb bone. This increases blood levels of Ca^{2+} as well as phosphate.
2. *Renal tubules.* PTH increases Ca^{2+} reabsorption from the kidney tubules. However, PTH stimulates phosphate excretion in the kidneys, which results in low blood levels of phosphate.
3. *Vitamin D_3.* PTH increases the rate of active vitamin D_3 formation, which indirectly increases Ca^{2+} levels through the actions of vitamin D_3.

Lack of PTH secretion causes a rapid reduction in blood Ca^{2+} levels. This could result in death primarily due to tetany of the respiratory muscles.

Vitamin D can be obtained from the diet or from vitamin D_3 synthesis. Normally, vitamin D_3 synthesis is adequate; however, because ultraviolet light is required for this process, prolonged lack of sun exposure reduces vitamin D_3 blood levels.

Without vitamin D_3, the transport of Ca^{2+} across the wall of the digestive tract is negligible. This leads to inadequate Ca^{2+} absorption, even though the person may be consuming a large amount of this ion. Thus, Ca^{2+} absorption depends on getting adequate amounts of calcium and vitamin D.

Calcitonin (KAL-sih-TOH-nin) is secreted by the parafollicular cells of the thyroid gland. Calcitonin lowers extracellular Ca^{2+} levels. However, greater-than-normal calcitonin levels in the blood do not reduce blood levels of Ca^{2+} to below-normal values. The major effect of calcitonin is in bone, where it inhibits osteoclasts. Thus, calcitonin prevents bone degradation, which keeps blood Ca^{2+} levels from rising (see chapter 6). However, PTH is more important than calcitonin for blood Ca^{2+} regulation.

Imbalances

Major symptoms develop when the extracellular concentration of Ca^{2+} moves out of its normal range. **Hypocalcemia** (HIGH-poh-kal-SEE-mee-ah) is due to a below-normal level of Ca^{2+} in the extracellular fluid (table 27.7). Changes in the extracellular concentration of Ca^{2+} markedly affect the electrical properties of excitable tissues. Hypocalcemia increases the plasma membrane's permeability to Na^+. As a result, nerve and muscle tissues undergo spontaneous action potential generation.

Hypercalcemia (HIGH-per-kal-SEE-mee-ah) is due to an above-normal level of Ca^{2+} in the extracellular fluid. Hypercalcemia decreases the plasma membrane's permeability to Na^+, preventing normal depolarization of nerve and muscle cells. High

TABLE 27.7 Consequences of Abnormal Concentrations of Calcium Ions

HYPOCALCEMIA		HYPERCALCEMIA	
Causes	Nutritional deficiencies Vitamin D deficiency Decreased PTH secretion Malabsorption of lipids (reduces vitamin D absorption) Bone tumors that increase Ca^{2+} deposition	**Causes**	Excessive PTH secretion Excess vitamin D
Symptoms	Confusion Muscle spasms Hyperreflexia Intestinal cramping Convulsions Tetany Inadequate respiratory movements Prolonged cardiac ventricular depolarization	**Symptoms**	Fatigue Weakness Lethargy Anorexia Nausea Constipation Reduced cardiac ventricular depolarization Kidney stones

extracellular Ca^{2+} levels cause the deposition of calcium carbonate salts in soft tissues, resulting in irritation and inflammation of those tissues (table 27.7).

ASSESS YOUR PROGRESS

21. *Describe the effects of hypocalcemia and hypercalcemia on membrane potentials.*
22. *Explain the role of PTH in regulating extracellular Ca^{2+} concentration.*
23. *Discuss the role of vitamin D in regulating extracellular Ca^{2+} concentration.*
24. *Describe the role of calcitonin in regulating extracellular Ca^{2+} concentration.*

Phosphate

Function

Mechanisms governing Ca^{2+} levels are tied to those governing phosphate levels. About 85% of the phosphate in the body is in the form of calcium phosphate salts in bone (hydroxyapatite) and teeth. Most of the remaining phosphate is inside cells. Many of the phosphate ions are covalently bound to other organic molecules. For example, phosphate ions are bound to lipids (to form phospholipids), proteins, and carbohydrates. In addition, they are important components of DNA, RNA, and ATP. Phosphates play important roles in regulating enzyme activity. Still other phosphate ions are dissolved in the intracellular fluid and act as buffers (see section 27.4). The most common phosphate ion is HPO_4^{2-}.

Regulation

The kidneys' capacity to reabsorb phosphate ions is limited. If the level of phosphate ions increases in the extracellular fluid, more phosphate is excreted in the urine. If the level of phosphate ions decreases in the extracellular fluid, less phosphate is excreted in the urine.

Over time, a diet low in phosphate can increase the rate of phosphate reabsorption. In addition, PTH increases extracellular phosphate levels by promoting bone reabsorption. Bone reabsorption releases Ca^{2+} and phosphate ions into the extracellular fluid. Thus, the kidneys do not need to conserve phosphate ions, and more are excreted in the urine. If phosphate levels in the extracellular fluid increase above normal levels, Ca^{2+} and phosphate ions precipitate as calcium phosphate salts in soft tissues.

Imbalances

Elevated blood levels of phosphate may occur with acute or chronic renal failure as a result of a critically reduced rate of filtrate formation by the kidneys. The rate of phosphate excretion is consequently reduced. Also, the chronic use of laxatives containing phosphates may cause elevated blood levels of phosphate. Symptoms of elevated phosphate levels are related to reduced blood Ca^{2+} levels because phosphate ions and Ca^{2+} precipitate out of solution and are deposited in the body's soft tissues. Prolonged elevation of blood levels of phosphate can result in calcium phosphate deposits in the joints and other tissues, such as the lungs and kidneys. A below-normal blood level of phosphate is called **hypophosphatemia** (HIGH-poh-fos-fay-TEE-mee-ah), and an above-normal blood level of phosphate is called **hyperphosphatemia** (HIGH-per-fos-fay-TEE-mee-ah). The consequences of increased and reduced plasma levels of phosphates are presented in table 27.8.

ASSESS YOUR PROGRESS

25. *Where is most of the phosphate in the body located? What is the most common phosphate ion?*
26. *Explain how the kidneys control plasma levels of phosphate ions.*
27. *How does an increased level of PTH affect tubular phosphate reabsorption?*
28. *What are the consequences of prolonged elevation of blood phosphate ions?*

TABLE 27.8 Consequences of Abnormal Concentrations of Phosphate Ions

	HYPOPHOSPHATEMIA		HYPERPHOSPHATEMIA
Causes	Reduced intestinal absorption due to vitamin D deficiency or alcohol abuse Hyperparathyroidism (elevated renal PO_4^- excretion)	**Causes**	Renal failure Tissue destruction from chemotherapy Hyperparathyroidism (reduced renal PO_4^- excretion)
Symptoms	Reduced metabolic rate Reduced O_2 transport Reduced blood clotting Reduced white blood cell functions	**Symptoms**	Formation of calcium phosphate deposits in tissues of lungs, kidneys, and joints Symptoms of reduced Ca^{2+} related to formation of deposits

TABLE 27.9 Consequences of Abnormal Concentrations of Magnesium Ions

	HYPOMAGNESEMIA (rare)		HYPERMAGNESEMIA (rare)
Causes	Malnutrition Alcoholism Reduced magnesium intestinal absorption Renal tubular dysfunction Some diuretics	**Causes**	Renal failure Magnesium-containing antacids
Symptoms	Irritability Muscle weakness Tetany Convulsions	**Symptoms**	Nausea Vomiting Muscle weakness Hypotension Bradycardia Reduced respiration

Magnesium

Function

Most of the magnesium in the body is stored in the bones or intracellular fluid. Less than 1% of the total are ions in the extracellular fluid. Approximately one-half of magnesium ions in the extracellular fluid are bound to plasma proteins, while the remaining **magnesium ions (Mg^{2+})** are free. Magnesium ions are cofactors for intracellular enzymes, such as the Na^+–K^+ pump involved in actively transporting Na^+ out of and K^+ into cells (see section 2.4).

Regulation

Free Mg^{2+} passes through the filtration membranes of the kidney into the filtrate. About 85–90% of those ions are reabsorbed from the filtrate, and only about 10–15% enter the urine. Of the Mg^{2+} reabsorbed, most is reabsorbed by the loop of Henle. The remainder is reabsorbed by the proximal convoluted tubule, distal convoluted tubule, and collecting duct.

The kidney's capacity to reabsorb Mg^{2+} is limited. If the level of free Mg^{2+} increases in the extracellular fluid, the excess Mg^{2+} remains in the filtrate, and the rate of Mg^{2+} loss in the urine increases. If the level of free Mg^{2+} decreases in the extracellular fluid, nearly all of the Mg^{2+} is reabsorbed, and the rate of Mg^{2+} loss in the urine decreases. The control of Mg^{2+} reabsorption is not clear, but a decreased extracellular concentration of Mg^{2+} causes an increased rate of reabsorption in the renal tubule.

Imbalance

Low and high levels of plasma magnesium produce symptoms associated with the effect of magnesium on Na^+–K^+ active transport (table 27.9). **Hypomagnesemia** is due to a below-normal blood level of magnesium. Hypomagnesemia as caused by alcoholism can lead to muscle weakness and muscle convulsions. Low levels of Mg^{2+} can also cause insulin resistance because Mg^{2+} is required for proper function of the insulin receptor. **Hypermagnesemia** is due to an above-normal blood level of magnesium. Hypermagnesemia such as that occurring in kidney failure results in nausea, low blood pressure, and a low respiratory rate.

ASSESS YOUR PROGRESS

29. *In what part of the renal tubule is most Mg^{2+} reabsorbed?*
30. *What effect does a decreased extracellular concentration of Mg^{2+} have on its reabsorption in the renal tubule?*

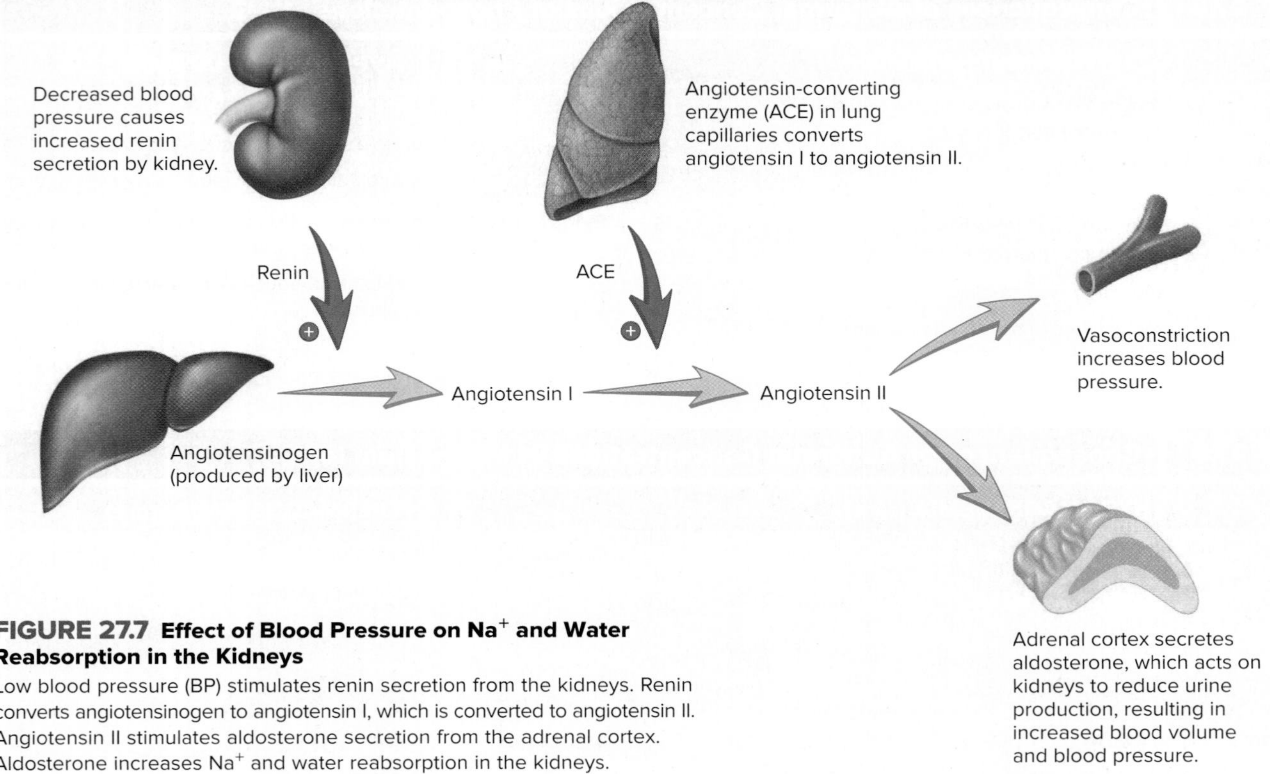

FIGURE 27.7 Effect of Blood Pressure on Na^+ and Water Reabsorption in the Kidneys

Low blood pressure (BP) stimulates renin secretion from the kidneys. Renin converts angiotensinogen to angiotensin I, which is converted to angiotensin II. Angiotensin II stimulates aldosterone secretion from the adrenal cortex. Aldosterone increases Na^+ and water reabsorption in the kidneys.

27.3 Hormonal Mechanisms Regulating Body Fluid Composition

LEARNING OUTCOMES

After reading this section, you should be able to

A. **Explain the mechanism of the renin-angiotensin-aldosterone system.**
B. **Explain the mechanism of atrial natriuretic hormone.**
C. **Explain the mechainsm of antidiuretic hormone.**

The volume of extracellular fluid can change even if its osmolality is maintained within a narrow range. Recall that blood volume is directly proportional to blood pressure. When blood volume increases, blood pressure goes up as well. The opposite is also true. Three important hormonal mechanisms that regulate body fluid composition are the renin-angiotensin-aldosterone mechanism, atrial natriuretic hormone, and antidiuretic hormone.

1. *Renin-angiotensin-aldosterone hormone mechanism.* The renin-angiotensin-aldosterone hormone mechanism acts to increase blood pressure (see chapter 26). When juxtaglomerular cells detect a drop in blood pressure in the afferent arterioles, they secrete the enzyme renin. Renin catalyzes the conversion of angiotensinogen to angiotensin I. Angiotensin I is converted to angiotensin II. Angiotensin II raises blood pressure in three ways: (1) vasoconstriction, (2) stimulation of thirst, and (3) stimulation of aldosterone secretion. Angiotensin II is a potent vasoconstrictor. Vasoconstriction increases peripheral resistance and thus blood pressure. Angiotensin II also stimulates the thirst center. Increased water intake will increase blood volume and, in turn, blood pressure. Finally, aldosterone from the adrenal cortex stimulates reabsorption of Na^+. The effect is to increase the osmolality of the blood, which increases water reabsorption in the kidneys. The water follows the Na^+ into the blood. Thus, because the volume of urine produced by the kidneys goes down, the extracellular fluid volume is increased, and blood pressure returns to the normal range (figure 27.7).
2. *Atrial natriuretic hormone (ANH) mechanism.* In response to a larger-than-normal blood volume, the heart's atrial walls are stretched to a greater degree. This stretch triggers ANH secretion. ANH reduces Na^+ reabsorption from the distal convoluted tubules and the collecting ducts, increasing the rate of Na^+ loss in the urine. Water will move by osmosis toward the higher Na^+ concentration in the filtrate. The increased water in the filtrate increases urine volume. Thus, increased ANH secretion decreases extracellular fluid volume and thus blood volume (figure 27.8).

   ANH does not appear to respond strongly to decreases in blood volume. However, a decrease in pressure in the atria of the heart inhibits the secretion of ANH.
3. *Antidiuretic hormone (ADH) mechanism.* The ADH mechanism plays an important role in regulating extracellular fluid volume in response to large changes in blood pressure (5–10%).

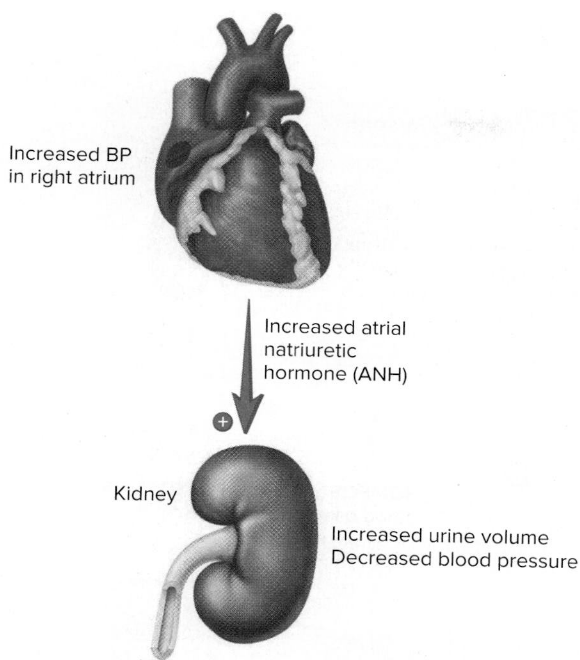

FIGURE 27.8 Effect of Blood Pressure in the Right Atrium on Na^+ and Water Excretion
Increased blood pressure (BP) in the right atrium of the heart causes increased secretion of atrial natriuretic hormone (ANH), which increases Na^+ excretion and water loss in urine.

Low blood pressure stimulates ADH secretion. ADH promotes the reabsorption of water from the distal convoluted tubules and collecting ducts, resulting in a small volume of concentrated urine. This response helps increase extracellular fluid volume, thereby increasing blood pressure (figures 27.9 and 27.10; see figure 27.5).

Clinical IMPACT 27.1

A Dangerous Contest

In 2007, a mother of three died from drinking too much water during a radio contest. The rules required the contestants to drink one 8-ounce bottle of water every 15 minutes without urinating. The person who could wait the longest without urinating would win a popular videogaming system. By the time the woman had dropped out of the contest, she had drunk almost 2 gallons of water. The woman called a friend on her way home complaining of a severe headache. The friend called the woman's mother, who found her daughter dead an hour later. Incredibly, during the contest, the DJs received warnings of the dangers of such a contest. The DJs joked that they weren't responsible because the contestants had signed liability waivers. The woman's death was found to be due to water intoxication. Two years after her death, a jury awarded the woman's family $16 million in wrongful death damages.

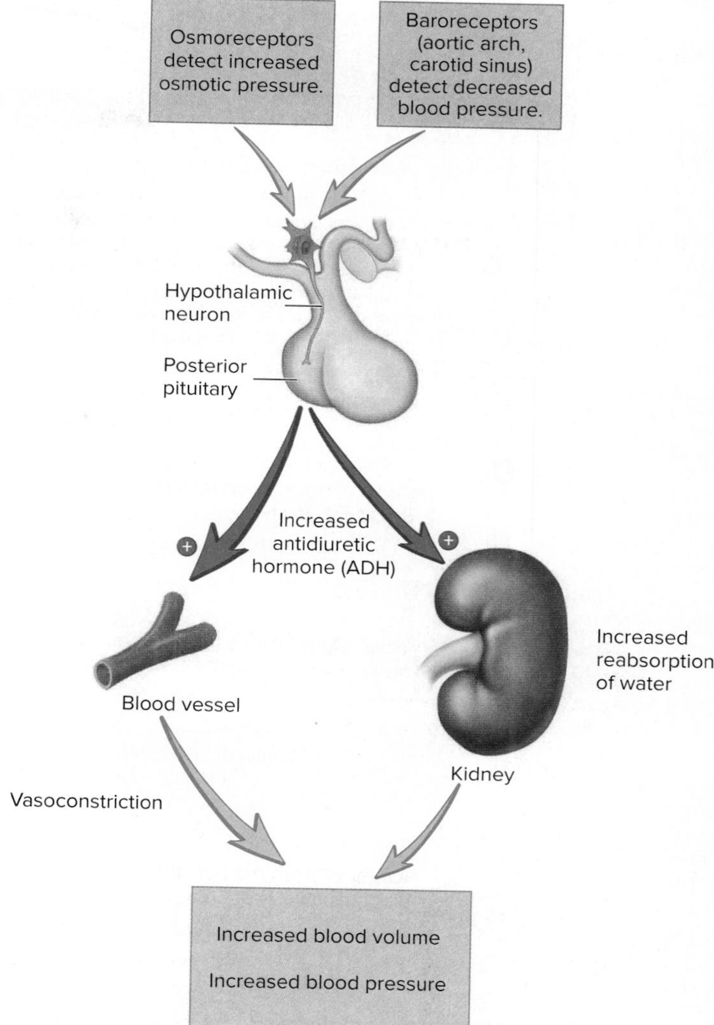

FIGURE 27.9 Effect of Blood Osmolality and Blood Pressure on Water Reabsorption in the Kidneys
Increased blood osmolality affects hypothalamic neurons, and decreased blood pressure (BP) affects baroreceptors in the aortic arch, carotid sinuses, and atrium. As a result of these stimuli, the rate of antidiuretic hormone (ADH) secretion from the posterior pituitary increases, which increases water reabsorption by the kidneys.

The mechanisms that maintain extracellular fluid concentration and volume function together. However, when the mechanisms do not function normally, extracellular fluid volume may increase, even though the extracellular concentration of fluids does not change substantially. For example, excessive aldosterone secretion from an enlarged adrenal cortex increases Na^+ reabsorption by the kidneys, and the total volume of extracellular fluid increases. Certain mechanisms, such as the regulation of ADH secretion, keep the concentration of the body fluids constant. Even if elevated blood pressure causes edema, the osmolality of the extracellular fluid is maintained between 285 and 300 mOsm/kg. Figure 27.11 summarizes the hormonal mechanisms involved in Na^+ regulation. Similarly, in people suffering from heart failure,

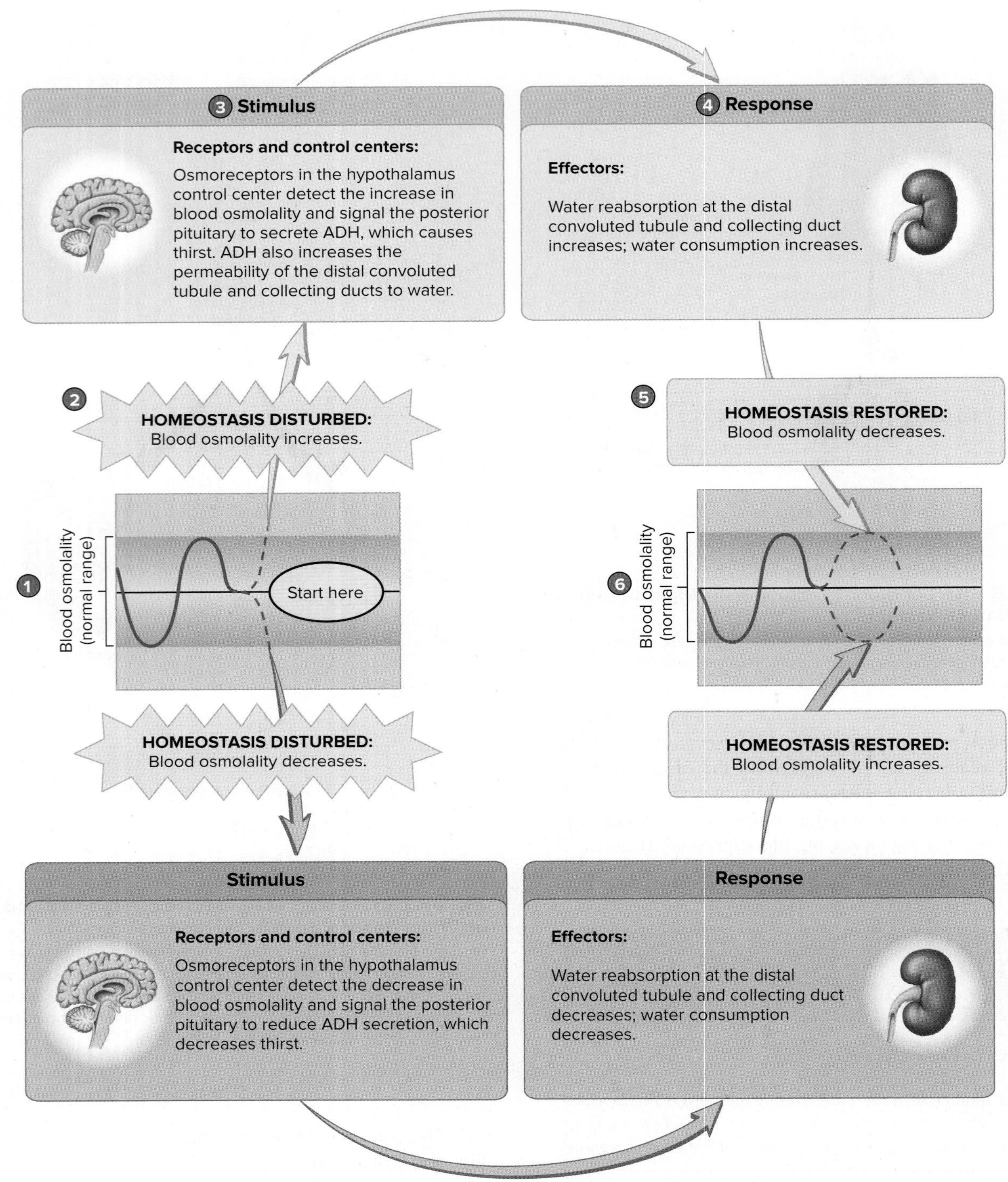

HOMEOSTASIS FIGURE 27.10 Blood Osmolality Regulation

(1) Blood osmolality is in the normal range. (2) Blood osmolality increases outside the normal range, which causes homeostasis to be disturbed. (3) The control center responds to the change in blood osmolality. (4) The control center causes ADH to be secreted, which increases water reabsorption at the distal convoluted tubule and the collecting duct. (5) These changes cause blood osmolality to decrease. (6) Blood osmolality returns to the normal range and homeostasis is restored. Observe the responses to a decrease in blood osmolality outside the normal range by following the *pink arrows*.

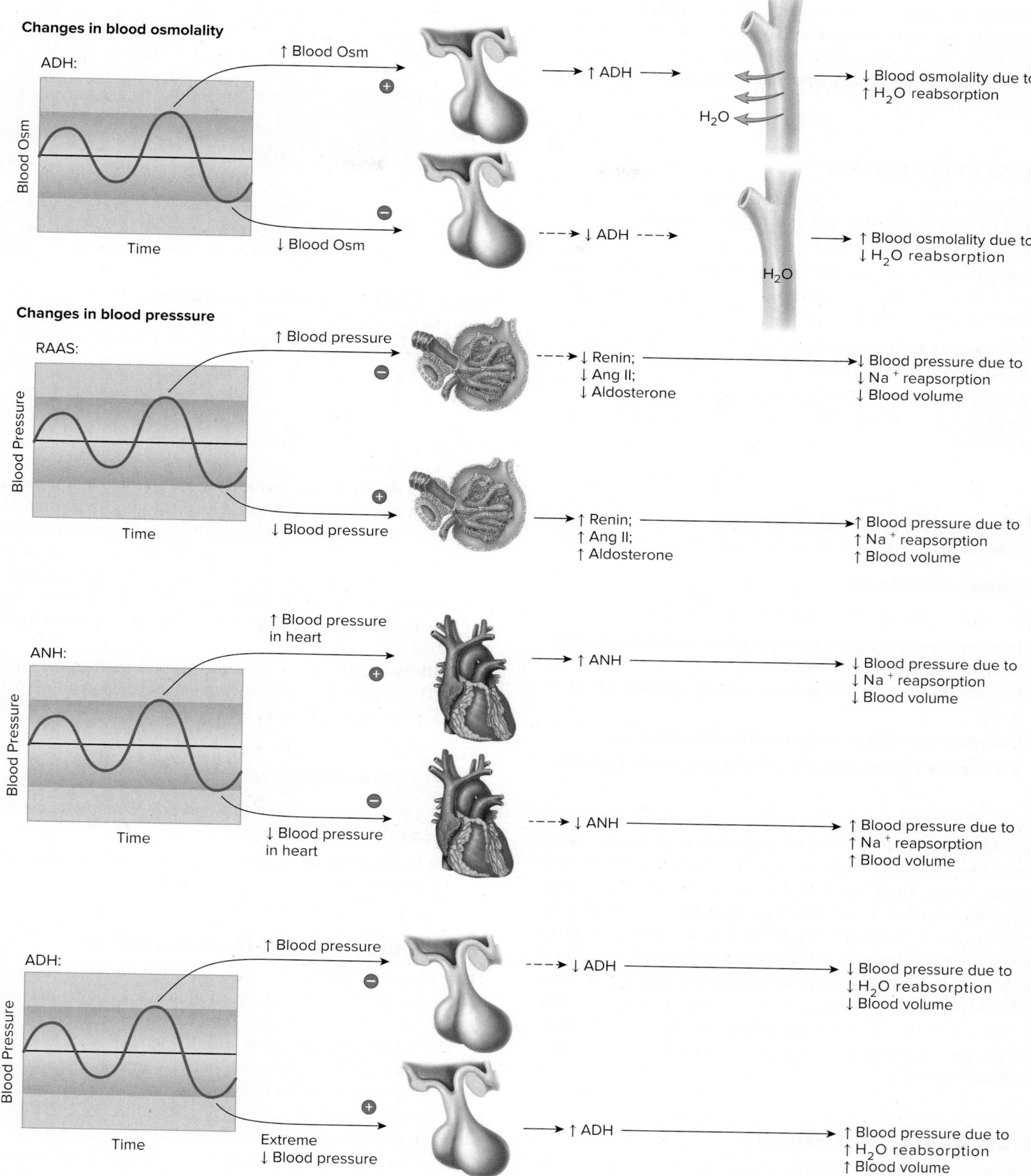

FIGURE 27.11 Summary of Sodium Regulation

Changes in blood osmolality trigger secretion of ADH, which induces water conservation in the kidney. A reduction in blood pressure induces the renin-angiotensin-aldosterone mechanism as well as the antidiuretic mechanism (severe decreases in blood pressure). Both hormonal mechanisms cause the kidney to conserve water. An increase in blood pressure stimulates the secretion of atrial natriuretic hormone, which results in the production of more urine by the kidney.

the resulting reduced blood pressure activates mechanisms, such as renin secretion, that increase blood pressure to its normal range. Consequently, aldosterone secretion increases, and the result is increased extracellular fluid volume and edema in the periphery, including the lungs.

ASSESS YOUR PROGRESS

31. *What sensory receptors are responsible for activating neural and hormonal mechanisms that regulate extracellular fluid volume?*
32. *Describe the response of the renin-angiotensin-aldosterone hormone mechanism to a decrease in blood pressure. How are extracellular fluid volume and urine volume affected?*
33. *What effect does atrial natriuretic hormone (ANH) have on extracellular fluid volume?*
34. *How does an increase in blood pressure affect the secretion of ADH? How does ADH affect extracellular fluid volume?*

27.4 Acid-Base Balance

LEARNING OUTCOMES

After reading this section, you should be able to

A. **Demonstrate an understanding of acids and bases and their relationship with buffers.**
B. **Explain the actions of the three buffer systems of the body.**
C. **Describe the mechanisms of acid-base balance.**
D. **Explain the causes and effects of acid-base imbalances.**

Hydrogen ions affect the activity of enzymes and interact with many electrically charged molecules. Consequently, most chemical reactions within the body are highly sensitive to the H^+ concentration of the fluid in which they occur. Maintaining the H^+ concentration within a narrow range of values is essential for normal metabolic reactions. The H^+ concentration is determined by acids and bases in the body. Recall from chapter 2 that the pH of a solution is a measure of H^+ concentration and that the relationship between the pH level and H^+ concentration is an inverse one: The lower the pH level, the greater the H^+ concentration. Likewise, the higher the pH level, the lower the H^+ concentration (see figure 2.15).

Acids, Bases, and Buffers

Acids release H^+ into a solution; bases remove H^+ from a solution. Acids and bases are classified as either strong or weak. A **strong acid** completely dissociates into its separate ions; for example, hydrochloric acid dissociates into H^+ and Cl^- (figure 27.12). A **strong base** also completely dissociates into its separate ions. For example, NaOH dissociates into Na^+ and OH^-.

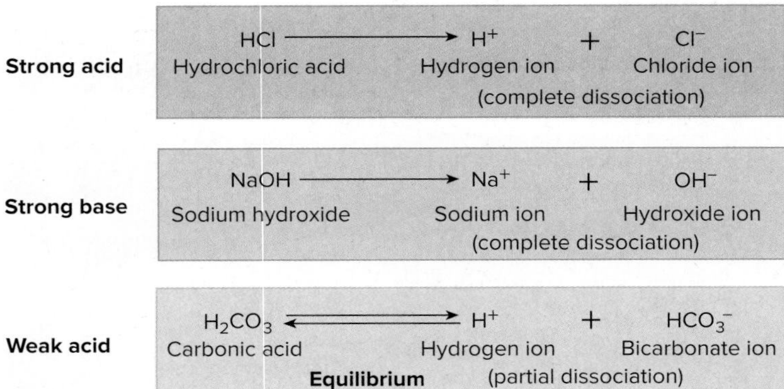

FIGURE 27.12 Types of Acids and Bases
Strong acids completely dissociate into their separate ions, while weak acids do not. Strong bases completely dissociate into their separate ions.

The OH^- can then react with H^+ to form H_2O, thus removing H^+ from the solution.

Like a strong acid, a **weak acid** releases H^+ into a solution; however, it does not completely dissociate into its separate ions. The weak acid releases H^+ until equilibrium with the surrounding solution is reached, and then no more H^+ dissociates. Weak acids are common in living systems, and they play important roles in preventing large changes in body fluid pH. A **weak base,** such as NH_3^+, reduces the concentration of H^+ ions in a solution by binding to free H^+.

Buffers (BUHF-erz; see chapter 2) prevent extreme changes in the pH of a solution. Buffers within body fluids stabilize the pH by binding to excess H^+ or by releasing H^+.

ASSESS YOUR PROGRESS

35. *Define acid and base. What is the relationship between pH and H^+ concentration?*
36. *Describe weak acids. Why are weak acids important in living systems?*

Regulation of Acid-Base Balance

There are two major mechanisms for regulation of H^+ concentration. These mechanisms are the following: (1) chemical buffer systems and (2) physiological buffer systems. Chemical buffers and physiological buffers work together to regulate acid-base balance (figure 27.13). Chemical buffers almost instantaneously resist changes in the pH of body fluids, but the physiological buffers also play essential roles. The two principal physiological buffer systems are (1) the respiratory system and (2) the renal system. The respiratory system provides a short-term response to changes in acid-base balance. It responds within a few minutes to bring the pH of body fluids back toward its normal range. The renal system provides a long-term, more substantial response to changes in acid-base balance. It responds within hours to days to alterations of body fluid pH.

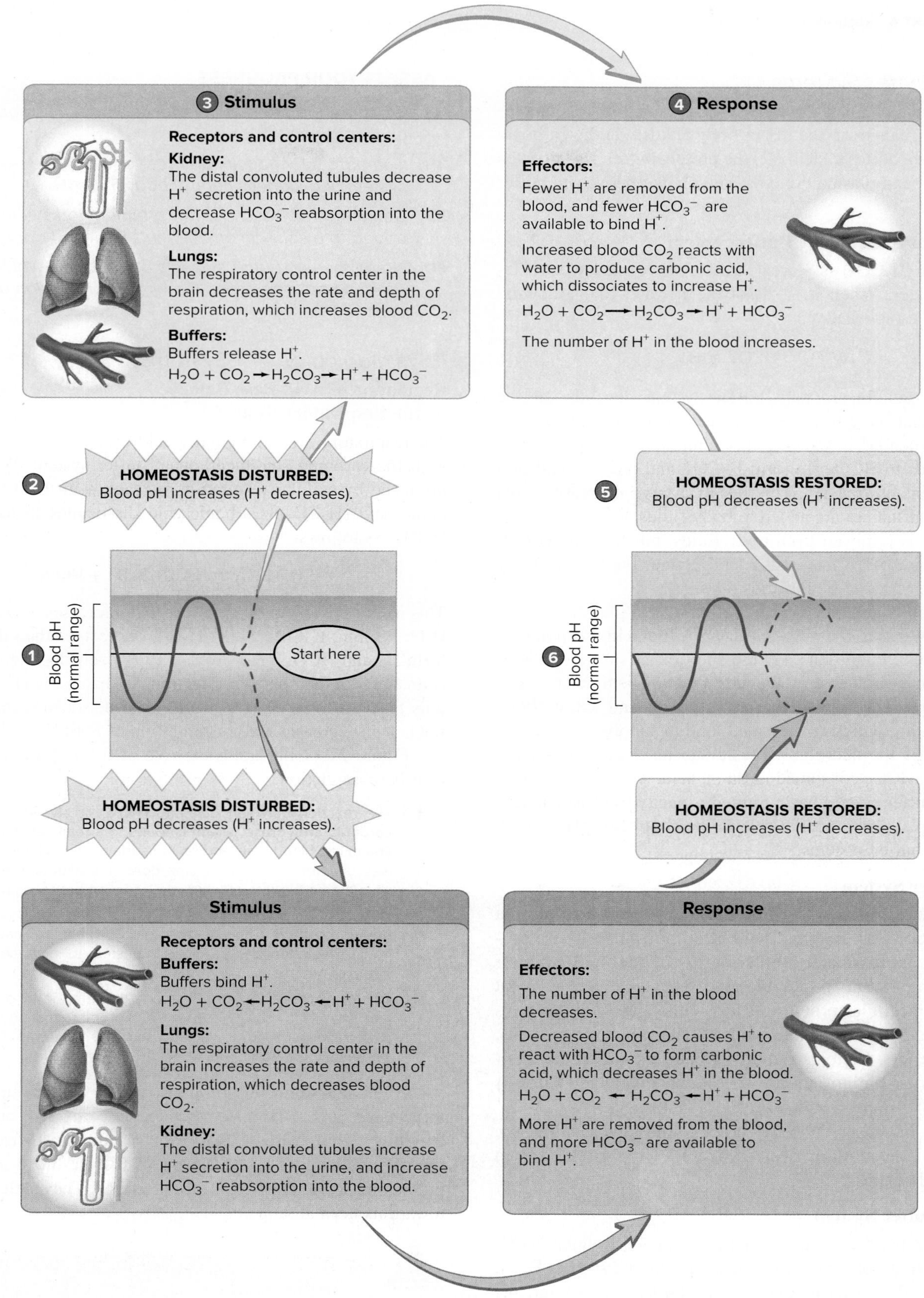

HOMEOSTASIS FIGURE 27.13 Summary of Acid-Base Balance Regulation

(1) Blood pH is in the normal range. (2) Blood pH increases outside the normal range, which causes homeostasis to be disturbed. (3) The blood pH control centers respond to the change in blood pH. (4) The control centers cause decreased H^+ secretion from the blood and increased carbonic acid production, which increases blood H^+ concentration. (5) These changes cause blood pH to decrease. (6) Blood pH returns to the normal range and homeostasis is restored. Observe the responses to a decrease in blood pH outside the normal range by following the *pink arrows*.

Chemical Buffer Systems

Three important chemical buffer systems function together to prevent major changes in the pH of body fluids: (1) the carbonic acid/bicarbonate buffer system; (2) the protein buffer system, such as hemoglobin and plasma proteins; and (3) the phosphate buffer system.

Carbonic Acid/Bicarbonate Buffer System

Carbonic acid (H_2CO_3) is a weak acid. It is formed when CO_2 reacts with water. When it is dissolved in water, the following equilibrium is established:

$$H_2CO_3 \rightleftarrows HCO_3^- + H^+$$

The carbonic acid/bicarbonate buffer system depends on the equilibrium that is quickly established between H_2CO_3 and H^+/HCO_3^-. When H^+ is added to this solution, a large proportion of the H^+ binds to HCO_3^- to form H_2CO_3, and only a small percentage remains as free H^+. This resists a large decrease in pH when acidic substances are added to body fluids.

When H^+ is removed from body fluids, much of the H_2CO_3 forms HCO_3^- and H^+. This resists a large change in pH when basic substances are added to body fluids.

The carbonic acid/bicarbonate buffer system plays an important role in regulating the *extra*cellular pH. It quickly responds to several metabolic conditions: (1) the addition of substances such as CO_2 or lactate produced by increased metabolism during exercise (see chapter 23), (2) increased fatty acid and ketone body production during periods of elevated lipid metabolism (see chapter 25), and (3) the addition of basic substances, such as large amounts of $NaHCO_3$ consumed as an antacid. The carbonic acid/bicarbonate buffer system has a limited capacity to resist changes in pH, but it plays an essential role in the control of pH by both physiological buffer systems.

Protein Buffer System

The high concentrations of intracellular proteins and plasma proteins function as a large pool of buffer molecules. These proteins provide approximately three-fourths of the body's buffer capacity. Hemoglobin in red blood cells is one of the most important intracellular protein buffers. Other intracellular molecules associated with nucleic acids, such as histone proteins, also act as buffers. Proteins function as buffers due to the functional groups of amino acids, such as carboxyl (–COOH) or amino ($–NH_2$) groups, which act as weak acids and bases. As H^+ concentration increases, more H^+ binds to the functional group, and when H^+ concentration decreases, more H^+ is released from the functional groups.

Phosphate Buffer System

The phosphate buffer system is an important *intra*cellular buffer system. Phosphate-containing molecules in solution, such as DNA, RNA, ATP, and phosphate ions, act as buffers. When the pH decreases, ions, such as HPO_4^-, bind H^+ to form $H_2PO_4^-$; however, when the pH becomes more basic, $H_2PO_4^-$ releases H^+ into solution. In this way, these two ions fluctuate between gaining and losing H^+ ions, which helps balance the pH.

ASSESS YOUR PROGRESS

37. *What are the three major mechanisms that regulate H^+ concentration?*
38. *Compare the capacity and rate at which the respiratory system and kidneys control body fluid pH.*
39. *Define* buffer. *Describe how a buffer works when H^+ is added to a solution or when it is removed from a solution.*
40. *Name the two buffer systems of the body. Which of these systems provides the largest proportion of buffer capacity?*

Physiological Buffer Systems

Regulation of Acid-Base Balance by the Respiratory System

The respiratory system regulates acid-base balance in partnership with the carbonic acid/bicarbonate buffer system. When CO_2 is produced by cellular respiration, it reacts with H_2O to form carbonic acid (H_2CO_3). Carbonic acid dissociates to form H^+ and HCO_3^- as follows:

$$H_2O + CO_2 \leftrightarrows H_2CO_3 \leftrightarrows H^+ + HCO_3^-$$

This reaction is in equilibrium. As CO_2 increases, CO_2 reacts with H_2O, forming H_2CO_3. Many H_2CO_3 molecules then dissociate to form H^+ and HCO_3^-. However, if CO_2 levels decline, the equilibrium shifts in the opposite direction, so that many H^+ and HCO_3^- ions react to form H_2CO_3, which then dissociates into CO_2 and H_2O. This decreases the concentration of both H^+ and HCO_3^-.

Figure 27.14 illustrates the role of the respiratory system in acid-base regulation.

1. The reaction between CO_2 and H_2O is catalyzed by the enzyme **carbonic anhydrase,** which is found in a relatively high concentration in red blood cells and on the surface of capillary epithelial cells (see chapter 23). This enzyme does not influence equilibrium but accelerates the rate at which the reaction proceeds in either direction, so that equilibrium is achieved quickly.
2. Chemoreceptors detect decreases in body fluid pH, causing neurons in the respiratory center in the brainstem to increase the rate and depth of breathing.
3. This eliminates CO_2 from the body through the lungs at a greater rate. The decline in CO_2 levels results in the formation of H_2CO_3, The dissociation of H_2CO_3 into CO_2 and H_2O lowers H^+ levels and pH becomes more basic.

Any increase in body fluid pH inhibits neurons in the respiratory center in the brainstem to decrease the rate and depth of breathing. This causes less CO_2 to be eliminated from the body through the lungs. Elevated levels of CO_2 result in more H_2CO_3 production and so more H^+ is also produced. The pH then decreases toward its normal range.

Predict 2

Under stressful conditions, some people hyperventilate. What effect does the rapid rate of ventilation have on blood pH? Explain why breathing into a paper bag helps a hyperventilating person.

PROCESS **Figure**

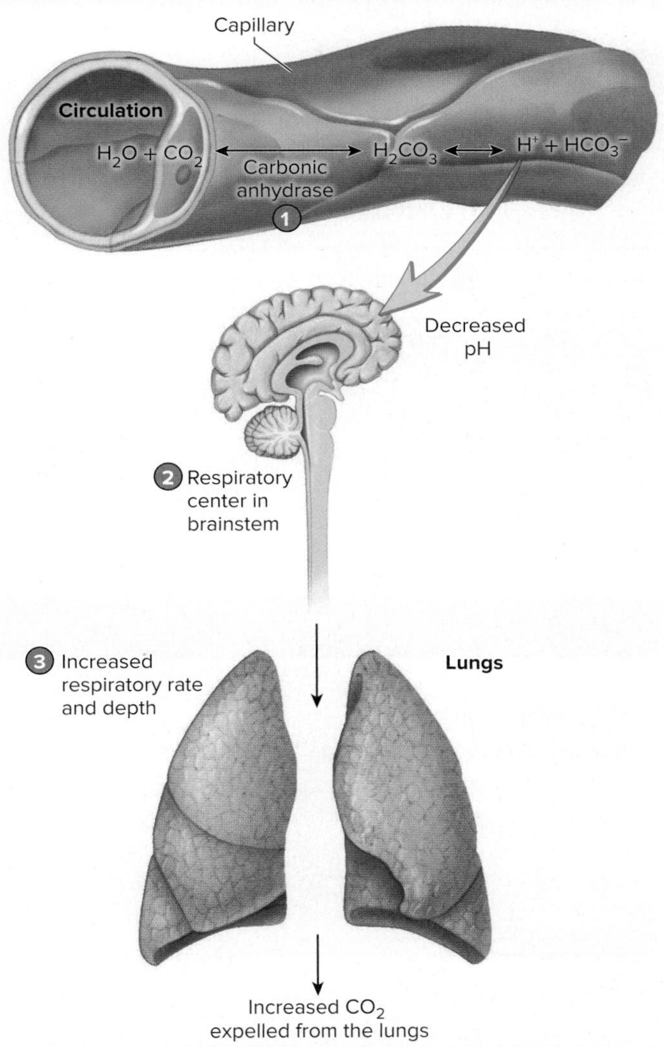

PROCESS **Figure 27.14**

Regulation of Body Fluid Acid-Base Balance by the Respiratory System

When CO_2 level increases in the blood, it reacts with water to create acid. The lungs help prevent the pH from becoming excessively low. CO_2 exits the blood within the lungs and pH rises again.

If the pH of the body fluids were to fall into the acidic range, how do you think blood pressure and heart rate would change in addition to the increased rate and depth of breathing?

Regulation of Acid-Base Balance by the Renal System

Cells in the kidney tubules directly regulate acid-base balance. Figure 27.15 details this process. These cells change both the rate of H^+ secretion into the filtrate and the rate of HCO_3^- reabsorption.

1. Carbonic anhydrase within tubule cells catalyzes the formation of H_2CO_3, which dissociates into H^+ and HCO_3^-.
2. An antiport system then exchanges H^+ for Na^+ across the apical membrane of the cells. Thus, tubule cells secrete H^+ into the filtrate and reabsorb Na^+.
3. The Na^+ and HCO_3^- are symported across the basal membrane.
4. After the Na^+ and HCO_3^- are symported from the tubule cells, they diffuse into the peritubular capillaries. As a result, H^+ is secreted into the lumens of the tubules, and HCO_3^- passes into the extracellular fluid.

The reabsorbed HCO_3^- combines with excess H^+ in the extracellular fluid to form H_2CO_3. This combination removes H^+ from the extracellular fluid and increases extracellular pH. The rate of H^+ secretion and HCO_3^- reabsorption increases when the pH of the body fluids decreases, and when the pH increases, H^+ secretion slows. Most HCO_3^- within the filtrate is returned to the extracellular fluid by the Na^+/HCO_3^- symporter in the basal membrane (figure 27.15). Unless the pH of the body fluids becomes overly basic, little HCO_3^- is excreted in the urine.

Although the tubule cells respond directly to H^+, the hormone aldosterone can also alter the H^+ permeability of the tubules. Aldosterone increases the rate of Na^+ reabsorption and K^+ secretion by the kidneys, but in high concentrations aldosterone also stimulates H^+ secretion. Elevated aldosterone levels, such as those occurring in patients with Cushing syndrome, can therefore elevate body fluid pH above normal (alkalosis). However, the major influence on the rate of H^+ secretion is the pH of the body fluids.

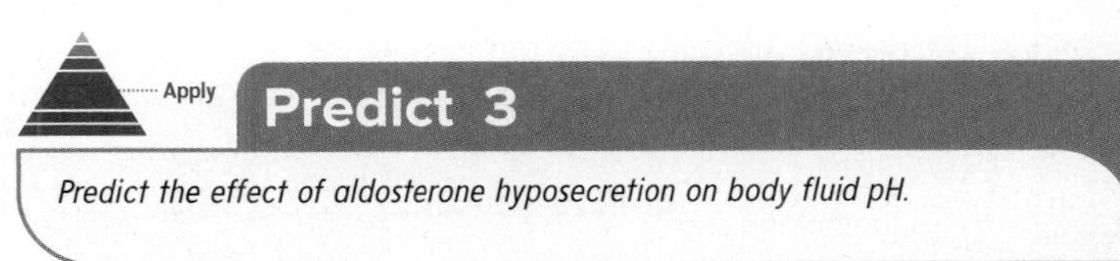

Predict 3

Predict the effect of aldosterone hyposecretion on body fluid pH.

The secretion of H^+ into the nephron can decrease the filtrate pH to approximately 4.5. A filtrate pH below 4.5 inhibits the secretion of additional H^+. The H^+ that passes into the filtrate is more than the amount required to decrease the pH of an unbuffered solution below 4.5. Buffers in the filtrate combine with many of the secreted H^+. The buffers in the filtrate include (1) HCO_3^-, (2) phosphate ions (HPO_4^{2-}), and (3) **ammonia (NH_3)**. HCO_3^- and HPO_4^{2-} enter the filtrate through the filtration membrane, and NH_3 diffuses across the wall of tubule cells into the filtrate. These ions combine with H^+ secreted by the renal tubule, lowering its concentration (figure 27.16).

NH_3 is produced in renal tubule cells when amino acids, such as glutamine, are deaminated. Subsequently, NH_3 diffuses from the tubule cells into the filtrate and combines with H^+ in the filtrate to form **ammonium ions (NH_4^+**; figure 27.16). The rate of NH_3 production increases when the pH of the body fluids has been depressed for 2–3 days, as occurs during prolonged respiratory or metabolic acidosis. The elevated ammonia production increases the buffering capacity of the filtrate, allowing the secretion of additional H^+ into the urine. Other weak acids, such as lactate in the filtrate, also bind to H^+ and increase the amount of H^+ that can be secreted into the filtrate.

PROCESS **Figure**

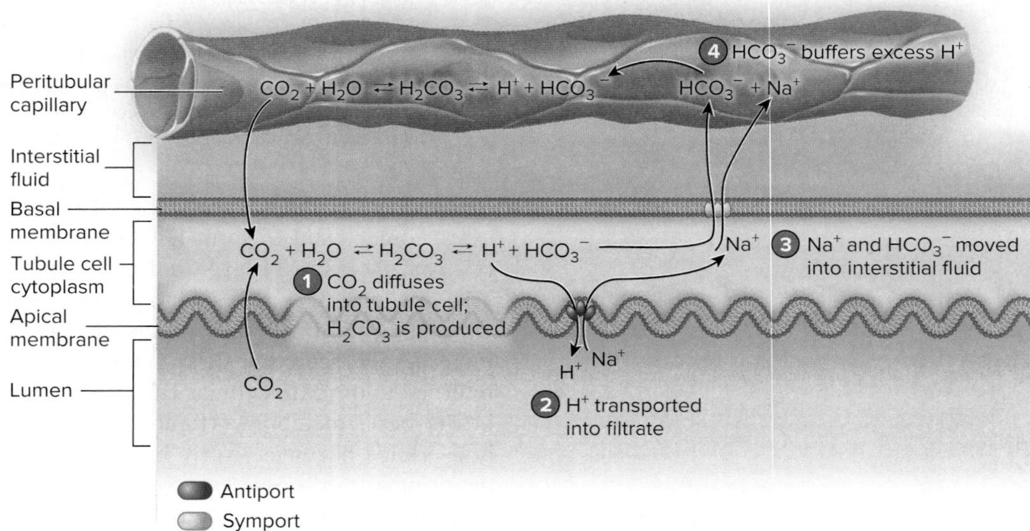

PROCESS **Figure 27.15**

Regulation of Body Fluid Acid-Base Balance by the Kidneys

As the extracellular pH decreases, the rate of H^+ secretion by the renal tubule cells and HCO_3 reabsorption increase.

Understand *If the activity of the Na^+/HCO_3^- symporter were increased, how would blood pH change? Why?*

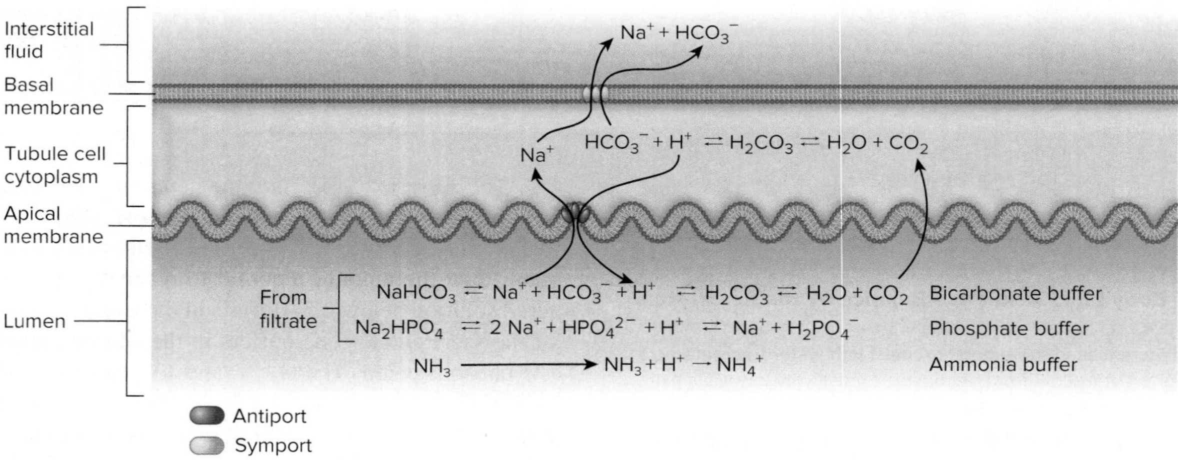

FIGURE 27.16 Hydrogen Ion Buffering in the Filtrate

The secretion of H^+ into the filtrate decreases filtrate pH. As the concentration of H^+ increases in the filtrate, the ability of tubule cells to secrete additional H^+ becomes limited. Buffering the H^+ in the filtrate decreases its concentration and enables tubule cells to secrete additional H^+.

ASSESS YOUR PROGRESS

41. *What happens to blood pH when blood CO_2 levels go up or down? What causes this change?*

42. *What effect do increased CO_2 levels or decreased pH have on ventilation? How does this change in breathing affect blood pH?*

43. *Describe the process by which tubule cells move H^+ into the tubule lumen and HCO_3^- into the extracellular fluid.*

44. *Name the factors that cause an increase and a decrease in H^+ secretion.*

45. *What is the purpose of buffers in the urine? Describe how the ammonia buffer system operates.*

Acid-Base Imbalance

The normal pH of the body fluids is between 7.35 and 7.45. **Acidosis** (ass-ih-DOH-sis) results when the pH falls below 7.35; **alkalosis** (al-kah-LOH-sis) occurs when the pH rises above 7.45. Acidosis and alkalosis are categorized according to the cause of the condition. **Respiratory acidosis** and **alkalosis** result from abnormalities in the respiratory system. **Metabolic acidosis** and **alkalosis** result from abnormal metabolism.

Acidosis

Metabolism produces acidic products that lower the pH of the body fluids. For example, CO_2 is a by-product of metabolism that combines with water to form H_2CO_3. Likewise, anaerobic respiration produces lactate, protein metabolism produces phosphoric and sulfuric acids, and lipid metabolism produces fatty acids. These acidic substances must continuously be eliminated from the body to maintain homeostatic pH. Failure to eliminate the acidic products of metabolism results in acidosis.

The major effect of acidosis is depression of the central nervous system. When blood pH falls below 7.35, the central nervous system malfunctions. The individual becomes disoriented, and possibly comatose as the condition worsens.

Inadequate ventilation causes respiratory acidosis because CO_2 is retained in the body rather than being eliminated (table 27.10). This increases the concentration of CO_2 in the body fluids. As CO_2 levels increase, there is an increase in H^+ concentration, which lowers the pH of the body fluids. A pH below 7.35, results in respiratory acidosis.

During respiratory acidosis, buffers help resist the decrease in pH. In addition, the kidneys increase the rate of H^+ secretion into the filtrate and also reabsorb HCO_3^-. However, the capacity of buffers to resist changes in pH can be exceeded, and a period of 1–2 days is required for the kidneys to become maximally functional. Thus, the kidneys are not effective if respiratory acidosis develops quickly. On the other hand, the kidneys are very effective if respiratory acidosis develops slowly, or if it lasts long enough for the kidneys to respond. For example, the kidneys cannot compensate for respiratory acidosis occurring in response to a severe asthma attack that begins quickly and subsides within hours. If, however, respiratory acidosis results from emphysema, which develops over a long time, the kidneys play a significant role in helping compensate.

Metabolic acidosis results from all conditions that decrease the pH of the body fluids below 7.35, except for certain respiratory system conditions (table 27.10). For example, if diabetes mellitus goes untreated, the body begins to metabolize lipid stores for energy. This tends to produce acidic metabolites, which cause the pH of body fluids to drop. As H^+ accumulates in the body fluids, buffers first resist a decline in pH. If the buffers cannot compensate for the increase in H^+, the respiratory center helps regulate body fluid pH. The reduced pH stimulates the respiratory center, which causes hyperventilation. During hyperventilation, CO_2 is eliminated at a greater rate. The elimination of CO_2 also eliminates excess H^+ and helps maintain the pH of the body fluids within a normal range.

If metabolic acidosis persists for many hours and if the kidneys are functional, the kidneys can also help compensate for metabolic acidosis by secreting H^+ at a greater rate and increasing the rate of HCO_3^- reabsorption. The symptoms of metabolic acidosis appear if the respiratory and renal systems are not able to maintain the pH of the body fluids within its normal range.

TABLE 27.10 Acidosis and Alkalosis

Acidosis	Alkalosis
Respiratory Acidosis	*Respiratory Alkalosis*
Reduced elimination of CO_2 from the body fluids	Reduced CO_2 levels in the extracellular fluid (e.g., hyperventilation due to emotions)
Asphyxia	Decreased atmospheric pressure, causing reduced O_2 levels, which stimulate the chemoreceptor reflex (e.g., cause hyperventilation at high altitudes)
Hypoventilation (e.g., impaired respiratory center function due to trauma, tumor, shock, or renal failure)	*Metabolic Alkalosis*
Advanced asthma	Elimination of H^+ and reabsorption of HCO_3^- in the stomach or kidneys (e.g., severe vomiting or formation of acidic urine in response to excess aldosterone)
Severe emphysema	Ingestion of alkaline substances (e.g., large amounts of sodium bicarbonate)
Metabolic Acidosis	
Elimination of large amounts of HCO_3^- resulting from mucous secretion (e.g., severe diarrhea and vomiting of lower intestinal contents)	
Direct reduction of body fluid pH as acid is absorbed (e.g., ingestion of acidic drugs, such as aspirin)	
Production of large amounts of fatty acids and other acidic metabolites, such as ketone bodies (e.g., untreated diabetes mellitus)	
Inadequate O_2 delivery to tissue, resulting in anaerobic respiration (e.g., exercise, heart failure, or shock)	

Case STUDY 27.1 Gastroenteritis

After work on a Friday night, Dan and some friends had a late dinner at a fast-food restaurant. Shortly afterward, Dan began feeling ill, so he went to his dorm room. By midnight, he was very nauseated and vomited repeatedly over the next several hours. The next morning, he was still vomiting at least once each hour, so he went to the student health center. At that point, it was about 12 hours since he had begun feeling nauseated. Each time he vomited, a significant volume of acidic gastric fluid was expelled. A physician examined him and ordered blood tests. The physician then diagnosed gastroenteritis caused by an unknown microorganism and prescribed medication for the infection. The next day, about 36 hours after Dan had begun to feel nauseated, he was reexamined.

Dan began to feel better by the end of the second day (about 48 hours after the nausea had begun). By 72 hours, he felt fairly normal again. After the nauseous feeling disappeared, Dan was very thirsty, and he drank a substantial amount of water and juice over several hours. Table 27.11 shows the results of Dan's physical examinations and blood analyses 12 hours and 36 hours after his illness began and compares them with normal values. After studying this table, explain the meaning of the various changes, as suggested in Predict 4.

TABLE 27.11

	12 Hours	36 Hours	Normal
Body Weight	71 kg	68 kg	Not known
Blood Pressure	115/75 mm Hg	90/60 mm Hg	120/80 mm Hg
Heart Rate	77 beats/min	105 beats/min	72 beats/min
Plasma pH	7.48	7.5	7.35 to 7.45
Plasma HCO_3^-	32 mEq/L	36 mEq/L	22 to 28 mEq/L
Plasma P_{CO_2}	44 mm Hg	48 mm Hg	35 to 43 mm Hg
Skin Color	Pallor	Pallor	

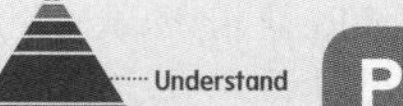

Predict 4

a. Explain the changes in weight, blood pressure, heart rate, and skin color that Dan experienced between 12 and 36 hours.

b. Explain the changes in plasma pH and plasma HCO_3^- between 12 and 36 hours.

c. Explain the plasma P_{CO_2} at 12 and 36 hours.

d. Explain why all the parameters had returned to normal by 72 hours.

Alkalosis

Excess elimination of the acidic products of metabolism results in alkalosis. A major effect of alkalosis is hyperexcitability of the nervous system. Peripheral nerves are affected first, resulting in spontaneous nervous stimulation of muscles. Spasms, tetanic contractions, and possibly extreme nervousness or convulsions result. Severe alkalosis can cause death as a result of tetany of the respiratory muscles.

Respiratory alkalosis results from hyperventilation, which eliminates greater-than-normal CO_2 from the body, resulting in a decrease of H^+ levels (table 27.10). A pH above 7.45 results in respiratory alkalosis.

During respiratory alkalosis, the kidneys decrease the rate of H^+ secretion into the filtrate and the rate of HCO_3^- reabsorption. If pH increases, the kidneys need 1–2 days to compensate. For example, the kidneys are not effective in compensating for respiratory alkalosis that occurs in response to hyperventilation triggered by emotions, which usually begins quickly and subsides within minutes or hours. However, if alkalosis results from staying at a high altitude over a 2- or 3-day period, the kidneys play a significant role in helping compensate.

Metabolic alkalosis results from all conditions that increase the pH of the body fluids above 7.45, with the exception of those resulting from altered function of the respiratory system. This occurs, for example, if an excessive amount of an antacid, such as that containing sodium bicarbonate, is consumed. As H^+ decreases in the body fluids, buffers first resist an increase in pH. If the buffers cannot compensate for the decrease in H^+, the respiratory center helps regulate body fluid pH. The increased pH inhibits respiration. Reduced respiration allows CO_2 to accumulate in the body fluids, which will help lower the pH. If metabolic alkalosis persists for several hours and if the kidneys are functional, the kidneys reduce the rate of H^+ secretion to help reverse alkalosis (table 27.10).

ASSESS YOUR PROGRESS

46. *What is acidosis? What are the two types, and what causes each? How does the body compensate for each of the changes?*

47. *What is alkalosis? What are the two types, and what causes each? How does the body compensate for each of the changes?*

Concept Check

27.1 Body Fluid Balance

Fluid Compartments

A. Intracellular fluid is inside cells.

B. Extracellular fluid is outside cells and includes interstitial fluid and plasma.

Exchange Between Compartments

A. Substances used or produced inside the cell and substances exchanged with the extracellular fluid determine the composition of intracellular fluid.

B. Intracellular fluid is different from extracellular fluid because the plasma membrane regulates the movement of materials.

C. The difference between intracellular and extracellular fluid concentrations determines water movement.

Fluid Input

A. Water crosses the wall of the digestive tract through osmosis.

B. An increase in extracellular osmolality or a decrease in blood pressure stimulates the sense of thirst.

C. Wetting of the oral mucosa or stretch of the digestive tract inhibits thirst.

D. Learned behavior plays a role in the amount of fluid ingested.

Fluid Output

Water leaves the body by the following routes:

- Through evaporation from the respiratory system and the skin (insensible perspiration and sweat)
- Through the digestive tract (this amount is normally small, but vomiting or diarrhea can significantly increase it)
- Through the kidneys, the primary regulator of water excretion; urine output can vary from a small amount of concentrated urine to a large amount of dilute urine

1. *The sensation of thirst increases when*

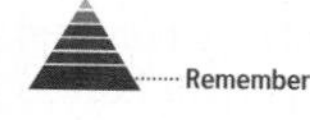

   a. the levels of angiotensin II increase.
   b. the osmolality of the blood decreases.
   c. blood pressure increases.
   d. renin secretion decreases.

2. *Insensible perspiration*

   a. is lost through sweat glands.
   b. results in heat loss from the body.
   c. increases when ADH secretion increases.
   d. results in the loss of solutes, such as Na^+ and Cl^-.

3. *The composition and volume of body fluids are regulated primarily by the*

   a. skin. *b. lungs.* *c. kidneys.* *d. heart.* *e. spleen.*

Regulation of Fluid Balance

Osmoreceptors and baroreceptors play a large role in regulating thirst by detecting changes in blood osmolality and volume.

Fluid Imbalances

A. Dehydration causes water to move out of cells and into the plasma.

B. Hyperhydration causes water to move out of the plasma and into cells.

27.2 Electrolyte Balance

The intake and elimination of substances from the body and the exchange of substances between the extracellular and intracellular fluids determine extracellular fluid composition.

Sodium

A. Sodium is responsible for 90–95% of extracellular osmotic pressure.

B. The amount of Na^+ excreted in the kidneys is the difference between the amount of Na^+ that enters the renal tubule and the amount that is reabsorbed from the renal tubule.
   - The glomerular filtration rate determines the amount of Na^+ entering the renal tubule.
   - Aldosterone determines the amount of Na^+ reabsorbed.

C. Small quantities of Na^+ are excreted in sweat.

D. Increased blood osmolality leads to the production of a small volume of concentrated urine and to thirst. Decreased blood osmolality leads to the production of a large volume of dilute urine and to decreased thirst.

E. Increased blood pressure increases water and salt loss.
   - Elevated extracellular fluid volume reduces ADH secretion.
   - Renin secretion is inhibited, leading to reduced aldosterone production.

4. *Which of these results in an increased blood Na^+ concentration?*

   a. decrease in ADH secretion
   b. decrease in aldosterone secretion
   c. increase in ANH
   d. decrease in renin secretion

5. *Which of these mechanisms is the most important for regulating blood osmolality?*

   Remember

   a. ADH
   b. renin-angiotensin-aldosterone
   c. ANH
   d. PTH

Chloride

Chloride ions are the dominant negatively charged ions in extracellular fluid.

Potassium

A. The extracellular concentration of K^+ affects resting membrane potentials.

B. The amount of K^+ excreted depends on the amount that enters with the glomerular filtrate, the amount actively reabsorbed by the renal tubule, and the amount secreted into the distal convoluted tubule.

C. Aldosterone increases the amount of K^+ secreted.

6. *A decrease in extracellular K^+*
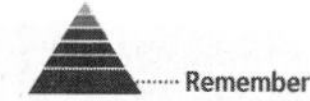

   a. *produces depolarization of the plasma membrane.*
   b. *results when aldosterone levels increase.*
   c. *occurs when tissues are damaged (e.g., in burn patients).*
   d. *increases ANH secretion.*
   e. *increases PTH secretion.*

Calcium

A. Elevated extracellular Ca^{2+} levels prevent membrane depolarization. Decreased levels lead to spontaneous action potential generation.
B. PTH increases extracellular Ca^{2+} levels and decreases extracellular phosphate levels. It stimulates osteoclast activity, increases Ca^{2+} reabsorption from the kidneys, and stimulates active vitamin D production.
C. Vitamin D stimulates Ca^{2+} uptake in the intestines.
D. Calcitonin decreases extracellular Ca^{2+} levels.

7. *Calcium ion concentration in the blood decreases when*

   a. *vitamin D levels are lower than normal.*
   b. *calcitonin secretion decreases.*
   c. *PTH secretion increases.*
   d. *All of these are correct.*

Phosphate

A. Under normal conditions, reabsorption of phosphate occurs at a maximum rate in the renal tubule.
B. An increase in plasma phosphate increases the amount of phosphate in the renal tubule beyond that which can be reabsorbed, and the excess is excreted in the urine.

Magnesium

The kidneys' capacity to reabsorb Mg^{2+} is limited, so excess Mg^{2+} is excreted in the urine, and decreased extracellular Mg^{2+} leads to increased Mg^{2+} reabsorption.

27.3 Hormonal Mechanisms Regulating Body Fluid Composition

A. Increased extracellular fluid volume results in decreased aldosterone secretion, increased ANH secretion, decreased ADH secretion, and decreased sympathetic stimulation of afferent arterioles. These changes decrease Na^+ reabsorption and increase urine volume so as to decrease extracellular fluid volume.
B. Decreased extracellular fluid volume results in increased aldosterone secretion, decreased ANH secretion, increased ADH secretion, and increased sympathetic stimulation of the afferent arterioles. These changes increase Na^+ reabsorption and decrease urine volume so as to increase extracellular fluid volume

8. *Which of these conditions* decreases *extracellular fluid volume?* Remember
   a. *constriction of afferent arterioles*
   b. *increased ADH secretion*
   c. *decreased ANH secretion*
   d. *decreased aldosterone secretion*
   e. *stimulation of sympathetic nerves to the kidneys*

9. *In patients with diabetes mellitus, not enough insulin is produced; as a consequence, blood glucose levels increase. If blood glucose levels rise high enough, the kidneys are unable to absorb the glucose from the glomerular filtrate, and glucose "spills over" into the urine. What effect does this glucose have on urine concentration and volume? How does the body adjust to the excess glucose in the urine?* Understand

10. *A patient suffering from a tumor in the hypothalamus produces excessive amounts of ADH, a condition called syndrome of inappropriate ADH (SIADH) production. For this patient, the excessive ADH production is chronic and has persisted for many months. A student nurse keeps a fluid input-output record on the patient. She is surprised to find that fluid input and urinary output are normal. What effect was she expecting? Can you explain why urinary output is normal?* Apply

27.4 Acid-Base Balance

Acids, Bases, and Buffers

Acids release H^+ into solution, and bases remove it.

11. *An acid* Remember
   a. *is a solution that has a pH greater than 7.*
   b. *is a substance that releases H^+ into a solution.*
   c. *is considered weak if it completely dissociates in water.*
   d. *All of these are correct.*

12. *Buffers* Remember
   a. *release H^+ when pH increases.*
   b. *resist changes in the pH of a solution.*
   c. *include the proteins of the blood.*
   d. *All of these are correct.*

Regulation of Acid-Base Balance

Buffers, the respiratory system, and the kidneys regulate acid-base balance.

Chemical Buffer Systems

A. A buffer resists changes in pH.
   - When H^+ is added to a solution, the buffer removes it.
   - When H^+ is removed from a solution, the buffer replaces it.
B. Three important buffers are carbonic acid/bicarbonate, proteins, and phosphate compounds.

Physiological Buffer Systems

Regulation of Acid-Base Balance by the Respiratory System

Respiratory regulation of pH is achieved through the carbonic acid/bicarbonate buffer system.

A. As CO_2 levels increase, pH decreases.
B. As CO_2 levels decrease, pH increases.
C. Carbon dioxide levels and pH affect the respiratory centers. Hypoventilation increases blood CO_2 levels, and hyperventilation decreases blood CO_2 levels.

Regulation of Acid-Base Balance by the Renal System

A. The secretion of H^+ into the filtrate and the reabsorption of HCO_3^- into extracellular fluid cause extracellular pH to increase.
   - Carbonic acid dissociates to form H^+ and HCO_3^- in tubule cells.
   - An antiport mechanism moves H^+ into the tubule lumen and Na^+ into the tubule cell.
   - Sodium ions and HCO_3^- diffuse into the extracellular fluid.

B. Bicarbonate ions in the filtrate are reabsorbed.
   - Bicarbonate ions combine with H^+ to form carbonic acid, which dissociates to form CO_2 and water.
   - Carbon dioxide diffuses into tubule cells and forms carbonic acid, which dissociates to form HCO_3^- and H^+.
   - Bicarbonate ions diffuse into the extracellular fluid, and H^+ is secreted into the filtrate.

C. The rate of H^+ secretion increases as body fluid pH decreases or as aldosterone levels increase.

D. Secretion of H^+ is inhibited when urine pH falls below 4.5.
   - Ammonia and phosphate buffers in the urine resist a drop in pH.
   - As the buffers absorb H^+, more H^+ is pumped into the urine.

13. *An increase in blood CO_2 levels is followed by a(n) ________ in H^+ and a(n) ________ in blood pH.* Remember
    a. *increase, increase*
    b. *increase, decrease*
    c. *decrease, increase*
    d. *decrease, decrease*

14. *High levels of bicarbonate ions in the urine indicate* 

    a. *a low level of H^+ secretion into the urine.*
    b. *that the kidneys are causing blood pH to increase.*
    c. *that urine pH is decreasing.*
    d. *All of these are correct.*

15. *High levels of ammonium ions in the urine indicate* 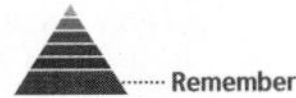

    a. *a high level of H^+ secretion into the urine.*
    b. *that the kidneys are causing blood pH to decrease.*
    c. *that urine pH is too basic.*
    d. *All of these are correct.*

16. *Blood plasma pH is normally* 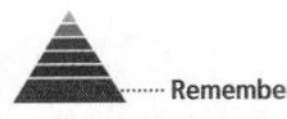

    a. *slightly acidic.*
    b. *strongly acidic.*
    c. *slightly basic.*
    d. *strongly basic.*
    e. *neutral.*

17. *Acetazolamide is a diuretic that blocks the activity of the enzyme carbonic anhydrase inside kidney tubule cells. This blockage prevents the formation of carbonic acid from CO_2 and water. Normally, carbonic acid dissociates to form H^+ and HCO_3^-, and the H^+ is exchanged for Na^+ from the urine. Blocking the formation of H^+ in the tubule cells blocks Na^+ reabsorption, thus inhibiting water reabsorption and producing the diuretic effect. With this information in mind, what effect does acetazolamide have on blood pH, urine pH, and respiratory rate?* Apply

18. *As part of a physiology experiment, an anatomy and physiology student is asked to breathe through a 3-foot-long glass tube. What effect does this action have on his blood pH, urine pH, and respiratory rate?* Apply

Acid-Base Imbalance

Acidosis occurs if pH falls below 7.35, and alkalosis occurs if pH rises above 7.45.

A. Acidosis results in insensitivity of the CNS.

B. Alkalosis results in overexcitability of the CNS.

19. *Acidosis* Remember
    a. *increases neuron excitability.*
    b. *can produce tetany by affecting the peripheral nervous system.*
    c. *may lead to coma.*
    d. *may produce convulsions through the central nervous system.*

20. *Respiratory alkalosis is caused by ________ and can be compensated for by the production of a more ________ urine.* Remember
    a. *hypoventilation, basic*
    b. *hypoventilation, acidic*
    c. *hyperventilation, acidic*
    d. *hyperventilation, basic*

21. *Harry ate a late meal at a cheap diner on the way home from work. A couple of hours later, he vomited three times, and then he consumed several packages of an antacid (mostly $NaHCO_3$) over the next several hours. By the evening of the next day, he was feeling better. During this ordeal, his blood pH did not deviate significantly. Select the mechanism(s) that helped maintain Harry's pH within a normal range.* Understand
    (1) *increased respiratory rate*
    (2) *increased H^+ secretion by the renal tubule*
    (3) *decreased respiratory rate*
    (4) *decreased H^+ secretion by the renal tubule*

    a. *1*
    b. *2*
    c. *1,2*
    d. *3*
    e. *3,4*

Answers to this chapter's odd-numbered Concept Check questions appear in Appendix F.

28 CHAPTER

Reproductive System

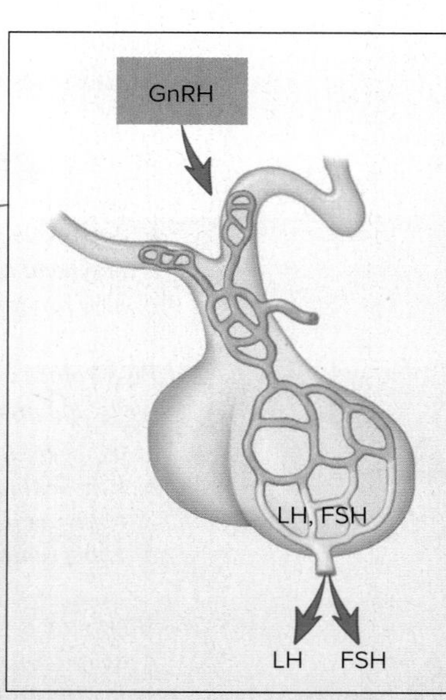

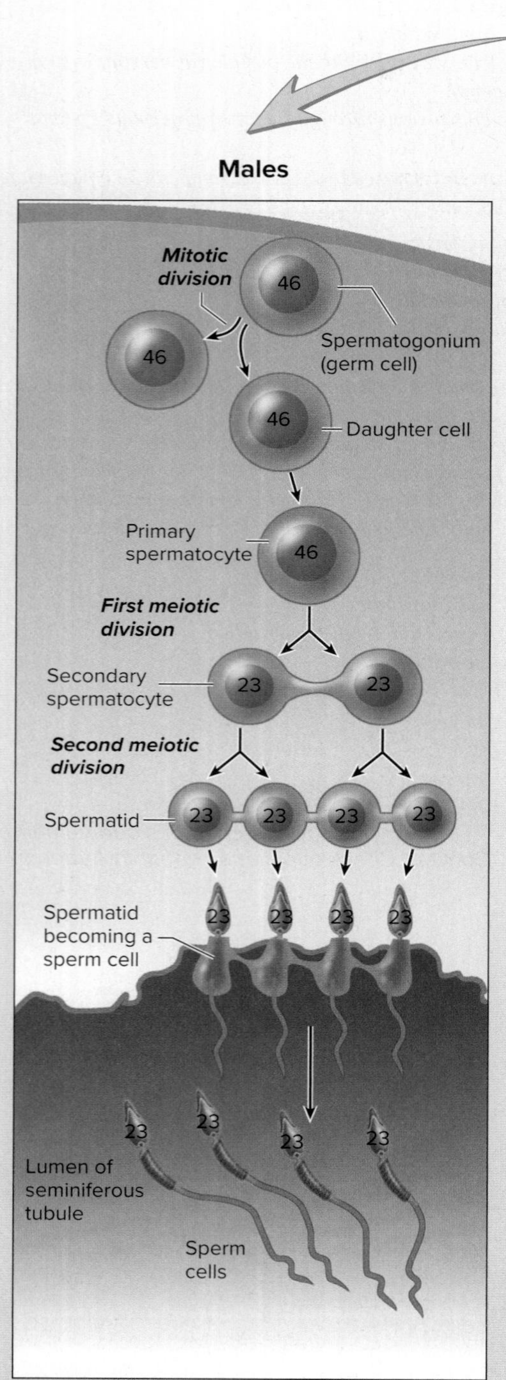

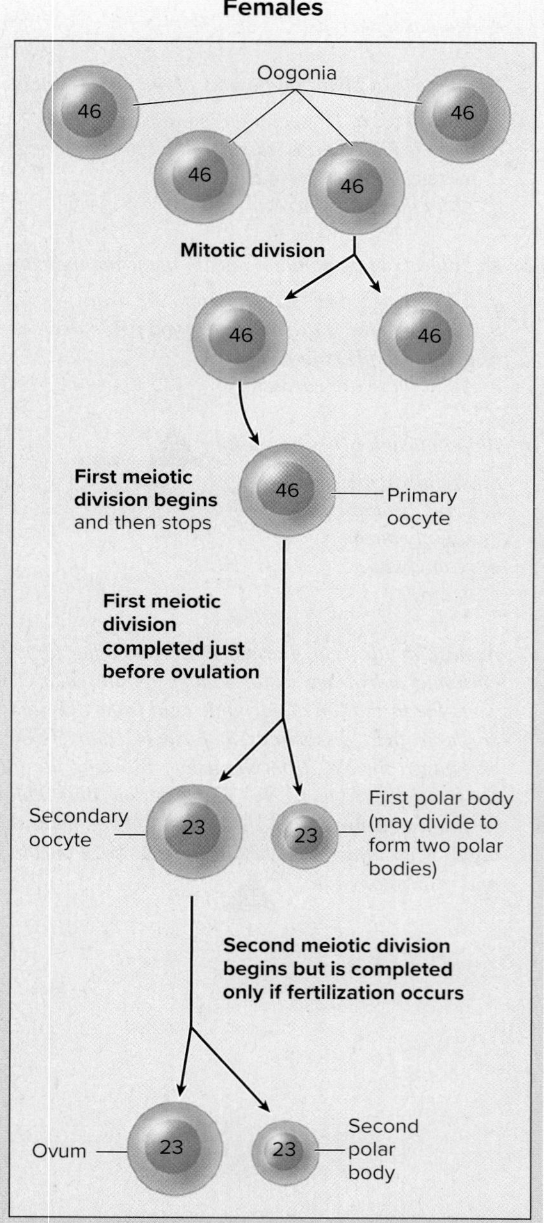

Both male and female reproduction involve production of specialized cells that merge to form offspring.

The reproductive system functions in **gametogenesis,** the process of gamete production, as well as the events involved in fertilization of these gametes. In addition, the female reproductive system ensures the product of fertilization, a new human, is protected and nourished. However, the reproductive systems also influence many other aspects of a person's life, anatomically, physiologically, as well as psychologically. In this chapter, the basic anatomical and physiological characteristics of the male and female reproductive systems will be discussed.

The male and female reproductive systems are obviously different, but these two systems also have numerous similarities. Many reproductive organs of males and females are derived from the same embryological structures (see chapter 29), and some of the same hormones function in both males and females, even though these hormones influence traits differently in males and females.

Learn to Predict

Chase and Christina were studying for their last anatomy and physiology exam of the semester. After reviewing his notes on meiosis, Chase said, "Well, since gametogenesis is exactly the same in males and females, I don't need to study the notes from the female reproductive system lecture." Christina quickly pointed out that he was wrong and that if he reviewed his notes he would see that gametogenesis is very different in males and females.

After reading chapter 28, explain the major differences between gametogenesis in males and females.

Answers to this question and the chapter's odd-numbered Predict questions can be found in Appendix E.

28.1 Functions of the Reproductive System

LEARNING OUTCOMES

After reading this section, you should be able to

A. **List the functions of the reproductive system.**
B. **Distinguish among the functions that occur in males, females, and both.**

Reproduction is an essential characteristic of living organisms, and functional male and female reproductive systems are necessary for humans to reproduce. In addition, even in individuals who do not reproduce, the reproductive system plays important roles. The reproductive system performs the following functions:

1. *Gametogenesis.* Gametogenesis is the production of gametes, which are reproductive cells that are produced in the gonads. The male gonads are the testes, which are the site of sperm cell production. The female gonads are the ovaries, which are the site of oocyte (egg) production.
2. *Fertilization.* The reproductive system enables fertilization of the oocyte by the sperm. The duct system in males nourishes sperm cells until they are mature and are deposited in the female reproductive tract by the penis. The female reproductive system receives the sperm cells from the male and provides a passageway for them to the fertilization site.
3. *Development and nourishment of a new individual.* The female reproductive system nurtures the developing fetus in the uterus until birth and provides nourishment (breast milk) after birth.
4. *Production of reproductive hormones.* Hormones produced by the reproductive system control its development and the development of the sex-specific body form (see tables 28.1 and 28.2 later in this chapter). These hormones are also essential for the routine functions of the reproductive system and for reproductive behavior.

ASSESS YOUR PROGRESS

Answers to these questions are found in the section you have just completed. Re-read the section if you need help in answering these questions.

1. *What are the functions of the reproductive system?*
2. *What functions occur in both males and females, and what functions occur only in females?*

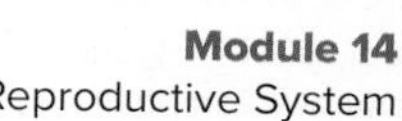

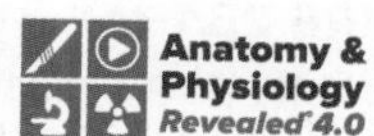

28.2 Meiosis

LEARNING OUTCOMES

After reading this section, you should be able to

A. **Describe the process of meiosis, highlighting the change in chromosome number and structure after each division.**

B. **Explain why meiosis is necessary in sexually reproducing organisms.**

C. **Describe the different events in meiosis that result in genetic variation among gametes.**

The testes in males and the ovaries in females (figure 28.1) produce **gametes** (GAM-eets), or reproductive cells. **Meiosis** (my-OH-sis) is a type of cell division specialized for producing gametes. In humans, meiosis occurs only in the testes and ovaries and produces sperm cells in males and oocytes in females.

In humans, the somatic cells normally have 46 chromosomes, called the **diploid** (DIP-loyd) number (2*n*). Chromosomes exist in 23 **homologous** (ho-MOL-oh-gus) **pairs**—22 autosomal pairs and 1 pair of sex chromosomes. One chromosome of each homologous pair is inherited from the male parent, and the other chromosome of each pair is inherited from the female parent. The chromosomes of each homologous pair are alike in size and shape and contain genes for the same traits, with the exception of the X chromosome and Y chromosome. The combination of sex chromosomes is known as the sexual karyotype. The female sexual karyotype is two X chromosomes; the male sexual karyotype includes one X chromosome and one Y chromosome. Though the X and Y chromosomes pair during meiosis, they are not the same size, nor do they carry the same genetic information (see figure 29.27).

Sperm cells and oocytes contain the **haploid** (HAP-loyd) number (*n*) of chromosomes, or 23. Each gamete contains one chromosome from each of the homologous pairs. Reduction in the number of chromosomes in sperm cells or oocytes to a haploid number is important. When a sperm cell and an oocyte fuse to form a fertilized egg, each provides a haploid number of chromosomes, which reestablishes a diploid number. If meiosis did not take place, the number of chromosomes in the fertilized oocyte would double each time fertilization occurred, and the extra chromosomal material would be lethal to the developing offspring.

Upon fertilization, the sex of the baby is determined by the sperm cell. The baby is male if the oocyte is fertilized by a Y-carrying sperm cell or female if it is fertilized by an X-carrying sperm cell. Though the sexual karyotype determines the development of the reproductive system (see section 29.1), other factors also influence the psychological development of an individual (see Clinical Impact 28.1).

The two divisions of meiosis are called **meiosis I** and **meiosis II.** The stages of meiosis have the same names as the stages of mitosis—that is, prophase, metaphase, anaphase, and

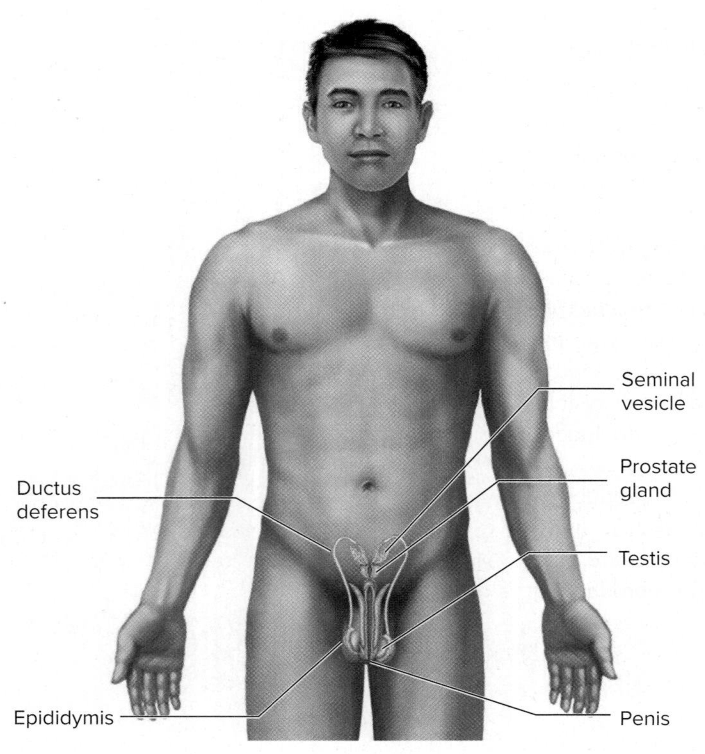

(a) Male reproductive system

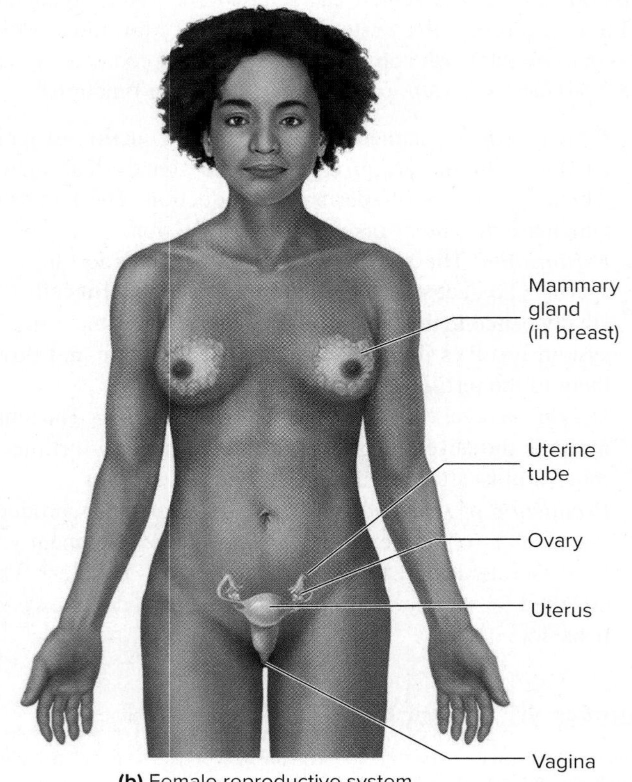

(b) Female reproductive system

FIGURE 28.1 Major Organs of the Reproductive Systems

(*a*) Major organs of the male reproductive system include the testes, epididymides, ducta deferentia, seminal vesicles, prostate gland, and penis. (*b*) Major organs of the female reproductive system include the ovaries, uterine tubes, uterus, vagina, and mammary glands.

Clinical IMPACT 28.1 Gender and Sex

At birth, people are assigned one of three biological sexes based solely on the anatomy of their external genitalia. Males have a penis, females have a vagina, and intersex people can have a wide variation in sexual characteristics. However, anatomy does not always dictate a person's gender identity. Gender identity is how people view and express themselves in the world. Biological sex also does not determine a person's sexual orientation. Sexual orientation is the interpersonal interactions people have with others with regard to physical, emotional, and romantic attraction. Sexual orientation also does not determine sexual preference. Sexual preference refers to the way a person wishes to receive and participate in physically intimate actions.

Until about the 1990s, the societal norm for humans in the United States consisted of a gender binary. The gender binary is the system of viewing gender as consisting of only two identities and two sexes: male and female. However, since the 1990s, it has been recognized that gender exists along a gender spectrum, sometimes referred to as nonbinary. The gender spectrum is a continuum of gender identity that includes male and female, but does not assert male and female as absolutes or as polar opposites. For parents of a gender-expansive child, one who goes against societal norms for gender identity, the first source of information is usually a medical professional. This means that physicians, nurses, and all medical professionals are put into a pivotal role of helping to provide understanding and resources to parents.

An immense set of terms exists to describe gender identity, sexual orientation, and sexual preference. Here, we provide a brief introduction to some of these terms:

1. Gender identity—how individuals view themselves; gender identity can be the same or different than the sex assigned to them at birth
2. Gender expression—how individuals present themselves in terms of appearance, behavior, clothing, haircut, etc.
3. Gender nonconforming—behaving in a way that does not conform to societal expectation of biological sex
4. Queer—a previously derogatory term used for certain sexual orientations, but now is used to express fluid identities and orientations; usually used by people who do not identify as straight (heterosexual)
5. Transgender—individuals whose gender identity and/or gender expression is not the same as societal expectations based on their assigned biological sex. Although this does not imply a particular sexual orientation, it can be described as an FtM (F2M), female to male, transition or an MtF (M2F), male to female, transition when individuals begin to express the knowledge of their internal identity by their outward appearance.
6. Gender dysphoria—the term used to describe the long-term distress individuals experience when their assigned biological sex does not align with their gender identity
7. Gay—the sexual attraction and affectional orientation between members of the same gender (assigned or expressed); refers to males and females
8. Pansexual—not limited in attraction to an individual with regard to biological sex, gender, or gender identity
9. Lesbian—the sexual attraction and affectional orientation between two females (assigned or expressed)
10. Bisexual—being sexually, emotionally, and physically attracted to people of both the same gender and another gender

telophase—but distinct differences exist between mitosis and meiosis. And just like in mitosis, before cell division begins, all the chromosomes are duplicated. See section 3.10 for a review of mitosis.

Figure 28.2 details the steps of meiosis I and meiosis II.

Meiosis I

1. ***Early prophase I:*** At the beginning of meiosis, each of the 46 duplicated chromosomes consists of two sister **chromatids** (KROH-mah-tidz) connected by a **centromere** (SEN-troh-meer).
2. ***Middle prophase I:*** The chromosomes become visible, and the homologous pairs come together in a process called **synapsis** (si-NAP-sis). Because each chromosome consists of two chromatids, the pairing of the homologous chromosomes brings two chromatids of each chromosome close together, an arrangement called a **tetrad.** Occasionally, part of a chromatid of one homologous chromosome breaks off and is exchanged with part of another chromatid from the other homologous chromosome. This exchange of genetic material between maternal and paternal chromosomes is called **crossing over** and may result in new gene combinations on the chromosomes.
3. ***Metaphase I:*** Homologous pairs of chromosomes line up near the center of the cell. For each homologous pair, however, the orientation of the maternal and paternal chromosomes is random. This random alignment and crossing over are responsible for the large degree of diversity in the genetic composition of sperm cells and oocytes produced by each individual.
4. ***Anaphase I:*** The chromosomes of homologous pairs separate and are moved to opposite sides of the cell.
5. ***Telophase I:*** New nuclei form, and the cell completes division of the cytoplasm to form two cells.

When meiosis I is complete, each daughter cell has 1 chromosome from each homologous pair. Because the chromosome number is reduced from a diploid number (46 chromosomes, or 23 pairs) to a haploid number (23 chromosomes, or 1 from each homologous pair) during meiosis I, this division is often called a **reduction division.**

At the end of meiosis I, each of the 23 chromosomes in the daughter cells still consists of two chromatids. The separation of the chromatids of the duplicated chromosomes occurs in meiosis II. The second meiotic division is similar to mitosis (see chapter 3).

Meiosis II

6. ***Prophase II:*** As the chromosomes condense, it is apparent that each is duplicated, consisting of two chromatids.
7. ***Metaphase II:*** The duplicated chromosomes line up near the middle of the cell.
8. ***Anaphase II:*** The chromatids are separated at the centromere and are moved to opposite sides of the cell so that each daughter cell receives one of the chromatids from each chromosome. When the centromere separates, each of the chromatids is called a chromosome.
9. ***Telophase II:*** New nuclei form around the chromosomes and the cells divide to form four daughter cells each containing 23 chromosomes.

PROCESS Figure

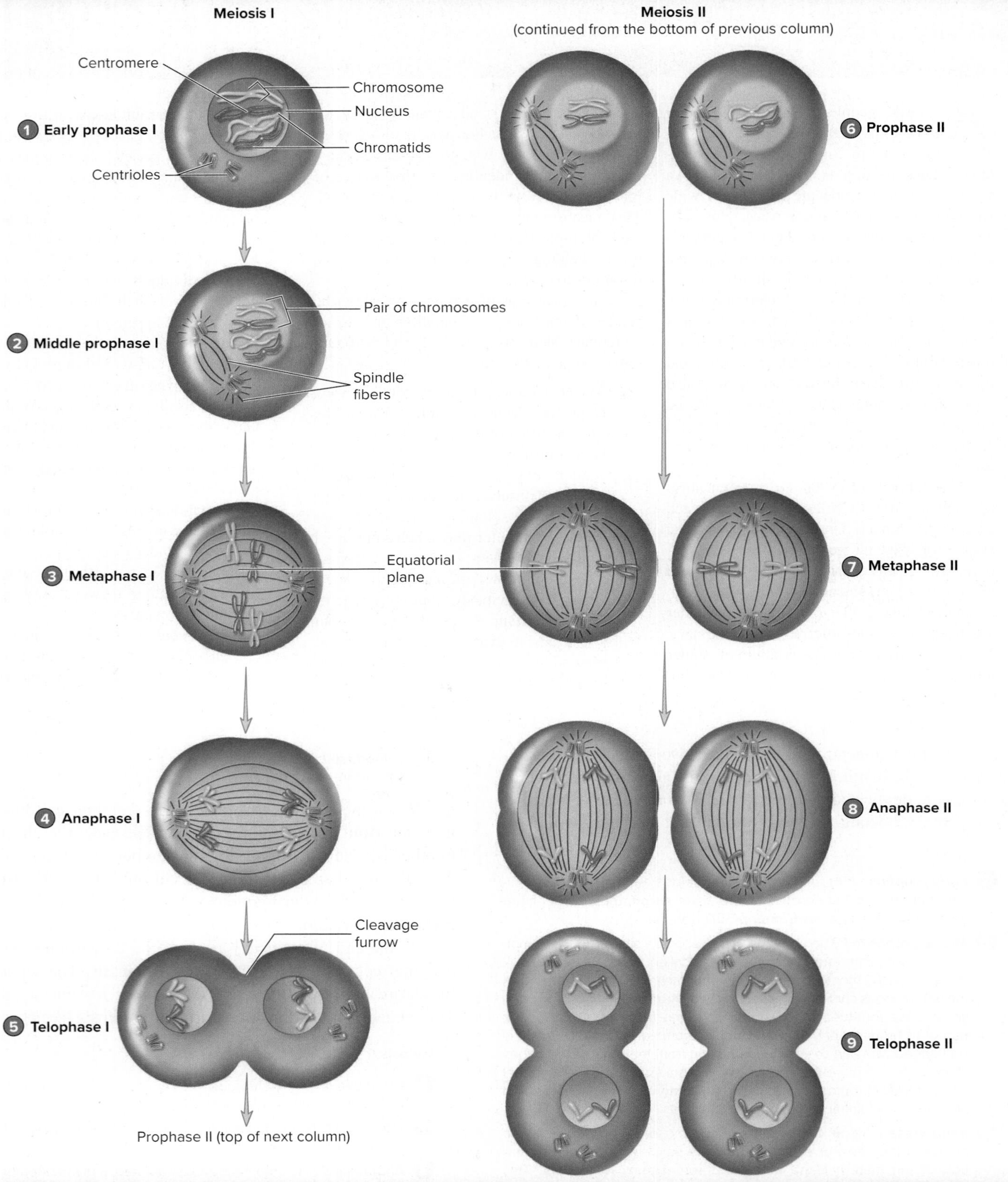

Meiosis I

Centromere
Chromosome
Nucleus
Chromatids
Centrioles

① **Early prophase I**

Pair of chromosomes
Spindle fibers

② **Middle prophase I**

Equatorial plane

③ **Metaphase I**

④ **Anaphase I**

Cleavage furrow

⑤ **Telophase I**

Prophase II (top of next column)

Meiosis II
(continued from the bottom of previous column)

⑥ **Prophase II**

⑦ **Metaphase II**

⑧ **Anaphase II**

⑨ **Telophase II**

PROCESS Figure 28.2

Meiosis

During meiosis, the chromosome number is halved in preparation for sexual reproduction. APR

How many chromosomes would an oocyte contain if, during anaphase II, the chromatids of one chromosome did not separate?

ASSESS YOUR PROGRESS

3. *Describe the events of meiosis I and meiosis II. How are the cells produced by meiosis I different from the cells produced by meiosis II?*
4. *Why is meiosis important in sexually reproducing organisms?*
5. *Describe two mechanisms that occur during meiosis that produce genetic variation among gametes.*

28.3 Anatomy of the Male Reproductive System

LEARNING OUTCOMES

After reading this section, you should be able to

A. **Describe the scrotum and its role in regulating the temperature of the testes.**
B. **Describe the structure of the testes.**
C. **List and describe the specialized cells of the testes.**
D. **Describe the process of spermatogenesis.**
E. **List the ducts of the male reproductive system and explain their functions.**
F. **Describe the structure and function of the penis.**
G. **Describe the structure and function of the three major glands of the male reproductive system: seminal vesicles, prostate gland, and bulbourethral glands.**

The male reproductive system consists of (1) the testes (sing. testis); (2) a series of ducts, which include the epididymides (sing. epididymis), the ducta deferentia (sing. ductus deferens; also vas deferens), and the urethra; (3) accessory glands, which include the seminal vesicles, the prostate gland, and the bulbourethral glands; and (4) supporting structures, which include the scrotum and the penis (figure 28.3). The testes and epididymides, in which the sperm cells develop, are located outside the body cavity in the scrotum. Sperm cells travel from each testis through the ducta deferentia into the pelvis, where they join the ducts of the seminal vesicles to form the ampullae. Extensions of the ampullae, called the ejaculatory ducts, pass into the prostate and empty into the urethra within the prostate. The urethra, in turn, exits the pelvis and passes through the penis to the outside of the body.

Scrotum

The **scrotum** (SKROH-tum) is a saclike structure that contains the testes. It is divided into two internal compartments by an incomplete connective tissue septum. Externally, the compartments of the scrotum are marked by a midline irregular ridge called the **raphe** (RAY-fee; a seam). The raphe extends posteriorly to the anus and anteriorly onto the inferior surface of the penis.

The wall of the scrotum includes the skin, a layer of superficial fascia consisting of loose connective tissue, and a layer of smooth muscle called the **dartos** (DAR-toss) **muscle.** In cold temperatures, the dartos muscle contracts, causing the skin of the scrotum

FUNDAMENTAL **Figure**

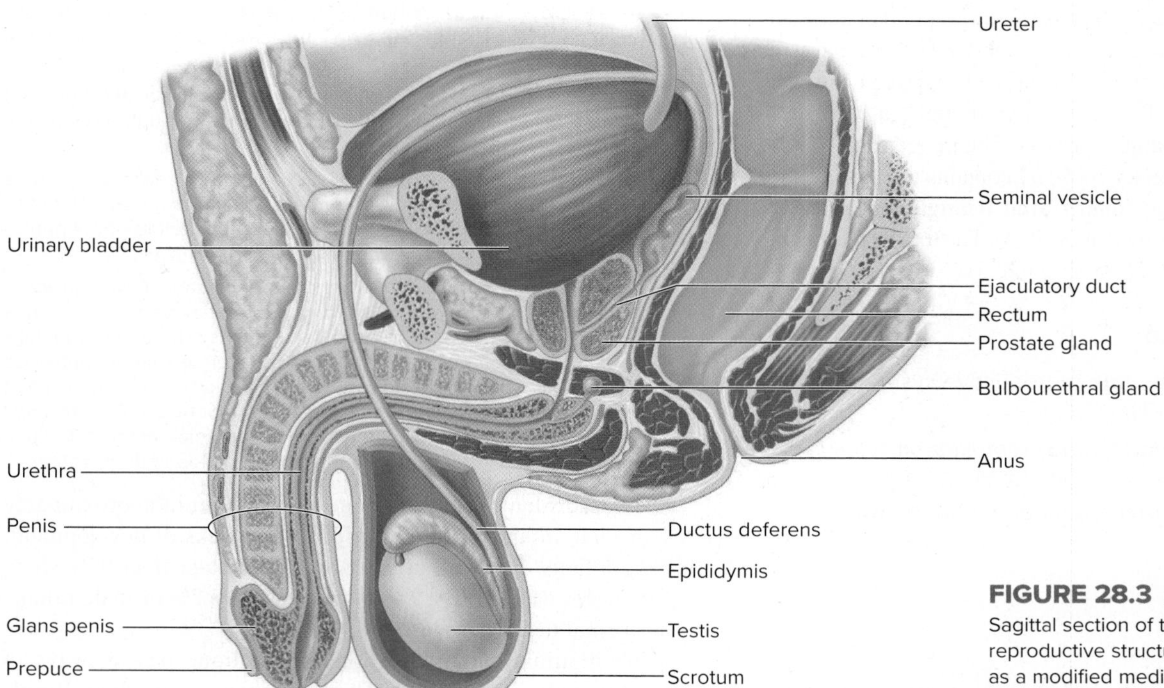

FIGURE 28.3 Male Reproductive System
Sagittal section of the male pelvis, showing the male reproductive structures. Some structures are drawn as a modified medial section to reveal the testis, epididymis, and seminal vesicles and to show the relationship of the ductus deferens to the ureter and urinary bladder. APR

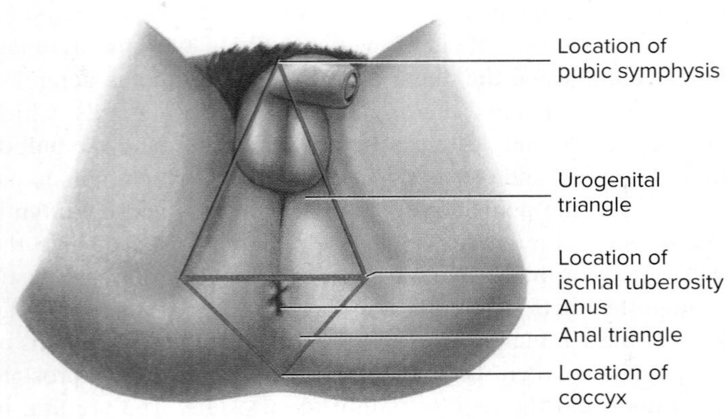

FIGURE 28.4 Male Perineum
Inferior view of the male perineum.

to become firm and wrinkled and reducing its overall size. At the same time, the **cremaster** (krih-MAS-ter) **muscles** (see figure 28.8), which are extensions of abdominal skeletal muscles into the scrotum, contract and help pull the testes nearer the body. These changes in size and position of the scrotum help keep the testes warm. When temperature increases due to a warmer environment or as a result of exercise or fever, the dartos and cremaster muscles relax, and the skin of the scrotum becomes loose and thin, allowing the testes to descend away from the body and keep cool. The response of the dartos and cremaster muscles is important because sperm cells are very temperature-sensitive and do not develop normally if the testes become too warm or too cool.

Perineum

The **perineum** (PER-ih-NEE-um) is the area between the thighs that is bounded by the pubic symphysis anteriorly, the coccyx posteriorly, and the ischial tuberosities laterally. The perineum is divided into two triangles by the superficial transverse muscles and the deep transverse perineal muscles. These muscles run transversely between the two ischial tuberosities (see figure 10.19). The two triangles are the urogenital triangle and the anal triangle. In males, the **urogenital** (YOO-roh-JEN-i-tal) **triangle,** or *anterior triangle,* contains the base of the penis and the scrotum, and the smaller **anal triangle,** or *posterior triangle,* contains the anal opening (figure 28.4). The female perineum is described later in the chapter (see section 28.5).

ASSESS YOUR PROGRESS

6. *List the structures of the male reproductive system.*
7. *Describe the structure of the scrotum.*
8. *Explain the role of the dartos and cremaster muscles in regulating the temperature of the testes.*
9. *Locate the boundaries of the perineum and the two triangles within it.*

Testes

Testicular Histology

The **testes** (TES-teez) are small, oval-shaped organs, each about 4–5 cm long, within the scrotum (see figure 28.3). The testes function as both exocrine and endocrine glands. Their major exocrine secretion is sperm cells, and their major endocrine secretion is the hormone testosterone.

The outer part of each testis is a thick, white capsule consisting mostly of fibrous connective tissue called the **tunica albuginea** (al-byoo-JIN-ee-ah). Extensions of the tunica albuginea extend into the testis and form incomplete **septa** (SEP-tah; figure 28.5*a*). The septa divide each testis into about 300–400 cone-shaped **lobules.** The lobules contain **seminiferous** (sem-ih-NIF-er-us; seed carriers) **tubules,** in which sperm cells develop. Loose connective tissue surrounding the seminiferous tubules contains clusters of endocrine cells called **interstitial cells,** or *Leydig cells* (figure 28.5*b*). The interstitial cells secrete testosterone.

The combined length of the seminiferous tubules in both testes is nearly half a mile. Considering that sperm cells are produced in the seminiferous tubules, it is not surprising that adult males are capable of producing more than 100 million mature sperm each day. The seminiferous tubules empty into a set of short, straight tubules called the **tubuli recti.** These in turn empty into a tubular network called the **rete** (REE-teh; net) **testis.** The rete testis empties into 15–20 tubules called **efferent ductules** (DUK-tools) that pass through the tunica albuginea to exit the testis. The efferent ductules have a ciliated pseudostratified columnar epithelium, which helps move sperm cells out of the testis.

Descent of the Testes

The testes first develop in the abdominal cavity, but eventually descend into the scrotum. Figure 28.6 illustrates the descent of the testes.

1. By approximately 8 weeks following fertilization, the testes have developed as nonmesenteric, or retroperitoneal, organs. Initially, the testes are located high in the abdominopelvic cavity near the developing kidneys. Each testis is connected to a labioscrotal swelling by a **gubernaculum** (GOO-ber-NAK-yoo-lum), a fibromuscular cord (see chapter 29). The labioscrotal swelling becomes the scrotum.
2. The testes descend toward the area where the **inguinal** (IN-gwin-al) **canals** will form. The gubernaculum extends through the inguinal canal, enlarging the canal.
3. Between 7 and 9 months of development, the testes move through the inguinal canals into the scrotum. As it moves into the scrotum, each testis is preceded by an outpocketing of the peritoneum called the **process vaginalis** (vaj-ih-NAH-lis).
4. Between birth and adulthood, the superior part of each process vaginalis usually degenerates, and the inferior part remains as a small, closed sac called the **tunica vaginalis.** The tunica vaginalis is a serous membrane consisting of a layer of simple squamous epithelium resting on a basement membrane that surrounds most of the testis in much the same way that the pericardium surrounds the heart. The tunica vaginalis secretes a small amount of fluid, which allows the testes to move without friction in the scrotum.

The testes have descended into the scrotum in approximately 79% of male infants delivered prior to 28 weeks of development. In male infants delivered after 28 weeks, greater than 97% show normal testes descent. By 9 months of age, 98.2% of male infants show normal testes descent.

The inguinal canals are bilateral, oblique passageways in the anterior abdominal wall. They originate at the **deep inguinal rings,** which open through the aponeuroses of the

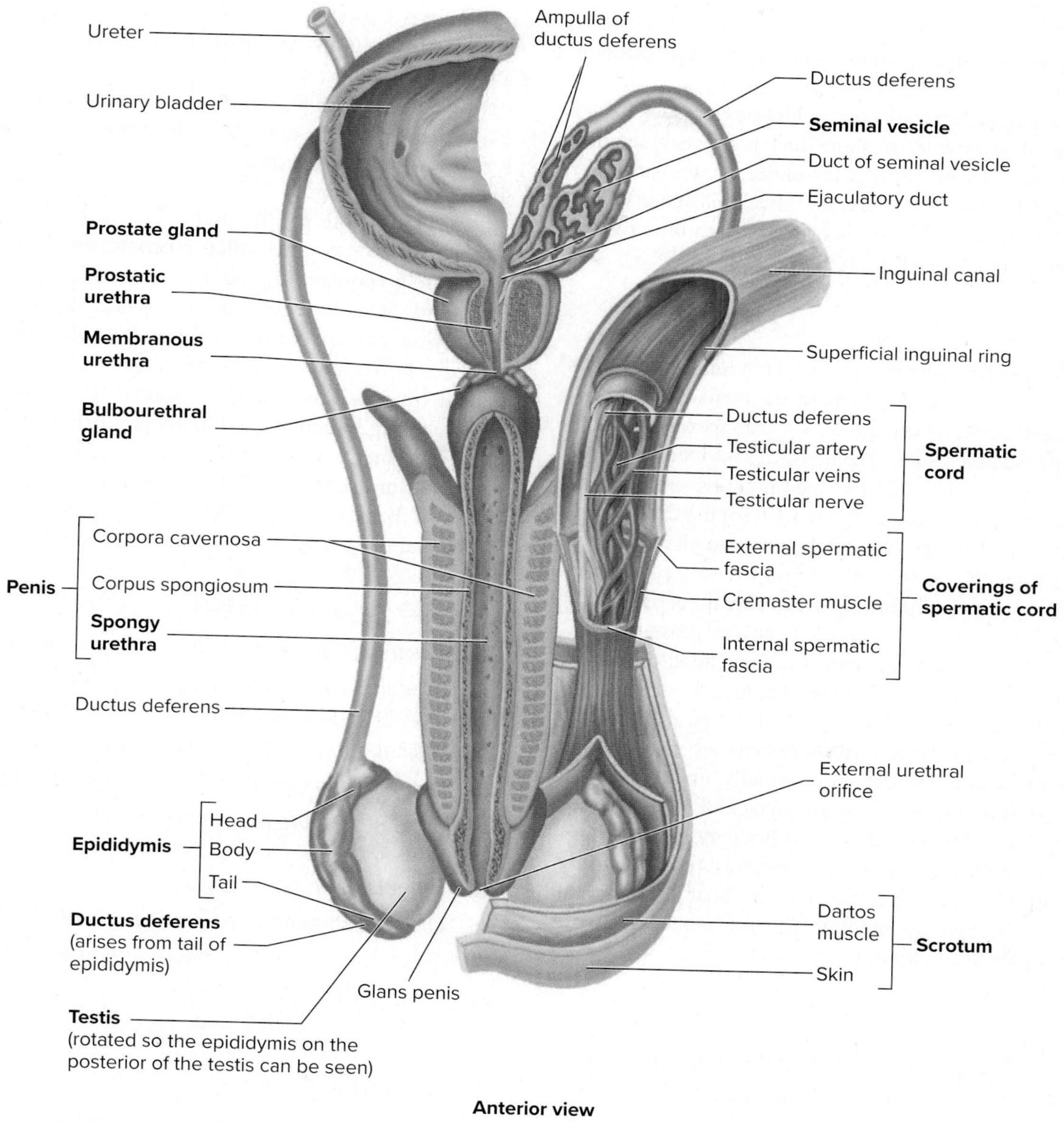

FIGURE 28.8 Male Reproductive Structures

Testis, epididymis, ductus deferens, and glands of the male reproductive system. The urethra is cut open along its dorsal side. 

secondary oocyte during fertilization (see section 28.5). Sperm cells taken from the head of the epididymis are unable to fertilize secondary oocytes, and they are not yet able to become motile; however, sperm cells taken from the tail of the epididymis are able to perform both functions.

Ductus Deferens and Ejaculatory Duct

The **ductus deferens** (pl. ducta deferentia), or *vas deferens,* emerges from the tail of the epididymis and ascends along the posterior side of the testis medial to the epididymis, where it associates with the blood vessels and nerves that supply the testis to form the **spermatic cord** (figure 28.8; see figures 28.3 and 28.5*a*). The spermatic cord consists of (1) the ductus deferens, (2) the testicular artery and venous plexus, (3) lymphatic vessels, (4) nerves, and (5) fibrous remnants of the process vaginalis. The coverings of the spermatic cord include (1) the **external spermatic fascia** (FASH-ee-ah); (2) the cremaster muscle, an extension of the muscle fibers of the internal abdominal oblique muscle of the abdomen; and (3) the **internal spermatic fascia** (figure 28.8).

The ductus deferens and the rest of the spermatic cord structures ascend and pass through the inguinal canal to enter the pelvic cavity (figure 28.8; see figure 28.3). The ductus deferens crosses the lateral and posterior walls of the pelvic cavity, travels over the ureter, and loops over the posterior surface of the urinary bladder to approach the prostate gland. Near the prostate gland, the end of the ductus deferens enlarges to form an **ampulla** (am-PUL-ah). The lumen of the ductus deferens is lined with pseudostratified columnar epithelium, which is surrounded by smooth muscle. Peristaltic contractions of the smooth muscle help propel sperm cells through the ductus deferens.

Adjacent to the ampulla of each ductus deferens is a sac-shaped gland called the seminal vesicle. A short duct from each seminal vesicle joins the ampulla of the ductus deferens to form the **ejaculatory** (ih-JACK-you-leh-toh-ree) **duct.** Each ejaculatory duct is approximately 2.5 cm long. These ducts extend into the prostate gland and open into the urethra (figure 28.8; see figure 28.3).

Urethra

The male **urethra** (you-REE-thra) is about 20 cm long and extends from the urinary bladder to the distal end of the penis (figure 28.9; see figures 28.3 and 28.8). The urethra is a passageway for both urine and male reproductive fluids. The urethra is divided into three parts: (1) the prostatic urethra, (2) the membranous urethra, and (3) the spongy urethra. The **prostatic** (pros-TAT-ik) **urethra** is connected to the bladder and passes through the prostate gland. Fifteen to 30 small ducts from the prostate gland and the two ejaculatory ducts empty into the prostatic urethra. The **membranous urethra** is the shortest part of the urethra, extending from the prostate gland through the perineum. The **spongy urethra,** also called the *penile* (PEE-nile) *urethra,* is the longest part of the urethra; it extends from the membranous urethra through the length of the penis, where it opens to the exterior at the **external urethral orifice** (figure 28.9*a*). In rare cases, the penis does not develop normally, and the urethra may open to the exterior along the inferior surface of the penis (see chapter 29). Stratified columnar epithelium lines most of the urethra, but transitional epithelium is in the prostatic urethra near the bladder, and stratified squamous epithelium is near the external urethral orifice of the spongy urethra. Several minute, mucus-secreting **urethral glands** empty into the urethra.

Penis

The **penis** is the male organ of copulation, through which sperm cells are transferred from the male to the female. The penis contains three columns of erectile tissue. Erectile tissue is composed of a network of connective tissue and smooth muscle tissue with many sinusoids, or spaces, that can fill with blood (figure 28.9*a,b*). This condition is referred to as engorgement. Engorgement of this erectile tissue causes the penis to enlarge and become firm, a process called **erection** (ee-REK-shun). The **corpora cavernosa** (KOHR-pohr-ah kav-er-NOHS-ah) are the erectile columns that form the dorsum and sides of the penis. The third column, the **corpus spongiosum** (KOHR-pus spun-gee-OH-sum), forms the ventral portion of the penis. The corpus spongiosum expands to form a cap, the **glans penis,** over the distal end of the penis. The spongy urethra passes through the corpus spongiosum, penetrates the glans penis, and opens as the external urethral orifice.

At the base of the penis, the corpus spongiosum expands to form the **bulb of the penis.** Each corpus cavernosum expands to form the **crus** (kroos; pl. crura, KROO-rah) **of the penis,** which attaches the penis to the pelvic bones (see figure 28.9*a*). Together, the bulb of the penis and the crura of the penis constitute the **root of the penis.**

Skin is loosely attached to the connective tissue that surrounds the erectile columns in the shaft of the penis. The skin is firmly attached at the base of the glans penis, and a thinner layer of skin tightly covers the glans penis. The skin of the penis, especially the glans penis, is well supplied with sensory receptors. A loose fold of skin called the **prepuce** (PREE-poos), or *foreskin,* covers the glans penis (see figure 28.3).

In many cultures, the prepuce is surgically removed shortly after birth, a procedure called **circumcision** (ser-kum-SIZH-un). There are no compelling medical reasons for circumcision. Uncircumcised males have a higher incidence of penile cancer, but the underlying causes seem related to chronic infections and poor hygiene. In the few cases in which the prepuce is "too tight" to be moved over the glans penis, circumcision may be necessary to avoid chronic infections and maintain normal circulation.

The primary nerves, arteries, and veins of the penis pass along its dorsal surface (figure 28.9*b*). Dorsal arteries, with dorsal nerves lateral to them, exist on each side of a single, midline dorsal vein. Additional deep arteries lie within the corpora cavernosa.

ASSESS YOUR PROGRESS

20. *Describe the structure and functions of the epididymis.*
21. *How do sperm move from the epididymis, and what changes occur in sperm cells while in the epididymis?*
22. *Describe the structure and functions of the ductus deferens.*
23. *List the components and coverings of the spermatic cord.*
24. *Relate the route by which the ductus deferens extends from the testis to the prostate gland.*
25. *What is the ejaculatory duct?*
26. *Distinguish among the three parts of the male urethra.*
27. *Describe the erectile tissue of the penis.*
28. *Describe the structures and locations of the glans penis, crus, bulb, and prepuce.*

Accessory Glands

The male reproductive system also includes three accessory glands that are important for normal reproductive function. The accessory glands are exocrine glands that secrete material into the ducts of the male reproductive tract. These glands are (1) the seminal vesicles, (2) the prostate gland, and (3) the bulbourethral glands.

Seminal Vesicles

The **seminal vesicles** (SEM-ih-nal VES-ih-kulz) are sac-shaped glands located next to the ampullae of the ducta deferentia (see figure 28.8). Each gland is about 5 cm long and tapers into a short excretory duct that joins the ampulla of the ductus deferens to form the ejaculatory duct. The seminal vesicles have a capsule containing fibrous connective tissue and smooth muscle cells.

Prostate Gland

The **prostate** (PROS-tate; one standing before) **gland** consists of both glandular and muscular tissue. It resembles a walnut in shape and size and is approximately 4 cm long and 2 cm wide. It is dorsal

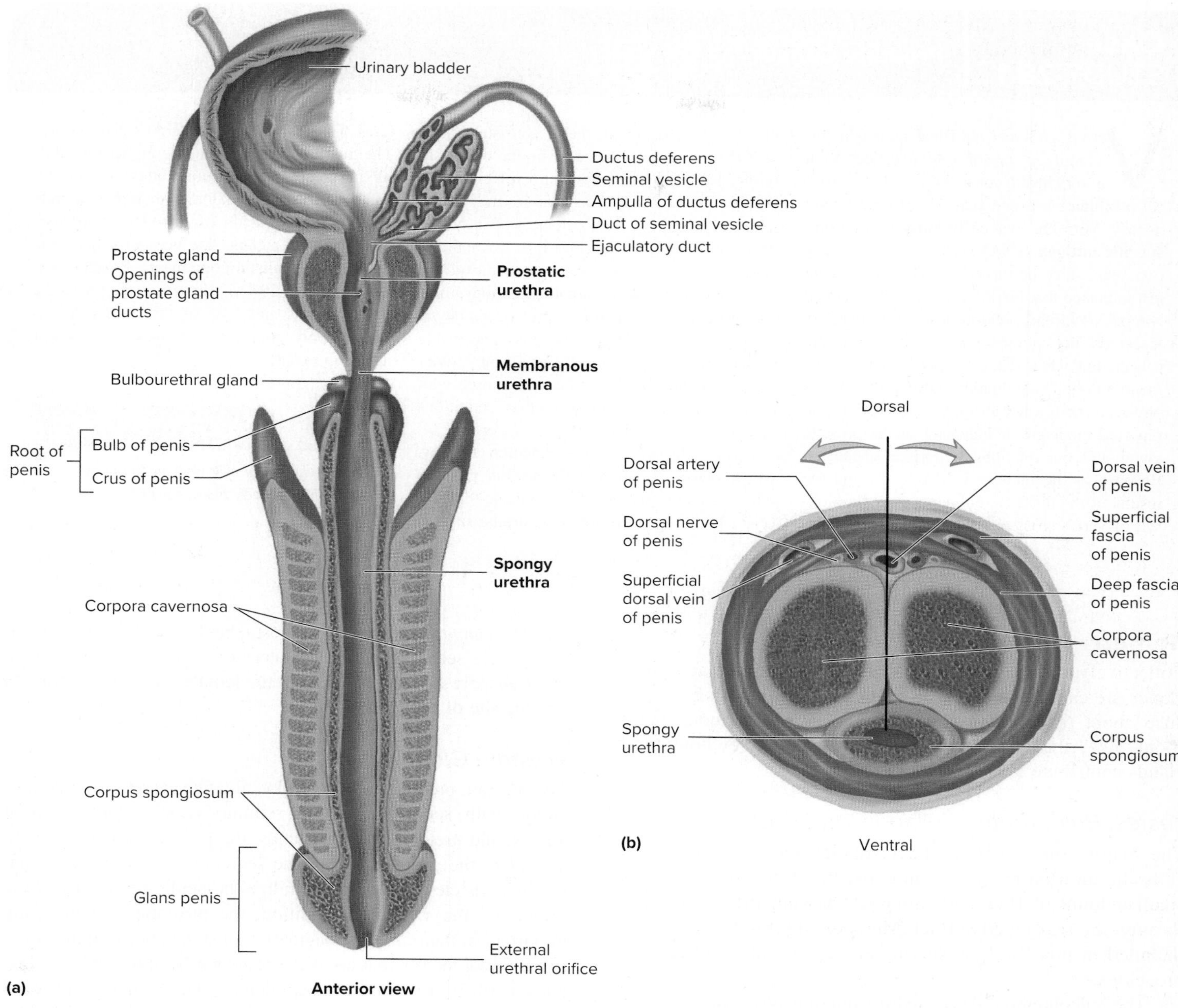

FIGURE 28.9 Penis

(*a*) Section through the spongy, or penile, urethra laid open and viewed from above. The prostate is also cut open to show the prostatic urethra. (*b*) Cross section of the penis, showing principal nerves, arteries, and veins along the dorsum of the penis. The *black solid line* and *blue arrows* above the image depict the manner in which (*a*) is cut and laid open.

to the pubic symphysis at the base of the urinary bladder, where it surrounds the prostatic urethra and the two ejaculatory ducts (see figure 28.3). The prostate gland is composed of a fibrous connective tissue capsule containing distinct smooth muscle cells and numerous fibrous partitions, also containing smooth muscle, that radiate inward toward the urethra. Covering these muscular partitions is a layer of columnar epithelial cells that form saccular dilations. The columnar cells secrete prostatic fluid into the saccular dilations. Fifteen to 30 small prostatic ducts carry these secretions into the prostatic urethra.

Bulbourethral Glands

The **bulbourethral** (BUL-boh-you-REE-thral) **glands,** or *Cowper glands,* are a pair of small glands located near the membranous urethra (see figures 28.3, 28.8, and 28.9). In young males, each gland is about the size of a pea, but they decrease in size with age and are almost impossible to detect in older males. Each bulbourethral gland is a compound mucous gland (see chapter 4). The small ducts of each gland unite to form a single duct, which empties into the spongy urethra at the base of the penis.

Case STUDY 28.1 Prostate Cancer

Vern is a 65-year-old Black male who has a family history of prostate cancer. Vern is very health conscious and has a physical examination every year. Due to his family history, Vern has elected to have his **prostate specific antigen (PSA)** levels evaluated every two years since he turned 55. His most recent test indicated that his PSA levels were elevated compared with his previous tests. Elevated PSA levels do not automatically indicate prostate cancer, but when detected, physicians recommend a digital examination of the prostate. His physician performed a digital examination and reported moderate enlargement of the prostate gland and two obvious tumorlike structures. Because of the increased PSA levels and the results of the digital examination, needle biopsies of Vern's prostate gland were taken through his rectum. Suspicious cells consistent with prostate cancer were detected in one of the six biopsy samples. The physician explained that, because the cancer had been discovered before it had metastasized, Vern's chances of surviving were high. Vern could choose to do nothing, have his prostate gland surgically removed, or treat the cancer with radiation therapy, hormonal therapy, or chemotherapy. Vern's physician indicated that doing nothing is a reasonable option for males who are significantly older than Vern because older males diagnosed with prostate cancer often die of other conditions before they succumb to prostate cancer.

Vern elected to have radiation therapy, which focuses radiation on the prostate gland to kill the cancer cells. Statistics indicate that surgery and radiation therapy have similar success rates for small, localized tumors like Vern's. The trauma of surgery and the higher probability of erectile dysfunction following surgery convinced Vern that radiation therapy was preferable. The physician explained that approximately 85% of patients like Vern are cancer-free 5 years after radiation treatments. Prostate cancer represents 29% of cancers in males in the United States and 14% of the deaths due to cancer. Only lung cancer causes more cancer deaths in males.

Predict 1

Explain why cancer cells were present in only one of the six needle biopsy samples.

Semen

Collectively, the sperm cells and secretions from the accessory glands are called **semen** (SEE-men). The seminal vesicles produce about 60% of the fluid, the prostate gland contributes about 30%, the testes contribute 5%, and the bulbourethral glands contribute 5%.

Testes, Bulbourethral Glands, and Urethra

The major component of the testicular secretions is sperm cells. In addition to the sperm cells, the testes also secrete a small amount of fluid necessary for moving the sperm cells through the reproductive tract. Metabolic by-products are also included in this fluid, as sperm cells carry out basic cellular processes.

The bulbourethral glands and urethral mucous glands produce a mucous secretion just before ejaculation. This alkaline mucous secretion has four major functions: (1) lubricating the urethra for sperm movement, (2) neutralizing the acidic fluids of the spongy urethra, (3) providing a small amount of lubrication during intercourse, and (4) reducing vaginal acidity.

Seminal Vesicles

The thick, mucuslike secretions of the seminal vesicles contain many substances, each with a specific function. The functions of these substances include:

1. *Nourishment of sperm cells.* Fructose, citric acid, and other nutrients nourish the sperm cells.
2. *Coagulation of semen.* The seminal vesicle secretions contain fibrinogen, which is involved in a weak coagulation reaction of the semen immediately after ejaculation.
3. *Movement of sperm cells.* Prostaglandins within the seminal vesicle secretions stimulate uterine contractions, which help transport sperm cells through the female reproductive tract to the site of fertilization.

Prostate Gland

The prostate produces a thin, milky, alkaline secretion. In combination with secretions of the seminal vesicles, bulbourethral glands, and urethral mucous glands, the prostatic secretions help neutralize the acidic urethra. The secretions of the prostate and seminal vesicles also help neutralize the acidic secretions of the testes and the vagina. In addition, the prostatic secretions are important in the transient coagulation of semen because they contain clotting factors that convert fibrinogen from the seminal vesicles to fibrin, resulting in coagulation. The coagulated material keeps the semen a sticky mass for a few minutes after ejaculation, and then fibrinolysin, also secreted by the prostate, causes the mass to dissolve. This releases the sperm cells to make their way through the female reproductive tract.

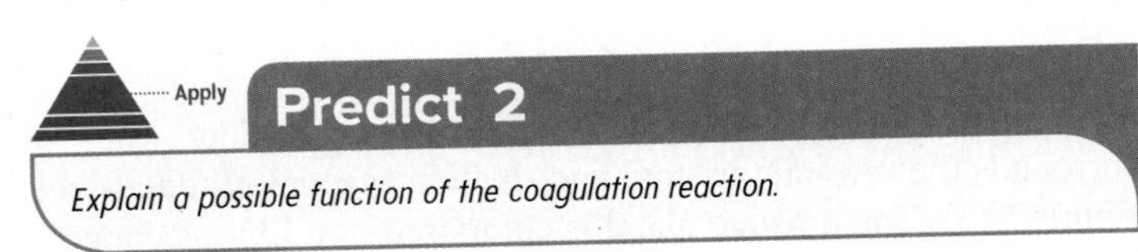

Predict 2

Explain a possible function of the coagulation reaction.

Normal sperm cell counts in the semen range from 75 to 400 million sperm cells per milliliter of semen, and a normal ejaculation usually consists of about 2–5 mL of semen. The semen with the highest sperm count is expelled from the penis first because it contains the greater percentage of sperm-containing fluid from the epididymis. Sperm cells become motile after

TABLE 28.1 Major Reproductive Hormones and Their Effects in Males

Hormone	Source	Target Tissue	Response
Gonadotropin-releasing hormone (GnRH)	Hypothalamus	Anterior pituitary	Stimulates secretion of LH and FSH
Luteinizing hormone (LH) (also called interstitial cell–stimulating hormone [ICSH] in males)	Anterior pituitary	Interstitial cells in the testes	Stimulates synthesis and secretion of testosterone
Follicle-stimulating hormone (FSH)	Anterior pituitary	Seminiferous tubules (sustentacular cells)	Supports spermatogenesis
Testosterone	Interstitial cells in the testes	Testes and body tissues	Supports spermatogenesis; stimulates development and maintenance of reproductive organs; causes development of secondary sexual characteristics
		Anterior pituitary and hypothalamus	Inhibits GnRH, LH, and FSH secretion through negative feedback

ejaculation once they are mixed with secretions of the male accessory glands and the female reproductive tract. The alkaline pH (an average of 7.5), nutrients, and removal of inhibitory substances from the surface of sperm cells appear to increase sperm cell motility. Enzymes carried in the acrosomal cap of each sperm cell help digest a path through the mucoid fluids of the female reproductive tract and through materials surrounding the oocyte. Once the acrosomal fluid is depleted from a sperm cell, the sperm cell is no longer capable of fertilization. As a result, most of the sperm cells (millions) are expended in moving the general group of sperm cells through the female reproductive tract.

ASSESS YOUR PROGRESS

29. *State where the seminal vesicles, prostate gland, and bulbourethral glands empty into the male reproductive duct system.*
30. *Describe the contributions to semen from the accessory glands.*
31. *What is the function of the secretions of each of the accessory glands?*

28.4 Physiology of Male Reproduction

LEARNING OUTCOMES

After reading this section, you should be able to

A. **List the hormones that influence the male reproductive system and describe their functions.**
B. **Demonstrate an understanding of the changes that occur in males during puberty.**
C. **Explain the events that occur during the male sex act.**

The male reproductive system is under hormonal and nervous control. Hormones are primarily responsible for the development of reproductive structures and the maintenance of their functional capacities, the development of secondary sexual characteristics, and the control of sperm cell formation. Hormones also influence sexual behavior (table 28.1). Neural mechanisms are primarily involved in sexual behavior and control of the sex act.

Regulation of Reproductive Hormone Secretion

Hormonal mechanisms that influence the male reproductive system involve the hypothalamus, the pituitary gland, and the testes. Figure 28.10 illustrates the hormonal regulation of male reproduction.

1. A small peptide hormone called **gonadotropin-releasing hormone (GnRH)** is released from neurons in the hypothalamus. GnRH passes through the hypothalamohypophysial portal system to the anterior pituitary gland (see chapter 18). In response to GnRH, cells within the anterior pituitary gland secrete two hormones, referred to as **gonadotropins** (GOH-nad-oh-TROH-pins) because they influence the function of the **gonads** (GOH-nadz; testes or ovaries). The two gonadotropins are **luteinizing hormone (LH)** and **follicle-stimulating hormone (FSH).** They are named for their functions in females, but they also have important functions in males. When discussing the male reproductive system, LH is sometimes called **interstitial cell–stimulating hormone (ICSH).**
2. LH binds to the interstitial cells in the testes and causes them to increase their rate of testosterone synthesis and secretion.
3. FSH binds primarily to sustentacular cells in the seminiferous tubules and promotes sperm cell development. It also increases the secretion of a hormone called **inhibin** (in-HIB-in; to inhibit).
4. Testosterone has a stimulatory effect on the sustentacular cells of the seminiferous tubules, as well as on the development of reproductive organs and secondary sexual characteristics.
5. The blood levels of reproductive hormones are under negative-feedback control. Testosterone has a negative-feedback effect on the secretion of GnRH from the hypothalamus and the secretion of LH and FSH from the anterior pituitary gland.
6. Inhibin has a negative-feedback effect on the secretion of FSH from the anterior pituitary gland.

For GnRH to stimulate the secretion of large quantities of LH and FSH and thereby influence sperm cell production, the anterior pituitary must be exposed to a series of pulses, or brief increases and decreases in GnRH. Interestingly, GnRH can be produced synthetically; if

PROCESS **Figure**

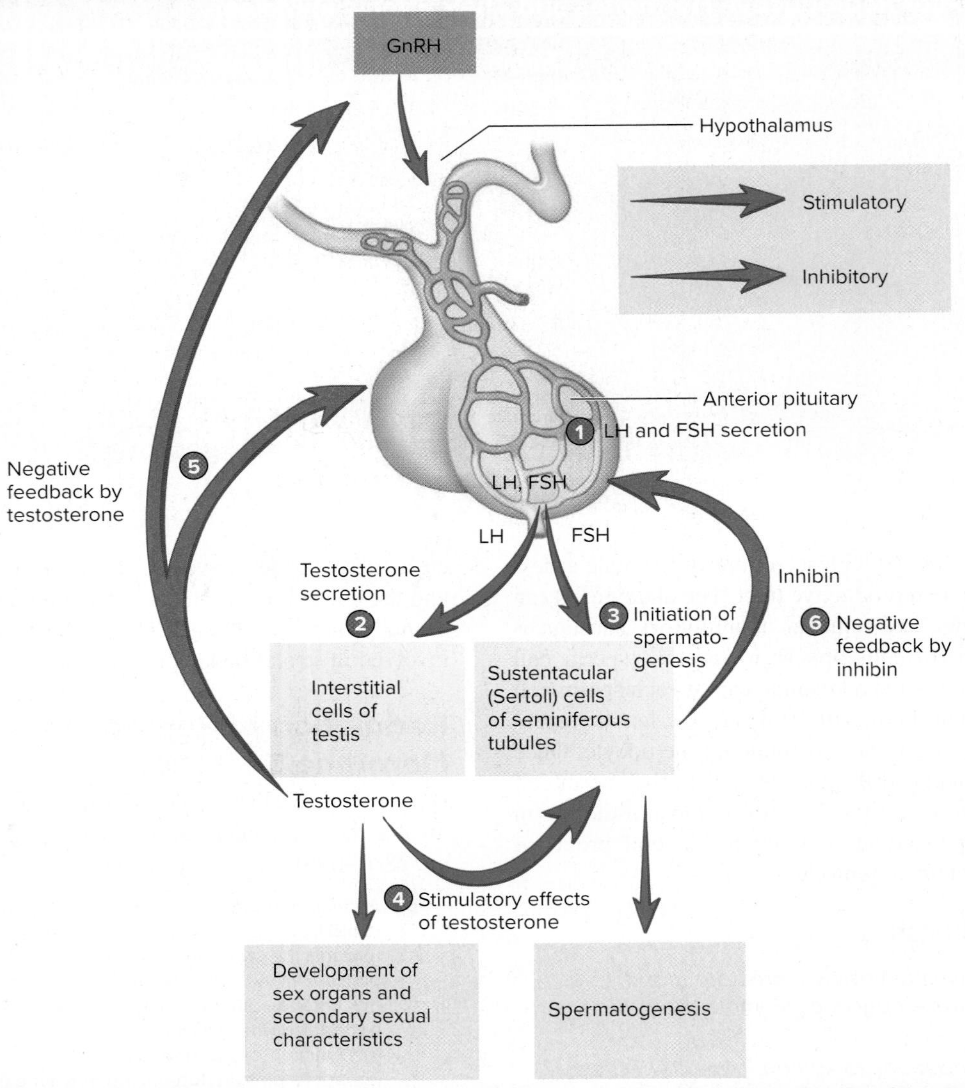

PROCESS **Figure 28.10**

Regulation of Reproductive Hormone Secretion in Males

Male reproductive hormones are produced by the hypothalamus, the anterior pituitary, and the testes.

Suppose an adult male developed a tumor in one of his testes that resulted in abnormally high levels of testosterone. What would happen to his levels of GnRH, FSH, and LH?

administered in small amounts in frequent pulses or surges, it can be useful in treating male infertility. However, chronically elevated GnRH levels in the blood cause the anterior pituitary cells to become insensitive to stimulation by GnRH molecules, and little LH or FSH is secreted. Long-term administration of synthetic GnRH, therefore, can reduce sperm cell production, causing infertility.

Testosterone is the major male hormone secreted by the testes. It is classified as an **androgen** (Gr. *andros,* male human) because it stimulates the development of male reproductive structures (see chapter 29) and male secondary sexual characteristics. The testes secrete other androgens, but they are produced in smaller concentrations and are less potent than testosterone. In addition, the testes secrete small amounts of estrogen and progesterone. Effects of testosterone are discussed later in the chapter.

Inside some target tissue cells, such as cells of the scrotum and penis, an enzyme converts testosterone to dihydrotestosterone, which is the active hormone for these cells. If the enzyme is not active, these structures do not develop normally. In other target tissue cells, an enzyme converts testosterone to estrogen, and estrogen becomes the active hormone. Some brain cells convert testosterone to estrogen. In these cells, estrogen may be the active hormone responsible for certain aspects of male sexual behavior.

Clinical IMPACT 28.3 Male Infertility

Infertility (in-fer-TIL-ih-tee) is the inability or the reduced ability to produce offspring. The most common cause of infertility in males is a low sperm cell count. A count of less than 20 million sperm cells per milliliter usually indicates infertility.

The sperm cell count can decrease because of damage to the testes as a result of trauma, radiation, cryptorchidism, or an infection, such as mumps. **Varicocele** (VAR-ih-koh-seel) is an abnormal dilation of a spermatic vein that results from incompetent or absent valves in spermatic veins, from thrombi, or from tumors. As a result, both testicular blood flow and spermatogenesis decrease. Reduced sperm cell counts can also result from inadequate secretion of LH and FSH, which can be caused by hypothyroidism, trauma to the hypothalamus, infarctions of the hypothalamus or anterior pituitary gland, or tumors. Decreased testosterone secretion reduces the sperm cell count as well. Some reports suggest that the average sperm cell count has decreased substantially since the end of World War II (1945), although there is some controversy about the accuracy of these reports. Researchers speculate that certain synthetic chemicals are responsible.

Even when the sperm cell count is normal, fertility can be reduced if sperm cell structure is abnormal, as occurs due to chromosomal abnormalities or other genetic factors. Reduced sperm cell motility also results in infertility. A major cause of reduced sperm cell motility is the presence of antisperm antibodies, which are produced by the immune system and bind to sperm cells.

In cases of infertility due to low sperm count or reduced motility, fertility can sometimes be achieved by collecting several ejaculations and concentrating the sperm cells before inserting them into the female reproductive tract, a process called **artificial insemination** (in-sem-ih-NAY-shun).

Puberty in Males

Before birth, a gonadotropin-like hormone called **human chorionic** (koh-ree-ON-ik) **gonadotropin (hCG),** secreted by the placenta, stimulates the synthesis and secretion of testosterone by the fetal testes. After birth, however, no source of stimulation is present, and the testes of the newborn baby atrophy slightly and secrete only small amounts of testosterone until puberty, which normally begins when a male is 12–14 years old.

Puberty (PYU-ber-tee) is the age at which individuals become capable of sexual reproduction. Before puberty, GnRH release from the hypothalamus is inhibited by small amounts of testosterone and other androgens. At puberty, the hypothalamus becomes much less sensitive to the inhibitory effect of these androgens, and the rate of GnRH secretion increases. This causes an increase in LH and FSH secretion from the anterior pituitary gland. Elevated FSH levels promote sperm cell formation, and elevated LH levels cause the interstitial cells to secrete larger amounts of testosterone. Testosterone still has a negative-feedback effect on GnRH secretion after puberty but is not capable of completely suppressing it.

Effects of Testosterone

Testosterone is by far the major androgen in males. Nearly all the androgens, including testosterone, are produced by the interstitial cells of the testes, with small amounts produced by the adrenal cortex and possibly by the sustentacular cells. Testosterone causes the enlargement and differentiation of the male genitals and reproductive duct system and is necessary for sperm cell formation. Testosterone affects the development of secondary sexual characteristics, which are those structural and behavioral changes, other than in the reproductive organs, that develop at puberty and distinguish males from females. Some of these characteristics are discussed below.

Testosterone stimulates growth of thicker, coarser, pigmented hair in the pubic area and extending up the linea alba, as well as on the legs, chest, axillary region, face, and back. Testosterone causes existing vellus hair to be converted to terminal hair, which is coarser and more pigmented.

Testosterone affects the appearance of the skin. Specifically, it causes the texture of the skin to become rougher or coarser. The quantity of melanin in the skin also increases, making the skin darker. In addition, testosterone increases the rate of secretion from the sebaceous glands, especially on the face. Near puberty, the increased testosterone level and increased sebaceous gland secretion frequently cause acne (see chapter 5).

Testosterone also causes hypertrophy of the larynx and reduced tension on the vocal folds, beginning near puberty. At first, the structural changes can make the voice difficult to control, but ultimately its normal masculine quality is achieved.

Testosterone stimulates metabolism so that males have a slightly higher metabolic rate than females. The red blood cell count increases by nearly 20% as a result of testosterone's effect on erythropoietin production. Testosterone also has a minor mineralocorticoid-like effect, causing Na^+ to be retained in the body and, consequently, an increased volume of body fluids. Testosterone promotes protein synthesis in most tissues; as a result, skeletal muscle mass increases at puberty. The average percentage of the body weight composed of skeletal muscle is greater for males than for females because of the effect of androgens.

Testosterone, historically, was believed to be the major hormone influencing bone growth in males. Recent studies though have found that testosterone is converted to estrogen, which affects bone growth. At puberty, the increase in sex hormone production, both testosterone and the subsequent production of estrogen, causes rapid bone growth and increases the deposition of Ca^{2+} in bone, resulting in increased height. However, the growth in height is limited because these sex hormones also stimulate ossification of the epiphyseal plates of long bones (see chapter 6). Males who mature sexually at an earlier age grow rapidly but reach their maximum height earlier. Males who mature sexually at a later age

Clinical IMPACT 28.4

Anabolic Steroids

In an attempt to improve their performance, some athletes, especially those who depend on muscle strength, may either ingest or inject synthetic androgens, commonly called **anabolic steroids,** or simply *steroids*. These hormones have testosterone-like effects, such as stimulating the development of male secondary sexual characteristics, but many anabolic steroids are structurally different from testosterone, and their effect on muscle is greater than their effect on the reproductive organs. However, when taken in large amounts, they can influence the reproductive system. Large doses of anabolic steroids have a negative-feedback effect on the hypothalamus and anterior pituitary, reducing GnRH, LH, and FSH levels. As a result, the testes can atrophy and sterility can develop. Other side effects of large doses of anabolic steroids include kidney and liver damage, heart attack, and stroke. In addition, anabolic steroids cause abrupt mood swings, usually toward intense anger and rage. Taking anabolic steroids is highly discouraged by medical professionals, violates the rules of most athletic organizations, and is illegal without a prescription.

do not exhibit a rapid period of growth, but they grow for a longer period and can become taller than those who mature sexually at an earlier age.

Male Sexual Behavior and the Male Sex Act

Testosterone is required to initiate and maintain male sexual behavior. Testosterone enters cells within the hypothalamus and the surrounding areas of the brain and influences their function, resulting in sexual behavior. However, male sexual behavior may depend, in part, on the conversion of testosterone to other steroids, such as estrogen, in cells of the brain.

The blood levels of testosterone remain relatively constant in a male from puberty until about 40 years of age. Thereafter, the levels slowly decline to about 20% of this value by 80 years of age, causing a slow decrease in sex drive and fertility.

The male sex act is a complex series of reflexes that result in erection of the penis, secretion of mucus into the urethra, emission, and ejaculation. **Emission** (ih-MISH-uhn) is the discharge of all these secretions from the ducta deferentia into the urethra. **Ejaculation** (ee-JACK-you-LAY-shun) is the forceful expulsion of semen from the urethra caused by contraction of the urethra, the skeletal muscles in the pelvic floor, and the muscles at the base of the penis. Sensations that are normally interpreted as pleasurable occur during the male sex act and result in a climactic sensation, called **orgasm** (OR-gaz-um), associated with ejaculation. After ejaculation, a phase called **resolution** occurs. Resolution is characterized by a flaccid penis, an overall feeling of satisfaction, and the inability to achieve erection and a second ejaculation for a period that can range from many minutes to many hours or longer.

Sensory Action Potentials and Integration

Male sexual reflexes are initiated by a variety of sensory stimuli. Action potentials are conducted by sensory neurons from the genitals through the pudendal nerve to the sacral region of the spinal cord, where reflexes that result in the male sex act are integrated. Action potentials travel from the spinal cord to the cerebrum to produce conscious sexual sensations.

Rhythmic massage of the penis, especially the glans penis, produces extremely important sensory action potentials that initiate erection and ejaculation. In addition, sensory action potentials produced in surrounding tissues, such as the scrotum and the anal, perineal, and pubic regions, reinforce sexual sensations. Engorgement of the prostate and seminal vesicles with their secretions also causes sexual sensations. In some cases, mild irritation of the urethra, as may result from an infection, can cause sexual sensations.

Psychological stimuli, including sight, sound, odor, and thoughts, have a major effect on male sexual reflexes. Thinking sexual thoughts or dreaming about erotic events tends to reinforce stimuli that trigger sexual reflexes, such as erection and ejaculation. Ejaculation while sleeping is a relatively common event in young males and is thought to be triggered by psychological stimuli associated with dreaming. Psychological stimuli can also inhibit the sex act, and thoughts that are not sexual tend to decrease the effectiveness of the male sex act.

Action potentials from the cerebrum that reinforce the sacral reflexes are not absolutely required for the culmination of the male sex act. The sex act can be performed by males who have suffered spinal cord injuries superior to the sacral region.

Erection, Emission, and Ejaculation

When erection occurs, the penis becomes enlarged and rigid. Erection is the first major component of the male sex act. Action potentials travel from the spinal cord through the pudendal nerve to the arteries that supply blood to the erectile tissues. The release of acetylcholine and nitric oxide (NO) causes smooth muscle cells to relax and blood vessels to dilate. At the same time, other arteries of the penis constrict to shunt blood to the erectile tissues. As a consequence, blood fills the sinusoids of the erectile tissue and compresses the veins. Because venous outflow is partially occluded, the blood pressure in the sinusoids causes inflation and rigidity of the erectile tissue. Nerve action potentials that result in erection come from parasympathetic centers (S2–S4) or sympathetic centers (T2–L1) in the spinal cord. Normally, the parasympathetic centers are more important for erection; however, in cases of damage to the sacral region of the spinal cord, erection can occur through the sympathetic system.

Parasympathetic action potentials also cause the mucous glands within the penile urethra and the bulbourethral glands at the base of the penis to secrete mucus.

Emission is the accumulation of sperm cells and secretions of the accessory glands in the urethra. Sympathetic centers in the spinal cord (T12–L1), which are stimulated as the level of sexual tension increases, control emission. Sympathetic action potentials cause peristaltic contractions of the reproductive ducts and stimulate the seminal vesicles and the prostate gland to release their secretions. Consequently, semen accumulates in the prostatic

Clinical IMPACT 28.5

Erectile Dysfunction

Failure to achieve erection, or **erectile dysfunction (ED),** sometimes called *impotence,* can be a major source of frustration for some males. ED can be due to reduced testosterone secretion resulting from hypothalamic, pituitary, or testicular complications. In other cases, ED is due to defective stimulation of the erectile tissue by nerve fibers or reduced response of the blood vessels to neural stimulation.

Some males can achieve erections by taking oral medication, such as sildenafil (Viagra), tadafil (Cialis), or vardenafil (Levitra). Sildenafil is a drug that blocks the activity of the enzyme that converts cGMP to GMP. Consequently, it allows cGMP to accumulate in smooth muscle cells in the arteries of erectile tissues. This response is effective in enhancing erection in males. Sildenafil's action is not specific to the erectile tissue of the penis, however. It causes vasodilation in other tissues and can increase the workload of the heart.

urethra and produces sensory action potentials that pass through the pudendal nerves to the spinal cord. Integration of these action potentials results in both sympathetic and somatic motor output. Sympathetic action potentials cause the internal sphincter of the urinary bladder to constrict so that semen and urine are not mixed. Somatic motor action potentials travel to the skeletal muscles of the urogenital diaphragm and the base of the penis, causing ejaculation by several rhythmic contractions that force the semen out of the urethra. Muscle tension increases throughout the body as well.

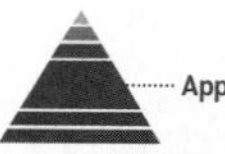

Predict 3

Mr. Grover suffers from the periodic inability to achieve an erection. His doctor could find no structural or physiological abnormalities, so he prescribed sildenafil. After taking the pills, Mr. Grover could sometimes, but not always, achieve an erection. Assuming no pathology affected Mr. Grover, explain his experiences.

ASSESS YOUR PROGRESS

32. *Where are GnRH, LH, FSH, and inhibin produced? What effects do they have on the male reproductive system?*
33. *Where is testosterone produced?*
34. *Explain the regulation of testosterone secretion.*
35. *What changes in hormone production occur at puberty?*
36. *Describe the effects of testosterone on the male body.*
37. *What effects do psychological, tactile, parasympathetic, and sympathetic stimulation have on the male sex act?*
38. *Describe the processes of erection, emission, ejaculation, orgasm, and resolution.*

28.5 Anatomy of the Female Reproductive System

LEARNING OUTCOMES

After reading this section, you should be able to

A. **Name the organs of the female reproductive system and describe their functions.**
B. **Describe the anatomy and histology of the ovaries.**
C. **Discuss the development of the oocyte and the follicle.**
D. **Describe ovulation.**
E. **Explain the likely location and result of fertilization.**
F. **Describe the structure and function of the uterine tubes.**
G. **Describe the structure of the uterus, including details about the tissues that make up the uterine wall.**
H. **Describe the anatomy and histology of the vagina.**
I. **Describe the anatomy of the female external genitalia.**
J. **Describe the anatomy and function of the mammary glands.**

The female reproductive system consists of (1) the ovaries, (2) the uterine tubes, (3) the uterus, (4) the vagina, (5) the external genital organs, and (6) the mammary glands (see figure 28.1*b*). The internal reproductive organs are within the pelvis between the urinary bladder and the rectum (figure 28.11). The uterus and the vagina are in the midline, with the ovaries to each side of the uterus. A group of ligaments holds the internal reproductive organs in place. The most conspicuous of these ligaments is the **broad ligament,** an extension of the peritoneum that spreads out on both sides of the uterus and attaches to the ovaries and uterine tubes (figure 28.12).

Ovaries

The two **ovaries** (OH-var-eez), the female gonads, are small organs about 2–3.5 cm long and 1–1.5 cm wide (figure 28.12). A peritoneal fold called the **mesovarium** (MEZ-oh-VAY-ree-um; mesentery of the ovary) attaches each ovary to the posterior surface of the broad ligament. Two other ligaments are associated with the ovary: (1) the **suspensory ligament,** which extends from the mesovarium to the body wall, and (2) the **ovarian ligament,** which attaches the ovary to the superior margin of the uterus. The ovarian arteries, veins, and nerves traverse the suspensory ligament and enter the ovary through the mesovarium.

Ovarian Histology

The ovary is covered by a portion of the visceral peritoneum, made up of simple cuboidal epithelium, called the **ovarian epithelium,** or *germinal epithelium.* Immediately below the ovarian epithelium is a capsule of dense fibrous connective tissue called the **tunica albuginea** (al-byoo-JIN-ee-ah). The tissue of the ovary is divided into two areas: the cortex and the medulla. The **cortex** is the denser, outer part of the ovary, and the **medulla** is the looser, inner part of the ovary (figure 28.13). The connective tissue of the ovary is called the **stroma.** Numerous **ovarian follicles,** each of which contains an **oocyte** (OH-oh-site), are distributed throughout the stroma of the cortex. Blood vessels, lymphatic vessels, and nerves from the mesovarium enter the medulla.

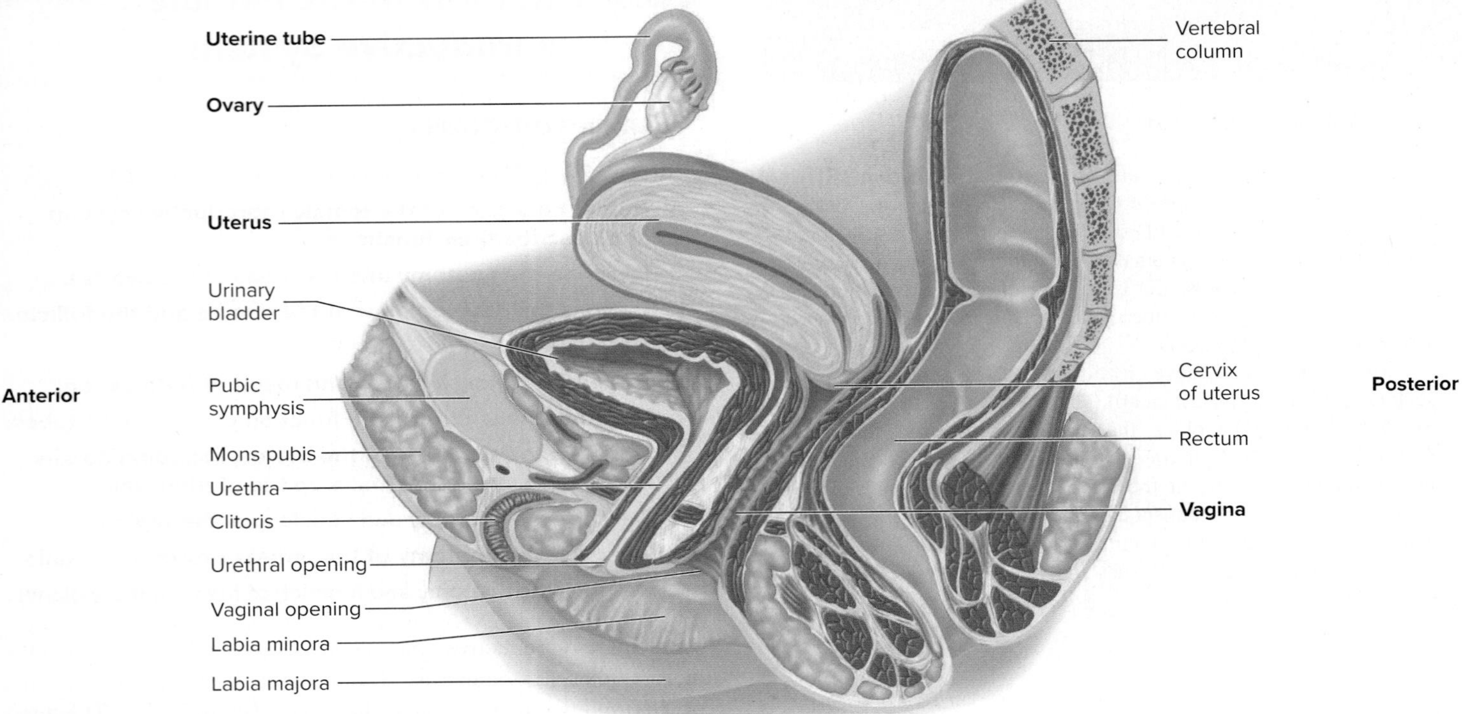

FIGURE 28.11 Female Reproductive Structures
The structures are depicted in sagittal section.

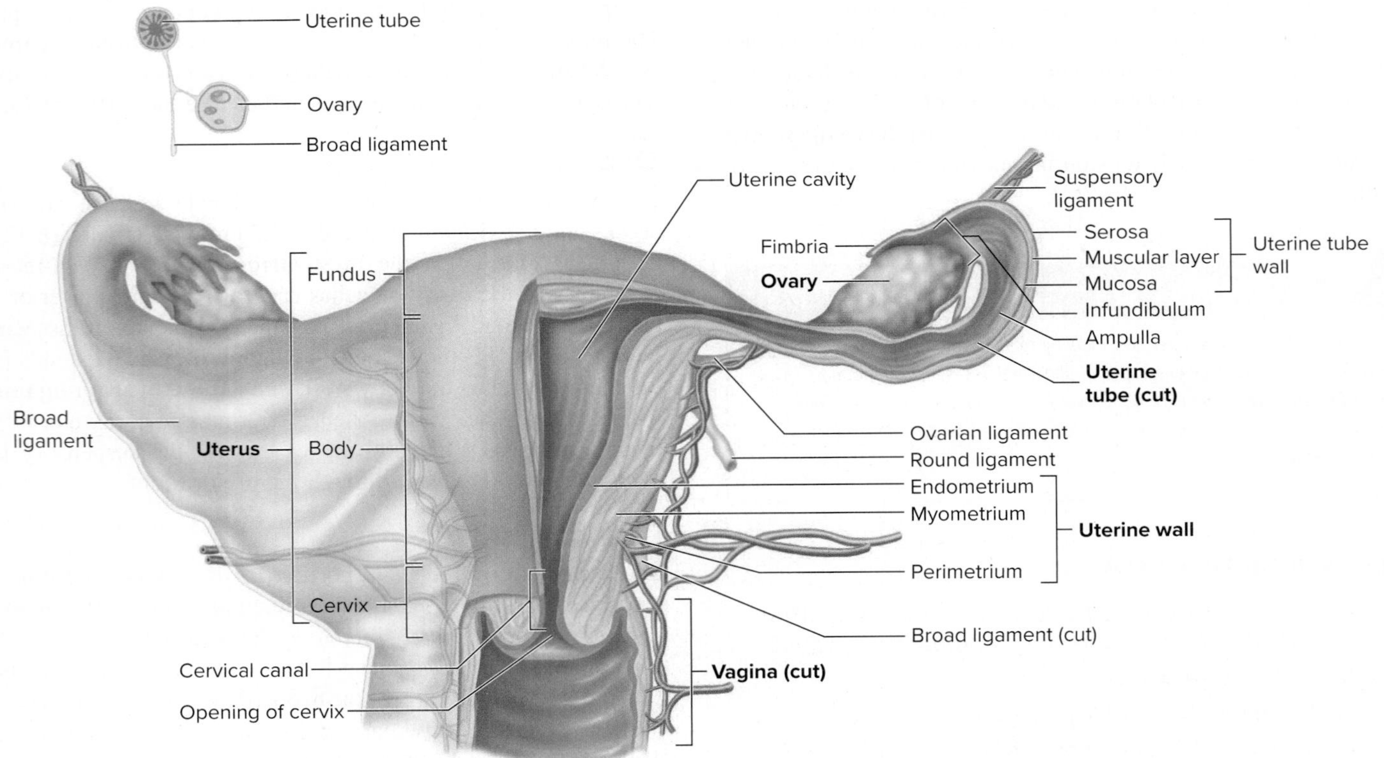

FIGURE 28.12 Uterus, Vagina, Uterine Tubes, Ovaries, and Supporting Ligaments
The uterus and uterine tubes are cut in section (on the left side), and the vagina is cut to show the internal anatomy. The inset (top, left) shows the relationships among the ovary, the uterine tube, and the ligaments that suspend them in the pelvic cavity.

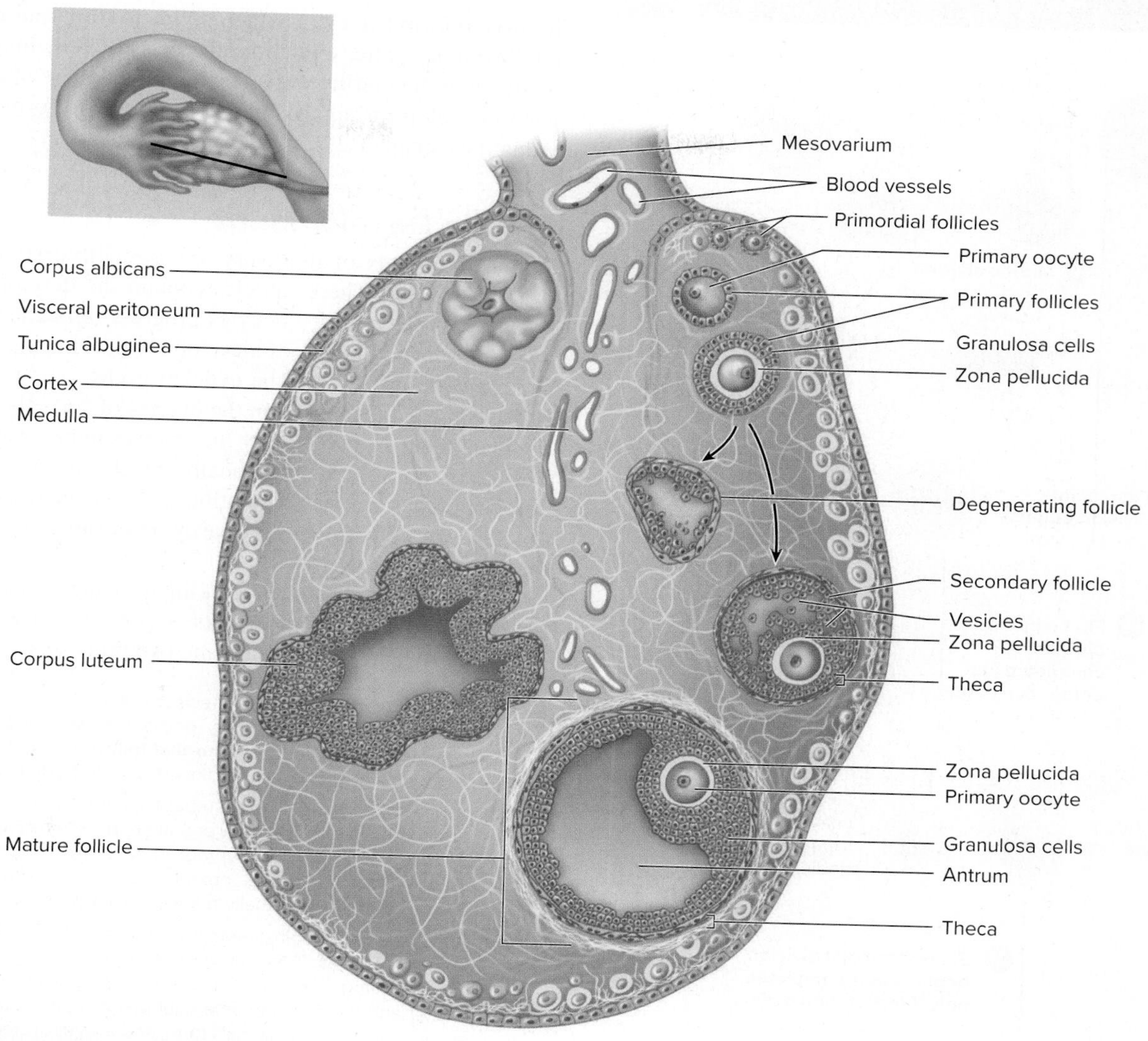

FIGURE 28.13 Histology of the Ovary
The ovary is sectioned to illustrate its internal structure (the inset shows plane of section). Ovarian follicles from each major stage of development are shown. APR

Oogenesis and Fertilization

The process of gamete production in females is called **oogenesis.** This process begins before a female is born. By the fourth month of development, the ovaries contain 5 million **oogonia** (oh-oh-GOH-nee-ah; *oon,* egg + *gone,* generation), the cells from which oocytes develop. By the time of birth, many of the oogonia have degenerated, and the remaining ones have differentiated into cells that have begun meiosis. Oogonia can form after birth from stem cells, but the extent to which this occurs, and how long it occurs, is not clear.

Figure 28.14 illustrates the process of oogenesis. After reviewing this information, compare and contrast the process of oogenesis and spermatogenesis, paying attention to the timing and number, as well as types, of cells produced. (*Note:* This will help with answering the Learn to Predict question at the beginning of the chapter.)

1. During development, oogonia increase in number by mitosis.
2. Before birth, most of the oogonia have differentiated into primary oocytes.
3. Primary oocytes, which are diploid cells, begin the process of meiosis I. Meiosis stops at birth, however, during the first meiotic division at prophase I.
4. At puberty, primary oocytes will reenter and complete meiosis I just before ovulation. Unlike meiosis in males, cytoplasm is split unevenly between the two haploid cells. Most of the cytoplasm remains with the secondary oocyte, resulting in a larger cell. The cytoplasm contains organelles, such as mitochondria, and nutrients that increase the viability of the secondary oocyte. The smaller **first polar body** has less cytoplasm and therefore few organelles and nutrients. It either degenerates or divides, producing second polar bodies, which eventually degenerate.
5. **Ovulation** (OV-you-LAY-shun) is the release of a **secondary oocyte** from an ovary. The secondary oocyte begins the second meiotic division, but stalls at metaphase II unless fertilization occurs. **Fertilization** (FER-til-ih-ZAY-shun) begins when a sperm cell binds to and penetrates the plasma membrane of a secondary oocyte. Subsequently, the secondary oocyte completes the second meiotic division to form two cells, each containing 23 chromosomes. One of these cells has very little cytoplasm and is called the second polar body, which degenerates. The other, larger cell is often called the ovum.

PROCESS **Figure**

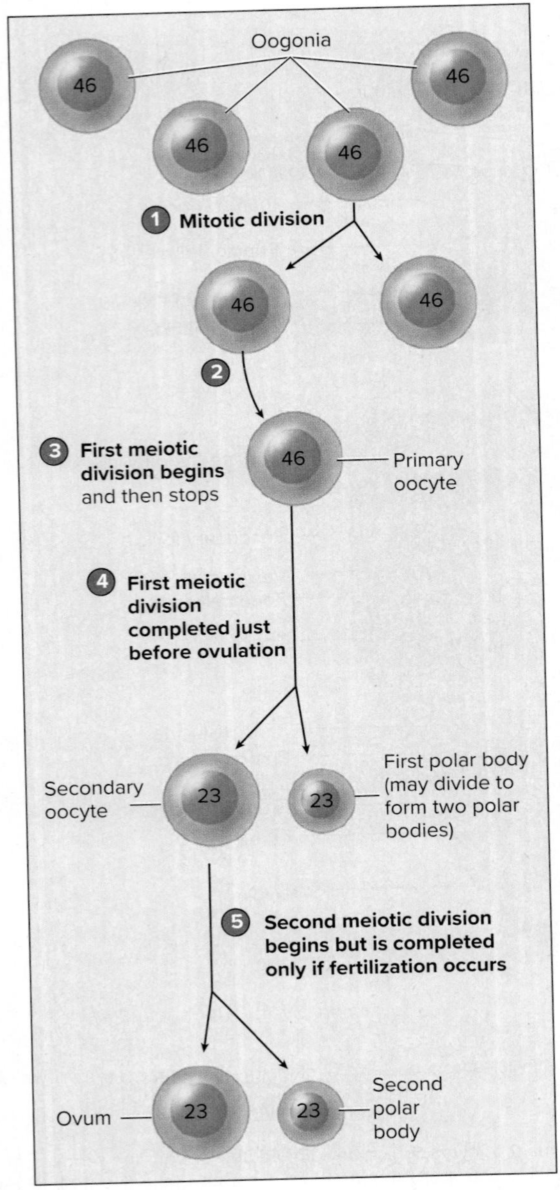

PROCESS **Figure 28.14**

Oogenesis

Oogenesis is the process of gamete formation in females.

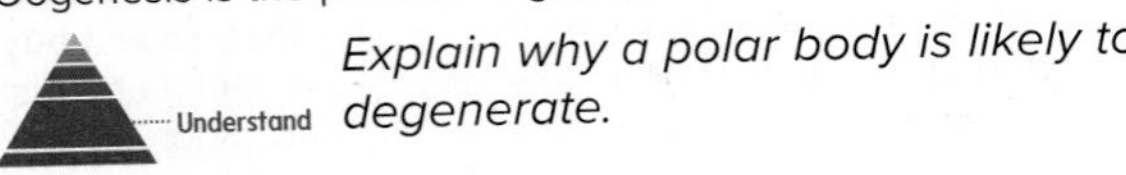

Explain why a polar body is likely to degenerate.

At fertilization, the 23 chromosomes from the sperm cell nucleus join with the 23 chromosomes from the oocyte to form a **zygote** (ZIE-goht; figure 28.15; see chapter 29). The zygote has 23 pairs of chromosomes (a total of 46 chromosomes). All cells of the human body contain 23 pairs of chromosomes, except for the male and female gametes. The zygote divides by mitosis to form two cells, which divide to form four cells, and so on. Seven days after ovulation, the mass of cells may implant in or attach to the uterine wall. The implanted mass of cells continues to develop for approximately 9 months to form a new individual (see chapter 29).

Follicle Development

Within the cortex of the ovary are specialized structures called ovarian follicles. These follicles contain the developing primary oocytes. As the primary oocytes progress through meiosis I, the ovarian follicle undergoes development, changing in size and structure (figure 28.15). The **ovarian cycle** refers to the reoccurring events that take place in the ovaries of sexually mature, nonpregnant females, particularly the changes in the ovarian follicles. The ovarian cycle is hormonally regulated. A more detailed description of hormonal regulation is presented in section 28.6. In this section, we will focus primarily on the anatomical changes in the ovarian follicle.

Figure 28.15 illustrates the follicle changes that occur during the ovarian cycle. The process of oogenesis is also illustrated in the figure to help you correlate the two processes.

1. As discussed earlier, oogenesis begins when a female is in her mother's uterus. The primary oocytes present at birth are located in primordial follicles. A **primordial follicle** is a primary oocyte surrounded by a single layer of flat cells, called **granulosa cells.**
2. At birth a female possesses about 2 million primary oocytes. From birth to puberty, the number of primary oocytes decreases to around 300,000–400,000. On average, about 400 primary oocytes will actually complete development and give rise to the secondary oocytes that are eventually released from the ovaries.
3. Once puberty begins, some of the primordial follicles become **primary follicles.** This transition to a primary follicle occurs as the oocyte enlarges and the single layer of granulosa cells becomes thicker and the cells become cuboidal in shape. Subsequently, several layers of granulosa cells form, and a layer of clear material called the **zona pellucida** (ZOH-nah peh-LOO-sih-dah; girdle + *pellucidus,* passage of light) is deposited around the primary oocyte.
4. Approximately every 28 days, hormonal changes stimulate some of the primary follicles to continue to develop. The primary follicle becomes a **secondary follicle** as fluid-filled spaces called **vesicles** form among the granulosa cells, and a capsule called the **theca** (THEE-kah; a box) forms around the follicle. Cells of the **theca interna** surround the granulosa cells, where they participate in the synthesis of ovarian hormones. The **theca externa** is primarily connective tissue that merges with the stroma of the ovary.
5. The secondary follicle continues to enlarge. When the fluid-filled vesicles fuse to form a single, fluid-filled chamber called the **antrum** (AN-trum), the follicle is called a **mature follicle,** or *Graafian* (GRAF-ee-an) *follicle.* In the mature follicle, the oocyte is pushed off to one side and lies in a mass of granulosa cells called the **cumulus cells,** or *cumulus oophorus* (KYOO-myoo-lus oh-OF-ohr-us).
6. The mature follicle forms a lump on the surface of the ovary. During ovulation, the mature follicle ruptures, releasing a small amount of blood, follicular fluid, and the oocyte, surrounded by the cumulus cells, into the peritoneal cavity. The cumulus cells resemble a crown radiating from the oocyte and are thus called the **corona radiata.** Usually, only one mature follicle reaches the most advanced stages of development and is ovulated. The other follicles that were undergoing this maturation process degenerate, a process called **atresia.**

FUNDAMENTAL **Figure**

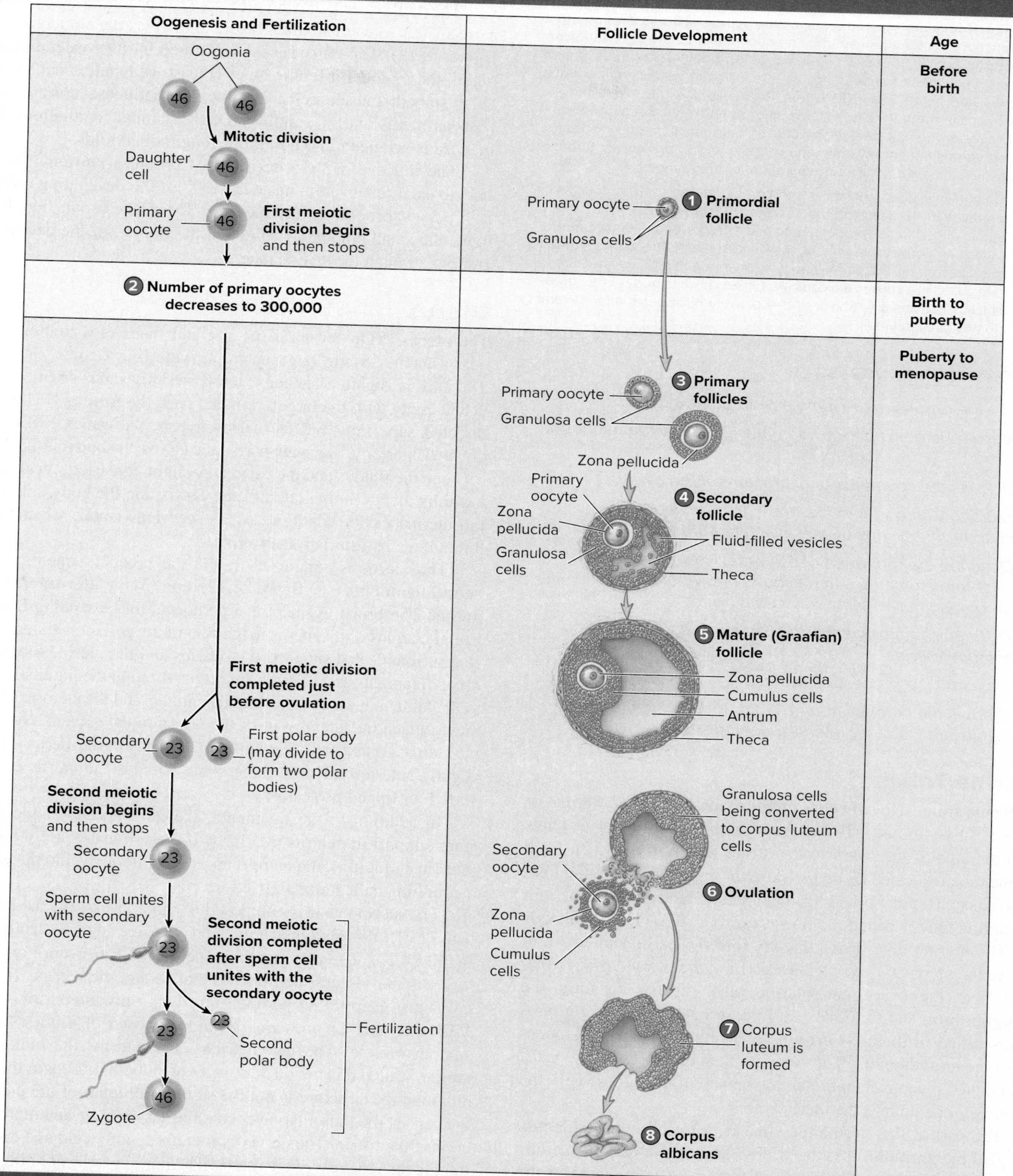

Oogenesis and Fertilization	Follicle Development	Age
Oogonia (46, 46) → **Mitotic division** → Daughter cell (46) → Primary oocyte (46): **First meiotic division begins** and then stops	Primary oocyte; Granulosa cells; ① **Primordial follicle**	**Before birth**
② **Number of primary oocytes decreases to 300,000**		**Birth to puberty**
First meiotic division completed just before ovulation → Secondary oocyte (23); First polar body (23) (may divide to form two polar bodies) → **Second meiotic division begins** and then stops → Secondary oocyte (23) → Sperm cell unites with secondary oocyte (23) → **Second meiotic division completed after sperm cell unites with the secondary oocyte** → 23; Second polar body (23) → Zygote (46) — Fertilization	③ **Primary follicles**: Primary oocyte; Granulosa cells; Zona pellucida. ④ **Secondary follicle**: Primary oocyte; Zona pellucida; Granulosa cells; Fluid-filled vesicles; Theca. ⑤ **Mature (Graafian) follicle**: Zona pellucida; Cumulus cells; Antrum; Theca. Granulosa cells being converted to corpus luteum cells; Secondary oocyte; Zona pellucida; Cumulus cells; ⑥ **Ovulation**. ⑦ **Corpus luteum is formed**. ⑧ **Corpus albicans**	**Puberty to menopause**

PROCESS **Figure 28.15**

Oogenesis and Follicle Development

The events of oogenesis and follicle development are closely linked. Once these structures are mature, fertilization can result. The numbers written in the cells are total numbers of chromosomes.

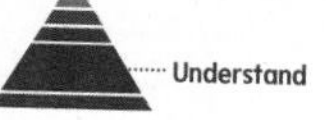

If fertilization does not occur, what happens to the secondary oocyte after ovulation?

7 After ovulation, the ruptured mature follicle still has an important function. It is transformed into an endocrine structure called the **corpus luteum** (KOR-pus LOO-tee-um; yellow body). The corpus luteum has a convoluted appearance as a result of its collapse after ovulation (see figure 28.13). The granulosa cells and the theca interna, now called **luteal cells,** enlarge and begin to secrete hormones—progesterone and smaller amounts of estrogen. If pregnancy occurs, the corpus luteum enlarges and remains active, particularly through the first trimester, as the **corpus luteum of pregnancy.**

8 If pregnancy does not occur, the corpus luteum remains functional for about 10–12 days and then begins to degenerate. As the corpus luteum degenerates, progesterone and estrogen secretion decreases. Within the corpus luteum, connective tissue cells become enlarged and clear, giving the whole structure a whitish color. The structure is then called the **corpus albicans** (AL-bih-kanz; white body). The corpus albicans continues to shrink and eventually disappears after several months or even years.

ASSESS YOUR PROGRESS

39. *List the organs of the female reproductive system.*
40. *Name and describe the ligaments that hold the ovaries in place.*
41. *Discuss the coverings and structure of the ovary.*
42. *Starting with oogonia, describe the formation of secondary oocytes by meiosis. What are polar bodies?*
43. *Describe the formation of a zygote. How many pairs of chromosomes are in a zygote, and where do the chromosomes within a pair come from?*
44. *Distinguish among primordial, primary, secondary, and mature follicles.*
45. *Describe the process of ovulation.*
46. *What is the corpus luteum? What happens to it if fertilization occurs? If fertilization does not occur?*

Uterine Tubes

A **uterine tube,** also called a *fallopian* (fah-LOH-pee-an) *tube* or *oviduct* (OH-vih-dukt), is associated with each ovary. It extends from the area of the ovary to the uterus (see figure 28.12). Each uterine tube is located along the superior margin of the broad ligament. The part of the broad ligament most directly associated with the uterine tube is called the **mesosalpinx** (MEZ-oh-SAL-pinks).

The uterine tube opens directly into the peritoneal cavity to receive the secondary oocyte released from the ovary during ovulation. Near the ovary, the uterine tube expands to form the **infundibulum** (IN-fun-DIB-you-lum; funnel). Long, thin processes called **fimbriae** (FIM-bree-ee; fringe) surround the opening of the infundibulum. The inner surfaces of the fimbriae consist of a ciliated mucous membrane. Movement of the cilia sweeps the secondary oocyte into the uterine tube.

The part of the uterine tube that is nearest the infundibulum is called the **ampulla.** It is the widest and longest part of the tube and accounts for about 7.5–8 cm of the total 10 cm length of the tube. Fertilization usually occurs in the ampulla. The part of the uterine tube nearest the uterus is the **isthmus.** It is much narrower and has thicker walls than the ampulla. The **uterine part,** or *intramural part,* of the uterine tube passes through the uterine wall and ends in a very small uterine opening.

The wall of each uterine tube consists of three layers: (1) the serosa, (2) the muscular layer, and (3) the mucosa (see figure 28.12). The outer **serosa** is formed by the visceral peritoneum, the middle **muscular layer** consists of longitudinal and circular smooth muscle cells, and the inner **mucosa** consists of a mucous membrane of simple ciliated columnar epithelium. The mucosa is arranged into numerous longitudinal folds.

The mucosa of the uterine tubes provides nutrients for the oocyte or, if fertilization has occurred, for the developing embryo as it passes through the uterine tube. The ciliated epithelium helps move the small amount of fluid and the oocyte, or the developing embryo, through the uterine tube.

Uterus

The **uterus** (YOU-ter-us) is the size and shape of a medium-sized pear—about 7.5 cm long and 5 cm wide (see figures 28.11 and 28.12). It is slightly flattened anteroposteriorly and is oriented in the pelvic cavity with the larger, rounded part, the **fundus** (FUN-dus), directed superiorly and the narrower part, the **cervix** (SER-viks), directed inferiorly. The main part of the uterus, the **body,** is the region between the fundus and the cervix. A slight constriction called the **isthmus** marks the junction of the cervix and the body. Internally, the uterine cavity continues as the **cervical canal,** which opens through the **ostium** into the vagina.

The uterus is supported by (1) the broad ligament, (2) the **round ligaments** (see figure 28.12), and (3) the **uterosacral ligaments.** The broad ligament is a peritoneal fold extending from the lateral margins of the uterus to the wall of the pelvis on either side. It also surrounds and supports the ovaries and the uterine tubes. The round ligaments extend from the uterus through the inguinal canals to the labia majora of the external genitalia, and the uterosacral ligaments attach the lateral wall of the uterus to the sacrum. Normally, the uterus is *anteverted,* meaning that the body of the uterus is tipped slightly anteriorly. However, in some females the uterus is retroverted, or tipped posteriorly.

In addition to the ligaments, skeletal muscles of the pelvic floor support the uterus inferiorly. If these muscles are weakened (e.g., in childbirth), the uterus can extend inferiorly into the vagina, a condition called a **prolapsed uterus.**

The uterine wall is composed of three layers: (1) the perimetrium, (2) the myometrium, and (3) the endometrium (see figure 28.12). The **perimetrium** (per-ih-MEE-tree-um), or *serous layer,* is the visceral peritoneum that covers the uterus. The next layer, just deep to the perimetrium, is the **myometrium** (my-oh-MEE-tree-um), or *muscular layer,* composed of a thick layer of smooth muscle. The myometrium accounts for the bulk of the uterine wall and is the thickest layer of smooth muscle in the body, although the structure is not the same in all areas of the uterus. In the cervix, the muscular layer contains less muscle and more dense connective tissue. The cervix is therefore more rigid and less contractile than the rest of the uterus. The innermost layer of the uterus is the **endometrium** (en-doh-MEE-tree-um). The endometrium is a mucous membrane that consists of a simple columnar epithelial lining and a connective tissue layer called the lamina propria. Simple tubular glands, called spiral glands, are scattered about the lamina propria and open through the epithelium into the uterine

MICROBES In Your Body 28.1 Human Papillomavirus and Cancer

In the majority of the Microbes in Your Body features we have focused on bacteria. However, recall from chapter 1 that the human microbiota also includes viruses, protists, and fungi. Human papillomaviruses (HPVs) belong to a family of DNA viruses that are naturally found on the skin soon after birth. Over 100 types of HPV have been identified, and most are not harmful. However, more than 13 types have been shown to be oncogenic, or cancer-causing, with two types, HPV 16 and HPV 18, being linked to 70% of all cervical cancer cases. In addition, the number of cases of mouth and throat cancers caused by HPV is on the rise, especially in males. HPV has also been linked to cancers of the anus, vulva, vagina, and penis. It is the most common viral infection of the reproductive tract and is easily transferred from one person to another. Viral transfer only requires direct contact of genital skin. Infection with noncancer-causing forms of HPV, such as types 6 and 11, can result in development of genital warts or respiratory papillomatosis (tumors in the air passages).

Viruses take over their host cell's machinery to replicate and form thousands of new individual viruses. In the case of HPV, the virus targets undifferentiated cells in the stratified squamous epithelium of the outer body skin, as well as the stratified squamous epithelium of the mucosal lining of the reproductive tract or pharynx (see chapter 4). Once the virus is inside the host cell nucleus, its DNA is replicated at the same time the host cell DNA is replicated. HPV induces uncontrolled division in its host's cells. The continued division causes an accumulation of mutations, and eventually the cell becomes cancerous. New HPVs are released through normal shedding of cells. Fortunately, full-blown metastasizing cancer from an HPV infection takes 15–20 years in females with normal immune systems and 5–10 years in females with weakened immune systems to develop, which gives enough time for screening, identification, and treatment.

Because HPV is present for years with no clinical symptoms, the most effective way to avoid the oncogenic forms is to be vaccinated against them. Acquisition of HPV is usually through sexual transmission, but the virus can also be passed from mother to child or from very close contact with an infected individual, such as providing personal hygienic care. Naturally acquired HPV does not usually elicit a strong immune response, which prevents development of a memory immune response. Immune memory protects against potential future exposures. Thus, the vaccine Gardasil® was developed to vaccinate against HPV types 16 and 18. There is now the Gardasil-9® vaccine that provides protection against 9 types of HPV. Additional HPV vaccines also protect against several other types of HPV. Vaccination for all male and female preteens and previously unvaccinated males and females through age 26 is recommended by the Centers for Disease Control and Prevention.

For males, genital warts caused by HPV are usually readily visible. However, there is not an approved HPV-related cancer test for males. For females, there are two types of HPV-related cancer screenings available. The first is the traditional Pap test for females. It is recommended that females ages 21–65 be screened with a Pap test every 3 years. The Pap test involves collecting cells from the surface of the cervix for examination under a microscope. If the cells are abnormally shaped, as precancerous or cancerous cells would be, it is indicative that further testing should be done. However, the Pap test can be negative for abnormal cells even if the female has HPV. If that is the case, the HPV test is recommended to test if HPV is present. The HPV test is also recommended for females over 30 years of age even if the female has been vaccinated for HPV because the vaccine does not target all oncogenic forms of HPV. HPV testing is not recommended for females under age 30 or for females who have had a hysterectomy. Eventually, with continued vaccination, the oncogenic types may become less relevant to human health.

Predict 4

The identity of the cell surface receptors used by HPV to enter their host cell has not been completely identified but will most likely be known within the next several years. Propose a future mechanism that could use the cell surface receptor protein to prevent HPV uptake and the subsequent development of cancer-inducing uncontrolled cell division.

cavity. The endometrium consists of two layers: (1) the basal layer and (2) the functional layer. The thin, deep **basal layer** is the deepest part of the lamina propria and is continuous with the myometrium. The thicker, superficial **functional layer** consists of most of the lamina propria and the endothelium and lines the uterine cavity itself. The functional layer is so named because it undergoes changes and sloughing during the uterine cycle (see section 28.6). Small **spiral arteries** of the lamina propria supply blood to the functional layer of the endometrium. These blood vessels play an important role in the cyclic changes of the endometrium.

Columnar epithelial cells line the cervical canal, which contains **cervical mucous glands.** The mucus fills the cervical canal and acts as a barrier to substances that could pass from the vagina into the uterus. Near ovulation, the consistency of the mucus changes, easing the passage of sperm cells from the vagina into the uterus.

ASSESS YOUR PROGRESS

47. *Describe the structure of the uterine tube.*
48. *How are the uterine tubes involved in moving the oocyte or the zygote?*
49. *Name the parts of the uterus.*
50. *Describe the major ligaments holding the uterus in place.*
51. *Describe the layers of the uterine wall.*

Vagina

The **vagina** (vah-JIE-nah) is the female organ of copulation, receiving the penis during intercourse. It also allows menstrual flow and childbirth. The vagina is a tube about 10 cm long that extends from the uterus to the outside of the body (see figure 28.12). Longitudinal ridges called **columns** extend the length of the anterior and posterior vaginal walls, and several transverse ridges called **rugae** (ROO-gee) extend between the anterior and posterior columns. The superior, domed part of the vagina, the **fornix** (FOHR-niks), is attached to the sides of the cervix so that a part of the cervix extends into the vagina.

The wall of the vagina consists of an outer muscular layer and an inner mucous membrane. The muscular layer is smooth muscle that allows the vagina to increase in size to accommodate the penis during intercourse and to stretch greatly during childbirth. The mucous membrane is moist, stratified squamous epithelium that forms a protective surface layer. Lubricating fluid passes through the epithelium into the vagina. During intercourse, increased lubrication is provided by increased fluid released from the vaginal wall as well a secretions from the cervix and glands of the external genitalia.

The **hymen** (HIGH-men) is a thin mucous membrane that covers the **vaginal opening,** or *orifice.* Sometimes, the hymen completely closes the vaginal opening (a condition called imperforate hymen), and it must be removed to allow menstrual flow. More commonly, the hymen is perforated by one or several holes. The openings in the hymen are usually greatly enlarged during the first sexual intercourse. In addition, the hymen can be perforated earlier in a young female's life, such as during strenuous physical exercise. Thus, the absence of an intact hymen is an unreliable indicator of virginity.

ASSESS YOUR PROGRESS

52. *What are the functions of the vagina?*
53. *Describe the layers of the vaginal wall. What are rugae and columns?*
54. *What is the hymen?*

Female External Genitalia

The female external genitalia are called the **vulva** (VUL-vah), or *pudendum* (poo-DEN-dum). It consists of the vestibule and its surrounding structures (figure 28.16). The **vestibule** (VES-tih-byul) is the space into which the vagina opens posteriorly and the urethra opens anteriorly. A pair of thin, longitudinal skin folds called the **labia** (LAY-bee-ah; lips) **minora** (sing. labium minus) form a border on each side of the vestibule. A small, erectile structure called the **clitoris** (KLIT-oh-ris) is located in the anterior margin of the vestibule. Anteriorly, the two labia minora unite over the clitoris to form a fold of skin called the **prepuce.**

The clitoris is usually less than 2 cm in length and consists of a shaft and a distal glans. Well supplied with sensory receptors, it initiates and intensifies levels of sexual sensation. The clitoris contains two erectile structures, the **corpora cavernosa,** each of which expands at the base end of the clitoris to form the **crus of the clitoris** and attaches the clitoris to the pelvic bones. The corpora cavernosa of the clitoris are comparable to the corpora cavernosa of the penis, and they become engorged with blood as a result of sexual excitement. In most females, this engorgement results in an increase in the diameter, but not the length, of the clitoris. With increased diameter, the clitoris makes better contact with the prepuce and surrounding tissues and is more easily stimulated.

FUNDAMENTAL **Figure**

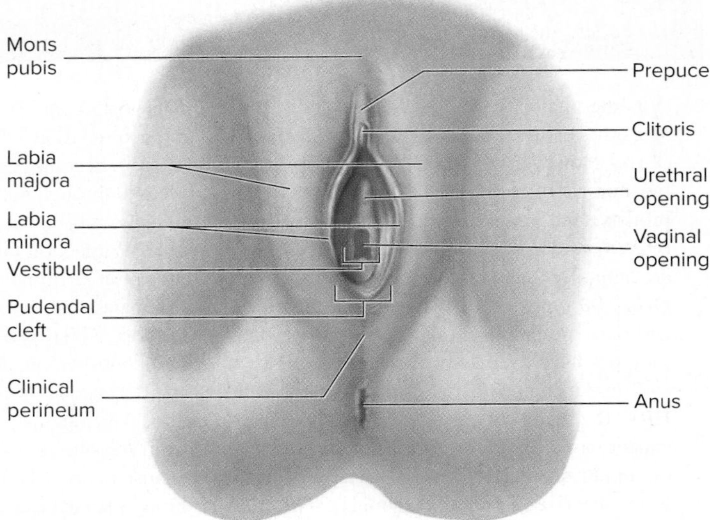

FIGURE 28.16 Female External Genitalia
The female external genitalia are called the vulva. It consists of the vestibule, labia majora, labia minora, and clitoris

Erectile tissue that corresponds to the corpus spongiosum of the male lies deep to and on the lateral margins of the vestibular floor on each side of the vaginal orifice. Each erectile body is called a **bulb of the vestibule.** Like other erectile tissue, it becomes engorged with blood and is more sensitive during sexual arousal. Expansion of the bulbs causes narrowing of the vaginal orifice and allows better contact of the vagina with the penis during intercourse.

Glands associated with the vestibule secrete a lubricating fluid that prevents drying of the vestibule. The ducts of the greater vestibular glands open on each side of the vestibule, between the vaginal opening and the labia minora. Additional small mucous glands, the **lesser vestibular glands,** or *paraurethral glands,* are located near the clitoris and urethral opening.

Lateral to the labia minora are two prominent, rounded folds of skin called the **labia majora** (sing. labium majus). Subcutaneous adipose tissue is primarily responsible for the prominence of the labia majora. The two labia majora unite anteriorly in an elevation over the pubic symphysis called the **mons pubis** (MONZ PYU-bis). The lateral surfaces of the labia majora and the surface of the mons pubis are covered with coarse hair. The medial surfaces are covered with numerous sebaceous and sweat glands. The space between the labia majora is called the **pudendal cleft.** Most of the time, the labia majora are in contact with each other across the midline, closing the pudendal cleft and concealing the deeper structures within the vestibule.

Perineum

Similar to the male perineum, the female **perineum** is divided into two triangles by the superficial and deep transverse perineal

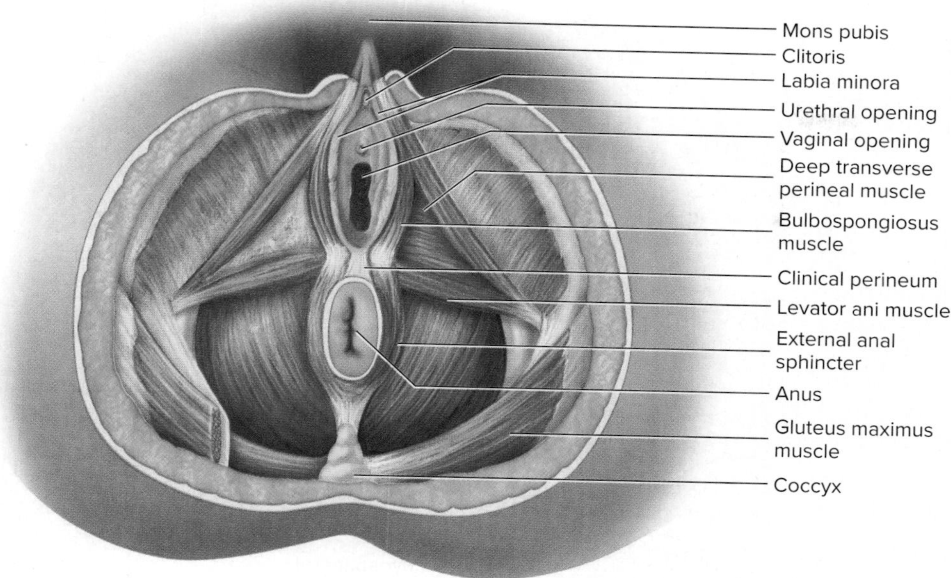

FIGURE 28.17 Inferior View of the Female Perineum
The perineum is divided into two regions by the superficial and deep transverse perineal muscles.

muscles (figure 28.17; see figure 28.3). The anterior urogenital triangle contains the external genitalia, and the posterior anal triangle contains the anal opening. The region between the vagina and the anus is the **clinical perineum.** The skin and muscle of this region can tear during childbirth. Allowing the perineum to stretch slowly during delivery may prevent tearing. Alternatively, an incision called an **episiotomy** (eh-peez-ee-OT-oh-mee) is sometimes made in the clinical perineum. This clean, straight incision is easier to repair than a tear would be. The use of episiotomy has decreased since the 1970s because research indicated that the procedure did not benefit the mother or the child in most cases.

ASSESS YOUR PROGRESS

55. *What are the vulva and vestibule?*
56. *What erectile tissue is in the clitoris and bulb of the vestibule?*
57. *What is the function of the clitoris and bulb of the vestibule?*
58. *Describe the labia minora, the prepuce, the labia majora, the pudendal cleft, and the mons pubis.*
59. *Where are the greater and lesser vestibular glands located? What is their function?*
60. *Describe the perineum.*
61. *What is the clinical perineum?*

Mammary Glands

The **mammary glands** are the organs of milk production and are located within the **breasts** (figure 28.18). The mammary glands are modified sweat glands. Externally, the breasts of both males and females have a raised **nipple** surrounded by a circular, pigmented region called the **areola** (ah-REE-oh-luh). The areolae normally have a slightly bumpy surface caused by **areolar glands** just below the surface. The areolar glands are actually rudimentary mammary glands. Secretions from these glands lubricate and protect the nipple and the areola from chafing during nursing.

Before puberty, the general structure of the breasts is similar in both males and females. The breasts possess a rudimentary glandular system, which consists mainly of ducts with sparse alveoli. The female breasts begin to enlarge during puberty, primarily under the influence of estrogen and progesterone. Increased sensitivity or pain in the breasts often accompanies this enlargement. Males often experience the same sensations during early puberty, and their breasts can even develop slight swellings; however, these symptoms usually disappear fairly quickly. On rare occasions, the breasts of a male become enlarged, a condition called **gynecomastia** (GUY-nih-koh-MAS-tee-ah).

Each adult female mammary gland usually consists of 15–20 glandular **lobes** covered by a considerable amount of adipose tissue. It is primarily this superficial adipose tissue that gives the breast its form. The lobes of each mammary gland form a conical mass, with the nipple located at the apex. Each lobe has a single **lactiferous** (lak-TIF-er-us; milk-producing) **duct,** which opens independently of other lactiferous ducts on the surface of the nipple. Just deep to the surface, each lactiferous duct enlarges to form a small, spindle-shaped **lactiferous sinus.** In lactating females, milk accumulates in the lactiferous sinuses during milk letdown. The lactiferous duct supplying a lobe subdivides to form smaller ducts, each of which supplies a **lobule.** Within a lobule, the ducts branch and become even smaller. In milk-producing, or lactating, mammary glands, the ends of these small ducts expand to form secretory sacs called **alveoli. Myoepithelial cells** surround the alveoli and contract to expel milk (see chapter 29). In nonlactating mammary glands, only the duct system is present.

A group of **suspensory ligaments,** or *Cooper ligaments,* support and hold the breasts in place. These ligaments extend from the fascia over the pectoralis major muscles to the skin over the mammary glands and prevent the breasts from excessive sagging.

The nipples are very sensitive to tactile stimulation and contain smooth muscle cells that contract, causing the nipple to become erect in response to stimulation. These smooth muscle cells respond to stimuli such as touch, cold, and sexual arousal.

ASSESS YOUR PROGRESS

62. *Describe the anatomy of the mammary glands.*
63. *Trace the route taken by a drop of milk from its site of production to the outside of the body.*

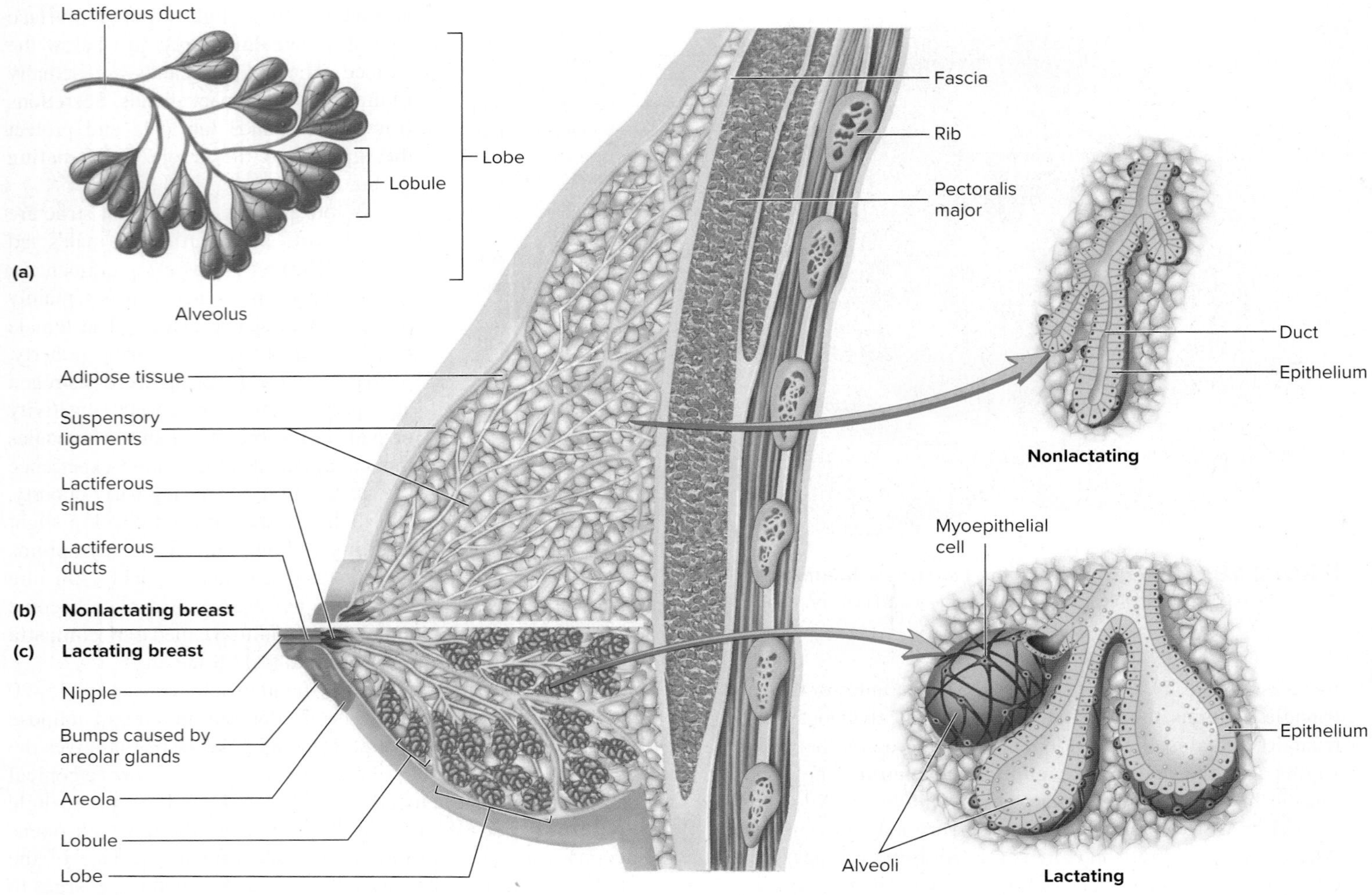

FIGURE 28.18 Anatomy of the Breast
(*a*) Lactiferous ducts divide to supply lobules, which form lobes. (*b*) In the nonlactating breast, only the duct system is present. (*c*) In the lactating breast, the ends of the mammary gland ducts have secretory sacs, called alveoli, that produce milk. Surrounding the alveoli are myoepithelial cells, which can contract, causing the milk to move out of the alveoli. APR

Clinical IMPACT 28.6

Fibrocystic Changes in the Breast

Fibrocystic changes in the breast are benign and include the formation of fluid-filled cysts, hyperplasia (accelerated growth) of the duct system of the breast, and the deposition of fibrous connective tissue. Breast pain sometimes occurs, especially during the luteal phase of the menstrual cycle and continuing until menstruation. These changes occur in approximately 10% of females who are less than 21 years of age, 25% of females in their reproductive years, and 50% of females who are postmenopausal. The cause of the condition is not known.

Some evidence suggests that females with certain types of duct hyperplasia, along with a family history of breast cancer, have an increased likelihood of developing breast cancer.

28.6 Physiology of Female Reproduction

LEARNING OUTCOMES

After reading this section, you should be able to

A. **Describe the changes that occur in females during puberty.**
B. **Explain the changes in the ovary during the ovarian cycle.**
C. **Explain the changes in the uterus during the uterine cycle.**
D. **List the hormones of the female reproductive system and explain their functions.**
E. **Explain how the secretion of female reproductive system hormones are regulated.**
F. **Explain the events that occur during the female sex act.**
G. **Describe the events that occur following fertilization of the oocyte.**

Clinical GENETICS 28.1 Breast Cancer

Breast cancer is a serious, often fatal disease that most often occurs in females. It is the most common cancer in North American females. Greater than 75% of the breast cancer cases occur in females older than 50 years of age, and 85% involve cancer of the epithelium of the mammary gland ducts (ductal carcinoma).

The risk for breast cancer appears to be lower if a female has had a child. Females who have never given birth are at a greater risk than those who have given birth. The younger a female is when her first child is born, the lower her risk of developing breast cancer. However, the risk for breast cancer is not lowered in young females who become pregnant but do not carry to full term. It appears that differentiation of the breast epithelium caused by the first pregnancy decreases the risk for cancer by reducing the amount of undifferentiated epithelium in the breast.

Breast cancer development correlates with long-term exposure to high levels of estrogen. Because pregnancy delays the menstrual cycle and decreases estrogen secretion, this may explain its effect on breast cancer risk. In addition, early menopause or removal of the ovaries also correlates with a reduced cancer risk. In both cases there is a decreased exposure of breast tissue to estrogen. Unfortunately, hormone replacement therapy for postmenopausal females correlates with an increased incidence of cancer; however, breast cancer incidence decreases with the use of drugs that block the effect of estrogen receptors.

A number of environmental factors have been associated with the development of breast cancer. Exposure to ionizing radiation, especially during adolescence and during pregnancy when epithelial cells are dividing more rapidly, is correlated with breast cancer. High dietary fat intake and obesity are also linked to breast cancer, although the fish oil–derived omega-3 fatty acids may help prevent cancer. Breast cancer rates are low in Japanese females; however, Japanese females who immigrate to the United States and adopt a Western diet have breast cancer rates close to those of females in the United States. A number of environmental factors that mimic estrogen, such as components of plastics, fuels, pharmaceuticals, and chlorine-based chemicals (such as DDT, PCBs, and chlorofluorocarbons), may increase the incidence of breast cancer.

Between 5% and 10% of breast cancers are hereditary. Females who have inherited specific gene mutations have an increased risk for breast cancer. Therefore, a history of breast cancer in a close relative, such as a mother or sister, makes breast cancer more likely, and the risk increases further if more than one close relative has had breast cancer, especially if the cancer affected both breasts and if it occurred before menopause. Genetic tests can identify breast cancer genes. However, the presence of breast cancer genes does not mean that cancer will develop. Some females who are known to be at high risk because of their genetic makeup have frequent breast examinations, whereas others elect to have their breasts surgically removed before cancer develops.

Mutations in the *BRCA1* and *BRCA2* genes are responsible for about 30–40% of inherited breast cancers. The *BRCA* genes are tumor suppressor genes, which normally suppress cell division. A person who has two mutated *BRCA* alleles is much more likely to develop breast cancer. Although a person with one normal and one mutated *BRCA* allele may have sufficient tumor suppressor activity, she has a greater risk of developing cancer because only one mutation in the remaining normal *BRCA* allele is necessary to eliminate tumor suppressor activity. Consequently, a person who has inherited two normal alleles is much less likely to develop breast cancer than a person who has inherited one or two mutated alleles.

Another tumor suppressor gene is called *p53*. The cells of almost 50% of all cancers have a mutated *p53* gene, and these cancers are more aggressive and more often fatal than cancers without a mutated *p53* gene. Approximately 20–40% of individuals with hereditary breast cancer have a mutated *p53* gene. *p53* is a regulatory gene that has been called the "guardian of the genome" because *p53* is activated when DNA is damaged. Once activated, *p53* arrests the cell cycle and initiates the repair of damaged DNA before the cell cycle continues. If the DNA damage is too extensive, *p53* causes cell death. Thus, the *p53* gene normally helps repair or eliminate cells that may become cancer cells. When *p53* is mutated, this protection against aberrant cell proliferation is reduced and there is a greatly increased risk for tumor formation.

H. **Describe the process of implantation of the embryo.**
I. **Discuss menopause, including the changes that result from it.**

Female reproduction is under hormonal and nervous control. The development of the female reproductive organs and their normal function depend on a number of hormones (table 28.2). Estrogen and progesterone are the female reproductive hormones. The term *estrogen* actually refers to several hormones, including estradiol, estrone, and estriol. Estradiol is the primary estrogen in humans and the most prevalent in the blood.

Puberty in Females

The initial change that results in puberty is most likely maturation of the hypothalamus. In females, puberty, which typically begins between ages 11 and 13 and is largely completed by age 16, is marked by the first episode of menstrual bleeding, which is called **menarche** (meh-NAR-key; *men,* month + *arche,* beginning). During puberty, the vagina, uterus, uterine tubes, and external genitalia begin to enlarge. Adipose tissue is deposited in the breasts and around the hips, causing them to enlarge and assume an adult form. In addition, pubic and axillary hair grow. The development of sexual drive is also associated with puberty.

The changes associated with puberty primarily result from the increasing rate of estrogen and progesterone secretion by the ovaries. Before puberty, estrogen and progesterone are secreted in very small amounts. At puberty, the cyclical adult pattern of hormone secretion is gradually established.

Before puberty, the rate of GnRH secretion from the hypothalamus and the rate of LH and FSH secretion from the anterior pituitary are very low. Estrogen and progesterone from the ovaries have a strong negative-feedback effect on the

TABLE 28.2 Major Reproductive Hormones and Their Effects in Females

Hormone	Source	Target Tissue	Response
Gonadotropin-releasing hormone (GnRH)	Hypothalamus	Anterior pituitary	Stimulates production of LH and FSH
Luteinizing hormone (LH)	Anterior pituitary	Ovaries	Causes follicles to complete maturation and undergo ovulation; causes ovulated follicle to become the corpus luteum
Follicle-stimulating hormone (FSH)	Anterior pituitary	Ovaries	Causes follicles to begin development
Prolactin	Anterior pituitary	Mammary glands	Stimulates milk secretion following childbirth
Estrogen	Follicles of ovaries	Uterus	Causes proliferation of endometrial cells
		Mammary glands	Causes development of mammary glands (especially duct systems)
		Anterior pituitary and hypothalamus	Has a positive-feedback effect before ovulation, resulting in increased LH and FSH secretion; has a negative-feedback effect, with progesterone, on the hypothalamus and anterior pituitary after ovulation, resulting in decreased LH and FSH secretion
		Other tissues	Causes development of secondary sexual characteristics
Progesterone	Corpus luteum of ovaries	Uterus	Causes hypertrophy of endometrial cells and secretion of fluid from uterine glands; helps maintain pregnancy
		Mammary glands	Causes development of mammary glands (especially alveoli)
		Anterior pituitary	Has a negative-feedback effect, with estrogen, on the hypothalamus and anterior pituitary after ovulation, resulting in decreased LH and FSH secretion
		Other tissues	Causes development of secondary sexual characteristics
Oxytocin*	Posterior pituitary	Uterus and mammary glands	Causes contraction of uterine smooth muscle during intercourse and childbirth; causes contraction of myoepithelial cells in the breast, resulting in milk letdown in lactating females
Human chorionic gonadotropin (hCG)	Placenta	Corpus luteum of ovaries	Maintains corpus luteum and increases its rate of progesterone secretion during the first one-third (first trimester) of pregnancy; increases testosterone production in testes of male fetuses

*Covered in chapter 29.

hypothalamus and pituitary. After the onset of puberty, the hypothalamus and anterior pituitary secrete larger amounts of GnRH, LH, and FSH. Estrogen and progesterone have less of a negative-feedback effect on the hypothalamus and pituitary, and a sustained increase in estrogen concentration has a positive-feedback effect. The normal cyclical pattern of reproductive hormone secretion that occurs during the menstrual cycle becomes established.

ASSESS YOUR PROGRESS

64. *Define* menarche. *Describe other physical changes that occur during female puberty.*

65. *What changes occur in LH, FSH, estrogen, and progesterone secretion during puberty?*

Menstrual Cycle

The term **menstrual** (MEN-stroo-al) **cycle** technically refers to the cyclic changes in sexually mature, nonpregnant females. Although the term *menstrual cycle* typically refers to the changes in the uterus, the term is often used to refer to all the cyclic events in the female reproductive system, including alterations in hormone secretion and changes in the ovaries.

In discussing the *menstrual cycle,* we normally describe it as 28 days long, although it can be as short as 18 days in some females and as long as 40 days in others (figure 28.19). Variation in duration of the menstrual cycle occurs among females, but can also occur from month to month in the same female, depending on many factors including nutrition, stress, and level of activity.

So that it is easier to discuss the processes occurring in different components of the female reproductive system, the menstrual cycle is divided into the ovarian cycle and the uterine cycle. The *ovarian cycle* describes the changes that are associated specifically with the ovaries, and the *uterine cycle* describes the changes that are associated specifically with the uterus.

Ovarian Cycle

The term **ovarian cycle** refers to the regular events that occur in the ovaries of sexually mature, nonpregnant females during the menstrual cycle. This cycle can be divided into the follicular phase, which occurs before ovulation, and the luteal phase, which occurs after ovulation (figure 28.19). During the follicular phase,

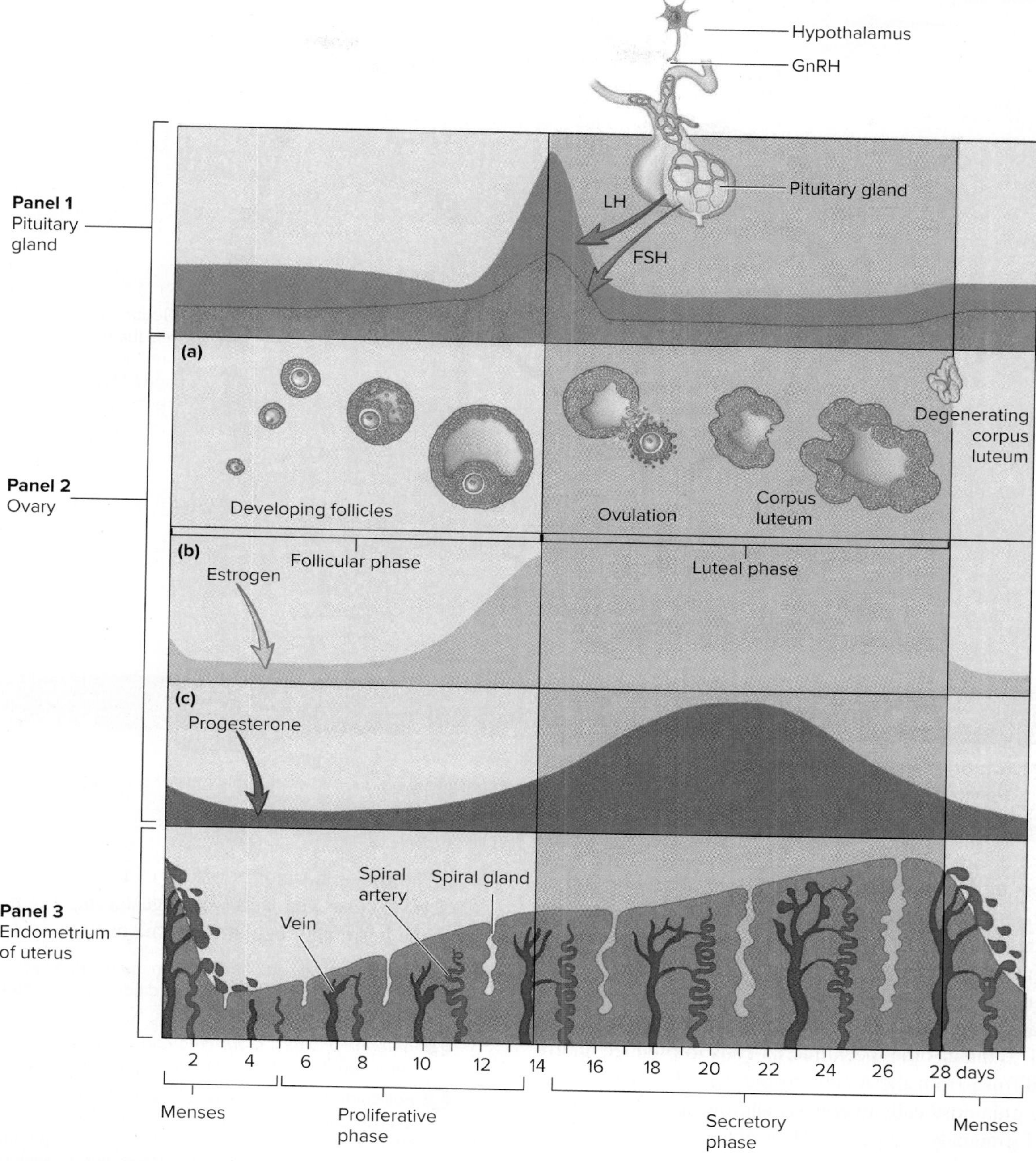

FIGURE 28.19 Menstrual Cycle
This graph depicts the changes that occur in blood hormone levels, follicles, and the endometrium during the menstrual cycle.

a primordial follicle develops into a mature follicle as the primary oocyte within undergoes the first meiotic division (see figure 28.15). Given the idealized 28-day cycle, the follicular phase occurs between days 1 and 14. On day 14, the mature follicle ruptures, releasing the newly formed secondary oocyte. Following ovulation, the follicle forms the endocrine structure, the corpus luteum. Ovulation marks the transition to the luteal phase (days 15–28). The corpus luteum secretes progesterone and a small amount of estrogen. If fertilization of the secondary oocyte occurs, the corpus luteum continues to secrete progesterone to maintain pregnancy, particularly in the first trimester, after which the placenta becomes the primary source for progesterone. If fertilization does not occur, the corpus luteum degenerates to form the corpus albicans (see figure 28.15).

As stated earlier, the menstrual cycle is hormonally regulated. We will first describe the hormonal changes that occur during the ovarian cycle. Figure 28.19 illustrates the hormonal fluctuations that occur during the menstrual cycle and will serve as a useful visual aid as we describe these changes. Panel 1 illustrates the levels of FSH and LH secretion by the anterior pituitary over the 28-day cycle. Panels 2*b*

PROCESS **Figure**

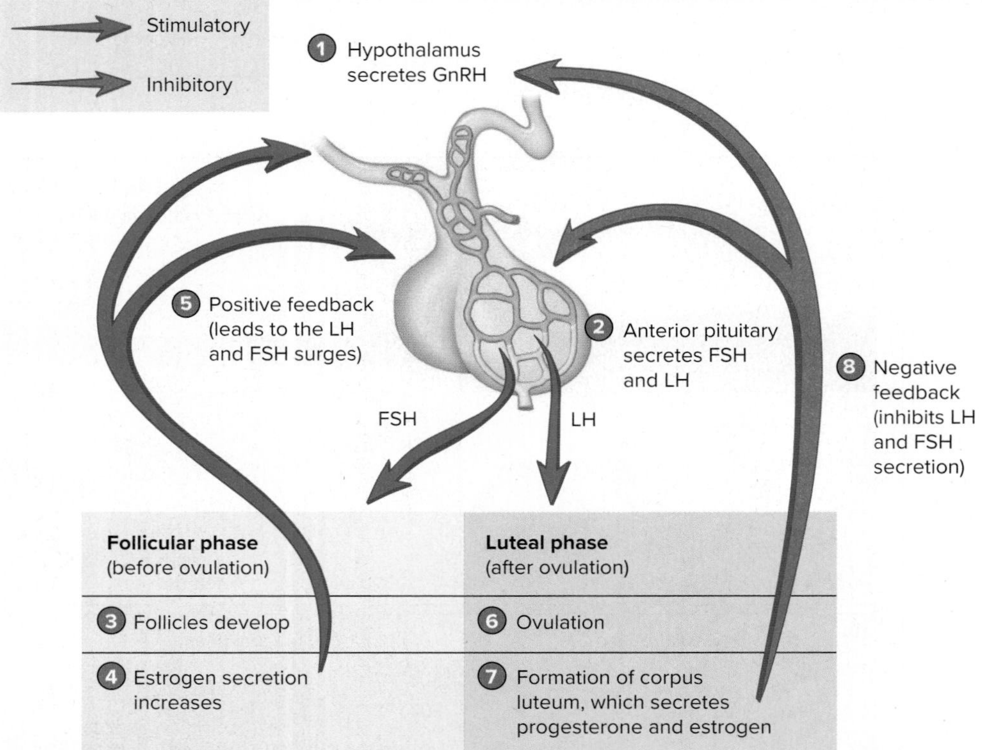

PROCESS **Figure 28.20**

Regulation of Hormone Secretion During the Ovarian Cycle

Hormone secretion is regulated from the anterior pituitary and the ovary before and after ovulation.

Explain how this process can involve positive feedback and negative feedback.

and 2*c* represent the levels of estrogen and progesterone secretion by structures of the ovary, respectively, over the same 28-day cycle.

Developing follicles of the ovary produce hormones important for the ovarian cycle. Hormone production by granulosa cells of the follicle involve a complex interplay among the gonadotropins (LH and FSH), granulosa cells of the follicle, and theca interna cells of the ovary. LH stimulates the theca interna cells to produce androgens, which diffuse from these cells to the granulosa cells. FSH stimulates the granulosa cells to convert androgens to estrogen. In addition, FSH gradually increases LH receptors in the granulosa cells. Estrogen produced by the granulosa cells increases LH receptors in the theca interna cells. Estrogen, in turn, increases receptors for LH in both theca interna cells and granulosa cells.

After LH receptors in the granulosa cells have increased, LH stimulates the granulosa cells to produce progesterone, which diffuses from the granulosa cells to the theca interna cells, where it is converted to androgens. These androgens are also converted to estrogen by the granulosa cells. Thus, the production of androgens by the theca interna cells increases, resulting in a gradual increase in estrogen secretion by granulosa cells throughout the follicular phase, even though only a small increase in LH secretion occurs. FSH levels actually decrease during the follicular phase because developing follicles produce inhibin, which has a negative-feedback effect on FSH secretion (figure 28.19).

The major hormones of the ovarian cycle include (1) FSH, (2) LH, (3) estrogen, and (4) progesterone. Figure 28.20 summarizes the hormonal regulation of the ovarian cycle.

1. *Hypothalamic secretion.* Early in the ovarian cycle, the hypothalamus increases release of GnRH. Additionally, the anterior pituitary sensitivity to GnRH increases.
2. *Anterior pituitary gland secretion.* As a result of increased GnRH secretion, the anterior pituitary increases secretion of FSH and LH.
3. *Follicular phase of ovarian cycle begins.* FSH and LH stimulate growth and maturation of ovarian follicles. FSH is primarily responsible for initiating the development of the primary follicles, and as many as 25 follicles begin to mature during each ovarian cycle. However, normally only 1 is ovulated. The follicles that start to develop in response to FSH may not ovulate during the same ovarian cycle in which they begin to mature, but they may ovulate one or two cycles later. The remaining follicles degenerate.
4. *Effects of estrogen secretion.* As follicles mature, they begin to secrete estrogens. Estrogen secretion by the follicle has three major effects: (a) stimulation of uterine endometrial proliferation, (b) positive feedback on hypothalamic and anterior pituitary secretion, and (c) determination of which follicles degenerate. Larger, more mature follicles appear to secrete estrogen and other substances that have an inhibitory effect on other, less mature follicles.
5. *LH surge and FSH surge.* As stated in step 4, estrogen has a positive-feedback effect on the hypothalamus and anterior pituitary, resulting in an increase in secretion of both LH and FSH, often referred to as the **LH surge** and **FSH surge.** The LH surge occurs

several hours earlier and to a greater degree than the FSH surge, and the LH surge can last up to 24 hours (see figure 28.19, *panel 1*).

6 *Ovulation and luteal phase of ovarian cycle begins.* The LH surge stimulates maturation of the follicle, including completion of meiosis I by the primary oocyte. Also, the LH surge triggers several events that are very much like inflammation in a mature follicle. These events result in ovulation, which involves the rupturing of the follicle and the release of the oocyte and corona radiata.

7 *Formation of corpus luteum.* Shortly after ovulation, the follicle's production of estrogen decreases and the remaining cells of the follicle differentiate into corpus luteum cells and begin to secrete progesterone and estrogen. Progesterone and estrogen secretion stimulate further development of the uterine endometrium (see "Uterine Cycle" later in this section).

8 *Negative-feedback effect of progesterone and estrogen secretion.* The increased progesterone and estrogen levels now have a negative-feedback effect on the hypothalamus and anterior pituitary, resulting in a decrease in FSH and LH secretion.

If the ovulated oocyte is fertilized, the developing embryo secretes the LH-like substance **human chorionic gonadotropin (hCG),** which keeps the corpus luteum from degenerating. As a result, blood levels of estrogen and progesterone do not decrease, and menses of the next uterine cycle (see description below) does not occur. If fertilization does not occur, hCG is not produced. The cells of the corpus luteum begin to atrophy after day 25 or 26, and the blood levels of estrogen and progesterone decrease rapidly, resulting in menses.

Predict 5

Predict the effect on the ovarian cycle of administering a relatively large amount of estrogen and progesterone just before the preovulatory LH surge. Also predict the consequences of continually administering high concentrations of GnRH.

Uterine Cycle

Recall that the endometrium of the uterus is composed of two layers: the basal layer and the functional layer. The term **uterine cycle** refers to changes that occur primarily in the functional layer of the endometrium during the menstrual cycle (figure 28.21; see figure 28.19). Other, more subtle changes also take place in the vagina and other structures during the menstrual cycle. Cyclic secretions of estrogen and progesterone are the primary cause of these changes.

The uterine cycle can be divided into three phases: (1) menses, (2) the proliferative phase, and (3) the secretory phase. Figure 28.21 illustrates these three phases. Table 28.3 summarizes these events as well.

1 **Menses** (MEN-seez) is a period of mild hemorrhage that occurs approximately once each month, during which the functional layer of the endometrium is sloughed and expelled from the uterus. **Menstruation** is the discharge of the sloughed endometrial tissue and blood.

2 The time between the ending of menses and ovulation is called the **proliferative phase.** During the proliferative phase, the endometrium of the uterus begins to regenerate. The remaining epithelial cells rapidly divide and replace the cells of the functional layer that were sloughed during the last menses. A relatively uniform layer of low cuboidal endometrial cells is produced. The cells later become columnar, and the layer of cells folds to form tubular **spiral glands.** Blood vessels called **spiral arteries** project through the delicate connective tissue that separates the individual spiral glands to supply nutrients to the endometrial cells.

3 The period after ovulation and before the next menses is called the **secretory phase** because of the maturation of and secretion by spiral glands. During the secretory phase, the endometrium becomes thicker, and the spiral glands develop to a greater extent and begin to secrete small amounts of a fluid rich in glycogen. Approximately 7 days after ovulation, or about day 21 of the menstrual cycle, the endometrium is prepared to receive a developing embryonic mass, if fertilization has occurred. If the developing embryonic mass arrives in the uterus too early or too late, the endometrium does not provide a suitable environment for it.

Clinical IMPACT 28.7

Menstrual Cramps and Amenorrhea

Menstrual cramps are the result of strong myometrial contractions that occur before and during menstruation. The cramps can result from excessive prostaglandin secretion. As the endometrium of the uterus sloughs off, it becomes inflamed, and prostaglandins are produced as part of the inflammatory process. Sloughing of the endometrium and uterine contractions are inhibited by progesterone but stimulated by estrogen. Many females can alleviate painful cramps by taking nonsteroidal anti-inflammatory drugs (NSAIDs), such as aspirin or ibuprofen, which inhibit prostaglandin biosynthesis, just before the onset of menstruation. These medications, however, are not effective in treating all painful menstruation, especially when the pain is not due to inflammation but to other conditions, such as tumors of the myometrium or obstruction of the cervical canal.

The absence of a menstrual cycle is called **amenorrhea** (ah-men-oh-REE-ah). If the pituitary gland does not function properly because of abnormal development, a female does not begin to menstruate at puberty. This condition is called **primary amenorrhea.** In contrast, if a female has had normal menstrual cycles and later stops menstruating, the condition is called **secondary amenorrhea.** One cause of secondary amenorrhea is anorexia, in which lack of food causes the hypothalamus to decrease GnRH secretion to levels so low that the menstrual cycle cannot occur. Many female athletes and ballet dancers who pursue rigorous training schedules have secondary amenorrhea. Physical stress coupled with inadequate food intake also results in very low GnRH secretion. Increased food intake, for anorexic females, and reduced training, for females who exercise intensely, generally restore normal hormone secretion and normal menstrual cycles.

Secondary amenorrhea can also result from a pituitary tumor that decreases FSH and LH secretion or from a lack of GnRH secretion from the hypothalamus due to head trauma or a tumor. In addition, secondary amenorrhea can occur due to a lack of normal hormone secretion from the ovaries, which can be caused by autoimmune diseases that attack the ovary or by polycystic ovarian disease, in which cysts in the ovary produce large amounts of androgens that are converted to estrogens by other body tissues. The increased estrogen prevents the normal cycle of FSH and LH secretion required for ovulation. Other hormone-secreting tumors of the ovary can also disrupt the normal menstrual cycle and result in amenorrhea.

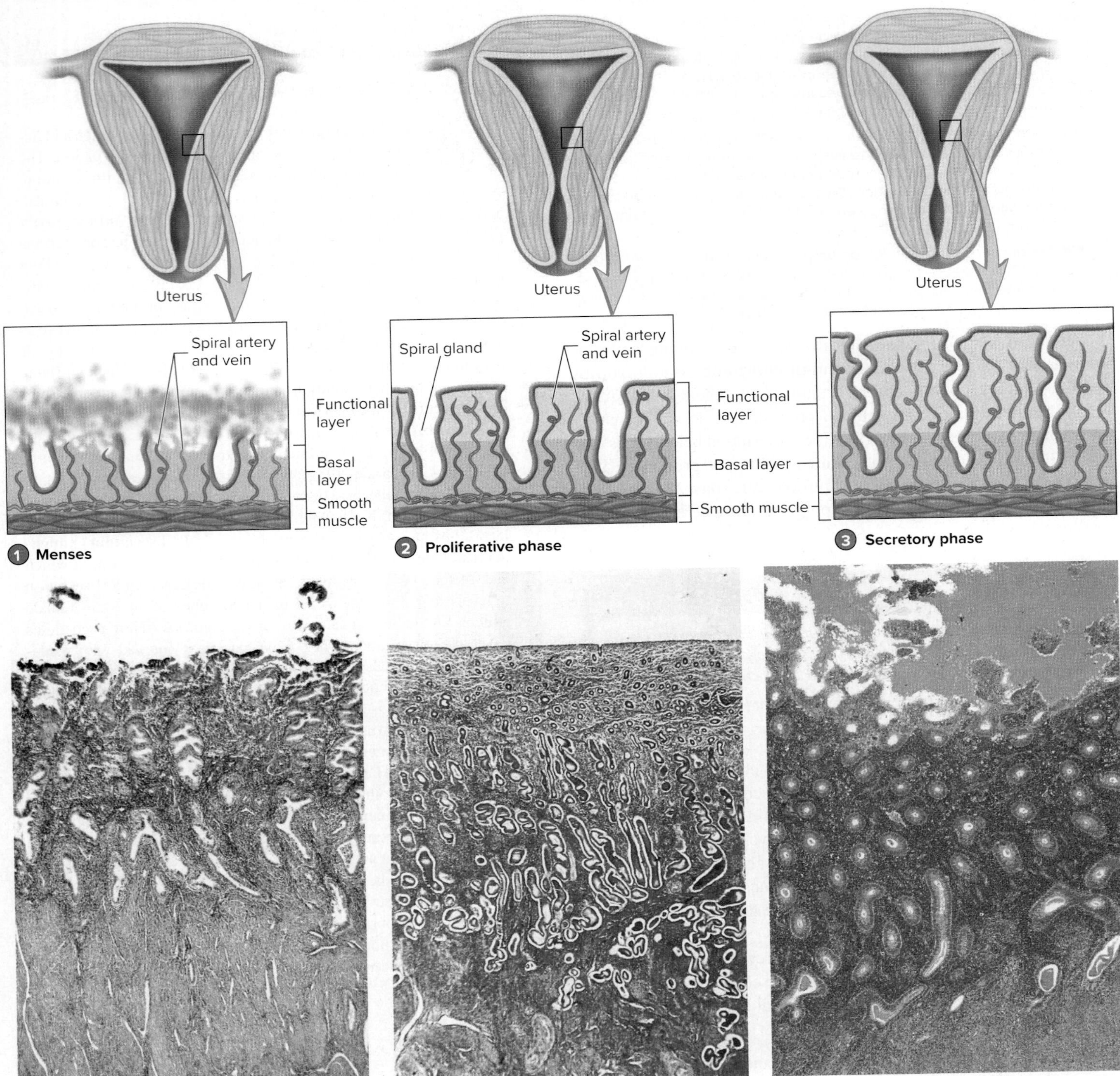

PROCESS Figure 28.21

Uterine Cycle

The uterine cycle is divided into three phases: (1) menses, (2) the proliferative phase, and (3) the secretory phase.

Understand *What events are occurring in the ovary during menses? At what point in the uterine cycle would a secondary oocyte form at the ovary?* (a) vetpathologist/Shutterstock; (b, c) Biophoto Associates/Science Source APR

TABLE 28.3 Events During the Menstrual Cycle

Menses (day 1 to day 4 or 5 of the menstrual cycle)	
Pituitary gland	The rate of FSH and LH secretion is low, but the rate of FSH secretion increases as progesterone levels decline.
Ovary	The rate of estrogen and progesterone secretion is low after degeneration of the corpus luteum produced during the previous menstrual cycle.
Uterus	In response to declining progesterone levels, the endometrial lining of the uterus sloughs off, resulting in menses followed by repair of the endometrium.
Proliferative Phase (from day 4 or 5 until ovulation on about day 14)	
Pituitary gland	The rate of FSH and LH secretion is only slightly elevated during most of the proliferative phase; FSH and LH secretions increase near the end of the proliferative phase in response to increasing estrogen secretion from the ovaries.
Ovary	Developing follicles secrete increasing amounts of estrogen, especially near the end of the proliferative phase; increasing FSH and LH cause additional estrogen secretion from the ovaries near the end of the proliferative phase.
Uterus	Estrogen causes endometrial cells of the uterus to divide. The endometrium of the uterus thickens, and tubelike glands form. Estrogen causes the cells of the uterus to be more sensitive to progesterone by increasing the number of progesterone receptors in uterine tissues.
Ovulation (about day 14)	
Pituitary gland	The rate of FSH and LH secretion increases rapidly just before ovulation in response to increasing estrogen levels. Increasing FSH and LH levels stimulate estrogen secretion, resulting in a positive-feedback cycle.
Ovary	LH causes final maturation of a mature follicle and initiates the process of ovulation. FSH acts on immature follicles and causes several of them to begin to enlarge.
Uterus	The endometrium continues to divide in response to estrogen.
Secretory Phase (from about day 14 to day 28)	
Pituitary gland	Estrogen and progesterone reach levels high enough to inhibit FSH and LH secretion from the pituitary gland.
Ovary	After ovulation, the follicle is converted to the corpus luteum; the corpus luteum secretes large amounts of progesterone and smaller amounts of estrogen from shortly after ovulation until about day 24 or 25. If fertilization does not occur, the corpus luteum degenerates after about day 25, and the rate of progesterone secretion rapidly declines to low levels.
Uterus	In response to progesterone, the endometrial cells enlarge, the endometrial layer thickens, and the glands of the endometrium reach their greatest degree of development; the endometrial cells secrete a small amount of fluid. After progesterone levels decline, the endometrium begins to degenerate.
Menses (day 1 to day 4 or 5 of the next menstrual cycle)	
Pituitary gland	The rate of LH remains low, and the rate of FSH secretion increases as progesterone levels decline.
Ovary	The rate of estrogen and progesterone secretion is low.
Uterus	In response to declining progesterone levels, the endometrial lining of the uterus sloughs off, resulting in menses followed by repair of the endometrium.

The first day of menses is considered day 1 of the uterine cycle, and menses typically lasts 4–5 days. Recall that ovulation occurs on about day 14 of a 28-day menstrual cycle; however, the timing of ovulation varies from individual to individual and even within a single individual from one menstrual cycle to the next. The time between ovulation (day 14) and the next menses is typically 14 days. The time between the first day of menses and the day of ovulation is more variable than the time between ovulation and the next menses.

Estrogen causes the endometrial cells and, to a lesser degree, the myometrial cells to divide during the proliferative phase. It also makes the uterine tissue more sensitive to progesterone by stimulating the synthesis of progesterone receptor molecules within the uterine cells. After ovulation, during the secretory phase, progesterone from the corpus luteum binds to the progesterone receptors, resulting in cellular hypertrophy in the endometrium and myometrium and causing the endometrial cells to become secretory. Estrogen increases the tendency of the smooth muscle cells of the uterus to contract in response to stimuli, but progesterone inhibits smooth muscle contractions. When progesterone levels increase while estrogen levels are low, contractions of the uterine smooth muscle are reduced.

In uterine cycles in which pregnancy does not occur, progesterone and estrogen levels decline to low levels as the corpus luteum degenerates (see figure 28.20, *step 8*). The drop in these hormones initiates the beginning of the next uterine cycle, beginning with the next menses. As a consequence of low progesterone and estrogen levels, the uterine lining begins to degenerate. The spiral arteries constrict in a rhythmic pattern for longer and longer periods as progesterone levels fall. As a result, all but the basal parts of the spiral glands become ischemic and then necrotic. As the cells become necrotic, they slough into the uterine lumen. The necrotic endometrium, mucous secretions, and a small amount of blood released from the spiral arteries make up the menstrual fluid. Decreases in progesterone levels and increases in inflammatory substances that stimulate myometrial smooth muscle cells cause uterine contractions, which expel the menstrual fluid from the uterus through the cervix and into the vagina.

Apply Predict 6

Predict the effect on the endometrium of maintaining high progesterone levels in the blood, including periods of time during which estrogen normally increases following menstruation.

ASSESS YOUR PROGRESS

66. *What are the major phases of the ovarian cycle? What happens during these phases?*
67. *On which day does ovulation occur?*
68. *What roles do FSH and LH play in the ovarian cycle?*
69. *Describe how the cyclic increase and decrease in FSH and LH is produced.*
70. *What is the importance of the LH surge and the FSH surge?*
71. *Where is hCG produced, and what effect does it have on the ovary?*
72. *What are the phases of the uterine cycle?*
73. *What is the length of a typical menstrual cycle? What event marks the beginning of a cycle?*
74. *What are the effects of estrogen and progesterone on the uterus?*

Female Sexual Behavior and the Female Sex Act

The female sex drive, like the sex drive in males, depends on hormones. The adrenal gland and other tissues, such as the liver, convert steroids, such as progesterone, to androgens. Androgens and possibly estrogens affect cells in the brain, especially in the hypothalamus, to influence sexual behavior. However, androgens and estrogen alone do not control sex drive. In other words, sex drive cannot be predictably increased simply by injecting these hormones into healthy individuals. Psychological factors also affect sexual behavior. For example, after removal of the ovaries or after menopause, many females report an increased sex drive because they no longer are concerned with the probability of pregnancy.

The neural pathways, both sensory and motor, involved in controlling sexual responses are the same for females and males. Sensory action potentials are conducted from the genitals to the sacral region of the spinal cord, where reflexes that govern sexual responses are integrated. Ascending pathways, primarily the spinothalamic tracts (see chapter 14), conduct sensory information through the spinal cord to the brain, and descending pathways conduct action potentials back to the sacral region of the spinal cord. As a result, cerebral influences modulate the sacral reflexes. Motor action potentials are conducted from the spinal cord to the reproductive organs by both parasympathetic and sympathetic nerve fibers and to skeletal muscles by the somatic motor nerve fibers.

During sexual excitement, as a result of parasympathetic stimulation, erectile tissue within the clitoris and around the vaginal opening becomes engorged with blood. The nipples of the breast often become erect as well. The mucous glands within the vestibule, especially the vestibular glands, secrete small amounts of mucus. Large amounts of mucuslike fluid are also extruded into the vagina through its wall, although no well-developed mucous glands are within the vaginal wall. These secretions provide lubrication that allows for easy entry of the penis into the vagina and easy movement of the penis during intercourse. Tactile stimulation of the female's genitals that occurs during sexual intercourse, along with psychological stimuli, normally triggers an orgasm. The vaginal, uterine, and perineal muscles contract rhythmically, and muscle tension increases throughout much of the body. After the sex act, a period of resolution characterized by an overall sense of satisfaction and relaxation occurs. In contrast to males, females can be receptive to further stimulation and can experience successive orgasms. Although orgasm is a pleasurable component of sexual intercourse, it is not necessary for females to experience an orgasm for fertilization to occur.

Female Fertility and Pregnancy

After sperm cells are ejaculated into the vagina during sexual intercourse, they are transported through the cervix, the body of the uterus, and the uterine tubes to the ampulla (figure 28.22). The forces responsible for moving sperm cells through the female reproductive tract include the swimming ability of the sperm cells and possibly the muscular contractions of the uterus and the uterine tubes. During sexual intercourse, oxytocin is released from the posterior pituitary of the female, and the semen introduced into the vagina contains prostaglandins. Both of these substances stimulate smooth muscle contractions in the uterus and uterine tubes, which may also enhance the movement of sperm cells through the female reproductive tract.

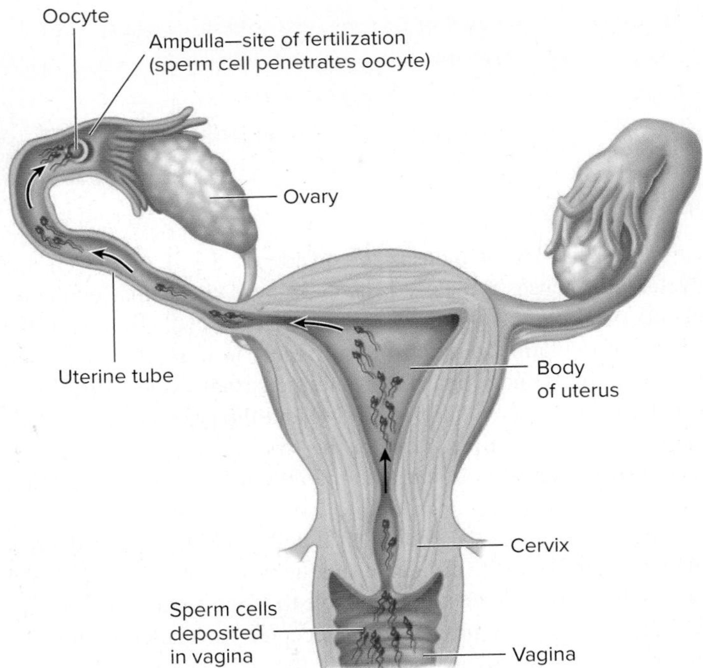

FIGURE 28.22 Sperm Cell Movement
Sperm cells are deposited into the vagina as part of the semen when the male ejaculates. Sperm cells pass through the cervix, the body of the uterus, and the uterine tube. Fertilization normally occurs when the oocyte is in the upper one-third of the uterine tube (the ampulla).

PROCESS **Figure**

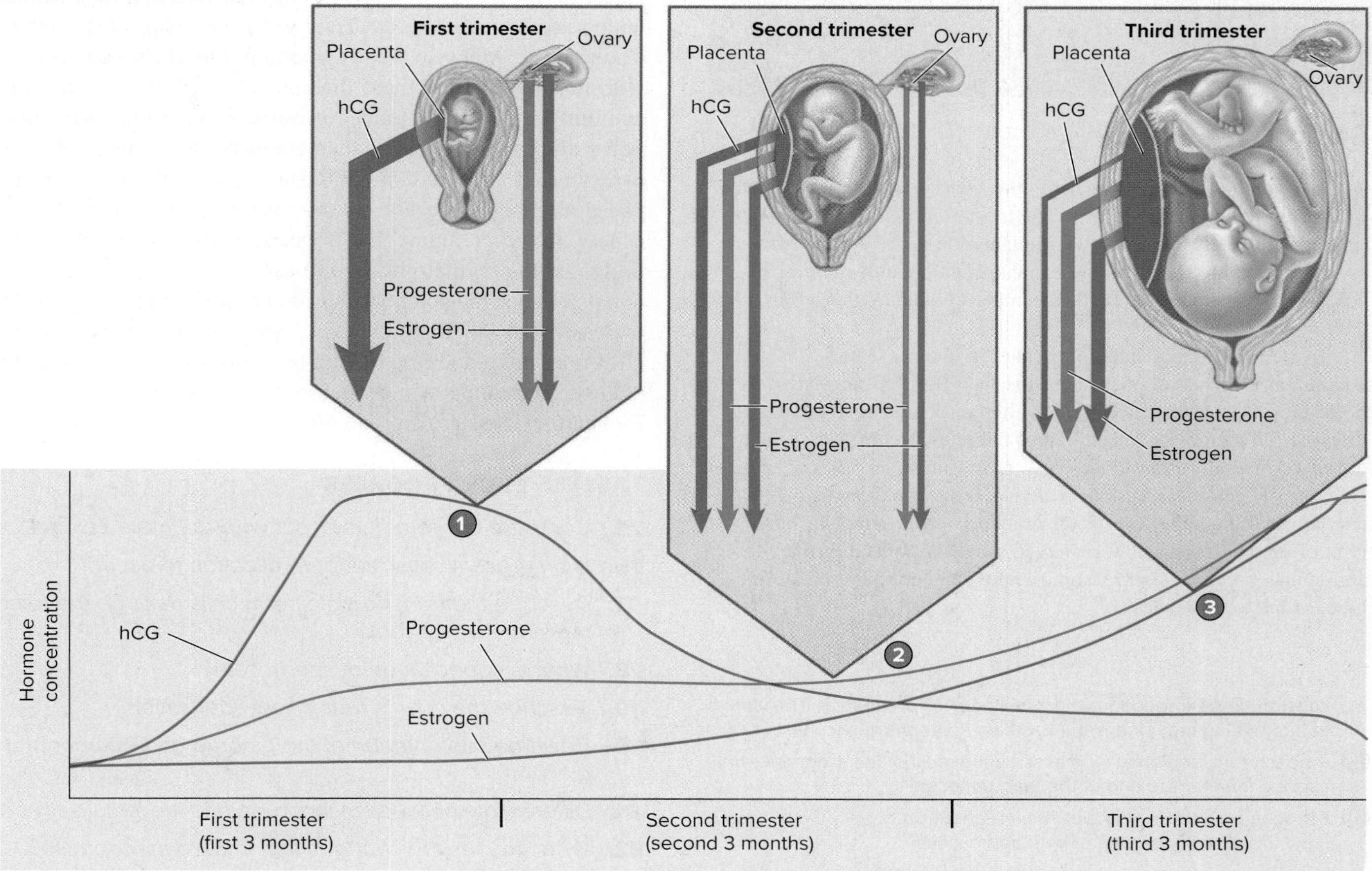

PROCESS **Figure 28.23**

Changes in Hormone Concentration and Changes in Hormone Secretion During Pregnancy

During pregnancy, hCG, progesterone, and estrogen are secreted. The placenta secretes hCG. Early in the pregnancy, the ovaries are responsible for progesterone and estrogen secretion; however, by midpregnancy, there is a shift to placental secretion of these two hormones.

Why is hCG secretion important during the first trimester?

While passing through the vagina, uterus, and uterine tubes, the sperm cells undergo **capacitation** (kuh-PAS-ih-tay-shun), which involves the removal of proteins and the modification of glycoproteins of the sperm cell plasma membranes. Following capacitation, as the sperm cells move through the female reproductive tract, some of them release acrosomal enzymes. These enzymes help the sperm cells penetrate the cervical mucus, cumulus mass, zona pellucida, and oocyte plasma membrane.

One sperm cell enters the secondary oocyte, and fertilization occurs (see figure 28.15 and chapter 29). The oocyte can be fertilized for up to 24 hours after ovulation, and some sperm cells remain viable in the female reproductive tract for up to 6 days, although most of them have degenerated after 24 hours. For fertilization to occur successfully, sexual intercourse must occur between 5 days before and 1 day after ovulation.

For the next several days following fertilization, a sequence of cell divisions occurs while the developing embryo passes through the uterine tube to the uterus. By 7 or 8 days after ovulation, which is day 21 or 22 of the average menstrual cycle, the endometrium of the uterus has been prepared for implantation. Estrogen and progesterone have caused it to reach its maximum thickness and secretory activity, and the developing embryo begins to implant. The outer layer of the developing embryo, the **trophoblast** (TROH-foh-blast), secretes proteolytic enzymes that digest the cells of the thickened endometrium (see chapter 29), and the developing embryo digests its way into the endometrium to form part of the **placenta** (plah-SEN-tah), the organ of nutrient and waste exchange between the embryo and the mother.

Throughout the pregnancy, several hormones are secreted by the placenta and ovary, including (1) human chorionic gonadotropin (hCG), (2) estrogen, and (3) progesterone. Figure 28.23 depicts the changes in these hormone levels over the course of the pregnancy.

1. The embryo and developing placenta secrete hCG, which is transported in the blood to the ovary and causes the corpus luteum to remain functional. As a consequence, both estrogen and progesterone levels continue to increase rather than decrease. The secretion of hCG increases rapidly and reaches a peak about 8–9 weeks after fertilization. Subsequently, hCG levels in the circulatory system have declined to a lower level by 16 weeks and remain at a relatively

Clinical IMPACT 28.8

Ectopic Pregnancy

If implantation occurs anywhere other than in the uterine cavity, an ectopic pregnancy results. The most common site of ectopic pregnancy is the uterine tube. Implantation in the uterine tube is eventually fatal to the fetus and can cause the tube to rupture. The possibility of hemorrhage makes ectopic pregnancy dangerous to the mother as well.

In rare cases, implantation occurs in the mesenteries of the abdominal cavity. Although the fetus may develop normally, the pregnancy is considered extremely high-risk due to the serious threat to the mother's life and that of the fetus. Severe hemorrhaging at or near the time of delivery is the most serious concern. Delivery by cesarean section, with special precautions to prevent uncontrolled bleeding, can result in a successful outcome for this type of ectopic pregnancy. However, maternal mortality rates for abdominal pregnancies are significantly higher than for uterine tube ectopic pregnancies.

constant level throughout the remainder of pregnancy. The detection of hCG in the urine is the basis for some pregnancy tests.

2. Progesterone secretion increases during most of the pregnancy until it levels off near the end of the third trimester.
3. Estrogen levels increase slowly throughout pregnancy, with a more rapid increase as the time of birth approaches.

The progesterone and estrogen secreted by the corpus luteum are essential for the maintenance of pregnancy. After the placenta forms from the trophoblast and uterine tissue, however, it also begins to secrete progesterone and estrogen. After the first 3 months of pregnancy, the corpus luteum is no longer needed to maintain pregnancy. Instead, the placenta, in addition to its function of nutrient and waste exchange between the fetus and the mother, functions as an endocrine gland that secretes sufficient quantities of progesterone and estrogen to maintain pregnancy. Progesterone and estrogen levels increase in the female's blood throughout pregnancy (figure 28.23).

Menopause

When a female is 40–50 years old, menstrual cycles become less regular, and ovulation often does not occur consistently. Eventually, menstrual cycles stop completely. The cessation of menstrual cycles is called **menopause** (MEN-oh-pawz). The time from the onset of irregular cycles to the complete cessation, which is often 3 to 5 years, is called **perimenopause,** or the *female climacteric* (KLIE-mak-ter-ik).

Menopause is associated with changes in the ovaries. The number of follicles remaining in the ovaries of menopausal females is small. In addition, the follicles that remain become less sensitive to stimulation by LH and FSH; therefore, fewer mature follicles and corpora lutea are produced.

Older females experience gradual changes in response to the reduced amount of estrogen and progesterone produced by the ovaries (table 28.4). For example, some females experience sudden episodes of uncomfortable sweating (hot flashes), fatigue, anxiety, temporary decreases in sex drive, and occasionally severe emotional disturbances. Many of these symptoms can be treated successfully with hormone replacement therapy (HRT). HRT usually involves administering small amounts of estrogen, or estrogen in combination with progesterone, and then gradually decreasing the treatment over time. It appears that administering estrogen following menopause also helps prevent osteoporosis and may reduce colorectal cancer. However, although estrogen therapy has been successful, it prolongs the symptoms associated with menopause in many females, and some potential side effects are of concern, including an increased risk for breast, ovarian, and uterine cancer. In addition, HRT does not reduce the risk for heart disease for the first few years after the beginning of menopause. Some data indicate that the risk for heart attacks, strokes, and blood clots is also increased.

ASSESS YOUR PROGRESS

75. *Compare the female sex act with the male sex act.*
76. *Is an orgasm required for fertilization to occur?*
77. *Describe the transport of sperm cells through the female reproductive system.*
78. *What is capacitation of sperm cells?*
79. *Describe the events that follow fertilization.*
80. *Describe implantation of the embryo and formation of the placenta.*
81. *Differentiate between menopause and the female climacteric.*
82. *What causes the changes that lead to menopause?*

Clinical IMPACT 28.9

Causes of Female Infertility

The causes of infertility in females include malfunctions of the uterine tubes, reduced hormone secretion from the pituitary gland or the ovaries, and interruption of implantation.

Uterine tube malfunction can occur when infections result in pelvic inflammatory disease (PID), which causes adhesions to form in one or both uterine tubes.

Inadequate secretion of LH and FSH can result in reduced ovulation. The insufficient amount of hormones may be caused by hypothyroidism, trauma to the hypothalamus, infarctions of the hypothalamus or anterior pituitary gland, or tumors.

Interruption of implantation may result from uterine tumors or conditions causing abnormal ovarian hormone secretion.

Endometriosis (EN-doh-mee-tree-OH-sis), in which endometrial tissue is present in abnormal locations, also reduces fertility. Generally, endometriosis is thought to result when some endometrial cells pass from the uterus through the uterine tubes into the pelvic cavity, where they invade the peritoneum. Because the endometrium is sensitive to estrogen and progesterone, the areas where the endometrial cells have invaded periodically become inflamed. Endometriosis is one possible cause of abdominal pain associated with menstruation.

TABLE 28.4 Possible Changes Caused by Decreased Ovarian Hormone Secretion in Postmenopausal Females

Affected Structures and Functions	Changes
Menstrual cycle	Five to 7 years before menopause, the cycle becomes less regular; finally, the number of cycles in which ovulation occurs decreases, and corpora lutea do not develop.
Uterine tubes	Little change occurs.
Uterus	Irregular menstruation is gradually followed by no menstruation; the chance of cystic glandular hypertrophy of the endometrium increases; the endometrium finally atrophies, and the uterus becomes smaller.
Vagina and external genitalia	The dermis and epithelial lining become thinner; the vulva becomes thinner and less elastic; the labia majora become smaller; pubic hair decreases; the vaginal epithelium produces less glycogen; vaginal pH increases; reduced secretion leads to dryness; the vagina is more easily inflamed and infected.
Skin	The epidermis becomes thinner; melanin synthesis increases.
Cardiovascular system	Hypertension and atherosclerosis occur more frequently.
Vasomotor instability	Hot flashes and increased sweating are correlated with the vasodilation of cutaneous blood vessels; hot flashes are not caused by abnormal FSH and LH secretion but are related to decreased estrogen levels.
Sex drive	Temporary changes, such as either decreases or increases in sex drive, are often associated with the onset of menopause.
Fertility	Fertility begins to decline approximately 10 years before the onset of menopause; by age 50, almost all oocytes and follicles have been lost; the loss is gradual, and no increased follicular degeneration is associated with the onset of menopause.

Clinical IMPACT 28.10 Birth Control Methods

Birth control methods, also called *contraception methods,* are procedures or devices used to prevent pregnancy (figure 28.24). In addition, protection from sexually transmitted infections (STIs, table 28.5) can be achieved with some birth control methods. There are six main types of birth control. They are listed in order from the most effective methods to the least effective methods: (1) long-acting reversible contraception, (2) sterilization, (3) hormonal methods, (4) barrier methods, (5) fertility awareness, and (6) emergency contraception. For each of these methods, there are measures of effectiveness for perfect use each time compared with typical use. We express the effectiveness of a particular birth control method as the number out of every 100 females who could become unintentionally pregnant with typical use within the first year of beginning a particular method. We present a few examples of each type of birth control rather than an exhaustive list of all birth control methods that are available.

Long-Acting Reversible Contraception

This type of birth control provides the highest rates of effectiveness with typical use (figure 28.24*a*). In addition, these methods do not require daily action or action with each incidence of sexual intercourse. However, none of these listed methods reduce the risk of STIs.

1. *Intrauterine devices*
   An **intrauterine device (IUD)** is a medical device that is placed in a female's uterus through the cervix by a medical caregiver. There are two main types of IUDs: (1) a copper IUD and (2) a synthetic progesterone-coated or levonorgestrel-releasing (LNG-IUD). Copper IUDs are effective for up to 10 years, while the LNG-IUDs are effective for approximately 5 years. Both types of IUDs work primarily by preventing fertilization through thickening of cervical mucus. The thicker mucus prevents sperm cells from entering the uterus. In addition, the copper from the copper IUDs damages sperm cells. Both types of IUDs result in less than 1 unintended pregnancy/100 females.
2. *Birth control implant*
   The **implant** is a small capsule containing etonogestrel, or synthetic progesterone, that a female's medical caregiver places under the skin of the upper arm. It slowly releases hormone for a period of 3–5 years. The hormone acts to thicken the cervical mucus, which prevents sperm cells from entering the uterus; the hormone also prevents ovulation. The implant results in less than 1 unintended pregnancy/100 females.

Permanent Methods of Birth Control

A male or female may choose a surgical sterilization method as a form of permanent birth control (figure 28.24*b*). None of these listed methods reduce the risk of STIs.

1. *Female sterilization*
   In females, the most common permanent birth control is **tubal ligation** where the uterine tubes are blocked or cut. The cutting or blocking of the uterine tubes prevents the oocyte and sperm cell from meeting, and thus prevents fertilization. Tubal ligations result in less than 1 unintended pregnancy/100 females.
2. *Male sterilization*
   The permanent form of birth control in males is a **vasectomy** where the ductus (vas) deferens is cut or blocked. A vasectomy prevents sperm cells from being ejaculated as part of the semen. Thus, no sperm cells enter the vagina. Three months after surgery, a vasectomy results in less than 1 unintended pregnancy/100 females.

Hormonal Methods of Birth Control

The principal mechanism of hormonal birth control methods is prevention of ovulation (figure 28.24*c*). Development of male hormonal birth control to inhibit sperm cell production is under investigation and is not widely available. Some of these methods require daily attention and none of these reduce the risk of STIs.

1. *Injectables*
   These hormonal methods must be injected under the skin every 2–3 months for progesterone-only injectables and into the muscle every month for combined injectable contraceptives. The progesterone-only injectable acts to thicken cervical mucus to prevent sperm cell entry into the uterus as well as preventing ovulation. The combined injectables prevent ovulation. Injectables result in about 6 unintended pregnancies/100 females. The challenge with injectables is being sure to receive repeat injections within the proper time frame.
2. *Pills*
   Oral contraceptives are taken almost exclusively by females since male oral contraceptives are not currently available. One form, referred to as "the pill," is a combination of estrogen and progestogen (synthetic progesterone) and works to prevent ovulation. Another form, "the minipill," contains only progestogen and works to thicken cervical mucus. Each of these pills results in about 9 unintended pregnancies/100 females. The challenge with the pills is remembering to take a pill each day.
3. *Patch and vaginal ring*
   Each of these methods continuously releases progestogen and estrogen for 3 weeks and then a new one is put into place. The transdermal contraceptive patch, also simply called the patch, is applied directly to the skin every 3 weeks. The vaginal ring is inserted into the vagina and remains in place for 3 weeks and is then removed. A new ring is inserted after 1 week. Each of these methods prevents ovulation and results in about 9 unintended pregnancies/100 females. The challenge is to remember to change the patch or ring on the appropriate schedule.

Barrier Methods of Birth Control

A barrier method is a device that physically prevents the sperm cells and oocyte from meeting (figure 28.24*d*). The major advantage of certain barrier methods is that these are the only contraceptive methods that also reduce the risk of STI transmission. To reduce the risk of STIs, the Centers for Disease Control and Prevention (CDC) recommends that condoms should always be used.

1. *Female condom*
   A female condom is made of thin, soft plastic, which fits inside the female's vagina. The condom traps any sperm cells released into the vagina and prevents them from reaching the oocyte. It also protects against HIV and other STIs. Use of the female condom results in about 21 unintended pregnancies/100 females. The challenge with the female condom is that it must be inserted before each incidence of sexual intercourse.
2. *Male condom*
   A male condom is a covering that is placed over a male's erect penis. Condoms can be made of several different materials, including natural latex, Vytex©, which has been treated to remove 90% of proteins responsible for latex allergies, or synthetic latex, called polyisoprene. There are also completely nonlatex condoms made of polyurethane, and "lambskin" condoms, which are made of sheep intestine. However, the latter have not been shown to reduce the risk of STIs. All other condoms reduce the risk of HIV transmission and many other STIs. Use of male condoms results in approximately 18 unintended pregnancies/100 females. The challenge is to use them correctly with every instance of intercourse.
3. *Diaphragm*
   A diaphragm is a flexible latex dome that a female inserts into her vagina along with a spermicide before each instance of sexual intercourse. The diaphragm will unfold and fit over the cervix to block sperm cells from entering the uterus. However, unlike the other barrier methods, such as the male and female condoms, a diaphragm does not prevent transmission of STIs. In addition, a diaphragm must be refitted in the event of a significant (20%) weight gain or loss. A diaphragm results in about 12 unintended pregnancies/100 females.

Fertility-Awareness-Based Methods of Birth Control

With fertility-awareness-based methods, a female determines and tracks the days when she is most fertile (figure 28.24*e*). In each menstrual cycle, there is approximately a 6–8 day window during which a female has the greatest chance of becoming pregnant if she has unprotected intercourse. This window is due to the fact that both the oocyte and sperm cell are viable for a period of time inside the female reproductive tract. Sperm cells are able to survive up to 5 days inside the female. The oocyte is viable for up to 24 hours after ovulation. Thus, fertility-awareness-based methods require focused attention. It is estimated that only 25–30% of females know when their most fertile period occurs.

1. *Standard days method*
   A female tracks her fertile period using a tracking tool such as cycle beads, or an app for her smartphone. This method is effective for females whose cycles are 26–32 days long. Using this method, around 12 in 100 females experienced an unintended pregnancy.
2. *Two-day method*
   Females monitor their cervical mucus traits such as color and consistency. Around 14 in 100 females become unintentionally pregnant using this method. When cervical mucus monitoring is combined with body temperature tracking, this method is called the symptothermal method and results in only 2 in 100 females becoming unintentionally pregnant.

Emergency Contraception

If unprotected intercourse occurs, ingestion of emergency contraceptive pills or insertion of a copper IUD significantly lowers the possibility of an unintended pregnancy. Both methods must be utilized within 5 days after unprotected intercourse. Emergency contraceptive pills such as Plan B (the morning-after pill) or Ella (the week-after pill) disrupt or delay ovulation. The copper IUD works to immobilize sperm cells, preventing them from reaching the oocyte. It also causes thinning of the endometrium and potentially inhibits the ability of oocytes to be fertilized. These methods result in only 1 in 100 unintended pregnancies.

Traditional Methods of Birth Control

Some traditional birth control methods are still in use; however, only abstinence is 100% effective in prevention of unintended pregnancies. Other traditional methods include the withdrawal method, where the male ejaculates outside the female's body, and the calendar method, or rhythm method, where fertile days are estimated. Each of these traditional methods results in approximately 15–17 in 100 females becoming unintentionally pregnant.

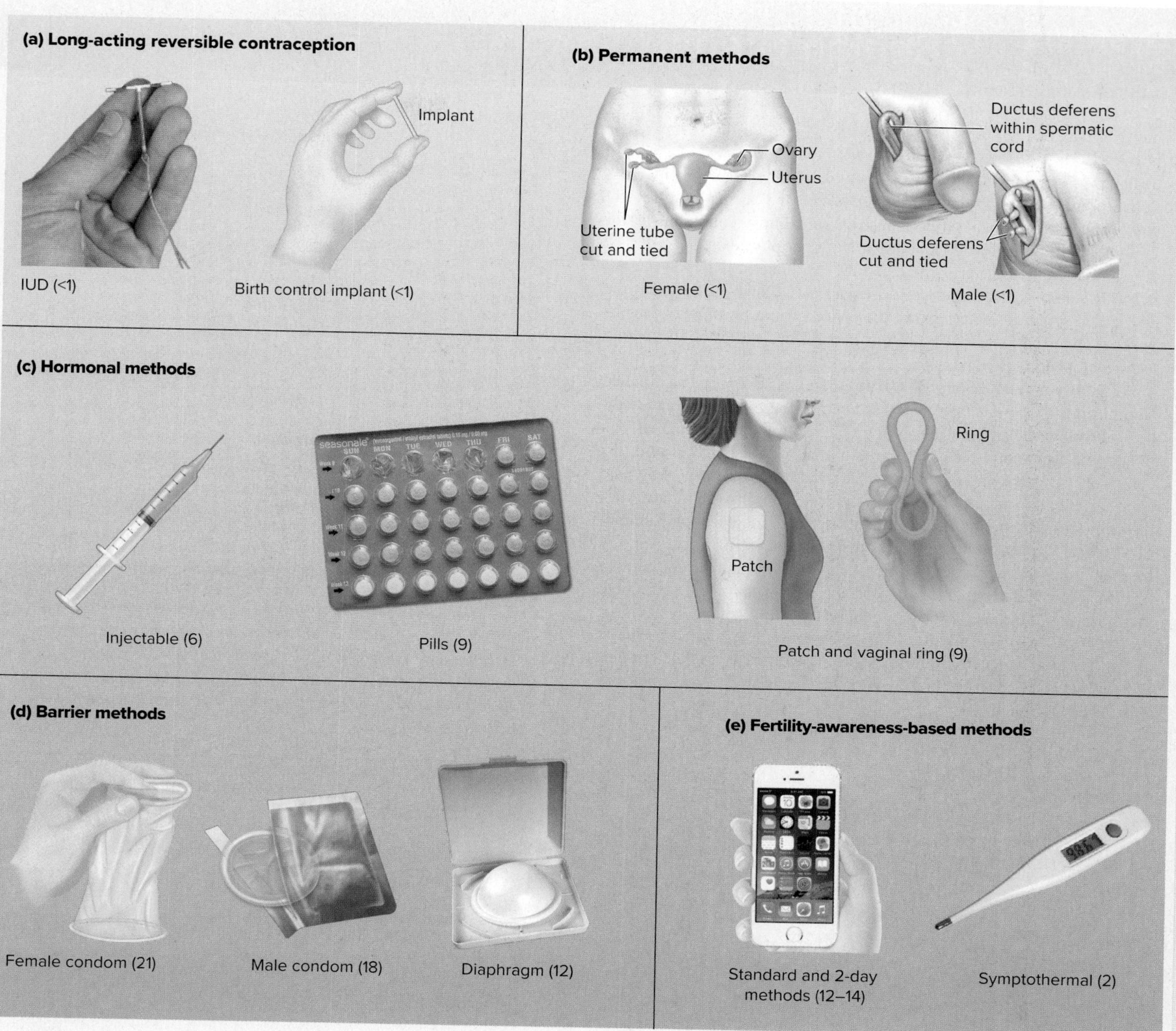

FIGURE 28.24 Methods of Birth Contol
The number in parentheses following each method label is the effectiveness, which is the number of females in 100 who become unintentionally pregnant with typical use. (a) Jill Braaten/McGraw Hill; (f) Martin Shields/Alamy Stock Photo; (j) McGraw Hill; (k) Alexey Boldin/Shutterstock; (l) D.Hurst/Alamy Stock Photo

Systems PATHOLOGY | Benign Uterine Tumors

Background Information

Molly is 43 years old and has four children. She noticed that menstruation was becoming gradually more severe and lasting up to several days longer each time. After menstruating almost continuously for 2 months, Molly made an appointment with her physician.

Palpation of the uterus indicated the presence of enlarged masses in Molly's uterus. The doctor performed a D&C, which is dilation of the cervix and scraping (curettage) of the endometrium to remove growths or other abnormal tissues. The results of the D&C indicated that Molly had developed leiomyomas.

Leiomyomas (LIE-oh-my-OH-mas; figure 28.25) are also called fibroid tumors of the uterus. They are one of the most common disorders of the uterus and are the most frequent tumor in females, affecting one of every four. However, three-fourths of the females with this condition experience no symptoms. The enlarged masses that originate from smooth muscle tissue compress the uterine lining (endometrium), resulting in ischemia and inflammation. The increased inflammation, which shares some characteristics with menstruation, results in frequent and severe menses, with associated abdominal cramping due to strong uterine contractions. Constant menstruation is a frequent manifestation of these tumors, and consequently, other systems of the body are affected (figure 28.26). The presence of these tumors and the constant menstruation are the most common reasons females elect to have the uterus removed, a procedure called a **hysterectomy** (his-ter-EK-toh-mee).

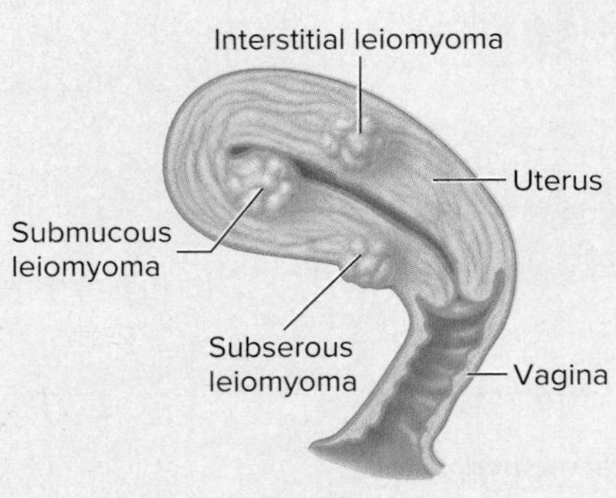

FIGURE 28.25 Leiomyomas

Leiomyomas, or fibroid tumors, are enlarged masses of smooth muscle. They can be located near the mucosa (submucous), within the myometrium (interstitial), or near the serosa (subserous).

Predict 7

When discussing her condition with her mother, Molly discovered that her mother had experienced frequent menses that were irregular and prolonged when she was in her late forties. Molly's mother did not have a hysterectomy, and in a few years the frequency of menstruation gradually began to subside. Explain.

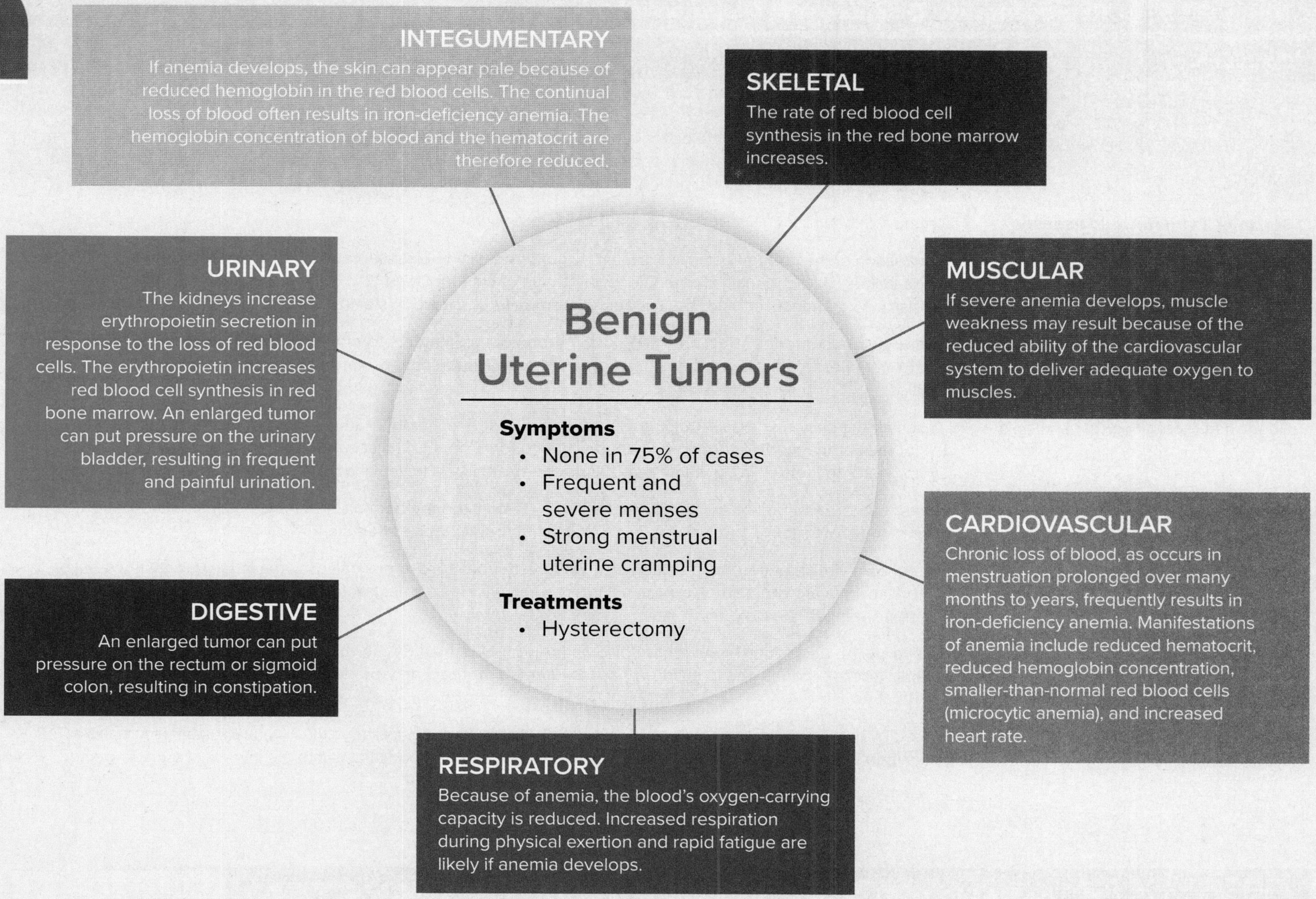

INTEGUMENTARY
If anemia develops, the skin can appear pale because of reduced hemoglobin in the red blood cells. The continual loss of blood often results in iron-deficiency anemia. The hemoglobin concentration of blood and the hematocrit are therefore reduced.

SKELETAL
The rate of red blood cell synthesis in the red bone marrow increases.

URINARY
The kidneys increase erythropoietin secretion in response to the loss of red blood cells. The erythropoietin increases red blood cell synthesis in red bone marrow. An enlarged tumor can put pressure on the urinary bladder, resulting in frequent and painful urination.

Benign Uterine Tumors

Symptoms
- None in 75% of cases
- Frequent and severe menses
- Strong menstrual uterine cramping

Treatments
- Hysterectomy

MUSCULAR
If severe anemia develops, muscle weakness may result because of the reduced ability of the cardiovascular system to deliver adequate oxygen to muscles.

CARDIOVASCULAR
Chronic loss of blood, as occurs in menstruation prolonged over many months to years, frequently results in iron-deficiency anemia. Manifestations of anemia include reduced hematocrit, reduced hemoglobin concentration, smaller-than-normal red blood cells (microcytic anemia), and increased heart rate.

DIGESTIVE
An enlarged tumor can put pressure on the rectum or sigmoid colon, resulting in constipation.

RESPIRATORY
Because of anemia, the blood's oxygen-carrying capacity is reduced. Increased respiration during physical exertion and rapid fatigue are likely if anemia develops.

FIGURE 28.26 **Effects of Benign Uterine Tumors on the Body's Organ Systems**

TABLE 28.5 Representative Diseases and Disorders of the Reproductive System

Condition	Description
Infectious Diseases	
Pelvic inflammatory disease (PID)	Bacterial infection of the female pelvic organs; commonly caused by vaginal or uterine infection by the bacteria that cause gonorrhea or chlamydia; early symptoms include increased vaginal discharge and pelvic pain; antibiotics are effective; if untreated, can lead to sterility or be life-threatening
Sexually Transmitted Diseases	Commonly known as STDs; spread by intimate sexual contact
Nongonococcal urethritis (non-GON-oh-kok-al you-ree-THRY-tis)	Inflammation of the urethra that is not caused by gonorrhea; can be caused by trauma, insertion of a nonsterile catheter, or sexual contact; usually due to infection with the bacterium *Chlamydia trachomatis* (klah-MID-ee-ah trah-KOH-mah-tis); may go unnoticed and result in pelvic inflammatory disease or sterility; antibiotics are effective treatment
Trichomoniasis (TRIK-oh-moh-NYE-ah-sis)	Caused by *Trichomonas* (TRIK-oh-MOH-nas), a protozoan commonly found in the vagina of females and in the urethra of males; results in a greenish-yellow discharge with a foul odor; more common in females than in males
Gonorrhea (gon-oh-REE-ah)	Caused by the bacterium *Neisseria gonorrhoeae* (nie-SEE-ree-ah gon-oh-REE-ah), which attaches to the epithelial cells of the vagina or male urethra and causes pus to form; pain and discharge from the penis occur in males; asymptomatic in females in the early stages; can lead to sterility in males and pelvic inflammatory disease in females
Genital herpes (HER-pees)	Caused by herpes simplex 2 virus; characterized by lesions on the genitals that progress into blisterlike areas, making urination, sitting, and walking painful; antiviral drugs can be effective
Genital warts	Caused by a viral infection; very contagious; warts vary from separate, small growths to large, cauliflower-like clusters; lesions are not painful, but sexual intercourse with lesions is; treatments include topical medicines and surgery to remove the lesions
Syphilis (SIF-ih-lis)	Caused by the bacterium *Treponema pallidum* (trep-oh-NEE-mah PAL-ih-dum); can be spread by sexual contact; multiple disease stages occur; children born to infected mothers may be developmentally delayed; antibiotics are effective
Acquired immunodeficiency syndrome (AIDS)	Caused by the human immunodeficiency virus (HIV), which ultimately destroys the immune system (see chapter 22); transmitted through intimate sexual contact or by allowing infected body fluids into the interior of another person

EFFECTS OF AGING ON THE REPRODUCTIVE SYSTEM

Aging affects the reproductive system in both males and females in several ways. Sexual activity is often maintained in males and females as they age, but the frequency of sexual intercourse usually decreases gradually.

In some but not all males, the size and weight of the testes decrease. In addition, there is an associated decrease in the number of interstitial cells and a thinning of the wall of the seminiferous tubules. These changes may be secondary to a decrease in blood flow to the testes or to a gradual decrease in reproductive hormone production. The rate of sperm cell production is also reduced, and the number of abnormal sperm cells produced increases. However, sperm cell production does not stop, and it remains adequate for fertility for most males.

Age-related changes become obvious in the prostate gland by age 40. By age 60, there is a clear decrease in blood flow to the prostate gland, an increased thickness in the epithelial cell lining of the prostate gland, and a decrease in the number of functional smooth muscle cells in the wall of the prostate. The changes in the prostate gland do not decrease fertility, but the incidence of benign prostatic hypertrophy (enlargement of the prostate) increases substantially and can lead to difficulty in urination due to compression of the prostatic urethra.

Although there is great variation among males, many exhibit decreases in the frequency of sexual activity and in sexual performance. Psychological changes, age-related changes in the nervous system, and decreased blood flow explain some of the decline. The side effects of medications taken for other conditions are responsible for decreased sexual activity in many older males. Erectile dysfunction increases in males with age.

The most significant age-related change in females is menopause. By age 50, the amount of estrogen and progesterone produced by the ovaries has decreased. The uterus decreases in size, and the endometrium decreases in thickness. The time between menses becomes irregular and longer until menstruations stop. The vaginal wall becomes thinner and less elastic. There is less lubrication of the vagina, and the epithelial lining is more fragile, resulting in an increased tendency for vaginal infections.

The incidence of breast cancer is greatest between 45 and 65 years of age and is greater for females who have a family history of breast cancer. Approximately 10% of all females will develop breast cancer. The most important measure to guard against death from breast cancer is early detection through breast self-exams and annual mammograms after age 45. The incidences of uterine cancer and cervical cancer increase between 50 and 65 years of age. Ovarian cancer increases in frequency in older females, and it is the second most common cancer of the reproductive system in older females. Regular medical checkups, including Pap smears, are important for early detection and treatment of these cancers.

Concept Check

28.1 Functions of the Reproductive System

The reproductive systems produce male and female gametes, enhance fertilization of an oocyte by a sperm cell, and produce reproductive hormones. In addition, the female reproductive system nurtures the new individual until birth.

28.2 Meiosis

The reproductive organs in males and females produce gametes by meiosis.

A. Two consecutive cell divisions halve the chromosome number from 46 total chromosomes to 23 total chromosomes.
B. Meiosis ensures that the diploid number (46, in humans) is maintained in each generation.
C. Crossing over and random sorting of chromosomes during meiosis I produce genetic variation in gametes.

1. *During meiosis I* 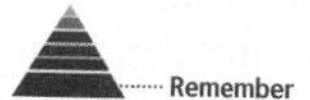

   a. *homologous chromosomes synapse.*
   b. *crossing over between homologous chromosomes occurs.*
   c. *the chromosomal number is reduced by half.*
   d. *two haploid cells are produced.*
   e. *All of these are correct.*

28.3 Anatomy of the Male Reproductive System

The male reproductive system includes the testes, ducts, accessory glands, and supporting structures.

Scrotum

A. The scrotum is a two-chambered sac that contains the testes.
B. The dartos and cremaster muscles help regulate testicular temperature.

Perineum

The perineum, the diamond-shaped area between the thighs, consists of a urogenital triangle and an anal triangle.

Testes

A. The tunica albuginea is the outer connective tissue capsule of the testes.
B. The testes are divided by septa into lobules that contain the seminiferous tubules and the interstitial cells.
C. The seminiferous tubules straighten to form the tubuli recti, which lead to the rete testis. The rete testis opens into the efferent ductules of the epididymis.
D. During development, the testes pass from the abdominal cavity through the inguinal canal to the scrotum.

Spermatogenesis

A. Spermatogenesis begins in the seminiferous tubules at the time of puberty.
B. Spermatogonia divide (mitosis) to form primary spermatocytes.
C. Primary spermatocytes divide (first division of meiosis) to form secondary spermatocytes, which divide (second division of meiosis) to form spermatids.
D. Spermatids develop an acrosome and a flagellum to become sperm cells.
E. Sustentacular cells nourish the sperm cells, form a blood-testis barrier, and produce hormones.

Ducts

A. Efferent ductules extend from the testes to the head of the epididymis.
B. The epididymis, a coiled tube system, is located on the testis and is the site of sperm cell maturation. It consists of a head, a body, and a tail.
C. The ductus deferens passes from the epididymis into the abdominal cavity.
D. The end of the ductus deferens, called the ampulla, and the seminal vesicle join to form the ejaculatory duct.
E. The prostatic urethra extends from the urinary bladder and joins with the ejaculatory ducts to form the membranous urethra.
F. The membranous urethra extends through the urogenital diaphragm and becomes the spongy urethra, which continues through the penis.
G. The spermatic cord consists of the ductus deferens, blood and lymphatic vessels, nerves, and remnants of the process vaginalis. Coverings of the spermatic cord consist of the external spermatic fascia, cremaster muscle, and internal spermatic fascia.
H. The spermatic cord passes through the inguinal canal into the abdominal cavity.

Penis

A. The penis consists of erectile tissue.
   - The two corpora cavernosa form the dorsum and the sides of the penis.
   - The corpus spongiosum forms the ventral part and the glans penis.

B. The bulb of the penis and the crura form the root of the penis, and the crura attaches the penis to the pelvic bones.
C. The prepuce covers the glans penis.

Accessory Glands

A. The seminal vesicles empty into the ejaculatory ducts.
B. The prostate gland consists of glandular and muscular tissue and empties into the prostatic urethra.
C. The bulbourethral glands are compound mucous glands that empty into the spongy urethra.

Semen

A. Semen is a mixture of sperm cells and glandular secretions.
B. The bulbourethral glands and the urethral mucous glands produce mucus, which neutralizes the acidic pH of the urethra.
C. The testicular secretions contain sperm cells.
D. The seminal vesicle fluid contains fructose and fibrinogen.
E. The prostate secretions make the seminal fluid more pH-neutral. Clotting factors activate fibrinogen, and fibrinolysin breaks down fibrin.

2. *Testosterone is produced in the* 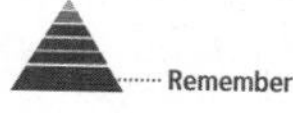

   a. *interstitial cells.*
   b. *seminiferous tubules of the testes.*
   c. *anterior lobe of the pituitary gland.*
   d. *sperm cells.*

3. *Early in development (4 months after fertilization), the testes*

   Remember

   a. *are found in the abdominal cavity.*
   b. *move through the inguinal canal.*
   c. *produce a membrane that becomes the scrotum.*
   d. *produce sperm cells.*
   e. *All of these are correct.*

4. *The site of spermatogenesis in the male is the* Remember

a. ductus deferens.
b. seminiferous tubules.
c. epididymis.
d. rete testis.
e. efferent ductule.

5. *The site of final maturation and storage of sperm cells before their ejaculation is the* Remember

a. seminal vesicles.
b. seminiferous tubules.
c. glans penis.
d. epididymis.
e. sperm bank.

6. *Given these structures:*

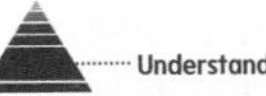

(1) ductus deferens
(2) efferent ductule
(3) epididymis
(4) ejaculatory duct
(5) rete testis

Choose the arrangement that lists the structures in the order a sperm cell passes through them from the seminiferous tubules to the urethra.

a. 2,3,5,4,1
b. 2,5,3,4,1
c. 3,2,4,1,5
d. 3,4,2,1,5
e. 5,2,3,1,4

7. *Concerning the penis,*

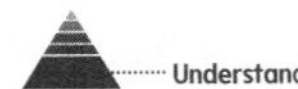

a. the membranous urethra passes through the corpora cavernosa.
b. the glans penis is formed by the corpus spongiosum.
c. the penis contains four columns of erectile tissue.
d. the crus of the penis is part of the corpus spongiosum.
e. the bulb of the penis is covered by the prepuce.

8. *Which of these glands is correctly matched with the function of its secretions?*

a. bulbourethral gland—neutralizes acidic contents of the urethra
b. seminal vesicles—contain large amounts of fructose, which nourishes the sperm cells
c. prostate gland—contains clotting factors that cause coagulation of the semen
d. All of these are correct.

9. *The left testis of a newborn baby failed to descend into his scrotal sac. For some reason, the condition was not treated, and the testis remained in that position until after puberty. Select the observation consistent with the fate of the left testis after puberty.* Apply

(1) normal testosterone secretion
(2) no interstitial cells in the testis
(3) no sustentacular cells in the testis
(4) no spermatogonia in the testis
(5) increased number of interstitial cells
(6) normal LH secretion

a. 1 *b. 1,2,3,4* *c. 1,2,3,6* *d. 1,4,6* *e. 4,6*

28.4 Physiology of Male Reproduction

Normal function of the male reproductive system depends on hormonal and neural mechanisms.

Regulation of Reproductive Hormone Secretion

A. GnRH is produced in the hypothalamus and released in surges.
B. GnRH stimulates LH and FSH release from the anterior pituitary.
- LH stimulates the interstitial cells to produce testosterone.
- FSH stimulates sperm cell formation.

C. Inhibin, produced by sustentacular cells, inhibits FSH secretion.

Puberty in Males

A. Before puberty, small amounts of testosterone inhibit GnRH release.
B. During puberty, testosterone does not completely suppress GnRH release, resulting in increased production of FSH, LH, and testosterone.

Effects of Testosterone

A. Interstitial cells, the adrenal cortex, and possibly the sustentacular cells produce testosterone.
B. Testosterone causes the development of male sex organs in the embryo and stimulates the descent of the testes.
C. Testosterone causes enlargement of the genitals and is necessary for sperm cell formation.
D. Other effects of testosterone
- Hair growth stimulation (pubic area, axilla, and beard) and inhibition (male pattern baldness)
- Enlargement of the larynx and deepening of the voice
- Increased skin thickness and melanin and sebum production
- Increased protein synthesis (muscle), bone growth as mediated by estrogen, blood cell synthesis, and blood volume
- Increased metabolic rate

Male Sexual Behavior and the Male Sex Act

A. Testosterone is required for normal sex drive.
B. Stimulation of the sex act can be tactile or psychological.
C. Afferent action potentials pass through the pudendal nerve to the sacral region of the spinal cord.
D. Parasympathetic stimulation
- Erection is due to vasodilation of the blood vessels that supply the erectile tissue.
- The glands of the urethra and the bulbourethral glands produce mucus.

E. Sympathetic stimulation causes erection, emission, and ejaculation.

10. *LH in the male stimulates*

a. the development of the seminiferous tubules.
b. spermatogenesis.
c. testosterone production.
d. Both a and b are correct.
e. All of these are correct.

11. *Which of these factors causes a decrease in GnRH release?*

a. decreased inhibin
b. increased testosterone
c. decreased FSH
d. decreased LH

12. *In the male, before puberty*

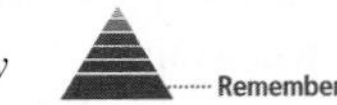

a. FSH levels are higher than after puberty.
b. LH levels are higher than after puberty.
c. GnRH release is inhibited by testosterone.
d. All of these are correct.

13. *Testosterone*

a. stimulates the development of terminal hairs.
b. decreases red blood cell count.
c. prevents closure of the epiphyseal plate.
d. decreases blood volume.
e. All of these are correct.

14. *Which of these events is consistent with erection of the penis?*
    a. *parasympathetic stimulation*
    b. *dilation of arterioles*
    c. *engorgement of sinusoids with blood*
    d. *occlusion of veins*
    e. *All of these are correct.*

Understand

15. *If an adult male were castrated (testes were removed), what would happen to the levels of GnRH, FSH, LH, and testosterone in his blood? What effect would these hormonal changes have on his sexual characteristics and sexual behavior?* Apply

16. *If a 9-year-old male were castrated, what would happen to the levels of GnRH, FSH, LH, and testosterone in his blood? What effect would these hormonal changes have on his sexual characteristics and sexual behavior as an adult?* Apply

17. *Suppose you want to produce a male birth control pill. On the basis of what you know about the male hormone system, what process should the pill affect? Discuss any possible side effects of the pill.* Apply

18. *Dr. Smith has two patients, one of whom has elevated blood PSA. A digital exam reveals that both patient 1 and patient 2 have enlarged prostate glands. Patient 1's enlarged prostate has the same shape as a smaller prostate, except that it is larger than normal, with a smooth contour. Patient 2's prostate is enlarged and asymmetrical, with a rough contour. In what way are these patients' lives probably being affected by their enlarged prostates? Explain how the doctor was able to conclude that one of the patients is likely to have prostate cancer.* Apply

19. *Norman had a stroke that decreased blood flow to his anterior pituitary gland. The condition had a sudden onset, and the manifestations lasted for about a week before collateral circulation developed and the manifestations disappeared. Which of the following are most consistent with this temporary interruption of anterior pituitary function?* Apply
    (1) increased testosterone levels in the blood
    (2) reduced sperm counts during the week Norman was in the hospital
    (3) decreased testosterone levels in the blood
    (4) normal sperm counts during the week Norman was in the hospital
    (5) increased LH secretion
    (6) decreased LH secretion

    a. *1,5* b. *3,5* c. *2,3,6* d. *3,4,6* e. *1,4,5*

28.5 Anatomy of the Female Reproductive System

The female reproductive system includes the ovaries, uterine tubes, uterus, vagina, external genitals, and mammary glands.

Ovaries

A. The broad ligament, the mesovarium, the suspensory ligaments, and the ovarian ligaments hold the ovaries in place.
B. The peritoneum (ovarian epithelium) covers the surface of the ovaries.
C. The ovary has an outer capsule called the tunica albuginea and is divided internally into a cortex, which contains follicles, and a medulla, which receives blood and lymphatic vessels and nerves.

Oogenesis and Fertilization

A. Oogonia proliferate and become primary oocytes that are in prophase I of meiosis.
B. Ovulation is the release of an oocyte from an ovary.
C. Prior to ovulation, a primary oocyte continues meiosis I and produces a secondary oocyte, which begins meiosis II, and a polar body, which either degenerates or divides to form two polar bodies.
D. Fertilization is the joining of a sperm cell and a secondary oocyte to form a zygote. A sperm cell enters a secondary oocyte, which then completes the second meiotic division and produces a polar body. A zygote is formed when the nuclei of the sperm cell and the oocyte fuse to form a diploid nucleus.

Follicle Development

A. Primordial follicles are surrounded by a single layer of flat granulosa cells.
B. Primary follicles are primary oocytes surrounded by cuboidal granulosa cells.
C. The primary follicles become secondary follicles as granulosa cells increase in number and fluid begins to accumulate in the vesicles. The granulosa cells increase in number, and a theca forms around the secondary follicles.
D. Mature follicles are enlarged secondary follicles at the surface of the ovary.
E. Ovulation occurs when the follicle swells and ruptures and the secondary oocyte is released from the ovary.
F. The mature follicle becomes the corpus luteum.
G. If pregnancy occurs, the corpus luteum persists. If no pregnancy occurs, it becomes the corpus albicans.

Uterine Tubes

A. The mesosalpinx holds the uterine tubes.
B. The uterine tubes transport the oocyte or zygote from the ovary to the uterus.
C. Structures
   - The ovarian end of the uterine tube is expanded as the infundibulum. The opening of the infundibulum is the ostium, which is surrounded by fimbriae.
   - The infundibulum connects to the ampulla, which narrows to become the isthmus. The isthmus is the part of the uterine tube nearest the uterus.
D. The uterine tube consists of an outer serosa, a middle muscular layer, and an inner mucosa composed of simple ciliated columnar epithelium.
E. Movement of the oocyte
   - Cilia move the oocyte over the fimbriae surface into the infundibulum.
   - Peristaltic contractions and cilia move the oocyte within the uterine tube.
   - Fertilization occurs in the ampulla, where the zygote remains for several days.

Uterus

A. The uterus consists of the body, the isthmus, and the cervix. The uterine cavity and the cervical canal are the spaces formed by the uterus.
B. The uterus is held in place by the broad, round, and uterosacral ligaments.
C. The wall of the uterus consists of the perimetrium (serous membrane), the myometrium (smooth muscle), and the endometrium (mucous membrane).

Vagina

A. The vagina connects the uterus (cervix) to the outside of the body.
B. The vagina consists of a layer of smooth muscle and an inner lining of moist, stratified squamous epithelium.

C. The vagina is folded into rugae and longitudinal folds.
D. The hymen covers the opening of the vagina.

Female External Genitalia

A. The vulva, or pudendum, comprises the external genitalia.
B. The vestibule is the space into which the vagina and the urethra open.
C. Erectile tissue
- The two corpora cavernosa form the clitoris.
- The corpora spongiosa form the bulbs of the vestibule.

D. The labia minora are folds that cover the vestibule and form the prepuce.
E. The greater and lesser vestibular glands produce a mucous fluid.
F. When closed, the labia majora cover the labia minora.
- The pudendal cleft is a space between the labia majora.
- The mons pubis is an elevated fat deposit superior to the labia majora.

Perineum

The clinical perineum is the region between the vagina and the anus.

Mammary Glands

A. The mammary glands are modified sweat glands located in the breasts.
- The mammary glands consist of glandular lobes and adipose tissue.
- The lobes consist of lobules that are divided into alveoli.
- The lobes connect to the nipple through the lactiferous ducts.
- The areola surrounds the nipple.

B. Suspensory ligaments support the breasts.

20. *After ovulation, the mature follicle collapses, taking on a yellowish appearance to become the* Remember

a. degenerating follicle.
b. corpus luteum.
c. corpus albicans.
d. tunica albuginea.
e. cumulus mass.

21. *The ampulla of the uterine tube* 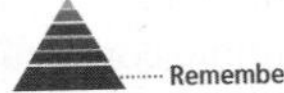

a. is the opening of the uterine tube into the uterus.
b. has long, thin projections called the ostium.
c. is connected to the isthmus of the uterine tube.
d. is lined with simple cuboidal epithelium.

22. *The layer of the uterus that undergoes the greatest change during the menstrual cycle is the* Remember

a. perimetrium.
b. hymen.
c. endometrium.
d. myometrium.
e. broad ligament.

23. *The vagina* Remember

a. consists of skeletal muscle.
b. has ridges called rugae.
c. is lined with simple squamous epithelium.
d. All of these are correct.

24. *During sexual excitement, which of these structures fills with blood and causes the vaginal opening to narrow?* Remember

a. bulbs of the vestibule
b. clitoris
c. mons pubis
d. labia majora
e. prepuce

25. *Concerning the breasts,* Remember

a. lactiferous ducts open on the areola.
b. each lactiferous duct supplies an alveolus.
c. they are attached to the pectoralis major muscles by suspensory ligaments.
d. even before puberty, the female breast is quite different from the male breast.

28.6 Physiology of Female Reproduction

Puberty in Females

A. The first menstrual bleeding (menarche) occurs during puberty.
B. Puberty begins when GnRH levels increase.

Menstrual Cycle

A. Ovarian cycle
- FSH initiates the development of the primary follicles.
- The follicles secrete a substance that inhibits the development of other follicles.
- LH stimulates ovulation and completion of the first meiotic division by the primary oocyte.
- The LH surge stimulates the formation of the corpus luteum. If fertilization occurs, hCG stimulates the corpus luteum to persist. If fertilization does not occur, the corpus luteum becomes the corpus albicans.

B. A positive-feedback mechanism causes FSH and LH levels to increase near the time of ovulation.
- Estrogen produced by the theca cells of the follicle stimulates GnRH secretion.
- GnRH stimulates the production and release of FSH and LH, which stimulate more estrogen secretion, and so on.
- Inhibition of GnRH levels causes FSH and LH levels to decrease after ovulation. Inhibition is due to the high levels of estrogen and progesterone produced by the corpus luteum.

C. Uterine cycle
- Menses (from day 1 to day 4 or 5). The spiral arteries constrict, and endometrial cells die. The menstrual fluid is composed of sloughed cells, secretions, and blood.
- Proliferative phase (from day 5 to day 14). Epithelial cells multiply and form glands, and the spiral arteries supply the glands.
- Secretory phase (from day 15 to day 28). The endometrium becomes thicker, and the endometrial glands secrete.
- Estrogen stimulates proliferation of the endometrium and synthesis of progesterone receptors.
- Increased progesterone levels cause hypertrophy of the endometrium, stimulate gland secretion, and inhibit uterine contractions. Decreased progesterone levels cause the spiral arteries to constrict and start menses.

Female Sexual Behavior and the Female Sex Act

A. Female sex drive is partially influenced by androgens (produced by the adrenal gland) and other steroids (produced by the ovaries).
B. Parasympathetic effects
- The erectile tissue of the clitoris and the bulbs of the vestibule become filled with blood.
- The vestibular glands secrete mucus, and the vagina extrudes a mucuslike substance.

Female Fertility and Pregnancy

A. If fertilization is to occur, intercourse must take place between 5 days before and 1 day after ovulation.
B. Sperm cell transport to the ampulla depends on the ability of the sperm cells to swim and possibly on contractions of the uterus and the uterine tubes.

C. Implantation of the developing embryo into the uterine wall occurs when the uterus is most receptive.

D. Estrogen and progesterone, secreted first by the corpus luteum and later by the placenta, are essential for the maintenance of pregnancy.

Menopause

The female climacteric begins with irregular menstrual cycles and ends with menopause, the cessation of the menstrual cycle.

26. *The major secretory product of the mature follicle is*

a. estrogen. *b. progesterone.* *c. LH.* *d. relaxin.* *e. FSH.*

27. *In the average adult female, ovulation occurs at day ________ of the menstrual cycle.*

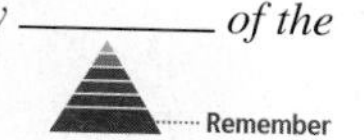

a. 1 *b. 7* *c. 14* *d. 21* *e. 28*

28. *Which of these processes or phases in the monthly reproductive cycle of the human female occur at the same time?* Understand
    a. *maximal LH secretion and menstruation*
    b. *early follicular development and the secretory phase of the uterus*
    c. *regression of the corpus luteum and an increase in ovarian progesterone secretion*
    d. *ovulation and menstruation*
    e. *proliferative stage of the uterus and increased estrogen production*

29. *During the proliferative phase of the uterine cycle, one would normally expect*

   a. *the highest levels of estrogen that occur during the menstrual cycle.*
   b. *the mature follicle to be present in the ovary.*
   c. *an increase in the thickness of the endometrium.*
   d. *Both a and b are correct.*
   e. *All of these are correct.*

30. *The cause of menses in the uterine cycle appears to be*

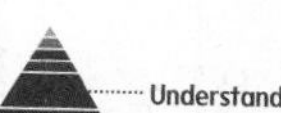

   a. *increased progesterone secretion from the ovary, which produces blood clotting.*
   b. *increased estrogen secretion from the ovary, which stimulates the muscles of the uterus to contract.*
   c. *decreased progesterone secretion by the ovary.*
   d. *decreased production of oxytocin, causing the muscles of the uterus to relax.*

31. *After fertilization, the successful development of a mature, full-term fetus depends on*

   a. *the release of human chorionic gonadotropin (hCG) by the developing placenta.*
   b. *the production of estrogen and progesterone by the placental tissues.*
   c. *maintenance of the corpus luteum for all 9 months.*
   d. *Both a and b are correct.*
   e. *All of these are correct.*

32. *A female with a 28-day menstrual cycle is most likely to become pregnant as a result of intercourse on days* Apply
    a. *1–3.*
    b. *5–8.*
    c. *9–14.*
    d. *15–20.*
    e. *21–28.*

33. *Menopause* Understand
    a. *develops when follicles become less responsive to FSH and LH.*
    b. *results from elevated estrogen levels in 40- to 50-year-old females.*
    c. *occurs because too many follicles develop during each cycle.*
    d. *results when follicles develop but contain no oocytes.*
    e. *occurs because FSH and LH levels decline.*

34. *If the ovaries are removed from a postmenopausal female, what happens to the levels of GnRH, FSH, LH, estrogen, and progesterone in her blood? What symptoms would you expect to observe?* Apply

35. *If the ovaries are removed from a 20-year-old female, what happens to the levels of GnRH, FSH, LH, estrogen, and progesterone in her blood? What side effects would these hormonal changes have on her sexual characteristics and sexual behavior?* Apply

36. *A study divides healthy females into two groups (A and B). Both groups are composed of those who have been sexually active for at least 2 years and are not pregnant at the beginning of the experiment. The subjects weigh about the same amount, and none smoke cigarettes, although some drink alcohol occasionally. Group A individuals receive a placebo in the form of a sugar pill each morning of their menstrual cycles. Group B individuals receive a pill containing estrogen and progesterone each morning of their menstrual cycles. Then plasma LH levels are measured before, during, and after ovulation. The results are as follows:* Analyze

Group	4 Days Before Ovulation	Day of Ovulation	4 Days After Ovulation
A	18 mg/100 mL	300 mg/100 mL	17 mg/100 mL
B	21 mg/100 mL	157 mg/100 mL	15 mg/100 mL

The number of pregnancies in group A is 37/100 females/year. The number of pregnancies in group B is 1.5/100 females/year. What conclusion can you reach on the basis of these data? Explain the mechanism involved.

37. *A female who is taking birth control pills that consist of only progesterone experiences the hot flashes of menopause. Explain why.* Understand

38. *GnRH can be used to treat some females who want to have children but have not been able to get pregnant. Explain why it is critical to administer the correct concentration of GnRH at the right time during the menstrual cycle.* Apply

Answers to this chapter's odd-numbered Concept Check questions appear in Appendix F.

29 CHAPTER
Development, Growth, Aging, and Genetics

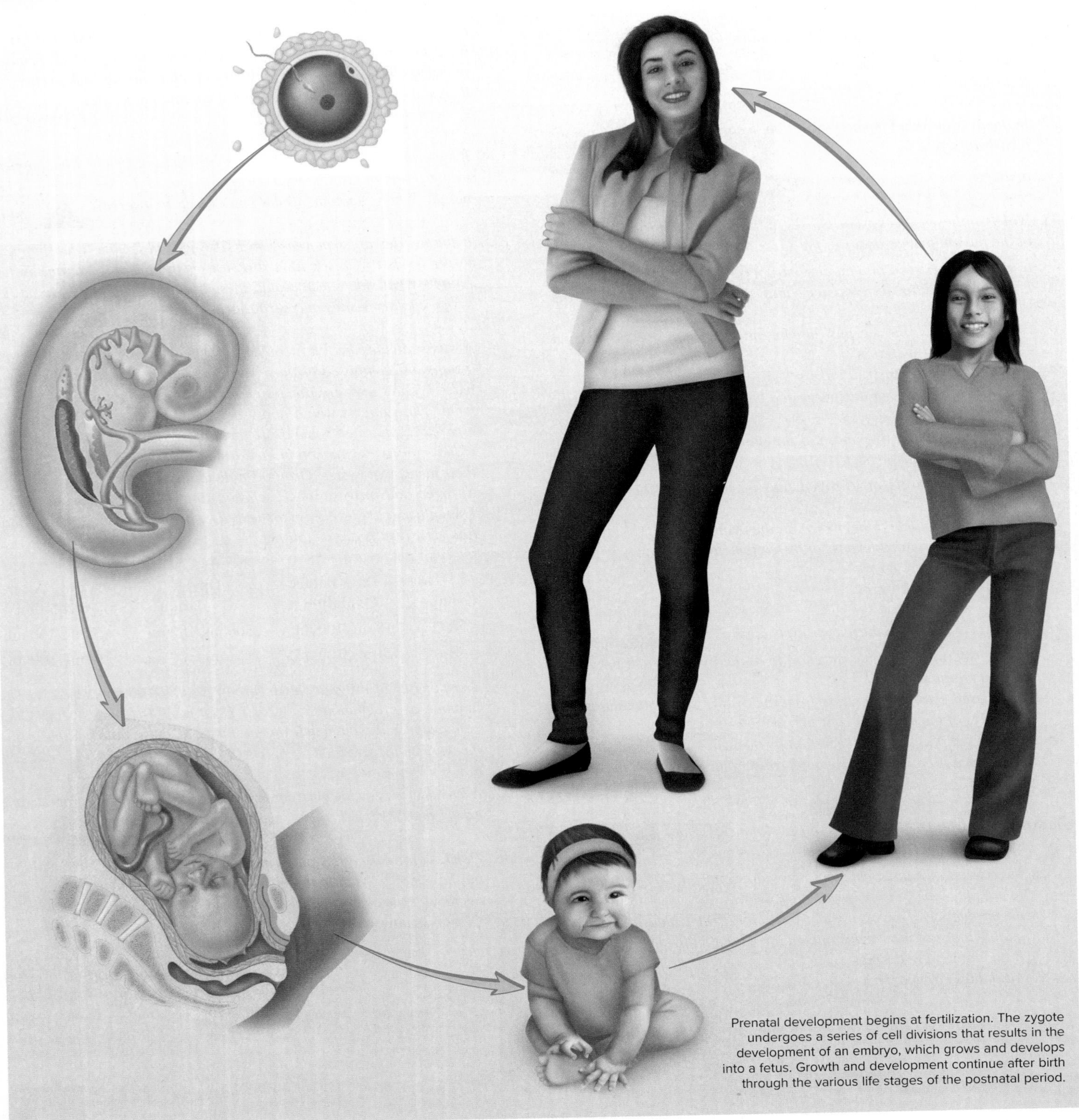

Prenatal development begins at fertilization. The zygote undergoes a series of cell divisions that results in the development of an embryo, which grows and develops into a fetus. Growth and development continue after birth through the various life stages of the postnatal period.

The stages of life and associated activities are issues of great interest in today's society. We tend to view life stages very differently today than in the past. For example, in 1960, 20% of males and 12% of females graduating from high school attended college. Today, over half of all people 25 and older have attended some college. In addition, there are many more nontraditional college students than there were 30 years ago.

The life span is usually considered the period between birth and death; however, the 9 months before birth are a critical part of a person's existence. What happens in these 9 months profoundly affects the rest of a person's life. Although most people develop normally and are born without defects, approximately 3 out of every 100 people are born with a birth defect so severe that it requires medical attention during the first year of life. Later in life, many more people discover previously unknown problems, such as the tendency to develop asthma, certain brain disorders, or cancer. This chapter discusses the topics of development, growth, aging, and genetics.

Learn to Predict

After reading about the benefits of breast milk, Ming was determined to breastfeed her baby until he was a year old. Unfortunately, 2 weeks after her son's birth, Ming developed a serious urinary tract infection. Her physician prescribed an antibiotic and explained that she must not breastfeed her son while taking it.

Predict the consequences if Ming stops breastfeeding for an extended time, and propose a strategy that would allow her to cease breastfeeding for a while but resume after she has finished the antibiotic.

Answers to this question and the chapter's odd-numbered Predict questions can be found in Appendix E.

29.1 Prenatal Development

LEARNING OUTCOMES

After reading this section, you should be able to

A. **List the prenatal periods and state the major developmental events associated with each.**
B. **List the postnatal periods and state the age range for each.**
C. **Describe the process of fertilization.**
D. **Describe the blastocyst.**
E. **Describe the process of implantation and placental formation.**
F. **List the three germ layers and describe their formation.**
G. **List the adult derivatives of each germ layer.**
H. **Discuss the formation of the neural tube and the neural crest cells.**
I. **Explain the formation of the digestive tract.**
J. **Describe the formation of the limbs.**
K. **Explain the formation of the face.**
L. **Demonstrate knowledge of the formation of the major organ systems.**

We recognize that during our lifetime we have and will pass through many different stages. Those stages may be characterized by many factors, such as biological factors or social factors. When discussing the human life span from a biological perspective, we subdivide it in multiple ways. From the broadest perspective, we divide the human life span into two major periods: prenatal (before birth) and postnatal (after birth). Each of these periods is then subdivided based on specific criteria (figure 29.1). The prenatal period, which extends from fertilization until birth, is subdivided into three stages:

1. The **germinal period** begins at fertilization and ends at 14 days (weeks 1 and 2 of development). This is the stage when the primitive germ layers form.
2. The **embryonic period** occurs during days 14–56 after fertilization (weeks 3–8 of development) and is the time when the major organ systems form. The developing human is called an **embryo** (EM-bree-oh) at this stage.
3. The **fetal period** extends from 56 days after fertilization to birth (the last 30 weeks of development). During this stage, the organ systems grow and become more mature, and the developing human is called a **fetus** (FEE-tus).

Module 14
Reproductive System

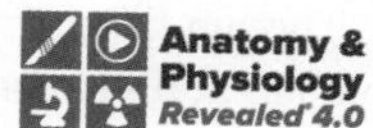

FIGURE 29.1 The Human Life Span

The human life span is divided into two major periods: the prenatal period and the postnatal period. These two periods are subdivided based on specific criteria.

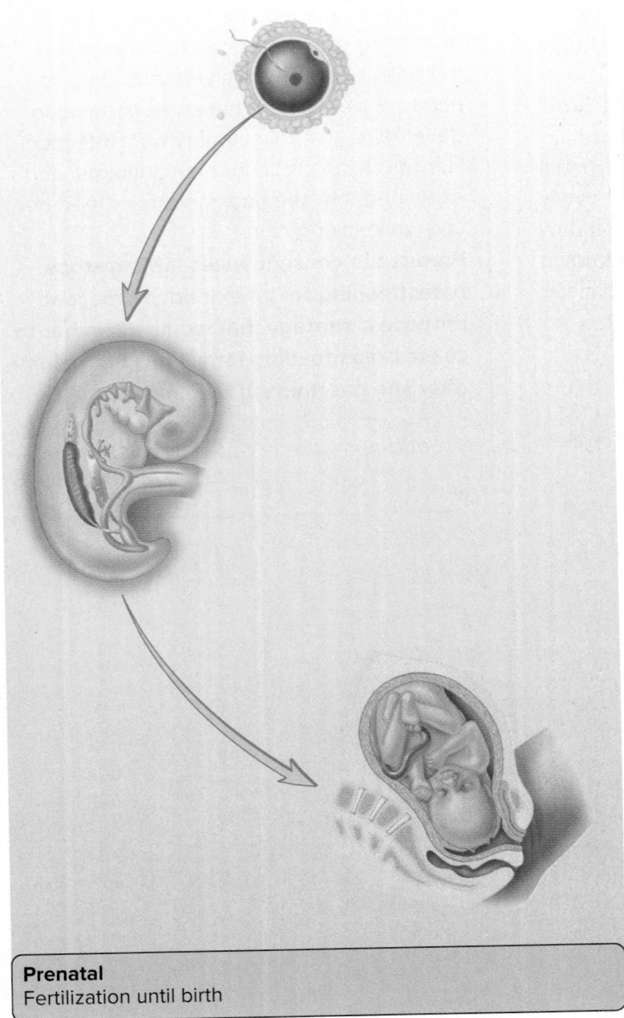

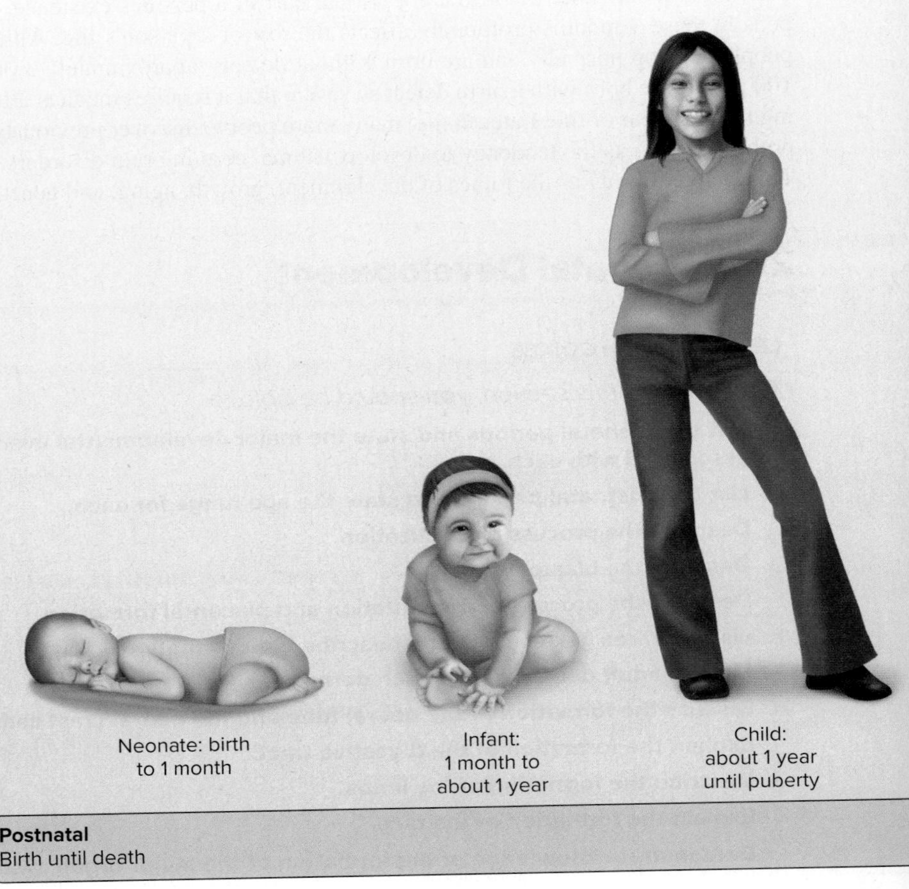

Altogether, the prenatal period extends about 9 months. The above description characterizes each period based on days from fertilization, or the postovulatory age. Most embryologists use this method to describe events of prenatal development. However, the medical community uses the mother's **last menstrual period (LMP)** to calculate the clinical age of the unborn child. Postovulatory age is used in this book. Because ovulation occurs about 14 days after LMP and fertilization occurs near the time of ovulation, postovulatory age is 14 days less than clinical age.

The prenatal period is acutely important for the remainder of a person's life. Essentially, the foundation of the human body is established early in this period and the first important steps of growth begin. Though these first 9 months of life are extremely important, the prenatal period is only a small part of the total life span.

The postnatal period begins at birth. This period is commonly divided into five stages:

1. **Neonatal period** extends from birth to 1 month after birth.
2. **Infancy** includes the time from 1 month to 1 or 2 years of age. The end of infancy is sometimes set at the time the child begins to walk.
3. **Childhood** includes the time from age 1 or 2 to puberty. During childhood, the individual develops considerably and forms many of the emotional characteristics that last throughout life.
4. **Adolescence** extends from puberty (age 11–14) to 20 years. Puberty usually occurs somewhat earlier in females (about age 11–13) than in males (about age 12–14). A period of rapid growth usually accompanies the onset of puberty.

5. **Adult** is the time from age 20 to death. Full adult stature is usually achieved by age 17 or 18 in females and by age 19 or 20 in males. Adulthood is sometimes divided into three periods: (1) young adult, age 20–40; (2) middle age, age 40–65; and (3) older adult, age 65 to death.

ASSESS YOUR PROGRESS

Answers to these questions are found in the section you have just completed. Re-read the section if you need help in answering these questions.

1. *Describe the three parts of the prenatal period, including the length of time for each part.*
2. *Distinguish between clinical age and postovulatory age.*
3. *List the stages of postnatal development, including the age range for each.*

Fertilization

Prenatal development begins at **fertilization.** Fertilization occurs when a sperm cell attaches to a secondary oocyte, and the contents of the sperm head enter the oocyte cytoplasm and join with the oocyte pronucleus. Figure 29.2 illustrates the process of fertilization.

1. Of the several hundred million sperm cells deposited in the vagina during sexual intercourse, only a few dozen reach the vicinity of the secondary oocyte in the ampulla of the uterine tube. Recall from chapter 28 that the secondary oocyte is surrounded by the **corona radiata,** which is composed of cumulus cells expelled from the follicle with the oocyte during ovulation (see figure 28.15). The corona radiata acts as a sort of barrier to those sperm cells that reach the oocyte; however, this barrier is not effective at completely blocking the sperm cells but rather slowing them down. The flagella on

FUNDAMENTAL **Figure**

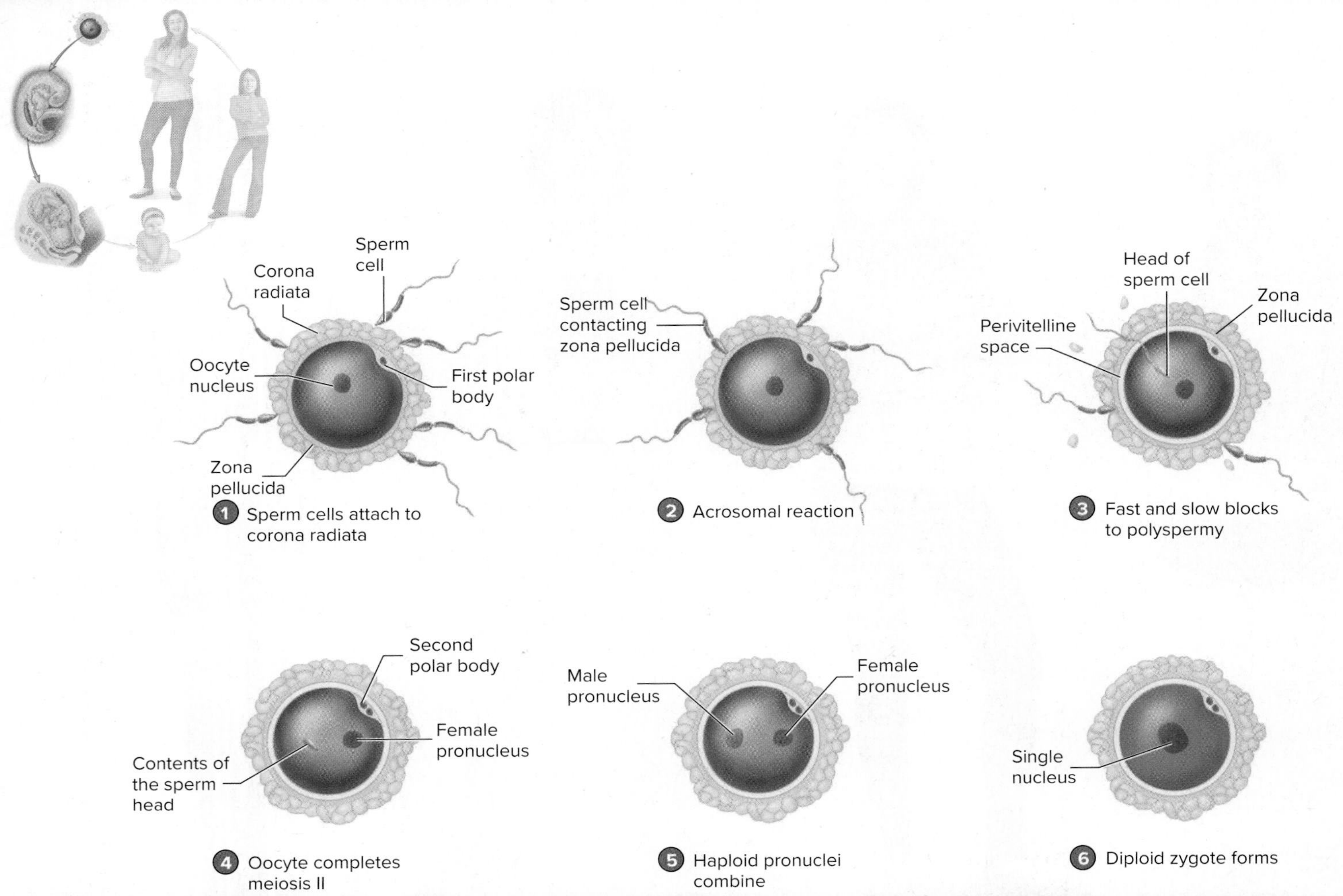

1 Sperm cells attach to corona radiata

2 Acrosomal reaction

3 Fast and slow blocks to polyspermy

4 Oocyte completes meiosis II

5 Haploid pronuclei combine

6 Diploid zygote forms

PROCESS **Figure 29.2**

Fertilization

Fertilization occurs when a sperm cell and an oocyte combine. APR

If two sperm cells were able to fertilize the same oocyte, how many chromosomes would the zygote have?

the sperm cells propel them through the loose matrix between the follicular cells of the corona radiata.

2 Between the corona radiata and the oocyte is the **zona pellucida,** an extracellular membrane comprised mostly of glycoproteins. One particular zona pellucida glycoprotein, called **ZP3,** is a species-specific sperm cell receptor, to which molecules on the acrosomal cap of the sperm cell bind. This binding initiates the **acrosomal reaction,** which activates digestive enzymes in the acrosome, primarily hyaluronidase.

3 The first sperm cell through the zona pellucida attaches to a receptor molecule (integrin α6β1) on the surface of the oocyte plasma membrane and causes depolarization of the membrane within 2–3 seconds. This depolarization, called the **fast block to polyspermy,** prevents additional sperm cells from attaching to the oocyte plasma membrane. Depolarization also stimulates the intracellular release of Ca^{2+}. This in turn causes the oocyte to release water and other molecules from secretory vesicles, referred to as cortical granules. These granules are located on the inner surface of the oocyte plasma membrane. The released fluid causes the oocyte to shrink and the zona pellucida to denature and expand away from the oocyte. This results in a fluid-filled space between the oocyte plasma membrane and the zona pellucida called the **perivitelline space.** As the result of denaturation of the zona pellucida, ZP3 is inactivated, and no additional sperm cells can attach. This reaction is referred to as the **slow block to polyspermy.** Together, the fast block and the slow block ensure that the oocyte is fertilized by only one sperm cell.

4 The entrance of a sperm cell into the oocyte stimulates the female nucleus to undergo the second meiotic division, and the second polar body is formed.

5 The nucleus that remains after the second meiotic division, called the **female pronucleus,** moves to the center of the oocyte, where it meets the **male pronucleus** of the sperm cell. Both the male and female pronuclei are haploid, each having one chromosome of each homologous pair (see chapter 28).

6 Fusion of the pronuclei completes the process of fertilization and restores the diploid number of chromosomes. The product of fertilization is a single diploid cell called a **zygote** (ZIE-goht; figure 29.3*a*).

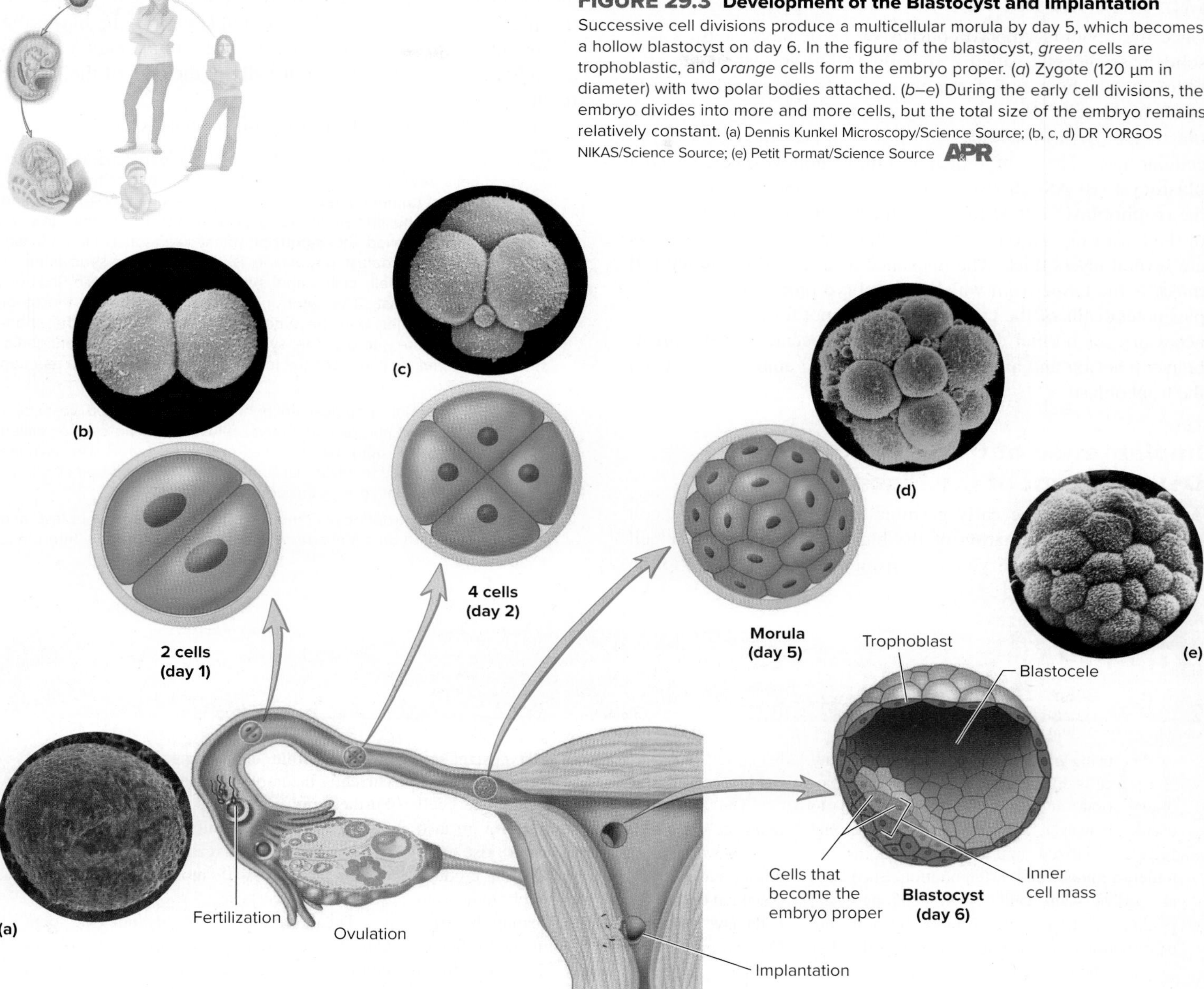

FIGURE 29.3 Development of the Blastocyst and Implantation
Successive cell divisions produce a multicellular morula by day 5, which becomes a hollow blastocyst on day 6. In the figure of the blastocyst, *green* cells are trophoblastic, and *orange* cells form the embryo proper. (*a*) Zygote (120 μm in diameter) with two polar bodies attached. (*b–e*) During the early cell divisions, the embryo divides into more and more cells, but the total size of the embryo remains relatively constant. (a) Dennis Kunkel Microscopy/Science Source; (b, c, d) DR YORGOS NIKAS/Science Source; (e) Petit Format/Science Source APR

Early Cell Division

About 18–36 hours after fertilization, the zygote divides to form two cells. Those two cells divide to form four cells, which divide to form eight cells, and so on (figure 29.3*b–d*). In the very early stages of development (days 1–4), the cells are said to be **totipotent** (toh-TIP-oh-tent; whole-powered), meaning that each cell has the potential to give rise to any tissue type necessary for development. However, the cells of the developing embryo soon undergo **differentiation,** or specialization. Once differentiation occurs, the dividing cells of the embryo are referred to as **pluripotent** (ploo-RIP-oh-tent; multiple-powered), which means that any given cell has the ability to develop into a wide range of tissues, but not into all the tissues necessary for development. From this point on, the total number of embryonic cells can decrease, increase, or reorganize without affecting the normal development of the embryo.

In rare cases, following early cell divisions, a totipotent cell separates from the embryo and develops to form another individual, producing "identical twins," or **monozygotic twins.** Identical twins have identical genetic information in their cells. Other mechanisms that occur a little later in development can also cause identical twins.

Occasionally, a female ovulates two or more secondary oocytes at the same time. Fertilization of two oocytes by different sperm cells results in "fraternal twins," or **dizygotic twins.** Dizygotic twins are not genetically identical. Multiple ovulations can occur naturally or result from the injection of drugs that stimulate gonadotropin release. These drugs are used to treat certain forms of infertility, and they sometimes result in multiple fetuses (see Clinical Impact 29.2).

Morula and Blastocyst

Once the dividing embryo consists of 12 or more cells, it is a solid mass of cells called a **morula** (MOR-you-lah; mulberry; figure 29.3*d*). Four or 5 days after ovulation, the morula consists of about 32 cells. Near this time, a fluid-filled cavity called the **blastocele** (BLAS-toe-seel) begins to form near the center of the cellular mass. The embryo then becomes a hollow sphere called a **blastocyst** (BLAS-toh-sist; figure 29.3*e*). A single layer of cells, the **trophoblast** (TROH-foh-blast; feeding layer), surrounds most of the blastocele. At one end of the blastocyst, however, the cells are several layers thick. The thickened area, called the **inner cell mass,** is the tissue from which the embryo proper develops. The pluripotent cells of the inner cell mass do not form all the tissues necessary for normal development. The placenta and the membranes (chorion and amnion) surrounding the embryo form from the trophoblast.

Implantation of the Blastocyst and Development of the Placenta

All the events of the early germinal phase, from the first cell division through formation of the blastocele and the inner cell mass, occur as the embryo moves from the site of fertilization in the ampulla of the uterine tube to the uterus, where **implantation** (im-plan-TAY-shun) occurs. During implantation, the blastocyst essentially burrows into the uterine wall. Implantation occurs about 7 days after fertilization, usually in the area of the uterine fundus.

Figure 29.4 depicts the process of implantation.

1. As the blastocyst invades the uterine wall, two populations of trophoblast cells develop and form the embryonic portion of the **placenta,** the organ of nutrient and waste exchange between the embryo and the mother. The first proliferating population of individual trophoblast cells is called the **cytotrophoblast** (sigh-toh-TROF-oh-blast). The other trophoblast population is a nondividing syncytium, or multinucleated cell, called the **syncytiotrophoblast** (sin-SISH-ee-oh-TROH-foh-blast). The cytotrophoblast remains nearer the other embryonic tissues, and the syncytiotrophoblast invades the endometrium of the uterus. The syncytiotrophoblast is nonantigenic, meaning that, as it invades the maternal tissue, no immune reaction is triggered.
2. As the syncytiotrophoblast encounters maternal blood vessels, it surrounds them and digests the vessel wall, forming cavities called **lacunae** (la-KOO-nee), which contain maternal blood. The lacunae are still connected to intact maternal vessels, so that blood circulates from the maternal vessels through the lacunae.
3. Cords of cytotrophoblast surround the syncytiotrophoblast and lacunae. Embryonic mesoderm and blood vessels grow into these cords.

Clinical IMPACT 29.1 — Stem Cell Research

During growth and development, many cells differentiate for a particular function, and many lose the ability to divide. However, some cells do not become fully specialized and retain the ability to undergo mitosis and differentiation. Such cells are called **stem cells.** Stem cells have the potential to treat many diseases by replacing dysfunctional cells with normal cells. For example, bone marrow transplants are a common treatment for certain types of leukemia. In this procedure, blood stem cells, found in the red bone marrow, are harvested from a donor and introduced into a leukemia patient. The stem cells provide a new source of normal blood cells for that individual. Bone marrow stem cells are being studied for treating other diseases, such as autoimmunity.

Stem cells can be obtained from different sources, including adult tissues. Adult stem cells, however, produce only a limited number of cell types, depending on the tissue source of the stem cell. For example, adult liver stem cells can give rise to many cell types found in the liver, but they cannot give rise to other tissue cell types, such as blood cells. The most versatile stem cell is the totipotent zygote because it can give rise to all cell types, including placental tissue.

The pluripotent cells of the inner cell mass, called **embryonic stem cells,** are also very versatile because they can give rise to all embryonic tissues, but they do not produce placental tissue. Theoretically, embryonic stem cells have great potential for treating diseases. One problem, however, lies in the ability to artificially stimulate embryonic stem cells to differentiate into the right type of cell. Scientists are still in the early stages of determining the biochemical processes of how embryonic stem cells communicate to allow for the proper development of all tissues in multicellular organisms. Ideally, scientists would prefer to limit the number of cell types a particular stem cell can give rise to.

Important ethical questions surround the use of embryonic stem cells. To harvest the embryonic cells, an embryo must be destroyed, which is unacceptable to those who argue that the zygote is a living human. Conversely, proponents of embryonic stem cell use maintain that the definition of a human life does not extend to the zygote and that preserving the sanctity and quality of human life for people suffering from debilitating, often fatal, and currently incurable diseases is worth the price. Furthermore, proponents argue that the zygotes providing the embryonic stem cells were produced for some other reason, such as infertility treatment, and will more than likely be destroyed.

The debate will probably not end soon. Current research is attempting to obtain embryonic stem cells without needing to destroy embryos. Indeed, the development of **induced pluripotent stem (iPS)** cells has raised the exciting prospect that fully differentiated adult cells—for example, skin cells—can be reprogrammed to create stem cells similar to embryonic stem cells. Alternatively, the ability to bypass iPS cells by directly transdifferentiating, or reprogramming, readily accessible adult skin cells to generate specific cell types is now becoming a reality. Whether iPS or transdifferentiated cells will be useful in treatment remains to be established, although in the near future the ability to create patient-specific cells will provide scientists with useful tools for researching disease mechanisms and possibly for screening new drugs.

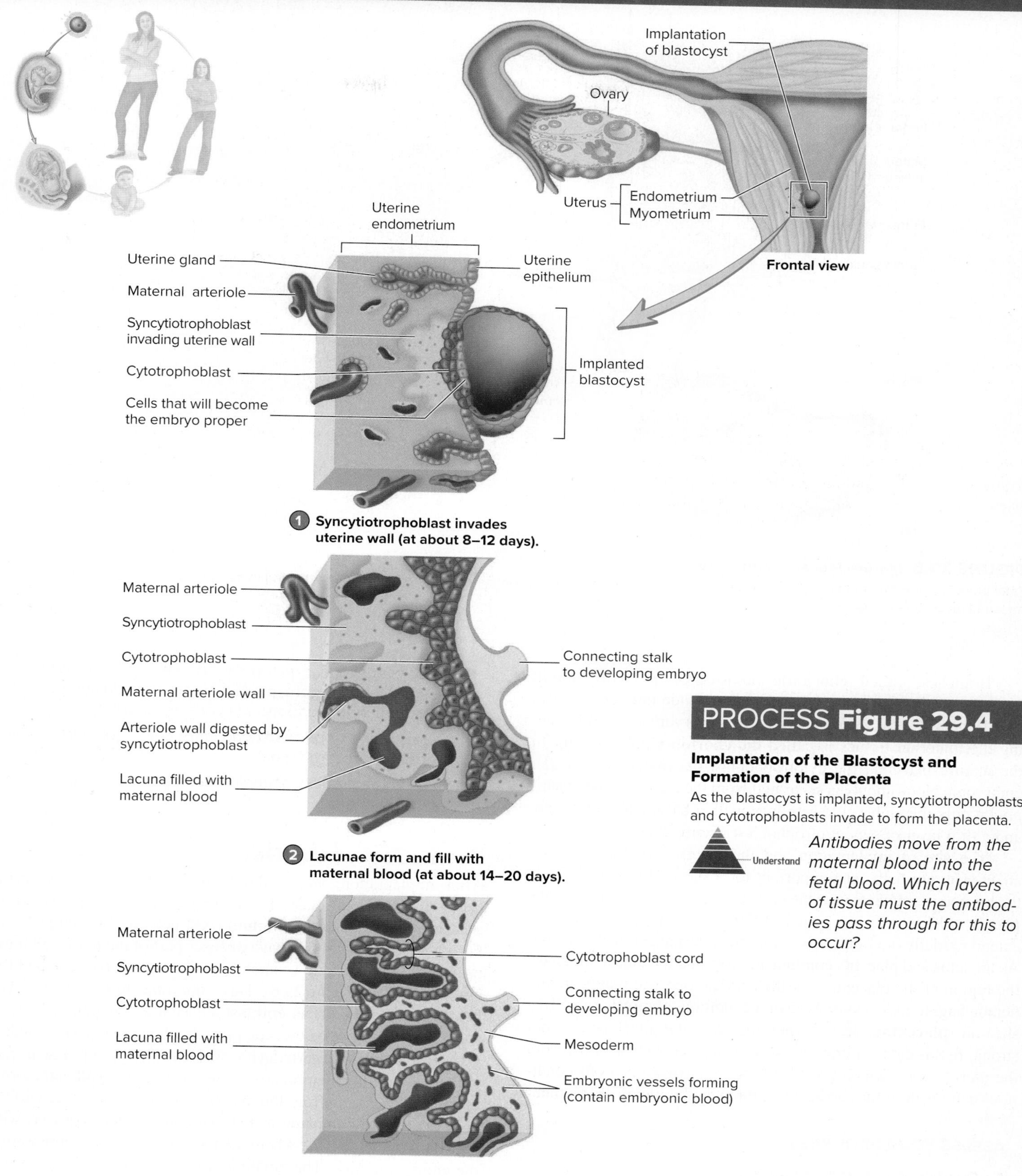

PROCESS **Figure 29.4**

Implantation of the Blastocyst and Formation of the Placenta

As the blastocyst is implanted, syncytiotrophoblasts and cytotrophoblasts invade to form the placenta.

Antibodies move from the maternal blood into the fetal blood. Which layers of tissue must the antibodies pass through for this to occur?

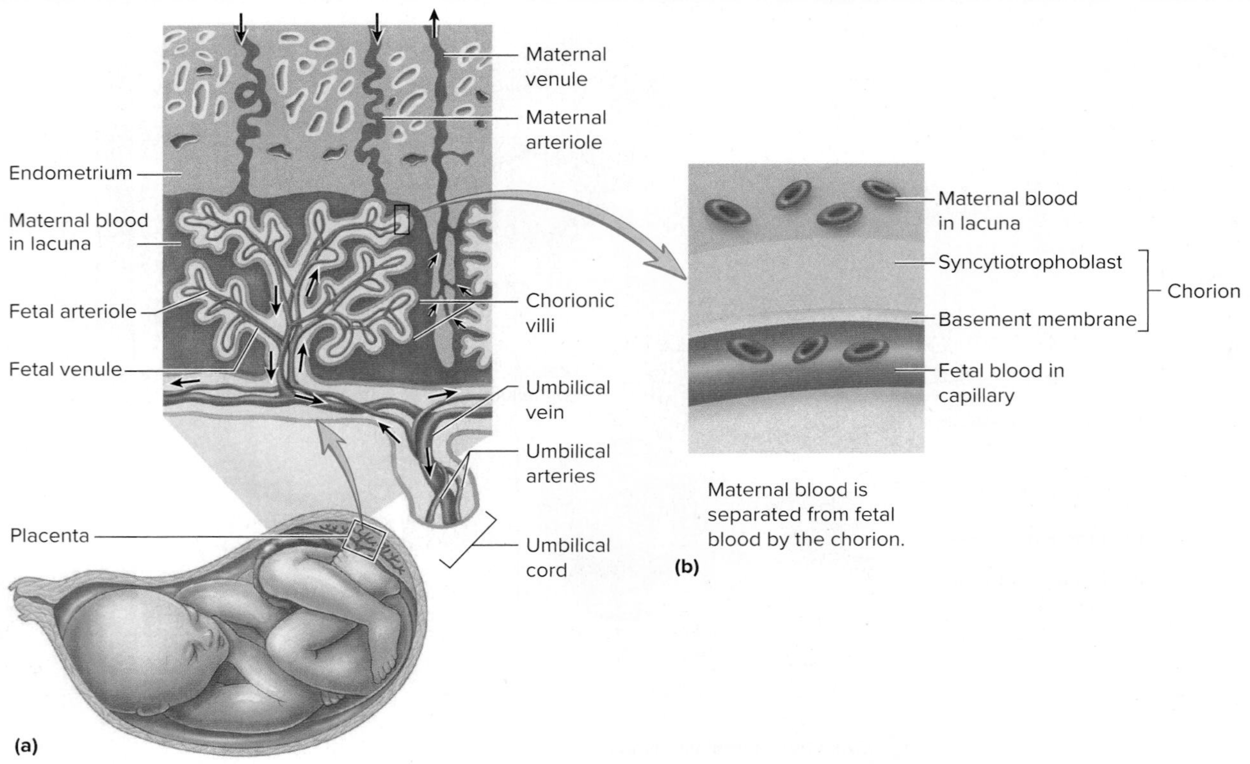

FIGURE 29.5 Mature Placenta and Fetus
Fetal blood vessels and maternal blood vessels are in close contact, and nutrients are exchanged between fetal and maternal blood. However, fetal and maternal blood do not mix.

Branches, called **chorionic** (koh-ree-ON-ik) **villi,** sprout from the cords of cytotrophoblasts and protrude into the lacunae, like fingers (figure 29.5*a*). This entire embryonic structure facing the maternal tissues is called the **chorion** (KOH-ree-on). In the mature placenta, the cytotrophoblast disappears so that the embryonic blood supply is separated from the maternal blood supply by only the embryonic capillary wall, a basement membrane, and a thin layer of syncytiotrophoblast (figure 29.5*b*).

The site of implantation and the integrity of the placental attachment are both very important for a successful pregnancy. If the blastocyst implants near the cervix, a condition called **placenta previa** (PREE-vee-ah) occurs. As the placenta grows, it may extend partially or completely across the internal cervical opening. As the fetus and placenta continue to grow and the uterus stretches, the region of the placenta over the cervical opening may tear, and hemorrhaging may occur. A second condition, **abruptio** (ab-RUP-shee-oh) **placentae,** occurs when the placental attachment is not strong. In this case, a normally positioned placenta tears away from the uterine wall, which also involves hemorrhaging. Both conditions can result in miscarriage and threaten the life of the mother.

ASSESS YOUR PROGRESS

4. *Describe the events of fertilization. Where does fertilization occur?*
5. *Explain what occurs to prevent polyspermy.*
6. *What events occur during the first week after fertilization? Use the terms* zygote, morula, blastocyst, blastocele, totipotent, *and* pluripotent *in your explanation.*
7. *Describe the trophoblast and inner cell mass, and explain what develops from each.*
8. *Explain the process of implantation and the development of the placenta.*

Formation of the Germ Layers

After implantation, an **amniotic** (am-nee-OT-ik) **cavity** forms inside the inner cell mass. The amniotic cavity is surrounded by a layer of cells called the **amnion** (AM-nee-on), or *amniotic sac.* Formation of the amniotic cavity causes part of the inner cell mass nearest the blastocele to separate as a flat disk of tissue called the **embryonic disk** (figure 29.6). This embryonic disk is composed of two layers of cells: (1) an **epiblast** adjacent to the amniotic cavity and (2) a **hypoblast** on the side opposite the amnion. The epiblast gives rise to the three germ layers, whereas the hypoblast gives rise to extraembryonic membranes. A third cavity, the **yolk sac,** forms inside the blastocele from the hypoblast. The amniotic sac and the yolk sac can be compared to two balloons pushed together, with the circular double layer where the two balloons meet representing the embryonic disk. The amniotic sac eventually enlarges to surround the developing embryo, providing a protective fluid environment, the "bag of waters," where the embryo forms.

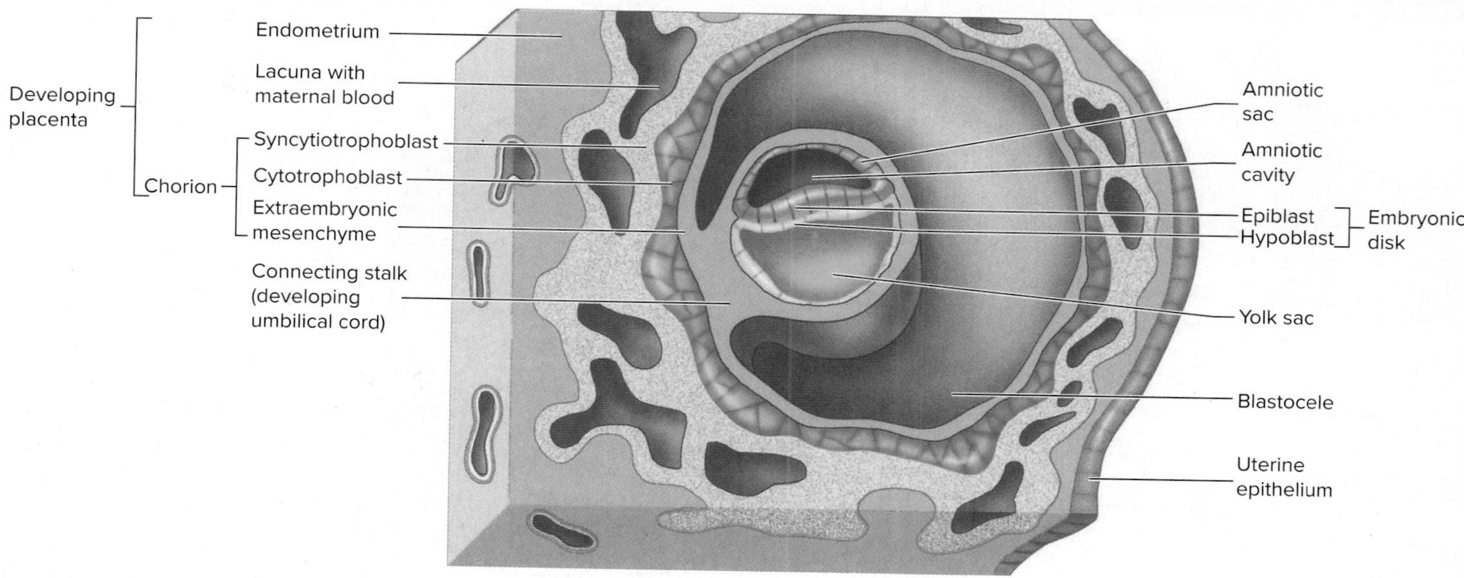

FIGURE 29.6 Embryonic Disk

The embryonic disk consists of epiblast (*blue*) and hypoblast (*yellow*), surrounded by the amniotic cavity and yolk sac. The connecting stalk, which attaches the embryo to the uterus, becomes part of the umbilical cord.

About 13 or 14 days after fertilization, the embryonic disk becomes a slightly elongated, oval structure. This phase of development, known as **gastrulation,** involves the movement of epiblast cells and results in the formation of three distinct germ layers that eventually give rise to the many body structures.

Gastrulation is illustrated in figure 29.7.

1. Proliferating cells of the epiblast migrate toward the center and the caudal (toward the tail or inferior) end of the disk, forming a thickened line called the **primitive streak.** Some epiblast cells migrate through the primitive streak. Those epiblast cells that do not migrate form the **ectoderm** (EK-toe-derm; outside layer).
2. A portion of the cells that moved through the primitive streak migrates toward and displaces the hypoblast to form the **endoderm** (EN-doh-derm; inside layer).
3. Other cells emerge between the ectoderm and the endoderm as the **mesoderm** (MEZ-oh-derm; middle layer). These three germ layers, the endoderm, mesoderm, and ectoderm, are the beginning of the embryo proper. All tissues of the adult can be traced to the three germ layers (table 29.1). The **notochord,** a rodlike structure, extends from the cephalic (toward the head or superior) end of the primitive streak.

The development of the germ layers and the subsequent development of the organ systems is heavily dependent on cell

Clinical IMPACT 29.2 In Vitro Fertilization and Embryo Transfer

In a small number of females, normal pregnancy is not possible because of an anatomical or physiological condition. In 87% of these cases, the uterine tubes are incapable of allowing sperm cells to reach the oocyte or transporting the zygote to the uterus. Since 1978, a two-stage process—(1) in vitro fertilization and (2) embryo transfer—has made pregnancy possible in hundreds of such females. **In vitro fertilization (IVF)** involves removing secondary oocytes from a female, placing the oocytes into a petri dish, and adding sperm cells to the dish, where fertilization and early development occur in vitro, which means "in glass." **Embryo transfer** involves removing the developing embryo from the petri dish and introducing the embryo into the uterus of a recipient female.

For IVF and embryo transfer to be accomplished, a female is first injected with a substance similar to luteinizing hormone (LH), which causes more than one follicle to ovulate at a time. Just before the follicles rupture, the secondary oocytes are surgically removed from the ovary. The oocytes are then incubated in a dish and maintained at body temperature for 6 hours, when sperm cells are added to the dish.

After 24–48 hours, when the embryos have divided to form cell masses of two to eight cells, several of the embryos are transferred to the uterus. Typically, three embryos are introduced into the uterus at a time to increase the success rate because only a small percentage of the embryos are expected to survive. However, the rate of complications, such as multiple pregnancies, miscarriage, and prematurity, also increases with the greater number of transferred embryos. About one-third of transfers of three embryos end in multiple pregnancies.

The success of IVF is dependent on many factors, including the reason for infertility and the mother's age. The success rate for achieving pregnancy following IVF treatment has increased dramatically in recent years.

FUNDAMENTAL Figure

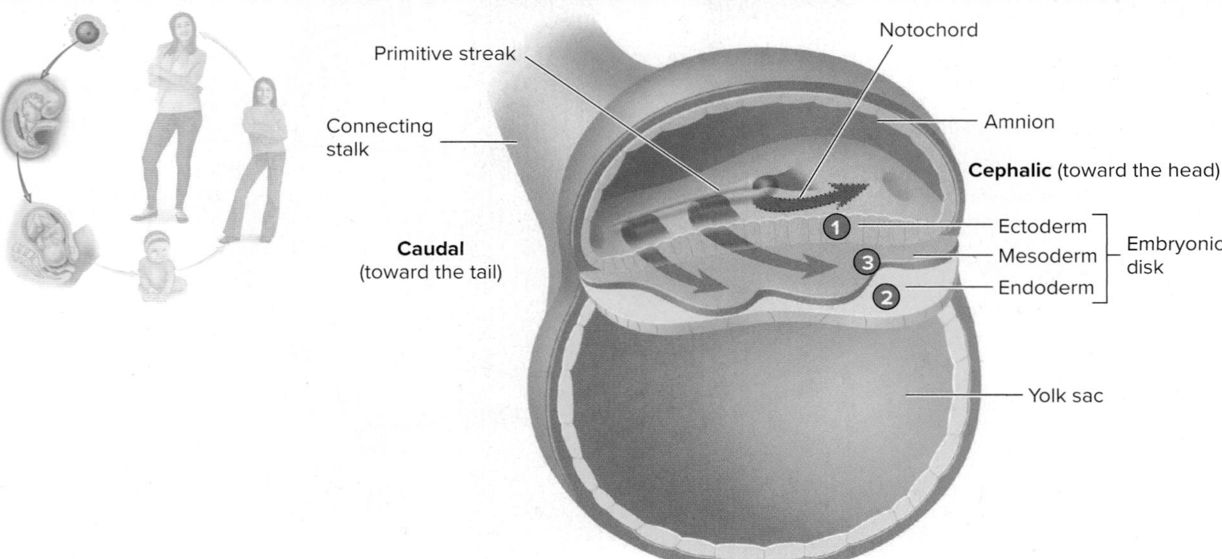

PROCESS Figure 29.7

Embryonic Disk with a Primitive Streak

During gastrulation, three germ layers form: the ectoderm, the mesoderm, and the endoderm.

How are the three germ layers depicted in this figure related to the two germ layers of the embryonic disk depicted in figure 29.6?

TABLE 29.1 Germ Layer Derivatives

Ectoderm	Mesoderm
Epidermis of skin	Dermis of skin
Tooth enamel	Cardiovascular system
Lens and cornea of eye	Parenchyma of glands
Outer ear	Muscle
Nasal cavity	Bones (except facial)
Anterior pituitary	Microglia
Neuroectoderm	Kidneys
Brain and spinal cord	**Endoderm**
Somatic motor neurons	Lining of digestive tract
Preganglionic autonomic neurons	Lining of lungs
Glial cells (except microglia)	Lining of hepatic, pancreatic, and other exocrine ducts
Posterior pituitary	Urinary bladder
Neural crest cells	Thymus
Melanocytes	Thyroid gland
Sensory neurons	Parathyroid glands
Postganglionic autonomic neurons	Tonsils
Adrenal medulla	
Facial bones	
Teeth (dentin, pulp, and cementum) and gingiva	
A few skeletal muscles in head	

PROCESS **Figure**

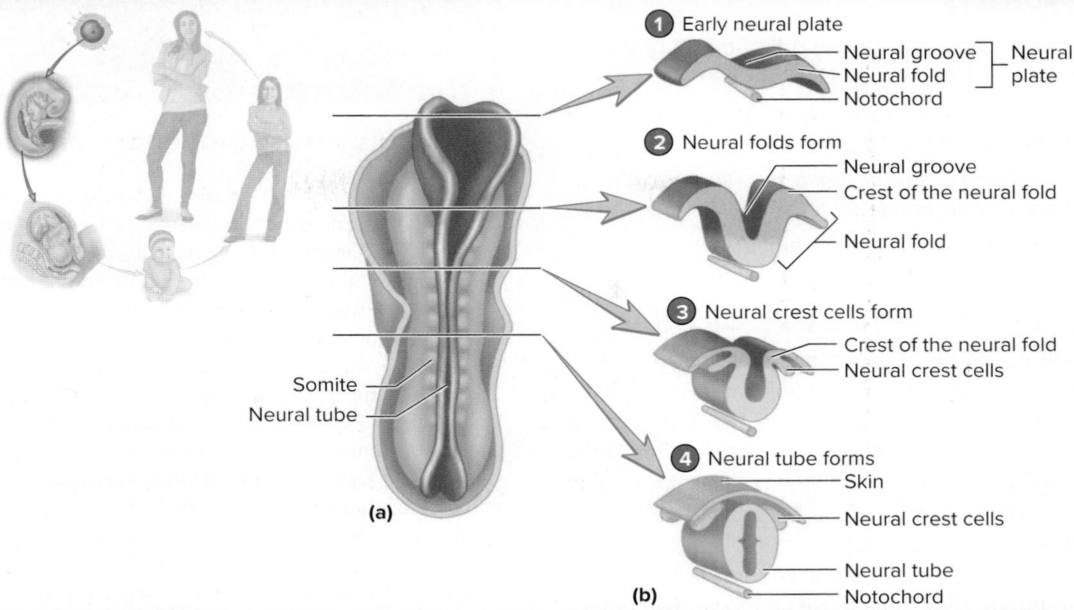

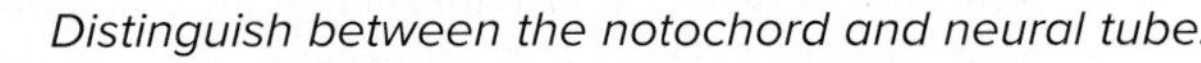

Formation of the Neural Tube

The neural folds come together in the midline and fuse to form a neural tube. This fusion begins in the center and moves both cranially and caudally. Shown is an embryo at about 21 days after fertilization. The insets to the right show progressive closure of the neural tube at various levels of cross section.

Understand *Distinguish between the notochord and neural tube.*

communication. Some communication requires direct cell-to-cell contact, whereas other communication depends on diffusable molecules, such as **growth factors.** Two important families of growth factors are epidermal growth factors (EGF) and fibroblast growth factors (FGF).

Predict 1

Occasionally, two primitive streaks form in one embryonic disk. Predict the result. What happens if the two primitive streaks are touching each other?

Neural Tube and Neural Crest Formation

Portions of the nervous system develop through specialization of ectoderm. Figure 29.8 illustrates the process.

1. About 18 days after fertilization, the ectoderm near the cephalic end of the primitive streak is stimulated to form a thickened **neural plate.**
2. The lateral edges of the plate begin to rise, like two ocean waves coming together. These edges are called the **neural folds,** and between them lies a **neural groove.** The underlying notochord stimulates the folding of the neural plate at the neural groove.
3. The crests of the neural folds begin to meet in the midline and fuse into a **neural tube.** The cells of the neural tube are called **neuroectoderm** (table 29.1). A population of cells, called **neural crest cells,** breaks away from the neuroectoderm all along the crests of the folds. We will discuss these cells in more detail later in this section.
4. Neuroectoderm becomes the brain, the spinal cord, and parts of the peripheral nervous system. The neural tube becomes completely closed by day 26. If the neural tube fails to close, major defects of the central nervous system can result (see Clinical Impact 29.4).

As stated earlier, a population of neuroectoderm cells, called neural crest cells, breaks away. These cells migrate along one of three distinct routes as they leave the neural folds: (1) those that migrate down along the side of the developing neural tube become autonomic ganglia neurons, adrenal medullary cells, or enteric nervous system neurons; (2) those that migrate into the somites (see the next section, "Somite Formation") become sensory ganglia neurons; and (3) those that migrate laterally between the somites and the ectoderm become melanocytes. In the head, neural crest cells contribute to the skull, the dentin of teeth, a few small skeletal muscles, and general connective tissue. Because neural crest cells in the head give rise to many of the same tissues as the mesoderm in the head and trunk, the general term **mesenchyme** (MEZ-en-kyme) is sometimes applied to cells of either neural crest or mesoderm origin.

Somite Formation

As the neural tube develops, distinct segments, called somites (SOH-mites), form from the mesoderm immediately adjacent to the tube (figure 29.8). In the head, the first few somites do not become clearly divided, but develop into indistinct, segmented structures called **somitomeres.** The somites and somitomeres eventually give rise to a part of the skull, the vertebral column, and skeletal muscle. Most of the head muscles are derived from the somitomeres.

ASSESS YOUR PROGRESS

9. *Describe the process of gastrulation and the role of the primitive streak.*
10. *List the major body tissues, organs, and systems that originate from each of the three germ layers.*
11. *Describe the formation of the neural tube. What are the three routes taken by neural crest cells?*
12. *What is a somite? What do they develop into?*

Formation of the Gut and Body Cavities

At the same time the neural tube is forming, the embryo itself is becoming a tube along the upper part of the yolk sac. The cephalic and caudal ends of the yolk sac separate from the main part of the sac to form the **foregut** and **hindgut,** respectively. This is the beginning of the digestive tract (figure 29.9*a*). The developing digestive tract pinches off from the yolk sac as a tube but remains attached to the yolk sac by a yolk stalk.

The ends of the foregut and hindgut (figure 29.9*b*) are in close relationship to the overlying ectoderm and form membranes called the oropharyngeal membrane and the cloacal membrane, respectively. The **oropharyngeal membrane** opens to form the mouth, and the **cloacal membrane** opens to form the urethra and anus. Thus, the digestive tract becomes a tube with openings at both ends.

A considerable number of outpocketings, or **evaginations** (ee-vaj-i-NAY-shunz), occur along the early digestive tract. The first to form is the allantois (figure 29.9*b*), part of which will form the urinary bladder. Other evaginations develop into structures such as the anterior pituitary, the thyroid gland, the lungs, the liver, and the pancreas. At the same time, solid bars of tissue known as **branchial arches** (figure 29.9*c;* see figure 29.10) form along the lateral sides of the head. The sides of the foregut expand as pockets between these branchial arches. The central expanded foregut is called the **pharynx,** and the pockets along both sides of the pharynx are called **pharyngeal pouches.** Adult derivatives of the pharyngeal pouches include the auditory tubes, tonsils, thymus, and parathyroid glands.

At about the same time the gut is developing, the **coelom** (SEE-lom), or body cavities, begins to form as a series of isolated cavities within the embryo (figure 29.9). The most cranial group of cavities enlarges and fuses to form the **pericardial cavity.** Shortly thereafter, the coelomic cavity extends toward the caudal end of the embryo as the **pleural cavities** and the **peritoneal cavity.** Initially, these cavities are continuous, but they eventually separate into distinct adult cavities (see chapter 1).

Limb Bud Development

At about 28 days, the arms and legs appear as limb buds (figure 29.10). The **apical ectodermal ridge,** a specialized thickening of the ectoderm, develops on the lateral margin of each limb bud and stimulates its outgrowth. As the buds elongate, limb tissues are laid down in a proximal-to-distal sequence. For example, in the upper limb, the arm forms before the forearm, which in turn forms before the hand.

Clinical IMPACT 29.3

Environmental Influences on Development

During the first 2 weeks of development, the embryo is quite resistant to environmental influences that may cause malformations. Factors that adversely affect the embryo at this age are more likely to kill it than cause malformations. However, between 2 weeks and the next 4–7 weeks (depending on the structure considered), the embryo is more sensitive to outside influences that cause malformations than at any other time.

A number of drugs and other environmental influences are known to affect the embryo and fetus during development. The two most common are alcohol and cigarette smoke. Alcohol consumption can result in **fetal alcohol syndrome,** which is primarily characterized by decreased mental function. Although excessive alcohol consumption, as occurs with alcoholism and binge drinking, is known to cause fetal alcohol syndrome, research results are inconsistent about the effects of lower levels of consumption. Most physicians recommend that alcohol not be consumed at all during pregnancy. Studies have shown that exposure to cigarette smoke throughout pregnancy can stunt the physical growth and mental development of the fetus.

Isotretinoin, more commonly known as Accutane, is a drug used to treat severe acne; however, it has been shown to cause severe birth defects, including malformation of the ears, eyes, face, skull, heart, and brain. The risk of detrimental effects on the developing embryo and fetus is so great that the manufacturer of Accutane requires both medical professionals who prescribe Accutane and their patients to participate in a pregnancy risk management program in order to obtain the medication. The program requires that females prescribed Accutane agree to use two forms of birth control and take monthly pregnancy tests while using the drug.

Development of the Face

The face develops by the fusion of five embryonic structures: the single frontonasal process, a pair of maxillary processes, and a pair of mandibular processes. Figure 29.11 illustrates some of the stages of the development of the face.

1. The **frontonasal process** forms the forehead, nose, and midportion of the upper jaw and lip. The **maxillary processes** form the lateral parts of the upper jaw and lip. The **mandibular processes** form the lower jaw and lip.
2. **Nasal placodes** (PLAK-ohdz), areas of thickening that develop at the lateral margins of the frontonasal process, develop into the nose and the center of the upper jaw and lip.
3. As the brain enlarges and the face matures, the nasal placodes approach each other in the midline. The medial edges of the placodes fuse to form the midportion of the upper jaw and lip. This part of the frontonasal process is between the two maxillary processes, which are expanding toward the midline, and fuses with them to form the upper jaw and lip, known as the **primary palate.** A **cleft lip** results if the frontonasal and one or both maxillary processes fail to fuse. Because the frontonasal process is a midline structure that normally fuses with the two lateral maxillary processes during formation of the primary palate, cleft lips usually do not occur in the midline but

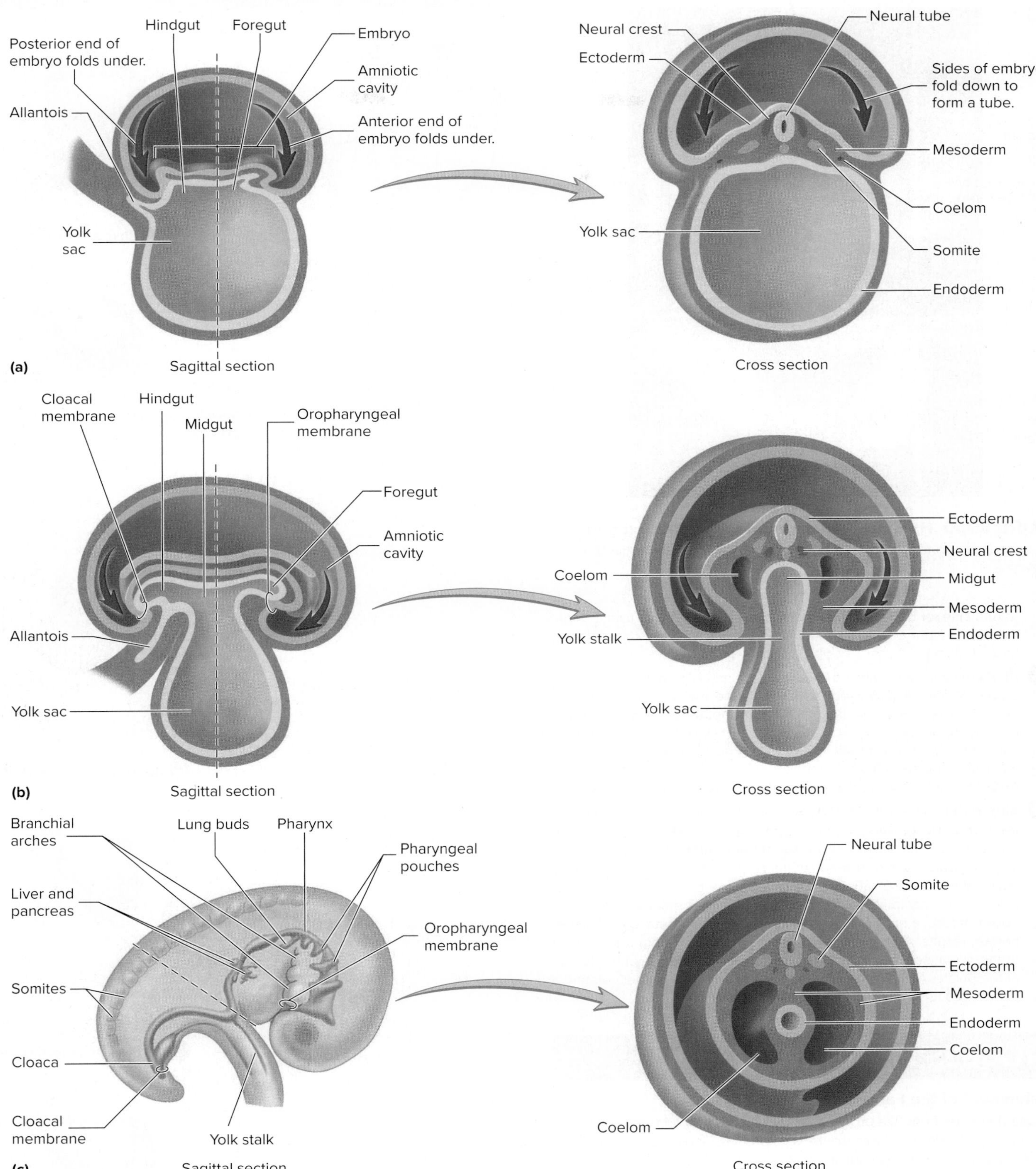

FIGURE 29.9 Formation of the Digestive Tract

Blue arrows show the folding of the digestive tract into a tube. *Dashed lines* show the plane from which the cross sections were taken. (*a*) Twenty days after fertilization. (*b*) Twenty-five days after fertilization. (*c*) Thirty days after fertilization. Evaginations are identified along the pharynx and the liver and pancreas.

FIGURE 29.10 Human Embryo 35 Days After Fertilization
Limb buds begin to form about 28 days after fertilization. John Giannicchi/Science Source

to one side (or both sides). The cleft can vary in severity from a slight indentation in the lip to a fissure that extends from the mouth to the nares (nostril).

4 At about the same time the primary palate is forming, the lateral edges of the nasal placodes fuse with the maxillary processes to close off the groove extending from the mouth to the eye. On rare occasions, these structures fail to meet, resulting in a facial cleft extending from the mouth to the eye. The inferior margins of the maxillary processes fuse with the superior margins of the mandibular processes to decrease the size of the mouth.

5 All of the previously described fusions and the growth of the brain give the face a recognizably "human" appearance by about 50 days. The roof of the mouth, known as the **secondary palate,** begins as vertical shelves, which swing to a horizontal position and begin to fuse with each other at about 56 days of development. Fusion of the entire palate is not completed until about 90 days. If the secondary palate does not fuse, a midline fissure in the roof of the mouth, called a **cleft palate,** results. A cleft palate can range in severity from a slight cleft of the uvula (see figure 24.6) to a fissure extending the entire length of the palate. A cleft lip and cleft palate can occur together, forming a continuous fissure.

PROCESS **Figure 29.11**

Development of the Face
The face develops from five processes that enlarge and fuse together. These processes are the single frontonasal process (indicated in *blue*), the two maxillary processes (indicated in *yellow*), and the two mandibular processes (indicated in *red*), which are illustrated in their fused state in this figure.

Which process(es) would be involved if the lower lip were not formed correctly? Which process(es) would be involved if there were abnormal development of the cheek?

PROCESS **Figure**

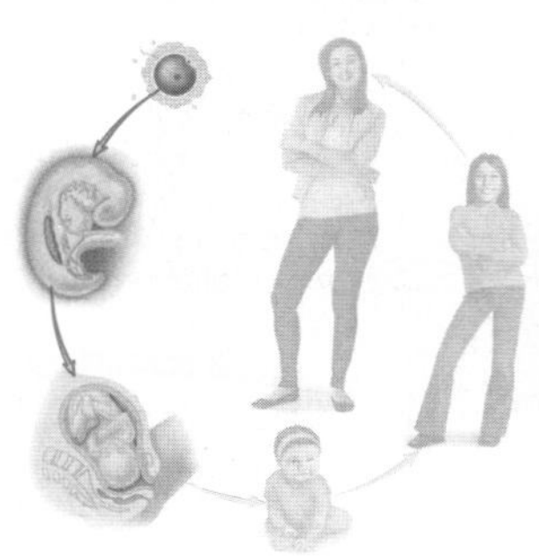

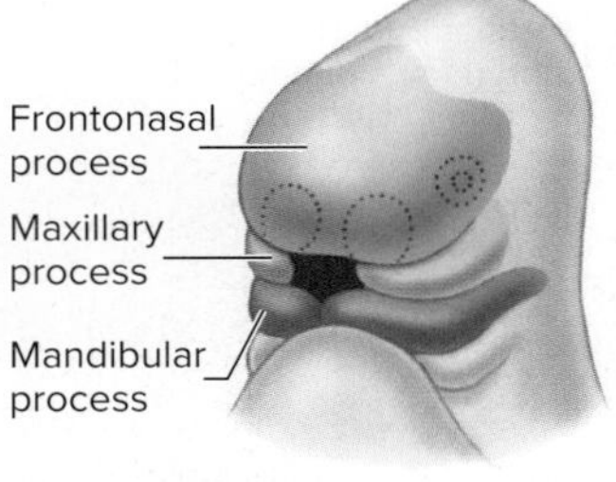

1 **28 days after fertilization**

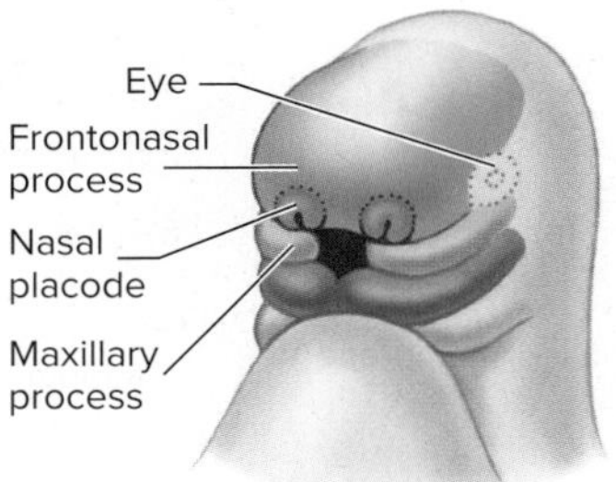

2 **33 days after fertilization**

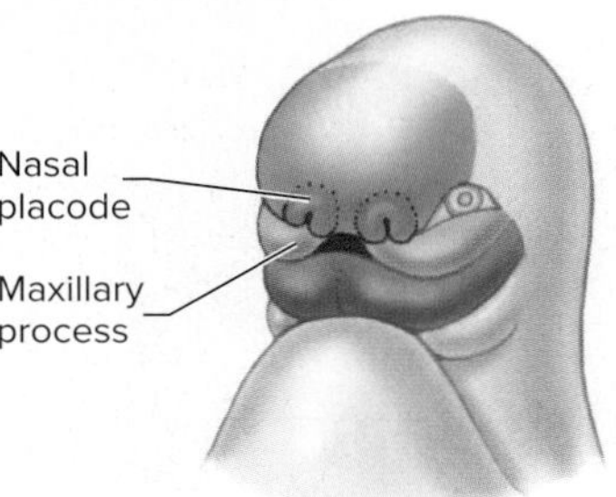

3 **40 days after fertilization**

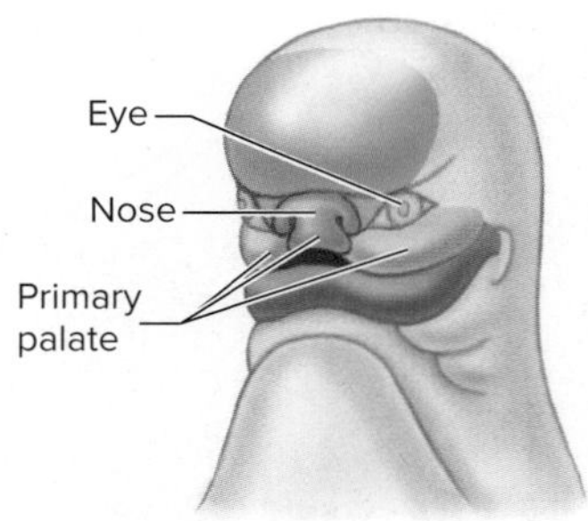

4 **48 days after fertilization**

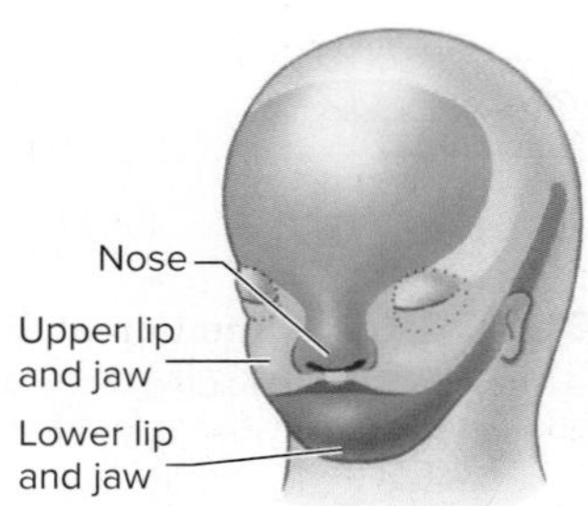

5 **14 weeks after fertilization**

ASSESS YOUR PROGRESS

13. *Describe the formation of the gut and the body cavities.*
14. *How do limb buds develop? What does proximal-to-distal growth sequence mean?*
15. *Describe the process involved in forming the face. What clefts may result if these tissues fail to fuse?*

Development of the Organ Systems

Organogenesis is the appearance and development of organs. The period of organogenesis occurs between 14 and 60 days after fertilization, which is primarily during the embryonic period of development (table 29.2).

Skin

Recall from chapter 5 that the skin is comprised of the epidermis and the dermis. The **epidermis** of the skin is derived from ectoderm, and the **dermis** is derived from mesoderm or, in the case of the face, from neural crest cells. Accesssory organs, such as the nails, hair, and glands, develop from the epidermis (see chapter 5). Melanocytes and sensory receptors in the skin are derived from neural crest cells.

Skeleton

The process of bone development was discussed in chapter 6. The bones of the skeleton develop from either mesoderm or the neural crest cells through intramembranous or endochondral bone formation (see chapter 6). The bones of the face develop from neural crest cells, whereas the rest of the skull, the vertebral column, and the ribs develop from somite- or somitomere-derived mesoderm. The appendicular skeleton develops from limb bud mesoderm.

Muscle

Recall from chapter 9 that skeletal muscles are comprised of multinucleated cells called muscle fibers. **Myoblasts** (MY-oh-blastz) are the early embryonic cells that give rise to skeletal muscle fibers. Myoblasts migrate from somites or somitomeres to sites of future muscle development, where they continue to divide and begin to fuse to form multinuclear cells called **myotubes.** Myotubes enlarge to become the muscle fibers of the skeletal muscles. Shortly after myotubes form, nerves grow into the area and innervate the developing muscle fibers. After the basic form of each muscle is established, muscle growth continues as the number of muscle fibers increases. The total number of muscle fibers is established before birth and remains relatively constant thereafter. Muscle enlargement after birth results from an increase in the size of individual muscle fibers.

Nervous System

The nervous system is derived from the neural tube and the neural crest cells. Neural tube closure begins at about 21 days of development in the upper cervical region and proceeds into the head and down the spinal cord. Severe birth defects result from failure of normal neural tube closure (figure 29.12) Soon after the neural tube has closed at about 25 days of development, the part of the neural tube that becomes the brain begins to expand and develop a series of pouches. The central cavity of the neural tube becomes the ventricles of the brain and the central canal of the spinal cord (see figure 13.13).

Within the neural tube are the neuron cell bodies of somatic motor neurons and preganglionic neurons of the autonomic nervous system, which provide axons to the peripheral nervous system. Sensory neurons and postganglionic neurons of the autonomic nervous system are derived from neural crest cells.

Special Senses

Recall from chapter 15 that the special senses are those senses where the receptors are localized to a specific organ. The sense of olfaction (smell) includes the olfactory organ, olfactory bulb, and olfactory nerves. The **olfactory bulbs** and **olfactory nerves** develop as an evagination from the telencephalon (see figures 13.3 and 13.15). The eyes, the organs of vision, develop as evaginations from the diencephalon. Each evagination elongates to form an **optic stalk,** and a bulb called the **optic vesicle** develops at the terminal end of each optic stalk. The optic vesicle reaches the side of the head and stimulates the overlying ectoderm to thicken into a **lens.** The sensory part of the ear, the organ of hearing and equilibrium, appears as an ectodermal thickening, or placode, that invaginates and pinches off from the overlying ectoderm.

Endocrine System

The structures of the endocrine system are found in many areas of the body (see chapter 18). A downward growth from the floor of the diencephalon forms the **posterior pituitary gland.** The **anterior pituitary gland** develops from an evagination of ectoderm in the roof of the embryonic oral cavity and grows toward the floor of the brain. It eventually loses its connection with the oral cavity and becomes attached to the posterior pituitary gland (see chapter 18).

The **thyroid gland** originates as an evagination from the floor of the pharynx in the region of the developing tongue and moves into the lower neck, eventually losing its connection with the pharynx. The **parathyroid glands,** which are derived from the third and fourth pharyngeal pouches, migrate inferiorly and become associated with the thyroid gland.

The **adrenal medulla** arises from neural crest cells and consists of specialized postganglionic neurons of the sympathetic division of the autonomic nervous system (see chapter 16). The **adrenal cortex** is derived from mesoderm.

The **pancreas** originates as two evaginations from the duodenum, which come together to form a single gland (see figure 29.9*c*).

Cardiovascular System

The cardiovascular system includes the heart, blood vessels, and blood (see chapters 19–21). The heart develops from two endothelial tubes, which lie side by side in the early embryo. Figure 29.13 illustrates the development of the heart.

1. At about 21 days after fertilization the two tubes fuse into a single, midline heart tube.
2. A series of dilations appears along the length of the primitive heart tube, and four major regions can be identified: (a) the **sinus venosus,** the site where blood enters the heart; (b) a single **atrium;** (c) a single **ventricle;** and (d) the **bulbus cordis,** where blood exits the heart. The

TABLE 29.2 **Development of the Organ Systems**

	Age (Days Since Fertilization)					
	1–5	**6–10**	**11–15**	**16–20**	**21–25**	**26–30**
General Features	Fertilization, morula, blastocyst	Blastocyst implants	Primitive streak, three germ layers	Neural plate	Neural tube closed	Limb buds and other "buds" appear.
Integumentary System			Ectoderm, mesoderm			Melanocytes form from neural crest.
Skeletal System			Mesoderm		Neural crest (will form facial bones)	Limb buds
Muscular System			Mesoderm	Somites begin to form.		Somites are all present.
Nervous System			Ectoderm	Neural plate	Neural tube complete; neural crest forms; eyes and ears begin to form.	Lens begins to form.
Endocrine System			Ectoderm, mesoderm, endoderm	Thyroid begins to develop.		Parathyroid glands and pancreas appear.
Cardiovascular System			Mesoderm	Blood islands form; two-tubed heart forms.	Single-tubed heart begins to beat.	Interatrial septum begins to form.
Lymphatic System			Mesoderm			Thymus appears.
Respiratory System			Mesoderm, endoderm		Diaphragm begins to form.	Trachea forms as single bud; lung buds (primary bronchi) form.
Digestive System			Mesoderm		Neural crest forms tooth dentin.	Liver and pancreas appear as buds.
			Endoderm		Foregut and hindgut form.	Tongue bud appears.
Urinary System			Mesoderm, endoderm		Pronephros develops; allantois appears.	Mesonephros appears.
Reproductive System			Mesoderm, endoderm		Primordial germ cells form on yolk sac.	Mesonephros appears; genital tubercle forms.

elongating heart, confined within the pericardium, becomes bent into a loop, the apex of which is the ventricle. The major chambers of the heart, the atrium and the ventricle, expand rapidly. The right part of the sinus venosus becomes absorbed into the atrium, and the bulbus cordis is absorbed into the ventricle. The embryonic sinus venosus initiates contraction at one end of the tubular heart. Later in development, part of the sinus venosus becomes the sinoatrial node, the pacemaker in the adult heart.

3. The **interatrial septum,** which separates the two atria in the adult heart, and the **interventricular septum,** which divides the single ventricle into two chambers, begin to grow toward the center of the heart.
4. The interatrial septum is formed from two parts: the **septum primum** (primary septum) and the **septum secundum** (secondary septum).
5. An opening in the interatrial septum called the **foramen ovale** (oh-VAL-ee) connects the two atria and allows blood to flow from the right to the left atrium in the embryo and fetus.

If the septum secundum fails to grow far enough or if the foramen ovale becomes too large, an **atrial septal defect (ASD)**

Age (Days Since Fertilization)					
31–35	**36–40**	**41–45**	**46–50**	**51–55**	**56–60**
Hand and foot plates on limbs	Fingers and toes appear; lips form; embryo is 15 mm long.	External ear is forming; embryo is 20 mm long.	Embryo is 25 mm long.	Limbs elongate to adult proportions; embryo is 35 mm long.	Face is distinctly human in appearance.
Sensory receptors appear in skin.		Collagen fibers are clearly present in skin.		Extensive sensory endings are present in skin.	
Mesoderm condenses in areas of future bone.	Cartilage in site of future humerus	Cartilage in site of future ulna and radius	Cartilage in site of hand and fingers		Ossification begins in clavicle and then in other bones.
Muscle precursor cells enter limb buds.			Functional muscle		Nearly all muscles are appearing in an adult form.
Nerve processes enter limb buds.		External ear is forming; olfactory nerves begin to form.		Semicircular canals in inner ear are complete.	Eyelids form; cochlea in inner ear is complete.
Pituitary gland appears as evaginations from brain and mouth.	Gonadal ridges form; adrenal glands are forming.		Pineal gland appears.	Thyroid gland is in adult position, and its attachment to tongue is lost.	Anterior pituitary loses its connection to mouth.
Interventricular septum begins to form.		Interventricular septum is complete.	Interatrial septum is complete but still has opening until birth.		
Large lymphatic vessels form in neck.	Spleen appears.			Adult lymph pattern forms.	
Secondary bronchi to lobes form.	Tertiary bronchi to bronchopulmonary segments form.		Tracheal cartilage begins to form.		
Oropharyngeal membrane ruptures.		Secondary palate begins to form; tooth buds begin to form.			Secondary palate begins to fuse (fusion complete by 90 days).
Metanephros begins to develop.				Mesonephros degenerates.	Anal portion of cloacal membrane ruptures.
	Gonadal ridges form.	Primordial germ cells enter gonadal ridges.	Paramesonephric ducts appear.		Uterus is forming; external genitalia begin to differentiate in male and female.

develops, allowing blood to flow from the left atrium to the right atrium in the newborn. If the interventricular septum does not grow enough to completely separate the ventricles, a **ventricular septal defect (VSD)** results. VSDs are more common than ASDs. Both ASDs and VSDs result in abnormal heart sounds, called a **heart murmur.** Blood passes through the ASD or the VSD from the left to the right side of the heart. The right side of the heart usually hypertrophies. In many cases, septal defects are not serious. However, in severe cases of VSD (Eisenmenger syndrome), increased pressure in the pulmonary blood vessels and decreased blood flow through the systemic blood vessels result in pulmonary edema, cyanosis (a bluish color to the skin due to deficient blood oxygenation), or heart failure.

Blood vessels and blood cells form from blood islands on the surface of the yolk sac and inside the embryo. Blood islands are small masses of mesoderm that become blood vessels on the

Clinical IMPACT 29.4 Neural Tube Defects

Proper neural tube formation is necessary for the development of the nervous system; otherwise, several birth defects can occur. **Anencephaly** (AN-en-SEF-ah-lee; no brain) is a birth defect in which much of the brain fails to form. It results because the neural tube did not close in the region of the head. A baby born with anencephaly cannot survive.

Spina bifida (SPY-nah BIH-fih-dah; split spine) is a general term describing defects of the spinal cord, vertebral column, or both (figure 29.12). Spina bifida can range from a simple defect, in which one or more vertebral spinous processes are split or missing but there is no clinical manifestation, to a severe defect that results in paralysis of the limbs or the bowels and bladder, depending on where the defect occurs.

The inclusion of **folic acid,** the B vitamin folate, in a mother's diet during the early stages of her pregnancy significantly reduces the risk for neural tube defects in her developing embryo.

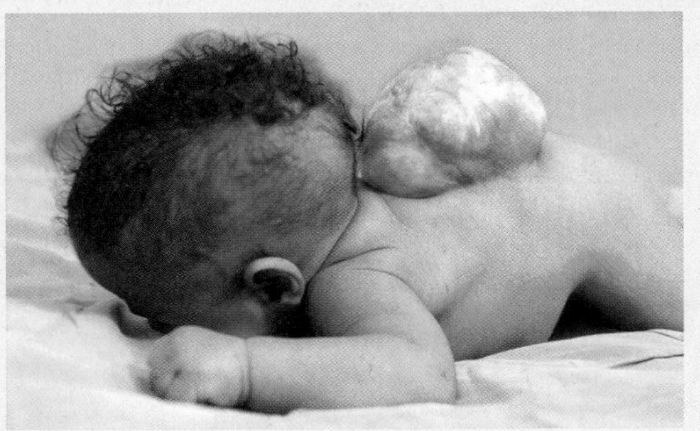

FIGURE 29.12 Spina Bifida
Spina bifida can result in severe malformation of the spinal cord, vertebral column, or both. Medicshots/Alamy Stock Photo

PROCESS Figure

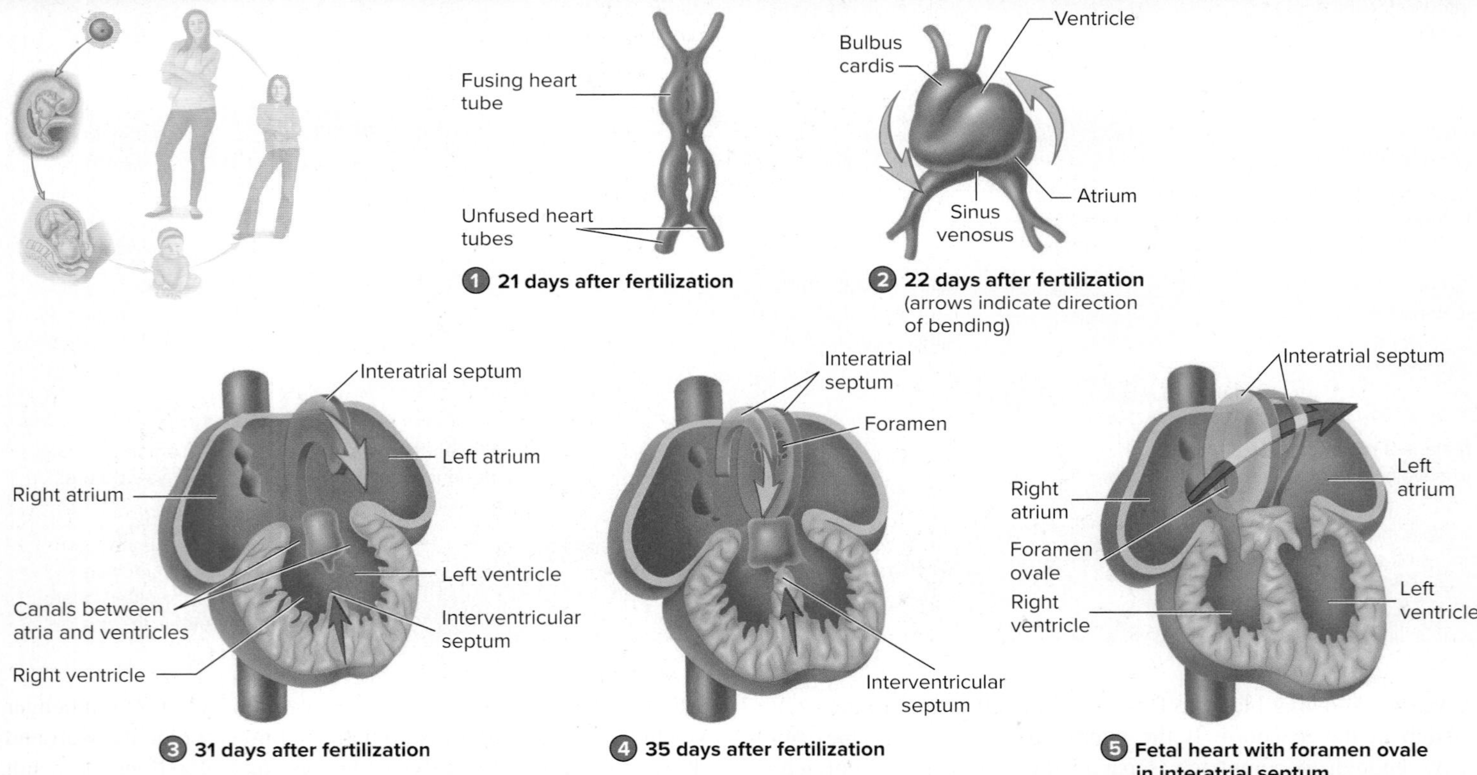

PROCESS Figure 29.13

Development of the Heart
The four-chambered adult heart develops from two parallel vessels that merge and then bend and elongate.

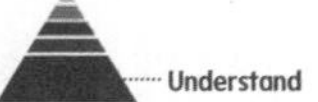

Why are interatrial septal defects more common than interventricular septal defects?

PROCESS **Figure**

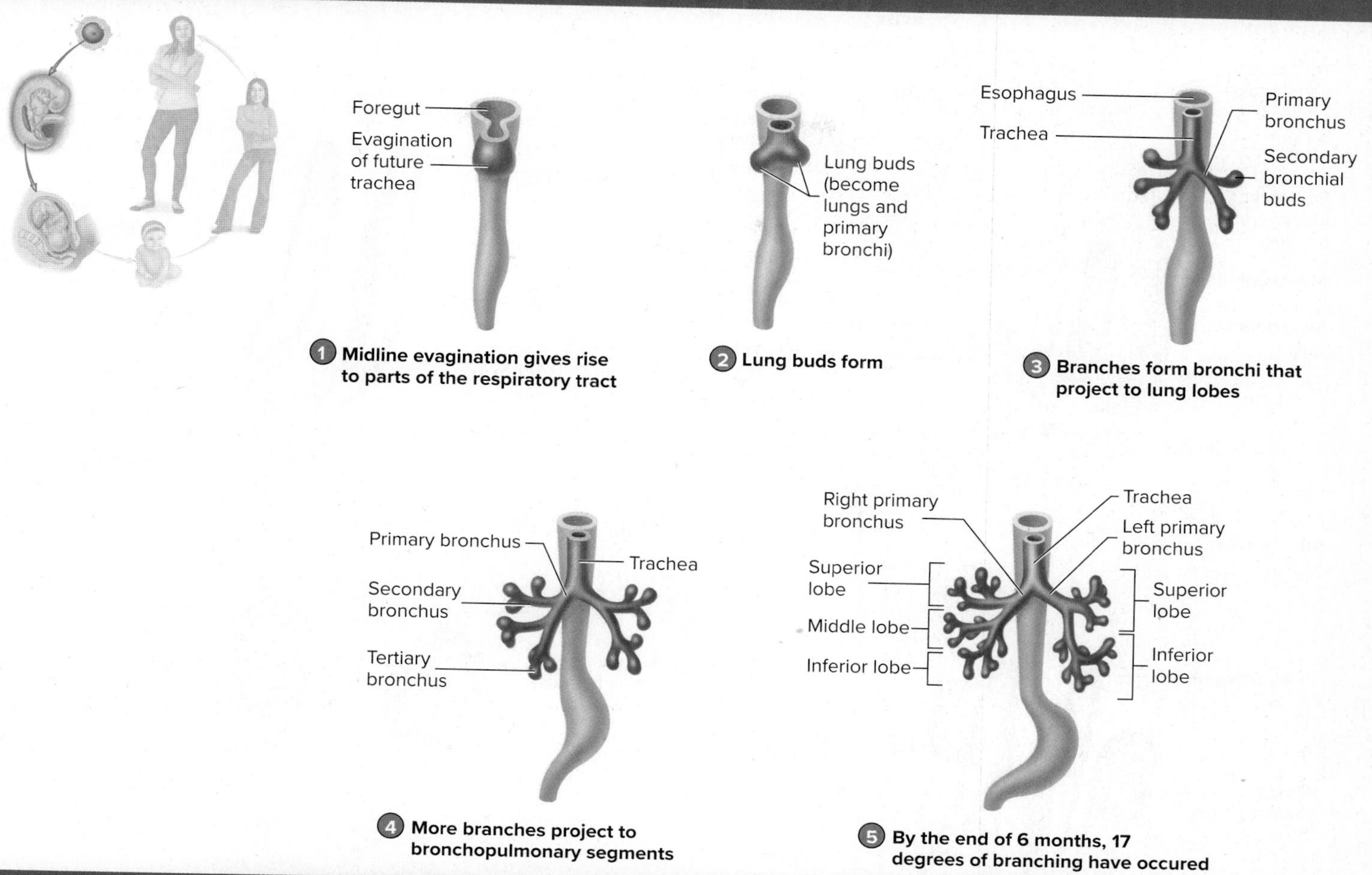

1 **Midline evagination gives rise to parts of the respiratory tract**

2 **Lung buds form**

3 **Branches form bronchi that project to lung lobes**

4 **More branches project to bronchopulmonary segments**

5 **By the end of 6 months, 17 degrees of branching have occured**

PROCESS **Figure 29.14**

Development of the Respiratory Tract

The air passageways within the lungs develop from an evagination of the foregut.

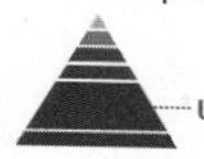

How would the branching of the embryonic tissue differ between the right lung and the left lung, and why?

outside and blood cells on the inside. These islands expand and fuse to form the blood vessels.

Respiratory System

The respiratory system includes the lungs and the structures of the respiratory tract (see chapter 23). Figure 29.14 depicts the development of the respiratory tract.

1. The lungs develop as a single, midline evagination from the foregut in the region of the future esophagus.
2. The midline evagination branches to form two **lung buds.**
3. The lung buds elongate and branch, first forming the bronchi that project to the lobes of the lungs.
4. Further branching forms the bronchi that project to the bronchopulmonary segments of the lungs.
5. The branching continues until, by the end of the sixth month, about 17 generations of branching have occurred. Even after birth, some branching continues as the lungs grow larger and, in the adult, about 24 generations of branches have been established.

Urinary System

The urinary system consists of the kidneys, ureters, urinary bladder, and urethra (see chapter 26). Unlike most of the organs discussed up to this point, kidney development actually involves the development of three different types of kidneys: (1) the pronephros, a short-lived structure; (2) the mesonephros, the embryonic kidney; and (3) the metanephros, the adult kidney.

The kidneys develop from mesoderm located between the somites and the lateral part of the embryo. About 21 days after fertilization, the mesoderm in the cervical region differentiates into the **pronephros** (figure 29.15*a*). The pronephros consists of a duct and simple tubules connecting the duct to the open coelomic cavity. This type of kidney is the functional adult kidney in some lower chordates, but it is probably not functional in the human embryo and soon disappears.

The **mesonephros** (figure 29.15*a,b*) is a functional organ in the embryo. It consists of a caudal extension of the pronephric duct and a number of minute tubules, which are smaller and more

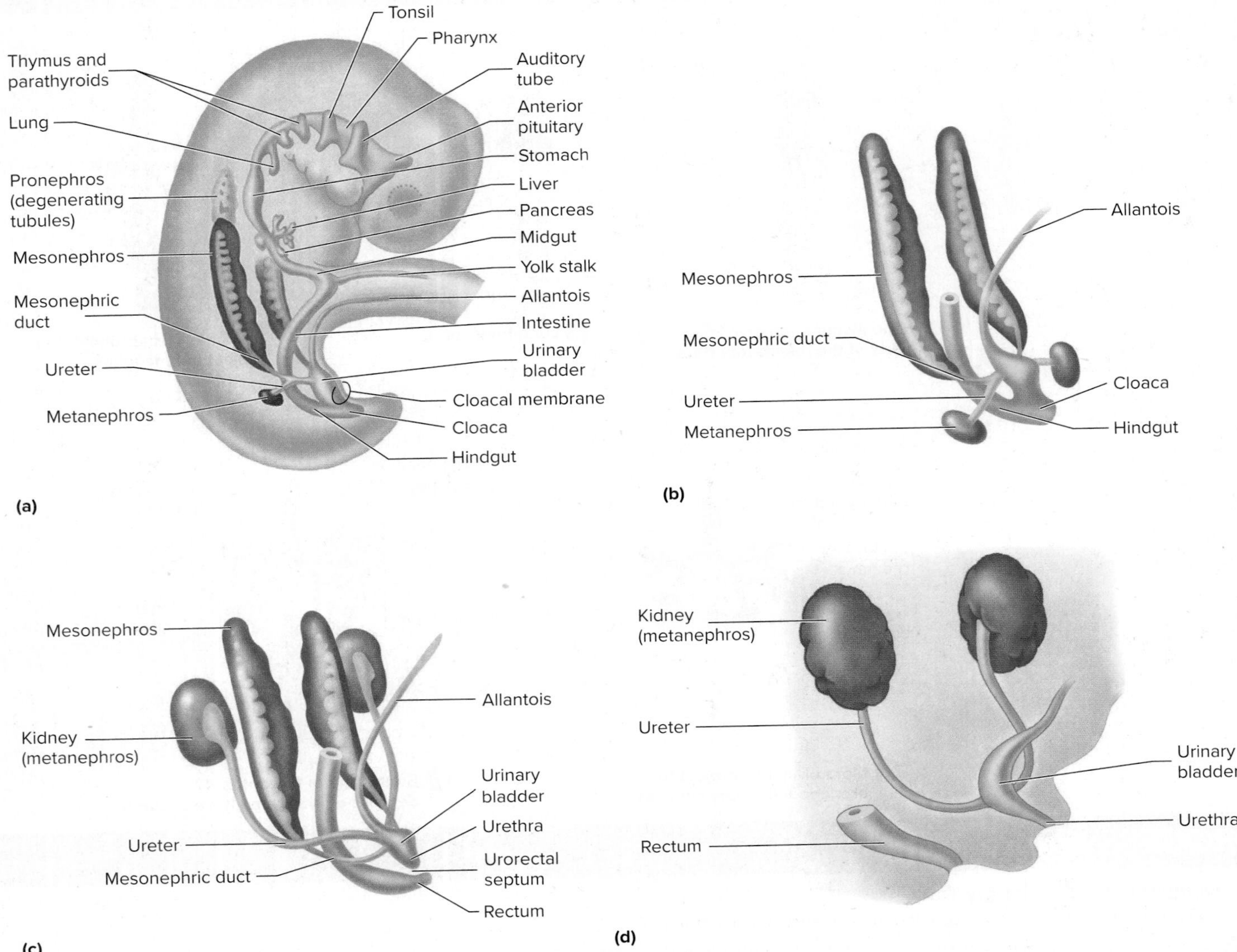

FIGURE 29.15 Development of the Kidneys and Urinary Bladder

(*a*) The developing kidney consists of three parts: pronephros, mesonephros, and metanephros. (*b*) The metanephros (adult kidney) enlarges as the mesonephros degenerates. (*c*) The kidneys continue to grow and develop. (*d*) Each kidney (formerly metanephros) is associated with a ureter, which extends to the urinary bladder.

complex than those of the pronephros. One end of each tubule opens into the mesonephric duct, and the other end forms a glomerulus (see chapter 26).

As the mesonephros is developing, the caudal end of the hindgut begins to enlarge to form the **cloaca** (kloh-AY-kah; sewer), the common junction of the digestive, urinary, and reproductive tracts (figure 29.15*b*). The cloaca is divided into two parts by a **urorectal septum:** a digestive part called the **rectum** and a urogenital part called the **urethra** (figure 29.15*c*). The cloaca is associated with two tubes: the hindgut and the **allantois** (ah-LAN-toh-is), a blind tube extending into the umbilical cord (see figure 29.9). The part of the allantois nearest the cloaca enlarges to form the urinary bladder, and the remainder, from the bladder to the umbilicus, forms the median umbilical ligament.

The mesonephric duct extends caudally as it develops and eventually joins the cloaca. Another tube, the **ureter,** begins to form at the point where the mesonephric duct joins the cloaca. Its distal end enlarges and branches to form the duct system of the **metanephros** (last kidney), which is the adult kidney. The metanephros takes over the function of the degenerating mesonephros (figure 29.15*d*).

Reproductive System

The term *gonads* refers to the organs in which gametogenesis occurs. The female gonad is the ovary, and the male gonad is the testis (see chapter 28). The male and female gonads appear as **gonadal ridges** along the ventral border of each mesonephros (figure 29.16*a*). **Primordial germ cells,** destined to become oocytes or sperm cells, form on the surface of the yolk sac, migrate into the embryo, and enter the gonadal ridge.

In the female, the ovaries descend from their original position high in the abdomen to a location within the pelvis. In the male,

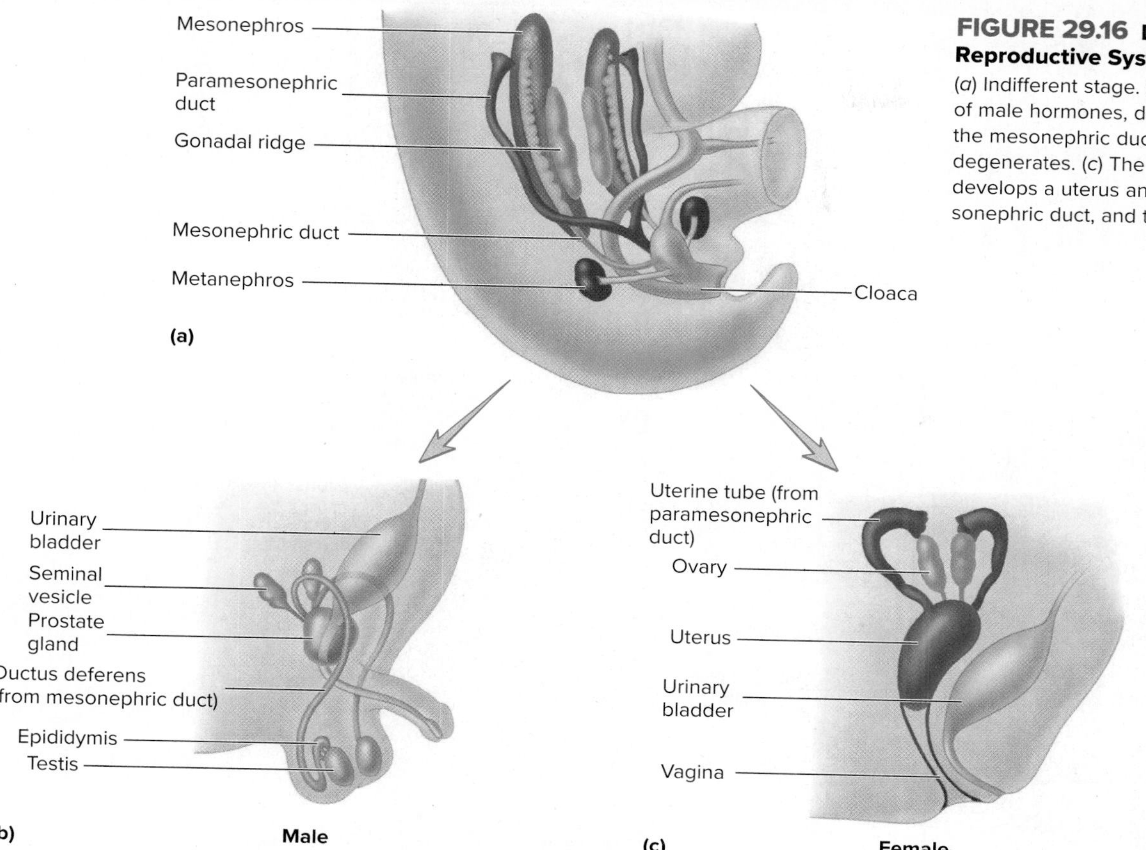

FIGURE 29.16 Differentiation of the Reproductive Systems

(*a*) Indifferent stage. (*b*) The male, under the influence of male hormones, develops a ductus deferens from the mesonephric duct, and the paramesonephric duct degenerates. (*c*) The female, without male hormones, develops a uterus and uterine tubes from the paramesonephric duct, and the mesonephros disappears.

the testes descend even farther. As the testes reach the anteroinferior abdominal wall, two tunnels called the **inguinal canals** form through the abdominal musculature. The testes pass through these canals, leaving the abdominal cavity and coming to lie within the **scrotum** (see figure 28.6). Descent of the testes through the inguinal canals begins about 7 months after fertilization, and the testes enter the scrotum about 1 month before the infant is born. In approximately 3% of male children, one or both testes fail to enter the scrotum. This condition is called undescended testes, or **cryptorchidism** (krip-TOR-kih-dizm). Because testosterone is required for the testes to descend into the scrotum, cryptorchidism is often the result of inadequate testosterone secreted by the fetal testes. If neither testis descends and the defect is not corrected, the male will be infertile because the slightly higher temperature of the body cavity, compared with that of the scrotal sac, causes the spermatogonia to degenerate. Cryptorchidism is treated with hormone therapy, or it can be surgically corrected. Cryptorchidism is an important risk factor for testicular cancer.

Paramesonephric ducts (also called müllerian ducts) are the precursors for the segments of the female reproductive tract. They begin to develop just lateral to the **mesonephric ducts** (also called wolffian ducts), which are the precursor for the segments of the male reproductive tract. These two ducts grow inferiorly until they meet one another and enter the cloaca as a single, midline tube.

In male embryos, the presence of the Y chromosome, specifically the *SRY* gene, influences the development of the male reproductive system. Genetic expression of the *SRY* stimulates the development of the testes and subsequent testosterone secretion. Testosterone causes the mesonephric duct system to enlarge and differentiate to form the epididymis, ductus deferens, seminal vesicles, and prostate gland (figure 29.16*b*). Müllerian-inhibiting hormone, also secreted by the testes, causes the paramesonephric ducts to degenerate. In female embryos, neither testosterone nor müllerian-inhibiting hormone is secreted. As a result, the mesonephric duct system atrophies, and the paramesonephric duct system develops to form the uterine tubes, the uterus, and part of the vagina in females (figure 29.16*c*).

Like the other sex organs, the external genitalia begin as the same structures in the male and female and then diverge. Figure 29.17 illustrates the development of the external genitalia in the male and female.

1. An enlargement called the **genital tubercle** develops in the groin of the embryo. **Genital folds** develop on each side of a **urethral groove,** and **labioscrotal swellings** develop lateral to the folds.
2. In the male, under the influence of dihydrotestosterone, derived from testosterone, the genital tubercle and the genital folds close over the urethral groove to form the penis. The testes move into the labioscrotal swellings, which become the scrotum of the male. If closure of the urethral groove does not proceed all the way to the end of the penis, a defect known as **hypospadias** (HIGH-poh-SPAY-dee-as) results.
3. In the female, in the absence of testosterone, the genital tubercle becomes the clitoris. The urethral groove disappears; genital folds do not fuse. As a result, the urethra opens somewhat posterior to the clitoris but anterior to the vaginal opening. The unfused genital folds become the labia minora, and the labioscrotal folds become the labia majora.

PROCESS **Figure**

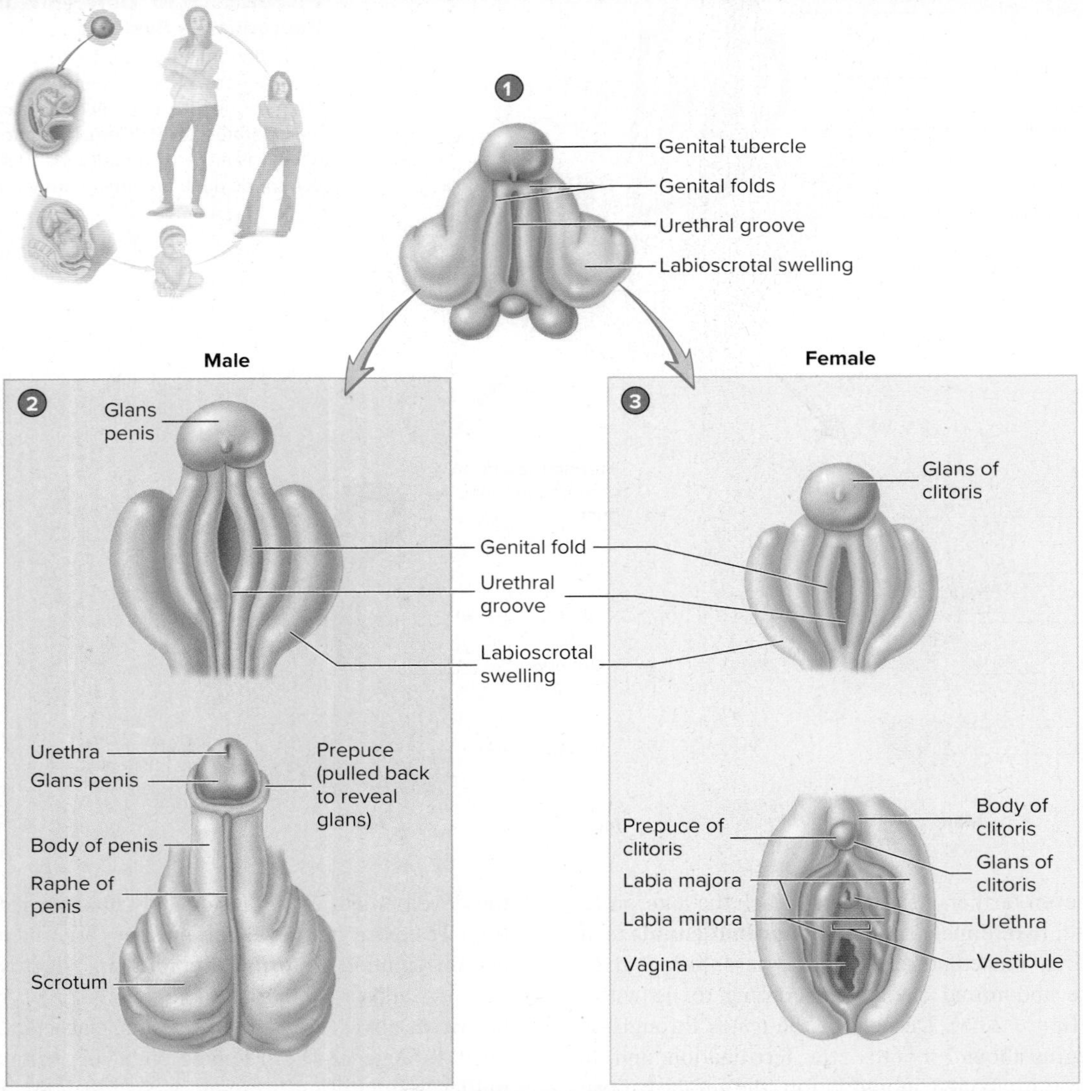

1

Genital tubercle
Genital folds
Urethral groove
Labioscrotal swelling

Male

2

Glans penis
Genital fold
Urethral groove
Labioscrotal swelling

Urethra
Glans penis
Prepuce (pulled back to reveal glans)
Body of penis
Raphe of penis
Scrotum

Female

3

Glans of clitoris

Prepuce of clitoris
Body of clitoris
Glans of clitoris
Labia majora
Labia minora
Urethra
Vagina
Vestibule

PROCESS **Figure 29.17**

Development of the External Genitalia

External genitalia for both sexes are derived from the same tissues.

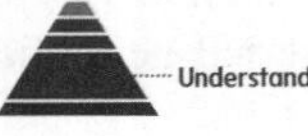

Homologous structures are those that are derived from the same tissue but have different appearances and/or functions in the adult form. What is the homologous structure of the female clitoris in the male? What is the homologous structure of the male scrotum in the female?

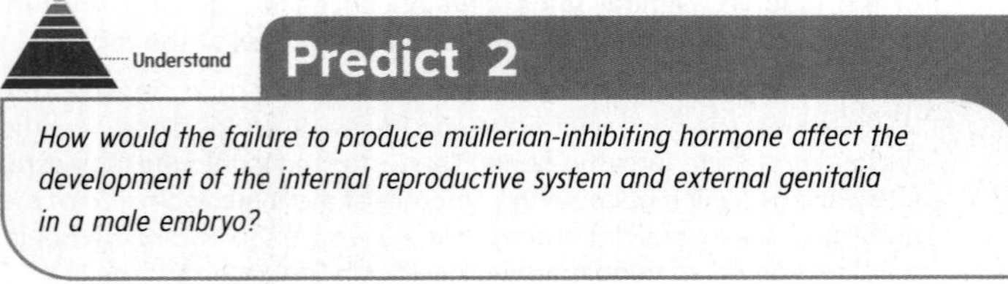

Predict 2

How would the failure to produce müllerian-inhibiting hormone affect the development of the internal reproductive system and external genitalia in a male embryo?

Growth of the Fetus

At approximately 60 days after fertilization, the embryo becomes a fetus (a 50-day-old embryo is shown in figure 29.18*a*). In the embryo, most of the organ systems are forming, whereas in the fetus the organs are present and continue to develop during the fetal period. Most morphological changes occur in the embryonic phase of development, whereas the fetal period is primarily a "growing phase."

The fetus grows from about 3 cm and 2.5 g at 60 days to 50 cm and 3300 g at term—more than a 15-fold increase in length and a 1300-fold increase in weight. The growth of the fetus also causes an increase in the size of the uterus (figure 29.19).

The fetus is covered with fine, soft hair called **lanugo** (lah-NYU-goh). The fetus is also covered with a waxy coat of sloughed epithelial cells called the **vernix caseosa**

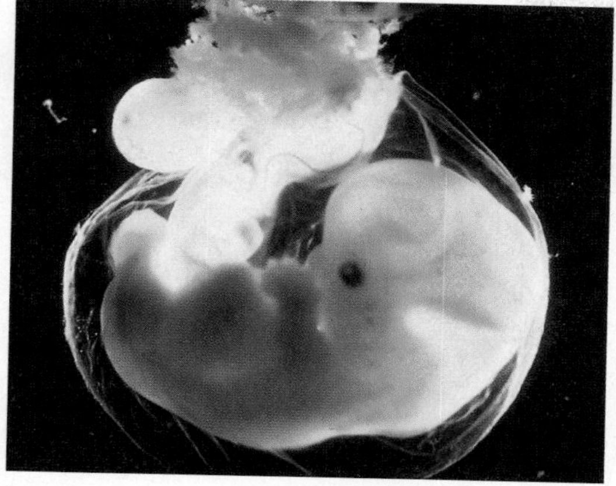

(a)

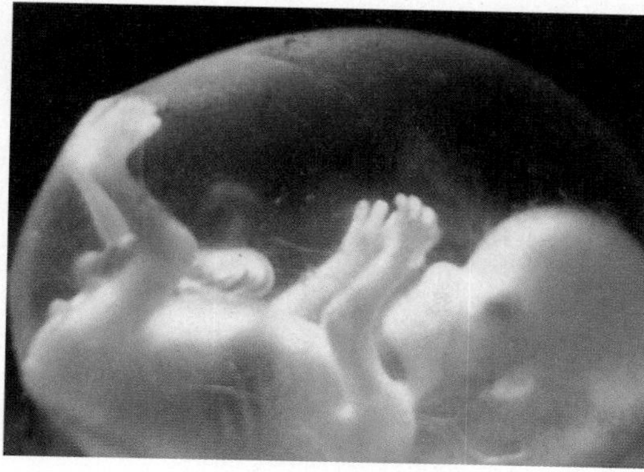

(b)

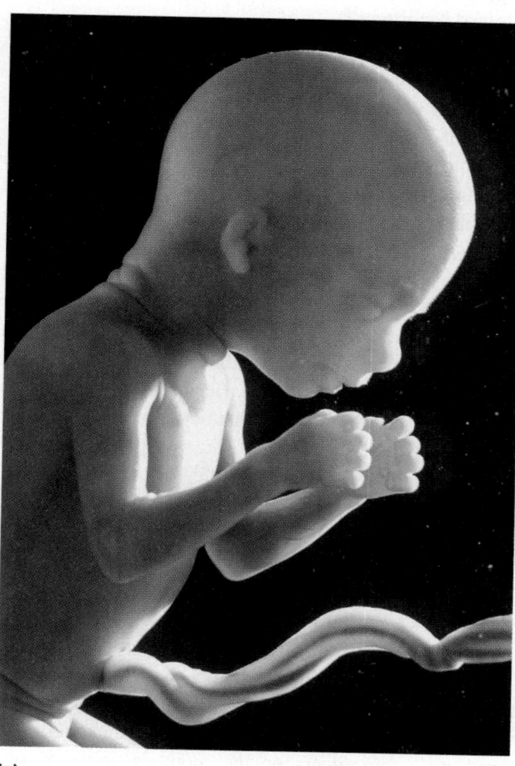

(c)

FIGURE 29.18 Embryos and Fetuses at Different Ages
(*a*) Fifty days after fertilization. (*b*) Three months after fertilization. (*c*) Four months after fertilization. (a) Claude Edelmann/Science Source (b) Petit Format/Nestle/Science Source; (c) Tissuepix/Science Source

(VER-niks kay-see-OH-sah). The vernix caseosa protects the fetus from the somewhat toxic amniotic fluid formed by the accumulation of fetal waste products.

Subcutaneous adipose tissue accumulates in the older fetus. This tissue provides nutrients and helps insulate the fetus after it is born. In addition, the subcutaneous adipose tissue aids the baby in sucking by strengthening and supporting the cheeks so that negative pressure can be developed in the oral cavity.

Peak body growth occurs late in gestation, but growth of the placenta essentially stops at about 35 weeks, thus restricting further intrauterine growth.

At about 38 weeks of development, the fetus can survive outside the mother and is ready to be delivered. The average weight at this point is 3250 g for a female fetus and 3300 g for a male fetus.

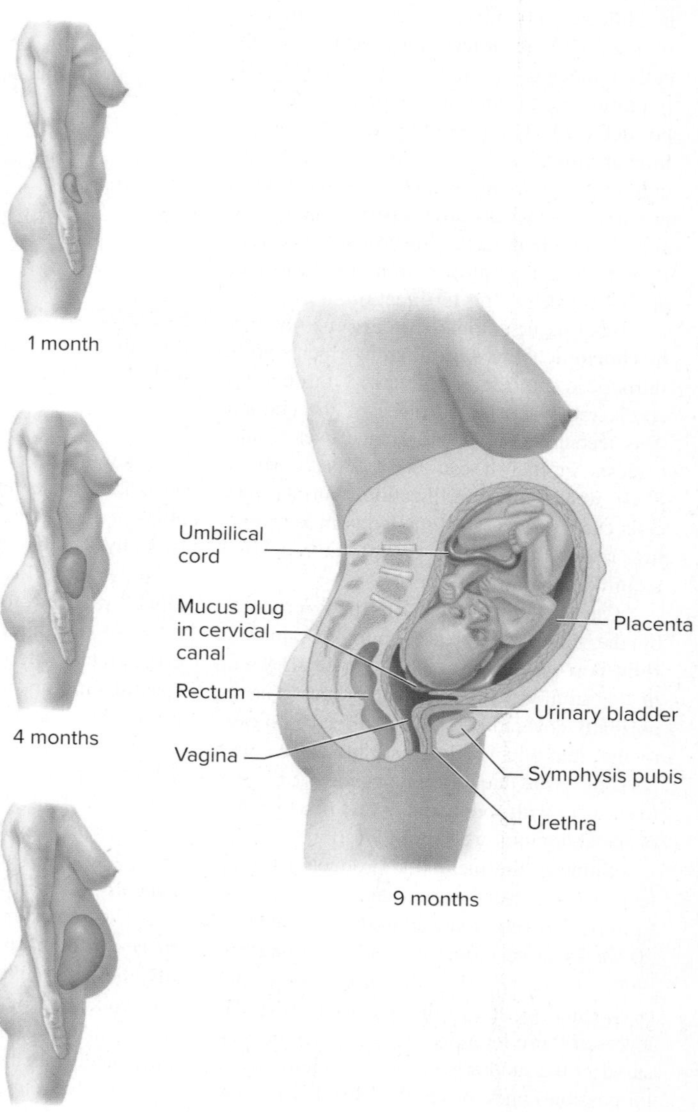

FIGURE 29.19 Enlargement of the Uterus During Fetal Development
The uterus expands in size as the embryo, and later the fetus, increases in size.

Clinical IMPACT 29.5 Fetal Monitoring

Monitoring of the fetus during pregnancy allows physicians to determine the likelihood of complications during delivery, as well as possible health conditions the fetus may have as a result of either genetics or a developmental error. **Amniocentesis** (AM-nee-oh-sen-TEE-sis) is the removal and analysis of amniotic fluid (figure 29.20). As the fetus develops, it expels molecules of various types, as well as living cells, into the amniotic fluid. These molecules and cells can be collected and analyzed to detect a number of metabolic disorders. Furthermore, if the cells collected by amniocentesis are grown in culture, additional metabolic disorders can be detected. Chromosome analysis, called **karyotyping,** can also be performed on the cultured cells. Amniocentesis has been done as early as 10 weeks after fertilization, but the success rate in detecting disorders at that time is quite low. It is most commonly performed at 13–16 weeks after fertilization.

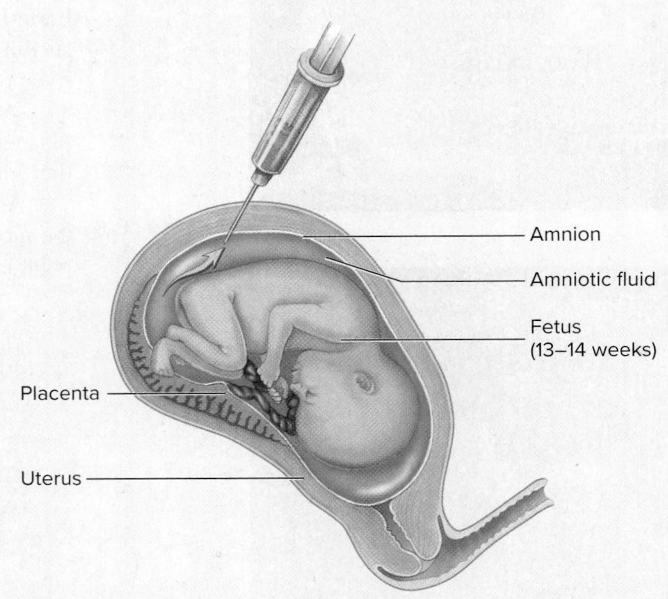

FIGURE 29.20 Amniocentesis
Amniotic fluid can be sampled by amniocentesis. The fluid, which contains fetal cells and various molecules, can be analyzed to detect different disorders.

Fetal tissue samples can also be obtained by **chorionic villus sampling,** in which a probe introduced into the uterine cavity through the cervix removes a small piece of the chorion. This technique has an advantage over amniocentesis in that it can be used as early as 8–10 weeks after fertilization. Furthermore, cells can be analyzed directly, as in karyotyping, rather than having to be cultured, as is required in amniocentesis.

One of the molecules normally produced by the fetus and released into the amniotic fluid is **α-fetoprotein.** This protein shows up in the amniotic fluid if fetal tissues that are normally covered by skin are directly exposed to the amniotic fluid. This can happen with nervous tissue due to failure of the neural tube to close, or with abdominal tissues due to failure of the abdominal wall to fully form.

Some of the metabolic products from the fetus, such as α-fetoprotein and estriol, a weak form of estrogen produced in the placenta after 20 weeks of gestation, can enter the maternal blood. In some cases, the products are processed and passed to the maternal urine. The levels of these fetal products can then be measured in the mother's blood or urine to screen for possible conditions of the fetus. Further tests are required to verify suspected fetal conditions indicated by elevated levels of fetal metabolic products in the maternal blood or urine.

New maternal blood tests have also been developed to screen for certain chromosomal abnormalities, such as Down syndrome (trisomy 21). Conducted in the first trimester of pregnancy, these procedures detect fetal DNA, referred to as **cell-free fetal DNA (cffDNA),** within the maternal blood. Certain cffDNA characteristics are valid indicators of specific chromosomal abnormalities. The benefit of this type of fetal monitoring is that it is less invasive than amniocentesis or chorionic villus sampling. Also, the detection rate is very high, as high as 99% in some studies. As with other types of fetal genetic testing, this procedure is reserved for at-risk or high-risk pregnancies as determined by the physician.

The fetus can be seen within the uterus by **ultrasound,** in which sound waves are bounced off the fetus like sonar and then analyzed and enhanced by computer. In another technique, called **fetoscopy,** a fiber-optic probe is introduced into the amniotic cavity and used to view the fetus. Because of the constantly increasing resolution in ultrasound technology and because it is noninvasive compared with fetoscopy, ultrasound is usually the preferred technique. However, some fetal defects cannot be adequately assessed by ultrasound and require fetoscopy. In that case, ultrasound is used to guide the fetoscope.

Ultrasound has not been found to pose any risk to the fetus or the mother. It is accomplished by placing a transducer on the mother's abdominal wall (transabdominal method) or by inserting the transducer into the female's vagina (transvaginal method). The latter technique produces much higher resolution because fewer layers of tissue exist between the transducer and the uterine cavity. Transvaginal ultrasound can be used to identify the yolk sac of a developing embryo as early as 17 days after fertilization, and the embryo can be visualized at 25 days. Transabdominal ultrasound allows for fetal monitoring by 6–8 weeks after fertilization.

Fetal heart rate can be detected with an ultrasound stethoscope by the tenth week after fertilization and with a conventional stethoscope by 20 weeks. Fetal heart rate is most commonly monitored electronically, either indirectly by transducers on the mother's abdomen or by a probe attached to the skin of the fetus. The normal fetal heart rate range is 110–160 bpm.

ASSESS YOUR PROGRESS

16. *Describe the formation of the following major organs and organ systems: skin, bones, skeletal muscles, nervous system, eyes, and respiratory system. When does each of these events occur?*
17. *Explain the formation of the following endocrine glands: anterior pituitary, posterior pituitary, thyroid, parathyroid, adrenal medulla, adrenal cortex, and pancreas.*
18. *Explain the process by which a one-chambered heart becomes a four-chambered heart.*
19. *Describe how the pronephros, mesonephros, and metanephros lead to the development of the kidneys.*
20. *Demonstrate your understanding of the effect hormones have on the development of the male and female reproductive systems.*
21. *Compare the male and female structures formed from each of the following: genital tubercle, genital folds, and labioscrotal swellings.*
22. *What major events distinguish between embryonic and fetal development?*

29.2 Parturition

LEARNING OUTCOMES

After reading this section, you should be able to

A. **Explain the events that occur during the three stages of parturition.**
B. **Discuss the hormonal changes of parturition for the fetus.**
C. **Describe the hormonal changes of parturition for the mother.**

Parturition (par-toor-ISH-un) is the process by which a baby is born. Physicians usually calculate the **gestation period,** or length of the pregnancy, as 280 days (40 weeks) from the last menstrual period (LMP) to the date of delivery of the infant. (In terms of postovulatory age, the fetus is ready for birth at 38 weeks.)

Predict 3

Compare and contrast clinical age and postovulatory age for fertilization, implantation, the beginning of the fetal period, and parturition.

Near the end of pregnancy, the uterus becomes progressively more excitable and usually exhibits occasional contractions, which become stronger and more frequent until parturition is initiated. The cervix gradually dilates, and strong uterine contractions help expel the fetus from the uterus through the vagina.

Stages of Labor

Labor is the period during which uterine contractions occur that eventually expel the fetus and placenta from the uterus. Figure 29.21 illustrates the three stages of labor.

FUNDAMENTAL **Figure**

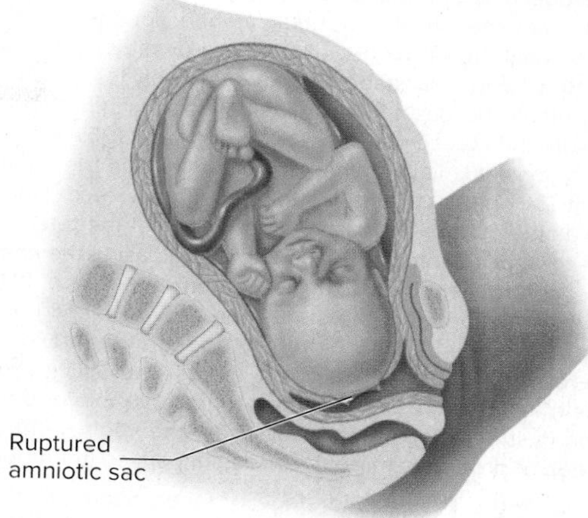

1 **First stage.** The cervix dilates, and the amniotic sac ruptures.

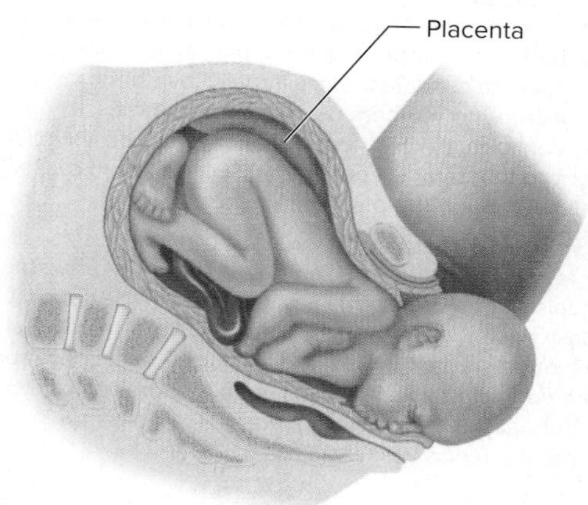

2 **Second stage.** The fetus is expelled from the uterus.

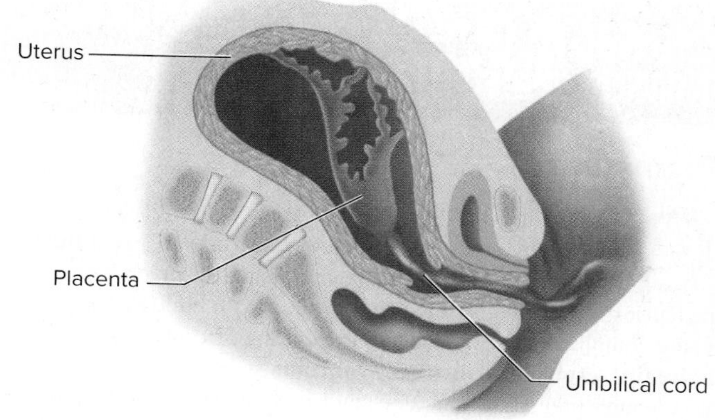

3 **Third stage.** The placenta is expelled.

PROCESS **Figure 29.21**

Parturition

During parturition, the fetus as well as the placenta are expelled from the uterus.

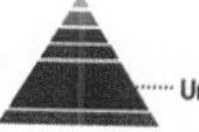

Which hormone is given to females during labor to increase uterine contractions?

1. *First stage.* The first stage of labor, often called the *dilation stage,* begins with the onset of regular uterine contractions. This stage extends until the cervix has dilated to a diameter about the size of the fetus's head. This stage of labor commonly lasts 8–24 hours, but it may be as short as a few minutes, especially in females who have had more than one child. Normally during labor (95% of the time), the head of the fetus is in an inferior position within the female's pelvis so that the head acts as a wedge, forcing the cervix and vagina to open as the uterine contractions push against the fetus. During this stage of labor, the amniotic sac ruptures, releasing the amniotic fluid.

   The **central tendon of the perineum** (see figure 10.19) is very important in supporting the uterus and vagina. Tearing or stretching of the tendon during childbirth may weaken the inferior support of these organs, and prolapse of the uterus may occur. **Prolapse** is a "sinking" of the uterus so that the uterine cervix moves down into the vagina (first degree), moves down near the vaginal orifice (second degree), or protrudes through the vaginal orifice (third degree).
2. *Second stage.* The second stage of labor, often called the *expulsion stage,* lasts from the time of maximum cervical dilation until the fetus exits the vagina. This stage may last from a minute to an hour or more. During this stage, contractions of the abdominal muscles assist the uterine contractions. The contractions generate enough pressure to compress blood vessels in the placenta so that blood flow to the fetus is stopped. During periods of relaxation, blood flow to the placenta resumes. Occasionally, synthetic oxytocin (pitocin) is administered to mothers during labor to increase the force of the uterine contractions. However, caution must be exercised in using this drug so that tetanic contractions, which would drastically reduce blood flow through the placenta, do not occur.
3. *Third stage.* The third stage of labor actually occurs after the birth of the fetus. This stage is often called the *placental stage* because during this stage the placenta is expelled from the uterus. Uterine contractions cause the placenta to tear away from the wall of the uterus. Some bleeding from the uterine wall occurs as a consequence of the intimate contact between the placenta and the uterus, but the bleeding is normally limited because uterine smooth muscle contractions compress the blood vessels to the placenta.

Blood levels of estrogen and progesterone fall dramatically after parturition because the source of these hormones is gone once the placenta has been dislodged from the uterus. In addition, during the 4 or 5 weeks after parturition, the uterus becomes much smaller, although it remains somewhat larger than it was before pregnancy. The cells of the uterine lining become smaller, and many of them degenerate. A vaginal discharge composed of small amounts of blood and degenerating endometrium persists for 1 week or more after parturition.

Clinical IMPACT 29.6

Prematurity

Occasionally, the fetus is delivered before it has sufficiently matured and is therefore considered **premature.** Prematurity is one of the most significant problems in pediatrics, the branch of medicine dealing with children, because many complications can result. The most significant complication is **infant respiratory distress syndrome,** which occurs because very young premature infants cannot produce **surfactant,** a mixture of phospholipids and protein that lines the inner surface of the lungs and allows them to expand as we breathe. Each year, 65,000 premature infants suffer from respiratory distress syndrome in the United States. Until recently, 10% of those infants died. Now, surfactant substitutes are being developed, and glucocorticoid administration can stimulate surfactant production. These therapies have cut the death rate in half, and more effective replacements are being investigated.

Hormonal Stimulation of Parturition

The precise signal that triggers parturition is unknown, but many supporting factors have been identified. Figure 29.22 illustrates the interactions of chemical signals from both the mother and fetus that are involved in stimulating parturition.

1. Before parturition, the progesterone concentration in the maternal blood is at its highest level and is exerting an inhibitory effect on uterine smooth muscle cells. Near the end of pregnancy, however, estrogen levels rapidly increase in the maternal blood, and their excitatory influence overcomes the inhibitory influence of progesterone.
2. Before parturition, the adrenal glands of the fetus are greatly enlarged, and the rate of adrenocorticotropic hormone (ACTH) secretion by the fetus's anterior pituitary gland increases. The increase in ACTH is due to the stress of the confined space and limited O_2 supply created in the uterus by the growing fetus.
3. ACTH causes the fetal adrenal cortex to produce glucocorticoids, which travel to the placenta, where they alter hormone secretion.
4. Specifically, the glucocorticoids from the fetal adrenal cortex decrease the rate of progesterone secretion and increase the rate of estrogen synthesis. Also, prostaglandin synthesis is initiated, which strongly stimulates uterine contractions.
5. During parturition, stretching of the uterine cervix stimulates the release of oxytocin from the maternal posterior pituitary gland.
6. Oxytocin stimulates uterine contractions, which move the fetus farther into the cervix, causing further stretch. Thus, by a positive-feedback mechanism, stretch stimulates oxytocin release and oxytocin causes further stretch until the time of delivery. After delivery of the fetus, the cervix is no longer stretched and oxytocin secretion decreases.

Besides the effects already described, progesterone and estrogen also influence the secretion of oxytocin. Progesterone inhibits oxytocin release and decreases the number of oxytocin receptors. Therefore, decreased progesterone levels in the maternal blood result in increased oxytocin secretion and the production of more oxytocin receptors in the uterus. In addition, estrogen makes the uterus more sensitive to oxytocin stimulation by also increasing the synthesis of oxytocin receptor sites. Estrogen may also increase the formation of gap junctions between myometrial cells, thereby enhancing the contractility of the uterus. Some evidence suggests that oxytocin also stimulates prostaglandin synthesis in the uterus. Recall that prostaglandins also stimulate smooth muscle contractions. All these events support the development of strong uterine contractions.

Predict 4

Samantha is having an extremely prolonged labor. From her anatomy and physiology course, she remembers the role of Ca^{2+} in muscle contraction and asks the doctor to give her a Ca^{2+} injection to speed the delivery. Explain why the doctor would or would not do as she requests.

PROCESS **Figure**

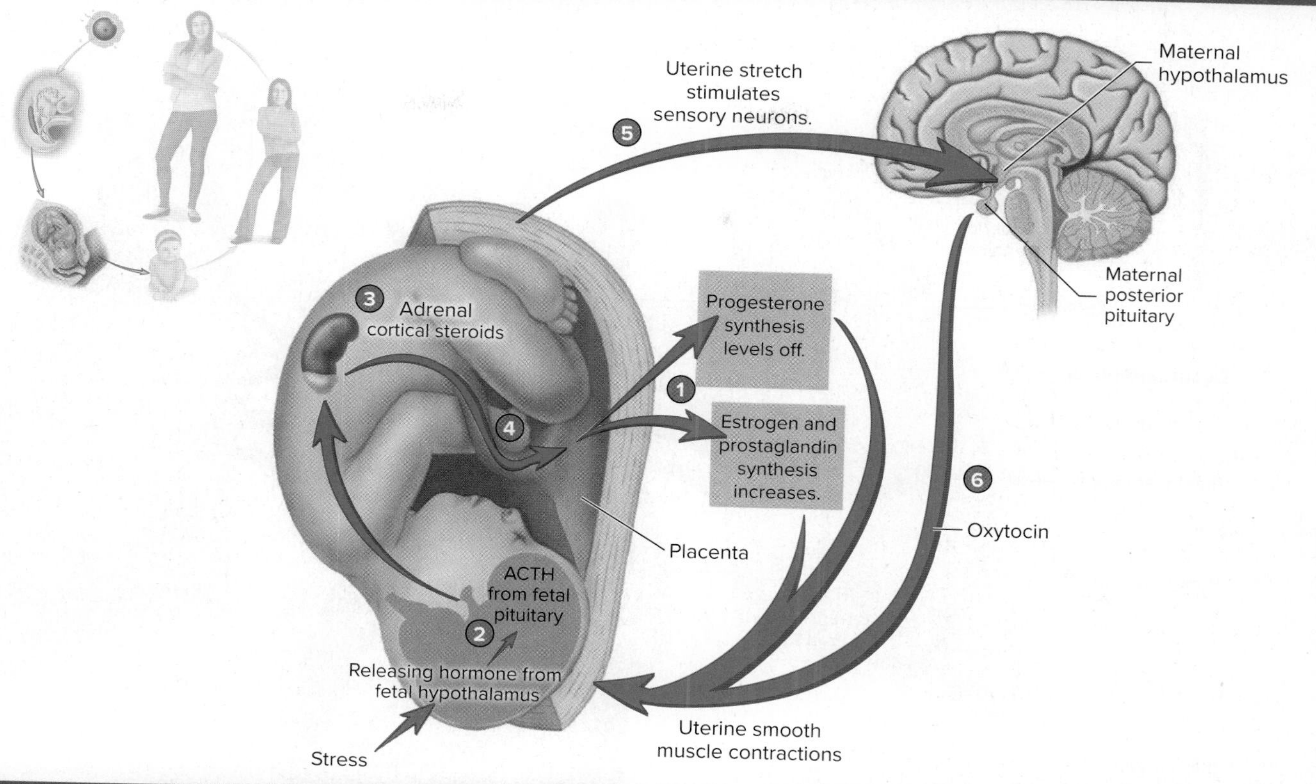

PROCESS **Figure 29.22**

Factors That Influence Parturition

Although the precise control of parturition is unknown, these changes appear to play a role.

Progesterone, estrogen, prostaglandins, and oxytocin all have important roles that influence parturition. For each of the substances listed, describe whether it has a stimulatory or inhibitory effect on the uterus.

ASSESS YOUR PROGRESS

23. *List the stages of labor; indicate when each stage begins and its approximate length.*
24. *Describe the hormonal changes that take place before and during delivery. How is stretch of the cervix involved in delivery?*

29.3 The Newborn

LEARNING OUTCOMES

After reading this section, you should be able to

A. **Discuss the respiratory and cardiovascular changes that occur in the newborn.**
B. **Explain the digestive changes that occur in the newborn.**
C. **Explain the significance of the Apgar score.**
D. **List the causes of congenital disorders.**

The newborn baby, which is also called a **neonate,** immediately experiences several dramatic changes due to being separated from the maternal blood and transferred from a fluid to a gaseous environment.

Respiratory and Cardiovascular Changes

The large, forced gasps of air taken in when the infant cries at the time of delivery help inflate the lungs. This initial inflation of the lungs causes important changes in the cardiovascular system. Figure 29.23*a* illustrates circulatory conditions of the fetus.

1. Prior to birth, blood bypasses the lungs by flowing from the pulmonary trunk through a vessel called the **ductus arteriosus** to the aorta.
2. Blood also bypasses the lungs by flowing from the right atrium directly to the left atrium through the foramen ovale.
3. Blood bypasses the liver sinusoids by flowing through the **ductus venosus** (vee-NOH-sus), which connects to the inferior vena cava.
4. Oxygenated blood from the placenta is passed to the fetus by the **umbilical vein.**
5. Deoxygenated blood is carried from the fetus to the placenta through the **umbilical arteries.**

Figure 29.23*b* illustrates the circulatory changes that occur at birth.

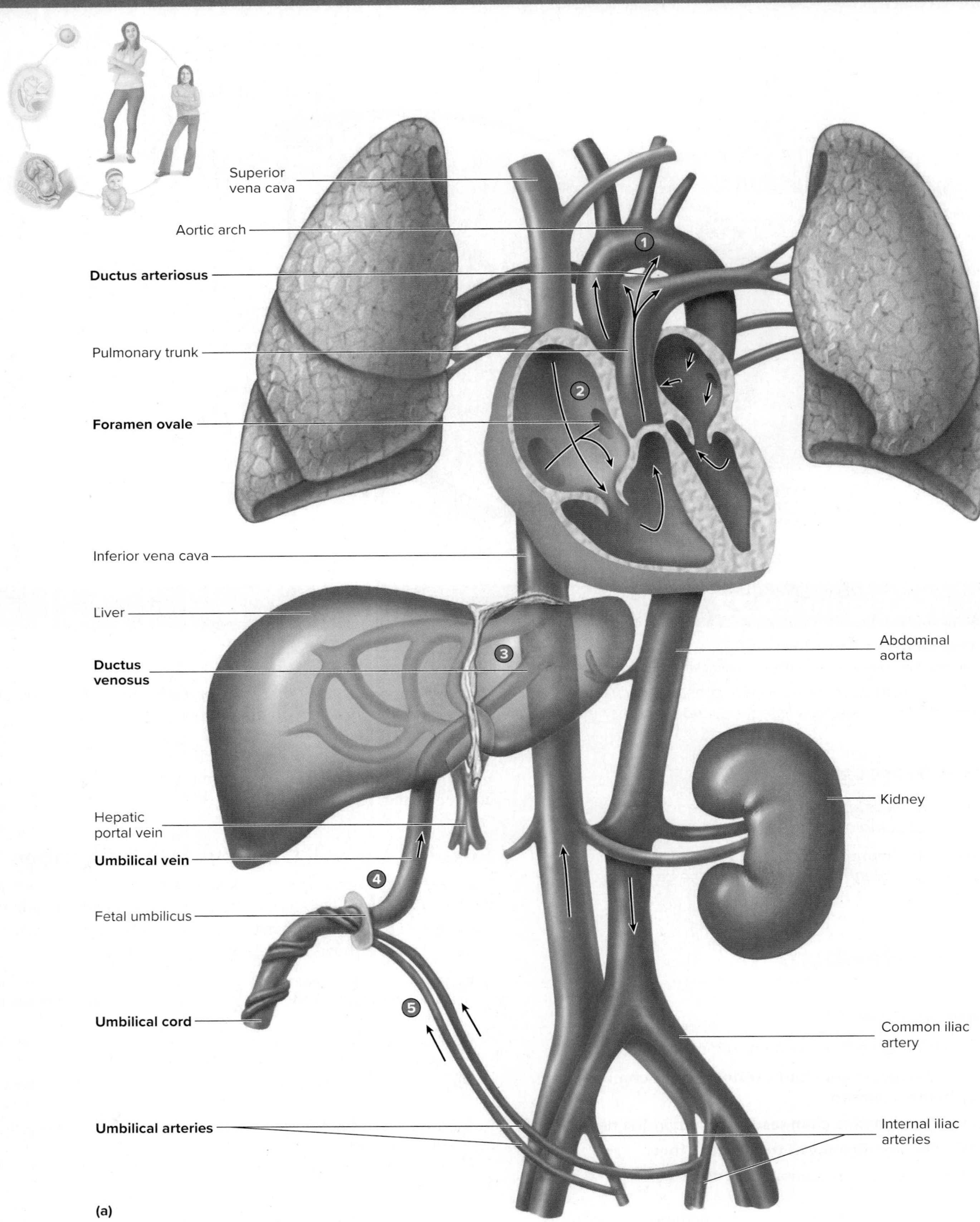
Superior vena cava
Aortic arch
Ductus arteriosus
Pulmonary trunk
Foramen ovale
Inferior vena cava
Liver
Ductus venosus
Hepatic portal vein
Umbilical vein
Fetal umbilicus
Umbilical cord
Umbilical arteries
Abdominal aorta
Kidney
Common iliac artery
Internal iliac arteries
1
2
3
4
5
(a)

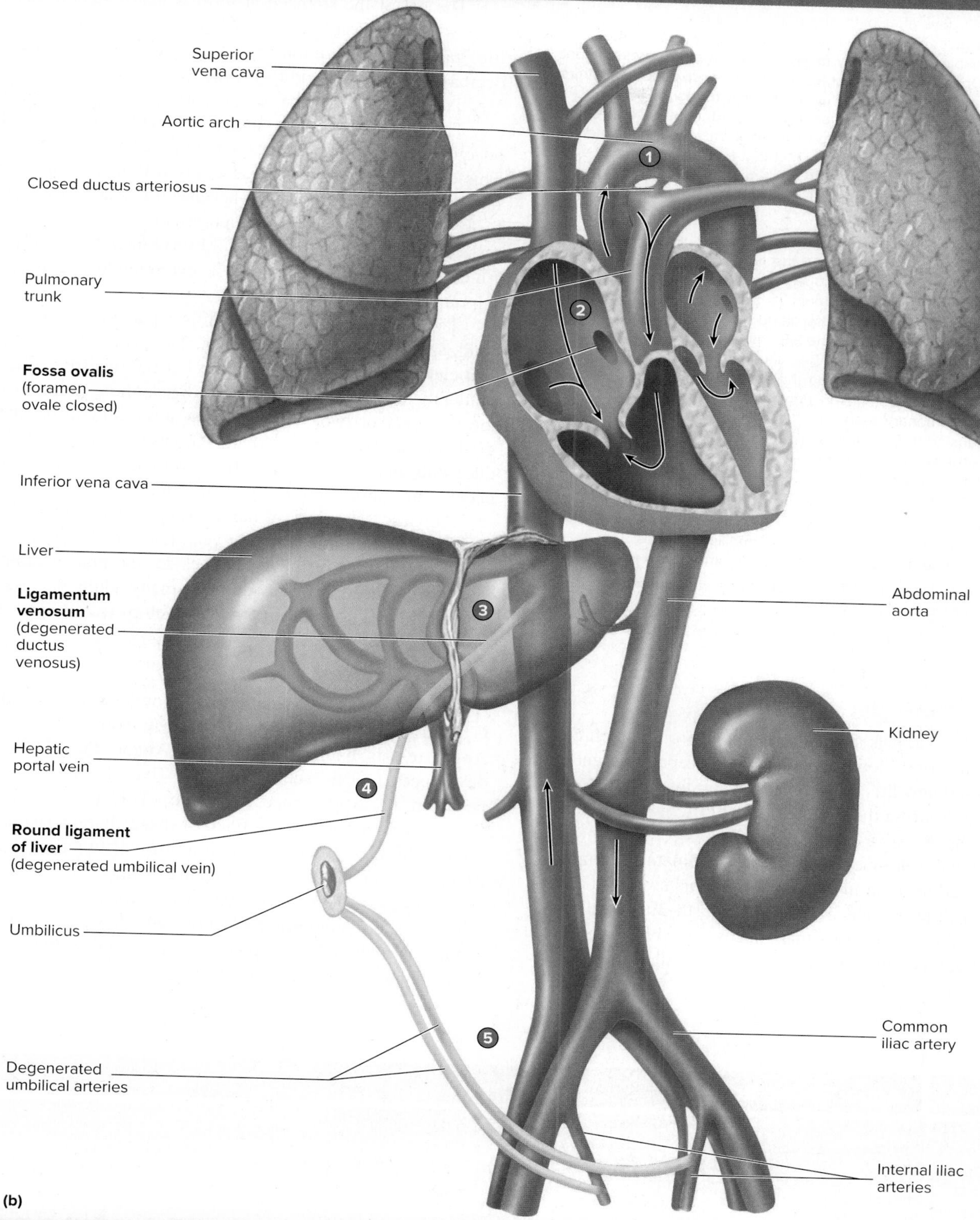

PROCESS Figure 29.23

Circulatory Changes at Birth

(*a*) Circulatory conditions in the fetus. Note the purple color of fetal vessels indicating a lower oxygenation level than what is found in arteries of the newborn (see panel *b*). This lower oxygenation level is the result of mixing of oxygenated blood from the umbilical cord and deoxygenated blood in the fetal vessels. (*b*) Circulatory changes that occur at birth.

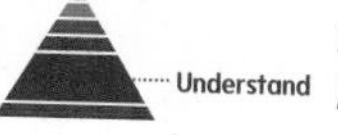

Describe the blood O_2 characteristics of the umbilical arteries and veins. How is this different than the normal blood O_2 levels in the arteries and veins after birth?

1. Within 1 or 2 days after birth, the ductus arteriosus closes off. This closure occurs because of the sphincterlike constriction of the artery and is probably stimulated by local changes in blood pressure and blood O_2. Once closed, the ductus arteriosus is replaced by connective tissue and is known as the **ligamentum arteriosum.** If the ductus arteriosus does not close completely, it is said to be **patent.** This is a serious birth defect, resulting in marked elevation in pulmonary blood pressure. This is due to the fact that blood flows from the left ventricle to the aorta, through the ductus arteriosus, and to the pulmonary arteries. If not corrected, it can lead to irreversible degenerative changes in the heart and lungs.
2. Expansion of the lungs following the baby's first breath reduces the resistance to blood flow through the lungs, resulting in increased blood flow through the pulmonary arteries. Consequently, more blood flows from the right atrium to the right ventricle and into the pulmonary arteries, and less blood flows from the right atrium through the foramen ovale to the left atrium. In addition, more blood returns from the lungs through the pulmonary veins to the left atrium, which increases the pressure in the left atrium. The increased left atrial pressure and decreased right atrial pressure, resulting from decreased pulmonary resistance, force blood against the septum primum, causing the foramen ovale to close. This action functionally completes the separation of the heart into two pumps: the right side of the heart and the left side of the heart. The closed foramen ovale becomes the **fossa ovalis.**
3. When the umbilical cord is tied and cut, no more blood flows through the ductus venosus, umbilical vein, or umbilical arteries. The ductus venosus degenerates and becomes the **ligamentum venosum.**
4. The remnant of the umbilical vein becomes the **ligamentum teres,** or *round ligament,* of the liver.
5. The remnants of the umbilical arteries become the cords of the umbilical arteries.

Digestive Changes

When a baby is born, it is suddenly separated from its source of nutrients, the maternal blood. Because of this separation and the stress of birth and new life, the neonate usually loses 5–10% of its total body weight during the first few days of life.

Although the digestive system of the fetus becomes somewhat functional late in development, it is still very immature, compared with that of an adult. Late in gestation, the fetus swallows amniotic fluid from time to time. Shortly after birth, this swallowed fluid plus intestinal cells, intestinal mucus, and bile pass from the digestive tract as a greenish anal discharge called **meconium** (meh-KOH-nee-um).

The pH of the stomach at birth is nearly neutral because of the swallowed basic amniotic fluid. Within the first 8 hours of life, gastric acid secretion increases, causing the stomach pH to decrease. Maximum acidity is reached at 4–10 days, and the pH gradually increases for the next 10–30 days.

The neonatal liver is also functionally immature. It lacks adequate amounts of the enzyme required to process bilirubin. This enzyme system usually develops within 2 weeks after birth in a healthy neonate; however, because it is not fully developed at birth, some full-term babies temporarily develop jaundice, characterized by elevated blood levels of bilirubin and a slightly yellowish cast to the skin or whites of the eye. Jaundice is also common in premature babies.

The newborn digestive system is capable of digesting lactose (milk sugar) from the time of birth. The pancreatic secretions are sufficiently mature for a milk diet, but the digestive system only gradually develops the ability to digest more solid foods over the first year or two; therefore, new foods should be introduced gradually during the first 2 years. Parents are also advised to introduce only one new food at a time so that, if an allergic reaction occurs, the cause is more easily determined.

Amylase secretion by the salivary glands and the pancreas remains low until after the first year. Lactase activity in the small intestine is high at birth but declines during infancy, although the levels still exceed those in adults. In many adults, lactase activity is lost, and an intolerance for milk develops (see chapter 24).

Apgar Scores

A physiological assessment tool known as the **Apgar score** is used to evaluate a newborn baby soon after birth. The Apgar test is named for Virginia Apgar, the physician who developed it. This score evaluates five characteristics of the newborn: (1) **A**ppearance, (2) **P**ulse, (3) **G**rimace, (4) **A**ctivity, and (5) **R**espiratory effort. Each of these characteristics is rated on a scale of 0–2, with 2 denoting normal function; 1, reduced function; and 0, seriously impaired function. More specific descriptions of the rankings for each characteristic are shown in table 29.3. For example, a newborn who has a pink complexion at birth is ranked 2 for appearance. The total Apgar score is the sum of the scores from the five characteristics, ranging from

TABLE 29.3 Apgar Rating Scales

Physiological Conditions	0	1	2
Appearance (skin color)	White or blue	Limbs blue, body pink	Pink
Pulse (rate)	No pulse	100 bpm	>100 bpm
Grimace (reflexive grimace initiated by stimulating the plantar surface of the foot)	No response	Facial grimaces, slight body movement	Facial grimaces, extensive body movement
Activity (muscle tone)	No movement, muscles flaccid	Limbs partially flexed, little movement, poor muscle tone	Active movement, good muscle tone
Respiratory effort (amount of breathing)	No breathing	Slow, irregular breathing	Good, regular breathing; strong cry

0 to 10. A total Apgar score of 8–10 at 1–5 minutes after birth is considered normal. Other systems that assess neonatal growth and development, including general external appearance and neurological development, also exist.

Congenital Disorders

The term *congenital* means "present at birth," and **congenital disorders** are abnormalities commonly referred to as birth defects. Approximately 70% of all congenital disorders are the result of an unknown cause, 15% have a known genetic cause, and the remaining 15% result from environmental factors or a combination of environmental and genetic factors. Environmental factors, referred to as **teratogens** (TER-ah-toh-jenz), damage the fetus during development. An example of a known teratogen is alcohol. Fetal alcohol syndrome results when a pregnant female drinks alcohol, which crosses the placenta and damages the fetus. The baby is born with a smaller-than-normal head, intellectual disability, and possibly other defects. Researchers are working to identify various other teratogens so that mothers can avoid known teratogens and reduce the risk for congenital disorders.

ASSESS YOUR PROGRESS

25. *What changes occur in the newborn's cardiovascular system shortly after birth? What do each of the following fetal structures become: foramen ovale, ductus arteriosus, umbilical vein, and ductus venosus?*

26. *What changes take place in the newborn's digestive system shortly after birth?*

27. *What does the Apgar score measure?*

28. *What are congenital disorders? What are some causes of these disorders?*

29. *What is a teratogen? Give an example.*

29.4 Lactation

LEARNING OUTCOMES

After reading this section, you should be able to

A. **Describe the events of lactation.**

B. **Relate the roles of hormones in milk production and release.**

Lactation is the production of milk by the mother's breasts (mammary glands) following parturition.

During pregnancy, the duct system and the secretory units of the breast expand as a result of the high concentration and continuous presence of estrogens and progesterone. The ducts grow and branch repeatedly to form an extensive network. Additional adipose tissue is deposited also; thus, the size of the breasts increases throughout pregnancy. Estrogen is primarily responsible for this breast growth, but normal development of the breast does not occur without the influence of several other hormones. Progesterone causes development of the breasts' secretory alveoli, which enlarge but do not usually secrete milk during pregnancy. The other necessary hormones are growth hormone, prolactin, thyroid hormones, glucocorticoids, and insulin. In addition, the placenta secretes a growth hormone–like substance (human somatotropin) and a prolactin-like substance (human placental lactogen), both of which support development of the breasts.

Prolactin, produced by the anterior pituitary gland, is responsible for milk production. Before parturition, high levels of estrogen stimulate increased prolactin production, but no milk is produced because high levels of estrogen and progesterone inhibit prolactin's effect on the mammary glands. After parturition, estrogen, progesterone, and prolactin levels decrease. However, these decreased levels of prolactin are still sufficient to stimulate milk production. Despite this overall decrease in the basal levels of prolactin following parturition, a reflex response produces surges of prolactin release. Figure 29.24 illustrates the hormonal control of lactation at the time of nursing.

1. During suckling, mechanical stimulation of the breasts initiates nerve impulses that reach the hypothalamus.
2. In response, the hypothalamus stimulates the release of prolactin from the anterior pituitary gland and oxytocin from the posterior pituitary gland.
3. Prolactin stimulates milk production in alveoli of the mammary glands. Oxytocin stimulates smooth muscle cells associated with the alveoli and ducts of the mammary glands to contract. As a result, milk flows from the breast in a process called **milk letdown.** In addition, higher brain centers can stimulate oxytocin release, and stimuli, such as hearing an infant cry, can result in milk letdown.

For the first few days after birth, the mammary glands secrete a high-protein material called **colostrum** (koh-LOSS-trum), which also contains many antibodies. Although colostrum is high in protein, it contains few lipids and less lactose than milk. Eventually, the breasts produce milk with a higher lipid and lactose content. The presence of maternal antibodies in the colostrum as well as milk helps protect the nursing baby from infections (see chapter 22).

Milk production in the breast takes time. Suckling also stimulates a surge in prolactin, as described earlier. This increase in prolactin results in the production of milk for the next feeding time. Repeated stimulation of prolactin release by suckling makes nursing (breastfeeding) possible for several years. If nursing stops, however, the ability to produce prolactin ceases, and milk production most often stops within a few days.

Predict 5

A first-time mother was breastfeeding her baby when she felt uterine cramps. Concerned, she consulted a nurse. What was the nurse's explanation?

ASSESS YOUR PROGRESS

30. *Which hormones are involved in preparing the breast for lactation?*

31. *Describe the events of milk production and milk letdown.*

32. *What is in colostrum?*

PROCESS **Figure**

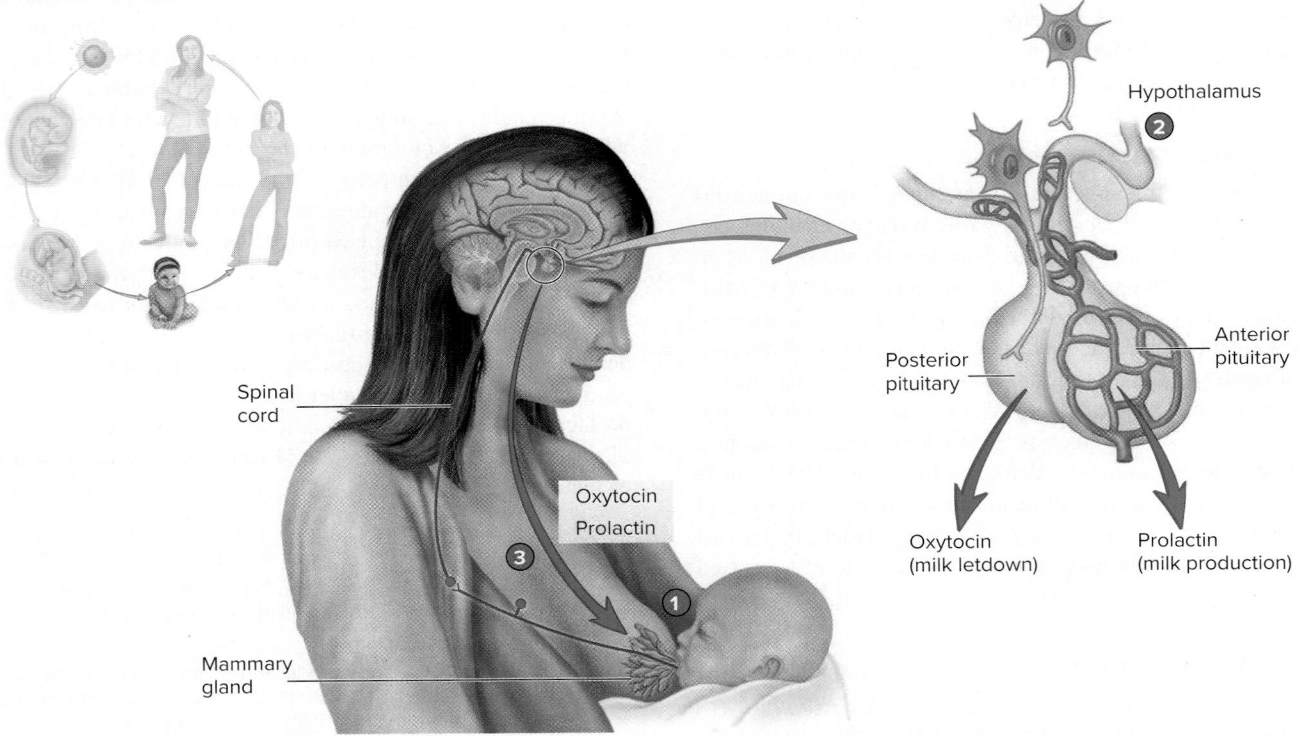

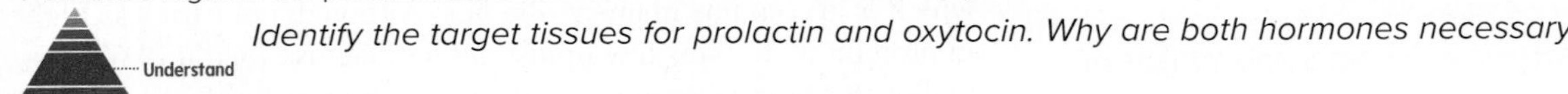
PROCESS **Figure 29.24**

Hormonal Control of Lactation

Hormones regulate the production and release of milk from the mammary glands.

Understand *Identify the target tissues for prolactin and oxytocin. Why are both hormones necessary for normal lactation?*

29.5 First Year After Birth

LEARNING OUTCOME

After reading this section, you should be able to

A. **Describe the changes that occur during the first year after birth.**

The infant experiences many changes from birth until 1 year of age. During this first year, the brain is still developing, and much of what the infant can do depends on how much brain development has occurred. It is estimated that the newborn's central nervous system contains the adult number of neurons, but subsequent brain growth and maturation add new glial cells, myelin sheaths, and new connections between neurons that may remain throughout life.

During the first year of life, infants typically pass certain developmental milestones. However, the timing of these events varies considerably from child to child, and the following time frames are only rough estimates. By 6 weeks of age, the infant usually can hold up their head when placed in a prone position and begins to smile in response to people or objects. At 3 months, the infant exercises their limbs aimlessly, but they can control their arms and hands enough to voluntarily suck their thumb. The infant can follow a moving person with their eyes. At 4 months, the infant begins to raise themselves by their arms. They can begin to grasp objects placed in their hand, coo and gurgle, roll from back to side, listen quietly to a person's voice or to music, hold their head erect, and play with their hands.

At 5 months, an infant can usually laugh, reach for objects, turn their head to follow an object, lift their head and shoulders, sit with support, and roll over. At 8 months, the infant recognizes familiar people, sits up without support, and reaches for specific objects. At 12 months, the infant may pull themselves to a standing position and may be able to walk without support. They can pick up objects with their hands and examine them carefully. They can understand much of what is said and may say several words of their own.

ASSESS YOUR PROGRESS

33. *List the major changes that occur during the first year of life. What do most of these activities depend on?*

29.6 Aging and Death

LEARNING OUTCOMES

After reading this section, you should be able to

A. **Describe the process of aging.**

B. **Explain the events that occur at the time of death.**

As with development, the process of aging begins at fertilization. Cells proliferate at an extremely rapid rate during early development, and then the process begins to slow as various cells become committed to specific body functions.

Many body cells, such as liver and skin cells, continue to proliferate throughout life, replacing dead or damaged tissue. However, many other cells, such as the neurons in the central nervous system, dramatically decrease the rate of proliferation once a certain number exist, and dead cells are not replaced quickly or at all. Though increases in the number of glial cells, myelin sheaths, and neuronal connections occur during the first year of life, the number of neurons reaches a peak, at about the time of birth. At that time, neuron numbers begin to decline. Neuronal loss is most rapid early in life and later decreases to a slower, steadier rate.

A natural, but as yet unexplained, decline occurs in mitochondrial DNA function with age. If this decline reaches a threshold, which apparently differs from tissue to tissue, the normal mitochondrial function is lost, and the tissue or organ may exhibit disease. In a small number of people, this mitochondrial degeneration occurs very early in life, resulting in premature aging.

The physical plasticity (i.e., the state of being soft and pliable) of young embryonic tissues results largely from the presence of large amounts of hyaluronate and relatively small amounts of collagen. Furthermore, the collagen and other related proteins that are present are not highly cross-linked; thus, the tissues are very flexible and elastic. Many of these proteins produced during development are permanent body components; as the person ages, more and more cross-links form between these protein molecules, thereby rendering the tissues more rigid and less elastic.

Because cross-linking of proteins is a normal part of the aging process, it is not surprising that the tissues with the highest content of collagen and other related proteins are the tissues that display the most tissue rigidity associated with aging. One of the first structures to exhibit pathological changes as a result of this increased rigidity is the lens of the eye. Seeing close objects becomes more difficult with advancing age until most middle-aged people require reading glasses. Loss of elasticity also affects other tissues, including the joints, blood vessels, kidneys, lungs, and heart, and greatly reduces their ability to function.

Like nervous tissue, mature muscle cells do not normally proliferate after terminal differentiation occurs before birth. As a result, the total number of skeletal and cardiac muscle fibers declines with age. The strength of skeletal muscle reaches a peak between 20 and 30 years of life and declines steadily thereafter. Furthermore, like the collagen of connective tissue, the macromolecules of muscle undergo biochemical changes during aging and render the muscle tissue less functional. A good exercise program, however, can slow or even reverse this process.

A decline in cardiac function with advanced aging is also related to the decline in muscular function. The heart loses elastic recoil ability and muscular contractility. As a result, total cardiac output declines, and less O_2 and fewer nutrients reach cells, such as neurons in the brain and chondrocytes in the joints. The lower amounts of O_2 and nutrients contribute to the decline in these tissues. Reduced cardiac function also may result in decreased blood flow to the kidneys, which decreases their filtration ability. Degeneration of the connective tissues as a result of collagen cross-linking and other factors also decreases the filtration efficiency of the glomerular basement membrane.

Atherosclerosis (ATH-er-oh-skler-OH-sis) is the deposit and subsequent hardening of a soft, gruel-like material, containing lipids, cholesterol, Ca^{2+}, and other materials, in lesions of the tunica intima of large and medium-sized arteries. These deposits then become fibrotic and calcified, resulting in **arteriosclerosis** (ar-TEER-ee-oh-skler-OH-sis; hardening of the arteries). Arteriosclerosis interferes with normal blood flow and can result in a **thrombus,** the formation of a clot or plaque inside a vessel. A piece of the plaque, called an **embolus** (EM-boh-lus), can break loose, float through the circulation, and lodge in smaller arteries, where it may cause myocardial infarctions or strokes. Atherosclerosis affects all middle-aged and older people to some extent and may even occur in young people. People with high blood cholesterol appear to be at increased risk of developing atherosclerosis. In addition to dietary influences, this condition seems to have a heritable component, and blood tests are available to screen people for high blood cholesterol.

Many other organs, including the liver, pancreas, stomach, and colon, undergo degenerative changes with age. The ingestion of harmful agents may accelerate such changes. For example, cigarette smoke induces degenerative changes in the lungs, and excessive alcohol consumption can cause sclerotic changes in the liver.

In addition to the previously described changes, cellular wear and tear contributes to aging. Progressive damage from many sources, including radiation and toxic substances, may result in irreversible cellular insults and may be one of the major factors leading to aging. Researchers have speculated that ingesting the antioxidant vitamins C and E in combination may help slow this part of aging by stimulating cell repair. Vitamin C also stimulates collagen production and may slow the loss of tissue plasticity associated with aging collagen.

One explanation for aging is the **free radical theory of aging.** Free radicals are atoms or molecules with an unpaired electron that can react with and alter the structure of molecules that are critical for normal cell function. Alteration of these molecules can result in cell dysfunction, cancer, or other types of cellular damage. Free radicals are produced as a normal part of metabolism and introduced into the body from the environment through the air we breathe and the food we eat. The damage caused by free radicals may accumulate with age. Antioxidants, such as beta carotene (provitamin A), vitamin C, and vitamin E, can donate electrons to free radicals, without themselves becoming harmful. Thus, antioxidants may prevent the damage caused by the free radicals and may ward off age-related disorders, ranging from wrinkles to cancer. Experiments designed to test this hypothesis, however, have not consistently produced positive results.

As a result of poor diet, many people over age 50 do not get the minimum daily allotment of several vitamins and minerals. Feeling "bad" is not necessarily a part of aging but is mostly a result of poor nutrition and lack of exercise. Engaging in moderate exercise and avoiding overeating can prolong life. Moderate exercise can reduce the risk for heart attack by as much as 20%. It can also reduce the risk for stroke, high blood pressure, and some forms of cancer. Exercise can also increase a person's ability to reason and remember. Walking 30 minutes a day is recommended.

One characteristic of aging is an overall decrease in ATP production. This decrease is associated with a decline in oxidative phosphorylation, which has been shown in many cases to result from **mitochondrial DNA mutations.** Mitochondria lack the DNA repair mechanisms that exist in the nucleus for nuclear DNA, and thus mutations can accumulate in mitochondrial DNA.

Immune system changes may also contribute to the effects of aging. The aging immune system loses its ability to respond to outside antigens but becomes more sensitive to the body's own antigens. These autoimmune changes add to the degeneration of the tissues and may be responsible for conditions such as arthritis, chronic glomerular nephritis, and hyperthyroidism. In addition, T lymphocytes tend to lose their functional capacity with aging and cannot destroy abnormal cells as efficiently. This change may be one reason that certain types of cancer occur more readily in older people.

Genetic traits may also cause many of the changes associated with aging. As a general rule, animals with a very high metabolic rate have a shorter life span than those with a lower metabolic rate. In humans, a very small number of exceptional people have a slightly reduced normal body temperature, suggesting a lower metabolic rate. The same people often have an unusually long life span. This tendency appears to run in families and probably has some genetic basis. Studies of the general population suggest that, if your parents and grandparents have lived a long time, so will you.

The genetic disorder **progeria** (proh-JEER-ee-ah; premature aging) also provides evidence of a strong genetic component to aging. This genetic disorder causes the degenerative changes of aging to begin shortly after the first year of life, and the child may look like a very old person by age 7.

One of the greatest disadvantages of aging is the increasing inability to adjust to stress. Older people have a far more precarious homeostatic balance than younger people, and eventually the body encounters some stressor so great that it cannot recover, and death results. Death is usually not attributed to old age. Another problem, such as heart failure, renal failure, or stroke, is usually the cause.

Death was once defined as the loss of heartbeat and respiration. In recent years, however, more precise definitions of death have been developed because medical science has learned how to keep both the heart and lungs working artificially, and the heart can even be replaced by an artificial device. Modern definitions of death are based on the permanent cessation of life functions and the cessation of integrated tissue and organ function. The most widely accepted indication of death in humans is **brain death,** which is defined as irreparable brain damage manifested clinically by the absence of (1) response to stimulation, (2) spontaneous breathing and heartbeat, and (3) brainstem reflexes, in addition to an electroencephalogram that remains isoelectric ("flat") for at least 30 minutes.

ASSESS YOUR PROGRESS

34. *How does the loss of cells that are not replaced affect the aging process? Give examples.*
35. *How does the loss of tissue plasticity affect the aging process? Give examples.*
36. *What tissue component is most affected by tissue rigidity?*
37. *Explain the free radical theory of aging.*
38. *How does aging affect the immune system?*
39. *What role does genetics play in aging?*
40. *What is the modern definition of death? How is death determined?*

29.7 Genetics

LEARNING OUTCOMES

After reading this section, you should be able to

A. **Define *genetics*.**
B. **Explain how chromosomes are related to inheritance.**
C. **Explain how Mendel's theories of genetics compare to modern concepts of genetics.**
D. **Define and give examples of *phenotypes* and *genotypes*.**
E. **Explain what a karyotype is.**
F. **Describe major patterns of inheritance.**
G. **Relate how mitosis differs from meiosis.**
H. **Explain how various genetic disorders can occur.**

Children resemble their parents in so many ways, whether it be appearance or behavior. This resemblance among relatives is due in large part to heredity. **Genetics** is the study of heredity—that is, the characteristics children inherit from their parents. Although the environment can influence gene expression, many of a person's physical characteristics, abilities, susceptibility to disease, and even life span are influenced by the genes inherited from their parents. Because many of the diseases caused by microorganisms are now preventable or treatable, diseases that have a genetic basis are receiving more attention.

An understanding of genetics is important for medical professionals. Knowing a patient's family medical history helps diagnose many diseases. The family medical history also allows a physician to determine the probability that a patient will develop certain diseases, such as heart disease or cancer, and to suggest preventive measures. Recent advances in genetics have shown how genes influence health and can provide new methods for treating certain diseases.

Some genetic diseases, such as hemophilia, have a simple pattern of inheritance, usually involving one or a few genes, and it is easy to predict whether a person will develop the disease. However, other genetic diseases have a more complex pattern of inheritance involving many more genes. **Mendelian genetics** is the study of how genetic traits are passed from parent to offspring. Mendelian genetics allows us to make predictions about the patterns of how traits are passed from one generation to the next. Understanding these patterns also allows us to make predictions of the probability that a trait will be inherited. From a medical perspective, Mendelian genetics has been used to determine an individual's risk of developing certain genetic diseases.

With the completion of the Human Genome Project in 2003, more than 99% of the genes in human chromosomes, collectively known as the *human genome,* have been sequenced. The results of this project have provided a wealth of useful information, allowing researchers to better identify the genes associated with particular diseases, to understand the biochemical relationship between genes and diseases, and to create new treatments. The genetic approach to the diagnosis and management of disease is known as **genomic medicine.** Mendelian genetics has indeed come a long way since its early beginnings.

Mendelian Genetics

Mendelian genetics is based on the studies of Gregor Mendel (1822–1884), an Austrian monk who made revolutionary discoveries about inheritance patterns in pea plants. Because of his discoveries, Mendel is known as the "father of genetics." Mendel found that certain traits, such as purple versus white flowers, are transmitted from one generation of pea plants to another by means of discrete units he called "heritable factors." He concluded that each pea plant has two heritable factors for a characteristic, such as flower color. He proposed that, during the production of **gametes,** or sex cells, each gamete receives one of these factors. Then two gametes combine to produce the next generation, so that each member of the next generation of pea plants has two heritable factors for each characteristic. Mendel's "heritable factors" are now called genes.

Notice that these studies focused on two different characteristics: the genes an individual possessed and how those genes influenced a particular trait. In the language of genetics, these two characteristics are referred to as the genotype and the phenotype. The **genotype** (JEN-oh-type, JEE-noh-type) is the genes an organism has for a given trait. The **phenotype** (FEE-noh-type) is the expression of the genes as a trait.

Environmental effects can influence gene expression to determine the phenotype of many traits. Even genetically identical twins can have different phenotypes because of environmental effects. For example, in addition to genes, height is affected by nutrition, and skin color is affected by exposure to the sun. Knowledge of environmental influences can be used to improve our genetic potential and to prevent harmful effects. For example, a healthy diet can promote growth or help prevent diabetes, and refraining from smoking can reduce the risk of developing cancer.

Mendel proposed that a gene for a given trait can exist in different forms, depending on how it is expressed. Specifically, Mendel stated that genes occur in dominant and recessive forms. Alternate forms of genes are now called **alleles** (ah-LEELZ). By definition, the effects of a **dominant allele** for a trait mask the effects of the **recessive allele** for that trait. For example, in pea plants, the allele for purple flowers is dominant over the allele for white flowers. By convention, dominant alleles are indicated by uppercase letters, and recessive alleles are indicated by lowercase letters. For example, the letter *P* designates the dominant allele for purple flower color, and the letter *p* represents the recessive allele for white flower color. A plant with the *Pp* genotype has purple flowers because purple is dominant over white.

Recall that genes are located on chromosomes, which exist in homologous pairs (see chapter 28). Because we possess pairs of alleles for a given gene, the combination of alleles can be two of the same alleles or two different alleles. An organism is **homozygous** (hoh-moh-ZY-gus) for a trait if the two alleles for the trait are identical. On the other hand, an organism is **heterozygous** (HET-er-oh-ZY-gus) for a trait if the two alleles for the trait are different. The possible genotypes and phenotypes for purple flower color are

Alleles	Genotype	Phenotype
PP	Homozygous dominant	Purple
Pp	Heterozygous	Purple
pp	Homozygous recessive	White

Note that the recessive trait is expressed only when it is not masked by the dominant trait.

The various alleles for a given trait provide information for protein synthesis in the cells of the body (see chapter 3). The relationship between genotype and phenotype can be understood on the molecular level if we consider how different alleles affect this protein synthesis. For example, a recessive trait in humans called **albinism** (AL-bih-niz-em) results in a lack of normal coloring of the skin, hair, and eyes. Several human genes produce the enzymes that are necessary for the synthesis of melanin, the pigment responsible for skin, hair, and eye color (see chapter 5). Alleles for these enzymes that do not produce a functional enzyme will result in the lack or complete absence of the pigment. An **albino,** a person with albinism, lacks the ability to produce the pigment melanin. Individuals with albinism have light blonde or white hair and light-colored eyes and skin, with shades of pink, blue, and yellow (figure 29.25). The pink and blue colors result from blood seen in the eyes or through the skin. The yellow is from the natural accumulation of ingested yellow plant pigments in the skin (see chapter 5).

FIGURE 29.25 Albinism

An albino male with his normally pigmented father. Norman Lightfoot/Science Source

The normal alleles for the melanin-synthesizing enzymes produce normal, functional enzymes capable of catalyzing the steps in melanin synthesis. When normal enzymes are produced, a person has normal pigmentation. But an abnormal allele for any one of the enzymes in the melanin pathway produces a defective enzyme, which blocks the pathway and stops the production of melanin. Type 1 albinism results from a defective enzyme that fails to initiate the synthesis of melanin from tyrosine. The normal allele of the gene for this enzyme, designated *A*, is dominant over the abnormal allele, designated *a*. The possible genotypes and phenotypes for albinism are

Alleles	Genotype	Phenotype
AA	Homozygous dominant	Normal pigmentation
Aa	Heterozygous	Normal pigmentation
aa	Homozygous recessive	Albino

A person with the genotype *AA* has the phenotype of normal pigmentation because the functional enzyme for melanin synthesis is produced by both alleles. A person with the genotype *Aa* also has the phenotype of normal pigmentation. Even though the *a* allele produces an abnormal, nonfunctional enzyme for melanin synthesis, the *A* allele produces sufficient amounts of the normal enzyme to keep pigmentation normal. A person with the genotype *aa* has the phenotype of albinism because only the abnormal, nonfunctional enzyme for melanin synthesis is produced.

Not all dominant traits are the normal condition, and not all recessive traits are abnormal. In some cases, the dominant trait is abnormal. For example, a person with **polydactyly** (pol-ee-DAK-tih-lee) has extra fingers or toes (figure 29.26). One allele for polydactyly is dominant over the recessive, normal allele that results in the normal number of fingers or toes.

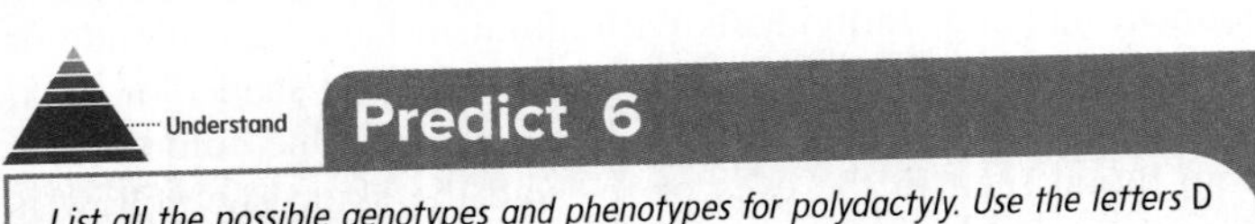
Understand **Predict 6**

List all the possible genotypes and phenotypes for polydactyly. Use the letters D *and* d *for the alleles.*

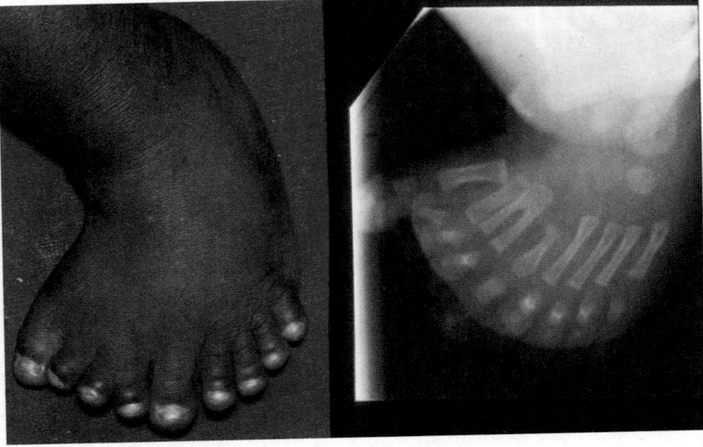

FIGURE 29.26 Polydactyly
Polydactyly, having extra fingers or toes, is determined by a dominant gene. Dr M.A. Ansary/Science Source

Modern Concepts of Genetics

Although the existence of chromosomes was known in Mendel's time, the relationship between genes and chromosomes was not confirmed until the studies of T. H. Morgan were able to connect different mutant traits to the pattern of chromosome inheritance in fruit flies in 1910. Researchers first isolated DNA as the genetic material in 1944, and James Watson and Francis Crick resolved the structure of DNA in 1953, which led to an understanding of the genetic code and protein synthesis (see chapter 3). The sequence of nucleotides of a human gene, specifically the gene that causes cystic fibrosis, was determined for the first time in 1989. The sequencing of more than 99% of the human genome was accomplished in 2003.

Chromosomes

In modern terminology, Mendel hypothesized that organisms have genes that control the expression of traits. Most genes, which are segments of DNA, occur in pairs of alleles. Chromosomes are made up of DNA and associated proteins found in the nuclei of cells of the body. The cells of the body can be divided into two major categories: somatic cells and gametes. **Somatic** (soh-MAT-ik) **cells** are all the cells of the body except the gametes. Examples of somatic cells are epithelial cells, muscle cells, neurons, fibroblasts, lymphocytes, and macrophages. In males, the gametes are **sperm cells;** in females, the gametes are **oocytes** (egg cells; see chapter 28).

The somatic cells have a normal number of chromosomes called the **diploid** (DIP-loyd; twofold) number. In chapter 28, we learned that the process of meiosis produces gametes with half the number of chromosomes as a somatic cell. The normal number of chromosomes in a gamete is the **haploid** (HAP-loyd; single) number. In humans, the diploid number of chromosomes is 46. The haploid number of chromosomes is 23.

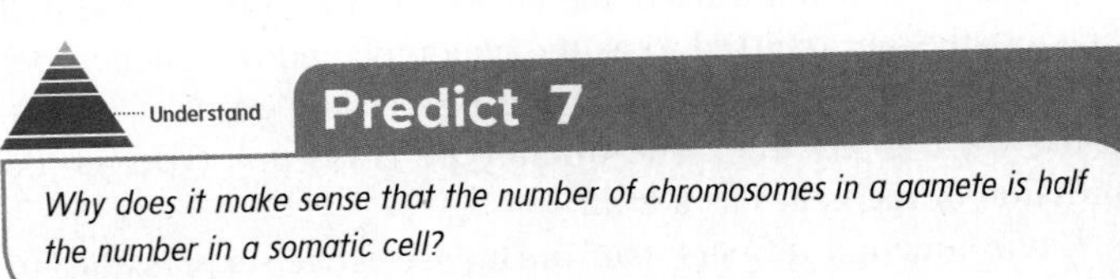
Understand **Predict 7**

Why does it make sense that the number of chromosomes in a gamete is half the number in a somatic cell?

The 23 pairs of chromosomes are divided into autosomal and sex chromosomes. Humans have 22 pairs of **autosomal** (aw-toh-SOH-mal) **chromosomes,** which are all the chromosomes except the sex chromosomes, and 1 pair of **sex chromosomes,** which determines the sex of the individual. Sex chromosomes are denoted as **X** or **Y chromosomes.** A normal female has two X chromosomes (XX) in each somatic cell. One X chromosome of a female is derived from her mother; the other is derived from her father. A normal male has one X chromosome and one Y chromosome (XY) in each somatic cell. The X chromosome of a male is derived from his mother; the Y chromosome is derived from his father.

Genetic traits can be classified by the type of chromosome their alleles are located on and by whether their alleles are dominant or recessive. Thus, traits can be autosomal dominant

TABLE 29.4 Genetic Disorders

Disorder	Description
Dominant Traits	
Achondroplasia	Dwarfism characterized by shortening of the upper and lower limbs
Huntington disease	Severe degeneration of the basal nuclei and frontal cerebral cortex; characterized by purposeless movements and mental deterioration; onset is usually between 40 and 50 years of age
Hypercholesterolemia	Elevated blood cholesterol levels that contribute to atherosclerosis and cardiovascular disease
Marfan syndrome	Abnormal connective tissue, resulting in increased height, elongated digits, and weakness in the aortic wall
Neurofibromatosis	Small, pigmented lesions (kah-FAY-oh-LAY spots) in the skin and disfiguring tumors (noncancerous) caused by the proliferation of Schwann cells along nerves
Osteogenesis imperfecta	Abnormal collagen synthesis, resulting in brittle bones that break repeatedly
Recessive Traits	
Albinism	Lack of an enzyme necessary to produce the pigment melanin; characterized by lack of coloration in skin, hair, and eyes
Cystic fibrosis	Impaired transport of chloride ions across plasma membranes; results in excessive production of thick mucus, which blocks the respiratory and gastrointestinal tracts; the most common fatal genetic disorder
Phenylketonuria	Lack of the enzyme necessary to convert the amino acid phenylalanine to the amino acid tyrosine; an accumulation of phenylalanine leads to intellectual disability
Severe combined immune deficiency	Inability to form the white blood cells (B cells, T cells, and phagocytes) necessary for an immune system response
Sickle-cell disease	Inability to produce normal hemoglobin; results in abnormally shaped red blood cells that clog capillaries or rupture
Tay-Sachs disease	Lack of the enzyme necessary to break down certain lipids; an accumulation of lipids impairs action potential propagation, resulting in deterioration of mental and physical functions and death by 3–4 years of age
Thalassemia	Decreased rate of hemoglobin synthesis; results in anemia, enlarged spleen, increased cell numbers in red bone marrow, and congestive heart failure
Sex-Linked Traits	
Duchenne muscular dystrophy	Deletion or alteration of part of the X chromosome; results in progressive weakness and wasting of muscles
Hemophilia	Most commonly, failure to produce blood clotting factors, caused by a recessive gene; results in prolonged bleeding
Red-green color blindness	Most commonly, deficiency in functional green-sensitive cones, caused by a recessive gene; inability to distinguish between red and green colors
Chromosomal Disorders	
Down syndrome	Caused by having three chromosomes 21; results in intellectual disability, short stature, and poor muscle tone
Klinefelter syndrome	Caused by two or more X chromosomes in a male (XXY); results in small testes, sterility, and development of femalelike breasts
Turner syndrome	Caused by having only one X chromosome (XO); results in immature uterus, lack of ovaries, and short stature

monosomies, in which a chromosome is missing, and trisomies, in which an extra chromosome is present. Aneuploidies are usually lethal and are one reason for a high rate of early embryo loss. **Down syndrome,** or *trisomy 21,* is a type of aneuploidy in which three chromosomes 21 are present. A **syndrome** (SIN-drohm) is a set of signs and symptoms occurring together as the result of a single cause, such as a single mutation or one extra chromosome (a trisomy). Down syndrome is an aneuploidy that is not always lethal. However, individuals with this genetic disorder exhibit physical and mental developmental problems, as well as an increased probability of developing certain cancers. These individuals also have a shortened life span.

A wide range of sex chromosome abnormalities exist. The presence of a Y chromosome makes a person genetically a male, and the absence of a Y chromosome makes a person genetically a female, regardless of the number of X chromosomes. Therefore, individuals with XO (Turner syndrome), XX, XXX, or XXXX karyotypes are females, and individuals with XY, XXY, XXXY, or XYY karyotypes are males. A YO condition is lethal because the genes on the X chromosome are necessary for survival. Secondary sexual characteristics are usually underdeveloped in both the XO female and the XXY male (called Klinefelter syndrome), and additional X chromosomes (XXXX or XXXY) are often associated with some degree of intellectual disability. Due to hormonal imbalances, the morphological features (phenotype) may be reversed from the genetic constitution (genotype). For example, a male with Klinefelter syndrome may display swelling of the breast.

Predict 10

Mr. and Mrs. Smith, both 40 years of age, are healthy with no known genetic conditions. Their newborn child has Down syndrome (trisomy 21). Explain the events that caused this condition.

ASSESS YOUR PROGRESS

51. *What is meiosis? How does it differ from mitosis? What is the end result of meiosis?*
52. *What is a carrier?*
53. *What is a mutagen? Describe a point mutation, structural mutation, and nondisjunction.*
54. *What causes the genetic disorder Down syndrome?*

Concept Check

29.1 Prenatal Development

A. Prenatal development is divided into three parts: the germinal period, during which the germ layers form; the embryonic period, when the organ systems form; and the fetal period, characterized by growth and maturation.

B. Postovulatory age is 14 days less than clinical age.

C. The stages of postnatal development are the neonatal period (birth to 1 month), infancy (1 month to 1–2 years), childhood (1–2 years to puberty), adolescence (puberty to 20 years), and adulthood (20 years to death).

1. *The major development of organ systems takes place in*

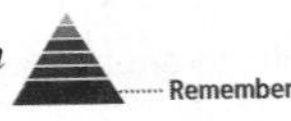

   a. weeks 1 and 2 of development.
   b. weeks 3–8 of development.
   c. weeks 8–20 of development.
   d. the last 30 weeks of development.

2. *Triploidy is the presence of three sets of chromosomes in a cell. Although rare, triploidy does occur in humans. What failures during fertilization can lead to triploidy?* Apply

3. *A physician tells Amanda that she is pregnant and is 44 days past her LMP. Approximately how many days has the embryo been developing, and what developmental events are occurring?* Apply

Fertilization

Fertilization, the union of the oocyte and sperm, results in a zygote.

Early Cell Division

The cells of the early embryo are pluripotent (capable of making any cell of the body). In the very early stages of development, the cells are totipotent, meaning that each cell can give rise to any tissue necessary for development.

Morula and Blastocyst

The product of fertilization undergoes divisions until it becomes a mass called a morula and then a hollow ball of cells called a blastocyst.

Implantation of the Blastocyst and Development of the Placenta

The blastocyst implants into the uterus about 7 days after fertilization. The placenta is derived from the trophoblast of the blastocyst.

Formation of the Germ Layers

All body tissues are derived from three primary germ layers: endoderm, mesoderm, and ectoderm.

Neural Tube and Neural Crest Formation

The nervous system develops from a neural tube that forms in the ectodermal surface of the embryo and from neural crest cells derived from the developing neural tube.

Somite Formation

Segments called somites, which develop along the neural tube, give rise to the musculature, vertebral column, and ribs.

Formation of the Gut and Body Cavities

A. The digestive tract forms as the developing embryo closes off part of the yolk sac.

B. The coelom develops from small cavities that fuse within the embryo.

4. *Given these structures:*

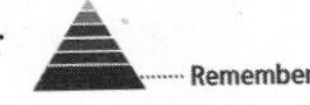

   (1) blastocyst
   (2) morula
   (3) zygote

   Choose the arrangement that lists the structures in the order in which they form during development.

   a. 1,2,3
   b. 1,3,2
   c. 2,3,1
   d. 3,1,2
   e. 3,2,1

5. *The embryo proper develops from the*

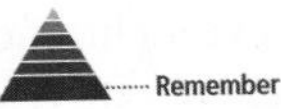

   a. inner cell mass.
   b. trophoblast.
   c. blastocele.
   d. yolk sac.

6. *The placenta*

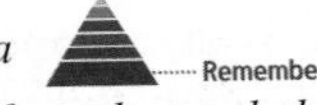

   a. develops from the trophoblast.
   b. allows maternal blood to mix with embryonic blood.
   c. invades the lacunae of the embryo.
   d. All of these are correct.

7. *The embryonic disk* Remember
   a. *forms between the amniotic cavity and the yolk sac.*
   b. *contains the primitive streak.*
   c. *becomes a three-layered structure.*
   d. *All of these are correct.*

8. *The brain develops from* Remember
   a. *ectoderm.*
   b. *endoderm.*
   c. *mesoderm.*

9. *Most of the skeletal system develops from*

   a. *ectoderm.*
   b. *endoderm.*
   c. *mesoderm.*

10. *The somites give rise to the*

   a. *circulatory system.*
   b. *skeletal muscle.*
   c. *lungs.*
   d. *kidneys.*
   e. *brain.*

11. *A high fever can prevent neural tube closure. If a female had a high fever approximately 35–45 days after her LMP, what kinds of congenital disorders might be seen in the developing embryo?* Apply

Limb Bud Development

The limbs develop from proximal to distal as outgrowths called limb buds.

Development of the Face

The face develops from the fusion of five major tissue processes.

Development of the Organ Systems

A. The epidermis of the skin develops from the ectoderm, and the dermis develops from the mesoderm or from neural crest cells. Melanocytes and sensory receptors develop from neural crest cells.
B. The skeletal system develops from mesoderm or neural crest cells.
C. Muscle develops from myoblasts, which migrate from somites.
D. The brain and spinal cord develop from the neural tube, and the peripheral nervous system develops from the neural tube and the neural crest cells.
E. The special senses develop mainly as neural tube or neural crest cell derivatives.
F. Many endocrine organs develop mainly as evaginations of the brain or digestive tract.
G. The heart develops as two tubes fuse into a single tube, which bends and develops septa to form four chambers.
H. The peripheral circulation develops from mesoderm as blood islands become hollow and fuse to form a network.
I. The lungs form as evaginations of the digestive tract. These evaginations undergo repeated branching.
J. The urinary system develops in three stages—pronephros, mesonephros, and metanephros—from the head to the tail of the embryo. The ducts join the allantois, part of which becomes the urinary bladder.
K. The reproductive systems develop in conjunction with the urinary system. The presence or absence of certain hormones is very important to sexual development.

Growth of the Fetus

A. The embryo becomes a fetus at 60 days.
B. The fetal period, from day 60 to birth, is a time of rapid growth.

12. *The pericardial cavity forms from*

   a. *evagination of the early digestive tract.*
   b. *the neural tube.*
   c. *the coelom.*
   d. *the branchial arches.*
   e. *pharyngeal pouches.*

13. *The parts of the limbs develop*

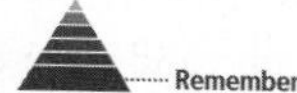

   a. *in a proximal-to-distal sequence.*
   b. *in a distal-to-proximal sequence.*
   c. *at approximately the same time.*
   d. *before the primitive streak is formed.*

14. *Concerning development of the face,*

   a. *the face develops by the fusion of five embryonic structures.*
   b. *the maxillary processes normally meet at the midline to form the lip.*
   c. *the primary palate forms the roof of the mouth.*
   d. *clefts of the secondary palate normally occur to one side of the midline.*

15. *Concerning the development of the heart,*

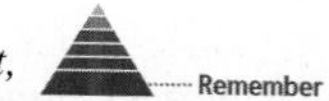

   a. *the heart develops from a single tube, which results from the fusion of two tubes.*
   b. *the SA node develops in the wall of the sinus venosus.*
   c. *the foramen ovale lets blood flow from the right atrium to the left atrium.*
   d. *the bulbus cordis is absorbed into the ventricle.*
   e. *All of these are correct.*

16. *Given these structures:* Remember
   (1) mesonephros
   (2) metanephros
   (3) pronephros

   Choose the arrangement that lists the structures in the order in which they form during development.
   a. *1,2,3*
   b. *1,3,2*
   c. *2,3,1*
   d. *3,1,2*
   e. *3,2,1*

17. *A study of the early embryo indicates that the glans penis of the male develops from the same embryonic structure as which of these female structures?* Remember
   a. *labia majora*
   b. *uterus*
   c. *clitoris*
   d. *vagina*
   e. *urinary bladder*

18. *Which hormones cause the differentiation of sex organs in the developing male fetus?*
    a. *FSH and LH*
    b. *LH and testosterone*
    c. *testosterone and dihydrotestosterone*
    d. *estrogen and progesterone*
    e. *GnRH and FSH*

29.2 Parturition

The total length of gestation is 280 days (clinical age).

Stages of Labor

Uterine contractions force the fetus out of the uterus during labor.

Hormonal Stimulation of Parturition

A. Increased estrogen and decreased progesterone help initiate parturition.
B. Fetal glucocorticoids act on the placenta to decrease progesterone synthesis and to increase estrogen and prostaglandin synthesis.
C. Stretch of the uterus and decreased progesterone levels stimulate oxytocin secretion, which stimulates uterine contraction.

19. *The onset of labor may be a result of* 

    a. *increased estrogen secretion by the placenta.*
    b. *increased glucocorticoid secretion by the fetus.*
    c. *increased secretion of oxytocin.*
    d. *stretch of the uterus.*
    e. *All of these are correct.*

20. *A female goes into labor during the thirtieth week of her pregnancy. What are the effects of administering progesterone at this stage?* 

29.3 The Newborn

Shortly after birth, the newborn baby experiences several dramatic changes when it is separated from the maternal circulation and transferred from a fluid to a gaseous environment.

Respiratory and Cardiovascular Changes

A. The foramen ovale closes, separating the two atria.
B. The ductus arteriosus closes, and blood no longer flows between the pulmonary trunk and the aorta.
C. The umbilical vein and arteries degenerate.

Digestive Changes

A. Meconium is a mixture of cells from the digestive tract, amniotic fluid, bile, and mucus excreted by the newborn.
B. The stomach begins to secrete acid.
C. The liver does not form adult bilirubin for the first 2 weeks.
D. The neonate can digest lactose, but other foods must be gradually introduced.

Apgar Scores

A. *Apgar* represents appearance, pulse, grimace, activity, and respiratory effort.
B. Apgar and other methods are used to assess the physiological condition of the newborn.

Congenital Disorders

A. Congenital disorders are abnormalities present at birth.
B. Teratogens are environmental agents that cause some congenital disorders.

21. *Following birth* 

    a. *the ductus arteriosus closes.*
    b. *the pH of the stomach increases.*
    c. *the fossa ovalis becomes the foramen ovale.*
    d. *blood flow through the pulmonary arteries decreases.*
    e. *All of these events occur.*

22. *Three minutes after birth, a newborn has an Apgar score of 5 as follows: A, 0; P, 1; G, 1; A, 1; and R, 2. What are some possible causes for this low score? What should be done for this neonate?*

29.4 Lactation

A. Estrogen, progesterone, and other hormones stimulate the growth of the breasts during pregnancy.
B. Suckling stimulates prolactin and oxytocin synthesis. Prolactin stimulates milk production, and oxytocin stimulates milk letdown.

23. *The hormone involved in milk production is* 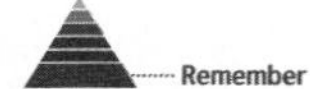

    a. *oxytocin.*
    b. *prolactin.*
    c. *estrogen.*
    d. *progesterone.*
    e. *ACTH.*

24. *When a mother breastfeeds, milk letdown can occur in the breast that is not being suckled. Explain how this response happens.*

29.5 First Year After Birth

A. The number of neuron connections and glial cells increases.
B. Motor skills develop gradually, especially head, eye, and hand movements.

25. *Which of these life stages is correctly matched with the time it occurs?*
    a. *neonate—birth to 1 month after birth*
    b. *infant—1 month to 6 months*
    c. *child—6 months to 5 years*
    d. *puberty—10–12 years*
    e. *middle age—20–40 years*

29.6 Aging and Death

A. Loss of cells that are not replaced contributes to aging.
   - A loss of neurons occurs.
   - Loss of muscle cells can affect skeletal and cardiac muscle function.
B. Loss of tissue plasticity results from cross-link formation between collagen molecules. The lens of the eye loses the ability to accommodate. Other organs, such as the joints, kidneys, lungs, and heart, also have reduced efficiency with advancing age.
C. The immune system loses the ability to act against foreign antigens and may attack self-antigens.

D. Many aging changes are probably genetic.
E. Death is the loss of brain functions.

26. *Which of these occurs as we get older?*

   a. Neurons replicate to replace lost neurons.
   b. Skeletal muscle cells replicate to replace lost muscle cells.
   c. Cross-links between collagen molecules increase.
   d. The immune system becomes less sensitive to the body's own antigens.
   e. Free radicals help prevent cancer.

29.7 Genetics

A. Genetics is the study of heredity, the characteristics children inherit from their parents.
B. Genomic medicine uses an understanding of the biochemical relationship between genes and disease to diagnose and manage disease.

Mendelian Genetics

A. The genes an organism has for a given trait are called the genotype. The expression of the genes is called the phenotype.
B. Alleles are alternate forms of genes. A dominant allele masks the effects of a recessive allele for the same trait.
C. An organism homozygous for a trait has two identical alleles for the trait, whereas an organism heterozygous for a trait has two different alleles for the trait.

Modern Concepts of Genetics

A. Chromosomes
   - Somatic cells have a diploid number of chromosomes, whereas gametes have a haploid number. In humans, the diploid number is 46 and the haploid number is 23.
   - Humans have 22 pairs of autosomal chromosomes and 1 pair of sex chromosomes. Females have the sex chromosomes XX, and males have XY.
   - A karyotype is a display of the chromosomes of a somatic cell during metaphase of mitosis.
   - Chromosome pairs are called homologous chromosomes.

B. The genome consists of all the genes found in the haploid number of chromosomes from one parent.
C. Each gene occupies a specific locus, or location, on a chromosome.
D. Alleles exist in many different forms, called multiple alleles.
E. Gene dominance
   - In complete dominance, the dominant allele masks the effects of the recessive allele.
   - In codominance, two alleles at the same locus are expressed, so that separate, distinguishable phenotypes occur at the same time.
   - In incomplete dominance, the dominant allele does not completely mask the effects of the recessive allele.

F. Polygenic traits result from the interaction of many genes.
G. Sex-linked traits
   - Sex-linked traits are traits affected by genes on the sex chromosomes.
   - X-linked traits are affected by genes on the X chromosome, and Y-linked traits are affected by genes on the Y chromosome.
   - X-linked traits are seen more frequently in males than in females because males have only one X chromosome.

Meiosis and the Transmission of Genes

A. Meiosis results in the production of gametes.
B. A Punnett square can be used to determine the probability of particular alleles being transmitted to the next generation.
C. A carrier for a recessive trait is heterozygous for the trait, having one normal allele and one disorder-causing allele.

Genetic Disorders

A. A mutation is a change in the number or kinds of nucleotides in DNA.
B. Some genetic disorders result from an abnormal distribution of chromosomes during gamete formation.

27. *A gene is* Remember
   a. the functional unit of heredity.
   b. a certain portion of a DNA molecule.
   c. a part of a chromosome.
   d. All of these are correct.

28. *Which of these terms is correctly matched with its definition?*

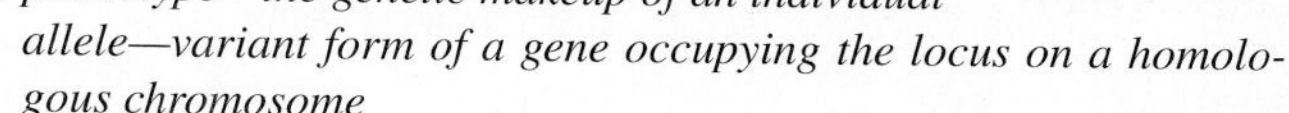

   a. autosome—an X or a Y chromosome
   b. phenotype—the genetic makeup of an individual
   c. allele—variant form of a gene occupying the locus on a homologous chromosome
   d. heterozygous—having two identical genes for a trait
   e. recessive—a trait expressed when the genes are heterozygous

29. *Which of these genotypes is heterozygous?*

   a. DD
   b. Dd
   c. dd
   d. Both a and c are correct.

30. *The AB blood type in the ABO blood group is an example of* Remember
   a. dominant versus recessive alleles.
   b. incomplete dominance.
   c. codominance.
   d. a polygenic trait.
   e. sex-linked inheritance.

31. *Assume that a trait is determined by an X-linked dominant gene. If the mother exhibits the trait but the father does not, then their*

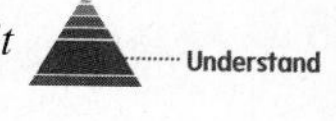

   a. sons are more likely than their daughters to exhibit the trait.
   b. daughters are more likely than their sons to exhibit the trait.
   c. sons and daughters are equally likely to exhibit the trait.

32. *An 18-year-old female consulted a physician because of her failure to initiate menses. She had experienced normal breast development at age 13, but no pubic or axillary hair had ever appeared. Her height was 5 feet 6 inches, weight 119 pounds, blood pressure 110/70, and pulse 60 beats/minute. Her physical examination confirmed the presence of well-developed breasts and the external genitalia of a normal female. However, the vagina ended in a blind pouch, and there was no evidence of a cervix, ovaries, or a uterus. Within the inguinal area, the examining physician could palpate a small, spherical mass on each side. Is this patient's genotype most likely XX, XO, or XY? Explain why the genotype you selected is consistent with the manifestations.* Apply

33. *Select the conditions that would be present in a genetic male fetus having a mutation that causes the synthesis of an ineffective müllerian-inhibiting hormone.* Apply

    (1) *Male internal reproductive structures develop.*
    (2) *Male internal reproductive structures do not develop.*
    (3) *Female internal reproductive structures develop.*
    (4) *Female internal reproductive structures do not develop.*
    (5) *Male external genitalia develop.*
    (6) *Female external genitalia develop.*

    a. 2,4,6
    b. 1,3,5
    c. 1,2,6
    d. 2,3,5

34. *The ability to roll the tongue to form a "tube" results from a dominant gene. Suppose that a female and her son can roll their tongues, but her husband cannot. Is it possible to determine if the husband is the father of her son?* Understand

35. *The ABO antigens are a group of molecules found on the surface of red blood cells. Can an individual who has blood type AB be a parent of a child with blood type O? Why or why not?* Understand

Answers to this chapter's odd-numbered Concept Check questions appear in Appendix F.

Appendix A

PERIODIC TABLE OF THE ELEMENTS

9 **F** Fluorine 19.00	
9	Atomic number
19.00	Atomic mass

1	2	3	4	5	6	7	8	9	10	11	12	13	14	15	16	17	18
1 **H** Hydrogen 1.008																	2 **He** Helium 4.003
3 **Li** Lithium 6.941	4 **Be** Beryllium 9.012											5 **B** Boron 10.81	6 **C** Carbon 12.01	7 **N** Nitrogen 14.01	8 **O** Oxygen 16.00	9 **F** Fluorine 19.00	10 **Ne** Neon 20.18
11 **Na** Sodium 22.99	12 **Mg** Magnesium 24.31											13 **Al** Aluminum 26.98	14 **Si** Silicon 28.09	15 **P** Phosphorus 30.97	16 **S** Sulfur 32.07	17 **Cl** Chlorine 35.45	18 **Ar** Argon 39.95
19 **K** Potassium 39.10	20 **Ca** Calcium 40.08	21 **Sc** Scandium 44.96	22 **Ti** Titanium 47.88	23 **V** Vanadium 50.94	24 **Cr** Chromium 52.00	25 **Mn** Manganese 54.94	26 **Fe** Iron 55.85	27 **Co** Cobalt 58.93	28 **Ni** Nickel 58.69	29 **Cu** Copper 63.55	30 **Zn** Zinc 65.39	31 **Ga** Gallium 69.72	32 **Ge** Germanium 72.59	33 **As** Arsenic 74.92	34 **Se** Selenium 78.96	35 **Br** Bromine 79.90	36 **Kr** Krypton 83.80
37 **Rb** Rubidium 85.47	38 **Sr** Strontium 87.62	39 **Y** Yttrium 88.91	40 **Zr** Zirconium 91.22	41 **Nb** Niobium 92.91	42 **Mo** Molybdenum 95.94	43 **Tc** Technetium (98)	44 **Ru** Ruthenium 101.1	45 **Rh** Rhodium 102.9	46 **Pd** Palladium 106.4	47 **Ag** Silver 107.9	48 **Cd** Cadmium 112.4	49 **In** Indium 114.8	50 **Sn** Tin 118.7	51 **Sb** Antimony 121.8	52 **Te** Tellurium 127.6	53 **I** Iodine 126.9	54 **Xe** Xenon 131.3
55 **Cs** Cesium 132.9	56 **Ba** Barium 137.3	57–71 Lanthanoids	72 **Hf** Hafnium 178.5	73 **Ta** Tantalum 180.9	74 **W** Tungsten 183.9	75 **Re** Rhenium 186.2	76 **Os** Osmium 190.2	77 **Ir** Iridium 192.2	78 **Pt** Platinum 195.1	79 **Au** Gold 197.0	80 **Hg** Mercury 200.6	81 **Tl** Thallium 204.4	82 **Pb** Lead 207.2	83 **Bi** Bismuth 209.0	84 **Po** Polonium (210)	85 **At** Astatine (210)	86 **Rn** Radon (222)
87 **Fr** Francium (223)	88 **Ra** Radium (226)	89–103 Actinoids	104 **Rf** Rutherfordium (257)	105 **Db** Dubnium (260)	106 **Sg** Seaborgium (263)	107 **Bh** Bohrium (262)	108 **Hs** Hassium (265)	109 **Mt** Meitnerium (266)	110 **Ds** Darmstadtium (269)	111 **Rg** Roentgenium (272)	112 **Cn** Copernicium	113 **Nh** Nihonium	114 **Fl** Flerovium	115 **Mc** Moscovium	116 **Lv** Livermorium	117 **Ts** Tennessine	118 **Og** Oganesson

Metals

Metalloids

Nonmetals

57 **La** Lanthanum 138.91	58 **Ce** Cerium 140.1	59 **Pr** Praseodymium 140.9	60 **Nd** Neodymium 144.2	61 **Pm** Promethium (147)	62 **Sm** Samarium 150.4	63 **Eu** Europium 152.0	64 **Gd** Gadolinium 157.3	65 **Tb** Terbium 158.9	66 **Dy** Dysprosium 162.5	67 **Ho** Holmium 164.9	68 **Er** Erbium 167.3	69 **Tm** Thulium 168.9	70 **Yb** Ytterbium 173.0	71 **Lu** Lutetium 175.0
89 **Ac** Actinium	90 **Th** Thorium 232.0	91 **Pa** Protactinium (231)	92 **U** Uranium 238.0	93 **Np** Neptunium (237)	94 **Pu** Plutonium (242)	95 **Am** Americium (243)	96 **Cm** Curium (247)	97 **Bk** Berkelium (247)	98 **Cf** Californium (249)	99 **Es** Einsteinium (254)	100 **Fm** Fermium (253)	101 **Md** Mendelevium (256)	102 **No** Nobelium (254)	103 **Lr** Lawrencium (257)

Layout published 2018 by the International Union of Pure and Applied Chemistry (IUPAC).

The modern periodic table of the elements lists the known elements in order of their atomic masses. Each element has a box that contains the name of the element and its chemical symbol, atomic number, and atomic mass. The boxes are organized into a grid of horizontal rows, called periods, and vertical columns, called groups. Within a period, the elements are listed in order of increasing atomic number from left to right. Elements in a period have different chemical properties, whereas elements in a group have similar chemical properties.

The atomic number is the number of protons in an element. Each element has a unique number of protons and therefore a unique atomic number. There are 90 naturally occurring elements. Scientists have been able to create new elements by changing the number of protons in the nuclei of existing elements. Protons, neutrons, or electrons from one atom are accelerated to very high speeds and then smashed into the nucleus of another atom. The resulting changes in the nucleus produce a new element with a new atomic number. These artificially produced elements are usually unstable, and they quickly convert back to more stable elements. The synthetic elements are technetium (Tc, atomic number 43), promethium (Pm, atomic number 61), and all the elements with an atomic number of 93 or higher. An element with an atomic number of 116 has the highest number officially recognized by the International Union of Pure and Applied Chemistry (IUPAC), but elements with higher atomic numbers have reportedly been made. In addition, the IUPAC gives standard atomic weights to only four significant figures, atomic weights now give a range of values when previously there was just one given, and atomic weights are no longer given for compounds without naturally occurring isotopes.

Appendix B

SELECTED ABBREVIATIONS, PREFIXES, SUFFIXES, AND COMBINING FORMS

Selected Abbreviations

α alpha
ACE angiotensin-converting enzyme
acetyl-CoA acetyl coenzyme A
ACh acetylcholine
ADH antidiuretic hormone
ADP adenosine diphosphate
ANH atrial natriuretic hormone
ANS autonomic nervous system
apo E apolipoprotein E
ATP adenosine triphosphate
AV atrioventricular beta
BCOP blood colloid osmotic pressure
BMI body mass index
BMR basal metabolic rate
BP blood pressure
BPG 2,3-bisphosphoglycerate
bpm beats per minute
BUN blood urea nitrogen
$C_6H_{12}O_6$ glucose
$Ca_{10}(PO_4)_6(OH)_2$ hydroxyapatite
Ca^{2+} calcium ion
cal calorie
cAMP cyclic adenosine monophosphate
CBC complete blood count
cGMP cyclic guanosine monophosphate
CH_3COOH acetic acid
Cl^- chloride ion
CNS central nervous system
CO cardiac output
CO carbon monoxide
CO_2 carbon dioxide
—COOH carboxyl group
COX-1 cyclooxygenase-1
CP capsule pressure
CRH corticotrophin-releasing hormone
CSF cerebrospinal fluid
DAG diacylglycerol
DNA deoxyribonucleic acid
ECG or EKG electrocardiogram
EEG electroencephalogram
EGF epidermal growth factor
ENS enteric nervous system
EPSP excitatory postsynaptic potential
FAD flavin adenine dinucleotide
$FADH_2$ reduced flavin adenine diphosphate
Fe^{2+} iron ion
FEV_1 forced expiratory volume in one second
FGF fibroblast growth factor
FSH follicle-stimulating hormone
g gram
GABA gamma-aminobutyric acid
GCP glomerular capillary pressure
GDP guanosine diphosphate
GFR glomerular filtration rate
GH growth hormone
GHIH growth hormone–inhibiting hormone
GHRH growth hormone–releasing hormone
GnRH gonadotropin-releasing hormone
GTP guanosine triphosphate
H^+ hydrogen ion
H_2CO_3 carbonic acid
H_2O water
H_2O_2 hydrogen peroxide
H_2PO^- dihydrogen phosphate ion
HCG human chorionic gonadotropin
HCl hydrochloric acid
HCO_3^- bicarbonate ion
HDL high-density lipoprotein
Hg mercury
HIV human immunodeficiency virus
HLA human leukocyte antigen
HPO_4^{2-} monohydrogen phosphate ion
HR heart rate
I^- iodide ion
ICSH interstitial cell–stimulating hormone
IFP interstitial fluid pressure
Ig immunoglobulin
IP_3 inositol triphosphate
IPSP inhibitory postsynaptic potential
IU international units
K^+ potassium ion
kcal kilocalorie
kg kilogram
L liter
LDL low-density lipoprotein
LH luteinizing hormone
LHRH luteinizing hormone–releasing hormone
MAC membrane attack complex
MALT mucosa-associated lymphoid tissue
MAO monoamine oxidase
MAP mean arterial pressure
mEq milliequivalent
Mg^{2+} magnesium ion
MHC major histocompatibility complex
mOsm milliosmole
mRNA messenger ribonucleic acid
mV millivolt
Na^+ sodium ion
NaCl sodium chloride
NAD^+ nicotinamide adenine dinucleotide
NADH reduced nicotinamide adenine dinucleotide
$NaHCO_3$ sodium bicarbonate
NaOH sodium hydroxide
NFP net filtration pressure
$—NH_2$ amine group
NH_3 ammonia
NH_4^+ ammonium ion
NK cells natural killer cells
NO nitric oxide
O_2 oxygen
OH^- hydroxide ion
PAH *para*-aminohippuric acid
P_{ALV} alveolar pressure
P_B barometric air pressure
PGE prostaglandin E
PGF prostaglandin F
P_i inorganic phosphate
PIF prolactin-inhibiting factor
PIH prolactin-inhibiting hormone
PIP_2 phosphoinositol
PMNs polymorphonuclear neutrophils
PNS peripheral nervous system
PO_4^{3-} phosphate ion
P_{PL} pleural pressure
PR peripheral resistance
PRF prolactin-releasing factor
PRH prolactin-releasing hormone
PTH parathyroid hormone
RANKL receptor activator of nuclear factor kappaβ ligand
RAS reticular activating system
RBC red blood count
RDA recommended daily allowances
RDI reference daily intake
RhoGAM Rh_o(D) immune globulin
RMP resting membrane potential
RNA ribonucleic acid
SA sinoatrial
SV stroke volume
T_3 triiodothyronine
T_4 tetraiodothyronine
TF tissue factor
TGF-β transforming growth factor beta
TMJ temporomandibular joint
TNF tumor necrosis factor
TRH thyroid-releasing hormone
TSH thyroid-stimulating hormone
V_A alveolar ventilation
VLDL very low-density lipoprotein
vWF von Willebrand factor
WBC white blood count

Process Figure 3.16

The cell is "paying" the energy cost through the use of ATP. Recall that the sodium-potassium pump is an active transport mechanism that requires ATP to move Na^+ and K^+ across the membrane. As such, the cell's energy cost is "paid" during the first step of the figure.

Process Figure 3.19

Receptor-mediated endocytosis is similar to facilitated diffusion in that the receptor proteins functioning in receptor-mediated endocytosis have many of the same characteristics as the carrier proteins involved in facilitated diffusion. These characteristics include specificity, competition, and saturation. These two processes differ in the number of molecules that can be transported in one "cycle." Facilitated diffusion transports individual molecules across the membrane per cycle. Receptor-mediated endocytosis moves many copies of the substance across the membrane with the formation of a single vesicle.

Process Figure 3.20

Exocytosis involves the release of substances from a cell, not the uptake of substances into the cell. Of the choices, secretion of newly synthesized proteins involves the release of material from the cell into the extracellular space, so this activity is most likely to involve exocytosis. The other two choices, ingestion of a bacterium and absorption of lipid-soluble material, both involve uptake of something into the cell, either by phagocytosis in the case of the ingestion of a bacterium or by simple diffusion in the case of absorption of lipid-soluble material.

Process Figure 3.24

From the figure we can see that ribosomal subunits are composed of ribosomal RNA (rRNA) and ribosomal proteins. Recall from chapter 2 that RNA is composed of nucleotides and proteins are composed of amino acids.

Process Figure 3.27

Recall that the rough ER is rough because of the presence of ribosomes; therefore, we would expect protein synthesis to occur there and the transport vesicles sent to the Golgi apparatus to contain proteins. Transport vesicles sent by the smooth ER to the Golgi apparatus are likely to contain lipids because the smooth ER is involved in lipid synthesis.

Process Figure 3.28

The digestive enzymes are isolated in the lysosomes to prevent the digestion of the normal parts of the cell.

Process Figure 3.33

As shown in the figure, transcription occurs in the nucleus and translation occurs in the cytoplasm, in association with ribosomes. Recall that our cells have membrane-bound nuclei and the nuclear envelope separates the contents of the nucleus from the cytoplasm. As a result, transcription must be completed before the mRNA molecule can exit the nucleus and enter the cytoplasm. Only then can the mRNA interact with the ribosome to complete the translation process. Bacterial cells do not have membrane-bound nuclei, so the ribosomes can associate with the mRNA as it is being synthesized before the process of transcription is completed.

Process Figure 3.34

Recall that each nucleotide of nucleic acids is composed of a sugar, a base, and a phosphate group. RNA nucleotides have ribose sugar, thus the name ribonucleic acid. DNA nucleotides have deoxyribose sugar, thus the name deoxyribonucleic acids.

Process Figure 3.35

The DNA gene sequence would be longer than the mRNA. The pre-mRNA has the same number of nucleotides as the coding section of the DNA gene sequence. The mRNA is shortened as introns are removed.

Process Figure 3.37

We learned that each codon specifies a single amino acid. That would mean that 50 codons specified the 50 amino acids in the polypeptide chain. Each codon is composed of 3 nucleotides, so the answer to the second question would be 150 (50×3) nucleotides specified the polypeptide chain.

Process Figure 3.39

The two processes are similar in that the DNA sequence is used to produce new RNA molecules during transcription and new DNA molecules during replication. The process of transcription produces RNA molecules; replication produces DNA molecules. Also, remember that transcription only involves specific genes, which are portions of a DNA molecule, but replication involves the entire DNA molecule.

Process Figure 3.41

We know that the process of mitosis produces daughter cells with the exact DNA as the parent and therefore the exact diploid number. The information provided suggests that one cell is lacking a chromosome (45) and one cell has an extra chromosome (47). It appears that the chromatids of a chromosome did not separate correctly and both moved into one new cell. Because the separation of chromatids occurs during anaphase, we can conclude that this is where the error occurred.

Process Figure 4.8

The characteristics of inflammation (redness, swelling, etc.) are due to increased blood flow to the site of injury. While it is very important to bring more blood to the injury site to provide more oxygen to the different cells as well as to increase the number of white blood cells, sometimes the inflammation response can become detrimental. RICE helps control the amount of blood arriving at the injured location. Rest reduces activity of the tissues so less oxygen is needed. Ice causes vasoconstriction, which reduces blood flow, and compression aids in moving excess fluid away from the area. Finally, elevation uses the force of gravity to aid in drawing fluid from the area. This is useful in recovery because excess swelling can actually prevent oxygen and nutrient delivery and can cause more damage than the original injury.

Process Figure 4.9

Recall from chapter 3 that the cellular division process called mitosis creates new cells. In preparation for mitosis, existing cells copy their DNA and then during mitosis each cell separates into two new, identical cells. This increases the total number of cells in an area. Mitosis creates cells to fill in the gap in the epidermis created by an injury.

Process Figure 5.3

DNA is primarily located in the nucleus. But recall that mitochondria also contain DNA. We can therefore assume that the melanosomes would congregate around the structures that contain DNA, the nucleus, and possibly the mitochondria.

Process Figure 5.12

Blood flows through the skin to release heat but also to ensure that the temperature of the skin is maintained at a homeostatic level. As the skin temperature drops due to the placement of the ice pack, blood vessels in that area will dilate to increase blood flow and therefore heat at the site.

Process Figure 5.13

The material passes through the blood three different times: once from the skin to the liver, a second time from the liver to the kidney, and a third time from the kidney to the small intestine.

Process Figure 6.10

Recall from chapter 3 and section 6.3 that cellular material is released in bulk by exocytosis. Thus, osteoblasts release the materials for bone matrix production by exocytosis.

Process Figure 6.11

You learned that regardless of starting material, bone ossification proceeds with osteoblasts secreting bony matrix until surrounded, at which point they are called osteocytes. In addition, you learned that bone is formed as woven bone first, followed by lamellar bone formation. Because osteoblasts produce bone matrix for each ossification type and osteoclasts remodel the new matrix, the basic process is the same. The primary difference is the starting material in the fetus.

Process Figure 6.12

Looking at figure 6.12, we can see that the mechanism promoting long bone growth is division of chondrocytes. This cell division increases the amount of hyaline cartilage in the epiphyseal plate, which makes the overall bone length greater. Therefore, the major effect of GH is to stimulate chondrocyte cell division.

Process Figure 6.16

Recall that increased mechanical stress stimulates osteoblast activity to secrete more bone matrix in the area where there is increased force on the bone. If a person were to become far less active, we would expect an overall decrease in bone density due to a reduction in osteoblast activity.

Process Figure 6.18

To answer this question, first recall stimuli for bone remodeling. One of the major promoters of bone remodeling and increased bone thickness is mechanical stress on the bone. Astronauts in very low gravity do not experience as much stress on their bones as do people living on Earth with its gravitational pull. Because there is less mechanical stimulation of osteoblasts, you would expect bones to heal more slowly in astronauts living in the international space station without the normal pull of gravity.

Process Figure 9.7

You learned that the charge on the inside of the membrane of an electrically excitable cell is negative (below zero). You also learned that K^+ is in higher concentration inside the cell membrane and constantly diffuses out of the cell through K^+ leak channels. Negatively charged proteins inside the cell cannot diffuse through the cell membrane. Thus, if the cell has a greater number of K^+ leak channels, the permeability of the membrane to K^+ is greater. Thus, more K^+ than normal will diffuse out of the cell. The negatively charged proteins left behind will cause the charge inside the cell to become even more negative. With the inside more negative, the resting membrane potential will be further from zero.

Process Figure 9.9

This is facilitated diffusion. Recall from chapter 3 that movement of a molecule or ion down its concentration gradient is a type of passive transport, specifically diffusion if the molecule or ion is a solute. However, diffusion of ions cannot occur directly through the phospholipid bilayer. Thus, a transport protein is required to "help" along the diffusion of the molecule or ion.

Process Figure 9.11

The action potential would be propagated in both directions, away from the point of stimulus. This is because an action potential is self-propagating. This means that it is the very Na^+ entering the cell causing the action potential that generates the action potential in the next section of the cell membrane. The Na^+ depolarizes the membrane, which stimulates voltage-gated Na^+ channels to open, letting more Na^+ into the cell.

Process Figure 9.12

To answer this question, recall that the neuromuscular junction is the structure where skeletal muscle contractions are stimulated. The neurotransmitter acetylcholine binds to acetylcholine receptors on the sarcolemma. Without acetylcholine receptors, no signal for contraction will be transmitted to the muscle fiber and skeletal muscles would remain flaccid (not contracted). Giving the patient an acetylcholinesterase inhibitor is effective because it prevents degradation of acetylcholine in the synaptic cleft. By keeping the concentration of acetylcholine elevated, the limited number of receptors will be stimulated to a greater degree.

Process Figure 9.13

Given that the primary symptom of malignant hyperthermia is uncontrolled muscle contraction and you learned that Ca^{2+} release into the sarcoplasm triggers contraction, a likely culprit is higher-than-normal levels of Ca^{2+} in the sarcoplasm. Indeed, malignant hyperthermia patients have a mutated Ca^{2+} channel in the terminal cisternae of the sarcoplasmic reticulum that is prevented from closing, which allows excess Ca^{2+} to diffuse into the sarcoplasm. At this time, the primary treatment's mechanism of action is uncertain, but in theory, inhibiting the Ca^{2+} channels in the sarcoplasmic reticulum to reduce the total Ca^{2+} released from the sarcoplasmic reticulum would minimize the excessive muscle contraction. Fewer muscle contractions would also, most likely, prevent the spike in body temperature because skeletal muscle contraction is a major source of our body heat. In addition, fewer muscle contractions would also avoid fatigue and damage to the muscle tissue and muscle tissue would be preserved instead of breaking down.

Process Figure 9.14

The question tells you that Ca^{2+} diffuses out of the sarcoplasmic reticulum after a person dies. Because the myosin heads are in their resting position in a relaxed muscle, the presence of Ca^{2+} will cause the myosin heads to automatically engage the actin myofilaments and the muscle will contract. However, ATP production ceases upon the death of a person. You learned that ATP is required for two steps in the cross-bridge cycle: (1) detachment of the myosin head and (2) returning the myosin head to its resting position. Thus, the absence of ATP in a corpse prevents the release of already formed cross-bridges and the muscles stay rigid. Rigor mortis does not happen in a living person because during life ATP does not get completely depleted. However, it can be significantly reduced when muscles have been overworked. In the case of severely overworked muscles, there is still enough ATP to allow a few cross-bridges to form, resulting in a weak contraction. However, there are not enough cross-bridges formed to allow a person to stand or walk.

Process Figure 9.15

Because the sarcoplasmic reticulum stores a high level of Ca^{2+} for rapid diffusion upon activation of a muscle contraction, during relaxation, Ca^{2+}

must be pumped against its concentration gradient. Movement of molecules or ions against their concentration gradient is called active transport.

Process Figure 9.19

The first part of the question refers to the "all-or-none" response, which in neurons refers solely to the electrical changes within the axon. We see this response due to the actions of the voltage-gated channels. These open or close only at a particular membrane voltage. Thus, at membrane potentials above +20mV the voltage-gated Na^+ gates close and the cell is incapable of further depolarization. However, in treppe of skeletal muscles, the all-or-none response we are referring to is tension of the muscle fiber, not just membrane potential. Thus, by increasing Ca^{2+} concentration in the sarcoplasm, it is possible to induce a greater number of cross-bridges to form, and the fiber can achieve greater tension in a subsequent stimulation up to a point. After that point, the strength of each contraction is equal to the previous.

Process Figure 9.20

The skeletal muscle fiber action potential is extremely short-lived (1–2 msec), and thus it has a very brief refractory period. A stronger stimulus can cause an action potential to be generated during the relative refractory period, and action potentials can occur before the tension in the fiber has reduced. Therefore, contractions can summate such that a muscle fiber does not relax before it contracts again, which results in a sustained contraction called tetanus.

Process Figure 9.26

ATP binds to myosin heads to detach them from the active sites in skeletal muscle. In smooth muscle, however, myosin phosphatase cleaves a phosphate from the myosin heads.

Process Figure 11.9

Ions are charged atoms or molecules. The charge of ions will affect the direction of movement because opposite charges are attracted to each other and same charges are repelled from each other. We learned that the inside surface of the cell membrane is slightly negative. Because Cl^- are also negative, we can conclude that the negative charge inside the cell repels Cl^-, thereby reducing the number that enter the cell.

Process Figure 11.12

Similar to what occurs between stimulus 4 and stimulus 5, we would expect the degree of depolarization to increase even more if another stimulus was applied before the 5th stimulus was able to disappear.

Process Figure 11.14

The process is active. In figure 11.14, we learned that the pump functions to maintain the differential levels of Na^+ and K^+ across the cell membrane. This membrane protein is an active-transport mechanism, requiring ATP to transport the ions from one side of the membrane to the other.

Process Figure 11.17

Recall that local currents are due to the movement of ions, specifically Na^+. In the area of the membrane that is experiencing the action potential, Na^+ is flowing into the cell. The Na^+ that is positioned around the adjacent areas of the membrane will also move due to the normal tendency to diffuse to areas of lower concentration. This leads to the local currents described along the adjacent areas of the membrane.

Process Figure 11.18

Looking at figure 11.18, imagine removing the regions of the axon that are myelinated. The nodes of Ranvier are the only areas that experience the action potential. The combined length of just the nodes of Ranvier of the myelinated axons is much shorter than the overall length of the axon.

Process Figure 11.19

The region of the plasma membrane where Na^+ diffuses through the gap junction is at resting membrane potential. Because ions diffuse in all directions away from their point of entry, any region of the membrane that reaches threshold will fire an action potential.

Process Figure 11.20

The ion channel depicted is a ligand-gated channel. Opening of these channels leads to graded potentials. If enough Na^+ enters through the ligand-gated channels, the cell will reach threshold and trigger the opening of voltage-gated Na^+ channels. Action potentials result from the opening of voltage-gated Na^+ channels.

Process Figure 11.21

MAO is the enzyme that degrades norepinephrine. If the enzyme is prevented from working properly, it cannot break down norepinephrine, and levels increase within the synaptic cleft. With higher levels of norepinephrine, the target can be stimulated to a greater degree and thus relieve anxiety.

Process Figure 11.22

We learned that action potential propagation is unidirectional toward the axon terminal due to the refractory period. In this scenario, the region of the membrane that reached threshold is not flanked by areas that are experiencing refractory periods. Because of that, the action potential could propagate in both directions.

Process Figure 12.5

Recall that the motor division of the PNS is divided into the somatic nervous system, which controls skeletal muscle tissue, and the autonomic nervous system, which controls cardiac and smooth muscle and glands. The reflex example in this figure is a somatic reflex because the effector is skeletal muscle.

Process Figure 12.7

The result we want for this particular reflex is for the upper limb to bend or flex. To determine this, we just need to identify the flexor muscles of the upper limb. By reviewing the muscles described in table 10.16, we can see that the biceps brachii and the brachialis are the flexor muscles; therefore, these are the muscles that must be stretched to initiate the reflex to flex or bend the arm.

Process Figure 12.8

First, recall that sensory nerves conduct signals from the Golgi tendon organs within the tendon near the muscle-tendon junction. These signals initiate the Golgi tendon reflex, which activates inhibitory interneurons in the spinal cord. These interneurons inhibit the motor neurons, leading to muscle relaxation and reduced tension on the tendons. In the absence of this reflex, the force may become so great that tendons, and even muscles, may be torn.

Process Figure 12.9

The key to understanding the difference between these two reflexes is the type of interneuron that is activated in the spinal cord. The withdrawal reflex activates an excitatory interneuron, while the Golgi tendon reflex activates an inhibitory interneuron. Thus, the withdrawal reflex activates the alpha motor neuron to cause contraction, while the Golgi tendon reflex inhibits the alpha motor neuron to cause relaxation.

Process Figure 12.10

Remember that stretching of a muscle stimulates the stretch reflex. During the withdrawal reflex, as the flexor muscles contract, the extensor muscles are stretching. The inhibition overrides the normal response of these muscles to contract and allows for the coordinated movement of the limb.

Process Figure 12.11

This hypothetical situation is meant to illustrate the importance of both the reciprocal innervation that inhibits the extensor muscle in the same limb and the crossed extensor reflex that stimulates the extensor muscle in the opposite limb. In this situation, the collateral branches of sensory neurons would have activated excitatory interneurons that do not cross to the opposite side of the spinal cord. As a result, there would be activation of the extensor muscles in the same leg, which would counteract the flexor muscles. This is the opposite of reciprocal innervation, which would normally have inhibited the extensor muscles. Likewise, the lack of a crossed extensor reflex would reduce the shifting of weight to the opposite, unaffected limb. Hence, the person would most likely have difficulty removing the limb from the source of pain and would likely fall in the effort.

Process Figure 13.2

The neural crest cells that migrate from the cephalic portion of the neural tube give rise to all the craniofacial bones and cartilage. Consequently, the cephalic neural crest is responsible for normal development of facial structures and altered cephalic neural crest development leads to craniofacial defects in newborns.

Process Figure 13.14

If production levels of CSF are normal, accumulation of CSF would result from problems with the movement and drainage of CSF into the venous system. We can conclude that either flow of CSF within the brain is blocked or the veins that drain CSF from the brain tissue are abnormal.

Process Figure 14.4

A primary sensory receptor can be activated only by stimulation of the type of receptor on its axon, for example, a Pacinian corpuscle. In contrast, a secondary sensory receptor is activated by neurotransmitters released by primary receptor cells. Consequently, the secondary neuron can be activated by multiple receptor cells responding to multiple stimuli. In addition, recall from section 11.7 that convergence of signals, such as occurs between multiple receptor cells and a sensory neuron, allows summation of signals. In this way, signals from multiple secondary receptor cells could contribute to activation of the sensory neuron.

Process Figure 14.11

The athletic trainer's conclusion is sensible considering the function of the cerebellum. Recall that the cerebellum ensures smooth and coordinated muscle contractions. The jerky, exaggerated movements exhibited by the kicker may be an indication of cerebellar damage. A thorough exam by a trained physician is needed to verify this diagnosis, so the athletic trainer was right to insist that the player be transported to a hospital.

Process Figure 14.13

The first step in the process would be most affected, which involves the visual cortex. Damage to the posterior region could possibly disrupt a person's ability to see and/or recognize a written word.

Process Figure 14.16

Recall that long-term potentiation involves both presynaptic and postsynaptic mechanisms. And, importantly, both mechanisms involve the neurotransmitter glutamate. Hence, inhibition of glutamate signaling activity would blunt both presynaptic and postsynaptic mechanisms.

Process Figure 15.2

The cholinergic synapse described in chapter 11 depended on neurotransmitters binding to receptor sites on the extracellular surface of the actual ion channel to open it, leading to depolarization. In the ion channels depicted in this figure, the ion channels open due to changes in the intracellular activity. Odorants do not directly interact with the ion channels but rather lead to opening of the ion channels through a G protein interaction.

Process Figure 15.3

The olfactory neuronal pathway from the olfactory bulb to the olfactory cortex areas represents a diverging pathway. Recall from section 11.7 that divergent pathways involve fewer presynaptic cells than postsynaptic cells. Essentially, presynaptic axons have collateral branches allowing them to communicate with more than one postsynaptic cell. We see this pattern as axons from the olfactory bulb synapse with multiple areas within the cerebrum.

Process Figure 15.6

Damage to the tractus solitarius would affect the sense of taste more because signals from all three cranial nerve pairs monitoring the taste buds synapse within the tractus solitarius. Damage to the glossopharyngeal nerve would only affect taste sensations from the posterior one-third of the tongue, the vallate papillae, and the superior pharynx.

Process Figure 15.8

If the lacrimal ducts are blocked, tears would not be released onto the surface of the eyeball. This could lead to irritation and damage of the eyeball due to the lack of lubrication and the protective enzyme lysozyme. Blocking the lacrimal canaliculi would result in "crying" as tears would not be able to drain from the surface of the eye and would eventually spill over the lower eyelid.

Process Figure 15.13

Recall from chapter 11 that action potentials occur when ions move across plasma membranes. Steps 2 and 3 both involve the generation of action potentials, so both involve ion movement across plasma membranes.

Process Figure 15.19

Recall from chapter 3 that mitochondria are the primary location for ATP production in the cell. In step 5 of this figure, we can see that ATP is needed for the recombination of rhodopsin molecules, which are necessary for the normal function of photoreceptors. We can hypothesize that mitochondrial diseases reduce normal ATP levels and therefore reduce the recycling of rhodopsin molecules in the photoreceptors.

Process Figure 15.20

The level of glutamate release from rods would be lower in the students sitting under the light. Recall that glutamate release is higher under dark conditions compared to bright conditions.

Process Figure 15.23

The superior colliculi of the midbrain are involved in reflexive movements of the head and body to visual and auditory stimuli. Essentially, we look in the directions of noises and movement in our periphery. Receiving visual stimuli is imperative for this reflex activity.

Process Figure 15.32

Remember that the middle ear is normally an air-filled space. If fluid accumulated in the middle ear, the auditory ossicles would not be able to move as easily. The auditory ossicles transmit vibrations of the tympanic membrane to the oval window, and therefore into the inner ear. If they cannot move as easily, the vibrations

the force of gravity from Earth is nearly nonexistent, the astronaut is "weightless." However, the definition of mass is the amount of matter present in the object itself. Thus, no matter the location of an object, the mass remains constant.

3. To answer this question, we must recall the relationship among CO_2, H_2O, and H^+ in solution. Carbon dioxide readily combines with water, resulting in the production of free H^+. Therefore, as the amount of CO_2 decreases, the reversible reaction will shift in the other direction to form CO_2. Similar to the trough of water example, if CO_2 levels decrease, it is like raising the right side of the trough, causing water to flow to the left. The reaction "flows" to the left: $CO_2 + H_2O \rightarrow H^+ + HCO_3^-$. In order for this to happen, free H^+ combines with HCO_3^-, decreasing its level in the blood. Section 2.3 explains that this decrease in H^+ levels changes the pH of the blood so that it becomes more basic.
5. During exercise, our body is doing work by muscular contractions. Work involves converting one form of energy into another, and as we read in the previous section, this conversion is not 100% efficient. As a result, heat energy is released. When contracting our muscles, potential energy is converted to kinetic energy and heat energy. Thus, more heat is produced when exercising than when at rest, and our body temperature increases.

Chapter 3

Learn to Predict

Consider first the important points made in the question itself. First, Carlos suffers from a genetic disease (diabetes insipidus) and, second, this disease results in excessive water loss at the kidneys. In this chapter, we learned that genes determine the structure of cellular proteins. But the question is, what type of protein? There are two possibilities. We also learned that cellular proteins have many functions, including membrane receptors and transport proteins. Mutations in the gene for either type can lead to disruption in water homeostasis. ADH is a hormone, or chemical signal, that regulates water loss from the kidneys. A mutation in the membrane receptor gene specific for ADH can, therefore, disrupt ADH regulation because the kidney cells cannot respond to ADH. On the other hand, aquaporins are membrane proteins that regulate osmosis or diffusion of water across the membrane. A mutation in an aquaporin gene can also lead to the disruption of water homeostasis.

1. Recall that a substance that binds to a protein receptor must be specific to the binding site. The drug is able to bind to the receptor as well, presumably, because it is structurally similar to the normal ligand. Similar to transport proteins, substances with similar structures compete for binding sites on the membrane. We can conclude that the lower dosage (250 mg) was not high enough to overwhelm the binding of the normal ligand. Increasing the dosage (750 mg) allowed the drug to outcompete and bind more often to the receptor, thereby blocking the normal activity.
3. If the membrane is freely permeable, there is no barrier to the movement of solutes or water. The solutes and water would each move down their concentration gradients. Because the solute concentration is higher in the tube, the solutes diffuse from the tube to the beaker until equal amounts of solutes exist inside the tube and beaker (i.e., equilibrium). In a similar fashion, water, which is at a higher concentration in the beaker compared with the tube, will diffuse into the tube until equal amounts of water are inside the tube and beaker. As a result of the diffusion of the water and solutes, the solution concentrations inside the tube and beaker will be the same because they both contain the same amounts of solutes and water.
5. a. We have learned that Na^+, as with other ions, must be transported across plasma membranes by transport proteins. We can therefore assume that aldosterone plays some role in stimulating Na^+ conservation at the kidneys through some type of membrane transport mechanism. We can also assume that because Na^+ is lost in the absence of aldosterone, the presence of aldosterone is involved in some type of active transport of Na^+, increasing the number of the ions that remain in the body as opposed to being lost as part of urine.
   b. Recall that osmosis, the diffusion of water, occurs when water moves from areas of low solute concentration to areas of higher solute concentration. Because the lack of aldosterone leads to an increase in the loss of Na^+ and water, we can conclude that water is diffusing to areas of higher Na^+ levels. As more water is lost in urine, blood volume will decrease. A decrease in blood volume leads to a decrease in blood pressure.
7. The first piece of relevant information is that viruses aren't cells. Antibiotics are drugs that attack features of cells. Bacteria are cells—independent, free-living organisms with their own, specific molecules and cellular mechanisms. Bacteria can synthesize their own proteins and reproduce on their own. Conversely, viruses occupy human cells and use human molecules for survival. In order to medically attack a virus, attack of human cells and human-specific molecules is often necessary. In general, antibiotics attack bacteria-specific molecules and processes.

Chapter 4

Learn to Predict

The question tells us that gluten enteropathy affects the intestinal lining, reducing its ability to absorb nutrients and water. It also reminds us that nutrient and water absorption occurs at the cellular level via several different transport processes.

Let us first identify the tissue type affected by gluten enteropathy. In chapter 4 we learned that epithelial tissue covers body surfaces, including the lining of the intestines. Further reading showed that the intestinal lining is composed of simple columnar epithelial tissue. Therefore, the tissue type affected by Matt's gluten enteropathy is simple columnar epithelium.

We are then asked to identify the specific cell parts affected by this disease. As stated in the question, the intestinal lining is organized into fingerlike projections called villi, which are covered by the simple columnar epithelium. Chapter 4 stated that the epithelial cells of this tissue have microvilli. In chapter 3, we learned that microvilli are extensions of the plasma membrane that increase the surface area for absorption. Matt's gluten enteropathy reduced his ability to absorb nutrients and water, so we can conclude that the cell parts affected by the disease are the microvilli.

Finally, the question asks us to explain why Matt suffers from bouts of diarrhea after eating gluten. We know that gluten damages the intestinal lining by decreasing the number of villi and microvilli. This reduces the surface area for absorption. If the surface area decreases, fewer nutrients are absorbed. Chapter 3 showed us that water moves by osmosis to areas of higher solute concentration. The nutrient molecules are solutes in the intestines. Because the solutes are not being absorbed, the solute concentration remains high in the intestines, and water absorption decreases. As a result, the nutrients and water accumulate in the intestines, resulting in the watery feces of diarrhea.

1. a. The question asks about the relationship between form and function of tissues. First, consider the name of the tissue type: nonkeratinized, stratified epithelium. The term *stratified* means more than one layer of cells, whereas the term *simple* means a single layer of cells. In

the digestive tract, a principal function is absorption, a process that would be hindered by the many layers of stratified epithelium. Stratified epithelium is more suited to areas where the layers would protect underlying tissues from abrasion. Cuboidal cells are specialized for secretion and absorption. These cells contain a large number of organelles that produce the secretions and transporters needed to support absorption.

b. In this scenario, both tissue types are stratified, but one type lacks keratin. The protein keratin provides a tough layer that retards water movement. If keratin were absent from the epidermis, the body could not retain water effectively and would be more prone to damage from abrasion.

c. In the mouth, because whole foods are sometimes very coarse, the tissue needs to be thick and tough like stratified squamous. If the mouth were lined with simple columnar, it would be severely damaged during chewing.

3. The question asks how the structure of a tissue's components contributes to its function. When the vertebrae flex, elastic ligaments attached to the vertebrae help them return to their normal, upright position. When a muscle contracts, the pull it exerts is transmitted along the length of its tendons. The tendons need to be very strong in that direction but not as strong in others. The collagen fibers, which are like microscopic ropes, are therefore all arranged in the same direction to maximize their strength. If tendons were elastic, muscle contraction tension would not move the bone effectively. Imagine trying to connect train cars end to end with rubber bands, rather than steel couplings. Movement of the train would be ineffective, as the engine would be able to move quite a distance before the next car would move, and so on.

5. First, consider the characteristics of hyaline cartilage that make it an effective tissue for ease of joint mobility. Hyaline cartilage provides a smooth surface, so that bones in joints can move easily. In contrast, dense irregular collagenous connective tissue is a fibrous meshwork that is noted for its strength and ability to withstand stretching—for example, in the dermis layer of the skin. When the smooth surface provided by hyaline cartilage is replaced by fibrous connective tissue, the smooth surface is replaced by a less smooth surface, and the movement of bones in joints is much more difficult. The increased friction helps increase the inflammation and pain that occur in the joints of people who have rheumatoid arthritis.

Chapter 5

Learn to Predict

To begin, we must identify the important information provided in the question. First, we are told that Laura is spending her summer at the pool, constantly exposed to the sun, and develops a "golden tan." Second, she returns to school in the fall, thus spending less time outside, and her tan fades.

We know that sun exposure leads to tanning of the skin, but to answer this question fully we must consider what specifically causes the skin to darken and why tanning is not permanent. We learned in this chapter that melanocytes in the epidermis produce melanin in response to sun exposure and package it in melanosomes. Keratinocytes phagocytize the tips of melanocyte processes containing the melanosomes, and the result is pigmented keratinocytes, and thus darker skin. We can therefore conclude that Laura's skin is darker due to increased sun exposure and increased melanin production during the summer.

We also learned in this chapter that the epidermis is a stratified squamous epithelium (described in chapter 4) composed of many layers of cells. Mitosis of cells in the deepest layer (stratum basale) of the epidermis produces new cells, which gradually undergo keratinization and eventually die. At the surface of the skin, keratinized (dead) keratinocytes are sloughed off and replaced by new ones daily.

So why did Laura's tan fade? It faded because the older, heavily pigmented keratinocytes were sloughed off each day and replaced with new cells. These new cells, produced *after* she returned to school, were less pigmented and her skin became a lighter color.

1. In the description of the epidermis, the superficial layer of the skin, we learned that the keratinized cells are coated with lipids to prevent fluid loss. Recall from chapter 3 that substances that are lipid-soluble easily diffuse through lipid layers, but water-soluble substances do not. By applying the same principles of diffusion across cell membranes to diffusion across the skin, we can predict that lipid-soluble substances diffuse easily, but water-soluble substances do not.

3. From the description of the injury, we know that the hammer struck Bob's nail bed. It is apparent that the hit was hard enough to rupture small blood vessels deep to the nail matrix. Blood accumulated between the nail and the nail bed, causing the dark area. In chapter 4 we learned that inflammation is the response that occurs when tissues are damaged, and a normal inflammatory event is edema, or swelling at the injury site. The accumulation of blood and edema increased the pressure deep to the nail body, which stimulated pain receptors. When a hole was drilled through the nail, the accumulated bloody fluid drained, reducing the pressure and, consequently, the pain. Because the nail matrix, which is proximal to the injury site, was not injured, the nail continued to grow over the next 2 months, until the injured area was pushed distally to the free edge of the nail.

5. We learned that one of the functions of the skin is to reduce water loss. Sam's burns resulted in severe damage to his skin, which most likely led to increased water loss at the injury site, causing dehydration and reduced urine production. We learned that Sam was administered large volumes of fluid to counteract his increased fluid loss. But how much fluid should be given? The amount of fluid given should match the amount that is lost, plus enough to keep the kidneys functioning properly. An adult receiving intravenous fluids should produce 30 to 50 mL of urine per hour, and children should produce 1 mL/kg of body weight per hour. By monitoring Sam's urine output, the nurse can determine if he is getting enough fluids. If his urine output is too low, more fluids can be given.

Chapter 6

Learn to Predict

After reading this chapter and its Systems Pathology, you learned that osteoporosis and Paget disease both result in overly weak bones due to unchecked bone reabsorption. Paget disease is different from osteoporosis in that bone turnover is greatly accelerated, resulting in bone being haphazardly constructed. Because osteoclasts are the primary affected cells in Paget disease, its principal manifestation is weakened bone. Some osteoporosis treatment medications are called bisphosphonates (see Systems Pathology). Bisphosphonates are osteoclast inhibitors. In Amir's case, his bones were becoming excessively demineralized and disproportionately composed of spongy bone. By inhibiting bone reabsorption, the excessive demineralization can be slowed, and bones remain able to support the mechanical stress of everyday movements.

1. First, let's consider the structure of cartilage. The book tells us that the perichondrium, which surrounds the cartilage, contains blood vessels, but the blood vessels do not enter the cartilage. The book also states that nutrients must diffuse through the matrix before reaching the chondrocytes. Logically, cells that aid in tissue repair would also enter cartilage more slowly than if blood vessels penetrated the cartilage. The question next asks whether the lack of perichondrium,

blood vessels, and nerves would be advantageous for articular cartilage. When considering the function of articular cartilage, the absence of such structures makes sense. Articular cartilage provides a smooth, low-friction surface for two bones to move past each other easily. If there were solid structures within the joint, the effect of smooth movement would be lost. Imagine trying to ice skate on a rink whose ice had garden hoses frozen just under and along the surface. We would spend more time trying to get back to our feet than skating.

3. This question requires knowledge of cartilage histology, bone formation, and bone histology. Recall that, to acquire O_2 and nutrients, cartilage relies on diffusion though the matrix. As osteoclasts migrate into the developing bone structure and start to remove the cartilage, the cartilage becomes calcified, no more diffusion is possible, and the chondrocytes die. However, when we examine bone histology, we see that adjacent osteocytes are connected via cell processes. As the matrix is laid down, the area where the cell processes meet does not become covered in ossified matrix, forming canaliculi. Therefore, osteocytes continue receiving oxygen and nutrients through the canaliculi or from one osteocyte to another through cell processes.
5. It is likely that Jill is still growing. Consequently, the epiphyseal plates in her long bones have not yet been converted to epiphyseal lines. If a break occurs in an epiphyseal plate, it can slow bone growth and interfere with bone elongation. As a result, the femur, and therefore her left leg, will be shorter than her right leg. Recovery is difficult because cartilage repairs slowly due to the fact that cartilage is much less vascular than bone.
7. The question tells us that Nellie's blood levels of estrogen are much higher than normal for a 12-year-old female. The text explained that important growth stimulators are reproductive hormones, which usually promote a burst of growth at puberty (approximately 12 years for females). Because Nellie's estrogen levels are higher than normal, she will most likely grow at a faster rate than she normally would have over the next 6 months. However, if the estrogen levels are not lowered back to normal, Nellie will probably be shorter at 18 than expected. Recall that, in addition to stimulating a burst of growth at puberty, estrogen causes a closure of the epiphyseal plate, and growth in bone length stops. Also, estrogen is more effective at this than testosterone, so Nellie may stop growing years before she would have with normal estrogen levels.
9. a. Henry's bone density is less than normal for a male his age. Less dense bone is more likely to break.
   b. Henry's eating habits have resulted in insufficient dietary intake of Ca^{2+} and vitamin D. Therefore, the absorption of Ca^{2+} from his intestine into his blood has been inadequate.
   c. We might expect Henry's blood Ca^{2+} to be low because of his diet. However, low blood Ca^{2+} levels stimulate increased PTH secretion. An increase in PTH maintains normal blood Ca^{2+} by increasing the number of osteoclasts, which break down bone and release Ca^{2+} into the blood. Thus, Henry's blood Ca^{2+} levels are maintained at the expense of his bones, which become less dense as more matrix than usual is broken down. Increased PTH levels also promote more Ca^{2+} reabsorption from the urine.
   d. Normally, exposure to sunlight activates a precursor molecule in the skin that eventually becomes activated vitamin D in the kidneys (see chapter 5). Henry produces few, if any, precursor molecules because of his nocturnal lifestyle. Therefore, Henry has low vitamin D levels and, so, has reduced absorption of Ca^{2+} from his small intestine.
   e. Exercise is a major source of mechanical stress on bones, which increases osteoblast activity. Because Henry does not exercise, his osteoblasts have not been as active as they might have otherwise been, which has allowed the osteoclasts to dissolve his bone to a greater degree than normal. The overactivity of the osteoclasts partially accounts for Henry's lower bone density.

Chapter 7

Learn to Predict

In this question we are asked to address four different topics: Two are identification of anatomy, and two relate to the function of the skeletal system. The description of the surgery provided useful information for addressing these topics.

The anatomy questions ask us to identify (1) the specific parts of the skeletal system and (2) the layers of bone tissue the surgeon cut. We are told exactly where the surgeon made the cut: a longitudinal midline incision through the sternum. We learned in this chapter that the sternum is composed of the manubrium, the body, and the xiphoid process. All three of these parts would have to be cut to allow the surgeon to spread the sternum halves apart to expose the heart. We learned in chapter 6 that a bone, such as the sternum, is surrounded by a periosteum and is composed of an outer layer of compact bone and internal spongy bone. Thus, the layers of bone tissue cut during the surgery were the periosteum, compact bone, and spongy bone.

Next we must explain why Dave experienced back discomfort following the surgery, and why he needed to wait two months before resuming his normal swimming routine. Chapter 6 explained that movements between bones occur at joints, and this chapter outlined the relationships among the sternum, the ribs, and the vertebrae. We can assume that, when the two halves of the sternum were spread apart, stress was applied to other structures of the thoracic cavity. Therefore, we can attribute Dave's discomfort in his back to stress on the joints between the ribs and the vertebrae when the two halves of the sternum were separated.

The last question we need to address is why Dave needed to wait two months before resuming his normal swimming routine. Chapter 6 stated that the skeletal system plays a major role in body movement, specifically as attachment sites for skeletal muscles. Movement occurs when muscles contract and pull on the bone. Just like the repair of a bone fracture, healing of the sternum requires time. Contraction of the muscles involved in swimming would apply undue stress to the sternum; therefore, Dave had to delay swimming until the sternum had healed properly.

1. After reading section 7.2, you probably realize that common structures, such as the "arm," the "hand," and the "nose," are actually a combination of multiple bones. Therefore, a "broken nose" could involve the nasal bones, the ethmoid bones, the vomer bone, the maxillae bones, or the inferior nasal conchae.
3. In this scenario, Dr. Smart is able to diagnose a broken clavicle without x-rays. To determine how this is possible, we first need to know the normal position of the arm and the clavicle's role in attaining this. The text explains that the clavicle's job is to hold the upper limb away from the body. In addition, if we look at figure 7.30, it shows that the clavicle supports the scapula anteriorly. Therefore, when Sarah arrived at the emergency room, Dr. Smart probably saw that her shoulder was more inferior and anterior than normal and that her arm was resting against the side of her body and not being held away from the body, as it normally is.
5. The top of ski boots is placed high up the leg to make the weakest point of the fibula less susceptible to great strain during a fall. Ski boots are also designed to reduce ankle mobility, which increases comfort and performance.
7. The question addresses the form and function of the femur, especially in older

people. Recall from chapter 6 that as people age, bone density declines because the reproductive hormones decline. We learned that estrogen in females and testosterone in males help bones grow and stay dense. However, because older females' estrogen levels tend to be lower than older males' testosterone levels, their bones are even more fragile than males'. Additionally, the femoral neck is commonly injured in older people because it is the smallest portion of the femur, which supports the weight of the body. It also forms an angle between the pelvis and the shaft of the femur, so the downward force of gravity on the body places enormous pressure on this part of the femur. That pressure is usually resisted in younger people with strong bones, but not as much in older adults.

Chapter 8

Learn to Predict

To answer this question, we first need to review the functions of the major knee ligaments that stabilize the knee joint: the cruciate and collateral ligaments. The anterior cruciate ligament (ACL) prevents extreme anterior movement of the tibia relative to the femur, which can occur from twisting the leg, such as when playing sports. The posterior cruciate ligament (PCL) prevents extreme posterior movement of the tibia relative to the femur, which can occur from a hard blow, such as in a car crash. The medial collateral ligament (MCL) prevents excessive abduction of the knee and can be damaged from a lateral blow to the knee, such as from a tackle in football. The lateral collateral ligament (LCL) prevents excessive adduction of the knee and can be damaged from a blow to the inside of the knee, such as from a tackle in soccer, but is less common than MCL injuries. Among these, the function of the ACL most closely fits the description of Andy's injury. The ACL and MCL are the most commonly injured ligaments in ski accidents. The ACL stabilizes the knee joint by stretching diagonally from the femur at the back of the joint to the tibia in the front, which normally prevents forward or anterior movement of the tibia from underneath the femur. It also resists medial rotation of the tibia. Thus, loss of the ACL increases mobility of the tibia in the anterior direction. This increased mobility can be detected using the anterior drawer test. In this test, the patient lies on his or her back with the hips flexed at a 45-degree angle, knees bent at a 90-degree angle, and feet flat on the examining table. A torn ACL yields increased mobility when the physician pulls the tibia forward (anterior direction) relative to the femur. Other physical tests can detect damage to the PCL, MCL, and LCL. In this case, the diagnosis of a torn ACL was confirmed by an MRI that revealed a complete tear of the ligament.

1. First, we must define a suture and its location. A suture is a seam between two skull bones. Second, we need to define a synostosis: an ossified joint, such that two bones have become one solid bone. Next, the question asks about the effect of skull bones fusing prematurely on a child's brain development. To address this, recall that, in a normal newborn, the sutures are more extensive than in an adult skull and are called fontanels (soft spots). The fontanels allow for expansion of the skull to accommodate brain growth. If a newborn's skull were completely solid, the brain's growth would be impeded, and developmental problems would arise in the child.
3. To begin, it is required to know what anatomical position is involved. Recall that, when a person is standing, the face is forward, the arms are to the sides, and the palms of the hands are facing forward. Next, it is necessary to know the different terms used to describe movements of limbs and body parts relative to others. Now, picture yourself in this anatomical position: Your right arm would move laterally out to the side (abduction) and then your hand would move closer to your head, bending at the elbow (flexion). Flexion at the shoulder and elbow also works.
5. This question requires you to apply your knowledge of the knee ligaments to a clinical situation involving two tests of ligament integrity (anterior and posterior drawer tests). For Ford, the normal anterior drawer test result indicates that the anterior cruciate ligament was not injured. However, the increased movement in the posterior direction indicates that his posterior cruciate ligament (PCL) was torn. The PCL connects the femur to the tibia at the back of the knee to limit the backward or posterior motion of the tibia. A PCL tear occurs most commonly when there is a strong direct blow to the front of the knee. The sudden force backward can tear the PCL, especially if the knee is flexed (bent) close to a 90-degree angle. Common incidents that cause PCL damage are car accidents when the knee hits the dashboard and contact sports such as when a football player is tackled from the front below the knee.

Chapter 9

Learn to Predict

We must address three issues: (1) Identify the bones involved when Bob is performing the exercise, (2) describe the joint movements involved, and (3) explain how Bob's muscles lift and lower the weight slowly. We know that Bob's movement engages the bones and muscles of the arm and forearm and that Bob is actively controlling the movement of the weight as he lifts the weight and lowers it.

Chapter 7 explained that the bones of the arm and forearm are the humerus, the radius, and the ulna. These are the bones involved in the exercise. In chapter 8 we learned that these bones articulate at the elbow. Chapter 8 also described the different types of joint movements, including flexion and extension. Flexion of his elbow causes Bob to lift the weight, and extension of his elbow allows him to lower it.

We learned in this chapter that muscle tension can vary depending on the number of motor units stimulated. Lifting the weight requires recruitment of motor units. As the number of stimulated motor units increases, the amount of tension produced by the muscle also increases until sufficient force is produced to lift the weight (multiple-motor-unit summation). The speed of the contraction depends on the rate of motor unit recruitment. Because the rate of recruitment is slow, Bob lifts the weight slowly. If the rate of motor unit recruitment were increased, Bob would lift the weight faster (wave summation). As Bob lowers the weight, the total tension in the arm is reduced as fewer motor units contract.

1. The first step to answering this question is to define the resting membrane potential and the distribution of ions across the cell membrane in a resting, electrically excitable cell. At rest, the concentration of K^+ is higher inside the cell than outside the cell. This means that a concentration gradient exists for K^+ from inside the plasma membrane to outside the plasma membrane. Therefore, if K^+ ion channels were opened, regardless of the stimulus that caused them to open, K^+ would diffuse out of the cell. Because K^+ is a positively charged ion and other, negatively charged particles, such as proteins, remain in the cell, the resting membrane potential would decrease or would become more negative.
3. To answer this question, we first need to understand what a motor unit is and how it works. In chapter 9 we learned that a motor unit is a motor neuron and all the muscle fibers it innervates. The pattern is that motor units with few muscle fibers perform more precise, delicate tasks (e.g., the motor units in our fingers), whereas motor units with a greater number of muscle fibers perform more gross movement tasks (e.g., the motor units in the gastrocnemius [calf] muscle). Therefore, upon recovery from poliomyelitis,

muscle control decreases when reinnervation of muscle fibers occurs because the number of motor units in the muscle is decreased. The greater the number of motor units in a muscle, the greater the potential for fine gradations of muscle contraction as motor units are recruited. A smaller number of motor units means that gradations of muscle contraction are not as fine.

5. As a weight is lifted, the muscle contractions are concentric contractions. When a weight lifter lifts a heavy weight above the head, most of the muscle groups contract with a force while the muscle is shortening. Concentric contractions are a category of isotonic contractions in which tension in the muscle increases or remains about the same while the muscle shortens. While the weight is held above the head, the contractions are isometric contractions because the length of the muscles does not change. While the weight is lowered, unless the weight lifter simply drops the weight, the length of the muscles increases as the weight is lowered for most of the muscle groups. Eccentric contractions are contractions in which tension is maintained in a muscle while the muscle increases in length. The major muscle groups are therefore contracting eccentrically while the weight is lowered. So Mary explained to the two students that they were each correct because the weight lifter used all three types of contractions.
7. The first step to answer this question is to define *glycogen* and its role in exercise in the nondisease state. Glycogen is the stored form of glucose. Free, immediately usable glucose is in limited supply, and the body quickly relies on glycogen for sustained exercise. Without the ability to break down glycogen to glucose molecules, muscle depends on the uptake of glucose from outside the cells (e.g., from the blood) or from the metabolism of fatty acids. Consequently, a person's ability to carry out vigorous exercise, including anaerobic exercise, is reduced. Fatigue and lower exercise tolerance are characteristic of the condition, but exercise can be maintained at a slow pace.
9. To answer this question, the first step is to refer to figure 9.26. We learned that a ligand is a chemical that, upon binding to its receptor, will stimulate a response. In figure 9.26, a smooth muscle cell is depicted, which shows that the ligand receptors are G protein–linked receptors. Binding of the ligand results in the opening of Ca^{2+} channels. Calcium ions diffuse into the cell and bind to calmodulin, which activates the enzyme myosin kinase to phosphorylate myosin heads and start the cross-bridge cycle. As long as intracellular Ca^{2+} levels are elevated, the cross-bridge cycle will take place. Because the cross-bridges release slowly, the contraction is sustained: Once a myosin head has been phosphorylated, it can form cross-bridges, move the actin, detach, and re-form cross-bridges again and again without breaking down new ATP molecules for each cycle.

Chapter 10

Learn to Predict

The description of Pedro's injury provided specific information about the regions of the body affected: the left hip and thigh. These facts will help us determine Pedro's symptoms and predict the movements that may be affected by his injury.

We read in this chapter that the muscles affected by Pedro's injury (psoas major, iliacus, pectineus, sartorius, vastus lateralis, vastus medius, vastus intermedius, and rectus femoris) are involved in flexing the hip, the knee, or both. Therefore, we can conclude that movements involving hip and knee flexion, such as walking up and down stairs, would be affected. Any tasks that require Pedro to walk up and down stairs would be more difficult for him. Sitting and standing may also be affected, but the weakness in Pedro's left hip and thigh may be compensated for by increased muscle strength on his right side.

1. The question is asking about which muscles of the tongue allow people to "stick their tongue out," or protrude it. Refer to table 10.6, where the actions of tongue muscles are described. There, we find it is the extrinsic muscle genioglossus that works to protrude the tongue. Further, the question tells us that Rachel's left mandible was broken and nerves were damaged. Recall from chapter 9 that skeletal muscles require a nerve impulse in order to contract. Therefore, we can conclude that the left genioglossus is unable to contract and the right is able to contract. So, when Rachel protrudes her tongue, it will only go to the left because it is only getting pushed out on the right side.
3. The first step is to remember what we learned in chapter 8: The definition of abduction is movement away from the body's midline. Next, it is necessary to know the location of the supraspinatus muscle to answer the question. The supraspinatus rests in the supraspinous fossa of the scapula. Then refer to table 10.15, where the function of the supraspinatus is summarized. Also recall that the supraspinatus is a member of the rotator cuff muscles. In extreme abduction, the supraspinatus would be compressed against the acromion process of the scapula.

Chapter 11

Learn to Predict

Multiple sclerosis (MS) results from the destruction of myelin sheaths around axons of CNS neurons. Although the exact mechanisms causing MS are still under scrutiny, MS is characterized as an immune-mediated disease, with the majority of MS specialists considering it to be an auto-immune disorder. Specific immune cells have been demonstrated to attack and destroy oligodendrocytes in the CNS. This is associated with a response by astrocytes called astrogliosis in which the blood-brain barrier is weakened, allowing further entry of the immune cells into the CNS. As a result of MS, Amanda is experiencing muscle weakness in her legs and left hand. In chapter 9 we learned that skeletal muscle contractions are stimulated by the nervous system and that the amount of muscle tension produced is determined by the frequency of the stimulation. This chapter explained that myelin sheaths increase the rate of action potential conduction in neurons and therefore increase the frequency of muscle stimulation. We can then conclude that the destruction of the myelin sheaths reduced the ability of Amanda's brain and spinal cord to communicate with the motor neurons supplying her leg and hand muscles. Because the brain and spinal cord neurons were conducting action potentials more slowly due to a reduction in saltatory conduction, the motor neurons were not being stimulated as quickly as normal. Therefore, Amanda's muscles could not produce as much tension as they could before the damage to the brain and spinal cord neurons occurred. Amanda's difficulty with climbing the steps suggests that the damaged spinal cord neurons include those that stimulate neurons that innervate muscles of her hip, thigh, and leg.

As the degeneration of myelin sheaths continues, Amanda is likely to experience increasing muscle weakness. Some muscle groups may become so weak that they cannot support Amanda's weight. She may have to use crutches, a cane, or eventually a wheelchair. Other muscle groups, including those involved in swallowing and breathing, will probably be compromised. In addition to motor functions, if Amanda's sensory neurons in her brain and spinal cord are affected, she may experience numbness, pain, and vision problems.

1. First, consider the basic function of the axon. At this point in the reading, we know that axons are a cellular projection from the neuron, sometimes called nerve fibers. We also know that the cell body is the site of protein synthesis for the entire cell. Therefore, if the distal portion of an axon is severed from the rest of the cell, it will die. There is no way for the distal axon to replenish

the enzymes and other proteins essential for survival. On the other hand, any remaining portion of axon still attached to the cell body survives and, in many cases, grows to replace the severed portion.

3. The first step to answer this question is to define the basis for the resting membrane potential. Recall that the inside of the plasma membrane is more negative than the outside of the plasma membrane due to a higher concentration of negatively charged proteins inside the cell. The K^+ is also in higher concentration inside the cell and tends to "offset" the negative charge of the proteins. However, the K^+ leak channels allow K^+ to diffuse out of the cell, down the concentration gradient. Removal of K^+ removes positive charge inside the cell, and the membrane potential becomes more negative. Therefore, because tissue A has more K^+ leak channels, more K^+ can leak out of tissue A cells than in tissue B cells, and the inside of tissue A cells becomes more negative. The resting membrane potential is larger for tissue A than for tissue B; it is further from threshold.
5. To answer this question, let us first describe the Na^+ concentration and its role in a normal excitable cell. We learned that, in a normal cell, the concentration of Na^+ is much higher outside the cell than inside the cell. As a result, when Na^+ channels open, Na^+ diffuses into the cell quickly, causing the changes in the membrane potential that result in an action potential. The movement of Na^+ into the cell is the result of its steep concentration gradient. Remember, also, that enough Na^+ must enter a cell for the membrane potential to reach threshold, opening the voltage-regulated Na^+ channels and causing an action potential. If the extracellular concentration of Na^+ were reduced, then the concentration gradient would also be reduced. The effect would be that, if the cell were stimulated, less Na^+ would enter the cell. The cell would not reach threshold, and an action potential would not occur.
7. First, what is the absolute refractory period? Recall that it is the time during which a neuron cannot fire an action potential no matter how strong the stimulus. This is due to all the voltage-gated Na^+ channels already being open. Thus, if the axon is nonresponsive for 1 ms, action potentials can be generated no faster than every millisecond. Because there are 1000 ms in 1 second, the maximal frequency is 1000 action potentials/second.
9. The key piece of information in the question is the fact that neuron B releases both a neurotransmitter and a neuromodulator, which is excitatory (produces EPSPs). EPSPs depolarize neuron C and bring it closer to threshold than it is when stimulated by only neuron A. Neuron C does not require as much time for temporal summation to reach threshold to fire an action potential when stimulated by neuron B vs. neuron A. Therefore, neuron C fires more action potentials with stimulation by neuron B alone than with temporal summation of neuron A alone. In other words, the neurotransmitter from neuron B is more effective when released with the neuromodulator from neuron B than it is when released alone from neuron A.

Chapter 12

Learn to Predict

Javier reacted to the pain of stepping on the toy cars not once but twice. We know that each time he stepped on a toy he switched the leg that supported his weight, first from the right to the left and then from the left to the right. This chapter described the withdrawal reflex that moves a limb away from a painful stimulus. Javier demonstrated this reflex when he stepped on the toys.

Javier displayed the withdrawal reflex and the crossed extensor reflex. Both of these reflexes are polysynaptic spinal reflexes, involving sensory neurons, interneurons, and motor neurons. Chapter 11 explained the functions of each of these neuron types. The sensory neurons delivered the painful stimulus to the central nervous system; the interneurons relayed the information between sensory and motor neurons; and the motor neurons regulated skeletal muscle activity. When Javier stepped on the toy car with his right foot, he transferred nearly all of his weight to his right leg before the withdrawal reflex was activated. The painful stimulus of stepping on the toy car activated the withdrawal reflex, causing Javier to pick up his right leg. At the same time, Javier extended his left leg because of the crossed extensor reflex. However, as Javier extended his left leg, he stepped on another toy car, activating the withdrawal reflex in his left leg and the crossed extensor reflex in his right leg. The repeated sequence of withdrawing one leg and stepping down on the other foot prevented Javier from falling down.

1. In chapter 11, we learned that a ganglion is a cluster of neuron cell bodies. Similarly, in this chapter we learned that the dorsal root ganglia are clusters of sensory cell bodies and the dorsal roots are bundles of sensory axons. The ganglia are larger in diameter than the roots because of the size difference between the cell bodies and axons. To answer the second question, refer to figure 12.4 to see the direction of action potential propagation in sensory axons and motor axons. Sensory axons carry action potentials from peripheral tissues to the central nervous system (CNS), which includes the brain and spinal cord. Motor axons carry action potentials from the CNS to peripheral tissues. Now, identify the types of axons in each structure listed. Recall that spinal nerves have both sensory and motor axons, so action potentials are propagated both to the spinal cord and away from the spinal cord. Dorsal roots contain only sensory axons, so action potentials are conducted to the spinal cord only. Finally, ventral roots contain only motor axons, so action potentials are conducted away from the spinal cord.
3. Recall that the phrenic nerve innervates the diaphragm, allowing for the contraction necessary for breathing. If the right phrenic nerve were damaged, then we would expect lack of muscle contraction in the right half of the diaphragm, affecting breathing. To answer the second part of the question, we need to consider the location of spinal cord injury to predict the effect it would have on the diaphragm. Remember that the phrenic nerve is part of the cervical plexus, which includes spinal nerves C1–C4. If the spinal cord were severed at the level of C2, the phrenic nerve would be damaged, and the contractions of the diaphragm would not occur, eliminating the person's ability to breathe. Death would likely occur if medical assistance were not administered quickly. On the other hand, if the spinal cord were completely severed at the level of C6, the phrenic nerve would not be damaged, and the diaphragm would not be affected.
5. Figure 12.26 indicates that the femoral nerve innervates several muscles involved in hip flexion and knee extension, both activities that were difficult for Carl. This indicates that the femoral nerve is involved. The sources of nerve fibers in the femoral nerve are L2, L3, and L4; therefore, the intervertebral disk involved compresses L2, L3, or L4 on the left side of the vertebral column. Recall that figure 12.15 includes a dermatomal map. We can see from the map that L3 innervates the dermatome of the medial thigh and is the most likely spinal nerve involved. Carl's motor movements were affected because the reduced control of action potentials from the femoral nerve to the muscles of the thigh caused muscle weakness. The referred pain results from compression of the spinal nerve that innervates the medial thigh and the knee. The compression stimulates action potentials in the nerves, and the pain is referred to the site of the sensory receptors for that nerve.

Chapter 13

Learn to Predict

In addition to Marvin's broken jaw, the question suggested that he experienced damage to a cranial nerve, specifically the one associated with controlling the muscles of the tongue. Chapter 11 explained that somatic motor neurons innervate skeletal muscle, so the cranial nerve associated with motor control of the tongue is the affected nerve. Tables 13.4 and 13.5 summarize the functional organization of the cranial nerves. By reviewing these tables, we find that the hypoglossal nerve (XII) innervates intrinsic and extrinsic tongue muscles; therefore, this cranial nerve was damaged during Marvin's accident. More specifically, the damage was on the right side and caused paralysis of the tongue muscles on the right side. Thus, only the left side of the tongue can stick out. The hypoglossal nerve also innervates some throat muscles, such as the thyrohyoid and the geniohyoid muscles, which may also be affected.

1. We learned in this chapter that reflexes that maintain blood pressure are integrated by the medulla oblongata. In response to blood loss, the reflexes increase the heart rate. Similarly, the reflexes cause the constriction of blood vessels in the skin and viscera to increase blood volume and therefore blood pressure. The lack of blood flow through the skin results in pallor. Recall that respiratory reflexes are integrated in the medulla oblongata and the pons.
3. To answer this question, let us first review the functions of the oculomotor, trochlear, and abducens nerves, listed in table 13.5. Besides innervating the levator palpebrae superioris muscle, the oculomotor nerve innervates the four eye muscles that move the eyeball so that the gaze is directed superiorly, inferiorly, medially, or superolaterally. If the patient can move the eyes in these directions, the oculomotor nerve is not damaged. Similarly, the abducens nerve directs the gaze laterally, and the trochlear nerve directs the gaze inferolaterally. If the patient can move the eyes in these directions, the associated nerves are intact.

Chapter 14

Learn to Predict

The students touched a hot (55°C) object with one hand and a cold (5°C) object with the other hand. We learned in this chapter that thermoreceptors allow us to distinguish between hot and cold stimuli. In section 14.1 we read that cold receptors respond to temperatures between 12°C and 35°C, whereas warm receptors respond to temperatures between 25°C and 47°C. However, temperatures both below 12°C and above 47°C stimulate pain receptors. Therefore, the students would most likely not be able to distinguish between the cold and hot objects. They would just feel pain.

The second part of the question asked us to identify the part of the CNS involved in making this distinction. In chapter 12 we learned that sensory neurons carry information from receptors in the skin to the spinal cord, which is then conveyed to the brain. This chapter explained more specifically that the sensations of pain and temperature are carried through the spinothalamic system to the thalamus, then to the primary sensory cortex. Chapter 13 taught us that the primary sensory cortex is located in the postcentral gyrus of the cerebrum. Stimulation of neurons in specific areas of the primary sensory cortex allows a person to perceive a particular sensation and locate the site of stimulation. The ability to recognize the stimulus also involves association areas of the cerebrum near the primary sensory cortex.

1. First, let us review the sensory information carried by the spinothalamic tract. From table 14.3 we can see that these include pain, temperature, light touch, pressure, tickle, and itch. Next, we can also see from table 14.3 and figure 14.5*b* that crossover of axons of the spinothalamic tract occurs in the spinal cord. From this we can conclude that a lesion on one side of the spinal cord that interrupts the spinothalamic tract would eliminate the specific sensations carried by that tract below the level of the lesion, but on the opposite side of the body. Not all sensations associated with the spinothalamic tract will be eliminated. Pain and temperature sensation from the opposite side of the body below the lesion would be eliminated. There would be few, if any, clinical changes in detecting light touch because other tracts still carry this information.
3. Before answering this question, consider the activities carried out by the two sets of limbs. We use the lower limbs primarily for standing and walking, both of which are activities on which we do not focus our attention. We use our upper limbs for all kinds of activities, including writing, texting on our cell phones, or even playing video games. These activities require much more conscious effort compared with the activities of the lower limbs.
5. Recall that stimulating the reticular activating system (RAS) promotes consciousness. Also, remember that acoustic stimuli, such as a dripping faucet, stimulate the RAS. Luke could not sleep because his RAS was stimulated, promoting consciousness and preventing sleep.
7. The vagus nerve supplies the muscles of the larynx that aid in voice production; therefore, minor injury to this nerve in the neck can lead to hoarseness or changes in the voice. In our reading of "Motor Output and Reflexes Projecting Through the Brainstem," we also learned that the vagus nerve controls muscles of the pharynx, larynx, and soft palate associated with swallowing and speech. Damage to the vagus nerve could therefore affect these two activities.
9. The first clue to answering this is to understand that these microbial metabolites are chemicals in the same way that the body's signal molecules are also chemicals. Therefore, as you learned in chapter 11, neurotransmitters are chemical signals, produced by neurons that bind to receptors on their targets. Once the neurotransmitters have bound to the receptor, many different types of cell processes can be initiated. In addition, you learned in chapter 3 that other chemical signals also bind to receptors in the cell membrane. In the same way, if gut bacterial metabolites function in our body as chemical signals, upon arriving at their target, these bacterial metabolites could also bind to receptors in neuron cell membranes and stimulate cellular mechanisms to begin. Recall that lipid-soluble molecules can easily cross plasma membranes, and because the short-chain fatty acids are lipid-based, they also easily cross the blood-brain barrier (see chapter 13). You will learn in the next chapter that our senses of smell and taste function in a similar fashion. Chemicals from the air or our food bind to receptors in neuron cell membranes in our nose and our taste buds. Thus, it is not out of the realm of possibilities that our body could utilize bacterial chemicals to regulate internal processes. In fact, this is a hallmark of a symbiotic relationship, such as what we have with our gut microbiota.

Chapter 15

Learn to Predict

We learn that Freddy's surgery replaced two of the three auditory ossicles. Recall that the auditory ossicles distribute sound waves from the tympanic membrane to the oval window of the inner ear, where the sound waves can then stimulate hair cells of the cochlear duct. If Freddy's auditory ossicles were not functional, we can predict that his loss of hearing was conductive hearing loss due to the absence of functional auditory ossicles. To address the question of sound location, recall that the brain can determine the direction from which a sound is coming because of the time interval between when the sound reaches one ear and the time it reaches the other. Because Freddy had complete hearing loss in one ear, his ability to determine the direction from which a sound came was probably diminished. Finally, by replacing the damaged auditory ossicles, Freddy's hearing was restored because sound waves can now be conducted from Freddy's tympanic membrane to his oval window.

1. Ernie's sensory neuropathy is the loss of taste sensation in the posterior one-third of the right half of his tongue. In reviewing "Neuronal Pathways for Taste" we learn that the glossopharyngeal nerves carry taste sensations from the posterior one-third of the tongue. Considering that only the right side of Ernie's tongue is affected, we can conclude that it is the right glossopharyngeal nerve that is damaged.
3. In this question, Max and his grandfather were looking at an object that was far away (the glacier) and an object that was close (the piece of ice). To answer this question, we need to consider three important factors for each scenario: accommodation, pupil constriction, and convergence. While Max and his grandfather were looking at the distant glacier, the ciliary muscles of their eyes were relaxed, and the suspensory ligaments of their ciliary bodies maintained elastic pressure on the lenses of the eyes, keeping the lenses relatively flat and allowing for distant vision. When they looked at the piece of ice that was close to them, accommodation occurred. The ciliary muscles contracted, pulling the choroids toward the lenses and reducing the tension on the suspensory ligaments. This allowed the lenses to assume a more spherical form because of their own elastic nature. More spherical lenses have more convex surfaces, causing greater refraction of light. Also, pupil constriction occurred when they were looking at the piece of ice. As the pupils constrict during close vision, the depth of focus is greater, and more light is required on the observed object. Convergence also occurs during close vision. As an object moves closer to the eye, the eyes must rotate medially so that the object is kept in focus on corresponding areas of each retina; otherwise, the object becomes blurry. The reason Max's grandfather had to reach for his glasses to view the piece of ice is because he suffers from presbyopia, which occurs because the lenses become sclerotic and less flexible as people age. Presbyopia is corrected by wearing reading glasses for close work and removing them when the person wants to see at a distance. Either bifocals or progressive lenses can also be used if a person also has myopia, or problems seeing distant objects clearly.
5. Before answering this question, let us review figure 15.24 to see the normal visual fields. We can see that each visual field is divided into temporal and nasal portions. The visual pathway is then color-coded to correlate with each portion for the right and left side. In the case of lesion *A*, we can see that the temporal part of the left visual field (light green) and the nasal part of the right visual field (dark blue) are affected. The black areas correlate with the same areas in the visual field. Using the same strategy, we can see that lesion *B* would affect both the temporal part (light blue) and the nasal part (dark blue) of the right visual field, so the entire right visual field would be affected, and an oval representing it would be black. The left visual field would be normal, with the temporal (light green) and nasal (dark green) parts indicated. Following is an illustration of the right and left visual fields.

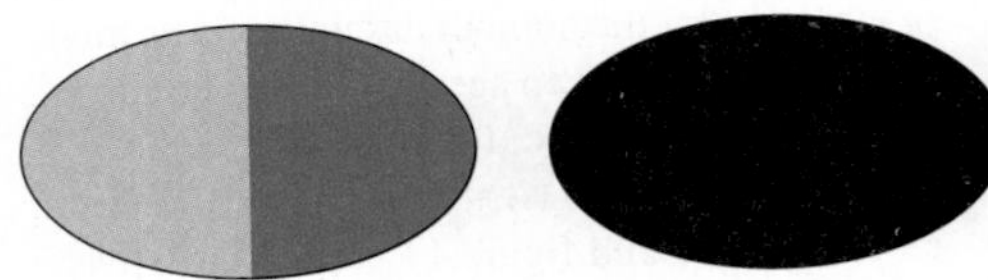

7. Recall that the sound wave amplitude determines the volume of a sound, whereas wave frequency determines the pitch of the sound. Loud sounds have sound waves with greater amplitude. This greater amplitude causes the basilar membrane to vibrate more violently over a wider range. The spreading of the wave in the basilar membrane to some extent counteracts the reflex from the superior olivary nucleus that is responsible for enabling a person to hear subtle tone differences.

Chapter 16

Learn to Predict

Describing the neural pathways involved in Officer Smith's muscular movements, increased heart rate, and changes in digestive functions requires an understanding of the somatic motor pathways described in chapter 14, the visual pathway described in chapter 15, and the autonomic pathways described in this chapter. The changes in Officer Smith's activity were initiated when she saw the speeding car. Action potentials were conducted from her eyes via the optic nerve (cranial nerve II) to the occipital lobe of the cerebral cortex, where conscious awareness of the situation occurred. The changes in her muscle movements occurred when action potentials were then conducted to the frontal lobe of the cerebrum, where voluntary motor activity is controlled. Action potentials initiated in the motor area of the frontal lobe traveled through descending pathways of the spinal cord. Somatic motor neurons carried action potentials from the spinal cord to the involved skeletal muscles, allowing the movements necessary for Officer Smith to drive her car.

In addition, action potentials also traveled from the cerebral cortex to the limbic system, including the hypothalamus, and from the hypothalamus to motor pathways of the autonomic nervous system. In the autonomic nervous system, action potentials were conducted to the sympathetic chain ganglia. Sympathetic neurons that regulate heart rate carried the action potentials to the heart, causing Officer Smith's heart rate to increase. Sympathetic neurons that regulate digestive function passed through the sympathetic chain ganglia to activate the splanchnic nerves and synapsed in the collateral ganglia. These neurons then conducted the action potentials to the digestive tract, where they decreased the activity of enteric neurons and decreased digestive secretion and motility.

1. This question is referring to the different types of cholinergic receptors: nicotinic receptors and muscarinic receptors. Remember that, even though these are cholinergic receptors to which acetylcholine normally binds, they were classified based on laboratory findings that nicotine binds to one type of cholinergic receptor and muscarine binds to the other type of cholinergic receptor. Also recall that all preganglionic neurons of the sympathetic and parasympathetic divisions and all postganglionic neurons of the parasympathetic division release acetylcholine. Also, the postganglionic neurons of the sympathetic division that innervate sweat glands also release acetylcholine. Figure 16.7 allows us to determine which of these synapses would be affected by nicotine and which of these synapses would be affected by muscarine. Nicotinic receptors are located within the autonomic ganglia in the membranes of postganglionic neurons of both the sympathetic and parasympathetic divisions. Consumption of nicotine would result in stimulation of the postganglionic neurons, and consequently, the stimulation of the effectors of both the sympathetic and parasympathetic divisions. Again, figure 16.7 illustrates that muscarinic receptors are located on the effectors of the parasympathetic division. After the consumption of muscarine, only the effectors that respond to acetylcholine would be affected. This includes all the effectors innervated by the parasympathetic division and the sweat glands, which are innervated by the sympathetic division.

3. a. Dilation of the pupil is caused by the contraction of the dilator pupillae, which are the radial muscles of the iris.
   b. Recall from the discussion of the iris that the sympathetic division innervates and therefore controls the radial muscles (dilator pupillae). The parasympathetic division innervates and therefore controls the circular muscles (sphincter pupillae).
   c. A drug that mimics sympathetic stimulation, such as an adrenergic drug, could activate α_1 receptor on the radial muscles of the iris and cause Sally's pupils to dilate. On the other hand, a drug that blocks parasympathetic stimulation, such as a muscarinic blocking agent, would prevent constriction of the pupil and therefore cause dilation.
   d. Remember from chapter 15 that the ciliary muscles constrict, changing the shape of the lenses when viewing close objects. Blurred vision indicates the eyedrops are inhibiting ciliary muscle contraction. From table 16.3 we can see that ciliary muscle contraction is a parasympathetic effect, so we would predict that the eyedrops contain a muscarinic blocking agent, one that would affect parasympathetic effectors.
   e. Notice that this scenario is essentially the opposite of that described in part c. Based on our answer for part c, we would expect that an adrenergic blocking agent that binds to α_1 receptors and prevents sympathetic stimulation would cause the pupils to constrict. Similarly, a muscarinic agent could stimulate the circular muscles of the iris, causing the pupils to constrict.
   f. Recall that sympathetic stimulation of blood vessels normally keeps them in a state of partial contraction. An adrenergic blocking agent that inhibits sympathetic stimulation allows the blood vessels in the conjunctiva of the eye to dilate, causing the appearance of blood-shot eyes.
5. Recall that the primary function of the autonomic nervous system is to maintain homeostasis. In both of the scenarios, Sarah's blood pressure changes. In chapter 1 we learned that most homeostasis control mechanisms are negative-feedback mechanisms that reverse the change. Also, notice that both questions address sympathetic reflexes controlling blood vessels. Remember that blood vessels are only innervated by the sympathetic nervous system. When Sarah does a headstand, blood drains toward her head, and the blood pressure in the arteries of her chest and head increases. Sensory receptors detect the increase in blood pressure, so the frequency of action potentials in sensory neurons increases. The brain, in turn, activates sympathetic stimulation of the blood vessels, which causes them to dilate. Consequently, the blood pressure in the arteries of the neck and head does not increase dramatically. When Sarah stands quickly after crouching for a short time, blood tends to drain away from her head, and the blood pressure in the arteries of her chest and head decreases. Sensory receptors detect the decrease in blood pressure, so the frequency of action potentials in sensory neurons decreases. The brain, in turn, activates sympathetic reflexes that cause blood vessels to constrict. Consequently, the blood pressure in her neck and head does not fall dramatically.

Chapter 17

Learn to Predict

After using anabolic steroids, Liu Dan's muscles increased in size, but he also experienced some unintended changes, including slight breast development, reduced testes size, and mood swings. We learned in this chapter that steroid hormones are all derived from cholesterol, a type of lipid, and are thus lipid-soluble. We also know that hormones, chemical messengers produced by the endocrine system, travel through the body via the bloodstream until they arrive at their target tissues. The cells of target tissues possess specific receptors that the hormones bind to and initiate changes in cellular metabolism or cell growth. Steroid hormones, because they are lipid-soluble, bind to intracellular receptors in the cell's cytoplasm or nucleus. Once the steroid hormone has bound to its receptor, the hormone-receptor complex stimulates increased gene expression and therefore increased protein production. In muscle cells, this leads to the increased muscle mass that Liu Dan experienced.

However, other tissues of the body contain receptors that can also bind the anabolic steroids, so using anabolic steroids can cause some unintended effects. The anabolic steroids Liu Dan used also led to the abnormal breast tissue growth, decreased testes size, and behavioral changes. Thus, although it may be tempting to take anabolic steroids to increase muscle mass, the risk for side effects is simply too great.

1. The question gives us two very important pieces of information: (1) Estrogen stimulates an increase in progesterone receptor number in the uterus and (2) progesterone action (binding to its receptors) is required for pregnancy. Thus, if too little estrogen is secreted, the up-regulation of receptors in the uterus for progesterone cannot occur. As a result, progesterone cannot prepare the uterus for the embryo to attach to its wall following ovulation, and pregnancy cannot occur. Because of the lack of up-regulation of progesterone receptors, the uterus cannot respond adequately to progesterone. If fewer-than-normal progesterone receptors are present, then a much larger-than-normal amount of progesterone is needed to produce its normal response.
3. Sarah's doctor explained to her that she is most likely experiencing insulin resistance. In order for a glucose transporter to allow glucose entry into a cell, the glucose transporter must be inserted into the cell's plasma membrane. Normal insulin action is to induce phosphorylation of intracellular regulatory proteins that control this insertion. Most instances of insulin resistance are due to the failure of the glucose transporter to be properly inserted into the plasma membrane, which has been linked to an impairment in the ability of the receptor to properly phosphorylate the intracellular regulatory proteins. Thus, Sarah's cells cannot receive adequate glucose because many of the glucose transporters never reach the plasma membrane of insulin target cells.

Chapter 18

Learn to Predict

We learn that Katie has androgen insensitivity syndrome. The name suggests that her tissues are not sensitive to androgens (male-like hormones). We learned that a tissue responds to hormones on the presence of specific receptors. With androgen insensitivity syndrome, the endocrine malfunction is not the production of the hormone, as in insulin-dependent (type I) diabetes mellitus, but the presence of the receptor in the target cells. Even though her cells produce plenty of the hormone testosterone, the target cells do not respond because the testosterone receptor has malfunctioned and does not recognize testosterone. Katie's feminine appearance is a direct result of the lack of a normal male body because her tissues were resistant to testosterone, which is responsible for growth of the male genitalia and other sex characteristics (see table 18.12 and chapter 29). Therefore, externally Katie looked female when she was born. Without testosterone working in her body or her brain and without normal social cues to associate with other males, she had always identified herself as female and was devastated to learn she could not have children. Her doctor and mother decided to wait until she was older before telling her the complete reason.

1. Secretions from the posterior pituitary are sometimes called neurohormones because the posterior pituitary is continuous with the brain and an extension of the nervous system. The neurons that secrete these hormones have their cell bodies in the hypothalamus of the brain, and their axons extend into the posterior pituitary. If the posterior pituitary is removed, the distal ends of the axons of the neurons that have their cell bodies in the hypothalamus are removed. The neurons survive, and after a few days, the proximal ends of the axons become capable of secreting the neuropeptides that the neurons normally secrete. Cells located entirely within the gland secrete the hormones of the anterior pituitary. They are released in response to neurohormones that travel through the hypothalamo-hypophysial portal system from the hypothalamus to the anterior pituitary. Removal of the anterior pituitary removes the cells that synthesize and secrete anterior pituitary hormones. Consequently, there is a permanent decrease in anterior pituitary hormones.
3. Recall that growth hormone (GH) targets cartilage in the epiphyseal plate of long bones and stimulates cell division of the chondrocytes. Administering GH to young people before the growth of their long bones is complete causes their long bones to grow. While Zach's son is actively growing, GH administration would cause him to grow taller. To accomplish this, GH has to be administered over a considerable length of time. However, there could also be unwanted changes consistent with acromegaly (oversecretion of GH). Other side effects, such as abnormal joint formation and diabetes mellitus, are also possible. In addition to undesirable changes in the skeleton, nerves frequently are compressed as a result of the proliferation of connective tissue. Because GH spares glucose usage, chronic hyperglycemia results, frequently leading to diabetes mellitus and severe atherosclerosis. Thus, Zach's doctor would not prescribe GH.
5. a. The major clue we are given is that Josie has low thyroid hormone levels, yet her TSH levels (the hormone that stimulates thyroid hormone release) are very high. Normally, thyroid hormone would provide negative feedback at the anterior pituitary to inhibit TSH secretion once thyroid hormone levels had reached their set point. But because Josie's thyroid is unable to produce thyroid hormone, there has been a loss of negative feedback, and TSH never receives the signal to shut off, so the TSH levels rise above normal.
   b. Usually, tumors create more cells than normal that contribute to the higher hormone levels. Therefore, if Josie had more thyroid hormone–secreting cells than normal, as with cancer, her thyroid hormone levels would be much higher than normal, not lower than normal as the tests indicated.
   c. The thyroid gland requires iodine to produce thyroid hormones because iodine is an integral part of the hormone molecule. Thus, lack of iodine prevented the synthesis of thyroid hormones and the lack of negative feedback on the anterior pituitary gland. Thus, TSH levels increased, overstimulated the thyroid gland, and caused it to grow larger than normal.
   d. By providing the thyroid gland with iodine, it was able to resume normal production of thyroid hormone. Once thyroid hormone levels reached their set point, they would provide negative feedback at the anterior pituitary to inhibit TSH release, and its levels would return to normal.
   e. Josie will probably need to continue taking thyroid hormone supplements for some time. After a large portion of the thyroid gland was destroyed by 131I, its ability to secrete T3 and T4 would fall below their normal range of values unless Josie took supplemental thyroid hormone. Theoretically, her doctor could slowly reduce her supplement, which could cause her thyroid to grow to compensate for the reduced intake levels.
7. To answer this question, you must first realize that, because cortisone mimics the normal adrenal cortex hormone cortisol, it will also act by negative feedback at the anterior pituitary. Cortisone inhibits ACTH secretion from the anterior pituitary. Second, it is important to understand that ACTH is required to prevent atrophy of the adrenal cortex. In the absence of ACTH, the adrenal cortex shrinks and may never recover to produce its normal secretions, even if ACTH secretion increases again.
9. Recall from chapter 16 that the parasympathetic nervous system is the "rest-and-digest" portion of the autonomic nervous system. Therefore, an increase in insulin secretion in response to parasympathetic stimulation and gastrointestinal hormones is consistent with the maintenance of homeostasis because parasympathetic stimulation and increased gastrointestinal hormones result from conditions such as eating a meal. Insulin levels therefore increase just before large amounts of glucose and amino acids enter the blood. The elevated insulin levels prevent a large increase in blood glucose and the loss of glucose in the urine.
11. Recall from chapter 16 that the sympathetic nervous system is activated during intense exercise and inhibits insulin secretion. Blood glucose levels are not high because skeletal muscle tissue continues to take up some glucose and metabolize it. In chapter 9, we learned that skeletal muscles store glucose as glycogen, and muscle contraction depends on glucose and fatty acid metabolism. During a long run, muscle glycogen levels are depleted as the cells metabolize more and more glucose. The "kick" at the end of a race results from increased energy produced by anaerobic respiration, which uses glucose or glycogen as an energy source. However, because blood glucose levels and glycogen levels are low at the end of a long-distance race, the runners' source of energy is insufficient for the greatly increased muscle activity a sprint to the finish would require.
13. Removal of part of the thyroid gland reduces the amount of thyroid hormone secreted by the gland. Usually, enough thyroid tissue can be removed to reduce secretion of thyroid hormone to within the normal range. In addition, the remaining thyroid tissue normally does not enlarge enough to produce more thyroid hormone, although there are exceptions. The removal of the thyroid tissue does not remove the influence of the abnormal antibodies on the tissues behind the eyes. Thus, in many cases, the condition's effect on the eyes is not improved.

Chapter 19

Learn to Predict

Frankie's feeling of fatigue and her blood test results are consistent with anemia. A low red blood cell count with microcytic cells, low hemoglobin, and a low hematocrit are all indicators of iron deficiency anemia.

The increased reticulocyte count indicated an increased rate of red blood cell production. But if red blood cell production was increased, why was Frankie's red blood cell count still low? We learned in this chapter that red blood cell production is regulated by the hormone erythropoietin. Specifically, reduced red blood cell numbers, as indicated by Frankie's blood test, caused less oxygen to be transported to her kidneys. Consequently, her kidneys secreted more erythropoietin, which resulted in increased red blood cell production in the red bone marrow. Because of Frankie's iron deficiency, which caused hemoglobin synthesis to slow, the newly synthesized red blood cells were smaller than normal, or microcytic. Remember, Frankie also complained of intense abdominal pain. The evidence of hemoglobin in her feces suggested that Frankie is losing blood into her digestive tract, which, considering her abdominal pain, would be consistent with having an ulcer. Frankie's doctor would need to order additional tests to confirm the presence of ulcers before determining treatment.

1. To develop the diagram, we must first determine the order we will use. Referring to table 19.2, column "Description," we can see the average size of the various formed elements. The smallest of the formed elements is platelets (2–4 μm). Based on the smallest number in a range, the second smallest would be lymphocyte (6–14 μm), followed by red blood cell (7.5 μm). Neutrophil and basophil have similar sizes (10–12 μm). Eosinophil is slightly larger (11–14 μm). The largest of the formed elements is the monocyte (12–20 μm). Using images from the table, you can create a visual representation of the formed elements in order of size from smallest to largest (platelet, lymphocyte, red blood cell, neutrophil and basophil, eosinophil, and monocyte).
3. We learned in this chapter that reticulocytes are immature red blood cells released from the red bone marrow into the circulation. Considering that, by donating a unit of blood, Juan's red blood cell count dropped below normal, we would expect his body to respond by producing more red blood cells. Erythropoietin secretion from the kidneys stimulates erythropoiesis, red blood cell production, in the red bone marrow to increase. As a result, we would expect Juan's reticulocyte count to increase during the week after he donated blood. This process continues at the increased rate until Juan's normal red blood cell count is reestablished.
5. Platelets are normally inactive; however, they become activated at sites of tissue injury. These are the areas where clot formation is needed to stop bleeding.
7. a. We learned that HDN is caused by an Rh incompatibility between a pregnant mother with Rh-negative blood and her Rh-positive child. If the mother is sensitized to the Rh antigen, she can produce anti-Rh antibodies that cross the placenta and cause agglutination and hemolysis of fetal red blood cells. A transfusion would replace the red blood cells lost by agglutination and hemolysis.
   b. Remember that erythropoietin stimulates red blood cell production. Even though new red blood cells were introduced during the exchange transfusion, administering erythropoietin will also increase Billy's red blood cell count.
   c. Erythropoietin levels increase as a result of low blood oxygen levels. This is directly related to the red blood cell count. Considering that Billy's red blood cell count was extremely low as a result of HDN, we would predict that his erythropoietin level would be higher than that of a fetus without HDN.
   d. A major physiological change that occurred after birth was that Billy was able to breathe on his own. The ability to oxygenate the blood using the lungs is greater than the ability to oxygenate the blood across the placenta. Billy's blood oxygen levels increased and his erythropoietin levels decreased. Thus, his production of red blood cells decreased and his anemia got worse.
   e. To treat HDN with an exchange transfusion, the donor's blood should be Rh-negative, even though the newborn is Rh-positive. Rh-negative red blood cells do not have Rh antigens. Therefore, any anti-Rh antibodies in the newborn's blood do not react with the transfused Rh-negative red blood cells. Eventually, all of the Rh-negative red blood cells die, and only Rh-positive red blood cells are produced by the newborn.
   f. Remember that blood types are genetically determined. Giving an Rh-postive newborn a transfusion of Rh-negative blood would not change the newborn's blood type. Even though Rh-negative blood is introduced to the body, over time all of the Rh-negative red blood cells die. The new red blood cells are produced from the bone marrow stem cells, which are genetically Rh-positive. Thus, only Rh-positive red blood cells are produced by the newborn.

Chapter 20

Learn to Predict

We learned in this chapter that the heart valves maintain a one-way flow of blood through the heart—from the atria to the ventricles. We also learned that an incompetent valve is one that leaks, or allows some blood to flow in the opposite direction—from the ventricles to the atria. An irregular swooshing noise following the first heart sound, as noted by Stan's regular physician, is a typical sign of an incompetent valve. The first heart sound is produced when the bicuspid and tricuspid valves close. The swooshing sound is the regurgitation of blood into the atria. The cardiologist determined that the bicuspid valve was incompetent, resulting in abnormal blood flow on the left side of the heart.

Stan's difficulty breathing resulted from the abnormal blood flow caused by his incompetent valve. After reviewing the blood flow through the heart in this chapter, we are aware that blood entering the left atrium is returning from the lungs through the pulmonary veins. As a result of the incompetent valve, the pressure in the left atrium, which is normally low, increases substantially during ventricular systole. The increased left atrial pressure causes the pressure in the pulmonary veins and pulmonary capillaries to increase. As a result, fluid leaks from the pulmonary capillaries into the lungs, causing pulmonary edema, or fluid accumulation in the lungs, making it difficult for Stan to breathe.

1. Pericarditis is an inflammation of the serous pericardium. In Tony's case, the pericarditis is a result of a viral infection. Pericarditis can lead to fluid accumulation in the pericardial sac. Tony's pain results from inflammation and distention of the pericardial membranes. His pulse was weak because the fluid in the pericardial sac compressed both the heart and the veins delivering blood to the heart; consequently, the heart could not fill with as much blood as normal. With less blood entering the heart, Tony's stroke volume, or volume of blood pumped from the heart, also decreased, causing a weak pulse and lower blood pressure. Recall from chapter 16 that increased sympathethic stimulation of the heart occurs when blood pressure begins to decrease, resulting in tachycardia. The increased heart rate helps maintain blood pressure. The jugular veins, which carry blood toward the heart, are distended because the accumulated fluid in the pericardial sac compresses the heart, preventing complete filling of the heart and reducing the flow of blood from the jugular veins toward the heart. Tony's physician used a needle to remove excess fluid from the pericardial space. Reviewing figure 20.2, we can see that the needle is most likely inserted in the fifth or sixth intercostal space near the sternum and penetrates the following body layers: the skin, the subcutaneous tissue, the intercostal muscles, the fibrous pericardium, and the parietal pericardium.
3. Before answering the question, we need to define tetanic contraction. Recall from chapter 9 that a tetanic contraction is a sustained contraction in which the frequency of stimulation of the muscle is so rapid that no relaxation occurs. The purpose of cardiac muscle contractions is to pump blood through the circulation by contracting and relaxing in a repeated cycle. Tetanic contractions in cardiac muscle would interrupt the pumping action produced by the cycle of contraction and relaxation, and the blood flow would cease. Tetanic skeletal muscle contractions are important to maintain posture or to hold a limb in a specific position.
5. In section 20.3, we learned that the left ventricle has the thicker wall. The pressure produced by the left ventricle is much

higher than the pressure produced by the right ventricle. It is important for each ventricle to pump the same amount of blood because, with two connected circulation loops (pulmonary circuit and systemic circuit), the volume of blood flowing into one must equal the volume of blood flowing into the other, so that one does not become overfilled at the expense of the other. For example, if the right ventricle pumps less blood than the left ventricle, blood accumulates in the systemic blood vessels. If the left ventricle pumps less blood than the right ventricle, blood accumulates in the pulmonary blood vessels.

7. Figure 20.18 will be very useful in answering this question. From the figure we can see that ventricular diastole occurs between the second heart sound of one cardiac cycle and the first heart sound of the next cardiac cycle. The second heart sound is produced as the aortic semilunar valve closes. The aortic pressure decreases from 95 mm Hg to approximately 80 mm Hg when the left ventricle contracts again. This causes the bicuspid valve to close, producing the first heart sound of the next cardiac cycle. Now, let us consider the pressure changes in the left atrium and ventricle. When the aortic semilunar valve closes (second heart sound), the pressure in the left ventricle decreases rapidly to nearly 0 mm Hg. As soon as the pressure decreases below the pressure in the left atrium, the bicuspid valve opens, and blood flows into the left ventricle. Pressure remains low in the left atrium and the left ventricle, with pressure in the left atrium slightly greater than in the left ventricle. Finally, pressure increases a few mm Hg when the left atrium contracts, causing additional blood to flow from the left atrium into the left ventricle. When the left ventricle begins to contract, the pressure in the left ventricle increases but, as soon as the pressure is greater in the left ventricle than in the left atrium, the bicuspid valve closes, causing the first heart sound of the next cardiac cycle.
9. Rupture of the left ventricle can occur several days after a myocardial infarction. As the necrotic tissues are being removed by macrophages, the wall of the ventricle becomes thinner and may bulge during systole. If the wall of the ventricle becomes very thin before new connective tissue is deposited, it can rupture. If the left ventricle ruptures, blood flows from the left ventricle into the pericardial sac, resulting in cardiac tamponade. As blood fills the pericardial sac, it compresses the ventricle from the outside. As a consequence, the ventricle is not able to fill with blood, and its pumping ability is rapidly eliminated. Rupture of the left ventricular wall, therefore, quickly results in death.

Chapter 21

Learn to Predict

After reading the Clinical Impact 21.6 "Circulatory Shock," in this chapter, we learned that circulatory shock is inadequate blood flow throughout the body. More specifically, septic shock results from infections that cause the release of toxic substances into the circulatory system that depress heart activity, cause vasodilation, and increase capillary permeability. After T.J. developed septic shock, we would expect his blood volume to decrease as fluid moved from the more permeable capillaries to the interstitial spaces. The reduction in blood volume would lead to a drop in his blood pressure, stimulating the baroreceptor reflex mechanism and subsequently an increase in heart rate. We would also expect T.J.'s stroke volume to decrease with a drop in blood volume. Increased sympathetic stimulation would cause vasoconstriction of blood vessels as T.J.'s body tried to maintain normal blood pressure. With the reduction in blood flow through the skin, T.J. would appear very pale. If T.J.'s blood pressure is not maintained, he could progress to irreversible shock, which is lethal.

1. As stated in the question, atherosclerosis of vessels occurs when lipid deposits block the vessels, which results in reduced blood flow through the vessel. The tissues to which the blocked vessels supply blood will therefore have reduced O_2 and nutrients. Because the carotid artery supplies blood to the brain, we would expect atherosclerosis of these vessels to lead to reduced brain function, which may include confusion and loss of memory.
3. Vasoconstriction of Richard's cutaneous blood vessels would cause a substantial increase in his systemic blood pressure. From Laplace's law, we learned that, as the diameter of a vessel increases, the force applied to the vessel wall increases. An aneurysm is a bulge that forms in an arterial wall that has weakened. The increase in Richard's blood pressure due to the sudden vasoconstriction of his cutaneous blood vessels would apply more force on the aneurysm. Because this is a weakened area of the artery wall, the increase in force applied to the aneurysm is more likely to rupture the wall. The rupture of an arterial wall is life threatening.
5. a. The blocked vein in Harry's right leg caused edema and led to tissue ischemia. Edema developed inferior to the blocked vein. Blockage of the vein increased the capillary hydrostatic pressure in the capillary beds drained by the blocked vein. The increased capillary hydrostatic pressure increased the amount of fluid that flowed from the capillaries into the tissue spaces and reduced the amount of fluid that returned to the capillaries. Consequently, fluid accumulated in the tissue spaces and caused edema (see figure 21.28). The ischemia resulted in pain, much the way ischemia of the heart causes pain during myocardial infarctions (see chapter 20).
   b. Emboli that originated in the posterior tibial vein would pass through the following parts of the circulatory system before lodging in the pulmonary arteries of the lungs: posterior tibial vein, popliteal vein, femoral vein, external iliac vein, common iliac vein, inferior vena cava, right atrium, right ventricle, pulmonary trunk, right or left pulmonary artery. Emboli lodge in branches of the pulmonary arteries and are most likely to lodge in the lungs because the pulmonary arteries branch many times before delivering blood to the pulmonary capillaries, and as they branch, their diameters decrease. Even small emboli eventually lodge in the smaller branches of the pulmonary arteries. The other parts of the circulatory system through which the emboli pass have much larger diameters, so emboli can pass readily through them.
   c. When emboli are large enough or numerous enough to block blood flow through a significant part of the lungs, resistance to blood flow through the lungs increases. The increased resistance increases the pulmonary venous pressure, which increases the afterload for the right ventricle. If the right ventricle is unable to overcome the increased afterload, failure of the right side of the heart can occur, and blood flow through the lungs is reduced.
   d. First let us address the effect of pulmonary emboli on blood oxygen levels. Pulmonary emboli large enough to significantly reduce blood flow through the lungs reduce the lungs' ability to carry out gas exchange with blood, and blood oxygen levels decrease. Next, let us address the effect of pulmonary emboli on the left ventricle's ability to pump blood. Pulmonary emboli block normal blood flow through the lungs, thereby reducing the blood volume returning to the left ventricle. This would also cause a reduction in cardiac output. Recall that cardiac output also affects blood pressure, so we would

expect hypotension, or a reduction in blood pressure, to occur. As blood pressure falls, the homeostatic mechanisms described in figure 21.32 are activated to increase blood pressure to normal levels. Manifestations of hypotension, such as increased heart rate, weak pulse, and pallor, would be present.

e. Heparin and coumadin are anticoagulants, discussed in chapter 19. They are prescribed to slow down the rate of blood clot formation. Heparin must be administered intravenously, but coumadin can be taken orally, which makes home use possible. Harry's prothrombin time will be checked periodically to ensure that enough anticoagulant is administered to prevent enlargement of the thrombus in the deep vein of his leg and to prevent additional emboli from forming. Remember that enzymes naturally found in our blood break down coagulated blood. In Harry's case, the clots are removed because the slower rate of coagulation allows the clots to be broken down faster than they can form.

7. During a headstand, gravity acts on the blood, causing it to settle in the vessels of the head and chest. Blood pressure in the area of the aortic arch and carotid sinus baroreceptors increases. Figure 21.32 illustrates how the baroreceptor reflexes regulate changes in blood pressure. The increased blood pressure activates the baroreceptor reflexes, increasing parasympathetic stimulation of the heart and decreasing sympathetic stimulation. Thus, the heart rate decreases. As blood from the periphery runs down to the heart, venous return increases, causing stroke volume to increase (Starling law of the heart). The activated baroreceptor reflexes also decrease vasomotor tone, and some peripheral vasodilation can occur.

Chapter 22

Learn to Predict

Maddie was correct; she was having an allergic, or hypersensitivity, reaction to one of the chemicals sprayed on the trees. After reviewing table 22.7, we can conclude that her symptoms are most consistent with a delayed hypersensitivity response because the itching and swelling did not occur until a day after she had been exposed to the chemicals. The chemicals on the leaves acted as haptens and combined with proteins, which were processed by the MHC class I processing system in the skin cells of her hands. In this chapter we learned that cytotoxic T cells can combine with MHC class I molecules on the surface of skin cells, destroying the cells. In addition, cytokines are released that attract macrophages to the area, thereby enhancing phagocytosis and inflammation.

1. a. Cancer cells can break free from a tumor and spread, or metastasize, to other parts of the body by entering lymphatic or blood capillaries (see chapter 3). If the cancer cells enter the lymphatic capillaries, they are carried to the lymph nodes, which filter lymph. The first lymph nodes in which cancer cells are likely to become trapped are the sentinel lymph nodes.

   b. Test results showed that all of the sentinel lymph nodes contained cancer cells, indicating that cancer cells had spread into her lymphatic system. Cindy's cancerous tumor is in her left breast, and the axillary lymph nodes drain the superficial thorax and upper limb. Removal of these lymph nodes minimizes the risk of further metastasis.

   c. Recall from chapter 21 approximately one-tenth of the fluid entering tissues is normally removed by the lymphatic system. Removal of the lymph nodes and their attached lymphatic vessels disrupts the normal removal of fluid from tissues, resulting in lymphedema, the accumulation of fluid in the tissues.

   d. Remember that contraction of skeletal muscle and the thoracic pressure changes associated with breathing are both mechanisms for moving lymph through lymphatic vessels. Exercise increases skeletal muscle contractions and breathing. Consequently, more fluid can enter lymphatic capillaries, reducing edema.

   e. The external force applied to tissues by a compression bandage or garment reduces the movement of fluid from the circulation into tissues (see chapter 21), thereby reducing lymphedema.

   f. Recall that contraction of lymphatic vessels and the presence of valves along these vessels ensure that lymph moves through lymphatic vessels in one direction, from the peripheral tissues toward the venous system of the thorax. A compression pump mimics the normal contraction and relaxation of the lymphatic vessels, moving the lymph in a distal-to-proximal direction.

3. Remember that the combination of an MHC class I molecule and an antigen is necessary to activate T cells. MHC molecules are genetically determined. Thus, unless mouse B is essentially genetically identical to mouse A, the T cells from mouse A that are introduced to mouse B will not respond to the antigen. The T cells are MHC-restricted, meaning they must interact with the MHC proteins of mouse A as well as the antigen from virus X, to be activated and respond.

5. The first exposure to the disease-causing agent (antigen) evokes a primary immune response, which destroys the existing pathogens but also produces memory cells that can respond to future infections. As time passes, the antibodies produced during the primary immune response will degrade, and memory cells will die. If, before all of the memory cells are eliminated, a second exposure to the antigen occurs, a secondary response results, increasing the number of antibodies and memory cells again. The newly produced memory cells can provide immunity until the next exposure to the antigen.

7. First, recall that vaccines are a form of artificial active immunity caused by deliberately introducing an antigen into the body, stimulating a primary response by the immune system. The immune system responds to the vaccine by increasing the number of specific memory cells and antibodies for the particular disease. This provides long-lasting immunity without disease symptoms. The booster shot stimulates a memory (secondary) response, resulting in the formation of even more memory cells and antibodies. A booster shot improves the effectiveness of the immune system's ability to fight the types of infections for which a person is vaccinated.

Chapter 23

Learn to Predict

Mr. Theron suffers from emphysema, a respiratory disorder that results in the destruction of alveoli. This chapter explained that the alveoli form the respiratory membrane, the site of gas exchange between the atmosphere and the blood. Alveolar destruction would directly reduce the respiratory membrane surface and therefore gas exchange. As a consequence, Mr. Theron has exaggerated respiratory movements to compensate for the reduction in surface area. Blood Po_2 is an important stimulus for the respiratory center, and the increased respiratory movements keep the pulmonary ventilation just adequate to maintain blood Po_2 in the low normal range. Because CO_2 diffuses across the respiratory membrane at a faster rate than O_2, the elevated pulmonary ventilation required to maintain blood Po_2 causes too much CO_2 to be expired, resulting in his blood Pco_2 level dropping below normal.

This chapter explained that a pneumothorax, or the introduction of air into the pleural cavity through an opening in the thoracic wall or lung, can cause a lung to collapse. Due to his emphysema, Mr. Theron's lung collapsed when alveoli near the surface of the lung ruptured, allowing air to enter the pleural space. The physician was able to diagnose Mr. Theron's collapsed lung by listening for respiratory sounds with a stethoscope. He detected respiratory sounds in the right lung but not in the left lung. We would expect Mr. Theron's respiratory movements to be even more exaggerated because the respiratory membrane was reduced by half when his left lung collapsed. The reduction in the respiratory membrane would cause a drop in Po_2 and an increase in Pco_2, both of which would stimulate respiratory centers to increase pulmonary ventilation.

1. It could be that Jake was fibbing when he claimed to be unafraid, trying to impress his girlfriend. But whether he was frightened or not, in order for his body to produce such a sound, certain muscles need to contract. The muscles of expiration cause airflow from the lungs to the exterior through the larynx. As air rushes past the vocal cords, they vibrate. If air is explosively pushed past the vocal cords, they vibrate to a greater degree than when air is pushed past them to a lesser degree, and they produce a louder sound. As for the high pitch of the scream, it is the position of the vocal cords that is important. More tension results in a higher frequency of vibration of the vocal cords, producing a higher-pitched sound. How does the tension increase? The arytenoid cartilages are rotated medially, which moves the vocal cords medially and posteriorly. Finally, the epiglottis-controlling muscles cause it to tip anteriorly so that air can flow past and out of the mouth. For Jake, the result was a high-pitched scream that either endeared him to his girlfriend or left him single.
3. To answer this question, knowledge you gained from chapter 22 about artificial active immunity is critical. Recall that a vaccination consists of isolated epitopes from the surface of a pathogen that are then injected into a person. In doing so, the vaccine serves to introduce the pathogen to the immune system. This exposure to the pathogen's isolated epitopes allows the immune system to activate specific cytotoxic T cells and B cells for that pathogen. The adaptive immune system will then create antibodies and memory cells for the pathogen, a central role of the immune system. By identifying and purifying the *B. pertussis* virulence factors that allow the bacterium to avoid the complement system, the vaccine would allow the immune system to create antibodies against both the virulence factors and *B. pertussis*'s epitopes. Binding of the antibodies to the complement avoidance virulence factors would neutralize these factors, thereby enabling complement to quickly attack and kill the bacteria. In addition, because complement and adaptive immunity work cooperatively, antibody production would occur more quickly. This provides protection against future exposures to *B. pertussis*.
5. The air the diver is breathing has a greater total pressure than atmospheric pressure at sea level. Consequently, the partial pressure of each gas in the air increases. According to Henry's law, as the partial pressure of a gas increases, the amount (concentration) of gas dissolved in the liquid (e.g., body fluids) with which the gas is in contact increases. When the diver suddenly ascends, the partial pressure of gases in the body returns toward sea level barometric pressure. As a result, the amount (concentration) of gas that can be dissolved in body fluids suddenly decreases. When the fluids can no longer hold all the gas, gas bubbles form.
7. When CO_2 moves from fetal blood into maternal blood, it increases CO_2 levels inside maternal red blood cells. As a result, pH inside maternal red blood cells decreases, the affinity of maternal hemoglobin for oxygen decreases, and more oxygen is released. In other words, the maternal oxygen-hemoglobin curve shifts to the right. Simultaneously, the movement of CO_2 from fetal blood into maternal blood decreases CO_2 levels inside fetal red blood cells and increases pH inside fetal red blood cells. This means that the affinity of fetal hemoglobin for oxygen increases, and more oxygen will bind to fetal hemoglobin. In other words, the fetal oxygen-hemoglobin dissociation curve shifts to the left. This shifting of the maternal and fetal oxygen-hemoglobin curves is called the double Bohr effect. The double Bohr effect increases the delivery of oxygen from maternal blood to fetal blood because maternal hemoglobin releases more oxygen and fetal hemoglobin is more effective at picking up that oxygen.
9. A person who cannot synthesize BPG has mild erythrocytosis because their hemoglobin releases less oxygen to tissues. Consequently, increased erythropoietin will probably be released from the kidneys, and increased red blood cell production will occur in red bone marrow.
11. To answer this question, we need to consider what types of stimuli affect the respiratory center. Look at figure 23.20. Notice that receptors for temperature (e.g., cold water), pain (e.g., very cold water), and touch (e.g., swatting on the buttocks) all stimulate the respiratory center. That is why we gasp when we jump into a cold swimming pool—it is involuntary—and babies were swatted on the buttocks—to stimulate their first breath of air.

Chapter 24

Learn to Predict

In this chapter we learned that the gallbladder stores bile, a secretion of the liver that neutralizes stomach acids and emulsifies lipids. We also learned that gallstones may form when there is an abundance of cholesterol in the bile, such as from a high-cholesterol diet. Gallstones can block the cystic duct, blocking the flow of bile from the gallbladder to the duodenum. Eating food high in fat causes gallbladder contractions. Specifically, gallbladder contraction is stimulated hormonally by cholecystokinin from the duodenum and parasympathetic stimulation. If Rebecca's cystic duct were blocked by gallstones, the increased pressure in the contracting gallbladder would result in pain and inflammation.

But why did Rebecca's skin turn yellow? Recall that bile contains bilirubin, a yellow pigment produced from the breakdown of hemoglobin that when further processed in the intestine turns brown and contributes to the normal color of feces. The gallstones blocked Rebecca's common bile duct, preventing bile from passing from the liver to the duodenum and reducing the amount of bilirubin removed from the blood. Rebecca's skin turned yellow due to the accumulation of bile pigments in the blood. Also, the reduced volume of bile entering the duodenum resulted in poor emulsification of lipids. The lipids remained in the small intestine, causing distension of the intestine, and the undigested lipids passing through the small and large intestines were responsible for the diarrhea. The lack of bilirubin resulted in the clay-colored feces.

1. Four. Recall that the greater omentum is a localized mesentery, which consists of serous membranes. Each single layer of the mesentery has two layers of simple squamous epithelium. Because the greater omentum is folded back on itself, that results in four layers of simple squamous epithelium.
3. Alice's physician concluded that the inflammation of her larynx was due to the reflux of gastric fluid into her esophagus while she was sleeping. In general, reflux is more likely after eating a meal and while lying down. Gastric acid secretion increases after a meal mainly because of the cephalic and gastric phases of gastric secretion, and gravity normally helps keep gastric fluid in the stomach. During the night, the gastric fluid moved through the esophagus and entered her larynx. An antacid was prescribed to neutralize the low pH of the

gastric secretions. Two classes of drugs decrease H^+ secretion. Both histamine receptor antagonists and proton pump inhibitors reduce the movement of H^+ into the lumen of the stomach, thereby increasing the pH of the gastric fluid secreted by the stomach mucosa. The histamine receptor antagonist binds to histamine receptors and blocks the action of histamine, and the proton pump inhibitor reduces the H^+–K^+ exchange pump. Either type could have been prescribed for Alice. The smaller volume of gastric acid secreted by the stomach mucosa and the higher pH of the stomach secretions reduce the acid reflux that cause inflammation of her larynx.

5. First, let us consider that acidic chyme in the small intestine is the stimulus. Stimuli are detected by receptors, and then control centers send a signal to initiate a response that will regulate homeostasis. In this case, the control center is the pancreas. In response to the acidic chyme, pancreatic secretin stimulates bicarbonate ion secretion from the pancreas (the effector), which neutralizes the acidic chyme. Thus, secretin prevents the acid levels in the chyme from becoming too high and keeps them in the normal range. The neutralization of the acidic chyme removes the stimulus for more secretin release, and bicarbonate ion is no longer secreted. Because the response was inhibited, this is an example of a negative-feedback system.
7. An enema is the introduction of fluid into the rectum, which causes it to distend. Recall that the defecation reflex is initiated by the movement of feces into the rectum and the subsequent stretch of the rectal wall. Therefore, because an enema stretches the rectal wall, it initiates the defecation reflex.

Chapter 25

Learn to Predict

Although Sadie's suggested snack did contain a lot of calories, which she and David needed for their day at the park, the food choices were not ideal. Most of the calories in the cookies and grape soda were actually from simple sugars. Eating large amounts of simple sugars, such as Sadie's suggested snack, could result in large fluctuations in blood glucose levels. Though the children may initially have an increase in energy, they will most likely experience a drastic decrease in energy as well. Foods that include complex carbohydrates, such as those in the snack Sadie's mom suggested, have other nutrients, such as vitamins, many of which are necessary for normal metabolism. In addition, complex carbohydrates are digested and absorbed at a slower rate and do not contribute to drastic changes in blood glucose levels. Essentially, Sadie's mom selected food that would provide the children with energy and additional beneficial nutrients.

1. Most of the vitamins, with the exception of A, D, and niacin, are essential vitamins, meaning they cannot be produced by the body but must be obtained from the diet. Recall that, after a vitamin is destroyed, its function is lost. If the vitamins were broken down by digestion before being absorbed, they would not be functional, and vitamin deficiencies would occur.
3. The last step in the electron-transport chain is when the electrons are passed to oxygen to form water. If this step is blocked, the citric acid and electron-transport chain cannot function, so ATP will not be produced aerobically. Anaerobic respiration alone cannot produce sufficient levels of ATP to maintain normal cellular activity, and death will occur.
5. Recall that catabolism of food releases energy that can be used by the body for normal biological work, such as muscle contraction. However, about 40% of the total energy released is actually used for biological work. The remaining energy is lost as heat. Exercise increases the amount of biological work and therefore requires more energy in the form of ATP. As more ATP is produced to fuel the exercise, more heat is also generated as lost energy, thereby increasing body temperature. Shivering consists of small, rapid muscle contractions that produce heat in an effort to prevent a decrease in body temperature in the cold.

Chapter 26

Learn to Predict

We read in this chapter that chronic renal failure is caused by a decrease in the number of functional nephrons in the kidneys, which is common in type 2 diabetics, such as Bobbie. Renal failure is most likely the result of damage to the glomerular basement membrane due to increased glomerular pressure and the production of advanced glycosylation end products, both of which are common side effects of type 2 diabetes.

Because Bobbie's renal failure means her kidneys have a dramatically reduced filtration function, we would expect Bobbie's blood tests to reveal high levels of glucose, K^+, and creatinine and low levels of Na^+. In addition, the creatinine clearance rate would be below normal, and there would be substantial protein in the urine. The increased blood glucose level results from a decrease in the transport maximum for glucose reabsorption due to fewer functional nephrons. Similarly, the transport maximum for Na^+ is decreased, and the kidneys' ability to secrete K^+ also decreases. Consequently, blood Na^+ levels decrease and blood K^+ levels increase. The low creatinine clearance rate is consistent with a decreased number of functional nephrons, and protein in the urine reflects the increased permeability of the filtration membrane in the remaining nephrons. The puffiness of Bobbie's face indicates that fluid is being retained, which is consistent with the increase in blood pressure.

The consequences for Bobbie are severe. She needs to take precautions to make it easier for the remaining nephrons to maintain homeostasis—for example, by carefully regulating her blood glucose and controlling the hypertension. If her condition continues to worsen, she may have to resort to dialysis and consider a kidney transplant.

1. Even though hemoglobin is a smaller molecule than albumin, it does not normally enter the filtrate because hemoglobin is contained within red blood cells, and these cells cannot pass through the filtration membrane. However, if red blood cells rupture, by a process called hemolysis, the hemoglobin is released into the plasma, and large amounts of hemoglobin enter the filtrate. Conditions that cause red blood cells to rupture in the circulatory system allow large amounts of hemoglobin to enter the urine.
3. Inhibition of ADH secretion is one of alcohol's numerous effects on the body. Lack of ADH causes the distal convoluted tubules and the collecting ducts to be relatively impermeable to water. Therefore, the water cannot move by osmosis from the distal nephrons and collecting ducts but remains in the nephrons to become urine. In addition, because other fluids are normally consumed with the alcohol, the increased water intake also results in an increase in dilute urine.
5. During the race, Amanda's blood volume decreased because of increased water loss through breathing and sweating. Because of Amanda's severe dehydration, her body immediately initiated the mechanism that maintains blood pressure. The vasoconstriction and reduced blood volume explain her pallor. Increased sympathetic stimulation caused the more rapid heart rate. The renal arteries also became vasoconstricted. Subsequently, the GFR decreased, and urine production was reduced. In addition, Amanda's ADH levels increased, which increased water reabsorption from the distal convoluted tubules and collecting ducts.
7. The first piece of information you need to make this prediction is that the micturition reflex is initiated by stretch receptors in the

bladder wall. However, when the volume of fluid in the bladder is below 300 mL, the urge to urinate can be repressed by centers in the pons and cerebrum. You also learned that a bacterial infection or another source of irritation could stimulate the urge to urinate, even if there is not much urine in the bladder. Purposeful infection of the bladder wall with tuberculosis bacteria during the BCG treatment causes irritation of the bladder wall and would stimulate an increased frequency of action potentials along the sensory neurons. The higher frequency of action potentials is interpreted as a greater urge to urinate. This is true for all bacterial infections in the bladder.

Chapter 27

Learn to Predict

Satish and Kiran suffered from dehydration due to lack of water intake and increased water loss. In this chapter we learned that water is normally lost through urine, sensible and insensible perspiration, respiratory passages, and feces. The students' rate of water loss due to perspiration and through the respiratory passages increased dramatically in the hot, dry environment. As water loss continued, blood volume decreased, and plasma osmolality increased. The decrease in blood volume caused their renal arteries to constrict, reducing renal blood flow and the glomerular filtration rate; stimulated the renin-angiotensin-aldosterone hormone mechanism, increasing Na^+ reabsorption; and increased ADH secretion, reducing water loss in the urine. Their increased plasma osmolality also increased ADH secretion. ADH and aldosterone together maximize the kidneys' ability to conserve water; thus, their urine was very concentrated and its volume was small. However, Satish and Kiran continued to lose water by evaporation of perspiration and from the respiratory passages. Their blood osmolality continued to increase and plasma volume continued to decrease. As the plasma volume decreased, Satish and Kiran's hematocrit increased. Consequently, their blood became more viscous, and their hearts had to work harder to pump blood. We also learned in this chapter that increased plasma osmolality causes water to move from cells into the interstitial spaces and into the plasma. As a result, cells became dehydrated and malfunctioned. Satish and Kiran almost died because of the increased workload on their hearts and the decreased ability of their nerve and muscle cells to function.

1. The first step is to define hemorrhagic shock. Hemorrhagic shock is due to excessive internal or external bleeding, which lowers blood volume. During hemorrhagic shock, blood pressure decreases and visceral blood vessels constrict. As a consequence, blood flow to the kidneys and the blood pressure in the glomeruli decrease dramatically. The total filtration pressure decreases, as does the amount of filtrate formed each minute. The rate at which Na^+ enters the nephron therefore decreases. In addition, the kidneys secrete large amounts of renin, which causes the formation of angiotensin I from angiotensinogen. Angiotensin I is converted to angiotensin II, which stimulates aldosterone secretion. Aldosterone increases the rate at which Na^+ is reabsorbed from the filtrate in the distal convoluted tubules and collecting ducts.
3. Aldosterone hyposecretion results in acidosis. Aldosterone increases the rate at which Na^+ is reabsorbed from nephrons, but it also increases the rate at which K^+ and H^+ are secreted. Hyposecretion of aldosterone decreases the rate at which H^+ is secreted by the nephrons and therefore can result in acidosis.

Chapter 28

Learn to Predict

In this chapter, we learned that gametogenesis involves meiosis, cell division that produces haploid cells. When comparing gametogenesis in males and females, we find that the processes differ in several ways: the stage in an individual's life when gametogenesis begins, the types of cells produced, the number of functional cells produced with each cell division, and the stage of life when gametogenesis ceases to occur.

In males, gametogenesis begins at puberty in the seminiferous tubules. Spermatogonia give rise to primary spermatocytes, which will undergo the process of meiosis. During this process, each primary spermatocyte eventually gives rise to four mature sperm cells. Males continue to produce sperm until death.

Gametogenesis in females is more complex. The process actually begins before a female is born. During fetal development, many of the oogonia in the ovaries degenerate. The remaining oogonia actually begin meiosis I and are called primary oocytes. At birth, the existing primary oocytes stop meiosis. After puberty and just before the ovulation of each oocyte, the primary oocyte that is ovulated completes the first meiotic division to produce one secondary oocyte and one polar body. The secondary oocyte begins the second meiotic division but will complete the process only if fertilized by a sperm cell. In the case of fertilization, the secondary oocyte divides to form two cells. One cell is another polar body and degenerates. In the other cell, the haploid sperm nucleus combines with the haploid oocyte nucleus to form a zygote. Thus, in females, each primary oocyte produces only one functional cell. For females, the process of gametogenesis stops at menopause.

1. We can assume that the six biopsy samples were of different regions of Vern's prostate gland. It appears that the cancerous tumor is small and the needle biopsy only passed through the tumor two of the six times.
3. Erection is the result of neural stimulation of arteries that supply the erectile tissue. Erectile dysfunction (ED) is caused by either defective stimulation of the erectile tissue by nerve fibers or reduced response of the blood vessels to neural stimulation. Recall from Clinical Impact 28.5 that sildenafil does not stimulate erection, but instead increases the effectiveness of stimulation by enhancing the response of blood vessels to action potentials by slowly breaking down cGMP. As cGMP accumulates in the smooth muscle cells of the blood vessels, they relax, allowing blood to flow into the erectile tissue. Mr. Grover is sometimes able to achieve erections, especially after treatment, so it is reasonable to assume that he is unable to achieve erections at other times because of dysfunction in neural stimulation. There could be fewer action potentials reaching the erectile tissue due to nerve damage or decreased ability of the central nervous system to increase action potentials in the nerves. Another possibility is that Mr. Grover is unable to achieve minimal sexual excitement, which would decrease action potentials in the appropriate nerves.
5. The question addresses the time period in the menstrual cycle just before the LH surge, which promotes ovulation. Referring to figure 28.19, it is evident that estrogen and progesterone are normally at their lowest levels before the LH surge. In contrast, progesterone is at its highest level after ovulation and prevents further development of follicles. Therefore, administration of a large amount of progesterone and estrogen just before the preovulatory LH surge inhibits the release of GnRH, LH, and FSH. Consequently, ovulation does not occur. However, progesterone is the more potent hormone when it comes to inhibiting ovulation. Injections of a small amount of estrogen just before ovulation could stimulate GnRH, LH, and FSH secretion with little negative effect on ovulation. Continual administration of high concentrations of GnRH causes the anterior pituitary cells to become insensitive to GnRH. Thus, LH and FSH levels remain low and the ovarian cycle stops.
7. Molly's mother could have had leiomyomas also, although, without direct data of

medical examinations, one cannot be certain. If that was the cause of her irregular menstruations, they may have become less frequent as Molly's mother experienced menopause. During menopause, the uterus gradually becomes smaller, and eventually the cyclical changes in the endometrial lining cease. If the condition was relatively mild, the onset of menopause could explain the gradual disappearance of the irregular and prolonged menstruations. (Note: If the tumors are large, constant, and severe, menstruations are likely even if regular menstrual cycles stop due to menopause.)

Chapter 29

Learn to Predict

In this chapter, we learned that the production of breast milk depends on a number of hormones. Estrogen causes the duct system of the breast to develop and is mainly responsible for the enlargement of the breasts during pregnancy. Progesterone causes the development of the breasts' secretory alveoli, which enlarge but do not usually secrete milk during pregnancy. Other hormones necessary for development of the breast include growth hormone, prolactin, thyroid hormones, glucocorticoids, and insulin. Human somatotropin and human placental lactogen are secreted from the placenta. The high levels of estrogen and progesterone inhibit the effect of prolactin on milk secretion during pregnancy. After parturition, blood levels of estrogen, progesterone, and prolactin decrease.

This chapter also explained that suckling stimulates the periodic pulses of prolactin and oxytocin. The pulses of prolactin, in the absence of high blood levels of estrogen and progesterone, cause the secretory units of the breasts to secrete milk. Oxytocin causes expulsion of the milk from the breast in response to suckling. Refraining from breastfeeding for a period of time results in no prolactin pulses. Consequently, the secretory units fail to secrete milk and quickly lose the capacity to do so. Ming can retain the capacity to breastfeed her baby by using a breast pump while she takes the prescribed antibiotic. The breast pump simulates suckling and stimulates the pulses of prolactin secretion. After finishing the antibiotic, Ming can then continue to breastfeed her baby.

1. The primitive streak essentially forms the central axis of an embryo. If two primitive streaks formed in one embryonic disk, we would expect two different embryos, or essentially twins, to develop. If the two primitive streaks were touching each other, conjoined twins would develop. The degree to which the two primitive streaks were touching would determine the severity of the attachment.
3. Recall that clinical age is dependent on LMP (last menstrual period) of the mother and that developmental age begins at fertilization, which is assumed to occur on day 14 after LMP. Most of the times reported in the text are developmental age. To determine the clinical age, add 14 to the developmental age. The one exception is parturition, which is reported as clinical age. To determine the developmental age, subtract 14 from the clinical age. We can easily construct a table to compare the ages:

	Clinical Age	Developmental Age
Fertilization	14 days	0 days
Implantation	21 days	7 days
Beginning of fetal period	70 days	56 days
Parturition	280 days	266 days

5. Suckling causes a reflex release of oxytocin from the mother's posterior pituitary. Oxytocin causes expulsion of milk from the breast, but it also causes contraction of the uterus. Contraction of the uterus is responsible for the sensation of cramps in her abdomen.
7. When fertilization occurs, the two haploid gametes combine to form a new diploid zygote. If the gametes had the same number of chromosomes as somatic cells, the chromosome number would double with each generation.
9. Duchenne muscular dystrophy is an X-linked condition. Remember that a male child receives an X chromosome from his mother and a Y chromosome from his father. We can therefore assume that Wilma is a "carrier" for Duchenne muscular dystrophy, meaning she is heterozygous for the condition. As a male, Wally has only one X chromosome in his cells, and his X chromosome must have the normal allele because Wally does not have Duchenne muscular dystrophy. Because each of their children will receive an X chromosome from Wilma, they may receive either an X chromosome with the normal allele or an X chromosome with the Duchenne muscular dystrophy allele. Males who receive a chromosome with a normal allele from Wilma and a Y chromosome from Wally will be normal. Males who receive an X chromosome with the muscular dystrophy allele from Wilma and the Y chromosome from Wally will have Duchenne muscular dystrophy. Therefore, the probability that their next child will have the condition is 0 if the child is female and 0.5 (or 1/2) if the child is male. However, the probability that each female child will be a carrier for the condition is 0.5 (or 1/2).

Appendix F

ANSWERS TO ODD-NUMBERED CONCEPT CHECK QUESTIONS

Chapter 1

1. a; 3. a; 5. e; 7. b; 9. d
11. Student B is correct. Body temperature begins to rise as a result of exposure to the hot environment. Sweating eliminates heat from the body and lowers body temperature. Body temperature returning to its ideal normal value is an example of negative feedback. Student A probably thought it was positive feedback because sweating continued to increase. However, sweating is the response. The variable being regulated by sweating is body temperature.
13. d
15. When a boy is standing on his head, his nose is superior to his mouth. Directional terms refer to a person's body in the anatomical position, not to the body's current position.
17. b; 19. c; 21. a
23. The uterus is located in the pelvic cavity. The pelvic cavity, however, is surrounded by the bones of the pelvis and does not increase in size during pregnancy. Instead, as the fetus grows, the expanding uterus must move into the abdominal cavity, thereby crowding the abdominal organs and dramatically increasing the size of the abdominal cavity.

Chapter 2

1. e
3. An atom of iron has 26 protons (the atomic number), 30 neutrons (the mass number minus the atomic number), and 26 electrons (because the number of electrons is equal to the number of protons). If an atom of iron loses 3 electrons, it has 3 more protons (positive charges) than electrons (negative charges). Therefore, the iron ion has an overall charge of +3, which is represented symbolically as Fe^{3+}.
5. a; 7. b; 9. c; 11. e; 13. d
15. Muscle contains proteins. To increase muscle mass, proteins must be synthesized from amino acids. The synthesis of molecules in living organisms requires the input of energy. That energy comes from the potential energy stored in the chemical bonds of food molecules, which is released during the decomposition of food molecules.
17. Heating (boiling) has destroyed the ability of the molecules in one or both of the solutions to function in the chemical reaction. This is called denaturation. There are two possibilities as to what is denatured: the reactants themselves or an enzyme that catalyzes the reaction.
19. c; 21. d; 23. d
25. pH is a measure of H^+ concentration. If equal amounts of solutions A and B are mixed, the resulting H^+ concentration is the average value of the two solutions—that is, the pH is $(8 + 2)/2 = 5$. A pH of 5 is acidic. This question illustrates an important point: The pH of a solution can be changed by adding a more acidic or more basic solution to it.
27. b; 29. b; 31. d; 33. a

Chapter 3

1. a; 3. c; 5. e; 7. a
9. The cells within the wound swell with water and lyse when a hypotonic solution is introduced. This kills potentially metastatic cells that may still be present in the wound.
11. Answer b is correct. Because the solution is isotonic, no exchange of water occurs. Because the solution contains the same concentration of all substances except that it has no urea, only a net movement of urea occurs across the membrane.
13. d; 15. b; 17. b; 19. c; 21. b
23. It is obvious that the heart and leg muscles of people who are jogging require the formation of ATP as a source of energy. As the heart and leg muscles increase in size, more ATP is produced by a greater number of mitochondria. Mitochondria are the critical membrane-bound organelles that increased in number by dividing. The genetic information for some of the proteins in mitochondria comes from the DNA of the mitochondria, and the genetic information for other proteins comes from DNA from the nuclei of the muscle cells.
25. a; 27. d; 29. d

Chapter 4

1. c; 3. a; 5. d; 7. d
9. The tissue is epithelial tissue because it is lining a free surface, and the epithelium is stratified because it consists of more than one layer. The types of stratified epithelium are stratified squamous, stratified cuboidal, stratified columnar, and transitional epithelium. The structure of the cells in the surface layers determines the tissue type. Flat cells in the surface layer indicate stratified squamous epithelium. Cuboidal cells in the surface layer indicate stratified cuboidal epithelium, and columnar cells in the surface layer point to stratified columnar epithelium. The surface cells of transitional epithelium are roughly cuboidal with cubelike or columnar cells beneath them. When transitional epithelium is stretched, the surface cells are still roughly cuboidal, but underlying layers can be somewhat flattened.
11. Pseudostratified squamous epithelium has goblet cells that secrete mucus. The cilia move the mucus over the surface of the epithelium toward the upper portion of the trachea. Stratified squamous epithelium does not secrete abundant mucus, and it does not have cilia. Consequently, mucus secreted by the area of the trachea that is still lined by pseudostratified columnar epithelium is not moved over the portion of the trachea lined by stratified squamous epithelium. The mucus accumulates below the area of the trachea lined by stratified squamous epithelium, causing Humphrey's frequent cough.
13. b
15. Glands producing merocrine secretions do so with no loss of actual cellular material, whereas glands producing holocrine secretions shed entire cells. The cells rupture and die, and the entire cell becomes part of the secretion. You can chemically analyze the secretions for the types of molecules found in cellular organelles. For example, if phospholipids and proteins normally found in membranes are in the secretion, the secretion is a holocrine secretion. If the secretion is watery or contains products that are not found in membranes or organelles, it is a merocrine secretion.
17. d; 19. a; 21. b
23. The tissue described is dense, regularly arranged, collagenic connective tissue. Injury to this type of tissue affects structures made up of this type of connective

tissue, which includes tendons. Damage to neck vertebrae can be ruled out because they are connected by ligaments containing abundant dense, regularly arranged elastic connective tissue. A ruptured intervertebral disk is not indicated because it would consist of dense, irregularly arranged collagenic connective tissue.

25. b; 27. c; 29. c; 31. b

Chapter 5

1. d; 3. b; 5. c
7. The stratum corneum, the outermost layer of the skin, consists of many rows of flat, dead epithelial cells. The many rows of cells, which are continuously shed and replaced, are responsible for the protective function of the integument. In infants, there are fewer rows of cells, resulting in skin that is more easily damaged than that of adults.
9. d; 11. b; 13. b
15. Carotene, a yellow pigment from ingested plants, accumulates in lipids. The stratum corneum of a callus has more layers of cells than other, noncallused parts of the skin, and the cells in each layer are surrounded by lipids. The carotene in the lipids makes the callus appear yellow.
17. b; 19. c; 21. b
23. The hair follicle, but not the hair, is surrounded with nerve endings that can detect movement and pulling of the hair. The hair is dead, keratinized epithelium, so cutting the hair is not painful.
25. b; 27. b
29. Probably not because, following removal of the nail from the nail fold, it may grow back into the nail fold and the ingrown toenail may recur. One solution is to remove the small part of the nail responsible for the ingrown toenail. Prior to this drastic approach, sterile gauze can be placed between the nail and the nail fold to force the nail away from the nail fold. After the nail fold is healed, the gauze can be removed.
31. c
33. Rickets is a disease of children resulting from inadequate vitamin D intake. Inadequate vitamin D leads to insufficient absorption of calcium from the small intestine, resulting in soft bones. If adequate vitamin D is ingested, rickets is prevented, whether a person is dark- or fair-skinned. However, if dietary vitamin D is inadequate, when the skin is exposed to ultraviolet light, 7-dehydrocholesterol is converted into cholecalciferol, which can be converted to vitamin D. Dark-skinned children are more susceptible to rickets because the additional melanin in their skin screens out the ultraviolet light and they produce less vitamin D.

Chapter 6

1. e; 3. a; 5. d; 7. c; 9. b; 11. d; 13. c; 15. e; 17. d; 19. c
21. Testosterone normally causes a growth spurt at puberty, followed by slower growth and closure of the epiphyseal plate. Without testosterone, growth is slower but proceeds longer, resulting in a taller-than-normal person.
23. Osteoporosis is depletion of bone matrix that results when more bone is destroyed than is formed. Because mechanical stress stimulates bone formation (osteoblast activity), running helps prevent osteoporosis in the bones being stressed. This includes the bones of the lower limbs and the spine.
25. c
27. Blood vessels in central canals run parallel to the long axis of the bone, and perforating canals run at approximately a right angle to the central canals. Thus, perforating canals connect to central canals, which allows blood vessels in the perforating canals to connect with blood vessels in the central canals. After a fracture, blood flow through the central canals stops back to the point where the blood vessels in the central canals connect to the blood vessels in the perforating canals. The regions of bone on both sides of the fracture associated with this lack of blood delivery die.
29. Hyperparathyroidism stimulates increased bone breakdown and can cause osteitis fibrosa cystica, a condition in which the bone is eaten away as Ca^{2+} is released from the bone. The result can be a deformed bone that is likely to fracture. Vitamin D therapy could help because vitamin D promotes an increase in blood Ca^{2+} and therefore increased deposition of Ca^{2+} in bone.

Chapter 7

1. c; 3. c; 5. c; 7. d; 9. b; 11. a; 13. a
15. Forceful rotation of the vertebral column is most likely to damage the articular processes, especially in the lumbar region, where the articular processes tend to prevent excessive rotation (the superior articular processes face medially and the inferior articular processes face laterally).
17. d; 19. b; 21. a; 23. b; 25. a
27. Females' hips are wider than males'. As the knees are positioned toward the midline, the slope of the femur from its proximal end toward its distal end is greater in females. As a result, more females than males tend to be knock-kneed.
29. Landing on the heels can fracture the calcaneus. A heavy object landing on the dorsal surface of the foot could fracture the metatarsal bones or even the tarsal bones.

Chapter 8

1. d; 3. c
5. If the sternocostal synchondrosis were to ossify, becoming a synostosis, there would no longer be any stretch through the costal cartilage, the thorax could not expand, and respiration would be severely hampered.
7. e; 9. c; 11. e; 13. b
15. a. suture, little or no movement
    b. syndesmosis, some movement
    c. complex synovial joints: the humeroulnoradial joint is a hinge joint and the radioulnar joint is a pivot joint; all have considerable movement
17. d; 19. b; 21. c

Chapter 9

1. c; 3. d; 5. e; 7. a; 9. d; 11. d
13. Muscular dystrophy results from gradual atrophy of skeletal muscle fibers and their replacement with connective tissue. Myasthenia gravis results from the degeneration of the receptors for acetylcholine on the postsynaptic membranes of skeletal muscle fibers. If an inhibitor of acetylcholinesterase is administered, the result should be an increase in the concentration of acetylcholine in the nerve muscle synapse. Thus, more acetylcholine is available to bind to acetylcholine receptors. In people suffering from myasthenia gravis, the increased concentration of acetylcholine in the synapse allows acetylcholine to bind a greater percentage of the acetylcholine receptors present and causes the muscle contractions to increase in strength. In people who have muscular dystrophy, the muscle contractions do not increase in strength because muscle atrophy is the cause of the weakness. The additional acetylcholine in the neuromuscular junction has no effect on the weakened muscle fibers.
15. e; 17. d; 19. c; 21. a; 23. d
25. The color of the meat depends on the number of capillaries (blood is red) within the muscle and is based on its myoglobin content (myoglobin is also red). After cooking, the tissues look darker, not red, because the blood and myoglobin have been broken down by the heat. Thus, the dark meat is darker because it contains more capillaries and more myoglobin. This is consistent with slow-twitch muscle fibers, which are used for maintaining posture and for performing slow movements, such as walking. The white muscle, with fewer capillaries and lower myoglobin content, is consistent

with fast-twitch muscle fibers, which are used for quick movements, such as running or flying.

27. a; 29. d

31. In experiment A, the students used anaerobic respiration as they started to run in place, but aerobic respiration also increased to meet most of their energy needs. When they stopped, their respiration rate was increased over resting levels because of the repayment of the oxygen deficit due to anaerobic respiration. In experiment B, almost all of the students' respiration came from anaerobic respiration because the students held their breath while running in place. Consequently, the students had a much larger oxygen deficit. The students' respiratory rate and depth would be greater than in experiment A, or their respiration rates would be elevated for a longer period of time than in experiment A.

33. c

35. The shape of an active tension curve for skeletal muscle can be seen in figure 9.22. In contrast, an active tension curve is much flatter for smooth muscle. That is, for each increase in the length of a muscle fiber, there is little change in the active tension produced by the smooth muscle fiber. Smooth muscle has the ability to increase in length without much increase in tension.

Chapter 10

1. d; 3. b; 5. c; 7. d; 9. b; 11. c;
13. a; 15. d; 17. b; 19. b; 21. a; 23. c

25. If you are sitting on a chair with the book open on the desk in front of you, very few muscles are required to turn the page. First the arm is extended slightly to push the forearm and hand along the edge of the book. This can be accomplished with the anterior portion of the deltoid muscle. The hand is then slightly supinated by means of the supinator muscle. The thumb and index finger are then flexed to grasp the page to be turned. This movement involves the flexor pollicis brevis and flexor digitorum superficialis to the index finger (the flexor digitorum profundus may also be involved). The page is then turned by extending the fingers (extensor digitorum), pronating the hand (pronator quadratus and pronator teres), and medially rotating the arm (pectoralis major, teres major, latissimus dorsi).

27. e; 29. b; 31. b

Chapter 11

1. b; 3. c; 5. c; 7. b; 9. a; 11. b;
13. a; 15. d; 17. e; 19. d; 21. b

23. Smooth muscle cells contract spontaneously in response to spontaneous depolarizations that produce action potentials. One way action potentials can be produced spontaneously is if membrane permeability to Na^+ spontaneously increases. As a result, some Na^+ enters the smooth muscle cells and causes a small depolarizing graded potential. The small depolarization can cause voltage-gated Na^+ channels to open, which results in further depolarization, thereby stimulating additional Na^+ voltage-gated ion channels to open. This positive-feedback cycle can continue until the plasma membrane is depolarized to its threshold level and an action potential is produced.

25. Action potential conduction along a myelinated nerve fiber is more energy-efficient because the action potential is propagated by saltatory conduction, which produces action potentials at the nodes of Ranvier. Compared with an unmyelinated nerve fiber, only a small portion of the myelinated neuron's membrane has action potentials. Thus, less Na^+ flows into the neuron (depolarization) and less K^+ flows out of the neuron (repolarization). Consequently, the sodium-potassium pump has to move fewer ions in order to restore ion concentrations. Because the sodium-potassium pump requires ATP, myelinated axons use less ATP than unmyelinated axons.

27. e

29. With aging, the amount of myelin surrounding axons decreases, which decreases the speed of action potential propagation. Also, at synapses, action potentials in the presynaptic terminal take longer to cause the production of action potentials in the postsynaptic membrane. It is believed this results from a reduced release of neurotransmitter by the presynaptic terminal and a reduced number of receptors in the postsynaptic membrane.

31. If the motor neurons supplying skeletal muscle are innervated by both excitatory and inhibitory neurons, blocking the activity of the inhibitory neurons with strychnine results in overstimulation of the motor neurons by the excitatory neurons.

33. When the neurotoxin binds to ligand-gated Na^+ channels in the postsynaptic membrane of a skeletal muscle fiber, they open, and Na^+ enters the cell, producing graded potentials. When the graded potentials reach threshold, an action potential is produced, stimulating the muscle fiber to contract. However, the neurotoxin tends to remain bound to the ligand-gated Na^+ channels, which prevents ACh from binding. Thus, the nervous system's ability to stimulate the muscle fiber decreases as more and more neurotoxin binds to ligand-gated Na^+ channels. Because the ligand-gated Na^+ channels with bound neurotoxin remain open, Na^+ continues to enter the muscle fiber, causing its resting membrane potential to depolarize. Eventually, the membrane becomes so depolarized that it is unresponsive to stimulation. Death from a cobra bite usually occurs because of paralysis of respiratory muscles.

35. e

Chapter 12

1. d; 3. c; 5. b; 7. c; 9. c; 11. a;
13. c; 15. e; 17. c

19. The sciatic nerve has rootlets from L4 to S3. Depending on the rootlet compressed, pain can be felt in different locations.

21. The plaster cast is pressing against the common fibular (peroneal) nerve at the neck of the fibula. Tingling is expected along the lateral and anterior leg and the dorsum of the foot.

Chapter 13

1. a; 3. c; 5. e; 7. b; 9. b; 11. e;
13. d; 15. c

17. The cerebellum, which is in charge of controlling coordinated muscle movement and maintaining muscle tone, was damaged in this patient.

19. b

21. Enlargement of the lateral and third ventricles, without enlargement of the fourth ventricle, suggests a blockage between the third and fourth ventricles in the cerebral aqueduct. This defect, called aqueductal stenosis, is a common congenital problem.

23. d; 25. b; 27. b; 29. c

31. I: Test vision; II: Have the person describe the smell of something placed under the nose; III: Test eye movement; IV: Test the ability to move the eye down and out; V: Test the sense of feeling in the face; VI: Test the ability to move the eye to the side; VII: Test the ability to taste an item on the front of the tongue and check for facial expression; VIII: Test the ability to hear; IX: Test the ability to swallow; X: Test the ability to swallow and check the uvula when the mouth is opened (the uvula will "point" away from the side where X is not working); XI: Test the ability to turn the head; XII: Have the person protrude their tongue (if XII is not functioning on one side, the tongue will "point" toward the damaged side).

33. The abducens nerves supply the lateral rectus muscles, which are responsible for moving the eyes laterally (abducting the eyes). Damage to the abducens nerve on the left side reduced or eliminated Stanley's ability to abduct his left eye. The inability

to move the left eye in concert with the right eye results in double vision.

35. It is likely that Afton experienced facial palsy (Bell palsy), which can be temporary. This condition may result from a stroke or a tumor, or it can be triggered by inflammation of the parotid gland, anesthesia, or exposure of the superficial branches of the nerve to cold (which is probably the cause in Afton's case). The loss of motor tone in the face is due to decreased innervation of the muscles of facial expression. Also, some muscles of the pharynx are affected, but these are not related to drooping of the face.

Chapter 14

1. c; 3. e; 5. a; 7. b; 9. a; 11. b; 13. c

15. a. The most likely explanation is that the olfactory neurons have adapted and no longer respond to the odor stimulus.
    b. The fact that people can hear the sound when they make a conscious effort indicates that the hair cells in the spiral organ have not adapted and are still able to detect the sound stimulus. Many action potentials arriving in the brain are prevented from causing conscious perception until we consciously "pay attention" to the stimulus. For example, you may not be paying attention to general conversations in a crowded room or hall until someone says your name. The sound of your name leaps out of the surrounding babble, and you are suddenly interested.

17. The fibers of the lateral spinothalamic tract carry impulses for pain and temperature. A lesion in the area where these fibers decussate results in the bilateral loss of pain and temperature sensations only at the level of the lesion, but no loss of sensation below the lesion. This occurs because fibers decussating above or below the lesion, as well as tracts that pass lateral to the lesion, are unaffected. This disorder, called syringomyelia, is often caused by a spinal cord tumor.

19. b; 21. a; 23. b

25. The damaged tracts are the lateral corticospinal tract, controlling motor functions on the right side of the body, and the lateral spinothalamic tract for pain and temperature sensations from the left side of the body. Damage to these tracts in the right side of the spinal cord produces the observed symptoms because within the cord the lateral spinothalamic tract crosses over at the level of entry and is therefore located on the opposite side of the cord from its peripheral nerve endings, whereas the corticospinal tract lies on the same side of the cord as its target muscles.

27. b; 29. d

31. The subdural hematoma is likely to be over the medial portion of the left side of the cerebral hemisphere in the area of the premotor cortex and expanding to the area of the primary motor cortex. The premotor area must be intact for a person to carry out complex, skilled, or learned movements, especially those requiring manual dexterity. If blood is removed from the hematoma and if no more bleeding occurs, it is likely that Perry's motor movements will improve rapidly.

33. d; 35. b; 37. e

39. Memory for the 10 minutes prior to the accident was stored in short-term memory and was disrupted before it could be transferred to long-term memory. Anytime a person suffers a concussion, there is a possibility that postconcussion syndrome will develop later. Symptoms include muscle tension or migraine headaches, reduced alcohol tolerance, difficulty learning new things, reduction in creativity and motivation, fatigue, and personality changes. The syndrome may last a month to a year. Postconcussion syndrome may be the result of a slowly occurring subdural hematoma, which may be missed in an early examination.

Chapter 15

1. e; 3. a; 5. b; 7. c; 9. c; 11. c; 13. a; 15. c; 17. a

19. Carrots contain vitamin A (retinoic acid), which can be used to form retinal. Retinal and opsin combine to form rhodopsin, which is found in rods. Rhodopsin is necessary for rods to respond to low levels of light. Lack of vitamin A can result in lack of rhodopsin and night blindness.

21. A lesion of the optic chiasm results in visual loss in both the right and left temporal fields, a condition called bitemporal hemianopsia, or tunnel vision. Tunnel vision can cause problems for normal functions, such as driving a car, because the peripheral vision is severely limited. This condition can also suggest a much more serious problem, such as a pituitary tumor just posterior to the optic chiasm.

23. d; 25. a; 27. b

29. The most likely area damaged is the spiral organ, where waves result in the production of action potentials. The action is much like ocean waves breaking on the shore during a violent storm, compared with those breaking in from a calm ocean. Specifically, damage likely occurs in the part of the spiral organ near the oval window because this part of the basilar membrane vibrates the most in response to high-frequency sounds.

31. Normally, airborne sounds cause the tympanic membrane to vibrate, resulting in the movement of the middle ear ossicles and the production of waves in the perilymph of the scala vestibuli. Vibration of the skull bones can also cause vibration of the perilymph in the scala vestibuli.

33. c

Chapter 16

1. e; 3. a; 5. b; 7. e; 9. d

11. The sympathetic division of the ANS is responsible for dilation of the pupil. Preganglionic fibers from the upper thoracic region of the spinal cord pass through spinal nerves (T1 and T2), into the white rami communicantes, and into the sympathetic chain ganglia. The preganglionic fibers ascend the sympathetic chain and synapse with postganglionic neurons in the superior cervical sympathetic chain ganglia. The axons of the postganglionic neurons leave the sympathetic chain ganglia as small nerves that project to the iris of the eye.

13. a. pelvic splanchic nerves
    b. outflow of gray ramus
    c. vagus nerve
    d. oculomotor nerve
    e. pelvic splanchnic nerve

15. a; 17. e

19. Epinephrine causes vasoconstriction and confines the drug to the site of administration. This increases the drug's duration of action locally and decreases its systemic effects. Vasoconstriction also reduces bleeding if a dry field (an area clear of blood on its surface) is required.

21. Because cutting the white rami of T1–T4 does not affect the drug's action, sympathetic preganglionic neurons in the spinal cord and sympathetic centers in the brain can be ruled out as a site of action. Because cutting the vagus nerves eliminates the drug's effect, the drug cannot be acting at the synapse between the preganglionic neurons and the postganglionic neurons, or between the synapse of the postganglionic neuron and the effector of either division of the ANS. The drug must therefore excite parasympathetic centers in the brainstem, resulting in decreased heart rate.

23. c

25. a. Responses in a person who is extremely angry are primarily controlled by the sympathetic division of the ANS. These responses include increased heart rate and blood pressure, decreased blood flow to the internal organs, increased blood flow to skeletal muscles, decreased

contractions of the intestinal smooth muscle, flushed skin in the face and neck region, and dilation of the pupils of the eyes.

b. For a person who has just finished eating and is relaxing, parasympathetic reflexes are more important than sympathetic reflexes. The blood pressure and heart rate are at normal resting levels, the blood flow to the internal organs is greater, contractions of smooth muscle in the intestines are greater, and secretions that achieve digestion are more active. If the urinary bladder or the colon becomes distended, autonomic reflexes that result in urination or defecation can result. Blood flow to the skeletal muscles is reduced.

Chapter 17

1. c; 3. e; 5. d; 7. b

9. Elevated GnRH levels in the blood as a result of the GnRH-secreting tumor would cause the down-regulation of GnRH receptors in the anterior pituitary. This would decrease the ability of GnRH to stimulate the anterior pituitary, and the rate of LH and FSH secretion by the anterior pituitary would decrease and remain decreased as long as the GnRH levels were chronically elevated. Therefore, the functions of the reproductive system controlled by LH and FSH would decrease.

11. Because thyroid hormones are important in regulating the basal metabolic rate, their long half-life is an advantage. Thyroid hormones are secreted and have a prolonged effect without large fluctuations in the basal metabolic rate. If thyroid hormones had a short half-life, the basal metabolic rate could fluctuate with changes in the rate of secretion of thyroid hormones. Certainly, the rate of secretion of thyroid hormones would have to be controlled within narrow limits if it did have a short half-life.

13. b

15. Insulin levels normally change in order to maintain normal blood sugar levels, despite periodic fluctuations in sugar intake. A constant supply of insulin from a skin patch might result in insulin levels that are too low when blood sugar levels are high (after a meal) and might be too high when blood sugar levels are low (between meals). In addition, insulin is a protein hormone that would not readily diffuse through the lipid barrier of the skin (see chapter 5).

17. c; 19. e; 21. e

23. When the hormone binds to its receptor, the α subunit of the G protein is released. However, GTP must bind to the α subunit before it can have its normal effect. If the α subunit cannot bind to GTP, the hormone has no effect on the target tissue.

25. a

Chapter 18

1. e; 3. e; 5. c; 7. b; 9. c

11. Polydipsia and polyuria are consistent with both diabetes mellitus and diabetes insipidus. Diabetes mellitus, however, is consistent with an increased urine osmolality because of the large amount of glucose lost in the urine. Diabetes insipidus is consistent with urine with a low specific gravity because little water is reabsorbed by the kidneys. Thus, urine has an osmolality close to that of the body fluids, and the rapid loss of dilute urine results in a decrease in blood pressure. Therefore, polyuria with a low specific gravity is consistent with diabetes insipidus but not with diabetes mellitus. The administration of ADH would reverse the symptoms of diabetes insipidus. Neither polydipsia nor polyuria results from a lack of glucagon or aldosterone.

13. d; 15. b; 17. c; 19. a; 21. d;
23. d; 25. e

27. It is likely that Julie's elevated ACTH levels are causing elevated blood levels of cortisol, which in turn are causing the observed symptoms. The elevated ACTH levels are probably due to a hormone-secreting tumor (adenoma) in the anterior pituitary gland. According to National Institutes of Health sources, pituitary adenomas cause 70% of Cushing syndrome cases, excluding those caused by glucocorticoid use. Most people with the disorder have a single adenoma. Cushing syndrome affects women five times more often than men. The most widely used treatment is surgical removal of the tumor, known as transsphenoidal adenomectomy. Using a special microscope and fine instruments, the surgeon approaches the pituitary gland through a nostril or an opening made below the upper lip. Because this procedure is extremely delicate, patients are often referred to centers specializing in this type of surgery. The success rate of this procedure is more than 80% when performed by a surgeon with extensive experience. If surgery fails or produces only a temporary cure, the surgery can be repeated, often with good results. Radiation of the pituitary gland is another possible treatment.

29. d; 31. a

33. The first piece of information is that, although Dylan is always hungry and eating, he is losing weight. You learned in this chapter that two of the most important hormones for metabolism and blood glucose regulation are insulin and glucagon. The disease most often affiliated with disruptions in insulin regulation is diabetes mellitus. Normally, insulin allows for glucose to enter the body's cells for energy production, but in cases of diabetes mellitus, insufficient insulin causes excessive circulating blood glucose. When coupled with Dylan's other symptoms, chronic thirst and urination, there is a clear link to diabetes mellitus. Recall from chapter 3 that membrane transport proteins can be saturated by their transport molecule. The reason Dylan is always thirsty is that too much glucose is filtered out of his blood in his kidneys to be reabsorbed; the excess filtered glucose saturates its transport molecule. In the filtrate, the glucose has an osmotic effect and prevents the kidneys from conserving water. The sweet, or acetone, breath is derived from the fact that, when starved from glucose, cells begin to catalyze lipids, and the by-products of this metabolism are acetone and other molecules chemically related to acetone. Dylan was treated with injectable insulin and began to feel much better. However, if Dylan keeps eating candy and drinking sugary soda, elevated blood glucose levels will continue to dehydrate Dylan and his neurons can become dehydrated. This would cause him to feel irritable and unwell. Dylan may also experience a sudden weight gain because of sugar intake while injecting insulin. His cells will be able to use the extra glucose and may convert it to adipose tissue. Dylan should eat a healthy diet and avoid sugary foods.

35. e; 37. c

Chapter 19

1. e; 3. a; 5. a; 7. c; 9. b

11. Blood doping increases the number of red blood cells in the blood, thereby increasing its oxygen-carrying capacity. The increased number of red blood cells also makes it more difficult for the blood to flow through the blood vessels, increasing the heart's workload.

13. a; 15. b; 17. e; 19. e; 21. a;
23. d; 25. c

27. Grace has hemolytic anemia. The RBC is lower than normal because the red blood cells are being destroyed faster than they are being replaced. With fewer red blood cells, hemoglobin and hematocrit are lower than normal. Bilirubin levels are above normal because of the breakdown of the hemoglobin released from the ruptured red blood cells.

Chapter 20

1. e; 3. a.
5. The walls of the ventricles are thicker than the walls of the atria because the ventricles must produce a greater pressure to pump blood into the arteries. Only a small pressure is required to pump blood from the atria into the ventricles during diastole. The wall of the left ventricle is thicker than the wall of the right ventricle because the left ventricle produces a much greater pressure to force blood through the aorta than the right ventricle produces to move blood through the pulmonary trunk and pulmonary arteries.
7. b; 9. a; 11. d; 13. b
15. A drug that prolongs the plateau of cardiac muscle cell action potentials prolongs the time each action potential exists and increases the refractory period. Therefore, the drug slows the heart. A drug that shortens the plateau shortens the length of time each action potential exists and shortens the refractory period. Therefore, the drug can allow the heart rate to increase further.
17. An ECG measures the electrical activity of the heart and would not indicate a slight heart murmur. Heart murmurs are detected by listening to the heart sounds. The boy may have a heart murmur, but the mother does not understand the basis for making such a diagnosis.
19. a
21. During systole, the cardiac muscle in the right and left ventricles contracts, which compresses the coronary arteries. During diastole, the cardiac muscle of the ventricles relaxes, and blood flow through the coronary arteries increases. The diastolic pressure is sufficient to cause blood to flow through the coronary arteries during diastole.
23. d; 25. a; 27. b; 29. d; 31. c; 33. e
35. When both common carotid arteries are clamped, the blood pressure within the internal carotid arteries drops dramatically. The decreased blood pressure is detected, and the baroreceptor reflex increases heart rate and stroke volume. The resulting increase in cardiac output causes the increase in blood pressure.

Chapter 21

1. b; 3. a; 5. d; 7. d; 9. a; 11. d; 13. c
15. a. great cardiac vein, coronary sinus; or anterior cardiac vein
    b. transverse sinus, sigmoid sinus, internal jugular vein, brachiocephalic vein, superior vena cava
    c. retromandibular vein, external jugular vein, subclavian vein, brachiocephalic vein, superior vena cava
    d. *deep:* vein of hand, radial or ulnar vein, brachial vein, axillary vein, subclavian vein, brachiocephalic vein, superior vena cava
    superficial: vein of hand, radial or ulnar vein, cephalic or basilic vein, axillary vein, subclavian vein, brachiocephalic vein, superior vena cava
    e. *deep:* vein of foot, dorsalis veins of foot, anterior tibial vein, popliteal vein, femoral vein, external iliac vein, common iliac vein, inferior vena cava
    superficial: vein of foot, great saphenous vein, external iliac vein, common iliac vein, inferior vena cava; or vein of foot, small saphenous vein, popliteal vein, femoral vein, external iliac vein, common iliac vein, inferior vena cava
    f. gastric vein or gastroepiploic vein, hepatic portal vein, hepatic sinusoids, hepatic vein, inferior vena cava
    g. renal vein, inferior vena cava
    h. hemiazygous vein or accessory hemiazygous vein, azygous vein, superior vena cava
17. b
19. According to Laplace's law, as the diameter of a blood vessel increases, the force applied to the vessel wall increases, even if the pressure remains constant. The increased connective tissue in the walls of the large blood vessels makes the wall of those vessels stronger and more capable of resisting the force applied to the wall.
21. b
23. Decreased liver function includes a decrease in the synthesis of plasma proteins. Consequently, the concentration of plasma proteins decreases, and the colloid osmotic pressure of the blood decreases. Less water moves by osmosis into the capillaries at the venous ends, and edemas result.
25. d
27. Chemoreceptors in the medulla oblongata detect carbon dioxide and the pH of the blood. The normal blood levels of CO_2 and pH stimulate these chemoreceptors, which in turn stimulate the vasomotor center. The vasomotor center keeps blood vessels partially constricted under resting conditions. This basal level of activity is called vasomotor tone. Blowing off CO_2 reduces the blood levels of carbon dioxide and increases the pH of the body fluids. These changes reduce vasomotor tone and result in vasodilation. If a person hyperventilates and blows off CO_2, the stimulus to the vasomotor center decreases, which results in a decrease in vasomotor tone. The decrease in vasomotor tone results in a decrease in systemic blood pressure. If the blood pressure decreases enough, the blood flow to the brain decreases and can cause a sensation of dizziness or even loss of consciousness.
29. b; 31. d; 33. b
35. Answer *b* is correct. Shortly after Jack was wounded, the loss of blood caused his blood pressure to decrease. Rapidly, the baroreceptor and adrenal medullary mechanisms were activated. His heart rate increased, and peripheral vasoconstriction increased as a result. There is no indication that the CNS ischemic response was activated because it requires a severe decrease in blood flow to the brain. The renin-angiotensin-aldosterone mechanism is activated as the systemic blood pressure decreases. Angiotensin II is a potent vasoconstrictor that helps the baroreceptor mechanism increase peripheral resistance. The increase in aldosterone secretion increases Na^+ and, consequently, water reabsorption in the kidneys, but it requires approximately 24 hours to be active. The fluid shift mechanism operates, but it takes several hours to function. The ADH mechanism is activated in response to a substantial decrease in blood pressure; it helps maintain blood volume by reducing the amount of urine produced.

Chapter 22

1. d; 3. e; 5. d
7. Elevating the limb reduces blood pressure in the limb, resulting in less fluid movement from the blood into the tissues (see chapter 21). Thus, the edema is reduced as fluid moves out of the tissues faster than it enters them. Massage moves lymph through the lymphatic vessels in the same fashion as the contraction of skeletal muscle does. The periodic application of pressure to lymphatic vessels forces lymph to flow toward the trunk of the body, but valves prevent flow in the reverse direction. The removal of lymph from the tissue helps relieve edema.
9. That there is no immediate effect indicates a reservoir of T cells exists in the lymphatic tissue. As the reservoir is depleted over time, the number of lymphocytes decreases and cell-mediated immunity is depressed, the animal becomes more susceptible to infections, and the ability to reject grafts decreases. The ability to produce antibodies decreases because of the loss of helper T cells that are normally involved with the activation of B cells.
11. e; 13. a; 15. d
17. The correct answer is *b*. The immune response that occurred in the next several hours was primarily the innate immune

response. Tissue was damaged, and mediators of inflammation were released. As a consequence, there were increases in capillary permeability, coagulation of blood, and chemotaxis of neutrophils; all are components of inflammation and the innate immune response. Increased mitosis of memory B cells is likely, but more than a few hours would be required, and it is most likely to occur in response to antigens. Bacteria and other antigens may enter the wound, and an adaptive immune response may result, but this, too, would take more than several hours to occur.

19. e; 21. b; 23. d

25. The correct answer is *a.* Upon first exposure to a type of antigen, the unprocessed antigens are ingested by macrophages, and the ingested antigens are broken down to fragments as they are processed. The processed antigen fragments are combined with MCH II molecules and transported to the cells' surfaces. A specific helper T cell recognizes the processed antigens bound to the MCH II molecules (the MHC II complex) at the macrophages' surfaces and binds to the MHC II complexes. Costimulation occurs, and interleukin-1 is released from the macrophages, while interleukin-2 is released from the T lymphocytes. As a result, the helper T cells undergo mitosis (see figure 22.19).

27. b; 29. a; 31. d

33. The infant's antibody-mediated immunity is not functioning properly, whereas his cell-mediated immunity is working properly. This explains his susceptibility to extracellular bacterial infections and his resistance to intracellular viral infections. It took so long to become apparent because IgG from the mother crossed the placenta and provided the infant with protection. The infant began to get sick after these antibodies degraded.

35. If the patient has already been vaccinated, the booster shot stimulates a memory (secondary) response and rapid production of antibodies against the toxin. If the patient has never been vaccinated, vaccinating now is not effective because there is not enough time for the patient to develop their own primary response. Therefore, antiserum is given to provide immediate, but temporary, protection. Sometimes both are given: The antiserum provides short-term protection, and the tetanus vaccine stimulates the patient's immune system to provide long-term protection. If the shots are given at the same location in the body, the antiserum (antibodies against the tetanus toxin) can cancel the effects of the tetanus vaccine (tetanus toxin is altered to be nonharmful).

Chapter 23

1. a; 3. d; 5. d

7. The left side of the diaphragm moves superiorly. During inspiration, thoracic volume increases as the right side of the diaphragm moves inferiorly and the intercostal muscles move the ribs outward. Increased thoracic volume causes a decrease in pressure in the thoracic cavity. As a result, the pressure on the superior surface of the diaphragm is less than on the inferior surface. The paralyzed left side of the diaphragm moves superiorly because of this pressure difference.

9. c; 11. d; 13. d; 15. c

17. The hose increases dead space and therefore decreases alveolar ventilation. Jenny has to compensate by increasing respiratory rate or tidal volume. If the hose is too long, she will not be able to compensate. Furthermore, with a long hose, air is simply moved back and forth in the hose so that little exchange of air between the atmosphere and the lungs takes place. Another consideration is the effect of water pressure on the thorax, which decreases compliance and increases the work of ventilation. In fact, a few feet under water, there is enough pressure on the thorax to prevent the intake of air, even through a short hose is connected to the atmosphere.

19. c

21. The increase in atmospheric pressure increases the partial pressure of oxygen. According to Henry's law, as the partial pressure of oxygen increases, the amount of oxygen dissolved in the body fluids increases. The increase in dissolved oxygen is detrimental to the gangrene bacteria. Because hemoglobin is already saturated with oxygen, the HBO treatment does not increase hemoglobin's ability to pick up oxygen in the lungs.

23. d; 25. b; 27. c; 29. c

31. While hyperventilating and making ready to leave your instructor behind, you might make the following arguments:
    - I would argue that hyperventilation increases the oxygen content of the air in the lungs; therefore, you would have more oxygen to use when holding your breath.
    - It is hemoglobin that is saturated. Hyperventilation increases the amount of oxygen dissolved in the blood plasma.
    - Hyperventilation decreases the amount of carbon dioxide in the blood. This makes it possible to hold your breath longer because of a decreased urge to take a breath.
    - Hyperventilation activates alveoli not in use because increasing alveolar oxygen and decreasing alveolar carbon dioxide cause lung arterioles to relax, thereby increasing blood flow through the lungs.

Chapter 24

1. a; 3. d; 5. b; 7. b; 9. a; 11. d

13. Without adequate amounts of hydrochloric acid, the pH in the stomach is not low enough for the activation of pepsin. This loss of pepsin function would result in inadequate protein digestion. However, if the food is well chewed, proteolytic enzymes in the small intestine (e.g., trypsin, chymotrypsin) can still digest the protein. If the stomach secretion of intrinsic factor decreases, the absorption of vitamin B12 is hindered. Inadequate amounts of vitamin B12 can result in decreased red blood cell production (pernicious anemia).

15. e

17. Cholera toxin irreversibly activates a G protein that causes persistent activation of the chloride channel. The activated channel allows excessive movements of chloride from the cells into the digestive tract. Water follows the osmotic gradient generated by the chloride, which leads to diarrhea. Conversely, mutations in the channel reduce the movement of chloride into the digestive tract. A thick mucus builds up on the surface of the epithelial cells, leading to some symptoms of cystic fibrosis.

19. e

21. Blockage of the common bile duct can result in jaundice (due to an accumulation of bile pigments in the blood) and clay-colored stools (due to lack of bile pigments in the feces). Other symptoms include abdominal pain, nausea, and vomiting. In addition, fat absorption is impaired because of the absence of bile salts in the duodenum, and a loose, bulky stool results. Lack of fat absorption reduces the absorption of fat-soluble vitamins, such as vitamin K, impairing normal clotting function.

23. a

25. The patient is still able to defecate. Following a meal, the gastrocolic and duodenocolic reflexes initiate mass movement of the feces into the rectum. In the rectum, local reflexes and the defecation reflex (integrated in the sacral level of the spinal cord and not requiring connections to high brain centers) cause defecation. However, the patient loses awareness of the need to defecate (due to loss of sensory input to the brain) and the ability to prevent defecation voluntarily via the external anal sphincter.

27. e; 29. c

31. Dietary changes are beneficial but alone would not likely be sufficient for FH patients. Only about 15% of the cholesterol in the body comes from diet; the remainder is synthesized, primarily in the liver.

A diet reduced in total fat and cholesterol, along with exercise, would help lower serum LDL cholesterol levels. However, because FH patients no longer have the normal LDL receptor-mediated feedback loop, increased cellular synthesis of cholesterol would continue. Often statin drug therapy is necessary to restore cholesterol levels to normal.

Chapter 25

1. d; 3. e; 5. d
7. The % Daily Values appearing on food labels are based on a 2000 kcal/day diet. Therefore, the % Daily Value for saturated fat for one serving of this food would be 10% (2/20 = 0.10, or 10%).
9. The % Daily Value is the amount of the nutrient in one serving divided by its Daily Value. Therefore, the % Daily Value is 10% (10/100 = 0.10, or 10%).
11. Copper is necessary for the proper functioning of the electron-transport chain. Inadequate copper in the diet results in reduced ATP production—that is, not enough energy.
13. This approach will not work because he is not losing stored energy from adipose tissue. In the sauna, he gains heat, primarily by convection from the hot air and by radiation from the hot walls. The evaporating sweat is removing heat gained from the sauna. The loss of water will make him thirsty, and he will regain the lost weight from fluids he drinks and food he eats.
15. b; 17. d; 19. e; 21. a
23. As ATP breakdown increased, more ATP would be produced to replace that used. Over an extended time, the ATP must be produced through aerobic respiration. Therefore, oxygen consumption and basal metabolic rate increase. The production of ATP requires the metabolism of carbohydrates, lipids, or proteins. As these molecules are used at a faster-than-normal rate, body weight decreases. Increased appetite and increased food consumption resist the loss in body weight. As ATP is produced and used, heat is released as a by-product. The heat raises body temperature, which is resisted by the dilation of blood vessels in the skin and by sweating.
25. During a fever, the body produces heat by shivering. The body also conserves heat by the constriction of blood vessels in the skin (producing pale skin) and by reduction in sweat loss (producing dry skin). When the fever breaks—that is, "the crisis is over"—heat is lost from the body to lower body temperature to normal. This is accomplished by the dilation of blood vessels in the skin (producing flushed skin) and increased sweat loss (producing wet skin).

Chapter 26

1. d; 3. c; 5. b; 7. e; 9. b; 11. a; 13. a; 15. c; 17. c
19. Answer *a* is correct. The respiratory system responds to below-normal pH by increasing the rate of respiration. However, Marvin's kidneys were not able to respond to the low pH because of the hypoxic injury. The hypoxic injury is responsible for the metabolic acidosis (lower-than-normal blood pH), and the damaged nephrons could not adequately increase HCO_3^- reabsorption or H^+ secretion.
21. d; 23. d; 25. d
27. The beer consumed composes a large volume of hyposmotic fluid, which increases blood volume and causes blood osmolality to decrease. The increased blood volume is detected by baroreceptors, and the decreased blood osmolality is detected by osmoreceptors in the hypothalamus. The response to these stimuli is inhibition of ADH secretion. The alcohol in the beer also inhibits ADH secretion. The increased volume inhibits the renin-angiotensin-aldosterone hormone mechanism, which in turn inhibits aldosterone secretion. The changes in aldosterone, however, take much longer to influence kidney function than changes in ADH. As a result of these changes, a large volume of dilute urine is produced until the blood osmolality and blood volume return to normal.
29. As aldosterone levels decrease, sodium reabsorption in the nephron decreases; consequently, plasma sodium levels decrease. The sodium is lost in the urine, and water follows the sodium by osmosis. Thus, a large amount of urine having a high concentration of sodium is produced. The loss of water reduces blood volume, which causes the low blood pressure. As aldosterone levels decrease, potassium secretion into the nephron also decreases, resulting in increased plasma potassium levels. The increased extracellular potassium causes the depolarization of nerve and muscle membranes, leading to tremors of skeletal muscles and cardiac arrhythmias, including fibrillation.
31. Urea is partially responsible for the high osmolality of the interstitial fluid in the medulla of the kidney. Because a high osmolality of the interstitial fluid must exist for the kidney to produce a concentrated urine, a small amount of urea in the kidney results in the production of dilute urine.
33. Answer *d* is correct. For at least 2 hours before help arrived, Marvin suffered from hemorrhagic shock, which was responsible for hypoxic injury to his kidneys. Hypoxic injury is the consequence of ischemia due to prolonged shock, and it results in cells sloughing off and blocking the lumen of the nephron so that the filtrate cannot flow through it. Marvin's urine volume decreased because cells of the nephron sloughed off and blocked the lumen of the nephron. The reabsorption of wastes was increased because the flow rate of the filtrate slowed and the wastes were able to pass through the wall of the nephron and reenter the circulatory system, rather than becoming part of the filtrate. This explains the increased blood volume and the distended neck veins. The high blood H^+ is due to decreased H^+ secretion; and the high blood K^+ is due to decreased K^+ secretion. There is no increase in blood HCO_3^- because the rate of HCO_3^- reabsorption is not increased. There is a decrease in erythropoietin secretion by the damaged kidney, which explains the reduced red blood cell count.
35. Water that moves into the collecting duct cells would diffuse into the interstitial fluid at a reduced rate because of the reduced number of aquaporins. Urine volume would increase because of water retention in the distal convoluted tubule and collecting ducts. Urine concentration would decrease because of dilution by the water. ADH can cause an increase in the number of aquaporin-2 water channel proteins in the apical membrane of the distal convoluted tubules and collecting ducts, but not in aquaporin-3 or aquaporin-4 channels in the basal membranes. These channels determine the permeability of the basal membranes to water. Therefore, ADH would not be an effective treatment. The net effect would be polyuria, which is similar to nephrogenic diabetes insipidus caused by an abnormal aquaporin-2 water channel protein.
37. d

Chapter 27

1. a; 3. c; 5. a; 7. a
9. When excess glucose is not reabsorbed, it osmotically obligates water to remain in the nephron. This results in the production of a large amount of urine, called polyuria, with a consequent loss of water, salts, and glucose. The loss of water can be compensated for by increasing fluid intake. The intense thirst that stimulates increased fluid intake is called polydipsia. The loss of salts can be compensated for by increasing the salt intake. The high glucose levels in the blood

increase the blood osmolality, thus stimulating the secretion of ADH. This increases the permeability of the distal convoluted tubule and collecting duct to water. Normally, this allows reabsorption of water from the collecting ducts and thus conserves water. However, if glucose levels in the urine are high enough, water loss increases even with high levels of ADH.

11. b; 13. b; 15. a
17. Blocking H^+ secretion produces acidosis. Because H^+ is exchanged for Na^+, the Na^+ remains in the urine as sodium bicarbonate. This effectively prevents the reabsorption of HCO_3^- and produces an alkaline urine. The blood pH is reduced because H^+ is not being secreted as rapidly by the nephron. The respiratory rate increases because of the stimulatory effect of decreased blood pH on the respiratory center.
19. c
21. Answer *e* is correct. The rate of stomach secretion increased prior to the time Harry vomited. Gastric secretions include a high concentration of HCl. As the stomach secretes HCl, it secretes H^+ into the stomach and absorbs HCO_3^- into the blood. Also, after Harry took the antacid, which is mostly $NaHCO_3$, the HCO_3^- was absorbed and entered the circulatory system. A significant amount of HCO_3^- entering the circulatory system causes an increase in the blood pH. The increased pH affects the regulatory centers of the respiratory system and causes respiration to slow. Although the kidney's response is slower, by 24 hours later, the rate of H^+ secretion by the kidney slows, and HCO_3^- absorption slows in response to an increase in the blood pH. The slower rates of respiration, H^+ secretion, and HCO_3^- absorption by the kidneys help keep the blood pH from becoming higher than normal.

Chapter 28

1. e; 3. a; 5. d; 7. b
9. The correct answer is *d*. If a testis fails to descend into the scrotal sac, the higher body temperature causes the spermatogonia to degenerate. Consequently, that testis produces no sperm cells. Sustentacular cells remain in the seminiferous tubules, and interstitial cells remain in the testis. Both testosterone secretion by the interstitial cells and LH secretion from the anterior pituitary gland remain normal.
11. b; 13. a
15. Removing the testes would eliminate the major source of testosterone. Blood levels of testosterone would therefore decrease. Because testosterone has a negative-feedback effect on the hypothalamus and pituitary gland, GnRH, FSH, and LH secretion would increase, and the blood levels of these hormones would increase. An adult male's primary and secondary sex characteristics are already developed; however, removal of the testes would eliminate sperm production. Also, the lack of testosterone would cause a decrease in sex drive and muscular strength.
17. Ideally, the pill would inhibit spermatogenesis. Using the same approach as the birth control pill in females, the inhibition of FSH and LH secretion should work. Chronic administration of GnRH suppresses FSH and LH levels enough to cause infertility through down-regulation. However, lack of LH can also result in reduced testosterone levels and loss of sex drive. Some evidence indicates that administering testosterone in the proper amounts reduces FSH and LH secretion, thus leading to less sperm cell production while still maintaining normal sex drive. For a large percentage of males, the technique results in a sperm concentration in the semen that is too low to allow fertilization. However, the technique is not sufficiently precise to be used as a standard birth control technique.
19. The correct answer is *d*. Decreased blood flow to the anterior pituitary gland would result in decreased LH secretion, not increased LH secretion. The decreased secretion of LH from the anterior pituitary causes a decrease in the blood level of testosterone. Because it takes approximately 74 days to produce a sperm cell, the sperm count is likely to remain normal during the week when the blood LH and FSH levels are reduced.
21. c; 23. b; 25. c; 27. c; 29. e;
31. d; 33. a
35. The removal of the ovaries from a 20-year-old female eliminates the major site of estrogen and progesterone production, thereby causing an increase in GnRH, FSH, and LH levels due to lack of negative feedback. We would expect to see the symptoms of menopause, such as cessation of menstruation and reduction in the size of the uterus, vagina, and breasts. A temporary reduction in sex drive may also occur.
37. The progesterone inhibits GnRH in the hypothalamus. Consequently, the anterior pituitary is not stimulated to produce LH and FSH. Lack of LH prevents ovulation, and lack of FSH prevents development of the follicles. LH is also required for the maturation of follicles prior to ovulation. Without follicle development, inadequate estrogen is produced, which causes the hot flashes.

Chapter 29

1. b
3. The approximate length of time the embryo has been developing, called the postovulatory age, is 14 days less than the time since the last menstrual period (LMP). In this case, the postovulatory age is 30 days (44 – 14). By this time, the neural tube has closed, the somites have formed, the digestive tract is developing, the limb buds have appeared, a tubular beating heart is present, and the lungs are developing. Because reproductive structures are still just forming, male and female embryos are indistinguishable at this age.
5. a; 7. d; 9. c
11. The fever occurred on days 21–31 of development, during the time of neural tube closure (days 18–25). If the fever prevented neural tube closure, the child could be born with anencephalus or spina bifida.
13. a; 15. e; 17. c; 19. e; 21. a;
23. b; 25. a; 27. d; 29. b; 31. c
33. Answer *b* is correct. Müllerian-inhibiting hormone causes the duct system that gives rise to female internal reproductive structures to degenerate in male fetuses. If the hormone is not effective, female internal reproductive structures, such as oviducts and a uterus, develop, at least to some degree, along with internal male reproductive structures. Because the developing testes produce testosterone, male external reproductive structures develop.
35. A person with blood type AB has the genotype I^AI^B but no *i* allele. A person with blood type O has a genotype of *ii*. Because the AB parent has no *i* allele, an AB individual cannot be the parent of a child with blood type O.

Glossary

Many of the words in this glossary and throughout the text are followed by a simplified phonetic spelling showing pronunciation. The pronunciation key reflects standard clinical usage, with minor modifications, as presented in *Stedman's Medical Dictionary* (27th edition), which has long been a leading reference volume in the health sciences.

A

A band Length of the myosin myofilament in a sarcomere.

abdomen (AB-doh-men) Belly, between the thorax and the pelvis.

abduction (ab-DUK-shun) [L., *abductio,* take away] Movement away from the midline.

absolute refractory period (AB-soh-loot ree-FRAK-tohr-ee) Portion of the action potential during which the membrane is insensitive to all stimuli, regardless of their strength.

absorptive cell (ab-SOHRP-tiv) Cell on the surface of villi of the small intestines and the luminal surface of the large intestine that is characterized by having microvilli; secretes digestive enzymes and absorbs digested materials on its free surface.

absorptive state Immediately after a meal when nutrients are being absorbed from the intestine into the circulatory system.

accommodation (ah-kom-oh-DAY-shun) [L., *ac* + *commodo,* to adapt] Ability of electrically excitable tissues, such as nerve or muscle cells, to adjust to a constant stimulus so that the magnitude of the local potential decreases through time; also called adaptation.

acetabulum (as-eh-TAB-you-lum) [L., shallow vinegar vessel or cup] Cup-shaped depression on the external surface of the coxa.

acetylcholine (ACh) (AS-eh-til-KOH-leen) Neurotransmitter substance released from motor neurons, all preganglionic neurons of the parasympathetic and sympathetic divisions, all postganglionic neurons of the parasympathetic division, some postganglionic neurons of the sympathetic division, and some central nervous system neurons.

acetylcholinesterase (AS-eh-til-KOH-leen-ESS-ter-ase) Enzyme found in the synaptic cleft that causes the breakdown of acetylcholine to acetic acid and choline, thus limiting the stimulatory effect of acetylcholine.

Achilles tendon *See* calcaneal tendon.

acid (ASS-id) Molecule that is a proton donor; any substance that releases hydrogen ions (H^+).

acidic Solution containing more than 10^{-27} mol of hydrogen ions per liter; has a pH less than 7.

acinus; pl. **acini** (ASS-ih-nus, AS-i-nie) [L., berry, grape] Grape-shaped secretory portion of a gland. The terms *acinus* and *alveolus* are sometimes used interchangeably. Some authorities differentiate the terms: Acini have a constricted opening into the excretory duct, whereas alveoli have an enlarged opening.

acromion (ah-CROH-mee-on) [Gr., *akron,* extremity + *omos,* shoulder] Bone comprising the tip of the shoulder.

acrosome (AK-roh-sohm) [Gr., *akron,* extremity + *soma,* body] Cap on the head of the spermatozoon, with hydrolytic enzymes that help the spermatozoon penetrate the ovum.

actin filament (AK-tin) Thin myofilament within the sarcomere; composed of two F actin molecules, tropomyosin, and troponin molecules.

action potential [L., *potentia,* power, potency] Change in membrane potential in an excitable tissue that acts as an electric signal and is propagated in an all-or-none fashion.

activation energy (ak-ti-VAY-shun) Energy that must be added to molecules to initiate a reaction.

active site Portion of an enzyme in which reactants are brought into close proximity and that plays a role in reducing activation energy of the reaction.

active tension Tension produced by the contraction of a muscle.

active transport Carrier-mediated process that requires ATP and can move substances against a concentration gradient.

adaptive immunity Immune status in which there is an ability to recognize, remember, and destroy a specific antigen.

adenohypophysis (AD-eh-noh-high-POF-i-sis) Portion of the hypophysis derived from the oral ectoderm; also called anterior pituitary.

adenosine diphosphate (ADP) (ah-DEN-oh-seen die-FOSS-fate) Adenosine, an organic base, with two phosphate groups attached to it. Adenosine diphosphate combines with a phosphate group to form adenosine triphosphate.

adenosine triphosphate (ATP) (ah-DEN-oh-seen try-FOS-fate) Adenosine, an organic base, with three phosphate groups attached to it. Energy stored in ATP is used in nearly all of the endergonic reactions in cells.

adenylate cyclase (a-DEN-i-late CY-klase) An enzyme acting on ATP to form 3′,5′-cyclic AMP plus pyrophosphate (two phosphate groups). A crucial step in the regulation and formation of the intracellular chemical signal 3′,5′-cyclic AMP.

adipocyte (AD-i-poh-syte) Fat cell.

adipose (AD-i-pose) [L., *adeps,* fat] Fat.

adrenal gland (ah-DREE-nal) [L., *ad,* to + *ren,* kidney] Located near the superior pole of each kidney, it is composed of a cortex and a medulla. The adrenal medulla is a highly modified sympathetic ganglion that secretes the hormones epinephrine and norepinephrine; the cortex secretes aldosterone and cortisol as its major secretory products. Also called suprarenal gland.

adrenergic neuron (ad-re-NER-jik) Nerve fiber that secretes norepinephrine (or epinephrine) as a neurotransmitter substance.

adrenergic receptor Receptor molecule that binds to adrenergic agents, such as epinephrine and norepinephrine.

adrenocorticotropic hormone (ACTH) (ah-DREE-noh-KOR-tih-koh-TROH-pik) Hormone of the adenohypophysis that governs the nutrition and growth of the adrenal cortex, stimulates it to functional activity, and causes it to secrete cortisol.

adventitia (ad-ven-TISH-ah) [L., *adventicius,* coming from abroad, foreign] Outermost covering of any organ or structure that is properly derived from outside the organ and does not form an integral part of the organ.

aerobic respiration (air-OH-bik) Breakdown of glucose in the presence of oxygen to produce carbon dioxide, water, and approximately 38 ATPs; includes glycolysis, the citric acid cycle, and the electron-transport chain.

afferent arteriole (AF-eh-rent ar-TEER-ee-ole) Branch of a cortical radiate of the kidney that conveys blood to the glomerulus.

afferent division Nerve fibers that send impulses from the periphery to the central nervous system.

agglutination (ah-glue-tih-NAY-shun) [L., *ad,* to + *gluten,* glue] Process by which blood cells, bacteria, or other particles are caused to adhere to one another and form clumps.

agglutinin (ah-GLOO-ti-nin) Antibody that binds to an antigen and causes agglutination.

agglutinogen (ah-gloo-TIN-oh-jen) Antigen on surface of red blood cells that can stimulate the production of antibodies (agglutinins) that combine with the antigen and cause agglutination.

agranulocyte (ay-GRAN-you-loh-site) Nongranular leukocyte (monocyte or lymphocyte).

ala; pl. **alae** (AY-la, AY-lee) [L., a wing] Wing-shaped structure.

aldosterone (al-DOS-ter-ohn) Steroid hormone produced by the zona glomerulosa of the adrenal cortex that facilitates potassium exchange for sodium in the distal renal tubule, causing sodium reabsorption and potassium and hydrogen secretion.

alkaline (AL-kah-line) Solution containing less than 10^{-7} mol of hydrogen ions per liter; has a pH greater than 7.0.

alkalosis (al-kah-LOH-sis) Condition characterized by blood pH of 7.45 or above.

allantois (ah-LAN-toh-is) Tube extending from the embryonic hindgut into the umbilical cord; forms the urinary bladder.

allele (ah-LEEL) [Gr., *allelon,* reciprocally] Any one of a series of two or more different genes that may occupy the same position or locus on a specific chromosome.

all-or-none principle When a stimulus is applied to a cell, an action potential is either produced or not. In muscle cells, the cell either contracts to the maximum extent possible (for a given condition) or does not contract.

alternative pathway Part of the nonspecific immune system for activation of complement.

alveolar duct (al-VEE-oh-lar) Part of the respiratory passages beyond a respiratory bronchiole; from it arise alveolar sacs and alveoli.

alveolar gland Gland in which the secretory unit has a saclike form and an obvious lumen.

alveolar sac Two or more alveoli that share an opening.

alveolus; pl. **alveoli** (al-VEE-oh-lus, al-VEE-oh-lie) Cavity. Examples include the sockets into which teeth fit, the endings of the respiratory system, and the terminal endings of secretory glands.

amino acid (ah-MEE-noh ASS-id) Class of organic acids that constitute the building blocks for proteins.

amplitude-modulated signal (AM-pli-tood) Signal that varies in magnitude or intensity, such as with large versus small concentrations of hormones.

ampulla; pl. **ampullae** (am-PUL-ah, am-PUL-lee) [L., two-handled bottle] Saclike dilatation of a semicircular canal; contains the crista ampullaris. Wide portion of the uterine tube between the infundibulum and the isthmus.

amygdala (ah-MIG-dah-lah) [L. fr. Gr., *amygydale,* almond] Nucleus in the temporal lobe of the brain, amygdaloid nucleus; also called amydaloid nuclear complex.

amylase (AM-il-ase) One of a group of starch-splitting enzymes that cleave starch, glycogen, and related polysaccharides.

anabolism (ah-NAB-oh-lizm) [Gr., *anabole,* a raising up] All of the synthesis reactions that occur within the body; requires energy.

anaerobic respiration (an-air-OH-bik) Breakdown of glucose in the absence of oxygen to produce lactic acid and two ATPs; consists of glycolysis and the reduction of pyruvic acid to lactic acid.

anal canal Terminal portion of the digestive tract.

anal triangle Posterior portion of the perineal region through which the anal canal opens.

analgesic (an-al-JEE-zik) Compound capable of producing analgesia, without producing anesthesia or loss of consciousness, characterized by reduced response to painful stimuli.

anaphase (AN-uh-faze) Time during cell division when chromatids divide (or, in the case of first meiosis, when the chromosome pairs divide).

anastomoses (ah-NAS-toh-MOH-seez) Natural communication, direct or indirect, between two blood vessels or other tubular structures. An opening created by surgery, trauma, or disease between two or more normally separate spaces or organs.

anatomical dead air space Volume of the conducting airways from the external environment down to the terminal bronchioles.

androstenedione (an-droh-STEEN-die-ohn) Androgenic steroid of weaker potency than testosterone; secreted by the testis, ovary, and adrenal cortex.

anencephaly (AN-en-SEF-ah-lee) [Gr., *an* + *enkephalos,* no brain] Defective development of the brain and absence of the bones of the cranium. Only a rudimentary brainstem and a trace of basal ganglia are present.

aneurysm (AN-you-rizm) [Gr., *eurys,* wide] Dilated portion of an artery.

angiotensin I (an-jee-oh-TEN-sin) Peptide derived when renin acts on angiotensinogen.

angiotensin II Peptide derived from angiotensin I; stimulates vasoconstriction and aldosterone secretion; also called active angiotensin.

anion (AN-eye-on) Ion carrying a negative charge.

antagonist (an-TAG-on-ist) Muscle that works in opposition to another muscle.

anterior chamber Chamber of the eye between the cornea and the iris.

anterior interventricular sulcus Groove on the anterior surface of the heart, marking the location of the septum between the two ventricles.

anterior pituitary gland *See* adenohypophysis.

antibody (AN-tih-body) Protein found in the plasma that is responsible for humoral immunity; binds specifically to antigen.

antibody-mediated immunity Immunity due to B cells and the production of antibodies.

anticoagulant (AN-tee-koh-AG-you-lant) Agent that prevents coagulation.

antidiuretic hormone (ADH) (an-tee-die-you-RET-ik) Hormone secreted from the neurohypophysis that acts on the kidney to reduce the output of urine; also called vasopressin because it causes vasoconstriction.

antigen (AN-tih-jen) [anti(body) + Gr., *gen,* producing] Substance that induces a state of sensitivity or resistance to infection or toxic substances after a latent period; substance that stimulates the specific immune system; also called epitope.

antigenic determinant (an-ti-JEN-ik) Specific part of an antigen that stimulates an immune system response by binding to receptors on the surface of lymphocytes; also called epitope.

antithrombin (an-tee-THROM-bin) Substance that inhibits or prevents the effects of thrombin so that blood does not coagulate.

antrum (AN-trum) [Gr., *antron,* a cave] Cavity of an ovarian follicle filled with fluid containing estrogen.

anulus fibrosus (AN-yoo-lus fye-BROH-sus) [L., fibrous ring] Fibrous material forming the outer portion of an intervertebral disk.

anus (AY-nus) Lower opening of the digestive tract through which fecal matter is extruded.

aorta (ay-OR-tuh) [Gr., *aorte* from *aeiro,* to lift up] Large, elastic artery that is the main trunk of the systemic arterial system; carries blood from the left ventricle of the heart and passes through the thorax and abdomen.

aortic arch [L., bow] Curve between the ascending and descending portions of the aorta.

aortic body One of the smallest bilateral structures, similar to the carotid bodies, attached to a small branch of the aorta near its arch; contains chemoreceptors that respond primarily to decreases in blood oxygen; less sensitive to decreases in blood pH or increases in carbon dioxide.

apex (AY-peks) [L., summit or tip] Extremity of a conical or pyramidal structure. The apex of the heart is the rounded tip directed anteriorly and slightly inferiorly.

Apgar score Named for U.S. anesthesiologist Virginia Apgar (1909–1974). Evaluation of a newborn infant's physical status by assigning numerical values to each of five criteria: appearance (skin color), pulse (heart rate), grimace (response to stimulation), activity (muscle tone), and respiratory effort; a score of 10 indicates the best possible condition.

apical ectodermal ridge Layer of surface ectodermal cells at the lateral margin of the embryonic limb bud; stimulates growth of the limb.

apical foramen [L., aperture] Opening at the apex of the root of a tooth; gives passage to the nerve and blood vessels.

apocrine sweat gland (AP-oh-krin) [Gr., *apo,* away from + *krino,* to separate] Gland whose cells contribute cytoplasm to its secretion (e.g., mammary glands). Sweat glands that produce organic secretions traditionally are called apocrine. These sweat glands, however, are actually merocrine glands.

appendicular skeleton (ah-pen-DIK-yoo-lar) The portion of the skeleton consisting of the upper limbs and the lower limbs and their girdles.

appositional growth (ap-oh-ZISH-uh-null) [L., *ap* + *pono,* to put or place] To place one layer of bone, cartilage, or other connective tissue against an existing layer.

aqueous humor (AYK-wee-us) Watery, clear solution that fills the anterior and posterior chambers of the eye.

arachnoid (ah-RAK-noyd) [Gr., *arachne,* spider, cobweb] Thin, cobweb-appearing meningeal layer surrounding the brain; the middle of the three layers.

arcuate artery (AR-kyu-ate) Artery that originates from the interlobar arteries of the kidney and forms an arch between the cortex and medulla of the kidney.

areola; pl. **areolae** (ah-REE-oh-luh, ah-REE-oh-lee) [L., area] Circular, pigmented area surrounding the nipple; its surface is dotted with little projections caused by the presence of the areolar glands beneath.

areolar gland (ah-REE-oh-lar) Gland forming small, rounded projections from the surface of the areola of the mamma.

arrectores pilorum; pl. **arrector pili** (ah-rek-TOH-reez pee-LOHR-um, ah-REK-tor PIE-lee) [L., that which raises; hair] Smooth muscle attached to the hair follicle and dermis that raises the hair when it contracts.

arterial capillary (ar-TEER-ee-al) Capillary opening from an arteriole or a metarteriole.

arteriole (ar-TEER-ee-ole) Minute artery with all three tunics that transports blood to a capillary.

arteriosclerosis (ar-TEER-ee-oh-skler-OH-sis) [L., *arterio* + Gr., *sklerosis,* hardness] Hardening of the arteries.

arteriovenous anastomosis (ar-TEER-ee-oh-VEE-nus ah-NAS-toh-MOH-sis) Vessel through which blood is shunted from an arteriole to a venule without passing through the capillaries.

artery (AR-ter-ee) Blood vessel that carries blood away from the heart.

articular cartilage (ar-TIK-yoo-lar KAR-tih-lij) Hyaline cartilage covering the ends of bones within a synovial joint.

articulation (ar-tik-you-LAY-shun) Place where two bones come together; also called joint.

arytenoid cartilages (ar-ih-TEE-noyd) Small, pyramidal laryngeal cartilages that articulate with the cricoid cartilage.

ascending aorta Part of the aorta from which the coronary arteries arise.

ascending colon (KOH-lon) Portion of the colon between the small intestine and the right colic flexure.

asthma (AZ-mah) Condition of the lungs in which widespread narrowing of airways occurs, caused by contraction of smooth muscle, edema of the mucosa, and mucus in the lumen of the bronchi and bronchioles.

astrocyte (ASS-troh-site) [Gr., *astron,* star + *kytos,* a hollow, a cell] Star-shaped neuroglia cell involved with forming the blood-brain barrier.

atherosclerosis (ATH-er-oh-skler-OH-sis) Arteriosclerosis characterized by irregularly distributed lipid deposits in the intima of large and medium-sized arteries.

atomic number (ah-TOM-ik) Number of protons in each type of atom.

atrial diastole (AY-tree-al die-AS-toh-lee) Dilation of the heart's atria.

atrial natriuretic hormone (ANH) (AY-tree-al nay-tree-yoo-RET-ik) Peptide released from the atria when atrial blood pressure is increased; lowers blood pressure by increasing the rate of urinary production, thus reducing blood volume.

atrial systole (ay-TREE-al SIS-toh-lee) Contraction of the atria.

atrioventricular (AV) bundle (AY-tree-oh-ven-TRIK-you-lar) Bundle of modified cardiac muscle fibers that projects from the AV node through the interventricular septum.

atrioventricular (AV) node Small node of specialized cardiac muscle fibers that gives rise to the atrioventricular bundle of the conduction system of the heart.

atrioventricular valve One of two valves closing the openings between the atria and ventricles.

atrium; pl. **atria** (AY-tree-um, AY-tree-ah) [L., entrance hall] One of two chambers of the heart into which veins carry blood.

auditory cortex (AW-dih-tor-ee KOR-teks) Portion of the cerebral cortex that is responsible for the conscious sensation of sound; in the dorsal portion of the temporal lobe within the lateral fissure and on the superolateral surface of the temporal lobe.

auditory ossicles (OS-ik-elz) Bones of the middle ear; include the malleus, incus, and stapes.

auditory tube Auditory canal; extends from the middle ear to the nasopharynx.

auricle (AW-ri-kul) [L., *auris,* ear] Part of the external ear that protrudes from the side of the head; also called pinna. Small pouch projecting from the superior, anterior portion of each atrium of the heart.

auscultatory (aw-SKUL-ta-to-ree) Relating to auscultation, listening to the sounds made by the various body structures as a diagnostic method.

autoimmune disease (aw-toh-im-YUNE) Disease resulting from a specific immune system reaction against self-antigens.

autonomic ganglia (aw-toh-NOM-ik GANG-glee-ah) Ganglia containing the nerve cell bodies of the autoimmune division of the nervous system.

autonomic nervous system (ANS) Nervous system composed of nerve fibers that send impulses from the central nervous system to smooth muscle, cardiac muscle, and glands.

autophagia (aw-toh-FAY-jee-uh) [Gr., *auto,* self + *phageia,* to eat] Segregation and disposal of organelles within a cell.

autoregulation (AW-toh-reg-yoo-LAY-shun) Maintenance of a relatively constant blood flow through a tissue despite relatively large changes in blood pressure; maintenance of a relatively constant glomerular filtration rate despite relatively large changes in blood pressure.

autorhythmic Spontaneous and periodic—for example, in smooth muscle, spontaneous (without nervous or hormonal stimulation) and periodic contractions.

autosome (AW-toh-zom) [Gr., *auto,* self + *soma,* body] Any chromosome other than a sex chromosome; normally exists in pairs in somatic cells and singly in gametes.

axial skeleton (AK-see-al) Skull, vertebral column, and rib cage.

axillary (AK-sil-air-ee) Relating to the axilla; the space below the shoulder joint, bounded by the pectoralis major anteriorly, the latissimus dorsi posteriorly, the serratus anterior medially, and the humerus laterally.

axolemma (AK-soh-LEM-ah) [Gr., *axo* + *lemma,* husk] Plasma membrane of the axon.

axon (AK-son) [Gr., axis] Main central process of a neuron that normally conducts action potentials away from the neuron cell body.

axon hillock Area of origin of the axon from the nerve cell body.

axoplasm (AK-soh-plazm) Neuroplasm or cytoplasm of the axon.

B

B cell Type of lymphocyte responsible for antibody-mediated immunity.

baroreceptor (bar-oh-ree-SEP-ter) Sensory nerve ending in the walls of the atria of the heart, venae cavae, aortic arch, and carotid sinuses; sensitive to stretching of the wall caused by increased blood pressure; also called pressoreceptor.

baroreceptor reflex Detects changes in blood pressure and produces changes in heart rate, heart force of contraction, and blood vessel diameter that return blood pressure to homeostatic levels.

basal ganglia (BAY-sal GANG-glee-ah) Nuclei at the base of the cerebrum involved in controlling motor functions.

base (bays) Molecule that is a proton acceptor; any substance that binds to hydrogen ions. Lower part or bottom of a structure; the base of the heart is the flat portion directed posteriorly and superiorly; veins and arteries project into and out of the base, respectively.

basement membrane (BAYS-ment MEM-brain) Specialized extracellular material located at the base of epithelial cells and separating them from the underlying connective tissues.

basilar membrane (BAS-ih-lar) Wall of the membranous labyrinth bordering the scala tympani; supports the organ of Corti.

basophil (BAY-so-fill) [Gr., *basis,* baso + *phileo,* to love] White blood cell with granules that stain specifically with basic dyes; promotes inflammation.

belly (BEL-ee) Largest portion of muscle between the origin and insertion.

beta-oxidation (BAY-tah ok-si-DAY-shun) Metabolism of fatty acids by removing a series of two-carbon units to form acetyl-CoA.

bicarbonate ion (bye-KAR-bon-ate) Anion (HCO_3^-) remaining after the dissociation of carbonic acid.

bicuspid valve (bi-KUS-pid) Valve closing the orifice between the left atrium and left ventricle of the heart; also called mitral valve.

bile (BYE-al) Fluid secreted from the liver into the duodenum; consists of bile salts, bile pigments, bicarbonate ions, cholesterol, fats, fat-soluble hormones, and lecithin.

bile canaliculus (BYE-al kan-ah-LIK-yoo-lus) One of the intercellular channels approximately 1 μm or less in diameter that occurs between liver cells into which bile is secreted; empties into the hepatic ducts.

bile salt Organic salt secreted by the liver that functions as an emulsifying agent.

bilirubin (bill-ee-RU-bin) [L., *bili* + *ruber,* red] Bile pigment derived from hemoglobin during the destruction of red blood cells.

biliverdin (bill-ee-VER-din) Green bile pigment formed from the oxidation of bilirubin.

binocular vision (bin-OK-yoo-lar) [L., *bini,* paired + *oculus,* eye] Vision using two eyes at the same time; responsible for depth perception when the visual fields of the eyes overlap.

bipolar neuron (bye-POH-ler) One of the three categories of neurons consisting of a neuron with two processes—one dendrite and one axon—arising from opposite poles of the cell body.

blastocele (BLAS-toe-seel) [Gr., *blastos,* germ + *koilos,* hollow] Cavity in the blastocyst.

blastocyst (BLAS-toh-sist) [Gr., *blastos,* germ + *kystis,* bladder] Stage of mammalian embryos that consists of the inner cell mass and a thin trophoblast layer enclosing the blastocele.

bleaching In response to light, retinal separates from opsin.

blind spot (blynd) Point in the retina where the optic nerve penetrates the fibrous tunic; contains no rods or cones and therefore does not respond to light.

blood clot Coagulated phase of blood.

blood colloid osmotic pressure (BCOP) Osmotic pressure due to the concentration difference of proteins across a membrane that does not allow passage of the proteins.

blood groups Classification of blood based on the type of antigen found on the surface of red blood cells.

blood island Aggregation of mesodermal cells in the embryonic yolk sac that forms vascular endothelium and primitive blood cells.

blood pressure [L., *pressus,* to press] Tension of the blood within the blood vessels; commonly expressed in units of millimeters of mercury (mm Hg).

blood-brain barrier Permeability barrier controlling the passage of most large-molecular compounds from the blood to the cerebrospinal fluid and brain tissue; consists of capillary endothelium and may include the astrocytes.

blood-thymic barrier Layer of reticular cells that separates capillaries from thymic tissue in the cortex of the thymus gland; prevents large molecules from leaving the blood and entering the cortex.

Bohr effect Named for Danish physiologist Christian Bohr (1855–1911). Shift of the oxygen-hemoglobin dissociation curve to the right or left because of changes in blood pH. The definition sometimes is extended to include shifts caused by changes in blood carbon dioxide levels.

bony labyrinth (LAB-ih-rinth) Part of the inner ear; contains the membranous labyrinth that forms the cochlea, vestibule, and semicircular canals.

Boyle's law The pressure of a gas is equal to the volume of a container times the constant, K, for a given temperature. Assuming a constant temperature, the pressure of a gas is inversely proportional to its volume.

brachial (BRAY-kee-al) [L., *brachium,* arm] Relating to the arm.

branchial arch Typically, six arches in vertebrates; in the lower vertebrates, they bear gills, but they appear transiently in the higher vertebrates and give rise to structures in the head and neck.

broad ligament Peritoneal fold passing from the lateral margin of the uterus to the wall of the pelvis on each side.

bronchiole (BRONG-key-ole) One of the finer subdivisions of the bronchial tubes, less than 1 mm in diameter; has no cartilage in its wall but does have relatively more smooth muscle and elastic fibers.

brush border Epithelial surface consisting of microvilli.

buffer (BUFF-er) Mixture of an acid and a base that reduces any changes in pH that would otherwise occur in a solution when acid or base is added to the solution.

bulb of the penis Expanded posterior part of the corpus spongiosum of the penis.

bulb of the vestibule Mass of erectile tissue on each side of the vagina.

bulbar conjunctiva (kon-junk-TIE-vah) Conjunctiva that covers the surface of the eyeball.

bulbourethral gland (BUL-boh-you-REE-thral) One of two small compound glands that produce a mucoid secretion; it discharges through a small duct into the spongy urethra.

bulbus cordis (BUL-bus) [L., plant bulb] End of the embryonic cardiac tube where blood leaves the heart; becomes part of the ventricle.

bursa; pl. **bursae** (BURR-sah, BURR-see) [L., purse] Closed sac or pocket containing synovial fluid, usually found in areas where friction occurs.

bursitis (burr-SIGH-tis) [L., *purse* + Gr., *ites,* inflammation] Inflammation of a bursa.

C

calcaneal tendon (kal-KAY-nee-uhl) Common tendon of the gastrocnemius, soleus, and plantaris muscle that attaches to the calcaneus; also called Achilles tendon.

calcitonin (kal-sih-TOH-nin) Hormone released from parafollicular cells that acts on tissues to cause a decrease in blood levels of calcium ions.

calmodulin (kal-MOD-yoo-lin) [*calcium* + *modulate*] Protein receptor for Ca^{2+} that plays a role in many Ca^{2+}-regulated processes, such as smooth muscle contraction.

calorie (cal) (KAL-oh-ree) [L., *calor,* heat] Unit of heat content or energy. The quantity of energy required to raise the temperature of 1 g of water 1°C.

calpain (KAL-payn) Enzyme involved in changing the shape of dendrites; involved with long-term memory.

calyx; pl. **calyces** (KAY-licks, KAL-i-seez) [Gr., cup of a flower] Flower-shaped or funnel-shaped structure; specifically, one of the branches or recesses of a renal pelvis into which the tips of the renal pyramids project.

cancer (KAN-ser) Any of various types of malignant neoplasms, most of which invade surrounding tissues, may metastasize to several sites, and are likely to recur after attempted removal and to cause death of the patient unless adequately treated.

canine (KAY-nine) Referring to the cuspid tooth.

cannula (KAN-yoo-lah) [L., *canna,* reed] Tube; often inserted into an artery or a vein.

capacitation (kuh-PAS-ih-tay-shun) [L., *capax,* capable of] Process whereby spermatozoa acquire the ability to fertilize ova; occurs in the female genital tract.

capitulum (kah-PIT-you-lum) [L., *caput,* head] Head-shaped structure.

carbaminohemoglobin (kar-BAM-i-noh-hee-moh-GLOH-bin) Carbon dioxide bound to hemoglobin by means of a reactive amino group on the hemoglobin.

carbohydrate (kar-boh-HIGH-drate) Monosaccharide (simple sugar) or the organic molecules composed of monosaccharides bound together by chemical bonds—for example, glycogen. For each carbon atom in the molecule, there are typically one oxygen molecule and two hydrogen molecules.

carbonic acid/bicarbonate buffer system One of the major buffer systems in the body; major components are carbonic acid and bicarbonate ions.

carbonic anhydrase Enzyme that catalyzes the reaction between carbon dioxide and water to form carbonic acid.

carcinoma (kar-sih-NOH-mah) Malignant neoplasm derived from epithelial tissue.

cardiac [Gr., *kardia,* heart] Related to the heart.

cardiac cycle [Gr., *kyklos,* circle] Complete round of cardiac systole and diastole.

cardiac nerve Nerve that extends from the sympathetic chain ganglia to the heart.

cardiac output (CO) Volume of blood pumped by the heart per minute; also called minute volume.

cardiac part Region of the stomach near the opening of the esophagus.

cardiac reserve [L., *re* + *servo,* to keep back, reserve] Work that the heart is able to perform beyond that required during ordinary circumstances of daily life.

carotid body (kah-ROT-id) One of the small organs near the carotid sinuses; contains chemoreceptors that respond primarily to decreases in blood oxygen; less sensitive to decreases in blood pH or increases in carbon dioxide.

carotid sinus Enlargement of the internal carotid artery near the point where the internal carotid artery branches from the common carotid artery; contains baroreceptors.

carpal (KAR-pal) [Gr., *karpos,* wrist] Bone of the wrist.

carrier Person in apparent health whose chromosomes contain a pathologic mutant gene, which may be transmitted to their children.

cartilage (KAR-tih-lij) [L., *cartilage,* gristle] Firm, smooth, resilient, nonvascular connective tissue.

cartilaginous joint (kar-ti-LAJ-i-nus) Bones connected by cartilage; includes synchondroses and symphyses.

catabolism (kah-TAB-oh-lizm) [Gr., *katabole,* a casting down] All of the decomposition reactions that occur in the body; releases energy.

catalyst (KAT-uh-list) Substance that increases the rate at which a chemical reaction proceeds without being changed permanently.

cataract (KAT-ah-rakt) Complete or partial opacity of the lens of the eye.

cation (KAT-eye-on) [Gr., *kation,* going down] Ion carrying a positive charge.

caveola; pl. **caveolae** (kav-ee-OH-la, kav-ee-OH-lee) [L., small pocket] Shallow invagination in the membranes of smooth muscle cells that may perform a function similar to that of both the T tubules and sarcoplasmic reticulum of skeletal muscle.

cecum (SEE-kum) [L., *caecus,* blind] Cul-de-sac forming the first part of the large intestine.

cell-mediated immunity Immunity due to the actions of T cells and null cells.

celom; pl. **celoma** (SEE-lom, see-LOH-mah) [Gr., *koilo* + *amma,* a hollow] Principal cavities of the trunk—for example, the pericardial, pleural, and peritoneal cavities. Separate in the adult, they are continuous in the embryo.

cementum (seh-MEN-tum) [L., *caementum,* rough quarry stone] Layer of modified bone covering the dentin of the root and neck of a tooth; blends with the fibers of the periodontal membrane.

central nervous system (CNS) Major subdivision of the nervous system, consisting of the brain and spinal cord.

central vein Terminal branches of the hepatic veins that lie centrally in the hepatic lobules and receive blood from the liver sinusoids.

centrosome (SEN-troh-sohm) Specialized zone of cytoplasm close to the nucleus and containing two centrioles.

cerebellum (ser-eh-BELL-um) [L., little brain] Separate portion of the brain attached to the brainstem at the pons; important in maintaining muscle tone, balance, and coordination of movement.

cerebrospinal fluid (CSF) (SER-eh-broh-SPY-nal) Fluid filling the ventricles and surrounding the brain and spinal cord.

ceruminous glands (seh-ROO-mi-nus) Modified sebaceous glands in the external acoustic meatus that produce cerumen (earwax).

cervical canal (SER-vih-kal) Canal extending from the isthmus of the uterus to the opening of the uterus into the vagina.

cervix; pl. **cervices** (SER-viks, SER-vi-seez) [L., neck] Lower part of the uterus extending from the isthmus of the uterus into the vagina.

chalazion (kah-LAY-zee-on) Chronic inflammation of a meibomian gland; also called meibomian cyst.

cheek (cheek) Side of the face forming the lateral wall of the mouth.

chemical signal Molecule that binds to a macromolecule, such as receptors or enzymes, and alters their function; also called ligand.

chemoreceptor (kee-moh-ree-SEP-ter) Sensory cell that is stimulated by a change in the concentration of chemicals to produce action potentials. Examples include taste receptors, olfactory receptors, and carotid bodies.

chemoreceptor reflex (kee-moh-ree-SEP-ter REE-fleks) Chemoreceptors detect a decrease in blood oxygen, an increase in carbon dioxide, or a decrease in pH and produce an increased rate and depth of respiration and, by means of the vasomotor center, vasoconstriction.

chemosensitive area (kem-oh-SEN-si-tiv, kee-moh-SEN-si-tiv) Chemosensitive neurons in the medulla oblongata detect changes in blood, carbon dioxide, and pH.

chemotactic factor (kee-moh-TAK-tik) Part of a microorganism or chemical released by tissues and cells that act as chemical signals to attract leukocytes.

chemotaxis (kee-moh-TAK-sis) [Gr., *chemo* + *taxis,* orderly arrangement] Attraction of living protoplasm (cells) to chemical stimuli.

chief cell Cell of the parathyroid gland that secretes parathyroid hormone. Cell of a gastric gland that secretes pepsinogen.

chloride (KLOHR-eyed) Compound containing chlorine—for example, salts of hydrochloric acid.

chloride shift Diffusion of chloride ions into red blood cells as bicarbonate ions diffuse out; maintains electrical neutrality inside and outside the red blood cells.

choana; pl. **choanae** (KOH-an-ee, KO-ah-nay) *See* internal naris.

cholecystokinin (KOH-leh-sis-toh-KIE-nin) Hormone liberated by the upper intestinal mucosa on contact with gastric contents; stimulates the contraction of the gallbladder and the secretion of pancreatic juice high in digestive enzymes.

cholinergic neuron (kol-in-ER-jik) Nerve fiber that secretes acetylcholine as a neurotransmitter substance.

chondroblast (KON-droh-blast) [Gr., *chondros,* gristle, cartilage + *blastos,* germ] Cartilage-producing cell.

chondrocyte (KON-droh-site) [Gr., *chondros,* gristle, cartilage + *kytos,* a cell] Mature cartilage cell.

chorda tympani; pl. **chordae** (KOR-dah TIM-pah-nee, KOHR-dee) Branch of the facial nerve that conveys taste sensation from the front two-thirds of the tongue.

chordae tendineae (KOHR-dee TEN-di-nee-ee) [L., cord] Tendinous strands running from the papillary muscles to the atrioventricular valves.

choroid (KOR-oid) Portion of the vascular tunic associated with the sclera of the eye.

choroid plexus [Gr., *chorioeides,* membranelike] Specialized plexus located within the ventricles of the brain that secretes cerebrospinal fluid.

chromatid (KROH-mah-tid) One-half of a chromosome; separates from its partner during cell division.

chromatin (KROH-ma-tin) Colored material; the genetic material in the nucleus.

chromosome (KROH-moh-sohm) Colored body in the nucleus, composed of DNA and proteins and containing the primary genetic information of the cell; 23 pairs in humans.

chronic pain Prolonged pain.

chylomicron (kigh-lo-MY-kron) [Gr., *chylos,* juice + *micros,* small] Microscopic particle of lipid surrounded by protein; in chyle and blood.

chymotrypsin (kigh-moh-TRIP-sin) Proteolytic enzyme formed in the small intestine from the pancreatic precursor chymotrypsinogen.

ciliary body (SILL-ee-air-ee) Structure continuous with the choroid layer at its anterior margin that contains smooth muscle cells; functions in accommodation.

ciliary gland Modified sweat gland that opens into the follicle of an eyelash, keeping it lubricated.

ciliary muscle Smooth muscle in the ciliary body of the eye.

ciliary process Portion of the ciliary body of the eye that attaches by suspensory ligaments to the lens.

ciliary ring Portion of the ciliary body of the eye that contains smooth muscle cells.

circumduction (ser-kum-DUK-shun) [L., around + *ductus,* to draw] Movement in a circular motion.

circumferential lamellae (ser-kum-fer-EN-shee-al la-MEL-ee) Lamellae covering the surface of and extending around compact bone inside the periosteum.

circumvallate papilla (ser-kum-VAL-ate pa-PIL-ah) Type of papilla on the surface of the tongue surrounded by a groove.

cisterna; pl. **cisternae** (sis-TER-na, sis-TER-nee) Interior space of the endoplasmic reticulum.

cisterna chyli (sis-TER-na KYE-lie) [L., tank + Gr., *chylos,* juice] Enlarged inferior end of the thoracic duct that receives chyle from the intestine.

citric acid cycle (SIT-rik) Series of chemical reactions in which citric acid is converted into oxaloacetic acid, carbon dioxide is formed, and energy is released. The oxaloacetic acid can combine with acetyl-CoA to form citric acid and restart the cycle. The energy released is used to form NADH, FADH, and ATP.

classical pathway Part of the specific immune system for activation of complement.

clavicle (KLAV-ih-kul) The collarbone, between the sternum and scapula.

cleavage furrow (KLEEV-ij) Inward pinching of the plasma membrane that divides a cell into two halves, which separate from each other to form two new cells.

cleft palate (kleft) Failure of the embryonic palate to fuse along the midline, resulting in an opening through the roof of the mouth.

clinical age (KLIN-i-kul) Age of the developing fetus from the time of the mother's last menstrual period before pregnancy.

clinical perineum (PER-ih-NEE-um) Portion of the perineum between the vaginal and anal openings.

clitoris (KLIT-oh-ris) Small, cylindrical, erectile body, rarely exceeding 2 cm in length, situated at the most anterior portion of the vulva and projecting beneath the prepuce.

cloaca (kloh-AY-kah) [L., sewer] In early embryos, the endodermally lined chamber into which the hindgut and allantois empty.

cloning (KLOHN-ing) Growing a colony of genetically identical cells or organisms.

clot retraction Condensation of a clot into a denser, compact structure; caused by the elastic nature of fibrin.

coagulation (koh-ag-you-LAY-shun) Process of changing from liquid to solid, especially of blood; formation of a blood clot.

cochlear duct (KOK-lee-ar) Interior of the membranous labyrinth of the cochlea; also called cochlear canal or scala media.

cochlear nerve Nerve that carries sensory impulses from the organ of Corti to the vestibulocochlear nerve.

cochlear nucleus Neurons from the cochlear nerve synapse within the dorsal or ventral cochlear nucleus in the superior medulla oblongata.

codon (KOH-don) Sequence of three nucleotides in mRNA or DNA that codes for a specific amino acid in a protein.

cofactor (KOH-FAK-ter, koh-FAK-tohr) Nonprotein component of an enzyme, such as coenzymes and inorganic ions essential for enzyme action.

collagen fibers (KOL-ah-jen) [Gr., *koila,* glue + *gen,* producing] Ropelike protein of the extracellular matrix.

collateral ganglia (koh-LAT-er-uhl GANG-glee-ah) Sympathetic ganglia at the origin of large abdominal arteries; include the celiac, superior, and inferior mesenteric arteries; also called prevertebral ganglia.

collecting duct Straight tubule that extends from the cortex of the kidney to the tip of the renal pyramid. Filtrate from the distal convoluted tubes enters the collecting duct and is carried to the calyces.

colloid (KOL-oyd) [Gr., *kolla,* glue + *eidos,* appearance] Atoms or molecules dispersed in a gaseous, liquid, or solid medium that resist separation from the liquid, gas, or solid.

colloidal solution (koh-LOYD-al) Fine particles suspended in a liquid; resistant to sedimentation or filtration.

colon (KOH-lon) Division of the large intestine that extends from the cecum to the rectum.

colostrum (koh-LOSS-trum) Thin, white fluid; the first milk secreted by the breast at the termination of pregnancy; contains less fat and lactose than the milk secreted later.

columnar Shaped like a column.

commissure (KOM-mih-shur) [L., *commissura,* a joining together] Connection of nerve fibers between the cerebral hemispheres or from one side of the spinal cord to the other.

common bile duct Duct formed by the union of the common hepatic and cystic ducts; it empties into the small intestine.

common hepatic duct Part of the biliary duct system formed by the joining of the right and left hepatic ducts.

compact bone Bone that is denser and has fewer spaces than cancellous bone.

competition Similar molecules binding to the same carrier molecule or receptor site.

complement (KOM-pleh-ment) Group of serum proteins that stimulates phagocytosis and inflammation.

complement cascade Series of reactions in which each component activates the next component, resulting in activation of complement proteins.

compliance (kom-PLY-ans) Change in volume (e.g., in lungs or blood vessels) caused by a given change in pressure.

compound (KOM-pound) Substance composed of two or more different types of atoms that are chemically combined.

concha; pl. **conchae** (KON-kah, KON-kee) [L., shell] Structure comparable to a shell in shape—for example, the three bony ridges on the lateral wall of the nasal cavity.

conduction (kon-DUCK-shun) [L., *con* + *ductus,* to lead, conduct] Transfer of energy, such as heat, from one point to another without evident movement in the conducting body.

cone (kohn) Photoreceptor in the retina of the eye; responsible for color vision.

congenital (kon-JEN-ih-tal) [L., *congenitus,* born with] Occurring at birth; may be genetic or due to some influence (e.g., drugs) during development.

conjunctiva (kon-junk-TIE-vah) [L., *conjungo,* to bind together] Mucous membrane covering the anterior surface of the eyeball and lining the lids.

conjunctival fornix (kon-junk-TYE-val FOHR-niks) Area in which the palpebral and bulbar conjunctiva meet.

constant region Portion of an antibody that does not combine with an antigen and is the same in different antibodies.

continuous capillary [L., *capillaris,* relating to hair] Capillary in which pores are absent; is less permeable to large molecules than are other types of capillaries.

contraction phase (kon-TRAK-shun) One of the three phases of muscle contraction; the time during which tension is produced by the contraction of muscle.

convection (kon-VEK-shun) [L., *con* + *vectus,* to carry or bring together] Transfer of heat in liquids or gases by movement of the heated particles.

coracoid (KOHR-a-koyd) [Gr., *korakodes,* crow's beak] Resembling a crow's beak—for example, a process on the scapula.

Cori cycle Named for Czech-U.S. biochemist and Nobel laureate Carl F. Cori (1896–1984). Lactic acid, produced by skeletal muscle, is carried in the blood to the liver, where it is aerobically converted into glucose. The glucose may return through the blood to skeletal muscle or may be stored as glycogen in the liver.

cornea (KOR-nee-ah) Transparent portion of the fibrous tunic that makes up the outer wall of the anterior portion of the eye.

corniculate cartilages (kor-NIK-you-late) Conical nodules of elastic cartilage surmounting the apex of each arytenoid cartilage.

corona radiata Single layer of columnar cells derived from the cumulus mass, which anchor on the zona pellucida of the oocyte in a secondary follicle.

coronary (KOR-oh-nair-ee) [L., *coronarius,* a crown] Resembling a crown; encircling.

coronary artery One of two arteries that arise from the base of the aorta and carry blood to the muscle of the heart.

coronary ligament Peritoneal reflection from the liver to the diaphragm at the margins of the bare area of the liver.

coronary sinus Short trunk that receives most of the veins of the heart and empties into the right atrium.

coronoid (KOR-oh-noyd) [Gr., *korone,* a crow] Shaped like a crow's beak—for example, a process on the mandible.

corpus; pl. **corpora** (KOHR-pus, KOHR-pohr-ah) [L., *body*] Any body or mass; the main part of an organ.

corpusalbicans(AL-bih-kanz) Atrophiedcorpus luteum, leaving a connective tissue scar in the ovary.

corpus callosum (kah-LOH-sum) [L., *body* + *callous*] Largest commissure of the brain, connecting the cerebral hemispheres.

corpus cavernosum; pl. **corpora cavernosa** (kav-er-NOHS-ah) One of two parallel columns of erectile tissue forming the dorsal part of the body of the penis or the body of the clitoris.

corpus luteum (LOO-tee-um) Yellow endocrine body formed in the ovary in the site of a ruptured vesicular follicle immediately after ovulation; secretes progesterone and estrogen.

corpus luteum of pregnancy Large corpus luteum in the ovary of a pregnant female; secretes large amounts of progesterone and estrogen.

corpus spongiosum (spun-gee-OH-sum) Median column of erectile tissue located between and ventral to the two corpora cavernosa in the penis; posteriorly it forms the bulb of the penis, and anteriorly it terminates as the glans penis; it is traversed by the urethra. In the female, it forms the bulb of the vestibule.

corpus striatum (stry-AY-tum) [L., *corpus,* body + *striatus,* striated or furrowed] Caudate nucleus, putamen, and globus pallidus; so-named because of the striations caused by intermixing of gray and white matter, which result from the number of tracts crossing the anterior portion of the corpus striatum.

cortex; pl. **cortices** (KOR-teks, KOHR-tih-seez) [L., bark] Outer portion of an organ (e.g., adrenal cortex or cortex of the kidney).

cortical radiate artery Artery that passes between lobules of an organ; branches of the interlobar arteries of the kidney pass outward through the cortex from the arcuate arteries and supply the afferent arterioles.

cortical radiate vein Vein that parallels the cortical radiate arteries; in the kidney, it drains the peritubular capillary plexus, emptying into arcuate veins.

corticotropin-releasing hormone (CRH) (KOHR-ti-koh-TROH-pin) Hormone from the hypothalamus that stimulates the anterior pituitary gland to release adrenocorticotropic hormone.

cortisol (KOR-tih-sol) Steroid hormone released by the zona fasciculata of the adrenal cortex; increases blood glucose and inhibits inflammation.

covalent bond (koh-VAY-lent) Chemical bond characterized by the sharing of electrons.

coxal bone (KOK-sal) Hip bone.

cranial nerve (KRAY-nee-al) Nerve that originates from a nucleus within the brain; there are 12 pairs of cranial nerves.

cranial vault Eight skull bones that surround and protect the brain; braincase.

craniosacral division (KRAY-nee-oh-SAY-kral) Parasympathetic division of the autonomic nervous system.

cranium (KRAY-nee-um) [Gr., *kranion,* skull] Skull; in a more limited sense, the braincase.

cremaster muscle (krih-MAS-ter) Extension of abdominal muscles originating from the internal oblique muscles; in the male, raises the testicles; in the female, envelops the round ligament of the uterus.

crenation (kreh-NAY-shun) [L., *crena,* notched] Denoting the outline of a shrunken cell.

cricoid cartilage (CRY-koyd) Most inferior laryngeal cartilage.

cricothyrotomy (CRY-koh-thigh-ROT-oh-mee) Incision through the skin and cricothyroid membrane for relief of respiratory obstruction.

crista; pl. **cristae** (KRIS-tah, KRIS-tee) [L., crest] Shelflike infolding of the inner membrane of a mitochondrion.

crista ampullaris (KRIS-tah am-pyoo-LAIR-is) [L., crest] Elevation on the inner surface of the ampulla of each semicircular duct for dynamic or kinetic equilibrium.

critical closing pressure Pressure in a blood vessel below which the vessel collapses, occluding the lumen and preventing blood flow.

crown Part of a tooth that is covered with enamel.

cruciate (KROO-shee-ate) [L., *cruciatus,* cross] Resembling or shaped like a cross.

crus of the penis (kroos) Posterior portion of the corpus cavernosum of the penis attached to the ischiopubic ramus.

crypt (kript) Pitlike depression or tubular recess.

cryptorchidism (krip-TOR-kih-dizm) Failure of the testis to descend.

crystallin (KRIS-tah-lin) Protein that fills the epithelial cells of the lens in the eye.

cuboidal Resembling a cube.

cumulus oophorus (oh-OF-ohr-us) [L., a heap] Mass of epithelial cells surrounding the oocyte; also called cumulus mass.

cuneiform cartilages (KYU-nee-ih-form) Small rods of elastic cartilage above each corniculate cartilage in the larynx.

cupula; pl. **cupulae** (KOO-poo-lah, KOO-poo-lee) [L., *cupa,* tub] Gelatinous mass that overlies the hair cells of the cristae ampullares of the semicircular ducts.

cuticle (KEW-tih-cul) [L., *cutis,* skin] Outer, thin layer, usually horny—for example, the outer covering of hair or the growth of the stratum corneum onto the nail.

cystic duct (SIS-tik) Duct leading from the gallbladder; joins the common hepatic duct to form the common bile duct.

cytokine (SIGH-toh-kine) Protein or peptide secreted by a cell that regulates the activity of neighboring cells.

cytokinesis (SIGH-toh-kih-NEE-sis) [Gr., *cyto,* cell + *kinesis,* movement] Division of the cytoplasm during cell division.

cytology (sigh-TOL-oh-jee) [Gr., *kytos,* a hollow (cell) + *logos,* study] Study of anatomy, physiology, pathology, and chemistry of the cell.

cytoplasm (SIGH-toh-plazm) Protoplasm of the cell surrounding the nucleus.

cytoplasmic inclusion (sigh-toh-PLAZ-mik) Any foreign or other substance contained in the cytoplasm of a cell.

cytotoxic reaction (SIGH-toh-TOK-sik) [Gr., *cyto,* cell + L., *toxic,* poison] Antibodies (IgG or IgM) combine with cells and activate complement, and cell lysis occurs.

cytotrophoblast (sigh-toh-TROF-oh-blast) Inner layer of the trophoblast, composed of individual cells.

D

Daily Reference Values (DRVs) Recommended amounts in the diet for total fat, saturated fat, cholesterol, total carbohydrate, dietary fiber, sodium, potassium, and protein. The values for total fat, saturated fat, cholesterol, and sodium are the uppermost limits considered desirable because of their link to certain diseases.

Daily Values Dietary reference values useful for planning a healthy diet. The Daily Values are taken from the Reference Daily Intakes (RDIs) and the Daily Reference Values.

Dalton's law Named for English chemist John Dalton (1766–1844). In a mixture of gases, the portion of the total pressure resulting from each type of gas is determined by the percentage of the total volume represented by each gas type.

dartos muscle (DAR-toss) Layer of smooth muscle in the skin of the scrotum; contracts in response to lower temperature and relaxes in response to higher temperature; raises and lowers testes in the scrotum.

deciduous tooth (dee-SID-yoo-us) Tooth of the first set of teeth; also called primary tooth.

decussate (DEE-ku-sate, dee-KUS-ate) [L., *decusso,* X-shaped, from *decussis,* ten (X)] To cross.

deep inguinal ring (IN-gwin-al) Opening in the transverse fascia through which the spermatic cord (or round ligament in the female) enters the inguinal canal.

defecation (def-eh-KAY-shun) [L., *defaeco,* to remove the dregs, purify] Discharge of feces from the rectum.

defecation reflex Combination of local and central nervous system reflexes initiated by distension of the rectum and resulting in the movement of feces out of the lower colon.

deglutition (dee-glue-TISH-un) [L., *de* + *glutio,* to swallow] Act of swallowing.

dendrite (DEN-dright) [Gr., *dendrites,* tree] Branching processes of a neuron; receives stimuli and conducts potentials toward the cell body.

dendritic cell (den-DRIT-ik) Large cells with long, cytoplasmic extensions that are capable of taking up and concentrating antigens, leading to the activation of B or T lymphocytes.

dendritic spine Extension of nerve cell dendrites where axons form synapses with the dendrites; also called gemmule.

dental arch (DEN-tahl) [L., *arcus,* bow] Curved maxillary or mandibular arch in which the teeth are located.

dentin (DEN-tin) Bony material forming the mass of the tooth.

deoxyhemoglobin (dee-OKS-ee-hee-moh-GLOH-bin) Hemoglobin without oxygen bound to it.

deoxyribonuclease (dee-OKS-ee-righ-boh-NOO-klee-ase) Enzyme that splits DNA into its component nucleotides.

deoxyribonucleic acid (DNA) (dee-OKS-ee-RYE-boh-noo-KLEE-ik) Type of nucleic acid containing deoxyribose as the sugar component, found principally in the nuclei of cells; constitutes the genetic material of cells.

depolarization phase (dee-POH-lar-ih-ZAY-shun) Change in the electric charge difference across the plasma membrane that causes the difference to be smaller or closer to 0 mV; phase of the action potential in which the membrane potential moves toward zero, or becomes positive.

depression (dee-PRESH-uhn) Movement of a structure in an inferior direction.

depth perception (per-SEP-shun) Ability to distinguish between near and far objects and to judge their distance.

dermatome (DER-mah-tohm) Area of skin supplied by a spinal nerve.

dermis (DER-miss) [Gr., *derma,* skin] Dense irregular connective tissue that forms the deep layer of the skin.

descending aorta Part of the aorta, further divided into the thoracic aorta and abdominal aorta.

descending colon Part of the colon extending from the left colonic flexure to the sigmoid colon.

desmosome (DEZ-moh-some) [Gr., *desmos,* a band + *soma,* body] Point of adhesion between cells. Each contains a dense plate at the point of adhesion and a cementing extracellular material between the cells.

desquamate (DES-kwah-mate) [L., *desquamo,* to scale off] Peeling or scaling off of the superficial cells of the stratum corneum.

diabetes insipidus (die-ah-BEE-teez in-SIP-i-dus) Chronic excretion of large amounts of urine of low specific gravity accompanied by extreme thirst; results from inadequate output of antidiuretic hormone.

diabetes mellitus (die-ah-BEE-teez MEL-ih-tus) Metabolic disease in which carbohydrate use is reduced and that of lipid and protein enhanced; caused by a deficiency of insulin or an inability to respond to insulin and is characterized, in more severe cases, by hyperglycemia, glycosuria, water and electrolyte loss, ketoacidosis, and coma.

diapedesis (DIE-ah-peh-DEE-sis) [Gr., *dia,* through + *pedesis,* a leaping] Passage of blood or any of its formed elements through the intact walls of blood vessels.

diaphragm (DIE-ah-fram) Musculomembranous partition between the abdominal and thoracic cavities.

diaphysis (die-AF-ih-sis) [Gr., growing between] Shaft of a long bone.

diastole (die-AS-toh-lee) [Gr., *diastole,* dilation] Relaxation of the heart chambers, during which they fill with blood; usually refers to ventricular relaxation.

diencephalon (die-en-SEF-a-lon) [Gr., *dia,* through + *enkephalos,* brain] Second portion of the embryonic brain; in the inferior core of the adult cerebrum.

diffuse lymphatic tissue Dispersed lymphocytes and other cells with no clear boundary; found beneath mucous membranes, around lymph nodules, and within lymph nodes and spleen.

diffusion (dih-FYU-zhun) [L., *diffundo,* to pour in different directions] Tendency for solute molecules to move from an area of high concentration to an area of low concentration in solution; the product of the constant random motion of all atoms, molecules, or ions in a solution.

diffusion coefficient Measure of how easily a gas diffuses through a liquid or tissue.

digestive tract (die-JEST-iv) Mouth, oropharynx, esophagus, stomach, small intestine, and large intestine.

digit (DIJ-it) Finger, thumb, or toe.

dilator pupillae (pyoo-PIL-ee) Radial smooth muscle cells of the iris diaphragm that cause the pupil of the eye to dilate.

diploid (DIP-loyd) Normal number of chromosomes (in humans, 46 chromosomes) in somatic cells.

disaccharide (die-SACK-ah-ride) Condensation product of two monosaccharides by the elimination of water.

dissociate (dih-SOH-see-ate) [L., *dis* + *socio,* to disjoin, separate] Ionization in which ions are dissolved in water and the cations and anions are surrounded by water molecules.

distal convoluted tubule Convoluted tubule of the nephron that extends from the ascending limb of the nephron loop and ends in a collecting duct.

distributing artery Medium-sized artery with a tunica media composed principally of smooth muscle; regulates blood flow to different regions of the body.

dominant (DOM-ih-nant) [L., *dominus,* a master] Gene that is expressed phenotypically to the exclusion of a contrasting recessive gene.

dorsal root (DOR-sal) Sensory (afferent) root of a spinal nerve.

dorsal root ganglion (GANG-lee-on) Collection of sensory neuron cell bodies within the dorsal root of a spinal nerve; also called spinal ganglion.

ductus arteriosus (DUK-tus ar-TEER-ee-oh-sus) Fetal vessel connecting the left pulmonary artery with the descending aorta.

ductus deferens (DUK-tus DEH-fuh-renz) Duct of the testicle, running from the epididymis to the ejaculatory duct; also called vas deferens.

duodenal gland (DOO-oh-DEE-nal, doo-OD-eh-nal) Small gland that opens into the base of intestinal glands; secretes a mucoid alkaline substance.

duodenocolic reflex (doo-oh-DEE-noh-koh-lik) Local reflex resulting in a mass movement of the contents of the colon; produced by stimuli in the duodenum.

duodenum (doo-oh-DEE-num) [L., *duodeni*] First division of the small intestine; connects to the stomach.

dura mater (DYU-rah MAY-ter) [L., hard mother] Tough, fibrous membrane forming the outer covering of the brain and spinal cord.

E

eardrum (EER-druhm) Cellular membrane that separates the external from the middle ear; vibrates in response to sound waves; also called tympanic membrane.

ectoderm (EK-toh-derm) Outermost of the three germ layers of an embryo.

ectopic focus; pl. **foci** (ek-TOP-ik FOH-kus, FOH-sigh) Any pacemaker other than the sinus node of the heart; abnormal pacemaker; an ectopic pacemaker.

edema (ee-DEE-mah) [Gr., *oidema,* a swelling] Excessive accumulation of fluid within or around cells, usually causing swelling.

effector T cell (ee-FEK-ter) Subset of T lymphocytes that is responsible for cell-mediated immunity.

efferent arteriole (ar-TEER-ee-ole) Vessel that carries blood from the glomerulus to the peritubular capillaries.

efferent division Nerve fibers that send impulses from the central nervous system to the periphery.

efferent ductule (DUCK-tool) [L., *ductus,* duct] One of a number of small ducts leading from the testis to the head of the epididymis.

ejaculation (ee-JACK-you-LAY-shun) Reflexive expulsion of semen from the penis.

ejaculatory duct (ih-JACK-you-leh-toh-ree) Duct formed by the union of the ductus deferens and the excretory duct of the seminal vesicle; opens into the prostatic urethra.

ejection period (ee-JEK-shun) Time in the cardiac cycle when the semilunar valves are open and blood is being ejected from the ventricles into the arterial system.

elastin (eh-LAS-tin) Yellow, elastic, fibrous mucoprotein that is the major connective tissue protein of elastic structures (e.g., large blood vessels and elastic ligaments).

electrocardiogram (ECG, EKG) (ee-LEK-troh-KAR-dee-oh-gram) [Gr., *elektron,* amber + *kardia,* heart + *gramma,* a drawing] Graphic record of the heart's electric currents obtained with an electrocardiograph.

electrolyte (ee-LEK-troh-light) [Gr., *electro* + *lytos,* soluble] Cation or anion in solution that conducts an electric current.

electron (ih-LEK-tron) Negatively charged subatomic particle in an atom.

electron-transport chain Series of electron carriers in the inner mitochondrial membrane; they receive electrons from NADH and $FADH_2$, using the electrons in the formation of ATP and water.

element (EL-ih-ment) [L., *elementum,* rudiment, beginning] Substance composed of atoms of only one kind.

elevation (el-eh-VAY-shun) Movement of a structure in a superior direction.

embolism (EM-boh-lizm) [Gr., *embolisma,* a piece of patch, literally something thrust in] Obstruction or occlusion of a vessel by a transported clot, a mass of bacteria, or other foreign material.

embolus; pl. **emboli** (EM-boh-lus, EM-boh-lie) [Gr., *embolos,* plug, wedge, or stopper] Plug, composed of a detached clot, a mass of bacteria, or another foreign body, occluding a blood vessel.

embryo (EM-bree-oh) Developing human from the first to the eighth week of development.

embryonic disk (em-bree-ON-ik) Point in the inner cell mass at which the embryo begins to be formed.

embryonic period From approximately the second to the eighth week of development, during which the major organ systems are organized.

emission (ih-MISH-uhn) [L., *emissio,* to send out] Discharge; accumulation of semen in the urethra prior to ejaculation. A nocturnal emission is a discharge of semen while asleep.

emmetropia (em-eh-TROH-pee-ah) [Gr., *emmetros,* according to measure + *ops,* eye] In the eye, the state of refraction in which parallel rays are focused exactly on the retina; no accommodation is necessary.

emulsify (eh-MUL-sih-fie) To form an emulsion.

enamel (ee-NAM-el) Hard substance covering the exposed portion of the tooth.

endocardium; pl. **endocardia** (EN-doh-KAR-dee-um, EN-doh-KAR-dee-ah) Innermost layer of the heart, including endothelium and connective tissue.

endocrine gland (EN-doh-krin) [Gr., *endon,* inside + *krino,* to separate] Ductless gland that secretes a hormone internally, usually into the circulation.

endocytosis (EN-doh-sigh-TOH-sis) Bulk uptake of material through the cell membrane.

endoderm (EN-doh-derm) Innermost of the three germ layers of an embryo.

endolymph (EN-doh-limf) [Gr., *endo* + L., *lympha,* clear fluid] Fluid found within the membranous labyrinth of the inner ear.

endometrium; pl. **endometria** (en-doh-MEE-tree-um, en-doh-MEE-tree-ah) Mucous membrane composing the inner layer of the uterine wall; consists of a simple columnar epithelium and a lamina propria that contains simple tubular uterine glands.

endomysium (EN-doh-MEE-see-um) [Gr., *endo,* within + *mys,* muscle] Fine connective tissue sheath surrounding a muscle fiber.

endoneurium (en-doh-NOO-ree-um) [Gr., *endo,* within + *neuron,* nerve] Delicate connective tissue surrounding individual nerve fibers within a peripheral nerve.

endoplasmic reticulum; pl. **reticula** (EN-doh-PLAZ-mik reh-TIK-you-lum, reh-TIK-you-lah) Double-walled membranous network inside the cytoplasm; rough has ribosomes attached to the surface; smooth does not have ribosomes attached.

endorphin (EN-dohr-fin) Opiate-like polypeptide found in the brain and other parts of the body; binds in the brain to the same receptors that bind exogenous opiates.

endosteum (en-DOSS-tee-um) [Gr., *endo,* within + *osteon,* bone] Membranous lining of the medullary cavity and the cavities of spongy bone.

endothelium; pl. **endothelia** (en-doh-THEE-lee-um, en-doh-THEE-lee-ah) [Gr., *endo,* within + *thele,* nipple] Layer of flat cells lining blood and lymphatic vessels and the chambers of the heart.

enkephalin (en-KEF-ah-lin) Pentapeptide found in the brain; binds to specific receptor sites, some of which may be pain-related opiate receptors.

enteric nervous system (ENS) Complex network of neuron cell bodies and axons within the wall of the digestive tract; capable of controlling the digestive tract independently of the central nervous system through local reflexes.

enterokinase (EN-teer-oh-KIE-nase) Intestinal proteolytic enzyme that converts trypsinogen into trypsin.

enzyme (EN-zyme) [Gr., *en,* in + *zyme,* leaven] Protein that acts as a catalyst.

eosinophil (ee-oh-SIN-oh-fill) [Gr., *eos,* dawn + *philos,* fond] White blood cell that stains with acidic dyes; inhibits inflammation.

epicardium (EP-ih-KAR-dee-um) [Gr., *epi,* on + *kardia,* heart] Serous membrane covering the surface of the heart; also called visceral pericardium.

epidermis (ep-ih-DER-miss) [Gr., *epi,* on + *derma,* skin] Outer portion of the skin formed of epithelial tissue that rests on or covers the dermis.

epididymis; pl. **epididymides** (EP-ih-DID-ih-miss, ep-ih-dih-DIM-ih-deez) [Gr., *epi,* on + *didymos,* twin] Elongated structure connected to the posterior surface of the testis, which consists of the head, body, and tail; site of storage and maturation of the spermatozoa.

epiglottis (ep-ih-GLOT-is) [Gr., *epi,* on + *glottis,* mouth of the windpipe] Plate of elastic cartilage covered with mucous membrane; serves as a valve over the glottis of the larynx during swallowing.

epimysium (ep-ih-MIS-ee-um) [Gr., *epi,* on + *mys,* muscle] Fibrous envelope surrounding a skeletal muscle.

epinephrine (ep-ih-NEF-rin) Hormone (amino acid derivative) similar in structure to the neurotransmitter norepinephrine; major hormone released from the adrenal medulla; increases cardiac output and blood glucose levels; also called adrenaline.

epineurium (ep-ih-NOO-ree-um) [Gr., *epi,* on + *neuron,* nerve] Connective tissue sheath surrounding a nerve.

epiphyseal line (eh-pih-FIZ-ee-al) Dense plate of bone in a bone that is no longer growing, indicating the former site of the epiphyseal plate.

epiphyseal plate Site at which bone growth in length occurs; located between the epiphysis and diaphysis of a long bone; area of hyaline cartilage where cartilage growth is followed by endochondral ossification; also called metaphysis or growth plate.

epiphysis; pl. **epiphyses** (eh-PIF-ih-sis, eh-PIF-ih-seez) [Gr., *epi,* on + *physis,* growth] Portion of a bone developed from a secondary ossification center and separated from the remainder of the bone by the epiphyseal plate.

epiploic appendage (eh-pih-PLOH-ik) One of a number of little processes of peritoneum projecting from the serous coat of the large intestine except the rectum; they are generally distended with fat.

epithelium (ep-ih-THEE-lee-um) [Gr., *epi,* on + *thele,* nipple] One of the four primary tissue types. *Nipple* refers to the tiny capillary-containing connective tissue in the lips, which is where the term was first used. The use of the term was later expanded to include all covering and lining surfaces of the body.

epitope (EP-ih-tohp) [Gr., *epi,* on + *top,* place] *See* antigenic determinant.

eponychium (ep-oh-NIK-ee-um) [Gr., *epi,* on + *onyx,* nail] Outgrowth of the skin that covers the proximal and lateral borders of the nail; also called cuticle.

erection (ee-REK-shun) [L., *erectio,* to set up] Condition of erectile tissue when filled with blood; tissue becomes hard and unyielding; especially refers to this state of the penis.

erythrocyte (eh-RITH-roh-site) [Gr., *erythros,* red + *kytos,* cell] Red blood cell; biconcave disk containing hemoglobin.

erythropoiesis (eh-RITH-roh-poy-EE-sis) [*erythrocyte* + Gr., *poiesis,* a making] Production of erythrocytes.

erythropoietin (EPO) (eh-RITH-roh-POY-ee-tin) Protein that enhances erythropoiesis by stimulating the formation of proerythroblasts and the release of reticulocytes from bone marrow.

esophagus; pl. **esophagi** (ee-SOF-ah-gus, ee-SOF-ah-jee) [Gr., *oisophagos,* gullet] Portion of the digestive tract between the pharynx and stomach.

essential amino acid Amino acid, required by animals, that must be supplied in the diet.

estrogen (ES-troh-jen) Substance that exerts biologic effects characteristic of estrogen hormone, such as stimulating female secondary sexual characteristics, growth, and maturation of long bones, and helps control the menstrual cycle.

evagination (ee-vaj-ih-NAY-shun) [L., *e,* out + *vagina,* sheath] Protrusion of some part or organ from its normal position.

evaporation (ee-vap-oh-RAY-shun) [L., *e,* out + *vaporare,* to emit vapor] Change from liquid to vapor form.

eversion (ee-VER-shun) [L., *everto,* to overturn] Turning outward.

excitation-contraction coupling (ek-sigh-TAY-shun kon-TRAK-shun KUP-ling) Stimulation of a muscle fiber produces an action potential that results in contraction of the muscle fiber.

excitatory postsynaptic potential (EPSP) (ek-SIGH-tay-toh-ree post-si-NAP-tik poh-TEN-shal) Depolarization in the postsynaptic membrane that brings the membrane potential close to threshold.

exocrine gland (EK-soh-krin) [Gr., *exo,* outside + *krino,* to separate] Gland that secretes to a surface or outward through a duct.

exocytosis (EK-so-sigh-TOH-sis) Elimination of material from a cell through the formation of vacuoles.

expiratory reserve volume Maximum volume of air that can be expelled from the lungs after a normal expiration.

extension (eks-TEN-shun) [L., *extensio,* to stretch out] To stretch out.

external anal sphincter Ring of striated muscular fibers surrounding the anus.

external auditory canal Short canal that opens to the exterior environment and terminates at the eardrum; part of the external ear.

external ear Portion of the ear that includes the auricle and external acoustic meatus; terminates at the eardrum.

external nose Nostril; anterior or external opening of the nasal cavity.

external spermatic fascia Outer fascial covering of the spermatic cord.

external urethral orifice Slitlike opening of the urethra in the glans penis.

external urinary sphincter Sphincter skeletal muscle around the base of the urethra external to the internal urinary sphincter.

exteroceptor (EKS-ter-oh-SEP-ter, EKS-ter-oh-SEP-tohr) [L., *exterus,* external + *receptor,* receiver] Sensory receptor in the skin or mucous membranes that responds to stimulation by external agents or forces.

extracellular (eks-trah-SELL-you-lar) Outside the cell.

extracellular matrix; pl. **matrices** (MAY-triks, MAY-tri-sees) Nonliving chemical substances located between connective tissue cells.

extrinsic clotting pathway (eks-TRIN-sik) Series of chemical reactions resulting in clot formation; begins with chemicals (e.g., tissue thromboplastin) found outside the blood.

extrinsic muscle Muscle located outside the structure being moved.

eyebrow Short hairs on the bony ridge above the eyes.

eyelash Hair at the margins of the eyelids.

eyelid Movable fold of skin in front of the eyeball; also called palpebra.

F

F actin (AK-tin) Fibrous actin molecule that is composed of a series of globular actin molecules (G actin).

facilitated diffusion Carrier-mediated process that does not require ATP and moves substances into or out of cells from a high to a low concentration.

falciform ligament (FAL-si-form LIG-ah-ment) Fold of peritoneum extending to the surface of the liver from the diaphragm and anterior abdominal wall.

fallopian tube (fah-LOH-pee-an) *See* uterine tube.

false pelvis Portion of the pelvis superior to the pelvic brim; composed of the bone on the posterior and lateral sides and by muscle on the anterior side; also called greater pelvis.

falx cerebelli (falks ser-eh-BEL-eye) Dural fold between the two cerebellar hemispheres.

falx cerebri (falks se-REE-bree) Dural fold between the two cerebral hemispheres.

far point of vision Distance from the eye where accommodation is not needed to have the image focused on the retina.

fascia; pl. **fasciae** (FASH-ee-ah, FASH-ee-ee) [L., band or fillet] Loose areolar connective tissue found beneath the skin (hypodermis) or dense connective tissue that encloses and separates muscles.

fasciculus (fah-SIK-you-lus) [L., *fascis,* bundle] Band or bundle of nerve or muscle fibers bound together by connective tissue.

fat [A.S., *faet*] Greasy, soft-solid material found in animal tissues and many plants; composed of two types of molecules: glycerol and fatty acids.

fatigue (fah-TEEG) [L., *fatigo,* to tire] Period characterized by a reduced capacity to do work.

fat-soluble vitamin Vitamin, such as A, D, E, and K, that is soluble in lipids and absorbed from the intestine along with lipids.

fauces (FAW-seez) [L., throat] Space between the cavity of the mouth and the pharynx.

female climacteric (KLIE-mak-ter-ik) Period of life occurring in females, encompassing termination of the reproductive period and characterized by endocrine, somatic, and transitory psychologic changes and ultimately menopause; also called perimenopause.

female pronucleus Nuclear material of the ovum after the ovum has been penetrated by the spermatozoon. Each pronucleus carries the haploid number of chromosomes.

fertilization (FER-til-ih-ZAY-shun) Process that begins with the penetration of the secondary oocyte by the spermatozoon and is completed with the fusion of the male and female pronuclei.

fetus (FEE-tus) Developing human following the embryonic period (after 8 weeks of development).

fibrin (FIGH-brin) Elastic filamentous protein derived from fibrinogen by the action of thrombin, which releases peptides from fibrinogen in coagulation of the blood.

fibroblast (FIGH-broh-blast) [L., *fibra,* fiber + Gr., *blastos,* germ] Spindle-shaped or stellate cells that form connective tissue.

fibrocyte (FIGH-broh-syte) Mature cell of fibrous connective tissue.

fibrous joint (FIGH-bruhs) Bones connected by fibrous tissue with no joint cavity; includes sutures, syndesmoses, and gomphoses.

fibrous tunic Outer layer of the eye; composed of the sclera and the cornea.

filiform (FIL-i-form) Filament-shaped.

filtrate (FIL-trait) Liquid that has passed through a filter—for example, fluid that enters the nephron through the filtration membrane of the glomerulus.

filtration (fil-TRAY-shun) Movement, due to a pressure difference, of a liquid through a filter that prevents some or all of the substances in the liquid from passing through.

filtration fraction Fraction of the plasma entering the kidney that filters into the glomerular capsule. Normally, it is around 19%.

filtration membrane Membrane formed by the glomerular capillary endothelium, the basement membrane, and the podocytes of the glomerular capsule.

filtration pressure Pressure gradient that forces fluid from the glomerular capillary through the filtration membrane into the glomerular capsule; glomerular capillary pressure minus glomerular capsule pressure minus colloid osmotic pressure.

fimbria; pl. **fimbriae** (FIM-bree-ah, FIM-bree-ee) [L., fringe] Fringelike structure located at the ostium of the uterine tube.

first messenger *See* intercellular chemical signal.

fixator (fik-SAY-ter) Muscle that stabilizes the origin of a prime mover.

flagellum; pl. **flagella** (fla-JELL-um, fla-JELL-ah) [L., whip] Whiplike locomotory organelle of constant structural arrangement consisting of double peripheral microtubules and two single central microtubules.

flatus (FLAY-tus) [L., a blowing] Gas or air in the gastrointestinal tract that may be expelled through the anus.

flexion (FLEK-shun) [L., *flectus*] Bending.

focal point Point at which light rays cross after passing through a concave lens, such as the lens of the eye.

foliate (FOH-lee-ate) Leaf-shaped.

follicle-stimulating hormone (FSH) (FOLL-ih-kull) Hormone of the adenohypophysis that, in females, stimulates the Graafian follicles of the ovary and assists in follicular maturation and the secretion of estrogen; in males, FSH stimulates the epithelium of the seminiferous tubules and is partially responsible for inducing spermatogenesis.

follicular phase (foh-LIK-yoo-lar) Time between the end of menses and ovulation, characterized by rapid division of endometrial cells and development of follicles in the ovary; also called proliferative phase.

foramen; pl. **foramina** (foh-RAY-men, foh-RAM-ih-nah) Hole.

foramen ovale (oh-VAL-ee) In the fetal heart, the oval opening in the septum secundum; the persistent part of septum primum acts as a valve for this interatrial communication during fetal life; postnatally, the septum primum becomes fused to the septum secundum to close the foramen ovale, forming the fossa ovale.

force That which produces a motion in the body; pull.

foregut Cephalic portion of the primitive digestive tube in the embryo.

foreskin *See* prepuce.

formed elements Cells (i.e., red and white blood cells) and cell fragments (i.e., platelets) of blood.

formula unit Relative number of cations and ions in an ionic compound.

fornix (FOHR-niks) [L., arch, vault] Recess at the cervical end of the vagina. Recess deep to each eyelid where the palpebral and bulbar conjunctivae meet.

fovea centralis (FOH-vee-ah) Depression in the middle of the macula where there are only cones and no blood vessels.

free energy Total amount of energy that can be liberated by the complete catabolism of food.

frenulum (FREN-you-lum) [L., *frenum,* bridle] Fold extending from the floor of the mouth to the midline of the undersurface of the tongue.

frequency-modulated signals Signals, all of which are identical in amplitude, that differ in their frequency—for example, strong stimuli may initiate a high frequency of action potentials and weak stimuli may initiate a low frequency of action potentials.

FSH surge Increase in plasma follicle-stimulating hormone (FSH) levels before ovulation.

fulcrum (F) (FUL-kruhm) Pivot point.

fundus (FUN-dus) [L., bottom] Bottom, or rounded end, of a hollow organ—for example, the fundus of the stomach or uterus.

fungiform (FUN-ji-form) Mushroom-shaped.

G

G actin (jee AK-tin) Globular protein molecules that, when bound together, form fibrous actin (F actin).

gallbladder (GAWL-blad-er) Pear-shaped receptacle on the inferior surface of the liver; serves as a storage reservoir for bile.

gamete (GAM-eet) Ovum or spermatozoon.

gamma globulin (GAM-ah GLOB-you-lin) [L., *globulus,* globule] Plasma proteins that include the antibodies.

ganglion; pl. **ganglia** (GANG-lee-on, GANG-lee-ah) [Gr., swelling, or knot] Any group of nerve cell bodies in the peripheral nervous system.

gap junction Small channel between cells that allows the passage of ions and small molecules between cells; provides means of intercellular communication.

gastric gland (GAS-trik) Gland located in the mucosa of the fundus and body of the stomach.

gastric inhibitory polypeptide Hormone secreted by the duodenum that inhibits gastric acid secretion.

gastric pit Small pit in the mucous membrane of the stomach, at the bottom of which are the mouths of the gastric glands that secrete mucus, hydrochloric acid, intrinsic factor, pepsinogen, and hormones.

gastrin (GAS-trin) Hormone secreted in the mucosa of the stomach and duodenum that stimulates the secretion of hydrochloric acid by the parietal cells of the gastric glands.

gastrocolic reflex (GAS-troh-KOL-ik) Local reflex resulting in mass movement of the contents of the colon, which occurs after the entrance of food into the stomach.

gastroesophageal opening (GAS-troh-ee-SOF-ah-JEE-al) Opening of the esophagus into the stomach; also called cardiac opening.

gene (jeen) [Gr., *genos,* birth, descent] Functional unit of heredity. Each gene occupies a specific place, or locus, on a chromosome; it is capable of reproducing itself exactly at each cell division; it often is capable of directing the formation of an enzyme or another protein.

genetics (jeh-NET-iks) [Gr., *genesis,* origin or production] Branch of science that deals with heredity.

genital fold (JEN-i-tahl) Paired longitudinal ridges developing in the embryo on each side of the urogenital orifice. In the male, they form part of the penis; in the female, they form the labia minora.

genital tubercle Median elevation just cephalic to the urogenital orifice of an embryo; gives rise to the penis of the male or the clitoris of the female.

genotype (JEN-oh-type, JEE-noh-type) [Gr., *genos,* birth, descent + *typos,* type] Genetic make-up of an individual.

germ cell (jerm) Spermatozoon or ovum.

germ layer One of three layers in the embryo (ectoderm, endoderm, or mesoderm) from which the four primary tissue types arise.

germinal center Lighter-staining center of a lymphatic nodule; area of rapid lymphocyte division.

gingiva (JIN-jih-vah) Dense fibrous tissue, covered by mucous membrane, that covers the alveolar processes of the upper and lower jaws and surrounds the necks of the teeth.

girdle (GIR-del) Belt or zone; the bony region where the limbs attach to the body.

gland [L., *glans,* acorn] Secretory organ from which secretions may be released into the blood, into a cavity, or onto a surface.

glans penis [L., *glans,* acorn] Conical expansion of the corpus spongiosum that forms the head of the penis.

globin (GLOH-bin) Protein portion of hemoglobin.

glomerular capillary pressure (GCP) (gloh-MAIR-yoo-lar) Blood pressure within the glomerulus.

glomerular filtration rate (GFR) Amount of plasma (filtrate) that filters into a glomerular capsule per minute.

glomerulus (gloh-MAIR-you-lus) [L., *glomus,* ball of yarn] Mass of capillary loops at the beginning of each nephron, nearly surrounded by a glomerular capsule.

glottis (GLOT-is) [Gr., aperture of the larynx] Vocal apparatus; includes vocal folds and the cleft between them.

glucocorticoid (glue-koh-KOR-tih-koyd) Steroid hormone (e.g., cortisol) released by zonula fasciculata of the adrenal cortex; increases blood glucose and inhibits inflammation.

gluconeogenesis (GLUE-koh-nee-oh-JEN-eh-sis) [Gr., *glykys,* sweet + *neos,* new + *genesis,* production] Formation of glucose from noncarbohydrates, such as proteins (amino acids) or lipids (glycerol).

glycogenesis (GLIGH-koh-JEN-eh-sis) Formation of glycogen from glucose molecules.

glycolysis (gligh-KOL-ih-sis) [Gr., *glykys,* sweet + *lysis,* a loosening] Anaerobic process during which glucose is converted to pyruvic acid; net of two ATP molecules is produced during glycolysis.

goblet cell Mucus-producing epithelial cell that has its apical end distended with mucin.

Golgi apparatus (GOL-jee) Named for Camillo Golgi, Italian histologist and Nobel laureate (1843–1926). Specialized endoplasmic reticulum that concentrates and packages materials for secretion from the cell.

Golgi tendon organ Proprioceptive nerve ending in a tendon.

gomphosis (gom-FOH-sis) [Gr., *gomphos,* bolt, nail + *osis,* condition] Fibrous joint in which a peglike process fits into a hole.

gonad (GOH-nad) [Gr., *gone,* seed] Organ that produces sex cells; testis of a male or ovary of a female.

gonadal ridge (goh-NAD-al) Elevation on the embryonic mesonephros; primordial germ cells become embedded in it, establishing it as a testis or an ovary.

gonadotropin (GOH-nad-oh-TROH-pin) Hormone capable of promoting gonadal growth and function. Two major gonadotropins are luteinizing hormone (LH) and follicle-stimulating hormone (FSH).

gonadotropin-releasing hormone (GnRH) Hypothalamic-releasing hormone that stimulates the secretion of gonadotropins (LH and FSH) from the adenohypophysis; also called luteinizing hormone–releasing hormone (LHRH).

granulocyte (GRAN-you-loh-site) Mature granular white blood cell (neutrophil, basophil, or eosinophil).

granulosa cell (gran-yoo-LOH-sah) Cell in the layer surrounding the primary follicle.

gray matter Collection of nerve cell bodies, their dendritic processes, and associated neuroglial cells within the central nervous system.

gray ramus communicans; pl. **rami communicantes** (RAY-mus koh-MYOO-nih-kans, RAY-my koh-myoo-nih-KAN-teez) Connection between a spinal nerve and a sympathetic chain ganglion through which unmyelinated postganglionic axons project.

greater omentum Peritoneal fold passing from the greater curvature of the stomach to the transverse colon, hanging like an apron in front of the intestines.

greater vestibular gland One of two mucus-secreting glands on each side of the lower part of the vagina. The equivalent of the bulbourethral glands in the male.

growth hormone Hormone that stimulates general growth of the individual; stimulates cellular amino acid uptake and protein synthesis; also called somatotropin.

gubernaculum (GOO-ber-NAK-yoo-lum) [L., helm] Column of tissue that connects the fetal testis to the developing scrotum; involved in testicular descent.

gustatory (GUS-tah-tohr-ee) Associated with the sense of taste.

gustatory hair Microvillus of gustatory cell in a taste bud.

gynecomastia (GUY-nih-koh-MAS-tee-ah) [Gr., *gyne,* woman + *mastos,* breast] Excessive development of the male mammary glands, which sometimes secrete milk.

H

H zone Area in the center of the A band in which there are no actin myofilaments; contains only myosin.

hair [A.S., hear] Columns of dead keratinized epithelial cells.

hair follicle Invagination of the epidermis into the dermis; contains the root of the hair and receives the ducts of sebaceous and apocrine glands.

Haldane effect Named for Scottish physiologist John S. Haldane (1860–1936). Hemoglobin that is not bound to carbon dioxide binds more readily to oxygen than hemoglobin that is bound to carbon dioxide.

half-life Time it takes for one-half of an administered substance to be lost through biologic processes.

haploid (HAP-loyd) One set of chromosomes, in contrast to diploid; characteristic of gametes.

hapten (HAP-ten) [Gr., *hapto,* to fasten] Small molecule that binds to a large molecule; together they stimulate the specific immune system.

hard palate Floor of the nasal cavity that separates the nasal cavity from the oral cavity; composed of the palatine processes of the maxillary bones and the horizontal plates of the palatine bones; also called bony palate.

haustra (HAW-strah) [L., machine for drawing water] Sacs of the colon, caused by contraction of the taeniae coli, which are slightly shorter than the gut so that the latter is thrown into pouches.

haversian canal (hah-VER-shan) Named for seventeenth-century English anatomist Clopton Havers (1650–1702). Canal containing blood vessels, nerves, and loose connective tissue and running parallel to the long axis of the bone.

heart skeleton Fibrous connective tissue that provides a point of attachment for cardiac muscle cells, electrically insulates the atria from the ventricles, and forms the fibrous rings around the valves.

heat energy Energy that results from the random movement of atoms, ions, or molecules; the greater the amount of heat energy in an object, the higher the object's temperature.

helicotrema (HEL-ih-koh-TREE-mah) [Gr., *helix,* spiral + *traema,* hole] Opening at the apex of the cochlea through which the scala vestibuli and the scala tympani of the cochlea connect.

helper T cell Subset of T lymphocytes that increases the activity of B cells and T cells.

hematocrit (hee-MAT-oh-krit) [Gr., *hemato,* blood + *krin,* to separate] Percentage of blood volume occupied by erythrocytes.

hematoma (hee-mah-TOH-mah) Localized mass of blood released from blood vessels but confined within an organ or a space; the blood is usually clotted.

heme (HEEM) Oxygen-carrying, color-furnishing part of hemoglobin.

hemidesmosome (hem-ee-DEZ-moh-sohm) Similar to half a desmosome, attaching epithelial cells to the basement membrane.

hemocytoblast (HEE-moh-SIGH-toh-blast) Blood stem cell derived from mesenchyme that can give rise to red and white blood cells and platelets.

hemoglobin (HEE-moh-GLOH-bin) Red, respiratory protein of red blood cells; consists of 6% heme and 94% globin; transports oxygen and carbon dioxide.

hemolysis (hee-MOL-ih-sis) [Gr., *haima* + *lysis,* destruction] Destruction of red blood cells in such a manner that hemoglobin is released.

hemolytic disease of the newborn (HDN) Destruction of erythrocytes in the fetus or newborn caused by antibodies produced in an Rh-negative mother acting on the Rh-positive blood of the fetus or newborn.

hemopoiesis (HEE-moh-poy-EE-sis) [Gr., *haima,* blood + *poiesis,* a making] Formation of the formed elements of blood—that is, red blood cells, white blood cells, and platelets; also called hematopoiesis.

hemopoietic tissue (HEE-moh-poy-EE-tik) [Gr., *haima,* blood + *poiesis,* to make] Blood-forming tissue.

hemostasis (HEE-moh-stay-sis, hee-MOS-tah-sis) Arrest of bleeding.

Henry's law Named for English chemist William Henry (1775–1837). The concentration of a gas dissolved in a liquid is equal to the partial pressure of the gas over the liquid times the solubility coefficient of the gas.

heparin (HEP-ah-rin) Anticoagulant that prevents platelet agglutination and thus prevents thrombus formation.

hepatic artery (heh-PAT-ik) Branch of the aorta that delivers blood to the liver.

hepatic cord Plate of liver cells that radiates away from the central vein of a liver lobule.

hepatic portal system System of portal veins that carries blood from the intestines, stomach, spleen, and pancreas to the liver.

hepatic portal vein Portal vein formed by the superior mesenteric and splenic veins and entering the liver.

hepatic sinusoid (SIGH-nuh-soyd) Terminal blood vessel having an irregular and larger caliber than an ordinary capillary within the liver lobule.

hepatic vein Vein that drains the liver into the inferior vena cava.

hepatocyte (HEP-ah-toh-site) Liver cell.

hepatopancreatic ampulla Dilation within the major duodenal papilla that normally receives both the common bile duct and the main pancreatic duct.

hepatopancreatic ampullar sphincter Smooth muscle sphincter of the hepatopancreatic ampulla; also called sphincter of Oddi.

Hering-Breuer reflex (HER-ing BROY-er) Named for German physiologist Heinrich Ewald Hering (1866–1948) and Austrian internist Josef Breuer (1842–1925). Sensory impulses from stretch receptors in the lungs arrest inspiration; expiration then occurs.

heterozygous (HET-er-oh-ZY-gus) [Gr., *heteros,* other + *zygon,* yoke] Having different allelic genes at one or more paired loci in homologous chromosomes.

hiatus (high-AY-tus) [L., aperture, to yawn] Opening.

hilum (HIGH-lum) [L., small bit or trifle] Indented surface on many organs, serving as a point where nerves and vessels enter or leave.

hindgut Caudal or terminal part of the embryonic gut.

histamine (HIS-tah-meen) Amine released by mast cells and basophils that promotes inflammation.

histology (his-TOL-oh-jee) [Gr., *histo,* web (tissue) + *logos,* study] Science that deals with the microscopic structure of cells, tissues, and organs in relation to their function.

holocrine gland (HOL-oh-krin) [Gr., *holos,* complete + *krino,* to separate] Gland whose secretion is formed by the disintegration of entire cells (e.g., sebaceous gland).

homeostasis (hoh-mee-oh-STAY-sis) [Gr., *homoio,* like + *stasis,* a standing] State of equilibrium in the body with respect to functions and composition of fluids and tissues.

homologous (hoh-MOL-oh-gus) [Gr., ratio or relation] Alike in structure or origin.

homozygous (hoh-moh-ZY-gus) [Gr., *homos,* the same + *zygon,* yoke] State of having identical allelic genes at one or more paired loci in homologous chromosomes.

hormone (HOR-mohn) [Gr., *hormon,* to set into motion] Substance secreted by endocrine tissues into the blood that acts on a target tissue to produce a specific response.

hormone receptor Protein or glycoprotein molecule of cells that specifically binds to hormones and produces a response.

horn Subdivision of gray matter in the spinal cord. The axons of sensory neurons synapse with neurons in the posterior horn, the cell bodies of motor neurons are in the anterior horn, and the cell bodies of autonomic neurons are in the lateral horn.

human chorionic gonadotropin (hCG) Hormone produced by the placenta; stimulates the secretion of testosterone by the fetus; during the first trimester, it stimulates ovarian secretion from the corpus luteum of the estrogen and progesterone required for the maintenance of the placenta. In a male fetus, it stimulates the secretion of testosterone by the fetal testis.

humoral immunity (HYU-mor-al im-YOU-nih-tee) [L., *humor,* a fluid] Immunity due to antibodies in serum.

hyaline cartilage (HIGH-ah-lin) [Gr., *hyalos,* glass] Gelatinous, glossy cartilage tissue consisting of cartilage cells and their matrix; contains collagen, proteoglycans, and water.

hyaluronic acid (HIGH-ah-loo-RON-ik) Mucopoly-saccharide made up of alternating β-(1,4)-linked residues of hyalobiuronic acid, forming a gelatinous material in the tissue spaces and acting as a lubricant and shock absorbant generally throughout the body.

hydrochloric acid (HCl) (high-droh-KLOHR-ik) Acid of gastric juice.

hydrogen bond (HIGH-droh-jen) Hydrogen atoms bound covalently to either N or O atoms have a small positive charge that is weakly attracted to the small negative charge of other atoms, such as O or N; it can occur within a molecule or between different molecules.

hydrophilic (high-droh-FIL-ik) [Gr., *hydro,* water + *philos,* love] Denoting the property of attracting or associating with water molecules, possessed by polar molecules and ions; the opposite of hydrophobic.

hydrophobic (high-droh-FOH-bik) [Gr., *hydro,* water + *phobos,* fear] Lacking an attraction to water, possessed by nonpolar molecules; the opposite of hydrophilic.

hydroxyapatite (high-DROK-see-ap-ah-tyte) Mineral with the empiric formula 3 $Ca_3(PO_4)_2 \cdot Ca(OH)_2$; the main mineral of bone and teeth.

hymen (HIGH-men) [Gr., membrane] Thin, membranous fold partly occluding the vaginal external orifice; normally disrupted by sexual intercourse or other mechanical phenomena.

hyoid bone (HIGH-oyd) (Gr., *hyoeides,* shaped like the Greek letter epsilon [ϵ]) U-shaped bone between the mandible and larynx.

hypercalcemia (HIGH-per-kal-SEE-mee-ah) Abnormally high levels of calcium in the blood.

hypercapnia (HIGH-per-KAP-nee-ah) Higher-than-normal levels of carbon dioxide in the blood or tissues.

hyperkalemia (HIGH-per-kah-LEE-mee-ah) Greater-than-normal concentration of potassium ions in the circulating blood.

hypernatremia (HIGH-per-nah-TREE-mee-ah) Abnormally high plasma concentration of sodium ions.

hyperosmotic (HIGH-per-oz-MOT-ik) [Gr., *hyper,* above + *osmos,* an impulsion] Having a greater osmotic concentration or pressure than a reference solution.

hyperpolarization (HIGH-per-POH-lar-ih-ZAY-shun) Increase in the charge difference across the plasma membrane; causes the charge difference to move away from 0 mV.

hypertonic (high-per-TON-ik) [Gr., *hyper,* above + *to-nos,* tension] Solution that causes cells to shrink.

hypertrophy (high-PER-troh-fee) [Gr., *hyper,* above + *trophe,* nourishment] Increase in bulk or size; not due to an increase in number of individual elements.

hypocalcemia (HIGH-poh-kal-SEE-mee-ah) Abnormally low levels of calcium in the blood.

hypocapnia (HIGH-poh-KAP-nee-ah) Lower-than-normal levels of carbon dioxide in the blood or tissues.

hypodermis (high-poh-DER-miss) [Gr., *hypo,* under + *dermis,* skin] Loose areolar connective tissue found deep to the dermis that connects the skin to muscle or bone.

hypokalemia (HIGH-poh-kah-LEE-mee-ah) Abnormally small concentration of potassium ions in the blood.

hyponatremia (HIGH-poh-nah-TREE-mee-ah) Abnormally low plasma concentration of sodium ions.

hyponychium (HIGH-poh-NIK-ee-um) [Gr., *hypo,* under + *onyx,* nail] Thickened portion of the stratum corneum under the free edge of the nail.

hypopolarization Change in the electric charge difference across the plasma membrane that causes the charge difference to be smaller or move closer to 0 mV.

hyposmotic (HIGH-pos-MOT-ik) [Gr., *hypo,* under + *osmos,* an impulsion] Having a lower osmotic concentration or pressure than a reference solution.

hypospadias (HIGH-poh-SPAY-dee-as) [Gr., one having the orifice of the penis too low; *hypospao,* to draw away from under] Developmental anomaly in the wall of the urethra so that the canal is open for a greater or lesser distance on the undersurface of the penis; a similar defect in the female in which the urethra opens into the vagina.

hypothalamohypophysial portal system (HIGH-poh-THAL-ah-moh-HIGH-poh-FIZ-ee-al) Series of blood vessels that carry blood from the area of the hypothalamus to the anterior pituitary gland; originates from capillary beds in the hypothalamus and terminates as a capillary bed in the anterior pituitary gland.

hypothalamohypophysial tract Nerve tract consisting of the axons of neurosecretory cells and extending from the hypothalamus into the posterior pituitary gland. Hormones produced in the neurosecretory cell bodies in the hypothalamus are transported through the hypothalamohypophyseal tract to the posterior pituitary gland, where they are stored for later release.

hypothalamus (high-poh-THAL-ah-muss) [Gr., *hypo,* under + *thalamus,* bedroom] Important autonomic and neuroendocrine control center beneath the thalamus.

hypothenar (high-poh-THEE-nar) [Gr., *hypo,* under + *thenar,* palm of the hand] Fleshy mass of tissue on the medial side of the palm; contains muscles responsible for moving the little finger.

hypotonic (high-poh-TON-ik) [Gr., *hypo,* under + *tonos,* tension] Solution that causes cells to swell.

I

I band Area between the ends of two adjacent myosin myofilaments within a myofibril; Z disk divides the I band into two equal parts.

ileocecal sphincter (ILL-ee-oh-SEE-cal) Thickening of circular smooth muscle between the ileum and the cecum, forming the ileocecal valve.

ileocecal valve Valve formed by the ileocecal sphincter between the ileum and the cecum.

ileum (ILL-ee-um) [Gr., *eileo,* to roll up, twist] Third portion of the small intestine, extending from the jejunum to the ileocecal opening into the large intestine; the posterior inferior bone of the coxal bone.

immunity (im-YOU-nih-tee) [L., *immunis,* free from service] Resistance to infectious disease and harmful substances.

immunization (im-MYOO-ni-ZAY-shun) Process by which a subject is rendered immune by deliberately introducing an antigen or antibody into the subject.

immunoglobulin (IG) (IM-you-noh-GLOB-you-lin) Antibody found in the gamma globulin portion of plasma.

implantation (im-plan-TAY-shun) Attachment of the blastocyst to the endometrium of the uterus, occurring 6 or 7 days after fertilization of the ovum.

impotence (IM-poh-tence) Inability to accomplish the male sexual act; caused by psychic or physical factors; also called erectile dysfunction (ED).

incisor (in-SIGH-zor) [L., *incido,* to cut into] One of the anterior, cutting teeth.

incisura (IN-sie-SOO-rah) [L., a cutting into] Notch or indentation at the edge of any structure.

incus (IN-cuss) [L., anvil] Middle of the three ossicles in the middle ear.

inferior colliculus (koh-LIK-yoo-lus) [L., *collis,* hill] One of two rounded eminences of the midbrain; involved with hearing.

inferior vena cava Vein that returns blood from the lower limbs and the greater part of the pelvic and abdominal organs to the right atrium.

inflammatory response (in-FLAM-ah-toh-ree) Complex sequence of events involving chemicals and immune cells that results in the isolation and destruction of antigens and tissues near the antigens.

infundibulum (IN-fun-DIB-you-lum) [L., funnel] Funnel-shaped structure or passage—for example, the infundibulum that attaches the hypophysis to the hypothalamus or the funnel-like expansion of the uterine tube near the ovary.

infusion Introduction of a fluid other than blood, such as a saline or glucose solution, into the blood.

inguinal canal (IN-gwin-al) Passage through the lower abdominal wall that transmits the spermatic cord in the male and the round ligament in the female.

inhibin (in-HIB-in) Polypeptide secreted from the testes that inhibits FSH secretion.

inhibitory neuron (in-HIB-i-tohr-ee) Neuron that produces IPSPs and has an inhibitory influence.

inhibitory postsynaptic potential (IPSP) Hyperpolarization in the postsynaptic membrane, which causes the membrane potential to move away from threshold.

innate immunity (IH-nate) Immune system response that is the same with each exposure to an antigen; there is no ability for the system to remember a previous exposure to the antigen.

inner cell mass Group of cells at one end of the blastocyst, part of which forms the body of the embryo.

inner ear Part of the ear that contains the sensory organs for hearing and balance; contains the bony and membranous labyrinth.

insensible perspiration [L., *per,* through + *spiro,* to breathe everywhere] Perspiration that evaporates before it is perceived as moisture on the skin; the term sometimes includes evaporation from the lungs.

insertion (in-SIR-shun) More movable attachment point of a muscle; usually, the lateral or distal end of a muscle associated with the limbs; also called mobile end.

inspiratory capacity (in-SPY-rah-toh-ree) Volume of air that can be inspired after a normal expiration; the sum of the tidal volume and the inspiratory reserve volume.

inspiratory reserve volume Maximum volume of air that can be inspired after a normal inspiration.

insulin (IN-syu-lin) Protein hormone secreted from the pancreas that increases the uptake of glucose and amino acids by most tissues.

interatrial septum (IN-ter-AY-tree-al) [L., *saeptum,* partition] Wall between the atria of the heart.

intercalated disk (in-TER-kah-lay-ted) Cell-to-cell attachment with gap junctions between cardiac muscle cells.

intercalated duct Minute duct of glands, such as the salivary gland, and the pancreas; leads from the acini to the interlobular ducts.

intercellular (in-ter-SEL-yoo-lar) Between cells.

intercellular chemical signal Chemical that is released from cells and passes to other cells; acts as a signal that allows cells to communicate with each other; also called first messenger.

interferons (in-ter-FEER-onz) Proteins that prevent viral replication.

interlobar artery (in-ter-LOH-bar) Branch of the segmental arteries of the kidney; runs between the renal pyramids and gives rise to the arcuate arteries.

interlobular duct Any duct leading from a lobule of a gland and formed by the junction of the intercalated ducts draining the acini.

intermediate olfactory area Part of the olfactory cortex responsible for the modulation of olfactory sensations.

internal anal sphincter [Gr., *sphinkter,* band or lace] Smooth muscle ring at the upper end of the anal canal.

internal naris; pl. **nares** (NAY-ris, NAY-res) Opening from the nasal cavity into the nasopharynx.

internal spermatic fascia Inner connective tissue covering of the spermatic cord.

internal urinary sphincter Traditionally recognized as a sphincter composed of a thickening of the middle smooth muscle layer of the bladder around the urethral opening.

interphase (IN-ter-FAYZ) Period between active cell divisions when DNA replication occurs.

interstitial (in-ter-STISH-al) [L., *inter,* between + *sisto,* to stand] Space within tissue. Interstitial growth is growth from within.

interstitial cell Cell between the seminiferous tubules of the testes; secretes testosterone; also called Leydig cell.

interventricular septum (IN-ter-ven-TRIK-you-lar) Wall between the ventricles of the heart.

intestinal gland (in-TES-tin-al) Tubular gland in the mucous membrane of the small and large intestines; also called crypt.

intracellular (in-trah-SELL-you-lar) Inside a cell.

intracellular mediator Molecule produced within a cell that binds to a macromolecule, such as receptors or enzymes inside that cell, that regulates their activities; also called second messenger.

intramural plexus (in-trah-MYOO-ral) Combined submucosal and myenteric plexuses.

intrinsic clotting pathway (in-TRIN-sik) Series of chemical reactions resulting in clot formation that begins with chemicals (e.g., plasma factor XII) within the blood.

intrinsic factor Factor secreted by the parietal cells of gastric glands and required for adequate absorption of vitamin B_{12}.

intrinsic muscles Muscles located within the structure being moved.

intubation (in-too-BAY-shun) Insertion of a tube into an opening, a canal, or a hollow organ.

inversion (in-VER-shun) [L., *inverto,* to turn about] Turning inward.

ion (EYE-on) [Gr., *ion,* going] Atom or group of atoms carrying a charge of electricity by virtue of having gained or lost one or more electrons.

ion channel Pore in the plasma membrane through which ions, such as sodium and potassium, move.

ionic bond (eye-ON-ik) Chemical bond that is formed when one atom loses an electron and another accepts that electron.

iris (EYE-ris) Specialized portion of the vascular tunic; the "colored" portion of the eye that can be seen through the cornea.

ischemia (ih-SKEE-mee-ah) [Gr., *ischo,* to keep back + *haima,* blood] Reduced blood supply to an area of the body.

ischium (IS-kee-um) Superior bone of the coxal bone.

isomers (EYE-soh-merz) [Gr., *isos,* equal + *meros,* part] Molecules having the same number and types of atoms but differing in their three-dimensional arrangement.

isometric contraction (eye-soh-MET-rik) [Gr., *isos,* equal + *metron,* measure] Muscle contraction in which the length of the muscle does not change but the tension produced increases.

isosmotic (EYE-sos-MOT-ik) [Gr., *isos,* equal + *osmos,* an impulsion] Having the same osmotic concentration or pressure as a reference solution.

isotonic (EYE-soh-TON-ik) [Gr., *isos,* equal + *tonos,* tension] Type of solution that causes cells to neither shrink nor swell.

isotope (EYE-soh-tope) [Gr., *isos,* equal + *topos,* part, place] Either of two or more atoms that have the same atomic number but a different number of neutrons.

isthmus (IS-muhs) Constriction connecting two larger parts of an organ, such as the constriction between the body and the cervix of the uterus or the portion of the uterine tube between the ampulla and the uterus.

J

jaundice (JAWN-dis) [Fr., *jaune,* yellow] Yellowish staining of the integument, the sclerae, and the other tissues with bile pigments.

jejunum (jeh-JEW-num) [L., *jejunus,* empty] Second portion of the small intestine; located between the duodenum and the ileum.

juxtaglomerular apparatus (JUKS-tah-gloh-MER-you-lar) Complex consisting of juxtaglomerular cells of the afferent arteriole and macular densa cells of the distal convoluted tubule near the renal corpuscle; secretes renin.

juxtaglomerular cell Modified smooth muscle cell of the afferent arteriole located at the renal corpuscle; a component of the juxtaglomerular apparatus.

juxtamedullary nephron (JUKS-ta-MED-you-lair-ee) Nephron located near the junction of the renal cortex and medulla.

K

karyotype (KAIR-ee-oh-type) Display of chromosomes arranged by pairs.

keratinization (KER-ah-tin-ih-ZAY-shun) Production of keratin and changes in the chemical and structural character of epithelial cells as they move to the skin surface.

keratinized (KER-ah-tih-nyezd) [Gr., *keras,* horn] Having become a structure that contains keratin, a protein found in skin, hair, nails, and horns.

keratinocyte (keh-RAT-ih-noh-syte) [Gr., *keras,* horn + *kytos,* cell] Epidermal cell that produces keratin.

keratohyalin (KER-ah-toh-HIGH-ah-lin) Nonmembrane-bound protein granule in the cytoplasm of stratum granulosum cells of the epidermis.

ketogenesis (kee-toh-JEN-eh-sis) Production of ketone bodies, such as from acetyl-CoA.

ketone body (KEE-tone) One of a group of ketones, including acetoacetic acid, β-hydrobutyric acid, and acetone.

ketosis (kee-TOH-sis) [*ketone* + *osis,* condition] Condition characterized by the enhanced production of ketone bodies, as in diabetes mellitus or starvation.

kidney (KID-nee) [A.S., *cwith,* womb, belly + *neere,* kidney] One of the two organs that excrete urine. The kidneys are bean-shaped organs approximately 11 cm long, 5 cm wide, and 3 cm thick lying on each side of the spinal column, posterior to the peritoneum, approximately opposite the twelfth thoracic and first three lumbar vertebrae.

kilocalorie (kcal) (KIL-oh-KAL-oh-ree) Quantity of energy required to raise the temperature of 1 kg of water 1°C; 1000 calories. Equal to one dietary calorie.

kinetic energy (kih-NET-ik) Motion energy or energy that can do work.

kinetic labyrinth (LAB-ih-rinth) Part of the membranous labyrinth composed of the semicircular canals; detects dynamic or kinetic equilibrium, such as movement of the head.

kinetochore (kih-NET-oh-kohr, kih-NEE-toh-kohr) [Gr., *kinēto,* moving + Gr., *chōra,* space] Structural portion of the chromosome to which microtubules attach.

Korotkoff sounds (koh-ROT-kof) Named for Russian physician Nikolai S. Korotkoff (1874–1920). Sounds heard over an artery when blood pressure is determined by the auscultatory method; caused by turbulent flow of blood.

L

labium majus; pl. **labia majora** (LAY-bee-uhm, LAY-bee-ah) One of two rounded folds of skin surrounding the labia minora and vestibule; homolog of the scrotum in males.

labium minus; pl. **labia minora** One of two narrow longitudinal folds of mucous membrane enclosed by the labia majora and bounding the vestibule; anteriorly they unite to form the prepuce.

lacrimal apparatus (LAK-rih-mal) Lacrimal, or tear, gland in the superolateral corner of the orbit of the eye and a duct system that extends from the eye to the nasal cavity.

lacrimal canaliculus Canal that carries excess tears away from the eye; located in the medial canthus and opening on the lacrimal papilla.

lacrimal gland Tear gland located in the superolateral corner of the orbit.

lacrimal papilla Small lump of tissue in the medial canthus or corner of the eye; the lacrimal canal opens within the lacrimal papilla.

lacrimal sac Enlargement in the lacrimal canal that leads into the nasolacrimal duct.

lactation (lak-TAY-shun) [L., *lactatio,* suckle] Period after childbirth during which milk is formed in the breasts.

lacteal (LAK-tee-al) Lymphatic vessel in the wall of the small intestine that carries chyle from the intestine and absorbs fat.

lactiferous duct (lak-TIF-er-us) One of 15–20 ducts that drain the lobes of the mammary gland and open onto the surface of the nipple.

lactiferous sinus Dilation of the lactiferous duct just before it enters the nipple.

lacuna; pl. **lacunae** (lah-KOO-nah, lah-KOO-nee) [L., *lacus,* a hollow, a lake] Small space or cavity; potential space within the matrix of bone or cartilage normally occupied by a cell that can be visualized only when the cell shrinks away from the matrix during fixation; space containing maternal blood within the placenta.

lag phase One of the three phases of muscle contraction; time between the application of the stimulus and the beginning of muscular contraction; also called latent phase.

lamella; pl. **lamellae** (lah-MEL-ah, lah-MEL-ee) Thin sheet or layer of bone.

lamellated corpuscle (LAM-eh-late-ed) Oval receptor found in the deep dermis or hypodermis (responsible for deep cutaneous pressure and vibration) and in tendons (responsible for proprioception); also called Pacinian corpuscle.

lamina; pl. **laminae** (LAM-ih-nah, LAM-ih-nee) [L., *lamina,* plate, leaf] Thin plate—for example, the thinner portion of the vertebral arch.

lamina propria (PROH-pree-ah) Layer of connective tissue underlying the epithelium of a mucous membrane.

laminar flow (LAM-ih-nar) Relative motion of layers of a fluid along smooth, concentric, parallel paths.

Langerhans cell Named for German anatomist Paul Langerhans (1847–1888); dendritic cell found in the skin.

lanugo (lah-NYU-goh) [L., *lana,* wool] Fine, soft, unpigmented fetal hair.

Laplace's law (lah-PLAS-sez) Named for French mathematician Pierre S. de Laplace (1749–1827); the force that stretches the wall of a blood vessel is proportional to the radius of the vessel times the blood pressure.

large intestine Portion of the digestive tract extending from the small intestine to the anus.

laryngitis (lair-in-JIE-tis) Inflammation of the mucous membrane of the larynx.

laryngopharynx (lah-RING-oh-FAIR-inks) Part of the pharynx lying posterior to the larynx.

larynx; pl. **larynges** (LAIR-inks, LAIR-in-jeez) Organ of voice production located between the pharynx and the trachea; it consists of a framework of cartilages and elastic membranes housing the vocal folds and the muscles that control the position and tension of these elements.

last menstrual period (LMP) Beginning of the last menstruation before pregnancy; used clinically to time events during pregnancy.

lateral geniculate nucleus (jeh-NIK-yoo-late) Nucleus of the thalamus where fibers from the optic tract terminate.

lateral olfactory area (ol-FAK-toh-ree) Part of the olfactory cortex involved in the conscious perception of olfactory stimuli.

lens Transparent biconvex structure lying between the iris and the vitreous humor.

lens fiber Epithelial cell that makes up the lens of the eye.

lesser omentum (oh-MEN-tum) [L., membrane that encloses the bowels] Peritoneal fold passing from the liver to the lesser curvature of the stomach and to the upper border of the duodenum for a distance of approximately 2 cm beyond the pylorus.

lesser vestibular gland (ves-TIB-you-lar) Number of minute mucous glands opening on the surface of the vestibule between the openings of the vagina and urethra; also called paraurethral gland.

leukocyte (LOO-koh-site) White blood cell.

leukocytosis (LOO-koh-sigh-TOH-sis) Abnormally large number of white blood cells in the blood.

leukopenia (loo-koh-PEE-nee-ah) Lower-than-normal number of white blood cells in the blood.

leukotriene (loo-koh-TRY-een) Specific class of physiologically active fatty acid derivatives present in many tissues.

lever Rigid shaft capable of turning about a fulcrum or pivot point.

LH surge Increase in plasma luteinizing hormone (LH) levels before ovulation and responsible for initiating it.

ligamentum arteriosum (LIG-ah-MEN-tum) Remains of the ductus arteriosus.

ligamentum venosum Remnant of the ductus venosus.

ligand *See* chemical signal.

ligand-gated ion channel Ion channel in a plasma membrane caused to either open or close by a ligand binding to a receptor.

limbic system (LIM-bic) [L., *limbus,* border] Part of the brain involved with emotions and olfaction; includes the cingulate gyrus, hippocampus, habenular nuclei, parts of the basal ganglia, and the hypothalamus (especially the mammillary bodies, the olfactory cortex, and various nerve tracts).

lingual tonsil (LING-gwal) Collection of lymphoid tissue on the posterior portion of the dorsum of the tongue.

lipase (LIE-pase) Any fat-splitting enzyme.

lipid (LIP-id) [Gr., *lipos,* fat] Substance composed principally of carbon, oxygen, and hydrogen; contains a lower ratio of oxygen to carbon and is less polar than carbohydrates; generally soluble in nonpolar solvents.

lipid bilayer Double layer of lipid molecules forming the plasma membrane and other cellular membranes.

lipochrome (LIP-oh-krohm) Lipid-containing pigment that is metabolically inert.

lipotropin (lih-poh-TROH-pin) One of the peptide hormones released from the adenohypophysis; increases lipolysis in fat cells.

liver (LIV-er) Largest gland of the body, lying in the upper-right quadrant of the abdomen just inferior to the diaphragm; secretes bile and is of great importance in carbohydrate and protein metabolism and in detoxifying chemicals.

lobar bronchi Branch from a primary bronchus that conducts air to each lobe of the lungs. There are two branches in the left lung and three branches from the primary bronchus in the right lung; also called secondary bronchus.

lobe (lohb) Rounded, projecting part, such as the lobe of a lung, the liver, or a gland.

lobule (LOB-yool) Small lobe or subdivision of a lobe, such as a lobule of the lung or a gland.

local inflammation Inflammation confined to a specific area of the body. Symptoms include redness, heat, swelling, pain, and loss of function.

local potential Depolarization that is not propagated and that is graded or proportional to the strength of the stimulus.

local reflex Reflex of the intramural plexus of the digestive tract that does not involve the brain or spinal cord.

locus; pl. **loci** (LOH-kus, LOH-sigh) Place; usually a specific site.

lower respiratory tract Larynx, trachea, and lungs.

lung recoil Decrease in the size of an expanded lung as a result of a decrease in the size (volume) of its alveoli; due to elastic recoil of elastic fibers surrounding alveoli and water surface tension of a thin film of water within alveoli.

lunula; pl. **lunulae** (LOO-noo-lah, LOO-noo-lee) [L., *luna,* moon] White, crescent-shaped portion of the nail matrix visible through the proximal end of the nail.

luteal phase (LOO-tee-al) Portion of the menstrual cycle extending from the time of formation of the corpus luteum after ovulation to the time when menstrual flow begins; usually 14 days in length; also called secretory phase.

luteinizing hormone (LH) (LOO-tee-ih-nyze-ing) In females, hormone stimulating the final maturation of the follicles and the secretion of progesterone by them, with their rupture releasing the ovum, and the conversion of the ruptured follicle into the corpus luteum; in males, stimulates the secretion of testosterone in the testes.

lymph (LIMF) [L., *lympha,* clear spring water] Clear or yellowish fluid derived from interstitial fluid and found in lymph vessels.

lymph node Encapsulated mass of lymph tissue found among lymph vessels.

lymphatic capillary Beginning of the lymphatic system of vessels; lined with flattened endothelium lacking a basement membrane.

lymphatic nodule Small accumulation of lymph tissue lacking a distinct boundary.

lymphatic sinus Channels in a lymph node crossed by a reticulum of cells and fibers.

lymphatic vessel One of the system of vessels carrying lymph from the lymph capillaries to the veins.

lymphedema (LIMF-eh-DEE-mah) Swelling of tissues resulting from the excessive accumulation of fluid caused by the removal, damage, or blockage of lymphatic vessels or lymph nodes; usually results in swelling of the arm or leg.

lymphoblast (LIM-foh-blast) Cell that matures into a lymphocyte.

lymphocyte (LIM-foh-site) Nongranulocytic white blood cell formed in lymphoid tissue.

lymphokine (LIM-foh-kyne) Chemical produced by lymphocytes that activates macrophages, attracts neutrophils, and promotes inflammation.

lysis (LYE-sis) [Gr., *lysis,* a loosening] Process by which a cell swells and ruptures.

lysosome (LIE-soh-sohm) [Gr., *lysis,* loosening + *soma,* body] Membrane-bounded vesicle containing hydrolytic enzymes that function as intracellular digestive enzymes.

lysozyme (LIE-soh-zime) Enzyme that is destructive to the cell walls of certain bacteria; present in tears and some other fluids of the body.

M

M line Line in the center of the H zone made of delicate filaments that holds the myosin myofilaments in place in the sarcomere of muscle fibers.

macrophage (MAK-roh-fayj) [Gr., *makros,* large + *phagein,* to eat] Any large, mononuclear phagocytic cell.

macula; pl. maculae (MAK-you-lah, MAK-you-lee) [L., a spot] Sensory structure in the utricle and saccule, consisting of hair cells and a gelatinous mass embedded with otoliths.

macula densa Cells of the distal convoluted tubule located at the renal corpuscle and forming part of the juxtaglomerular apparatus.

main bronchus; pl. **bronchi** (BRONG-kuss, BRONG-kye) One of two tubes arising at the inferior end of the trachea; each primary bronchus extends into one of the lungs; also called primary bronchus.

major duodenal papilla Point of opening of the common bile duct and pancreatic duct into the duodenum.

major histocompatibility complex (MHC) molecules Genes that control the production of major histocompatibility complex proteins, which are glycoproteins found on the surfaces of cells. The major histocompatibility proteins serve as self-markers for the immune system and are used by antigen-presenting cells to present antigens to lymphocytes.

male pronucleus Nuclear material of the sperm cell after the ovum has been penetrated by the sperm cell.

malignant (mah-LIG-nant) Resistant to treatment; occurring in severe form and frequently fatal; having locally invasive and destructive growth and metastasis.

malleus; pl. **mallei** (MAL-ee-us, MAL-ee-eye) [L., hammer] Largest of the three auditory ossicles; attached to the tympanic membrane.

mamillary bodies (MAM-ih-lair-ee) [L., breast- or nipple-shaped] Nipple-shaped structures at the base of the hypothalamus.

mamma; pl. **mammae** (MAM-ah, MAM-ee) Breast; the organ of milk secretion; one of two hemispheric projections of variable size situated in the subcutaneous layer over the pectoralis major muscle on each side of the chest; it is rudimentary in the male.

mammary ligaments (MAM-ah-ree) Well-developed ligaments that extend from the overlying skin to the fibrous stroma of the mammary gland; also called Cooper's ligaments.

manubrium; pl. **manubria** (mah-NOO-bree-um, mah-NOO-bree-ah) [L., handle] Part of a bone representing the handle, such as the manubrium of the sternum representing the handle of a sword.

mass movement Forcible peristaltic movement of short duration, occurring only three or four times a day, which moves the contents of the large intestine.

mass number Number of protons plus the number of neutrons in each atom.

mastication (mas-tih-KAY-shun) [L., *mastico,* to chew] Process of chewing.

mastication reflex Repetitive cycle of relaxation and contraction of the muscles of mastication.

mastoid (MAS-toyd) [Gr., *mastos,* breast] Resembling a breast.

mastoid air cells Spaces within the mastoid process of the temporal bone connected to the middle ear by ducts.

mature follicle Ovarian follicle in which the oocyte attains its full size. The follicle contains a fluid-filled antrum and is surrounded by the theca interna and externa; also called Graafian follicle.

maximal stimulus Stimulus resulting in a local potential just large enough to produce the maximum frequency of action potentials.

meatus (mee-AY-tus) [L., to go, pass] Passageway or tunnel.

mechanoreceptor (MEK-an-noh-ree-SEP-ter) Sensory receptor that responds to mechanical pressures—for example, pressure receptors in the carotid sinus or touch receptors in the skin.

meconium (meh-KOH-nee-um) [Gr., *mekon,* poppy] First intestinal discharges of the newborn infant, greenish in color and consisting of epithelial cells, mucus, and bile.

medial olfactory area Part of the olfactory cortex responsible for the visceral and emotional reactions to odors.

medulla oblongata (ob-lon-GAH-tah) Inferior portion of the brainstem that connects the spinal cord to the brain and contains autonomic centers controlling functions such as heart rate, respiration, and swallowing.

medullary cavity (MEH-dyoo-lair-ee) Large, marrow-filled cavity in the diaphysis of a long bone.

medullary ray Extension of the kidney medulla into the cortex, consisting of collecting ducts and nephron loops.

megakaryoblast (meg-ah-KAR-ee-oh-blast) [Gr., *mega* + *karyon,* nut, nucleus + *blastos,* germ] Cell that gives rise to platelets or thrombocytes.

meibomian cyst (my-BOH-mee-an) Named for German anatomist Hendrik Meibom (1638–1700); a chronic inflammation of a meibomian gland.

meibomian gland Sebaceous gland near the inner margins of the eyelid; secretes sebum that lubricates the eyelid and retains tears.

meiosis (my-OH-sis) [Gr., a lessening] Cell division that results in the formation of gametes. Consists of two divisions, which result in one (female) or four (male) gametes, each of which contains one-half the number of chromosomes in the parent cell.

Meissner corpuscle (MICE-ner KOR-pus-ul) Named for German histologist Georg Meissner (1829–1905). *See also* tactile corpuscle.

melanin (MEL-ah-nin) [Gr., *melas,* black] Group of related molecules responsible for skin, hair, and eye color. Most melanins are brown to black pigments; some are yellowish or reddish.

melanocyte (MEL-an-oh-syte) [Gr., *melas,* black + *kytos,* cell] Cell found mainly in the stratum basale; produces the brown or black pigment melanin.

melanocyte-stimulating hormone (MSH) Peptide hormone secreted by the anterior pituitary; increases melanin production by melanocytes, making the skin darker in color.

melanosome (MEL-ah-noh-sohm) [Gr., *melas,* black + *soma,* body] Membranous organelle containing the pigment melanin.

melatonin (mel-ah-TONE-in) Hormone (amino acid derivative) secreted by the pineal body; inhibits the secretion of gonadotropin-releasing hormone from the hypothalamus.

membrane attack complex (MAC) Channel through a plasma membrane produced by activated complement proteins, primarily complement protein C9; in nucleated cells, water enters the channel, causing lysis of cells.

membrane-bound receptor Receptor molecule, such as a hormone receptor, that is bound to the plasma membrane of the target cell.

membranous labyrinth (MEM-brah-nus LAB-ih-rinth) Membranous structure within the inner ear consisting of the cochlea, vestibule, and semicircular canals.

membranous urethra (you-REE-thrah) Portion of the male urethra, approximately 1 cm in length, extending from the prostate gland to the beginning of the penile urethra.

memory cell Small lymphocyte that is derived from a B cell or T cell and that rapidly responds to a subsequent exposure to the same antigen.

menarche (meh-NAR-key) [Gr., *mensis,* month + *arche,* beginning] Establishment of menstrual function; the time of the first menstrual period or flow.

meninx; pl. **meninges** (MEN-inks, meh-NIN-jeez) [Gr., membrane] Connective tissue membrane surrounding the brain.

meniscus; pl. **menisci** (meh-NIS-kuss, meh-NIS-sigh) Crescent-shaped intraarticular fibrocartilage found in certain joints, such as the crescent-shaped fibrocartilaginous structure of the knee.

menopause (MEN-oh-pawz) [Gr., *mensis,* month + *pausis,* cessation] Permanent cessation of the menstrual cycle.

menses (MEN-seez) [L., *mensis,* month] Periodic hemorrhage from the uterine mucous membrane, occurring at approximately 28-day intervals.

menstrual cycle (MEN-stroo-al) Series of changes that occur in sexually mature, nonpregnant females and result in menses. Specifically refers to the uterine cycle but is often used to include both the uterine and ovarian cycles.

Merkel (tactile) disk (MER-kel) Named for German anatomist Friedrich Merkel (1845–1919).

merocrine gland (MARE-oh-krin) [Gr., *meros,* part + *krino,* to separate] Gland that secretes products with no loss of cellular material—for example, water-producing sweat glands.

mesencephalon (mez-en-SEF-ah-lon) [Gr., *mesos,* middle + *enkephalos,* brain] Midbrain in both the embryo and adult; consists of the cerebral peduncle and the corpora quadrigemini.

mesentery (MESS-en-ter-ree) [Gr., *mesos,* middle + *enteron,* intestine] Double layer of peritoneum extending from the abdominal wall to the abdominal viscera, conveying to it its vessels and nerves.

mesoderm (MEZ-oh-derm) Middle of the three germ layers of an embryo.

mesonephros (MEZ-oh-NEF-ros) One of three excretory organs appearing during embryonic development; forms caudal to the pronephros as the pronephros disappears. It is well developed and is functional for a time before the establishment of the metanephros, which gives rise to the kidney. It undergoes regression as an excretory organ, but its duct system is retained in the male as the efferent ductule and epididymis.

mesosalpinx (MEZ-oh-SAL-pinks) [Gr., *mesos,* middle + *salpinx,* trumpet] Part of the broad ligament supporting the uterine tube.

mesothelium (mez-oh-THEE-lee-um) Single layer of flattened cells forming an epithelium that lines serous cavities, such as peritoneum, pleura, pericardium.

mesovarium (MEZ-oh-VAY-ree-um) Short peri-toneal fold connecting the ovary with the broad ligament of the uterus.

messenger ribonucleic acid (mRNA) Type of RNA that moves out of the nucleus and into the cytoplasm, where it is used as a template to determine the structure of proteins.

metabolism (meh-TAB-oh-lizm) [Gr., *metabole,* change] Sum of all the chemical reactions that take place in the body, consisting of anabolism and catabolism. *Cellular metabolism* refers specifically to the chemical reactions within cells.

metacarpal (MET-ah-KAR-pal) Relating to the fine bones of the hand between the carpus (wrist) and the phalanges.

metanephros (met-ah-NEF-ros) Most caudally located of the three excretory organs appearing during embryonic development; becomes the permanent kidney of mammals. In mammalian embryos, it is formed caudal to the mesonephros and develops later as the mesonephros undergoes regression.

metaphase (MET-ah-fayz) Time during cell division when the chromosomes line up along the equator of the cell.

metarteriole (MET-ar-TEER-ee-ohl) One of the small peripheral blood vessels that contain scattered groups of smooth muscle fibers in their walls; located between the arterioles and the true capillaries.

metastasis (meh-TAS-tah-sis) Shifting of a disease or its local manifestations or the spread of a disease from one part of the body to another, as in a malignant neoplasm.

metatarsal (MET-ah-TAR-sal) [Gr., *meta,* after + *tarsos,* sole of the foot] Distal bone of the foot.

metencephalon (MET-en-SEF-ah-lon) [Gr., *meta,* after + *enkephalos,* brain] Second-most posterior division of the embryonic brain; becomes the pons and cerebellum in the adult.

micelle (my-SEL) [L., *micella,* small morsel] Droplets of lipid surrounded by bile salts in the small intestine.

microfilament (migh-kroh-FIL-ah-ment) Small fibril forming bundles, sheets, or networks in the cytoplasm of cells; provides structure to the cytoplasm and mechanical support for microvilli and stereocilia.

microglia (my-KROH-glee-ah) [Gr., *micro* + *glia,* glue] Small neuroglial cells that become phagocytic and mobile in response to inflammation; considered to be macrophages within the central nervous system.

microtubule (my-kroh-TOO-bule) Hollow tube composed of tubulin, measuring approximately 25 nm in diameter and usually several micrometers long. Helps provide support to the cytoplasm of the cell and is a component of certain cell organelles, such as centrioles, spindle fibers, cilia, and flagella.

microvillus; pl. **microvilli** (my-kroh-VIL-us, my-kroh-VIL-eye) Minute projection of the cell membrane that greatly increases the surface area.

micturition reflex (mik-choo-RISH-un) Contraction of the urinary bladder stimulated by stretching of the bladder wall; results in emptying of the bladder.

middle ear Air-filled space within the temporal bone; contains auditory ossicles; between the external and internal ear.

milk letdown Expulsion of milk from the alveoli of the mammary glands; stimulated by oxytocin.

mineral Inorganic nutrient necessary for normal metabolic functions.

mineralocorticoid (MIN-er-al-oh-KOR-tih-koyd) Steroid hormone (e.g., aldosterone) produced by the zona glomerulosa of the adrenal cortex; facilitates exchange of potassium for sodium in the distal renal tubule, causing sodium reabsorption and potassium and hydrogen ion secretion.

minor duodenal papilla Site of the opening of the accessory pancreatic duct into the duodenum.

minute ventilation Product of tidal volume times the respiratory rate.

mitochondrion; pl. **mitochondria** (my-toh-KON-dree-on, mye-toh-KON-dree-ah) [Gr., *mitos,* thread + *chandros,* granule] Small, spherical, rod-shaped or thin filamentous structure in the cytoplasm of cells that is a site of ATP production.

mitosis (my-TOH-sis) [Gr., thread] Cell division resulting in two daughter cells with exactly the same number and type of chromosomes as the mother cell.

modiolus (moh-DIE-oh-lus) [L., nave of a wheel] Central core of spongy bone about which turns the spiral canal of the cochlea.

molar (MOH-lar) Tricuspid tooth; the three posterior teeth of each dental arch.

molecule (MOLL-eh-kyul) Substance composed of two or more atoms chemically combined to form a structure that behaves as an independent unit.

monoblast (MON-oh-blast) Cell that matures into a monocyte.

monocyte (MON-oh-site) Type of white blood cell; large phagocytic white blood cell that moves from the blood into tissues and becomes a macrophage.

mononuclear phagocytic system (mon-oh-NOO-klee-ar fag-oh-SIT-ik) Phagocytic cells, each with a single nucleus; derived from monocytes; also called reticuloendothelial system.

monosaccharide (MON-oh-SACK-ah-ride) Simple sugar carbohydrate that cannot form any simpler sugar by hydrolysis.

mons pubis (MONZ PYU-bis) [L., mountain; the genitals] Prominence caused by a pad of fatty tissue over the symphysis pubis in the female.

morula (MOR-you-lah) [L., *morus,* mulberry] Mass of 12 or more cells resulting from the early cleavage divisions of the zygote.

motor neuron Neuron that innervates skeletal, smooth, or cardiac muscle fibers.

motor unit Single neuron and the muscle fibers it innervates.

mucosa (myu-KOH-sah) [L., *mucosus* mucous] Mucous membrane consisting of epithelium and lamina propria. In the digestive tract, there is also a layer of smooth muscle.

mucous membrane (MYU-kus) Thin sheet consisting of epithelium and connective tissue (lamina propria) that lines cavities that open to the outside of the body; many contain mucous glands that secrete mucus.

mucous neck cell One of the mucus-secreting cells in the neck of a gastric gland.

mucus (MYU-kus) Viscous secretion produced by and covering mucous membranes; lubricates mucous membranes and traps foreign substances.

multiple motor unit summation Increased force of contraction of a muscle due to recruitment of motor units.

multiple-wave summation Increased force of contraction of a muscle due to increased frequency of stimulation.

multipolar neuron One of three categories of neurons consisting of a neuron cell body, an axon, and two or more dendrites.

muscarinic receptor (mus-kah-RIN-ik) Class of cholinergic receptor that is specifically activated by muscarine in addition to acetylcholine.

muscle fiber Muscle cell.

muscle spindle Three to 10 specialized muscle fibers supplied by gamma motor neurons and wrapped in sensory nerve endings; detects stretch of the muscle and is involved in maintaining muscle tone.

muscle tone Relatively constant tension produced by a muscle for long periods as a result of asynchronous contraction of motor units.

muscle twitch Contraction of a whole muscle in response to a stimulus that causes an action potential in one or more muscle fibers.

muscular fatigue Fatigue due to a depletion of ATP within the muscle fibers.

muscularis (muss-kyu-LAR-is) [Modern L., muscular] Muscular coat of a hollow organ or tubular structure.

muscularis mucosa Thin layer of smooth muscle found in most parts of the digestive tube; located outside the lamina propria and adjacent to the submucosa.

musculi pectinati (mus-kyoo-ligh PEK-ti-NAH-tie) Prominent ridges of atrial myocardium located on the inner surface of much of the right atrium and both auricles.

mutation (myoo-TAY-shun) Change in the number or kinds of nucleotides in the DNA of a gene.

myelencephalon (MY-el-en-SEF-ah-lon) [Gr., *myelos,* medulla, marrow + *enkephalos,* brain] Most caudal portion of the embryonic brain; also called medulla oblongata.

myelin sheath (MY-eh-lin) Envelope surrounding most axons; formed by Schwann cell membranes being wrapped around the axon.

myelinated axon (MY-eh-lin-ay-ted AK-son) Nerve fiber having a myelin sheath.

myeloblast (MY-eh-loh-blast) Immature cell from which the different granulocytes develop.

myenteric plexus (my-en-TER-ik) Plexus of unmelinated fibers and postganglionic autonomic cell bodies lying in the muscular coat of the esophagus, stomach, and intestines; communicates with the submucosal plexuses.

myoblast (MY-oh-blast) [Gr., *mys,* muscle + *blastos,* germ] Primitive, multinucleated cell with the potential to develop into a muscle fiber.

myofilament (my-oh-FIL-ah-ment) Extremely fine molecular thread helping form the myofibrils of muscle; thick myofilaments are formed of myosin, and thin myofilaments are formed of actin.

myometrium (my-oh-MEE-tree-um) Muscular wall of the uterus; composed of smooth muscle; also called muscular layer.

myosin myofilament (MY-oh-sin) Thick myofilament of muscle fibrils; composed of myosin molecules.

N

nail (NAYL) [A.S., naegel] Several layers of dead epithelial cells containing hard keratin on the ends of the digits.

nail bed Epithelial tissue resting on dermis under the nail between the nail matrix and hyponychium; contributes to the formation of the nail.

nail matrix Epithelial tissue resting on dermis under the proximal end of a nail; produces most of the nail.

nasal cavity (NAY-zal) Cavity between the external nares and the pharynx. It is divided into two chambers by the nasal septum and is bounded inferiorly by the hard and soft palates.

nasal septum Bony partition that separates the nasal cavity into left and right parts; composed of the vomer, the perpendicular plate of the ethmoid, and hyaline cartilage.

nasolacrimal duct (NAY-zoh-LAK-rim-al) Duct that leads from the lacrimal sac to the nasal cavity.

nasopharynx (NAY-zoh-FAIR-inks) Part of the pharynx that lies above the soft palate; anteriorly it opens into the nasal cavity.

near point of vision Closest point from the eye at which an object can be held without appearing blurred.

neck Slightly constricted part of a tooth, between the crown and the root.

neoplasm (NEE-oh-plazm) Abnormal tissue that grows by cellular proliferation more rapidly than normal and continues to grow after the stimuli that initiated the new growth ceases.

nephron (NEF-ron) [Gr., *nephros,* kidney] Functional unit of the kidney, consisting of the renal corpuscle, the proximal convoluted tubule, the nephron loop, and the distal convoluted tubule.

nephron loop U-shaped part of the nephron extending from the proximal to the distal convoluted tubule and consisting of descending and ascending limbs. Some of the nephron loops extend into the renal pyramids. Also known as the loop of Henle, named for Friedrich G. J. Henle (1809-1885).

nerve tract Bundles of parallel axons with their associated sheaths in the central nervous system.

neural crest (NOOR-al) Edge of the neural plate as it rises to meet at the midline to form the neural tube.

neural crest cells Cells derived from the crests of the forming neural tube in the embryo; together with the mesoderm, they form the mesenchyme of the embryo; they give rise to part of the skull, the teeth, melanocytes, sensory neurons, and autonomic neurons.

neural layer Portion of the retina containing rods and cones.

neural plate Region of the dorsal surface of the embryo that is transformed into the neural tube and neural crest.

neural tube Tube formed from the neuroectoderm by the closure of the neural groove; develops into the spinal cord and brain.

neuroectoderm (noor-oh-EK-toh-derm) Part of the ectoderm of an embryo giving rise to the brain and spinal cord.

neurohormone (NOOR-oh-HOHR-mohn) Hormone secreted by a neuron.

neuromodulator Substance that influences the sensitivity of neurons to neurotransmitters but neither strongly stimulates nor strongly inhibits neurons by itself.

neuromuscular junction (NOOR-oh-MUSS-kyu-lar) Specialized synapse between a motor neuron and a muscle fiber.

neuron (NOOR-on) [Gr., nerve] Morphologic and functional unit of the nervous system, consisting of the nerve cell body, the dendrites, and the axon; also called nerve cell.

neuron cell body Enlarged portion of the neuron containing the nucleus and other organelles; also called nerve cell body.

neurotransmitter (NOOR-oh-trans-MIT-er) [Gr., *neuro,* nerve + L., *transmitto,* to send across] Any specific chemical agent released by a presynaptic cell on excitation that crosses the synaptic cleft and stimulates or inhibits the postsynaptic cell.

neutral solution (NOO-trahl) Solution, such as pure water, that has 10^{-7} mol of hydrogen ions per liter and an equal concentration of hydroxide ions; has a pH of 7.

neutron (NOO-tron) [L., *neuter,* neither] Electrically neutral particle in the nuclei of atoms (except hydrogen).

neutrophil (NOO-troh-fill) [L., *neuter,* neither + Gr., *philos,* fond] Type of white blood cell; small phagocytic white blood cell with a lobed nucleus and small granules in the cytoplasm.

nicotinic receptor (nik-oh-TIN-ik) Class of cholinergic receptor molecule that is specifically activated by nicotine and by acetylcholine.

nipple (NIP-l) Projection at the apex of the mamma, on the surface of which the lactiferous ducts open; surrounded by a circular pigmented area, the areola.

Nissl substance (NIS-il) Named after German neurologist Franz Nissl (1860–1919). Areas in the neuron cell body containing rough endoplasmic reticulum.

nociceptor (noh-sih-SEP-ter) [L., *noceo,* to injure + *capio,* to take] Sensory receptor that detects painful or injurious stimuli; also called pain receptor.

nonelectrolyte (non-ee-LEK-troh-light) [Gr., *electro* + *lytos,* soluble] Molecules that do not dissociate and do not conduct electricity.

norepinephrine (NOR-ep-ih-NEF-rin) Neurotransmitter substance released from most of the postganglionic neurons of the sympathetic division; hormone released from the adrenal cortex that increases cardiac output and blood glucose levels; also called noradrenaline.

nose, or **nasus** (NOHZ, NAY-sus) Visible structure that forms a prominent feature of the face; nasal cavities.

notochord (NOH-toh-kord) [Gr., *notor,* back + *chords,* cord] Small rod of tissue lying ventral to the neural tube. A characteristic of all vertebrates, in humans it becomes the nucleus pulposus of the intervertebral disks.

nuchal (NOO-kal) Back of the neck.

nuclear envelope (NOO-klee-ar) Double membrane structure surrounding and enclosing the nucleus.

nuclear pores Porelike openings in the nuclear envelope where the inner and outer membranes fuse.

nucleic acid (noo-KLEE-ik) Polymer of nucleotides, consisting of DNA and RNA, forms a family of substances that comprise the genetic material of cells and control protein synthesis.

nucleolus; pl. **nucleoli** (noo-KLEE-oh-lus, noo-KLEE-oh-lie) Somewhat rounded, dense, well-defined nuclear body with no surrounding membrane; contains ribosomal RNA and protein.

nucleotide (NOO-klee-oh-tide) Basic building block of nucleic acids consisting of a sugar (either ribose or deoxyribose) and one of several types of organic bases.

nucleus; pl. **nuclei** (NOO-klee-us, noo-KLEE-eye) [L., inside of a thing] Cell organelle containing most of the genetic material of the cell; collection of nerve cell bodies within the central nervous system; center of an atom consisting of protons and neutrons.

nucleus pulposus (pul-POH-sus) [L., central pulp] Soft central portion of the intervertebral disk.

nutrient (NOO-tree-ent) [L., *nutriens,* to nourish] Chemicals taken into the body that are used to produce energy, provide building blocks for new molecules, or function in other chemical reactions.

O

olecranon process (oh-LEK-rah-non) Process on the distal end of the ulna, forming the point of the elbow.

olfaction (ol-FAK-shun) [L., *olfactus,* smell] Sense of smell.

olfactory area (ol-FAK-toh-ree) Extreme superior region of the nasal cavity.

olfactory bulb Ganglion-like enlargement at the rostral end of the olfactory tract that lies over the cribriform plate; receives the olfactory nerves from the nasal cavity.

olfactory cortex Termination of the olfactory tract in the cerebral cortex within the lateral fissure of the cerebrum.

olfactory epithelium Epithelium of the olfactory recess containing olfactory receptors.

olfactory tract Nerve tract that projects from the olfactory bulb to the olfactory cortex.

oligodendrocyte (OL-ih-goh-DEN-droh-site) Neuroglial cell that has cytoplasmic extensions that form myelin sheaths around axons in the central nervous system.

oncogene (ONG-koh-jeen) Gene that can change or be activated to cause cancer.

oncology (on-KOL-oh-jee) Study of neoplasms.

oocyte (OH-oh-site) [Gr., *oon,* egg + *kytos,* a hollow (cell)] Immature ovum.

oogenesis (oh-oh-JEN-eh-sis) Formation and development of a secondary oocyte or ovum.

oogonium (oh-oh-GOH-nee-um) [Gr., *oon,* egg + *gone,* generation] Primitive cell from which oocytes are derived by meiosis.

opposition Movement of the thumb and little finger toward each other; movement of the thumb toward any of the fingers.

opsin (OP-sin) Protein portion of the rhodopsin molecule; a class of proteins that bind to retinal to form the visual pigments of the rods and cones of the eye.

opsonin (OP-soh-nin) [Gr., *opsonein,* to prepare food] Substance, such as antibody or complement, that enhances phagocytosis.

optic chiasm (OP-tik KIE-azm) [Gr., two crossing lines; *chi,* the letter χ] Point of crossing of the optic tracts.

optic disc Point at which axons of ganglion cells of the retina converge to form the optic nerve, which then penetrates through the fibrous tunic of the eye.

optic nerve Nerve carrying visual signals from the eye to the optic chiasm.

optic stalk Constricted proximal portion of the optic vesicle in the embryo; develops into the optic nerve.

optic tract Tract that extends from the optic chiasm to the lateral geniculate nucleus of the thalamus.

optic vesicle One of the paired evaginations from the walls of the embryonic forebrain from which the retina develops.

oral cavity (OR-al) The mouth; consists of the space surrounded by the lips, cheeks, teeth, and palate; limited posteriorly by the fauces.

orbit (OR-bit) Eye socket; formed by seven skull bones that surround and protect the eye.

organ of Corti (OR-gan) Named for Italian anatomist Marquis Alfonso Corti (1822–1888). Spiral organ; rests on the basilar membrane and supports the hair cells that detect sounds.

organelle (OR-gah-nell) [Gr., *organon,* tool] Specialized part of a cell with one or more specific individual functions.

orgasm (OR-gaz-um) [Gr., *orgao,* to swell, be excited] Climax of the sexual act, associated with a pleasurable sensation.

origin (OR-ih-jin) Less movable attachment point of a muscle; usually the medial or proximal end of a muscle associated with the limbs; also called fixed end.

oropharynx (OR-oh-FAIR-inks) Portion of the pharynx that lies posterior to the oral cavity; it is continuous above with the nasopharynx and below with the laryngopharynx.

oscillating circuit Neuronal circuit arranged in a circular fashion that allows action potentials produced in the circuit to keep stimulating the neurons of the circuit.

osmolality (os-moh-LAL-ih-tee) Osmotic concentration of a solution; the number of moles of solute in 1 kg of water times the number of particles into which the solute dissociates.

osmoreceptor cell (os-moh-ree-SEP-ter, OS-moh-ree-SEP-tohr) [Gr., *osmos,* impulsion] Receptor in the central nervous system that responds to changes in the osmotic pressure of the blood.

osmosis (oz-MOH-sis) [Gr., *osmos,* thrusting or an impulsion] Diffusion of solvent (water) through a membrane from a less concentrated solution to a more concentrated solution.

osmotic pressure (os-MOT-ik) Force required to prevent the movement of water across a selectively permeable membrane.

ossification (OS-ih-fih-KAY-shun) [L., *os,* bone + *facio,* to make] Bone formation; also called osteogenesis.

osteoblast (OS-tee-oh-blast) [Gr., *osteon,* bone + *blastos,* germ] Bone-forming cell.

osteoclast (OS-tee-oh-klast) [Gr., *osteon,* bone + *klastos,* broken] Large, multinucleated cell that absorbs bone.

osteocyte (OS-tee-oh-site) [Gr., *osteon,* bone + *kytos,* cell] Mature bone cell surrounded by bone matrix.

osteomalacia (OS-tee-oh-mah-LAY-shee-ah) Softening of bones due to calcium depletion; adult rickets.

osteon (OS-tee-on) Central canal containing blood capillaries and the concentric lamellae around it; occurs in compact bone; also called haversian system.

osteoporosis (OS-tee-oh-poh-ROH-sis) [Gr., *osteon,* bone + *poros,* pore + *osis,* condition] Reduction in quantity of bone, resulting in porous bone.

ostium (OS-tee-um) [L., door, entrance, mouth] Small opening—for example, the opening of the uterine tube near the ovary or the opening of the uterus into the vagina.

otolith (OH-toh-lith) Crystalline particles of calcium carbonate and protein embedded in the maculae.

oval window (OH-val) Membranous structure to which the stapes attaches; transmits vibrations to the inner ear.

ovarian cycle (oh-VAIR-ee-an) Series of events that occur in a regular fashion in the ovaries of sexually mature, nonpregnant females; results in ovulation and the production of the hormones estrogen and progesterone.

ovarian epithelium Peritoneal covering of the ovary; also called germinal epithelium.

ovarian ligament Bundle of fibers passing to the uterus from the ovary.

ovary (OH-vuh-ree) One of two female reproductive glands located in the pelvic cavity; produces the secondary oocyte, estrogen, and progesterone.

oviduct (OH-vih-dukt) *See* uterine tube.

ovulation (OV-you-LAY-shun) Release of an ovum, or secondary oocyte, from the vesicular follicle.

oxidation (ok-si-DAY-shun) Loss of one or more electrons from a molecule.

oxidation-reduction reaction Reaction in which one molecule is oxidized and another is reduced.

oxidative deamination (ok-sih-DAY-tiv) Removal of the amine group of an amino acid to form a keto acid, ammonia, and NADH.

oxygen deficit (OK-see-jen) Oxygen necessary for the synthesis of the ATP required to remove lactic acid produced by anaerobic respiration.

oxygen-hemoglobin dissociation curve Graph describing the relationship between the percentage of hemoglobin saturated with oxygen and a range of oxygen partial pressures.

oxyhemoglobin (OK-see-hee-moh-GLOH-bin) Oxygenated hemoglobin.

P

P wave First complex of the electrocardiogram representing depolarization of the atria.

Pacinian corpuscle (pa-SIN-ee-an, pa-CHIN-ee-an) Named for Italian anatomist Filippo Pacini (1812–1883). *See also* lamellated corpuscle.

palate (PAL-uht) [L., *palatum,* palate] Roof of the mouth.

palatine tonsil (PAL-ah-tine) One of two large, oval masses of lymphoid tissue embedded in the lateral wall of the oral pharynx.

palpebra; pl. **palpebrae** (pal-PEE-brah, pal-PEE-bree) [L., eyelid] Eyelid.

palpebral conjunctiva (pal-PEE-bral kon-junk-TIE-vah) Conjunctiva that covers the inner surface of the eyelids.

palpebral fissure Space between the upper and lower eyelids.

pancreas (PAN-kree-as) [Gr., *pankreas,* sweetbread] Abdominal gland that secretes pancreatic juice into the intestine and insulin and glucagon from the pancreatic islets into the bloodstream.

pancreatic duct (pan-kree-AT-ik) Excretory duct of the pancreas that extends through the gland from tail to head, where it empties into the duodenum at the greater duodenal papilla.

pancreatic islet Cellular mass varying from a few to hundreds of cells lying in the interstitial tissue of the pancreas; composed of different cell types that make up the endocrine portion of the pancreas and are the source of insulin and glucagon; also called islets of Langerhans.

pancreatic juice [L., *jus,* broth] External secretion of the pancreas; clear, alkaline fluid containing several enzymes.

papilla (pah-PILL-ah) [L., nipple] Small, nipple-like process; projection of the dermis, containing blood vessels and nerves, into the epidermis; projections on the surface of the tongue.

papillary muscle (PAP-ih-lar-ee) Nipplelike, conical projection of myocardium within the ventricle; the chordae tendineae are attached to the apex of the papillary muscle.

parafollicular cell (pair-ah-foh-LIK-yoo-lar) Endocrine cell in the thyroid gland; secretes the hormone calcitonin.

paramesonephric duct (pair-ah-mes-oh-NEF-rik) One of two embryonic tubes extending along the mesonephros and emptying into the cloaca; in the female, the duct forms the uterine tube, the uterus, and part of the vagina; in the male, it degenerates.

paranasal sinus (pair-ah-NAY-zal) Air-filled cavities within certain skull bones that connect to the nasal cavity; located in the frontal, maxillary, sphenoid, and ethmoid bones.

parasympathetic division (pair-ah-sim-pah-THET-ik) Subdivision of the autonomic nervous system; characterized by having the cell bodies of its preganglionic neurons located in the brainstem and the sacral region of the spinal cord (craniosacral division); usually involved in activating vegetative functions, such as digestion, defecation, and urination.

parathyroid gland (pair-ah-THIGH-royd) One of four glandular masses embedded in the posterior surface of the thyroid gland; secretes parathyroid hormone.

parathyroid hormone (PTH) Peptide hormone produced by the parathyroid gland; increases bone breakdown and blood calcium levels.

parietal (pah-RYE-eh-tal) [L., *paries,* wall] Relating to the wall of any cavity.

parietal cell Gastric gland cell that secretes hydrochloric acid.

parietal pericardium Serous membrane lining the fibrous portion of the pericardial sac.

parietal peritoneum Layer of peritoneum lining the abdominal walls.

parietal pleura Serous membrane that lines the different parts of the wall of the pleural cavity.

parotid gland (pah-ROT-id) Largest of the salivary glands; situated anterior to each ear.

partial pressure Pressure exerted by a single gas in a mixture of gases.

passive tension Tension applied to a load by a muscle without contracting; produced when an external force stretches the muscle.

patella (pah-TEL-ah) [L., *patina,* shallow disk] Kneecap.

pectoral girdle (PEK-toh-ral) Site of attachment of the upper limb to the trunk; consists of the scapula and the clavicle; also called shoulder girdle.

pedicle (PED-ih-kul) [L., *pes,* feet] Stalk or base of a structure, such as the pedicle of the vertebral arch.

pelvic brim (PEL-vic) Imaginary plane passing from the sacral promontory to the pubic crest.

pelvic girdle Site of attachment of the lower limb to the trunk; ring of bone formed by the sacrum and the coxal bones.

pelvic inlet Superior opening of the true pelvis.

pelvic outlet Inferior opening of the true pelvis.

pelvis (PEL-vis) [L., basin] Any basin-shaped structure; cup-shaped ring of bone at the lower end of the trunk, formed from the ossa coxal bones, sacrum, and coccyx.

pennate (bipennate) (PEN-ate) [L., *penna,* feather] Muscles with fasciculi arranged like the barbs of a feather along a common tendon.

pepsin (PEP-sin) [Gr., *pepsis,* digestion] Principal digestive enzyme of the gastric juice, formed from pepsinogen; digests proteins into smaller peptide chains.

pepsinogen (pep-SIN-oh-jen) [*pepsin* + Gr. *gen,* producing] Proenzyme formed and secreted by the chief cells of the gastric mucosa; the acidity of the gastric juice and pepsin itself converts pepsinogen into pepsin.

peptidase (PEP-ti-dase) Enzyme capable of hydrolyzing one of the peptide links of a peptide.

peptide bond (PEP-tide) Chemical bond between amino acids.

Percent Daily Value (% Daily Value) Percentage of the recommended daily value of a nutrient found in one serving of a particular food.

perforating canal Canal containing blood vessels and nerves and running through bone perpendicular to the haversian canals; also called Volkmann's canal.

periarterial lymphatic sheath (PER-ee-ar-TEE-ree-al) Dense accumulation of lymphocytes (white pulp) surrounding arteries within the spleen.

pericapillary cell One of the slender connective tissue cells in close relationship to the outside of the capillary wall; it is relatively undifferentiated and may become a fibroblast, macrophage, or smooth muscle cell.

pericardial cavity (per-ih-KAR-dee-al) Space within the mediastinum in which the heart is located.

pericardial fluid Viscous fluid contained within the pericardial cavity between the visceral and parietal pericardium; functions as a lubricant.

pericardium (per-ih-KAR-dee-um) [Gr., *pericardion,* membrane around the heart] Membrane covering the heart; also called pericardial sac.

perichondrium (per-ih-KON-dree-um) [Gr., *peri,* around + *chondros,* cartilage] Double-layered connective tissue sheath surrounding cartilage.

perilymph (PER-ih-limf) [Gr., *peri,* around + L., *lympha,* clear fluid (lymph)] Fluid contained within the bony labyrinth of the inner ear.

perimetrium (per-ih-MEE-tree-um) Outer serous coat of the uterus; also called serous layer.

perimysium (PER-ih-MIS-ee-um) [Gr., *peri,* around + *mys,* muscle] Fibrous sheath enveloping a bundle of skeletal muscle fibers (muscle fascicle).

perineum (PER-ih-NEE-um) Area inferior to the pelvic diaphragm between the thighs; extends from the coccyx to the pubis.

perineurium (per-ih-NOO-ree-um) [L., *peri,* around + Gr., *neuron,* nerve] Connective tissue sheath surrounding a nerve fascicle.

periodontal ligament (PER-ee-oh-DON-tal) Connective tissue that surrounds the tooth root and attaches it to its bony socket.

periosteum (PER-ee-OSS-tee-um) [Gr., *peri,* around + *osteon,* bone] Thick, double-layered connective tissue sheath covering the entire surface of a bone, except the articular surface, which is covered with cartilage.

peripheral nervous system (PNS) (peh-RIF-eh-ral) Major subdivision of the nervous system consisting of nerves and ganglia.

peripheral resistance (PR) Resistance to blood flow in all the blood vessels.

peristaltic wave (per-ih-STAL-tik) Contraction in a tube, such as the intestine, characterized by a wave of contraction in smooth muscle preceded by a wave of relaxation that moves along the tube.

peritubular capillary Capillary network located in the cortex of the kidney; associated with the distal and proximal convoluted tubules.

permanent tooth One of the 32 teeth belonging to the permanent dentition; also called secondary tooth.

peroneal (per-oh-NEE-uhl) [Gr., *perone,* fibula] Associated with the fibula.

peroxisome (per-OK-sih-sohm) Membrane-bounded body similar to a lysosome in appearance but often smaller and irregular in shape; contains enzymes that either decompose or synthesize hydrogen peroxide.

Peyer patch Named for Swiss anatomist Johann K. Peyer (1653–1712). Lymphatic nodule found in the lower half of the small intestine and the appendix.

phagocyte (FAG-oh-site) Cell that ingests bacteria, foreign particles, and other cells.

phagocytosis (FAG-oh-sigh-TOH-sis) [Gr., *phagein,* to eat + *kytos,* cell + *osis,* condition] Cells' ingestion of solid substances, such as other cells, bacteria, bits of necrosed tissue, and foreign particles.

phalange; pl. **phalanges** (fah-LANJ, fah-LAN-jeez) [Gr., *phalanx,* line of soldiers] Bone of a finger or toe.

pharyngeal pouch (fah-RIN-jee-al) Paired evagination of embryonic pharyngeal endoderm between the brachial arches that gives rise to the thymus, thyroid gland, tonsils, and parathyroid glands.

pharyngeal tonsil One of two collections of aggregated lymphoid nodules on the posterior wall of the nasopharynx.

pharynx (FAIR-inks) [Gr., *pharynx,* throat, the joint opening of the gullet and windpipe] Upper expanded portion of the digestive tube between the esophagus below and the oral and nasal cavities above and in front.

phenotype (FEE-noh-type) [Gr., *phaino,* to display, show forth + *typos,* model] Characteristic observed in an individual due to the expression of their genotype.

phosphodiesterase (FOS-foh-die-ES-ter-ase) Enzyme that splits phosphodiester bonds—that is, that breaks down cyclic AMP to AMP.

phospholipid (fos-foh-LIP-id) Lipid with phosphorus, resulting in a molecule with a polar end and a nonpolar end; main component of the lipid bilayer.

phosphorylation (FOS-fohr-ih-LAY-shun) Addition of phosphate to an organic compound.

photoreceptor (foh-toh-ree-SEP-tor) [L., *photo,* light + *ceptus,* to receive] Sensory receptor that is sensitive to light—for example, rods and cones of the retina.

phrenic nerve (FREN-ik) Nerve derived from spinal nerves C3–C5; supplies the diaphragm.

physiologic contracture (fiz-ee-oh-LOJ-ik kon-TRAK-chur) Temporary inability of a muscle to either contract or relax because of a depletion of ATP so that active transport of calcium ions into the sarcoplasmic reticulum cannot occur.

physiologic shunt Deoxygenated blood from the alveoli plus deoxygenated blood from the bronchi and bronchioles.

physiological dead space Sum of anatomical dead air space plus the volume of any nonfunctional alveoli.

pia mater (PEE-ah MAY-ter) [L., tender mother] Delicate membrane forming the inner covering of the brain and spinal cord.

pigmented layer Pigmented portion of the retina.

pineal gland (PIN-ee-al) [L., *pineus,* relating to pine trees] A small, pine cone–shaped structure that projects from the epiphysis of the diencephalon; produces melatonin; also called pineal body.

pinna (PIN-ah) [L., *pinna* or *penna,* feather] *See* auricle.

pinocytosis (PIN-oh-sigh-TOH-sis) [Gr., *pineo,* to drink + *kytos,* cell + *osis,* condition] Cell drinking; uptake of liquid by a cell.

pituitary gland (pih-TOO-ih-tair-ee) Endocrine gland attached to the hypothalamus by the infundibulum; also called hypophysis.

plane (playn) [L., *planus,* flat] Flat surface; an imaginary surface formed by extension through any axis or two points—for example, a midsagittal plane, a coronal plane, and a transverse plane.

plasma (PLAZ-mah) [Gr., something formed] Fluid portion of blood.

plasma cell Cell derived from B cells; produces antibodies.

plasma clearance Volume of plasma per minute from which a substance can be completely removed by the kidneys.

plasmin (PLAZ-min) Enzyme derived from plasminogen; dissolves clots by converting fibrin into soluble products.

plateau phase Prolongation of the depolarization phase of a cardiac muscle cell membrane; results in a prolonged refractory period.

platelet (PLAYT-let) Irregularly shaped disk found in blood; contains granules in the central part and clear protoplasm peripherally but has no definite nucleus; also called thrombocyte.

platelet plug Accumulation of platelets that stick to each other and to connective tissue; prevents blood loss from damaged blood vessels.

pleural cavity (PLUR-al) Potential space between the parietal and visceral layers of the pleura.

plexus; pl. **plexuses** (PLEK-sus, PLEK-sus-ez) [L., a braid] Intertwining of nerves or blood vessels.

plicae circulares (PLY-see) Numerous folds of the mucous membrane of the small intestine.

pluripotent (ploo-RIP-oh-tent) [L., *pluris,* more + *potentia,* power] In development, a cell or group of cells that have not yet become fixed or determined as to what specific tissues they are going to become.

podocytes (POD-oh-sites) [Gr., *pous, podos,* foot + *kytos,* a hollow (cell)] Epithelial cell of the glomerular capsule attached to the outer surface of the glomerular capillary basement membrane by cytoplasmic foot processes.

Poiseuille's law (pwah-ZUH-yes) Named for French physiologist and physicist Jean Léonard Marie Poiseuille (1797–1869). The volume of a fluid passing per unit of time through a tube is directly proportional to the pressure difference between its ends and to the fourth power of the internal radius of the tube and inversely proportional to the tube's length and the viscosity of the fluid.

polar body (POH-lar) One of the two small cells formed during oogenesis because of unequal division of the cytoplasm.

polar covalent bond Covalent bond in which atoms do not share their electrons equally.

polarization Development of differences in potential between two points in living tissues, as between the inside and outside of the plasma membrane.

polycythemia (POL-ee-sigh-THEE-mee-ah) Increase in red blood cell number above the normal.

polygenic (pol-ee-JEN-ik) Relating to a hereditary disease or normal characteristic controlled by the interaction of genes at more than one locus.

polysaccharide (pol-ee-SACK-ah-ride) Carbohydrate containing a large number of monosaccharide molecules.

polyunsaturated fat Fatty acid that contains two or more double covalent bonds between its carbon atoms.

pons (PONZ) [L., bridge] Portion of the brainstem between the medulla and midbrain.

popliteal (pop-LIT-ee-al) [L., ham] Posterior region of the knee.

porta (POR-tah) [L., gate] Fissure on the inferior surface of the liver where the portal vein, hepatic artery, hepatic nerve plexus, hepatic ducts, and lymphatic vessels enter or exit the liver.

portal system (POR-tal) System of vessels in which blood, after passing through one capillary bed, is conveyed through a second capillary network.

portal triad Branches of the portal vein, hepatic artery, and hepatic duct bound together in the connective tissue that divides the liver into lobules.

postabsorptive state State following the absorptive state; blood glucose levels are maintained because of the conversion of other molecules to glucose.

posterior chamber (pos-TEER-ee-or) Chamber of the eye between the iris and the lens.

posterior interventricular sulcus Groove on the diaphragmatic surface of the heart, marking the location of the septum between the two ventricles.

posterior pituitary gland Portion of the hypophysis derived from the brain. Major secretions include antidiuretic hormone and oxytocin; also called neurohypophysis.

postganglionic neuron (POST-gang-glee-ON-ik) Autonomic neuron that has its cell body located within an autonomic ganglion and sends its axon to an effector organ.

postovulatory age Age of the developing fetus based on the assumption that fertilization occurs 14 days after the last menstrual period before the pregnancy.

postsynaptic (post-sih-NAP-tik) Relating to the membrane of a nerve, muscle, or gland that is in close association with a presynaptic terminal. The postsynaptic membrane has receptor molecules within it that bind to neurotransmitter molecules.

potential difference (poh-TEN-shal) Difference in electrical potential, measured as the charge difference across the plasma membrane.

potential energy [Gr., *en,* in + *ergon,* work] Energy in a chemical bond that is not being exerted or used to do work.

PQ interval Time elapsing between the beginning of the P wave and the beginning of the QRS complex in the electrocardiogram; also called PR interval.

PR interval *See* PQ interval.

precapillary sphincter (pree-KAP-ih-lair-ee SFINK-ter) Smooth muscle sphincter that regulates blood flow through a capillary.

preganglionic neuron (PREE-gang-glee-ON-ik) Autonomic neuron that has its cell body located within the central nervous system and sends its axon through a nerve to an autonomic ganglion, where it synapses with postganglionic neurons.

premolar (pree-MOH-lar) Bicuspid tooth.

prenatal (pree-NAY-tal) [*pre* + L., *natus,* born] Preceding birth.

prepuce (PREE-poos) In males, the free fold of skin that more or less completely covers the glans penis; the foreskin. In females, the external fold of the labia minora that covers the clitoris.

pressoreceptor (PRES-oh-ree-SEP-ter, PRES-oh-ree-SEP-tohr) *See* baroreceptor.

presynaptic terminal (PREE-sih-NAP-tik) Enlarged axon terminal or terminal bouton.

primary palate In the early embryo, the structure that gives rise to the upper jaw and lips.

primary response Immune response that occurs as a result of the first exposure to an antigen.

primary spermatocyte (SPER-mah-toh-site) Spermatocyte arising by a growth phase from a spermatogonium; gives rise to secondary spermatocytes after the first meiotic division.

prime mover Muscle that plays a major role in accomplishing a movement.

primitive streak (PRIM-ih-tiv) Ectodermal ridge in the midline of the embryonic disk, from which arises the mesoderm by the inward and then lateral migration of cells.

primordial germ cell (pry-MOHR-dee-al) Most primitive undifferentiated sex cell, found initially outside the gonad on the surface of the yolk sac.

process (PROS-es) Projection on a bone.

process vaginalis (proh-SES-us vaj-ih-NAH-lis) Peritoneal outpocketing in the embryonic lower anterior abdominal wall that traverses the inguinal canal; in the male, it forms the tunica vaginalis testis and normally loses its connection with the peritoneal cavity.

proerythroblast Cell that matures into an erythrocyte.

progeria (proh-JEER-ee-ah) [Gr., *pro,* before + *ge* + *amras,* old age] Severe retardation of growth after the first year accompanied by a senile appearance and death at an early age.

progesterone (proh-JESS-ter-ohn) Steroid hormone secreted by the corpus luteum and one of the hormones secreted by the placenta.

prolactin (proh-LAK-tin) Hormone of the adenohypophysis that stimulates the production of milk.

prolactin-inhibiting hormone (PIH) Neurohormone released from the hypothalamus that inhibits prolactin release from the adenohypophysis.

prolactin-releasing hormone (PRH) Neurohormone released from the hypothalamus that stimulates prolactin release from the adenohypophysis.

proliferative phase (proh-LIF-er-ah-tiv) *See* follicular phase.

pronation (proh-NAY-shun) [L., *pronare,* to bend forward] Rotation of the forearm so that the anterior surface is down (prone).

pronephros (proh-NEF-ros) In the embryos of higher vertebrates, a series of tubules emptying into the celomic cavity. It is a temporary structure in the human embryo, followed by the mesonephros and still later by the metanephros, which gives rise to the kidney.

prophase (PROH-fayz) First stage in cell division when chromatin strands condense to form chromosomes.

proprioception (proh-pree-oh-SEP-shun) [L., *proprius,* one's own + *capio,* to take] Information about the position of the body and its various parts.

proprioceptor (PROH-pree-oh-SEP-ter) Sensory receptor associated with joints and tendons.

prostaglandin (PROS-tah-GLAN-din) Class of physiologically active substances present in many tissues; among its effects are vasodilation, stimulation and contraction of uterine smooth muscle and the promotion of inflammation and pain.

prostate gland (PROS-tate) [Gr., *prostates,* one standing before] Gland that surrounds the beginning of the urethra in the male. The secretion of the gland is a milky fluid that is discharged by 20–30 excretory ducts into the prostatic urethra as part of the semen.

prostatic urethra (pros-TAT-ik) Part of the male urethra, approximately 2.5 cm in length, that passes through the prostate gland.

protease (PROH-tee-ase) Enzyme that breaks down proteins.

protein (PROH-teen) [Gr., *proteios,* primary] Macromolecule consisting of long sequences of amino acids linked together by peptide bonds.

protein kinase (KIE-nase) Class of enzymes that phosphorylates other proteins. Many of these kinases are responsive to other chemical signals (e.g., cAMP, cGMP, insulin, epidermal growth factor, calcium, and calmodulin).

proteoglycan (PROH-tee-oh-GLYE-kan) Macromolecule consisting of numerous polysaccharides attached to a common protein core.

prothrombin (proh-THROM-bin) Glycoprotein present in blood that, in the presence of prothrombin activator, is converted to thrombin.

proton (PROH-ton) [Gr., *protos*, first] Positively charged particle in the nuclei of atoms.

protraction (proh-TRAK-shun) [L., *protractus*, to draw forth] Movement forward or in the anterior direction.

provitamin (proh-VITE-ah-min) Substance that may be converted into a vitamin.

proximal convoluted tubule (PROK-sih-mal) Part of the nephron that extends from the glomerulus to the descending limb of the nephron loop.

pseudostratified epithelium Epithelium consisting of a single layer of cells but having the appearance of multiple layers.

pseudo-unipolar neuron One of the three categories of neurons consisting of a nerve cell body with a single axon projecting from it.

psychologic fatigue (sigh-koh-LOJ-ik) Fatigue caused by the central nervous system.

ptosis (TOH-sis) [G., *ptosis*, a falling] Falling down of an organ—for example, the drooping of the upper eyelid.

puberty (PYU-ber-tee) [L., *pubertas*, grown up] Series of events that transform a child into a sexually mature adult; involves an increase in the secretion of GnRH.

pubis (PYU-bis) Anterior inferior bone of the coxal bone.

pudendal cleft (poo-DEN-dal) Cleft between the labia majora.

pudendum (poo-DEN-dum) *See* vulva.

pulmonary artery (PULL-moh-NAIR-ee) One of the arteries that extend from the pulmonary trunk to the right or left lungs.

pulmonary capacity Sum of two or more pulmonary volumes.

pulmonary trunk Large, elastic artery that carries blood from the right ventricle of the heart to the right and left pulmonary arteries.

pulmonary vein One of the veins that carry blood from the lungs to the left atrium of the heart.

pulp (PULP) [L., *pulpa*, flesh] Soft tissue within the pulp cavity of the tooth, consisting of connective tissue containing blood vessels, nerves, and lymphatics.

pulse pressure (puhls) Difference between systolic and diastolic pressure.

pupil (PYU-pill) Circular opening in the iris through which light enters the eye.

Purkinje fiber (per-KIN-jee) Named for Bohemian anatomist Johannes E. von Purkinje (1787–1869). Modified cardiac muscle cells found beneath the endocardium of the ventricles. Specialized to conduct action potentials.

pus (puhs) Fluid product of inflammation; contains white blood cells, the debris of dead cells, and tissue elements liquefied by enzymes.

pyloric opening (pie-LOHR-ik) Opening between the stomach and the superior part of the duodenum.

pyloric sphincter Thickening of the circular layer of the gastric musculature encircling the junction between the stomach and duodenum; also called pylorus.

pyrogen (PIE-roh-jen) Chemical released by microorganisms, neutrophils, monocytes, and other cells that stimulates fever production by acting on the hypothalamus.

Q

QRS complex Principal deflection in the electrocardiogram, representing ventricular depolarization.

QT interval Time elapsing from the beginning of the QRS complex to the end of the T wave, representing the total duration of electrical activity of the ventricles.

R

radial pulse (RAY-dee-al) Pulse detected in the radial artery.

radiation (RAY-dee-AY-shun) [L., *radius*, ray, beam] Sending forth of light, short radiowaves, ultraviolet or x-rays, or any other rays for treatment or diagnosis or for other reasons; radiant heat.

radioactive isotope (RAY-dee-oh-AK-tiv) Isotope with a nuclear composition that is unstable from which subatomic particles and electromagnetic waves are emitted.

ramus; pl. **rami** (RAY-mus, RAY-mye) [L., branch] One of the primary subdivisions of a nerve or blood vessel; the part of a bone that forms an angle with the main body of the bone.

raphe (RAY-fee) [Gr., *rhaphe*, suture, seam] Central line running over the scrotum from the anus to the root of the penis.

receptor Structural protein or glycoprotein molecule on the cell surface or within the cytoplasm that binds to a specific factor (chemical signal).

recessive (ree-SES-iv) Gene that may not be expressed because of suppression by a contrasting dominant gene.

Recommended Daily Intake (RDI) Generally, the highest RDA value in each of four categories: infants, toddlers, people over 4 years of age, and pregnant or lactating females. The RDIs used to determine the Daily Values are based on the 1968 RDAs.

Recommended Dietary Allowances (RDAs) Guide for estimating the nutritional needs of groups of people based on their age, sex, and other factors; first established in 1941.

rectum (RECK-tum) [L., *rectus*, straight] Portion of the digestive tract that extends from the sigmoid colon to the anal canal.

red marrow (MARE-oh) Soft, pulpy connective tissue filling the cavities of bones; consists of reticular fibers and the development stages of blood cells and platelets; gradually replaced by yellow marrow in long bones and the skull.

red pulp [L., *pulpa*, flesh] Reddish-brown substance of the spleen consisting of venous sinuses and the tissues intervening between them, called pulp cords.

reduction (ree-DUK-shun) Gain of one or more electrons by a molecule.

refraction (ree-FRAK-shun) Bending of a light ray when it passes from one medium into another of different density.

refractory period (ree-FRAK-tohr-ee) [Gr., *periodos*, a way around, a cycle] Period following effective stimulation during which excitable tissue, such as heart muscle, fails to respond to a stimulus of threshold intensity.

regeneration (ree-JEN-eh-RAY-shun) Reproduction or reconstruction of a lost or injured part.

regulatory gene Gene involved with controlling the activity of structural genes.

relative refractory period Portion of the action potential following the absolute refractory period during which another action potential can be produced with a greater-than-threshold stimulus strength.

relaxation phase (ree-lak-SAY-shun) Phase of muscle contraction following the contraction phase; the time from maximal tension production until tension decreases to its resting level.

relaxin Polypeptide hormone secreted by the corpus luteum and placenta during pregnancy; facilitates the birth process by causing a softening and lengthening of the pubic symphysis and cervix.

renal artery (REE-nal) Artery that originates from the aorta and delivers blood to the kidney.

renal blood flow rate Volume at which blood flows through the kidneys per minute; an average of approximately 1200 mL/min.

renal column Cortical substance separating the renal pyramids.

renal corpuscle Glomerulus and glomerular capsule that encloses it.

renal fascia (FASH-ee-ah) Connective tissue surrounding the kidney that forms a sheath or capsule for the organ.

renal fat pad Fat layer that surrounds the kidney and functions as a shock-absorbing material.

renal fraction Portion of the cardiac output that flows through the kidneys; averages 21%.

renal pelvis Funnel-shaped expansion of the upper end of the ureter that receives the calyces.

renal pyramid One of a number of pyramidal masses seen on longitudinal section of the kidney; they contain part of the nephron loops and the collecting tubules.

renal threshold Amount of a substance per minute that crosses the filtration membrane into the glomerular capsule.

renin (REE-nin) Enzyme secreted by the juxtaglomerular apparatus that converts angiotensinogen to angiotensin I.

renin-angiotensin-aldosterone mechanism Renin, released from the kidneys in response to low blood pressure, converts angiotensinogen to angiotensin I. Angiotensin I is converted by angiotensin-converting enzyme to angiotensin II, which causes vasoconstriction, resulting in increased blood pressure. Angiotensin II also increases aldosterone secretion, which increases blood pressure by increasing blood volume.

repolarization phase (REE-poh-lar-ih-ZAY-shun) Phase of the action potential in which the membrane potential moves from its maximum degree of depolarization toward the value of the resting membrane potential.

reposition Return of a structure to its original position.

residual volume (ree-ZID-yoo-al) Volume of air remaining in the lungs after a maximum expiratory effort.

resolution (rez-oh-LOO-shun) [L., *resolutio*, a slackening] Phase of the male sexual act after ejaculation during which the penis becomes flaccid; feeling of satisfaction; inability to achieve erection and second ejaculation. Last phase of the female sexual act, characterized by an overall sense of satisfaction and relaxation.

respiration (RES-pih-RAY-shun) [L., *respiratio*, to exhale, breathe] Process of life in which oxygen is used to oxidize organic fuel molecules, providing a source of energy, carbon dioxide, and water; movement of air into and out of the lungs, the exchange of gases with blood, the transportation of gases in the blood, and gas exchange between the blood and the tissues.

respiratory bronchiole (RES-pir-ah-TOR-ee) Smallest bronchiole (0.5 mm in diameter) that connects the terminal bronchiole to the alveolar duct.

respiratory membrane Membrane in the lungs across which gas exchange occurs with blood.

resting membrane potential (RMP) Electric charge difference inside a plasma membrane, measured relative to just outside the plasma membrane.

reticular (reh-TIK-you-lar) [L., *rete*, net] Relating to a fine network of cells or collagen fibers.

reticular cell Cell with processes making contact with those of other similar cells to form a cellular network; along with the network of reticular fibers, the reticular cells form the framework of bone marrow and lymphatic tissues.

reticulocyte (reh-TIK-yoo-loh-site) Young red blood cell with a network of basophilic endoplasmic reticulum occurring in larger numbers during the process of active red blood cell synthesis.

reticuloendothelial system (reh-TIK-yoo-loh-en-doh-THEE-lee-al) *See* mononuclear phagocytic system.

retina (RET-ih-nah) Nervous tunic of the eyeball.

retinaculum (ret-ih-NAK-you-lum) [L., band, halter, to hold back] Dense regular connective tissue sheath holding down the tendons at the wrist, ankle, or other sites.

retraction (ree-TRAK-shun) [L., *retractio*, a drawing back] Movement in the posterior direction.

retroperitoneal (REH-troh-PER-ih-toh-NEE-uhl) Behind the peritoneum.

rhodopsin (roh-DOP-sin) Light-sensitive substance found in the rods of the retina; composed of opsin loosely bound to retinal.

ribonuclease (rye-boh-NOO-klee-ase) Enzyme that splits RNA into its component nucleotides.

ribonucleic acid (RNA) (RYE-boh-noo-KLEE-ik) Nucleic acid containing ribose as the sugar component; found in all cells in both nuclei and cytoplasm; helps direct protein synthesis.

ribosomal RNA (rRNA) (RYE-boh-sohm-al) RNA that is associated with certain proteins to form ribosomes.

ribosome (RYE-boh-sohm) Small, spherical, cytoplasmic organelle where protein synthesis occurs.

right lymphatic duct Lymphatic duct that empties into the right subclavian vein; drains the right side of the head and neck, the right-upper thorax, and the right-upper limb.

rigor mortis (RIG-er MOHR-tis) Increased rigidity of muscle after death due to cross-bridge formation between actin and myosin as calcium ions leak from the sarcoplasmic reticulum.

rod Photoreceptor in the retina of the eye; responsible for noncolor vision in low-intensity light.

root Part below the neck of a tooth covered by cementum rather than enamel and attached by the periodontal ligament to the alveolar bone.

root of the penis Proximal attached part of the penis, including the two crura and the bulb.

rotation (roh-TAY-shun) Movement of a structure about its axis.

rotator cuff (roh-TAY-tor) Four deep muscles that attach the humerus to the scapula.

round ligament Fibromuscular band that is attached to the uterus on each side in front of and below the opening of the uterine tube; it passes through the inguinal canal to the labium majus.

round ligament of the liver Remains of the umbilical vein.

round window Membranous structure separating the scala tympani of the inner ear from the middle ear.

Ruffini end organ (roo-FEE-nee) Named for Italian histologist Angelo Ruffini (1864–1929); receptor located deep in the dermis and responding to continuous touch or pressure.

ruga; pl. **rugae** (ROO-gah, ROO-gee) [L., a wrinkle] Fold or ridge; fold of the mucous membrane of the stomach when the organ is contracted; transverse ridge in the mucous membrane of the vagina.

S

saccule (SAK-yool) Part of the membranous labyrinth; contains a sensory structure, the macula, that detects static equilibrium.

salivary amylase (SAL-ih-var-ee AM-il-ase) Enzyme secreted in the saliva that breaks down starch to maltose and isomaltose.

salivary gland (SAL-ih-var-ee) Gland that produces and secretes saliva into the oral cavity. The three major pairs of salivary glands are the parotid, submandibular, and sublingual glands.

salt Molecule consisting of a cation other than hydrogen and an anion other than hydroxide.

sarcolemma (SAR-koh-LEM-ah) [Gr., *sarco*, muscle + *lemma*, husk] Plasma membrane of a muscle fiber.

sarcoma (sar-KOH-mah) Malignant neoplasm derived from connective tissue.

sarcomere (SAR-koh-meer) [Gr., *sarco*, muscle + *meros*, part] Part of a myofibril between adjacent Z disks.

sarcoplasm (SAR-koh-plazm) [Gr., *sarco*, muscle + *plasma*, a thing formed] Cytoplasm of a muscle fiber, excluding the myofilaments.

sarcoplasmic reticulum (SAR-koh-PLAZ-mik reh-TIK-you-lum) [Gr., *sarco*, muscle + *plasma*, a thing formed + *reticulum*, net] Endoplasmic reticulum of muscle.

satellite cell (SAT-eh-lyte) Specialized cell that surrounds the cell bodies of neurons within ganglia.

saturated (SATCH-yoo-rayt-ed) Fatty acid in which the carbon chain contains only single bonds between carbon atoms.

saturation (satch-yoo-RAY-shun) Point when all carrier molecules or enzymes are attached to substrate molecules and no more molecules can be transported or reacted.

scala tympani (SKAY-lah tim-PAH-nee) [L., stairway] Division of the spiral canal of the cochlea lying below the spiral lamina and basilar membrane.

scala vestibuli (SKAY-lah ves-TIB-you-lie) Division of the cochlea lying above the spiral lamina and vestibular membrane.

scapula (SKAP-you-lah) Bone forming the shoulder blade.

scar (skar) [Gr., *eschara*, scab] Fibrous tissue replacing normal tissue; also called cicatrix.

sciatic nerve (sigh-AT-ik) Tibial and common peroneal nerves bound together; also called ischiadic nerve.

sclera (SKLAIR-ah) White of the eye; white, opaque portion of the fibrous tunic of the eye.

scleral venus sinus Series of veins at the base of the cornea that drain excess aqueous humor from the eye.

scrotum; pl. scrota, scrotums (SKROH-tum, SKROH-tah, SKROH-tums) Musculocutaneous sac containing the testes.

sebaceous gland (se-BAY-shus) [L., *sebum,* tallow] Gland of the skin, usually associated with a hair follicle, that produces sebum.

second messenger *See* intracellular mediator.

secondary follicle Follicle in which the secondary oocyte is surrounded by granulosa cells at the periphery; contains fluid-filled antral spaces.

secondary oocyte (OH-oh-site) Oocyte in which the second meiotic division stops at metaphase II unless fertilization occurs.

secondary palate Roof of the mouth in the early embryo that gives rise to the hard and the soft palates.

secondary response Immune response that occurs when the immune system is exposed to an antigen against which it has already produced a primary response; also called memory response.

secondary spermatocyte (SPER-mah-toh-site) Spermatocyte derived from a primary spermatocyte by the first meiotic division; each secondary spermatocyte gives rise by the second meiotic division to two spermatids.

secretin (seh-KREE-tin) Hormone formed by the epithelial cells of the duodenum; stimulates secretion of pancreatic juice high in bicarbonate ions.

secretion (seh-KREE-shun) Substance produced inside a cell and released from the cell.

secretory phase (seh-KREET-eh-ree, SEE-kreh-tohr-ee) *See* luteal phase.

segmental artery One of five branches of the renal artery, each supplying a segment of the kidney.

segmental bronchi Extend from the secondary bronchus and conducts air to each lobule of the lungs.

self-antigen Antigen produced by the body that is capable of initiating an immune response against the body.

semen (SEE-men) [L., seed (of plants, men, animals)] Penile ejaculate; thick, yellowish white, viscous fluid containing spermatozoa and secretions of the testes, seminal vesicles, prostate, and bulbourethral glands.

semicircular canal (SEM-ee-SIR-kyoo-lar) Canal in the petrous portion of the temporal bone that contains sensory organs that detect kinetic or dynamic equilibrium. Three semicircular canals are within each inner ear.

seminal vesicle (SEM-ih-nal VES-ih-kul) One of two glandular structures that empty into the ejaculatory ducts; its secretion is one of the components of semen.

seminiferous tubule (sem-ih-NIF-er-us) Tubule in the testis in which spermatozoa develop.

sensible perspiration (SEN-sih-bl pers-pih-RAY-shun) Perspiration excreted by the sweat glands that appears as moisture on the skin; produced in large quantity when there is much humidity in the atmosphere.

septum primum (SEP-tum PRY-mum) First septum in the embryonic heart that arises on the wall of the originally single atrium of the heart and separates it into right and left chambers.

septum secundum (seh-KUN-dum) Second of two major septal structures involved in the partitioning of the atrium, arising later than the septum primum and located to the right of it; it remains an incomplete partition until after birth, with its unclosed area constituting the foramen ovale.

serosa (seh-ROH-sah) [L., *serosus,* serous] Outermost covering of an organ or a structure that lies in a body cavity.

serous fluid (SEER-us) Fluid similar to lymph that is produced by and covers the serous membrane; it lubricates the serous membrane.

serous membrane Thin sheet composed of epithelial and connective tissues; it lines cavities that do not open to the outside of the body or contain glands but do secrete serous fluid.

serous pericardium Lining of the pericardial sac composed of a serous membrane.

Sertoli cell (seer-TOH-lee) Named for Italian histologist Enrico Sertoli (1842–1910). Elongated cell in the wall of the seminiferous tubules to which spermatids are attached during spermatogenesis.

serum (SEER-um) [L., whey] Fluid portion of blood after the removal of fibrin and blood cells.

sesamoid bone (SES-ah-moyd) [Gr., *sesamoceies,* like a sesame seed] Bone found within a tendon, such as the patella.

sex chromosomes Pair of chromosomes responsible for sex determination, XX in female and XY in male.

sex-linked trait Characteristic resulting from the expression of a gene on a sex chromosome.

sigmoid colon (SIG-moyd) Part of the colon between the descending colon and the rectum.

sigmoid mesocolon Fold of peritoneum attaching the sigmoid colon to the posterior abdominal wall.

simple epithelium Epithelium consisting of a single layer of cells.

sinoatrial (SA) node (sigh-noh-AY-tree-al) Mass of specialized cardiac muscle fibers; acts as the "pacemaker" of the cardiac conduction system.

sinus (SIGH-nus) [L., cavity] Hollow in a bone or other tissue; enlarged channel for blood or lymph.

sinus venosus End of the embryonic cardiac tube where blood enters the heart; becomes a portion of the right atrium, including the SA node.

sinusoid (sigh-nuh-SOYD) [L., sinus + Gr., *eidos,* resemblance] Terminal blood vessel having a larger diameter than an ordinary capillary.

sinusoidal capillary (sigh-nuh-SOY-dal) Capillary with caliber of 10–20 μm or more; lined with a fenestrated type of endothelium.

small intestine [L., *intestinus,* entrails] Portion of the digestive tube between the stomach and the cecum; consists of the duodenum, jejunum, and ileum.

sodium-potassium (Na^+-K^+) pump Biochemical mechanism that uses energy derived from ATP to achieve the active transport of potassium ions opposite to that of sodium ions; also called sodium potassium ATP-ase.

soft palate Posterior muscular portion of the palate, forming an incomplete septum between the mouth and the oropharynx and between the oropharynx and the nasopharynx.

solute (SOL-yoot) [L., *solutus,* dissolved] Dissolved substance in a solution.

solution (soh-LOO-shun) [L., *solutio*] Homogenous mixture formed when a solute is dissolved in a solvent.

solvent (SOL-vent) [L., *solvens,* to dissolve] Liquid that holds another substance in solution.

soma (SOH-mah) [Gr., body] Neuron cell body or the enlarged portion of the neuron containing the nucleus and other organelles.

somatic (soh-MAT-ik) [Gr., *somatikos,* bodily] Relating to the body; the cells of the body except the reproductive cells.

somatic nervous system Composed of nerve fibers that send impulses from the central nervous system to skeletal muscle.

somatomedin (SOH-mah-toh-MEE-din) Peptide synthesized in the liver capable of stimulating certain anabolic processes in bone and cartilage, such as synthesis of DNA, RNA, and protein.

somatotropin (SOH-mah-toh-TROH-pin) Protein hormone of the anterior pituitary gland; it promotes body growth, fat mobilization, and inhibition of glucose utilization.

somite (SOH-mite) [Gr., *soma,* body + *ite*] One of the paired segments consisting of cell masses formed in the early embryonic mesoderm on each side of the neural tube.

somitomere (SOH-mite-oh-meer) Indistinct somite in the head region of the embryo.

spatial summation Summation of the local potentials in which two or more action potentials arrive simultaneously at two or more presynaptic terminals that synapse with a single neuron.

specific heat Heat required to raise the temperature of any substance 1°C compared with the heat required to raise the same volume of water 1°C.

speech Use of the voice in conveying ideas.

spermatic cord (sper-MAT-ik) Cord formed by the ductus deferens and its associated structures; extends through the inguinal canal into the scrotum.

spermatid (SPER-mah-tid) [Gr., *sperma,* seed + *id*] Cell derived from the secondary spermatocyte; gives rise to a spermatozoon.

spermatogenesis (SPER-mat-oh-JEN-eh-sis) Formation and development of the spermatozoon.

spermatogonium (SPER-mah-toh-GOH-nee-um) [Gr., *sperma,* seed + *gone,* generation] Cell that divides by mitosis to form primary spermatocytes.

spermatozoon; pl. **spermatozoa** (SPER-mah-toh-ZOH-on, SPER-mah-toh-ZOH-ah) [Gr., *sperma,* seed + *zoon,* animal] Male gamete or sex cell, composed of a head and a tail. The spermatozoon contains the genetic information transmitted by the male; also called sperm cell.

sphenoid (SFEE-noyd) [Gr., *shen,* wedge] Wedge-shaped.

sphincter pupillae (SFINK-ter pyoo-PIL-ee) Circular smooth muscle fibers of the iris's diaphragm that constrict the pupil of the eye.

sphygmomanometer (SFIG-moh-mah-NOM-ih-ter) [Gr., *sphygmos,* pulse + *manos,* thin, scanty + *metron,* measure] Instrument for measuring blood pressure.

spinal nerve (SPY-nal) One of 31 pairs of nerves formed by the joining of the dorsal and ventral roots that arise from the spinal cord.

spindle fiber (SPIN-dl) Specialized microtubule that develops from each centrosome and extends toward the chromosomes during cell division.

spiral artery (SPY-ral) One of the corkscrewlike arteries in premenstrual endometrium; most obvious during the secretory phase of the uterine cycle.

spiral ganglion Cell bodies of sensory neurons that innervate hair cells of the organ of Corti are located in the spiral ganglion.

spiral lamina Attached to the modiolus and supports the basilar and vestibular membranes.

spiral ligament Attachment of the basilar membrane to the lateral wall of the bony labyrinth.

spiral organ Organ of Corti; rests on the basilar membrane and consists of the hair cells that detect sound.

spiral tubular gland Well-developed simple or compound tubular gland; spiral in shape; within the endometrium of the uterus; prevalent in the secretory phase of the uterine cycle.

spirometer (spy-ROM-eh-ter) [L., *spiro,* to breathe + Gr., *metron,* measure] Gasometer used for measuring the volume of respiratory gases; usually understood to consist of a counterbalanced cylindrical bell sealed by dipping into a circular trough of water.

spirometry (spy-ROM-eh-tree) Making pulmonary measurements with a spirometer.

spleen (SPLEEN) Large lymphatic organ in the upper part of the abdominal cavity on the left side between the stomach and diaphragm, composed of white and red pulp. It responds to foreign substances in the blood, destroys worn-out red blood cells, and is a storage site for blood cells.

spongy urethra Portion of the male urethra, approximately 15 cm in length, that traverses the corpus spongiosum of the penis.

squamous (SKWAY-mus) [L., *squama,* a scale] Scalelike, flat.

stapedius (stay-PEE-dee-us) Small skeletal muscles attached to the stapes.

stapes (STAY-pees) [L., stirrup] Smallest of the three auditory ossicles; attached to the oval window.

Starling law of the heart Named for English physiologist Ernest H. Starling (1866–1927). Force of contraction of cardiac muscle is a function of the length of its muscle fibers at the end of diastole; the greater the ventricular filling, the greater the stroke volume produced by the heart.

sternum (STER-num) [L., *sternon,* chest] Breastbone.

steroid (STEER-oyd) Large family of lipids, including some reproductive hormones, vitamins, and cholesterol.

stomach (STUM-uck) Large sac between the esophagus and the small intestine, lying just beneath the diaphragm.

stratified epithelium (STRAT-ih-fide ep-i-THEE-lee-um) Epithelium consisting of more than one layer of cells.

stratum basale (STRAH-tum ba-SAL-eh) [L., layer; basal] Basal, or deepest, layer of the epidermis; also called stratum germinativum.

stratum corneum (COR-nee-um) [L., layer + *corneus,* horny] Most superficial layer of the epidermis consisting of flat, keratinized, dead cells.

stratum granulosum (gran-yoo-LOH-sum) [L., layer; granulum, a small grain] Layer of cells in the epidermis filled with granules of keratohyalin.

stratum lucidum (LOO-see-dum) [L., layer + *lucidus,* clear] Clear layer of the epidermis found in thick skin between the stratum granulosum and the stratum corneum.

stratum spinosum (spy-NOH-sum) [L., layer + *spina,* spine] Layer of many-sided cells in the epidermis with intercellular connections (desmosomes) that give the cells a spiny appearance.

stria; pl. **striae** (STRY-ah, STRY-ee) [L., channel] Line or streak in the skin that is a different texture or color from the surrounding skin; also called stretch mark.

striated (STRY-ate-ed) [L., *striatus,* furrowed] Striped; marked by stripes or bands.

stroke volume (SV) [L., *volumen,* something rolled up, scroll, from *volvo,* to roll] Volume of blood pumped out of one ventricle of the heart in a single beat.

structural gene Gene that determines the structure of a specific protein or peptide.

sty (STIE) Inflamed ciliary gland of the eye.

subcutaneous (sub-kew-TAY-nee-us) [L., *sub,* under + *cutis,* skin] Under the skin; same tissue as the hypodermis.

sublingual gland (sub-LING-wal) One of two salivary glands in the floor of the mouth beneath the tongue.

submandibular gland (sub-man-DIB-you-lar) One of two salivary glands in the neck, located in the space bounded by the two bellies of the digastric muscle and the angle of the mandible.

submucosa (sub-myu-KOH-sa) Layer of tissue beneath a mucous membrane.

submucosal plexus (sub-myu-KOH-sal) [L., a braid] Gangliated plexus of unmyelinated nerve fibers in the intestinal submucosa.

substantia nigra (sub-STAN-shee-ah NYE-grah) [L., substance; black] Black nuclear mass in the midbrain; involved in coordinating movement and maintaining muscle tone.

subthreshold stimulus Stimulus resulting in a local potential so small that it does not reach threshold and produce an action potential.

sucrose (SOO-krohs) Disaccharide composed of glucose and fructose; table sugar.

sulcus; pl. **sulci** (SUL-cuss, SUL-sigh) [L., furrow or ditch] Furrow or groove on the surface of the brain between the gyri; may also refer to a fissure.

superficial inguinal ring (IN-gwin-al) Slitlike opening in the aponeurosis of the external oblique muscle of the abdominal wall through which the spermatic cord (round ligament in the female) emerges from the inguinal canal.

superior colliculus (koh-LIK-yoo-lus) [L., *collis,* hill] One of two rounded eminences of the midbrain; aids in coordination of eye movements.

superior vena cava (VEE-nah KAY-vah) Vein that returns blood from the head and neck, upper limbs, and thorax to the right atrium.

supination (soo-pih-NAY-shun) [L., *supino,* to bend backward, place on back] Rotation of the forearm (when the forearm is parallel to the ground) so that the anterior surface is up (supine).

suppressor T cell Subset of T lymphocytes that decreases the activity of B cells and T cells.

supramaximal stimulus Stimulus of greater magnitude than a maximal stimulus; however, the frequency of action potentials is not increased above that produced by a maximal stimulus.

surfactant (ser-FAK-tant) Lipoproteins forming a monomolecular layer over pulmonary alveolar surfaces; stabilizes alveolar volume by reducing surface tension and the tendency for the alveoli to collapse.

suspension (sus-PEN-shun) Liquid through which a solid is dispersed and from which the solid separates unless the liquid is kept in motion.

suspensory ligament (sus-PEN-soh-ree) Band of peritoneum that extends from the ovary to the body wall; contains the ovarian vessels and nerves. Small ligament attached to the margin of the lens in the eye and the ciliary body to hold the lens in place.

suture (SOO-chur) [L., *sutura,* a seam] Junction between flat bones of the skull.

sweat (SWET) [A.S., *swat*] Perspiration; secretions produced by the sweat glands of the skin; also called sensible perspiration.

sweat gland Usually means structure that produces a watery secretion called sweat. Some sweat glands, however, produce viscous organic secretions; also called sudoriferous gland.

sympathetic chain ganglion (sim-pah-THET-ik) Collection of sympathetic postganglionic neurons that are connected to each other to form a chain along both sides of the spinal cord; also called paravertebral ganglion.

sympathetic division Subdivision of the autonomic division of the nervous system characterized by having the cell bodies of its preganglionic neurons located in the thoracic and upper lumbar regions of the spinal cord (thoracolumbar division); usually involved in preparing the body for physical activity; also called thoracolumbar division.

symphysis; pl. **symphyses** (SIM-fih-sis, SIM-fih-seez) [Gr., a growing together] Fibrocartilage joint between two bones.

synapse; pl. **synapses** (SIN-aps, sih-NAP-seez) [Gr., *syn,* together + *haptein,* to clasp] Functional membrane-to-membrane contact of a nerve cell with another nerve cell, muscle cell, gland cell, or sensory receptor; functions in the transmission of action potentials from one cell to another; also called neuromuscular junction.

synaptic cleft (sih-NAP-tik) Space between the presynaptic and the postsynaptic membranes.

synaptic fatigue Fatigue due to depletion of neurotransmitter vesicles in the presynaptic terminals.

synaptic vesicle Secretory vesicle in the presynaptic terminal containing neurotransmitter substances.

synchondrosis; pl. **synchondroses** (SIN-kon-DROH-sis, SIN-kon-DROH-seez) [Gr., *syn,* together + *chondros,* cartilage + *osis,* condition] Union between two bones formed by hyaline cartilage.

syncytiotrophoblast (sin-SISH-ee-oh-TROH-foh-blast) Outer layer of the trophoblast composed of multinucleated cells.

syndesmosis; pl. **syndesmoses** (SIN-dez-MOH-sis, SIN-dez-MOH-seez) [Gr., *syndeo,* to bind + *osis,* condition] Form of fibrous joint in which opposing surfaces that are some distance apart are united by ligaments.

synergist (SIN-er-jist) Muscle that works with other muscles to cause a movement.

synovial (sih-NOH-vee-al) [Gr., *syn,* together + *oon,* egg] Relating to or containing synovia (a substance that serves as a lubricant in a joint, tendon sheath, or bursa).

synovial fluid Slippery fluid found inside synovial joints and bursae; produced by the synovial membranes.

systemic inflammation (sis-TEM-ik) Inflammation that occurs in many areas of the body. In addition to symptoms of local inflammation, increased neutrophil numbers in the blood, fever, and shock can occur.

systole (SIS-toh-lee) [Gr., *systole,* a contracting] Contraction of the heart chambers during which blood leaves the chambers; usually refers to ventricular contraction.

T

T cell Thymus-derived lymphocyte of immunologic importance; it is of long life and is responsible for cell-mediated immunity.

T wave Deflection in an electrocardiogram following the QRS complex, representing ventricular repolarization.

tactile corpuscle (TAK-til) Oval receptor found in the papillae of the dermis; responsible for fine, discriminative touch; also called Meissner corpuscle.

tactile disk Cuplike receptor found in the epidermis; responsible for light touch and superficial pressure; also called Merkel's disk.

talus (TAY-lus) [L., ankle bone, heel] Tarsal bone contributing to the ankle.

target tissue Tissue on which a hormone acts.

tarsal bone (TAR-sahl) [Gr., *tarsos,* sole of foot] One of seven ankle bones.

tarsal plate Crescent-shaped layer of connective tissue that helps maintain the shape of the eyelid.

taste (tayst) Sensations created when a chemical stimulus is applied to the taste receptors in the tongue.

taste bud Sensory structure, mostly on the tongue, that functions as a taste receptor.

tectum (TEK-tum) Roof of the midbrain.

tegmentum (teg-MEN-tum) Floor of the midbrain.

telencephalon (tel-en-SEF-ah-lon) [Gr., *telos,* end + *enkephalos,* brain] Anterior division of the embryonic brain from which the cerebral hemispheres develop.

telophase (TEL-oh-fayz) Time during cell division when the chromosomes are pulled by spindle fibers away from the cell equator and into the two halves of the dividing cell.

temporal summation (TEM-por-al) Summation of the local potential that results when two or more action potentials arrive at a single synapse in rapid succession.

tendon (TEN-dun) Band or cord of dense connective tissue that connects a muscle to a bone or another structure.

tensor tympani (TEN-sohr TIM-pan-ee) Small skeletal muscle attached to the malleus.

tentoriumcerebelli(ten-TOH-ree-umser-eh-BEH-lie) Dural folds between the cerebrum and the cerebellum.

terminal bouton (byoo-TON) [Fr., button] Enlarged axon terminal or presynaptic terminal.

terminal cisterna (sis-TER-nah) [L., *terminus,* limit + *cista,* box] Enlarged end of the sarcoplasmic reticulum in the area of the T tubules.

terminal hair [L., *terminus,* a boundary, limit] Long, coarse, usually pigmented hair found in the scalp, eyebrows, and eyelids and replacing vellus hair.

terminal sulcus (SUL-cuss) [L., furrow or ditch] V-shaped groove on the surface of the tongue at the posterior margin.

testis; pl. **testes** (TES-tis, TES-teez) One of two male reproductive glands located in the scrotum; produces spermatozoa, testosterone, and inhibin.

testosterone (tes-TOSS-ter-ohn) Steroid hormone secreted primarily by the testes; aids in spermatogenesis, maintenance and development of male reproductive organs, secondary sexual characteristics, and sexual behavior.

tetraiodothyronine (T_4) (TET-rah-eye-oh-doh-THIGH-roh-neen) One of the iodine-containing thyroid hormones; also called thyroxine.

thalamus (THAL-ah-mus) [Gr., *thalamos,* bed, bedroom] Large mass of gray matter that forms the larger dorsal subdivision of the diencephalon.

theca (THEE-kah) [Gr., *theke,* box] Sheath or capsule.

theca externa External fibrous layer of the theca of a vesicular follicle.

theca interna Inner vascular layer of the theca of the secondary and mature follicle; produces estrogen and contributes to the formation of the corpus luteum after ovulation.

thenar eminence (THEE-nar) [Gr., palm of the hand] Fleshy mass of tissue at the base of the thumb; contains muscles responsible for thumb movements.

thick skin Skin in the palms, soles, and tips of the digits; has all five epidermal strata.

thin skin Skin over most of the body, usually without a stratum lucidum; has fewer layers of cells than thick skin.

thoracic cavity (thor-ASS-ik) Space within the thoracic walls, bounded below by the diaphragm and above by the neck.

thoracic duct Largest lymph vessel in the body, beginning at the cisterna chyli and emptying into the left subclavian vein; drains the left side of the head and neck, the left-upper thorax, the left-upper limb, and the inferior half of the body.

thoracolumbar division (THOR-ah-koh-LUM-bar) *See* sympathetic division.

thoroughfare channel Channel for blood through a capillary bed from an arteriole to a venule.

threshold potential (THRESH-ohld) Value of the membrane potential at which an action potential is produced as a result of depolarization in response to a stimulus.

threshold stimulus Stimulus resulting in a local potential just large enough to reach threshold and produce an action potential.

thrombocyte (THROM-boh-site) Platelet.

thrombocytopenia (THROM-boh-sigh-toh-PEE-nee-ah) [*thrombocyte* + Gr., *penia,* poverty] Condition in which there is an abnormally small number of platelets in the blood.

thromboxane (THROM-bok-zane) Specific class of physiologically active fatty acid derivatives present in many tissues.

thrombus; pl. **thrombi** (THROM-bus, THROM-bie) [Gr., *thrombos,* a clot] Clot in the cardiovascular system formed from constituents of blood; may be occlusive or attached to the vessel or heart wall without obstructing the lumen.

thymus (THIGH-mus) [Gr., *thymos,* sweetbread] Bilobed lymph organ located in the inferior neck and superior mediastinum; secretes the hormone thymosin.

thyroid cartilage (THIGH-royd) Largest laryngeal cartilage. It forms the laryngeal prominence, or Adam's apple.

thyroid gland [Gr., *thyreoeides,* shield] Endocrine gland located inferior to the larynx and consisting of two lobes connected by the isthmus; secretes the thyroid hormones triiodothyronine (T_3) and tetraiodothyronine (T_4).

thyroid-stimulating hormone (TSH) Glycoprotein hormone released from the hypothalamus; stimulates thyroid hormone secretion from the thyroid gland; also called thyrotropin.

thyrotropin (thigh-ROT-roh-pin, thigh-roh-TROH-pin) *See* thyroid-stimulating hormone (TSH).

thyroxine (thigh-ROK-seen) *See* tetraiodothyronine.

tidal volume (TYE-dahl) Volume of air that is inspired or expired in a single breath during regular, quiet breathing.

tissue repair (TISH-you) Substitution of viable cells for damaged or dead cells by regeneration or replacement.

tolerance (TOL-er-ans) Failure of the specific immune system to respond to an antigen.

tongue (TUHNG) Muscular organ occupying most of the oral cavity when the mouth is closed; major attachment is through its posterior portion.

tonicity (toh-NIS-ih-tee) [Gr., *tonos,* tone] Osmotic pressure or tension of a solution, usually relative to that of blood; a state of continuous activity or tension caused by muscle contraction beyond the tension related to physical properties of muscle.

tonsil; pl. **tonsils** (TON-sill, TON-sillz) [L., *tonsilla,* stake] Collection of lymphoid tissue; usually refers to a large collection of lymphatic tissue beneath the mucous membrane of the oral cavity and pharynx; lingual, pharyngeal, and palatine tonsils.

total lung capacity Volume of air contained in the lungs at the end of a maximum inspiration; equals vital capacity plus residual volume.

total tension Sum of active and passive tension.

trabecula; pl. **trabeculae** (trah-BEK-yoo-lah, trah-BEK-yoo-lee) [L., *trabs,* beam] One of the supporting bundles of fibers traversing the substance of a structure, usually derived from the capsule or one of the fibrous septa, such as trabeculae of lymph nodes, testes; a beam or plate of cancellous bone.

trachea (TRAY-kee-ah) [Gr., *tracheia arteria,* rough artery] Air tube extending from the larynx into the thorax, where it divides to form the bronchi; composed of 16–20 rings of hyaline cartilage.

tracheostomy (tray-kee-OST-oh-mee) [*tracheo, trachea* + Gr., *stoma,* mouth] Operation to make an opening into the trachea; usually the opening is intended to be permanent, and a tube is inserted into the trachea to allow airflow.

tracheotomy (tray-kee-OT-oh-mee) [*tracheo, trachea* + Gr., *tome,* incision] Act of cutting into the trachea.

transcription (tran-SKRIP-shun) Process of forming RNA from a DNA template.

transfer RNA (tRNA) RNA that attaches to individual amino acids and transports them to the ribosomes, where they are connected to form a protein polypeptide chain.

transfusion (trans-FYOO-zhun) [L., *trans,* across + *fundo,* to pour from one vessel to another] Transfer of blood from one person to another.

transitional epithelium (tran-SISH-un-ahl) Stratified epithelium that may be either cuboidal or squamouslike, depending on the presence or absence of fluid in the organ (as in the urinary bladder).

translation (trans-LAY-shun) Synthesis of polypeptide chains at the ribosome in response to information contained in mRNA molecules.

transport maximum Maximum rate of secretion or reabsorption of a substance by the renal tubules.

transverse colon (trans-VERS KOH-lon) Part of the colon between the right and left colic flexures.

transverse mesocolon (MEZ-oh-KOH-lon) Fold of peritoneum attaching the transverse colon to the posterior abdominal wall.

transverse (T) tubule [L., *tubus,* tube] Tubule that extends from the sarcolemma to a myofibril of striated muscles.

treppe (TREP-ee) [Ger., staircase] Series of successively stronger contractions that occur when a rested muscle fiber receives closely spaced stimuli of the same strength but with a sufficient stimulus interval to allow complete relaxation of the fiber between stimuli.

triacylglycerol (try-AS-il-GLIS-er-ol) *See* triglyceride.

triad (TRY-ad) Two terminal cisternae and a T tubule between them.

tricuspid valve (try-KUS-pid) Valve closing the orifice between the right atrium and the right ventricle of the heart.

triglyceride (try-GLIS-eh-ride) Three-carbon glycerol molecule with a fatty acid attached to each carbon; constitutes approximately 95% of the fats in the human body. Also called triacylglycerol.

trigone (TRY-gohn) [Gr., *trigonon,* triangle] Triangular, smooth area at the base of the bladder between the openings of the two ureters and that of the urethra.

triiodothyronine (T_3) (try-EYE-oh-doh-THIGH-roh-neen) One of the iodine-containing thyroid hormones.

trochlea (TROK-lee-ah) [L., pulley] Structure shaped like or serving as a pulley or spool.

trochlear nerve (TROK-lee-ar) [L., *trochlea,* pulley] Cranial nerve IV, to the muscle (superior oblique) turning around a pulley.

trophoblast (TROH-foh-blast) [Gr., *trophe,* nourishment + *blastos,* germ] Cell layer forming the outer layer of the blastocyst, which erodes the uterine mucosa during implantation; the trophoblast does not become part of the embryo but contributes to the formation of the placenta.

tropomyosin (troh-poh-MY-oh-sin) Fibrous protein found as a component of the actin myofilament.

troponin (TROH-poh-nin) Globular protein component of the actin myofilament.

true pelvis Portion of the pelvis inferior to the pelvic brim.

true rib Rib that attaches by an independent costal cartilage directly to the sternum; also called vertebrosternal (ver-TEE-broh-STER-nal) rib.

trypsin (TRIP-sin) Proteolytic enzyme formed in the small intestine from the inactive pancreatic precursor trypsinogen.

tubercle (TOO-ber-kul) Lump on a bone.

tubular reabsorption Movement of materials, by means of diffusion, active transport, or symport, from the filtrate within a nephron to the blood.

tubular secretion Movement of materials, by means of active transport, from the blood into the filtrate of a nephron.

tumor (TOO-mer) Any swelling or growth; a neoplasm.

tunic (TOO-nik) [L., coat] One of the enveloping layers of a part; one of the coats of a blood vessel; one of the coats of the eye; one of the coats of the digestive tract.

tunica adventitia (TOO-ni-kah ad-ven-TISH-ah) Outermost fibrous coat of a vessel or an organ that is derived from the surrounding connective tissue.

tunica albuginea (al-byoo-JIN-ee-ah) Dense, white, collagenous tunic surrounding a structure, such as the capsule around the testis.

tunica intima (IN-tih-mah) Innermost coat of a blood vessel; consists of endothelium, a lamina propria, and an inner elastic membrane.

tunica media Middle, usually muscular, coat of an artery or another tubular structure.

turbulent flow Flow characterized by eddy currents exhibiting nonparallel blood flow.

tympanic membrane (tim-PAN-ik) Eardrum; cellular membrane that separates the external from the middle ear; vibrates in response to sound waves.

U

unmyelinated axon (un-MIGH-eh-li-NAY-ted) Nerve fibers lacking a myelin sheath.

unsaturated (un-SACH-yoor-ate-ed) Carbon chain of a fatty acid that possesses one or more double or triple bonds.

upper respiratory tract Nasal cavity, pharynx, and associated structures.

up-regulation Increase in the concentration of receptors in response to a signal.

ureter (you-REET-er) [Gr., *oureter,* urinary canal] Tube conducting urine from the kidney to the urinary bladder.

urethral gland (you-ree-thral) One of numerous mucous glands in the wall of the spongy urethra in the male.

urogenital triangle Anterior portion of the perineal region containing the openings of the urethra and vagina in the female and the urethra and root structures of the penis in the male.

uterine cycle (YOU-ter-in, YOU-ter-eyen) Series of events that occur in a regular fashion in the uterus of sexually mature, nonpregnant females; prepares the uterine lining for implantation of the embryo.

uterine part Portion of the uterine tube that passes through the wall of the uterus.

uterine tube One of the tubes leading on each side from the uterus to the ovary; consists of the infundibulum, ampulla, isthmus, and uterine parts; also called fallopian tube or oviduct.

uterus (YOU-ter-us) Hollow, muscular organ in which the fertilized ovum develops into a fetus.

utricle (YOU-trih-kul) Part of the membranous labyrinth; contains a sensory structure, the macula, that detects static equilibrium.

uvula (YOU-vyou-lah) [L., *uva,* grape] Small, grapelike appendage at the posterior margin of the soft palate.

V

vaccination (vak-sih-NAY-shun) Deliberate introduction of an antigen into a subject to stimulate the immune system and produce immunity to the antigen.

vaccine (vak-SEEN) [L., *vaccinus,* relating to a cow] Preparation of killed microbes, altered microbes, or derivatives of microbes or microbial products intended to produce immunity. The method of administration is usually inoculation, but ingestion is preferred in some instances, and nasal spray is used occasionally.

vagina (vah-JIE-nah) [L., sheath] Genital canal in the female, extending from the uterus to the vulva.

vapor pressure Partial pressure exerted by water vapor.

variable region Part of an antibody that combines with an antigen.

vas deferens (VAS DEH-fuh-renz) *See* ductus deferens.

vasa recta (VAH-sah REK-tah) Specialized capillary that extends from the cortex of the kidney into the medulla and then back to the cortex.

vasa vasorum (VAY-sah vay-SOH-rum) [L., vessel, dish] Small vessels distributed to the outer and middle coats of larger blood vessels.

vascular tunic (VAS-kyoo-lar) Middle layer of the eye; contains many blood vessels.

vasoconstriction (VAY-soh-con-STRIK-shun) Decreased diameter of blood vessels.

vasodilation (VAY-soh-die-LAY-shun) Increased diameter of blood vessels.

vasomotion (vay-soh-MOH-shun, vas-oh-MOH-shun) Periodic contraction and relaxation of the precapillary sphincter, resulting in cyclic blood flow through capillaries.

vasomotor center (vay-soh-MOH-tor) Area within the medulla oblongata that regulates the diameter of blood vessels by way of the sympathetic nervous system.

vasomotor tone Relatively constant frequency of sympathetic impulses that keep blood vessels partially constricted in the periphery.

vasopressin (vay-soh-PRESS-in) *See* antidiuretic hormone.

vellus hair (VEL-us) [L., fleece] Short, fine, usually unpigmented hair that covers the body except for the scalp, eyebrows, and eyelids. Much of the vellus is replaced at puberty by terminal hairs.

venous capillary (VEE-nus) Capillary opening into a venule.

venous return Volume of blood returning to the heart.

venous sinus Endothelium-lined venous channel in the dura mater that receives cerebrospinal fluid from the arachnoid granulations.

ventilation (ven-tih-LAY-shun) [L., *ventus,* the wind] Movement of gases into and out of the lungs.

ventral root (VEN-tral) Motor (efferent) root of a spinal nerve.

ventricle (VEN-trih-kul) [L., *venter,* belly] Chamber of the heart that pumps blood into arteries (i.e., the left and right ventricles); in the brain, a fluid-filled cavity.

ventricular diastole (ven-TRIK-you-lar) Dilation of the heart ventricles.

ventricular systole Contraction of the ventricles.

venule (VEN-yool) Minute vein, consisting of endothelium and a few scattered smooth muscles, that carries blood away from capillaries.

vermiform appendix (VER-mih-form) [L., *vermis,* worm + *forma,* form; appendage] Wormlike sac extending from the blind end of the cecum.

vesicle (VES-ih-kull) [L., *vesica,* bladder] Small sac containing a liquid or gas, such as a blister in the skin or an intracellular, membrane-bounded sac.

vestibular fold (ves-TIB-you-lar) One of two folds of mucous membrane stretching across the laryngeal cavity from the angle of the thyroid cartilage to the arytenoid cartilage superior to the vocal cords; helps close the glottis; also called false vocal cord.

vestibular membrane Membrane separating the cochlear duct and the scala vestibuli.

vestibule (VES-tih-byul) [L., antechamber, entrance court] Anterior part of the nasal cavity just inside the external nares that is enclosed by cartilage; space between the lips and the alveolar processes and teeth; middle region of the inner ear containing the utricle and saccule; space behind the labia minora containing the openings of the vagina, urethra, and vestibular glands.

vestibulocochlear nerve (ves-TIB-yoo-loh-KOK-lee-ar) Nerve formed by the cochlear and vestibular nerves; extends to the brain.

villus; pl. villi (VIL-us, VIL-eye) [L., shaggy hair (of beasts)] Projection of the mucous membrane of the intestine; leaf-shaped in the duodenum; becomes shorter, more finger-shaped, and sparser in the ileum.

visceral (VISS-er-al) Relating to the internal organs.

visceral pericardium (per-ih-KAR-dee-um) Serous membrane covering the surface of the heart; also called epicardium.

visceral peritoneum (per-ih-toh-NEE-um) [Gr., *periteino,* to stretch over] Layer of peritoneum covering the abdominal organs.

visceral pleura (PLUR-aa) Serous membrane investing the lungs and dipping into the fissures between the several lobes.

visceroreceptor (VISS-er-oh-ree-SEP-ter) Sensory receptor associated with the organs.

viscosity (vis-KOS-ih-tee) [L., *viscosus,* viscous] Resistance to flow or alteration of shape by any substance as a result of molecular cohesion.

visual cortex (VIZH-oo-al) Area in the occipital lobe of the cerebral cortex that integrates visual information and produces the sensation of vision.

visual field Area of vision for each eye.

vital capacity (VYTE-all) Greatest volume of air that can be exhaled from the lungs after a maximum inspiration.

vitamin (VIE-tah-min) [L., *vita,* life + amine] One of a group of organic substances present in minute amounts in natural foodstuffs that are essential to normal metabolism; insufficient amounts in the diet may cause deficiency diseases.

vitamin D Fat-soluble vitamin produced from precursor molecules in skin exposed to ultraviolet light; increases calcium and phosphate uptake from the intestines.

vitreous humor (VIT-ree-us) Transparent, jellylike material that fills the space between the lens and the retina.

Volkmann's canal Named for German surgeon Richard Volkmann (1830–1889). Canal in bone containing blood vessels; not surrounded by lamellae; runs perpendicular to the long axis of the bone and the haversian canals, interconnecting the latter with each other and the exterior circulation.

vulva (VUL-vah) [L., wrapper or covering, seed covering, womb] External genitalia of the female, composed of the mons pubis, the labia majora and minora, the clitoris, the vestibule of the vagina and its glands, and the opening of the urethra and of the vagina; also called pudendum.

W

water-soluble vitamin Vitamin, such as B complex and C, that is absorbed with water from the intestinal tract.

white matter Bundles of parallel axons with their associated sheath in the central nervous system.

white pulp Part of the spleen consisting of lymphatic nodules and diffuse lymphatic tissue; associated with arteries.

white ramus communicans; pl. **rami communicantes** (RAY-mis koh-MYOO-ni-kans, RAY-my koh-myoo-ni-KAN-teez) Connection between a spinal nerve and a sympathetic chain ganglion through which myelinated preganglionic axons project.

wisdom tooth Third molar tooth on each side in each jaw.

X

xiphoid (ZI-foyd) [Gr., *xiphos,* sword] Sword-shaped, with special reference to the sword tip; the inferior part of the sternum.

X-linked Gene located on an X chromosome.

Y

yellow marrow (MARE-oh) Connective tissue filling the cavities of bones; consists primarily of reticular fibers and fat cells; replaces red marrow in long bones and the skull.

Y-linked Gene located on a Y chromosome.

yolk sac (YOKE SACK) Highly vascular layer surrounding the yolk of an embryo.

Z

Z disk Delicate, membranelike structure found at each end of a sarcomere to which actin myofilaments attach.

zona fasciculata (ZOH-nah fa-SIK-yoo-lah-tah) [L., *zone,* a girdle, one of the zones of the sphere] Middle layer of the adrenal cortex that secretes cortisol.

zona glomerulosa (gloh-MARE-yoo-lohs-ah or gloh-MAR-yoo-loh-sah) Outer layer of the adrenal cortex that secretes aldosterone.

zona pellucida (peh-LOO-sih-dah) Layer of viscous fluid surrounding the oocyte.

zona reticularis (re-TIK-yoo-LAR-is) Inner layer of the adrenal cortex that secretes androgens and estrogens.

zonula adherens (ZOH-nyoo-lah ad-HER-enz) [L., a small zone; adhering] Small zone holding or adhering cells together.

zonula occludens (ok-LOOD-enz) [L., occluding] Junction between cells in which the plasma membranes may be fused; occludes or blocks off the space between the cells.

zygomatic (zie-goh-MAT-ik) [Gr., *zygon,* yoke] Yoking or joining; bony arch created by the junction of the zygomatic and temporal bones.

zygote (ZIE-goht) [Gr., *zygotos,* yoked] Diploid cell resulting from the union of a sperm cell and an oocyte.

Index

Page numbers followed by *f* indicate figures and *t* indicate tables; numbers in *italics* indicate photos.

A

B

C

H

I

M

N

O

S

T

W

X

Y

Z